Hoover's
MasterList
of U.S. Companies

2009

Hoover's Business Press
Austin, Texas

Hoover's MasterList of U.S. Companies is intended to provide readers with accurate and authoritative information about the enterprises covered in it. The information contained herein is as accurate as we could reasonably make it. In many cases we have relied on third-party material that we believe to be trustworthy but were unable to independently verify. We do not warrant that the book is absolutely accurate or without error. Readers should not rely on any information contained herein in instances where such reliance might cause loss or damage. The publisher, the editors, and their data suppliers specifically disclaim all warranties, including the implied warranties of merchantability and fitness for a specific purpose. This book is sold with the understanding that neither the publisher, the editors, nor any content contributors are engaged in providing investment, financial, accounting, legal, or other professional advice.

EDGAR Online provided financial data for most public companies in this book. For private companies and historical information on public companies prior to their becoming public, we obtained information directly from the companies. Hoover's, Inc., is solely responsible for the presentation of all data.

Many of the names of products and services mentioned in this book are the trademarks or service marks of the companies manufacturing or selling them and are subject to protection under U.S. law. Space has not permitted us to indicate which names are subject to such protection, and readers are advised to consult with the owners of such marks regarding their use. Hoover's is a trademark of Hoover's, Inc.

10 9 8 7 6 5 4 3 2 1

Publishers Cataloging-in-Publication Data

Hoover's MasterList of U.S. Companies 2009, Vol. 1

Includes indexes.

ISBN: 978-1-57311-126-3

ISSN 1549-6457

1. Business enterprises — Directories. 2. Corporations — Directories.

HF3010 338.7

Hoover's Company Information is also available on the Internet at Hoover's Web site (www.hoovers.com). A catalog of Hoover's products is available on the Internet at www.hooversbooks.com.

This book was produced for Hoover's Business Press by:

Sycamore Productions, Inc.
5808 Balcones Drive, Suite 205
Austin, Texas 78731
info@sycamoreproductions.com

Cover design is by Jim Neeley. Electronic prepress and printing are by Yurchak Printing Inc. of Landisville, PA.

U.S. AND WORLD BOOK SALES

Hoover's, Inc.
5800 Airport Blvd.
Austin, TX 78752
Phone: 512-374-4500
Fax: 512-374-4538
e-mail: orders@hoovers.com
Web: www.hooversbooks.com

EUROPEAN BOOK SALES

William Snyder Publishing Associates
5 Five Mile Drive
Oxford OX2 8HT
England
Phone & fax: +44-186-551-3186
e-mail: snyderpub@aol.com

Hoover's, Inc.

Founder: Gary Hoover
President: David Mather
EVP Sales: Karen Kennedy
EVP Editorial and First Research: Russell Secker
VP SMB Sales: Jim Currie
VP Finance: Michael (Mike) Clark
VP Technology: Mamie Jones
VP Operations: Shannon Kovar
VP Product Development and Management: Chris Warwick
VP Advertising Sales and Operations: Mark Walters
Leader Human Resources: Robin Pfahler

EDITORIAL

Managing Editor: Margaret C. Lynch
Senior Editors: Larry Bills, Jason Cother, Kathleen Cottay, Zack Gonzales, Nancy Kay, Kathleen Kelly, Greg Perliski, Barbara Redding, Dennis Sutton
Editors: Sally Alt, Adam Anderson, Jenn Barnier, Victoria Bernard, Alex Biesada, Joe Bramhall, James Bryant, Anthony Buchanan, Ryan Caione, Jason Cella, Catherine Colbert, Danny Cummings, Jennifer DeShaw, Jeff Dorsch, Bobby Duncan, Lesley Epperson, Rachel Gallo, Stuart Hampton, Jim Harris, Dan Hayes, Chris Huston, Donna Iroabuchi, Jessica Jimenez, Linnea Anderson Kirgan, Julie Krippel, Anne Law, Josh Lower, John MacAyeal, Rebecca Mallett, Erin McInnis, Barbara Murray, Nell Newton, Lynett Oliver, Kristi Park, Peter Partheymuller, Tracey Panek, David Ramirez, Melanie Robertson, Patrice Sarath, Matt Saucedo, Amy Schein, Seth Shafer, Paula Smith, Anthony Staats, Diane Stimets, Barbara Strickland, Tracy Uba, Vanessa Valencia, Ryan Wade, Tim Walker, Kathi Whitley, Randy Williams, David Woodruff
QA Editors: Carrie Geis, Rosie Hatch, Diane Lee, John Willis
Project Analyst: Tara LoPresti
Editorial Customer Advocates: Adi Anand, Kenny Jones

HOOVER'S BUSINESS PRESS

Senior Director: Jim Currie
Distribution Manager: Rhonda Mitchell
Customer Support and Fulfillment Manager: Michael Febonio

ABOUT HOOVER'S, INC.

Hoover's, a D&B company, provides its customers the fastest path to business with insight and actionable information about companies, industries and key decision makers, along with the powerful tools to find and connect to the right people to get business done. Hoover's provides this information for sales, marketing, business development, and other professionals who need intelligence on U.S. and global companies, industries, and the people who lead them. Hoover's unique combination of editorial expertise and one-of-a-kind data collection with user-generated and company-supplied content gives customers a 360-degree view and competitive edge. This information, along with powerful tools to search, sort, download and integrate the content, is available through Hoover's (http://www.hoovers.com), the company's premier online service. Hoover's is headquartered in Austin, Texas.

Abbreviations

AFL-CIO – American Federation of Labor and Congress of Industrial Organizations
AMA – American Medical Association
AMEX – American Stock Exchange
ARM – adjustable-rate mortgage
ASP – application services provider
ATM – asynchronous transfer mode
ATM – automated teller machine
CAD/CAM – computer-aided design/computer-aided manufacturing
CD-ROM – compact disc – read-only memory
CD-R – CD-recordable
CEO – chief executive officer
CFO – chief financial officer
CMOS – complimentary metal oxide silicon
COO – chief operating officer
DAT – digital audiotape
DOD – Department of Defense
DOE – Department of Energy
DOS – disk operating system
DOT – Department of Transportation
DRAM – dynamic random-access memory
DSL – digital subscriber line
DVD – digital versatile disc/digital video disc
DVD-R – DVD-recordable
EPA – Environmental Protection Agency
EPROM – erasable programmable read-only memory
EPS – earnings per share
ESOP – employee stock ownership plan
EU – European Union
EVP – executive vice president
FCC – Federal Communications Commission
FDA – Food and Drug Administration
FDIC – Federal Deposit Insurance Corporation
FTC – Federal Trade Commission
FTP – file transfer protocol
GATT – General Agreement on Tariffs and Trade
GDP – gross domestic product
HMO – health maintenance organization
HR – human resources
HTML – hypertext markup language
ICC – Interstate Commerce Commission
IPO – initial public offering
IRS – Internal Revenue Service
ISP – Internet service provider
kWh – kilowatt-hour
LAN – local-area network
LBO – leveraged buyout
LCD – liquid crystal display

LNG – liquefied natural gas
LP – limited partnership
Ltd. – limited
mips – millions of instructions per second
MW – megawatt
NAFTA – North American Free Trade Agreement
NASA – National Aeronautics and Space Administration
Nasdaq – National Association of Securities Dealers Automated Quotations
NATO – North Atlantic Treaty Organization
NYSE – New York Stock Exchange
OCR – optical character recognition
OECD – Organization for Economic Cooperation and Development
OEM – original equipment manufacturer
OPEC – Organization of Petroleum Exporting Countries
OS – operating system
OSHA – Occupational Safety and Health Administration
OTC – over-the-counter
PBX – private branch exchange
PCMCIA – Personal Computer Memory Card International Association
P/E – price to earnings ratio
RAID – redundant array of independent disks
RAM – random-access memory
R&D – research and development
RBOC – regional Bell operating company
RISC – reduced instruction set computer
REIT – real estate investment trust
ROA – return on assets
ROE – return on equity
ROI – return on investment
ROM – read-only memory
S&L – savings and loan
SCSI – Small Computer System Interface
SEC – Securities and Exchange Commission
SEVP – senior executive vice president
SIC – Standard Industrial Classification
SOC – system on a chip
SVP – senior vice president
USB – universal serial bus
VAR – value-added reseller
VAT – value-added tax
VC – venture capitalist
VP – vice president
VoIP – Voice over Internet Protocol
WAN – wide-area network
WWW – World Wide Web

CONTENTS

Volume 1

Volume 2

About *Hoover's MasterList of U.S. Companies 2009*

Hoover's MasterList of U.S. Companies is one of the most comprehensive, but still affordable, sources for information on the vast array of enterprises that power the U.S. economy. This fifteenth edition is packed with information, and we believe, represents a true value for the information seeker.

In this two-volume set, we continue to feature our capsule summaries for each company. Additionally, we have included lists of the Top 500 companies in this book, organized by sales, employees, five-year annualized sales growth, and market value.

Hoover's MasterList of U.S. Companies 2009 contains essential information on about 10,000 companies taken from our internal database. We supplemented and expanded that database by obtaining sales information on most public companies from EDGAR Online.

In our selection process, we have endeavored to cover all US companies traded on the major stock exchanges, the largest and most important private enterprises in the US, as well as many other organizations that contribute to our economy, including government-owned enterprises (the United States Postal Service), foundations (the Bill & Melinda Gates Foundation), and major subsidiaries of US and non-US corporations.

We selected companies using the following criteria:

Public Companies (5,697)

We've included all US companies that trade on the New York Stock Exchange (NYSE), the American Stock Exchange (AMEX), and the NASDAQ Global (NASDAQ GM) and Global Select Markets (NASDAQ GS), as well as many of the companies in Hoover's database that trade on the NASDAQ Capital Market (NASDAQ CM), OTC, or Pink Sheets.

Private and Other Enterprises (4,303)

Our coverage of privately held businesses and other non-public entities includes:

- the largest privately held companies in the US;
- hundreds of the largest mutual insurance companies, agricultural co-ops, foundations, sports teams and leagues, universities, and not-for-profits;
- major subsidiaries of US and non-US corporations that have strong identities independent of the parent organizations;
- major government-owned enterprises.

INFORMATION PROVIDED ABOUT THE COMPANIES

Each entry contains a description of the company's products and operations, ownership, and market position if available, as well as the basic information that most people need to locate, communicate with, and evaluate a company. We have included each company's legal name at the top of the entry (or in the text if it is too long), and if available:

- The street address, phone number, fax number, and Web site address;
- The names of the chief executive officer (CEO), chief financial officer (CFO), and human resources (HR) contact;
- The company's status (privately held, public, subsidiary, etc.).

Headquarters for companies that are incorporated in Bermuda, but whose operational headquarters are in the US, are listed under their US address. The same applies for companies with joint US and non-US headquarters (such as KPMG International).

For public companies, we have provided trading symbols and exchanges. Sales numbers are provided for all companies, if available, with generally two major exceptions: Corporate parents do not break out sales for many subsidiaries or business segments, and venture capital firms and investment bankers do not provide revenue numbers. Sales for private companies are the most recent available; some are estimated or approximate, as the companies would not divulge exact figures. (Estimated sales numbers are identified as such.)

Some companies have joint CEOs or even no one with the title CEO, although there is someone who functions as the chief executive. In these cases, we have listed after the CEO heading the name of the person who appears first in the company's materials. In smaller companies, sometimes no one individual has the official title of CFO. In those cases, we have listed after the CFO heading the name of the principal financial officer (i.e., the officer who signs off on the company's financial statements).

INDEXES

To help readers easily locate information, we have included three indexes: companies by headquarters location, by industry, and by stock exchange symbol. The indexes for the two volumes are combined and are located at the end of Volume 2.

OTHER HOOVER'S RESOURCES

Companies in *Hoover's MasterList of U.S. Companies* that have more in-depth coverage on Hoover's Online (www.hoovers.com) are indicated by this symbol: ⊞

Many of these in-depth profiles are also available in the Hoover's Handbook series, including *Hoover's Handbook of American Business* and *Hoover's Handbook of Emerging Companies*. Information on non-US and private companies can be found in *Hoover's Handbook of World Business* and *Hoover's Handbook of Private Companies*. For more information about these or other Hoover's products, call us at 800-486-8666, e-mail us at orders@hoovers.com, or check out www.hooversbooks.com.

The best suggestions we receive come from our readers. If you would like to see any additional information included in future editions of this book, we invite your comments via telephone (512-374-4500), fax (512-374-4538), mail (5800 Airport Blvd., Austin, TX 78752), or e-mail (info@hoovers.com).

As always, we hope you find our books useful.

The Editors
Hoover's, Inc.
August 2008

Hoover's MasterList
of U.S. Companies

Company
Rankings

Top 500 Companies by Sales in
Hoover's MasterList of U.S. Companies 2009

Rank	Company	Headquarters	Sales ($ mil.)	Rank	Company	Headquarters	Sales ($ mil.)
1	Exxon Mobil Corporation	Irving, TX	404,552.0	51	Chrysler LLC	Auburn Hills, MI	49,000.0
2	Wal-Mart Stores, Inc.	Bentonville, AR	378,799.0	52	Pfizer Inc.	New York, NY	48,418.0
3	Chevron Corporation	San Ramon, CA	220,904.0	53	Lowe's Companies, Inc.	Mooresville, NC	48,283.0
4	ConocoPhillips	Houston, TX	194,495.0	54	Time Warner Inc.	New York, NY	46,482.0
5	General Motors Corporation	Detroit, MI	181,122.0	55	Caterpillar Inc.	Peoria, IL	44,958.0
6	General Electric Company	Fairfield, CT	172,738.0	56	Sunoco, Inc.	Philadelphia, PA	44,728.0
7	Ford Motor Company	Dearborn, MI	172,455.0	57	Medco Health Solutions, Inc.	Franklin Lakes, NJ	44,506.2
8	Citigroup Inc.	New York, NY	159,229.0	58	SUPERVALU INC.	Eden Prairie, MN	44,048.0
9	Bank of America Corporation	Charlotte, NC	124,321.0	59	Archer Daniels Midland Company	Decatur, IL	44,018.0
10	AT&T Inc.	San Antonio, TX	118,928.0	60	Cellco Partnership	Basking Ridge, NJ	43,900.0
11	Berkshire Hathaway Inc.	Omaha, NE	118,245.0	61	Federal Home Loan Mortgage Corporation	McLean, VA	43,104.0
12	JPMorgan Chase & Co.	New York, NY	116,353.0	62	Safeway Inc.	Pleasanton, CA	42,286.0
13	American International Group, Inc.	New York, NY	110,064.0	63	Lockheed Martin Corporation	Bethesda, MD	41,862.0
14	Hewlett-Packard Company	Palo Alto, CA	104,286.0	64	Sprint Nextel Corporation	Overland Park, KS	40,146.0
15	McKesson Corporation	San Francisco, CA	101,703.0	65	Best Buy Co., Inc.	Richfield, MN	40,023.0
16	International Business Machines	Armonk, NY	98,786.0	66	PepsiCo, Inc.	Purchase, NY	39,474.0
17	Koch Industries, Inc.	Wichita, KS	98,000.0	67	Intel Corporation	Santa Clara, CA	38,334.0
18	Valero Energy Corporation	San Antonio, TX	95,327.0	68	Kaiser Permanente	Oakland, CA	37,800.0
19	Verizon Communications Inc.	New York, NY	93,469.0	69	Kraft Foods Inc.	Northfield, IL	37,241.0
20	Cargill, Incorporated	Wayzata, MN	88,266.0	70	The Allstate Corporation	Northbrook, IL	36,769.0
21	The Goldman Sachs Group, Inc.	New York, NY	87,968.0	71	Motorola, Inc.	Schaumburg, IL	36,622.0
22	Cardinal Health, Inc.	Dublin, OH	86,852.0	72	The Walt Disney Company	Burbank, CA	35,510.0
23	Morgan Stanley	New York, NY	85,328.0	73	FedEx Corporation	Memphis, TN	35,214.0
24	The Home Depot, Inc.	Atlanta, GA	77,349.0	74	Ingram Micro Inc.	Santa Ana, CA	35,047.1
25	The Procter & Gamble Company	Cincinnati, OH	76,476.0	75	SYSCO Corporation	Houston, TX	35,042.1
26	CVS Caremark Corporation	Woonsocket, RI	76,329.5	76	Cisco Systems, Inc.	San Jose, CA	34,922.0
27	UnitedHealth Group Incorporated	Minnetonka, MN	75,431.0	77	Johnson Controls, Inc.	Milwaukee, WI	34,624.0
28	United States Postal Service	Washington, DC	74,800.0	78	Honeywell International Inc.	Morristown, NJ	34,589.0
29	Altria Group, Inc.	Richmond, VA	73,801.0	79	Prudential Financial, Inc.	Newark, NJ	34,401.0
30	The Kroger Co.	Cincinnati, OH	70,235.0	80	Northrop Grumman Corporation	Los Angeles, CA	32,018.0
31	The Boeing Company	Chicago, IL	66,387.0	81	Hess Corporation	New York, NY	31,647.0
32	AmerisourceBergen Corporation	Chesterbrook, PA	66,074.3	82	American Express Company	New York, NY	31,557.0
33	Marathon Oil Corporation	Houston, TX	65,207.0	83	Comcast Corporation	Philadelphia, PA	30,895.0
34	Costco Wholesale Corporation	Issaquah, WA	64,400.2	84	Alcoa Inc.	Pittsburgh, PA	30,748.0
35	Target Corporation	Minneapolis, MN	63,367.0	85	E. I. du Pont de Nemours and Company	Wilmington, DE	30,653.0
36	Merrill Lynch & Co., Inc.	New York, NY	62,675.0	86	The Coca-Cola Company	Atlanta, GA	28,857.0
37	WellPoint, Inc.	Indianapolis, IN	61,134.3	87	News Corporation	New York, NY	28,655.0
38	Dell Inc.	Round Rock, TX	61,133.0	88	Aetna Inc.	Hartford, CT	27,599.6
39	Johnson & Johnson	New Brunswick, NJ	61,095.0	89	General Dynamics Corporation	Falls Church, VA	27,240.0
40	Lehman Brothers Holdings Inc.	New York, NY	59,003.0	90	Bechtel Group, Inc.	San Francisco, CA	27,000.0
41	Wachovia Corporation	Charlotte, NC	56,662.0	91	Tyson Foods, Inc.	Springdale, AR	26,900.0
42	United Technologies Corporation	Hartford, CT	54,759.0	92	HCA Inc.	Nashville, TN	26,900.0
43	Walgreen Co.	Deerfield, IL	53,762.0	93	Enterprise GP Holdings L.P.	Houston, TX	26,713.8
44	Wells Fargo & Company	San Francisco, CA	53,593.0	94	Washington Mutual, Inc.	Seattle, WA	26,523.0
45	The Dow Chemical Company	Midland, MI	53,513.0	95	Macy's, Inc.	Cincinnati, OH	26,313.0
46	MetLife, Inc.	New York, NY	53,007.0	96	The Travelers Companies, Inc.	St. Paul, MN	26,017.0
47	Federal National Mortgage Association	Washington, DC	51,176.0	97	The Hartford Financial Services Group, Inc.	Hartford, CT	25,916.0
48	Microsoft Corporation	Redmond, WA	51,122.0	98	Abbott Laboratories	Abbott Park, IL	25,914.2
49	Sears Holdings Corporation	Hoffman Estates, IL	50,703.0	99	Humana Inc.	Louisville, KY	25,290.0
50	United Parcel Service, Inc.	Atlanta, GA	49,692.0	100	PricewaterhouseCoopers International Limited	New York, NY	25,150.0

Top 500 Companies by Sales in
Hoover's MasterList of U.S. Companies 2009 (continued)

Rank	Company	Headquarters	Sales ($ mil.)	Rank	Company	Headquarters	Sales ($ mil.)
101	Mars, Incorporated	McLean, VA	25,000.0	151	Xerox Corporation	Norwalk, CT	17,228.0
102	3M Company	St. Paul, MN	24,462.0	152	CHS Inc.	Inver Grove Heights, MN	17,216.0
103	Rite Aid Corporation	Camp Hill, PA	24,326.8	153	Enterprise Products Partners L.P.	Houston, TX	16,950.1
104	Merck & Co., Inc.	Whitehouse Station, NJ	24,197.7	154	Freeport-McMoRan Copper & Gold Inc.	Phoenix, AZ	16,939.0
105	Deere & Company	Moline, IL	24,082.2	155	United States Steel Corporation	Pittsburgh, PA	16,873.0
106	Apple Inc.	Cupertino, CA	24,006.0	156	Fluor Corporation	Irving, TX	16,691.0
107	Schlumberger Limited	Houston, TX	23,708.0	157	Anheuser-Busch Companies, Inc.	St. Louis, MO	16,685.7
108	Tech Data Corporation	Clearwater, FL	23,423.1	158	Google Inc.	Mountain View, CA	16,594.0
109	Publix Super Markets, Inc.	Lakeland, FL	23,193.6	159	Nucor Corporation	Charlotte, NC	16,593.0
110	Deloitte Touche Tohmatsu	New York, NY	23,100.0	160	Computer Sciences Corporation	Falls Church, VA	16,499.5
111	AMR Corporation	Fort Worth, TX	22,935.0	161	Kohl's Corporation	Menomonee Falls, WI	16,473.7
112	McDonald's Corporation	Oak Brook, IL	22,786.6	162	Lenovo Group Limited	Morrisville, NC	16,352.0
113	Emerson Electric Co.	St. Louis, MO	22,572.0	163	NIKE, Inc.	Beaverton, OR	16,325.9
114	Oracle Corporation	Redwood City, CA	22,430.0	164	Weyerhaeuser Company	Federal Way, WA	16,308.0
115	Wyeth	Madison, NJ	22,399.8	165	Union Pacific Corporation	Omaha, NE	16,283.0
116	Delphi Corporation	Troy, MI	22,283.0	166	Illinois Tool Works Inc.	Glenview, IL	16,170.6
117	Electronic Data Systems Corporation	Plano, TX	22,134.0	167	Lear Corporation	Southfield, MI	15,995.0
118	Tesoro Corporation	San Antonio, TX	21,915.0	168	Arrow Electronics, Inc.	Melville, NY	15,985.0
119	International Paper Company	Memphis, TN	21,890.0	169	Time Warner Cable Inc.	New York, NY	15,955.0
120	Accenture Ltd	New York, NY	21,452.8	170	Anadarko Petroleum Corporation	The Woodlands, TX	15,892.0
121	Raytheon Company	Waltham, MA	21,301.0	171	Burlington Northern Santa Fe Corporation	Fort Worth, TX	15,802.0
122	Constellation Energy Group, Inc.	Baltimore, MD	21,193.2	172	The Gap Inc.	San Francisco, CA	15,763.0
123	Ernst & Young Global Limited	United Kingdom	21,160.0	173	Avnet, Inc.	Phoenix, AZ	15,681.1
124	New York Life Insurance Company	New York, NY	21,123.0	174	Dominion Resources, Inc.	Richmond, VA	15,674.0
125	Coca-Cola Enterprises Inc.	Atlanta, GA	20,936.0	175	Office Depot, Inc.	Delray Beach, FL	15,527.5
126	Manpower Inc.	Milwaukee, WI	20,500.3	176	Aflac Incorporated	Columbus, GA	15,393.0
127	Plains All American Pipeline, L.P.	Houston, TX	20,394.0	177	Southern Company	Atlanta, GA	15,353.0
128	U.S. Bancorp	Minneapolis, MN	20,308.0	178	Halliburton Company	Houston, TX	15,264.0
129	U.S. Foodservice, Inc.	Columbia, MD	20,200.0	179	FPL Group, Inc.	Juno Beach, FL	15,263.0
130	UAL Corporation	Chicago, IL	20,143.0	180	PACCAR Inc	Bellevue, WA	15,221.7
131	Occidental Petroleum Corporation	Los Angeles, CA	20,013.0	181	Cox Enterprises, Inc.	Atlanta, GA	15,000.0
132	J. C. Penney Company, Inc.	Plano, TX	19,860.0	182	FMR LLC	Boston, MA	14,900.0
133	The Goodyear Tire & Rubber Company	Akron, OH	19,644.0	183	Amazon.com, Inc.	Seattle, WA	14,835.0
134	C&S Wholesale Grocers, Inc.	Keene, NH	19,500.0	184	Amgen Inc.	Thousand Oaks, CA	14,771.0
135	Whirlpool Corporation	Benton Harbor, MI	19,408.0	185	TRW Automotive Holdings Corp.	Livonia, MI	14,702.0
136	Staples, Inc.	Framingham, MA	19,372.7	186	The Progressive Corporation	Mayfield Village, OH	14,686.8
137	Bristol-Myers Squibb Company	New York, NY	19,348.0	187	Health Care Service Corporation	Chicago, IL	14,348.4
138	Delta Air Lines, Inc.	Atlanta, GA	19,154.0	188	Continental Airlines, Inc.	Houston, TX	14,232.0
139	Capital One Financial Corporation	McLean, VA	19,132.4	189	SemGroup, L.P.	Tulsa, OK	14,200.0
140	Exelon Corporation	Chicago, IL	18,916.0	190	Health Net, Inc.	Woodland Hills, CA	14,108.3
141	Tyco International Ltd.	Princeton, NJ	18,781.0	191	The Chubb Corporation	Warren, NJ	14,107.0
142	The TJX Companies, Inc.	Framingham, MA	18,647.1	192	CBS Corporation	New York, NY	14,072.9
143	Eli Lilly and Company	Indianapolis, IN	18,633.5	193	L-3 Communications Holdings, Inc.	New York, NY	13,960.5
144	Murphy Oil Corporation	El Dorado, AR	18,439.1	194	Sun Microsystems, Inc.	Santa Clara, CA	13,873.0
145	Loews Corporation	New York, NY	18,380.0	195	Texas Instruments Incorporated	Dallas, TX	13,835.0
146	Express Scripts, Inc.	St. Louis, MO	18,273.6	196	SunTrust Banks Inc.	Atlanta, GA	13,826.3
147	Kimberly-Clark Corporation	Irving, TX	18,266.0	197	Toys "R" Us, Inc.	Wayne, NJ	13,794.0
148	AutoNation, Inc.	Fort Lauderdale, FL	17,691.5	198	Colgate-Palmolive Company	New York, NY	13,789.7
149	CIGNA Corporation	Philadelphia, PA	17,623.0	199	Qwest Communications International Inc.	Denver, CO	13,778.0
150	The DIRECTV Group, Inc.	El Segundo, CA	17,246.0	200	World Fuel Services Corporation	Miami, FL	13,729.6

Top 500 Companies by Sales in
Hoover's MasterList of U.S. Companies 2009 (continued)

Rank	Company	Headquarters	Sales ($ mil.)	Rank	Company	Headquarters	Sales ($ mil.)
201	General Mills, Inc.	Minneapolis, MN	13,652.1	251	Smithfield Foods, Inc.	Smithfield, VA	11,351.2
202	The Pepsi Bottling Group, Inc.	Somers, NY	13,591.0	252	Marsh & McLennan Companies, Inc.	New York, NY	11,350.0
203	The AES Corporation	Arlington, VA	13,588.0	253	D.R. Horton, Inc.	Fort Worth, TX	11,296.5
204	Medtronic, Inc.	Minneapolis, MN	13,515.0	254	Visteon Corporation	Van Buren Township, MI	11,266.0
205	H. E. Butt Grocery Company	San Antonio, TX	13,500.0	255	Baxter International Inc.	Deerfield, IL	11,263.0
206	ONEOK, Inc.	Tulsa, OK	13,477.4	256	Reliant Energy, Inc.	Houston, TX	11,208.7
207	Tyco Electronics Ltd.	Berwyn, PA	13,460.0	257	PPG Industries, Inc.	Pittsburgh, PA	11,206.0
208	Viacom Inc.	New York, NY	13,423.1	258	Genworth Financial, Inc.	Richmond, VA	11,125.0
209	American Electric Power Company, Inc.	Columbus, OH	13,380.0	259	Dairy Farmers of America, Inc.	Kansas City, MO	11,100.0
210	Waste Management, Inc.	Houston, TX	13,310.0	260	DISH Network Corporation	Englewood, CO	11,090.4
211	PG&E Corporation	San Francisco, CA	13,237.0	261	Danaher Corporation	Washington, DC	11,025.9
212	EMC Corporation	Hopkinton, MA	13,230.2	262	Regions Financial Corporation	Birmingham, AL	10,939.0
213	Textron Inc.	Providence, RI	13,225.0	263	Principal Financial Group, Inc.	Des Moines, IA	10,906.5
214	Consolidated Edison, Inc.	New York, NY	13,120.0	264	Genuine Parts Company	Atlanta, GA	10,843.2
215	Edison International	Rosemead, CA	13,113.0	265	Harrah's Entertainment, Inc.	Las Vegas, NV	10,825.2
216	Cummins, Inc.	Columbus, IN	13,048.0	266	Parker Hannifin Corporation	Cleveland, OH	10,718.1
217	Eaton Corporation	Cleveland, OH	13,033.0	267	The Trump Organization	New York, NY	10,700.0
218	Carnival Corporation	Miami, FL	13,033.0	268	BB&T Corporation	Winston-Salem, NC	10,671.0
219	Marriott International, Inc.	Bethesda, MD	12,990.0	269	SLM Corporation	Reston, VA	10,627.2
220	Chevron Phillips Chemical Company LLC	The Woodlands, TX	12,986.0	270	Lincoln National Corporation	Radnor, PA	10,594.0
221	Penske Automotive Group, Inc.	Bloomfield Hills, MI	12,957.7	271	The Williams Companies, Inc.	Tulsa, OK	10,558.0
222	Public Service Enterprise Group	Newark, NJ	12,853.0	272	Unum Group	Chattanooga, TN	10,519.9
223	FirstEnergy Corp.	Akron, OH	12,802.0	273	Baker Hughes Incorporated	Houston, TX	10,428.2
224	Duke Energy Corporation	Charlotte, NC	12,720.0	274	YUM! Brands, Inc.	Louisville, KY	10,416.0
225	Omnicom Group Inc.	New York, NY	12,694.0	275	Sanmina-SCI Corporation	San Jose, CA	10,384.3
226	Schering-Plough Corporation	Kenilworth, NJ	12,690.0	276	Eastman Kodak Company	Rochester, NY	10,301.0
227	Northwest Airlines Corporation	Eagan, MN	12,528.0	277	Integrys Energy Group, Inc.	Chicago, IL	10,292.4
228	ARAMARK Corporation	Philadelphia, PA	12,384.3	278	Lennar Corporation	Miami, FL	10,186.8
229	Highmark Inc.	Pittsburgh, PA	12,352.6	279	Limited Brands, Inc.	Columbus, OH	10,134.0
230	Ascension Health	St. Louis, MO	12,322.0	280	Reyes Holdings LLC	Rosemont, IL	10,100.0
231	Navistar International Corporation	Warrenville, IL	12,295.0	281	The PNC Financial Services Group, Inc.	Pittsburgh, PA	10,088.0
232	Jabil Circuit, Inc.	St. Petersburg, FL	12,290.6	282	H. J. Heinz Company	Pittsburgh, PA	10,070.8
233	Sara Lee Corporation	Downers Grove, IL	12,278.0	283	Air Products and Chemicals, Inc.	Allentown, PA	10,037.8
234	JM Family Enterprises, Inc.	Deerfield Beach, FL	12,200.0	284	Xcel Energy Inc.	Minneapolis, MN	10,034.2
235	ConAgra Foods, Inc.	Omaha, NE	12,028.2	285	CSX Corporation	Jacksonville, FL	10,030.0
236	National City Corporation	Cleveland, OH	11,829.6	286	Apache Corporation	Houston, TX	9,977.9
237	Dean Foods Company	Dallas, TX	11,821.9	287	Avon Products, Inc.	New York, NY	9,938.7
238	State Street Corporation	Boston, MA	11,818.0	288	CNA Financial Corporation	Chicago, IL	9,885.0
239	Kellogg Company	Battle Creek, MI	11,776.0	289	Coventry Health Care, Inc.	Bethesda, MD	9,879.5
240	Masco Corporation	Taylor, MI	11,770.0	290	Southwest Airlines Co.	Dallas, TX	9,861.0
241	Circuit City Stores, Inc.	Richmond, VA	11,743.7	291	Blue Cross Blue Shield of Michigan	Detroit, MI	9,849.0
242	Genentech, Inc.	South San Francisco, CA	11,724.0	292	National Oilwell Varco, Inc.	Houston, TX	9,789.0
243	US Airways Group, Inc.	Tempe, AZ	11,700.0	293	Thermo Fisher Scientific Inc.	Waltham, MA	9,746.4
244	Tenaska, Inc.	Omaha, NE	11,600.0	294	Applied Materials, Inc.	Santa Clara, CA	9,734.9
245	R.R. Donnelley & Sons Company	Chicago, IL	11,587.1	295	TEPPCO Partners, L.P.	Houston, TX	9,658.1
246	Knight Inc.	Houston, TX	11,500.0	296	Huntsman Corporation	Salt Lake City, UT	9,650.8
247	Entergy Corporation	New Orleans, LA	11,484.4	297	CenterPoint Energy, Inc.	Houston, TX	9,623.0
248	Sempra Energy	San Diego, CA	11,438.0	298	YRC Worldwide Inc.	Overland Park, KS	9,621.3
249	Devon Energy Corporation	Oklahoma City, OK	11,362.0	299	Enterprise Rent-A-Car Company	St. Louis, MO	9,500.0
250	Seagate Technology LLC	Scotts Valley, CA	11,360.0	300	Dollar General Corporation	Goodlettsville, TN	9,495.3

Top 500 Companies by Sales in
Hoover's MasterList of U.S. Companies 2009 (continued)

Rank	Company	Headquarters	Sales ($ mil.)	Rank	Company	Headquarters	Sales ($ mil.)
301	Norfolk Southern Corporation	Norfolk, VA	9,432.0	351	Chesapeake Energy Corporation	Oklahoma City, OK	7,800.0
302	Liberty Media Corporation	Englewood, CO	9,423.0	352	Catholic Health Initiatives	Denver, CO	7,731.5
303	Starbucks Corporation	Seattle, WA	9,411.5	353	Crown Holdings, Inc.	Philadelphia, PA	7,727.0
304	Praxair, Inc.	Danbury, CT	9,402.0	354	MGM MIRAGE	Las Vegas, NV	7,691.6
305	Pepco Holdings, Inc.	Washington, DC	9,366.4	355	eBay Inc.	San Jose, CA	7,672.3
306	Pulte Homes, Inc.	Bloomfield Hills, MI	9,263.1	356	Owens-Illinois, Inc.	Perrysburg, OH	7,659.1
307	Tennessee Valley Authority	Knoxville, TN	9,244.0	357	Pilgrim's Pride Corporation	Pittsburg, TX	7,598.6
308	Kinder Morgan Energy Partners, L.P.	Houston, TX	9,217.7	358	Mohawk Industries, Inc.	Calhoun, GA	7,586.0
309	Progress Energy, Inc.	Raleigh, NC	9,153.0	359	Ameren Corporation	St. Louis, MO	7,546.0
310	Terex Corporation	Westport, CT	9,137.7	360	Ball Corporation	Broomfield, CO	7,475.3
311	OfficeMax Incorporated	Naperville, IL	9,082.0	361	Aon Corporation	Chicago, IL	7,471.0
312	The Bank of New York Mellon Corporation	New York, NY	9,031.0	362	Trane Inc.	Piscataway, NJ	7,449.6
313	Reynolds American Inc.	Winston-Salem, NC	9,023.0	363	Gannett Co., Inc.	McLean, VA	7,439.5
314	BJ's Wholesale Club, Inc.	Natick, MA	9,005.0	364	Smurfit-Stone Container Corporation	Chicago, IL	7,420.0
315	ITT Corporation	White Plains, NY	9,003.3	365	Sunoco Logistics Partners L.P.	Philadelphia, PA	7,405.8
316	Liberty Global, Inc.	Englewood, CO	9,003.3	366	Dillard's, Inc.	Little Rock, AR	7,370.8
317	SAIC, Inc.	San Diego, CA	8,935.0	367	C.H. Robinson Worldwide, Inc.	Eden Prairie, MN	7,316.2
318	Ameriprise Financial, Inc.	Minneapolis, MN	8,909.0	368	Western Refining, Inc.	El Paso, TX	7,305.0
319	Rohm and Haas Company	Philadelphia, PA	8,897.0	369	Thomson Reuters Corporation	New York, NY	7,296.0
320	QUALCOMM Incorporated	San Diego, CA	8,871.0	370	Enbridge Energy Partners, L.P.	Houston, TX	7,282.6
321	Tenet Healthcare Corporation	Dallas, TX	8,852.0	371	Reliance Steel & Aluminum Co.	Los Angeles, CA	7,265.6
322	Nordstrom, Inc.	Seattle, WA	8,828.0	372	Dover Corporation	New York, NY	7,226.1
323	ALLTEL Corporation	Little Rock, AR	8,803.1	373	V.F. Corporation	Greensboro, NC	7,219.4
324	Smith International, Inc.	Houston, TX	8,764.3	374	Community Health Systems, Inc.	Franklin, TN	7,127.5
325	KBR, Inc.	Houston, TX	8,745.0	375	GameStop Corp.	Grapevine, TX	7,094.0
326	Dana Holding Corporation	Toledo, OH	8,721.0	376	Bed Bath & Beyond Inc.	Union, NJ	7,048.9
327	Hertz Global Holdings, Inc.	Park Ridge, NJ	8,685.6	377	The Estée Lauder Companies Inc.	New York, NY	7,037.5
328	CIT Group Inc.	New York, NY	8,605.0	378	SYNNEX Corporation	Fremont, CA	7,004.1
329	Fortune Brands, Inc.	Deerfield, IL	8,563.1	379	AK Steel Holding Corporation	West Chester, OH	7,003.0
330	Monsanto Company	St. Louis, MO	8,563.0	380	Yahoo! Inc.	Sunnyvale, CA	6,969.3
331	DTE Energy Company	Detroit, MI	8,506.0	381	Dole Food Company, Inc.	Westlake Village, CA	6,931.0
332	Fifth Third Bancorp	Cincinnati, OH	8,494.0	382	The Pantry, Inc.	Sanford, NC	6,911.2
333	Jacobs Engineering Group Inc.	Pasadena, CA	8,474.0	383	MeadWestvaco Corporation	Glen Allen, VA	6,906.0
334	Assurant, Inc.	New York, NY	8,453.5	384	National Football League	New York, NY	6,900.0
335	Boston Scientific Corporation	Natick, MA	8,357.0	385	Precision Castparts Corp.	Portland, OR	6,852.1
336	Sonic Automotive, Inc.	Charlotte, NC	8,336.9	386	Family Dollar Stores, Inc.	Matthews, NC	6,834.3
337	Commercial Metals Company	Irving, TX	8,329.0	387	Eastman Chemical Company	Kingsport, TN	6,830.0
338	CarMax, Inc.	Richmond, VA	8,285.4	388	AGCO Corporation	Duluth, GA	6,828.1
339	Centex Corporation	Dallas, TX	8,275.6	389	Clear Channel Communications, Inc.	San Antonio, TX	6,816.9
340	The First American Corporation	Santa Ana, CA	8,195.6	390	Owens & Minor, Inc.	Mechanicsville, VA	6,800.5
341	Virgin Media Inc.	New York, NY	8,136.4	391	Energy Transfer Partners, L.P.	Dallas, TX	6,792.0
342	The Sherwin-Williams Company	Cleveland, OH	8,005.3	392	Energy Transfer Equity, L.P.	Dallas, TX	6,792.0
343	Calpine Corporation	San Jose, CA	7,970.0	393	The McGraw-Hill Companies, Inc.	New York, NY	6,772.3
344	NiSource Inc.	Merrillville, IN	7,939.8	394	Global Partners LP	Waltham, MA	6,757.8
345	KeyCorp	Cleveland, OH	7,925.0	395	Catholic Healthcare West	San Francisco, CA	6,730.1
346	Campbell Soup Company	Camden, NJ	7,867.0	396	Quest Diagnostics Incorporated	Madison, NJ	6,704.9
347	Ashland Inc.	Covington, KY	7,834.0	397	Whole Foods Market, Inc.	Austin, TX	6,591.8
348	Weatherford International Ltd.	Houston, TX	7,832.1	398	Ryder System, Inc.	Miami, FL	6,566.0
349	Liberty Interactive Group	Englewood, CO	7,802.0	399	The Black & Decker Corporation	Towson, MD	6,563.2
350	Automatic Data Processing, Inc.	Roseland, NJ	7,800.0	400	The Interpublic Group of Companies, Inc.	New York, NY	6,554.2

Top 500 Companies by Sales in
Hoover's MasterList of U.S. Companies 2009 (continued)

Rank	Company	Headquarters	Sales ($ mil.)	Rank	Company	Headquarters	Sales ($ mil.)
401	CMS Energy Corporation	Jackson, MI	6,504.0	451	Anixter International Inc.	Glenview, IL	5,852.9
402	PPL Corporation	Allentown, PA	6,498.0	452	ONEOK Partners, L.P.	Tulsa, OK	5,831.6
403	Cablevision Systems Corporation	Bethpage, NY	6,484.5	453	Northeast Utilities	Berlin, CT	5,822.2
404	ArvinMeritor, Inc.	Troy, MI	6,449.0	454	Gerdau Ameristeel Corporation	Tampa, FL	5,806.6
405	Celanese Corporation	Dallas, TX	6,444.0	455	The Mosaic Company	Plymouth, MN	5,773.7
406	Discover Financial Services	Riverwoods, IL	6,434.3	456	Affiliated Computer Services, Inc.	Dallas, TX	5,772.5
407	W.W. Grainger, Inc.	Lake Forest, IL	6,418.0	457	The Shaw Group Inc.	Baton Rouge, LA	5,723.7
408	KB Home	Los Angeles, CA	6,416.5	458	Freescale Semiconductor, Inc.	Austin, TX	5,722.0
409	Newell Rubbermaid Inc.	Atlanta, GA	6,407.3	459	Reinsurance Group of America, Incorporated	Chesterfield, MO	5,718.4
410	The Great Atlantic & Pacific Tea Company	Montvale, NJ	6,401.1	460	Asbury Automotive Group, Inc.	New York, NY	5,713.0
411	Group 1 Automotive, Inc.	Houston, TX	6,393.0	461	Dr Pepper Snapple Group, Inc.	Plano, TX	5,700.0
412	Goodrich Corporation	Charlotte, NC	6,392.2	462	Micron Technology, Inc.	Boise, ID	5,688.0
413	Transocean Inc.	Houston, TX	6,377.0	463	Brunswick Corporation	Lake Forest, IL	5,671.2
414	IAC/InterActiveCorp	New York, NY	6,373.4	464	Kelly Services, Inc.	Troy, MI	5,667.6
415	Pension Benefit Guaranty Corporation	Washington, DC	6,372.0	465	Unisys Corporation	Blue Bell, PA	5,652.5
416	Embarq Corporation	Overland Park, KS	6,365.0	466	McDermott International, Inc.	Houston, TX	5,631.6
417	Becton, Dickinson and Company	Franklin Lakes, NJ	6,359.7	467	The Charles Schwab Corporation	San Francisco, CA	5,617.0
418	Avery Dennison Corporation	Pasadena, CA	6,307.8	468	Allegis Group, Inc.	Hanover, MD	5,570.0
419	Oshkosh Corporation	Oshkosh, WI	6,307.3	469	Darden Restaurants, Inc.	Orlando, FL	5,567.1
420	Performance Food Group Company	Richmond, VA	6,304.9	470	Core-Mark Holding Company, Inc.	South San Francisco, CA	5,560.9
421	Omnicare, Inc.	Covington, KY	6,220.0	471	W. R. Berkley Corporation	Greenwich, CT	5,553.6
422	Safeco Corporation	Seattle, WA	6,208.8	472	Blockbuster Inc.	Dallas, TX	5,542.4
423	Franklin Resources, Inc.	San Mateo, CA	6,205.8	473	Newmont Mining Corporation	Denver, CO	5,526.0
424	ProLogis	Denver, CO	6,204.7	474	Fidelity National Financial, Inc.	Jacksonville, FL	5,524.0
425	Hormel Foods Corporation	Austin, MN	6,193.0	475	XTO Energy Inc.	Fort Worth, TX	5,513.0
426	Molson Coors Brewing Company	Denver, CO	6,190.6	476	UGI Corporation	King of Prussia, PA	5,476.9
427	Tenneco Inc.	Lake Forest, IL	6,184.0	477	Ecolab Inc.	St. Paul, MN	5,469.6
428	AutoZone, Inc.	Memphis, TN	6,169.8	478	Western Digital Corporation	Lake Forest, CA	5,468.0
429	TravelCenters of America LLC	Westlake, OH	6,166.2	479	Allegheny Technologies Incorporated	Pittsburgh, PA	5,452.5
430	Starwood Hotels & Resorts Worldwide, Inc.	White Plains, NY	6,153.0	480	Foot Locker, Inc.	New York, NY	5,437.0
431	Royal Caribbean Cruises Ltd.	Miami, FL	6,149.1	481	Host Hotels & Resorts, Inc.	Bethesda, MD	5,426.0
432	Harley-Davidson, Inc.	Milwaukee, WI	6,143.0	482	Agilent Technologies, Inc.	Santa Clara, CA	5,420.0
433	Pitney Bowes Inc.	Stamford, CT	6,129.8	483	Barnes & Noble, Inc.	New York, NY	5,410.8
434	Major League Baseball	New York, NY	6,100.0	484	Northern Trust Corporation	Chicago, IL	5,395.1
435	Allied Waste Industries, Inc.	Phoenix, AZ	6,068.7	485	Wm. Wrigley Jr. Company	Chicago, IL	5,389.1
436	CB Richard Ellis Group, Inc.	Los Angeles, CA	6,034.3	486	URS Corporation	San Francisco, CA	5,383.0
437	Advanced Micro Devices, Inc.	Sunnyvale, CA	6,013.0	487	BorgWarner Inc.	Auburn Hills, MI	5,328.6
438	WESCO International, Inc.	Pittsburgh, PA	6,003.5	488	Sovereign Bancorp, Inc.	Philadelphia, PA	5,274.1
439	Charter Communications, Inc.	St. Louis, MO	6,002.0	489	DaVita Inc.	El Segundo, CA	5,264.1
440	Stryker Corporation	Kalamazoo, MI	6,000.5	490	Longs Drug Stores Corporation	Walnut Creek, CA	5,262.6
441	NRG Energy, Inc.	Princeton, NJ	5,989.0	491	The Timken Company	Canton, OH	5,236.0
442	Avis Budget Group, Inc.	Parsippany, NJ	5,986.0	492	Expeditors International	Seattle, WA	5,235.2
443	Ross Stores, Inc.	Pleasanton, CA	5,975.2	493	USG Corporation	Chicago, IL	5,202.0
444	Mattel, Inc.	El Segundo, CA	5,970.1	494	Frontier Oil Corporation	Houston, TX	5,188.7
445	EMCOR Group, Inc.	Norwalk, CT	5,927.1	495	Energy East Corporation	New Gloucester, ME	5,178.1
446	Henry Schein, Inc.	Melville, NY	5,920.2	496	NVR, Inc.	Reston, VA	5,156.4
447	Cooper Industries, Ltd.	Houston, TX	5,903.1	497	Foster Wheeler Ltd.	Clinton, NJ	5,107.2
448	Atmos Energy Corporation	Dallas, TX	5,898.4	498	Tribune Company	Chicago, IL	5,063.0
449	Symantec Corporation	Cupertino, CA	5,874.4	499	Rockwell Automation, Inc.	Milwaukee, WI	5,003.9
450	Corning Incorporated	Corning, NY	5,860.0	500	Owens Corning	Toledo, OH	4,978.0

Top 500 Companies by Employees in
Hoover's MasterList of U.S. Companies 2009

Rank	Company	Headquarters	Employees	Rank	Company	Headquarters	Employees
1	Manpower Inc.	Milwaukee, WI	5,033,000	51	The Procter & Gamble Company	Cincinnati, OH	138,000
2	Wal-Mart Stores, Inc.	Bentonville, AR	2,100,000	52	Emerson Electric Co.	St. Louis, MO	137,700
3	United States Postal Service	Washington, DC	786,000	53	The Walt Disney Company	Burbank, CA	137,000
4	Kelly Services, Inc.	Troy, MI	760,000	54	National Amusements Inc.	Dedham, MA	133,269
5	International Business Machines	Armonk, NY	426,969	55	PricewaterhouseCoopers LLP	New York, NY	130,000
6	United Parcel Service, Inc.	Atlanta, GA	425,300	56	Costco Wholesale Corporation	Issaquah, WA	127,000
7	McDonald's Corporation	Oak Brook, IL	390,000	57	Northrop Grumman Corporation	Los Angeles, CA	122,600
8	Citigroup Inc.	New York, NY	387,000	58	Honeywell International Inc.	Morristown, NJ	122,000
9	Target Corporation	Minneapolis, MN	366,000	59	Ernst & Young Global Limited	New York, NY	121,000
10	The Home Depot, Inc.	Atlanta, GA	331,000	60	Wachovia Corporation	Charlotte, NC	120,000
11	General Electric Company	Fairfield, CT	327,000	61	Tyco International Ltd.	Princeton, NJ	118,000
12	The Kroger Co.	Cincinnati, OH	323,000	62	Administaff, Inc.	Kingwood, TX	117,301
13	AT&T Inc.	San Antonio, TX	310,000	63	American International Group, Inc.	New York, NY	116,000
14	YUM! Brands, Inc.	Louisville, KY	301,000	64	Brinker International, Inc.	Dallas, TX	113,900
15	Robert Half International Inc.	Menlo Park, CA	272,300	65	Rite Aid Corporation	Camp Hill, PA	112,800
16	General Motors Corporation	Detroit, MI	266,000	66	Alcoa Inc.	Pittsburgh, PA	107,000
17	ARAMARK Corporation	Philadelphia, PA	250,000	67	ABM Industries Incorporated	San Francisco, CA	107,000
18	Ford Motor Company	Dearborn, MI	246,000	68	Ascension Health	St. Louis, MO	106,000
19	Verizon Communications Inc.	New York, NY	235,000	69	Tyson Foods, Inc.	Springdale, AR	104,000
20	Berkshire Hathaway Inc.	Omaha, NE	233,000	70	Kraft Foods Inc.	Northfield, IL	103,000
21	Walgreen Co.	Deerfield, IL	226,000	71	Caterpillar Inc.	Peoria, IL	101,333
22	United Technologies Corporation	Hartford, CT	225,600	72	Comcast Corporation	Philadelphia, PA	100,000
23	Lowe's Companies, Inc.	Mooresville, NC	216,000	73	Abercrombie & Fitch Co.	New Albany, OH	99,000
24	Bank of America Corporation	Charlotte, NC	210,000	74	Limited Brands, Inc.	Columbus, OH	97,500
25	Safeway Inc.	Pleasanton, CA	201,000	75	Tyco Electronics Ltd.	Berwyn, PA	94,000
26	CVS Caremark Corporation	Woonsocket, RI	200,000	76	Lear Corporation	Southfield, MI	91,000
27	SUPERVALU INC.	Eden Prairie, MN	192,000	77	The Coca-Cola Company	Atlanta, GA	90,500
28	PepsiCo, Inc.	Purchase, NY	185,000	78	Dell Inc.	Round Rock, TX	88,200
29	Macy's, Inc.	Cincinnati, OH	182,000	79	Harrah's Entertainment, Inc.	Las Vegas, NV	87,000
30	JPMorgan Chase & Co.	New York, NY	180,667	80	Pfizer Inc.	New York, NY	86,600
31	Starbucks Corporation	Seattle, WA	172,000	81	Time Warner Inc.	New York, NY	86,400
32	Accenture Ltd	New York, NY	170,000	82	Intel Corporation	Santa Clara, CA	86,300
33	Delphi Corporation	Troy, MI	169,500	83	AMR Corporation	Fort Worth, TX	85,500
34	HCA Inc.	Nashville, TN	161,000	84	Altria Group, Inc.	Richmond, VA	84,000
35	Wells Fargo & Company	San Francisco, CA	159,800	85	General Dynamics Corporation	Falls Church, VA	83,500
36	Kaiser Permanente	Oakland, CA	159,700	86	Exxon Mobil Corporation	Irving, TX	83,000
37	The Boeing Company	Chicago, IL	159,300	87	Cox Enterprises, Inc.	Atlanta, GA	82,000
38	Cargill, Incorporated	Wayzata, MN	158,000	88	Carnival Corporation	Miami, FL	81,200
39	Darden Restaurants, Inc.	Orlando, FL	157,000	89	Schlumberger Limited	Houston, TX	80,000
40	Starwood Hotels & Resorts Worldwide, Inc.	White Plains, NY	155,000	90	Koch Industries, Inc.	Wichita, KS	80,000
41	J. C. Penney Company, Inc.	Plano, TX	155,000	91	Microsoft Corporation	Redmond, WA	79,000
42	Marriott International, Inc.	Bethesda, MD	151,000	92	3M Company	St. Paul, MN	76,239
43	The Gap Inc.	San Francisco, CA	150,000	93	Coca-Cola Enterprises Inc.	Atlanta, GA	73,000
44	Best Buy Co., Inc.	Richfield, MN	150,000	94	Whirlpool Corporation	Benton Harbor, MI	73,000
45	PricewaterhouseCoopers International	New York, NY	146,767	95	Raytheon Company	Waltham, MA	72,100
46	Deloitte Touche Tohmatsu	New York, NY	146,600	96	Chrysler LLC	Auburn Hills, MI	72,000
47	Publix Super Markets, Inc.	Lakeland, FL	144,000	97	The Goodyear Tire & Rubber Company	Akron, OH	72,000
48	FedEx Corporation	Memphis, TN	143,000	98	Toys "R" Us, Inc.	Wayne, NJ	72,000
49	Johnson Controls, Inc.	Milwaukee, WI	140,000	99	Dollar General Corporation	Goodlettsville, TN	71,500
50	Electronic Data Systems Corporation	Plano, TX	139,500	100	Omnicom Group Inc.	New York, NY	70,000

Top 500 Companies by Employees in
Hoover's MasterList of U.S. Companies 2009 (continued)

Rank	Company	Headquarters	Employees	Rank	Company	Headquarters	Employees
101	The Pepsi Bottling Group, Inc.	Somers, NY	69,100	151	Halliburton Company	Houston, TX	51,000
102	Cellco Partnership	Basking Ridge, NJ	69,000	152	The Great Atlantic & Pacific Tea Company	Montvale, NJ	51,000
103	Abbott Laboratories	Abbott Park, IL	68,000	153	SYSCO Corporation	Houston, TX	50,900
104	American Express Company	New York, NY	67,700	154	Wyeth	Madison, NJ	50,527
105	MGM MIRAGE	Las Vegas, NV	67,400	155	Catholic Healthcare West	San Francisco, CA	50,000
106	UnitedHealth Group Incorporated	Minnetonka, MN	67,000	156	Danaher Corporation	Washington, DC	50,000
107	Enterprise Rent-A-Car Company	St. Louis, MO	66,700	157	Thomson Reuters Corporation	New York, NY	50,000
108	TRW Automotive Holdings Corp.	Livonia, MI	66,300	158	Dillard's, Inc.	Little Rock, AR	49,938
109	Motorola, Inc.	Schaumburg, IL	66,000	159	Washington Mutual, Inc.	Seattle, WA	49,403
110	Catholic Health Initiatives	Denver, CO	65,296	160	Office Depot, Inc.	Delray Beach, FL	49,000
111	R.R. Donnelley & Sons Company	Chicago, IL	65,000	161	MetLife, Inc.	New York, NY	49,000
112	Chevron Corporation	San Ramon, CA	65,000	162	Weight Watchers International, Inc.	New York, NY	49,000
113	L-3 Communications Holdings, Inc.	New York, NY	64,600	163	Morgan Stanley	New York, NY	48,256
114	Merrill Lynch & Co., Inc.	New York, NY	64,000	164	Mars, Incorporated	McLean, VA	48,000
115	Eaton Corporation	Cleveland, OH	64,000	165	Hanesbrands Inc.	Winston-Salem, NC	47,600
116	CBRL Group, Inc.	Lebanon, TN	64,000	166	Waste Management, Inc.	Houston, TX	47,400
117	Tenet Healthcare Corporation	Dallas, TX	63,264	167	FMR LLC	Boston, MA	46,400
118	H. E. Butt Grocery Company	San Antonio, TX	63,000	168	Gannett Co., Inc.	McLean, VA	46,100
119	Regis Corporation	Minneapolis, MN	62,000	169	Baxter International Inc.	Deerfield, IL	46,000
120	Jabil Circuit, Inc.	St. Petersburg, FL	61,000	170	Automatic Data Processing, Inc.	Roseland, NJ	46,000
121	Sprint Nextel Corporation	Overland Park, KS	60,000	171	The Dow Chemical Company	Midland, MI	45,856
122	Illinois Tool Works Inc.	Glenview, IL	60,000	172	Continental Airlines, Inc.	Houston, TX	45,610
123	E. I. du Pont de Nemours and Company	Wilmington, DE	60,000	173	Time Warner Cable Inc.	New York, NY	45,600
124	Merck & Co., Inc.	Whitehouse Station, NJ	59,800	174	Dole Food Company, Inc.	Westlake Village, CA	45,000
125	Blockbuster Inc.	Dallas, TX	59,643	175	Advance Auto Parts, Inc.	Roanoke, VA	44,065
126	Xerox Corporation	Norwalk, CT	57,400	176	Family Dollar Stores, Inc.	Matthews, NC	44,000
127	Parker Hannifin Corporation	Cleveland, OH	57,338	177	Textron Inc.	Providence, RI	44,000
128	Watson Pharmaceuticals, Inc.	Corona, CA	56,400	178	Wendy's International, Inc.	Dublin, OH	44,000
129	Marsh & McLennan Companies, Inc.	New York, NY	56,000	179	SAIC, Inc.	San Diego, CA	43,800
130	Cognizant Technology Solutions	Teaneck, NJ	55,400	180	Quest Diagnostics Incorporated	Madison, NJ	43,500
131	Delta Air Lines, Inc.	Atlanta, GA	55,044	181	GameStop Corp.	Grapevine, TX	43,000
132	Nordstrom, Inc.	Seattle, WA	55,000	182	Volt Information Sciences, Inc.	New York, NY	43,000
133	Schering-Plough Corporation	Kenilworth, NJ	55,000	183	Dollar Tree, Inc.	Chesapeake, VA	42,600
134	AutoZone, Inc.	Memphis, TN	55,000	184	Jack in the Box Inc.	San Diego, CA	42,500
135	UAL Corporation	Chicago, IL	55,000	185	Bechtel Group, Inc.	San Francisco, CA	42,500
136	Pilgrim's Pride Corporation	Pittsburg, TX	54,900	186	Aon Corporation	Chicago, IL	42,500
137	V.F. Corporation	Greensboro, NC	54,200	187	The Bank of New York Mellon Corporation	New York, NY	42,100
138	U.S. Bancorp	Minneapolis, MN	54,000	188	Res-Care, Inc.	Louisville, KY	42,000
139	Seagate Technology LLC	Scotts Valley, CA	54,000	189	H Group Holding, Inc.	Chicago, IL	42,000
140	The Brink's Company	Richmond, VA	53,900	190	Avon Products, Inc.	New York, NY	42,000
141	Kimberly-Clark Corporation	Irving, TX	53,000	191	Bristol-Myers Squibb Company	New York, NY	42,000
142	News Corporation	New York, NY	53,000	192	WellPoint, Inc.	Indianapolis, IN	41,700
143	Sanmina-SCI Corporation	San Jose, CA	52,607	193	Visteon Corporation	Van Buren Township, MI	41,500
144	Whole Foods Market, Inc.	Austin, TX	52,600	194	The Veritas Capital Fund, L.P.	New York, NY	41,300
145	Sara Lee Corporation	Downers Grove, IL	52,400	195	Fluor Corporation	Irving, TX	41,260
146	Deere & Company	Moline, IL	52,000	196	Prudential Financial, Inc.	Newark, NJ	40,703
147	Winn-Dixie Stores, Inc.	Jacksonville, FL	52,000	197	Eli Lilly and Company	Indianapolis, IN	40,600
148	KBR, Inc.	Houston, TX	52,000	198	Burlington Northern Santa Fe Corporation	Fort Worth, TX	40,000
149	Masco Corporation	Taylor, MI	52,000	199	Barnes & Noble, Inc.	New York, NY	40,000
150	International Paper Company	Memphis, TN	51,500	200	Ruby Tuesday, Inc.	Maryville, TN	40,000

Top 500 Companies by Employees in
Hoover's MasterList of U.S. Companies 2009 (continued)

Rank	Company	Headquarters	Employees	Rank	Company	Headquarters	Employees
201	Universal Health Services, Inc.	King of Prussia, PA	39,900	251	Genuine Parts Company	Atlanta, GA	32,000
202	ITT Corporation	White Plains, NY	39,700	252	Amphenol Corporation	Wallingford, CT	32,000
203	Ross Stores, Inc.	Pleasanton, CA	39,100	253	AECOM Technology Corporation	Los Angeles, CA	32,000
204	Burger King Holdings, Inc.	Miami, FL	39,000	254	The Sherwin-Williams Company	Cleveland, OH	31,572
205	Bed Bath & Beyond Inc.	Union, NJ	39,000	255	Cooper Industries, Ltd.	Houston, TX	31,504
206	Williams-Sonoma, Inc.	San Francisco, CA	39,000	256	Fortune Brands, Inc.	Deerfield, IL	31,027
207	UPMC	Pittsburgh, PA	39,000	257	Fidelity National Information Services, Inc.	Jacksonville, FL	31,000
208	Kindred Healthcare, Inc.	Louisville, KY	38,200	258	DaVita Inc.	El Segundo, CA	31,000
209	Big Lots, Inc.	Columbus, OH	38,153	259	Mattel, Inc.	El Segundo, CA	31,000
210	The Allstate Corporation	Northbrook, IL	38,000	260	The Hartford Financial Services Group, Inc.	Hartford, CT	31,000
211	Weatherford International Ltd.	Houston, TX	38,000	261	Anheuser-Busch Companies, Inc.	St. Louis, MO	30,849
212	Cummins, Inc.	Columbus, IN	37,800	262	Norfolk Southern Corporation	Norfolk, VA	30,806
213	EMC Corporation	Hopkinton, MA	37,700	263	The Goldman Sachs Group, Inc.	New York, NY	30,522
214	The First American Corporation	Santa Ana, CA	37,354	264	NIKE, Inc.	Beaverton, OR	30,200
215	Avery Dennison Corporation	Pasadena, CA	37,300	265	Charming Shoppes, Inc.	Bensalem, PA	30,200
216	Qwest Communications International Inc.	Denver, CO	37,000	266	Texas Instruments Incorporated	Dallas, TX	30,175
217	Sun Healthcare Group, Inc.	Irvine, CA	36,850	267	Unisys Corporation	Blue Bell, PA	30,000
218	Apollo Group, Inc.	Phoenix, AZ	36,418	268	Avis Budget Group, Inc.	Parsippany, NJ	30,000
219	Jacobs Engineering Group Inc.	Pasadena, CA	36,400	269	PayStaff Corporation	Rockville, MD	30,000
220	Mohawk Industries, Inc.	Calhoun, GA	36,200	270	Brunswick Corporation	Lake Forest, IL	29,920
221	Pitney Bowes Inc.	Stamford, CT	36,165	271	Trane Inc.	Piscataway, NJ	29,600
222	OfficeMax Incorporated	Naperville, IL	36,000	272	Six Flags, Inc.	New York, NY	29,594
223	Colgate-Palmolive Company	New York, NY	36,000	273	Western Digital Corporation	Lake Forest, CA	29,572
224	Baker Hughes Incorporated	Houston, TX	35,800	274	Sykes Enterprises, Incorporated	Tampa, FL	29,560
225	RadioShack Corporation	Fort Worth, TX	35,800	275	Borders Group, Inc.	Ann Arbor, MI	29,500
226	Health Management Associates, Inc.	Naples, FL	35,645	276	The Cheesecake Factory Incorporated	Calabasas Hills, CA	29,400
227	Aetna Inc.	Hartford, CT	35,200	277	BB&T Corporation	Winston-Salem, NC	29,400
228	The American National Red Cross	Washington, DC	35,000	278	Hertz Global Holdings, Inc.	Park Ridge, NJ	29,350
229	Dana Holding Corporation	Toledo, OH	35,000	279	Medical Staffing Network Holdings, Inc.	Boca Raton, FL	29,150
230	CSX Corporation	Jacksonville, FL	35,000	280	Centerplate, Inc.	Spartanburg, SC	29,050
231	Mariner Health Care, Inc.	Atlanta, GA	35,000	281	CB Richard Ellis Group, Inc.	Los Angeles, CA	29,000
232	PPG Industries, Inc.	Pittsburgh, PA	34,900	282	EMCOR Group, Inc.	Norwalk, CT	29,000
233	Southwest Airlines Co.	Dallas, TX	34,378	283	P.F. Chang's China Bistro, Inc.	Scottsdale, AZ	28,800
234	Sun Microsystems, Inc.	Santa Clara, CA	34,200	284	Ryder System, Inc.	Miami, FL	28,800
235	Northwest Airlines Corporation	Eagan, MN	34,000	285	Lehman Brothers Holdings Inc.	New York, NY	28,600
236	Cintas Corporation	Cincinnati, OH	34,000	286	The Estée Lauder Companies Inc.	New York, NY	28,500
237	Dover Corporation	New York, NY	33,400	287	McDermott International, Inc.	Houston, TX	28,400
238	The Travelers Companies, Inc.	St. Paul, MN	33,300	288	The PNC Financial Services Group, Inc.	Pittsburgh, PA	28,320
239	Wyndham Worldwide Corporation	Parsippany, NJ	33,200	289	Burlington Coat Factory Warehouse	Burlington, NJ	28,005
240	Molex Incorporated	Lisle, IL	33,200	290	The AES Corporation	Arlington, VA	28,000
241	Regions Financial Corporation	Birmingham, AL	33,161	291	Las Vegas Sands Corp.	Las Vegas, NV	28,000
242	Thermo Fisher Scientific Inc.	Waltham, MA	33,000	292	United States Steel Corporation	Pittsburgh, PA	28,000
243	McKesson Corporation	San Francisco, CA	32,900	293	University System of Maryland	Adelphi, MD	28,000
244	The Bon-Ton Stores, Inc.	York, PA	32,700	294	Praxair, Inc.	Danbury, CT	27,992
245	Brookdale Senior Living, Inc.	Chicago, IL	32,700	295	Vishay Intertechnology, Inc.	Malvern, PA	27,900
246	Jones Lang LaSalle Incorporated	Chicago, IL	32,700	296	Boston Scientific Corporation	Natick, MA	27,500
247	ConocoPhillips	Houston, TX	32,600	297	Archer Daniels Midland Company	Decatur, IL	27,300
248	SunTrust Banks Inc.	Atlanta, GA	32,323	298	Anschutz Company	Denver, CO	27,205
249	DineEquity, Inc.	Glendale, CA	32,300	299	U.S. Foodservice, Inc.	Columbia, MD	27,160
250	National City Corporation	Cleveland, OH	32,064	300	State Street Corporation	Boston, MA	27,110

Top 500 Companies by Employees in
Hoover's MasterList of U.S. Companies 2009 (continued)

Rank	Company	Headquarters	Employees	Rank	Company	Headquarters	Employees
301	The Shaw Group Inc.	Baton Rouge, LA	27,000	351	Willis Stein & Partners, L.L.C.	Chicago, IL	22,715
302	Ernst & Young L.L.P.	New York, NY	27,000	352	Smurfit-Stone Container Corporation	Chicago, IL	22,700
303	Eastman Kodak Company	Rochester, NY	26,900	353	Fifth Third Bancorp	Cincinnati, OH	22,678
304	The Progressive Corporation	Mayfield Village, OH	26,851	354	The Trump Organization	New York, NY	22,450
305	Southern Company	Atlanta, GA	26,742	355	Allina Hospitals and Clinics	Minneapolis, MN	22,347
306	Triarc Companies, Inc.	Atlanta, GA	26,605	356	Air Products and Chemicals, Inc.	Allentown, PA	22,100
307	CIGNA Corporation	Philadelphia, PA	26,600	357	CH2M HILL Companies, Ltd.	Englewood, CO	22,000
308	Sun Capital Partners, Inc.	Boca Raton, FL	26,467	358	HealthSouth Corporation	Birmingham, AL	22,000
309	Dick's Sporting Goods, Inc.	Pittsburgh, PA	26,400	359	The Steak n Shake Company	Indianapolis, IN	22,000
310	Technitrol, Inc.	Trevose, PA	26,100	360	Newell Rubbermaid Inc.	Atlanta, GA	22,000
311	Ecolab Inc.	St. Paul, MN	26,050	361	Liberty Global, Inc.	Englewood, CO	22,000
312	Maxim Healthcare Services, Inc.	Columbia, MD	26,000	362	Longs Drug Stores Corporation	Walnut Creek, CA	21,900
313	CKE Restaurants, Inc.	Carpinteria, CA	26,000	363	Psychiatric Solutions, Inc.	Franklin, TN	21,800
314	Laboratory Corporation of America Holdings	Burlington, NC	26,000	364	PACCAR Inc	Bellevue, WA	21,800
315	Duke University	Durham, NC	26,000	365	Jo-Ann Stores, Inc.	Hudson, OH	21,707
316	Kellogg Company	Battle Creek, MI	26,000	366	Loews Corporation	New York, NY	21,700
317	Viasystems Group Inc.	St. Louis, MO	25,738	367	Westaff, Inc.	Walnut Creek, CA	21,694
318	Dean Foods Company	Dallas, TX	25,585	368	Valero Energy Corporation	San Antonio, TX	21,651
319	Red Robin Gourmet Burgers, Inc.	Greenwood Village, CO	25,285	369	Amkor Technology, Inc.	Chandler, AZ	21,600
320	The Timken Company	Canton, OH	25,175	370	Apple Inc.	Cupertino, CA	21,600
321	Jarden Corporation	Rye, NY	25,000	371	The University of Texas at Austin	Austin, TX	21,513
322	Fiserv, Inc.	Brookfield, WI	25,000	372	Harsco Corporation	Camp Hill, PA	21,500
323	CHRISTUS Health	Irving, TX	25,000	373	The McGraw-Hill Companies, Inc.	New York, NY	21,171
324	Humana Inc.	Louisville, KY	25,000	374	Transocean Inc.	Houston, TX	21,100
325	Banner Health	Phoenix, AZ	25,000	375	IAC/InterActiveCorp	New York, NY	21,000
326	The Black & Decker Corporation	Towson, MD	25,000	376	Denny's Corporation	Spartanburg, SC	21,000
327	AutoNation, Inc.	Fort Lauderdale, FL	25,000	377	LifePoint Hospitals, Inc.	Brentwood, TN	21,000
328	Ruddick Corporation	Charlotte, NC	24,800	378	Terex Corporation	Westport, CT	21,000
329	Corning Incorporated	Corning, NY	24,800	379	American Electric Power Company, Inc.	Columbus, OH	20,861
330	ConAgra Foods, Inc.	Omaha, NE	24,500	380	BJ's Wholesale Club, Inc.	Natick, MA	20,800
331	Leggett & Platt, Incorporated	Carthage, MO	24,000	381	Medco Health Solutions, Inc.	Franklin Lakes, NJ	20,800
332	SSM Health Care System Inc.	St. Louis, MO	24,000	382	Jefferson Health System Inc.	Radnor, PA	20,700
333	Chiquita Brands International, Inc.	Cincinnati, OH	24,000	383	PepsiAmericas, Inc.	Minneapolis, MN	20,700
334	MeadWestvaco Corporation	Glen Allen, VA	24,000	384	Service Corporation International	Houston, TX	20,591
335	The Day & Zimmermann Group	Philadelphia, PA	24,000	385	Vanderbilt University	Nashville, TN	20,571
336	CBS Corporation	New York, NY	23,970	386	On Assignment, Inc.	Calabasas, CA	20,350
337	The Children's Place Retail Stores, Inc.	Secaucus, NJ	23,800	387	Iron Mountain Incorporated	Boston, MA	20,100
338	Micron Technology, Inc.	Boise, ID	23,500	388	PG&E Corporation	San Francisco, CA	20,050
339	Clear Channel Communications, Inc.	San Antonio, TX	23,400	389	Rockwell Automation, Inc.	Milwaukee, WI	20,000
340	Goodrich Corporation	Charlotte, NC	23,400	390	The Cleveland Clinic Foundation	Cleveland, OH	20,000
341	Allied Waste Industries, Inc.	Phoenix, AZ	23,300	391	Dr Pepper Snapple Group, Inc.	Plano, TX	20,000
342	Regal Entertainment Group	Knoxville, TN	23,292	392	Addus Healthcare, Inc.	Palatine, IL	20,000
343	NCR Corporation	Dayton, OH	23,200	393	Smith International, Inc.	Houston, TX	19,865
344	Freescale Semiconductor, Inc.	Austin, TX	23,200	394	Tribune Company	Chicago, IL	19,600
345	Perot Systems Corporation	Plano, TX	23,100	395	Rockwell Collins, Inc.	Cedar Rapids, IA	19,500
346	DISH Network Corporation	Englewood, CO	23,000	396	Agilent Technologies, Inc.	Santa Clara, CA	19,400
347	Texas Roadhouse, Inc.	Louisville, KY	23,000	397	Sonic Corp.	Oklahoma City, OK	19,357
348	MedStar Health	Columbia, MD	23,000	398	ICT Group, Inc.	Newtown, PA	19,006
349	TOPS Markets, LLC	Williamsville, NY	23,000	399	The Washington Post Company	Washington, DC	19,000
350	Hewitt Associates, Inc.	Lincolnshire, IL	23,000	400	Liberty Media Corporation	Englewood, CO	19,000

Top 500 Companies by Employees in
Hoover's MasterList of U.S. Companies 2009 (continued)

Rank	Company	Headquarters	Employees	Rank	Company	Headquarters	Employees
401	National Railroad Passenger Corporation	Washington, DC	19,000	451	Memorial Hermann Healthcare System	Houston, TX	16,500
402	COMFORCE Corporation	Woodbury, NY	19,000	452	Health Care Service Corporation	Chicago, IL	16,500
403	Bon Secours Health System, Inc.	Marriottsville, MD	19,000	453	Charter Communications, Inc.	St. Louis, MO	16,500
404	KeyCorp	Cleveland, OH	18,934	454	Liz Claiborne, Inc.	New York, NY	16,500
405	Chipotle Mexican Grill, Inc.	Denver, CO	18,800	455	Wynn Resorts, Limited	Las Vegas, NV	16,500
406	Rent-A-Center, Inc.	Plano, TX	18,600	456	Advanced Micro Devices, Inc.	Sunnyvale, CA	16,420
407	The Pep Boys - Manny, Moe & Jack	Philadelphia, PA	18,564	457	Wm. Wrigley Jr. Company	Chicago, IL	16,400
408	CEC Entertainment, Inc.	Irving, TX	18,500	458	Pier 1 Imports, Inc.	Fort Worth, TX	16,400
409	Hormel Foods Corporation	Austin, MN	18,500	459	Emeritus Corporation	Seattle, WA	16,205
410	Sally Beauty Holdings, Inc.	Denton, TX	18,500	460	Detroit Medical Center	Detroit, MI	16,144
411	Highmark Inc.	Pittsburgh, PA	18,500	461	ALLTEL Corporation	Little Rock, AR	16,104
412	The Stanley Works	New Britain, CT	18,400	462	Stryker Corporation	Kalamazoo, MI	16,026
413	The Men's Wearhouse, Inc.	Houston, TX	18,400	463	Harris Corporation	Melbourne, FL	16,000
414	Bright Horizons Family Solutions, Inc.	Watertown, MA	18,400	464	Pacific Sunwear of California, Inc.	Anaheim, CA	16,000
415	Five Star Quality Care, Inc.	Newton, MA	18,301	465	Pentair, Inc.	Golden Valley, MN	16,000
416	W.W. Grainger, Inc.	Lake Forest, IL	18,036	466	Hallmark Cards, Inc.	Kansas City, MO	15,900
417	Emergency Medical Services Corporation	Greenwood Village, CO	18,015	467	Penske Automotive Group, Inc.	Bloomfield Hills, MI	15,800
418	Texas Health Resources Inc.	Arlington, TX	18,000	468	The McClatchy Company	Sacramento, CA	15,748
419	Fairview Health Services	Minneapolis, MN	18,000	469	Rohm and Haas Company	Philadelphia, PA	15,710
420	Vanguard Health Systems, Inc.	Nashville, TN	18,000	470	CarMax, Inc.	Richmond, VA	15,637
421	Building Materials Holding Corporation	San Francisco, CA	18,000	471	Fidelity National Financial, Inc.	Jacksonville, FL	15,500
422	Embarq Corporation	Overland Park, KS	18,000	472	Clayton, Dubilier & Rice, Inc.	New York, NY	15,500
423	Nucor Corporation	Charlotte, NC	18,000	473	Ball Corporation	Broomfield, CO	15,500
424	PETCO Animal Supplies, Inc.	San Diego, CA	17,900	474	CommScope, Inc.	Hickory, NC	15,500
425	Regal Beloit Corporation	Beloit, WI	17,900	475	Gentiva Health Services, Inc.	Melville, NY	15,450
426	Papa John's International, Inc.	Louisville, KY	17,800	476	Cameron International Corporation	Houston, TX	15,400
427	Omnicare, Inc.	Covington, KY	17,800	477	Applied Materials, Inc.	Santa Clara, CA	15,328
428	SPX Corporation	Charlotte, NC	17,800	478	Penn National Gaming, Inc.	Wyomissing, PA	15,289
429	Capital One Financial Corporation	McLean, VA	17,800	479	Quanta Services, Inc.	Houston, TX	15,261
430	Duke Energy Corporation	Charlotte, NC	17,800	480	Consolidated Edison, Inc.	New York, NY	15,214
431	Exelon Corporation	Chicago, IL	17,800	481	Virgin Media Inc.	New York, NY	15,060
432	BorgWarner Inc.	Auburn Hills, MI	17,700	482	Boston Market Corporation	Golden, CO	15,041
433	Amgen Inc.	Thousand Oaks, CA	17,500	483	Coventry Health Care, Inc.	Bethesda, MD	15,000
434	Edison International	Rosemead, CA	17,275	484	Newmont Mining Corporation	Denver, CO	15,000
435	Navistar International Corporation	Warrenville, IL	17,200	485	ALLETE, Inc.	Duluth, MN	15,000
436	Multi-Fineline Electronix, Inc.	Anaheim, CA	17,178	486	Cabela's Incorporated	Sidney, NE	15,000
437	BearingPoint, Inc.	McLean, VA	17,100	487	Saint Vincent Catholic Medical Centers	New York, NY	15,000
438	Forstmann Little & Co.	New York, NY	17,034	488	eBay Inc.	San Jose, CA	15,000
439	Amazon.com, Inc.	Seattle, WA	17,000	489	Girling Health Care, Inc.	Austin, TX	15,000
440	C&S Wholesale Grocers, Inc.	Keene, NH	17,000	490	Lennox International Inc.	Richardson, TX	15,000
441	Dominion Resources, Inc.	Richmond, VA	17,000	491	Akal Security, Inc.	Española, NM	15,000
442	NPC International, Inc.	Overland Park, KS	17,000	492	Ingram Micro Inc.	Santa Ana, CA	15,000
443	Partners HealthCare System, Inc.	Boston, MA	16,981	493	Life Time Fitness, Inc.	Chanhassen, MN	15,000
444	Google Inc.	Mountain View, CA	16,805	494	Columbia Sussex Corporation	Crestview Hills, KY	15,000
445	A. O. Smith Corporation	Milwaukee, WI	16,800	495	Navy Exchange Service Command	Virginia Beach, VA	15,000
446	DynCorp International Inc.	Falls Church, VA	16,800	496	Flowserve Corporation	Irving, TX	15,000
447	BJ Services Company	Houston, TX	16,700	497	IKON Office Solutions, Inc.	Malvern, PA	15,000
448	Saks Incorporated	New York, NY	16,700	498	Inova Health System Foundation	Falls Church, VA	14,911
449	The Talbots, Inc.	Hingham, MA	16,600	499	New York Life Insurance Company	New York, NY	14,847
450	Principal Financial Group, Inc.	Des Moines, IA	16,585	500	Freeman Spogli & Co. Incorporated	Los Angeles, CA	14,841

Top 500 Companies by Sales Growth in
Hoover's MasterList of U.S. Companies 2009

Rank	Company	Headquarters	Five-Year Annualized Sales Growth	Rank	Company	Headquarters	Five-Year Annualized Sales Growth
1	Portsmouth Square, Inc.	Los Angeles, CA	10,466.7%	51	Dune Energy, Inc.	Houston, TX	338.5%
2	Solera Holdings, Inc.	San Ramon, CA	4,758.0%	52	MPC Corporation	Nampa, ID	337.1%
3	Hughes Communications, Inc.	Germantown, MD	3,922.2%	53	Concho Resources Inc.	Midland, TX	334.0%
4	The Pampered Chef, Ltd.	Addison, IL	3,779.7%	54	American Trucking Associations	Alexandria, VA	331.6%
5	US Farms, Inc.	San Diego, CA	2,275.0%	55	Lyris, Inc.	Emeryville, CA	321.0%
6	The Methodist Hospital System	Houston, TX	2,091.9%	56	CombinatoRx, Incorporated	Cambridge, MA	320.8%
7	Tercica, Inc.	Brisbane, CA	1,966.7%	57	Tortoise Energy Capital Corporation	Overland Park, KS	316.0%
8	CareFirst, Inc.	Owings Mills, MD	1,690.3%	58	Chamber of Commerce of The United States of America	Washington, DC	312.6%
9	Aircastle Limited	Stamford, CT	1,462.0%	59	Allegro Biodiesel Corporation	Los Angeles, CA	311.1%
10	Leonard Green & Partners, L.P.	Los Angeles, CA	1,134.8%	60	Santarus, Inc.	San Diego, CA	307.0%
11	ACT-1 Personnel Services	Torrance, CA	1,093.7%	61	FiberTower Corporation	San Francisco, CA	305.7%
12	SECURUS Technologies, Inc.	Dallas, TX	1,083.4%	62	First Acceptance Corporation	Nashville, TN	304.4%
13	Graebel Companies, Inc.	Aurora, CO	1,052.4%	63	NorthStar Realty Finance Corp.	New York, NY	301.4%
14	Healthy Fast Food, Inc.	Henderson, NV	900.0%	64	Westside Energy Corporation, Inc.	Oklahoma City, OK	300.0%
15	Specialty Underwriters' Alliance, Inc.	Chicago, IL	714.3%	65	Alnylam Pharmaceuticals, Inc.	Cambridge, MA	299.4%
16	MAKO Surgical Corp.	Fort Lauderdale, FL	700.0%	66	Command Center, Inc.	Post Falls, ID	296.3%
17	Infinera Corporation	Sunnyvale, CA	642.8%	67	Samaritan Pharmaceuticals, Inc.	Las Vegas, NV	295.8%
18	Wynn Resorts, Limited	Las Vegas, NV	620.0%	68	NovaBay Pharmaceuticals, Inc.	Emeryville, CA	293.3%
19	Entropic Communications, Inc.	San Diego, CA	574.0%	69	InSite Vision Incorporated	Alameda, CA	292.8%
20	Jacques Moret, Inc.	New York, NY	571.1%	70	Auriga Laboratories, Inc.	Norcross, GA	290.6%
21	Hercules Technology Growth Capital	Palo Alto, CA	545.9%	71	Osiris Therapeutics, Inc.	Columbia, MD	289.9%
22	Halozyme Therapeutics, Inc.	San Diego, CA	516.4%	72	Cafe Rio, Inc.	Orem, UT	286.7%
23	Silver Lake Partners, L.P.	Menlo Park, CA	512.5%	73	Affymax, Inc.	Palo Alto, CA	285.8%
24	Franklin Wireless Corp.	San Diego, CA	488.8%	74	NxStage Medical, Inc.	Lawrence, MA	276.1%
25	Teton Energy Corporation	Denver, CO	481.9%	75	ISTA Pharmaceuticals, Inc.	Irvine, CA	274.3%
26	International Fight League, Inc.	New York, NY	470.0%	76	PokerTek, Inc.	Matthews, NC	265.1%
27	Bimini Capital Management, Inc.	Vero Beach, FL	465.8%	77	Pain Therapeutics, Inc.	South San Francisco, CA	259.7%
28	Giant Motorsports, Inc.	Salem, OH	460.5%	78	Medical Mutual of Ohio	Cleveland, OH	259.0%
29	Veronis Suhler Stevenson LLC	New York, NY	459.5%	79	Tidelands Bancshares, Inc.	Mt. Pleasant, SC	257.9%
30	Rand Logistics, Inc.	New York, NY	454.9%	80	Tri-Isthmus Group, Inc.	Beverly Hills, CA	257.1%
31	Global Telecom & Technology, Inc.	McLean, VA	448.6%	81	Gramercy Capital Corp.	New York, NY	256.9%
32	Data Domain, Inc.	Santa Clara, CA	436.6%	82	The Hunt Corporation	Scottsdale, AZ	255.1%
33	The Broe Companies, Inc.	Denver, CO	432.0%	83	First Solar, Inc.	Tempe, AZ	254.3%
34	Interim HealthCare Inc.	Sunrise, FL	420.5%	84	ICx Technologies, Inc.	Arlington, VA	252.9%
35	Benchmark Hospitality International	The Woodlands, TX	418.2%	85	SunPower Corporation	San Jose, CA	252.8%
36	Crocs, Inc.	Niwot, CO	415.5%	86	A. Duda & Sons, Inc.	Oviedo, FL	247.5%
37	The Orchard Enterprises, Inc.	New York, NY	408.9%	87	NGP Capital Resources Company	Houston, TX	246.7%
38	Genomic Health, Inc.	Redwood City, CA	403.0%	88	The Segal Group, Inc.	New York, NY	244.2%
39	ICOP Digital, Inc.	Lenexa, KS	390.5%	89	Vertafore, Inc.	Bothell, WA	242.9%
40	NewStar Financial, Inc.	Boston, MA	387.4%	90	Biophan Technologies, Inc.	Pittsford, NY	242.1%
41	Syntax-Brillian Corporation	Tempe, AZ	372.5%	91	Ambient Corporation	Newton, MA	239.1%
42	Evergreen Energy Inc.	Denver, CO	369.8%	92	Patriot Capital Funding, Inc.	Westport, CT	237.7%
43	KKR Financial Holdings LLC	San Francisco, CA	368.1%	93	CBRE Realty Finance, Inc.	Hartford, CT	237.2%
44	Gener8Xion Entertainment, Inc.	Hollywood, CA	362.6%	94	ViroPharma Incorporated	Exton, PA	235.9%
45	Genco Shipping & Trading Limited	New York, NY	360.4%	95	TWL Corporation	Carrollton, TX	231.3%
46	Hythiam, Inc.	Los Angeles, CA	358.0%	96	Bruegger's Enterprises, Inc.	Burlington, VT	222.8%
47	Technology Investment Capital Corp.	Greenwich, CT	357.5%	97	First Investors Corporation	New York, NY	222.1%
48	International Assets Holding	Altamonte Springs, FL	349.8%	98	Insurance Services Office, Inc.	Jersey City, NJ	217.7%
49	Airvana, Inc.	Chelmsford, MA	339.6%	99	Ascendant Solutions, Inc.	Dallas, TX	217.5%
50	Genoptix, Inc.	Carlsbad, CA	339.2%	100	American Apparel, Inc.	Los Angeles, CA	216.6%

Top 500 Companies by Sales Growth in
Hoover's MasterList of U.S. Companies 2009 (continued)

Rank	Company	Headquarters	Five-Year Annualized Sales Growth	Rank	Company	Headquarters	Five-Year Annualized Sales Growth
101	DCT Industrial Trust Inc.	Denver, CO	213.3%	151	NewMarket Technology Inc.	Dallas, TX	152.2%
102	Woodforest Financial Group, Inc.	The Woodlands, TX	210.9%	152	Atrinsic, Inc.	Irvine, CA	150.4%
103	Altair Nanotechnologies Inc.	Reno, NV	208.9%	153	Terra Nova Financial Group, Inc.	Chicago, IL	148.7%
104	Southern National Bancorp of Virginia	Charlottesville, VA	206.2%	154	Novacea, Inc.	South San Francisco, CA	147.6%
105	SoftNet Technology Corp.	Iselin, NJ	204.5%	155	Insmed Incorporated	Richmond, VA	147.5%
106	New World Brands, Inc.	Eugene, OR	204.1%	156	AMDL, Inc.	Tustin, CA	147.5%
107	Replidyne, Inc.	Louisville, CO	202.5%	157	Glu Mobile Inc.	San Mateo, CA	146.9%
108	Helicos BioSciences Corporation	Cambridge, MA	200.0%	158	PTS, Inc.	Las Vegas, NV	146.6%
109	Santa Fe Financial Corporation	Los Angeles, CA	199.5%	159	Parking Company of America	Downey, CA	144.1%
110	Cubist Pharmaceuticals, Inc.	Lexington, MA	198.7%	160	MobilePro Corp.	Bethesda, MD	143.8%
111	LRN Corporation	Los Angeles, CA	197.8%	161	Carolinas HealthCare System	Charlotte, NC	142.8%
112	National Coal Corp.	Knoxville, TN	196.5%	162	Diamond Hill Investment Group, Inc.	Columbus, OH	142.2%
113	CytRx Corporation	Los Angeles, CA	194.3%	163	NutriSystem, Inc.	Horsham, PA	142.1%
114	True Religion Apparel Inc.	Vernon, CA	191.5%	164	Acme Packet, Inc.	Burlington, MA	142.0%
115	Sirius Satellite Radio Inc.	New York, NY	190.8%	165	WideOpenWest Holdings, LLC	Englewood, CO	141.5%
116	FTS Group, Inc.	Oldsmar, FL	189.3%	166	Groen Brothers Aviation, Inc.	Salt Lake City, UT	141.5%
117	Discount Drug Mart Inc.	Medina, OH	188.9%	167	totes»Isotoner Corporation	Cincinnati, OH	140.9%
118	KIT digital, Inc.	New York, NY	188.7%	168	Covanta Holding Corporation	Fairfield, NJ	140.8%
119	Petrohawk Energy Corporation	Houston, TX	187.7%	169	MVC Capital, Inc.	Purchase, NY	138.5%
120	Isilon Systems, Inc.	Seattle, WA	187.6%	170	Veri-Tek International, Corp.	Bridgeview, IL	138.3%
121	Caneum, Inc.	Newport Beach, CA	187.6%	171	Hoku Scientific, Inc.	Kapolei, HI	137.8%
122	VeraSun Energy Corporation	Brookings, SD	185.9%	172	PQ Corporation	Malvern, PA	137.8%
123	Thoma Cressey Bravo	Chicago, IL	185.4%	173	Wave Systems Corp.	Lee, MA	136.9%
124	Depomed, Inc.	Menlo Park, CA	184.6%	174	AmeriResource Technologies, Inc.	Las Vegas, NV	136.0%
125	Vera Bradley Designs Inc	Fort Wayne, IN	184.2%	175	Paladin Holdings, Inc	Kingsport, TN	136.0%
126	Innuity, Inc.	Redmond, WA	183.9%	176	Compellent Technologies, Inc.	Eden Prairie, MN	135.9%
127	VeriChip Corporation	Delray Beach, FL	183.1%	177	Argan, Inc.	Rockville, MD	134.8%
128	Dice Holdings, Inc.	New York, NY	182.8%	178	Payment Data Systems, Inc.	San Antonio, TX	134.0%
129	instaCare Corp.	Westlake Village, CA	181.7%	179	McMoRan Exploration Co.	New Orleans, LA	133.8%
130	Odyssey Marine Exploration, Inc.	Tampa, FL	180.6%	180	Homeland Security Capital Corporation	Arlington, VA	132.7%
131	A&R Transport, Inc.	Morris, IL	179.9%	181	TurboChef Technologies, Inc.	Atlanta, GA	132.5%
132	Barrier Therapeutics, Inc.	Princeton, NJ	178.6%	182	Universal Insurance Holdings, Inc.	Fort Lauderdale, FL	132.1%
133	YTB International, Inc.	Wood River, IL	177.0%	183	NeoGenomics, Inc.	Fort Myers, FL	131.6%
134	Acorda Therapeutics, Inc.	Hawthorne, NY	175.6%	184	Micromet, Inc.	Bethesda, MD	130.6%
135	Quick-Med Technologies, Inc.	Gainesville, FL	171.4%	185	EXCO Resources, Inc.	Dallas, TX	130.5%
136	Atlas Pipeline Partners, L.P.	Moon Township, PA	170.3%	186	NuStar GP Holdings, LLC	San Antonio, TX	130.4%
137	Deerfield Capital Corp.	Rosemont, IL	169.2%	187	Pacific Ethanol, Inc.	Sacramento, CA	129.5%
138	Evolution Petroleum Corporation	Houston, TX	166.8%	188	DUSA Pharmaceuticals, Inc.	Wilmington, MA	129.4%
139	MRU Holdings, Inc.	New York, NY	166.6%	189	Nephros, Inc.	New York, NY	128.9%
140	Incentra Solutions Inc.	Boulder, CO	166.3%	190	Arena Resources, Inc.	Tulsa, OK	128.1%
141	Darwin Professional Underwriters, Inc.	Farmington, CT	165.4%	191	Ashford Hospitality Trust, Inc.	Dallas, TX	127.3%
142	SkyTerra Communications, Inc.	Reston, VA	164.2%	192	IA Global, Inc.	San Francisco, CA	126.8%
143	Inovio Biomedical Corporation	San Diego, CA	163.2%	193	Tix Corporation	Studio City, CA	126.5%
144	Acacia Research Corporation	Newport Beach, CA	163.0%	194	Duff & Phelps Corporation	New York, NY	126.4%
145	BioCryst Pharmaceuticals, Inc.	Birmingham, AL	158.3%	195	Hiland Partners, LP	Enid, OK	126.3%
146	CarBiz Inc.	Sarasota, FL	156.2%	196	International Coffee & Tea, LLC	Los Angeles, CA	124.8%
147	JER Investors Trust Inc.	McLean, VA	155.8%	197	Highland Capital Management, L.P.	Dallas, TX	124.4%
148	Transmeridian Exploration, Inc.	Houston, TX	155.3%	198	Prospect Capital Corporation	New York, NY	124.2%
149	ImaRx Therapeutics, Inc.	Tucson, AZ	154.6%	199	Houston American Energy Corp.	Houston, TX	123.6%
150	JWM Partners, LLC	Greenwich, CT	152.5%	200	Compass Diversified Holdings	Westport, CT	123.4%

Top 500 Companies by Sales Growth in
Hoover's MasterList of U.S. Companies 2009 (continued)

Rank	Company	Headquarters	Five-Year Annualized Sales Growth	Rank	Company	Headquarters	Five-Year Annualized Sales Growth
201	Redpoint Bio Corporation	Ewing, NJ	122.4%	251	Douglas Emmett, Inc.	Santa Monica, CA	97.6%
202	Bronco Drilling Company, Inc.	Edmond, OK	121.2%	252	Dental Patient Care America, Inc.	Salt Lake City, UT	96.8%
203	FiberMark, Inc.	Brattleboro, VT	120.9%	253	NutraCea	Phoenix, AZ	96.1%
204	Luminent Mortgage Capital, Inc.	Philadelphia, PA	119.1%	254	Amalgamated Bank	New York, NY	96.0%
205	Diversified Thermal Solutions, Inc.	Memphis, TN	118.5%	255	Virtual Radiologic Corporation	Minnetonka, MN	95.5%
206	NuState Energy Holdings, Inc.	Boca Raton, FL	118.3%	256	POZEN Inc.	Chapel Hill, NC	94.9%
207	Vonage Holdings Corp.	Holmdel, NJ	118.2%	257	Momenta Pharmaceuticals, Inc.	Cambridge, MA	94.8%
208	Hercules Offshore, Inc.	Houston, TX	118.0%	258	WorldWater & Solar Technologies Corp.	Ewing, NJ	94.2%
209	Sucampo Pharmaceuticals, Inc.	Bethesda, MD	117.6%	259	Cavium Networks, Inc.	Mountain View, CA	94.2%
210	China DongSheng International, Inc.	Hackensack, NJ	117.4%	260	InPlay Technologies, Inc.	Mesa, AZ	93.9%
211	Pharmasset, Inc.	Princeton, NJ	116.6%	261	Auxilio, Inc.	Mission Viejo, CA	93.4%
212	The Amacore Group, Inc.	Tampa, FL	115.3%	262	Accuray Incorporated	Sunnyvale, CA	92.8%
213	Ambassadors International, Inc.	Newport Beach, CA	113.9%	263	First Citizens Bancorporation, Inc.	Columbia, SC	91.8%
214	Peter Piper, Inc.	Scottsdale, AZ	113.2%	264	Trimeris, Inc.	Morrisville, NC	91.2%
215	Nuvelo, Inc.	San Carlos, CA	112.5%	265	Mirapoint, Inc.	Sunnyvale, CA	90.3%
216	Williams Partners L.P.	Tulsa, OK	112.1%	266	Illumina, Inc.	San Diego, CA	90.2%
217	Akeena Solar, Inc.	Los Gatos, CA	111.5%	267	Approach Resources Inc.	Fort Worth, TX	90.0%
218	Cleveland BioLabs, Inc.	Buffalo, NY	111.5%	268	DOR BioPharma Inc.	Ewing, NJ	89.9%
219	BIO-key International, Inc.	Wall, NJ	111.5%	269	NexMed, Inc.	East Windsor, NJ	89.9%
220	American Oil & Gas, Inc.	Denver, CO	111.5%	270	Lithium Technology Corporation	Plymouth Meeting, PA	89.9%
221	TomoTherapy Incorporated	Madison, WI	110.8%	271	WPCS International Incorporated	Exton, PA	89.7%
222	United Foods, Inc.	Bells, TN	110.0%	272	Critical Therapeutics, Inc.	Lexington, MA	89.5%
223	BioMed Realty Trust, Inc.	San Diego, CA	109.9%	273	Sonic Foundry, Inc.	Madison, WI	89.3%
224	Limelight Networks, Inc.	Tempe, AZ	109.6%	274	Alpha Innotech Corp.	San Leandro, CA	89.0%
225	DexCom, Inc.	San Diego, CA	109.1%	275	Novatel Wireless, Inc.	San Diego, CA	88.8%
226	Sovereign Exploration Associates	Newtown, PA	108.8%	276	Indevus Pharmaceuticals, Inc.	Lexington, MA	88.8%
227	XenoPort, Inc.	Santa Clara, CA	107.0%	277	OSG America L.P.	Tampa, FL	88.8%
228	Javo Beverage Company, Inc.	Vista, CA	106.0%	278	GMX Resources Inc.	Oklahoma City, OK	88.4%
229	Avery Weigh-Tronix, LLC	Fairmont, MN	105.5%	279	Hersha Hospitality Trust	Harrisburg, PA	88.0%
230	InnerWorkings, Inc.	Chicago, IL	105.4%	280	XM Satellite Radio Holdings Inc.	Washington, DC	87.6%
231	Apollo Investment Corporation	New York, NY	105.1%	281	Microlslet, Inc.	San Diego, CA	87.1%
232	Dynavax Technologies Corporation	Berkeley, CA	104.9%	282	The Parent Company	Denver, CO	86.5%
233	Allis-Chalmers Energy Inc.	Houston, TX	104.4%	283	Columbia Sussex Corporation	Crestview Hills, KY	86.2%
234	Vertical Branding, Inc.	Encino, CA	103.9%	284	Vertical Communications, Inc.	Cambridge, MA	86.1%
235	Gasco Energy, Inc.	Englewood, CO	103.3%	285	Natural Nutrition, Inc.	Houston, TX	86.1%
236	Infinite Group, Inc.	Pittsford, NY	102.5%	286	Security With Advanced Technology, Inc.	Loveland, CO	86.1%
237	Sirona Dental Systems, Inc.	Long Island City, NY	102.3%	287	Windstream Corporation	Little Rock, AR	85.9%
238	NACO Industries, Inc.	Logan, UT	101.9%	288	Energy Transfer Partners, L.P.	Dallas, TX	85.7%
239	Omniture, Inc.	Orem, UT	101.4%	289	TheLadders.com, Inc.	New York, NY	85.0%
240	EverBank Financial Corporation	Jacksonville, FL	100.2%	290	BioMimetic Therapeutics, Inc.	Franklin, TN	84.8%
241	Complete Production Services, Inc.	Houston, TX	100.1%	291	SpaceDev, Inc.	Poway, CA	84.4%
242	Ivivi Technologies, Inc.	Northvale, NJ	100.0%	292	Constant Contact, Inc.	Waltham, MA	84.0%
243	ASI Technology Corporation	Henderson, NV	100.0%	293	Trading Technologies International, Inc.	Chicago, IL	84.0%
244	Cardium Therapeutics, Inc.	San Diego, CA	100.0%	294	Atlas America, Inc.	Moon Township, PA	83.9%
245	EGPI Firecreek, Inc.	Scottsdale, AZ	100.0%	295	SuccessFactors, Inc.	San Mateo, CA	83.8%
246	Fairfield Residential LLC	San Diego, CA	99.2%	296	Aurora Oil & Gas Corporation	Traverse City, MI	83.7%
247	Alexion Pharmaceuticals, Inc.	Cheshire, CT	98.9%	297	Google Inc.	Mountain View, CA	83.4%
248	Legacy Reserves LP	Midland, TX	98.7%	298	Access Integrated Technologies, Inc.	Morristown, NJ	83.1%
249	Rentech, Inc.	Los Angeles, CA	98.6%	299	Sport Supply Group, Inc.	Farmers Branch, TX	83.1%
250	M & F Worldwide Corp.	New York, NY	98.1%	300	NetSuite Inc.	San Mateo, CA	83.0%

Top 500 Companies by Sales Growth in
Hoover's MasterList of U.S. Companies 2009 (continued)

Rank	Company	Headquarters	Five-Year Annualized Sales Growth	Rank	Company	Headquarters	Five-Year Annualized Sales Growth
301	Palatin Technologies, Inc.	Cranbury, NJ	82.4%	351	Amylin Pharmaceuticals, Inc.	San Diego, CA	73.7%
302	VMware, Inc.	Palo Alto, CA	82.3%	352	CapLease, Inc.	New York, NY	73.3%
303	The Blackstone Group L.P.	New York, NY	82.3%	353	ShoreTel, Inc.	Sunnyvale, CA	73.3%
304	DivX, Inc.	San Diego, CA	82.2%	354	uVuMobile, Inc.	Duluth, GA	73.2%
305	IceWEB, Inc.	Herndon, VA	82.1%	355	Wherify Wireless, Inc.	San Mateo, CA	73.2%
306	Consulier Engineering, Inc.	Riviera Beach, FL	82.1%	356	WSB Financial Group, Inc.	Bremerton, WA	72.8%
307	Allied Security Innovations, Inc.	Sea Girt, NJ	82.1%	357	Optium Corporation	Chalfont, PA	72.7%
308	AVI BioPharma, Inc.	Portland, OR	82.1%	358	Idera Pharmaceuticals, Inc.	Cambridge, MA	72.7%
309	Titan Global Holdings, Inc.	Fremont, CA	81.7%	359	Neurobiological Technologies, Inc.	Emeryville, CA	72.5%
310	Arrowhead Research Corporation	Pasadena, CA	81.7%	360	Silicon Mountain Holdings, Inc.	Boulder, CO	72.4%
311	Hollis-Eden Pharmaceuticals, Inc.	San Diego, CA	81.7%	361	Rex Energy Corporation	State College, PA	72.4%
312	Auxilium Pharmaceuticals, Inc.	Malvern, PA	81.6%	362	Bank of Florida Corporation	Naples, FL	72.2%
313	Sunair Services Corporation	Boca Raton, FL	81.6%	363	Oscient Pharmaceuticals Corporation	Waltham, MA	72.2%
314	GeoEye, Inc.	Dulles, VA	81.0%	364	Icahn Enterprises L.P.	New York, NY	72.1%
315	Flotek Industries, Inc.	Houston, TX	80.8%	365	NPS Pharmaceuticals, Inc.	Bedminster, NJ	71.8%
316	TGC Industries, Inc.	Plano, TX	80.6%	366	ATP Oil & Gas Corporation	Houston, TX	71.5%
317	OSI Pharmaceuticals, Inc.	Melville, NY	80.1%	367	BioForm Medical, Inc.	San Mateo, CA	71.1%
318	Quest Resource Corporation	Oklahoma City, OK	80.0%	368	Galaxy Energy Corporation	Denver, CO	71.0%
319	ONEOK Partners, L.P.	Tulsa, OK	80.0%	369	3PAR Inc.	Fremont, CA	70.5%
320	GTCR Golder Rauner, LLC	Chicago, IL	80.0%	370	ProLogis	Denver, CO	70.5%
321	Anadys Pharmaceuticals, Inc.	San Diego, CA	79.9%	371	Targa Resources Partners LP	Houston, TX	70.5%
322	Knight Inc.	Houston, TX	79.9%	372	Limco-Piedmont Inc.	Tulsa, OK	70.4%
323	L-1 Identity Solutions, Inc.	Stamford, CT	79.6%	373	Conceptus, Inc.	Mountain View, CA	70.1%
324	Wizzard Software Corporation	Pittsburgh, PA	79.6%	374	GeoResources, Inc.	Williston, ND	70.0%
325	Think Partnership Inc.	Clearwater, FL	79.4%	375	North American Technologies Group, Inc.	Marshall, TX	70.0%
326	CirTran Corporation	West Valley City, UT	79.3%	376	Global Traffic Network, Inc.	New York, NY	69.9%
327	Terremark Worldwide, Inc.	Miami, FL	79.1%	377	Heelys, Inc.	Carrollton, TX	69.6%
328	Emisphere Technologies, Inc.	Cedar Knolls, NJ	78.9%	378	Brookdale Senior Living, Inc.	Chicago, IL	69.5%
329	Fortune Industries, Inc.	Indianapolis, IN	78.8%	379	Mellanox Technologies, Ltd.	Santa Clara, CA	69.5%
330	Spirit AeroSystems Holdings, Inc.	Wichita, KS	78.7%	380	Resource Capital Corp.	New York, NY	69.4%
331	Smith Micro Software, Inc.	Aliso Viejo, CA	78.7%	381	West Texas Gas, Inc.	Midland, TX	69.3%
332	American Electric Technologies, Inc.	Houston, TX	78.4%	382	Hansen Natural Corporation	Corona, CA	69.2%
333	Progenics Pharmaceuticals, Inc.	Tarrytown, NY	78.2%	383	Clean Diesel Technologies, Inc.	Stamford, CT	69.0%
334	BioMarin Pharmaceutical Inc.	Novato, CA	78.0%	384	EnergySolutions, Inc.	Salt Lake City, UT	68.9%
335	Crimson Exploration, Inc.	Houston, TX	77.6%	385	NuStar Energy L.P.	San Antonio, TX	68.9%
336	Avanex Corporation	Fremont, CA	77.6%	386	Gold Reserve Inc.	Spokane, WA	68.8%
337	TorreyPines Therapeutics, Inc.	La Jolla, CA	77.4%	387	BlackRock, Inc.	New York, NY	68.7%
338	Penn Virginia Resource Partners, L.P.	Radnor, PA	77.3%	388	NetLogic Microsystems, Inc.	Mountain View, CA	68.6%
339	The First Marblehead Corporation	Boston, MA	76.2%	389	Pinnacle Financial Partners, Inc.	Nashville, TN	68.5%
340	Agar Supply, Inc.	Taunton, MA	76.1%	390	Delek US Holdings, Inc.	Brentwood, TN	68.4%
341	DiamondRock Hospitality Company	Bethesda, MD	76.0%	391	Startech Environmental Corporation	Wilton, CT	68.2%
342	Wireless Ronin Technologies, Inc.	Minneapolis, MN	76.0%	392	American Soil Technologies, Inc.	Pacoima, CA	68.2%
343	SIGA Technologies, Inc.	New York, NY	75.9%	393	Avalon Pharmaceuticals, Inc.	Germantown, MD	68.2%
344	Greystone Logistics, Inc.	Tulsa, OK	75.7%	394	Metals USA Holdings Corp.	Houston, TX	68.0%
345	Occam Networks, Inc.	Santa Barbara, CA	75.1%	395	LaPolla Industries, Inc.	Houston, TX	67.9%
346	Inspire Pharmaceuticals, Inc.	Durham, NC	74.9%	396	Jarden Corporation	Rye, NY	67.8%
347	NightHawk Radiology Holdings, Inc.	Coeur d'Alene, ID	74.9%	397	Arbor Realty Trust, Inc.	Uniondale, NY	67.8%
348	Epoch Holding Corporation	New York, NY	74.1%	398	Talent Plus, Inc.	Lincoln, NE	67.5%
349	Western Refining, Inc.	El Paso, TX	73.9%	399	Stereotaxis, Inc.	St. Louis, MO	67.4%
350	Och-Ziff Capital Management Group LLC	New York, NY	73.8%	400	SemGroup Energy Partners, L.P.	Tulsa, OK	67.4%

Top 500 Companies by Sales Growth in
Hoover's MasterList of U.S. Companies 2009 (continued)

Rank	Company	Headquarters	Five-Year Annualized Sales Growth	Rank	Company	Headquarters	Five-Year Annualized Sales Growth
401	FX Energy, Inc.	Salt Lake City, UT	67.3%	451	Starent Networks Corporation	Tewksbury, MA	61.8%
402	U.S. Global Investors, Inc.	San Antonio, TX	67.2%	452	NetQoS, Inc.	Austin, TX	61.6%
403	salesforce.com, inc.	San Francisco, CA	67.1%	453	Superior Well Services, Inc.	Indiana, PA	61.6%
404	Beacon Power Corporation	Tyngsboro, MA	67.1%	454	Green Mountain Energy Company	Austin, TX	61.5%
405	PDS Technical Services, Inc.	Irving, TX	66.8%	455	NuVasive, Inc.	San Diego, CA	61.5%
406	Corcept Therapeutics Incorporated	Menlo Park, CA	66.7%	456	First Potomac Realty Trust	Bethesda, MD	61.3%
407	Cheniere Energy, Inc.	Houston, TX	66.7%	457	Source Interlink Companies, Inc.	Bonita Springs, FL	61.3%
408	NetSol Technologies, Inc.	Calabasas, CA	66.6%	458	Intellon Corporation	Ocala, FL	61.1%
409	Pinnacle Gas Resources, Inc.	Sheridan, WY	66.6%	459	LoopNet, Inc.	San Francisco, CA	61.1%
410	Spectrum Pharmaceuticals, Inc.	Irvine, CA	66.6%	460	eMagin Corporation	Bellevue, WA	61.1%
411	Convio, Inc.	Austin, TX	66.6%	461	UNIFI Mutual Holding Company	Lincoln, NE	61.1%
412	International Card Establishment, Inc.	Camarillo, CA	66.4%	462	Iomai Corporation	Gaithersburg, MD	60.8%
413	Freeport-McMoRan Copper & Gold Inc.	Phoenix, AZ	66.3%	463	Rackable Systems, Inc.	Fremont, CA	60.7%
414	The Bank Holdings	Reno, NV	66.3%	464	Gulfport Energy Corporation	Oklahoma City, OK	60.6%
415	Alesco Financial Inc.	Philadelphia, PA	66.2%	465	The Riverside Company	New York, NY	60.6%
416	American Technology Corporation	San Diego, CA	66.1%	466	8x8, Inc.	Santa Clara, CA	60.5%
417	Tennessee Commerce Bancorp, Inc.	Franklin, TN	65.9%	467	Lakes Entertainment, Inc.	Minnetonka, MN	60.5%
418	EV Energy Partners, L.P.	Houston, TX	65.7%	468	Entertainment Distribution	New York, NY	60.3%
419	Evergreen Solar, Inc.	Marlboro, MA	65.6%	469	Extra Space Storage Inc.	Salt Lake City, UT	60.2%
420	Synchronoss Technologies, Inc.	Bridgewater, NJ	65.4%	470	Intuitive Surgical, Inc.	Sunnyvale, CA	60.0%
421	Ceradyne, Inc.	Costa Mesa, CA	65.2%	471	ExlService Holdings, Inc.	New York, NY	59.5%
422	Macquarie Infrastructure Company LLC	New York, NY	65.2%	472	Hungarian Telephone and Cable Corp.	Seattle, WA	59.4%
423	Protocall Technologies Incorporated	Commack, NY	65.1%	473	Regency Energy Partners LP	Dallas, TX	59.3%
424	AtheroGenics, Inc.	Alpharetta, GA	65.0%	474	Annaly Capital Management, Inc.	New York, NY	59.0%
425	CV Therapeutics, Inc.	Palo Alto, CA	64.5%	475	Geron Corporation	Menlo Park, CA	58.6%
426	ImClone Systems Incorporated	New York, NY	64.4%	476	Drury Inns, Inc.	St. Louis, MO	58.4%
427	Altus Pharmaceuticals Inc.	Cambridge, MA	64.4%	477	Neose Technologies, Inc.	Horsham, PA	58.3%
428	Energy Transfer Equity, L.P.	Dallas, TX	64.3%	478	CapitalSource Inc.	Chevy Chase, MD	58.3%
429	Sigma Designs, Inc.	Milpitas, CA	64.1%	479	Digital Realty Trust, Inc.	San Francisco, CA	58.2%
430	U.S. TelePacific Corp.	Los Angeles, CA	64.0%	480	R.H. Donnelley Corporation	Cary, NC	57.9%
431	Axesstel, Inc.	San Diego, CA	64.0%	481	Caspian Services, Inc.	Salt Lake City, UT	57.7%
432	Perficient, Inc.	Austin, TX	63.9%	482	Alkermes, Inc.	Cambridge, MA	57.6%
433	Organic To Go Food Corporation	Seattle, WA	63.9%	483	American Vantage Companies	Las Vegas, NV	57.6%
434	Sun American Bancorp	Boca Raton, FL	63.9%	484	Mariner Energy, Inc.	Houston, TX	57.4%
435	Allegiant Travel Company	Las Vegas, NV	63.9%	485	IntercontinentalExchange, Inc.	Atlanta, GA	57.3%
436	Acacia Technologies Group	Newport Beach, CA	63.8%	486	Theravance, Inc.	South San Francisco, CA	57.2%
437	Basin Water, Inc.	Rancho Cucamonga, CA	63.5%	487	National Lampoon, Inc.	West Hollywood, CA	57.2%
438	Gateway Financial Holdings, Inc.	Virginia Beach, VA	63.1%	488	Marchex, Inc.	Seattle, WA	56.9%
439	S & B Engineers and Constructors, Ltd.	Houston, TX	62.9%	489	Aruba Networks, Inc.	Sunnyvale, CA	56.8%
440	Aaron Industries, Inc.	Clinton, SC	62.7%	490	DealerTrack Holdings, Inc.	Lake Success, NY	56.8%
441	AIMS Worldwide, Inc.	Fairfax, VA	62.7%	491	Rackspace, Inc.	San Antonio, TX	56.7%
442	Cepheid	Sunnyvale, CA	62.7%	492	American Capital Strategies, Ltd.	Bethesda, MD	56.6%
443	Distributed Energy Systems Corp.	Wallingford, CT	62.7%	493	Pacific Sands, Inc.	Racine, WI	56.5%
444	FinancialContent, Inc.	Foster City, CA	62.7%	494	National Scientific Corporation	Scottsdale, AZ	56.5%
445	One Voice Technologies, Inc.	La Jolla, CA	62.7%	495	Patriot Scientific Corporation	Carlsbad, CA	56.5%
446	ValueClick, Inc.	Westlake Village, CA	62.5%	496	MIRENCO, Inc.	Radcliffe, IA	56.5%
447	Global Entertainment Corporation	Phoenix, AZ	62.5%	497	MathStar, Inc.	Hillsboro, OR	56.5%
448	Mueller Water Products, Inc.	Atlanta, GA	62.4%	498	Alliance Pharmaceutical Corp.	La Jolla, CA	56.5%
449	Endologix, Inc.	Irvine, CA	62.4%	499	AmTrust Financial Services, Inc.	New York, NY	56.3%
450	First Clover Leaf Financial Corp.	Edwardsville, IL	62.0%	500	Zavata, Inc.	Atlanta, GA	56.3%

Top 500 Companies by Market Value in
Hoover's MasterList of U.S. Companies 2009

Rank	Company	Headquarters	Mkt. Value* ($ mil.)	Rank	Company	Headquarters	Mkt. Value ($ mil.)
1	Exxon Mobil Corporation	Irving, TX	504,240	51	The Home Depot, Inc.	Atlanta, GA	51,461
2	General Electric Company	Fairfield, CT	370,240	52	Amgen Inc.	Thousand Oaks, CA	50,480
3	Microsoft Corporation	Redmond, WA	276,429	53	Kraft Foods Inc.	Northfield, IL	50,047
4	AT&T Inc.	San Antonio, TX	251,170	54	Merrill Lynch & Co., Inc.	New York, NY	49,582
5	Wal-Mart Stores, Inc.	Bentonville, AR	201,590	55	United Parcel Service, Inc.	Atlanta, GA	48,938
6	Chevron Corporation	San Ramon, CA	195,100	56	WellPoint, Inc.	Indianapolis, IN	48,796
7	The Procter & Gamble Company	Cincinnati, OH	191,641	57	Target Corporation	Minneapolis, MN	46,709
8	Johnson & Johnson	New Brunswick, NJ	191,374	58	Honeywell International Inc.	Morristown, NJ	45,965
9	Bank of America Corporation	Charlotte, NC	183,107	59	eBay Inc.	San Jose, CA	45,421
10	Cisco Systems, Inc.	San Jose, CA	176,717	60	Transocean Inc.	Houston, TX	45,410
11	Google Inc.	Mountain View, CA	163,256	61	News Corporation	New York, NY	45,381
12	Intel Corporation	Santa Clara, CA	155,690	62	Caterpillar Inc.	Peoria, IL	45,276
13	Pfizer Inc.	New York, NY	153,678	63	MetLife, Inc.	New York, NY	44,935
14	Berkshire Hathaway Inc.	Omaha, NE	153,122	64	Texas Instruments Incorporated	Dallas, TX	44,863
15	International Business Machines	Armonk, NY	149,744	65	Walgreen Co.	Deerfield, IL	44,671
16	American International Group, Inc.	New York, NY	147,475	66	Marathon Oil Corporation	Houston, TX	43,211
17	Citigroup Inc.	New York, NY	147,040	67	Schering-Plough Corporation	Kenilworth, NJ	43,183
18	JPMorgan Chase & Co.	New York, NY	146,986	68	Lockheed Martin Corporation	Bethesda, MD	42,959
19	ConocoPhillips	Houston, TX	142,502	69	Gilead Sciences, Inc.	Foster City, CA	42,904
20	The Coca-Cola Company	Atlanta, GA	142,256	70	Emerson Electric Co.	St. Louis, MO	41,960
21	Apple Inc.	Cupertino, CA	133,876	71	Dell Inc.	Round Rock, TX	41,921
22	Hewlett-Packard Company	Palo Alto, CA	133,334	72	Prudential Financial, Inc.	Newark, NJ	41,623
23	Verizon Communications Inc.	New York, NY	129,076	73	Colgate-Palmolive Company	New York, NY	39,684
24	Merck & Co., Inc.	Whitehouse Station, NJ	126,244	74	E. I. du Pont de Nemours and Company	Wilmington, DE	39,652
25	PepsiCo, Inc.	Purchase, NY	123,633	75	Devon Energy Corporation	Oklahoma City, OK	39,494
26	Schlumberger Limited	Houston, TX	117,819	76	Freeport-McMoRan Copper & Gold Inc.	Phoenix, AZ	39,235
27	Oracle Corporation	Redwood City, CA	117,626	77	EMC Corporation	Hopkinton, MA	38,954
28	Publix Super Markets, Inc.	Lakeland, FL	92,294	78	Federal National Mortgage Association	Washington, DC	38,945
29	The Goldman Sachs Group, Inc.	New York, NY	88,544	79	Amazon.com, Inc.	Seattle, WA	38,538
30	Abbott Laboratories	Abbott Park, IL	87,027	80	Monsanto Company	St. Louis, MO	38,051
31	United Technologies Corporation	Hartford, CT	75,281	81	Corning Incorporated	Corning, NY	37,616
32	Wachovia Corporation	Charlotte, NC	74,539	82	Valero Energy Corporation	San Antonio, TX	37,582
33	UnitedHealth Group Incorporated	Minnetonka, MN	72,925	83	Comcast Corporation	Philadelphia, PA	37,498
34	Genentech, Inc.	South San Francisco, CA	70,558	84	Anheuser-Busch Companies, Inc.	St. Louis, MO	37,431
35	QUALCOMM Incorporated	San Diego, CA	69,560	85	Sprint Nextel Corporation	Overland Park, KS	37,355
36	McDonald's Corporation	Oak Brook, IL	68,648	86	Lowe's Companies, Inc.	Mooresville, NC	37,252
37	Occidental Petroleum Corporation	Los Angeles, CA	67,530	87	The Dow Chemical Company	Midland, MI	37,069
38	The Walt Disney Company	Burbank, CA	67,480	88	Baxter International Inc.	Deerfield, IL	36,783
39	The Boeing Company	Chicago, IL	67,173	89	Las Vegas Sands Corp.	Las Vegas, NV	36,611
40	U.S. Bancorp	Minneapolis, MN	62,612	90	CME Group Inc.	Chicago, IL	36,549
41	Eli Lilly and Company	Indianapolis, IN	60,561	91	Motorola, Inc.	Schaumburg, IL	36,300
42	American Express Company	New York, NY	60,239	92	General Dynamics Corporation	Falls Church, VA	35,950
43	3M Company	St. Paul, MN	59,796	93	Apache Corporation	Houston, TX	35,803
44	Time Warner Inc.	New York, NY	59,320	94	FedEx Corporation	Memphis, TN	34,379
45	Wyeth	Madison, NJ	59,117	95	Deere & Company	Moline, IL	34,050
46	CVS Caremark Corporation	Woonsocket, RI	57,458	96	The Travelers Companies, Inc.	St. Paul, MN	33,776
47	Morgan Stanley	New York, NY	55,688	97	Halliburton Company	Houston, TX	33,361
48	Medtronic, Inc.	Minneapolis, MN	55,594	98	Lehman Brothers Holdings Inc.	New York, NY	33,312
49	Exelon Corporation	Chicago, IL	53,964	99	Hess Corporation	New York, NY	32,336
50	Bristol-Myers Squibb Company	New York, NY	52,350	100	State Street Corporation	Boston, MA	31,366

*Market value at the latest available fiscal year-end

Top 500 Companies by Market Value in
Hoover's MasterList of U.S. Companies 2009 (continued)

Rank	Company	Headquarters	Mkt. Value ($ mil.)	Rank	Company	Headquarters	Mkt. Value ($ mil.)
101	Franklin Resources, Inc.	San Mateo, CA	31,297	151	The Williams Companies, Inc.	Tulsa, OK	20,967
102	Yahoo! Inc.	Sunnyvale, CA	31,102	152	First Solar, Inc.	Tempe, AZ	20,904
103	Anadarko Petroleum Corporation	The Woodlands, TX	30,743	153	Kellogg Company	Battle Creek, MI	20,642
104	Stryker Corporation	Kalamazoo, MI	30,724	154	General Mills, Inc.	Minneapolis, MN	20,618
105	Aflac Incorporated	Columbus, GA	30,471	155	Safeway Inc.	Pleasanton, CA	20,596
106	Alcoa Inc.	Pittsburgh, PA	30,242	156	The Chubb Corporation	Warren, NJ	20,448
107	The Charles Schwab Corporation	San Francisco, CA	29,659	157	MEMC Electronic Materials, Inc.	St. Peters, MO	20,212
108	Southern Company	Atlanta, GA	29,590	158	SYSCO Corporation	Houston, TX	20,185
109	The Allstate Corporation	Northbrook, IL	29,405	159	PACCAR Inc	Bellevue, WA	20,070
110	Kimberly-Clark Corporation	Irving, TX	29,187	160	Chesapeake Energy Corporation	Oklahoma City, OK	20,037
111	Burlington Northern Santa Fe Corporation	Fort Worth, TX	28,939	161	Becton, Dickinson and Company	Franklin Lakes, NJ	20,012
112	Aetna Inc.	Hartford, CT	28,651	162	Genzyme Corporation	Cambridge, MA	19,802
113	Illinois Tool Works Inc.	Glenview, IL	28,381	163	Simon Property Group, Inc.	Indianapolis, IN	19,780
114	Carnival Corporation	Miami, FL	28,155	164	Diamond Offshore Drilling, Inc.	Houston, TX	19,720
115	Praxair, Inc.	Danbury, CT	27,987	165	Allergan, Inc.	Irvine, CA	19,651
116	Danaher Corporation	Washington, DC	27,900	166	Reynolds American Inc.	Winston-Salem, NC	19,459
117	FPL Group, Inc.	Juno Beach, FL	27,610	167	Starbucks Corporation	Seattle, WA	19,343
118	Dominion Resources, Inc.	Richmond, VA	27,379	168	YUM! Brands, Inc.	Louisville, KY	19,231
119	The Hartford Financial Services Group, Inc.	Hartford, CT	27,364	169	Norfolk Southern Corporation	Norfolk, VA	19,132
120	Medco Health Solutions, Inc.	Franklin Lakes, NJ	26,995	170	MasterCard Incorporated	Purchase, NY	18,792
121	Costco Wholesale Corporation	Issaquah, WA	26,986	171	American Electric Power Company, Inc.	Columbus, OH	18,644
122	Loews Corporation	New York, NY	26,664	172	Celgene Corporation	Summit, NJ	18,628
123	Northrop Grumman Corporation	Los Angeles, CA	26,567	173	Newmont Mining Corporation	Denver, CO	18,492
124	The DIRECTV Group, Inc.	El Segundo, CA	26,548	174	Express Scripts, Inc.	St. Louis, MO	18,423
125	National Oilwell Varco, Inc.	Houston, TX	26,224	175	Constellation Energy Group, Inc.	Baltimore, MD	18,243
126	Applied Materials, Inc.	Santa Clara, CA	26,135	176	The Western Union Company	Englewood, CO	18,205
127	Thomson Reuters Corporation	New York, NY	26,026	177	CSX Corporation	Jacksonville, FL	18,056
128	Cardinal Health, Inc.	Dublin, OH	26,003	178	Textron Inc.	Providence, RI	17,912
129	Automatic Data Processing, Inc.	Roseland, NJ	25,970	179	Principal Financial Group, Inc.	Des Moines, IA	17,836
130	Raytheon Company	Waltham, MA	25,870	180	Best Buy Co., Inc.	Richfield, MN	17,659
131	Baker Hughes Incorporated	Houston, TX	25,579	181	Coach, Inc.	New York, NY	17,654
132	Duke Energy Corporation	Charlotte, NC	25,455	182	Tyco Electronics Ltd.	Berwyn, PA	17,624
133	Public Service Enterprise Group	Newark, NJ	24,979	183	Capital One Financial Corporation	McLean, VA	17,621
134	XTO Energy Inc.	Fort Worth, TX	24,925	184	Edison International	Rosemead, CA	17,389
135	Time Warner Cable Inc.	New York, NY	24,895	185	Juniper Networks, Inc.	Sunnyvale, CA	17,357
136	MGM MIRAGE	Las Vegas, NV	24,682	186	The Kroger Co.	Cincinnati, OH	17,225
137	Accenture Ltd	New York, NY	24,558	187	Boston Scientific Corporation	Natick, MA	17,207
138	Adobe Systems Incorporated	San Jose, CA	24,079	188	Clear Channel Communications, Inc.	San Antonio, TX	17,188
139	Thermo Fisher Scientific Inc.	Waltham, MA	23,951	189	Nucor Corporation	Charlotte, NC	17,058
140	Johnson Controls, Inc.	Milwaukee, WI	23,377	190	American Tower Corporation	Boston, MA	17,019
141	NYSE Euronext, Inc.	New York, NY	23,259	191	Fortune Brands, Inc.	Deerfield, IL	16,997
142	Entergy Corporation	New Orleans, LA	23,082	192	Biogen Idec Inc.	Cambridge, MA	16,948
143	The PNC Financial Services Group, Inc.	Pittsburgh, PA	22,387	193	Avon Products, Inc.	New York, NY	16,907
144	FirstEnergy Corp.	Akron, OH	22,052	194	Northern Trust Corporation	Chicago, IL	16,894
145	Tyco International Ltd.	Princeton, NJ	22,006	195	Staples, Inc.	Framingham, MA	16,862
146	EOG Resources, Inc.	Houston, TX	22,002	196	BB&T Corporation	Winston-Salem, NC	16,744
147	NIKE, Inc.	Beaverton, OR	21,798	197	CBS Corporation	New York, NY	16,688
148	SunTrust Banks Inc.	Atlanta, GA	21,772	198	Peabody Energy Corporation	St. Louis, MO	16,647
149	Archer Daniels Midland Company	Decatur, IL	21,277	199	Regions Financial Corporation	Birmingham, AL	16,404
150	Air Products and Chemicals, Inc.	Allentown, PA	21,053	200	Union Pacific Corporation	Omaha, NE	16,385

Top 500 Companies by Market Value in
Hoover's MasterList of U.S. Companies 2009 (continued)

Rank	Company	Headquarters	Mkt. Value ($ mil.)	Rank	Company	Headquarters	Mkt. Value ($ mil.)
201	Waste Management, Inc.	Houston, TX	16,339	251	Fluor Corporation	Irving, TX	12,923
202	ProLogis	Denver, CO	16,334	252	Cummins, Inc.	Columbus, IN	12,877
203	Spectra Energy Corp	Houston, TX	16,332	253	Wynn Resorts, Limited	Las Vegas, NV	12,824
204	PG&E Corporation	San Francisco, CA	16,305	254	Humana Inc.	Louisville, KY	12,804
205	Sempra Energy	San Diego, CA	16,151	255	Coca-Cola Enterprises Inc.	Atlanta, GA	12,675
206	Murphy Oil Corporation	El Dorado, AR	16,117	256	Wm. Wrigley Jr. Company	Chicago, IL	12,670
207	T. Rowe Price Group, Inc.	Baltimore, MD	16,109	257	Ecolab Inc.	St. Paul, MN	12,639
208	Electronic Arts Inc.	Redwood City, CA	15,875	258	Sara Lee Corporation	Downers Grove, IL	12,605
209	The Mosaic Company	Plymouth, MN	15,486	259	Progress Energy, Inc.	Raleigh, NC	12,592
210	Paychex, Inc.	Rochester, NY	15,439	260	ConAgra Foods, Inc.	Omaha, NE	12,568
211	Zimmer Holdings, Inc.	Warsaw, IN	15,406	261	NYMEX Holdings, Inc.	New York, NY	12,556
212	Lincoln National Corporation	Radnor, PA	15,384	262	Ameriprise Financial, Inc.	Minneapolis, MN	12,551
213	Omnicom Group Inc.	New York, NY	15,352	263	Qwest Communications International Inc.	Denver, CO	12,529
214	Weyerhaeuser Company	Federal Way, WA	15,301	264	Weatherford International Ltd.	Houston, TX	12,472
215	Noble Corporation	Sugar Land, TX	15,157	265	Forest Laboratories, Inc.	New York, NY	12,459
216	CIGNA Corporation	Philadelphia, PA	15,022	266	Intuitive Surgical, Inc.	Sunnyvale, CA	12,426
217	Xerox Corporation	Norwalk, CT	14,849	267	Broadcom Corporation	Irvine, CA	12,256
218	Smith International, Inc.	Houston, TX	14,826	268	Marriott International, Inc.	Bethesda, MD	12,184
219	H. J. Heinz Company	Pittsburgh, PA	14,648	269	Rockwell Collins, Inc.	Cedar Rapids, IA	12,110
220	Aon Corporation	Chicago, IL	14,512	270	El Paso Corporation	Houston, TX	12,077
221	McKesson Corporation	San Francisco, CA	14,506	271	Washington Mutual, Inc.	Seattle, WA	12,012
222	The AES Corporation	Arlington, VA	14,339	272	ITT Corporation	White Plains, NY	11,986
223	Sears Holdings Corporation	Hoffman Estates, IL	14,297	273	Crown Castle International Corp.	Houston, TX	11,752
224	Ford Motor Company	Dearborn, MI	14,295	274	Macy's, Inc.	Cincinnati, OH	11,752
225	United States Steel Corporation	Pittsburgh, PA	14,267	275	Seagate Technology LLC	Scotts Valley, CA	11,647
226	Kohl's Corporation	Menomonee Falls, WI	14,260	276	PPG Industries, Inc.	Pittsburgh, PA	11,504
227	Campbell Soup Company	Camden, NJ	14,209	277	CA, Inc.	Islandia, NY	11,470
228	The Gap Inc.	San Francisco, CA	14,196	278	Ameren Corporation	St. Louis, MO	11,292
229	Eaton Corporation	Cleveland, OH	14,155	279	Foster Wheeler Ltd.	Clinton, NJ	11,242
230	The McGraw-Hill Companies, Inc.	New York, NY	14,123	280	Harley-Davidson, Inc.	Milwaukee, WI	11,140
231	Symantec Corporation	Cupertino, CA	14,118	281	SunPower Corporation	San Jose, CA	11,101
232	Precision Castparts Corp.	Portland, OR	14,090	282	Genworth Financial, Inc.	Richmond, VA	11,096
233	General Motors Corporation	Detroit, MI	14,089	283	Boston Properties, Inc.	Boston, MA	10,972
234	St. Jude Medical, Inc.	St. Paul, MN	14,081	284	Ultra Petroleum Corp.	Houston, TX	10,868
235	NVIDIA Corporation	Santa Clara, CA	13,900	285	TD AMERITRADE Holding Corporation	Omaha, NE	10,835
236	Enterprise Products Partners L.P.	Houston, TX	13,823	286	J. C. Penney Company, Inc.	Plano, TX	10,767
237	Marsh & McLennan Companies, Inc.	New York, NY	13,775	287	Biomet, Inc.	Warsaw, IN	10,716
238	International Paper Company	Memphis, TN	13,765	288	Allegheny Energy, Inc.	Greensburg, PA	10,637
239	Noble Energy, Inc.	Houston, TX	13,664	289	Electronic Data Systems Corporation	Plano, TX	10,569
240	International Game Technology	Reno, NV	13,658	290	KLA-Tencor Corporation	San Jose, CA	10,515
241	Agilent Technologies, Inc.	Santa Clara, CA	13,634	291	Cameron International Corporation	Houston, TX	10,493
242	Vornado Realty Trust	New York, NY	13,463	292	Leucadia National Corporation	New York, NY	10,483
243	IntercontinentalExchange, Inc.	Atlanta, GA	13,419	293	National City Corporation	Cleveland, OH	10,435
244	Fifth Third Bancorp	Cincinnati, OH	13,386	294	Rohm and Haas Company	Philadelphia, PA	10,394
245	McDermott International, Inc.	Houston, TX	13,326	295	Rockwell Automation, Inc.	Milwaukee, WI	10,385
246	Consolidated Edison, Inc.	New York, NY	13,288	296	Quest Diagnostics Incorporated	Madison, NJ	10,265
247	L-3 Communications Holdings, Inc.	New York, NY	13,155	297	NRG Energy, Inc.	Princeton, NJ	10,260
248	CONSOL Energy Inc.	Pittsburgh, PA	13,037	298	General Growth Properties, Inc.	Chicago, IL	10,044
249	The Progressive Corporation	Mayfield Village, OH	13,033	299	Analog Devices, Inc.	Norwood, MA	9,980
250	The TJX Companies, Inc.	Framingham, MA	12,933	300	Equity Residential	Chicago, IL	9,831

Top 500 Companies by Market Value in
Hoover's MasterList of U.S. Companies 2009 (continued)

Rank	Company	Headquarters	Mkt. Value ($ mil.)	Rank	Company	Headquarters	Mkt. Value ($ mil.)
301	Cognizant Technology Solutions	Teaneck, NJ	9,775	351	Waters Corporation	Milford, MA	7,970
302	Apollo Group, Inc.	Phoenix, AZ	9,730	352	Plum Creek Timber Company, Inc.	Seattle, WA	7,933
303	Intuit Inc.	Mountain View, CA	9,713	353	Assurant, Inc.	New York, NY	7,881
304	Expeditors International	Seattle, WA	9,517	354	Molson Coors Brewing Company	Denver, CO	7,799
305	C. R. Bard, Inc.	Murray Hill, NJ	9,498	355	Hudson City Bancorp, Inc.	Paramus, NJ	7,789
306	Autodesk, Inc.	San Rafael, CA	9,465	356	BJ Services Company	Houston, TX	7,775
307	SLM Corporation	Reston, VA	9,396	357	Legg Mason, Inc.	Baltimore, MD	7,756
308	The Clorox Company	Oakland, CA	9,393	358	Masco Corporation	Taylor, MI	7,756
309	Questar Corporation	Salt Lake City, UT	9,348	359	V.F. Corporation	Greensboro, NC	7,710
310	Cooper Industries, Ltd.	Houston, TX	9,321	360	Genuine Parts Company	Atlanta, GA	7,689
311	C.H. Robinson Worldwide, Inc.	Eden Prairie, MN	9,245	361	AmerisourceBergen Corporation	Chesterbrook, PA	7,682
312	Kimco Realty Corporation	New Hyde Park, NY	9,202	362	Range Resources Corporation	Fort Worth, TX	7,679
313	Kinder Morgan Energy Partners, L.P.	Houston, TX	9,190	363	Marvell Technology Group Ltd.	Santa Clara, CA	7,656
314	Coventry Health Care, Inc.	Bethesda, MD	9,162	364	Harman International Industries	Washington, DC	7,620
315	Fiserv, Inc.	Brookfield, WI	9,161	365	Embarq Corporation	Overland Park, KS	7,583
316	Icahn Enterprises L.P.	New York, NY	9,144	366	Parker Hannifin Corporation	Cleveland, OH	7,582
317	CNA Financial Corporation	Chicago, IL	9,129	367	HCP, Inc.	Long Beach, CA	7,559
318	Jacobs Engineering Group Inc.	Pasadena, CA	9,086	368	SanDisk Corporation	Milpitas, CA	7,519
319	Reliant Energy, Inc.	Houston, TX	9,042	369	Iron Mountain Incorporated	Boston, MA	7,430
320	Royal Caribbean Cruises Ltd.	Miami, FL	9,018	370	Bed Bath & Beyond Inc.	Union, NJ	7,338
321	Moody's Corporation	New York, NY	8,975	371	FMC Technologies, Inc.	Houston, TX	7,331
322	Southwest Airlines Co.	Dallas, TX	8,965	372	Annaly Capital Management, Inc.	New York, NY	7,305
323	M&T Bank Corporation	Buffalo, NY	8,961	373	Owens-Illinois, Inc.	Perrysburg, OH	7,303
324	The Pepsi Bottling Group, Inc.	Somers, NY	8,951	374	Denbury Resources Inc.	Plano, TX	7,281
325	Dover Corporation	New York, NY	8,943	375	AvalonBay Communities, Inc.	Alexandria, VA	7,279
326	Host Hotels & Resorts, Inc.	Bethesda, MD	8,905	376	DTE Energy Company	Detroit, MI	7,176
327	Gannett Co., Inc.	McLean, VA	8,801	377	Newell Rubbermaid Inc.	Atlanta, GA	7,161
328	Goodrich Corporation	Charlotte, NC	8,799	378	H&R Block, Inc.	Kansas City, MO	7,130
329	Nordstrom, Inc.	Seattle, WA	8,783	379	Energy Transfer Partners, L.P.	Dallas, TX	7,129
330	Allegheny Technologies Incorporated	Pittsburgh, PA	8,777	380	The Sherwin-Williams Company	Cleveland, OH	7,128
331	Mirant Corporation	Atlanta, GA	8,646	381	Citrix Systems, Inc.	Fort Lauderdale, FL	7,122
332	ENSCO International Incorporated	Dallas, TX	8,579	382	Harris Corporation	Melbourne, FL	7,068
333	Sunoco, Inc.	Philadelphia, PA	8,519	383	Sigma-Aldrich Corporation	St. Louis, MO	7,065
334	Micron Technology, Inc.	Boise, ID	8,496	384	VMware, Inc.	Palo Alto, CA	7,048
335	GameStop Corp.	Grapevine, TX	8,456	385	DISH Network Corporation	Englewood, CO	6,964
336	Starwood Hotels & Resorts Worldwide, Inc.	White Plains, NY	8,410	386	W.W. Grainger, Inc.	Lake Forest, IL	6,954
337	Laboratory Corporation of America Holdings	Burlington, NC	8,384	387	Newfield Exploration Company	Houston, TX	6,921
338	VeriSign, Inc.	Mountain View, CA	8,381	388	Mattel, Inc.	El Segundo, CA	6,881
339	Linear Technology Corporation	Milpitas, CA	8,309	389	The NASDAQ OMX Group, Inc.	New York, NY	6,873
340	Discover Financial Services	Riverwoods, IL	8,297	390	Liberty Global, Inc.	Englewood, CO	6,846
341	Amphenol Corporation	Wallingford, CT	8,293	391	Whole Foods Market, Inc.	Austin, TX	6,817
342	UST Inc.	Stamford, CT	8,271	392	IAC/InterActiveCorp	New York, NY	6,794
343	NII Holdings, Inc.	Reston, VA	8,210	393	DENTSPLY International Inc.	York, PA	6,789
344	Expedia, Inc.	Bellevue, WA	8,205	394	The Goodyear Tire & Rubber Company	Akron, OH	6,776
345	Energy Transfer Equity, L.P.	Dallas, TX	8,189	395	MetroPCS Communications, Inc.	Dallas, TX	6,771
346	Pitney Bowes Inc.	Stamford, CT	8,160	396	Discovery Holding Company	Englewood, CO	6,767
347	R.R. Donnelley & Sons Company	Chicago, IL	8,148	397	Hospira, Inc.	Lake Forest, IL	6,767
348	AutoZone, Inc.	Memphis, TN	8,130	398	UnionBanCal Corporation	San Francisco, CA	6,742
349	National Semiconductor Corporation	Santa Clara, CA	8,089	399	The Washington Post Company	Washington, DC	6,592
350	NetApp, Inc.	Sunnyvale, CA	8,010	400	KBR, Inc.	Houston, TX	6,585

Top 500 Companies by Market Value in
Hoover's MasterList of U.S. Companies 2009 (continued)

Rank	Company	Headquarters	Mkt. Value ($ mil.)	Rank	Company	Headquarters	Mkt. Value ($ mil.)
401	Terex Corporation	Westport, CT	6,577	451	Wisconsin Energy Corporation	Milwaukee, WI	5,696
402	AllianceBernstein Holding L.P.	New York, NY	6,566	452	New York Community Bancorp, Inc.	Westbury, NY	5,693
403	Cincinnati Financial Corporation	Fairfield, OH	6,564	453	Cablevision Systems Corporation	Bethpage, NY	5,660
404	Lam Research Corporation	Fremont, CA	6,561	454	Pride International, Inc.	Houston, TX	5,658
405	The Hershey Company	Hershey, PA	6,550	455	Virgin Media Inc.	New York, NY	5,622
406	Tesoro Corporation	San Antonio, TX	6,537	456	BorgWarner Inc.	Auburn Hills, MI	5,622
407	Comerica Incorporated	Dallas, TX	6,529	457	Torchmark Corporation	McKinney, TX	5,579
408	Applera Corporation	Norwalk, CT	6,514	458	Total System Services, Inc.	Columbus, GA	5,568
409	Equitable Resources, Inc.	Pittsburgh, PA	6,508	459	Henry Schein, Inc.	Melville, NY	5,560
410	Xilinx, Inc.	San Jose, CA	6,477	460	Roper Industries, Inc.	Sarasota, FL	5,552
411	American Capital Strategies, Ltd.	Bethesda, MD	6,457	461	Covance Inc.	Princeton, NJ	5,547
412	Celanese Corporation	Dallas, TX	6,437	462	CenterPoint Energy, Inc.	Houston, TX	5,533
413	Arch Coal, Inc.	St. Louis, MO	6,432	463	SL Green Realty Corp.	New York, NY	5,492
414	Darden Restaurants, Inc.	Orlando, FL	6,408	464	Sovereign Bancorp, Inc.	Philadelphia, PA	5,488
415	Energizer Holdings, Inc.	St. Louis, MO	6,353	465	Martin Marietta Materials, Inc.	Raleigh, NC	5,479
416	The Manitowoc Company, Inc.	Manitowoc, WI	6,342	466	Janus Capital Group Inc.	Denver, CO	5,463
417	Eastman Kodak Company	Rochester, NY	6,299	467	MeadWestvaco Corporation	Glen Allen, VA	5,441
418	SEI Investments Company	Oaks, PA	6,253	468	SPX Corporation	Charlotte, NC	5,430
419	AGCO Corporation	Duluth, GA	6,228	469	White Mountains Insurance Group, Ltd.	Hanover, NH	5,425
420	Whirlpool Corporation	Benton Harbor, MI	6,204	470	Flowserve Corporation	Irving, TX	5,417
421	BMC Software, Inc.	Houston, TX	6,198	471	Harsco Corporation	Camp Hill, PA	5,411
422	salesforce.com, inc.	San Francisco, CA	6,193	472	Huntington Bancshares	Columbus, OH	5,406
423	CF Industries Holdings, Inc.	Deerfield, IL	6,190	473	Exterran Holdings, Inc.	Houston, TX	5,369
424	Computer Sciences Corporation	Falls Church, VA	6,166	474	Health Net, Inc.	Woodland Hills, CA	5,327
425	Gerdau Ameristeel Corporation	Tampa, FL	6,150	475	People's United Financial, Inc.	Bridgeport, CT	5,310
426	Cintas Corporation	Cincinnati, OH	6,087	476	Avery Dennison Corporation	Pasadena, CA	5,255
427	Ventas, Inc.	Louisville, KY	6,048	477	Varian Medical Systems, Inc.	Palo Alto, CA	5,241
428	Joy Global Inc.	Milwaukee, WI	6,045	478	Stericycle, Inc.	Lake Forest, IL	5,192
429	DaVita Inc.	El Segundo, CA	6,037	479	NiSource Inc.	Merrillville, IN	5,179
430	McAfee, Inc.	Santa Clara, CA	6,036	480	Penn National Gaming, Inc.	Wyomissing, PA	5,174
431	Plains Exploration and Production Company	Houston, TX	6,035	481	AK Steel Holding Corporation	West Chester, OH	5,156
432	Microchip Technology Incorporated	Chandler, AZ	6,033	482	The Macerich Company	Santa Monica, CA	5,138
433	Plains All American Pipeline, L.P.	Houston, TX	6,031	483	The Estée Lauder Companies Inc.	New York, NY	5,121
434	Fastenal Company	Winona, MN	6,027	484	SandRidge Energy, Inc.	Oklahoma City, OK	5,118
435	Cypress Semiconductor Corporation	San Jose, CA	5,949	485	Hertz Global Holdings, Inc.	Park Ridge, NJ	5,114
436	Pepco Holdings, Inc.	Washington, DC	5,940	486	Tyson Foods, Inc.	Springdale, AR	5,105
437	Avnet, Inc.	Phoenix, AZ	5,938	487	Affiliated Computer Services, Inc.	Dallas, TX	5,086
438	Altera Corporation	San Jose, CA	5,934	488	Mohawk Industries, Inc.	Calhoun, GA	5,086
439	SUPERVALU INC.	Eden Prairie, MN	5,923	489	MDU Resources Group, Inc.	Bismarck, ND	5,036
440	Windstream Corporation	Little Rock, AR	5,918	490	The Dun & Bradstreet Corporation	Short Hills, NJ	5,034
441	Conexant Systems, Inc.	Newport Beach, CA	5,908	491	AMETEK, Inc.	Paoli, PA	5,029
442	Alliance Data Systems Corporation	Dallas, TX	5,906	492	DST Systems, Inc.	Kansas City, MO	5,019
443	Eaton Vance Corp.	Boston, MA	5,893	493	Zions Bancorporation	Salt Lake City, UT	5,001
444	Office Depot, Inc.	Delray Beach, FL	5,853	494	Amylin Pharmaceuticals, Inc.	San Diego, CA	4,997
445	Republic Services, Inc.	Fort Lauderdale, FL	5,754	495	Safeco Corporation	Seattle, WA	4,994
446	Akamai Technologies, Inc.	Cambridge, MA	5,751	496	Hormel Foods Corporation	Austin, MN	4,992
447	The Blackstone Group L.P.	New York, NY	5,750	497	Teradata Corporation	Miamisburg, OH	4,961
448	Pioneer Natural Resources Company	Irving, TX	5,750	498	SCANA Corporation	Columbia, SC	4,932
449	Barr Pharmaceuticals, Inc.	Montvale, NJ	5,725	499	BE Aerospace, Inc.	Wellington, FL	4,924
450	AMB Property Corporation	San Francisco, CA	5,711	500	Markel Corporation	Glen Allen, VA	4,890

Hoover's
MasterList
of U.S. Companies

Company
Listings

1-800 CONTACTS, INC.

66 E. Wadsworth Park Dr., 3rd Fl.	CEO: Jonathan C. Coon
Draper, UT 84020	CFO: Robert G. Hunter
Phone: 801-316-5000	HR: Max Neves
Fax: 801-924-9905	FYE: Saturday nearest December 31
Web: www.1800contacts.com	Type: Private

Lose a contact? If you can still find your phone or computer, you can get replacement lenses from 1-800 CONTACTS. The firm sells lenses by phone and through its Web site. It offers thousands of lenses that it buys from major manufacturers and distributors and encourages its customers to provide prescriptions for their lenses. 1-800 CONTACTS sells a wide array of contact lenses, including the AquaSoft Singles, Johnson & Johnson Vision Care, CIBA Vision, Bausch & Lomb, Ocular Sciences, and CooperVision brands. Founded in 1995 by entrepreneurs Jonathan Coon and John Nichols, the company was taken private by affiliates of the New York-based private equity firm Fenway Partners in 2007 for about $340 million.

	Annual Growth	12/02	12/03	12/04	12/05	12/06
Sales ($ mil.)	10.2%	168.6	187.3	211.7	237.9	248.7
Net income ($ mil.)	—	(4.0)	(1.4)	(0.6)	(2.6)	(22.5)
Employees	18.7%	555	819	892	1,135	1,101

1-800-FLOWERS.COM, INC.

NASDAQ (GS): FLWS

1 Old Country Rd.	CEO: James F. (Jim) McCann
Carle Place, NY 11514	CFO: William E. Shea
Phone: 516-237-6000	HR: –
Fax: 516-237-6060	FYE: Sunday nearest June 30
Web: www.1800flowers.com	Type: Public

Some say it's all in the name, but 1-800-FLOWERS.COM does more than just peddle petunias online. The Internet flower company sells fresh flowers and plants from its toll-free number, several Web sites, some 125 million catalogs, and about 95 franchised and 10 company-owned shops, in California, New York, and four other states. It also partners with such companies as Microsoft, Yahoo!, and Google to sell its products, which include gift baskets, gourmet foods, popcorn, greeting cards, home and garden items, and toys. It added wines to the menu in 2004. Founder and CEO James F. McCann, a former social worker, got into the flower business in 1976; he controls more than 95% of 1-800-FLOWERS.COM's voting power.

	Annual Growth	6/03	6/04	6/05	6/06	6/07
Sales ($ mil.)	12.7%	565.6	604.0	670.7	781.7	912.6
Net income ($ mil.)	8.8%	12.2	40.9	7.8	3.2	17.1
Market value ($ mil.)	0.7%	235.9	281.4	202.4	163.4	242.4
Employees	23.3%	—	—	3,000	3,700	—

1800MATTRESS.COM

31-10 48th Ave.	CEO: Napoleon Barragan
Long Island City, NY 11101	CFO: William A. Johnson
Phone: 718-472-1200	HR: Kathy Desmond
Fax: 718-482-6561	FYE: December 31
Web: www.mattress.com	Type: Private

Some phone services may leave you hot and bothered, but 1800mattress.com (formerly Dial-A-Mattress Operating Corp.) hopes to leave you comfy and rested. The firm allows customers to order name-brand and private-label mattresses over the phone or the Internet, 24 hours a day. As competitors have started their own phone shopping services, the company has countered by opening showrooms where customers can feel the merchandise before buying. The firm sells products at more than 140 showrooms across the country and on its Web site. CEO Napoleon Barragan, who founded the company in the 1970s, and his wife, Kay, own 1800mattress.com.

1-DAY PAINT & BODY CENTERS, INC.

21801 S. Western Ave.	CEO: Javier Ricardo Uribe
Torrance, CA 90501	CFO: –
Phone: 310-328-0390	HR: –
Fax: 310-212-5493	FYE: December 31
	Type: Private

1-Day Paint & Body Centers sees a lot of cars in one year. The company owns and operates more than 30 auto-paint shops in California, Nevada, and New Mexico. In most cases, paint jobs take about two to three days, a little longer because new environmentally safe paints take longer to apply. Body work is available at most locations. Half of the company's business is from wholesale and fleet customers. The company estimates that it paints more than 25,000 new and used wholesale vehicles annually. 1-Day Paint & Body Centers was founded in 1967 by chairman Javier Uribe, who had previously worked for rival car-painting chain Earl Scheib.

	Annual Growth	12/03	12/04	12/05	12/06	12/07
Est. sales ($ mil.)	—	—	—	—	—	15.1
Employees	—	—	—	—	—	343

1ST CENTENNIAL BANCORP

OTC: FCEN

218 E. State St.	CEO: Thomas E. (Tom) Vessey
Redlands, CA 92373	CFO: Beth Sanders
Phone: 909-798-3611	HR: Sheri Passerino
Fax: 909-335-2363	FYE: December 31
Web: www.1stcent.com	Type: Public

1st Centennial Bancorp is the holding company for 1st Centennial Bank, which has about a half-dozen branches in Southern California. It also operates some five loan production offices that focus on real estate, construction, commercial, and religious lending. Construction and development real estate loans make up the largest segment (about two-thirds) of the bank's lending portfolio, followed by business loans and commercial and multifamily mortgages. The bank also offers standard services such as checking and savings accounts, CDs, IRAs, and credit cards. Investment products and services are offered through a third-party provider.

	Annual Growth	12/03	12/04	12/05	12/06	12/07
Assets ($ mil.)	28.3%	254.4	356.7	456.2	551.1	689.5
Net income ($ mil.)	39.3%	2.1	3.0	5.1	7.4	7.9
Market value ($ mil.)	62.0%	14.5	29.0	30.3	72.3	99.8
Employees	—	—	—	—	—	—

1ST CONSTITUTION BANCORP

NASDAQ (GM): FCCY

2650 Rte. 130	CEO: Robert F. Mangano
Cranbury, NJ 08512	CFO: Joseph M. Reardon
Phone: 609-655-4500	HR: Beverly Tindall
Fax: 609-655-5653	FYE: December 31
Web: www.1stconstitution.com	Type: Public

In order to "secure the blessings of liberty," the founding fathers established the US Constitution. As for promoting the general welfare, some banks share the same dedication to "We the people." 1st Constitution Bancorp is the parent of 1st Constitution Bank, which serves consumers, small businesses, and not-for-profits through about a dozen branches in North Jersey. Services and products include demand, savings, and time deposits, as well as loans and mortgages. Commercial mortgages, business loans, and construction loans make up more than 90% of the company's lending portfolio.

	Annual Growth	12/03	12/04	12/05	12/06	12/07
Assets ($ mil.)	10.0%	293.5	335.8	372.5	392.7	429.1
Net income ($ mil.)	14.0%	3.2	3.8	4.6	5.3	5.4
Market value ($ mil.)	32.5%	19.6	49.4	62.5	66.3	60.3
Employees	8.0%	81	97	91	102	—

1ST FRANKLIN FINANCIAL CORPORATION

213 E. Tugalo St.
Toccoa, GA 30577
Phone: 706-886-7571
Fax: 706-886-7953
Web: www.1ffc.com

CEO: Ben F. Cheek III
CFO: A. Roger Guimond
HR: C. Michael Haynie
FYE: December 31
Type: Private

Benjamin Franklin was known for doling out sage financial advice to "common folk." Today, 1st Franklin Financial is known for doling out direct cash loans and real estate loans to a similar demographic. Secured direct cash loans make up the lion's share (about 85%) of the company's loan portfolio. 1st Franklin Financial also buys and services sales finance contracts from retailers and offers credit insurance to borrowers. The firm operates through around 240 branch offices in Alabama, Georgia, Louisiana, Mississippi, and South Carolina. The family of chairman and CEO Ben Cheek III owns more than 90% of the company.

	Annual Growth	12/03	12/04	12/05	12/06	12/07
Est. sales ($ mil.)	—	—	—	—	—	106.5
Employees	—	—	—	—	—	964

1ST INDEPENDENCE FINANCIAL GROUP, INC.

NASDAQ (GM): FIFG

8620 Biggin Hill Ln.
Louisville, KY 40250
Phone: 812-944-1400
Fax: 812-944-1460
Web: www.1stindependence.com

CEO: N. William (Bill) White
CFO: R. Michael Wilborn
HR: –
FYE: December 31
Type: Public

1st Independence Financial Group is the holding company for 1st Independence Bank, which operates around 10 locations in Kentucky and Indiana. The company's 1st Independence Mortgage operates through the bank's branches. In addition to standard deposit products and services, the bank focuses on residential mortgages (about 40% of its portfolio), but also offers construction, commercial real estate, and other loans. The company was formed in 2004 when Harrodsburg First Financial Bancorp bought Indiana's privately held Independence Bancorp. Indiana-based MainSource Financial Group is buying 1st Independence Financial Group.

	Annual Growth	9/04	*12/04	12/05	12/06	12/07
Assets ($ mil.)	2.1%	320.0	337.2	336.2	342.8	347.7
Net income ($ mil.)	—	(1.1)	0.2	4.5	1.9	(4.8)
Market value ($ mil.)	(19.2%)	—	36.4	36.1	32.7	19.2
Employees	(4.6%)	89	—	81	—	—

*Fiscal year change

1ST SOURCE CORPORATION

NASDAQ (GS): SRCE

100 N. Michigan St.
South Bend, IN 46601
Phone: 574-235-2000
Fax: 574-235-2882
Web: www.1stsource.com

CEO: Christopher J. (Chris) Murphy III
CFO: Larry E. Lentych
HR: –
FYE: December 31
Type: Public

Need a bank? Don't give it a 2nd thought. Contact 1st Source Corporation, parent of 1st Source Bank, which provides commercial and consumer banking services through some 75 branches in 17 northern Indiana and southwestern Michigan counties. The bank's specialty finance group provides financing for aircraft, automobile fleets, trucks, and construction and environmental equipment through nearly 25 offices nationwide; such loans account for approximately half of 1st Source's portfolio. Subsidiaries offer insurance, mortgage banking, and investment advisory services. The bank acquired the family-owned First National Bank, Valparaiso for $135 million in 2008.

	Annual Growth	12/03	12/04	12/05	12/06	12/07
Assets ($ mil.)	7.5%	3,330.1	3,563.7	3,511.3	3,807.3	4,447.1
Net income ($ mil.)	12.4%	19.1	25.0	33.8	39.3	30.5
Market value ($ mil.)	0.7%	409.9	486.2	478.0	731.2	422.0
Employees	6.1%	—	—	1,200	1,200	1,350

1SYNC, INC.

Princeton Pike Corporate Center, 1009 Lenox Dr., Ste. 115
Lawrenceville, NJ 08648
Phone: 312-463-4000
Fax: 609-620-4601
Web: www.1sync.org

CEO: Robert (Bob) Noe
CFO: Kumar Yegneswaran
HR: –
FYE: December 31
Type: Subsidiary

1SYNC hopes to help you synchronize all sorts of trading relationships and product information. The company provides collaborative software used to synchronize data in multiple locations, formats, and languages. 1SYNC's products are used for functions such as supply chain management, business intelligence, collaborating with trading partners, and managing catalog information. The company also offers services such as consulting, implementation, maintenance, support, and training. Its customers include consumer products manufacturers, membership organizations, and retailers. The company was formed in 2005 when the operations of Transora and UCCnet were combined. 1SYNC is a not-for-profit subsidiary of GS1 US.

	Annual Growth	12/03	12/04	12/05	12/06	12/07
Est. sales ($ mil.)	—	—	—	—	—	16.4
Employees	—	—	—	—	—	159

II-VI INCORPORATED

NASDAQ (GS): IIVI

375 Saxonburg Blvd.
Saxonburg, PA 16056
Phone: 724-352-4455
Fax: 724-352-5284
Web: www.ii-vi.com

CEO: Francis J. Kramer
CFO: Craig A. Creaturo
HR: –
FYE: June 30
Type: Public

II-VI maintains a laser-like focus on focusing lasers. The company (pronounced "two-six") makes lenses, mirrors, prisms, and other optical components used to manipulate laser beams. The company's 5,000-plus clients — drawn from the health care, industrial, military, and telecom equipment sectors — employ these components in lasers for precision manufacturing, fiber-optic transmission and reception, and other applications. Through its eV Products unit, II-VI makes X-ray and gamma-ray sensors for nuclear radiation detection; subsidiary VLOC makes laser and sensing system parts and materials. The company gets about one-third of sales outside the US.

	Annual Growth	6/03	6/04	6/05	6/06	6/07
Sales ($ mil.)	19.7%	128.2	150.9	194.0	232.5	263.2
Net income ($ mil.)	34.5%	11.6	17.3	24.8	10.8	38.0
Market value ($ mil.)	48.8%	163.9	221.5	537.0	533.3	803.8
Employees	18.2%	1,094	1,242	1,548	1,690	2,138

2WIRE, INC.

1704 Automation Pkwy.
San Jose, CA 95131
Phone: 408-428-9500
Fax: 408-428-9590
Web: www.2wire.com

CEO: Pasquale (Pat) Romano
CFO: Roop Lakkaraju
HR: –
FYE: December 31
Type: Private

2Wire, or not 2Wire, that is the question: Whether 'tis nobler in networks to suffer the slings and arrows of outrageous dial-up connections, or to take up broadband against a sea of troubles, and with a 2Wire gateway end them? 2Wire's HomePortal and OfficePortal networking devices combine router and firewall functions, and allow multiple PCs and telephones to share a single broadband DSL or cable hookup. Its gateways connect devices to each other wirelessly or via phone or Ethernet wires. 2Wire also makes DSL filters and adapters. Alcatel-Lucent owns one-quarter of 2Wire. For in broadband what dreams may come when we have shuffled off these slow connections, must give us pause.

	Annual Growth	12/03	12/04	12/05	12/06	12/07
Est. sales ($ mil.)	—	—	—	—	—	219.7
Employees	—	—	—	—	—	298

An in-depth profile of this company is available to Hoover's Online members at hoovers.com.

25

3 DAY BLINDS, INC.

2220 E. Cerritos Ave.
Anaheim, CA 92806
Phone: 714-634-4600
Fax: 714-634-1041
Web: www.3day.com

CEO: Micheal Bush
CFO: Opal Ferraro
HR: Tikie Holewski
FYE: December 31
Type: Private

3 Day Blinds is not a personal account of a very serious hangover, but the time frame 3 Day Blinds committed to a long time ago when it challenged the custom blinds industry to deliver finished products to customers in days, not weeks. The company makes a wide range of window blinds and shades using wood, fabrics, and plastics. 3 Day Blinds operates 170 Showrooms in 17 US states, where customers can order the custom crafted window coverings of their choice. It also operates a store at all 17 of The Great Indoors retail locations. The company's brands include Christopher Lowell, Disney, Eddie Bauer, Transitions, Ultima, Laura Ashley, and ViewPointe.

	Annual Growth	12/03	12/04	12/05	12/06	12/07
Est. sales ($ mil.)	—	—	—	—	—	66.8
Employees	—	—	—	—	—	1,000

3COM CORPORATION

NASDAQ (GS): COMS

350 Campus Dr.
Marlborough, MA 01752
Phone: 508-323-5000
Fax: 508-323-1111
Web: www.3com.com

CEO: Robert Y. L. (Bob) Mao
CFO: Jay Zager
HR: Eileen Nelson
FYE: May 31
Type: Public

3Com has gotten down to business. 3Com sells networking hardware and software, including LAN-level infrastructure gear (switches, routers, gateways), Internet telephony systems, network intrusion prevention systems, and wireless networking equipment for enterprises. The company also provides services ranging from technical support to high-end consulting and systems integration. 3Com sells directly and though resellers and distributors. Once active in the consumer and telecom carrier markets, 3Com is now focused primarily on enterprise customers. The company agreed to be acquired by private equity firm Bain Capital for more than $2 billion in 2007, but the deal collapsed in 2008.

	Annual Growth	5/03	5/04	5/05	5/06	5/07
Sales ($ mil.)	8.0%	932.9	698.9	651.2	794.8	1,267.5
Net income ($ mil.)	—	(283.8)	(349.3)	(195.7)	(100.7)	(88.6)
Market value ($ mil.)	0.9%	1,805.9	2,541.0	1,410.0	1,872.8	1,871.6
Employees	201.2%	—	—	1,850	5,572	—

3D SYSTEMS CORPORATION

NASDAQ (GM): TDSC

333 Three D Systems Circle
Rock Hill, SC 29730
Phone: 803-326-3900
Fax: 803-324-8810
Web: www.3dsystems.com

CEO: Abraham N. (Abe) Reichental
CFO: Damon J. Gregoire
HR: —
FYE: December 31
Type: Public

3D Systems helps product designers and engineers bring their 3-D dreams to life. The company's stereolithography apparatuses (SLAs) and other machines create 3-D prototypes of everything from toys to airplane parts. 3D Systems' SLAs rapidly produce 3-D objects using CAD/CAM software in a process called solid imaging (using a laser to cut successive layers from resin to form a physical model). Its ThermoJet solid object printer fabricates plastic models using a modified ink jet printing system. 3D Systems' customers have included General Electric, Hasbro, Motorola, and Texas Instruments.

	Annual Growth	12/03	12/04	12/05	12/06	12/07
Sales ($ mil.)	9.2%	110.0	125.4	139.7	134.8	156.5
Net income ($ mil.)	—	(26.0)	2.6	10.1	(29.3)	(6.7)
Market value ($ mil.)	27.2%	131.0	290.5	275.2	304.6	342.4
Employees	(2.7%)	—	—	351	341	332

3DLABS INC., LTD.

1901 McCarthy Blvd.
Milpitas, CA 95035
Phone: 408-432-6700
Fax: 408-432-6701
Web: www.3dlabs.com

CEO: C. Hock Leow
CFO: —
HR: —
FYE: June 30
Type: Subsidiary

When you want 3-D graphics in your hand, 3Dlabs has a product for you. 3Dlabs' three-dimensional graphics accelerator products are intended for the portable handheld device market. The company's Embedded Graphics and IP Cores division supplies graphics chips and flexible intellectual property cores for embedded applications. Customers include the BBC, Jaguar, Stargate Digital, and Trek Bicycle. 3Dlabs is a subsidiary of computer board maker Creative Technology. The company has shifted its product emphasis, introducing the DMS-02 media processor in late 2006 for applications in automotive infotainment systems, mobile handsets, navigation systems, portable media players, and videoconferencing equipment.

3E COMPANY, INC.

1905 Aston Ave.
Carlsbad, CA 92008
Phone: 760-602-8700
Fax: 760-602-8852
Web: www.3ecompany.com

CEO: Robert S. Christie
CFO: Steven L. Wolkenstein
HR: Linda S. Allen
FYE: December 31
Type: Private

3E won't touch your hazardous materials, but the company will tell you what you need to know about them. 3E's Ariel unit provides environmental, health, and safety (EH&S) information management services to help customers respond to emergencies and comply with federal regulations. The company maintains databases containing information about materials used at more than 75,000 of its customers' facilities, and it provides around-the-clock telephone access to hazardous materials experts. Customers have included companies such as Anheuser-Busch, Continental Airlines, and Pepsi.

	Annual Growth	12/03	12/04	12/05	12/06	12/07
Est. sales ($ mil.)	—	—	—	—	—	14.9
Employees	—	—	—	—	—	180

3H TECHNOLOGY L.L.C.

1767 Business Center Dr., Ste. 100
Reston, VA 20190
Phone: 703-521-5200
Fax: 703-521-5201
Web: www.3ht.com

CEO: Sam Haidar
CFO: —
HR: —
FYE: December 31
Type: Subsidiary

3H Technology can think of more than three ways in which to improve your information technology (IT) operations. The company provides IT services such as custom software development, network design and integration, computer-based training, and Web site design. The company's clients have included the US Navy, General Services Administration, the Department of Health & Human Services, and the Department of Treasury, as well as local governments and commercial businesses. 3H also offers software for implementing and managing corporate portals as well as applications for document imaging. QinetiQ acquired the company in 2007 for about $52 million.

	Annual Growth	12/03	12/04	12/05	12/06	12/07
Est. sales ($ mil.)	—	—	—	—	—	29.1
Employees	—	—	—	—	—	200

3I INFOTECH LTD.

450 Raritan Center Pkwy., Ste. B
Edison, NJ 08837
Phone: 732-225-4242
Fax: 732-346-1823
Web: www.3i-infotech.com

CEO: V. Srinivasan
CFO: Amar Chintopanth
HR: Manoj Mandavgane
FYE: December 31
Type: Private

3i Infotech (formerly ICICI Infotech) is informed about technology. The information technology (IT) service provider offers software development, technology security consulting, and IT infrastructure services for the insurance, financial, retail, and government markets. Services include network design, systems integration, legacy migration, application development, training, support, and consulting. 3i also offers a variety of outsourced services addressing tasks such as business process management, application development, and support. The company's customers have included Dow Jones, GlaxoSmith-Kline, and Panasonic.

	Annual Growth	12/03	12/04	12/05	12/06	12/07
Est. sales ($ mil.)	—	—	—	—	—	16.5
Employees	—	—	—	—	—	200

⬛ 3M COMPANY

NYSE: MMM

3M Center
St. Paul, MN 55144
Phone: 651-733-1110
Fax: 651-733-9973
Web: www.mmm.com

CEO: George W. Buckley
CFO: Patrick D. (Pat) Campbell
HR: Janice K. Angell
FYE: December 31
Type: Public

Loath to be stuck on one thing, 3M makes everything from masking tape to asthma inhalers. The company has six operating segments: display and graphics (specialty film, traffic control materials); health care (dental and medical supplies, and health IT); safety, security, and protection (commercial care, occupational health and safety products); electro and communications (connecting, splicing, and insulating products); industrial and transportation (specialty materials, tapes, and adhesives); and consumer and office. Well-known brands include Scotchgard fabric protectors, Post-it Notes, Scotch-Brite scouring products, and Scotch tapes. Sales outside the US account for about two-thirds of 3M's sales.

	Annual Growth	12/03	12/04	12/05	12/06	12/07
Sales ($ mil.)	7.6%	18,232.0	20,011.0	21,167.0	22,923.0	24,462.0
Net income ($ mil.)	14.3%	2,403.0	2,990.0	3,199.0	3,851.0	4,096.0
Market value ($ mil.)	(2.7%)	66,673.5	63,482.6	58,476.7	57,228.9	59,796.0
Employees	3.3%	67,072	67,071	69,315	75,333	76,239

3PAR INC.

NYSE Arca: PAR

4209 Technology Dr.
Fremont, CA 94538
Phone: 510-413-5999
Fax: 510-413-5699
Web: www.3par.com

CEO: David C. Scott
CFO: Adriel G. Lares
HR: Jeannette Robinson
FYE: March 31
Type: Public

3PAR has taken a swing at the high-end storage market. The company's storage servers and software let large enterprises pool their storage assets across multiple departments or lines of business, consolidating data management while allowing differentiated service levels. Its customers include medium and large corporations and government agencies worldwide. It markets primarily through a direct sales force, utilizing resellers to handle US government accounts and business in some foreign countries. The company was founded by veterans of Sun Microsystems.

	Annual Growth	3/04	3/05	3/06	3/07	3/08
Sales ($ mil.)	70.5%	—	23.8	38.2	66.2	118.0
Net income ($ mil.)	—	—	(17.4)	(16.3)	(15.5)	(10.1)
Employees	—	—	—	—	352	—

3SG CORPORATION

344 Cramer Creek Ct.
Dublin, OH 43017
Phone: 614-761-8394
Fax: 614-761-2716
Web: www.3sg.com

CEO: K. A. (Ranjan) Manoranjan
CFO: Anton Rasiah
HR: –
FYE: December 31
Type: Private

Drowning in documents? 3SG Corp. wants businesses to throw out their file cabinets and let it convert their paper, microfiche, and microfilm documents to digital images. The firm provides document imaging and conversion, management solutions, and business process outsourcing services to some 400 clients in state and local government, and industries such as insurance, education, and health care. Other services include data entry and processing, custom software development, and HIPAA compliance services. Founded in 2000, 3SG's business plan was to provide its clients with the three S's: software, service, and solutions. Today 3SG focuses on helping clients cope in a digital age.

	Annual Growth	12/03	12/04	12/05	12/06	12/07
Est. sales ($ mil.)	—	—	—	—	—	10.7
Employees	—	—	—	—	—	302

4KIDS ENTERTAINMENT, INC.

NYSE: KDE

1414 Avenue of the Americas
New York, NY 10019
Phone: 212-758-7666
Fax: 212-980-0933
Web: www.4kidsentertainmentinc.com

CEO: Alfred R. (Al) Kahn
CFO: Bruce R. Foster
HR: –
FYE: December 31
Type: Public

If your youth are into *Yu-Gi-Oh!*, thank (or blame) 4Kids Entertainment. The company makes money by licensing rights to third-party entertainment properties for use in cartoons, games, toys, and apparel. In addition, 4Kids leases a four-hour block of time Saturday mornings on FOX; 4Kids is responsible for ad sales and content for the *4Kids TV* line-up, which showcases such 4Kids properties as *Teenage Mutant Ninja Turtles, Winx Club,* and *Yu-Gi-Oh!*. Other youth-oriented properties under the 4Kids umbrella include *Cabbage Patch Kids, Dinosaur King,* and *Viva Piñata*; in addition, 4Kids handles licensing for the American Kennel Club, the Cat Fanciers' Association, and the UK's Royal Air Force.

	Annual Growth	12/03	12/04	12/05	12/06	12/07
Sales ($ mil.)	(14.1%)	102.1	103.3	86.7	71.8	55.6
Net income ($ mil.)	—	14.8	12.7	5.1	(1.0)	(23.3)
Market value ($ mil.)	(16.7%)	363.4	287.2	205.2	240.2	175.3
Employees	(1.1%)	—	—	238	209	233

4LIFE RESEARCH, LC

9850 S. 300 West
Sandy, UT 84070
Phone: 801-256-3102
Fax: 801-562-3611
Web: www.4life.com

CEO: David Lisonbee
CFO: Mark Ostler
HR: –
FYE: December 31
Type: Private

4Life Research believes in good health and good wealth, or at least optimism in pill form. The multilevel marketing company manufactures nutritional supplements for humans and animals and sells them through its network of independent distributors. The company's flagship product is Transfer Factor, a supplement made from egg yolks and cow colostrum that is meant to enhance the body's immune system. The firm makes Transfer Factor formulations for humans, dogs, cats, horses, and livestock. 4Life's other (human) products include weight management supplements, nutritionals to support various systems of the body for general health, and cleansers, moisturizers, and other personal care items.

	Annual Growth	12/03	12/04	12/05	12/06	12/07
Est. sales ($ mil.)	—	—	—	—	—	20.6
Employees	—	—	—	—	—	150

⬛ An in-depth profile of this company is available to Hoover's Online members at hoovers.com.

27

5G WIRELESS COMMUNICATIONS, INC.

Pink Sheets: FGWI

2771 Plaza Del Amo, Ste. 805
Torrance, CA 90503
Phone: 310-328-0493
Fax: 310-328-0498
Web: www.5gwireless.com

CEO: Jerry Dix
CFO: Jay Wilkins
HR: –
FYE: December 31
Type: Public

5G Wireless Communications provides the equipment necessary to set up a new generation of networks. The company develops and manufactures indoor and outdoor base stations for broadband wireless networks based on the 802.11, or Wi-Fi, standard. It sells directly and through distributors and resellers to government and military bodies, health care providers, university and corporate campuses, and wireless Internet service providers. The company also offers wireless Internet services to the hospitality market. 5G's auditor has expressed concern that the company may not have the financial resources to stay in business.

	Annual Growth	12/02	12/03	12/04	12/05	*12/06
Sales ($ mil.)	68.2%	0.1	0.2	0.6	1.6	0.8
Net income ($ mil.)	—	(6.2)	(2.2)	(5.0)	(4.0)	(6.1)
Employees	—	—	—	—	—	18

*Most recent year available

7-ELEVEN, INC.

1722 Routh St.
Dallas, TX 75202
Phone: 972-828-7011
Fax: 972-828-7848
Web: www.7-eleven.com

CEO: Joseph M. (Joe) DePinto
CFO: Stanley W. Reynolds
HR: Krystin Mitchell
FYE: February 28
Type: Subsidiary

"If convenience stores are open 24 hours, why the locks on their doors?" If anyone knows, it's 7-Eleven. The North American subsidiary of Seven-Eleven Japan, 7-Eleven operates more than 6,000 company-owned and licensed stores in the US and Canada under the 7-Eleven name. The retailer also has an interest in about 675 stores in Mexico. Globally, 7-Eleven operates, franchises, or licenses more than 33,200 stores worldwide. The US's leading convenience store chain was taken private in late 2005 by its largest shareholder, the Japanese retail conglomerate Seven & I Holdings, the holding company for Seven-Eleven Japan, Ito-Yokado, Denny's restaurants, and other businesses.

8E6 TECHNOLOGIES

828 W. Taft Ave.
Orange, CA 92865
Phone: 714-282-6111
Fax: 714-282-6117
Web: www.8e6.com

CEO: George Y. Shih
CFO: Rodney S. Miller
HR: –
FYE: December 31
Type: Private

8e6 wants to give the ol' heave-ho to inappropriate material in the workplace and the classroom. 8e6 Technologies provides Internet filtering and reporting products for a variety of customers, including businesses, schools, and ISPs. The company's network appliances can be used to filter and restrict access to Web and e-mail content. 8e6 sells its products through a direct sales force in the US as well as through resellers and distributors in Europe and Asia. The company was founded in 1995 and has received funding from the Darwin Group. 8e6 has offices in China, Taiwan, and the US.

	Annual Growth	12/03	12/04	12/05	12/06	12/07
Est. sales ($ mil.)	—	—	—	—	—	23.8
Employees	—	—	—	—	—	117

8X8, INC.

NASDAQ (CM): EGHT

3151 Jay St.
Santa Clara, CA 95054
Phone: 408-727-1885
Fax: 408-980-0432
Web: www.8x8.com

CEO: Bryan R. Martin
CFO: Daniel (Dan) Weirich
HR: –
FYE: March 31
Type: Public

8x8 is no square when it comes to Internet telephony. The company offers software, services, and equipment that enable voice and video communication over Internet Protocol (IP) networks. Through its Packet8 software suite and related services, 8x8 allows subscribers to make phone calls and perform other broadband networking functions using voice-over-IP (VoIP) technology, such as voice mail, caller ID, call waiting, call forwarding, and 3-way conferencing. The company sells its products directly as well as through resellers, distributors, and retailers.

	Annual Growth	3/04	3/05	3/06	3/07	3/08
Sales ($ mil.)	60.5%	9.3	11.5	31.9	53.1	61.7
Net income ($ mil.)	—	(3.0)	(19.1)	(24.1)	(9.9)	0.0
Market value ($ mil.)	(18.1%)	134.9	89.9	107.0	90.2	60.8
Employees	—	—	158	—	—	—

10-K WIZARD TECHNOLOGY, LLC

3232 McKinney St., Ste. 750
Dallas, TX 75204
Phone: 214-800-4560
Fax: 214-800-4567
Web: www.10kwizard.com

CEO: Martin X. Zacarias
CFO: Martin X. Zacarias
HR: Martin X. Zacarias
FYE: December 31
Type: Private

Need a little magic to sort through SEC filings? Having access to a wizard certainly helps. 10-K Wizard Technology provides subscription-based online access to US Securities and Exchange Commission (SEC) document filings, including more than 400 types of forms, as well as powerful searching and parsing tools to sort through the information. Users can search by company name, ticker, SIC code, industry type, or keyword. Registered users of its Alert Wizard service can receive personal custom e-mail alerts of new filings. 10-K Wizard also uses its technology to power the SEC portions of Web sites. CEO Martin Zacarias and CTO Kee Kimbrell founded the company in 1999.

21ST CENTURY HOLDING COMPANY

NASDAQ (GM): TCHC

3661 W. Oakland Park Blvd., Ste. 300
Lauderdale Lakes, FL 33311
Phone: 954-581-9993
Fax: 954-316-9201
Web: www.21stcenturyholding.com

CEO: Edward J. (Ted) Lawson
CFO: Peter J. Prygelski III
HR: –
FYE: December 31
Type: Public

Trashed trailer? 21st Century can help. Through Federated National Insurance and other subsidiaries, the company underwrites a variety of personal property/casualty insurance lines in Florida. Products include homeowners, manufactured home, flood, liability, and nonstandard automobile coverage. Through its American Vehicle Insurance subsidiary, the company offers commercial general liability insurance in nearly a dozen primarily southeastern states. 21st Century underwrites policies and handles claims for third-party insurers through its Assurance MGA and Superior Adjusting subsidiaries. The company distributes its products through independent agents.

	Annual Growth	12/03	12/04	12/05	12/06	12/07
Assets ($ mil.)	19.7%	106.7	163.6	290.1	212.1	219.4
Net income ($ mil.)	26.2%	8.4	(10.9)	12.1	13.9	21.3
Market value ($ mil.)	18.1%	54.4	88.3	115.9	187.6	105.8
Employees	(13.9%)	—	—	135	122	100

An in-depth profile of this company is available to Hoover's Online members at hoovers.com.

21ST CENTURY TOYS, INC.

2456 Verna Ct.
San Leandro, CA 94577
Phone: 510-483-5700
Fax: 510-483-2141
Web: www.21stcenturytoys.com

CEO: James Allen
CFO: Cynthia Majors
HR: –
FYE: –
Type: Private

21st Century Toys looks to the last century for its action figure inspiration. The company makes realistic military, police, and other action figures and scaled models of vehicles. Its product series include figures, weapons, and vehicles from World War II and Vietnam, as well as law enforcement and public safety agencies. Product lines are sold online and through hobby and specialty toy stores under names such as The Villains, America's Finest, and The Ultimate Soldier. The company also offers vehicles and action figures from movies, including *Platoon* and *Sky Captain and the World of Tomorrow*. 21st Century Toys was founded in 1997.

24/7 REAL MEDIA, INC.

132 W. 31st St.
New York, NY 10001
Phone: 212-231-7100
Fax: 212-760-1774
Web: www.247realmedia.com

CEO: David J. Moore
CFO: Kristopher Heinrichs
HR: John Hughes
FYE: December 31
Type: Subsidiary

Keeping it real — 24/7. 24/7 Real Media provides key elements in the rapidly changing Internet advertising arena: search marketing services, software to host and manage ads, and a network of Web sites that run the ads. The company's Media Solutions segment provides advertisers access to its network of Web sites and permission-based e-mail marketing database. 24/7 also offers search engine optimization services (an increasingly important business segment for the company). Technology offerings revolve around the company's ad delivery and management software, which allows advertisers to plan, manage, and measure their online campaigns. 24/7 was acquired by communications conglomerate WPP in July 2007.

	Annual Growth	12/02	12/03	12/04	12/05	12/06
Sales ($ mil.)	47.2%	42.6	49.2	85.3	139.8	200.2
Net income ($ mil.)	—	(17.5)	(12.0)	(3.2)	0.0	(8.6)
Employees	11.1%	256	255	325	368	390

22SQUARED, INC.

1170 Peachtree St. Northeast, 15th Fl.
Atlanta, GA 30309
Phone: 404-347-8700
Fax: 404-347-8800
Web: www.22squared.com

CEO: Richard Ward
CFO: Tom Fuller
HR: –
FYE: December 31
Type: Private

For this agency, advertising + marketing = 22squared. Formerly known as Westwayne, 22squared provides the whole shebang of marketing services (media buying and planning, direct marketing, event marketing, interactive, and public relations) through its two offices in Atlanta, Georgia and Tampa, Florida. The independent agency serves clients across the Southeast, including such notable brands as the Atlanta Falcons, Lincoln Financial Group, and SunTrust Banks. 22squared traces its roots back to 1922 when it was founded as Westwayne.

	Annual Growth	12/03	12/04	12/05	12/06	12/07
Est. sales ($ mil.)	—	—	—	—	—	87.6
Employees	—	—	—	—	—	225

84 LUMBER COMPANY

1019 Rte. 519
Eighty Four, PA 15330
Phone: 724-228-8820
Fax: 724-228-8058
Web: www.84lumber.com

CEO: Joseph A. Hardy Sr.
CFO: Dan Wallach
HR: Jim Guest
FYE: First Sunday following December 31
Type: Private

With its utilitarian stores (most don't have heat or air conditioning), 84 Lumber has built itself up to be a leading low-cost provider of lumber and building materials and services. Through some 380 stores in more than 35 states the company, which is the nation's largest privately held building-materials supplier, sells lumber, siding, drywall, windows, and other supplies, as well as kits to make barns, play sets, decks, and even homes. Its 84 Components subsidiary operates about a dozen manufacturing plants that make floor and roof trusses and wall panels. Its stores are mainly in the East, Southeast, and Midwest; the firm also sells products internationally. CEO Joseph Hardy Sr. founded 84 Lumber in 1956.

	Annual Growth	12/02	12/03	12/04	12/05	12/06
Sales ($ mil.)	16.3%	2,139.3	2,537.7	3,460.0	4,000.0	3,920.0
Employees	13.1%	5,800	6,500	8,000	10,500	9,500

24 HOUR FITNESS WORLDWIDE, INC.

12647 Alcosta Blvd., 5th Fl.
San Ramon, CA 94583
Phone: 925-543-3100
Fax: 925-543-3200
Web: www.24hourfitness.com

CEO: Carl C. Liebert III
CFO: Colin Heggie
HR: –
FYE: December 31
Type: Private

If you're holding too much weight, 24 Hour Fitness Worldwide has the solution. It owns and operates more than 350 fitness centers that offer aerobic, cardiovascular, and weight lifting activities to the company's more than 3 million members. Some facilities also feature squash, racquetball, and basketball courts; swimming pools; steam and sauna rooms; tanning rooms; and whirlpools. It is one of the only fitness chains open 24 hours a day. The centers are located in 16 states in the US, as well as in Asia. Investment partnership McCown De Leeuw & Co. was a leading investor in 24 Hour Fitness, which was founded in 1983 by chairman Mark Mastrov. Financier Theodore J. Forstmann acquired the company for $1.6 billion.

	Annual Growth	12/02	12/03	12/04	12/05	12/06
Sales ($ mil.)	16.5%	1,000.0	1,000.0	1,004.0	1,077.0	1,840.0
Employees	(13.9%)	20,000	16,000	—	19,660	11,000

99 CENT STUFF, INC.

Pink Sheets: NNCT

1801 Clint Moore Rd., Ste. 205
Boca Raton, FL 33487
Phone: 561-999-9815
Fax: 561-999-9817
Web: www.99centstuff.com

CEO: Raymond Zimmerman
CFO: Barry Bilmes
HR: –
FYE: December 31
Type: Public

Thrifty Floridians look to 99 Cent Stuff for bargains under a buck. The company has about 10 stores in South Florida, selling items ranging from baby products and clothing to hardware and toys. Everything in the store is 99 cents or less. 99 Cent Stuff buys closeouts from manufacturers, wholesalers, and others, and emphasizes name-brand items from companies such as General Mills, Mattel, Procter & Gamble, The Hershey Company, and Revlon. 99 Cent Stuff also sells food, including produce, to encourage customers to visit frequently. Former Service Merchandise CEO Raymond Zimmerman founded 99 Cent Stuff in 1999. The company went public in 2003 and filed for Chapter 11 bankruptcy protection in early 2007.

	Annual Growth	12/03	12/04	12/05	12/06	12/07
Est. Sales ($ mil.)	—	—	—	—	—	56.1
Employees	—	—	—	—	—	525

An in-depth profile of this company is available to Hoover's Online members at hoovers.com.

29

99 CENTS ONLY STORES

NYSE: NDN

4000 Union Pacific Ave.
Commerce, CA 90023
Phone: 323-980-8145
Fax: 323-980-8160
Web: www.99only.com

CEO: Eric Schiffer
CFO: Robert (Rob) Kautz
HR: Howard Derman
FYE: March 31
Type: Public

Pass the buck, get a penny back. 99 Cents Only Stores sells closeout and regular general merchandise for 99 cents or less. With about 265 stores, the company sells name-brand and private-label food and beverages, health and beauty aids, household goods, toys, and more. Most of the company's stores are in Southern California, but there are also a few in central California, Las Vegas, Phoenix, and Texas. The firm's Bargain Wholesale unit distributes discounted merchandise to retailers, distributors, and exporters. The Gold family owns more than one-third of the company and is actively involved in running it. (Chairman David is the founder; his son Jeff is president, and son-in-law Eric Schiffer is its CEO.)

	Annual Growth	12/03	12/04	*3/06	3/07	3/08
Sales ($ mil.)	8.6%	862.5	972.2	1,023.6	1,104.7	1,199.4
Net income ($ mil.)	(52.4%)	56.5	27.8	11.4	9.8	2.9
Market value ($ mil.)	(23.1%)	1,961.5	1,123.4	943.4	1,030.2	687.3
Employees	7.6%	—	8,636	9,690	10,000	

*Fiscal year change

123GREETINGS.COM, INC.

1674 Broadway, Ste. 403
New York, NY 10019
Phone: 212-246-0044
Fax: 212-202-4738
Web: www.123greetings.com

CEO: Sharad Kajaria
CFO: Manish Saraf
HR: –
FYE: –
Type: Private

Sending an electronic greeting is easier than counting to three. 123Greetings.com seems to think so, anyway. With an offering of more than 20,000 free e-mail cards, the company's greetings run the gamut, offering a variety of religious cards (for Buddhist, Christian, Hindi, Islamic, Shinto, Sikh, and Jewish holidays and observances, among others), as well cards celebrating secular occasions (birthdays, anniversaries, and the other usual suspects plus unique holidays such as Fluffernutter Day and Fly a Kite Day). 123Greetings.com also provides a wireless service that allows subscribers to access, personalize, and send greeting cards through their mobile phones.

170 SYSTEMS, INC.

36 Crosby Dr.
Bedford, MA 01730
Phone: 781-743-1900
Fax: 781-743-2200
Web: www.170systems.com

CEO: David J. (Dave) Ellenberger
CFO: Paul G. Smith Jr.
HR: Chris McMahon
FYE: December 31
Type: Private

170 Systems hopes to help you gain a complete view of all your business operations. Its 170 MarkView product is a document management and imaging system that captures and manages data used in core business functions such as accounts payable and receivable, expense management, purchasing, project management, records management, order management, and contract management. 170 Systems also offers services such as consulting, installation, maintenance, support, and training.

	Annual Growth	12/03	12/04	12/05	12/06	12/07
Est. sales ($ mil.)	—	—	—	—	—	12.8
Employees	—	—	—	—	—	120

180 CONNECT INC.

OTC: CNCT

6501 E. Belleview Ave.
Englewood, CO 80111
Phone: 303-395-6001
Fax: 303-395-6197
Web: www.180connect.net

CEO: Peter Giacalone
CFO: Steven Westberg
HR: Charles Storey
FYE: December 31
Type: Public

180 Connect makes connections both coming and going. The company is one of the largest providers of installation and integration services for home entertainment, communications, and security systems in the US; it also does business in Canada. 180 Connect provides cable, satellite, and telephone-system installation and maintenance services from more than 80 locations through contracts with cable and broadband communications providers; most of its business comes from services provided to US broadcast satellite leader DIRECTV. Other clients include Rogers Communications and Time Warner Cable. 180 Connect agreed in 2008 to be acquired by The DIRECTV Group for about $46 million.

	Annual Growth	12/03	12/04	12/05	12/06	12/07
Sales ($ mil.)	16.3%	—	—	280.7	335.4	379.8
Net income ($ mil.)	—	—	—	—	(15.3)	(24.9)
Employees	3.9%	—	—	4,400	4,500	4,750

180S, INC.

701 E. Pratt St., Ste. 180
Baltimore, MD 21202
Phone: 410-534-6320
Fax: 410-534-6321
Web: www.180s.com

CEO: Susan Shafton
CFO: –
HR: –
FYE: December 31
Type: Private

Cold weather sports fanatics ought to thank their lucky stars for 180s, Inc. The company, a performance wear manufacturer, makes apparel, ear warmers, sunglasses, and gloves to aid athletes in battling the rigors of outdoor training and exercise. Its products are sold at sporting goods and department stores nationwide. 180s also makes Gorgonz Performance Work Gear (sold at gorgonz.com), a line of apparel and gear that helps tradesmen and other workers stay comfortable in all conditions. The company was founded by Ron L. Wilson II and Brian Le Gette in 1995. The two were classmates at The Wharton School of the University of Pennsylvania where they began by selling ear warmers on campus.

	Annual Growth	12/03	12/04	12/05	12/06	12/07
Est. sales ($ mil.)	—	—	—	—	—	25.4
Employees	—	—	—	—	—	40

360I LLC

1 Peachtree Pt., 1545 Peachtree St., Ste. 450
Atlanta, GA 30309
Phone: 404-876-6007
Fax: 404-876-9097
Web: www.360i.com

CEO: Bryan Wiener
CFO: –
HR: –
FYE: December 31
Type: Private

If you are ready to tune-up your online marketing campaign, keep this company on your short list. 360i provides search engine optimization, paid placement management, and performance analytics services for US and international clients including H&R Block, NBC Universal, and Office Depot. In addition to turning Web searches into marketing opportunities (through optimization and paid placement) the company also provides development and management services for targeted marketing campaigns using banner ads, e-mails, and Web sites. 360i got off the ground in 1998.

	Annual Growth	12/03	12/04	12/05	12/06	12/07
Est. sales ($ mil.)	—	—	—	—	—	25.5
Employees	—	—	—	—	—	74

1105 MEDIA, INC.

9121 Oakdale Ave., Ste. 101
Chatsworth, CA 91311
Phone: 818-734-1520
Fax: 818-734-1522
Web: www.101com.com

CEO: Neal Vitale
CFO: Richard Vitale
HR: Michael J. (Mike) Valenti
FYE: December 31
Type: Private

1105 Media has a myriad of ways to distribute business-to-business information. Its products and operations include publications (*Redmond Magazine* for the Microsoft IT community), e-newsletters (*Federal Employees News Digest*), Web sites (EduHound.com), and conferences and events (Web Design World). The company covers markets such as Government, Education, Network & Enterprise Computing, Business Intelligence, Office Equipment, Industrial Health & Safety, Compliance, Security, Environmental Protection, Water & Wastewater, and Home Medical Equipment. 1105 Media was founded in 2006 by Nautic Partners, Alta Communications, and publishing and marketing executive Neal Vitale.

	Annual Growth	12/03	12/04	12/05	12/06	12/07
Est. sales ($ mil.)	—	—	—	—	—	40.0
Employees	—	—	—	—	—	400

1867 WESTERN FINANCIAL CORPORATION

301 E. Miner Ave.
Stockton, CA 95202
Phone: 209-929-1600
Fax: –
Web: www.bankofstockton.com

CEO: Douglass M. Eberhardt
CFO: John F. Dentoni
HR: Deborah A. Collard Montiel
FYE: December 31
Type: Private

1867 Western Financial Corporation is the holding company for Bank of Stockton, one of California's oldest banks and the oldest bank still operating under its original charter. The bank has about 20 branches in and around San Joaquin County, including Sacramento to the north. It offers standard banking products and services including checking and savings accounts, CDs, and commercial and retail loans and mortgages; real estate loans account for more than half of the company's loan book. Bank of Stockton also operates under division names Elk Grove Commerce Bank (opened in 2006) and Modesto Commerce Bank and Turlock Commerce Bank (both acquired in 2003).

	Annual Growth	12/03	12/04	12/05	12/06	12/07
Est. sales ($ mil.)	—	—	—	—	—	81.0
Employees	—	—	—	—	—	370

2929 ENTERTAINMENT LP

2425 Olympic Blvd., Ste. 6040W
Santa Monica, CA 90404
Phone: 310-309-5701
Fax: 310-309-5716
Web: www.2929entertainment.com

CEO: Todd R. Wagner
CFO: –
HR: –
FYE: –
Type: Private

It doesn't hurt to name an entertainment firm after a few lucky numbers. 2929 Entertainment is owned by business partners Mark Cuban (owner of the Dallas Mavericks) and Todd Wagner, who struck gold when they sold their Broadcast.com business to Yahoo! for more than $5 billion at the height of the dot-com boom. (2929 Entertainment is named after Broadcast.com's address at 2929 Elm St.) The company has ownership stakes in movie distribution firms (Magnolia Pictures), high definition television networks (HDNet and HDNet Movies), and movie exhibition (Landmark Theatres). 2929 Entertainment also partners with movie studios such as Warner Bros. to release various film and TV projects.

9278 COMMUNICATIONS INC.

1942 Williamsbridge Rd.
Bronx, NY 10461
Phone: 718-887-9278
Fax: 718-792-5130
Web: www.9278.com

CEO: Sajid Kapadia
CFO: Jim Scigliano
HR: –
FYE: December 31
Type: Private

9278 Communications makes long-distance calling as easy as 1, 2, 3. The company distributes prepaid phone cards and prepaid wireless products through a network of distributors with more than 150,000 retail locations in North America and Europe. It also sells the cards through an Internet site. The prepaid calling cards can be used for domestic and international long-distance, as well as local exchange access, and can be purchased with calling options for virtually any country around the globe. 9278 Communications acquired NTSE Holding, a private firm owned by CEO Sajid Kapadia, which resulted in the company going private in 2003.

	Annual Growth	12/03	12/04	12/05	12/06	12/07
Est. sales ($ mil.)	—	—	—	—	—	16.3
Employees	—	—	—	—	—	102

A. DAIGGER & COMPANY, INC.

620 Lakeview Parkway
Vernon Hills, IL 60061
Phone: 847-816-5060
Fax: –
Web: www.daigger.com

CEO: Jim Woldenberg
CFO: Mike Dost
HR: –
FYE: December 31
Type: Private

A. Daigger & Company mixes up a well-stocked lab. Founded in 1894, A. Daigger has been distributing laboratory equipment and supplies for more than a century. The company sells products under its own Daigger brand, as well as under hundreds of other brand names, such as Brinkmann/Eppendorf, Corning, Ohaus, and Sartorius. Striving for the lowest prices in the industry, A. Daigger offers a wide range of products — anatomical models, beakers, burners, cell cultures, centrifuges, cylinders, dissecting equipment, freeze dryers, incubators, microscopes, pipettes, safety equipment, thermometers, and many more items.

	Annual Growth	12/03	12/04	12/05	12/06	12/07
Est. sales ($ mil.)	—	—	—	—	—	28.0
Employees	—	—	—	—	—	181

A. DUDA & SONS, INC.

1200 Duda Tr.
Oviedo, FL 32765
Phone: 407-365-2111
Fax: 407-365-2010
Web: www.duda.com

CEO: Joseph A. Duda
CFO: Barton (Bart) Weeks
HR: Angelo Toro
FYE: August 31
Type: Private

DUDA has been around the block — er, the vegetable chopping block. In business for some 80 years, A. Duda & Sons (DUDA) grows and markets fresh fruits and vegetables, as well as value-added produce products. The company sells its produce to retail and foodservice customers through it shipping and import/export operations. Its main offerings include celery — DUDA is the one of the world's largest celery producers — radishes, lettuce, onions, and sweet corn, as well as citrus fruits. DUDA also grows and processes sugarcane and sod and has cattle operations. Its Viera subsidiary develops and manages commercial and residential properties in Florida.

	Annual Growth	8/03	8/04	8/05	8/06	8/07
Est. sales ($ mil.)	—	—	—	—	—	476.1
Employees	—	—	—	—	—	1,600

An in-depth profile of this company is available to Hoover's Online members at hoovers.com.

31

A. DUIE PYLE INC.

650 Westtown Rd.	CEO: Stephen M. (Steve) O'Kane
West Chester, PA 19381	CFO: Kurt V. Christensen
Phone: 610-696-5800	HR: –
Fax: 610-696-3768	FYE: December 31
Web: www.aduiepyle.com	Type: Private

A. Duie Pyle has piled up a collection of transportation-related businesses. The company's services include less-than-truckload (LTL) and truckload freight hauling, warehousing, third-party logistics, and equipment leasing. A. Duie Pyle's LTL business operates primarily in the eastern US and in Canada from a network of about a dozen terminals. (LTL carriers consolidate freight from multiple shippers into a single trailer.) The LTL unit maintains a fleet of about 630 tractors and 1,575 trailers; another 200 tractors are devoted to truckload hauling. The company offers service outside its core region through alliances with other carriers. A. Duie Pyle maintains about 2 million sq. ft. of warehouse space.

	Annual Growth	12/03	12/04	12/05	12/06	12/07
Est. sales ($ mil.)	—	—	—	—	—	77.9
Employees	—	—	—	—	—	1,400

A. FINKL & SONS COMPANY

2011 N. Southport Ave.	CEO: Bruce C. Liimatainen
Chicago, IL 60614	CFO: Joe Curci
Phone: 773-975-2510	HR: Steve Denten
Fax: 773-348-5347	FYE: January 31
Web: www.finkl.com	Type: Private

Thanks to Mrs. O'Leary's cow A. Finkl & Sons has chiseled a niche for itself in the steel industry. The company was founded in 1879 when Anton Finkl developed a chisel to clean bricks rescued from buildings destroyed in the Great Chicago Fire. Since then Finkl has forged ahead to become a leading global supplier of forging die steels (a forging die is a steel block used in a hammer or press for shaping metal). The firm also produces plastic mold steels, die casting tool steels, and custom open-die forging. German steel company SCHMOLZ+BICKENBACH acquired Finkl in 2007.

A. H. BELO CORPORATION

NYSE: AHC

400 S. Record St.	CEO: Robert W. Decherd
Dallas, TX 75202	CFO: Alison K. Engel
Phone: 214-977-8200	HR: Sheila Hartley
Fax: 214-977-8201	FYE: December 31
Web: www.ahbelo.com	Type: Public

This company gives the Big D a helping of news with breakfast. A. H. Belo is a leading newspaper publisher with a portfolio of three daily newspapers anchored by *The Dallas Morning News*, one of the country's top papers with a circulation of more than 460,000. It also owns *The Press-Enterprise* (Riverside, California) and *The Providence Journal* (published in Rhode Island by subsidiary The Providence Journal Company). In addition to its flagship papers, A. H. Belo publishes the *Denton Record-Chronicle* (Texas) and several niche papers such as the Spanish-language paper Al Dia (Dallas), along with Web sites serving most of its publications. The company was spun off from TV station operator Belo Corp. in 2008.

	Annual Growth	12/03	12/04	12/05	12/06	12/07
Sales ($ mil.)	—	—	—	—	—	738.7
Net income ($ mil.)	—	—	—	—	—	(347.0)
Employees	—	—	—	—	—	3,800

A. RUIZ CONSTRUCTION COMPANY & ASSOCIATES, INC.

1601 Cortland Ave.	CEO: Antonio (Tony) Ruiz
San Francisco, CA 94110	CFO: Thomas Cotter
Phone: 415-647-4010	HR: –
Fax: 415-647-1796	FYE: December 31
Web: www.aruizconstruction.com	Type: Private

Tony Bennett may have left his heart in San Francisco, but Antonio Ruiz has left his blood, sweat, and tears. Ruiz owns and operates A. Ruiz Construction Company & Associates, a firm which he founded in 1978. A general engineering and building contractor, it has expertise in civil engineering, as well as residential construction and remodeling. It has worked on everything from reservoir repair to street improvements to utilities installation in both the public and private sectors. Clients include the City of San Francisco, Pacific Gas & Electric, and Bombardier Transportation. A. Ruiz Construction primarily serves the Bay Area with offices in San Francisco and San Leandro, California.

	Annual Growth	12/03	12/04	12/05	12/06	12/07
Est. sales ($ mil.)	—	—	—	—	—	7.6
Employees	—	—	—	—	—	50

A. SCHULMAN, INC.

NASDAQ (GS): SHLM

3550 W. Market St.	CEO: Joseph M. (Joe) Gingo
Akron, OH 44333	CFO: Paul F. DeSantis
Phone: 330-666-3751	HR: Cathy Brown
Fax: 330-668-7204	FYE: August 31
Web: www.aschulman.com	Type: Public

A. Schulman adds color to plastic resins but keeps them from getting red hot. Schulman adds chemicals to basic plastics such as polypropylene, polyethylene, and PVC to give them color and desired characteristics like flexibility or the ability to retard flame. Its products include color and additive concentrates, engineered compounds (such as reinforced plastics), elastomers, and value-added PVC. Customers range from makers of plastics to auto parts. The company also distributes plastic resins made by ExxonMobil Chemical. In 2007 investor Barington Group threw up a fight about the direction of the company. It managed to win the right to name a director and get Schulman to consider a merger or sale.

	Annual Growth	8/03	8/04	8/05	8/06	8/07
Sales ($ mil.)	12.8%	1,102.5	1,241.3	1,435.6	1,616.4	1,787.1
Net income ($ mil.)	9.2%	15.9	27.9	32.1	32.7	22.6
Market value ($ mil.)	5.9%	473.7	610.3	559.3	645.5	596.0
Employees	1.5%	—	—	2,399	2,480	2,471

A. SMITH BOWMAN DISTILLERY, INC.

1 Bowman Dr.	CEO: John B. (Jay) Adams Jr.
Fredericksburg, VA 22408	CFO: Kent Broussard
Phone: 540-373-4555	HR: –
Fax: 540-371-2236	FYE: December 31
Web: www.asmithbowman.com	Type: Private

Let the good times (and the barrels) roll. Shortly after Prohibition's end, Abram Bowman decided to boost profits from his corn field by making bourbon (whiskey made from corn). Thus was born the A. Smith Bowman Distillery, which today produces a variety of small-batch spirits — vodka, scotch, tequila, rum, gin, and whiskey — under its namesake Bowman's brand and the Virginia Gentleman brand. The distillery is owned by the New Orleans spirits operation the Sazerac Company.

	Annual Growth	12/03	12/04	12/05	12/06	12/07
Est. sales ($ mil.)	—	—	—	—	—	116.7
Employees	—	—	—	—	—	350

A2D TECHNOLOGIES

2345 Atascocita Rd.
Humble, TX 77396
Phone: 281-319-4944
Fax: 281-319-4945
Web: www.tgsnopec.com

CEO: H. H. (Hank) Hamilton III
CFO: Arne Helland
HR: Michelle Hobbs
FYE: December 31
Type: Subsidiary

A2D Technologies provides digital well log data, interpretive software, and data management services. Through subscribing to A2D's LOG-LINE system, geoscientists access and download well log data from their workstations. A2D customers use its well log data to calibrate seismic data to known geologic conditions in well bores. A2D was founded in 1993 by Dave Kotowych (president), Brenda Sigurdson (VP), and Joe Carroll. Seismic data company TGS-NOPEC Geophysical acquired A2D in 2002. Along with affiliate Riley Electric Log, A2D Technologies has made TGS-NOPEC one of the largest owners of digital well log data in North America.

	Annual Growth	12/03	12/04	12/05	12/06	12/07
Est. sales ($ mil.)	—	—	—	—	—	13.0
Employees	—	—	—	—	—	210

A21, INC.

OTC: ATWO

7660 Centurion Pkwy.
Jacksonville, FL 32256
Phone: 904-565-0066
Fax: 904-565-1620
Web: www.a21group.com

CEO: John Z. Ferguson
CFO: Thomas (Tom) Costanza
HR: —
FYE: December 31
Type: Public

a21 is an online marketplace of digital stock images. Its clients include photographers, artists, advertisers, publishers, and other members of the professional creative community. The company offers full service photo management, including conversion, storage, distribution, marketing, customer service, and media rights management, to image buyers and sellers. a21 operates through subsidiaries SuperStock and the UK-based Ingram Publishing. In addition, its ArtSelect subsidiary is a supplier of framed and unframed wall décor.

	Annual Growth	12/03	12/04	12/05	12/06	12/07
Sales ($ mil.)	45.9%	—	7.5	9.6	19.6	23.3
Net income ($ mil.)	—	—	(2.5)	(4.8)	(9.1)	(4.7)
Market value ($ mil.)	(20.7%)	—	4.8	23.9	21.5	2.4
Employees	—	—	—	77	—	—

AAA COOPER TRANSPORTATION

1751 Kinsey Rd.
Dothan, AL 36302
Phone: 334-793-2284
Fax: 334-794-3353
Web: www.aaacooper.com

CEO: G. Mack Dove
CFO: Steve Roy
HR: —
FYE: December 31
Type: Private

It might not give you maps like that other AAA, but AAA Cooper Transportation will design a route for your freight. A regional less-than-truckload (LTL) freight hauler, AAA Cooper operates primarily in the southeastern US and in Puerto Rico; it also maintains facilities in Chicago and a few other industrial areas. (LTL carriers combine freight from multiple shippers into a single truckload.) AAA Cooper Transportation operates from about 80 terminals, and the company's fleet includes about 2,300 tractors and 6,000 trailers. AAA Cooper Transportation also offers freight brokerage services and dedicated contract carriage. Chairman and CEO Mack Dove owns the company, which was founded by his father in 1955.

	Annual Growth	12/03	12/04	12/05	12/06	12/07
Est. sales ($ mil.)	—	—	—	—	—	528.8
Employees	—	—	—	—	—	4,668

AAC GROUP HOLDING CORP.

7211 Circle S Rd.
Austin, TX 78745
Phone: 512-444-0571
Fax: 512-443-5213
Web: www.cbi-rings.com

CEO: Donald J. Percenti
CFO: Kris G. Radhakrishnan
HR: Ann Broome
FYE: Last Saturday in August
Type: Private

AAC Group (doing business as American Achievement) wants you to show off its class ring, sign its yearbook, and wear its jacket. The firm manufactures and supplies those items of high school and college memorabilia, as well as graduation products such as caps and gowns, diplomas, letter jackets, and announcements. Its ring brands include Balfour and ArtCarved. Scholastic products account for most of the company's sales. It also makes commemorative jewelry for families, sports fans, employee awards, and professional sports events such as the World Series and the Super Bowl. American Achievement is majority-owned by Fenway Partners, which has agreed to sell the company to rival Herff Jones.

	Annual Growth	8/02	8/03	8/04	8/05	8/06
Sales ($ mil.)	1.3%	304.4	308.4	314.1	315.6	320.9
Employees	(6.4%)	2,400	2,344	2,170	1,930	1,840

AAF-MCQUAY INC.

10300 Ormsby Park Place, #600
Louisville, KY 40223
Phone: 502-637-0011
Fax: 502-637-0452

CEO: Ho Nyuk Choy
CFO: Bruce D. Krueger
HR: —
FYE: Saturday nearest June 30
Type: Subsidiary

AAF-McQUAY is into AC. The company, a part of Daikin Industries, makes and markets commercial air-conditioning and air-filtration products and systems for commercial, institutional, and industrial clients worldwide. Its AAF International division makes air-filtration products that include replacement filters and environmental products (air pollution-control products and systems, machinery filtration products, and acoustical systems). The McQuay International unit produces commercial air-conditioning and refrigeration equipment (chiller products, applied air handling systems, applied terminal systems, and industrial refrigeration). The company operates plants worldwide.

AAIPHARMA INC.

2320 Scientific Park Dr.
Wilmington, NC 28405
Phone: 910-254-7000
Fax: 910-815-2300
Web: www.aaipharma.com

CEO: Ludo Reynders
CFO: Rachel R. Selisker
HR: John W. Harrington
FYE: December 31
Type: Private

AAIPharma has undergone its own drug trials and has begun its rebuilding phase. A provider of contract research services to the pharmaceutical, biotech, and medical device industries, the company emerged from Chapter 11 bankruptcy in 2006 focused on its drug development and support operations and minus its pharmaceuticals business. It sold the unit, which had marketed the narcotic Darvocet among other things, to Xanodyne Pharmaceuticals as part of its reorganization. Its outsourcing services run the gamut from drug candidate selection and feasibility studies, to bioanalytical testing and clinical trials management. Other services include regulatory support, clinical supplies manufacturing, and data management.

An in-depth profile of this company is available to Hoover's Online members at hoovers.com.

33

AALFS MANUFACTURING COMPANY

1005 4th St.
Sioux City, IA 51101
Phone: 712-252-1877
Fax: 712-252-5205
Web: www.aalfs.com

CEO: John (Jack) Aalfs
CFO: Barbara Benson
HR: –
FYE: March 31
Type: Private

Aalfs Manufacturing Company, owned and run by the founding Aalfs family, just might have a gene for the jeans business. The company designs, makes, and markets clothing (primarily jeans and denimwear) to big-name retailers nationwide. Clients include J.C. Penney, Tommy Hilfiger, Gap, Old Navy, and even Harley Davidson. Founded in Iowa in 1892 by H.A. Baker and renamed the Aalfs-Baker Manufacturing Company in 1929, when Wilbur Aalfs held the presidential title, the apparel manufacturer officially became Aalfs Manufacturing Company in 1959. The company also operates offices in several other states.

	Annual Growth	3/03	3/04	3/05	3/06	3/07
Est. sales ($ mil.)	—	—	—	—	—	46.0
Employees	—	—	—	—	—	1,425

AAMCO TRANSMISSIONS, INC.

201 Gibraltar Rd.
Horsham, PA 19044
Phone: 215-643-5885
Fax: 215-956-0340
Web: www.aamcotransmissions.com

CEO: Todd P. Leff
CFO: Michael Sumsky
HR: Linda Etter
FYE: December 31
Type: Private

AAMCO Transmissions is geared for transmission repair. The company is a leading franchiser of transmission fix-it facilities, with more than 800 independently owned and operated shops throughout the US. Along with transmission work, AAMCO stores provide automotive cooling system and electrical system repairs and other maintenance services. Investment firm American Capital Strategies acquired a controlling stake in the company in 2006 in order to combine AAMCO with its portfolio company Cottman Transmission, which offers similar services.

	Annual Growth	12/03	12/04	12/05	12/06	12/07
Est. sales ($ mil.)	—	—	—	—	—	10.5
Employees	—	—	—	—	—	160

A&E TELEVISION NETWORKS

235 E. 45th St.
New York, NY 10017
Phone: 212-210-1400
Fax: 212-850-9370
Web: www.aetn.com

CEO: Abbe Raven
CFO: Gerard Gruosso
HR: Rosalind Clay Carter
FYE: December 31
Type: Joint venture

A&E Television Networks is defying the notion that TV rots the brain. The company offers a smorgasbord of programming in history, the arts, current events, and popular culture through its two main cable networks A&E and The History Channel, each of which reach about 95 million US homes. A&E Television also operates five other channels (Biography Channel, Crime & Investigation, Military History, History Channel International, and The History Channel en Español) and a handful of associated Web sites. Internationally, A&E's channels reach about 235 million subscribers in 130 countries. A&E is a joint venture of Hearst (37.5%), Disney ABC Cable (37.5%), and NBC Universal Cable (25%).

A & H SPORTSWEAR CO., INC.

500 William St.
Pen Argyl, PA 18072
Phone: 610-863-4176
Fax: –
Web: www.miraclesuit.com

CEO: Mark Waldman
CFO: Randy Finelli
HR: –
FYE: October 31
Type: Private

When swimsuit season rolls around, Houdini has nothing on A & H Sportswear. The company's Miraclesuit makes 10 pounds disappear! The Miraclesuit bathing suits suck in that tummy using three times as much Lycra as most other swimwear. The company also makes beachwear and cruise wear using its patented Miratex fabric. A & H Sportswear's swimsuits and beachwear are sold in the US through retailers (such as Bloomingdale's, Lane Bryant, and Saks Fifth Avenue), catalogs (including Eddie Bauer, Norm Thompson, and Nordstrom), and online retailers (Cyberswim.com, everythingbutwater.com). A & H Sportswear's apparel is also sold internationally through retailer locations in Australia.

	Annual Growth	10/03	10/04	10/05	10/06	10/07
Est. sales ($ mil.)	—	—	—	—	—	100.0
Employees	—	—	—	—	—	650

A & L, INC.

4201 State Rte. 51
Belle Vernon, PA 15012
Phone: 724-929-2125
Fax: 724-929-3011
Web: www.alconstruction.com

CEO: Louis D. (Lou) Ruscitto
CFO: Michelle Herron
HR: –
FYE: September 30
Type: Private

An alternate way to spell heavy civil and highway construction might be A & L. The construction company provides demolition, site development, construction, and site management services on such projects as airports, bridges, dams, roads, tunnels, manufacturing facilities, railways, toll plazas, and water treatment plants. Clients run the gamut from businesses to school districts to government agencies and include Volkswagen, Westinghouse, Pennsylvania's Gateway School District, and the New York State Department of Transportation. A & L, which was founded in 1963 by president Louis Ruscitto, operates offices in Illinois, New York, and Pennsylvania.

	Annual Growth	9/03	9/04	9/05	9/06	9/07
Est. sales ($ mil.)	—	—	—	—	—	32.3
Employees	—	—	—	—	—	250

A&R TRANSPORT, INC.

8440 S. Tabler Rd.
Morris, IL 60450
Phone: 815-941-5200
Fax: 800-406-5703
Web: artransport.com

CEO: James E. Bedeker
CFO: Craig Stimpert
HR: Brenda Barnhart
FYE: December 31
Type: Private

A&R Transport offers over-the-road transportation of dry and liquid bulk commodities. The company operates from some 20 terminals, mainly in the eastern half of the US; its fleet of equipment includes some 600 tractors, more than 1,800 dry bulk tanks and containers, about 120 liquid tanks, and some 30 liquid tank container chassis. A&R Transport's customers include companies in the plastics and chemicals manufacturing industries. Affiliate A&R Packaging & Distribution Services operates four warehouses with a total of more than 800,000 sq. ft. of space.

	Annual Growth	12/03	12/04	12/05	12/06	12/07
Est. sales ($ mil.)	—	—	—	—	—	150.0
Employees	—	—	—	—	—	750

A&W RESTAURANTS, INC.

1900 Colonel Sanders Ln.
Louisville, KY 40213
Phone: 502-874-3000
Fax: 502-874-8848
Web: www.awrestaurants.com

CEO: Andy Rosen
CFO: –
HR: Ruth Melchior
FYE: December 31
Type: Subsidiary

The old fashioned root beer stand lives on thanks to this business. A subsidiary of fast-food giant YUM! Brands, A&W Restaurants operates and franchises about 625 quick-service restaurants in the US and 10 other countries offering hamburgers, hot dogs, onion rings, and fries, along with its signature root beer. In addition to its traditional drive-up format, the chain includes food court locations and restaurants co-branded with sister chains KFC and Taco Bell. A handful of locations are corporate-owned. A&W traces its roots back to a California root beer stand business started by Roy Allen in 1919.

AARON INDUSTRIES, INC.

28966 Hwy. 76 East
Clinton, SC 29325
Phone: 864-833-0178
Fax: 864-833-5493
Web: www.aaronindustriesinc.com

CEO: James L. Medford
CFO: Kenneth R. Rodgers
HR: –
FYE: December 31
Type: Private

Aaron Industries makes a lot of the products you might be familiar with, but under different names. The pharmaceutical company makes approximately 80 different branded and private-label generic products, including alcohol, hydrogen peroxide, mouthwash, hair gel, and antacids and laxatives. It also produces cold and cough suppressants and personal care products such as body sprays and lotions. Aaron Industries provides contract manufacturing and logistics services. The company operates two manufacturing facilities, one in California and one in South Carolina.

	Annual Growth	12/03	12/04	12/05	12/06	12/07
Est. sales ($ mil.)	—	—	—	—	—	50.1
Employees	—	—	—	—	—	400

AAON, INC.

NASDAQ (GS): AAON

2425 S. Yukon Ave.
Tulsa, OK 74107
Phone: 918-583-2266
Fax: 918-583-6094
Web: www.aaon.com

CEO: Norman H. (Norm) Asbjornson
CFO: Kathy I. Sheffield
HR: Robert G. (Bob) Fergus
FYE: December 31
Type: Public

Whichever way the thermostat turns, it generates cool cash for AAON. Through subsidiaries, the company manufactures rooftop air-conditioning and heating equipment for commercial and industrial uses primarily in the US. AAON produces five series of rooftop air-conditioning products with cooling sizes ranging from two tons to 230 tons. (Typical commercial buildings require one ton of cool air for every 300 to 400 sq. ft.) The company estimates that it owns 13% of the rooftop market. AAON also makes air handlers, condensing units, chillers, coils, and boilers. It serves the new construction and replacement markets.

	Annual Growth	12/03	12/04	12/05	12/06	12/07
Sales ($ mil.)	15.2%	148.8	173.3	185.2	231.5	262.5
Net income ($ mil.)	13.1%	14.2	7.5	11.5	17.1	23.2
Market value ($ mil.)	21.9%	162.0	132.3	145.8	216.2	357.8
Employees	(0.8%)	—	—	1,413	—	1,391

AARON RENTS, INC.

NYSE: RNT

309 E. Paces Ferry Rd. NE
Atlanta, GA 30305
Phone: 404-231-0011
Fax: 678-402-3560
Web: www.aaronrents.com

CEO: Robert C. Loudermilk Jr.
CFO: Gilbert L. Danielson
HR: D. Chad Strickland
FYE: December 31
Type: Public

For all those customers who crave a credenza, desire a desk, seek a sofa, or wish for a washer, Aaron Rents rents — and sells — all of the above and more. One of the leading furniture rental and rent-to-own companies in the US (behind industry leader Rent-A-Center), Aaron Rents purveys home and office furniture in the US, Puerto Rico, and Canada through some 1,560 Aaron's Sales & Lease Ownership for Less and Aaron's Rent-to-Rent stores. Its stores also offer consumer electronics and household appliances. Aaron Rents' MacTavish Furniture Industries makes nearly half of the firm's furniture at facilities across four US states. Chairman Charles Loudermilk owns about 64% of the company's Class A shares.

	Annual Growth	12/03	12/04	12/05	12/06	12/07
Sales ($ mil.)	18.2%	766.8	946.5	1,125.5	1,326.6	1,494.9
Net income ($ mil.)	21.9%	36.4	52.6	58.0	78.6	80.3
Market value ($ mil.)	24.3%	364.7	1,034.1	877.6	1,304.8	871.4
Employees	12.4%	—	—	7,600	8,400	9,600

AAR CORP.

NYSE: AIR

1100 N. Wood Dale Rd.
Wood Dale, IL 60191
Phone: 630-227-2000
Fax: 630-227-2039
Web: www.aarcorp.com

CEO: David P. Storch
CFO: Richard J. (Rick) Poulton
HR: Timothy O. Skelly
FYE: May 31
Type: Public

With much more than a wing and a prayer, AAR provides a wide range of products and services for the aviation industry. The company's aviation supply chain unit, which accounts for about half of AAR's sales, buys and sells a variety of engine and airframe parts and components and offers inventory management services. Other AAR units manufacture containers, pallets, and in-plane cargo loading and handling systems; provide maintenance, repair, and overhaul (MRO) of commercial and military aircraft and components; and sell and lease used commercial jet aircraft. Customers include airlines, business aircraft operators, aviation OEMs, and militaries. The US Department of Defense accounts for nearly a third of sales.

	Annual Growth	5/03	5/04	5/05	5/06	5/07
Sales ($ mil.)	15.0%	606.3	652.0	747.8	897.3	1,061.2
Net income ($ mil.)	—	(12.4)	3.5	15.4	35.2	58.7
Market value ($ mil.)	71.0%	143.3	308.9	522.7	882.6	1,226.2
Employees	26.9%	—	—	2,600	3,300	—

AARP

601 E. St. NW
Washington, DC 20049
Phone: 202-434-7700
Fax: 202-434-7710
Web: www.aarp.org

CEO: William D. (Bill) Novelli
CFO: Robert R. Hagans Jr.
HR: Ellie Hollander
FYE: December 31
Type: Not-for-profit

Turn 50 and the doors of the AARP will open for you, as they have for more than 35 million current members. On behalf of its members, the not-for-profit AARP acts as an advocate on public policy issues, publishes information (including the monthly *AARP Bulletin* and the bimonthly *AARP The Magazine*), promotes community service, and works with business partners to offer products and services (including discounts on insurance and travel). The group is organized into some 3,500 local chapters throughout the US. Royalties from businesses eager to reach AARP members account for about 40% of the group's revenue; membership dues ($12.50 per year) account for about 25%.

	Annual Growth	12/03	12/04	12/05	12/06	12/07
Sales ($ mil.)	—	—	—	—	—	1,009.6
Employees	—	—	—	—	—	—

An in-depth profile of this company is available to Hoover's Online members at hoovers.com.

35

AASTROM BIOSCIENCES, INC.

NASDAQ (CM): ASTM

Domino's Farms, Lobby K, 24 Frank Lloyd Wright Dr.
Ann Arbor, MI 48105
Phone: 734-930-5555
Fax: 734-665-0485
Web: www.aastrom.com

CEO: George W. Dunbar Jr.
CFO: George W. Dunbar Jr.
HR: Carol Duman
FYE: June 30
Type: Public

Aastrom Biosciences brings new life to dying tissue. Its Tissue Repair Cell (TRC) technology takes a small amount of bone marrow from a patient and uses it to grow stem and progenitor cells. The new cells, created through a sterile, automated process, are then used in tissue regeneration therapies for the donor patient. The company hopes the technology will treat various types of conditions, including degenerative bone, vascular, cardiac, and central nervous system diseases. The TRC system is in clinical trials for bone and vascular regeneration; it has received orphan drug status for the treatment of osteonecrosis, or bone death caused by poor blood supply.

	Annual Growth	6/03	6/04	6/05	6/06	6/07
Sales ($ mil.)	(3.3%)	0.8	1.3	0.9	0.9	0.7
Net income ($ mil.)	—	(9.6)	(10.5)	(11.8)	(16.5)	(17.6)
Market value ($ mil.)	25.4%	65.5	73.2	319.3	158.9	162.0
Employees	—	—	—	49	—	—

A. B. BOYD COMPANY

600 S. McClure Rd.
Modesto, CA 95357
Phone: 209-236-1111
Fax: 209-236-0154
Web: www.boydcorp.com

CEO: Mitchell F. (Mitch) Aiello
CFO: Kurt Wetzel
HR: –
FYE: December 31
Type: Private

A. B. Boyd Company puts a little zip in rubber manufacturing. Originally set up as a zipper distributor, the company, which does business as Boyd Corporation, now manufactures rubber, plastic, and fiber products for OEMs in the aerospace, electronics, medical, telecommunications, and transportation industries. A. B. Boyd can provide custom design and manufacturing services and works with materials such as silicone, Mylar, polypropylene, neoprene, Teflon, copper and aluminum foils, and coated fabrics. A list of the suppliers that the company works with includes SABIC Innovative Plastics (formerly GE Plastics), 3M Company, and Gaska Tape.

	Annual Growth	12/03	12/04	12/05	12/06	12/07
Est. sales ($ mil.)	—	—	—	—	—	50.0
Employees	—	—	—	—	—	273

ABACUS TECHNOLOGY CORPORATION

5454 Wisconsin Ave., Ste. 1100
Chevy Chase, MD 20815
Phone: 301-907-8500
Fax: 301-907-8508
Web: www.abacustech.com

CEO: Dennis J. Yee
CFO: Marjorie Holman
HR: –
FYE: December 31
Type: Private

If you're a government bureaucrat or a military officer who needs computers, chances are that Abacus Technology can help you. The company provides installation, implementation, maintenance, and training services for products from Microsoft and other tech vendors. Established in 1983, Abacus does work for all three branches of the US military, along with federal civilian agencies, and for state and local governments. The company also counts many clients in the private sector, including The Aerospace Corporation, Caterpillar, Keane, and KPMG. President Dennis Yee owns the company, which has offices around the US and in Saudi Arabia.

	Annual Growth	12/03	12/04	12/05	12/06	12/07
Est. sales ($ mil.)	—	—	—	—	—	24.2
Employees	—	—	—	—	—	435

ABATIX CORP.

Pink Sheets: ABIX

2400 Skyline Dr., Ste. 400
Mesquite, TX 75149
Phone: 214-381-0322
Fax: 214-381-9513
Web: www.abatix.com

CEO: Terry W. Shaver
CFO: Frank J. Cinatl IV
HR: Andrea Staub
FYE: December 31
Type: Public

Abatix helps companies clean up. Through eight US distribution centers, Abatix supplies more than 22,000 personal protection and safety products to environmental contractors, construction companies, and industrial safety companies. Abatix's products are used by workers involved in cleanup projects such as asbestos and lead abatement and mold remediation. The company imports protective clothing through subsidiary International Enviroguard Systems (IESI). Abatix serves some 4,000 customers primarily located in the Southeast, Southwest, Midwest, Pacific Coast, and Alaska and Hawaii. CEO Terry Shaver owns about 30% of Abatix.

	Annual Growth	12/03	12/04	12/05	12/06	12/07
Sales ($ mil.)	9.0%	48.9	52.9	70.6	66.4	69.0
Net income ($ mil.)	89.9%	0.1	0.2	2.1	1.0	1.3
Employees	0.0%	—	—	105	105	—

ABAXIS, INC.

NASDAQ (GS): ABAX

3240 Whipple Rd.
Union City, CA 94587
Phone: 510-675-6500
Fax: 510-441-6150
Web: www.abaxis.com

CEO: Clinton H. Severson
CFO: Alberto R. Santa Ines
HR: –
FYE: March 31
Type: Public

Abaxis makes a praxis of producing what the facts is when analyzing patients' blood. Its point-of-care blood analyzers can perform more than 20 types of tests on animals and humans. The analyzers are portable, require little training, provide on-the-spot results, and offer built-in quality control and calibration. They come with reagent discs for performing common blood tests. Abaxis markets the system under the name VetScan in the veterinary market (where it makes most of its sales) and Piccolo in the human medical market. It is developing a wider range of tests to better penetrate the human diagnostic market. Abaxis sells its products to veterinarians, hospitals, managed care companies, and the military.

	Annual Growth	3/04	3/05	3/06	3/07	3/08
Sales ($ mil.)	21.0%	46.9	52.8	68.9	86.2	100.6
Net income ($ mil.)	(15.0%)	24.0	4.8	7.5	10.1	12.5
Market value ($ mil.)	6.1%	396.7	176.0	456.7	516.8	502.9
Employees	20.0%	—	184	217	265	—

ABB INC.

501 Merritt 7
Norwalk, CT 06851
Phone: 203-750-2200
Fax: 203-750-2263
Web: www.abb.us

CEO: Enrique Santacana
CFO: –
HR: Phil Lloyd
FYE: December 31
Type: Subsidiary

When robots take over the world you can blame ABB. The US operations of global manufacturing conglomerate ABB Ltd. have built a presence in dozens of industries. Like its German parent company, ABB Inc. operates in two main areas, automation technologies and power technologies, and serves customers including power utilities, commercial and residential buildings, and industrial process plants. ABB's products include controls and instrumentation, robotics, switches, motors, transformers, and power electronics. It also offers various consulting services. Although ABB has acted independently in the past, its parent has brought it under the umbrella of a central management structure.

ABBEY CARPET COMPANY, INC.

3471 Bonita Bay Blvd.
Bonita Springs, FL 34134
Phone: 239-948-0900
Fax: 239-948-0999
Web: www.abbeycarpet.com

CEO: Philip (Phil) Gutierrez
CFO: Herb Gray
HR: –
FYE: December 31
Type: Private

Beating out McDonald's as the first registered franchise in California, Abbey Carpet Company has become one of the nation's top franchise operations. The company runs a network of about 800 independently owned and operated stores across the US, the Bahamas, and Puerto Rico. It sells brand-name carpet at mill-direct prices, as well as area rugs; hardwood, laminate, and vinyl floorings; ceramic tile; and window coverings. It also offers its own line of carpet and home fashion products. Founded in 1958 by Milton Levinson, Abbey Carpet began as a single floor-covering store in Sacramento, California. Chairman and CEO Phil Gutierrez has owned Abbey Carpet since 1983.

	Annual Growth	12/03	12/04	12/05	12/06	12/07
Est. sales ($ mil.)	—	—	—	—	—	22.6
Employees	—	—	—	—	—	43

ABBOTT LABORATORIES

NYSE: ABT

100 Abbott Park Rd.
Abbott Park, IL 60064
Phone: 847-937-6100
Fax: 847-937-9555
Web: www.abbott.com

CEO: Miles D. White
CFO: Thomas C. (Tom) Freyman
HR: Stephen R. (Steve) Fussell
FYE: December 31
Type: Public

Filling baby bottles and soothing tummies are a habit for Abbot. Abbott Laboratories is one of the US's top health care products makers. The company's pharmaceuticals include HIV treatment Norvir, rheumatoid arthritis therapy Humira, and obesity drug Meridia. Its nutritional products division makes such well-known brands as Similac infant formula and the Ensure line of nutrition supplements. Abbott Labs also makes laboratory diagnostic systems and devices to treat vascular disease. The company sells its products in more than 130 countries through affiliates and distributors.

	Annual Growth	12/03	12/04	12/05	12/06	12/07
Sales ($ mil.)	7.1%	19,680.6	19,680.0	22,337.8	22,476.3	25,914.2
Net income ($ mil.)	7.0%	2,753.2	3,235.9	3,372.1	1,716.8	3,606.3
Market value ($ mil.)	6.2%	68,521.2	72,775.1	60,692.0	74,879.1	87,027.5
Employees	6.7%	—	—	59,735	66,663	68,000

ABC APPLIANCE, INC.

1 Silverdome Industrial Park
Pontiac, MI 48343
Phone: 248-335-4222
Fax: 248-335-2568
Web: www.abcwarehouse.com

CEO: Gordon W. (Gordy) Hartunian
CFO: Don Behrendt
HR: –
FYE: October 31
Type: Private

ABC Appliance sells audio equipment, electronics, computers, appliances, and other products at more than 40 stores in Michigan, Ohio, and Indiana. The company's inventory includes products made by such manufacturers as Audiovox, Canon, Sony, and Whirlpool. The retail outlets operate under the ABC Warehouse, Mickey Shorr (mobile electronics), and Hawthorne Appliance banners. Stores are set up like warehouses with what the company calls a "no frills" approach. President and CEO Gordy Hartunian, who founded the company in 1964, and his family own ABC Appliance.

	Annual Growth	10/03	10/04	10/05	10/06	10/07
Est. sales ($ mil.)	—	—	—	—	—	338.3
Employees	—	—	—	—	—	1,750

ABC HOME FURNISHINGS, INC.

888 Broadway
New York, NY 10003
Phone: 212-473-3000
Fax: 212-505-3125
Web: www.abchome.com

CEO: Paulette Cole
CFO: David E. Lauber
HR: –
FYE: September 30
Type: Private

Do your ABCs start with armoires, beds, and carpets? Then ABC Home Furnishings (aka ABC Carpet & Home) is the store for you. The specialty home furnishings retailer operates four stores in the US, plus a store in Harrods in London, offering high-quality furniture, linens, window treatments, mattresses, rugs, and related accessories. It also sells upscale electronics from Harvey. The company is owned by CEO and creative director Paulette Cole, the daughter of ABC's founder, Jerry Weinrib, who started the company as a single carpet store in 1961. In 1981 Paulette and then-husband Evan Cole joined the business. In 2003 the Coles separated; shortly thereafter, Evan sold his share of the business to Paulette.

	Annual Growth	9/03	9/04	9/05	9/06	9/07
Est. sales ($ mil.)	—	—	—	—	—	65.5
Employees	—	—	—	—	—	600

ABCO LABORATORIES, INC.

2450 S. Watney Way
Fairfield, CA 94533
Phone: 707-432-2200
Fax: 707-432-2240
Web: www.abcolabs.com

CEO: Allen Baron
CFO: Jessica Chua
HR: Jessica Chua
FYE: December 31
Type: Private

ABCO Laboratories knows the ABCs of custom food-ingredient manufacturing. The company offers contract manufacturing, custom blending, private labeling, packaging, encapsulation, and other services for the natural-food industry. Its products include Gourmet Naturally baking mixes, soups, and vegetarian entrees; Spiceworks seasonings, herbs, and marinades; Nutra Naturally juice-bar products; and Homeopathics natural remedies and tonics. ABCO also makes ingredients for use by nutritional supplement, pharmaceutical, cosmetic, and homeopathic product manufacturers. ABCO Laboratories was founded in 1964.

	Annual Growth	12/03	12/04	12/05	12/06	12/07
Est. sales ($ mil.)	—	—	—	—	—	8.2
Employees	—	—	—	—	—	100

ABENGOA BIOENERGY CORPORATION

1400 Elbridge Payne Rd., Ste. 212
Chesterfield, MO 63017
Phone: 636-728-0508
Fax: 636-728-1148
Web: www.abengoabioenergy.com

CEO: Javier Salgado Leirado
CFO: Ignacio García
HR: –
FYE: June 30
Type: Subsidiary

Among the largest US producers of ethanol, Abengoa Bioenergy owns five plants in the US and another half dozen in Europe. The company's primary product is fuel-grade ethanol, which, when blended with gasoline, raises oxygen levels and reduces exhaust emissions of pollutants such as carbon monoxide. As part of a search for new revenue streams, Abengoa Bioenergy launched a research and development subsidiary that works in partnership with universities and other companies to develop improved processing technology for ethanol. In 2007 it acquired Brazilian ethanol maker Dedini Agro for about $300 million. It's been a part of Spanish engineering firm Abengoa since 2002.

	Annual Growth	6/03	6/04	6/05	6/06	6/07
Est. sales ($ mil.)	—	—	—	—	—	40.6
Employees	—	—	—	—	—	165

An in-depth profile of this company is available to Hoover's Online members at hoovers.com.

ABERCROMBIE & FITCH CO.

NYSE: ANF

6301 Fitch Path
New Albany, OH 43054
Phone: 614-283-6500
Fax: 614-283-6710
Web: www.abercrombie.com

CEO: Michael S. (Mike) Jeffries
CFO: Michael W. Kramer
HR: Ron Grzymkowski
FYE: Saturday nearest January 31
Type: Public

Trading on its century-old name, Abercrombie & Fitch (A&F) sells upscale men's, women's, and kids' casual clothes and accessories — quite a change from when the company outfitted Ernest Hemingway and Teddy Roosevelt for safaris. A&F has 1,000-plus stores in North America (mostly in malls) and also sells via its catalog and online. It targets college students, and has come under fire for some of its ad campaigns, as well as for some of its short-run products. The company also runs a fast-growing chain of some 450 teen stores called Hollister Co., and a chain targeted at boys and girls ages seven to 14 called abercrombie. RUEHL, a Greenwich Village-inspired concept for the post-college set, debuted in 2004.

	Annual Growth	1/04	1/05	1/06	1/07	1/08
Sales ($ mil.)	21.7%	1,707.8	2,021.3	2,784.7	3,318.2	3,749.8
Net income ($ mil.)	23.5%	204.8	216.4	334.0	422.2	475.7
Employees	34.6%	30,200	62,140	76,100	86,400	99,000

ABF FREIGHT SYSTEM, INC.

3801 Old Greenwood Rd.
Fort Smith, AR 72903
Phone: 479-785-6000
Fax: 800-599-2810
Web: www.abfs.com

CEO: Robert A. (Bob) Davidson
CFO: Frank Ward
HR: –
FYE: December 31
Type: Subsidiary

ABF Freight System knows the ABCs of freight transportation. The primary subsidiary of Arkansas Best, ABF Freight System specializes in long-haul, less-than-truckload (LTL) transportation of general commodities such as apparel, appliances, chemicals, food, furniture, plastics, rubber, and textiles. (LTL carriers combine freight from multiple shippers into a single truckload.) ABF Freight System operates from a network of about 290 terminals throughout the US and Canada and in Puerto Rico. It maintains a fleet of some 4,000 tractors and 20,000 trailers. The company offers service in Mexico through arrangements with Mexican carriers.

ABIGAIL ADAMS NATIONAL BANCORP, INC.

NASDAQ (GM): AANB

1130 Connecticut Ave. NW, Ste. 200
Washington, DC 20036
Phone: 202-772-3600
Fax: 202-835-3871
Web: www.adamsbank.com

CEO: Jeanne Delaney Hubbard
CFO: Karen E. Troutman
HR: Everett Hitchner
FYE: December 31
Type: Public

Abigail Adams National Bancorp is sure to "remember the ladies." The holding company owns The Adams National Bank, which was founded in 1977 as the first federally chartered bank owned and operated by women. With six branches in the Washington, DC, area, it caters to women, minorities, small businesses, not-for-profit organizations, and government contractors. Another bank subsidiary, Consolidated Bank & Trust, operates three branches in Virginia's Richmond and Hampton Roads areas. The banks offer standard retail products such as checking and savings accounts, money market accounts, IRAs, and loans and mortgages.

	Annual Growth	12/03	12/04	12/05	12/06	12/07
Assets ($ mil.)	17.8%	231.9	251.2	343.0	405.5	445.9
Net income ($ mil.)	(0.8%)	3.2	3.6	3.3	3.7	3.1
Market value ($ mil.)	(8.8%)	52.1	64.2	48.5	46.2	36.0
Employees	1.9%	—	—	103	108	107

ABINGTON BANCORP, INC.

NASDAQ (GS): ABBC

180 Old York Rd.
Jenkintown, PA 19046
Phone: 215-887-3200
Fax: 215-887-4100
Web: www.abingtonbankonline.com

CEO: Robert W. White
CFO: Jack J. Sandoski
HR: –
FYE: December 31
Type: Public

Abington Bancorp is young, but its bank is old. Formed in 2004, the holding company (formerly Abington Community Bancorp) owns Abington Bank, which was established in 1867. It has about 15 branches in southeastern Pennsylvania, north of Philadelphia. The bank offers such standard products as checking and savings accounts, debit cards, and loans. Residential mortgages account for more than half of the company's loan portfolio, which also includes construction loans, commercial and multi-family real estate loans, and home equity lines of credit.

	Annual Growth	12/03	12/04	12/05	12/06	12/07
Assets ($ mil.)	14.6%	—	718.0	844.1	925.2	1,079.7
Net income ($ mil.)	15.6%	—	4.6	6.3	6.8	7.1
Employees	8.7%	—	—	144	148	170

ABINGTON MEMORIAL HOSPITAL

1200 Old York Rd.
Abington, PA 19001
Phone: 215-481-2000
Fax: 215-481-3619
Web: www.amh.org

CEO: Richard L. Jones Jr.
CFO: Michael Walsh
HR: Meghan Patton
FYE: June 30
Type: Not-for-profit

Abington Memorial Hospital brings health care to residents of southeastern Pennsylvania. Serving Montgomery, Bucks, and Philadelphia counties, the not-for-profit community hospital has some 570 beds. In addition to general medical and surgical care, Abington Memorial Hospital offers specialized care centers for cancer and cardiovascular conditions, and serves as a regional trauma care facility. It also runs an inpatient pediatric unit in affiliation with The Children's Hospital of Philadelphia. Along with its main hospital facility, Abington Memorial has several other outpatient campuses and physicians' offices.

	Annual Growth	6/03	6/04	6/05	6/06	6/07
Est. sales ($ mil.)	—	—	—	—	—	535.2
Employees	—	—	—	—	—	4,018

ABIOMED, INC.

NASDAQ (GM): ABMD

22 Cherry Hill Dr.
Danvers, MA 01923
Phone: 978-777-5410
Fax: 978-777-8411
Web: www.abiomed.com

CEO: Michael R. Minogue
CFO: Daniel J. (Dan) Sutherby
HR: –
FYE: March 31
Type: Public

ABIOMED is no heartless company. On the contrary, it helps troubled hearts regain their vigor with its BVS 5000 and AB5000 ventricular assist devices. The FDA-approved products temporarily take over the heart's pumping function and improve circulatory flow in patients with acute heart failure, thus allowing their hearts to rest and recover. The company has also developed a battery-powered, implantable replacement heart system called AbioCor, which has received Humanitarian Device Exemption approval from the FDA. The device can be used to extend life for dying patients who aren't eligible for a heart transplant. ABIOMED markets its products through both a direct sales force and distributors.

	Annual Growth	3/04	3/05	3/06	3/07	3/08
Sales ($ mil.)	23.0%	25.7	38.2	43.7	50.7	58.9
Net income ($ mil.)	—	(9.4)	(2.3)	(29.5)	(27.9)	(40.9)
Market value ($ mil.)	25.2%	175.2	233.6	341.4	440.4	430.6
Employees	3.1%	—	305	300	324	—

ABLE ENERGY, INC.

Pink Sheets: ABLE

198 Green Pond Rd.
Rockaway, NJ 07866
Phone: 973-625-1012
Fax: 973-586-9866
Web: www.ableenergy.com

CEO: Gregory D. Frost
CFO: Daniel L. Johnston
HR: Colleen Harrington
FYE: June 30
Type: Public

An able consolidator in the fragmented heating-oil market, Able Energy provides retail distribution of heating oil and other fuels to more than 30,000 residential and commercial customers in Florida, New Jersey, New York, and Pennsylvania through subsidiary Able Oil. Able Energy also installs and repairs HVAC equipment and markets gasoline and other refined petroleum products and natural gas. In 2007 Able acquired All American Plazas' truck stops in return for a 75% stake in Able, making AAP Able's largest shareholder. Able Energy plans to use AAP's locations to sell its energy products.

	Annual Growth	6/02	6/03	6/04	6/05	*6/06
Sales ($ mil.)	29.5%	26.7	46.3	42.9	62.0	75.1
Net income ($ mil.)	—	(1.5)	0.2	(0.1)	(2.2)	(6.2)
Employees	11.8%	68	—	—	95	—

*Most recent year available

ABLEST INC.

1511 N. Westshore Blvd., Ste. 900
Tampa, FL 33607
Phone: 813-830-7700
Fax: 813-830-7029
Web: www.ablest.com

CEO: Kurt R. Moore
CFO: John Horan
HR: —
FYE: December 31
Type: Subsidiary

Q: Which company is most ready and willing to provide temporary staffing? A: The company that is Ablest, a subsidiary of Select Family of Staffing Companies. Ablest provides temporary and contract employees from about 55 locations in the eastern and southwestern US that operate under the Select Staffing and RemX brands. The company specializes in placement for clerical and light industrial jobs; in addition, it helps fill positions in information technology fields. Koosharem, a holding company that does business as the Select Family of Staffing Companies, acquired Ablest in 2007 and rebranded the company's operations.

	Annual Growth	12/02	12/03	12/04	12/05	12/06
Sales ($ mil.)	8.6%	101.2	104.1	116.3	137.5	140.8
Net income ($ mil.)	16.7%	0.7	2.9	0.9	0.5	1.3
Employees	(15.6%)	—	—	—	43,850	37,000

ABM INDUSTRIES INCORPORATED

NYSE: ABM

160 Pacific Ave., Ste. 222
San Francisco, CA 94111
Phone: 415-733-4000
Fax: 415-733-7333
Web: www.abm.com

CEO: Henrik C. Slipsager
CFO: James S. Lusk
HR: Erin M. Andre
FYE: October 31
Type: Public

ABM Industries makes a clean sweep of things. A leading facility services contractor, the company offers cleaning, engineering, and maintenance services to owners and operators of office parks and buildings, hospitals, manufacturing plants, schools, and transportation centers throughout the US. Its Ampco System Parking unit operates about 1,600 parking lots and garages, mainly at airports, in some 30 states, while its American Commercial Security Services (ACSS) subsidiary offers electronic safety monitoring, investigative, and security consulting services. ABM's largest division, however, remains its ABM Janitorial segment. In 2007, ABM expanded by acquiring rival facility services company OneSource Services.

	Annual Growth	10/03	10/04	10/05	10/06	10/07
Sales ($ mil.)	5.9%	2,262.5	2,416.2	2,587.8	2,792.7	2,842.8
Net income ($ mil.)	(12.8%)	90.5	30.5	57.9	93.2	52.4
Market value ($ mil.)	11.8%	752.6	1,010.7	970.2	965.9	1,176.5
Employees	21.1%	—	—	73,000	75,000	107,000

ABRAXAS PETROLEUM CORPORATION

AMEX: ABP

500 N. Loop 1604 E., Ste. 100
San Antonio, TX 78232
Phone: 210-490-4788
Fax: 210-490-8816
Web: www.abraxaspetroleum.com

CEO: Robert L. G. (Bob) Watson
CFO: Chris E. Williford
HR: Carol O'Brien
FYE: December 31
Type: Public

Abraxas is a mythical Gnostic symbol that represents the number 365 in Greek, and Abraxas Petroleum is working hard as a 365-day-a-year oil and gas company. The independent energy company is engaged in natural gas and crude oil exploration, development, and production. It operates primarily in Texas (along the Gulf Coast and in the Permian Basin) and in Wyoming, and in 2007 it reported estimated proved reserves of 106.8 billion cu. ft. of natural gas equivalent. Abraxas also owns interests in 104,205 gross acres (80,281 net acres) primarily in mature fields.

	Annual Growth	12/03	12/04	12/05	12/06	12/07
Sales ($ mil.)	3.1%	39.0	33.8	48.6	51.7	44.0
Net income ($ mil.)	0.4%	55.9	11.2	19.1	0.7	56.7
Market value ($ mil.)	43.9%	44.1	84.7	221.8	132.0	189.2
Employees	—	—	—	48	—	—

ABRAXIS BIOSCIENCE INC.

NASDAQ (GS): ABII

11755 Wilshire Blvd., 20th Fl.
Los Angeles, CA 90025
Phone: 310-883-1300
Fax: 310-998-8553
Web: www.abraxisbio.com

CEO: Patrick Soon-Shiong
CFO: David O'Toole
HR: —
FYE: December 31
Type: Public

Cancer patients will hopefully get a helpful shot in the arm thanks to Abraxis BioScience. Having spun off its generic injectable drug business, the company's oncology and research division is now devoted to developing its own line of injectable drugs starting with Abraxane, its patented version of cancer drug paclitaxel. Abraxis BioScience is working to quickly develop a market for Abraxane, which is approved for use in the treatment of metastatic breast cancer. The company owns manufacturing and development facilities in the US, Puerto Rico, and Switzerland. Chairman and CEO Patrick Soon-Shiong holds more than 80% of the company.

	Annual Growth	12/03	12/04	12/05	12/06	12/07
Sales ($ mil.)	(1.3%)	351.3	405.0	518.8	765.5	333.7
Net income ($ mil.)	—	71.7	56.7	86.4	(46.9)	(41.6)
Market value ($ mil.)	—	—	—	—	—	2,751.8
Employees	25.3%	—	—	1,488	1,864	—

ABRY PARTNERS, LLC

111 Huntington Ave.
Boston, MA 02199
Phone: 617-859-2959
Fax: 617-859-8797
Web: www.abry.com

CEO: Royce G. Yudkoff
CFO: Deb Johnson
HR: —
FYE: December 31
Type: Private

Extra! Extra! ABRY Partners specializes in financing companies that get the word out. The private equity firm has invested in more than 450 media concerns, from newspaper companies to broadband providers. Its portfolio includes Muzak, Atlantic Broadband, Charleston Newspapers, the quaintly named Country Road Communications, and Dolan Media Company. Operations include leveraged buyouts, expansions, acquisitions, and recapitalizations. The company usually invests $20 million to $100 million in equity transactions, or $10 million to $50 million in mezzanine capital. The company has $2.75 billion in capital under management. ABRY Partners was founded in 1989 by chairman Andrew Banks and president Royce Yudkoff.

	Annual Growth	12/03	12/04	12/05	12/06	12/07
Est. sales ($ mil.)	—	—	—	—	—	157.9
Employees	—	—	—	—	—	2,214

An in-depth profile of this company is available to Hoover's Online members at hoovers.com.

39

ABS COMPUTER TECHNOLOGIES INC.

18045 Rowland St.	CEO: Fred F. Chang
City of Industry, CA 91748	CFO: –
Phone: 626-271-1580	HR: –
Fax: 626-271-9500	FYE: December 31
Web: www.abspc.com	Type: Private

ABS Computer Technologies designs and builds made-to-order personal computers. Based on processors from either AMD or Intel, its Ultimate desktop and Mayhem notebook systems can be customized for gaming, multimedia, or professional applications. ABS has grown into one of the largest custom specialty PC suppliers. The company also resells third-party software and accessories. ABS was established in 1990. Founder and CEO Fred Chang is the majority shareholder. ABS helped give birth to Newegg.com, the popular Web portal for electronics, and now it is a subsidiary of the younger venture.

	Annual Growth	12/03	12/04	12/05	12/06	12/07
Est. sales ($ mil.)	—	—	—	—	—	12.7
Employees	—	—	—	—	—	110

ABT ASSOCIATES INC.

55 Wheeler St.	CEO: Wendell J. Knox
Cambridge, MA 02138	CFO: Richard Small
Phone: 617-492-7100	HR: Richard A. Kulka
Fax: 617-492-5219	FYE: March 31
Web: www.abtassociates.com	Type: Private

Abt Associates offers a wide array of research-based consulting services to government agencies, businesses, and other organizations worldwide. The firm specializes in issues related to social, economic, and health policy; clinical research; and international development. Its services include consulting, implementation, and technical assistance; research and evaluation; survey data collection, management, and analysis; and strategy, planning, and policy. Abt Associates does business from several US offices and from about 35 project sites around the globe. Employees own the company, which was founded in 1965 by Clark Abt.

	Annual Growth	3/02	3/03	3/04	3/05	3/06
Est. sales ($ mil.)	—	—	—	—	—	193.0
Employees	—	—	—	—	—	1,000

ABT ELECTRONICS, INC.

1200 N. Milwaukee Ave.	CEO: Robert J. (Bob) Abt
Glenview, IL 60025	CFO: Richard (Rich) Cawley
Phone: 847-967-8800	HR: Rosemary Wald
Fax: 847-544-2270	FYE: December 31
Web: www.abt.com	Type: Private

Looking for a $60,000 stereo amplifier or just a moderately priced clothes dryer? Abt Electronics & Appliance is apt to have it. Abt has just one store — a massive 37-acre megastore with a parking lot that accommodates 1,000 cars in suburban Chicago, where the natives tend to incorrectly call the store A.B.T. One of the country's largest independent retailers of electronics and appliances, the company carries mostly name brands and targets affluent Chicagoans with high-end products such as Bang & Olufsen audio systems and Sub-Zero refrigerators. It also sells online through AbtElectronics.com and services everything it sells. Founded in 1936 by David and Jewel Abt, the company is still family-owned.

A.C. MOORE ARTS & CRAFTS, INC.

NASDAQ (GS): ACMR

130 A.C. Moore Dr.	CEO: Rick A. Lepley
Berlin, NJ 08009	CFO: Marc D. Katz
Phone: 856-768-4930	HR: Roxanne Stankiewicz
Fax: 856-753-4723	FYE: December 31
Web: www.acmoore.com	Type: Public

Some are content to merely collect and dust their tchotchkes, but others are compelled to make them. A.C. Moore Arts & Crafts is ready and willing to serve them (focusing on women 25-55). The crafty superstores stock silk and dried flowers, as well as art and scrapbooking supplies and picture frames (which account for about one-third of sales), yarn, seasonal items, fashion crafts, beads, and everything else needed to glue, paint, or arrange. A.C. Moore also offers in-store arts-and-crafts classes for children and adults. Its about 135 stores (up from just 17 in 1997) are located along the East Coast. The company was founded in 1985 by its former chairman William Kaplan and ex-CEO Jack Parker.

	Annual Growth	12/03	12/04	12/05	12/06	12/07
Sales ($ mil.)	6.6%	433.9	497.6	539.4	589.5	559.7
Net income ($ mil.)	(31.5%)	17.3	16.9	10.0	2.4	3.8
Market value ($ mil.)	(7.0%)	372.8	566.3	288.8	437.0	279.1
Employees	3.6%	—	—	5,090	4,941	5,459

ACA CAPITAL HOLDINGS, INC.

Pink Sheets: ACAH

140 Broadway, 47th Fl.	CEO: Alan S. Roseman
New York, NY 10005	CFO: Lisa Mumford
Phone: 212-375-2000	HR: Eileen Hatcher
Fax: 212-375-2100	FYE: December 31
Web: www.aca.com	Type: Public

ACA Capital, through its ACA Management subsidiary, provides asset management services for collateralized debt obligations (CDOs) built by pooling fixed-income assets, including bonds, loans, and credit swaps; investors in the company's CDOs include banks, money managers, hedge funds, and insurance companies. Its ACA Financial Guaranty subsidiary offers financial guaranty insurance for municipal and other public finance bonds, as well as credit protection on some structured financings. Chairman David King is a stockholder through Bear Stearns Merchant Banking which holds nearly 30% of the company's stock.

	Annual Growth	12/02	12/03	12/04	12/05	*12/06
Assets ($ mil.)	60.3%	915.6	3,468.4	5,692.0	5,798.2	6,038.2
Net income ($ mil.)	89.0%	4.6	17.2	(3.8)	28.8	58.7
Employees	6.9%	88	87	—	—	115

*Most recent year available

ACACIA RESEARCH CORPORATION

500 Newport Center Dr., 7th Fl.	CEO: Paul R. Ryan
Newport Beach, CA 92660	CFO: Clayton J. Haynes
Phone: 949-480-8300	HR: –
Fax: 949-480-8301	FYE: December 31
Web: www.acaciaresearch.com	Type: Holding company

It's the stuff you'd expect to see in a George Orwell novel. Acacia Research acquires, develops, licenses, and protects patented technologies for individual inventors and small companies that have limited resources to protect against infringement. The company owns or controls the rights to approximately 90 patent portfolios in the US and abroad. It typically buys portfolios and pays its clients an upfront fee or becomes the exclusive licensing agent and doles out royalties. It has out-licensed to such companies as 3M, Dell, and Walt Disney Company. Acacia Research formerly operated as two business groups, Acacia Technologies and CombiMatrix, but it split CombiMatrix off into a separate public company in 2007.

	Annual Growth	12/03	12/04	12/05	12/06	12/07
Est. sales ($ mil.)	—	—	—	—	—	52.6
Net income ($ mil.)	—	—	—	—	—	(15.4)
Employees	—	—	—	—	—	

ACACIA TECHNOLOGIES GROUP

NASDAQ (GM): ACTG

500 Newport Center Dr., 7th Fl.
Newport Beach, CA 92660
Phone: 949-480-8300
Fax: 949-480-8301
Web: www.acaciatechnologies.com

CEO: Paul R. Ryan
CFO: Clayton J. Haynes
HR: –
FYE: December 31
Type: Public

Acacia Technologies Group offers shade to more than 60 patent portfolios held by Acacia Research. The group acquires and licenses patent rights to various technologies related to digital audio-on-demand and video-on-demand transmission. It markets these patents under the DMT brand to makers of electronics gear, who incorporate the technologies into applications for cable, satellite, and Internet distribution of digital content. Acacia Research created tracking stocks for Acacia Technologies and sister group CombiMatrix as part of a corporate recapitalization in 2002. Acacia Technologies has reached licensing agreements with Fujitsu, Pioneer, Sony, and Union Pacific, among other companies.

	Annual Growth	12/03	12/04	12/05	12/06	12/07
Sales ($ mil.)	63.8%	—	—	19.6	34.8	52.6
Net income ($ mil.)	—	—	—	(18.7)	(25.5)	(15.4)
Employees	36.4%	—	—	—	33	45

ACADEMY BUS TOURS, INC.

111 Paterson Ave.
Hoboken, NJ 07030
Phone: 201-420-7000
Fax: 201-420-8087
Web: www.academybus.com

CEO: Francis Tedesco
CFO: Kim Hansen
HR: Bill Reinhold
FYE: December 31
Type: Private

Passengers who have been rewarded with pleasant journeys by bus can stand up and thank the Academy. Academy Bus Tours offers charter bus services in the eastern US. The company operates throughout New Jersey and in the New York and Philadelphia metropolitan areas, as well as in New England and in the mid-Atlantic states. Customers have included school and tour groups, including those bound for Atlantic City's casinos; in addition, Academy Bus has provided transportation services under contract with state-owned New Jersey Transit. The company operates a fleet of about 600 buses. Academy Bus was founded in 1968.

	Annual Growth	12/03	12/04	12/05	12/06	12/07
Est. sales ($ mil.)	—	—	—	—	—	14.1
Employees	—	—	—	—	—	380

ACADEMY SPORTS & OUTDOORS, LTD.

1800 N. Mason Rd.
Katy, TX 77449
Phone: 281-646-5200
Fax: 281-646-5000
Web: www.academy.com

CEO: David Gochman
CFO: Rodney (Rod) Faldyn
HR: Sylvia Barrera-Moses
FYE: January 31
Type: Private

Academy Sports & Outdoors is near the head of the class among sporting goods retailers. The company is one of the top full-line sporting goods chains in the US with more than 100 stores in about a dozen states throughout the South and Southwest. Academy's low-frills stores carry clothing, shoes, and equipment for almost any sport and outdoor activity, including camping, golf, hunting, fishing, and boating. The company, which also operates a catalog operation, dates back to a San Antonio tire shop opened by Max Gochman in 1938. The business moved into military surplus items and during the 1980s began focusing on sports and outdoor merchandise. The Gochman family still owns Academy.

	Annual Growth	1/02	1/03	1/04	1/05	1/06
Sales ($ mil.)	24.1%	775.0	941.1	1,059.0	1,215.1	1,840.0
Employees	21.8%	5,000	6,000	6,995	7,000	11,000

ACADIA PHARMACEUTICALS INC.

NASDAQ (GM): ACAD

3911 Sorrento Valley Blvd.
San Diego, CA 92121
Phone: 858-558-2871
Fax: 858-558-2872
Web: www.acadia-pharm.com

CEO: Uli Hacksell
CFO: Thomas H. Aasen
HR: Natasha Bowman
FYE: December 31
Type: Public

ACADIA Pharmaceuticals puts genes and drugs together to fight disease. The development-stage company uses its proprietary R-SAT technology to identify and evaluate genomic targets for drug therapies, primarily for central nervous system disorders. ACADIA hopes its lead drug candidate pimavanserin will effectively treat psychosis in patients with Parkinson's disease. The company is also testing the drug in conjunction with schizophrenia treatments as a means to reduce the side effects of antipsychotic drugs. ACADIA has a second schizophrenia treatment in clinical trials and, in partnership with eye-care heavyweight Allergan, is developing therapies for glaucoma and chronic pain.

	Annual Growth	12/03	12/04	12/05	12/06	12/07
Sales ($ mil.)	0.7%	7.4	4.6	11.0	8.1	7.6
Net income ($ mil.)	—	(14.1)	(25.9)	(34.1)	(45.0)	(56.4)
Market value ($ mil.)	53.0%	—	114.6	231.7	263.2	410.0
Employees	10.9%	—	101	112	—	—

ACADIA REALTY TRUST

NYSE: AKR

1311 Mamaroneck Ave., Ste. 260
White Plains, NY 10605
Phone: 914-288-8100
Fax: 914-428-2760
Web: www.acadiarealty.com

CEO: Kenneth F. Bernstein
CFO: Michael L. Nelsen
HR: –
FYE: December 31
Type: Public

The magical creatures within this Acadia frolic in movie theaters, grocery stores, and toy stores rather than woodlands, lakes, or mountains. A self-managed real estate investment trust (REIT), Acadia Realty acquires, redevelops, and manages commercial retail properties primarily in the Northeast, Mid-Atlantic, and Midwest. The REIT specializes in urban area shopping and mixed-use centers; it owns some 75 properties comprising 8 million sq. ft., mostly grocery store- and big box-anchored shopping centers. It also has private equity investments in other retail real estate. The company's largest tenants include Albertsons, Sears, and T.J. Maxx.

	Annual Growth	12/03	12/04	12/05	12/06	12/07
Sales ($ mil.)	10.0%	69.4	72.9	83.3	102.7	101.6
Net income ($ mil.)	36.8%	7.8	19.6	20.6	39.0	27.3
Market value ($ mil.)	24.5%	342.6	510.9	636.8	795.0	824.2
Employees	—	—	—	158	—	—

ACC CAPITAL CORPORATION

1787 E. Ft. Union Blvd., Ste. 200
Salt Lake City, UT 84121
Phone: 801-733-2300
Fax: 801-733-2274
Web: www.acccapital.com

CEO: Loni Lowder
CFO: R. Jeffrey MacArtney
HR: –
FYE: March 31
Type: Private

ACC Capital helps companies ace their equipment leasing quandaries. The middle-market financial services company provides equipment leasing and financing to businesses in the US. It specializes in structuring, originating, and servicing lease products. Typical transactions range from $50,000 to $10 million. It has financed leases for equipment ranging from heavy industry and mining machinery to restaurant, food processing, and telecom equipment. ACC also serves a network of brokers that sells its products, and it targets community banks, offering them direct origination through a private label program or consulting services for in-house origination. The company is no relation to lender ACC Capital Holdings.

	Annual Growth	3/03	3/04	3/05	3/06	3/07
Est. sales ($ mil.)	—	—	—	—	—	7.5
Employees	—	—	—	—	—	40

An in-depth profile of this company is available to Hoover's Online members at hoovers.com.

ACCEL PARTNERS

428 University Ave.
Palo Alto, CA 94301
Phone: 650-614-4800
Fax: 650-614-4880
Web: www.accel.com

CEO: James W. (Jim) Breyer
CFO: –
HR: –
FYE: December 31
Type: Private

How fast can you make money? Accel Partners hopes to accelerate that. Founded in 1984, the firm focuses on early-stage investments in only two sectors, software and networking, and has some $3 billion under management. The company's investment history includes a who's who of tech powerhouses such as UUNET, Brightmail, Macromedia, and Facebook. Based in Silicon Valley and China (through its alliance with IDG Technology Venture Investment), Accel looks for investments in companies that were founded by entrepreneurs but are run by experienced management teams. It provides strategic financing, recruiting, and business development, among other services.

ACCELERATED BUILDING CONCEPTS CORPORATION

OTC: ABCC

500 5th Ave., Ste. 1650
New York, NY 10110
Phone: 212-810-2430
Fax: –
Web: www.acceleratedbuildingconcepts.com

CEO: Joseph (Joe) Sorci
CFO: Bruce Harmon
HR: –
FYE: December 31
Type: Public

Engineering and construction company Accelerated Building Concepts has been accelerating the building of its own new business plan. Once a Web consulting and design firm known as K2 Digital, the company was acquired in 2007 by New Century Structures, which then adopted the Accelerated Building Concepts name. As a subsidiary of Accelerated Building Concepts, New Century Structures designs and constructs modular buildings using concrete, steel, and structural insulated panels. Customers have included several Florida school districts, NASA, and commercial enterprises. Through subsidiary Sustainable Structures Leasing, Accelerated Building Concepts enables customers to lease modular buildings.

	Annual Growth	12/03	12/04	12/05	12/06	12/07
Sales ($ mil.)	—	—	—	—	0.0	2.0
Net income ($ mil.)	—	—	—	—	0.0	(0.6)
Market value ($ mil.)	143.9%	—	—	—	3.0	7.3
Employees	—	—	—	—	—	—

ACCELLENT INC.

100 Fordham Rd.
Wilmington, MA 01887
Phone: 978-570-6900
Fax: 978-657-0878
Web: www.accellent.com

CEO: Robert E. (Bob) Kirby
CFO: Jeremy A. Friedman
HR: Tricia M. McCall
FYE: December 31
Type: Private

Accellent provides the nuts and bolts for the medical device industry. The company provides outsourced design, engineering, and manufacturing of custom components, subassemblies, and completed devices, primarily for medical device firms. Its customers include such industry leaders as Medtronic, Abbott Labs, Stryker, and Johnson & Johnson. Accellent specializes in equipment used for cardiac rhythm management, interventional cardiology, and orthopedics, as well as urology and minimally invasive procedures (especially in the field of endoscopy). The company has locations in North America and Europe.

	Annual Growth	12/02	12/03	12/04	12/05	12/06
Sales ($ mil.)	21.7%	—	—	320.2	461.1	474.1
Net income ($ mil.)	—	—	—	—	—	(18.6)
Employees	—	—	—	—	—	3,289

ACCELR8 TECHNOLOGY CORPORATION

AMEX: AXK

7000 N. Broadway, Bldg. 3, Unit 307
Denver, CO 80221
Phone: 303-863-8088
Fax: 303-863-1218
Web: www.accelr8.com

CEO: Thomas V. Geimer
CFO: Thomas V. Geimer
HR: –
FYE: July 31
Type: Public

Accelr8 Technology wants to speed up your lab results. Using its BACcel technology, the company is working on quicker methods for identifying bacterial infections. Its BACcelr8r system is being designed for use in clinical settings to provide bacterial identification within two hours. If successful, the system will be an improvement over existing methods which depend upon identifying bacteria in a culture grown over two to five days from a patient sample. Instead, BACcelr8r will look directly at the sample itself, sort through the tens of thousands of bacterial cells to identify any pathogenic bacteria, and determine if any are resistant to antibiotics.

	Annual Growth	7/03	7/04	7/05	7/06	7/07
Sales ($ mil.)	(31.3%)	0.9	0.1	0.5	0.2	0.2
Net income ($ mil.)	—	(1.4)	(0.9)	(2.1)	(3.0)	(1.9)
Market value ($ mil.)	(9.5%)	35.0	23.3	30.8	23.8	23.4
Employees	—	—	—	19	—	—

ACCELRYS, INC.

NASDAQ (GM): ACCL

10188 Telesis Ct., Ste. 100
San Diego, CA 92121
Phone: 858-799-5000
Fax: 858-799-5100
Web: www.accelrys.com

CEO: Mark J. Emkjer
CFO: Rick E. Russo
HR: Judith Ohrn Hicks
FYE: March 31
Type: Public

Accelrys knows nothing can accelerate research like good software. It develops software for managing data generated by studying genomes and proteins (bioinformatics) and through developing chemicals and other industrial materials (cheminformatics). The firm also offers simulation and modeling software to help researchers develop new drugs and materials. Accelrys' workflow software allows users to comb through extra large sets of data in real time. It also provides training and contract research services. Clients include drug and chemical makers, government agencies, and academic research labs. The company sells its software and related products and services to customers around the globe.

	Annual Growth	12/03	*3/05	3/06	3/07	3/08
Sales ($ mil.)	(8.8%)	115.1	69.6	82.0	81.0	79.7
Net income ($ mil.)	—	(3.5)	(25.2)	(7.7)	(1.5)	1.3
Market value ($ mil.)	(12.1%)	251.6	154.2	190.6	169.1	150.3
Employees	(19.5%)	713	525	479	372	—

ACCENT MARKETING SERVICES, L.L.C.

400 Missouri Ave., Ste. 107
Jeffersonville, IN 47130
Phone: 812-206-6200
Fax: 812-206-6201
Web: www.accentonline.com

CEO: Kevin Foley
CFO: Chris Dauk
HR: Laura Carpenter
FYE: December 31
Type: Subsidiary

ACCENT Marketing Services provides customer relationship marketing (CRM) services with an emphasis on contact center support. Among ACCENT's services are inbound and outbound call support, mail, e-mail, and Web chat. The company also offers loyalty marketing programs and customer satisfaction tracking. It has call centers in Arkansas, Florida, Indiana, and Missouri, as well as in the Caribbean and the Philippines. The company was founded in 1993 and serves a variety of industries from telecommunications to financial services to automotive. It is owned by marketing communications services firm MDC Partners.

	Annual Growth	12/03	12/04	12/05	12/06	12/07
Est. sales ($ mil.)	—	—	—	—	—	56.9
Employees	—	—	—	—	—	1,570

ACCENTIA BIOPHARMACEUTICALS, INC.
NASDAQ (GM): ABPI

324 S. Hyde Park Ave., Ste. 350	CEO: Francis E. O'Donnell Jr.
Tampa, FL 33606	CFO: Alan M. Pearce
Phone: 813-864-2554	HR: –
Fax: 813-258-6912	FYE: September 30
Web: www.accentia.net	Type: Public

Accentia Biopharmaceuticals emphasizes runny noses. The company acquires and develops treatments for respiratory conditions, as well as other ailments. Accentia has several pharmaceutical products on the market, including Respi-TANN and Zinotic. Its development-stage drugs include sinus inflammation treatment SinuNase, multiple sclerosis drug Revimmune, and BiovaxID, a possible vaccine for non-Hodgkin's lymphoma being developed by majority owned subsidiary Biovest International. Accentia also develops cell production instruments, including the AutovaxID system, and offers pharmaceutical product consulting services.

	Annual Growth	9/03	9/04	9/05	9/06	9/07
Sales ($ mil.)	16.6%	9.9	25.9	25.2	25.1	18.3
Net income ($ mil.)	—	(16.7)	(23.2)	(44.7)	(43.4)	(76.0)
Market value ($ mil.)	33.0%	—	—	—	81.8	108.9
Employees	(27.2%)	—	—	264	—	140

ACCENTURE LTD
NYSE: ACN

1345 Avenue of the Americas	CEO: William D. (Bill) Green
New York, NY 10105	CFO: Pamela J. Craig
Phone: 917-452-4400	HR: Kedrick Adkins
Fax: 917-527-9915	FYE: August 31
Web: www.accenture.com	Type: Public

For Accenture, the accent is on trying to help businesses improve their performance. The world's largest consulting firm, Accenture offers management consulting, information technology and systems integration, and business process outsourcing (BPO) services to customers around the globe. The company divides its practices into five main operating groups — communications and high technology, financial services, public service, products, and resources — that encompass more than 15 industries. Accenture, which is domiciled in Bermuda but headquartered in New York, operates from more than 150 locations in about 50 countries.

	Annual Growth	8/03	8/04	8/05	8/06	8/07
Sales ($ mil.)	12.5%	13,397.2	15,113.6	17,094.4	18,228.4	21,452.8
Net income ($ mil.)	25.7%	498.2	690.8	940.5	973.3	1,243.2
Market value ($ mil.)	26.5%	9,593.9	15,278.9	13,918.7	17,219.9	24,557.9
Employees	19.3%	—	100,000	123,000	140,000	170,000

ACCESS INTEGRATED TECHNOLOGIES, INC.
NASDAQ (GM): AIXD

55 Madison Ave., Ste. 300	CEO: A. Dale (Bud) Mayo
Morristown, NJ 07960	CFO: Brian D. Pflug
Phone: 973-290-0080	HR: –
Fax: 973-290-0081	FYE: March 31
Web: www.accessitx.com	Type: Public

Access Integrated Technologies provides data services with a Hollywood flair. The company operates in two primary areas. Its Media Services division provides software and services that enable the digital distribution of films and other content to movie theaters and other venues. Top customers include projector maker Christie and Twentieth Century Fox. The company's Data Center Services division provides managed data storage and consulting services from three data centers in New Jersey and New York. It primarily serves telecommunications service providers and entertainment companies; clients include the Weinstein Company and Rothschild.

	Annual Growth	3/04	3/05	3/06	3/07	3/08
Sales ($ mil.)	83.1%	7.2	10.6	16.8	47.1	81.0
Net income ($ mil.)	—	(4.8)	(6.8)	(16.8)	(26.0)	(35.7)
Market value ($ mil.)	22.6%	36.4	62.3	282.8	130.0	82.2
Employees	50.5%	—	93	140	—	—

ACCESS INTELLIGENCE, LLC

4 Choke Cherry Rd., 2nd Fl.	CEO: Donald (Don) Pazour
Rockville, MD 20850	CFO: Ed Pinedo
Phone: 301-354-2000	HR: Macy Fecto
Fax: 301-309-3847	FYE: December 31
Web: www.pbimedia.com	Type: Private

The mission of Access Intelligence (formerly PBI Media) is to provide business information. The company publishes some 10 magazines, 20 newsletters, two subscription-based Web sites, more than 20 directories and databases, and dozens of mailing lists. It also organizes trade shows and conferences and publishes or distributes more than 100 studies, manuals, and market research reports. Access Intelligence's products include offerings on industry specializations such as aviation, cable, chemical, defense, energy, media & PR (magazine, advertising, and marketing), satellite, studio (TV, film, and video production), and telecommunications.

	Annual Growth	12/03	12/04	12/05	12/06	12/07
Est. sales ($ mil.)	—	—	—	—	—	53.8
Employees	—	—	—	—	—	480

ACCESS NATIONAL CORPORATION
NASDAQ (GM): ANCX

1800 Robert Fulton Dr., Ste. 310	CEO: Michael W. Clarke
Reston, VA 20191	CFO: Charles Wimer
Phone: 703-871-2100	HR: –
Fax: 703-766-3386	FYE: December 31
Web: www.accessnationalbank.com	Type: Public

Enabling easy access to your money is Access National's aim. The holding company for Access National Bank, a thrift founded in 1999, serves the Washington, DC area. It offers standard services including checking and savings accounts, IRAs, CDs, and loans to consumers and small to midsized businesses. Bank subsidiary Access National Mortgage originates residential real estate loans. Commercial real estate loans make up more than 40% of the company's portfolio; residential real estate accounts for about another third. Consumer, home equity, real estate construction, and business loans round out its lending activities.

	Annual Growth	12/03	12/04	12/05	12/06	12/07
Assets ($ mil.)	14.0%	—	420.1	537.0	644.8	622.4
Net income ($ mil.)	3.9%	—	3.3	5.9	7.6	3.7
Market value ($ mil.)	67.3%	—	14.0	113.4	113.0	65.5
Employees	(8.4%)	—	242	—	203

ACCESS PLANS USA, INC.
NASDAQ (CM): AUSA

4929 W. Royal Ln.	CEO: Ian R. Stuart
Irving, TX 75063	CFO: Ian R. Stuart
Phone: 972-915-3200	HR: –
Fax: –	FYE: December 31
Web: www.accessplansusa.com	Type: Public

Access Plans USA (formerly known as Precis) wants to provide you with cheaper access to health care. The company's consumer health care savings program, Care Entrée, allows subscribers access to its network of 400,000 health care providers offering discounted fees (similar to a PPO). It manages wholesale membership programs targeting clients in the banking, consumer finance, retail, and rent-to-own industries. It also provides administration services such as payment processing, claims management, and plan designing through its Access Administrators subsidiary. Access Plans USA is the result of the early 2007 merger between two companies: Precis and Insurance Capital Management USA.

	Annual Growth	12/03	12/04	12/05	12/06	12/07
Sales ($ mil.)	(0.8%)	42.1	38.3	30.1	22.0	40.7
Net income ($ mil.)	—	4.1	(2.0)	(13.4)	(7.7)	(13.2)
Market value ($ mil.)	(17.2%)	46.1	32.1	20.3	27.1	21.7
Employees	—	—	—	180	—	—

An in-depth profile of this company is available to Hoover's Online members at hoovers.com.

43

ACCESS WORLDWIDE COMMUNICATIONS, INC.
OTC: AWWC

1820 N. Fort Myer Dr., 3rd Fl.	CEO: Shawkat Raslan
Arlington, VA 22209	CFO: Richard Lyew
Phone: 703-292-5210	HR: –
Fax: 703-465-8642	FYE: December 31
Web: www.accessww.com	Type: Public

Access Worldwide Communications gives clients access to its wide array of business process outsourcing (BPO) capabilities. Operating from locations in the US and in the Philippines, Access Worldwide offers inbound/outbound sales, lead generation, order entry, appointment setting, billing management, and hardware/software support services. The company caters to the banking, retail/catalog, telecommunications, and media/publishing industries, providing BPO support in more than 15 different languages across all forms of media. Two clients (AT&T and E*TRADE) accounted for 82% of its revenue in 2007. Access Worldwide was established in 1983.

	Annual Growth	12/03	12/04	12/05	12/06	12/07
Sales ($ mil.)	(10.5%)	51.1	47.5	38.9	27.7	32.8
Net income ($ mil.)	—	(11.6)	(1.4)	(4.7)	2.9	(5.0)
Market value ($ mil.)	16.6%	9.0	9.8	8.5	11.4	16.5
Employees	—	—	—	—	—	—

ACCESSORY NETWORK GROUP

350 5th Ave., 4th Fl.	CEO: Abe Chehebar
New York, NY 10118	CFO: –
Phone: 212-842-3000	HR: –
Fax: 212-842-3242	FYE: December 31
Web: www.accessorynetwork.com	Type: Private

To the company's customers, accessories are the spice of life. Accessory Network Group (ANG) designs, manufactures, and markets fashion bags, small leather goods, stationery, and accessories for women, men, and children. The firm's products are sold in department, discount, and specialty stores in the US, Canada, South America, Europe, and Australia. It distributes out of facilities in New Jersey, California, and Canada. ANG's affiliate company, Brand Science LLC, acquired handbag maker LeSportsac, Inc., through an alliance with ITOCHU Corporation in early 2006.

	Annual Growth	12/03	12/04	12/05	12/06	12/07
Est. sales ($ mil.)	—	—	—	—	—	42.4
Employees	—	—	—	—	—	300

ACCO BRANDS CORPORATION
NYSE: ABD

300 Tower Pkwy.	CEO: David D. Campbell
Lincolnshire, IL 60069	CFO: Neal V. Fenwick
Phone: 847-541-9500	HR: David L. Kaput
Fax: 847-484-4492	FYE: December 31
Web: www.accobrands.com	Type: Public

Reach into the recesses of your desk drawer for that trusty box of staples or paperclips, and you've entered the realm of holding company ACCO Brands. The company, formerly known as ACCO World and a unit of Fortune Brands, is the maker of Swingline staplers, Kensington computer accessories, Wilson Jones binders and accounting supplies, Day-Timer personal organizers, and other products. Its other brands include Rexel, NOBO, Quartet, and GBC. ACCO's products are sold to office and computer products wholesalers, retailers, and mail order companies around the world. Ariel Capital Management owns about a 15% stake in ACCO.

	Annual Growth	12/03	12/04	12/05	12/06	12/07
Sales ($ mil.)	15.2%	1,101.9	1,175.7	1,487.5	1,951.0	1,938.9
Net income ($ mil.)	—	26.7	68.5	59.5	7.2	(0.9)
Market value ($ mil.)	(18.1%)	—	—	1,294.3	1,423.3	867.8
Employees	4.7%	4,990	4,375	7,770	6,846	6,000

ACCOR NORTH AMERICA

4001 International Pkwy.	CEO: Olivier Poirot
Carrollton, TX 75007	CFO: Didier Bosc
Phone: 972-360-9000	HR: Kelley Johnson
Fax: 972-716-6590	FYE: December 31
Web: www.accor-na.com	Type: Business segment

This company is keeping the light on for budget-minded travelers. Accor North America, a division of global hotel giant Accor, is a leading operator and franchisor of economy hotels, with more than 900 properties. Its flagship chain, Motel 6, caters primarily to vacationing families in the US and Canada with a limited menu of amenities. It also operates economy extended-stay lodging chain Studio 6 in the US and Canada, as well as the upscale Sofitel in the US and Canada, and mid-scale Novotel in the US, Canada, and Mexico, and four Ibis hotel locations in Mexico. The company sold its smaller Red Roof Inns chain in 2007 to focus on growing its Motel 6 holdings.

ACCREDITED HOME LENDERS HOLDING CO.

15090 Avenue of Science, Ste. 200	CEO: Jeff Walton
San Diego, CA 92128	CFO: Stuart D. (Stu) Marvin
Phone: 858-676-2100	HR: Joseph F. (Joe) Weinbrecht
Fax: 858-676-2170	FYE: December 31
Web: www.accredhome.com	Type: Private

Accredited Home Lenders is willing to give credit where it's due . . . or not. The mortgage banker originates, acquires, services, and sells subprime single-family mortgages for homebuyers in the US and Canada who may not otherwise qualify. It primarily operates through a network of some 12,600 independent mortgage brokers. In addition to its wholesale operations, the firm also has a retail division, Home Funds Direct, which has about 120 offices across the country (about a quarter of which are in California) responding to leads from the Internet, telemarketing, and direct marketing. Private equity firm Lone Star Funds bought Accredited Home Lenders for some $400 million in 2007.

	Annual Growth	12/02	12/03	12/04	12/05	12/06
Assets ($ mil.)	58.3%	1,807.3	3,501.4	6,688.4	9,853.3	11,349.0
Net income ($ mil.)	—	28.8	100.0	130.8	155.4	(205.6)
Employees	—	—	—	—	2,762	—

ACCREDO HEALTH, INCORPORATED

1640 Century Center Pkwy.	CEO: Timothy C. Wentworth
Memphis, TN 38134	CFO: –
Phone: 901-385-3688	HR: Chantal Vaete
Fax: 901-385-3689	FYE: December 30
Web: www.accredohealthgroup.com	Type: Subsidiary

Accredo Health is one pharmacy where you won't be able to pick up a bottle of aspirin. The specialty pharmacy segment of pharmacy benefits manager Medco Health, Accredo dispenses high-tech, injectable drugs for chronic and serious illnesses such as multiple sclerosis, hemophilia, pulmonary arterial hypertension (PAH), and certain autoimmune disorders. Under contracts with managed care organizations and drugmakers, it delivers drugs and related supplies in temperature-controlled packaging to patient homes or to clinics where they are administered. It also provides clinical monitoring to make sure patients are complying with their drug regimens and files claims on behalf of patients and doctors.

	Annual Growth	12/03	12/04	12/05	12/06	12/07
Est. sales ($ mil.)	—	—	—	—	—	163.3
Employees	—	—	—	—	—	1,977

ACCRETIVE SOLUTIONS, INC.

888 Veterans Hwy., Ste. 440
Hauppauge, NY 11788
Phone: 631-348-9100
Fax: 631-348-7788
Web: www.accretivesolutions.com

CEO: Patrick S. (Pat) Persons
CFO: Dirk D. Hobgood
HR: Mike G. Reinecke
FYE: December 31
Type: Partnership

Block by block by block by block, Accretive Solutions is working to build the selection of services that will answer clients' needs. The company, which specializes in accounting and finance, corporate governance and information technology, provides services through its consulting and executive search divisions. It was formed to, well, accrete the strengths of member firms Horn Murdock Cole (auditing, accounting, and consulting services) and Dickson Allan (search and interim management services). Accretive Solutions targets such industries as energy, financial services, health care, and telecommunications.

	Annual Growth	12/03	12/04	12/05	12/06	12/07
Est. sales ($ mil.)	—	—	—	—	—	56.4
Employees	—	—	—	—	—	925

ACCRUENT, INC.

1601 Cloverfield Blvd., Ste. 500 South
Santa Monica, CA 90404
Phone: 310-526-5700
Fax: 310-526-6300
Web: www.accruent.com

CEO: Mark Friedman
CFO: Robert Pape
HR: –
FYE: December 31
Type: Private

Accruent can help you accrue much better management skills. The company provides software that enterprises use to manage real estate and other related assets. Accruent's products are used to manage tasks such as construction, vendor performance, site selection, market planning, budgeting, and facilities management. The company also provides professional services including consulting, support, training, and implementation. Accruent's customers come from industries such as retail, consumer goods, and food and beverage. The company was founded in 1995.

	Annual Growth	12/03	12/04	12/05	12/06	12/07
Est. sales ($ mil.)	—	—	—	—	—	17.7
Employees	—	—	—	—	—	138

ACCUMED, INC.

2572 Brunswick Pike
Lawrenceville, NJ 08648
Phone: 609-883-1818
Fax: 609-883-2288
Web: www.accumed.org

CEO: Burgise Palkhiwala
CFO: Frank Petranich
HR: Archana Khanna
FYE: December 31
Type: Private

AccuMed believes in both medicine and the power of accuracy. The company develops and manufactures OTC pharmaceutical tablets, powders, and liquids, as well as edible breath strip products. AccuMed's products address a variety of conditions and ailments, including constipation, indigestion, skin conditions, stomach problems, and nose and throat soreness. The company's products are sold in drug stores, groceries, convenience stores, and wholesale locations. AccuMed also provides contract manufacturing services to national brands and pharmaceutical companies.

	Annual Growth	12/03	12/04	12/05	12/06	12/07
Est. sales ($ mil.)	—	—	—	—	—	28.3
Employees	—	—	—	—	—	222

ACCURAY INCORPORATED

NASDAQ (GM): ARAY

1310 Chesapeake Terrace
Sunnyvale, CA 94089
Phone: 408-716-4600
Fax: 408-716-4601
Web: www.accuray.com

CEO: Euan S. Thomson
CFO: Robert E. McNamara
HR: –
FYE: June 30
Type: Public

Accuray's CyberKnife radiosurgery system zaps tumors with precisely aimed, high-dose radiation. The system, approved for use in the US, the EU, and several Asian countries, improves upon older radiosurgery systems that have limited mobility and are mostly used to treat brain tumors. Doctors can use CyberKnife to treat tumors anywhere in the body; the system tracks, and adjusts for movement in real time, allowing for patient and tumor movement. Procedures with CyberKnife require no anesthesia and can be performed on an outpatient basis. More than 100 of the systems have been installed in hospitals around the world, around 70 of them in the US.

	Annual Growth	6/03	6/04	6/05	6/06	6/07
Sales ($ mil.)	92.8%	—	19.6	22.4	52.9	140.4
Net income ($ mil.)	—	—	(11.7)	(25.2)	(33.7)	(5.6)
Market value ($ mil.)	—	—	—	—	—	1,193.3
Employees	—	—	—	—	—	—

ACCURIDE CORPORATION

NYSE: ACW

7140 Office Cir.
Evansville, IN 47715
Phone: 812-962-5000
Fax: 812-962-5400
Web: www.accuridecorp.com

CEO: John R. Murphy
CFO: David K. Armstrong
HR: James (Jim) Maniatis
FYE: December 31
Type: Public

If you're driving a big rig, Accuride offers the goods to keep you rolling — or to stop you in your tracks. The company is a leading manufacturer of steel and forged aluminum wheels for vehicles ranging from commercial trucks and trailers to pickup trucks. Accuride also makes truck body and chassis parts, seating assemblies, and other components. In addition, its Gunite unit produces wheel-end assemblies, including drum and disc brakes, for commercial trucks. Accuride's customers include commercial vehicle OEMs (Daimler Trucks North America, trailer manufacturers (Wabash National), and automakers (General Motors). The company markets its products under brands such as Imperial, Fabco, and Bostrom.

	Annual Growth	12/03	12/04	12/05	12/06	12/07
Sales ($ mil.)	29.2%	364.3	494.0	1,229.3	1,408.2	1,013.7
Net income ($ mil.)	—	(8.7)	21.8	51.2	65.1	(8.6)
Market value ($ mil.)	(20.3%)	—	—	437.4	392.4	277.9
Employees	(14.1%)	—	—	4,745	4,622	3,500

ACCURIDE INTERNATIONAL INC.

12311 Shoemaker Ave.
Santa Fe Springs, CA 90670
Phone: 562-903-0200
Fax: 562-903-0208
Web: www.accuride.com

CEO: Scott Jordan
CFO: Larry Campbell
HR: –
FYE: December 31
Type: Private

Slides rule at Accuride International. Accuride International designs and makes ball bearing slides for such uses as drawers in residential and office furniture, appliances, and enclosures for servers and telecommunications. The company's slides are also found in automotive accessories, including storage units and arm rests, and industrial equipment, such as cash registers and assembly lines. Accuride International builds and maintains its own tools and machinery for manufacturing its products. The company was founded in 1962 by Fred Jordan. It is still owned and operated by the Jordan family.

	Annual Growth	12/03	12/04	12/05	12/06	12/07
Est. sales ($ mil.)	—	—	—	—	—	164.9
Employees	—	—	—	—	—	2,000

ACE CASH EXPRESS, INC.

1231 Greenway Dr., Ste. 600	CEO: Jay B. Shipowitz
Irving, TX 75038	CFO: Douglas A. Lindsay
Phone: 972-550-5000	HR: James E. Gibbs
Fax: 972-582-1406	FYE: June 30
Web: www.acecashexpress.com	Type: Private

Ace Cash Express (ACE) takes care of bankless Americans. The company operates a leading chain of check-cashing stores, some under the name ACE Cash Advance, that provide services for people who are unable (or unwilling) to do business with commercial banks. For a fee, customers can cash checks, buy money orders, transfer money, and pay bills at nearly 1,600 ACE locations in almost 40 states and the District of Columbia, nearly 15% of which are franchised. Its Ace Cash Advance (ACA) stores offer short-term payday loans. Senior management and private equity firm JLL Partners took ACE private in 2006 in an estimated $420 million deal.

	Annual Growth	6/03	6/04	6/05	6/06	6/07
Est. sales ($ mil.)	—	—	—	—	—	366.2
Employees	—	—	—	—	—	3,061

ACE HARDWARE CORPORATION

2200 Kensington Ct.	CEO: Ray A. Griffith
Oak Brook, IL 60523	CFO: Dorvin D. Lively
Phone: 630-990-6600	HR: Jimmy Alexander
Fax: 630-990-6838	FYE: Saturday nearest December 31
Web: www.acehardware.com	Type: Cooperative

Luckily, Ace has John Madden up its sleeve. Despite the growth of warehouse-style competitors, Ace Hardware has remained a household name, thanks to ads featuring Madden, a former Oakland Raiders football coach and TV commentator. By sales the company is the #1 hardware cooperative in the US, ahead of Do It Best. Ace dealer-owners operate more than 4,700 Ace Hardware stores, home centers, and lumber and building materials locations in all 50 US states and about 70 other countries. From about 15 warehouses Ace distributes such products as electrical and plumbing supplies, garden equipment, hand tools, housewares, and power tools. Ace's paint division is a major paint manufacturer in the US.

	Annual Growth	12/02	12/03	12/04	12/05	12/06
Sales ($ mil.)	5.6%	3,029.1	3,159.3	3,288.7	3,466.0	3,770.0
Net income ($ mil.)	6.9%	82.1	100.7	101.9	100.4	107.4
Employees	(1.3%)	5,268	5,100	5,000	4,976	5,000

ACE PARKING MANAGEMENT, INC.

645 Ash St.	CEO: John Baumgardner
San Diego, CA 92101	CFO: Charles Blottin
Phone: 619-233-6624	HR: Cynthia Heu
Fax: –	FYE: December 31
Web: www.aceparking.com	Type: Private

When you're betting on finding a convenient parking spot in the western US, your chances of drawing an Ace are pretty good. Ace Parking Management oversees more than 450 parking locations in Arizona, California, Oregon, Texas, and Washington. The company manages facilities at locations such as airports, hospitals, hotels, medical centers, office and retail buildings, and stadiums. Customers have included Bank of America and the San Diego Padres baseball team. Chairman Scott Jones owns Ace Parking, which was founded in San Diego by his father in 1950.

	Annual Growth	12/03	12/04	12/05	12/06	12/07
Est. sales ($ mil.)	—	—	—	—	—	149.5
Employees	—	—	—	—	—	3,500

ACE*COMM CORPORATION
OTC: ACEC

704 Quince Orchard Rd., Ste. 100	CEO: James (Jim) Greenwell
Gaithersburg, MD 20878	CFO: Steven R. Delmar
Phone: 301-721-3000	HR: Loretta L. Rivers
Fax: 301-721-3001	FYE: June 30
Web: www.acecomm.com	Type: Public

ACE*COMM's got a whole lot of network data up its sleeve. The company provides data collection and analysis products for voice and data networks. ACE*COMM's products are used by telecommunications service providers to collect, manage, analyze, and distribute data collected from network elements. The company also offers products that enable corporations, government agencies, and educational institutions to automate certain network operations, such as performance and fault management. ACE*COMM markets its products directly and works with resellers and systems integrators.

	Annual Growth	6/03	6/04	6/05	6/06	6/07
Sales ($ mil.)	(0.9%)	13.8	13.7	20.0	26.7	13.3
Net income ($ mil.)	—	(2.0)	(5.9)	(6.5)	0.3	(9.5)
Market value ($ mil.)	17.1%	9.8	33.2	39.4	48.6	18.5
Employees	(12.3%)	—	—	146	128	—

ACER AMERICA CORPORATION

333 West San Carlos St., Ste. 1500	CEO: Rudi Schmidleithner
San Jose, CA 95110	CFO: Ming Wang
Phone: 408-533-7700	HR: Lenny Pollak
Fax: 408-533-4555	FYE: December 31
Web: www.acer.com/us	Type: Subsidiary

Whether it's monitors in the Midwest or servers in Saskatchewan, Acer America has Canada and the US covered. The company, a subsidiary of Taiwanese computer giant Acer, sells to businesses, government agencies, schools, and individual consumers. Its personal computer offerings include desktop, notebook, and tablet PCs. Other products include servers, flat-panel LCD displays, and digital projectors. The company sells through resellers and online retail partners. Established in 1977, Acer America serves the Canadian market with its Acer Canada division.

	Annual Growth	12/03	12/04	12/05	12/06	12/07
Est. sales ($ mil.)	—	—	—	—	—	1,104.2
Employees	—	—	—	—	—	180

ACETO CORPORATION
NASDAQ (GS): ACET

1 Hollow Ln.	CEO: Leonard S. Schwartz
Lake Success, NY 11042	CFO: Douglas Roth
Phone: 516-627-6000	HR: –
Fax: 516-627-6093	FYE: June 30
Web: www.aceto.com	Type: Public

Distributor Aceto (pronounced "a-seat-o") is getting bigger through chemicals — namely generic drugs. The company sources and distributes roughly 1,000 chemicals through four segments. Its largest segment is health sciences, which sources and distributes bulk generic drugs, advanced pharmaceutical intermediates, and nutritionals. Aceto's other business units include chemicals and colorants (which distributes intermediates and chemicals for coatings, inks, and electronics) and crop protection (herbicides, insecticides, and fungicides). Aceto sources about two-thirds of its products from Asia and turns around to sell more than half of them in the US.

	Annual Growth	6/03	6/04	6/05	6/06	6/07
Sales ($ mil.)	3.7%	271.3	297.7	313.4	297.1	313.5
Net income ($ mil.)	7.6%	7.6	13.1	10.0	9.2	10.2
Market value ($ mil.)	27.7%	84.7	188.3	181.6	168.0	225.1
Employees	(3.8%)	—	—	242	216	224

ACF INDUSTRIES LLC

101 Clark St.
St. Charles, MO 63301
Phone: 636-949-2399
Fax: 636-949-2825
Web: www.acfindustries.com

CEO: William L. (Bill) Finn
CFO: James E. Bowles
HR: Gary Rager
FYE: December 31
Type: Private

ACF Industries has been around for more than a century, and the company is still on track as a maker of railcar components. ACF Industries has manufacturing operations in Pennsylvania and West Virginia. The company is owned by billionaire financier Carl Icahn, who serves as its chairman. Affiliates American Railcar Leasing and American Railcar Industries lease the railroad freight cars formerly owned by ACF Industries.

ACG HOLDINGS, INC.

100 Winners Cir.
Brentwood, TN 37027
Phone: 615-377-0377
Fax: 615-377-0370
Web: www.americancolor.com

CEO: Stephen M. Dyott
CFO: Patrick W. Kellick
HR: –
FYE: March 31
Type: Private

If you spend part of your Sunday morning reading the newspaper sale flyers in search of good deals, thank ACG Holdings. The company's American Color Graphics unit makes many newspapers pudgy by printing advertising inserts for about 220 retailers and Sunday comics for about 150 newspapers. American Color Graphics also prints TV listings, local newspapers, comic books (for Marvel Publishing), and other publications. In addition to its print capabilities, the company provides digital imaging, pre-press, and photographic services. Funds affiliated with Morgan Stanley own a combined 52% of the company. Founded in 1926, ACG Holdings has agreed to be acquired by rival Vertis Communications.

	Annual Growth	3/03	3/04	3/05	3/06	3/07
Sales ($ mil.)	(3.8%)	520.3	471.1	449.5	434.5	445.0
Net income ($ mil.)	—	(0.3)	(28.8)	(25.7)	(14.6)	(21.0)
Employees	(4.4%)	2,465	2,250	2,010	2,040	2,060

ACH FOOD COMPANIES, INC.

7171 Goodlett Farms Pkwy.
Memphis, TN 38016
Phone: 901-381-3000
Fax: 901-381-2968
Web: www.achfood.com

CEO: Daniel S. (Dan) Antonelli
CFO: Jeffrey A. (Jeff) Atkins
HR: Deborah Murdock
FYE: September 30
Type: Subsidiary

ACH Food Companies is ACH-ing to help the cook. The company's products include edible oils, shortenings, and other oil-based products, as well as food ingredients such as cornstarch, syrup, spices, and cake decorations. The company has two divisions (consumer products and commercial products) that serve the retail, industrial food, and foodservice markets. Its brands include Mazola Oil, Argo Corn Starch, Karo Corn Syrup, and Spice Islands. ACH is the US subsidiary of UK food, ingredient, and retail giant Associated British Foods, which purchased ACH in 1995.

ACHILLION PHARMACEUTICALS, INC.

NASDAQ (GM): ACHN

300 George St.
New Haven, CT 06511
Phone: 203-624-7000
Fax: 203-624-7003
Web: www.achillion.com

CEO: Michael D. Kishbauch
CFO: Mary Kay Fenton
HR: –
FYE: December 31
Type: Public

Achillion Pharmaceuticals is looking for the Achilles heel of infectious disease. The firm is developing biopharmaceutical treatments for infectious diseases, including antiviral treatments for HIV infection and hepatitis C, as well as antibacterials for fighting drug-resistant hospital-based infections. Lead candidate elvucitabine is in clinical trials for the treatment of HIV; the drug is designed specifically for patients who have become resistant to existing antiviral drugs. Achillion is working in collaboration with biotech firm Gilead Sciences to develop a possible treatment for chronic hepatitis C. Another candidate in development is aimed at combating staph and other drug-resistant infections.

	Annual Growth	12/03	12/04	12/05	12/06	12/07
Sales ($ mil.)	—	0.0	0.8	8.5	3.3	4.0
Net income ($ mil.)	—	(15.8)	(17.5)	(13.6)	(24.1)	(28.1)
Market value ($ mil.)	(37.6%)	—	—	—	125.1	78.0
Employees	—	—	—	—	—	—

⊞ ACI WORLDWIDE, INC.

NASDAQ (GS): ACIW

120 Broadway, Ste. 3350
New York, NY 10271
Phone: 646-348-6700
Fax: 212-479-4000
Web: www.aciworldwide.com

CEO: Philip G. (Phil) Heasley
CFO: Scott W. Behrens
HR: –
FYE: September 30
Type: Public

ACI Worldwide (formerly Transaction Systems Architects) helps money go mobile. The company develops e-payment and electronic funds transfer (EFT) software for companies around the world. Customers use its software to process transactions involving ATMs, credit and debit cards, home banking services, point-of-sale terminals, smart cards, and wire transfers. ACI also makes network integration software, and it offers services such as design, implementation, and facilities management. Clients include banks, retailers, and third-party transaction processors.

	Annual Growth	9/03	9/04	9/05	9/06	9/07
Sales ($ mil.)	7.2%	277.3	292.8	313.2	347.9	366.2
Net income ($ mil.)	—	14.3	46.7	43.3	55.4	(9.1)
Market value ($ mil.)	7.4%	599.2	699.5	1,041.2	1,278.8	797.4
Employees	14.3%	—	—	1,674	1,960	2,186

ACME BRICK COMPANY

3101 Bryant Irvin Rd. South
Fort Worth, TX 76109
Phone: 817-332-4101
Fax: 817-390-2404
Web: www.brick.com

CEO: Dennis Knautz
CFO: Judy B. Hunter
HR: Ben P. Muro
FYE: December 31
Type: Subsidiary

Troy Aikman doesn't lob bricks, but the former Cowboys quarterback does pitch products for Acme Brick. The Berkshire Hathaway subsidiary produces and distributes more than a billion bricks annually for its construction customers in a variety of colors, shapes, and sizes. It operates more than 20 brick manufacturing plants; it also makes all-brick woodburning fireplace systems. Acme Brick operates a family of companies that includes American Tile Supply (residential, commercial, and natural stone tiles), Featherlite (masonry materials), IBP Glass Block Grid System (glass blocks set in custom-made aluminum grids), and Texas Quarries (limestone).

	Annual Growth	12/03	12/04	12/05	12/06	12/07
Est. sales ($ mil.)	—	—	—	—	—	176.2
Employees	—	—	—	—	—	2,602

⊞ An in-depth profile of this company is available to Hoover's Online members at hoovers.com.

47

ACME COMMUNICATIONS, INC.

NASDAQ (GM): ACME

2101 E. 4th St., Ste. 202A
Santa Ana, CA 92705
Phone: 714-245-9499
Fax: 714-245-9494
Web: www.acmecommunications.com

CEO: Jamie Kellner
CFO: Thomas D. (Tom) Allen
HR: –
FYE: December 31
Type: Public

ACME Communications' relationship with Warner Bros. has nothing to do with a wily coyote, rockets, or any other explosives. The company owns and operates a half dozen television stations in midsized markets in five states, most of which are affiliated with The CW Network, a joint venture between Time Warner's Warner Bros. Entertainment and CBS Corporation. It also has one station that is affiliated with MyNetworkTV, a network owned by News Corp. Both networks focus on programming skewed towards younger audiences. In addition to its stations, ACME Communications produces a syndicated morning program called *The Daily Buzz* that airs on about 140 stations.

	Annual Growth	12/03	12/04	12/05	12/06	12/07
Sales ($ mil.)	(7.4%)	43.5	46.9	40.9	34.8	32.0
Net income ($ mil.)	(32.8%)	75.0	(17.5)	(15.9)	(4.2)	15.3
Market value ($ mil.)	(26.1%)	147.2	117.6	59.5	80.6	43.8
Employees	—	—	—	195	—	—

ACME PACKET, INC.

NASDAQ (GM): APKT

71 3rd Ave.
Burlington, MA 01803
Phone: 781-328-4400
Fax: 781-425-5077
Web: www.acmepacket.com

CEO: Andrew (Andy) Ory
CFO: Keith Seidman
HR: –
FYE: December 31
Type: Public

Acme Packet brings networks together. The company makes communications equipment designed to route voice and data across Internet Protocol (IP) networks. Acme's family of Net-Net session border controllers (SBCs) are used to connect networks operated by service providers and enterprise customers. SBCs handle interactive services including voice-over-IP. Acme Packet has distribution partnerships with Ericsson and Sonus Networks. It counts Charter Communications, China Unicom, and Telstra among its customers. Menlo Ventures owns a 22% stake in the company.

	Annual Growth	12/03	12/04	12/05	12/06	12/07
Sales ($ mil.)	142.0%	3.3	16.0	36.1	84.1	113.1
Net income ($ mil.)	—	(7.5)	(7.0)	0.0	28.9	19.6
Market value ($ mil.)	(37.1%)	—	—	—	1,208.8	760.8
Employees	30.4%	—	—	—	247	322

ACME UNITED CORPORATION

AMEX: ACU

60 Round Hill Road
Fairfield, CT 06824
Phone: 203-254-6060
Fax: 203-254-6019
Web: www.acmeunited.com

CEO: Walter C. Johnsen
CFO: Paul G. Driscoll
HR: –
FYE: December 31
Type: Public

Acme United has taken measures to trim its business. It sold its medical equipment division to focus on its core products: scissors, rulers, and first aid kits. Its products are used in schools, offices, and homes. (The kits come complete with bandages, gloves, and over-the-counter medications.) Its name brands include Westcott, Clauss, and PhysiciansCare. Acme sells its products to stationery and school supply distributors, office supply stores, and mass merchants, such as Staples, Office Max, and United Stationers. Its operations span Canada, Germany, Hong Kong, China, and the US (which contributes most of sales). President and CEO Walter Johnsen owns 17% of company stock.

	Annual Growth	12/03	12/04	12/05	12/06	12/07
Sales ($ mil.)	15.9%	35.0	43.4	50.0	56.9	63.2
Net income ($ mil.)	35.1%	1.2	3.2	2.9	3.9	4.0
Market value ($ mil.)	30.2%	17.6	53.6	48.6	50.6	50.6
Employees	—	—	—	116	—	—

ACN, INC.

32991 Hamilton Ct.
Farmington Hills, MI 48334
Phone: 248-699-4000
Fax: 248-489-5883
Web: www.acninc.com

CEO: Gregory (Greg) Provenzano
CFO: Jim Mulzahy
HR: –
FYE: December 31
Type: Private

What do Tupperware and telephone service have in common? For ACN, it's all in how you sell it. The telecommunications reseller makes its money through multi-level marketing (the selling strategy used by the likes of consumer goods distributors Tupperware Brands and Amway). Its commission-based independent distributors operate in 19 countries, reselling local and long-distance phone service, as well as DSL Internet access. ACN purchases network resources from such leading carriers as BellSouth, Telstra, and Verizon. Chairman Robert Stevanovski, president Gregory Provenzano, and vice presidents Anthony and Michael Cupisz founded ACN in 1993.

	Annual Growth	12/03	12/04	12/05	12/06	12/07
Est. sales ($ mil.)	—	—	—	—	—	76.4
Employees	—	—	—	—	—	600

ACNB CORPORATION

OTC: ACNB

16 Lincoln Sq.
Gettysburg, PA 17325
Phone: 717-334-3161
Fax: 717-334-9319
Web: www.acnb.com

CEO: Thomas A. Ritter
CFO: David W. Cathell
HR: Sandra A. Deaner
FYE: December 31
Type: Public

Seven score and a few years ago, ACNB Corporation's fathers brought forth a small-town bank. Now ACNB is dedicated to the proposition of being the holding company for Adams County National Bank, operating more than 20 branches in the Gettysburg and Newville areas of Pennsylvania. It is altogether fitting and proper that the bank offers traditional retail banking services. The world may long note and remember that the bank also provides residential mortgage (about 60% of the portfolio), commercial real estate, consumer, and business loans. ACNB also gives a full measure of devotion to insurance products; the company also provides trust services and hopes that community banking shall not perish from the earth.

	Annual Growth	12/03	12/04	12/05	12/06	12/07
Assets ($ mil.)	1.5%	872.7	924.2	945.1	964.8	926.7
Net income ($ mil.)	(7.5%)	10.8	9.3	7.4	7.3	7.9
Market value ($ mil.)	(8.8%)	131.7	127.7	98.1	108.4	91.1
Employees	—	—	—	—	—	266

ACNIELSEN CORPORATION

770 Broadway
New York, NY 10003
Phone: 646-654-5000
Fax: 646-654-5002
Web: www.acnielsen.com

CEO: Susan D. Whiting
CFO: Kirk Miller
HR: John Moses
FYE: December 31
Type: Subsidiary

When you shop till you drop, ACNielsen keeps track of every blow. A subsidiary of business information giant Nielsen, ACNielsen is a leading collector of retail sales data. It compiles data from retail store scanners and in-store audits in about 100 countries, providing information on market share, pricing, and promotional effectiveness. It also collects information on brand loyalty, purchases, and demographics through its consumer panel of more than 125,000 households in about two dozen countries. In addition, ACNielsen offers custom research services and several lines of support software designed to help its clients use its data. Sister company Nielsen Media Research measures TV viewing habits.

	Annual Growth	12/03	12/04	12/05	12/06	12/07
Est. sales ($ mil.)	—	—	—	—	—	679.5
Employees	—	—	—	—	—	21,068

ACORDA THERAPEUTICS, INC.

NASDAQ (GM): ACOR

15 Skyline Dr.
Hawthorne, NY 10532
Phone: 914-347-4300
Fax: 914-347-4560
Web: www.acorda.com

CEO: Ron Cohen
CFO: David Lawrence
HR: Denise J. Duca
FYE: December 31
Type: Public

Acorda Therapeutics hopes its products really get on your nerves. The company is developing therapeutics that would restore neurological function for patients with spinal cord injury and other central nervous system disorders. The company markets and sells muscle relaxant Zanaflex in the US through a licensing agreement with Elan Corporation. Its lead drug candidate is Fampridine-SR, which enhances conduction in the myelin layer of nerves damaged by blunt trauma or from multiple sclerosis (MS). The drug is delivered by a sustained release system developed for the firm by Elan. Acorda's other drug candidates include drugs for MS and spinal cord injuries.

	Annual Growth	12/03	12/04	12/05	12/06	12/07
Sales ($ mil.)	175.6%	—	—	5.2	27.4	39.5
Net income ($ mil.)	—	—	—	(35.5)	(24.0)	(38.0)
Market value ($ mil.)	67.4%	—	—	—	374.7	627.5
Employees	—	—	—	80	—	—

⊞ ACORN ENERGY, INC.

OTC: ACFN

4 W. Rockland Rd.
Montchanin, DE 19710
Phone: 302-656-1707
Fax: 302-994-3086
Web: www.acornfactor.com

CEO: John A. Moore
CFO: Michael Barth
HR: Tali Rappaport
FYE: December 31
Type: Public

Acorn Energy is nuts about its investments. The company, formerly known as Data Systems & Software, is a holding company that maintains controlling or equity positions in a variety of companies, including Comverge, Paketeria, and dsIT Solutions. Comverge is a demand response company that enables utilities, industry, and consumers to better manage peak electricity usage. Paketeria combines five service businesses, including eBay dropshops, shipping services, photo processing, and photocopying and printer cartridge refilling. dsIT Solutions is a provider of software consulting and development services operating in the areas of port security, oncology treatment, and health-care billing.

	Annual Growth	12/03	12/04	12/05	12/06	12/07
Sales ($ mil.)	(36.5%)	35.0	30.1	21.9	4.1	5.7
Net income ($ mil.)	—	(6.3)	(1.2)	(1.3)	(6.1)	32.5
Market value ($ mil.)	22.8%	27.1	8.1	13.2	33.0	61.6
Employees	—	—	—	—	—	—

ACOSTA, INC.

6600 Corporate Center Pkwy.
Jacksonville, FL 32216
Phone: 904-281-9800
Fax: 904-281-9966
Web: www.acosta.com

CEO: Gary Chartrand
CFO: Gregory (Greg) Delaney
HR: Michael W. Rotelle III
FYE: December 31
Type: Private

Acosta spends a lot of time thinking about which products are top-shelf. The company offers sales and marketing services that intersect with consumers at the shelves of retail food service and grocery businesses. Some 1,000 US consumer products manufacturers (including Coca-Cola and Pepsi) call on Acosta to help them position their products in grocery and convenience stores, drug stores, and mass merchandisers in the US and Canada. Acosta specializes in inventory and merchandising services and business consulting for promotions, marketing campaigns, and sales. Acosta was established in 1927. It was acquired by AEA Investors LLC, a New York private equity firm, in mid-2006.

	Annual Growth	12/03	12/04	12/05	12/06	12/07
Est. sales ($ mil.)	—	—	—	—	—	2,147.5
Employees	—	—	—	—	—	11,000

ACR GROUP, INC.

3200 Wilcrest Dr., Ste. 440
Houston, TX 77042
Phone: 713-780-8532
Fax: 713-780-4067
Web: www.acrgroup.com

CEO: Alex Trevino Jr.
CFO: Anthony R. Maresca
HR: Carol Russell
FYE: December 31*
Type: Subsidiary

Whether the mercury is rising or it's 10 below, ACR Group is in the cool business of climate control. The company is a wholesale distributor of heating, ventilating, air conditioning, and refrigeration (HVACR) equipment and supplies, which are sold to contractors and dealers responsible for the installation, repair, and maintenance of HVACR systems. ACR operates about 55 distribution centers in 10 states, including three of the largest HVACR markets: California, Florida, and Texas. The company has been expanding in the Sunbelt and in other high-growth regions of the US. Founded in 1990, ACR Group was acquired by rival Watsco in mid-2007 for about $74 million.

	Annual Growth	2/03	2/04	2/05	2/06	2/07
Sales ($ mil.)	10.3%	161.8	174.4	199.6	204.3	239.6
Net income ($ mil.)	75.6%	0.6	2.4	4.2	2.8	5.7
Employees	7.1%	—	—	421	451	483

*Fiscal year change

ACS INDUSTRIES, INC.

191 Social St.
Woonsocket, RI 02895
Phone: 401-769-4700
Fax: 401-766-2191
Web: www.acsindustries.com

CEO: Steven Buckler
CFO: Paul Pimentel
HR: –
FYE: October 31
Type: Private

When it comes to making wire mesh products, ACS Industries doesn't mess around. The company makes wire products, primarily knitted wire and woven mesh, but also specialty wire, and wire cable. The company serves customers in the automotive and industrial manufacturing industries with products including air-bag filters, exhaust components, joint seals, filters, and mufflers. The diversified manufacturer also makes a line of household and institutional cleaning products, including scouring pads, mops, brooms, and brushes through its Scrubble Products division. ACS Industries was founded in 1939 as a manufacturer of knitted copper pot cleaners.

	Annual Growth	10/03	10/04	10/05	10/06	10/07
Est. sales ($ mil.)	—	—	—	—	—	142.9
Employees	—	—	—	—	—	2,000

ACSIS, INC.

3000 Lincoln Dr. East
Marlton, NJ 08053
Phone: 856-673-3000
Fax: 856-810-3597
Web: www.acsisinc.com

CEO: Steven G. (Steve) Selfridge
CFO: Tonya Zweier
HR: –
FYE: December 31
Type: Subsidiary

Acsis assists companies in assembling data. The company provides supply chain execution technologies and services designed to help large manufacturers make the most of their SAP-based supply chain systems. Its products and services improve data collection and help users integrate supply chain and enterprise resource planning systems. Acsis's DataPass software makes supply chain data accessible throughout an organization; its online DPExchange service lets customers share information with trading partners. Founded in 1996, Acsis was acquired by Safeguard Scientifics in 2005.

	Annual Growth	12/03	12/04	12/05	12/06	12/07
Est. sales ($ mil.)	—	—	—	—	—	12.7
Employees	—	—	—	—	—	110

⊞ An in-depth profile of this company is available to Hoover's Online members at hoovers.com.

49

ACSYS INC.

111 Anza Blvd., Ste. 400
Burlingame, CA 94010
Phone: 650-579-1111
Fax: 650-579-1927
Web: www.acsysinc.com

CEO: Jack Unroe
CFO: Joe Prusko
HR: —
FYE: December 31
Type: Subsidiary

Acsys wants to be the name that businesses can "account" on to provide temporary staffing services. The company provides temporary accounting, finance, and administrative professionals to clients in a variety of industries. It also offers information technology consultants and permanent placement services and provides specialized placement services for customers in the health care and legal industries, among others. Headquartered in Atlanta, Acsys operates almost 15 offices in major metropolitan markets throughout the US, primarily along the East Coast. Amsterdam-based staffing giant Vedior purchased the company in 2000.

	Annual Growth	12/03	12/04	12/05	12/06	12/07
Est. sales ($ mil.)	—	—	—	—	—	59.4
Employees	—	—	—	—	—	160

ACT, INC.

500 ACT Dr.
Iowa City, IA 52243
Phone: 319-337-1000
Fax: 319-339-3021
Web: www.act.org

CEO: Richard L. Ferguson
CFO: Thomas J. Goedken
HR: Jim Friel
FYE: August 31
Type: Not-for-profit

These three little letters strike fear in the hearts of high school students across the US. ACT most famously develops and administers the national college admission exam that bears its name, but the company also designs educational assessment programs for students of all ages. Its EXPLORE program, for example, helps students determine how prepared they are for college. In addition, the not-for-profit company offers workforce development services. Its Workforce Solutions division provides assessment, training, and consulting to employers. ACT, which was founded in 1959 as The American College Testing Program, has offices across the US and in Australia, China, South Korea, and Spain.

	Annual Growth	8/03	8/04	8/05	8/06	8/07
Est. sales ($ mil.)	—	—	—	—	—	190.0
Employees	—	—	—	—	—	1,200

ACT TELECONFERENCING, INC.

Pink Sheets: ACTT

1526 Cole Blvd., Ste. 300
Golden, CO 80401
Phone: 303-233-3500
Fax: 303-238-0096
Web: www.acttel.com

CEO: Peter E. Salas
CFO: —
HR: Jennie McQuade
FYE: December 31
Type: Public

ACT Teleconferencing helps its customers get their acts together over communications lines. The company provides audio-conferencing services, including operator-assisted and unattended conferencing. The company also has video and Web conferencing options. ACT's primary customers are multinational corporations, such as BP, Ernst & Young, KLM Royal Dutch Airlines, and Philips Electronics. It also serves educational organizations and governmental entities worldwide. Through an odd-lot tender offer, ACT completed a stock buyback and deregistered with the SEC in 2007.

	Annual Growth	12/02	12/03	12/04	12/05	*12/06
Sales ($ mil.)	(0.1%)	53.9	55.8	53.5	51.0	53.6
Net income ($ mil.)	—	(7.7)	(8.5)	(21.2)	(18.1)	1.8
Employees	(7.1%)	416	—	—	333	—

*Most recent year available

ACT-1 PERSONNEL SERVICES

1999 W. 190th St.
Torrance, CA 90504
Phone: 310-750-3400
Fax: 310-750-1104
Web: www.act1personnel.com

CEO: Janice Bryant Howroyd
CFO: Jeff Kornreich
HR: —
FYE: December 31
Type: Private

ACT-1 Personnel Services offers permanent placement and temporary staffing services from more than 70 branch locations in the US. The company provides administrative, professional, and light industrial personnel for companies in the entertainment, medical, financial services, telecommunications, and manufacturing sectors, among others. Its technical and professional services unit supplies contract IT and engineering professionals. Other affiliated businesses offer a range of business services including background screening, print purchasing, document scanning, and workforce training. ACT-1 Personnel Services was founded in 1978.

	Annual Growth	12/03	12/04	12/05	12/06	12/07
Est. sales ($ mil.)	—	—	—	—	—	627.0
Employees	—	—	—	—	—	375

ACTEL CORPORATION

NASDAQ (GM): ACTL

2061 Stierlin Ct.
Mountain View, CA 94043
Phone: 650-318-4200
Fax: 650-318-4600
Web: www.actel.com

CEO: John C. East
CFO: Jon A. Anderson
HR: Barbara L. McArthur
FYE: December 31
Type: Public

Actel acts to design and sell programmable chips. The company makes field-programmable gate arrays (FPGAs), a type of integrated circuit that can be programmed by users for specific functions. Actel sells FPGAs to a broad range of manufacturers in the telecommunications, military, industrial equipment, computer, consumer electronics, and automotive industries. Actel makes high-speed, anti-fuse FPGAs, as well as flash-based FPGAs; it also offers design software and programming hardware used to configure and test its chips. The fabless semiconductor company's customers include Boeing, Cisco Systems, Magna Electronics, Nortel Networks, and Siemens. The US represents about half of sales.

	Annual Growth	12/03	12/04	12/05	12/06	12/07
Sales ($ mil.)	7.1%	149.9	165.5	179.4	191.5	197.0
Net income ($ mil.)	—	6.2	2.4	7.0	(2.2)	(2.9)
Market value ($ mil.)	(13.6%)	604.8	445.7	327.6	481.5	337.6
Employees	1.8%	543	557	565	574	584

ACTION PRODUCTS INTERNATIONAL, INC.

NASDAQ (GM): APII

1101 N. Keller Rd., Ste. E
Orlando, FL 32810
Phone: 407-481-8007
Fax: 407-481-2781
Web: www.apii.com

CEO: Ronald S. (Ron) Kaplan
CFO: Robert L. Burrows
HR: —
FYE: December 31
Type: Public

Kids like to stay away when education is involved, but this firm hopes they go where the action is. Action Products International designs, makes, and markets nonviolent, educational products with a focus on science, nature, and space. Toys include ClimbTron suction-cup climbing robots, Space Voyagers astronaut action figures and model spacecrafts, I Dig Dinosaurs excavation kits, arts & crafts kits, and puzzle-like wood kits. Toy stores, museum shops, and other specialty retailers are all part of Action Products' worldwide customer base. (The firm generates most of its sales in the US.) The Kaplan family (including founder Judith Kaplan and son Ron, chairman) owns about 55% of the firm.

	Annual Growth	12/03	12/04	12/05	12/06	12/07
Sales ($ mil.)	(7.1%)	8.2	9.1	9.5	7.4	6.1
Net income ($ mil.)	—	(0.5)	(0.1)	0.0	(2.7)	1.3
Market value ($ mil.)	(18.3%)	11.6	18.0	12.1	8.0	5.2
Employees	(21.1%)	—	—	38	30	—

ACTIONTEC ELECTRONICS, INC.

760 N. Mary Ave.
Sunnyvale, CA 94085
Phone: 408-752-7700
Fax: 408-541-9003
Web: www.actiontec.com

CEO: Dean Chang
CFO: Brian Paul
HR: –
FYE: December 31
Type: Private

Actiontec Electronics aims to broaden your approach to networking. The company makes gateways, routers, modems, and other broadband connection equipment used to create wireless home networks. It also makes VoIP (Voice over Internet Protocol) products, including a speakerphone (Chatterbox) that plugs into a computer's USB port and works with Skype's VoIP software. The company sells its equipment through partnerships with telecommunication service providers and equipment makers, such as Qwest, America Online, Dell, and Hewlett-Packard. It also sells through retailers. The company was founded in 1993.

	Annual Growth	12/03	12/04	12/05	12/06	12/07
Est. sales ($ mil.)	—	—	—	—	—	28.5
Employees	—	—	—	—	—	440

ACTIVANT SOLUTIONS INC.

7683 Southfront Rd.
Livermore, CA 94551
Phone: 925-449-0606
Fax: –
Web: www.activant.com

CEO: Pervez A. Qureshi
CFO: Kathleen M. (Kathy) Crusco
HR: Beth A. Taylor
FYE: September 30
Type: Private

Activant Solutions wants all parts of a business holding hands, singing in perfect harmony. The company provides enterprise resource planning (ERP) software for more than 20,000 small and medium-sized businesses in the automotive parts aftermarket, hardware and home center, wholesale trade, and lumber and building materials industries. Activant's software automates functions such as inventory management, parts selection, general accounting, and point-of-sale analysis. Customers have included members of the Ace Hardware, True Value, and Do it Best cooperatives.

ACTIVE MEDIA SERVICES, INC.

1 Blue Hill Plaza
Pearl River, NY 10965
Phone: 845-735-1700
Fax: 845-735-0717
Web: www.activeinternational.com

CEO: Alan S. Elkin
CFO: Richard Vendig
HR: –
FYE: June 30
Type: Private

Active Media Services, which does business as Active International, has turned corporate barter into an art form, and a profitable one at that. The corporate trading firm acquires underperforming assets, including surplus inventory, capital equipment, real estate, and receivables. It exchanges these for cash and/or trade credit, which is used to offset expenses or purchase such services as advertising, freight, printing, shipping, sports and event planning, and travel. Active International serves a variety of industries from offices in some 20 countries around the globe. The firm acquires assets in one part of the world and remarkets them in another; clients can use their trade credits internationally.

	Annual Growth	6/03	6/04	6/05	6/06	6/07
Est. sales ($ mil.)	—	—	—	—	—	39.4
Employees	—	—	—	—	—	525

ACTIVE POWER, INC.

NASDAQ (GM): ACPW

2128 W. Braker Ln., Bldg. 12
Austin, TX 78758
Phone: 512-836-6464
Fax: 512-836-4511
Web: www.activepower.com

CEO: James (Jim) Clishem
CFO: John K. Penver
HR: Shannon Harding
FYE: December 31
Type: Public

Active Power keeps the juices flowing. The company's CleanSource DC and CleanSource UPS (uninterruptible power system) are designed to replace conventional UPS products that use lead-acid batteries. The CleanSource DC/UPS products use a flywheel that stores kinetic energy by spinning. When a power quality problem is detected, the products convert the kinetic energy into electricity. The CleanSource UPS was developed in partnership with heavy equipment maker Caterpillar (about 31% of sales), which markets the product with its generator sets. CleanSource is marketed to Internet service providers, as well as telecommunications, industrial, and commercial customers. US customers provide more than half of sales.

	Annual Growth	12/03	12/04	12/05	12/06	12/07
Sales ($ mil.)	39.4%	8.9	15.8	17.8	25.0	33.6
Net income ($ mil.)	—	(21.7)	(27.8)	(22.9)	(21.1)	(20.5)
Market value ($ mil.)	2.1%	122.1	199.0	188.0	131.2	132.8
Employees	5.7%	124	135	164	145	155

ACTIVIDENTITY CORPORATION

NASDAQ (GM): ACTI

6623 Dumbarton Cir.
Fremont, CA 94555
Phone: 510-574-0100
Fax: 510-574-0101
Web: www.actividentity.com

CEO: Grant Evans
CFO: –
HR: –
FYE: September 30
Type: Public

ActivIdentity isn't passive when it comes to security. The company provides a variety of authentication and user management products, including smart cards, biometric readers, tokens, and USB keys. Its products are used to control and monitor access to intranets, extranets, and the Internet, enabling businesses to authenticate and manage the digital identities of employees, customers, and trading partners. The company's customers have included Citibank, France Telecom, and Sun Microsystems. ActivIdentity also offer professional services such as consulting, support, and training.

	Annual Growth	12/03	*9/04	9/05	9/06	9/07
Sales ($ mil.)	11.6%	38.3	26.9	42.2	53.4	59.5
Net income ($ mil.)	—	(29.8)	(27.4)	(47.9)	(22.5)	(9.3)
Market value ($ mil.)	(8.2%)	331.9	260.9	197.4	215.0	236.0
Employees	—	—	—	313		

*Fiscal year change

⊞ ACTIVISION, INC.

NASDAQ (GS): ATVI

3100 Ocean Park Blvd.
Santa Monica, CA 90405
Phone: 310-255-2000
Fax: 310-255-2100
Web: www.activision.com

CEO: Robert A. (Bobby) Kotick
CFO: Thomas Tippl
HR: Ann Weiser
FYE: March 31
Type: Public

Video game maker Activision is a firm believer that action speaks louder than words. The video game publisher is best known for title franchises such as *Tony Hawk, Guitar Hero, Doom,* and *Call of Duty.* It also makes games based on licensed properties from LucasArts (*Star Wars*), Marvel (*Spider-Man* and *X-Men*), and DreamWorks Animation (*Shrek*). Its titles are produced for console game systems and handheld devices from Sony, Microsoft, and Nintendo. The company also distributes third-party titles. In late 2007 the company agreed to sell a 52% stake in the company to Vivendi in a deal valued at $9.8 billion; Vivendi plans to combine the company with Vivendi Games.

	Annual Growth	3/04	3/05	3/06	3/07	3/08
Sales ($ mil.)	32.2%	947.7	1,405.9	1,468.0	1,513.0	2,898.1
Net income ($ mil.)	45.2%	77.7	138.3	40.3	85.8	344.9
Market value ($ mil.)	60.2%	1,222.1	2,231.4	3,820.1	5,365.9	8,046.9
Employees	10.9%	—	1,728	2,149	2,125	

ACTS RETIREMENT-LIFE COMMUNITIES, INC.

375 Morris Rd.
West Point, PA 19486
Phone: 215-661-8330
Fax: 215-661-8320
Web: www.actsretirement.com

CEO: Marvin Mashner
CFO: Jerry Grant
HR: Warren Johnson
FYE: December 31
Type: Not-for-profit

When mom can still live on her own but needs some help, it's time to act. ACTS develops, owns, and operates retirement communities in the Southeastern US. The company's properties feature resort-style amenities in Christian environments (ACTS comes from a Biblical reference). It owns nearly 20 properties, located in Florida, Georgia, North Carolina, Pennsylvania, and South Carolina. ACTS builds most of its holdings but does acquire existing communities; it bought its 18th property, a continuing-care retirement community in South Carolina, in 2005. The not-for-profit organization was founded as Open Door Estates by a group of Pennsylvania church members in 1971.

	Annual Growth	12/03	12/04	12/05	12/06	12/07
Est. sales ($ mil.)	—	—	—	—	—	131.5
Employees	—	—	—	—	—	5,500

ACTUANT CORPORATION

NYSE: ATU

13000 W. Silver Spring Dr.
Butler, WI 53007
Phone: 414-352-4160
Fax: 414-247-5550
Web: www.actuant.com

CEO: Robert C. (Bob) Arzbaecher
CFO: Andrew G. (Andy) Lampereur
HR: Susan S. Korthase
FYE: August 31
Type: Public

Actual results may vary, but Actuant consistently produces a range of tools and hydraulic equipment. It makes electrical and industrial tools, such as wire connectors, fasteners, plugs, sockets, and electrical hand tools, for wholesale and retail distribution under such brand names as Acme Electric, Gardner Bender, and Kopp. The company also offers hydraulic motion-control systems to OEMs. Products include RV slide-out systems, hydraulic cab-tilt systems for heavy-duty trucks, and electro-hydraulic automotive convertible top systems, while brands include Milwaukee Cylinder and Power-Packer. The US accounts for more than half of the company's sales.

	Annual Growth	8/03	8/04	8/05	8/06	8/07
Sales ($ mil.)	25.6%	585.4	726.8	976.1	1,201.2	1,458.8
Net income ($ mil.)	37.9%	29.0	34.8	71.3	92.6	104.9
Market value ($ mil.)	29.2%	302.7	449.6	573.4	615.5	843.9
Employees	22.4%	3,300	3,600	5,850	6,300	7,400

ACTUATE CORPORATION

NASDAQ (GM): ACTU

2207 Bridgepointe Pkwy., Ste. 500
San Mateo, CA 94404
Phone: 650-645-3000
Fax: 650-645-3700
Web: www.actuate.com

CEO: Peter I. (Pete) Cittadini
CFO: Daniel A. (Dan) Gaudreau
HR: –
FYE: December 31
Type: Public

Actuate accentuates reporting. The company provides enterprise reporting and analytics software that corporations use to analyze business data and design, publish, and distribute report content through company networks and the Internet. Actuate's customers, which have included Bank of America, Dell, Johnson & Johnson, and Lockheed Martin, use the company's software to publish financial statements, performance metrics, manufacturing and distribution reports, and customer account information. Actuate's service offerings include training and support, as well as professional consulting.

	Annual Growth	12/03	12/04	12/05	12/06	12/07
Sales ($ mil.)	7.7%	104.5	104.7	106.4	128.6	140.6
Net income ($ mil.)	—	(4.5)	1.3	11.6	13.8	20.2
Market value ($ mil.)	25.8%	190.4	158.0	188.9	361.7	477.3
Employees	18.5%	—	—	491	582	—

ACUITY, A MUTUAL INSURANCE COMPANY

2800 S. Taylor Dr.
Sheboygan, WI 53081
Phone: 920-458-9131
Fax: 920-458-1618
Web: www.acuity.com

CEO: Benjamin M. (Ben) Salzmann
CFO: Wendy Schuler
HR: John Signer
FYE: December 31
Type: Mutual company

For Acuity, keeping an eye on the prize means meeting its customers' insurance needs. The company writes a variety of personal and commercial property/casualty insurance plans for policyholders in nearly 20 states, primarily in the Midwest. Its products include automobile, homeowners, liability, marine, umbrella, and workers' compensation coverage. Acuity provides policies for such businesses as construction contractors, manufacturers, and small service businesses. More than 800 independent agencies sell the company's policies. Acuity was founded in 1925 as Mutual Auto Insurance Company of the Town of Herman.

	Annual Growth	12/03	12/04	12/05	12/06	12/07
Est. sales ($ mil.)	—	—	—	—	—	741.2
Employees	—	—	—	—	—	730

ACUITY BRANDS, INC.

NYSE: AYI

1170 Peachtree St. Northeast, Ste. 2400
Atlanta, GA 30309
Phone: 404-853-1400
Fax: 404-853-1411
Web: www.acuitybrands.com

CEO: Vernon J. (Vern) Nagel
CFO: Richard K. (Ricky) Reece
HR: –
FYE: August 31
Type: Public

To keep things light, Acuity Brands has made a clean sweep of its specialty consumer cleaning products business. The company spun off its specialty products business as Zep Inc. in 2007. Now Acuity is strictly a maker of lighting products. The company makes products that range from residential and commercial lighting fixtures to the high-mast systems used to illuminate highways, parking lots, rail yards, and seaports. Brand names include Hydrel, MetalOptics, and Peerless. Zep, now an independent company, makes cleaners, deodorizers, disinfectants, herbicides, and pesticides primarily geared for the industrial, institutional, and retail markets.

	Annual Growth	8/03	8/04	8/05	8/06	8/07
Sales ($ mil.)	5.4%	2,049.3	2,104.2	2,172.9	2,393.1	2,530.7
Net income ($ mil.)	32.7%	47.8	67.2	52.2	106.6	148.1
Market value ($ mil.)	32.1%	746.4	980.1	1,328.2	1,840.1	2,275.8
Employees	0.0%	—	—	10,000	10,600	10,000

ACUNETX, INC.

OTC: ANTX

2301 W. 205th St., Ste. 102
Torrance, CA 90501
Phone: 310-328-0477
Fax: 310-328-0697
Web: www.acunetx.com

CEO: Ronald A. (Ron) Waldorf
CFO: Colis Woodard
HR: –
FYE: December 31
Type: Public

If you find yourself humming "Catch me now, I'm falling" then AcuNetx can help. The company's IntelliNetx division markets patented medical devices that assist in the diagnosis of dizziness and vertigo, and rehabilitate those in danger of falling as a result of balance disorders. Through its majority-owned VisioNetx subsidiary AcuNetx makes diagnostic equipment that can tell employers and police if someone is impaired by alcohol, some other substance, or by fatigue or illness. The company's OrthoNetx unit is a medical subsidiary which provides surgery devices that create new bone in order to correct deformities and deficiencies of the skeleton.

	Annual Growth	12/03	12/04	12/05	12/06	12/07
Sales ($ mil.)	(5.1%)	3.2	2.1	1.4	2.2	2.6
Net income ($ mil.)	—	1.0	0.4	(0.4)	(8.2)	(0.9)
Employees	50.0%	—	—	—	4	6

ACURA PHARMACEUTICALS, INC.

NASDAQ (CM): ACUR

616 N. North Ct., Ste. 120
Palatine, IL 60067
Phone: 847-705-7709
Fax: 847-705-5399
Web: acurapharm.com

CEO: Robert B. Jones
CFO: Peter A. Clemens
HR: –
FYE: December 31
Type: Public

Acura Pharmaceuticals is working to make it harder to abuse otherwise good drugs. The company has developed a technology to add abuse-deterring agents to commonly abused pharmaceuticals. If a drug with these agents (what Acura calls Aversion Technology) is taken in excess, the ingredients cause unpleasant symptoms shortly after ingestion. If a tablet is crushed and inhaled other ingredients will cause nasal irritation; and if an abuser attempts to dissolve the powder, it will form a non-injectable gel. Lead product candidate Acurox combines Aversion Technology with the commonly abused opioid painkiller oxycodone HCl.

	Annual Growth	12/03	12/04	12/05	12/06	12/07
Sales ($ mil.)	—	—	—	—	—	6.4
Net income ($ mil.)	—	—	—	—	—	(4.3)
Market value ($ mil.)	—	—	—	—	—	29.5
Employees	—	—	—	—	—	—

ACUSHNET COMPANY

333 Bridge St.
Fairhaven, MA 02719
Phone: 508-979-2000
Fax: 508-979-3927
Web: www.acushnet.com

CEO: Walter R. (Wally) Uihlein
CFO: William C. Burke Sr.
HR: Dennis Doherty
FYE: December 31
Type: Subsidiary

Acushnet stays teed off all the time. Owned by Fortune Brands, Acushnet Company is a leading maker of golf balls, clubs, shoes, gloves, and other golfing equipment and accessories. Its Titleist brand of golf balls is the #1 seller in the US. Its FootJoy golf shoes are also #1 nationwide. The company makes value-priced Pinnacle golf balls, Cobra golf clubs, and Scotty Cameron putters, as well. Acushnet's products are sold to golf pro shops, sporting goods stores, and mass merchants throughout the US, Canada, and South Africa, and in parts of Europe and Asia. Some 35% of sales are from outside the US. Players who use Titleist equipment include Bart Bryant, Ernie Els, Zach Johnson, and Tommy Armour.

	Annual Growth	12/03	12/04	12/05	12/06	12/07
Est. sales ($ mil.)	—	—	—	—	—	481.3
Employees	—	—	—	—	—	4,600

ACUSPHERE, INC.

NASDAQ (GM): ACUS

500 Arsenal St.
Watertown, MA 02472
Phone: 617-648-8800
Fax: 617-926-4750
Web: www.acusphere.com

CEO: Sherri C. Oberg
CFO: Frederick W. Ahlholm
HR: –
FYE: December 31
Type: Public

Acusphere micromanages its products, but then how else would you handle microparticles? Using proprietary technology, Acusphere creates porous microparticles smaller than red blood cells to develop cardiovascular drugs for the detection of coronary artery disease. Its lead injectable candidate, Imagify, is in clinical trials. The company has granted the European development and marketing rights for Imagify to Nycomed Danmark ApS. It intends to seek a similar marketing partnership in the US. Additional candidates in Acusphere's pipeline include two separate drug delivery systems designed to enhance the formulation of certain cancer drugs and improve the delivery of certain asthma treatments.

	Annual Growth	12/03	12/04	12/05	12/06	12/07
Sales ($ mil.)	16.7%	—	1.7	3.4	1.8	2.7
Net income ($ mil.)	—	—	(30.0)	(44.6)	(61.1)	(53.7)
Market value ($ mil.)	(34.9%)	—	109.2	122.1	92.9	30.1
Employees	—	—	—	110	—	—

⊞ ACXIOM CORPORATION

NASDAQ (GS): ACXM

1 Information Way, Ste. 200
Little Rock, AR 72202
Phone: 501-342-1000
Fax: 501-342-3913
Web: www.acxiom.com

CEO: John A. Meyer
CFO: Christopher W. (Chris) Wolf
HR: Cindy K. Childers
FYE: March 31
Type: Public

Acxiom will help you make sense of customer information. Acxiom is one of the world's leading providers of data and software used for direct marketing and customer relationship management (CRM). It collects and maintains a storehouse of consumer information covering nearly every household in the US and real estate records on more than 90 million properties that it offers to clients needing addresses, telephone numbers, and demographics for their direct mail and telemarketing efforts. Its CRM applications help companies manage customer data and can integrate that information into marketing systems. In 2007, Acxiom agreed to be taken private by two prominent investment firms, but the deal fell through.

	Annual Growth	3/04	3/05	3/06	3/07	3/08
Sales ($ mil.)	8.2%	1,010.8	1,223.0	1,332.6	1,395.1	1,384.1
Net income ($ mil.)	—	58.3	69.7	64.1	70.7	(7.8)
Market value ($ mil.)	(16.5%)	1,887.2	1,992.8	2,274.7	1,723.7	917.6
Employees	0.1%	—	6,600	6,765	7,100	6,610

ACXIOM DIGITAL

177 Bovet Rd.
San Mateo, CA 94402
Phone: 650-356-3400
Fax: 650-356-3410
Web: www.acxiomdigital.com

CEO: Kevin H. Johnson
CFO: Joelle Werich
HR: –
FYE: March 31
Type: Subsidiary

Acxiom Digital (formerly Digital Impact) leaves a big impression on Web surfers. As a business segment of Acxiom Corporation, the company provides the tools and services that clients need to create and manage online marketing campaigns using e-mail, search engines, targeted Web sites, and banner ads. It offers consulting, media buying, campaign management, and hosting of its IMPACT direct marketing application. IMPACT allows clients such as Marriott, Gap, and Hewlett-Packard to plan, manage, and analyze their own campaigns. Acxiom Digital owns offices in San Mateo, California; New York City; and London.

ADAC AUTOMOTIVE INC.

5920 Tahoe Dr.
Grand Rapids, MI 49546
Phone: 616-957-0311
Fax: 616-974-0582
Web: www.adacplastics.com

CEO: Ken Hungerford
CFO: Thomas Kowieski
HR: –
FYE: December 31
Type: Private

ADAC Automotive, formerly ADAC Plastics, has got a handle on what automakers need. The company supplies automakers worldwide with interior and exterior door handles and components, exterior trim, and marker lighting. Other products include cowl vent grilles and fuel filler doors. Its ADAC Technologies is a leading supplier of plastic moldings, subassemblies, and decorative finishes. Services provided by ADAC Automotive include design, molding, painting, and assembly. in 2006 the company joined with STRATTEC SECURITY and Witte-Velbert to form Vehicle Access Systems Technology (VAST), a marketing alliance.

	Annual Growth	12/03	12/04	12/05	12/06	12/07
Est. sales ($ mil.)	—	—	—	—	—	177.2
Employees	—	—	—	—	—	900

⊞ An in-depth profile of this company is available to Hoover's Online members at hoovers.com.

53

ADA-ES, INC.

NASDAQ (CM): ADES

8100 SouthPark Way, Unit B
Littleton, CO 80120
Phone: 303-734-1727
Fax: 303-734-0330
Web: www.adaes.com

CEO: Michael D. (Mike) Durham
CFO: Mark H. McKinnies
HR: Beth Turner-Graziano
FYE: December 31
Type: Public

ADA-ES is trying to make "clean coal" more than just a marketing term. The company, which was spun off from Earth Sciences in 2003, makes environmental technology systems and specialty chemicals that reduce emissions at coal-burning power plants. It offers integrated mercury control systems, as well as flue gas conditioning and combustion aid chemicals. ADA-ES also provides consulting and testing services and mercury measurement equipment. In 2006 ADA-ES set up a joint venture with NexGen Refined Coal to market proprietary coal technology that reduces emissions of nitrogen oxides and mercury from some treated coals.

	Annual Growth	12/03	12/04	12/05	12/06	12/07
Sales ($ mil.)	34.5%	5.9	8.4	11.0	15.5	19.3
Net income ($ mil.)	(6.9%)	0.4	0.3	0.7	0.4	0.3
Market value ($ mil.)	14.0%	25.4	115.1	102.3	91.3	43.0
Employees	31.3%	—	—	32	42	—

A.D.A.M., INC.

NASDAQ (CM): ADAM

1600 RiverEdge Pkwy., Ste. 100
Atlanta, GA 30328
Phone: 770-980-0888
Fax: 770-955-3088
Web: www.adam.com

CEO: Kevin S. Noland
CFO: Mark B. Adams
HR: –
FYE: December 31
Type: Public

A.D.A.M. (formerly adam.com) has prescribed itself a healthy dose of information distribution. The firm provides interactive health and medical content and applications in media ranging from the Internet to newsletters and CD-ROMs. Consumers, as well as media and health care companies, use A.D.A.M.'s library, which features such content as 40,000 medical illustrations, color graphics, animation, 3D models, video content, and printed reference guides. It also offers 4,000 health reference articles. A.D.A.M. additionally provides a Web-based HR benefits management product, the Benergy Communications Platform, to employers, and offers educational software that teaches students gross anatomy and human physiology.

	Annual Growth	12/03	12/04	12/05	12/06	12/07
Sales ($ mil.)	37.1%	7.9	8.4	10.1	16.5	27.9
Net income ($ mil.)	59.7%	0.6	1.6	7.1	2.5	3.9
Market value ($ mil.)	52.4%	15.0	31.3	66.2	55.4	81.1
Employees	67.3%	—	—	40	108	112

ADAMS EXPRESS COMPANY

NYSE: ADX

7 St. Paul St., Ste. 1140
Baltimore, MD 21202
Phone: 410-752-5900
Fax: 410-659-0080
Web: www.adamsexpress.com

CEO: Douglas G. (Doug) Ober
CFO: Maureen A. Jones
HR: –
FYE: December 31
Type: Public

The Adams Express Company will be quick to tell you it administers a closed-end investment fund (a fund with a limited number of shares). The bulk of its portfolio is invested in such sectors as banking (Bank of America, Wachovia), health care (Johnson & Johnson, Wyeth), industrials (Emerson Electric, United Technologies), and consumer products (Procter & Gamble, Target); its largest non-affiliated holding is General Electric. Adams Express was founded in 1840 as a courier service for financial documents; it was one of a handful of closed-end funds to survive the Great Depression. It shares headquarters and most of its executives with fellow closed-end fund Petroleum & Resources.

	Annual Growth	12/03	12/04	12/05	12/06	12/07
Sales ($ mil.)	(22.5%)	257.3	140.6	77.8	185.1	92.6
Net income ($ mil.)	(25.5%)	252.3	135.3	44.9	178.5	77.8
Market value ($ mil.)	4.1%	1,053.4	1,130.1	1,080.6	1,204.4	1,237.9
Employees	—	—	—	—	—	—

ADAMS GOLF, INC.

OTC: ADGF

2801 East Plano Pkwy.
Plano, TX 75074
Phone: 972-673-9000
Fax: 972-398-8818
Web: www.adamsgolf.com

CEO: Oliver G. (Chip) Brewer III
CFO: Eric T. Logan
HR: Ann Neff
FYE: December 31
Type: Public

Like any golfer, Adams Golf believes the problem isn't in the swing, it's in the clubs. The company's Tight Lies fairway woods are designed to quickly lift a golf ball from any lie — even from bunkers, rough, or divots — and achieve longer distance. Adams Golf also sells drivers, wedges, and custom-fitted clubs. Sales to specialty retailers, mass merchants, pro shops, and sporting goods stores account for more than 80% of Adams' sales. In addition to endorsing its products, pro golfer Tom Watson assists in design and testing. Adams Golf was founded by chairman Barney Adams in 1987.

	Annual Growth	12/03	12/04	12/05	12/06	12/07
Sales ($ mil.)	16.8%	50.9	56.8	56.4	76.0	94.6
Net income ($ mil.)	47.2%	2.0	3.1	3.2	9.0	9.4
Market value ($ mil.)	(3.2%)	63.8	126.6	109.7	188.8	56.0
Employees	—	—	—	—	—	—

ADAM'S MARK HOTELS & RESORTS

11330 Olive Blvd.
St. Louis, MO 63141
Phone: 314-567-9000
Fax: 314-567-5485
Web: www.adamsmark.com

CEO: Fred S. Kummer
CFO: Michael Chan
HR: –
FYE: December 31
Type: Private

Adam's Mark Hotels & Resorts wants to leave its mark on the hotel industry. The company owns and operates a handful of hotel properties, including Adam's Mark Buffalo-Niagara and Adam's Mark Indianapolis. In 2008 former parent HBE Corporation, a medical construction company, sold the hotel chain to San Francisco hotel investment and advisory firm Chartes Lodging Group LLC for $18.6 million. Concurrent with the purchase, the new parent announced a $238 million renovation, rebranding, and repositioning plan for the acquired properties. Kokua Hospitality, a property management firm affiliated with Chartres Lodging, manages the Adam's Mark hotels.

ADAMS RESOURCES & ENERGY, INC.

AMEX: AE

4400 Post Oak Pkwy., Ste. 2700
Houston, TX 77027
Phone: 713-881-3600
Fax: 713-881-3491
Web: www.adamsresources.com

CEO: K. S. (Bud) Adams Jr.
CFO: Richard B. (Rick) Abshire
HR: –
FYE: December 31
Type: Public

Bud Adams may have moved his football team to Tennessee, but his Adams Resources & Energy remains a Houston oiler. Subsidiary Gulfmark Energy buys crude oil at the wellhead for transport to refiners and other customers, and the company's Ada Resources subsidiary markets refined petroleum products such as gasoline and diesel fuel. With exploration and production mainly in Texas and Louisiana, Adams Resources boasts proved reserves of 7.1 billion cu. ft. of natural gas and 297,000 barrels of oil. Chairman and CEO Adams, owner of the NFL's Tennessee Titans, controls 49.3% of the company.

	Annual Growth	12/03	12/04	12/05	12/06	12/07
Sales ($ mil.)	11.2%	1,721.9	2,069.8	2,364.8	2,246.6	2,636.2
Net income ($ mil.)	53.3%	3.1	8.6	17.6	10.5	17.1
Market value ($ mil.)	17.4%	57.1	74.4	96.3	127.0	108.4
Employees	(0.2%)	—	—	745	748	742

ADAMS RESPIRATORY THERAPEUTICS, INC.

4 Mill Ridge Ln., Mill Ridge Farm
Chester, NJ 07930
Phone: 908-879-1400
Fax: 908-879-9191
Web: www.adamslaboratories.com

CEO: Michael J. (Mike) Valentino
CFO: Rita M. O'Connor
HR: –
FYE: June 30
Type: Subsidiary

Adams Respiratory Therapeutics is responsible for more productive coughs. Formerly known as Adams Laboratories, the firm makes over-the-counter remedies for respiratory ailments. The drugmaker's best-selling Mucinex-branded products are extended-release expectorants based upon on guaifenesin to help the body rid itself of excess mucus. The Mucinex line of products now includes tablets, nasal sprays, and formulations for children. Its other products include time-released cough suppressants under the Delsym brand. Adams' products are sold at food, drug, and mass retail stores in the US. The company is a subsidiary of consumer products giant Reckitt Benckiser.

	Annual Growth	6/03	6/04	6/05	6/06	6/07
Sales ($ mil.)	120.6%	14.0	61.3	160.2	239.1	331.6
Net income ($ mil.)	—	(22.6)	35.8	27.0	46.3	30.5
Employees	62.2%	—	—	176	209	463

ADAPTEC, INC.

NASDAQ (GM): ADPT

691 S. Milpitas Blvd.
Milpitas, CA 95035
Phone: 408-945-8600
Fax: 408-262-2533
Web: www.adaptec.com

CEO: Subramanian (Sundi) Sundaresh
CFO: Mary Dotz
HR: Shirley Olerich
FYE: March 31
Type: Public

Connection is in the cards for Adaptec. The company's adapters and controllers connect computers to storage devices and speed data transfer. In addition to its RAID controllers and host bus adapters (HBAs), Adaptec provides network-attached storage (NAS) systems and storage management software. Adaptec sells directly and through resellers and distributors to OEMs, retailers, and system integrators. Its products are sold under its own brand and the brands of its OEM customers. Adaptec outsources the manufacturing of its products, primarily to Sanmina-SCI.

	Annual Growth	3/04	3/05	3/06	3/07	3/08
Sales ($ mil.)	(22.0%)	452.9	475.0	310.1	255.2	167.4
Net income ($ mil.)	—	62.9	(145.1)	(148.4)	30.8	(9.6)
Market value ($ mil.)	(22.0%)	961.9	538.1	638.5	460.2	355.5
Employees	(37.4%)	—	1,525	1,128	598	—

ADC TELECOMMUNICATIONS, INC.

NASDAQ (GS): ADCT

13625 Technology Dr.
Eden Prairie, MN 55344
Phone: 952-938-8080
Fax: 952-917-1717
Web: www.adc.com

CEO: Robert E. (Bob) Switz
CFO: James G. (Jim) Mathews
HR: –
FYE: October 31
Type: Public

The transmission overhauls ADC Telecommunications performs don't leave grease stains on the driveway. The company provides broadband data access and infrastructure equipment. Its products — central office service platforms, broadband switches and routers, and wireless gear — are used to transmit voice and data signals and connect communications providers with their subscribers. ADC also provides network management software and integration services. The company caters to local, long-distance, and wireless telephone and cable TV providers; it also sells to distributors and other equipment makers. Customers include BellSouth, Ciena, Graybar Electric, and Time Warner Cable.

	Annual Growth	10/03	10/04	10/05	10/06	10/07
Sales ($ mil.)	14.4%	773.2	784.3	1,169.2	1,281.9	1,322.2
Net income ($ mil.)	—	(76.7)	16.4	110.7	65.7	106.3
Market value ($ mil.)	(37.6%)	14,510.7	12,532.2	2,032.9	1,677.1	2,199.1
Employees	5.1%	—	—	8,200	8,600	9,050

ADCARE HEALTH SYSTEMS, INC.

AMEX: ADK

5057 Troy Rd.
Springfield, OH 45502
Phone: 937-964-8974
Fax: 937-964-8961
Web: www.adcarehealth.com

CEO: Gary L. Wade
CFO: Scott Cunningham
HR: Jackie Potter
FYE: December 31
Type: Public

Retirement keeps AdCare Health Systems working. The company manages about 15 assisted living facilities, nursing homes, and independent retirement communities in Ohio with a total of 800 beds. It owns all or part of seven of its facilities, including the Hearth & Home assisted living facilities. Services include Alzheimer's and subacute care. AdCare also operates a home health care business, Assured Health Care, which offers nursing, therapy, and aide services, as well as administrative services for insurance coordination and caregiver hiring.

	Annual Growth	12/03	12/04	12/05	12/06	12/07
Sales ($ mil.)	9.5%	16.5	18.3	21.9	22.5	23.7
Net income ($ mil.)	—	0.0	0.2	(0.8)	(2.4)	(0.2)
Market value ($ mil.)	(71.4%)	—	—	—	10.6	3.0
Employees	—	—	850	—	—	—

ADDUS HEALTHCARE, INC.

2401 S. Plum Grove Rd.
Palatine, IL 60067
Phone: 847-303-5300
Fax: 847-303-5376
Web: www.addus.com

CEO: Mark S. Heaney
CFO: Dave Stasiewicz
HR: Paul Diamond
FYE: December 31
Type: Private

Having difficulties juggling caregiving with the rest of your life? Addus hopes you add them to your list of options. Addus Healthcare provides home health care and related services such as nursing, rehabilitation, disease management, and staffing. The company also offers adult day care (health, social, and support services), assisted care (short visits over short-term), long-term home care for the elderly, family services, and in-home support services (such as bathing, dressing, and cleaning). Addus serves about 40,000 patients each year at nearly 100 locations in 12 states. The company, founded in 1979, provides nurses; physical, occupational, and speech therapists; medical social workers; and home health aides.

	Annual Growth	12/03	12/04	12/05	12/06	12/07
Est. sales ($ mil.)	—	—	—	—	—	163.7
Employees	—	—	—	—	—	20,000

ADDVANTAGE TECHNOLOGIES GROUP, INC.

AMEX: AEY

1221 E. Houston St.
Broken Arrow, OK 74012
Phone: 918-251-9121
Fax: 918-268-7771
Web: www.addvantagetech.com

CEO: Kenneth A. (Ken) Chymiak
CFO: Daniel E. O'Keefe
HR: –
FYE: September 30
Type: Public

ADDvantage Technologies has used change to its advantage. The company took its present form in 1999, when it bought Oklahoma-based cable TV parts and services provider TULSAT in a deal that gave TULSAT's owners control over the company. ADDvantage sells new and remanufactured cable TV equipment and provides repair services to cable operators. Its products include headend equipment (satellite receivers, amplifiers, and antennas), fiber products (couplers, optical transmitters), and distribution gear (directional taps, line extenders). ADDvantage gets more than 90% of its sales in the US.

	Annual Growth	9/03	9/04	9/05	9/06	9/07
Sales ($ mil.)	18.5%	33.3	47.1	50.3	52.5	65.7
Net income ($ mil.)	13.2%	4.5	5.8	5.8	4.8	7.4
Market value ($ mil.)	21.6%	38.0	38.7	39.3	43.1	83.2
Employees	5.8%	—	141	159	167	167

An in-depth profile of this company is available to Hoover's Online members at hoovers.com.

55

ADEA, INC.

7701 Las Colinas Ridge, 3rd Fl.
Irving, TX 75063
Phone: 972-764-1700
Fax: 972-764-1701
Web: www.adea.com

CEO: Shouvik Bhattacharyya
CFO: Daniel G. (Dan) Cross
HR: Karen George
FYE: December 31
Type: Private

Adea has an idea or two about how to optimize your business operations. The company offers information technology and consulting services, including systems integration, applications development, and project management. Adea's SAP Services unit specializes in software customization, support, and systems design and integration related to products made by leading global enterprise software developer SAP. Other services include network design, legacy migration, and business process optimization. The company's clients come from such fields as health care, retail, telecommunications, and the federal government. Top customers have included the US Department of Agriculture. Adea was founded in 1996.

	Annual Growth	12/03	12/04	12/05	12/06	12/07
Est. sales ($ mil.)	—	—	—	—	—	41.6
Employees	—	—	—	—	—	700

ADEPT TECHNOLOGY, INC.

NASDAQ (GM): ADEP

3011 Triad Dr.
Livermore, CA 94551
Phone: 925-245-3400
Fax: 925-960-0452
Web: www.adept.com

CEO: Robert H. Bucher
CFO: Lisa M. Cummins
HR: Laurie Hioki
FYE: June 30
Type: Public

Adept Technology makes "intelligent automation hardware," or, for the sci-fi fan in all of us: robots. Its robots are designed to handle, assemble, and package products in the electronics, food processing, automotive component, and pharmaceutical industries. Adept Technology's robots replicate the movements of human shoulders, elbows, and wrists. The company also sells the software that runs its robots; the V+ programming language allows operators to control robots from a PC. Adept Technology's customers include Boeing, Corning, Ford, Honeywell, IBM, Nokia, Procter & Gamble, Seagate, and Xerox. Investors Austin Marxe and David Greenhouse control nearly 40% of the company.

	Annual Growth	6/03	6/04	6/05	6/06	6/07
Sales ($ mil.)	2.1%	44.8	49.1	50.5	57.6	48.7
Net income ($ mil.)	—	(29.0)	(7.3)	1.3	0.5	(11.5)
Market value ($ mil.)	10.2%	34.0	173.5	50.0	107.7	50.1
Employees	(2.8%)	—	179	174	—	—

ADERANT HOLDINGS, INC.

3525 Piedmont Rd., Bldg. 6, Ste. 620
Atlanta, GA 30305
Phone: 404-720-3600
Fax: 404-720-3601
Web: www.aderant.com

CEO: Michael E. (Mike) Kohlsdorf
CFO: Roger Maloch
HR: –
FYE: December 31
Type: Private

Does your company live to serve? ADERANT Holdings provides software and services for professional services firms, especially in the fields of accounting, consulting, and law. The company's services software suite includes applications for managing time and billing, business analytics, staffing, pricing, and other front- and back-office functions. Products include Executive Office for profitability analysis and other strategic decision support; CMS.Net for Web-based financial and practice management; and Novient for resources management. ADERANT counts Accenture, Computacenter, Ernst & Young, Mayer, Brown, Rowe & Maw, PKF International, and Winston & Strawn among its clients.

	Annual Growth	12/03	12/04	12/05	12/06	12/07
Est. sales ($ mil.)	—	—	—	—	—	20.4
Employees	—	—	—	—	—	260

ADESA, INC.

13085 Hamilton Crossing Blvd.
Carmel, IN 46032
Phone: 317-815-1100
Fax: 317-249-4651
Web: www.adesa.com

CEO: James P. (Jim) Hallett
CFO: Paul Lips
HR: –
FYE: December 31
Type: Subsidiary

ADESA (Auto Dealers Exchange Services of America) doesn't sell cars, it sells fleets of cars to dealers. The company offers used- and salvage-vehicle redistribution services to automakers, lessors, and dealers in the US, Canada, and Mexico. ADESA operates about 60 used-vehicle auctions and more than 40 salvage auctions; it also offers such ancillary services as logistics, inspections, evaluation, titling, and settlement administration. The company collects fees from buyers and sellers on each auction and from its extra services. Its AFC (Automotive Finance Corporation) unit offers dealer floorplan financing services. In mid-2007, ADESA was acquired by an investment group for $3.7 billion.

	Annual Growth	12/02	12/03	12/04	12/05	12/06
Sales ($ mil.)	7.3%	832.4	911.9	931.6	968.8	1,103.9
Net income ($ mil.)	9.4%	88.3	115.1	105.3	125.5	126.3
Employees	6.9%	—	—	10,418	10,740	11,915

ADEXA INC.

5933 W. Century Blvd., 12th Fl.
Los Angeles, CA 90045
Phone: 310-642-2100
Fax: 310-338-9878
Web: www.adexa.com

CEO: K. Cyrus Hadavi
CFO: Mario A. DiSandro
HR: –
FYE: January 31
Type: Private

Adexa wants to help manufacturers become more adept at planning. The company's Enterprise Global Planning System (eGPS) software includes applications designed to help manufacturers manage a wide range of operations, including costs, factory scheduling, sales, inventory and materials management, and supply chain planning. The integrated application suite also includes tools for managing product information and collaborating with suppliers, distributors, and customers. Adexa targets clients in the semiconductor, aerospace, soft goods, industrial, automotive, electronics, chemicals, and consumer packaged goods industries; its customers include Advanced Micro Devices, Boeing, General Motors, and Samsung.

	Annual Growth	12/01	*1/03	1/04	1/05	1/06
Sales ($ mil.)	(16.6%)	41.0	30.0	24.0	20.6	19.8
Employees	(24.4%)	337	200	150	133	110
						*Fiscal year change

ADHEREX TECHNOLOGIES INC.

AMEX: ADH

4620 Creekstone Dr., Ste. 200
Durham, NC 27703
Phone: 919-484-8484
Fax: 919-484-8001
Web: www.adherex.com

CEO: William P. (Bill) Peters
CFO: James A. (Jim) Klein Jr.
HR: –
FYE: December 31
Type: Public

Working nimbly with a very sticky subject, Adherex Technologies researches and develops cancer treatments. Its lead drug candidate, Exherin, targets a tumor's blood supply and makes those blood vessels weak and leaky by disrupting a key protein. Other drug candidates could help prevent hearing loss in children undergoing certain types of chemotherapy; make cancer cells more vulnerable to anti-cancer drugs; and prevent thrombocytopenia, the loss of blood platelets during chemotherapy. Adherex Technologies' pipeline is strongly based on compounds that disrupt cadherins, proteins that adhere like molecules together in cell adhesion. Southpoint Capital Advisors control more than 42% of the company.

	Annual Growth	6/03	*12/04	12/05	12/06	12/07
Sales ($ mil.)	—	0.0	0.0	0.0	0.0	0.0
Net income ($ mil.)	—	(6.1)	(6.9)	(13.9)	(16.4)	(13.4)
Employees	(10.8%)	30	23	29	25	19
						*Fiscal year change

An in-depth profile of this company is available to Hoover's Online members at hoovers.com.

ADIR INTERNATIONAL EXPORT LTD INC

1605 W. Olympic Blvd.
Los Angeles, CA 90015
Phone: 213-386-4412
Fax: 213-386-2601
Web: www.lacuracao.com

CEO: Ron Azarkman
CFO: –
HR: –
FYE: December 31
Type: Private

Adir International Export Ltd. (dba La Curacao) operates half a dozen La Curacao department stores in downtown Los Angeles and Orange County, California, that cater to Hispanics. The stores sell consumer electronics as well as appliances, furniture, books, music, and other merchandise, which it will ship to Mexico or Central America. La Curacao sells most of its merchandise on credit to some 400,000 customers who carry the La Curacao credit card. It also operates a travel agency, and offers Internet and long-distance calling services. The company was founded by a pair of Israeli brothers, CEO Ron and Jerry Azarkman, who also own the franchise for Pollo Campero, the popular Guatemalan fried-chicken restaurants.

	Annual Growth	12/03	12/04	12/05	12/06	12/07
Est. sales ($ mil.)	—	—	—	—	—	84.6
Employees	—	—	—	—	—	1,300

ADM TRONICS UNLIMITED, INC.

OTC: ADMT

224-S Pegasus Ave.
Northvale, NJ 07647
Phone: 201-767-6040
Fax: 201-784-0620
Web: www.admtronics.com

CEO: Andre' A. DiMino
CFO: Andre' A. DiMino
HR: –
FYE: March 31
Type: Public

ADM Tronics has had its own Industrial Revolution. While the company previously focused on the making of medical devices, ADM has shifted its main focus to water-based chemical products for industrial use. These products include coatings, resins, primers, and additives, primarily for the printing and packaging industries. The firm licenses many of its medical products, which include the Sonotron line of devices (used to treat osteoarthritis and inflammatory joint ailments with radio waves). Its Pros-Aide unit makes adhesives used in professional makeup products. ADM spun off Ivivi Technologies in 2006, though it still owns a third of the company. The founding DiMino family owns more than half of ADM Tronics.

	Annual Growth	3/04	3/05	3/06	3/07	3/08
Sales ($ mil.)	12.2%	1.2	1.4	1.7	1.5	1.9
Net income ($ mil.)	—	(0.1)	(3.1)	(7.2)	(8.2)	(2.9)
Market value ($ mil.)	(17.0%)	18.2	21.6	14.5	12.9	8.6
Employees	—	—	—	—	23	—

ADMINISTAFF, INC.

NYSE: ASF

19001 Crescent Springs Dr.
Kingwood, TX 77339
Phone: 281-358-8986
Fax: 281-348-3718
Web: www.administaff.com

CEO: Paul J. Sarvadi
CFO: Douglas S. (Doug) Sharp
HR: Betty L. Collins
FYE: December 31
Type: Public

Administaff handles the payroll so you don't have to. The company is one of the leading professional employer organizations (PEOs) in the US, providing small and midsized companies such services as payroll and benefits administration, workers' compensation programs, personnel records management, and employee recruiting. As a PEO, it is a co-employer of its clients' workers. Administaff also offers Web-based services through its Employee Service Center and operates a business-to-business e-commerce site. Most of its client companies are engaged in the business, financial, and computer services industries.

	Annual Growth	12/03	12/04	12/05	12/06	12/07
Sales ($ mil.)	15.2%	891.7	969.5	1,169.6	1,389.5	1,570.0
Net income ($ mil.)	38.5%	12.9	19.2	30.0	46.5	47.5
Market value ($ mil.)	12.4%	464.4	321.3	1,147.6	1,183.1	741.4
Employees	14.9%	—	—	88,780	104,325	117,301

ADOBE SYSTEMS INCORPORATED

NASDAQ (GS): ADBE

345 Park Ave.
San Jose, CA 95110
Phone: 408-536-6000
Fax: 408-537-6000
Web: www.adobe.com

CEO: Shantanu Narayen
CFO: Mark S. Garrett
HR: Donna Morris
FYE: Friday nearest November 30
Type: Public

Adobe Systems' role as a leading desktop publishing software provider is well documented. The company offers the ubiquitous Acrobat Reader (distributed free of charge), a tool that displays portable document format (PDF) files on the Internet. The company's Web and print publishing products include Photoshop, Illustrator, and PageMaker. Adobe's offerings also include print technology geared toward manufacturers, as well as Web design (GoLive) and electronic book publishing software. Its InDesign publishing package provides professional layout and design applications. Adobe's Professional Services group offers implementation, training, and support.

	Annual Growth	11/03	11/04	11/05	11/06	11/07
Sales ($ mil.)	25.0%	1,294.8	1,666.6	1,966.3	2,575.3	3,157.9
Net income ($ mil.)	28.4%	266.3	450.4	602.8	505.8	723.8
Market value ($ mil.)	48.7%	4,922.1	9,310.7	20,685.7	23,642.8	24,079.2
Employees	10.2%	—	—	5,734	6,082	6,959

ADOLOR CORPORATION

NASDAQ (GM): ADLR

700 Pennsylvania Dr.
Exton, PA 19341
Phone: 484-595-1500
Fax: 484-595-1520
Web: www.adolor.com

CEO: Michael R. Dougherty
CFO: Thomas P. (Tom) Hess
HR: Denise Kerton
FYE: December 31
Type: Public

If you haven't got time for the pain, or the side effects brought on by painkillers, Adolor might be able to help. In keeping with the movement toward improved pain management (including the increased use of opioids like hydrocodone), the company is developing drugs that alleviate the side effects of some pain treatments. Adolor won FDA approval in 2008 for Entereg as a treatment for post-operative ileus, or bowel dysfunction in patients following bowel resection surgery; the condition is associated with the use of opioids used to treat post-operative pain. The company partnered with GlaxoSmithKline on the development of Entereg.

	Annual Growth	12/03	12/04	12/05	12/06	12/07
Sales ($ mil.)	(18.6%)	20.7	25.5	15.7	15.1	9.1
Net income ($ mil.)	—	(51.2)	(43.6)	(56.8)	(69.7)	(48.4)
Market value ($ mil.)	(27.7%)	775.5	387.7	571.0	345.9	211.7
Employees	—	—	—	179	—	—

ADRIAN STEEL COMPANY

906 James St.
Adrian, MI 49221
Phone: 517-265-6194
Fax: –
Web: www.adriansteel.com

CEO: David (Dave) Pilmore
CFO: Joseph E. Emens
HR: Susan Grof
FYE: September 30
Type: Private

A cluttered work truck is a business opportunity for Adrian Steel. The company makes cargo management products for service trucks and vans such as bins, drawers, files, ladder racks, shelving units, and tool boxes. Chrysler, Ford, and General Motors have offered programs in which they subsidize purchases and installation of Adrian Steel products for buyers of new trucks and vans. The company's products are also sold through more than 300 independent distributors throughout the US and Canada. Adrian Steel was founded in 1953 by Bob Westfall, a former All-Pro football player with the Detroit Lions and the father of company president Harley Westfall.

	Annual Growth	9/03	9/04	9/05	9/06	9/07
Est. sales ($ mil.)	—	—	—	—	—	196.1
Employees	—	—	—	—	—	390

An in-depth profile of this company is available to Hoover's Online members at hoovers.com.

57

ADS MEDIA GROUP, INC.

OTC: AMGU

12758 Cimarron Path, Ste. B-128
San Antonio, TX 78249
Phone: 210-655-6613
Fax: 210-655-6269
Web: www.adsmediagroup.com

CEO: Clark R. (Dub) Doyal
CFO: Michael Wofford
HR: —
FYE: December 31
Type: Public

ADS Media Group through its Alternative Delivery Solutions subsidiary specializes in direct marketing for businesses in the US, Canada, Mexico, and Puerto Rico. The company focuses on door-to-door delivery of promotional products to homes, apartments, and businesses in North America. ADS can target its marketing efforts down to the neighborhood level, delivering materials to households based on specific demographic information. One key branded product includes its La Canasta de Valores campaign, a door-delivered package containing advertising inserts and promotional material geared towards the Hispanic consumer. The company was founded in 2001.

	Annual Growth	12/03	12/04	12/05	12/06	12/07
Sales ($ mil.)	14.2%	2.0	3.7	5.5	4.8	3.4
Net income ($ mil.)	—	(1.7)	0.0	0.3	0.0	(2.2)
Market value ($ mil.)	(43.7%)	21.7	4.7	2.4	7.6	2.2
Employees	—	—	—	—	—	—

ADSTAR, INC.

Pink Sheets: ADST

4553 Glencoe Ave., Ste. 300
Marina del Rey, CA 90292
Phone: 310-577-8255
Fax: 310-577-8266
Web: www.adstar.com

CEO: Leslie Bernhard
CFO: James Linesch
HR: —
FYE: December 31
Type: Public

Adstar deals with matters that are strictly classified. More than 25 newspapers use Adstar's technology, which enables advertisers to compose, format, schedule, and submit classified ads electronically. After a brief stint running a Web portal selling classified ad space, Adstar is back to providing the software and services that allow clients to buy and sell print classified ads online. Through subsidiary Edgil Associates, Adstar markets and sells its EdgCapture credit card payment processing software, which processes more than 12 million transactions for the publishing sector each year.

	Annual Growth	12/03	12/04	12/05	12/06	12/07
Sales ($ mil.)	14.4%	2.8	4.9	5.2	5.1	4.8
Net income ($ mil.)	—	(2.8)	(3.7)	(1.1)	(1.4)	(3.3)
Market value ($ mil.)	—	—	—	—	—	7.7
Employees	(11.6%)	—	—	32	—	25

ADT WORLDWIDE

1 Town Center Rd.
Boca Raton, FL 33486
Phone: 561-988-3600
Fax: 561-988-3673
Web: www.tyco.com

CEO: Naren K. Gursahaney
CFO: —
HR: Rich Lovely
FYE: September 30
Type: Subsidiary

ADT Worldwide, formerly Tyco Fire & Security, provides fire protection and electronic security systems and services to more than 5 million residential customers worldwide, as well as millions of additional commercial and industrial clients. A division of Tyco International, the company operates through subsidiaries such as ADT Security Services and SimplexGrinnell in North America, and Tyco Fire and Integrated Services in Europe. In 2007 parent company Tyco split its operations into three companies. Tyco Fire & Security became ADT Worldwide, remaining under the control of Tyco International.

ADTRAN, INC.

NASDAQ (GS): ADTN

901 Explorer Blvd.
Huntsville, AL 35806
Phone: 256-963-8000
Fax: 256-963-8030
Web: www.adtran.com

CEO: Thomas R. Stanton
CFO: James E. (Jim) Matthews
HR: —
FYE: December 31
Type: Public

ADTRAN turns copper into gold. The company offers more than 1,600 network access products and systems used to enable Internet access, telephony, data transport, and video over all kinds of voice and data networks, from traditional copper wire to optical. ADTRAN sells its switches, routers, and multiplexing systems to wireline and wireless carriers and service providers, such as Verizon, AT&T, and Sprint. It also markets to the enterprise sector. The company sells directly and through a network of distributors that includes Ingram Micro and Tech Data.

	Annual Growth	12/03	12/04	12/05	12/06	12/07
Sales ($ mil.)	4.7%	396.7	454.5	513.2	472.7	476.8
Net income ($ mil.)	5.5%	61.5	75.1	101.2	78.3	76.3
Market value ($ mil.)	(13.4%)	2,466.0	1,524.5	2,366.5	1,577.0	1,387.8
Employees	(0.5%)	—	—	1,628	1,601	1,611

ADVANCE AMERICA, CASH ADVANCE CENTERS, INC.

NYSE: AEA

135 N. Church St.
Spartanburg, SC 29306
Phone: 864-342-5600
Fax: 864-342-5612
Web: www.advanceamerica.net

CEO: Kenneth E. (Ken) Compton
CFO: J. Patrick O'Shaughnessy
HR: —
FYE: December 31
Type: Public

Money problems? Don't jump from the bridge. Instead, just bridge your short-term cash crunch with Advance America, Cash Advance Centers. Advance America is one of the nation's leading payday advance firms. To cover unexpected expenses, customers visit one of the lender's 2,800 locations in 35 states, show two forms of ID, bank statement, paycheck stub, and personal check, and the company loans them $100 or more until payday. Advance America also offers money orders and money transfer services. In an industry criticized for preying upon the vulnerable, using strong-arm collection tactics, and slamming borrowers with outrageous rates, Advance America charges $15 for a $100 loan and uses a soft collections touch.

	Annual Growth	12/03	12/04	12/05	12/06	12/07
Assets ($ mil.)	7.9%	348.0	397.5	436.4	525.1	471.7
Net income ($ mil.)	(13.3%)	96.2	83.1	63.0	70.2	54.4
Market value ($ mil.)	(27.2%)	—	1,922.6	1,019.5	1,165.2	741.1
Employees	3.8%	—	—	6,500	7,000	7,000

ADVANCE AUTO PARTS, INC.

NYSE: AAP

5008 Airport Rd.
Roanoke, VA 24012
Phone: 540-362-4911
Fax: 540-561-1448
Web: www.advanceautoparts.com

CEO: Darren R. Jackson
CFO: Michael (Mike) Norona
HR: Keith A. Oreson
FYE: Saturday nearest December 31
Type: Public

Advance Auto Parts has turned auto parts retailing into less of a one-company race. The company is now the #2 chain (AutoZone is #1) after its 1998 acquisition of Sears, Roebuck's Western Auto Supply and its 2001 purchase of Discount Auto Parts. Advance Auto Parts operates more than 3,100 stores under the Advance Auto Parts and Discount Auto Parts names in about 40 states; the company's stores operate under the Western Auto and Advance Auto Parts names in Puerto Rico and the Virgin Islands. Sales to commercial customers including garages, service stations, and auto dealers account for about 25% of revenues. The company is also a partner in online auto parts seller PartsAmerica.com.

	Annual Growth	12/03	12/04	12/05	12/06	12/07
Sales ($ mil.)	8.5%	3,493.7	3,770.3	4,265.0	4,616.5	4,844.4
Net income ($ mil.)	17.5%	124.9	188.0	234.7	231.3	238.3
Market value ($ mil.)	17.2%	2,005.2	2,103.8	4,702.3	3,746.3	3,781.1
Employees	1.9%	—	—	42,427	43,772	44,065

ADVANCE DISPLAY TECHNOLOGIES, INC. OTC: ADTI

7334 S. Alton Way, Ste. F CEO: Matthew W. (Matt) Shankle
Centennial, CO 80112 CFO: Matthew W. (Matt) Shankle
Phone: 303-267-0111 HR: –
Fax: 303-267-0330 FYE: June 30
Web: www.advancedisplaytechnologies.com Type: Public

Advance Display Technologies (ADT) develops large-screen fiber-optic video displays. The company plans to license or sell its intellectual property assets. After a brief foray into theater operations, ADT is looking to raise capital and restructure its debt in order to continue development of its displays. It has also acquired the rights to LED technologies that are patented and have patents pending. These LED display technologies are trademarked as PMV and UltraNet. The company's auditor has issued a "going-concern" warning about ADT's ability to continue operations. Including convertible notes and preferred stock, director Lawrence DeGeorge owns about 68% of ADT.

	Annual Growth	6/03	6/04	6/05	6/06	6/07
Sales ($ mil.)	—	0.0	0.1	0.1	0.1	0.0
Net income ($ mil.)	—	(0.9)	(0.6)	(0.8)	(1.2)	(2.1)
Market value ($ mil.)	0.0%	—	—	—	3.7	3.7
Employees	25.0%	—	—	4	5	—

ADVANCE FOOD COMPANY, INC.

301 W. Broadway CEO: Greg Allen
Enid, OK 73701 CFO: Frank Merritt
Phone: 580-237-6656 HR: Brian Hayden
Fax: 580-213-4707 FYE: December 31
Web: www.advf.com Type: Private

Advance Food Company helps restaurants and cafeterias prepare their food in advance. The company manufactures more than 2,000 portion-controlled and processed beef, pork, poultry, lamb, and veal products for foodservice customers in the restaurant industry. Its other clients include convenience stores, health care facilities, and the US military, along with colleges, universities, and schools. Its brands include Steak-EZE Philly steaks and Shorty's chili and taco meats. Advance Food operates eight manufacturing facilities in five states as well as a nationwide distribution network. Internationally, its products are available in Canada, Mexico, French Polynesia, Germany, Japan, Central America, and the Caribbean.

ADVANCE PUBLICATIONS, INC.

950 Fingerboard Rd. CEO: Samuel I. (Si) Newhouse Jr.
Staten Island, NY 10305 CFO: –
Phone: 212-286-2860 HR: –
Fax: 718-981-1456 FYE: December 31
Web: www.advance.net Type: Private

Advance Publications gets its marching orders from the printed page. A leading US newspaper publisher, Advance owns daily newspapers in some 20 cities around the country, including *The Star-Ledger* (New Jersey), *The Cleveland Plain Dealer*, and its namesake *Staten Island Advance*. It also owns American City Business Journals (more than 40 weekly papers) and Parade Publications (*Parade Magazine* Sunday insert). The company is a top magazine publisher through its Condé Nast unit. Aside from print publishing, Advance is a major online publisher through its Advance Internet network of local news sites; Advance additionally owns television assets. Samuel "Si" Newhouse Jr. and his brother, Donald, own the company.

	Annual Growth	12/02	12/03	12/04	12/05	12/06
Est. sales ($ mil.)	5.3%	—	—	—	7,315.0	7,700.0
Employees	(6.7%)	—	—	—	30,000	28,000

ADVANCED ACCESSORY HOLDINGS CORPORATION

12900 Hall Rd., Ste. 200 CEO: Alan C. Johnson
Sterling Heights, MI 48313 CFO: Clifford Suing
Phone: 586-997-2900 HR: –
Fax: 586-997-6868 FYE: December 31
Web: www.advancedaccessorysystems.com Type: Private

Advanced Accessory Holdings knows there's no better way to rack up the cash than by hitching your wagon to the likes of GM, Ford, and Chrysler LLC. Through its subsidiaries, Advanced Accessory Holdings makes rack systems for many of the world's automakers. The company's line of rack systems includes fixed and detachable racks designed for carrying items such as bikes, canoes, luggage, and skis. Other products include roof rack lighting systems, bed cleats and other pickup bed cargo management systems, running boards, and air dams. Private equity firm Castle Harlan controls the company.

ADVANCED ANALOGIC TECHNOLOGIES NASDAQ (GS): AATI

830 E. Arques Ave. CEO: Richard K. Williams
Sunnyvale, CA 94085 CFO: Brian R. McDonald
Phone: 408-737-4600 HR: –
Fax: 408-737-4611 FYE: December 31
Web: www.analogictech.com Type: Public

Advanced Analogic Technologies Incorporated tries to take an advanced approach to analog chip technology. The company, known as AnalogicTech, provides specialized power management semiconductors for use in a variety of computing, communications, and consumer electronics applications. AnalogicTech's chips go into digital audio players, digital still cameras, notebook and tablet computers, and wireless handsets. The company's investors include Samsung Electronics. Another Korean company, LG Electronics, accounts for 20% of sales; Samsung, 11%. AnalogicTech gets most of its revenues from Asian customers.

	Annual Growth	12/03	12/04	12/05	12/06	12/07
Sales ($ mil.)	42.6%	26.5	51.3	68.3	81.2	109.6
Net income ($ mil.)	20.5%	0.9	15.2	2.1	(2.1)	1.9
Market value ($ mil.)	(7.5%)	—	—	597.8	237.5	511.6
Employees	17.3%	—	183	200	252	295

ADVANCED BIONICS CORPORATION

12740 San Fernando Rd. CEO: Alfred E. (Al) Mann
Sylmar, CA 91342 CFO: Russ Ramanayake
Phone: 661-362-1400 HR: –
Fax: 661-362-1500 FYE: December 31
Web: www.advancedbionics.com Type: Subsidiary

Steve Austin, television's Six Million Dollar Man, isn't working at Advanced Bionics. The company has the technology not to make a person "better, faster, and stronger" but instead to help people with severe to profound hearing loss to hear. Advanced Bionics makes the HiResolution Bionic Ear System, which includes a cochlear implant, sound processor, and other equipment that together can restore hearing to the deaf. Boston Scientific bought Advanced Bionics in 2004, but the two companies parted ways in 2008. Boston Scientific retained the former pain management operations of Advanced Bionics.

	Annual Growth	12/03	12/04	12/05	12/06	12/07
Est. sales ($ mil.)	—	—	—	—	—	38.1
Employees	—	—	—	—	—	500

ADVANCED CELL TECHNOLOGY, INC.

OTC: ACTC

1201 Harbor Bay Pkwy., Ste. 120
Alameda, CA 94502
Phone: 510-748-4900
Fax: 510-748-4950
Web: www.advancedcell.com

CEO: William M. (Bill) Caldwell IV
CFO: –
HR: –
FYE: December 31
Type: Public

No need to choose between embryonic and adult stem cells — Advanced Cell Technology (ACT) works with both to develop possible means to regenerate human tissue. The company has an assortment of patented means of creating new human stem cells from either embryos or adult stem cells. It hopes to find applications of its regenerative cell methods to address acute, chronic, and degenerative diseases, as well as regenerative conditions (e.g., trauma, infarction, burns). ACT is conducting research at both the pre-clinical and clinical trial levels. Its research with adult stem cells is focused on restoring cardiac function in patients with advanced heart disease.

	Annual Growth	12/03	12/04	12/05	12/06	12/07
Sales ($ mil.)	—	0.0	0.0	0.4	0.4	0.6
Net income ($ mil.)	—	0.0	(0.1)	(9.4)	(18.7)	(15.9)
Employees	—	—	—	—	—	—

ADVANCED DRAINAGE SYSTEMS, INC.

4640 Trueman Blvd.
Hilliard, OH 43026
Phone: 614-658-0050
Fax: 614-658-0204
Web: www.ads-pipe.com

CEO: Joseph A. (Joe) Chlapaty
CFO: Mark B. Sturgeon
HR: Paul Cash
FYE: December 31
Type: Private

Advanced Drainage Systems' work isn't down the drain, it *is* the drain. The company manufactures high density polyethylene (HDPE) pipes for use in drainage systems for residential and commercial construction projects. Advanced Drainage Systems' plastic products include culverts, drains, fittings, gaskets, grates, screens, leaching chambers, and storm sewers. Customers include mining and timber operations and companies specializing in construction of highways and waste management systems. Advanced Drainage Systems products are also found under some of the more fabled athletic fields and complexes in the US, such as Augusta National, Dodger Stadium, and Lambeau Field.

	Annual Growth	12/02	12/03	12/04	12/05	12/06
Sales ($ mil.)	0.0%	—	—	—	1,200.0	1,200.0
Employees	2.6%	—	—	—	3,800	3,900

ADVANCED ENERGY INDUSTRIES, INC.

NASDAQ (GM): AEIS

1625 Sharp Point Dr.
Fort Collins, CO 80525
Phone: 970-221-0108
Fax: 970-407-6550
Web: www.advanced-energy.com

CEO: Douglas S. (Doug) Schatz
CFO: Lawrence D. (Larry) Firestone
HR: –
FYE: December 31
Type: Public

Advanced Energy Industries (AE) advances ordinary electrical power to the head of the high-tech class. The company's power conversion and control products transform raw electricity, making it uniform enough to ensure consistent production in high-precision manufacturing. Top clients include semiconductor equipment makers Applied Materials (29% of sales), Axcelis, Lam Research, Novellus, and ULVAC. AE's gear also is used in the production of data storage devices (including hard disks, CD-ROMs, and DVDs) and flat-panel displays, and for a variety of industrial processes, such as applying coatings to windows, eyeglasses, and solar panels. The company gets more than half of its sales in the US.

	Annual Growth	12/03	12/04	12/05	12/06	12/07
Sales ($ mil.)	10.0%	262.4	395.3	325.5	410.7	384.7
Net income ($ mil.)	—	(44.2)	(12.8)	12.8	88.3	34.4
Market value ($ mil.)	(8.6%)	848.5	299.1	526.4	846.4	592.4
Employees	4.6%	1,347	1,651	1,527	1,583	1,611

ADVANCED ENVIRONMENTAL RECYCLING

NASDAQ (CM): AERT

914 N. Jefferson St.
Springdale, AR 72764
Phone: 479-756-7400
Fax: 479-756-7410
Web: www.aertinc.com

CEO: Joe G. Brooks
CFO: Eric E. Barnes
HR: –
FYE: December 31
Type: Public

It may not turn straw into gold, but Advanced Environmental Recycling Technologies, Inc. (AERT) does practice a kind of alchemy by turning waste wood fiber and recycled plastics into building materials for homes. Its products are mainly used in residential renovation by individual homeowners, homebuilders, and contractors as a more environmentally-conscious alternative to traditional wood and plastic products used to make decking, railing, and trim. AERT markets its products under such names as ChoiceDek and MoistureShield; they are sold to do-it-yourself retailers like Lowe's through Weyerhaeuser (some three-quarters of sales). The founding Brooks family owns about 40% of AERT.

	Annual Growth	12/03	12/04	12/05	12/06	12/07
Sales ($ mil.)	17.2%	43.5	63.6	87.3	97.8	82.2
Net income ($ mil.)	—	2.3	1.3	7.8	1.8	(9.5)
Market value ($ mil.)	(7.4%)	46.0	40.7	67.4	86.9	33.8
Employees	(0.6%)	—	—	670	664	662

ADVANCED EQUITIES FINANCIAL CORPORATION

311 S. Wacker Dr., Ste. 1650
Chicago, IL 60606
Phone: 312-377-5300
Fax: 312-377-5314
Web: www.advancedequities.com

CEO: Dwight Badger
CFO: Gregg S. Glaser
HR: –
FYE: December 31
Type: Private

Advanced Equities Financial likes to help small companies advance. The investment bank specializes in private equity placements, particularly mezzanine and late-stage development financing for emerging companies in technology-related fields. Advanced Equities Financial also offers retail brokerage (through its First Allied Securities subsidiary) and private client services for wealthy individuals. The company, founded in 1999, has financial advisors working from some 200 branch locations nationwide; its venture capital business has offices in Chicago, New York, and San Francisco. Advanced Equities Financial has more than $20 billion in assets under management.

	Annual Growth	12/03	12/04	12/05	12/06	12/07
Est. sales ($ mil.)	—	—	—	—	—	22.3
Employees	—	—	—	—	—	235

ADVANCED FRESH CONCEPTS CORPORATION

19205 S. Laurel Park Rd.
Rancho Dominguez, CA 90220
Phone: 310-604-3200
Fax: 310-604-6449
Web: www.afcsushi.com

CEO: Ryuji Ishii
CFO: Ryuji Ishii
HR: Ryuji Ishii
FYE: December 31
Type: Private

This company brings hand-crafted Japanese food to your local supermarket. Advanced Fresh Concepts operates a chain of more than 2,500 franchised fresh sushi bars in supermarkets, sports arenas, and on college campuses in 45 states and in Canada. Operating under the name Southern Tsunami, the outlets offer traditional fresh sushi, as well as salads and party trays. Advanced Fresh Concepts also manufactures a line of sushi-related dressings, sauces, soups, teas, sushi-making kits, gift baskets, and other products. The company was founded by president Ryuji Ishii in 1986.

	Annual Growth	12/03	12/04	12/05	12/06	12/07
Est. sales ($ mil.)	—	—	—	—	—	13.1
Employees	—	—	—	—	—	85

ADVANCED LIFE SCIENCES HOLDINGS, INC.

NASDAQ (CM): ADLS

1440 Davey Rd.
Woodridge, IL 60517
Phone: 630-739-6744
Fax: 630-739-6754
Web: www.advancedlifesciences.com

CEO: Michael T. Flavin
CFO: John L. Flavin
HR: –
FYE: December 31
Type: Public

Advanced Life Sciences is a biopharmaceutical company working to develop clinical and preclinical drug candidates for infectious disease, cancer, and inflammation. Its antibiotic candidate cethromycin is in clinical trials for treatment of respiratory infections and pneumonia. The biopharmaceutical company's other drug candidates include possible treatments for metastatic melanoma and inflammation-related tissue damage as a result of acute respiratory distress syndrome. The company has licensed the development and commercialization rights to cethromycin from Abbott Laboratories.

	Annual Growth	12/02	12/03	12/04	12/05	*12/06
Sales ($ mil.)	—	0.5	0.2	0.3	0.1	0.0
Net income ($ mil.)	—	(1.3)	(2.5)	(27.2)	(6.4)	(20.5)
Market value ($ mil.)	9.1%	—	—	—	70.5	76.9
Employees	8.8%	20	—	—	18	28

*Most recent year available

ADVANCED LIGHTING TECHNOLOGIES, INC.

32000 Aurora Rd.
Solon, OH 44139
Phone: 440-519-0500
Fax: 440-519-0501
Web: www.adlt.com

CEO: Wayne R. Hellman
CFO: Wayne J. Vespoli
HR: –
FYE: Sunday nearest June 30
Type: Private

And then there was metal halide light. Advanced Lighting Technologies' (ADLT) metal halide simulates sunlight more closely than other lighting technologies. Through subsidiary Venture Lighting, ADLT makes metal halide lamps ranging from 50 to 2,000 watts. Other lighting products include lamp components, power supplies, and lamp-making equipment. A vertically integrated company, ADLT makes the metal halide salts used in its own products; metal halide salts are also sold to other manufacturers. ADLT's Deposition Sciences subsidiary makes passive optical telecommunications devices and deposition coating equipment. The company is 99%-owned by Saratoga Partners.

	Annual Growth	6/02	6/03	6/04	6/05	6/06
Sales ($ mil.)	4.1%	—	145.1	144.6	157.8	163.9
Net income ($ mil.)	—	—	(28.9)	(13.6)	5.8	(6.1)
Employees	(6.4%)	—	1,425	1,480	1,384	1,168

ADVANCED MATERIALS GROUP, INC.

Pink Sheets: ADMG

3303 Lee Pkwy., Ste. 105
Dallas, TX 75219
Phone: 972-432-0602
Fax: 972-432-0595
Web: www.ami4.com

CEO: Ricardo G. Brutocao
CFO: William G. Mortensen
HR: –
FYE: November 30
Type: Public

Advanced Materials Group (AMG) has a cushy job. The company converts raw materials such as foam, foil, film, and adhesive components into a variety of products, primarily for customers in the medical and consumer industries. Its products include padding and cushions for helmets, soft luggage, and neck braces; foam inserts and inking felts for computer printer cartridges; car air-conditioner insulation; water and dust seals; and surgical pads. It serves customers in the aerospace, medical, automotive, consumer, and technology industries. Foamex International is AMG's top materials supplier.

	Annual Growth	11/03	11/04	11/05	11/06	11/07
Sales ($ mil.)	(7.3%)	14.5	8.0	8.7	10.0	10.7
Net income ($ mil.)	—	(0.6)	0.7	0.2	1.3	0.8
Employees	—	52	—	—	—	—

ADVANCED MEDICAL OPTICS, INC.

NYSE: EYE

1700 E. St. Andrew Place
Santa Ana, CA 92705
Phone: 714-247-8200
Fax: 714-247-8672
Web: www.amo-inc.com

CEO: James V. (Jim) Mazzo
CFO: Michael J. Lambert
HR: Francine D. Meza
FYE: December 31
Type: Public

Advanced Medical Optics helps patients see optical illusions and real life more clearly. The company makes eye care products in three key segments: ophthalmic surgery, laser vision correction, and contact lens care. The company's surgical products include intraocular lenses used in cataract surgery, as well as devices, equipment, and accessories used in cataract and laser vision correction procedures. Its contact lens division makes multi-purpose cleaning and disinfecting solutions, daily and enzymatic cleaners, and lens moisturizing drops. Surgery products are marketed to eye surgeons and surgery centers through a direct sales force.

	Annual Growth	12/03	12/04	12/05	12/06	12/07
Sales ($ mil.)	16.0%	601.5	742.1	920.7	997.5	1,090.8
Net income ($ mil.)	—	10.4	(129.4)	(453.2)	79.5	(192.9)
Market value ($ mil.)	26.7%	577.3	1,525.0	2,835.3	2,094.8	1,487.6
Employees	9.2%	—	—	3,440	3,800	4,100

ADVANCED MICRO DEVICES, INC.

NYSE: AMD

1 AMD Place
Sunnyvale, CA 94088
Phone: 408-749-4000
Fax: 408-982-6164
Web: www.amd.com

CEO: Hector de J. Ruiz
CFO: Robert J. (Bob) Rivet Sr.
HR: Reid Linney
FYE: Last Sunday in December
Type: Public

Advanced Micro Devices (AMD) has made some advances in its battle against Intel. AMD ranks #2 in PC and server microprocessors, far behind its archrival. Though Intel commands about three-quarters of the world processor market, AMD has at times eroded that market share thanks to the popularity of its Athlon and Opteron processor families. The company also makes embedded processors and other chips for communications and networking applications. AMD has spun off its flash memory device business into another company, Spansion. Hewlett-Packard is AMD's biggest customer. Chinese OEMs account for about 40% of the company's sales.

	Annual Growth	12/03	12/04	12/05	12/06	12/07
Sales ($ mil.)	14.3%	3,519.2	5,001.4	5,847.6	5,649.0	6,013.0
Net income ($ mil.)	—	(274.5)	91.2	165.5	(166.0)	(3,379.0)
Market value ($ mil.)	(3.7%)	5,148.7	8,665.3	13,283.6	11,131.5	4,435.9
Employees	3.5%	14,300	15,900	9,860	16,500	16,420

ADVANCED NEUROMODULATION SYSTEMS, INC.

6901 Preston Rd.
Plano, TX 75024
Phone: 972-309-8000
Fax: 972-309-8150
Web: www.ans-medical.com

CEO: Christopher G. Chavez
CFO: R. J. Steines
HR: James P. (Jim) Calhoun
FYE: December 31
Type: Subsidiary

If you've got chronic pain, Advanced Neuromodulation Systems (ANS) will get on your nerves — literally — with its spinal cord stimulation devices. The company makes products that treat chronic pain by stimulating nerves in the spinal cord with electrical impulses, delivered through leads connected to an implantable device; the process works by disrupting pain signals that are traveling to the brain. ANS sells several versions of these systems, with either internal or external power sources, under the names Eon, Genesis, and Renew. It also makes implantable leads and software (Rapid Programmer) used to program its neuromodulation systems. The company is a subsidiary of St. Jude Medical.

	Annual Growth	12/03	12/04	12/05	12/06	12/07
Est. sales ($ mil.)	—	—	—	—	—	52.9
Employees	—	—	—	—	—	529

An in-depth profile of this company is available to Hoover's Online members at hoovers.com.

61

ADVANCED PHOTONIX, INC.　　　　　AMEX: API

2925 Boardwalk	CEO: Richard D. (Rick) Kurtz
Ann Arbor, MI 48104	CFO: Robin F. (Rob) Risser
Phone: 734-864-5600	HR: –
Fax: 734-998-3474	FYE: Sunday nearest March 31
Web: www.advancedphotonix.com	Type: Public

Advanced Photonix, Inc. (API) senses more with light. The company makes devices that detect light and radiation, including photodiodes, photodetectors, and optoelectronic assemblies, which are used by manufacturers in analysis and imaging equipment for applications ranging from missile guidance and satellite positioning to baggage scanning and blood analysis. API's large-area avalanche photodiodes (LAAPD) are used to sense low levels of light and radiation. Its FILTRODE technology applies optical coatings to photodiode chips to filter out bright background light. Most of API's sales are to customers located in the US.

	Annual Growth	3/04	3/05	3/06	3/07	3/08
Sales ($ mil.)	17.0%	12.4	14.8	23.6	23.6	23.2
Net income ($ mil.)	—	0.8	5.1	(5.3)	(4.7)	(9.6)
Market value ($ mil.)	3.8%	27.5	28.5	51.2	37.7	31.9
Employees	9.9%	96	156	152	162	140

ADVANCED PLANT PHARMACEUTICALS, INC.　　　OTC: APPIE

43 W. 33rd St.	CEO: David Lieberman
New York, NY 10001	CFO: –
Phone: 212-695-3334	HR: –
Fax: 212-695-2882	FYE: December 31
Web: www.advancedplantpharm.com	Type: Public

Advanced Plant Pharmaceuticals, Inc. (APPI) develops and markets dietary supplements derived from plants. Products include ACACaplets (energy and immune booster); Sinusol mist to clear nasal passages; and Lo-Chol to promote lipid balance. APPI's Mazal Plant Pharmaceuticals subsidiary is developing a drug candidate to lower and control cholesterol. However, because its supplements haven't had much market success, the company hopes its future might lie in other plant-based energy products. Its World Health Energy subsidiary is exploring biodiesel production which may become the company's primary activity. A tiny three-employee company, APPI is controlled by CEO David Lieberman and his brother, C. J. Lieberman.

	Annual Growth	12/02	12/03	12/04	12/05	*12/06
Sales ($ mil.)	—	0.0	0.1	0.1	0.0	0.0
Net income ($ mil.)	—	(2.3)	(3.9)	(3.7)	(4.5)	(1.6)
Employees	—	—	—	—	—	—

*Most recent year available

ADVANCED TECHNOLOGIES GROUP, LTD.　　　OTC: AVGG

32 Broadway, 3rd Fl.	CEO: Alex J. Stelmak
New York, NY 10004	CFO: –
Phone: 212-968-0941	HR: –
Fax: 212-968-7238	FYE: January 31
Web: www.atgworld.com	Type: Public

Advanced Technologies Group (ATG) is looking to enter the e-commerce software market. The company — which has a 25% interest in FX Direct Dealer, a developer of software for conducting online foreign currency exchange transactions — hopes to acquire and commercialize technologies for Internet-based marketplaces. The company also offers PromotionStat, a Web-based statistical and analytical traffic-monitoring tool, as well as online portals Promote4Free and LuxuryLounge.

	Annual Growth	1/04	1/05	1/06	1/07	1/08
Sales ($ mil.)	(42.3%)	—	—	0.9	0.5	0.3
Net income ($ mil.)	—	—	—	(0.9)	(0.6)	(0.2)
Market value ($ mil.)	(89.2%)	—	—	—	13.5	1.5
Employees	—	—	—	—	23	—

ADVANSTAR COMMUNICATIONS INC.

6200 Canoga Ave., 2nd Fl.	CEO: Joseph (Joe) Loggia
Woodland Hills, CA 91367	CFO: Theodore S. (Ted) Alpert
Phone: 818-593-5000	HR: Nancy Nugent
Fax: 818-593-5020	FYE: December 31
Web: www.advanstar.com	Type: Private

Advanstar Communications offers a constellation of business-to-business publishing and marketing services related to fashion, life sciences, and powersports. The company has a portfolio of nearly 70 print publications and directories and some 150 electronic publications and Web sites. It stages more than 90 expositions and conferences annually. Titles include *Motor Age*, *Medical Economics*, and *Dermatology Times*; trade shows include apparel show MAGIC Marketplace; and marketing offerings include direct mail services and custom publishing. A consortium of investors led by private-equity firm Veronis Suhler Stevenson owns Advanstar.

	Annual Growth	12/02	12/03	12/04	12/05	12/06
Sales ($ mil.)	1.3%	307.2	325.9	380.5	288.9	323.7
Net income ($ mil.)	—	(124.3)	(70.1)	(67.1)	8.6	(41.7)
Employees	(4.5%)	1,200	1,400	1,400	1,000	1,000

⊞ ADVANTA CORP.　　　NASDAQ (GS): ADVNA

Welsh and McKean Roads, P.O. Box 844	CEO: Dennis Alter
Spring House, PA 19477	CFO: Philip M. (Phil) Browne
Phone: 215-657-4000	HR: Paul Jeffers
Fax: 215-444-6121	FYE: December 31
Web: www.advanta.com	Type: Public

Advanta gives small business owners credit. Through Advanta Bank Corp. the company is one of the nation's largest issuers of MasterCard business credit cards to small businesses and professionals (to a lesser extent, it issues Visa business cards as well). The bank also offers deposit products and online banking. To grow its customer base, Advanta markets its cards through direct mail, telemarketing, and the Internet. The company operates two insurance subsidiaries, Advanta Insurance and Advanta Life Insurance, that offer specialty credit-related insurance and other ancillary products to existing customers.

	Annual Growth	12/03	12/04	12/05	12/06	12/07
Assets ($ mil.)	13.1%	1,687.6	1,692.9	2,127.4	2,413.1	2,764.4
Net income ($ mil.)	26.5%	28.2	44.7	110.4	85.0	72.1
Market value ($ mil.)	6.2%	82.8	144.9	193.0	255.0	105.2
Employees	8.4%	—	—	878	952	—

ADVANTAGE RENT A CAR

6660 1st Park Ten Blvd., Ste. 116	CEO: William (Bill) Plamondon
San Antonio, TX 78213	CFO: Paul McClintock
Phone: 210-344-4712	HR: Janice Bunch
Fax: 210-679-2589	FYE: December 31
Web: www.arac.com	Type: Private

Advantage Rent-A-Car hopes to gain an advantage by focusing on its home territory. The company operates a fleet of about 15,000 vehicles in more than 10 states, primarily in the Southwest. Besides serving business and leisure travelers, it cultivates government accounts and vehicle replacement rental business. Outside the US, Advantage Rent-A-Car offers service through affiliates in more than 30 countries in the Americas, Australasia, the Caribbean, Europe, and the Middle East. Investor group ARC Venture Holding (led by Rosedale Leasing) owns the company, which was founded by Kenneth and Helen Walker in 1963 with a fleet of five cars. The Walker family sold Advantage Rent-A-Car to ARC Venture Holding in 2006.

	Annual Growth	12/03	12/04	12/05	12/06	12/07
Est. sales ($ mil.)	—	—	—	—	—	150.0
Employees	—	—	—	—	—	1,100

ADVANTAGE SALES AND MARKETING, LLC

19100 Von Karman Ave., Ste. 600
Irvine, CA 92612
Phone: 949-797-2900
Fax: 949-797-9112
Web: www.asmnet.com

CEO: Sonny King
CFO: Brian Stevens
HR: Stephanie Neuvirth
FYE: December 31
Type: Private

Making consumer products is one thing, but selling them is another, and that's where Advantage Sales & Marketing aims to do business. The company provides outsourced sales, merchandising, and marketing services to consumer goods and food product manufacturers and suppliers. It works to win optimal placement of clients' products at retail locations throughout the US and Canada, and it offers a variety of promotional programs aimed at boosting sales. Advantage Sales & Marketing has counted Del Monte, S.C. Johnson, and Unilever among its more than 1,200 clients. Investment firms J.W. Childs Associates and Merrill Lynch Global Private Equity own a controlling stake in the company.

	Annual Growth	12/03	12/04	12/05	12/06	12/07
Est. sales ($ mil.)	—	—	—	—	—	2,147.5
Employees	—	—	—	—	—	12,000

ADVANT-E CORPORATION

OTC: AVEE

2680 Indian Ripple Rd.
Dayton, OH 45440
Phone: 937-429-4288
Fax: 937-429-4309
Web: www.advant-e.com

CEO: Jason K. Wadzinski
CFO: James E. Lesch
HR: James E. Lesch
FYE: December 31
Type: Public

Advant-e makes software that helps companies establish e-commerce Web sites. The company's EnterpriseEC platform is a building system for online business transactions and trading communities. In addition, Advant-e's subsidiary Edict Systems provides hosted trading community management software used to develop industry-specific business-to-business portals such as CPGSupplier.com, LogisticsEC.com, MfgEC.com, and RetailEC.com. Advant-e also provides consulting services, as well as professional services such as training, support, and maintenance.

	Annual Growth	12/03	12/04	12/05	12/06	12/07
Sales ($ mil.)	25.5%	2.9	3.6	4.5	5.4	7.2
Net income ($ mil.)	49.5%	0.2	0.5	0.6	0.9	1.0
Market value ($ mil.)	10.9%	8.8	9.1	9.0	13.5	13.3
Employees	—	—	—	—	—	—

ADVENT INTERNATIONAL CORPORATION

75 State St.
Boston, MA 02109
Phone: 617-951-9400
Fax: 617-951-0566
Web: www.adventinternational.com

CEO: Peter A. Brooke
CFO: Thomas H. (Tom) Lauer
HR: –
FYE: December 31
Type: Private

Buyout firm Advent International invests in later-stage companies in a variety of industries in North America and Western Europe. Target firms use the company's infusions of cash (up to $500 million) for international expansion, restructuring, or to fuel growth. Advent International finances companies in developing markets such as Central Europe, Brazil, Mexico, and Argentina to the tune of $20 million to $60 million. The company also invests venture capital in companies in the health care and technology fields. Advent International has offices in more than a dozen countries.

	Annual Growth	12/03	12/04	12/05	12/06	12/07
Est. sales ($ mil.)	—	—	—	—	—	277.5
Employees	—	—	—	—	—	3,900

ADVENT SOFTWARE, INC.

NASDAQ (GS): ADVS

600 Townsend St.
San Francisco, CA 94103
Phone: 415-543-7696
Fax: 415-556-0607
Web: www.advent.com

CEO: Stephanie G. DiMarco
CFO: Craig B. Collins
HR: John P. Brennan
FYE: December 31
Type: Public

Advent Software manages investments from beginning to end. A provider of enterprise investment management software for investment advisors, banks, and corporations, Advent offers applications for managing everything from client relationships to trade order executions. The company's products are used for managing portfolio accounting, trading and order execution, hedge and venture fund allocation, securities clients, reconciliation, and other functions. Advent also offers services such as consulting, support, maintenance, systems integration, and installation.

	Annual Growth	12/03	12/04	12/05	12/06	12/07
Sales ($ mil.)	11.9%	137.2	150.0	168.7	184.1	215.3
Net income ($ mil.)	—	(97.5)	(16.2)	14.1	82.6	12.6
Market value ($ mil.)	25.7%	574.1	670.4	901.4	961.0	1,433.5
Employees	13.4%	—	—	736	824	946

ADVENTIST HEALTH

2100 Douglas Blvd.
Roseville, CA 95661
Phone: 916-781-2000
Fax: 916-783-9909
Web: www.adventisthealth.org

CEO: Donald R. Ammon
CFO: Douglas E. Rebok
HR: –
FYE: December 31
Type: Not-for-profit

Not simply waiting around for the advent of good health, Adventist Health operates about 20 hospital systems (with 2,800 beds) in the western portion of the US. Its hospital systems — sprinkled throughout California, Hawaii, Oregon, and Washington — also include physicians' clinics and outpatient centers. Additionally, the organization runs more than a dozen home health care agencies and has established a handful of joint-venture nursing homes in California, Oregon, and Washington. Adventist Health maintains strong ties to the Seventh-Day Adventist Church but is independently owned. A sister organization, Adventist Health System, operates in the central and southern parts of the country.

ADVENTIST HEALTH SYSTEM

111 N. Orlando Ave.
Winter Park, FL 32789
Phone: 407-647-4400
Fax: 407-975-1469
Web: www.ahss.org

CEO: Donald L. Jernigan
CFO: Terry D. Shaw
HR: Donald G. (Don) Jones
FYE: December 31
Type: Not-for-profit

Adventist Health System (AHS) operates nearly 40 hospitals, 15 nursing homes, and more than 20 home health care agencies. Its acute care hospitals have more than 6,200 beds combined, and its long-term care facilities offer more than 2,500 beds total. While it operates in ten southeastern and midwestern states, Florida is a key market: Its Florida Hospital system serves residents of the central part of the state and has nearly 1,800 beds. The health system is sponsored by the Seventh-Day Adventist Church as part of its legacy of providing health care.

	Annual Growth	12/02	12/03	12/04	12/05	12/06
Sales ($ mil.)	9.0%	3,519.1	4,085.9	4,379.2	4,637.2	4,968.7
Net income ($ mil.)	17.5%	170.6	203.1	236.2	251.4	325.4
Employees	0.6%	42,000	44,000	—	43,000	43,000

An in-depth profile of this company is available to Hoover's Online members at hoovers.com.

63

ADVENTIST HEALTHCARE, INC.

1801 Research Blvd., Ste. 400
Rockville, MD 20850
Phone: 301-315-3030
Fax: 301-315-3043
Web: www.adventisthealthcare.com

CEO: William G. (Bill) Robertson
CFO: James G. Lee
HR: –
FYE: December 31
Type: Not-for-profit

Adventist HealthCare serves metropolitan Washington, DC, and portions of northwestern New Jersey, through a network that includes three acute care hospitals (Shady Grove Adventist Hospital, Washington Adventist Hospital, and Hackettstown Regional Medical Center); two inpatient rehabilitation facilities (operating as the Adventist Rehabilitation Hospital of Maryland); and the Potomac Ridge Behavioral Health System, which provides inpatient and outpatient mental health services. Owned by the Seventh-Day Adventist Church, Adventist HealthCare also operates a number of home health care agencies and nursing homes. Combined, the health care network has more than 850 acute care, rehab, and behavioral health beds.

	Annual Growth	12/03	12/04	12/05	12/06	12/07
Est. sales ($ mil.)	—	—	—	—	—	246.4
Employees	—	—	—	—	—	5,236

ADVENTNET, INC.

5200 Franklin Dr., Ste. 115
Pleasanton, CA 94588
Phone: 925-924-9500
Fax: 925-924-9600
Web: www.adventnet.com

CEO: Sridhar Vembu
CFO: Jai Anand
HR: –
FYE: December 31
Type: Private

AdventNet sees the coming of a new technological age. The company provides enterprise software development services. Its software covers a broad range of applications, including collaboration, customer relationship management (CRM), network management, security, and testing. AdventNet's customers come from a variety of industries including financial services, transportation, energy, manufacturing, electronics, telecommunications, and technology. The company also offers services such as consulting, maintenance, support, training, and installation. AdventNet was founded in 1996.

	Annual Growth	12/03	12/04	12/05	12/06	12/07
Est. sales ($ mil.)	—	—	—	—	—	40.3
Employees	—	—	—	—	—	400

ADVENTRX PHARMACEUTICALS, INC.

AMEX: ANX

6725 Mesa Ridge Rd., Ste. 100
San Diego, CA 92121
Phone: 858-552-0866
Fax: 858-552-0876
Web: www.adventrx.com

CEO: Evan M. Levine
CFO: Mark N. K. Bagnall
HR: –
FYE: December 31
Type: Public

ADVENTRX Pharmaceuticals hopes to balance adventure with profits with its investigational drug treatments for cancer and infectious diseases. Its lead cancer candidates are improved formulations of existing treatments that aim to reduce the toxic side effects of most chemotherapies. The company is also developing CoFactor, which may enhance the effectiveness of popular chemotherapy 5-FU. Though its cancer programs are its main focus, ADVENTRX also owns the rights to a number of potential infectious disease compounds, including treatments for bacterial infections, HIV, and influenza.

	Annual Growth	12/03	12/04	12/05	12/06	12/07
Sales ($ mil.)	—	—	—	—	—	0.5
Net income ($ mil.)	—	—	—	—	—	(22.1)
Market value ($ mil.)	—	—	—	—	—	40.6
Employees	—	—	—	—	—	

ADVENTURELAND PARK

305 34th NW
Altoona, IA 50009
Phone: 515-266-2121
Fax: 515-266-9831
Web: www.adventureland-usa.com

CEO: Jan Krantz
CFO: Dan Bohner
HR: –
FYE: December 31
Type: Private

Adventureland is indeed a land within itself. The family resort boasts an amusement park with more than 100 attractions (Adventureland Park), an inn (Adventureland Inn), and a full-service campground (Adventureland Campground). Rides range from roller coasters to kiddie-sized fun and shows include live music, magic, and musicals. The Adventureland Inn features a tropical themed pool and free shuttle service to and from the amusement park. Adventureland Campground offers its own pool along with RV and tent camping spots. Former CEO John Krantz founded Adventureland in 1974. Krantz died in 2006.

	Annual Growth	12/03	12/04	12/05	12/06	12/07
Est. sales ($ mil.)	—	—	—	—	—	20.0
Employees	—	—	—	—	—	150

ADVERTISING SPECIALTY INSTITUTE, INC.

4800 Street Rd.
Trevose, PA 19053
Phone: 215-953-4000
Fax: 800-564-1399
Web: www.asicentral.com

CEO: Timothy M. Andrews
CFO: Vincent (Vince) Mendola
HR: Carol Albright
FYE: December 31
Type: Private

Did you ever wonder where all the freebies at trade shows come from? So did the folks at ASI, or The Advertising Specialty Institute. Founded in 1950, the group began by creating a database of promotional products suppliers and manufacturers. Today, it produces catalogs, directories and newsletters, runs various Web sites, such as asicentral.com and promomart.com, and holds trade shows all over the US. More than 22,000 promotional products sellers and manufactures are members of ASI.

	Annual Growth	12/03	12/04	12/05	12/06	12/07
Est. sales ($ mil.)	—	—	—	—	—	101.7
Employees	—	—	—	—	—	1,000

ADVERTISING.COM, INC.

1020 Hull St., Ivory Bldg.
Baltimore, MD 21230
Phone: 410-244-1370
Fax: 410-244-1699
Web: www.advertising.com

CEO: Lynda M. Clarizio
CFO: Scott Yinger
HR: Tracy-Lee Nobin
FYE: December 31
Type: Subsidiary

This aptly named business helps companies get their advertisements online. Advertising.com offers targeted ad placement across its network of more than 3,000 Web sites using its proprietary AdLearn targeting system. It also places ads through search-driven advertising systems operated by Google, Yahoo! Search Marketing, and LookSmart, as well as rich-media and interactive advertising services. In addition to online ads, Advertising.com offers a wide range of direct e-mail advertising services as well as campaign reporting and analytical services. Founded as TeknoSurf.com in 1998, the company was acquired by AOL in 2004.

	Annual Growth	12/03	12/04	12/05	12/06	12/07
Est. sales ($ mil.)	—	—	—	—	—	27.0
Employees	—	—	—	—	—	270

THE ADVISORY BOARD COMPANY

NASDAQ (GS): ABCO

2445 M St., NW
Washington, DC 20037
Phone: 202-266-5600
Fax: 202-266-5700
Web: www.advisoryboardcompany.com

CEO: Frank J. Williams
CFO: Michael T. Kirshbaum
HR: Mary D. Van Hoose
FYE: December 31*
Type: Public

Here's where a hospital might go for a second opinion. The Advisory Board Company specializes in providing best practices consulting to member-clients in the health care industry, including more than 2,700 hospitals, pharmaceutical companies, insurance firms, and medical device manufacturers in the US. The Advisory Board offers more than 35 programs in areas such as strategy, operations, and management. Members buy annual subscriptions to one or more programs and participate in the firm's research efforts. Programs typically include best practices research studies, seminars, customized reports, and decision-support tools.

	Annual Growth	3/04	3/05	3/06	3/07	3/08
Sales ($ mil.)	15.8%	121.8	141.6	165.1	189.8	219.0
Net income ($ mil.)	14.5%	18.7	23.4	25.6	27.4	32.1
Market value ($ mil.)	9.7%	659.7	841.9	1,055.9	914.4	955.6
Employees	11.3%	—	—	768	855	—

*Fiscal year change

ADVOCARE INTERNATIONAL, L.P.

2727 Realty Rd., Ste. 134
Carrollton, TX 75006
Phone: 972-478-4500
Fax: 972-478-4758
Web: www.advocare.com

CEO: Bob Ulrich
CFO: –
HR: –
FYE: December 31
Type: Private

AdvoCare International can be your ticket to good health, or your ticket to entrepreneurship. The direct sales company offers a variety of vitamin supplements and nutritional products for weight management, sport and athletic performance, skin care, and general wellness. In addition to its grown-up offerings, the firm also sells products for children. AdvoCare markets its products through a force of over 100,000 independent distributors throughout the world. Bolstering the company's image is its slate of endorsers, ranging from professional and collegiate athletes, and bodybuilders, to musicians.

	Annual Growth	12/03	12/04	12/05	12/06	12/07
Est. sales ($ mil.)	—	—	—	—	—	80.0
Employees	—	—	—	—	—	247

ADVOCAT INC.

NASDAQ (CM): AVCA

1621 Galleria Blvd.
Brentwood, TN 37027
Phone: 615-771-7575
Fax: 615-771-7409
Web: www.irinfo.com/avc

CEO: William R. Council III
CFO: L. Glynn Riddle Jr.
HR: –
FYE: December 31
Type: Public

Spelling errors notwithstanding, Advocat strives to be an advocate for the elderly through its nursing homes and assisted-living facilities, most of which are located in the southeastern and southwestern US. The company operates some 50 nursing homes and assisted-living centers with a total of some 5,800 beds. Advocat, which focuses on rural areas, offers a range of health care services including skilled nursing, recreational therapy, and social services, as well as nutritional support, respiratory treatments, rehabilitative therapy, and other specialized ancillary services.

	Annual Growth	12/03	12/04	12/05	12/06	12/07
Sales ($ mil.)	5.8%	195.8	202.8	203.7	216.8	245.1
Net income ($ mil.)	—	(11.2)	2.8	25.3	21.9	9.4
Market value ($ mil.)	161.2%	1.4	28.3	30.2	94.3	64.0
Employees	—	—	—	—	—	—

ADVOCATE HEALTH CARE

2025 Windsor Dr.
Oak Brook, IL 60523
Phone: 630-572-9393
Fax: 630-990-4752
Web: www.advocatehealth.com

CEO: James H. (Jim) Skogsbergh
CFO: Dominic J. Nakis
HR: Ben Grigaliunas
FYE: December 31
Type: Not-for-profit

Advocating wellness in Chicagoland from Palos Heights to Palatine, Advocate Health Care is an integrated health care network with more than 200 sites serving the Chicago area. Advocate's operations include eight acute care hospitals (including Christ Medical Center and Lutheran General Hospital) with 3,500 beds, and two children's hospitals, as well as home health care and ambulatory care services. Advocate also has teaching affiliations with area medical schools such as the University of Illinois at Chicago. The health system's Advocate Medical Group has over 400 physician members serving Chicago.

	Annual Growth	12/02	12/03	12/04	12/05	12/06
Sales ($ mil.)	5.8%	2,603.6	2,715.9	2,779.7	2,973.9	3,268.3
Net income ($ mil.)	—	(6.8)	123.6	143.6	140.6	288.8
Employees	3.6%	25,293	25,000	24,500	29,600	29,100

AEARO TECHNOLOGIES INC.

5457 W. 79th St.
Indianapolis, IN 46268
Phone: 317-692-6666
Fax: 317-692-6772
Web: www.aearo.com

CEO: Michael A. McLain
CFO: Jeffrey S. Kulka
HR: James M. Phillips
FYE: –
Type: Subsidiary

When the sparks fly, it helps to be under the aegis of Aearo Technologies. The company sells personal protection equipment in more than 70 countries under brand names such as AOSafety, E-A-R, Peltor, and SafeWaze. Products include earplugs, goggles, face shields, respirators, hard hats, safety clothing, first-aid kits, and communication headsets. Aearo also sells safety prescription eyewear and makes energy-absorbing foams that control noise, vibration, and shock. Bear Stearns Merchant Banking previously owned a controlling stake in Aearo, which in 2006 was acquired by private equity firm Permira for $765 million. The company is a subsidiary of 3M Company.

AECOM TECHNOLOGY CORPORATION

NYSE: ACM

555 S. Flower St., Ste. 3700
Los Angeles, CA 90071
Phone: 213-593-8000
Fax: 213-593-8730
Web: www.aecom.com

CEO: John M. Dionisio
CFO: Michael S. (Mike) Burke
HR: Robert Kelleher
FYE: September 30
Type: Public

AECOM Technology means never having to say Architecture, Engineering, Consulting, Operations, and Maintenance. One of the world's leading engineering and design groups, AECOM provides planning, consulting, and construction management services for civil and infrastructure construction, including airports, highways, and water/wastewater and power transmission facilities. It is a top design firm in Asia and the Middle East. It offers logistics, facilities management, training, and support for US government agencies. Company projects include general building work for the BBC, water/wastewater projects, and design and development of Spaceport America, the launch site for Virgin's private space program.

	Annual Growth	9/03	9/04	9/05	9/06	9/07
Sales ($ mil.)	23.0%	1,850.0	2,012.0	2,395.3	3,421.5	4,237.3
Net income ($ mil.)	25.8%	—	50.4	53.8	53.7	100.3
Market value ($ mil.)	—	—	—	—	—	3,460.2
Employees	17.5%	16,800	17,700	22,000	27,300	32,000

⊞ An in-depth profile of this company is available to Hoover's Online members at hoovers.com.

65

AEGIS COMMUNICATIONS GROUP, INC.

8001 Bent Branch Dr.
Irving, TX 75063
Phone: 972-830-1800
Fax: 972-830-1877
Web: www.aegiscomgroup.com

CEO: Kannan Ramasamy
CFO: C. M. Sharma
HR: Mary Mullen
FYE: December 31
Type: Private

This is not a pre-recorded message. Aegis Communications Group provides outsourced telemarketing and customer care services through half a dozen contact centers in the US. The company handles both inbound and outbound calling services, order provisioning, and multilingual communications programs. In addition to teleservices, Aegis offers online customer services such as e-mail responses, real-time chat, and data collection. Major clients have included AT&T, American Express, Qwest Communications, and Western Union. The Essar Group, an investment firm, owns a majority stake in the company.

	Annual Growth	12/03	12/04	12/05	12/06	12/07
Est. sales ($ mil.)	—	—	—	—	—	111.9
Employees	—	—	—	—	—	3,700

AEGIS CORPORATION

614 Dartmouth Terrace Ct.
Wildwood, MO 63011
Phone: 636-273-1011
Fax: 636-273-1015
Web: www.goaegis.com

CEO: M. David (Dave) Kramer
CFO: Marcia Murphy
HR: –
FYE: December 31
Type: Private

Aegis customers might consider themselves in good company. The company's primary product is Aegis Guard, a leather case that protects against radiation and dangerous by-products of cordless and wireless telephones. "Aegis" was the word for a goatskin shield carried by the heroes of Greek mythology. Aegis also makes radiation shields for telephone headsets and a variety of other electronic equipment. The company additionally makes a line of laser products that include laser pointers, sound-activated laser light displays, and layout tools for construction and engineering applications.

	Annual Growth	12/03	12/04	12/05	12/06	12/07
Est. sales ($ mil.)	—	—	—	—	—	910.0
Employees	—	—	—	—	—	4,300

AEGON USA, INC.

4333 Edgewood Rd. NE
Cedar Rapids, IA 52499
Phone: 319-398-8511
Fax: 319-369-2209
Web: www.aegonins.com

CEO: Patrick S. (Pat) Baird
CFO: Darryl D. Button
HR: –
FYE: December 31
Type: Business segment

AEGON USA has realized the impact of pyramid power: Dutch insurance giant AEGON's nearly $10 billion acquisition of Transamerica (of San Francisco skyline fame) helped transform AEGON USA into a powerful force on the US insurance market once Transamerica was fully integrated. AEGON USA provides life insurance and accident and health insurance (such as cancer and long-term care policies) throughout the US. The company also offers annuity and investment products and mutual funds. Subsidiaries include Life Investors Insurance, Monumental Life, and Transamerica Life. AEGON's purchase of J. C. Penney's direct marketing and life insurance business boosted the US unit's marketing efforts.

AEHR TEST SYSTEMS

NASDAQ (GM): AEHR

400 Kato Terrace
Fremont, CA 94539
Phone: 510-623-9400
Fax: 510-623-9450
Web: www.aehr.com

CEO: Rhea J. Posedel
CFO: Gary L. Larson
HR: –
FYE: May 31
Type: Public

Aehr Test Systems' products don't test air, but rather silicon. Aehr (pronounced "air") makes gear that tests logic and memory semiconductors to weed out defective devices. Its burn-in systems test chips' reliability under stress by exposing them to high temperatures and voltages. Aehr also makes massively parallel test systems for handling thousands of chips simultaneously, die carriers for testing unpackaged chips, custom-designed fixtures for test equipment, and other memory test products. Top customers include Spansion (about 39% of sales) and Texas Instruments (nearly 23%). Aehr gets about 80% of its business from the US.

	Annual Growth	5/03	5/04	5/05	5/06	5/07
Sales ($ mil.)	16.1%	15.1	15.8	16.1	23.8	27.4
Net income ($ mil.)	—	(4.5)	(4.0)	(4.9)	0.8	2.4
Market value ($ mil.)	23.2%	20.5	30.4	22.6	49.1	47.3
Employees	—	—	—	—	—	108

AEI

1221 Lamar St., Ste. 800
Houston, TX 77010
Phone: 713-345-5200
Fax: –
Web: www.aeienergy.com

CEO: James Hughes
CFO: John G. Fulton
HR: –
FYE: December 31
Type: Private

When Enron got into trouble AEI got into the energy game. The company was created as Prisma Energy International to manage Enron's international energy interests (35 businesses in 12 countries) and has grown through acquisitions since then. AEI's business includes natural gas transmission and distribution, and power distribution and power generation, as well as retail fuel operations. It serves 6 million customers throughout Asia, Europe, and South America with approximately 39,000 KM of oil and gas pipelines, 160,000 KM of power distribution lines, a gross installed capacity of approximately 1,750 MW, and indirect ownership of more than 1,500 gas stations. Investment firm the Ashmore Group owns AEI.

	Annual Growth	12/03	12/04	12/05	12/06	12/07
Est. sales ($ mil.)	—	—	—	—	—	2,147.5
Employees	—	—	—	—	—	8,300

AEOLUS PHARMACEUTICALS, INC.

OTC: AOLS

23811 Inverness Place
Laguna Niguel, CA 92677
Phone: 949-481-9825
Fax: 949-481-9829
Web: www.aeoluspharma.com

CEO: John L. McManus
CFO: Michael P. (Mike) McManus
HR: –
FYE: September 30
Type: Public

Aeolus Pharmaceuticals wants to put an end to free radicals' free-wheeling, cell-damaging fun. The development-stage company is focusing its attention on developing catalytic antioxidant drugs, which can neutralize free radicals. Aeolus' drug candidates could battle amyotrophic lateral sclerosis (ALS, better known as Lou Gehrig's disease), stroke, Parkinson's disease, and other neurodegenerative conditions. The company is also developing antioxidant drugs to treat respiratory conditions and protect healthy tissue from cancer-fighting radiation. Chairman David Cavalier controls about half of the company through investment company XMark Asset Management.

	Annual Growth	9/02	9/03	9/04	9/05	*9/06
Sales ($ mil.)	(42.3%)	—	—	0.3	0.3	0.1
Net income ($ mil.)	—	—	—	(17.2)	(6.9)	(5.7)
Market value ($ mil.)	5.1%	—	—	21.2	15.7	23.4
Employees	(50.0%)	—	—	4	1	1

*Most recent year available

AEP INDUSTRIES INC.

NASDAQ (GM): AEPI

125 Phillips Ave.
South Hackensack, NJ 07606
Phone: 201-641-6600
Fax: 201-807-2490
Web: www.aepinc.com

CEO: J. Brendan Barba
CFO: Paul M. Feeney
HR: Linda Roskos
FYE: October 31
Type: Public

Making plastic cling is its thing. AEP Industries manufactures plastic packaging film products, including stretch wrap for pallets, packaging for meats and other foods, and films for agricultural uses (such as wrapping bales of hay). AEP Industries also makes dispenser boxes with plastic wrap, which it sells to consumers and to institutions (schools and hospitals). Other industries served by AEP Industries include packaging, transportation, food, auto, chemical, and electronics. Founder Brendan Barba (chairman, president, and CEO) and his family own about 13% of the company.

	Annual Growth	10/03	10/04	10/05	10/06	10/07
Sales ($ mil.)	0.9%	759.5	811.0	732.7	802.1	786.0
Net income ($ mil.)	—	(25.5)	(17.5)	(50.6)	62.9	30.0
Market value ($ mil.)	45.3%	61.3	93.0	173.6	415.4	273.0
Employees	4.3%	—	—	1,700	1,800	1,850

AEP TEXAS CENTRAL COMPANY

1 Riverside Plaza
Columbus, OH 43215
Phone: 614-716-1000
Fax: 614-716-1823
Web: www.aep.com

CEO: Michael G. (Mike) Morris
CFO: Susan Tomasky
HR: —
FYE: December 31
Type: Subsidiary

The lights are big and bright deep in the heart of the Lone Star State thanks to AEP Texas Central (TCC). The utility, formerly named Central Power and Light, provides regulated electric utility services to approximately 753,000 customers in Texas. TCC operates more than 29,650 miles of transmission and distribution lines in Texas; its transmission assets are managed by ERCOT. At one time, more than half of its revenues came from wholesale power transactions, but parent American Electric Power is in the process of divesting the unit's generation assets. TCC has sold its stake in STP Nuclear (STP) to STP, NRG Texas, and the city of San Antonio.

	Annual Growth	12/03	12/04	12/05	12/06	12/07
Est. sales ($ mil.)	—	—	—	—	—	664.7
Employees	—	—	—	—	—	1,224

AERA ENERGY LLC

10000 Ming Ave.
Bakersfield, CA 93311
Phone: 661-665-5000
Fax: 661-665-5169
Web: www.aeraenergy.com

CEO: Eugene J. (Gene) Voiland
CFO: Kate Shae
HR: —
FYE: December 31
Type: Joint venture

Aera Energy covers a large area of California. The state's leading oil and gas producer, Aera Energy's properties extend from the Los Angeles Basin in the south to Coalinga in the north. It has daily production of 185,000 barrels of oil and 67 million cu. ft. of natural gas and boasts proved onshore and offshore reserves of more than 900 million barrels of oil equivalent. Aera Energy also has interests in real estate operations (in partnership with homebuilder Toll Brothers). The exploration and production company is a joint venture of affiliates of Exxon Mobil and Royal Dutch Shell.

	Annual Growth	12/03	12/04	12/05	12/06	12/07
Est. sales ($ mil.)	—	—	—	—	—	2,147.5
Employees	—	—	—	—	—	1,100

AEROCENTURY CORP.

AMEX: ACY

1440 Chapin Ave., Ste. 310
Burlingame, CA 94010
Phone: 650-340-1888
Fax: 650-696-3929
Web: www.aerocentury.com

CEO: Neal D. Crispin
CFO: Toni M. Perazzo
HR: Toni M. Perazzo
FYE: December 31
Type: Public

With a high-flyin' inventory, AeroCentury leases used turboprop aircraft and engines to regional airlines and other commercial customers. The company often buys equipment from an airline, then leases it back to the seller, usually for a term of three to five years. AeroCentury also buys assets already under lease. The company only makes a purchase when it has a customer committed to a lease. Typically, lessees are responsible for any maintenance costs. AeroCentury owns about 30 aircraft, mainly de Havilland and Fokker models. The majority of the company's lease revenues come from airlines headquartered outside the US.

	Annual Growth	12/03	12/04	12/05	12/06	12/07
Sales ($ mil.)	28.0%	8.9	10.9	13.5	18.3	23.9
Net income ($ mil.)	—	(1.3)	0.3	0.2	0.8	3.8
Market value ($ mil.)	66.1%	4.9	4.1	5.3	10.4	37.3
Employees	—	—	—	0	0	—

AEROFLEX INCORPORATED

35 S. Service Rd.
Plainview, NY 11803
Phone: 516-694-6700
Fax: 516-694-0658
Web: www.aeroflex.com

CEO: Leonard (Len) Borow
CFO: John Adamovich Jr.
HR: —
FYE: June 30
Type: Private

Aeroflex flexes its high-tech muscle with aerospace and communications components. The company's diverse offerings include integrated circuits, microelectronic modules, and thin-film interconnects used in military aircraft, satellites, and fiber-optic and broadband cable networks. Aeroflex also makes test and measurement gear for communications networks and motion control applications. The company's largest customer base is the US government and its contractors; Aeroflex sells to such blue-chip clients as Lockheed Martin and Teradyne. In 2007 the company was acquired by Veritas Capital, Golden Gate Private Equity, and Goldman Sachs for about $1.1 billion in cash.

	Annual Growth	6/02	6/03	6/04	6/05	6/06
Sales ($ mil.)	28.5%	202.6	291.8	414.1	463.4	551.8
Net income ($ mil.)	—	(10.8)	6.4	12.1	17.0	27.0
Employees	9.2%	2,030	1,860	2,398	2,640	—

AEROGROUP INTERNATIONAL INC.

201 Meadow Rd.
Edison, NJ 08817
Phone: 732-985-0495
Fax: 732-985-3697
Web: www.aerosoles.com

CEO: Jules Schneider
CFO: Richard Morris
HR: —
FYE: June 30
Type: Private

AeroGroup International wants women to feel like they're walking on air or, at least, feel like buying a pair of its Aerosoles. The company designs the Aerosoles brand of women's footwear and sells it in more than 250 Aerosoles stores in about 15 states, by catalog, online, and through thousands of department (Boscovs, Gottschalks, and Macy's) and specialty stores (Burlington Coat Factory) in North America and abroad. Originally a division of Kenneth Cole, CEO Jules Schneider gathered a group of investors and took the business private in 1987. AeroGroup's consumer base is expanding past 40- and 50-something women, thanks in part to appearances on popular television programs like *Sex and the City*.

	Annual Growth	6/03	6/04	6/05	6/06	6/07
Est. sales ($ mil.)	—	—	—	—	—	162.9
Employees	—	—	—	—	—	800

AEROJET-GENERAL CORPORATION

Highway 50 and Aerojet Road
Rancho Cordova, CA 95670
Phone: 916-355-4000
Fax: 916-351-8667
Web: www.aerojet.com

CEO: J. Scott Neish
CFO: –
HR: Bryan Ramsey
FYE: November 30
Type: Subsidiary

It *did* take a bunch of rocket scientists to come up with the idea for Aerojet-General. The company, a maker of missile propulsion systems, was founded by a professor at the California Institute of Technology and several of his colleagues. Aerojet's propulsion technologies are used in both defense- and space-related applications. The company's defense products include liquid, solid, and air-breathing propulsion systems for missiles and for interceptors used in missile defense systems, as well as armament systems. Among Aerojet's space-related products are liquid, solid, and electric propulsion systems for launch vehicles, transatmospheric vehicles, and spacecraft. Aerojet is the primary subsidiary of GenCorp.

AÉROPOSTALE, INC.

NYSE: ARO

112 W. 34th St., 22nd Fl.
New York, NY 10120
Phone: 646-485-5410
Fax: 646-485-5430
Web: www.aeropostale.com

CEO: Julian R. Geiger
CFO: Michael J. Cunningham
HR: Frederick B. Lamster
FYE: Saturday nearest January 31
Type: Public

Aéropostale wants to fly high in the teen fashion world. The retailer operates about 825 mostly mall-based stores that target teens under the Aéropostale and Jimmy'Z Surf Co. banners in some 47 US states and Canada. Aéropostale stocks the usual teen outerwear (jeans, T-shirts, accessories), mostly under the Aéropostale and Aéro names. It designs and sources its own merchandise so that it can quickly respond to trends. The Aéropostale name originated from a 1920s airmail firm, Compagnie Generale Aéropostale. The brand was created by R.H. Macy & Co. as a private label in the 1980s and later made into a specialty store concept. Macy's sold Aéropostale to its management and Bear Stearns Merchant Banking in 1998.

	Annual Growth	1/04	1/05	1/06	1/07	1/08
Sales ($ mil.)	21.3%	734.9	964.2	1,204.3	1,413.2	1,590.9
Net income ($ mil.)	24.2%	54.3	84.1	83.9	106.7	129.2
Market value ($ mil.)	51.6%	494.0	1,008.8	1,097.6	1,241.2	2,610.0
Employees	131.9%	—	—	9,621	22,310	—

AEROSONIC CORPORATION

AMEX: AIM

1212 N. Hercules Ave.
Clearwater, FL 33765
Phone: 727-461-3000
Fax: 727-447-5926
Web: www.aerosonic.com

CEO: Douglas Hillman
CFO: Charles L. (Charlie) Pope
HR: Sheryl Vaughn
FYE: December 31*
Type: Public

Aerosonic helps pilots straighten up and fly right. The company makes a broad range of mechanical aircraft instruments, including altimeters, airspeed indicators, vertical speed indicators, mach airspeed gauges, artificial horizon indicators, cabin differential indicators, cabin altimeters, maximum allowable airspeed indicators, and stall warning systems. To ensure that everything's working before the wheels leave the ground, Aerosonic also makes aircraft instrument testing equipment. The company's customers include the US military and aircraft manufacturers.

	Annual Growth	1/04	1/05	1/06	1/07	1/08
Sales ($ mil.)	(4.9%)	31.1	30.7	34.8	31.3	25.4
Net income ($ mil.)	—	0.5	1.5	2.5	0.6	(3.4)
Market value ($ mil.)	(12.7%)	30.8	20.8	27.5	25.0	17.9
Employees	(5.3%)	269	286	279	240	216

*Fiscal year change

THE AEROSPACE CORPORATION

2350 E. El Segundo Blvd.
El Segundo, CA 90245
Phone: 310-336-5000
Fax: 310-336-7055
Web: www.aero.org

CEO: William F. Ballhaus Jr.
CFO: Dale E. Wallis
HR: Marlene M. Dennis
FYE: September 30
Type: Not-for-profit

A not-for-profit company, The Aerospace Corporation provides space-related research, development, and advisory services for US government programs, as well as for international organizations and foreign governments. Its chief sponsor is the US Air Force, and its main customers have included the Space and Missile Systems Center of Air Force Space Command and the National Reconnaissance Office. Areas of expertise include launch certification, process implementation, systems engineering, and technology application. The Aerospace Corporation was established in 1960.

	Annual Growth	9/02	9/03	9/04	9/05	9/06
Sales ($ mil.)	8.5%	—	—	—	663.5	719.7
Employees	26.7%	—	—	—	3,000	3,800

AEROTECH LABORATORIES, INC.

1501 W. Knudsen Dr.
Phoenix, AZ 85027
Phone: 623-780-4800
Fax: 623-780-7695
Web: www.aerotechpk.com

CEO: Rachel Brydon Jannetta
CFO: –
HR: Lori Thomas
FYE: December 31
Type: Private

Aerotech Laboratories (which operates as Aerotech P&K) wants you to breathe easier about what you're breathing. The company, a subsidiary of Severn Trent Laboratories, offers a full array of indoor air quality (IAQ) testing services to analyze allergens, bacteria, chemicals, and mold. The group even screens nasal swabs for the microbial agent that causes anthrax. Aerotech also offers industrial hygiene, consumer product and food safety, water/wastewater, and hazardous waste services to ensure that work and consumer environments maintain desirable levels of hygiene and cleanliness.

	Annual Growth	12/03	12/04	12/05	12/06	12/07
Est. sales ($ mil.)	—	—	—	—	—	11.2
Employees	—	—	—	—	—	200

AEROVIRONMENT, INC.

NASDAQ (GM): AVAV

181 W. Huntington Dr., Ste. 202
Monrovia, CA 91016
Phone: 626-357-9983
Fax: 626-359-9628
Web: www.avinc.com

CEO: Timothy E. Conver
CFO: Stephen C. Wright
HR: –
FYE: April 30
Type: Public

AeroVironment is giving US soldiers their own birds-eye view. The company designs, manufactures, and supports a variety of small unmanned aircraft systems (UAS) for the Department of Defense and its component military branches. Small enough for one-man transport, launchable by a single person, and operated through a hand-held control unit, AeroVironment's aircraft can provide intelligence, surveillance, and reconnaissance for small tactical units or individual soldiers. The company also makes fast-charge systems for industrial vehicle batteries under the PosiCharge brand, and makes power processing test equipment through its Energy Technology Center business segment.

	Annual Growth	4/04	4/05	4/06	4/07	4/08
Sales ($ mil.)	45.8%	47.7	105.2	139.4	173.7	215.8
Net income ($ mil.)	76.6%	2.2	14.7	11.4	20.7	21.4
Market value ($ mil.)	22.0%	—	—	—	403.9	492.9
Employees	—	—	—	—	495	—

AERUS LLC

5956 Sherry Ln.
Dallas, TX 75225
Phone: 214-378-4000
Fax: 214-378-4053
Web: www.aerusonline.com

CEO: Joseph P. Urso
CFO: Bret Holland
HR: —
FYE: December 31
Type: Private

A pioneer in the vacuum business, Aerus LLC (formerly Electrolux LLC) has been dirt's worst enemy since 1924. The manufacturer sells vacuums and air purifiers, as well as bags and allergy control accessories, through in-home demonstrations and more than 500 Aerus sales centers in North America; its brands include Guardian, Lux, and Floor Pro. In 2000 AB Electrolux bought the North American rights to the Electrolux trademark from what is now Aerus. By 2004 Aerus had stopped selling products under the Electrolux brand. Aerus is owned by investment firm Engles Urso Follmer.

	Annual Growth	12/03	12/04	12/05	12/06	12/07
Est. sales ($ mil.)	—	—	—	—	—	41.3
Employees	—	—	—	—	—	120

THE AES CORPORATION

NYSE: AES

4300 Wilson Blvd., 11th Fl.
Arlington, VA 22203
Phone: 703-522-1315
Fax: 703-528-4510
Web: www.aes.com

CEO: Paul T. Hanrahan
CFO: Victoria D. Harker
HR: Rita Trehan
FYE: December 31
Type: Public

The right place at the right time — is it kismet? No, it's AES, one of the world's leading independent power producers. The company has interests in more than 120 generation facilities in 26 countries in the Americas, Europe, Asia, Africa, and the Caribbean that give it a combined net generating capacity of 43 gigawatts of power (primarily fossil-fueled). AES sells electricity to utilities and other energy marketers through wholesale contracts or on the spot market. AES also sells power directly to customers worldwide through its interests in distribution utilities, mainly in Latin America. The company is also developing alternative energy power plants.

	Annual Growth	12/03	12/04	12/05	12/06	12/07
Sales ($ mil.)	12.7%	8,415.0	9,463.0	11,086.0	11,564.0	13,588.0
Net income ($ mil.)	—	(403.0)	292.0	630.0	204.0	(95.0)
Market value ($ mil.)	24.8%	5,909.4	8,886.8	10,382.6	14,659.4	14,338.6
Employees	(3.4%)	—	—	30,000	32,000	28,000

AETNA INC.

NYSE: AET

151 Farmington Ave.
Hartford, CT 06156
Phone: 860-273-0123
Fax: 860-273-3971
Web: www.aetna.com

CEO: Ronald A. Williams
CFO: Joseph M. Zubretsky
HR: Elease E. Wright
FYE: December 31
Type: Public

Whether you live or die, Aetna's got an insurance policy to cover it. The company, one of the largest health insurers in the US, also offers life, disability, and long-term care insurance, as well as retirement savings products. Its Health Care division offers managed care plans, health savings accounts, and traditional indemnity coverage, along with dental, vision, behavioral health, and Medicare plans. The division covers about 17 million medical members. Aetna's Group Insurance segment sells life, disability, and long-term care insurance nationwide. And its Large Case Pensions segment offers pensions, annuities, and other retirement savings products.

	Annual Growth	12/03	12/04	12/05	12/06	12/07
Sales ($ mil.)	11.3%	17,976.4	19,904.1	22,491.9	25,145.7	27,599.6
Net income ($ mil.)	18.3%	933.8	2,245.1	1,634.5	1,701.7	1,831.0
Market value ($ mil.)	82.6%	2,576.9	4,569.1	26,713.3	22,280.9	28,651.4
Employees	11.7%	—	—	28,200	30,000	35,200

AETRIUM INCORPORATED

NASDAQ (GM): ATRM

2350 Helen St.
North St. Paul, MN 55109
Phone: 651-770-2000
Fax: 651-770-7975
Web: www.aetrium.com

CEO: Joseph C. Levesque
CFO: Paul H. Askegaard
HR: Mary Kvall
FYE: December 31
Type: Public

Aetrium can attribute whatever success it reaps to its semiconductor testing equipment. The company makes systems used in testing integrated circuits (ICs) and other electronic components. Its main products are test handlers, which work with testers to thermally condition and sort ICs. Other product lines include automated IC handling products, reliability test systems, and gear for adapting test handlers to different types of IC packages. Aetrium's customers include analog chip maker Maxim Integrated Products (40% of sales). The company gets about two-thirds of sales outside the US.

	Annual Growth	12/03	12/04	12/05	12/06	12/07
Sales ($ mil.)	18.7%	14.1	27.8	16.4	28.2	28.0
Net income ($ mil.)	—	(1.6)	3.4	(1.9)	(0.6)	6.7
Market value ($ mil.)	20.4%	30.0	37.7	43.6	36.5	63.2
Employees	(2.1%)	85	90	91	74	78

AF FINANCIAL GROUP

Pink Sheets: ASFE

21 E. Ashe St.
West Jefferson, NC 28694
Phone: 336-246-4344
Fax: 336-246-3966
Web: www.ashefederal.com

CEO: Robert E. Washburn
CFO: Melanie P. Miller
HR: —
FYE: June 30
Type: Public

Well, goll-ee! Deep in the heart of "The Andy Griffith Show" country, AF Financial Group provides good ol' traditional banking and insurance services through subsidiaries AF Bank and AF Insurance Services. The bank operates seven offices in northwestern North Carolina's Alleghany, Ashe, and Watauga counties. It provides standard deposit products such as checking and savings accounts and CDs. Residential mortgages make up about half of its loan portfolio. The bank also offers investment products and services through a pact with a third-party provider. AF Insurance Services sells bonds and auto, home-owners, health, and life insurance. Mutual holding company AsheCo owns 51% of AF Financial Group.

	Annual Growth	6/03	6/04	6/05	6/06	6/07
Assets ($ mil.)	6.3%	192.0	211.6	214.1	229.4	245.3
Net income ($ mil.)	39.2%	0.4	(0.3)	0.6	1.0	1.5
Employees	—	—	—	—	—	—

AFC ENTERPRISES, INC.

NASDAQ (GM): AFCE

5555 Glendridge Connector NE, Ste. 300
Atlanta, GA 30342
Phone: 404-459-4450
Fax: —
Web: www.afce.com

CEO: Cheryl A. Bachelder
CFO: H. Melville (Mel) Hope III
HR: Stanley F. Stout
FYE: Last Sunday in December
Type: Public

This company rests its hopes on chowhounds choosing chicken. AFC Enterprises operates Popeyes Chicken & Biscuits, the #2 quick-service chain specializing in chicken (behind YUM! Brands' KFC). It operates and franchises more than 1,800 Popeyes locations in the US and in more than two dozen other countries. The restaurants feature Cajun-style fried chicken that is typically served with buttermilk biscuits and a variety of sides, including Cajun rice, cole slaw, mashed potatoes, and French fries. Customers can also select such items as chicken sandwiches, chicken strips, and fried fish and shrimp. The company owns and operates about 65 locations and franchises the rest.

	Annual Growth	12/03	12/04	12/05	12/06	12/07
Sales ($ mil.)	0.7%	—	163.9	143.4	153.0	167.3
Net income ($ mil.)	(2.1%)	—	24.6	149.6	22.4	23.1
Market value ($ mil.)	(24.3%)	—	663.9	458.4	521.0	287.8
Employees	2.4%	—	—	1,527	1,751	1,600

An in-depth profile of this company is available to Hoover's Online members at hoovers.com.

AFFILIATED COMPUTER SERVICES, INC.

NYSE: ACS

2828 N. Haskell
Dallas, TX 75204
Phone: 214-841-6111
Fax: 214-821-8315
Web: www.acs-inc.com

CEO: Lynn R. Blodgett
CFO: Kevin Kyser
HR: Lora J. Villarreal
FYE: June 30
Type: Public

Affiliated Computer Services (ACS) handles jobs its clients would rather hand off. The company provides business process outsourcing and technology-related services for commercial enterprises and government agencies. As an outsourcer, ACS handles functions such as administration, including health care claims processing; finance and accounting; human resources; payment processing; sales, marketing, and customer care call centers; and supply chain management. Business process outsourcing accounts for about 75% of sales. ACS also provides information technology and systems integration services.

	Annual Growth	6/03	6/04	6/05	6/06	6/07
Sales ($ mil.)	11.1%	3,787.2	4,106.4	4,351.2	5,353.7	5,772.5
Net income ($ mil.)	(4.7%)	306.8	529.8	415.9	358.8	253.1
Market value ($ mil.)	(3.2%)	5,789.7	7,198.8	6,062.0	5,499.5	5,086.0
Employees	11.5%	—	—	52,000	58,000	—

AFFILIATED FOODS INCORPORATED

1401 W. Farmers Ln.
Amarillo, TX 79118
Phone: 806-372-3851
Fax: 806-372-3647
Web: www.afiama.com

CEO: George Lankford
CFO: Tammie Coffee
HR: Renee Havens
FYE: September 30
Type: Cooperative

This company helps keep pantries stocked in the Panhandle and elsewhere. Affiliated Foods is a leading wholesale distribution cooperative that supplies more than 700 member grocery stores and restaurants in Texas, Oklahoma, and five other states. It distributes fresh produce, meat, and non-food products, as well as dairy products and beverages through its Plains Dairy unit. Its Tri State Baking Company supplies bread to about 500 members. In addition, Affiliated Foods owns a stake in private-label products supplier Western Family Foods. The company was founded in 1946 as Panhandle Associated Grocers, which merged with South Plains Associated Grocers to form Affiliated Foods in 1968.

	Annual Growth	9/03	9/04	9/05	9/06	9/07
Est. sales ($ mil.)	—	—	—	—	—	1,137.2
Employees	—	—	—	—	—	1,010

AFFILIATED FOODS MIDWEST

1301 Omaha Ave.
Norfolk, NE 68702
Phone: 402-371-0555
Fax: 402-371-1884
Web: afmidwest.com

CEO: Martin (Marty) Arter
CFO: Dwayne Severson
HR: Audry Cravatt
FYE: June 30
Type: Cooperative

Affiliated Foods Midwest is a wholesale food distribution cooperative that supplies more than 850 independent grocers in a dozen Midwestern states. From its two distribution centers in Kansas and Nebraska, it distributes fresh produce, meats, deli products, baked goods, dairy items, and frozen foods, as well as general merchandise and equipment. The co-op distributes goods under the Shurfine brand (from Topco Associates) and IGA labels. In addition to distribution, Affiliated Foods Midwest provides marketing, merchandising, and warehousing support services for its members. The cooperative was formed in 1931 to make wholesale purchases for a group of Nebraskan grocers.

	Annual Growth	6/03	6/04	6/05	6/06	6/07
Est. sales ($ mil.)	—	—	—	—	—	1,024.8
Employees	—	—	—	—	—	800

AFFILIATED FOODS SOUTHWEST

12103 Interstate 30
Little Rock, AR 72209
Phone: 501-455-3590
Fax: 501-455-6525
Web: www.affiliatedfoods.com

CEO: John R. Mills
CFO: Ron Rivers
HR: Robert (Bob) Southern
FYE: July 31
Type: Cooperative

Affiliated Foods Southwest (AFS) is a leading wholesale distribution cooperative that supplies hundreds of independent member stores in Arkansas, Louisiana, Mississippi, Oklahoma, Tennessee, and Texas. It distributes nationally-branded food and general merchandise, as well as products sold under the Price Saver, Shurfine, and Shurfresh labels. The co-op was established in the 1940s as Model Markets.

	Annual Growth	7/03	7/04	7/05	7/06	7/07
Est. sales ($ mil.)	—	—	—	—	—	639.3
Employees	—	—	—	—	—	2,444

AFFILIATED MANAGERS GROUP, INC.

NYSE: AMG

600 Hale St.
Prides Crossing, MA 01965
Phone: 617-747-3300
Fax: 617-747-3380
Web: www.amg.com

CEO: Sean M. Healey
CFO: Darrell W. Crate
HR: –
FYE: December 31
Type: Public

AMG knows a good asset when it sees one — and it knows how to make the most of the ones it finds. Affiliated Managers Group (AMG) is an asset management company that owns interests in more than 30 midsized investment management firms in the US and Canada. The company typically acquires majority stakes of between 50% and 70% in its affiliates, firms that cater to institutional investors and wealthy individuals. Its structure lets affiliates retain partial ownership of their firms and operate with relative autonomy. AMG usually contracts to allocate a percentage of revenues to affiliates for operating expenses such as compensation.

	Annual Growth	12/03	12/04	12/05	12/06	12/07
Assets ($ mil.)	22.3%	1,519.2	1,933.4	2,321.6	2,665.9	3,395.7
Net income ($ mil.)	31.7%	60.5	77.2	119.1	151.3	182.0
Market value ($ mil.)	43.2%	1,091.1	2,620.2	3,131.7	4,102.6	4,583.8
Employees	11.5%	—	—	1,270	1,275	1,580

AFFINA

2001 Ruppman Plaza
Peoria, IL 61614
Phone: 309-685-5901
Fax: 309-679-4199
Web: www.affina.com

CEO: Donna Malone
CFO: Polly Sappington
HR: Wendy Basham
FYE: December 31
Type: Private

AFFINA has more than 30 years of experience in providing inbound contact center services for clients in the telecommunications, health care, consumer products, and other industries, as well as for many federal government agencies. The company handles about 18 million phone calls annually through its six call centers in the US and Canada. It provides customer service support, inbound sales support, analytics and marketing, and actionable customer relationship management services. In early 2007, the company was acquired by Hinduja TMT, an information technology group based in India, for $30 million.

	Annual Growth	12/03	12/04	12/05	12/06	12/07
Est. sales ($ mil.)	—	—	—	—	—	109.5
Employees	—	—	—	—	—	2,001

AFFINIA HOSPITALITY

500 W. 37th St.	CEO: Brooke D. Barrett
New York, NY 10018	CFO: David Duncan
Phone: 212-465-3700	HR: Doug O'Neill
Fax: 212-465-3697	FYE: December 31
Web: www.affinia.com	Type: Private

Indulge your affinity for New York and Chicago with Affinia Hospitality. The city's all-suite hotel group has four locations in Manhattan. The company added a fifth hotel in Chicago (on the city's Magnificent Mile) to its portfolio in 2006. Accommodating both business and leisure travelers, its hotels offer spacious rooms, executive desks, gourmet restaurants, and full-service spas to pamper its customers in comfort and style. Benjamin "Bud" Denihan, Sr. founded the first hotel, Lyden Gardens, in 1962, and the Denihan family still owns and operates the company.

	Annual Growth	12/03	12/04	12/05	12/06	12/07
Est. sales ($ mil.)	—	—	—	—	—	32.5
Employees	—	—	—	—	—	965

AFFINION GROUP HOLDINGS, INC.

100 Connecticut Ave.	CEO: Nathaniel J. Lipman
Norwalk, CT 06850	CFO: Thomas A. Williams
Phone: 203-956-1000	HR: —
Fax: 203-956-8502	FYE: December 31
Web: www.affiniongroup.com	Type: Private

Through its partners and affiliations, Affinion Group aims to make fans of its customers' customers. The company operates membership and loyalty programs on behalf of corporate clients seeking to strengthen their ties to consumers. It specializes in launching a variety of media services, through direct mail and the Internet, and packaging these benefits to its clients' customers. Programs overseen include AutoVantage, Buyers Advantage, and Travelers Advantage. Overall the group offers its programs to more than 70 million members worldwide through more than 5,200 partners; it has offices in Europe, South Africa, and the US. Owned by investment firm Apollo Management, Affinion Group has filed to go public.

	Annual Growth	12/02	12/03	12/04	12/05	12/06
Sales ($ mil.)	(13.8%)	—	—	1,530.9	1,198.7	1,137.7
Net income ($ mil.)	—	—	—	376.4	(89.0)	(452.6)
Employees	0.0%	—	—	—	3,000	3,000

AFFINITY GROUP, INC.

2575 Vista Del Mar	CEO: Michael A. Schneider
Ventura, CA 93001	CFO: Thomas F. Wolfe
Phone: 805-667-4100	HR: Laura A. James
Fax: 805-667-4419	FYE: December 31
Web: www.affinitygroup.com	Type: Private

Recreation is serious business for Affinity Group (AGI). The direct marketing firm sells goods and services through its clubs, such as Good Sam, Coast to Coast, President's Club (which provides discounts for the RV crowd), and Golf Card (discounts for green fees). In 28 states, it runs about 75 Camping World retail stores, which sell RV products (air conditioners, sanitation systems, repair items, and furnishings) not usually found in general merchandise stores. AGI also organizes related trade shows and publishes magazines and travel guides, from which it derives subscription fees and ad sales revenue. Chairman Steve Adams is the majority owner of both AGI and, through another entity, RV retailer FreedomRoads.

	Annual Growth	12/03	12/04	12/05	12/06	12/07
Sales ($ mil.)	—	—	—	—	—	514.6
Net income ($ mil.)	—	—	—	—	—	(5,731.0)
Employees	—	—	—	—	—	2,006

AFFINITY MODEL & TALENT AGENCY, INC.

8721 Santa Monica Blvd., Ste. 27	CEO: Ross Kenneth Grossman
West Hollywood, CA 90069	CFO: —
Phone: 323-525-0577	HR: —
Fax: 323-843-9696	FYE: —
Web: www.affinitytalent.com	Type: Private

Affinity Model & Talent Agency caters to those with an affinity for the camera, catwalk, and curious crowds. The agency provides models, actors, musicians, and other talent for a variety of industries, including film, TV, radio, fashion, advertising, tradeshow, promotion, and special events. Its talent has been featured in the *Wall Street Journal*, *San Francisco Chronicle*, Amazon.com, CNET, MTV, NewLine Films, Dimension Films, TNT, and Macy's Passport Fashion, among others. Some models also have appeared in advertising for Pantene, Levi's, DKNY, Estée Lauder, Joe Boxer, L'Oréal, and Jaguar, and other clients. Affinity Model & Talent Agency has offices in Chicago, New York, Los Angeles, and San Francisco.

AFFINITY TECHNOLOGY GROUP, INC.

OTC: AFFI

1310 Lady St., Ste. 601	CEO: Joseph A. (Joe) Boyle
Columbia, SC 29201	CFO: Joseph A. (Joe) Boyle
Phone: 803-758-2511	HR: —
Fax: 803-758-2560	FYE: December 31
Web: www.affi.net	Type: Public

Affinity Technology Group's DeciSys/RT and Automated Loan Machine (ALM) software systems were created to process loans, capture consumer information entered by loan officers, and automatically communicate with credit bureaus and third-party financial services firms. Finding little success offering its software under the application service provider model, the company slashed its workforce and focused its efforts on its mortgage processing business; in 2002 Affinity discontinued its mortgage processing operations, hoping to license its patents to other companies.

	Annual Growth	12/03	12/04	12/05	12/06	12/07
Sales ($ mil.)	—	0.5	0.3	0.0	0.0	0.0
Net income ($ mil.)	—	(0.6)	(0.2)	(0.6)	(2.7)	(1.5)
Employees	(15.9%)	4	3	2	2	2

AFFIRMATIVE INSURANCE HOLDINGS, INC.

NASDAQ (GS): AFFM

4450 Sojourn Dr., Ste. 500	CEO: Kevin R. Callahan
Addison, TX 75001	CFO: Michael J. McClure
Phone: 972-728-6300	HR: Randy Smith
Fax: 972-991-0882	FYE: December 31
Web: www.affirmativeholdings.com	Type: Public

If you've got a bad driving record or let your insurance lapse, can you still get auto coverage? This company answers in the Affirmative. Affirmative Insurance Holdings, through its subsidiaries, writes and sells non-standard auto insurance policies — that is, coverage for drivers in high-risk categories due to their age, driving records, and other factors — in about a dozen states. It markets its own policies, as well as non-standard coverage from other insurers, through some 250 owned and franchised retail locations; its retail stores operate under several different names, including USAgencies, Yellow Key, and A-Affordable. Affirmative Insurance also sells through independent agencies in some markets.

	Annual Growth	12/03	12/04	12/05	12/06	12/07
Assets ($ mil.)	30.1%	314.6	520.9	544.1	557.3	901.9
Net income ($ mil.)	(15.6%)	19.1	24.4	18.3	9.7	9.7
Market value ($ mil.)	(17.4%)	—	283.6	225.2	249.8	160.0
Employees	2.0%	—	—	1,203	942	1,252

An in-depth profile of this company is available to Hoover's Online members at hoovers.com.

71

AFFYMAX, INC.

NASDAQ (GM): AFFY

4001 Miranda Ave.
Palo Alto, CA 94304
Phone: 650-812-8700
Fax: 650-424-0832
Web: www.affymax.com

CEO: Arlene M. Morris
CFO: Paul B. Cleveland
HR: Kay Slocum
FYE: December 31
Type: Public

Affymax is designing peptides to give red blood cells a pep talk. The biotechnology firm is researching and developing possible drugs based upon these biological process regulators. Its leading drug candidate Hematide is an erythropoietin (EPO) mimetic, designed to stimulate red blood cell production like EPO itself. Hematide is being investigated as a possible treatment for anemia caused by chronic renal failure and chemotherapy. Affymax believes Hematide will be cheaper, and longer lasting than the EPO stimulants currently used on dialysis patients.

	Annual Growth	12/03	12/04	12/05	12/06	12/07
Sales ($ mil.)	285.8%	0.2	0.2	0.1	11.7	44.3
Net income ($ mil.)	—	(28.2)	(21.4)	(32.6)	(48.3)	(43.1)
Market value ($ mil.)	(33.2%)	—	—	—	506.5	338.3
Employees	—	—	—	—	105	—

AFFYMETRIX, INC.

NASDAQ (GS): AFFX

3420 Central Expwy.
Santa Clara, CA 95051
Phone: 408-731-5000
Fax: 408-731-5441
Web: www.affymetrix.com

CEO: Stephen P. A. (Steve) Fodor
CFO: John C. Batty
HR: –
FYE: December 31
Type: Public

Affymetrix detects the secrets of human genetics. Its GeneChip system and other products are used to identify, analyze, and manage genetic data in the development of new treatments for infectious diseases, cancer, and other ailments. Affymetrix sells its products directly to drugmakers, academic research labs, and government agencies in its key North American and European markets. It has partnerships with such companies as Roche and Johnson & Johnson subsidiary Veridex to develop disease diagnostics using its GeneChip technology. The company owns about 20% of Perlegen Sciences, which uses Affymetrix's technology to map genetic variations and tie them to human health for drug development.

	Annual Growth	12/03	12/04	12/05	12/06	12/07
Sales ($ mil.)	5.4%	300.8	346.0	367.6	355.3	371.3
Net income ($ mil.)	(3.1%)	14.3	47.6	65.8	(13.7)	12.6
Market value ($ mil.)	2.3%	1,463.2	2,251.0	3,209.8	1,566.3	1,601.7
Employees	1.8%	—	—	1,101	1,128	1,141

AFG INDUSTRIES, INC.

11175 Cicero Dr., Ste. 400
Alpharetta, GA 30022
Phone: 404-446-4200
Fax: 404-446-4220
Web: www.afgglass.com

CEO: Brad Kitterman
CFO: Phil Barnes
HR: Richard (Rick) Stapleton
FYE: December 31
Type: Subsidiary

In AFG Industries' line of work, if the boss catches you staring out the window you can claim that you're doing research. The company lays claim to being North America's largest manufacturer of construction/specialty glass, and the continent's second-largest maker of flat glass. AFG offers its coated, insulated, solar, laminated, store-front, and fire-rated glass products to customers in the residential, commercial, remodeling, specialty, and automotive markets. AFG Industries, which was formed by the 1978 merger of Fourco Glass and ASG, is a direct subsidiary of Asahi Glass America, Inc., which is itself a subsidiary of Asahi Glass Company, Limited (Japan).

AFLAC INCORPORATED

NYSE: AFL

1932 Wynnton Rd.
Columbus, GA 31999
Phone: 706-323-3431
Fax: 706-324-6330
Web: www.aflac.com

CEO: Daniel P. (Dan) Amos
CFO: Kriss Cloninger III
HR: Brenda Mullins
FYE: December 31
Type: Public

Aflac's clients may not welcome accidents and illness any more than a visit from Gilbert Gottfried, but at least their coverage will keep them from financial ruin. Aflac (whose popular ads feature a valiant duck voiced by comedian Gottfried) sells supplemental health and life insurance policies that cover special conditions, primarily cancer. It is one of the largest sellers of supplemental insurance in the US and is an industry leader in Japan's cancer-insurance market (with 14 million policies in force). Aflac, which is marketed through and is an acronym for American Family Life Assurance Company, sells policies that pay cash benefits for hospital confinement, emergency treatment, and medical appliances.

	Annual Growth	12/03	12/04	12/05	12/06	12/07
Assets ($ mil.)	6.6%	50,964.0	59,326.0	56,361.0	59,805.0	65,805.0
Net income ($ mil.)	19.7%	795.0	1,299.0	1,483.0	1,483.0	1,634.0
Market value ($ mil.)	13.4%	18,447.9	20,063.7	23,158.6	30,162.9	30,471.4
Employees	6.8%	6,186	6,531	6,970	7,411	8,048

AFP IMAGING CORPORATION

OTC: AFPC

250 Clearbrook Rd.
Elmsford, NY 10523
Phone: 914-592-6100
Fax: 914-592-6148
Web: www.afpimaging.com

CEO: David Vozick
CFO: Elise Nissen
HR: Aida McKinney
FYE: June 30
Type: Public

Getting ready for a dental implant, or just wanting to look that gift horse in the mouth? AFP Imaging can assist you. The company makes imaging systems, for medical, dental, veterinary, and industrial markets. Products range from good old fashioned film-based X-ray machines and film processors to digital computed tomography scanners and digital radiography systems (including both the sensors and software to display images on computer screens). Its digital radiography systems are designed for use in both human and animal dental diagnostics. In addition to selling its own products, AFP Imaging distributes products from third-party manufacturers.

	Annual Growth	6/03	6/04	6/05	6/06	6/07
Sales ($ mil.)	12.4%	18.0	19.8	23.1	25.0	28.7
Net income ($ mil.)	—	(1.5)	1.4	1.9	1.0	(4.7)
Market value ($ mil.)	109.7%	1.6	13.9	19.8	29.0	30.5
Employees	11.5%	—	83	84	83	115

AFTER HOURS FORMALWEAR

1835 Shackleford Ct.
Norcross, GA 30093
Phone: 770-448-8381
Fax: 770-449-6707
Web: www.afterhours.com

CEO: Bob Huth
CFO: Gary Walker
HR: Bob White
FYE: Saturday nearest January 31
Type: Subsidiary

After Hours Formalwear has the duds for a dance around the clock. The company is the US leader in tuxedo sales and rentals, with more than 500 stores in some 35 states under the After Hours Formalwear and Mr. Tux (in New England) banners. The men's formalwear chain also offers its tuxes through David's Bridal stores and Web site. After Hours offers its own label of tuxes as well as designs by Tommy Hilfiger, Nicole Miller, and FUBU, among others. Weddings and proms account for most of the company's sales. The Men's Wearhouse acquired After Hours Formalwear from Federated Department Stores (now Macy's, Inc.) for about $100 million in April 2007.

AFTERMARKET TECHNOLOGY CORP.

NASDAQ (GS): ATAC

1400 Opus Place, Ste. 600
Downers Grove, IL 60515
Phone: 630-271-8100
Fax: 630-663-8210
Web: www.goatc.com

CEO: Donald T. (Don) Johnson Jr.
CFO: John M. Pinkerton
HR: John J. Machota
FYE: December 31
Type: Public

Hold the phone, old transmissions are gold for Aftermarket Technology Corp. (ATC). The company provides supply chain management services for the communication industry and also remanufactures automatic transmissions and other drivetrain components. The logistics business includes packaging and distribution, order fulfillment, and warehousing. Drivetrain customers include the North American service and parts operations of Chrysler LLC, Ford, and Honda, along with Ford's European operations. ATC also sells to independent auto repair shops and parts retailers.

	Annual Growth	12/03	12/04	12/05	12/06	12/07
Sales ($ mil.)	9.7%	367.1	395.6	442.0	498.0	530.7
Net income ($ mil.)	17.9%	20.5	5.8	31.0	8.0	39.6
Market value ($ mil.)	16.1%	332.6	342.4	423.1	464.0	603.9
Employees	8.7%	—	—	3,300	—	3,900

A.G. EDWARDS, INC.

1 N. Jefferson Ave.
St. Louis, MO 63103
Phone: 314-955-3000
Fax: 314-955-2890
Web: www.agedwards.com

CEO: Robert L. Bagby
CFO: Douglas L. Kelly
HR: Mary V. Atkin
FYE: Last day in February
Type: Subsidiary

With an attitude that's more Main Street than Wall Street, A.G. Edwards brings a midwestern sensibility to the investment business. The company's primary subsidiary, A. G. Edwards & Sons, was founded in 1887 and is one of the oldest and largest US retail brokerages. The firm offers securities and commodities brokerage, asset management, trust services, mutual funds, and insurance to individuals through offices nationwide. The company also serves government and corporate clients. Subsidiary A.G. Edwards Capital is a general partner in several private equity partnerships that invest in both established and startup firms. In 2007 superregional bank Wachovia purchased A.G. Edwards for $6.8 billion.

	Annual Growth	2/03	2/04	2/05	2/06	2/07
Sales ($ mil.)	9.2%	2,199.2	2,498.9	2,611.8	2,750.8	3,126.1
Net income ($ mil.)	29.2%	118.8	159.5	186.5	238.3	331.4
Employees	(0.9%)	—	—	—	15,480	15,338

AG INTERACTIVE

1 American Rd.
Cleveland, OH 44144
Phone: 216-889-5000
Fax: 216-889-5371
Web: www.aginteractive.com

CEO: Josef A. Mandelbaum
CFO: Michael Waxman-Lenz
HR: –
FYE: December 31
Type: Subsidiary

This company has just the thing for those special occasions when an e-mail just won't do. AG Interactive is a leading operator of online greeting card sites, boasting a portfolio that includes AmericanGreetings.com, BlueMountain.com, and Egreetings.com. Its sites offer free e-card services as well as subscription services used by more than 3.4 million customers. In addition, AG Interactive's e-cards can be accessed through Instant Messaging or online partnerships with AOL, MSN, and Yahoo!. AG Interactive is a subsidiary of greeting card publisher American Greetings.

AG PROCESSING INC

12700 W. Dodge Rd.
Omaha, NE 68154
Phone: 402-496-7809
Fax: 402-498-2215
Web: www.agp.com

CEO: Martin P. (Marty) Reagan
CFO: J. Keith Spackler
HR: Judith V. Ford
FYE: August 31
Type: Cooperative

Soy far, soy good for Ag Processing (AGP), one of the largest soybean processors in the US. AGP's chief soybean products include vegetable oil and commercial animal feeds. The agricultural cooperative provides grain marketing and transportation services for its members. The cooperative also offers corn-based ethanol and soybean oil-based bio-fuels, fuel additives, and solvents. AGP processes some 15,000 acres of soybeans a day from its members' farms. The co-op's owners include approximately 250,000 member-farmers in the US and Canada. Mostly Midwestern farmers, AGP's members are represented through about 200 local and regional co-ops.

	Annual Growth	8/02	8/03	8/04	8/05	8/06
Sales ($ mil.)	7.0%	1,801.6	2,126.7	2,663.6	2,349.8	2,360.5
Net income ($ mil.)	17.9%	32.4	11.0	26.1	42.4	62.7
Employees	(26.3%)	2,500	1,500	—	1,000	—

A. G. SPANOS COMPANIES

10100 Trinity Pkwy., 5th Fl.
Stockton, CA 95219
Phone: 209-478-7954
Fax: 209-473-3703
Web: www.agspanos.com

CEO: Dean A. Spanos
CFO: Jeremiah T. (Jerry) Murphy
HR: Charlene Flynn
FYE: September 30
Type: Private

Spanning the land from California to Florida, A.G. Spanos Companies bridges many operations: from building, managing, and selling multi-family housing units to constructing master-planned communities, to developing land, to building commercial space. The firm currently has around 20 multifamily properties in seven states. Operations include luxury apartments in the Sunbelt, some 2 million square feet of office and retail space, master-planned and mixed-use development, and property management. Alex Spanos, owner of the NFL's San Diego Chargers, operates the company with his sons Dean (president and CEO) and Michael Spanos (EVP).

	Annual Growth	9/02	9/03	9/04	9/05	9/06
Est. sales ($ mil.)	—	—	—	—	—	1,580.0
Employees	—	—	—	—	—	600

AGAR SUPPLY, INC.

Myles Standish Industrial Park, 225 John Hancock Rd.
Taunton, MA 02780
Phone: 508-821-2060
Fax: 617-880-5113
Web: www.agarsupply.com

CEO: Karen Bressler
CFO: Greg Burgess
HR: Edward (Ed) Boylan
FYE: September 30
Type: Private

Agar Supply is a leading independent supplier for the foodservice industry. The company delivers fresh beef and seafood, as well as appetizers, sauces, and non-food items to restaurants and other foodservice operators in New England. Agar also supplies some independent grocery chains and other retail customers. Karl Bressler founded the family-owned business in 1940.

	Annual Growth	9/03	9/04	9/05	9/06	9/07
Est. sales ($ mil.)	—	—	—	—	—	474.0
Employees	—	—	—	—	—	375

An in-depth profile of this company is available to Hoover's Online members at hoovers.com.

73

AGCO CORPORATION

NYSE: AG

4205 River Green Pkwy.
Duluth, GA 30096
Phone: 770-813-9200
Fax: 770-813-6118
Web: www.agcocorp.com

CEO: Martin H. Richenhagen
CFO: Andrew H. (Andy) Beck
HR: Norman L. (Norm) Boyd
FYE: December 31
Type: Public

AGCO's annual harvests might be smaller than those of larger rivals John Deere and CNH Global, but it's still able to reap profits worldwide. AGCO sells its tractors, combines, hay tools, sprayers, forage equipment, and replacement parts through a global network of more than 3,200 independent dealers and distributors. Brand names include Massey Ferguson, Gleaner, and Fendt. The company also offers financing services to some customers and dealers through a joint venture with Netherlands-based Rabobank. AGCO sells its products in more than 140 countries.

	Annual Growth	12/03	12/04	12/05	12/06	12/07
Sales ($ mil.)	18.2%	3,495.3	5,273.3	5,449.7	5,435.0	6,828.1
Net income ($ mil.)	34.9%	74.4	158.8	31.6	(64.9)	246.3
Market value ($ mil.)	42.3%	1,518.8	1,978.7	1,499.7	2,821.0	6,227.6
Employees	2.7%	—	—	13,000	12,800	13,700

AGENCY.COM LTD.

488 Madison Ave., 4th Fl.
New York, NY 10022
Phone: 212-358-2600
Fax: 212-358-2604
Web: www.agency.com

CEO: Chan Suh
CFO: Rob Elliot
HR: –
FYE: December 31
Type: Subsidiary

Sometimes the name says it all. Agency.com is a leading interactive marketing firm that specializes in creating Web sites for large corporate clients. Its work includes corporate branding sites, online marketing sites, and e-commerce systems. The company creates online advertising and offers media planning and buying services. In addition, Agency.com is active in creating new types of interactive marketing using outdoor displays, mobile phones, and interactive television. Serving such clients as British Airways, Energizer, and Visa, it operates about 10 offices in the US and Europe. Agency.com is a part of the Diversified Agency Services division of advertising and media services giant Omnicom Group.

AGENTRICS LLC

625 N. Washington St.
Alexandria, VA 22314
Phone: 703-234-5100
Fax: 703-234-5200
Web: www.agentrics.com

CEO: Christopher K. (Chris) Sellers
CFO: Chris DeChene
HR: –
FYE: December 31
Type: Private

Agentrics is an international business-to-business exchange serving the retail e-marketplace. It connects more than 250 retail customers with 80,000 suppliers that provide members with supply-chain and e-commerce services. The company was formed in the late 2005 merger of the WorldWide Retail Exchange (WWRE) with GlobalNetXchange (GNX), another supplier of e-commerce software and services. Both WWRE and GNX were established in 2000.

	Annual Growth	12/03	12/04	12/05	12/06	12/07
Est. sales ($ mil.)	—	—	—	—	—	40.0
Employees	—	—	—	—	—	200

AGFIRST FARM CREDIT BANK

1401 Hampton St.
Columbia, SC 29202
Phone: 803-799-5000
Fax: 803-254-1776
Web: www.agfirst.com

CEO: F. A. (Andy) Lowrey
CFO: Leon T. (Timmy) Amerson
HR: Pat N. Roche
FYE: December 31
Type: Cooperative

AgFirst puts farmers first. A large and growing agricultural lender, AgFirst Farm Credit Bank operates in 15 eastern states and Puerto Rico, offering more than $17 billion in loans to some 80,000 farmers, ranchers, rural homeowners, and agribusiness owners. The lender originates real estate, operating, and rural home mortgage loans. Additionally, it offers crop, life, and timber insurance; equipment leasing; tax services; record keeping; and other products and services designed to meet customers' business and personal needs. The bank does not accept deposits; it raises money by selling bonds and notes on the capital markets.

AGILENT TECHNOLOGIES, INC.

NYSE: A

5301 Stevens Creek Blvd.
Santa Clara, CA 95051
Phone: 408-345-8886
Fax: 408-345-8474
Web: www.agilent.com

CEO: William P. (Bill) Sullivan
CFO: Adrian T. Dillon
HR: Jean M. Halloran
FYE: October 31
Type: Public

Agilent Technologies keeps scientists on their toes. A leading manufacturer of scientific instruments and analysis equipment, Agilent is the #1 supplier of electronic test and measurement products, including data generators, multimeters, and oscilloscopes. Its life sciences and chemical analysis unit manufactures laboratory equipment and other scientific instruments. Agilent's 30,000 customers include global giants, such as Cisco, Dow Chemical, GlaxoSmithKline, Intel, Merck, and Samsung. Operations outside the US account for about two-thirds of sales.

	Annual Growth	10/03	10/04	10/05	10/06	10/07
Sales ($ mil.)	(2.7%)	6,056.0	7,181.0	5,139.0	4,973.0	5,420.0
Net income ($ mil.)	—	(2,058.0)	349.0	327.0	3,307.0	638.0
Market value ($ mil.)	4.8%	11,300.4	11,619.4	15,334.5	13,833.2	13,634.5
Employees	(9.6%)	29,000	28,000	21,000	18,700	19,400

AGILYSYS, INC.

NASDAQ (GS): AGYS

2255 Glades Rd., Ste. 301E
Boca Raton, FL 33431
Phone: 561-999-8700
Fax: 561-999-8765
Web: www.agilysys.com

CEO: Arthur Rhein
CFO: Martin F. Ellis
HR: Richard A. (Rick) Sayers II
FYE: March 31
Type: Public

Agilysys serves as an agile ally for systems procurement. Specializing in the retail and hospitality markets, the company provides IT services to enterprise and government customers. It implements hardware and software from partners including Cisco Systems, EMC, Hewlett-Packard, IBM, Microsoft and Oracle. The company's services range from disaster planning to document and storage management, and it provides industry-specific software tools such as property management applications. Agilysys markets to the education, financial services, government, health care, manufacturing, and transportation sectors. In 2008 Agilysys announced it was exploring strategic alternatives including a possible sale of the company.

	Annual Growth	3/03	3/04	3/05	3/06	3/07
Sales ($ mil.)	(20.2%)	1,171.6	1,403.2	1,622.9	1,742.5	474.6
Net income ($ mil.)	—	(42.1)	8.7	19.5	28.1	232.9
Market value ($ mil.)	27.0%	270.6	378.6	566.6	459.7	704.4
Employees	(15.2%)	—	—	1,386	1,483	996

AGL RESOURCES INC.

NYSE: ATG

10 Peachtree Place NE	CEO: John W. Somerhalder II
Atlanta, GA 30309	CFO: Andrew W. (Drew) Evans
Phone: 404-584-4000	HR: Melanie M. Platt
Fax: 404-584-3714	FYE: December 31
Web: www.aglresources.com	Type: Public

AGL Resources is resourcefully tackling deregulation. Although its customers now choose a natural gas supplier, AGL Resources' Atlanta Gas Light unit delivers natural gas to 1.6 million customers in Georgia. AGL Resources also operates natural gas utilities in Tennessee (Chattanooga Gas) and Virginia (Virginia Natural Gas), and it has operations in Florida, Maryland, and New Jersey via its acquisition of NUI. Overall, the company distributes natural gas to almost 2.3 million customers. Through its nonregulated subsidiaries, AGL Resources markets natural gas to retail and wholesale customers, stores and transports gas, offers asset and risk management services, and operates telecommunications networks.

	Annual Growth	12/03	12/04	12/05	12/06	12/07
Sales ($ mil.)	26.2%	983.7	1,832.0	2,718.0	2,621.0	2,494.0
Net income ($ mil.)	13.3%	127.9	153.0	193.0	212.0	211.0
Market value ($ mil.)	11.2%	1,879.5	2,557.9	2,704.7	3,023.3	2,875.7
Employees	(1.1%)	—	—	2,385	2,369	2,332

AGREE REALTY CORPORATION

NYSE: ADC

31850 Northwestern Hwy.	CEO: Richard Agree
Farmington Hills, MI 48334	CFO: Kenneth R. Howe
Phone: 248-737-4190	HR: –
Fax: 248-737-9110	FYE: December 31
Web: www.agreerealty.com	Type: Public

Shopping sprees really agree with Agree Realty. The self-managed real estate investment trust (REIT) owns, develops, and manages retail real estate, primarily freestanding big-box properties. It owns some 60 retail properties in 16 mostly Midwestern states, though more than half of its properties are located in Michigan. A dozen of the REIT's properties are anchored strip malls. All told, Agree Realty owns a total of more than 3 million sq. ft. of leasable space. Its largest tenants are Borders (which accounts for about one-third of its rental revenue), Walgreen (more than 20% of rent), and Kmart (more than 10%).

	Annual Growth	12/03	12/04	12/05	12/06	12/07
Sales ($ mil.)	5.8%	27.5	29.9	31.6	32.9	34.5
Net income ($ mil.)	10.2%	10.5	13.1	16.0	14.0	15.5
Market value ($ mil.)	6.4%	182.0	205.6	222.7	266.4	233.4
Employees	11.8%	—	—	8	—	10

AGRI BEEF CO.

1555 Shoreline Dr., 3rd Fl.	CEO: Robert N. Rebholtz Jr.
Boise, ID 83702	CFO: Bill Rawlings
Phone: 208-338-2500	HR: Joan Bargholz
Fax: 208-338-2605	FYE: September 30
Web: www.agribeef.com	Type: Private

So where did that steak you threw on the barbecue last night come from? Perhaps it was from Agri Beef, an Idaho-based company that raises cattle on its ranches and then fattens them up on its four feedlots in Idaho, Kansas, and Washington. Its processing plant is also in Washington. Offering both fresh and processed meat items, Agri Beef's brands include St. Helen's and Snake River Farms (American Kobe beef and Kurobuta pork), and Double R Ranch Beef. Its Washington Beef subsidiary slaughters and processes beef for sale in the US and Japan. The family-owned business also operates Performix, a cattle-feed and -supplement manufacturer.

	Annual Growth	9/03	9/04	9/05	9/06	9/07
Est. sales ($ mil.)	—	—	—	—	—	280.6
Employees	—	—	—	—	—	1,000

AGRIBANK, FCB

375 Jackson St.	CEO: L. William (Bill) York
St. Paul, MN 55101	CFO: Brian J. O'Keane
Phone: 651-282-8800	HR: Sandi Schmiesing
Fax: 651-282-8666	FYE: December 31
Web: www.agribank.com	Type: Cooperative

AgriBank puts the "green" in green acres. A financial intermediary, AgriBank provides wholesale lending and business services to Farm Credit System (FCS) associations in America's heartland. Established by Congress, the FCS is a nationwide network of cooperatives that provides loans and financial services for farmers, ranchers, agribusiness owners, timber producers, and rural homeowners. Farm Credit Service's co-ops write loans for land, equipment, and other farm operating costs; they in turn own AgriBank. Formed in 1992, AgriBank also provides credit to rural electric, water, and telephone systems.

	Annual Growth	12/03	12/04	12/05	12/06	12/07
Est. sales ($ mil.)	—	—	—	—	—	1,035.2
Employees	—	—	—	—	—	283

AGUSTA AEROSPACE CORPORATION

3050 Red Lion Rd.	CEO: Bruno Cellemme
Philadelphia, PA 19114	CFO: Vincent Genovese
Phone: 215-281-1400	HR: –
Fax: 215-281-0447	FYE: December 31
Web: www.agustausa.com	Type: Subsidiary

Agusta Aerospace sells and services helicopters made by its parent, UK-based AgustaWestland. Agusta Aerospace offers sales support and services for customers in the US, Canada, and Central and South America. Services include airframe and sheet metal fabrication, inspections, pilot and mechanic training, component repair, overhaul, inventory support, and replacement services. Helicopters supported include the A109E, A119 KOALA, A109K2, A109C, A109MAX, and A109A. Customers come from the corporate, emergency medical, law enforcement, offshore, and utility markets.

	Annual Growth	12/03	12/04	12/05	12/06	12/07
Est. sales ($ mil.)	—	—	—	—	—	216.7
Employees	—	—	—	—	—	375

AHOLD USA, INC.

1385 Hancock St., Quincy Center Plaza	CEO: Lawrence S. (Larry) Benjamin
Quincy, MA 02169	CFO: Kimberly Ross
Phone: 781-380-8000	HR: Ward Kraemer
Fax: 617-770-8190	FYE: Saturday nearest December 31
Web: www.ahold.com	Type: Subsidiary

Ahold USA is the shrinking American arm of Netherlands-based Royal Ahold — one of the world's leading grocery retailers. The subsidiary oversees some 700 supermarkets in three chains. The largest supermarket chain, Stop & Shop in New England, runs about 375 stores. The other two chains have similar names: Giant-Carlisle (Giant Food stores in four northeastern states) and Giant-Landover (mostly in the Baltimore-Washington, DC, area). Royal Ahold sold its 70-store TOPS Markets supermarket chain to Morgan Stanley in late 2007. In mid-2007 the company sold its U.S. Foodservice business (46% of 2006 sales) to Clayton, Dubilier & Rice Fund VII, and KKR & Co. for about $7.1 billion.

An in-depth profile of this company is available to Hoover's Online members at hoovers.com.

AIM INTERNATIONAL, INC.

3923 E. Flamingo Ave.
Nampa, ID 83687
Phone: 208-465-5116
Fax: 208-442-3105
Web: www.theaimcompanies.com

CEO: Ronald A (Ron) Wright
CFO: David N. (Dave) Taylor
HR: –
FYE: December 31
Type: Private

With green barley and beet powders, some friendly bacteria, a few minerals and amino acids AIM International is pointed at selling better health. The company manufactures and markets food concentrates, nutritional supplements, and personal care products though direct sales and through "members" who sell and distribute in a multi-level marketing arrangement. The company has offices in Australia, Canada, New Zealand, South Africa, the UK, and the US. Lead products include AIM BarleyLife, AIM Herbal Fiberblend, and AIMega. It also has a line of products designed for athletes. In all it offers about 25 products. VP and director Dennis Itami founded the company in 1982.

	Annual Growth	12/03	12/04	12/05	12/06	12/07
Est. sales ($ mil.)	—	—	—	—	—	21.4
Employees	—	—	—	—	—	80

AIMCO PROPERTIES, L.P.

4582 S. Ulster Street Pkwy., Ste. 1100
Denver, CO 80237
Phone: 303-757-8101
Fax: 303-757-8735
Web: www.aimco.com

CEO: Terry Considine
CFO: Thomas M. (Tom) Herzog
HR: James G. Purvis
FYE: December 31
Type: Subsidiary

AIMCO Properties' aim is true. The operating arm of residential real estate leader Apartment Investment and Management Company (AIMCO) is laser-focused on apartment complexes, which it owns, manages, and redevelops. The company owns or manages some 1,170 garden style, mid-rise, and high-rise apartment communities with more than 200,000 units located throughout the US and in Puerto Rico. The company divides its operations into "conventional" and "affordable" operations (the latter are often subsidized by government agencies). AIMCO controls about 90% of AIMCO Properties.

	Annual Growth	12/02	12/03	12/04	12/05	12/06
Sales ($ mil.)	7.5%	1,266.9	1,394.7	1,468.9	1,521.5	1,691.0
Net income ($ mil.)	(1.1%)	206.2	177.9	293.1	80.7	197.1
Employees	(5.4%)	7,500	7,300	6,800	6,400	6,000

AIMS WORLDWIDE, INC.

OTC: AMWW

10400 Eaton Place, Ste. 450
Fairfax, VA 22030
Phone: 703-621-3875
Fax: 703-621-3865
Web: www.aimsworldwide.com

CEO: Gerald Garcia Jr.
CFO: Patrick J. Summers
HR: –
FYE: December 31
Type: Public

With a name like that, AIMS Worldwide has certainly set its sights sky-high. AIMS, which stands for Accurate Integrated Marketing Solutions, provides one-to-one marketing and consulting services through branded products such as AIMSolutions and its marketing model, One-2-One. The company operates via business segments that provide advertising, strategic planning, market research, public relations, training, and digital media services. AIMS intends to acquire additional media and marketing services businesses, and in mid-2007 the company acquired digital marketing specialist Target America, marketing consultancy Bill Main & Associates, and political consulting firm IKON Public Affairs.

	Annual Growth	12/03	12/04	12/05	12/06	12/07
Sales ($ mil.)	62.7%	0.3	0.6	1.2	1.7	2.1
Net income ($ mil.)	—	(0.7)	(3.1)	(1.9)	(3.2)	(3.2)
Market value ($ mil.)	7.9%	8.5	16.6	18.8	11.9	11.6
Employees	—	—	—	—	—	—

AIR CRUISERS COMPANY

1740 Hwy. 34
Wall, NJ 07719
Phone: 732-681-3527
Fax: 732-681-9163
Web: www.aircruisers.com

CEO: Jose Redento
CFO: John Melone
HR: Scott Ernst
FYE: August 31
Type: Subsidiary

Air Cruisers can be an aviator's best buddy if the skies turn unfriendly. The company makes life vests, life rafts, helicopter floats, and evacuation slides for corporate, military, and commercial aircraft. Air Cruisers' smallest life rafts hold four people while the largest can accommodate nearly 60. Its life vests come in yellow for passengers and orange for crew members. The company has two US manufacturing facilities and distributes its products through sales offices in China, France, Singapore, and the US. It also operates over a half dozen FAA-approved service centers. Founded in 1935, Air Cruisers is now a subsidiary of Groupe Zodiac.

	Annual Growth	8/03	8/04	8/05	8/06	8/07
Est. sales ($ mil.)	—	—	—	—	—	201.6
Employees	—	—	—	—	—	2,759

AIR METHODS CORPORATION

NASDAQ (GS): AIRM

7301 S. Peoria
Englewood, CO 80112
Phone: 303-792-7400
Fax: 303-790-0499
Web: www.airmethods.com

CEO: Aaron D. Todd
CFO: Trent J. Carman
HR: Jackie Forker
FYE: December 31
Type: Public

Air Methods flies to the rescue for people needing intensive medical care. With a fleet of about 340 medically equipped aircraft, mainly helicopters, the company provides emergency medical air transportation services throughout the US. The company's community-based division, which accounts for most of Air Methods' sales, provides transportation and in-flight medical care from its own bases in more than 20 states. Its hospital-based division contracts with hospitals in more than 30 states to transport critically ill patients to trauma centers or tertiary care facilities; under the hospital-based model, the hospitals themselves provide in-flight medical personnel.

	Annual Growth	12/03	12/04	12/05	12/06	12/07
Sales ($ mil.)	13.1%	242.5	273.1	337.0	319.5	396.4
Net income ($ mil.)	52.4%	5.1	11.8	11.8	17.2	27.5
Market value ($ mil.)	57.9%	97.1	94.5	200.7	331.5	603.6
Employees	26.4%	—	—	1,961	—	3,133

AIR PRODUCTS AND CHEMICALS, INC.

NYSE: APD

7201 Hamilton Blvd.
Allentown, PA 18195
Phone: 610-481-4911
Fax: 610-481-5900
Web: www.airproducts.com

CEO: John E. McGlade
CFO: Paul E. Huck
HR: Lynn C. Minella
FYE: September 30
Type: Public

Much like Jumpin' Jack Flash, business at Air Products and Chemicals is a gas gas gas. The company provides gases such as argon, hydrogen, nitrogen, and oxygen to manufacturers, health care facilities, and other industries. Not all is light and airy, however. It also makes gas containers and equipment that separates air, purifies hydrogen, and liquefies gas. The company distributes industrial gases by building on-site plants (a strategy nearly as old as the company itself) or by truck for companies with less extensive needs. It had produced chemicals, including catalysts, surfactants, and intermediates used to make polyurethane and emulsions derived from vinyl acetate monomer (VAM) until it sold that unit in 2008.

	Annual Growth	9/03	9/04	9/05	9/06	9/07
Sales ($ mil.)	12.4%	6,297.3	7,411.4	8,143.5	8,850.4	10,037.8
Net income ($ mil.)	27.1%	397.3	604.1	711.7	723.4	1,035.6
Market value ($ mil.)	19.7%	10,249.7	12,360.7	12,235.5	14,418.9	21,053.2
Employees	6.5%	—	—	19,500	20,700	22,100

AIR SERV CORPORATION

3399 Peachtree Rd. NE, Ste. 1800
Atlanta, GA 30326
Phone: 404-926-4200
Fax: 404-267-2230
Web: www.airservcorp.com

CEO: Thomas J. (Tom) Marano
CFO: David L. Gamsey
HR: Teddy Gil
FYE: December 31
Type: Private

Airlines hire Air Serv to provide the ground-based services that help passengers and cargo take to the skies. The company's offerings include cargo handling, ground transportation, passenger services (such as baggage handling and ticket verification), and ramp services. Air Serv operates at about 20 airports throughout the US; the company also does business in the UK. Customers have included Delta Air Lines, FedEx, and UAL's United Airlines. Air Serv was established in 2002 by chairman Frank Argenbright, who previously had founded Argenbright Security.

	Annual Growth	12/03	12/04	12/05	12/06	12/07
Est. sales ($ mil.)	—	—	—	—	—	454.2
Employees	—	—	—	—	—	5,400

AIR SYSTEM COMPONENTS, INC.

1401 N. Plano Rd.
Richardson, TX 75081
Phone: 972-680-9126
Fax: 972-575-3372
Web: www.airsysco.com

CEO: Terry J. O'Halloran
CFO: Ron Dewey
HR: –
FYE: December 31
Type: Subsidiary

An air conditioner is nothing but a sum of its parts, with Air System Components (ASC) supplying the parts. The company also makes components — grilles, registers, diffusers, and terminal devices — for heating and ventilation systems. Its products are used in industrial facilities, schools, hospitals, universities, and commercial and residential buildings, as well as the International Space Station. ASC's major brands include Titus, Krueger, Tuttle & Bailey, Reliable, Superior Rex, and PennBarry, and are distributed through wholesalers, independent distributors, and manufacturer representatives. ASC, which has seven manufacturing facilities, is a subsidiary of UK-based manufacturer Tomkins plc.

	Annual Growth	12/03	12/04	12/05	12/06	12/07
Est. sales ($ mil.)	—	—	—	—	—	184.4
Employees	—	—	—	—	—	2,079

AIR T, INC.

NASDAQ (CM): AIRT

3524 Airport Rd.
Maiden, NC 28650
Phone: 828-464-8741
Fax: 828-465-5281
Web: www.airt.net/home.html

CEO: Walter Clark
CFO: John Parry
HR: –
FYE: March 31
Type: Public

So FedEx can deliver for you, Air T flies for FedEx. Air T owns two overnight air cargo subsidiaries, Mountain Air Cargo and CSA Air, which operate under contracts with the express delivery giant. Mountain Air Cargo flies mainly in the southeastern US, the Caribbean, and South America; CSA Air operates primarily in the upper Midwest. The carriers' combined fleet consists of about 90 turboprop aircraft, nearly all of which are leased from FedEx. Air cargo operations account for about half of Air T's sales. The company's other businesses, Global Ground Support and Global Aviation Services, make de-icing and scissor-lift equipment used at airports and provide related maintenance services.

	Annual Growth	3/04	3/05	3/06	3/07	3/08
Sales ($ mil.)	8.8%	56.0	70.0	79.5	67.3	78.4
Net income ($ mil.)	18.9%	1.7	2.1	2.0	2.5	3.4
Market value ($ mil.)	13.1%	14.2	46.2	30.2	20.1	23.3
Employees	(2.7%)	—	414	390	392	—

AIR TRANSPORT SERVICES GROUP, INC.

NASDAQ (GM): ATSG

145 Hunter Dr.
Wilmington, OH 45177
Phone: 937-382-5591
Fax: 937-383-3838
Web: www.atsginc.com

CEO: Joseph C. (Joe) Hete
CFO: Quint O. Turner
HR: Gene Rhodes
FYE: December 31
Type: Public

Air Transport Services Group (ATSG, formerly ABX Holdings) aims to help ensure that your packages get to where they're going on time. Its main unit, cargo airline ABX Air, works for express delivery company DHL (USA) under an ACMI (aircraft, crew, maintenance, insurance) contract and a hub services agreement, in which ABX Air provides package sorting services. ABX Air operates a fleet of about 100 aircraft from the hub it shares with DHL in Wilmington, Ohio, and about 15 regional hubs; it offers overnight service throughout the US and Canada. ATSG also owns airfreight carriers Air Transport International and Capital Cargo International Airlines.

	Annual Growth	12/03	12/04	12/05	12/06	12/07
Sales ($ mil.)	0.3%	1,161.0	1,202.5	1,464.4	1,260.4	1,174.5
Net income ($ mil.)	—	(446.9)	37.0	30.3	90.1	19.6
Market value ($ mil.)	1.1%	250.6	518.0	458.3	405.7	261.9
Employees	(6.1%)	—	—	11,500	9,700	10,150

AIR WISCONSIN AIRLINES CORPORATION

W6390 Challenger Dr., Ste. 203
Appleton, WI 54914
Phone: 920-739-5123
Fax: –
Web: www.airwis.com

CEO: James P. (Jim) Rankin
CFO: Christine Deister
HR: Joel Kuplack
FYE: December 31
Type: Private

Not bound by the borders of the state that shares its name, Air Wisconsin Airlines flies throughout the eastern half of the US. The regional carrier operates under the US Airways Express banner, providing connecting service for US Airways to about 70 cities in more than 25 states and in two Canadian provinces. Air Wisconsin maintains a fleet of about 70 aircraft, consisting of 50-seat Canadair regional jets (CRJs) made by Bombardier. In addition to its passenger transportation operations, Air Wisconsin Airlines provides ground-based services, such as passenger check-in and baggage handling, on behalf of United Airlines and Northwest Airlines. Air Wisconsin Airlines began operations in 1965.

	Annual Growth	12/03	12/04	12/05	12/06	12/07
Est. sales ($ mil.)	—	—	—	—	—	361.6
Employees	—	—	—	—	—	3,100

AIR2WEB, INC.

1230 Peachtree St. NE, 12th Fl.
Atlanta, GA 30309
Phone: 404-942-5300
Fax: 404-815-7708
Web: www.air2web.com

CEO: Bill Jones
CFO: Donald (Don) Dysert
HR: –
FYE: December 31
Type: Private

Air2Web believes that all sorts of Web data should be freed, allowed to roam throughout air, land, and sea. The company offers networking and server software for delivering Web pages, e-mail, and other data to wireless devices. In early 2004, the company acquired Wokup SA, a European wireless software company. Air2Web has offices in France, India, the UK, and the US.

	Annual Growth	12/03	12/04	12/05	12/06	12/07
Est. sales ($ mil.)	—	—	—	—	—	9.8
Employees	—	—	—	—	—	95

An in-depth profile of this company is available to Hoover's Online members at hoovers.com.

77

AIRBORNE, INC.

26811 S. Bay Dr., Ste. 300	CEO: Elise Donahue
Bonita Springs, FL 34134	CFO: Lucy Morris
Phone: 239-948-8545	HR: –
Fax: 239-948-8551	FYE: December 31
Web: www.airbornehealth.com	Type: Private

Airborne wants to keep users from being grounded. The company makes a dietary supplement that contains herbal extracts, vitamins, electrolytes, amino acids, and antioxidants meant to boost immune systems and combat germs. The product, which comes in numerous flavors and formulas including one for kids and another for nighttime, is available nationwide in pharmacies, supermarkets, and mass merchant retailers (including Costco, CVS, Target, and Wal-Mart), as well as online for an average price of $6.99. The company was established in 1997 by former second grade teacher Victoria Knight-McDowell and is currently majority owned by Summit Partners. However, Summit put Airborne on the auction block in late 2006.

	Annual Growth	12/02	12/03	12/04	12/05	12/06
Sales ($ mil.)	—	—	—	—	—	151.6
Employees	—	—	—	—	—	18

AIRBUS NORTH AMERICA HOLDINGS, INC.

198 Van Buren St., Ste. 300	CEO: Barry Eccleston
Herndon, VA 20170	CFO: Robert Hein
Phone: 703-834-3400	HR: Robert N. Ehrenfeld
Fax: 703-834-3340	FYE: December 31
Web: www.airbusnorthamerica.com	Type: Subsidiary

Airbus North America Holdings, the US-based arm of France's Airbus S.A.S., serves the company's important US and Canadian customer base. Historically the world's #2 aircraft maker, Airbus is giving Boeing a run for its money. Airbus' single-aisle (A318, A319, A320, A321) and wide-body (A300, A310, A330, A340) jets can accommodate between 109 and 400 passengers. Airbus delivered the first of its newest planes, the superjumbo A380 jet (capable of carrying more than 550 passengers) in 2007. Airbus is also at work developing the A350 — an updated plane based on the A330 platform. The European Aeronautic Defence & Space Company (EADS) owns Airbus.

	Annual Growth	12/03	12/04	12/05	12/06	12/07
Est. sales ($ mil.)	—	—	—	—	—	13.5
Employees	—	—	—	—	—	240

AIRCASTLE LIMITED

NYSE: AYR

300 First Stamford Place, 5th Fl.	CEO: Ron Wainshal
Stamford, CT 06902	CFO: Michael J. Inglese
Phone: 203-504-1020	HR: –
Fax: 203-504-1021	FYE: December 31
Web: www.aircastle.com	Type: Public

Not to be confused with the inflatable palaces parents rent for their for kids' birthday parties, Aircastle Limited is an aircraft leasing concern. The company owns a portfolio of jet aircraft which it leases to passenger and cargo airlines. Aircastle boasts a portfolio of more than 130 aircraft which are leased to about 60 different lessees. The lessees of Aircastle's aircraft are responsible for maintaining the planes as well as paying operational and insurance expenses. The company's leases are managed from offices in Ireland, Singapore, and the US. Aircastle also invests in debt securities secured by commercial jet aircraft.

	Annual Growth	12/03	12/04	12/05	12/06	12/07
Sales ($ mil.)	1,462.0%	—	0.1	36.0	189.3	381.1
Net income ($ mil.)	—	—	(1.5)	0.2	51.2	127.3
Market value ($ mil.)	35.9%	—	—	—	1,522.8	2,068.9
Employees	—	—	—	—	45	

AIRCRAFT SERVICE INTERNATIONAL GROUP, INC.

201 S. Orange Ave., Ste. 1100-A	CEO: Keith P. Ryan
Orlando, FL 32801	CFO: David F. Pittman
Phone: 407-648-7373	HR: –
Fax: 407-206-5391	FYE: December 31
Web: www.asig.com	Type: Subsidiary

Rather than soaring through the skies, Aircraft Service International Group (ASIG) takes care of planes when they're on the ground. The company provides fueling, ground handling, cargo handling, and related services to the commercial aviation industry. (Ground handling includes services such as baggage loading and unloading, cabin cleaning, and passenger check-in.) ASIG operates at more than 65 airports worldwide, primarily in the US and the UK but also elsewhere in Europe and in Asia. The company is a unit of UK-based BBA Aviation. Sister company Signature Flight Support serves the general aviation community as a leading fixed-base operator (FBO). ASIG was founded in 1947 and acquired by BBA Aviation in 2001.

	Annual Growth	12/03	12/04	12/05	12/06	12/07
Est. sales ($ mil.)	—	—	—	—	—	72.0
Employees	—	—	—	—	—	250

AIRGAS, INC.

NYSE: ARG

259 N. Radnor-Chester Rd., Ste. 100	CEO: Peter McCausland
Radnor, PA 19087	CFO: Robert M. McLaughlin
Phone: 610-687-5253	HR: Dwight T. Wilson
Fax: 610-225-3271	FYE: March 31
Web: www.airgas.com	Type: Public

Airgas has floated to the top of the industrial gas distribution industry by buying up more than 350 companies since its founding in 1986. The company's extensive North American network of more than 1,000 locations includes retail stores, gas fill plants, specialty gas labs, production facilities, and distribution centers. Airgas distributes argon, helium, hydrogen, nitrogen, oxygen, welding gases, and a variety of medical and specialty gases, as well as dry ice and protective equipment (hard hats, goggles). Its Merchant Gases unit operates air-separation plants that produce oxygen, nitrogen, and argon. It also sells welding machines, rents industrial gas tanks, and produces acetylene and nitrous oxide.

	Annual Growth	3/04	3/05	3/06	3/07	3/08
Sales ($ mil.)	20.7%	1,895.5	2,411.4	2,829.6	3,205.1	4,017.0
Net income ($ mil.)	29.2%	80.2	92.0	123.6	154.4	223.4
Market value ($ mil.)	23.4%	1,612.2	1,818.3	3,020.8	3,315.9	3,741.6
Employees	2.2%	—	11,000	10,300	11,500	—

AIRNET SYSTEMS, INC.

7250 Star Check Dr.	CEO: Bruce D. Parker
Columbus, OH 43217	CFO: Ray L. Druseikis
Phone: 614-409-4900	HR: –
Fax: 614-409-7852	FYE: December 31
Web: www.airnet.com	Type: Private

Air cargo carrier AirNet Systems helps banks keep their records straight. Transporting canceled checks and other bank documents accounts for the majority of the company's sales. AirNet also offers express delivery of such cargo as human organs and time-sensitive medications, as well as general freight. It provides both scheduled and charter cargo services. Overall, AirNet operates a fleet of about 100 aircraft, including jets and turboprops. It serves more than 95 cities in the US. In 2008, AirNet was acquired by an affiliate of investment firm Bayside Capital.

	Annual Growth	12/03	12/04	12/05	12/06	12/07
Sales ($ mil.)	1.9%	149.2	174.9	196.4	172.8	161.0
Net income ($ mil.)	5.0%	2.8	(34.2)	(4.3)	(13.3)	3.4
Employees	—	—	—	790	—	—

AIRSPAN NETWORKS INC.

NASDAQ (GM): AIRN

777 Yamato Rd., Ste. 310
Boca Raton, FL 33431
Phone: 561-893-8670
Fax: 561-893-8671
Web: www.airspan.com

CEO: Eric D. Stonestrom
CFO: David Brant
HR: –
FYE: December 31
Type: Public

Airspan Networks covers a lot of ground, mostly through the air. The company supplies equipment based on the WiMax wireless networking standard. Phone companies, ISPs, utility companies, and other network operators use Airspan's base stations and subscriber terminals to provide fixed and mobile broadband wireless access. The company's other products include Wi-Fi-based networking equipment, as well as voice-over-IP (VoIP) soft switches and gateways. Airspan sells directly and through OEMs, resellers and systems integrators to customers worldwide.

	Annual Growth	12/03	12/04	12/05	12/06	12/07
Sales ($ mil.)	32.7%	30.6	94.7	111.0	127.8	95.0
Net income ($ mil.)	—	(29.5)	(10.0)	(15.1)	(29.2)	(30.5)
Market value ($ mil.)	(4.6%)	124.2	204.4	225.7	149.4	103.0
Employees	58.1%	—	—	118	—	295

AIRTRAN HOLDINGS, INC.

NYSE: AAI

9955 AirTran Blvd.
Orlando, FL 32827
Phone: 407-318-5600
Fax: 407-318-5900
Web: www.airtran.com

CEO: Robert L. (Bob) Fornaro
CFO: Arne G. Haak
HR: Loral Blinde
FYE: December 31
Type: Public

The Atlanta airport is one of the world's busiest, and AirTran Holdings is partly responsible. Through its main subsidiary, AirTran Airways, the company offers low-fare passenger transportation, primarily from its hub in Atlanta. AirTran Airways flies to about 55 cities, mainly in the eastern US. The airline operates a fleet of about 140 Boeing aircraft, including the 717-200 and the 737-700. It is a leading carrier in the Atlanta market, behind Delta, which handles the largest share of the traffic at Hartsfield-Jackson Atlanta International Airport.

	Annual Growth	12/03	12/04	12/05	12/06	12/07
Sales ($ mil.)	25.9%	918.0	1,041.4	1,450.5	1,892.1	2,310.0
Net income ($ mil.)	(14.9%)	100.5	12.3	8.1	14.7	52.7
Market value ($ mil.)	(10.0%)	1,002.1	926.8	1,423.3	1,070.2	657.9
Employees	11.5%	5,500	6,100	6,900	7,700	8,500

AIRVANA, INC.

NASDAQ (GM): AIRV

19 Alpha Rd.
Chelmsford, MA 01824
Phone: 978-250-3000
Fax: 978-250-3910
Web: www.airvana.com

CEO: Randall S. Battat
CFO: Jeffrey D. (Jeff) Glidden
HR: –
FYE: Sunday nearest December 31
Type: Public

Airvana can help you rock out to Nirvana. The company makes mobile broadband infrastructure products for wireless carriers. Its products enable wireless networks to deliver broadband multimedia services — such as Internet access, e-mail, music downloads, and video streaming — to cell phones, laptops, and other mobile devices. Airvana sells its software and hardware to service providers such as Verizon Wireless in the US, TELUS in Canada, Telstra in Australia, Israel's Pelephone, and Eurotel in the Czech Republic; however, nearly all of its revenue (about 99% in 2007) is derived from Nortel Networks.

	Annual Growth	12/03	12/04	12/05	12/06	12/07
Sales ($ mil.)	339.6%	—	3.6	2.3	170.3	305.8
Net income ($ mil.)	—	—	(29.1)	(63.0)	74.1	153.3
Market value ($ mil.)	—	—	—	—	—	355.3
Employees	14.1%	—	—	—	491	560

AIRXCEL, INC.

3050 N. St. Francis
Wichita, KS 67204
Phone: 316-832-3400
Fax: 316-832-3493
Web: www.airxcel.com

CEO: Melvin L. (Mel) Adams
CFO: Richard L. Schreck
HR: –
FYE: December 31
Type: Private

Airxcel manufactures air conditioners, furnaces, water heaters, cooking appliances, and compressor refrigeration units mainly for recreational vehicle OEMs (almost 70% of sales), including Fleetwood Enterprises, Thor Industries, and Winnebago. The RV products unit makes Coleman-brand air-conditioning equipment; the Marvair unit makes specialty wall-mount ACs, environmental control units, and heat pumps for utilities and schools and for modular construction and telecom companies. Subsidiary Suburban Manufacturing Company makes RV gas furnaces, water heaters, ranges, and cooktops; the InstaFreeze unit makes compressor refrigerators for RV, marine, and ambulance OEMs.

AISIN WORLD CORP. OF AMERICA

46501 Commerce Center Dr.
Plymouth, MI 48170
Phone: 734-453-5551
Fax: 734-453-4670
Web: www.aisinworld.com

CEO: Don Whitsitt
CFO: –
HR: –
FYE: March 31
Type: Private

The core of AISIN World Corp. of America's business is automotive parts and systems. These include brake systems, suspensions, chassis components, engine parts, drivetrain components, body parts, and information devices. AISIN World Corp.'s aftermarket products include clutch plates, water pumps, master cylinders, and brake pads. The company also makes life and amenity-related products including home sewing and embroidery machines, and energy system-related products that include indoor and outdoor gas heat pump air-conditioning systems. Automotive customers include Toyota Motor Engineering & Manufacturing North America, General Motors, Honda of America, and Johnson Controls.

	Annual Growth	3/03	3/04	3/05	3/06	3/07
Est. sales ($ mil.)	—	—	—	—	—	964.1
Employees	—	—	—	—	—	1,278

AIT WORLDWIDE LOGISTICS, INC.

701 N. Rohlwing Rd.
Itasca, IL 60143
Phone: 630-766-8300
Fax: 630-766-0205
Web: www.aitworldwide.com

CEO: Steve Leturno
CFO: Joe Kayser
HR: –
FYE: December 31
Type: Private

Arranging the transportation of its customers' cargo by air, by land, and by sea, AIT Worldwide Logistics provides domestic and international freight forwarding services, including customs brokerage. The company also offers supply chain management, including information services that help customers keep track of their freight. Customers have come from a variety of industries; the company's specialties include service to government agencies and handling of perishable products. AIT Worldwide Logistics maintains more than 30 offices throughout the US, and the company operates overseas through a network of agents. Steven Leturno and Dan Lisowski founded the company in 1979.

	Annual Growth	12/03	12/04	12/05	12/06	12/07
Est. sales ($ mil.)	—	—	—	—	—	318.0
Employees	—	—	—	—	—	600

An in-depth profile of this company is available to Hoover's Online members at hoovers.com.

79

AJC INTERNATIONAL, INC.

5188 Roswell Rd., NW
Atlanta, GA 30342
Phone: 404-252-6750
Fax: 404-252-9340
Web: www.ajcfood.com

CEO: Gerald L. Allison
CFO: –
HR: –
FYE: July 31
Type: Private

This company helps keep refrigerators and freezers stocked around the world. AJC International is a leading distributor of refrigerated and frozen food products, serving customers in about 140 countries. It supplies retail and foodservice customers with a variety of products, including meat, poultry, and pork, as well as seafood and vegetables. It also offers its own branded products under such labels as Early Dawn, Golden Phoenix, and Mity Fresh. Chairman and CEO Gerald Allison and president Eric Joiner founded AJC in 1972 and continue to control the company.

	Annual Growth	7/03	7/04	7/05	7/06	7/07
Est. sales ($ mil.)	—	—	—	—	—	30.4
Employees	—	—	—	—	—	201

AJILON CONSULTING

210 W. Pennsylvania Ave., Ste. 650
Towson, MD 21204
Phone: 410-821-0435
Fax: 410-828-0106
Web: www.ajilonconsulting.com

CEO: Roy Haggerty
CFO: Tom Sinnott
HR: Samantha O'Neil
FYE: December 31
Type: Subsidiary

Systems integration is just one of the jillion things this company does for its clients. A unit of Switzerland-based global staffing giant Adecco, Ajilon Consulting is a leading provider of consulting and technology services to both private corporations and government agencies. The company specializes in such areas as software and systems development, networking and infrastructure management, and technology procurement. Ajilon also provides data management, software testing, and outsourced help desk and other technology support services. It operates through more than 70 locations worldwide.

AJS BANCORP, INC.

OTC: AJSB

14757 S. Cicero Ave.
Midlothian, IL 60445
Phone: 708-687-7400
Fax: 708-687-7466
Web: www.ajsmithbank.com

CEO: Thomas R. Butkus
CFO: Pamela N. Favero
HR: –
FYE: December 31
Type: Public

There is no need for an alias: A. J. Smith Federal is the primary operating subsidiary of holding company AJS Bancorp. The bank serves customers in suburban Chicago from three branches in Midlothian and Orland Park, Illinois. A. J. Smith Federal offers area businesses and residents traditional products such as checking and savings accounts, various insurance and investment products, and loans. One- to four-family real estate loans comprise about two-thirds of the bank's lending portfolio; multi-family and commercial mortgages, another 25%. Arthur J. Smith founded A. J. Smith Federal in 1892 as a building and loan cooperative. It wasn't until 1984 that it became a federally chartered savings bank.

	Annual Growth	12/03	12/04	12/05	12/06	12/07
Assets ($ mil.)	1.0%	238.4	270.9	257.9	266.5	248.4
Net income ($ mil.)	(19.1%)	1.4	1.6	1.1	0.9	0.6
Market value ($ mil.)	(7.2%)	55.0	54.4	49.4	55.8	40.7
Employees	—	—	—	—	—	—

⊞ AK STEEL HOLDING CORPORATION

NYSE: AKS

9227 Centre Pointe Dr.
West Chester, OH 45069
Phone: 513-425-5000
Fax: 513-425-2676
Web: www.aksteel.com

CEO: James L. Wainscott
CFO: Albert E. Ferrara Jr.
HR: Lawrence F. Zizzo Jr.
FYE: December 31
Type: Public

Automobile sales help AK Steel's business keep rolling. The company manufactures carbon, stainless, and electrical steel. It sells hot- and cold-rolled carbon steel to construction companies, steel distributors and service centers, and automotive and industrial machinery producers. AK Steel also sells cold-rolled and aluminum-coated stainless steel to automakers. The company produces electrical steels (iron-silicon alloys with unique magnetic properties) for makers of power transmission and distribution equipment. In addition, it makes carbon and stainless steel tubular products through AK Tube. Sales to automakers make up nearly half of AK Steel's business; GM is its largest customer, generating 10% of sales.

	Annual Growth	12/03	12/04	12/05	12/06	12/07
Sales ($ mil.)	14.7%	4,041.7	5,217.3	5,647.4	6,069.0	7,003.0
Net income ($ mil.)	—	(560.4)	238.4	(2.3)	12.0	387.7
Market value ($ mil.)	74.7%	553.7	1,579.4	873.0	1,864.5	5,155.7
Employees	(7.1%)	—	—	8,000	7,000	6,900

AKAL SECURITY, INC.

7 Infinity Loop
Española, NM 87532
Phone: 505-692-6600
Fax: 505-753-8689
Web: www.akalsecurity.com

CEO: Sat Nirmal K. Khalsa
CFO: Sukhwinder Singh
HR: –
FYE: December 31
Type: Private

Akal Security provides security guard services for customers throughout the US. The company specializes in contract judicial security services, protecting federal courthouses in 40 states. Akal also provides security officers for detention facilities and military installations, and offers electronic security, surveillance, and access control system design, installation, and integration. In addition to federal customers, the company serves commercial clients and state and local government facilities. Clients have included the US Army, the Department of Homeland Security, and the US Marshals Service.

	Annual Growth	12/03	12/04	12/05	12/06	12/07
Est. sales ($ mil.)	—	—	—	—	—	557.3
Employees	—	—	—	—	—	15,000

AKAMAI TECHNOLOGIES, INC.

NASDAQ (GS): AKAM

8 Cambridge Center
Cambridge, MA 02142
Phone: 617-444-3000
Fax: 617-444-3001
Web: www.akamai.com

CEO: Paul L. Sagan
CFO: J. Donald (J. D.) Sherman
HR: –
FYE: December 31
Type: Public

Akamai Technologies offers an accelerated course on Internet delivery. The company's technology enables companies and government agencies to deliver Web content and applications, such as ads, business transaction tools, streaming video, and Web sites. Through its network of some 30,000 servers in about 70 countries, Akamai analyzes and manages Web traffic, transmitting content from the server geographically closest to the end user. The company's customers include Airbus, Apple, Best Buy, FedEx, Microsoft, MTV Networks, Sony Ericsson Mobile Communications, the US Department of Defense, the US Department of Labor, Victoria's Secret, and XM Satellite Radio.

	Annual Growth	12/03	12/04	12/05	12/06	12/07
Sales ($ mil.)	40.9%	161.3	210.0	283.1	428.7	636.4
Net income ($ mil.)	—	(29.3)	34.4	328.0	57.4	101.0
Market value ($ mil.)	44.7%	1,311.4	1,651.8	3,047.7	8,515.1	5,751.0
Employees	28.8%	—	—	784	1,058	1,300

AKEBONO CORPORATION (NORTH AMERICA)

310 Ring Rd.
Elizabethtown, KY 42701
Phone: 248-489-7400
Fax: 270-766-1352
Web: www.akebonobrakes.com

CEO: Tsuyoshi (Go) Kashiwagi
CFO: Ron Jones
HR: Carl Lay
FYE: December 31
Type: Private

You may be able to make you own breaks, but Akebono Corporation (North America) makes original-equipment brake systems for carmakers, as well as brake components for the automotive aftermarket. The company, which operates as Akebono Brake Corporation, makes products such as disc brake calipers and pads, parking brake components, and drum brakes. It operates brake plants in Kentucky and an R&D and engineering center in Michigan. Customers have included Audi, GM, Ford, Honda, Toyota, and Nissan. Akebono Corporation (North America) is a unit of Tokyo-based Akebono Brake Industry Co., Ltd., which entered the US market in 1980.

	Annual Growth	12/03	12/04	12/05	12/06	12/07
Est. sales ($ mil.)	—	—	—	—	—	49.8
Employees	—	—	—	—	—	1,529

AKEENA SOLAR, INC.

NASDAQ (CM): AKNS

16005 Los Gatos Blvd.
Los Gatos, CA 95032
Phone: 408-395-7774
Fax: –
Web: www.akeena.net

CEO: Barry Cinnamon
CFO: Gary R. Effren
HR: Thomas Gerner
FYE: December 31
Type: Public

Ask anyone at Akeena about their company's name, and they'll tell you Akeena was the mistress of the Greek sun god Apollo. The company designs, markets, and sells solar power systems for residential and small commercial customers. They serve five states: California, Connecticut, New Jersey, New York, and Pennsylvania. Akeena was founded in 2001 and has installed more than 675 solar power systems to date, at schools, wineries, restaurants, and affordable housing developments. It uses components (such as solar modules and inverters) from Sharp, Kyocera, and SunPower.

	Annual Growth	12/03	12/04	12/05	12/06	12/07
Sales ($ mil.)	111.5%	—	—	7.2	13.4	32.2
Net income ($ mil.)	—	—	—	0.0	(1.8)	(11.1)
Market value ($ mil.)	428.5%	—	—	—	41.3	218.2
Employees	—	—	—	—	165	—

AKER CONSTRUCTION, INC.

701 Technology Dr.
Canonsburg, PA 15317
Phone: 724-416-6900
Fax: –
Web: www.akersolutions.com

CEO: Steve Harker
CFO: Leif Borge
HR: Robert C. (Bob) Hoover
FYE: December 31
Type: Subsidiary

Aker Construction is part of the North American union construction and maintenance division of Norway-based Aker Solutions, providing heavy and civil construction and renovation services for power generation plants and other industrial projects. The company provides services such as prime contracting, electrical work, equipment setting, heavy mechanical contracting, steel erection, piping, and construction management. Aker Construction acquired McCartin McAuliffe Mechanical, an Indiana-based piping contractor, in 2006. Customers have included AK Steel, BASF, and TransCanada.

	Annual Growth	12/03	12/04	12/05	12/06	12/07
Est. sales ($ mil.)	—	—	—	—	—	337.0
Employees	—	—	—	—	—	1,500

AKIBIA, INC.

4 Technology Dr.
Westborough, MA 01581
Phone: 508-621-5100
Fax: 508-621-5206
Web: www.akibia.com

CEO: Thomas (Tom) Willson
CFO: Thomas (Tom) Tucker
HR: Karen Wall
FYE: March 31
Type: Private

Maybe Akibia means IT services and business consulting in some language? The company's infrastructure management division provides technical support services for UNIX, Linux, and Windows computing environments; areas of operation include security, desktop management, and infrastructure design and maintenance. Its consulting division specializes in installing and customizing customer relationship management (CRM) software. Founded in 1988 as Polaris Service, Akibia changed its name in 2000. (Akibia is actually from Akebia Quinata, a fast-growing vine that supports surrounding plants.)

	Annual Growth	3/03	3/04	3/05	3/06	3/07
Est. sales ($ mil.)	—	—	—	—	—	88.1
Employees	—	—	—	—	—	350

AKIN GUMP STRAUSS HAUER & FELD LLP

Robert S. Strauss Bldg., 1333 New Hampshire Ave. NW
Washington, DC 20036
Phone: 202-887-4000
Fax: 202-887-4288
Web: www.akingump.com

CEO: R. Bruce McLean
CFO: Janet L. Mourges
HR: Julie Dressing
FYE: December 31
Type: Partnership

Known for its work inside Washington's Beltway, law firm Akin Gump Strauss Hauer & Feld has a staff peppered with political insiders. Co-founder Robert Strauss is a former chairman of the Democratic National Committee who has advised several presidents. Overall, the firm has more than 900 attorneys in some 15 offices, mainly in the US but also in the Asia/Pacific region, Europe, and the Middle East. Beyond its work related to public policy and government contracts, Akin Gump maintains a wide range of practices, such as corporate and securities, energy, intellectual property, litigation, and project and infrastructure development.

AKORN, INC.

NASDAQ (GM): AKRX

2500 Millbrook Dr.
Buffalo Grove, IL 60089
Phone: 847-279-6100
Fax: 800-943-3694
Web: www.akorn.com

CEO: Arthur S. Przybyl
CFO: Jeffrey A. Whitnell
HR: Neill Shanahan
FYE: December 31
Type: Public

Akorn works hard to grow roots in several segments of the pharmaceutical industry. The company makes and sells specialty therapeutic and diagnostic pharmaceuticals in categories including ophthalmology, rheumatology, and anesthesia. Akorn's ophthalmic segment includes antibiotics, glaucoma treatments, lubricating ointments, diagnostic stains and dyes, and contact lens accessories. The firm's injectable segment includes drugs for rheumatoid arthritis and pain management. Akorn's products are sold nationally to hospitals, physicians, pharmacies, and wholesalers. Akorn also provides contract manufacturing services for other drugmakers. Chairman John Kapoor controls about a third of the company.

	Annual Growth	12/03	12/04	12/05	12/06	12/07
Sales ($ mil.)	3.8%	45.5	50.7	44.5	71.3	52.9
Net income ($ mil.)	—	(12.3)	(3.0)	(8.6)	(6.0)	(19.2)
Market value ($ mil.)	99.0%	41.6	96.3	125.9	537.4	652.5
Employees	—	—	—	327	—	—

An in-depth profile of this company is available to Hoover's Online members at hoovers.com.

81

AKZO NOBEL INC.

525 W. Van Buren St., Ste. 1600	CEO: Conrad S. Kent
Chicago, IL 60607	CFO: Philip Radtke
Phone: 312-544-7000	HR: –
Fax: 312-544-7137	FYE: December 31
Web: www.akzonobel.com	Type: Subsidiary

Akzo Nobel Inc. works hard to create the right chemistry. The US subsidiary of Dutch paints and chemicals giant Akzo Nobel N.V., the company develops and makes chemicals, coatings, and health care products. Its chemicals business includes catalysts, functional chemicals, polymers, pulp and paper chemicals, and surfactants. The coatings sector includes car refinishes, decorative coatings, and industrial coatings and finishes. While the parent company is the world's largest coatings maker, its American subsidiary is driven by its chemicals business. In 2007 Akzo Nobel sold its pharmaceuticals operations, which included oral contraceptives, antidepressants, and pharmaceutical raw materials.

	Annual Growth	12/03	12/04	12/05	12/06	12/07
Est. sales ($ mil.)	—	—	—	—	—	2,147.5
Employees	—	—	—	—	—	8,210

ALA CARTE ENTERTAINMENT, INC.

2330 Hammond Dr., Ste. G	CEO: Fred Hoffman
Schaumburg, IL 60173	CFO: Bob Steder
Phone: 847-303-4400	HR: Debbie Vanacora
Fax: 847-303-0112	FYE: December 31
Web: www.aceplaces.com	Type: Private

This company caters to many tastes with a varied menu of dining and drinking options. Ala Carte Entertainment (ACE) operates more than 30 nightspots in the Chicago area, including such popular night clubs as Apartment, Deja Vu, and Excalibur. It also has several pub establishments, including The Celtic Crown and The Full Shilling. ACE's portfolio of restaurants includes Chandler's Chophouse, Magnum's Steakhouse, and Moretti's Ristorante and Pizzeria. The company also provides catering services through its restaurants. Owner and company president Fred Hoffman started his dining and entertainment empire in the early 1970s when he opened the Snuggery singles bar.

	Annual Growth	12/03	12/04	12/05	12/06	12/07
Est. sales ($ mil.)	—	—	—	—	—	71.3
Employees	—	—	—	—	—	1,300

ALABAMA AIRCRAFT INDUSTRIES, INC.

NASDAQ (GM): AAII

1943 N. 50th St.	CEO: Ronald A. Aramini
Birmingham, AL 35212	CFO: Randall C. Shealy
Phone: 205-592-0011	HR: –
Fax: 205-592-6306	FYE: December 31
Web: www.alabamaaircraft.com	Type: Public

Alabama Aircraft Industries or AAII (formerly Pemco Aviation Group) has found a sweet home maintaining aircraft and helping to launch things into space — at least for now. AAII provides airframe maintenance and modification services, primarily for large military transport aircraft. AAII's Space Vector division, which the company has plans to sell, offers launch services for scientific and military missions. The US government accounts for nearly 90% of AAII's sales. Chairman Michael Tennenbaum controls a 25% stake in the company. AAII's World Air Services unit was sold in 2007.

	Annual Growth	12/03	12/04	12/05	12/06	12/07
Sales ($ mil.)	(21.4%)	190.4	201.2	150.3	160.7	72.8
Net income ($ mil.)	(45.2%)	10.0	(3.0)	(5.8)	0.5	0.9
Market value ($ mil.)	(46.2%)	139.5	111.8	72.4	32.1	11.7
Employees	(12.8%)	—	—	1,728	1,506	—

ALABAMA FARMERS COOPERATIVE, INC.

121 Somerville Rd. SE	CEO: Tommy Paulk
Decatur, AL 35601	CFO: Dan Groscost
Phone: 256-353-6843	HR: Tina Johnson
Fax: 256-350-1770	FYE: May 31
Web: www.alafarm.com	Type: Cooperative

Alabama Farmers Cooperative (AFC) provides farmers in the Yellowhammer State a full range of agricultural supplies and services including feed, fertilizer, seed, grain storage, and marketing, along with home-gardening items such as seeds and hardware. The co-op also serves members in parts of Florida, Georgia, and Mississippi. AFC owns Bonnie Plant Farms, one of the largest suppliers of vegetable plants and annual flowers in the US. Its Anderson's Peanuts division was sold to Birdsong in 2007. Originally called the Tennessee Valley Fertilizer Cooperative, it was established in 1936.

	Annual Growth	5/02	5/03	5/04	5/05	5/06
Sales ($ mil.)	(3.9%)	298.6	324.1	286.4	267.4	254.7
Employees	—	—	—	—	—	2,300

ALABAMA POWER COMPANY

600 N. 18th St.	CEO: Charles D. McCrary
Birmingham, AL 35291	CFO: Art P. Beattie
Phone: 205-257-1000	HR: –
Fax: 205-257-2445	FYE: December 31
Web: www.alabamapower.com	Type: Subsidiary

Alabama Power powers up Southern Rockers and others in the heart of Dixie. The Southern Company subsidiary provides electricity to nearly 1.4 million residential and business customers in Alabama. The utility operates more than 78,000 miles of transmission and distribution lines, and it has nuclear, hydroelectric, and fossil-fueled power plant interests that give it a generating capacity of more than 13,000 MW. Alabama Power sells wholesale power to more than 15 municipal and rural distribution utilities; it also provides steam transmission (used for heating and cooling buildings) in downtown Birmingham, Alabama, and sells electric appliances (such as thermostats, ovens, and washing machines).

	Annual Growth	12/03	12/04	12/05	12/06	12/07
Sales ($ mil.)	7.9%	3,960.2	4,236.0	4,647.8	5,014.7	5,360.0
Net income ($ mil.)	5.8%	491.1	504.8	532.2	542.5	615.7
Employees	—	—	—	—	6,796	—

ALAMO GROUP INC.

NYSE: ALG

1627 E. Walnut	CEO: Ronald A. (Ron) Robinson
Seguin, TX 78155	CFO: Ronald A. (Ron) Robinson
Phone: 830-379-1480	HR: Gabrielle Garcia
Fax: 830-372-9683	FYE: December 31
Web: www.alamo-group.com	Type: Public

Remember the Alamo Group for tractor-mounted mowing equipment (rotary, flail, and sickle-bar). The company's Alamo Industrial and Tiger hydraulically powered tractor-mounted mowers are primarily sold to government entities. Its Rhino and M&W subsidiaries sell rotary cutters and other equipment to farmers and ranchers for pasture maintenance. McConnel, Bomford, and S.M.A. units sell hydraulic boom-mounted hedge and grass cutters. Reaching across the Atlantic, Alamo acquired Rivard Development, a France-based vacuum truck maker, in 2008. Third Avenue Management owns 31% of Alamo Group; Capital Southwest Venture Corporation, 29%.

	Annual Growth	12/03	12/04	12/05	12/06	12/07
Sales ($ mil.)	15.9%	279.1	342.2	368.1	456.5	504.4
Net income ($ mil.)	11.6%	8.0	13.4	11.3	11.5	12.4
Market value ($ mil.)	4.7%	148.4	264.5	199.9	230.0	178.3
Employees	12.3%	—	—	1,862	2,215	2,347

ALANCO TECHNOLOGIES, INC.   NASDAQ (CM): ALAN

15575 N. 83rd Way, Ste. 3
Scottsdale, AZ 85260
Phone: 480-607-1010
Fax: 480-607-1515
Web: www.alanco.com

CEO: Robert R. Kauffman
CFO: John A. Carlson
HR: John A. Carlson
FYE: June 30
Type: Public

Having failed to strike gold in the pollution business and feeling fried, Alanco Technologies turned to data storage and tracking. The company once made pollution control systems, owned gold mines, and made an unsuccessful foray into the restaurant fryer business. It now operates subsidiaries involved in data storage products (Excel/Meridian Data), radio-frequency identification (RFID) tracking devices for correctional facilities (Technology Systems International), and GPS tracking systems for the refrigerated transport industry (StarTrak Systems).

	Annual Growth	6/03	6/04	6/05	6/06	6/07
Sales ($ mil.)	25.7%	7.4	4.9	7.2	6.7	18.5
Net income ($ mil.)	—	(2.6)	(3.2)	(3.8)	(4.0)	(5.2)
Market value ($ mil.)	33.5%	15.2	90.6	62.7	70.5	48.4
Employees	33.6%	—	—	42	80	75

⊞ ALASKA AIR GROUP, INC.   NYSE: ALK

19300 International Blvd.
Seattle, WA 98188
Phone: 206-392-5040
Fax: 206-392-2804
Web: www.alaskaair.com

CEO: William S. (Bill) Ayer
CFO: Bradley D. (Brad) Tilden
HR: Marne K. McCluskey
FYE: December 31
Type: Public

Whether you want to capture a Kodiak moment or down a daiquiri by the Sea of Cortez, an Alaska Air Group unit can fly you there. The company serves as holding company for Alaska Airlines and Horizon Air Industries. Alaska Airlines serves some 40 cities in Alaska, other western states, and western Canada; it also flies to selected major cities elsewhere in the US and about 10 cities in Mexico. It has a fleet of some 115 jets (Boeing 737s and MD-80s). Alaska Airlines operates from hubs in Anchorage, Alaska; Portland, Oregon; Los Angeles; and Seattle. Regional carrier Horizon Air flies to another 40 cities in the western US and Canada with a fleet of some 20 jets and 50 turboprops.

	Annual Growth	12/03	12/04	12/05	12/06	12/07
Sales ($ mil.)	9.4%	2,444.8	2,723.8	2,975.3	3,334.4	3,506.0
Net income ($ mil.)	74.4%	13.5	(15.3)	(5.9)	(52.6)	125.0
Market value ($ mil.)	6.8%	730.3	908.5	1,195.0	1,591.6	951.6
Employees	3.4%	—	—	13,768	14,485	14,710

ALASKA COMMUNICATIONS SYSTEMS GROUP   NASDAQ (GS): ALSK

600 Telephone Ave.
Anchorage, AK 99503
Phone: 907-297-3000
Fax: 907-297-3100
Web: www.acsalaska.com

CEO: Liane J. Pelletier
CFO: David Wilson
HR: S. Lynn Erwin
FYE: December 31
Type: Public

Alaska Communications Systems Group, Inc. (ACS Group) has outgrown the igloo. The facilities-based integrated telecommunications carrier operates the leading local-exchange network in the state and provides local and long-distance voice services, as well as Internet access and wireless communications services under the "ACS" brand to retail, enterprise, and wholesale customers. It also provides interexchange long-distance services as well as Internet phone service. The company has about 250,000 traditional phone access lines in service and about 180,000 wireless subscribers.

	Annual Growth	12/03	12/04	12/05	12/06	12/07
Sales ($ mil.)	4.5%	323.5	302.7	326.8	349.8	385.8
Net income ($ mil.)	—	(6.6)	(39.3)	(41.6)	20.0	144.1
Market value ($ mil.)	46.6%	139.1	264.9	423.5	642.9	643.2
Employees	(2.8%)	—	—	1,030	1,001	—

ALASKA PACIFIC BANCSHARES, INC.   OTC: AKPB

2094 Jordan Ave.
Juneau, AK 99801
Phone: 907-789-4844
Fax: 907-790-5110
Web: www.alaskapacificbank.com

CEO: Craig E. Dahl
CFO: Julie Pierce
HR: Bill Abbott
FYE: December 31
Type: Public

If you hail from Alaska, *Juneau* about Alaska Pacific Bancshares. It is the holding company for Alaska Pacific Bank, which serves the communities of Juneau, Ketchikan, and Sitka through about a half-dozen branches. The bank offers deposit products including checking and savings accounts, CDs, IRAs, and check cards. Single- to four-family residential mortgages and commercial real estate loans each account for about a quarter of the company's loan portfolio. The bank also originates construction, business, and consumer loans. Alaska Pacific Bank was founded in 1935.

	Annual Growth	12/03	12/04	12/05	12/06	12/07
Assets ($ mil.)	3.3%	164.6	163.8	177.2	178.9	187.5
Net income ($ mil.)	15.8%	0.5	0.7	0.7	1.1	0.9
Market value ($ mil.)	7.0%	—	—	12.6	15.3	14.4
Employees	—	—	—	—	—	73

ALBANY INTERNATIONAL CORP.   NYSE: AIN

1373 Broadway
Albany, NY 12204
Phone: 518-445-2200
Fax: 518-445-2265
Web: www.albint.com

CEO: Joseph G. Morone
CFO: Michael C. Nahl
HR: Ralph M. Polumbo
FYE: December 31
Type: Public

Albany International's products look good on paper and on papermaking machines. The company makes paper machine clothing (PMC, custom-made fabric belts that move paper stock through each phase of production). Albany produces about 45% of the monofilament yarn used in its paper machine clothing and relies on independent suppliers for the remainder. It markets these products to paper mills worldwide through a direct sales staff. Albany also makes industrial fabric doors (Rapid Roll Doors), such as aircraft hangar doors and dock doors, as well as synthetic insulation, and industrial fabric filters.

	Annual Growth	12/03	12/04	12/05	12/06	12/07
Sales ($ mil.)	5.9%	869.0	919.8	978.7	1,011.5	1,093.0
Net income ($ mil.)	(24.3%)	54.1	10.4	71.8	58.0	17.8
Market value ($ mil.)	(0.9%)	1,014.6	990.6	1,053.2	854.9	977.1
Employees	1.7%	—	—	5,900	6,150	6,100

ALBANY MEDICAL CENTER

43 New Scotland Ave.
Albany, NY 12208
Phone: 518-262-3125
Fax: 518-262-3165
Web: www.amc.edu

CEO: James J. Barba
CFO: William C. Hasselbarth
HR: Catherine (Cathy) Halakan
FYE: December 31
Type: Not-for-profit

Albany Medical Center provides upscale medical care to the residents of upstate New York. Serving 25 counties in eastern New York and western New England, the health system has at its heart the 650-bed Albany Medical Center Hospital, a general medical-surgical facility that also provides specialty care in areas such as oncology, rehabilitation, and organ transplantation. Additionally, Albany Medical Center features a children's hospital, an outpatient surgery center, and a group medical practice. Its Albany Medical College, one of the nation's first private medical schools, offers undergraduate and graduate medical degrees and residency programs, as well as fellowships and continuing medical education.

	Annual Growth	12/03	12/04	12/05	12/06	12/07
Est. sales ($ mil.)	—	—	—	—	—	480.7
Employees	—	—	—	—	—	6,050

ALBANY MOLECULAR RESEARCH, INC.
NASDAQ (GM): AMRI

21 Corporate Cir.
Albany, NY 12212
Phone: 518-464-0279
Fax: 518-464-0289
Web: www.albmolecular.com

CEO: Thomas E. D'Ambra
CFO: Mark T. Frost
HR: Walter Foust
FYE: December 31
Type: Public

Albany Molecular Research, doing business as AMRI, provides contract research and manufacturing services to pharmaceutical and biotechnology firms. The company's services run the gamut, from compound screening and other drug discovery services to the contract manufacturing of drugs and drug ingredients for clinical trials and commercial sale. In addition to its work for other drug companies, Albany Molecular conducts some of its own research, with the goal of licensing its compounds to other firms for further development. The contract company has one winner already: it owns a patent for fexofenadine HCl, the key ingredient in Sanofi-Aventis' antihistamine Allegra.

	Annual Growth	12/03	12/04	12/05	12/06	12/07
Sales ($ mil.)	(0.5%)	196.4	169.5	183.9	179.8	192.5
Net income ($ mil.)	(26.7%)	30.9	(11.7)	16.3	2.2	8.9
Market value ($ mil.)	(0.0%)	474.6	355.0	393.7	345.0	474.5
Employees	—	—	—	847	—	—

ALBECCA INC.

3900 Steve Reynolds Blvd.
Norcross, GA 30093
Phone: 770-279-5200
Fax: 770-279-5297
Web: www.larsonjuhl.com

CEO: Stephen E. (Steve) McKenzie
CFO: R. Bradley Goodson
HR: Patrick R. Cronin
FYE: December 31
Type: Subsidiary

Albecca has a clear picture of the custom framing industry. The company (which operates under the name Larson-Juhl) designs, makes, and distributes framing products, including wood and metal molding. Wood products are sold under the Larson-Juhl Classic Collection and the Craig Ponzio Signature Collection names; metal moldings are sold under the Clark name. The company also sells mat (Artique) and foam board, glass, and related supplies (joining machines, matboard cutters). Albecca sells its nearly 20,000 products through retail custom framers and home decorating centers worldwide. Warren Buffett and his investment group, Berkshire Hathaway, bought the company from designer Craig Ponzio and his wife in 2002.

	Annual Growth	12/03	12/04	12/05	12/06	12/07
Est. sales ($ mil.)	—	—	—	—	—	127.0
Employees	—	—	—	—	—	2,070

ALBEMARLE CORPORATION
NYSE: ALB

330 S. Fourth St.
Richmond, VA 23219
Phone: 804-788-6000
Fax: 804-788-5688
Web: www.albemarle.com

CEO: Mark C. Rohr
CFO: Richard J. (Rich) Diemer Jr.
HR: Jack P. Harsh
FYE: December 31
Type: Public

Albemarle has family chemistry. A spinoff from Ethyl Corp. (now called NewMarket), the company produces polymer additives, fine chemicals, and catalysts used by a variety of industries. Its polymer additives — flame retardants, stabilizers, and curatives — add desired properties to various plastics. Albemarle's catalysts segment makes polyolefin and refinery catalysts. Its fine chemicals include bromine-based chemicals, agricultural chemicals, and bulk ibuprofen (used to make the pain reliever). Customers include chemical, plastics, pharmaceutical, petroleum, and paper companies.

	Annual Growth	12/03	12/04	12/05	12/06	12/07
Sales ($ mil.)	20.4%	1,110.2	1,513.7	2,107.5	2,368.5	2,336.2
Net income ($ mil.)	33.7%	71.9	54.8	114.9	143.0	229.7
Market value ($ mil.)	58.7%	616.7	810.9	896.4	3,405.5	3,907.8
Employees	5.7%	—	—	3,700	3,560	4,130

ALBERICI CORPORATION

8800 Page Ave.
St. Louis, MO 63114
Phone: 314-733-2000
Fax: 314-733-2001
Web: www.alberici.com

CEO: Gregory J. (Greg) Kozicz
CFO: Gregory T. (Greg) Hesser
HR: R. Denay Davis
FYE: December 31
Type: Private

Alberici helped shape the St. Louis skyline; it now sets its sights — or its construction sites — across North America. Alberici Corporation, parent of Alberici Constructors (formerly J.S. Alberici Construction Co.), encompasses a group of enterprises with a presence in the US, Canada, and Mexico as well as in Brazil. Operations include construction equipment, building materials, and steel fabrication and erection units. Alberici offers general contracting, design/build services, construction management, demolition, and specialty contracting. It also offers facilities management. The Alberici family still holds the largest share of the employee-owned firm, founded in 1918 by John S. Alberici.

	Annual Growth	12/02	12/03	12/04	12/05	12/06
Sales ($ mil.)	(0.3%)	—	—	—	1,033.0	1,030.0
Employees	0.0%	—	—	—	511	511

▣ ALBERTO-CULVER COMPANY
NYSE: ACV

2525 Armitage Ave.
Melrose Park, IL 60160
Phone: 708-450-3000
Fax: 708-450-3409
Web: www.alberto.com

CEO: V. James Marino
CFO: Ralph J. Nicoletti
HR: –
FYE: September 30
Type: Public

From the bath to the kitchen, Alberto-Culver has it covered. It makes products for hair care (Alberto VO5, Nexxus, TRESemmé, Consort, Motions), skin care (St. Ives Swiss Formula), and personal care (FDS); sweeteners and seasonings (Molly McButter, Mrs. Dash, SugarTwin, Baker's Joy); and laundrycare items (Static Guard). A plan to sell the business to Regis Corporation fell through in early 2006. In November 2006, however, Alberto-Culver parted ways with its Sally Beauty unit, the world's #1 beauty supply retailer and distributor to professionals and consumers. The move included a split with its Beauty Systems Group, as well. It's selling its Cederroth business, which serves Nordic countries, to CapMan.

	Annual Growth	9/03	9/04	9/05	9/06	9/07
Sales ($ mil.)	(14.5%)	2,891.4	3,258.0	3,531.2	3,772.0	1,541.6
Net income ($ mil.)	(16.6%)	162.1	141.8	210.9	205.3	78.3
Market value ($ mil.)	—	—	—	—	—	2,301.2
Employees	(31.2%)	17,000	18,300	19,000	3,800	3,800

▣ ALBERTSONS LLC

250 Parkcenter Blvd.
Boise, ID 83706
Phone: 208-395-6200
Fax: 208-395-6349
Web: albertsonsmarket.com

CEO: Robert (Bob) Miller
CFO: Richard J. (Rick) Navarro
HR: Jack Snow
FYE: Thursday nearest January 31
Type: Private

Call it the incredible shrinking grocery chain. Albertsons LLC (formerly Albertson's) is all that's left of what was once the nation's #2 supermarket operator. Stung by competition, the 2,500-store chain sold itself in mid-2006 to a consortium that included rival grocer SUPERVALU, drugstore chain CVS, investment firm Cerberus Capital Management, and Kimco Realty for about $9.7 billion. SUPERVALU and CVS cherry picked the company's best supermarket and drugstore assets. Subsequent divestments (most notably 132 stores in Northern California) have left the company with more than 315 Albertsons supermarkets and about 115 Express fuel centers in about 10 states.

	Annual Growth	1/02	1/03	1/04	1/05	1/06
Sales ($ mil.)	1.6%	37,931.0	35,626.0	35,436.0	39,897.0	40,358.0
Net income ($ mil.)	(2.9%)	501.0	485.0	556.0	444.0	446.0
Employees	1.6%	220,000	202,000	—	—	234,000

ALCAN BALTEK CORPORATION

10 Fairway Ct.
Northvale, NJ 07647
Phone: 201-767-1400
Fax: 201-387-6631
Web: www.baltek.com

CEO: Daniel Duclos
CFO: Gustavo Chavez
HR: Mauricio Valdivieso
FYE: December 31
Type: Subsidiary

Alcan Baltek is a model of modern manufacturing. The company, a unit of Rio Tinto Alcan (formerly Alcan) through its Alcan Composites subsidiary, and part of its Core Composites unit, makes composites and other materials that go into the manufacture of yachts, aircraft, wind turbines, and high-speed trains. Alcan Baltek supplies end grain balsa core material, PVC foam products, and nonwoven polyester mats to manufacturers for use as lamination between fiberglass or metal skins in the production of fiberglass boats, aircraft flooring, and other applications. The hobby industry uses Alcan Baltek's balsa wood (produced in Ecuador) for model airplanes. Alcan Composites bought Baltek in 2003.

	Annual Growth	12/03	12/04	12/05	12/06	12/07
Est. sales ($ mil.)	—	—	—	—	—	110.6
Employees	—	—	—	—	—	977

ALCAS CORPORATION

1116 E. State St.
Olean, NY 14760
Phone: 716-372-3111
Fax: 716-790-7191
Web: www.alcas.com

CEO: James E. Stitt
CFO: −
HR: −
FYE: December 31
Type: Private

Alcas cuts up in the kitchen and on the battlefield. The company's CUTCO Cutlery subsidiary makes butcher knives, paring knives, carving forks, and other household cutlery. It also makes hunting and fishing knives. CUTCO's cutlery is sold in North America via home demonstrations by Vector Marketing, an Alcas subsidiary. Alcas' KA-BAR Knives subsidiary manufactures fighting and utility knives for the US military, along with hunting, fishing, and pocket knives that are sold through retailers worldwide. Another Alcas subsidiary, CUTCO International, sells CUTCO's products outside North America. Formed in 1949 by Alcoa and W.R. Case & Sons Cutlery Company, Alcas was bought by company management from Alcoa in 1982.

ALCATEL-LUCENT HOLDING INC.

3400 W. Plano Pkwy.
Plano, TX 75075
Phone: 972-519-3000
Fax: 972-519-2240
Web: www.usa.alcatel.com

CEO: Cindy Christy
CFO: −
HR: −
FYE: December 31
Type: Subsidiary

Alcatel-Lucent Holding, a regional subsidiary of France-based Alcatel-Lucent, designs, develops, and builds communications networks. It supplies equipment, software applications, and related services to telecom carriers and network service providers, as well as enterprise and government customers. A leading supplier of broadband Internet access products, the company pioneered the development of digital subscriber line (DSL) technology for residential and small business end-users. Alcatel-Lucent was formed from the 2006 merger of telecom rivals Alcatel and Lucent Technologies.

	Annual Growth	12/03	12/04	12/05	12/06	12/07
Est. sales ($ mil.)	—	—	—	—	—	651.3
Employees	—	—	—	—	—	6,800

⊞ ALCOA INC.

NYSE: AA

201 Isabella St.
Pittsburgh, PA 15212
Phone: 412-553-4545
Fax: 412-553-4498
Web: www.alcoa.com

CEO: Klaus Kleinfeld
CFO: Charles D. (Chuck) McLane Jr.
HR: Regina M. Hitchery
FYE: December 31
Type: Public

Alcoa is among the world's top producers of alumina (aluminum's principal ingredient, processed from bauxite) and aluminum. Its vertically integrated operations include bauxite mining, alumina refining, and aluminum smelting; primary products include alumina and its chemicals, automotive components, and sheet aluminum for beverage cans. The company's non-aluminum products include fiber-optic cables. Major markets include the aerospace, automotive, and construction industries. In 2007 Alcoa offered to buy what was then the world's #3 aluminum producer, Alcan, for $33 billion but was trumped by Rio Tinto's $40 billion offer. The next year it sold its packaging business to the Rank Group.

	Annual Growth	12/03	12/04	12/05	12/06	12/07
Sales ($ mil.)	9.4%	21,504.0	23,478.0	26,159.0	30,379.0	30,748.0
Net income ($ mil.)	28.6%	938.0	1,310.0	1,233.0	2,248.0	2,564.0
Market value ($ mil.)	(2.2%)	33,002.6	27,366.2	25,779.7	26,094.8	30,241.5
Employees	(8.9%)	—	—	129,000	123,000	107,000

ALDEN MANAGEMENT SERVICES, INC.

4200 W. Peterson Ave., Ste. 140
Chicago, IL 60646
Phone: 773-286-3883
Fax: 773-286-2128
Web: www.thealdennetwork.com

CEO: Floyd A. Schlossberg
CFO: Steve Kroll
HR: −
FYE: December 31
Type: Private

Alden Management Services operates independent living, assisted living, and skilled rehabilitation and nursing facilities primarily throughout Illinois, but also in Wisconsin. Its facilities provide a wide range of services such as rehabilitation, Alzheimer's care, hospice, and infectious disease management. The company also offers programs for children with special needs. Alden's pediatric services include behavioral management, nursing care, and physical therapy.

	Annual Growth	12/03	12/04	12/05	12/06	12/07
Est. sales ($ mil.)	—	—	—	—	—	91.8
Employees	—	—	—	—	—	4,000

ALDILA, INC.

NASDAQ (GM): ALDA

13450 Stowe Dr.
Poway, CA 92064
Phone: 858-513-1801
Fax: 858-513-1870
Web: www.aldila.com

CEO: Peter R. Mathewson
CFO: Scott M. Bier
HR: Maryann Jacoub
FYE: December 31
Type: Public

Without Aldila, golf clubs just wouldn't look the same. Under the Aldila brand name, the company makes graphite golf club shafts for companies such as Callaway Golf, Ping, and Acushnet (which combine for more than 50% of sales). Other customers include custom club builders, distributors, pro shops, and repair centers. Aldila is protecting itself against any erratic swings in the industry by producing its own graphite and selling the excess to other sporting goods manufacturers. Aldila makes its shafts in China, Mexico, and Vietnam.

	Annual Growth	12/03	12/04	12/05	12/06	12/07
Sales ($ mil.)	16.3%	37.8	52.8	77.0	72.4	69.2
Net income ($ mil.)	—	(1.7)	9.3	13.4	11.2	15.9
Market value ($ mil.)	48.7%	17.3	78.2	137.2	82.4	84.5
Employees	—	—	—	1,274	—	—

⊞ An in-depth profile of this company is available to Hoover's Online members at hoovers.com.

ALERIS INTERNATIONAL, INC.

25825 Science Park Dr., Ste. 400
Beachwood, OH 44122
Phone: 216-910-3400
Fax: 216-910-3650
Web: www.aleris.com

CEO: Steven J. (Steve) Demetriou
CFO: Sean M. Stack
HR: –
FYE: December 31
Type: Private

Aleris International was formed in 2004 when aluminum recycler IMCO Recycling bought Commonwealth Industries. It got a lot bigger with the 2006 acquisition of Corus Group's downstream aluminum operations and has continued to grow through acquisitions. Its rolled and extruded products unit makes alloy aluminum sheet from recycled metal as well as extruded profiles for the construction and engineering markets. Aleris' recycling unit processes recycled aluminum (beverage cans and scrap) and metal alloys (aluminum scrap and other metals). It operates in China, the Americas, and throughout Europe. In 2006 Texas Pacific Group acquired Aleris for about $3.5 billion in cash and assumed debt.

	Annual Growth	12/02	12/03	12/04	12/05	12/06
Sales ($ mil.)	62.1%	687.2	892.0	1,226.6	2,429.0	4,748.8
Net income ($ mil.)	—	(51.9)	(0.8)	(23.8)	74.3	70.3
Employees	51.2%	1,627	1,788	3,200	4,200	8,500

ALESCO FINANCIAL INC.

NYSE: AFN

2929 Arch St., 17th Fl.
Philadelphia, PA 19104
Phone: 215-701-9555
Fax: 215-701-8281
Web: www.alescofinancial.com

CEO: James J. McEntee III
CFO: John J. Longino
HR: –
FYE: December 31
Type: Public

Alesco Financial (formerly Sunset Financial Resources) is a real estate investment trust (REIT) that acquires and invests in collateralized debt and loan obligations. Its portfolio largely consists of trust-preferred securities issued by banks and insurance companies, mortgage-backed securities, and commercial loans made primarily to small and midsized companies in the consumer products and manufacturing industries. The company is externally managed by investment bank and asset manager Cohen & Company (founded by Alesco chairman). In 2006 Sunset Financial merged with Alesco Financial Trust, a specialty finance REIT formed earlier that year, and the combined entity took the Alesco name.

	Annual Growth	12/03	12/04	12/05	12/06	12/07
Sales ($ mil.)	66.2%	—	18.2	46.4	217.7	83.6
Net income ($ mil.)	—	—	0.6	(4.7)	22.0	(1,261.3)
Market value ($ mil.)	(66.2%)	—	—	—	587.7	198.6
Employees	251.6%	—	—	11	—	136

ALEX LEE, INC.

120 4th St. SW
Hickory, NC 28602
Phone: 828-725-4424
Fax: 828-725-4435
Web: www.alexlee.com

CEO: Boyd L. George
CFO: Ronald W. Knedlik
HR: Glenn DeBiasi
FYE: September 30
Type: Private

Wholesale groceries are only part of the story for this company. Alex Lee is a leading wholesale distributor of food and other products to retailers and foodservice operators. Through Merchants Distributors, Inc. (MDI), it supplies food and related merchandise to more than 600 retailers in about 10 states, mostly in the Southeast. Its Institutional Food House (IFH) unit is a foodservice supplier serving customers in the hospitality industry. Alex Lee also operates a chain of more than 100 grocery stores through Lowe's Food Stores, and it provides warehousing services through Consolidation Services. Alex and Lee George started the company in 1931; the George family continues to control Alex Lee.

	Annual Growth	9/02	9/03	9/04	9/05	9/06
Sales ($ mil.)	9.0%	1,980.0	2,140.0	2,320.0	2,500.0	2,800.0
Employees	3.9%	9,000	9,500	10,300	10,300	10,500

ALEXANDER & BALDWIN, INC.

NASDAQ (GS): ALEX

822 Bishop St.
Honolulu, HI 96813
Phone: 808-525-6611
Fax: 808-525-6652
Web: www.alexanderbaldwin.com

CEO: W. Allen Doane
CFO: Christopher J. (Chris) Benjamin
HR: Son-Jai Paik
FYE: December 31
Type: Public

Alexander & Baldwin (A&B) helps connect Hawaii with North America. The company's ocean transportation subsidiary, Matson Navigation, carries freight mainly between ports in Hawaii, Guam, Alaska, and Puerto Rico and the continental US. Its fleet of more than 15 vessels includes containerships and barges. Matson also provides intermodal services (arrangement of freight transportation by a combination of road and rail) and logistics services in North America. In addition to its transportation-related businesses, A&B has subsidiaries that engage in real estate development and property management, both in Hawaii and on the US mainland. Other units produce sugar and coffee in Hawaii.

	Annual Growth	12/03	12/04	12/05	12/06	12/07
Sales ($ mil.)	8.1%	1,233.0	1,494.0	1,607.0	1,607.0	1,681.0
Net income ($ mil.)	15.1%	81.0	101.0	126.0	122.0	142.0
Market value ($ mil.)	11.4%	1,424.3	1,836.8	2,386.6	1,888.9	2,190.4
Employees	0.9%	—	—	2,177	2,197	

ALEXANDER'S, INC.

NYSE: ALX

210 Rte. 4 East
Paramus, NJ 07652
Phone: 201-587-8541
Fax: 201-708-6214
Web: www.alx-inc.com

CEO: Steven Roth
CFO: Joseph Macnow
HR: –
FYE: December 31
Type: Public

Alexander's knows what's great about real estate. The real estate investment trust (REIT) owns, manages, and leases a handful of properties totaling about 2.3 million sq. ft. in New York City and New Jersey. Once a department store chain, Alexander's held on to its property interests, including the site of its erstwhile flagship store — an entire block on Manhattan's Lexington Avenue. The REIT leases space at the mixed-use Lexington site to tenants such as Bloomberg, Citibank, The Home Depot, and The Container Store. The Lexington site is also home to about 100 condos. Bloomberg accounts for about a third of sales. Vornado Realty Trust owns 33% of the company and manages its real estate business.

	Annual Growth	12/03	12/04	12/05	12/06	12/07
Sales ($ mil.)	24.3%	87.2	148.9	187.1	198.8	208.0
Net income ($ mil.)	—	(17.7)	(33.5)	82.2	(75.0)	114.3
Market value ($ mil.)	30.0%	623.4	1,078.0	1,270.1	2,113.3	1,781.8
Employees	1.6%	—	—	96	—	99

ALEXANDRIA REAL ESTATE EQUITIES, INC.

NYSE: ARE

385 E. Colorado Blvd., Ste. 299
Pasadena, CA 91101
Phone: 626-578-0777
Fax: 626-578-0896
Web: www.labspace.com

CEO: Joel S. Marcus
CFO: Dean A. Shigenaga
HR: –
FYE: December 31
Type: Public

Alexandria Real Estate Equities sheds a little light on properties that can be useful to life science firms. The real estate investment trust (REIT) owns, develops, and operates offices and laboratories, with more than 160 properties in ten states and about five additional properties in Canada. Biotechnology and pharmaceutical companies, research institutions, government agencies, and similar tenants occupy its properties. The REIT's properties, which contain more than 12 million sq. ft. of rentable space, are mainly located in high-tech hotbeds such as North Carolina's Research Triangle, the San Francisco Bay area, San Diego, Seattle, Washington, DC, and Boston.

	Annual Growth	12/03	12/04	12/05	12/06	12/07
Sales ($ mil.)	26.0%	160.6	183.3	244.1	316.8	405.4
Net income ($ mil.)	12.0%	59.6	60.2	63.4	73.4	93.7
Market value ($ mil.)	30.3%	1,115.4	1,458.2	1,806.5	2,912.8	3,213.1
Employees	27.0%	—	—	93	105	150

ALEXIAN BROTHERS HEALTH SYSTEM

3040 Salt Creek Ln.
Arlington Heights, IL 60005
Phone: 847-818-5100
Fax: 847-483-7039
Web: www.alexianhealthsystems.org

CEO: Thomas Keusenkothen
CFO: James J. Sances
HR: Jim Lewandowski
FYE: December 31
Type: Not-for-profit

O brother, can you spare some health care? Alexian Brothers Health System — which follows the principles set forth by St. Alexius of Rome, the patron of beggars and pilgrims — runs two medical centers, two psychiatric hospitals, a rehabilitation institute, and several occupational health and community health clinics in the Chicago area. In Missouri, Tennessee, and Wisconsin, the Roman Catholic brotherhood operates continuing care retirement communities, assisted-living residences, nursing facilities, and independent living assistance. With more than 800 beds, the system's hospitals emphasize such specialties as cardiology, obstetrics, and oncology.

ALEXION PHARMACEUTICALS, INC.

NASDAQ (GM): ALXN

352 Knotter Dr.
Cheshire, CT 06410
Phone: 203-272-2596
Fax: 203-271-8190
Web: www.alexionpharmaceuticals.com

CEO: Leonard Bell
CFO: Vikas Sinha
HR: Glenn R. Melrose
FYE: December 31
Type: Public

Alexion Pharmaceuticals can't suppress its enthusiasm for treating immune functions gone awry. The firm develops drugs that inhibit certain immune system functions that cause autoimmune disorders, cancers, and other diseases. The company's first marketed product, Soliris, won US and European approval in 2007 for the treatment of a rare genetic blood disorder known as paroxysmal nocturnal hemoglobinuria. Alexion is developing the same antibody (eculizumab) as a potential treatment for other autoimmune and inflammatory conditions, including myasthenia gravis, multifocal neuropathy, and severe asthma. It has other antibodies at early stages of development that may treat leukemia and other cancers.

	Annual Growth	7/04	7/05	*12/05	12/06	12/07
Sales ($ mil.)	98.9%	4.6	1.1	0.7	1.6	72.0
Net income ($ mil.)	—	(74.1)	(108.8)	(58.0)	(131.5)	(92.3)
Market value ($ mil.)	59.5%	438.1	398.0	626.3	1,434.3	2,837.3
Employees	0.0%	—	241	241	—	—

*Fiscal year change

ALEXZA PHARMACEUTICALS, INC.

NASDAQ (GM): ALXA

2091 Stierlin Court
Mountain View, CA 94043
Phone: 650-944-7000
Fax: 650-944-7999
Web: www.alexza.com

CEO: Thomas B. King
CFO: August J. Moretti
HR: Emily Lee Kelley
FYE: December 31
Type: Public

Alexza Pharmaceuticals has found that some good can come out of smoking cigarettes. Though they deliver harmful chemicals, cigarettes deliver those chemicals almost instantly. That is the basis for Alexza Pharmaceutical's primary product, Staccato inhalers. The inhalers contain a heating element coated with a thin layer of medicine. Before use, the patient triggers the heating element which vaporizes the medicine, allowing the patient to inhale it. The medicine is then rapidly absorbed through the lungs at a rate typically faster than oral and intravenous mediations. The company has been targeting acute pain treatments and anxiety treatments.

	Annual Growth	12/02	12/03	12/04	12/05	*12/06
Sales ($ mil.)	49.5%	0.2	1.0	2.4	2.2	1.0
Net income ($ mil.)	—	(8.2)	(14.3)	(16.6)	(32.4)	(41.8)
Market value ($ mil.)	—	—	—	—	—	271.3
Employees	17.5%	—	—	—	120	141

*Most recent year available

ALFA CORPORATION

2108 E. South Blvd.
Montgomery, AL 36116
Phone: 334-288-3900
Fax: 334-613-4709
Web: www.alfains.com

CEO: Jerry A. Newby
CFO: Stephen G. Rutledge
HR: Thomas E. Bryant
FYE: December 31
Type: Private

Alfa Corporation wants to be the top dog in the Alabama insurance pack. As a subsidiary of the Alfa Mutual group of companies (Alfa Mutual Insurance, Alfa Mutual Fire Insurance, and Alfa Mutual General Insurance) Alfa Corporation provides personal property/casualty insurance in a dozen central and southeastern states. It also offers life insurance policies in Alabama, Georgia, and Mississippi. The company enjoys a pooling arrangement between all of the Alfa companies. President and chairman Jerry Newby is also president of the Alabama Farmers Federation, which founded the company in 1946.

	Annual Growth	12/03	12/04	12/05	12/06	12/07
Assets ($ mil.)	6.6%	2,045.1	2,222.7	2,381.9	2,534.2	2,641.8
Net income ($ mil.)	4.5%	78.5	89.4	99.0	105.9	93.5
Employees	—	—	—	0	4,161	—

ALFA LAVAL INC.

5400 International Trade Dr.
Richmond, VA 23231
Phone: 804-222-5300
Fax: 804-236-3672
Web: www.alfalaval.us

CEO: Alessandro Terenghi
CFO: Stephen Pratt
HR: –
FYE: December 31
Type: Subsidiary

There's a "whole lotta shaking going on" at Alfa Laval. The subsidiary of Sweden-based Alfa Laval AB makes separators (centrifuges), heat exchangers (evaporators and condensers), decanters, tank equipment, pumps, and valves. Alfa Laval's products are used in a host of industries from dairy and food processing to petrochemicals and steel manufacturing. The company also offers spare parts, reconditioned heat exchangers, and round-the-clock equipment monitoring systems. The company has 11 locations in the US, including three manufacturing facilities.

	Annual Growth	12/03	12/04	12/05	12/06	12/07
Est. sales ($ mil.)	—	—	—	—	—	323.2
Employees	—	—	—	—	—	632

ALFACELL CORPORATION

NASDAQ (CM): ACEL

300 Atrium Dr.
Somerset, NJ 08873
Phone: 732-652-4525
Fax: 732-652-4575
Web: www.alfacell.com

CEO: Kuslima (Tina) Shogen
CFO: Lawrence A. (Larry) Kenyon
HR: –
FYE: July 31
Type: Public

Development-stage Alfacell may kiss a few frogs in hopes one will transform into a princely product. The biotechnology firm has isolated proteins from Northern Leopard frog eggs and embryos as possible therapies for cancerous tumors that have become resistant to chemotherapy. The company's lead drug candidate, Onconase, is in late-stage clinical trials to treat mesothelioma, a cancer afflicting the lungs and stomach caused by exposure to asbestos. Onconase is also in early clinical trials for small cell lung cancer. Alfacell is researching applications for Onconase and other amphibian proteins for applications in other areas of oncology, as well as infectious diseases including HIV.

	Annual Growth	7/02	7/03	7/04	7/05	*7/06
Sales ($ mil.)	—	0.0	0.0	0.0	0.2	0.1
Net income ($ mil.)	—	(2.6)	(2.4)	(5.1)	(6.5)	(7.8)
Market value ($ mil.)	83.9%	7.7	33.0	226.7	77.5	88.6
Employees	2.5%	—	13	15	14	14

*Most recent year available

An in-depth profile of this company is available to Hoover's Online members at hoovers.com.

87

ALFRED NICKLES BAKERY INCORPORATED

26 N. Main St.
Navarre, OH 44662
Phone: 330-879-5635
Fax: 330-879-5896
Web: www.nicklesbakery.com

CEO: David A. Gardner
CFO: Mark Sponseller
HR: Gary Prado
FYE: December 31
Type: Private

It was 1909 when Swiss immigrant Alfred Nickles began counting his nickels and dimes as a one-man bakery-shop operator. The company he founded, Alfred Nickles Bakery, now operates three large-scale bakeries in Ohio, as well as 37 distribution centers in five Midwestern states (Indiana, Michigan, Ohio, Pennsylvania, and West Virginia). It runs a fleet of more than 600 delivery trucks. It makes and delivers fresh-baked goods — bagels, bread, breadsticks, dinner rolls, hot dog and hamburger buns, cakes, pastries, donuts, snack cakes, and muffins — to retail food and foodservice operations in the Midwest.

	Annual Growth	12/03	12/04	12/05	12/06	12/07
Est. sales ($ mil.)	—	—	—	—	—	176.2
Employees	—	—	—	—	—	1,700

ALIBRIS, INC.

1250 45th St., Ste. 100
Emeryville, CA 94608
Phone: 510-500-0856
Fax: –
Web: www.alibris.com

CEO: Brian P. Elliott
CFO: Richard Hewitt
HR: Peggy J. DeLeon
FYE: December 31
Type: Private

When the average bookstore just won't do, there's Alibris. The online retailer provides more than 70 million out-of-print and hard-to-find books, music, and videos; manuscripts; photos; prints; and autographs. Independent booksellers worldwide from 45 countries supply Alibris with books. Customers include libraries, wholesalers, retailers, and consumers in the US and the UK. The company was founded as Interloc in 1994 and relaunched as Alibris in 1998. Under its previous backers (which included CMGI and Lightspeed Venture Partners), Alibris planned to go public but eventually withdrew the offer. Oak Hill Capital Partners then bought the company in mid-2006 and appointed a new CEO in 2007.

ALICO, INC.

NASDAQ (GS): ALCO

640 S. Main St.
La Belle, FL 33935
Phone: 863-675-2966
Fax: 863-675-6928
Web: www.alicoinc.com

CEO: John R. Alexander
CFO: Patrick W. Murphy
HR: Michael Talaga
FYE: August 31
Type: Public

Alico is bullish on cattle, but citrus generates more revenue. The company, which owns some 135,000 acres of land in Florida, also dabbles in sugarcane, vegetable and sod, forestry, and land leases. Alico's citrus is packed or processed with fruit from other growers through produce marketer Ben Hill Griffin. It has a breeding herd of approximately 11,000 cattle and sells stock primarily to packing and processing plants. Alico's sugarcane is sold through a pooling agreement with a nearby sugar mill; sod is marketed through a US wholesaler. The company's timberland operations primarily consist of growing and selling sabal palms, palm fans, oak trees, and other plants.

	Annual Growth	8/03	8/04	8/05	8/06	8/07
Sales ($ mil.)	29.3%	48.3	52.1	70.9	77.4	134.8
Net income ($ mil.)	—	12.7	17.8	6.1	6.5	(13.8)
Market value ($ mil.)	16.9%	201.4	321.7	383.1	433.3	376.3
Employees	21.3%	—	—	155	—	228

ALIENWARE CORPORATION

14591 SW 120th St.
Miami, FL 33186
Phone: 305-251-9797
Fax: 305-259-9874
Web: www.alienware.com

CEO: Nelson Gonzalez
CFO: –
HR: –
FYE: December 31
Type: Subsidiary

Aliens have landed in Miami and they're spreading! Relax, they come in peace. Alienware caters to video game enthusiasts, digital video editors, and professionals in the market for high-end PCs made with top-of-the-line components. Sporting names like Area-51, Alienware's colorful systems utilize the highest-performance processors, video cards, and storage components available for PCs. Alienware systems are further differentiated by customized cases, upgraded power supplies, and multiple cooling fans. CEO Nelson Gonzalez and president Alex Aguila, Alienware co-founders and childhood friends, started the company in 1996. Dell acquired Alienware in 2006.

ALIGN TECHNOLOGY, INC.

NASDAQ (GM): ALGN

881 Martin Ave.
Santa Clara, CA 95050
Phone: 408-470-1000
Fax: 408-470-1010
Web: www.aligntech.com

CEO: Thomas M. Prescott
CFO: Kenneth B. (Ken) Arola
HR: Sonia Clark
FYE: December 31
Type: Public

Brace-face begone! Align Technology produces and sells the Invisalign System, which corrects malocclusion, or crooked teeth. Instead of using metal or ceramic mounts that are cemented on the teeth and connected by wires, the system involves using an array of clear and removable dental Aligners to move a patient's teeth into a desired tooth alignment. The company markets its products to orthodontists and dentists worldwide. Align also provides training for practitioners to model treatment schemes using its Internet-based application called ClinCheck, which simulates tooth movement and suggests the appropriate Aligner.

	Annual Growth	12/03	12/04	12/05	12/06	12/07
Sales ($ mil.)	23.4%	122.7	172.8	207.1	206.4	284.3
Net income ($ mil.)	—	(20.1)	8.8	1.4	(35.0)	35.7
Market value ($ mil.)	4.2%	970.0	654.4	401.7	906.1	1,144.9
Employees	9.2%	—	—	1,097	1,253	1,307

ALION SCIENCE AND TECHNOLOGY CORPORATION

1750 Tysons Blvd., Ste. 1300
McLean, VA 22102
Phone: 703-918-4480
Fax: 703-714-6508
Web: www.alionscience.com

CEO: Bahman Atefi
CFO: Michael J. Alber
HR: Katherine C. Madeleno
FYE: September 30
Type: Private

Ah, Alion! Alion Science and Technology creates an alliance between science, technology, and big government. Alion is a development and research company that provides consulting and technology services primarily to federal agencies. The majority of its revenues come from contracts with the US Department of Defense (DoD), especially the Navy. Its areas of specialty include marine and naval architecture and engineering, wargaming, lab support and chemical decontamination, wireless operations, military transformation, wireless communications engineering, and more. Employee-owned Alion operates from offices and facilities throughout the US, generally near government military bases and other installations.

	Annual Growth	9/02	9/03	9/04	9/05	9/06
Sales ($ mil.)	26.0%	201.7	165.9	269.9	369.2	508.6
Net income ($ mil.)	—	4.7	(12.6)	(15.1)	(40.2)	(31.1)
Employees	21.8%	1,622	1,604	1,880	2,508	3,575

ALIXPARTNERS LLP

2000 Town Center, Ste. 2400
Southfield, MI 48075
Phone: 248-358-4420
Fax: 248-358-1969
Web: www.alixpartners.com

CEO: Frederick A. (Fred) Crawford
CFO: Douglas E. (Doug) Barnett
HR: –
FYE: October 1
Type: Private

Is your company headed in the wrong direction? AlixPartners can help you turn things around. Founded by Jay Alix in 1981, the firm provides operational management, corporate restructuring, and legal and financial advisory services to underperforming as well as healthy companies worldwide. It evaluates each client's organization to identify operational weaknesses, and works quickly to develop and implement changes that address trouble issues and improve operational performance. The turnaround firm's clients include leading companies in a wide range of industries, such as automotive, retail, manufacturing, health care, power generation, and financial services.

	Annual Growth	9/02	9/03	9/04	9/05	9/06
Sales ($ mil.)	—	—	—	—	—	375.0
Employees	—	—	—	—	—	600

ALJ REGIONAL HOLDINGS, INC.

Pink Sheets: ALJJ

244 Madison Ave., PMB #358
New York, NY 10016
Phone: 212-883-0083
Fax: 212-622-7301

CEO: John Scheel
CFO: Donald Reisenberg
HR: –
FYE: September 30
Type: Public

ALJ Regional Holdings owns a steel mini-mill in Kentucky, which it acquired in 2005. The mill is operated by Kentucky Electric Steel, which produces bar flat products that it sells to service centers as well as makers of truck trailers, steel springs, and cold drawn bars. Kentucky Electric Steel produces steel in both Merchant Bar Quality and Special Bar Quality.

	Annual Growth	9/03	9/04	9/05	9/06	9/07
Sales ($ mil.)	47.7%	—	—	69.2	139.8	150.9
Net income ($ mil.)	—	—	—	(3.4)	2.4	6.6
Employees	2.1%	—	—	143	146	149

ALKERMES, INC.

NASDAQ (GS): ALKS

88 Sidney St.
Cambridge, MA 02139
Phone: 617-494-0171
Fax: 617-494-9263
Web: www.alkermes.com

CEO: David A. Broecker
CFO: James M. (Jim) Frates
HR: –
FYE: March 31
Type: Public

Alkermes, whose name is Arabic for "magic potion," is working some biotech alchemy. The firm uses its proprietary drug-delivery systems to make fragile biotech compounds that require less frequent dosing or provide more targeted delivery. It has a couple of drugs on the market that use its injectable extended-release technology, which lets patients take a drug once or twice a month, rather than once or twice a day. One such drug is Risperdal Consta, a long-acting version of Janssen's schizophrenia medication Risperdal. Another is Vivitrol, a treatment for alcohol dependence that partner Cephalon markets in the US.

	Annual Growth	3/04	3/05	3/06	3/07	3/08
Sales ($ mil.)	57.6%	39.0	76.1	166.6	240.0	240.7
Net income ($ mil.)	—	(102.4)	(73.9)	3.8	9.4	167.0
Market value ($ mil.)	(5.7%)	1,428.0	934.2	2,023.0	1,555.2	1,129.8
Employees	25.4%	—	528	760	830	—

ALL AMERICAN SEMICONDUCTOR, LLC

16115 NW 52nd Ave.
Miami, FL 33014
Phone: 305-621-8282
Fax: 305-620-7831
Web: www.allamerican.com

CEO: Jamil Nizam
CFO: Howard L. Flanders
HR: –
FYE: December 31
Type: Private

They couldn't be more patriotic at All American Semiconductor. They take pride in distributing electronic components from more than 55 suppliers. The company primarily sells active semiconductor components, such as transistors, diodes, integrated circuits, microprocessors, and memory products; it also offers passive components, including capacitors, resistors, and switches. Through its Aved Memory Products subsidiary, All American assembles memory packages. After filing for Chapter 11 protection from creditors in 2007, All American sold substantially all of its assets to Rock River Capital for about $15 million. The new ownership brought in new management to run the company.

ALL-AMERICAN SPORTPARK, INC

OTC: AASP

6730 S. Las Vegas Blvd.
Las Vegas, NV 89119
Phone: 702-798-7777
Fax: 702-739-9509

CEO: Ronald S. Boreta
CFO: Ronald S. Boreta
HR: –
FYE: December 31
Type: Public

If golf is your sport, then this company has a park for you. All-American SportPark operates Callaway Golf Center (CGC), a 42-acre golf practice facility located at the end of the famous Las Vegas Strip. Amenities include 110 driving stations in two tiers, 10 impact greens, and an island green. The center also features Divine Nine, a lighted nine-hole, par three course. CGC's clubhouse offers electronic swing analysis and the St. Andrews Golf Shop. The founding Boreta family owns about a third of the company. Tennis pro Andre Agassi and partner Perry Rogers together own almost 20% of All-American SportPark.

	Annual Growth	12/03	12/04	12/05	12/06	12/07
Sales ($ mil.)	0.0%	2.2	2.2	2.2	2.2	2.2
Net income ($ mil.)	—	0.3	(0.6)	(1.6)	(1.0)	(0.8)
Market value ($ mil.)	—	—	—	—	—	—
Employees	—	—	—	—	—	—

ALLBRITTON COMMUNICATIONS COMPANY

1000 Wilson Blvd., Ste. 2700
Arlington, VA 22209
Phone: 703-647-8700
Fax: 703-236-9268

CEO: Robert L. Allbritton
CFO: Stephen P. Gibson
HR: –
FYE: September 30
Type: Private

This company has a real affinity for the Alphabet Network. Allbritton Communications is a leading television broadcaster with about 10 TV stations all affiliated with Walt Disney's ABC network. The stations serve markets in Alabama, Arkansas, Oklahoma, Pennsylvania, South Carolina, and Virginia, as well as Washington, DC. The company also owns and operates a 24-hour cable news channel (NewsChannel 8) that serves the nation's capitol, and it publishes *The Politico*, a newspaper that targets members of Congress, congressional staffers, and others interested in politics. Joe Allbritton started the family-owned business in 1975.

	Annual Growth	9/02	9/03	9/04	9/05	9/06
Sales ($ mil.)	3.3%	196.2	202.6	203.3	200.4	223.4
Net income ($ mil.)	—	—	—	13.6	13.6	(17.2)
Employees	1.3%	—	936	936	960	972

An in-depth profile of this company is available to Hoover's Online members at hoovers.com.

89

ALLEGHANY CORPORATION

NYSE: Y

7 Times Square Tower	CEO: Weston M. Hicks
New York, NY 10036	CFO: Roger B. Gorham
Phone: 212-752-1356	HR: –
Fax: 212-759-8149	FYE: December 31
Web: www.alleghany.com	Type: Public

After a spell as an conglomerate with interests ranging from minerals to steel fasteners, Alleghany Corporation has found that it really prefers property/casualty insurance, with a smattering of good-old real estate. Alleghany's subsidiaries include Capitol Transamerica (property/casualty, fidelity, and surety insurance) and Darwin Professional Underwriters (55% owned), which writes specialty property/casualty insurance. The company's RSUI Group is a leading underwriter of wholesale specialty insurance while its Employers Direct Insurance provides workers' compensation coverage. Alleghany also has commercial and residential real estate interests in California.

	Annual Growth	12/03	12/04	12/05	12/06	12/07
Assets ($ mil.)	17.2%	3,568.0	4,427.7	5,913.7	6,178.7	6,733.0
Net income ($ mil.)	17.1%	162.4	117.7	52.3	251.2	305.3
Market value ($ mil.)	19.0%	1,602.7	2,104.6	2,157.8	2,781.6	3,215.7
Employees	18.6%	—	—	676	713	951

ALLEGHENY ENERGY, INC.

NYSE: AYE

800 Cabin Hill Dr.	CEO: Paul J. Evanson
Greensburg, PA 15601	CFO: Philip L. Goulding
Phone: 724-837-3000	HR: Edward (Ed) Dudzinski
Fax: 724-830-5284	FYE: December 31
Web: www.alleghenyenergy.com	Type: Public

Even when the Allegheny Moon isn't shining, Allegheny Energy (AE) can provide plenty of light. The company's Allegheny Power unit provides electricity to almost 1.5 million customers in Maryland, Pennsylvania, West Virginia, and Virginia through regulated utilities Monongahela Power, Potomac Edison, and West Penn Power. Subsidiary Allegheny Energy Supply provides power to AE's utilities and sells electricity to wholesale and retail customers. Subsidiary Allegheny Ventures controls Allegheny Communications Connect (telecommunications) and Allegheny Energy Solutions (energy consulting). It also has transmission line design and management units (TrAIL Company and PATH, LLC).

	Annual Growth	12/03	12/04	12/05	12/06	12/07
Sales ($ mil.)	7.5%	2,472.4	2,756.1	3,037.9	3,121.5	3,307.0
Net income ($ mil.)	—	(355.0)	(310.6)	63.1	319.3	412.2
Market value ($ mil.)	60.1%	1,620.1	2,707.8	5,157.5	7,591.7	10,637.1
Employees	(1.2%)	—	—	4,460	4,362	4,355

ALLEGHENY TECHNOLOGIES INCORPORATED

NYSE: ATI

1000 Six PPG Place	CEO: L. Patrick (Pat) Hassey
Pittsburgh, PA 15222	CFO: Richard J. (Rich) Harshman
Phone: 412-394-2800	HR: Jon D. Walton
Fax: 412-394-3034	FYE: December 31
Web: www.alleghenytechnologies.com	Type: Public

Allegheny Technologies, Inc. (ATI) manufactures stainless and specialty steels, nickel- and cobalt-based alloys and superalloys, titanium and titanium alloys, tungsten materials, and such exotic alloys as niobium and zirconium. The company's flat-rolled products (sheet, strip, and plate) account for a great majority of its sales. Its high-performance metals unit produces metal bar, coil, foil, ingot, plate, rod, and wire. Allegheny Technologies' largest markets include aerospace, the chemical process, and oil and gas industries. Three-fourths of its sales are in the US. ATI was formed from the 1996 merger of Teledyne and stainless-steel producer Allegheny Ludlum.

	Annual Growth	12/03	12/04	12/05	12/06	12/07
Sales ($ mil.)	29.5%	1,937.4	2,733.0	3,539.9	4,936.6	5,452.5
Net income ($ mil.)	—	(314.6)	19.8	359.8	571.9	747.1
Market value ($ mil.)	69.4%	1,066.3	2,075.6	3,543.1	9,176.9	8,777.1
Employees	2.1%	—	—	9,300	9,500	9,700

ALLEGHENY VALLEY BANCORP, INC.

OTC: AVLY

5137 Butler St.	CEO: Edward J. Bartosiewicz
Pittsburgh, PA 15201	CFO: Nelson L. Person
Phone: 412-781-0318	HR: Edward Sullivan
Fax: 412-781-6474	FYE: December 31
Web: www.avbpgh.com	Type: Public

Allegheny Valley Bancorp is the holding company for Allegheny Valley Bank, which has about 10 branches in Pittsburgh and its suburbs. The bank offers standard services such as checking and savings accounts, CDs, money market accounts, IRAs, and debit cards. One- to four-family residential mortgages make up the largest portion of the bank's loan portfolio, followed by commercial mortgages, business loans, and equipment leases. The company's asset management subsidiary, AVB Advisors, provides financial planning, trust services, and investment products. Allegheny Valley Bancorp bought Pittsburgh-area bank RSV Bancorp in 2006.

	Annual Growth	12/03	12/04	12/05	12/06	12/07
Est. sales ($ mil.)	—	—	—	—	—	17.6
Employees	—	—	—	—	—	100

ALLEGIANT TRAVEL COMPANY

NASDAQ (GM): ALGT

3301 N. Buffalo Dr., Ste. B-9	CEO: Maurice J. (Maury) Gallagher Jr.
Las Vegas, NV 89129	CFO: Andrew C. Levy
Phone: 702-851-7300	HR: –
Fax: 702-256-7209	FYE: December 31
Web: www.allegiantair.com	Type: Public

Allegiant Travel pledges to serve the vacation needs of residents of more than 50 small US cities in more than 30 states. Through Allegiant Air, the company provides nonstop service to tourist destinations such as Las Vegas and Orlando, Florida, from places such as Cedar Rapids, Iowa; Fargo, North Dakota; and Toledo, Ohio. It maintains a fleet of about 35 MD-80 series aircraft. Besides scheduled service, Allegiant Air offers charter flights for casino operator Harrah's and other customers. Sister company Allegiant Vacations works with partners to allow customers to book hotel rooms and rental cars with their airline tickets.

	Annual Growth	12/03	12/04	12/05	12/06	12/07
Sales ($ mil.)	63.9%	50.0	90.4	132.5	243.4	360.6
Net income ($ mil.)	64.5%	4.3	9.1	7.3	8.7	31.5
Market value ($ mil.)	20.0%	—	—	—	555.5	666.5
Employees	54.8%	282	—	—	1,046	—

ALLEGIS GROUP, INC.

7301 Parkway Dr.	CEO: Steve Bisciotti
Hanover, MD 21076	CFO: Dave Standeven
Phone: 410-579-4800	HR: Neil Mann
Fax: 410-540-7556	FYE: December 31
Web: www.allegisgroup.com	Type: Private

Clients in need of highly skilled technical and other personnel might want to take the pledge of Allegis. One of the world's largest staffing and recruitment firms, Allegis Group operates from more than 260 offices in North America and Europe. Among its operating companies are Aerotek (engineering, automotive, and scientific professionals for short- and long-term assignments), Stephen James Associates (recruitment for accounting, financial, and cash management positions), and TEKsystems (information technology staffing and consulting). In 1983 co-chairman Jim Davis helped found the company (originally known as Aerotek) in order to provide contract engineering personnel to two clients in the aerospace industry.

	Annual Growth	12/03	12/04	12/05	12/06	12/07
Sales ($ mil.)	19.3%	2,750.0	3,600.0	4,400.0	5,000.0	5,570.0
Employees	21.4%	4,600	6,000	7,000	8,000	10,000

ALLEGRA NETWORK LLC

21680 Haggerty Rd.
Northville, MI 48167
Phone: 248-596-8600
Fax: 248-596-8601
Web: www2.allegranetwork.com

CEO: Carl Gerhardt
CFO: Laura Pierce
HR: –
FYE: December 31
Type: Private

Think fast! Allegra Network franchises quick printing centers under a number of names, including Allegra Print & Imaging, American Speedy Printing Centers, Speedy Printing Centers, Instant Copy, Insty-Prints, and Zippy Print. Allegra has more than 600 centers in Canada, the US, and the UK. The company's printing centers offer graphic design, copying, and finishing services in addition to digital and traditional printing services. Allegra also operates sign shops franchised under the Signs Now name. Founded in 1976, Allegra Network is privately owned by an investor group led by the company's management, including chairman William McIntyre. Other shareholders include Michael Marcantonio and Domino's founder Thomas S. Monaghan.

	Annual Growth	12/03	12/04	12/05	12/06	12/07
Est. sales ($ mil.)	—	—	—	—	—	16.4
Employees	—	—	—	—	—	65

ALLEGRO BIODIESEL CORPORATION

OTC: ABDS

6033 W. Century Blvd., Ste. 1090
Los Angeles, CA 90045
Phone: 310-670-2093
Fax: 310-670-4107
Web: www.allegrobiodiesel.com

CEO: W. Bruce Comer III
CFO: –
HR: –
FYE: December 31
Type: Public

Allegro Biodiesel (formerly Diametrics Medical) is looking to biodiesel as its prescription for financial health. The company, which had operated as a shell since 2005, purchased Vanguard Synfuels in 2006 and shifted its focus from medical devices to biodiesel production. It made the nearly $30 million acquisition with funding from private investment firm M.A.G. Capital. Allegro Biodiesel owns and operates a biodiesel production facility in Louisiana capable of producing 12 million gallons of fuel per year. It uses soybean oil as the raw ingredient for its biodiesel.

	Annual Growth	12/03	12/04	12/05	12/06	12/07
Sales ($ mil.)	311.1%	—	—	—	1.8	7.4
Net income ($ mil.)	—	—	—	—	(75.3)	(29.6)
Market value ($ mil.)	(86.9%)	—	—	—	51.2	6.7
Employees	—	—	—	—	—	—

ALLEGRO MICROSYSTEMS, INC.

115 Northeast Cutoff
Worcester, MA 01606
Phone: 508-853-5000
Fax: 508-853-3353
Web: www.allegromicro.com

CEO: Dennis H. Fitzgerald
CFO: Mark A. Feragne
HR: Marybeth Perry
FYE: March 31
Type: Subsidiary

Allegro MicroSystems makes its microchips to do their jobs at a lively tempo. The company is one of the world's top makers of Hall-effect sensors. Automotive manufacturers use these specialized components — named after an electromagnetic phenomenon called the Hall effect — in braking, steering, suspension, and other systems. Allegro also makes power integrated circuits used for a variety of purposes in printers, scanners, photocopiers, industrial motors, and automotive systems. The company, a subsidiary of Sanken Electric, entered the chip business four decades ago as Sprague Semiconductor Group before taking the Allegro name in 1990.

	Annual Growth	3/03	3/04	3/05	3/06	3/07
Sales ($ mil.)	6.6%	—	—	282.4	285.1	320.7
Net income ($ mil.)	16.3%	—	—	15.6	11.6	21.1
Employees	—	—	—	—	—	2,673

ALLEN SYSTEMS GROUP, INC.

1333 3rd Ave. South
Naples, FL 34102
Phone: 239-435-2200
Fax: 239-263-3692
Web: www.asg.com

CEO: Arthur L. (Art) Allen
CFO: –
HR: Tom Romnios
FYE: December 31
Type: Private

When it comes to enterprise computing, Allen Systems Group (ASG) strives to make all systems go. The company provides a variety of software and services for enterprise performance, operations, and application management. Its products are used for functions such as migrating legacy data, business performance management, and developing business applications. ASG also offers business information portals and applications for identity and user access management, in addition to consulting, implementation, and training services. Customers have included Coca-Cola, General Electric, and Procter & Gamble.

	Annual Growth	12/03	12/04	12/05	12/06	12/07
Est. sales ($ mil.)	—	—	—	—	—	160.3
Employees	—	—	—	—	—	975

ALLEN-EDMONDS SHOE CORPORATION

201 E. Seven Hills Rd.
Port Washington, WI 53074
Phone: 262-235-6000
Fax: 262-268-7427
Web: www.allenedmonds.com

CEO: Mark Birmingham
CFO: Jay Schauer
HR: Sandy Sirra
FYE: December 31
Type: Private

Allen-Edmonds' shoes stand their ground in the US. Maker of high-end men's dress and casual shoes, boots, belts, leather care goods, and hosiery, Allen-Edmonds makes most of its shoes in Maine and Wisconsin, resisting the trend of moving production abroad. Its upscale shoes are handmade by skilled craftsmen and Allen-Edmonds is known for its full range of shoe sizes for men. Allen-Edmonds also offers a namesake cologne. Products are sold in about 30 company-owned stores in the US, Belgium, and Italy, as well as in department stores, other specialty retailers, and a company catalog. Founded by Elbert Allen in 1922, the company was sold to Goldner Hawn Johnson & Morrison in 2006.

	Annual Growth	12/03	12/04	12/05	12/06	12/07
Est. sales ($ mil.)	—	—	—	—	—	32.4
Employees	—	—	—	—	—	600

ALLENS, INC.

305 E. Main St.
Siloam Springs, AR 72761
Phone: 479-524-6431
Fax: 479-524-3291
Web: www.allencanning.com

CEO: Roderick L. Allen
CFO: Lori Sherrell
HR: James Phillips
FYE: December 31
Type: Private

Popeye himself would probably approve of Allens business. The company, formerly called Allen Canning, produces a full line of canned and frozen vegetables (including Popeye's fave, spinach) for the retail food and foodservice industries. Its brands include Allens, Butterfield, Popeye, Princella, Royal Prince, Sunshine, Sugary Sam, and Trappey's, along with Freshlike and Veg-All (both of which it purchased from Birds Eye in 2002 and 2003 respectively). The company's veggies are sold in grocery stores throughout the US. Allens, founded in 1926, is a family-owned and -operated company.

	Annual Growth	12/03	12/04	12/05	12/06	12/07
Est. sales ($ mil.)	—	—	—	—	—	200.0
Employees	—	—	—	—	—	2,000

An in-depth profile of this company is available to Hoover's Online members at hoovers.com.

91

ALLERGAN, INC.

NYSE: AGN

2525 Dupont Dr.
Irvine, CA 92612
Phone: 714-246-4500
Fax: 714-246-4971
Web: www.allergan.com

CEO: David E. I. Pyott
CFO: Jeffrey L. Edwards
HR: Douglas S. Ingram
FYE: December 31
Type: Public

Don't let the name fool you, Allergan can't help you with that runny nose. Instead, the company is a leading maker of eye care and skin care products; it also produces best-selling pharmaceutical Botox. Originally used to treat muscle spasms (as well as eye spasms and misalignment), Botox has found a more popular application in diminishing facial wrinkles. Allergan's eye care products include medications for glaucoma, allergic conjunctivitis, chronic dry eye, and pink eye. The company's skin care products include treatments for acne, wrinkles, and psoriasis. Allergan also sells implants used in breast augmentation and weight-loss surgery. Its products are sold in 100 countries via direct sales and distributors.

	Annual Growth	12/03	12/04	12/05	12/06	12/07
Sales ($ mil.)	22.1%	1,771.4	2,045.6	2,319.2	3,063.3	3,938.9
Net income ($ mil.)	—	(52.5)	377.1	403.9	(127.4)	499.3
Market value ($ mil.)	40.8%	4,998.1	5,327.0	7,169.8	9,116.3	19,651.5
Employees	24.9%	—	—	5,055	6,772	7,886

ALLERGY RESEARCH GROUP, INC.

OTC: ALRG

2300 North Loop Rd.
Alameda, CA 94502
Phone: 510-263-2000
Fax: 510-263-2100
Web: www.allergyresearchgroup.com

CEO: Stephen Levine
CFO: Stephen Levine
HR: —
FYE: December 31
Type: Public

You might think about allergies once a year, but Allergy Research Group thinks about them every day. Through its Nutricology subsidiary, the company develops and markets hypoallergenic vitamins and nutritional supplements including amino acids, bioflavonoids, fatty acids, glandular tissue products, minerals, and multivitamins. It markets more than 250 products directly to doctors, nutritionists, and other health care professionals under the Allergy Research Group label, and it distributes products to health food stores and pharmacies through its NutriCology label. US customers account for nearly 90% of the company's sales. CEO Stephen Levine founded Allergy Research Group and holds 70% of the company's stock.

	Annual Growth	12/03	12/04	12/05	12/06	12/07
Sales ($ mil.)	5.3%	13.6	15.1	15.9	16.3	16.7
Net income ($ mil.)	(8.9%)	1.6	1.3	1.2	1.1	1.1
Market value ($ mil.)	2.1%	11.3	15.2	12.5	11.9	12.3
Employees	—	—	—	—	—	—

ALLETE, INC.

NYSE: ALE

30 W. Superior St.
Duluth, MN 55802
Phone: 218-279-5000
Fax: 218-720-2502
Web: www.allete.com

CEO: Donald J. (Don) Shippar
CFO: Mark A. Schober
HR: Glen Porter
FYE: December 31
Type: Public

ALLETE, formerly Minnesota Power, has lost its drive but none of its power. After having spun off ADESA, one of North America's largest vehicle auctioneers and a dealership creditor (Automotive Finance Corporation), the company now has three primary operating units: regulated utilities (electric, gas, and water located in northeastern Minnesota and northwestern Wisconsin), nonregulated utilities (coal mining and wholesale power marketing), and real estate (large land tracts in Florida). Subsidiary BNI Coal operates a mine in North Dakota that supplies, primarily, two generating co-ops, Minnkota Power and Square Butte. ALLETE also has interests in emerging technologies related to electric utilities.

	Annual Growth	12/03	12/04	12/05	12/06	12/07
Sales ($ mil.)	(15.1%)	1,618.8	751.4	737.4	767.1	841.7
Net income ($ mil.)	(22.0%)	236.4	104.4	13.3	76.4	87.6
Market value ($ mil.)	(17.8%)	2,671.4	1,091.5	1,324.4	1,414.8	1,219.1
Employees	216.2%	—	—	1,500	1,500	15,000

ALLIANCE BANCSHARES CALIFORNIA

OTC: ABNS

100 Corporate Pointe
Culver City, CA 90230
Phone: 310-410-9281
Fax: 310-216-4275
Web: www.allbank.com

CEO: Curtis S. Reis
CFO: Daniel L. (Dan) Erickson
HR: —
FYE: December 31
Type: Public

Alliance Bancshares California is the holding company for Alliance Bank, which has six branches in Southern California. Catering to small to midsized businesses, builders, and professionals, the bank offers deposit accounts such as checking and savings accounts, NOW and money market accounts, CDs, and IRAs. It also issues credit cards. While the bank's loan portfolio is dominated by real estate, commercial, and construction loans, it also performs specialized lending services such as equipment leasing and asset-based lending. Due to a downturn in new housing starts, the company ceased making residential construction and land development loans in 2007.

	Annual Growth	12/03	12/04	12/05	12/06	12/07
Assets ($ mil.)	39.4%	282.7	409.8	675.0	875.8	1,066.6
Net income ($ mil.)	16.8%	2.2	3.9	6.2	8.0	4.1
Market value ($ mil.)	2.4%	40.0	55.7	79.8	103.0	43.9
Employees	—	—	—	—	—	149

ALLIANCE BANK

NASDAQ (GM): ALLB

541 Lawrence Rd.
Broomall, PA 19008
Phone: 610-353-2900
Fax: 610-359-6908
Web: www.allianceanytime.com

CEO: Dennis D. Cirucci
CFO: Peter J. Meier
HR: Janette Wyman-Babikian
FYE: December 31
Type: Public

Alliance Bank (formerly operating as Greater Delaware Valley Savings Bank) has about 10 branch offices and a loan center serving individuals and local businesses in Pennsylvania's Delaware County and Chester County. The bank's deposit products include checking, savings, money market, term certificate, and NOW accounts. Commercial real estate loans make up about half of the bank's loan portfolio, which also includes residential mortgages (more than 40%), construction and land development, and industrial loans. The bank is converting into a mid-tier stock holding company from a mutual holding structure.

	Annual Growth	12/03	12/04	12/05	12/06	12/07
Assets ($ mil.)	3.2%	374.4	382.1	389.0	410.4	424.5
Net income ($ mil.)	(15.9%)	2.2	2.1	1.2	1.4	1.1
Employees	22.5%	—	—	—	80	98

ALLIANCE BANKSHARES CORPORATION

NASDAQ (CM): ABVA

14200 Park Meadow Dr., Ste. 200 South
Chantilly, VA 20151
Phone: 703-814-7200
Fax: 703-378-7210
Web: www.alliancebankva.com

CEO: Thomas A. Young Jr.
CFO: Paul M. Harbolick Jr.
HR: —
FYE: December 31
Type: Public

Alliance Bankshares has enjoyed a healthy partnership with mortgages since 1996. The financial institution is the holding company for Alliance Bank and its mortgage subsidiary Alliance Home Funding. Alliance Bankshares operates branches and loan production offices in the DC suburbs of northern Virginia. The bank offers such services as checking and savings accounts, CDs, corporate credit cards, and cash management. Its lending activities mainly consist of residential and commercial mortgages, with business and consumer loans rounding out its portfolio.

	Annual Growth	12/03	12/04	12/05	12/06	12/07
Assets ($ mil.)	11.0%	356.7	479.7	611.5	644.4	541.3
Net income ($ mil.)	—	4.0	2.8	4.1	4.5	(2.8)
Market value ($ mil.)	(11.3%)	53.7	64.8	67.0	86.9	33.3
Employees	(4.4%)	—	—	115	115	105

ALLIANCE DATA SYSTEMS CORPORATION
NYSE: ADS

17655 Waterview Pkwy.
Dallas, TX 75252
Phone: 972-348-5100
Fax: 972-348-5335
Web: www.alliancedata.com

CEO: J. Michael (Mike) Parks
CFO: Edward J. (Ed) Heffernan
HR: Dwayne H. Tucker
FYE: December 31
Type: Public

Hoping to forge an alliance between consumers and retailers, Alliance Data Systems performs such private-label credit card operations as credit and transaction services and marketing, serving more than 800 clients, including retailers, supermarkets, oil companies, utilities, and financial services companies. Activities include loyalty programs, billing and payment processing, point-of-sale services, risk management, and database marketing. Alliance Data Systems has about a dozen facilities in the US and Canada. Private equity giant The Blackstone Group agreed to buy the company for more than $6 billion, but Alliance Data Systems has terminated the deal.

	Annual Growth	12/03	12/04	12/05	12/06	12/07
Sales ($ mil.)	21.6%	1,049.1	1,257.4	1,552.4	1,998.7	2,291.2
Net income ($ mil.)	25.0%	67.3	102.4	138.7	189.6	164.1
Market value ($ mil.)	27.9%	2,204.0	3,909.8	2,862.4	4,976.0	5,906.4
Employees	10.7%	—	—	8,000	9,300	9,800

ALLIANCE ENTERTAINMENT CORPORATION

4250 Coral Ridge Dr.
Coral Springs, FL 33065
Phone: 954-255-4000
Fax: 954-255-4078
Web: www.aent.com

CEO: Alan Tuchman
CFO: George Campagna
HR: —
FYE: December 31
Type: Private

Alliance Entertainment Corp. (AEC) rolls out the rock 'n' roll. The company distributes music and video items — CDs, videos, DVDs, games, and related products — to home entertainment retailers including Best Buy, Barnes and Noble, and Hastings Entertainment. AEC provides retailer support services (including e-commerce software) through its IDN and AEC Direct subsidiaries. It also owns astrological PC software maker Matrix Software. Its NCircle Entertainment unit distributes children's and family programming. Investment firm The Yucaipa Companies owns half of Alliance; magazine wholesaler Source Interlink owns the rest (after its 2005 purchase).

	Annual Growth	12/03	12/04	12/05	12/06	12/07
Est. sales ($ mil.)	—	—	—	—	—	166.5
Employees	—	—	—	—	—	900

ALLIANCE FIBER OPTIC PRODUCTS, INC.
NASDAQ (CM): AFOP

275 Gibraltar Dr.
Sunnyvale, CA 94089
Phone: 408-736-6900
Fax: 408-736-4882
Web: www.afop.com

CEO: Peter C. Chang
CFO: Anita K. Ho
HR: —
FYE: December 31
Type: Public

Alliance Fiber Optic Products (AFOP) unites with light. Communications equipment manufacturers incorporate AFOP's fiber-optic components into products used to build networks that connect cities, regions within cities, and telecom service providers with their individual customers. Its optical path integration and optical fiber amplifier components, which include attenuators, couplers, depolarizers, multiplexers, and splitters, account for most of sales. The company sells directly to telecom equipment makers, primarily in North America, where it gets 60% of sales. AFOP has more than 200 customers.

	Annual Growth	12/03	12/04	12/05	12/06	12/07
Sales ($ mil.)	30.9%	11.5	14.6	21.0	26.8	33.8
Net income ($ mil.)	—	(8.5)	(9.3)	(2.6)	0.7	3.4
Market value ($ mil.)	7.9%	61.7	58.5	45.3	82.7	83.6
Employees	15.6%	387	494	581	684	691

ALLIANCE FINANCIAL CORPORATION
NASDAQ (GM): ALNC

120 Madison St., Tower 2, 18th Fl.
Syracuse, NY 13202
Phone: 315-475-4478
Fax: 315-475-4421
Web: www.alliancebankna.com

CEO: Jack H. Webb
CFO: J. Daniel Mohr
HR: Colleen K. Lefeve
FYE: December 31
Type: Public

Alliance Financial Corporation is the holding company for Alliance Bank, which operates about 30 branches in central New York state. Targeting individuals and small to midsized businesses, Alliance offers such retail banking products as checking and savings accounts, IRAs, and CDs. Its loan and lease portfolio mainly contains residential mortgages (about 30%), commercial loans (nearly 25%), and indirect auto loans (around 20%). The company provides commercial equipment leasing in more than 30 states through its Alliance Leasing subsidiary. Alliance Financial also operates a trust department that manages some $1 billion worth of investment assets.

	Annual Growth	12/03	12/04	12/05	12/06	12/07
Assets ($ mil.)	12.2%	826.3	893.9	980.4	1,273.0	1,307.3
Net income ($ mil.)	4.4%	8.0	7.3	7.5	7.3	9.5
Market value ($ mil.)	1.7%	112.9	108.9	114.4	152.9	121.0
Employees	11.6%	—	—	269	—	335

ALLIANCE HEALTHCARD, INC.
OTC: ALHC

3500 Parkway Ln., Ste. 720
Norcross, GA 30092
Phone: 770-734-9255
Fax: 770-734-9253
Web: www.alliancehealthcard.com

CEO: Danny C. Wright
CFO: Rita W. McKeown
HR: —
FYE: September 30
Type: Public

Alliance HealthCard is an ally for people without health insurance. The company provides health care savings programs, serving individuals and families with limited health benefits or no insurance. Its membership programs offer access to hospitals, doctors, dentists, mental health services, pharmacies, physical therapy, and outpatient clinics at discounted rates for an annual fee. In addition, subsidiary Benefit Marketing Solutions (BMS) provides grocery, entertainment, automobile, property insurance, and rent-to-own membership programs, and BMS Insurance Agency provides leased property and other insurance coverage. Alliance HealthCard markets its service through retailers and financial services partners.

	Annual Growth	9/03	9/04	9/05	9/06	9/07
Sales ($ mil.)	42.2%	4.3	4.0	3.6	3.3	17.6
Net income ($ mil.)	—	(1.0)	0.7	0.8	0.6	1.4
Market value ($ mil.)	106.8%	1.5	4.1	3.5	2.5	27.8
Employees	—	—	—	—	—	—

ALLIANCE HOLDINGS GP, L.P.
NASDAQ (GS): AHGP

1717 S. Boulder Ave.
Tulsa, OK 74119
Phone: 918-295-1415
Fax: 918-295-7361
Web: www.arlp.com

CEO: Joseph W. Craft III
CFO: Brian L. Cantrell
HR: —
FYE: December 31
Type: Public

When it comes to coal mining, it takes more than one company to make an Alliance. Alliance Holdings GP owns Alliance Resource Management GP, which is the managing general partner of coal mining company Alliance Resource Partners, L.P. That company has eight coal mining complexes in Illinois, Indiana, Kentucky, and Maryland, plus other coal interests in West Virginia. Alliance Holdings GP generates revenue from its general partnership interest and its 42% ownership stake in Alliance Resource Partners, L.P. The Alliance companies have been assembled by Joseph Craft III, who is chairman, president, CEO, and majority owner of Alliance Holdings GP.

	Annual Growth	12/03	12/04	12/05	12/06	12/07
Sales ($ mil.)	6.8%	—	—	—	967.2	1,033.0
Net income ($ mil.)	2.6%	—	—	—	85.7	87.9
Market value ($ mil.)	20.1%	—	—	—	1,182.9	1,420.5
Employees	—	—	—	—	2,500	—

ALLIANCE IMAGING, INC.
NYSE: AIQ

1900 S. State College Blvd., Ste. 600
Anaheim, CA 92806
Phone: 714-688-7100
Fax: 714-688-3397
Web: www.allianceimaging.com

CEO: Paul S. Viviano
CFO: Howard K. Aihara
HR: –
FYE: December 31
Type: Public

Alliance Imaging can see right through you. The company operates around 500 diagnostic imaging systems for more than 1,000 hospitals and other health care providers in more than 40 states. For most of its customers, the company provides imaging systems and the staff to run and maintain them, as well as ancillary services such as marketing and billing support. In addition to MRI equipment and services (which account for most of revenue), Alliance Imaging offers positron emission tomography (PET), computed tomography (CT), combination PET/CT scanning, X-rays, and ultrasound, among other imaging services. The company also runs a handful of cancer centers that provide radiation therapy.

	Annual Growth	12/03	12/04	12/05	12/06	12/07
Sales ($ mil.)	1.7%	415.3	432.1	430.8	455.8	444.9
Net income ($ mil.)	—	(31.6)	(0.5)	19.9	18.6	16.2
Market value ($ mil.)	28.9%	177.4	551.5	295.0	331.9	489.9
Employees	(0.5%)	—	—	2,092	1,955	2,070

ALLIANCE LAUNDRY HOLDINGS LLC

119 Shepard St.
Ripon, WI 54971
Phone: 920-748-3121
Fax: 920-748-4334
Web: www.comlaundry.com

CEO: Thomas F. (Tom) L'Esperance
CFO: Bruce P. Rounds
HR: –
FYE: December 31
Type: Private

Laundry day can't come often enough for Alliance Laundry Holdings (ALH). Through its wholly owned subsidiary, Alliance Laundry Systems, the company makes commercial laundry equipment used in laundromats, multi-housing laundry facilities (apartments, dormitories, military bases), and on-premise laundries (hotels, hospitals, prisons). Its washers and dryers are made under the brands Speed Queen, UniMac, Huebsch, IPSO, and Cissell. They're sold in North America and in 90 countries. Investment firm Teachers' Private Capital (private equity arm of Ontario Teachers' Pension Plan) acquired more than 91% of ALH for about $450 million in 2005. The company was founded in 1908.

	Annual Growth	12/02	12/03	12/04	12/05	12/06
Sales ($ mil.)	9.4%	255.2	267.6	281.0	296.6	366.1
Net income ($ mil.)	—	1.3	15.9	11.8	(0.7)	(1.8)
Employees	3.9%	1,300	1,309	1,312	1,312	1,517

ALLIANCE ONE INTERNATIONAL, INC.
NYSE: AOI

8001 Aerial Center Pkwy.
Morrisville, NC 27560
Phone: 919-379-4300
Fax: 919-379-4346
Web: www.aointl.com

CEO: Robert E. (Pete) Harrison
CFO: Robert A. Sheets
HR: Michael K. McDaniel
FYE: March 31
Type: Public

Alliance One International keeps one eye on the world's tobacco farmers and the other eye on the cigarette makers. The company is a leading global leaf-tobacco merchant, behind slightly larger rival Universal Corporation. Alliance One buys leaf tobacco directly from growers in more than 45 countries. It also processes flue-cured, burley, and oriental tobaccos and sells them to large, multi-national cigarette and cigar manufacturers, such as Altria Group, in some 90 countries. Alliance One was formed through the mid-2005 merger of tobacco processor DIMON and Standard Commercial.

	Annual Growth	3/04	3/05	3/06	3/07	3/08
Sales ($ mil.)	25.2%	817.4	1,311.4	2,112.7	1,979.1	2,011.5
Net income ($ mil.)	—	(32.9)	13.3	(447.5)	(21.6)	16.9
Market value ($ mil.)	13.8%	320.7	283.6	461.5	890.4	536.9
Employees	5.8%	—	4,200	5,400	4,700	—

ALLIANCE PHARMACEUTICAL CORP.
OTC: ALLP

7590 Fay Ave., Ste. 402
La Jolla, CA 92037
Phone: 858-410-5200
Fax: 858-410-5201
Web: www.allp.com

CEO: Duane J. Roth
CFO: –
HR: –
FYE: June 30
Type: Public

Watch out red blood cells — Alliance Pharmaceutical may be taking over your job. The firm is developing a chemical emulsion called Oxygent for use as a temporary oxygen carrier in surgery patients. Oxygent delivers oxygen to vital organs to prevent tissue damage or organ failure during surgery. The company is also developing Oxygent as a therapy to protect gastrointestinal organs. (Often the body will conserve blood for the heart and brain and deprive the intestines of blood during surgery.) In addition, Oxygent could reduce the need for blood transfusions during surgery. Alliance Pharmaceutical is working with LEO Pharma to get Oxygent approved in the European Union and Canada.

	Annual Growth	6/03	6/04	6/05	6/06	6/07
Sales ($ mil.)	56.5%	0.1	0.6	1.5	0.1	0.6
Net income ($ mil.)	—	(20.3)	10.0	(5.7)	(9.6)	(4.1)
Market value ($ mil.)	(12.8%)	7.3	21.6	7.0	4.3	4.2
Employees	—	—	—	—	—	4

ALLIANCE RESOURCE PARTNERS, L.P.
NASDAQ (GS): ARLP

1717 S. Boulder Ave., Ste. 600
Tulsa, OK 74119
Phone: 918-295-7600
Fax: 918-295-7358
Web: www.arlp.com

CEO: Joseph W. Craft III
CFO: Brian L. Cantrell
HR: –
FYE: December 31
Type: Public

Coal is the main resource of Alliance Resource Partners. The company has eight coal mining complexes (seven underground, one surface) in Illinois, Indiana, Kentucky, Maryland, Pennsylvania, and West Virginia. Alliance controls more than 700 million tons of reserves. The company produces about 20 million tons of coal annually, nearly all of which is sold to electric utilities. Alliance bought out River View Coal in early 2006, giving it 100 million more tons of high-sulfur coal reserves, and the company acquired nearly another 100 million tons the next year from Consol Energy. President and CEO Joseph Craft III controls a 44% stake in Alliance Resource Partners.

	Annual Growth	12/03	12/04	12/05	12/06	12/07
Sales ($ mil.)	17.5%	542.8	653.3	838.7	967.6	1,033.3
Net income ($ mil.)	37.3%	47.9	76.6	160.0	172.9	170.4
Market value ($ mil.)	51.4%	252.6	670.8	1,355.1	1,257.2	1,325.7
Employees	8.7%	—	—	2,300	2,500	—

ALLIANCE SEMICONDUCTOR CORPORATION
Pink Sheets: ALSC

2575 Augustine Dr.
Santa Clara, CA 95054
Phone: 408-855-4900
Fax: 408-855-4999
Web: www.alsc.com

CEO: Melvin L. (Mel) Keating
CFO: Karl H. Moeller Jr.
HR: –
FYE: Saturday nearest March 31
Type: Public

Alliance Semiconductor was taken over by an alliance of dissident shareholders and stopped selling semiconductors. The company's bread and butter products were its static random-access memories (SRAMs) and DRAMs, which are used for high-performance memory storage in PCs and in multimedia, networking, and telecommunications devices. After a threatened proxy battle over the company's strategic direction in the fall of 2005, a new majority took over the board of directors and began selling Alliance Semi's assets. After selling the company's operating businesses in 2006, the board divested many of Alliance's investments in 2007. The board gave shareholders a special cash dividend as a result.

	Annual Growth	3/02	3/03	3/04	3/05	*3/06
Sales ($ mil.)	(26.8%)	26.5	18.5	26.7	23.6	7.6
Net income ($ mil.)	—	(240.7)	(106.1)	(19.4)	(49.8)	(26.6)
Employees	(1.6%)	210	261	261	281	197

*Most recent year available

ALLIANCE SHIPPERS, INC.

516 Sylvan Ave.
Englewood Cliffs, NJ 07632
Phone: 201-227-0400
Fax: 201-227-0924
Web: www.alliance.com

CEO: Ronald Lefcourt
CFO: –
HR: –
FYE: June 30
Type: Private

Alliance Shippers knows that it often it takes more than one company to move freight from origin to destination. A logistics provider, Alliance Shippers arranges the transportation of freight by rail, road, air, and sea from a network of more than 50 offices in the US, Canada, and Mexico. The company specializes in arranging intermodal freight transportation, in which goods move by multiple methods, such as train and truck. Alliance Shippers operates through about a dozen divisions, including units devoted to government customers and to temperature-controlled transportation. The company was founded in 1977.

	Annual Growth	6/03	6/04	6/05	6/06	6/07
Est. sales ($ mil.)	—	—	—	—	—	740.8
Employees	—	—	—	—	—	550

ALLIANCEBERNSTEIN HOLDING L.P.

NYSE: AB

1345 Avenue of the Americas
New York, NY 10105
Phone: 212-969-1000
Fax: 212-969-2229
Web: www.alliancebernstein.com

CEO: Lewis A. (Lew) Sanders
CFO: Robert H. Joseph Jr.
HR: –
FYE: December 31
Type: Public

The *raison d'etre* of AllianceBernstein Holding is its approximately 30% ownership of investment manager AllianceBernstein. (French insurer AXA, through its AXA Financial unit, owns a majority of the subsidiary.) AllianceBernstein administers about 80 mutual funds, including value equity, growth equity, fixed income, index, and structured investments. The subsidiary serves institutional clients such as pension funds, corporations, and not-for-profits, as well retail investors. The company also owns Sanford C. Bernstein, known for investment research and private client services. It changed its name to AllianceBernstein in early 2006 to more closely align itself with the well-regarded research firm.

	Annual Growth	12/03	12/04	12/05	12/06	12/07
Assets ($ mil.)	(11.6%)	—	—	—	10,601.1	9,368.8
Net income ($ mil.)	13.7%	—	—	—	1,108.6	1,260.4
Market value ($ mil.)	(3.6%)	—	—	—	6,811.9	6,565.7
Employees	—	—	—	—	—	5,580

⊞ ALLIANCEBERNSTEIN L.P.

1345 Avenue of the Americas
New York, NY 10105
Phone: 212-969-1000
Fax: 212-969-2229
Web: www.alliancebernstein.com

CEO: Lewis A. (Lew) Sanders
CFO: Robert H. Joseph Jr.
HR: –
FYE: December 31
Type: Private

AllianceBernstein has tons of funds. As one of the world's largest investment managers, the company (formerly Alliance Capital Management) administers about 80 domestic and international mutual funds. It serves such institutional investors as pension funds, foundations, endowments, government entities, and insurance firms. For retail investors, the company provides private client services, managed accounts, annuities, retirement plans, and college savings plans. AllianceBernstein also owns money manager and research firm Sanford C. Bernstein. French insurer AXA holds nearly 60% of AllianceBernstein; publicly traded AllianceBernstein Holding owns more than 30%.

	Annual Growth	12/02	12/03	12/04	12/05	12/06
Assets ($ mil.)	10.1%	7,218.0	8,171.7	8,779.3	9,490.5	10,601.1
Net income ($ mil.)	16.1%	611.0	329.8	705.2	868.3	1,108.6
Employees	4.2%	4,172	4,096	4,100	4,312	4,914

ALLIANT CREDIT UNION

11545 W. Touhy Ave.
Chicago, IL 60666
Phone: 773-462-2000
Fax: –
Web: www.alliantcreditunion.org

CEO: David W. Mooney
CFO: –
HR: –
FYE: December 31
Type: Not-for-profit

Alliant Credit Union is spreading its wings. Formerly United Airlines Employees' Credit Union, the company offers a fleet of financial services to the families of current and retired employees of United Airlines and its affiliates, as well as residents of the Chicago suburbs surrounding O'Hare Airport and employees of other select Employee Groups. It provides such standard products as checking, certificates and savings accounts, home and auto loans, and credit cards. The company, which has about 10 branches across the US (located near major airports), ranks among the largest credit unions in the nation, with some $4.4 billion in assets and more than 207,000 members worldwide.

	Annual Growth	12/02	12/03	12/04	12/05	12/06
Est. sales ($ mil.)	—	—	—	—	—	228.8
Employees	—	—	—	—	—	277

ALLIANT ENERGY CORPORATION

NYSE: LNT

4902 N. Biltmore Ln.
Madison, WI 53718
Phone: 608-458-3311
Fax: 608-458-4824
Web: www.alliantenergy.com

CEO: William D. (Bill) Harvey
CFO: Eliot G. Protsch
HR: –
FYE: December 31
Type: Public

Alliant would like you to increase your reliance on energy. Alliant Energy's utilities, Interstate Power and Light (IP&L) and Wisconsin Power and Light (WPL), provide electricity to 980,850 customers and natural gas to more than 410,260 customers in four states; the utility operations also own power plants that generate some 5,600 MW of capacity. Nonregulated operations include rail and marine transportation services, independent power production (including wind farms), and real estate. Alliant Energy also provides engineering, consulting, and management services.

	Annual Growth	12/03	12/04	12/05	12/06	12/07
Sales ($ mil.)	2.4%	3,128.2	2,958.7	3,279.6	3,359.4	3,437.6
Net income ($ mil.)	23.4%	183.5	145.5	(7.7)	315.7	425.3
Market value ($ mil.)	12.9%	2,763.0	3,310.2	3,281.7	4,386.1	4,490.5
Employees	(1.7%)	—	—	5,239	5,151	—

⊞ ALLIANT TECHSYSTEMS INC.

NYSE: ATK

5050 Lincoln Dr.
Edina, MN 55436
Phone: 952-351-3000
Fax: 952-351-3009
Web: www.atk.com

CEO: Daniel J. (Dan) Murphy
CFO: John L. Shroyer
HR: Paula J. Patineau
FYE: March 31
Type: Public

You wouldn't want to hold a candle to Alliant Techsystems (ATK), maker of ammunition, smart bombs, and rocket propulsion systems. A leader in the production of solid propulsion rocket motors, ATK builds motors for space launch vehicles such as the Trident II and the Delta II. ATK is also one of the top suppliers of ammunition — from small-caliber rounds to tank ammunition — to the US and its allies. Additional lethal offerings include anti-tank mines, aircraft weapons systems, and high-tech weapons components. The US government and its prime contractors account for nearly 80% of sales.

	Annual Growth	3/04	3/05	3/06	3/07	3/08
Sales ($ mil.)	15.2%	2,366.2	2,801.1	3,216.8	3,565.1	4,171.7
Net income ($ mil.)	8.2%	162.3	153.5	153.9	184.1	222.4
Market value ($ mil.)	13.6%	2,036.7	2,661.4	2,717.0	2,908.0	3,395.3
Employees	6.9%	—	14,000	15,200	16,000	—

⊞ An in-depth profile of this company is available to Hoover's Online members at hoovers.com.

ALLIANZ GLOBAL INVESTORS OF AMERICA INC.

680 Newport Ctr. Dr., Ste. 250
Newport Beach, CA 92660
Phone: 949-219-2200
Fax: –
Web: www.allianzinvestors.com

CEO: Marna C. Whittington
CFO: –
HR: –
FYE: December 31
Type: Subsidiary

Allianz Global Investors of America (formerly Allianz Dresdner Asset Management of America, or ADAM of America) is the US arm of Allianz's asset management operations, Allianz Global Investors. Allianz Global Investors of America offers institutional and individual investors such products and services as mutual funds, separate account management, and financial advice. It oversees such subsidiaries and affiliates as PIMCO, Nicholas-Applegate Capital Management, NFJ Investment Group, Oppenheimer Capital, and RCM Capital Management. The firm has some $690 billion in assets under management.

	Annual Growth	12/03	12/04	12/05	12/06	12/07
Est. sales ($ mil.)	—	—	—	—	—	244.5
Employees	—	—	—	—	—	1,800

ALLIANZ GLOBAL RISKS US INSURANCE COMPANY

2350 Empire Ave.
Burbank, CA 91504
Phone: 818-260-7500
Fax: 818-260-7207
Web: www.allianzglobalrisks.com

CEO: Wolfgang Schatz
CFO: Randy Renn
HR: Daniel Barker
FYE: December 31
Type: Subsidiary

International enterprise is a risky business and that's where Allianz Global Risks US steps in. Also known as Allianz Global Corporate & Specialty, the company is the US arm of Allianz Global Risks, which provides international corporate insurance to large industrial clients of Munich-based mega-insurer Allianz SE. Allianz Global Risks US provides complex property/casualty insurance. It also provides fronting arrangements for the underwriting of insurance for US-based companies worldwide. The company breaks its underwriters out across 13 industries including construction, energy, retail, power generation, public entities, real estate, and both standard and special industrial hazards.

	Annual Growth	12/03	12/04	12/05	12/06	12/07
Est. sales ($ mil.)	—	—	—	—	—	56.4
Employees	—	—	—	—	—	425

ALLIANZ LIFE INSURANCE COMPANY OF NORTH AMERICA

5701 Golden Hills Dr.
Minneapolis, MN 55416
Phone: 763-765-6500
Fax: –
Web: www.allianzlife.com

CEO: Gary C. Bhojwani
CFO: Jill E. Paterson
HR: Jeffrey B. (Jeff) Reeves
FYE: December 31
Type: Subsidiary

There's more to Allianz Life than life. The subsidiaries and affiliates of Allianz Life Insurance Company of North America (Allianz Life) offer a range of insurance, investment, and savings products throughout the US. Allianz Life boasts a network of more than 100,000 independent agents and financial planners selling such products as life insurance, variable and fixed life annuity products, and long-term care insurance. It offers mutual funds and other broker-dealer services through its Questar Capital affiliate. Allianz Life operates in New York through its Allianz Life Insurance Company of New York unit. Allianz Life became a subsidiary of Allianz SE in 1979.

ALLIED BEVERAGE GROUP LLC

600 Washington Ave.
Carlstadt, NJ 07072
Phone: 201-842-6200
Fax: 201-842-6327
Web: www.alliedbeverage.com

CEO: Eric Perlmutter
CFO: –
HR: –
FYE: January 31
Type: Private

Allied Beverage Group is considered the largest New Jersey-based wine and spirits distributor and one of the 10 largest in the US. The company, which specializes in fine wines, sells beverages to restaurants and other establishments that serve alcohol. Among its divisions are Flagstaff Distributors, Meritage Wine Group, and J&J Distributing. Its Majestic Wine & Spirits USA is a brokerage and direct wholesale business in Pennsylvania. Allied Beverage, which is a distributor for Diageo, was created in 1996 from the merger of the Baxter Group, F&A Distributing Company, and Jaydor (companies that date back to the 1930s).

	Annual Growth	1/03	1/04	1/05	1/06	1/07
Est. sales ($ mil.)	—	—	—	—	—	521.5
Employees	—	—	—	—	—	800

ALLIED CAPITAL CORPORATION   NYSE: ALD

1919 Pennsylvania Ave. NW
Washington, DC 20006
Phone: 202-721-6100
Fax: 202-721-6101
Web: www.alliedcapital.com

CEO: William L. (Bill) Walton
CFO: Penni F. Roll
HR: Diane E. Murphy
FYE: December 31
Type: Public

One of the largest business development companies in the US, Allied Capital invests mainly in private middle-market enterprises. Targeting such industries as business and financial services, consumer and industrial products, health care, retail, and energy, the company typically provides funds for buyouts, acquisitions, and restructuring, and to fuel growth. It seeks out established businesses that have solid market share and management with significant equity stakes in their firms. The company does not provide early-stage or seed funding. On occasion, Allied Capital may take a controlling equity position in a company, but usually assumes a minority interest and holds on to it long-term.

	Annual Growth	12/03	12/04	12/05	12/06	12/07
Sales ($ mil.)	8.8%	329.2	367.1	374.1	452.6	461.7
Net income ($ mil.)	(5.5%)	192.0	249.5	872.8	245.1	153.3
Market value ($ mil.)	(1.2%)	3,571.9	3,439.3	4,014.8	4,858.2	3,397.0
Employees	4.1%	—	—	—	170	177

THE ALLIED DEFENSE GROUP, INC.   AMEX: ADG

8000 Towers Crescent Dr., Ste. 260
Vienna, VA 22182
Phone: 703-847-5268
Fax: 703-847-5334
Web: www.allieddefensegroup.com

CEO: John J. Marcello
CFO: Deborah F. Ricci
HR: –
FYE: December 31
Type: Public

The Allied Defense Group can supply real or fake explosions. The company's ammunition and weapons effects division is composed of MECAR (medium-caliber ammunition and mortars). Allied Defense's Electronic Security division includes The VSK Group (a maker of electronic security and fire detection systems), and SynthetiVision (microwave surveillance systems, electronic security systems, and communications systems used in broadcast news and law enforcement). Titan Dynamics Systems (pyrotechnics used in warfare training and simulation) was sold to Chemring Group in early 2008 for a reported $4.7 million.

	Annual Growth	12/03	12/04	12/05	12/06	12/07
Sales ($ mil.)	(24.5%)	171.4	150.1	112.2	128.7	55.6
Net income ($ mil.)	—	8.8	3.9	(38.9)	(41.1)	(21.3)
Market value ($ mil.)	(23.2%)	132.7	124.6	136.2	136.9	46.2
Employees	—	—	—	—	—	—

ALLIED ELECTRONICS, INC.

7151 Jack Newell Blvd. South
Fort Worth, TX 76118
Phone: 817-595-3500
Fax: 817-595-6444
Web: www.alliedelec.com

CEO: Lee Davidson
CFO: Mark McKone
HR: –
FYE: March 31
Type: Subsidiary

Allied Electronics allies itself to customers looking for a wide variety of electronic gear. The company distributes a wide variety of electronic products from such companies as Agilent, Honeywell, National Semiconductor, Panduit, and Vishay. Allied has 300,000-plus parts available online and more than 135,000 products in its popular catalog. Its offerings include test and measurement equipment (analyzers, meters, probes, and oscilloscopes), cable and wire assemblies, enclosure hardware, power supplies and transformers, switches, timers, passive components, and soldering equipment. Allied Electronics, which was founded in 1928 as Allied Radio, was acquired by UK-based Electrocomponents in 1999.

	Annual Growth	3/03	3/04	3/05	3/06	3/07
Est. sales ($ mil.)	—	—	—	—	—	134.0
Employees	—	—	—	—	—	675

ALLIED HEALTHCARE INTERNATIONAL INC.

NASDAQ (GS): AHCI

555 Madison Ave.
New York, NY 10022
Phone: 212-750-0064
Fax: 212-750-7221
Web: www.alliedhealthcare.com

CEO: Alexander (Sandy) Young
CFO: David Moffatt
HR: –
FYE: September 30
Type: Public

Allied Healthcare International (formerly Transworld HealthCare) offers temporary staffing services to the UK health care industry. The company operates through a network of about 100 branches across the UK. Allied Healthcare places its staff, which includes more than 12,000 nurses, nurses aides, and home health aides, in hospitals, nursing homes, care homes, and private homes. Allied Healthcare also provided medical-grade oxygen for respiratory therapy to pharmacies and patients at home in northern Ireland. However, in October 2007 the company divested these operations (primarily its Allied Respiratory Ltd. and Medigas subsidiaries) to industrial gas supplier Air Liquide Group for about $75 million.

	Annual Growth	9/03	9/04	9/05	9/06	9/07
Sales ($ mil.)	(1.4%)	294.4	325.3	351.2	294.6	277.8
Net income ($ mil.)	53.3%	12.0	9.9	18.7	(123.8)	66.3
Market value ($ mil.)	5.3%	87.3	245.9	253.4	89.5	107.5
Employees	(8.5%)	—	—	980	—	821

⊞ ALLIED HEALTHCARE PRODUCTS, INC.

NASDAQ (GM): AHPI

1720 Sublette Ave.
St. Louis, MO 63110
Phone: 314-771-2400
Fax: 314-771-0650
Web: www.alliedhpi.com

CEO: Earl R. Refsland
CFO: Daniel C. Dunn
HR: –
FYE: June 30
Type: Public

No point holding your breath for Allied Healthcare Products — the company has ways of getting oxygen into those lungs. The medical equipment maker produces respiratory equipment used in hospitals, surgery centers, ambulances, and other medical facilities, as well as in patient homes. Its products include anesthesia equipment, oxygen cylinders and nebulizers used in home respiratory therapy, and emergency resuscitation products. It also makes medical gas system components installed in hospital walls during construction, as well as spine immobilization backboards and other items used in trauma situations. Allied Healthcare sells directly to hospitals and through equipment dealers in the US and abroad.

	Annual Growth	6/03	6/04	6/05	6/06	6/07
Sales ($ mil.)	(1.9%)	60.9	59.1	56.1	57.5	56.5
Net income ($ mil.)	—	(0.2)	1.9	2.3	1.6	1.6
Market value ($ mil.)	17.0%	27.9	40.2	38.4	45.5	52.3
Employees	(3.5%)	—	—	412	—	384

ALLIED HOME MORTGAGE CAPITAL CORPORATION

6110 Pinemont
Houston, TX 77092
Phone: 713-353-0400
Fax: 713-353-0489
Web: www.alliedmtgcapital.com

CEO: Jim C. Hodge
CFO: James (Jim) Hagen
HR: Eric Klenk
FYE: June 30
Type: Private

Seeking home mortgage detente? Allied Home Mortgage wants to be your ally. One of the nation's largest privately held mortgage banker/brokers, Allied Home Mortgage Capital (formerly AllQuest.com) originates, sells, and brokers loans. Founded in 1991, the company offers a variety of mortgages — conforming, government-insured, jumbo, home equity, second, and subprime — from more than 800 lenders. It operates through hundreds of branches in all 50 US states and the Virgin Islands, as well as through the Internet (it closed the first paperless mortgage). Allied Home Mortgage Capital sells all of its loans, retaining the servicing. CEO Jim Hodge owns the company.

ALLIED MOTION TECHNOLOGIES INC.

NASDAQ (CM): AMOT

23 Inverness Way East, Ste. 150
Englewood, CO 80112
Phone: 303-799-8520
Fax: 303-799-8521
Web: www.alliedmotion.com

CEO: Richard D. (Dick) Smith
CFO: Richard D. (Dick) Smith
HR: –
FYE: December 31
Type: Public

Allied Motion Technologies has the drive to put you in control of your own motions. The company makes specialized motors, optical encoders, and frequency converters used in mechanical motion control applications. Its products are incorporated into a number of end products, including high-definition printers, robotic systems, and satellite tracking systems. Allied Motion targets applications in the aerospace and military, computer, industrial automation, medical equipment, and semiconductor manufacturing markets. The company operates through five subsidiaries. The US accounts for about three-quarters of sales.

	Annual Growth	12/03	12/04	12/05	12/06	12/07
Sales ($ mil.)	21.1%	39.4	62.7	74.3	82.8	84.6
Net income ($ mil.)	27.8%	0.9	2.3	0.9	1.9	2.4
Market value ($ mil.)	13.1%	19.7	43.8	26.6	44.9	32.3
Employees	10.2%	343	495	515	517	505

ALLIED SECURITY HOLDINGS LLC

3606 Horizon Dr.
King of Prussia, PA 19406
Phone: 610-239-1100
Fax: 610-239-1107
Web: www.alliedbarton.com

CEO: William C. (Bill) Whitmore Jr.
CFO: William A. (Bill) Torzolini
HR: Jim Gillece
FYE: December 31
Type: Subsidiary

Allied Security Holdings offers a secure ally for its customers. One of the largest private security firms in the US, the company does business as AlliedBarton Security Services, and primarily provides security guards for shopping malls, office buildings, hospitals, corporate complexes, residential communities, government facilities, and universities. The company also provides background verification services through its Van Ella subsidiary. Allied Security began doing business as AlliedBarton Security Services after acquiring Barton Protective Services in 2004. AlliedBarton is nearly 70%-owned by Ronald Perelman's MacAndrews & Forbes Holdings.

	Annual Growth	12/02	12/03	12/04	12/05	12/06
Sales ($ mil.)	26.0%	500.0	550.0	873.4	1,124.5	1,261.8
Employees	28.2%	19,000	23,000	37,000	39,200	51,400

⊞ An in-depth profile of this company is available to Hoover's Online members at hoovers.com.

97

ALLIED SECURITY INNOVATIONS, INC.

OTC: ASVN

2150 Hwy. 35, Ste. 250
Sea Girt, NJ 08750
Phone: 732-751-1115
Fax: 732-751-1130
Web: www.ddsi-cpc.com

CEO: Anthony R. (Tony) Shupin
CFO: Michael J. Pellegrino
HR: –
FYE: December 31
Type: Public

Allied Security Innovations (formerly Digital Descriptor Systems) sells computer-based image capture devices and management systems. Its Compu-Capture system incorporates such features as fingerprint matching and description text identifying aliases, hair color, facial scars, or physical deformities, to law enforcement agencies and correctional facilities worldwide. The company expanded by buying CGM Security Solutions, a maker of security seals and tapes. The deal marks Allied's shift in focus from the law enforcement market to the security market in general. In 2007 the company implemented a one-for-500 reverse stock split and changed its name from Digital Descriptor Systems to Allied Security Innovations.

	Annual Growth	12/03	12/04	12/05	12/06	12/07
Sales ($ mil.)	82.1%	0.4	0.4	3.3	4.5	4.4
Net income ($ mil.)	—	(1.3)	(2.0)	(4.0)	(4.3)	(16.3)
Employees	71.0%	4	17	20	20	—

ALLIED SUPPLY COMPANY

120 E. Industry Ct.
Deer Park, NY 11729
Phone: 631-254-9300
Fax: 631-254-0064
Web: www.alliedondemand.com

CEO: Marc J. Bodner
CFO: –
HR: Pamela (Pam) Knopman
FYE: December 31
Type: Private

Stocking shelves? Allied Supply is a wholesale distributor of a wide variety of household and personal care products, stationery items, toys, and sundries to supermarkets, independent pharmacies, and discount and stationery stores. Its offerings have ranged from ACE bandages to Zippo lighters and from Wiffle balls to baby wipes. The company operates throughout the US through a network of about half a dozen distribution facilities; among its key partners have been pharmaceutical distributors such as McKesson and Cardinal Health. Allied Supply has been assembled via a string of transactions dating to the 1950s, including the 1986 merger of E&N Sales Corp. and Ortner Drug Co.

	Annual Growth	12/03	12/04	12/05	12/06	12/07
Est. sales ($ mil.)	—	—	—	—	—	55.1
Employees	—	—	—	—	—	200

▥ ALLIED SYSTEMS HOLDINGS, INC.

2302 Parklake Dr., Bldg. 15, Ste. 600
Atlanta, GA 30345
Phone: 404-373-4285
Fax: 404-370-4206
Web: www.alliedholdings.com

CEO: Mark Gendregske
CFO: Thomas H. (Tom) King
HR: Brenda Ragsdale
FYE: December 31
Type: Private

Carrying more than 7 million cars, trucks, and SUVs every year, Allied Systems Holdings leads the North American automobile-hauling market. Subsidiary Allied Automotive Group moves vehicles with a fleet of more than 3,400 tractor-trailer rigs. Vehicles are transported from manufacturing plants, railway distribution points, ports, and auctions to auto dealers; an average haul is less than 200 miles. Automakers are the company's main customers — Chrysler, Ford, General Motors, Honda, and Toyota together account for more than 85% of sales. Allied Automotive Group operates from some 75 terminals in the US and Canada. The holding company emerged from Chapter 11 bankruptcy protection in May 2007.

	Annual Growth	12/02	12/03	12/04	12/05	12/06
Sales ($ mil.)	(0.1%)	898.1	865.5	895.2	892.9	893.8
Employees	(4.0%)	6,600	6,200	6,400	—	5,600

ALLIED TELESIS, INC.

19800 N. Creek Pkwy., Ste. 200
Bothell, WA 98011
Phone: 800-424-4284
Fax: 425-481-3895
Web: www.alliedtelesyn.com

CEO: Takayoshi Oshima
CFO: Joseph J. Italiano III
HR: Joseph J. Italiano III
FYE: December 31
Type: Subsidiary

Allied Telesis provides hubs, media conversion devices, network adapters, switches, routers, and other networking equipment. It sells its products worldwide to customers in the education, enterprise, and government markets. Customers include Agilent, General Electric, Hewlett-Packard, Ohio State University, Stanford University, and the US Department of Homeland Security. The company is part of Japan's Allied Telesis Group. Formerly called Allied Telesyn, the company changed its name in 2006 to align its North American brand with that of its parent. Allied Telesis was founded in 1987.

	Annual Growth	12/03	12/04	12/05	12/06	12/07
Est. sales ($ mil.)	—	—	—	—	—	39.0
Employees	—	—	—	—	—	362

▥ ALLIED WASTE INDUSTRIES, INC.

NYSE: AW

18500 N. Allied Way
Phoenix, AZ 85054
Phone: 480-627-2700
Fax: 480-627-2701
Web: www.alliedwaste.com

CEO: John J. Zillmer
CFO: Peter S. Hathaway
HR: Edward A. Evans
FYE: December 31
Type: Public

Allied Waste Industries proves every day that one person's trash is another person's treasure. The company is the US's second-largest waste-hauler, behind only Waste Management, Inc. Allied Waste picks up the garbage of about 8 million residential, commercial, and industrial customers throughout the US. Its vast collection, recycling, and landfill operations include a network of 291 collection companies, 161 transfer stations, 161 active landfills, and 53 recycling facilities in 124 markets in 37 states. Residential, commercial, and roll-off (dumpsters) collection accounts for about two-thirds of sales. Officers and directors control about 36% of the company.

	Annual Growth	12/03	12/04	12/05	12/06	12/07
Sales ($ mil.)	3.7%	5,247.7	5,362.0	5,734.8	6,028.8	6,068.7
Net income ($ mil.)	20.7%	128.7	49.3	203.8	160.9	273.6
Market value ($ mil.)	(2.1%)	4,443.0	2,946.4	2,894.7	4,521.5	4,081.8
Employees	(5.3%)	—	—	26,000	24,200	23,300

ALLIN CORPORATION

OTC: ALLN

381 Mansfield Ave., Ste. 400
Pittsburgh, PA 15220
Phone: 412-928-8800
Fax: 412-928-0887
Web: www.allin.com

CEO: Richard W. (Rich) Talarico
CFO: Dean C. Praskach
HR: –
FYE: December 31
Type: Public

Allin wants to be an all-in-one information technology (IT) provider on the high seas and dry land. A provider of Microsoft-focused services, the company (pronounced "all in") performs IT consulting, applications development, and systems integration services for cruise lines and small and midsized businesses. Allin offers interactive media development and integration for cruise lines, technology infrastructure services, and e-business consulting. The company uses video equipment and services provided by On Command for its interactive TV operations. With warrants, Pittsburgh investor Henry Posner controls just over 50% of Allin.

	Annual Growth	12/03	12/04	12/05	12/06	12/07
Sales ($ mil.)	18.1%	12.9	12.6	14.3	19.0	25.1
Net income ($ mil.)	42.5%	0.8	0.3	(0.9)	1.9	3.3
Market value ($ mil.)	32.3%	2.6	1.8	4.0	3.8	8.1
Employees	—	—	—	—	—	—

An in-depth profile of this company is available to Hoover's Online members at hoovers.com.

ALLINA HOSPITALS AND CLINICS

2925 Chicago Ave.
Minneapolis, MN 55407
Phone: 612-775-5000
Fax: 612-863-5667
Web: www.allina.com

CEO: Richard R. (Dick) Pettingill
CFO: Michael McAnder
HR: –
FYE: December 31
Type: Not-for-profit

Allina Hospitals and Clinics is a not-for-profit health care system that focuses on protecting people's number one asset — "Their Good Health." Allina Hospitals and Clinics owns and operates 11 hospitals and medical centers, more than 60 clinics, and 15 pharmacies. The Allina network serves Minnesota and western Wisconsin. Allina Hospitals and Clinics also provides disease prevention programs, specialized inpatient and outpatient services, medical equipment, and emergency medical transportation service. About 5,000 physicians provide services through the health care system. Its emergency department treats more than 200,000 patients each year.

	Annual Growth	12/03	12/04	12/05	12/06	12/07
Est. sales ($ mil.)	—	—	—	—	—	2,147.5
Employees	—	—	—	—	—	22,347

ALLION HEALTHCARE, INC.

NASDAQ (GM): ALLI

1660 Walt Whitman Rd., Ste. 105
Melville, NY 11747
Phone: 631-547-6520
Fax: 631-249-5863
Web: www.allionhealthcare.com

CEO: Michael P. Moran
CFO: Russell J. Fichera
HR: –
FYE: December 31
Type: Public

Allion Healthcare is a specialty drug distributor focusing on patients with HIV and AIDS. Through its subsidiary MOMS Pharmacy, the company fulfills prescriptions for necessary medications at about a dozen distribution centers and delivers them to patients, doctors' offices, and clinics nationwide. Allion also provides ancillary drugs and nutritional supplies, and it offers special software and packaging of drug orders — pre-filled pill boxes, for instance — that are intended to help patients stick with their medication regimens. Most of Allion's customers rely on Medicaid or state programs such as the AIDS Drug Assistance Program for payment of their prescriptions.

	Annual Growth	12/03	12/04	12/05	12/06	12/07
Sales ($ mil.)	55.2%	42.5	60.1	123.1	209.5	246.7
Net income ($ mil.)	—	(3.0)	(2.7)	(1.0)	3.2	3.3
Market value ($ mil.)	(23.2%)	—	—	150.9	116.0	89.0
Employees	30.6%	—	—	170	222	—

ALLIS-CHALMERS ENERGY INC.

NYSE: ALY

5075 Westheimer, Ste. 890
Houston, TX 77056
Phone: 713-369-0550
Fax: 713-369-0555
Web: www.alchenergy.com

CEO: Munawar H. (Micki) Hidayatallah
CFO: Victor M. Perez
HR: –
FYE: December 31
Type: Public

This company knows the drill. Allis-Chalmers Energy provides drilling and oil field services to oil and gas exploration companies operating primarily in the western and southern US. It operates in six segments of the oil and natural gas service industry: Rental Services; International Drilling; Directional Drilling; Tubular Services; Underbalanced Drilling; and Production Services. Its Strata Directional Technology subsidiary offers drilling services to clients in Texas and Louisiana. Through its AirComp unit, Allis-Chalmers operates a fleet of 260 compressors, 105 full-time directional drillers, 30 measurement-while-drilling tools, and 300 downhole motors used for well production enhancement and completion.

	Annual Growth	12/03	12/04	12/05	12/06	12/07
Sales ($ mil.)	104.4%	32.7	47.7	105.3	307.3	571.0
Net income ($ mil.)	104.2%	2.9	0.9	7.2	35.6	50.4
Market value ($ mil.)	78.5%	51.0	67.9	210.2	650.5	518.0
Employees	108.7%	—	—	700	2,567	3,050

ALLISON TRANSMISSION, INC.

4700 W. 10th St.
Indianapolis, IN 46222
Phone: 317-242-5000
Fax: –
Web: www.allisontransmission.com

CEO: Lawrence E. Dewey
CFO: –
HR: –
FYE: December 31
Type: Private

You can't have a tractor pull without Allison Transmission. The company builds automatic transmissions for commercial vehicles. Allison Transmission's customers include makers of everything from garbage trucks and city transit buses to military vehicles and dump trucks. Allison also makes a line of electric drives for use primarily on buses and shuttles, and remanufactures automatic transmissions for the commercial replacement aftermarket. Allison also builds transmissions for GM's Silverado HD and GMC Sierra HD pickups. In 2007 General Motors sold Allison to The Carlyle Group and Onex Corp. for $5.6 billion. GM kept one Allison plant that builds transmissions for its light trucks.

	Annual Growth	12/03	12/04	12/05	12/06	12/07
Est. sales ($ mil.)	—	—	—	—	—	2,000.0
Employees	—	—	—	—	—	3,400

ALLOY, INC.

NASDAQ (GM): ALOY

151 W. 26th St., 11th Fl.
New York, NY 10001
Phone: 212-244-4307
Fax: 212-244-4311
Web: www.alloy.com

CEO: Matthew C. (Matt) Diamond
CFO: Joseph D. Frehe
HR: Kerry Genza
FYE: January 31
Type: Public

Alloy has its eye on Generation Y. The company, through its chief promotional division Alloy Media + Marketing, provides advertising and marketing services and produces content for online and print media, all designed to help customers reach people between the ages of 10 and 24. It also helps customers place advertising in print and broadcast media focused on high school and college students and military personnel. In addition to its Channel One subsidiary, which broadcasts youth-oriented news and public affairs programming, Alloy's other media offerings include Web sites and social networks (alloy.com, TEEN.com, sconex.com), print publications, and display boards placed on school and college campuses.

	Annual Growth	1/04	1/05	1/06	1/07	1/08
Sales ($ mil.)	(14.5%)	372.0	402.5	195.3	196.1	199.1
Net income ($ mil.)	—	(75.2)	(91.8)	(35.5)	(7.2)	(64.4)
Market value ($ mil.)	(26.9%)	420.9	152.6	33.4	174.5	119.9
Employees	(49.0%)	—	5,094	2,723	601	674

ALLSCRIPTS HEALTHCARE SOLUTIONS, INC.

NASDAQ (GS): MDRX

222 Merchandise Mart Plaza, Ste. 2024
Chicago, IL 60654
Phone: 866-358-6869
Fax: 312-506-1201
Web: www.allscripts.com

CEO: Glen E. Tullman
CFO: William J. (Bill) Davis
HR: Bonnie Schirato
FYE: December 31
Type: Public

Jokes about doctors' handwriting may go the way of house calls thanks to Allscripts Healthcare — a provider of clinical software and information systems for doctors. The company sells prescription-management software and services that let doctors enter prescription information over computer networks, including tools that give doctors access (via desktop or wireless handheld devices) to patient drug history, drug interactions, and generic alternatives. Other services include electronic document imaging and scanning and physician feedback services. Allscripts bought ChannelHealth from IDX Systems, adding thousands of physicians to its clientele. IDX Systems owns about 20% of Allscripts.

	Annual Growth	12/03	12/04	12/05	12/06	12/07
Sales ($ mil.)	34.6%	85.8	100.8	120.6	228.0	281.9
Net income ($ mil.)	—	(5.0)	3.1	9.7	11.9	20.6
Market value ($ mil.)	52.0%	207.7	428.0	547.7	1,467.1	1,108.9
Employees	73.0%	—	—	386	914	1,155

An in-depth profile of this company is available to Hoover's Online members at hoovers.com.

99

THE ALLSTATE CORPORATION

NYSE: ALL

2775 Sanders Rd.
Northbrook, IL 60062
Phone: 847-402-5000
Fax: 847-326-7519
Web: www.allstate.com

CEO: Thomas J. Wilson II
CFO: Samuel H. Pilch
HR: Anise D. Wiley-Little
FYE: December 31
Type: Public

Ya gotta hand it to Allstate. The "good hands" company is the second-largest US personal lines insurer, behind rival State Farm. The company sells auto, homeowners, property/casualty, and life insurance products in Canada and the US. The company's life insurance subsidiaries include Allstate Life, American Heritage Life, and Lincoln Benefit Life. Allstate Financial provides life insurance and investment products, targeting affluent and middle-income consumers. Allstate Motor Club provides emergency road service, and adding to its repertoire, the company also offers the nationwide online Allstate Bank.

	Annual Growth	12/03	12/04	12/05	12/06	12/07
Assets ($ mil.)	3.9%	134,142.0	149,725.0	156,072.0	157,554.0	156,408.0
Net income ($ mil.)	14.4%	2,705.0	3,181.0	1,765.0	4,993.0	4,636.0
Market value ($ mil.)	(0.7%)	30,286.1	35,324.8	34,929.2	40,498.4	29,405.5
Employees	(0.4%)	—	—	38,300	37,900	38,000

ALLSUP'S CONVENIENCE STORES INC.

2112 Thornton St.
Clovis, NM 88101
Phone: 505-769-2311
Fax: 505-769-2564
Web: www.allsups.com

CEO: Lonnie Allsup
CFO: Barbara Allsup
HR: Stacy Owens
FYE: March 31
Type: Private

Whether it's your gas tank or your stomach, you can fill up at Allsup's. Allsup's Convenience Stores operates about 300 locations in small towns and along roadsides in New Mexico and Texas. The company's stores offer hot southwestern-style foods, such as burritos and barbecue, as well as other food items and traditional convenience store fare, including cigarettes, snacks, and sodas. Exxon, Fina, ConocoPhillips, and Shell brand gasoline is also sold at Allsup's locations. Cutting horse aficionado Lonnie Allsup opened his first convenience store in 1956. His family continues to own and run the company.

	Annual Growth	3/03	3/04	3/05	3/06	3/07
Est. sales ($ mil.)	—	—	—	—	—	134.1
Employees	—	—	—	—	—	1,238

ALLTEL CORPORATION

1 Allied Dr.
Little Rock, AR 72202
Phone: 501-905-8000
Fax: 501-905-5444
Web: www.alltel.com

CEO: Scott T. Ford
CFO: Sharilyn S. Gasaway
HR: C. J. Duvall Jr.
FYE: December 31
Type: Private

All together, ALLTEL is a leading wireless telecommunications network operator. The company has more than 13 million customers and its network covers most of the US. ALLTEL has transitioned in recent years into a wireless-only provider, with an eye toward expanding its wireless operations through acquisitions. TPG Capital and Goldman Sachs unit GS Capital Partners acquired ALLTEL in 2007 for about $27.5 billion. In June 2008 Verizon Wireless announced plans to acquire ALLTEL in a deal worth about $28.1 billion; the purchase would make Verizon Wireless the largest wireless operator in the US.

	Annual Growth	12/03	12/04	12/05	12/06	12/07
Sales ($ mil.)	2.5%	7,979.9	8,246.1	9,487.0	7,884.0	8,803.1
Net income ($ mil.)	(39.1%)	1,330.1	1,046.2	1,331.4	1,129.4	183.2
Employees	(13.2%)	—	—	21,373	14,899	16,104

ALMOST FAMILY, INC.

NASDAQ (CM): AFAM

9510 Ormsby Station Rd., Ste. 300
Louisville, KY 40223
Phone: 502-891-1000
Fax: 502-891-8067
Web: www.almost-family.com

CEO: William B. Yarmuth
CFO: C. Steven (Steve) Guenthner
HR: Mark Sutton
FYE: December 31
Type: Public

If you live in California and you're worried about Mom's failing faculties back in Florida, you could call Almost Family. With its home health nursing services, Almost Family offers senior citizens in nine states (including Florida) an alternative to spending their days in nursing homes. The company operates through two segments: Its visiting nurse unit provides skilled nursing care under the Caretenders and Mederi-Caretenders names, while its personal care segment (operating under the Almost Family banner) offers custodial care, such as housekeeping, meal preparation, and medication management. The company has about 50 skilled nursing and 20 personal care branch locations.

	Annual Growth	12/03	12/04	12/05	12/06	12/07
Sales ($ mil.)	11.0%	86.9	86.8	75.6	91.8	132.1
Net income ($ mil.)	37.9%	2.1	1.3	7.9	4.2	7.6
Market value ($ mil.)	79.8%	10.3	17.1	19.2	118.7	107.5
Employees	—	—	—	3,200	—	—

ALNYLAM PHARMACEUTICALS, INC.

NASDAQ (GM): ALNY

300 3rd St., 3rd Fl.
Cambridge, MA 02142
Phone: 617-551-8200
Fax: 617-551-8101
Web: www.alnylam.com

CEO: John M. Maraganore
CFO: Patricia L. Allen
HR: Eric Raichle
FYE: December 31
Type: Public

Call it *The Silence of the Genes*. Alnylam Pharmaceuticals runs interference with RNA to prevent disease. RNA interference (RNAi) technology developed by the biotech firm can selectively shut off harmful genes. The company is developing its own pipeline, including its treatment for respiratory syncytial virus (RSV), a viral infection that is a leading cause of respiratory ailments in children and can be fatal in preemies and children with weak immune systems. Other R&D programs target neurological disorders, cystic fibrosis, and Ebola virus infection. Alnylam has R&D alliances with Roche, Novartis, Biogen Idec, and Medtronic, as well as more than 20 licensing agreements with other biotechnology firms.

	Annual Growth	12/03	12/04	12/05	12/06	12/07
Sales ($ mil.)	299.4%	0.2	4.3	5.7	26.9	50.9
Net income ($ mil.)	—	(25.0)	(32.7)	(42.9)	(34.6)	(85.5)
Market value ($ mil.)	96.7%	—	155.7	355.9	792.9	1,185.7
Employees	—	—	—	94	—	—

ALOETTE COSMETICS, INC.

4900 Highlands Pkwy.
Smyrna, GA 30082
Phone: 678-444-2563
Fax: 678-444-2564
Web: www.aloettecosmetics.com

CEO: Robert (Bob) Cohen
CFO: Loren Burnett
HR: –
FYE: December 31
Type: Private

Aloette Cosmetics loves a good party. Best known for selling aloe-based skin care products, Aloette also markets cosmetics and perfume, as well as other personal care items. The products, most of which contain aloe, are sold mainly through home parties held by Aloette's direct-sales network of about 10,000 consultants, who operate through approximately 50 franchises in the US, Canada, and Mexico. Top sellers for the company include their anti-aging and spa indulgence lines. The company also sells products online and on television shopping channels. Former franchisee Christie Cohen (chairman) and her husband, Bob (CEO), bought Aloette in 1998. Christie also serves as Aloette's spokesmodel.

	Annual Growth	12/03	12/04	12/05	12/06	12/07
Est. sales ($ mil.)	—	—	—	—	—	12.6
Employees	—	—	—	—	—	50

ALON USA ENERGY, INC.

NYSE: ALJ

7616 LBJ Fwy., Ste. 300
Dallas, TX 75251
Phone: 972-367-3600
Fax: 972-367-3728
Web: www.alonusa.com

CEO: Jeff D. Morris
CFO: Shai Even
HR: –
FYE: December 31
Type: Public

Could anything be finer than FINA? Alon USA Energy is the driving force behind FINA-branded marketing and refining operations throughout the US Southwest. Alon USA Energy, a subsidiary of Alon Israel Oil, was formed in 2000 to acquire FINA Inc.'s downstream assets. The company provides fuel to almost 1,100 FINA-branded retail sites. It also owns or operates more than 300 convenience stores under the 7-Eleven brand. Alon USA Energy's refineries in Texas (one), California (two), and Oregon (one), have a combined throughput capacity of 170,000 barrels per day. Alon USA Energy is also a top asphalt producer. Alon Israel Oil owns 72% of Alon USA Energy.

	Annual Growth	12/03	12/04	12/05	12/06	12/07
Sales ($ mil.)	34.0%	1,410.8	1,707.6	2,328.5	3,198.1	4,542.1
Net income ($ mil.)	64.8%	14.1	25.1	104.0	157.4	103.9
Market value ($ mil.)	17.6%	—	—	919.8	1,231.5	1,272.3
Employees	38.1%	—	—	1,415	2,029	2,697

ALORICA INC.

14726 Ramona Ave., 3rd Fl.
Chino, CA 91710
Phone: 909-606-3600
Fax: 909-606-7708
Web: www.alorica.com

CEO: Andy Lee
CFO: Jack Pollock
HR: –
FYE: –
Type: Private

Alorica is here to remedy your front- and back-office ailments. The company provides outsourced customer service operations through its call centers located in the US and the Philippines. Alorica's contact center services include technical support, customer service, help desk, billing, and sales (inbound and outbound). The company also offers fulfillment and service logistics including returns management, warranty support management, and field service dispatch. Based in California, the company was founded in 1999.

ALPHA INNOTECH CORP.

OTC: APNO

2401 Merced St.
San Leandro, CA 94577
Phone: 510-483-9620
Fax: 510-483-3227
Web: alphainnotech.com

CEO: Ronald H. (Ron) Bissinger
CFO: Ronald H. (Ron) Bissinger
HR: –
FYE: December 31
Type: Public

Alpha Innotech has found a singular purpose in the double helix. The company makes digital imaging systems used by life sciences researchers to study DNA and RNA, proteins, and cells. Drug companies, biotechs, and research institutions use its instruments (FluorChem, AlphaImager, and AlphaDigiDoc, among others) to run tests on genes, bacterial colonies, and proteins for a number of purposes, including drug discovery, molecular diagnostics, and biomarker screening. The company sells through a direct sales force, manufacturers' representatives, and internationally through a network of distributors. It also sells its products as components to GE Healthcare.

	Annual Growth	12/03	12/04	12/05	12/06	12/07
Sales ($ mil.)	89.0%	1.2	0.1	12.1	13.3	15.3
Net income ($ mil.)	—	(2.8)	1.3	(2.5)	(1.0)	(0.7)
Employees	7.0%	—	—	48	48	55

ALPHA NATURAL RESOURCES, INC.

NYSE: ANR

1 Alpha Place
Abingdon, VA 24212
Phone: 276-619-4410
Fax: –
Web: www.alphanr.com

CEO: Michael J. (Mike) Quillen
CFO: David C. Stuebe
HR: Gary W. Banbury
FYE: December 31
Type: Public

Alpha Natural Resources doesn't mind going underground. The company produces steam and metallurgical coal at 45 underground mines and 25 surface mines, primarily in central and northern Appalachia. Low-sulfur steam coal, which is used mainly as fuel for electricity generation, accounts for most of Alpha's sales. The company produces about 25 million tons of coal annually, and purchases another 5 million from other mining companies. Most of the purchased coal is blended with coal from Alpha's mines before being sold. It sells about a third of its product internationally. Alpha controls somewhere near 600 million tons of proved and probable coal reserves.

	Annual Growth	12/03	12/04	12/05	12/06	12/07
Sales ($ mil.)	24.1%	792.6	1,269.7	1,627.3	1,910.7	1,877.6
Net income ($ mil.)	86.3%	2.3	20.0	21.2	128.2	27.7
Market value ($ mil.)	31.4%	—	—	1,237.5	924.4	2,136.2
Employees	12.4%	2,500	—	3,591	3,546	—

ALPHAGRAPHICS, INC.

268 S. State St., Ste. 300
Salt Lake City, UT 84111
Phone: 801-595-7270
Fax: 801-595-7271
Web: www.alphagraphics.com

CEO: Kevin K. Cushing
CFO: Randall A. (Randy) Plant
HR: Stacy Stetner
FYE: June 30
Type: Private

AlphaGraphics wants to be the beginning — and the end — of printing services. The franchise company provides print-related and digital publishing services through some 300 shops in over 10 countries. Besides printing and copying, it also offers graphic design, corporate identity, and sales materials consultation. Through its subsidiary Creative Media Group, AlphaGraphics provides Web site design, database programming, and Internet hosting, as well as strategic planning and marketing analysis. AlphaGraphics was founded in 1970 by Tucson, Arizona entrepreneur Rodger Ford. British print and electronic media company Pindar holds a majority stake in the company.

	Annual Growth	6/03	6/04	6/05	6/06	6/07
Est. sales ($ mil.)	—	—	—	—	—	18.4
Employees	—	—	—	—	—	99

[logo] ALPHARMA INC.

NYSE: ALO

440 Rte. 22 East
Bridgewater, NJ 08807
Phone: 908-566-3800
Fax: 908-566-4137
Web: www.alpharma.com

CEO: Dean J. Mitchell
CFO: Jeffrey S. Campbell
HR: Peter M. Watts
FYE: December 31
Type: Public

Alpharma makes medicines for all of the world's creatures. The company operates in two segments, human pharmaceuticals and animal health. Alpharma's human pharmaceuticals business makes branded drugs for chronic pain control, including Kadian, an extended-release morphine in capsule form, and Flector, an anti-inflammatory pain relief patch. The company's animal health segment caters to the rest of the animal kingdom; its animal antibiotics and feed additives are sold to livestock producers and feed makers. Alpharma's products are manufactured by a third party.

	Annual Growth	12/03	12/04	12/05	12/06	12/07
Sales ($ mil.)	(13.6%)	1,297.3	1,339.5	553.6	653.8	722.4
Net income ($ mil.)	—	13.8	(314.7)	133.8	82.5	(13.6)
Market value ($ mil.)	2.0%	813.7	699.7	1,212.6	1,038.7	882.4
Employees	19.5%	—	—	1,400	1,400	2,000

ALPHATEC HOLDINGS, INC.

NASDAQ (GM): ATEC

2051 Palomar Airport Rd., Ste. 100
Carlsbad, CA 92011
Phone: 760-431-9286
Fax: 760-431-9823
Web: www.alphatecspine.com

CEO: Dirk Kuyper
CFO: Charles O. Boyles
HR: Susan L. Johnson
FYE: December 31
Type: Public

Alphatec Holdings aims to help people stand up straight and keep moving. The company develops and manufactures products used to treat spinal disorders including scoliosis and degenerating disks. Through its Alphatec Spine subsidiary, the company makes a variety of FDA-approved products primarily for the spine fusion market in the US. Its product line includes grafting materials, spinal implant systems, and surgical instruments. Alphatec markets its products to surgeons through a network of independent distributors, as well as a direct sales force. The company's Alphatec Pacific subsidiary sells spine fusion and orthopedic trauma devices in Japan.

	Annual Growth	12/03	12/04	12/05	12/06	12/07
Sales ($ mil.)	8.1%	—	—	—	74.0	80.0
Net income ($ mil.)	—	—	—	—	(25.8)	(20.2)
Market value ($ mil.)	83.3%	—	—	—	129.7	237.8
Employees	(10.8%)	—	—	—	295	263

ALPINE AIR EXPRESS, INC.

OTC: APNX

1177 Alpine Air Way
Provo, UT 84601
Phone: 801-373-1508
Fax: 801-377-3781
Web: www.alpine-air.com

CEO: Eugene R. (Gene) Mallette
CFO: Don T. Squire Jr.
HR: —
FYE: October 31
Type: Public

Alpine Air Express flies the western skies to cart cargo for its customers. The air cargo company provides scheduled transportation of mail, packages, and other time-sensitive freight to more than 20 cities in the western half of the US mainland and in Hawaii. Its primary customers, the United States Postal Service and United Parcel Service, together account for more than 80% of sales. Alpine Air operates a fleet of about 25 Beechcraft turboprop planes from bases in Hawaii, Montana, and Utah. Along with its cargo operations, the company provides pilot training and aircraft maintenance services. CEO Eugene Mallette owns a controlling stake in Alpine Air.

	Annual Growth	10/03	10/04	10/05	10/06	10/07
Sales ($ mil.)	15.6%	10.3	15.0	22.6	20.2	18.4
Net income ($ mil.)	—	(1.4)	(1.4)	(1.4)	0.4	2.5
Market value ($ mil.)	34.9%	4.6	2.4	5.6	16.0	15.2
Employees	—	—	—	—	—	—

ALPINE ELECTRONICS OF AMERICA, INC.

19145 Gramercy Place
Torrance, CA 90501
Phone: 310-326-8000
Fax: 310-782-8127
Web: www.alpine-usa.com

CEO: Toru Usami
CFO: —
HR: —
FYE: March 31
Type: Subsidiary

Alpine prefers to be on top of the electronics market. Alpine Electronics of America, a subsidiary of Japanese electronics manufacturer Alps Electric, makes and distributes mobile electronics equipment to customers in Canada and the US. The company produces amplifiers, subwoofers, speakers, monitors, CD and DVD players, and navigation systems designed primarily for use in automobiles. Other products include adapters designed to connect Apple's iPod products to car stereos. It operates research and development facilities in Asia, Europe, and the US. Alpine Electronics was formed in 1978.

	Annual Growth	3/03	3/04	3/05	3/06	3/07
Est. sales ($ mil.)	—	—	—	—	—	183.8
Employees	—	—	—	—	—	550

THE ALPINE GROUP, INC.

Pink Sheets: APNI

1 Meadowlands Plaza, Ste. 801
East Rutherford, NJ 07073
Phone: 201-549-4400
Fax: 201-549-4428
Web: www.alpine-group.net

CEO: Steven S. Elbaum
CFO: —
HR: —
FYE: December 31
Type: Public

The Alpine Group has experienced the peaks and valleys of various metals and wires business. The company's Exeon subsidiary specializes in the reclamation of metal and copper wires and produces copper chops. Exeon was formerly part of Alpine's Essex Electric wire and cable subsidiary, which was divested in 2006. Other operations include subsidiary Posterloid (menuboard and signage systems) and majority-owned Synergy Cables (formerly Superior Cables, power and telecommunications cables). Alpine also holds a stake in Wolverine Tube (small copper and alloy tubes).

	Annual Growth	12/03	12/04	12/05	12/06	12/07
Sales ($ mil.)	(36.5%)	330.5	315.9	447.8	23.1	53.6
Net income ($ mil.)	(78.8%)	834.8	13.4	4.6	20.5	1.7
Employees	—	—	—	—	—	—

ALR TECHNOLOGIES INC.

OTC: ALRT

114M Reynolda Village
Winston-Salem, NC 27106
Phone: 336-722-2254
Fax: 336-722-2775
Web: www.alrt.com

CEO: Sidney Chan
CFO: Sidney Chan
HR: —
FYE: December 31
Type: Public

ALR Technologies helps patients remember to take their medicine. The company makes medication compliance products and compliance home-monitoring and intervention systems. Its devices can be programmed to provide up to eight daily audio and visual alerts to indicate that it is time to take a medication. ALR Technologies also makes pet medication reminders with alerts that can be set for every day or every month. In addition, the company provides contact lens replacement reminders. ALR Technologies has offices in the US, as well as in Hong Kong to serve Pacific Rim countries.

	Annual Growth	12/03	12/04	12/05	12/06	12/07
Sales ($ mil.)	0.0%	0.2	0.4	0.3	0.2	0.2
Net income ($ mil.)	—	(2.8)	(4.3)	(1.8)	(2.6)	(1.6)
Employees	0.0%	—	9	10	9	9

ALRO STEEL CORPORATION

3100 E. High St.
Jackson, MI 49204
Phone: 517-787-5500
Fax: 517-787-6390
Web: www.alro.com

CEO: Alvin Glick
CFO: —
HR: —
FYE: May 31
Type: Private

Service center operator Alro Steel provides processing services such as aluminum circle cutting, CNC flame cutting, forming, and machining. The company carries an extensive inventory of steel products, along with industrial tools and supplies. It offers plastic sheet, rod, tube, and film through its Alro Plastics division. The company also distributes industrial tools and materials through subsidiary Alro Industrial Supplies. Alro Steel operates from some 40 locations in 12 states, though about half of them are in Michigan. The company was founded in 1948.

	Annual Growth	5/03	5/04	5/05	5/06	5/07
Est. sales ($ mil.)	—	—	—	—	—	997.6
Employees	—	—	—	—	—	1,500

ALSCO, INC.

505 E. South Temple
Salt Lake City, UT 84102
Phone: 801-328-8831
Fax: 801-363-5680
Web: www.alsco.com

CEO: Kevin Steiner
CFO: Kevin Steiner
HR: Tim Weiler
FYE: June 30
Type: Private

Alsco tells its clients, "It pays to keep clean," and then provides uniforms, linens, and related products and services in 10 countries to achieve that goal. The company (whose name stands for American linen supply company) supplies towels, linens, and uniforms to the medical and hospitality industries, among others. It also manufactures, rents, and sells uniforms, provides workplace restroom services, launders specialized garments, and manages gown rooms at high-tech sites. The company expanded in 2006 by buying the assets of National Linen and Uniform Service. Founded in 1889 by George Steiner, Alsco is owned and operated by the Steiner family.

	Annual Growth	6/02	6/03	6/04	6/05	6/06
Est. sales ($ mil.)	(0.8%)	—	—	—	1,169.0	1,160.0
Employees	45.8%	—	—	—	12,000	17,500

ALSTON & BIRD LLP

1 Atlantic Center, 1201 W. Peachtree St.
Atlanta, GA 30309
Phone: 404-881-7000
Fax: 404-881-7777
Web: www.alston.com

CEO: Richard R. Hays
CFO: Richard G. Levinson
HR: Cathy A. Benton
FYE: December 31
Type: Partnership

One of the South's leading law firms, Alston & Bird groups its 80-plus practices into four main areas: corporate and finance; intellectual property; litigation; and tax. The firm's intellectual property practice group is one of the nation's largest. Overall, Alston & Bird has about 750 attorneys, policy advisers, and patent agents. The firm serves a wide range of domestic and international clients, which have included Bank of America, Duke University, General Electric, and UPS. Besides its Atlanta home base, Alston & Bird has offices in Charlotte and Raleigh, North Carolina; New York; and Washington, DC. The firm traces its roots to a law practice founded in 1893.

	Annual Growth	12/03	12/04	12/05	12/06	12/07
Est. sales ($ mil.)	—	—	—	—	—	128.5
Employees	—	—	—	—	—	1,485

⊞ ALTADIS U.S.A., INC.

5900 N. Andrews Ave., Ste. 1100
Fort Lauderdale, FL 33309
Phone: 954-772-9000
Fax: 954-267-1198
Web: www.altadisusa.com

CEO: Theo W. Folz
CFO: Gary R. Ellis
HR: Rick McKenzie
FYE: December 31
Type: Subsidiary

The cigar-smoking fad may have lost some steam in other markets, but Altadis USA keeps rolling along. Created from the 2000 consolidation of HavaTampa Inc. and Consolidated Cigar Holdings, Altadis USA is a leading cigar maker nationwide that generates more than half of its parent Altadis, S.A.'s worldwide cigar sales. Altadis USA manufactures and markets both premium and mass-market cigars under such well-known brand names as Don Diego, El Producto, H. Upmann, and Montecristo. It also sells little cigars under the Dutch Treats and Supre Sweets brands, as well as humidors and cigar cases. Altadis USA's Spanish parent company was acquired by Britain's Imperial Tobacco Group in February 2008.

	Annual Growth	12/03	12/04	12/05	12/06	12/07
Est. sales ($ mil.)	—	—	—	—	—	37.0
Employees	—	—	—	—	—	1,400

ALTAIR ENGINEERING, INC.

1820 E. Big Beaver Rd.
Troy, MI 48083
Phone: 248-614-2400
Fax: 248-614-2411
Web: www.altair.com

CEO: James R. (Jim) Scapa
CFO: Thomas M. (Tom) Perring
HR: –
FYE: December 31
Type: Private

Founded in 1985, Altair Engineering is a product design consulting and technology company that provides software and services to clients which have included Boeing, Caterpillar, Ford Motor, General Electric, Motorola, Nokia, Procter & Gamble, Whirlpool, and the US Departments of Defense and Energy. The company operates through three primary business lines: product design and development, commercial software, and enterprise process management.

	Annual Growth	12/03	12/04	12/05	12/06	12/07
Est. sales ($ mil.)	—	—	—	—	—	44.6
Employees	—	—	—	—	—	700

ALTAIR NANOTECHNOLOGIES INC.

NASDAQ (CM): ALTI

204 Edison Way
Reno, NV 89502
Phone: 775-856-2500
Fax: 775-856-1619
Web: www.altairinc.com

CEO: Terry M. Copeland
CFO: John C. Fallini
HR: Stephen A. Balogh
FYE: December 31
Type: Public

When Altair Nanotechnologies paints the town, its pigment of choice is titanium dioxide ($TiO2$). The company produces titanium dioxide particles used in paints, coatings, and sensors. Altair intends to create new applications and products with its nanocrystalline technology. Its major development thus far has been its nano lithium Titanate battery materials, which offer superior performance, the company says, to other rechargeable batteries. The company has licensing agreements with Western Oil Sands to use Altair's technology to extract titanium from raw materials. Other large customers include Phoenix Motorcars, Spectrum Pharmaceuticals, and the US Department of Energy.

	Annual Growth	12/03	12/04	12/05	12/06	12/07
Sales ($ mil.)	208.9%	0.1	1.1	2.8	4.3	9.1
Net income ($ mil.)	—	(6.2)	(7.0)	(9.9)	(17.2)	(31.5)
Market value ($ mil.)	33.1%	113.6	134.9	120.4	181.7	356.8
Employees	—	—	—	62	—	—

ALTEC INDUSTRIES, INC.

210 Inverness Center Dr.
Birmingham, AL 35242
Phone: 205-991-7733
Fax: 205-991-7747
Web: www.altec.com

CEO: Lee J. Styslinger III
CFO: J. D. Williams
HR: –
FYE: December 31
Type: Private

Altec Industries is not all talk and no action. On the contrary, Altec manufactures lift trucks, digger derricks, and specialty equipment for use by linemen in the electric utility, telecommunications, and tree care industries. The company also provides after-sale support and services equipment worldwide. Altec sells used equipment through National Utility Equipment Co., and rents equipment through Global Rental Co. Altec offers financing services through Altec Capital Services. Altec Industries operates manufacturing, final assembly, and service facilities throughout Canada and the US. The company, founded in 1929, is controlled by third-generation family management, led by CEO Lee Styslinger III.

	Annual Growth	12/03	12/04	12/05	12/06	12/07
Est. sales ($ mil.)	—	—	—	—	—	173.3
Employees	—	—	—	—	—	1,500

⊞ An in-depth profile of this company is available to Hoover's Online members at hoovers.com.

103

ALTERA CORPORATION

NASDAQ (GS): ALTR

101 Innovation Dr.
San Jose, CA 95134
Phone: 408-544-7000
Fax: 408-544-6408
Web: www.altera.com

CEO: John P. Daane
CFO: Timothy R. Morse
HR: Kevin H. Lyman
FYE: December 31
Type: Public

Altera chips are just made to be altered. The company is a top maker of high-density programmable logic devices (PLDs) — integrated circuits that customers can program using software also provided by Altera. PLDs offer an attractive alternative to custom-designed chips because they help manufacturers cut development costs and time to market. Altera's PLDs are used by thousands of customers in computing, telecommunications, industrial, and automotive applications. Virtually all of the fabless semiconductor company's sales are made through distributors; distribution giant Arrow accounts for about 45% of sales. End customers outside North America provide about three-quarters of Altera's sales.

	Annual Growth	12/03	12/04	12/05	12/06	12/07
Sales ($ mil.)	11.2%	827.2	1,016.4	1,123.7	1,285.5	1,263.6
Net income ($ mil.)	16.9%	155.1	275.1	278.8	323.2	290.0
Market value ($ mil.)	(8.6%)	8,518.2	7,736.8	6,660.0	7,088.8	5,934.1
Employees	7.4%	1,995	2,164	2,361	2,654	2,651

ALTEX INDUSTRIES, INC.

OTC: ALTX

217 S. Ridge Rd.
Breckenridge, CO 80424
Phone: 303-265-9312
Fax: 303-265-9312

CEO: Steven H. Cardin
CFO: Steven H. Cardin
HR: –
FYE: September 30
Type: Public

More OilRockies than AllTex(as), Altex Industries buys and sells oil and gas properties, participates in drilling exploratory wells, and sells oil and gas production to refineries, pipeline operators, and processing plants. The oil and gas exploration and production independent owns interests in 41 gross productive oil wells and 20,000 gross developed acres in Utah and Wyoming. In 2005 Altex Industries reported estimated proved reserves of 123,000 barrels of oil and 817 million cu. ft. of natural gas. CEO Steven Cardin controls about 49% of the company.

	Annual Growth	9/03	9/04	9/05	9/06	9/07
Sales ($ mil.)	(21.7%)	0.8	0.9	1.0	3.1	0.3
Net income ($ mil.)	—	0.0	0.0	0.2	2.3	(0.2)
Market value ($ mil.)	32.6%	—	1.3	4.2	3.4	3.1
Employees	—	—	—	—	—	—

ALTICOR INC.

7575 Fulton St. East
Ada, MI 49355
Phone: 616-787-1000
Fax: 616-682-4000
Web: www.alticor.com

CEO: Doug DeVos
CFO: Russell A. (Russ) Evans
HR: Kelly Savage
FYE: August 31
Type: Private

At the core of Alticor, there is Amway. Alticor was formed in 2000 as a holding company and operates five businesses: direct-selling giant Amway, Web-based sales firm Quixtar, Amway Hotel Corp. (corporate development for Alticor and affiliates), upscale cosmetics company Gurwitch Products, and Access Business Group (manufacturing, logistics services). Access Business' biggest customers are Amway and Quixtar, but Access also serves outsiders. Amway, which accounts for most of Alticor's revenues, sells more than 450 different products through 3 million independent distributors. Quixtar sells Amway and other products online. Alticor is owned by Amway founders, the DeVos and Van Andel families.

	Annual Growth	8/02	8/03	8/04	8/05	8/06
Sales ($ mil.)	8.8%	4,500.0	4,900.0	6,200.0	6,400.0	6,300.0
Employees	5.5%	10,500	11,500	13,000	13,000	13,000

ALTIGEN COMMUNICATIONS, INC.

NASDAQ (CM): ATGN

4555 Cushing Pkwy.
Fremont, CA 94538
Phone: 510-252-9712
Fax: 510-252-9738
Web: www.altigen.com

CEO: Gilbert Hu
CFO: Philip M. (Phil) McDermott
HR: –
FYE: September 30
Type: Public

AltiGen Communications helps communications networks find a new calling. The company's AltiServe Office phone systems utilize both Internet protocol (IP) and public telephone networks to transmit voice signals and support between eight and 400 users. AltiServe systems include voicemail, auto attendant menus, and other features of traditional business PBX systems; its AltiContact Manager product adds advanced call center functionality. The company also sells traditional analog and IP telephones. AltiGen deals primarily through distributors including AltiSys, Graybar, and Synnex.

	Annual Growth	9/03	9/04	9/05	9/06	9/07
Sales ($ mil.)	11.0%	11.8	14.8	15.4	17.9	17.9
Net income ($ mil.)	—	(3.5)	0.0	(0.3)	0.0	(0.9)
Market value ($ mil.)	(12.6%)	45.0	38.8	27.5	24.4	26.3
Employees	9.4%	—	—	91	—	109

ALTRA HOLDINGS, INC.

NASDAQ (GM): AIMC

14 Hayward St.
Quincy, MA 02171
Phone: 617-328-3300
Fax: 617-479-6238
Web: www.altramotion.com

CEO: Michael L. Hurt
CFO: Christian Storch
HR: Timothy McGowan
FYE: December 31
Type: Public

Altra Holdings brings things to a stop. Doing business as Altra Industrial Motion, the company designs, makes, and markets industrial power transmission products under a variety of brand names, including Warner Electric and Boston Gear. The company's industrial clutches and brakes, gear drives, couplings, and bearing assemblies are used in the braking systems of elevators and wheelchairs. Altra sells directly and through distributors to industrial equipment makers in industries such as material handling, mining, and transportation. The company gets about 70% of its sales from North America.

	Annual Growth	12/03	12/04	12/05	12/06	12/07
Sales ($ mil.)	21.6%	266.9	303.7	363.5	462.3	584.4
Net income ($ mil.)	—	(9.3)	1.0	2.5	8.9	11.5
Market value ($ mil.)	38.6%	—	—	—	301.6	417.9
Employees	12.2%	—	—	2,745	2,500	3,455

ALTRIA GROUP, INC.

NYSE: MO

6601 West Broad St.
Richmond, VA 23230
Phone: 804-274-2200
Fax: 804-484-8231
Web: www.altria.com

CEO: Michael E. Szymanczyk
CFO: David R. (Dave) Beran
HR: –
FYE: December 31
Type: Public

The house the Marlboro Man built, Altria Group is the largest cigarette company in the US. Altria operates its cigarette business through subsidiary Philip Morris USA, which sells Marlboro — the world's best-selling cigarette brand since 1972. Altria controls about half of the US tobacco market. It manufactures cigarettes under the Parliament, Virginia Slims, and Basic cigarette brands. The company owns about 29% of brewer SABMiller, as well. Altria spun off its Kraft Foods (Jell-O, Maxwell House) business to shareholders in March 2007. It also spun off its international tobacco arm, Philip Morris International, in March 2008. Altria bought US cigar maker John Middleton in 2007.

	Annual Growth	12/03	12/04	12/05	12/06	12/07
Sales ($ mil.)	(2.5%)	81,832.0	89,610.0	97,854.0	101,407.0	73,801.0
Net income ($ mil.)	1.5%	9,204.0	9,416.0	10,435.0	12,022.0	9,786.0
Employees	(35.0%)	—	—	199,000	175,000	84,000

ALTUS PHARMACEUTICALS INC.

NASDAQ (GM): ALTU

125 Sidney St.
Cambridge, MA 02139
Phone: 617-299-2900
Fax: 617-299-2999
Web: www.altus.com

CEO: Georges Gemayel
CFO: Jonathan I. Lieber
HR: –
FYE: December 31
Type: Public

Altus Pharmaceuticals plans to release the power of protein crystals in medicine. The company is developing oral and injectable therapies based on its protein crystallization technology to treat gastrointestinal and metabolic disorders. Its main candidate is Trizytek, an enzyme replacement used to treat pancreatic insufficiency disorders that involve malabsorption of nutrients, malnutrition, and impaired growth. Two other potential therapies in Altus' pipeline include a candidate for the treatment of growth hormone deficiency and another for the treatment of kidney stones and crystal formations in other organs. Altus Pharmaceuticals plans to commercialize its products among physician specialists in North America.

	Annual Growth	12/03	12/04	12/05	12/06	12/07
Sales ($ mil.)	64.4%	3.9	4.2	8.3	5.1	28.5
Net income ($ mil.)	—	(15.2)	(21.0)	(27.1)	(55.7)	(63.2)
Market value ($ mil.)	(64.7%)	—	—	—	452.3	159.5
Employees	—	—	—	102	—	—

ALUMINUM SHAPES, LLC

9000 River Rd.
Delair, NJ 08110
Phone: 856-662-5500
Fax: 888-329-6061
Web: www.shapesllc.com

CEO: Stephen Grabell
CFO: –
HR: –
FYE: August 31
Type: Private

Aluminum shapes Aluminum Shapes, which makes aluminum shapes. The company's aluminum extrusion processes begins with the manufacturing of precision-formulated billets in its foundry. Its reverberatory furnaces melt and process aluminum ingots, which are eventually cast into finished logs. Aluminum Shapes creates billets for all its extrusion needs, as well as billets for sales to external customers. The company's major customers include architectural, defense, and transportation industries. Aluminum Shapes offers full-service aluminum extrusion capabilities at its 1.5-million-sq.-ft. manufacturing and distribution facility in Pennsauken, New Jersey.

	Annual Growth	8/03	8/04	8/05	8/06	8/07
Est. sales ($ mil.)	—	—	—	—	—	64.3
Employees	—	—	—	—	—	800

ALVAREZ & MARSAL HOLDINGS, LLC

600 Lexington Ave., 6th Fl.
New York, NY 10022
Phone: 212-759-4433
Fax: 212-759-5532
Web: www.alvarezandmarsal.com

CEO: Antonio C. (Tony) Alvarez II
CFO: Mark Dominick (Nick) Alvarez
HR: –
FYE: December 31
Type: Private

A&M specializes in M&A, along with restructuring, right-sizing, and other corporate turnaround processes. Alvarez & Marsal provides advisory and consulting services surrounding mergers and acquisitions, crisis and interim management, divestitures, performance improvement, restructuring, and strategic planning. The firm has served clients including U-Haul International parent AMERCO and underwear maker The Warnaco Group. Alvarez & Marsal has more than 30 offices in the Americas, Asia, and Europe. Managing directors Bryan Marsal and Tony Alvarez II started the firm in 1983.

	Annual Growth	12/03	12/04	12/05	12/06	12/07
Est. sales ($ mil.)	—	—	—	—	—	7.2
Employees	—	—	—	—	—	97

ALYESKA PIPELINE SERVICE COMPANY

900 E. Benson St.
Anchorage, AK 99519
Phone: 907-787-8700
Fax: 907-787-8240
Web: www.alyeska-pipe.com

CEO: Kevin Hostler
CFO: Art Mitchell
HR: Kristi J. Acuff
FYE: December 31
Type: Consortium

Named after the Aleut word for mainland, The Alyeska Pipeline Service Company operates the 800-mile long, 48-inch diameter pipeline that transports crude oil from Alaska's North Slope to the marine oil terminal of Valdez in Prince William Sound. Founded in 1970 to make the newly discovered finds in Prudhoe Bay commercially accessible, the company was assigned the task of designing, building, operating, and maintaining the Trans-Alaska Pipeline System (TAPS). The $8 billion pipeline was completed in 1977. The volume of oil flowing through the pipeline averages about 1 million barrels per day. TAPS is owned by a consortium of oil and gas firms, including BP (47%), ConocoPhillips (28%), and Exxon Mobil (20%).

	Annual Growth	12/03	12/04	12/05	12/06	12/07
Est. sales ($ mil.)	—	—	—	—	—	182.9
Employees	—	—	—	—	—	850

ALZA CORPORATION

1900 Charleston Rd.
Mountain View, CA 94039
Phone: 650-564-5000
Fax: 732-342-9819
Web: www.alza.com

CEO: Michael R. Jackson
CFO: –
HR: –
FYE: December 31
Type: Subsidiary

ALZA helps medicine get under your skin. The company concentrates on drug-delivery systems, primarily transdermal patches; GlaxoSmithKline's #1 smoking-cessation product NicoDerm CQ uses ALZA technology. Other drug delivery systems offered by ALZA include electro-transport systems that use electricity to push the drug through skin, implants designed to regulate drug delivery for up to a full year, depot injections, liposomal technology for intravenous drugs, and timed-release tablets and capsules. The company has been a subsidiary of health care giant Johnson & Johnson since its 2001 acquisition.

	Annual Growth	12/03	12/04	12/05	12/06	12/07
Est. sales ($ mil.)	—	—	—	—	—	198.4
Employees	—	—	—	—	—	1,845

A. M. CASTLE & CO.

NYSE: CAS

3400 N. Wolf Rd.
Franklin Park, IL 60131
Phone: 847-455-7111
Fax: 847-455-6930
Web: www.amcastle.com

CEO: Michael H. (Mike) Goldberg
CFO: Lawrence A. (Larry) Boik
HR: Paul J. Winsauer
FYE: December 31
Type: Public

Providing alloys for its allies, metals service company A. M. Castle distributes highly engineered metals and metal alloys to a broad range of industrial manufacturers. The company sells steel (alloy, carbon, and stainless), aluminum, copper, brass, and titanium in bar, sheet, plate, and tube form. A. M. Castle operates throughout North America as well as in France and the UK. The company also engages in industrial plastics distribution through subsidiary Total Plastics. It acquired Transtar Metals in mid-2006. Investor Patrick Herbert controls about a quarter of A. M. Castle.

	Annual Growth	12/03	12/04	12/05	12/06	12/07
Sales ($ mil.)	27.2%	543.0	761.0	959.0	1,177.6	1,420.3
Net income ($ mil.)	—	(18.0)	16.9	38.9	55.1	51.8
Market value ($ mil.)	51.1%	115.3	188.7	361.6	434.8	600.8
Employees	10.1%	—	—	1,604	2,016	1,945

An in-depth profile of this company is available to Hoover's Online members at hoovers.com.

105

THE AMACORE GROUP, INC.

OTC: ACGI

1211 N. Westshore Blvd., Ste. 512
Tampa, FL 33607
Phone: 813-289-5552
Fax: 813-289-5553
Web: www.amacoregroup.com

CEO: Clark A. Marcus
CFO: Giuseppe (Joe) Crisafi
HR: –
FYE: December 31
Type: Public

The Amacore Group wants you to be able to see a smaller optometry bill. Amacore is a provider of non-insurance based discount plans for eyewear and eye-care services, including surgery. Amacore Group's products are marketed to individuals, families, and businesses, as well as through the company's affiliations with insurance companies and other membership groups. The company has expanded its discount program offerings to include dental, hearing, chiropractic, and other health services. It also offers traditional health plans through partnerships with insurance providers.

	Annual Growth	12/03	12/04	12/05	12/06	12/07
Sales ($ mil.)	115.3%	0.2	0.2	0.5	0.4	4.3
Net income ($ mil.)	—	(1.5)	(38.4)	(4.3)	(1.7)	(21.2)
Market value ($ mil.)	103.2%	2.9	17.8	2.0	3.4	49.6
Employees	—	—	—	—	—	—

AMADA AMERICA, INC.

7025 Firestone Blvd.
Buena Park, CA 90621
Phone: 714-739-2111
Fax: 714-739-4099
Web: www.amada.com

CEO: Mike Guerin
CFO: John Kaminski
HR: Cathy Gonzalez
FYE: December 31
Type: Private

Amada America manufactures and sells sheet metal fabricating equipment, including CNC turret punch presses, lasers, press brakes, shears, flexible manufacturing systems, and software. The company primarily sells its fabricating equipment to the aerospace, appliance, electronics, farm equipment, medical, and telecommunications industries. Through its Amada Capital Corp. subsidiary, Amada America finances and leases its equipment. Amada America was founded in 1971.

	Annual Growth	12/03	12/04	12/05	12/06	12/07
Est. sales ($ mil.)	—	—	—	—	—	173.0
Employees	—	—	—	—	—	500

AMAG PHARMACEUTICALS, INC.

NASDAQ (GM): AMAG

61 Mooney St.
Cambridge, MA 02138
Phone: 617-497-2070
Fax: 617-547-2445
Web: www.amagpharma.com

CEO: Brian J.G. Pereira
CFO: David A. Arkowitz
HR: –
FYE: December 31
Type: Public

AMAG Pharmaceuticals' magnetic technology doesn't make things stick, it makes things stick out. The company, formerly called Advanced Magnetics, uses its expertise in iron oxide nanoparticles to create organ-specific diagnostic contrast agents used in magnetic resonance imaging (MRI) tests. It has two products on the market: Feridex I.V. (for the diagnosis of liver lesions) and GastroMARK (used for delineating the bowel in abdominal imaging). The firm is developing Combidex as a contrast agent for the diagnosis of metastatic lymph nodes and another product, ferumoxytol, as an iron replacement therapy for anemic patients.

	Annual Growth	9/03	9/04	9/05	9/06	*12/07
Sales ($ mil.)	(15.0%)	4.8	3.8	2.5	2.7	2.5
Net income ($ mil.)	—	0.9	(4.5)	(12.7)	(25.4)	(33.9)
Market value ($ mil.)	94.6%	71.0	111.0	95.9	407.2	1,018.9
Employees	—	—	—	36	—	—

*Fiscal year change

AMALGAMATED BANK

275 7th Ave.
New York, NY 10001
Phone: 212-255-6200
Fax: 212-895-4507
Web: www.amalgamatedbank.com

CEO: Derrick Cephas
CFO: Michael J. Indiveri
HR: –
FYE: December 31
Type: Private

Founded in 1923 by the Amalgamated Clothing Workers of America, Amalgamated Bank serves working-class consumers and trade unions through about 10 branches in New York City, as well as locations in California, New Jersey, and Washington, DC. In addition to standard services like deposits, mortgages and other loans, and investments, the bank also administers union-related trust funds and multi-employer benefits plans. It is an active investor, monitoring corporate governance of its portfolio companies regarding such issues as executive salaries and working conditions.

	Annual Growth	12/03	12/04	12/05	12/06	12/07
Est. sales ($ mil.)	—	—	—	—	—	212.5
Employees	—	—	—	—	—	433

AMALGAMATED SUGAR COMPANY LLC

3184 Elder St.
Boise, ID 83705
Phone: 208-383-6500
Fax: 208-383-6684
Web: www.amalgamatedsugar.com

CEO: Victor J. (Vic) Jaro
CFO: David L. Budge
HR: –
FYE: December 31
Type: Cooperative

This fusion of beet growers makes for a sweet mix. A top US sugar producer, Amalgamated Sugar (ASC) processes sugar beets in Idaho. The company makes granulated, coarse, powdered, and brown sugar products marketed under the brand name White Satin. It also provides private-label products for grocery chains. In addition Amalgamated Sugar produces beet pulp, molasses, and other beet by-products for use by food and animal-feed manufacturers. The company, which started out in 1994, became a grower-owned beet-sugar cooperative in 1997 and changed its name to Amalgamated Sugar Company.

	Annual Growth	12/03	12/04	12/05	12/06	12/07
Est. sales ($ mil.)	—	—	—	—	—	617.7
Employees	—	—	—	—	—	1,500

AMANASU ENVIRONMENT CORPORATION

OTC: AMSU

115 East 57th St., 11th Fl.
New York, NY 10022
Phone: 212-939-7278
Fax: 206-262-8199

CEO: Atsushi Maki
CFO: Atsushi Maki
HR: –
FYE: December 31
Type: Public

Development stage company Amanasu Environment Corporation owns the licensing rights to produce and market positive ion breeder incinerators for nuclear wastes, hot-water boilers that extract heat energy from waste tires, and a patented process for purifying seawater and removing hazardous pollutants from wastewater. Amanasu Environment, however, has not developed any products for commercial sale, although it has developed prototypes. The firm was incorporated in 1999. Chairman and president Atsushi Maki and his wife, Lina Lei, who is the company's secretary and a director, together own about 73% of the company.

	Annual Growth	12/03	12/04	12/05	12/06	12/07
Sales ($ mil.)	18.3%	—	—	0.5	0.5	0.7
Net income ($ mil.)	—	—	—	(0.6)	(1.1)	(0.8)
Market value ($ mil.)	(21.4%)	—	—	24.2	4.4	15.0
Employees	—	—	—	—	—	—

AMARILLO BIOSCIENCES, INC.

OTC: AMAR

4134 Business Park Dr.
Amarillo, TX 79110
Phone: 806-376-1741
Fax: 806-376-9301
Web: www.amarbio.com

CEO: Joseph M. (Joe) Cummins
CFO: Gary W. Coy
HR: Chrystal Shelton
FYE: December 31
Type: Public

Amarillo: home to cattlemen, prairies, and . . . interferon? Development-stage Amarillo Biosciences hopes its low-dose interferon alpha (IFNa), which modulates the immune system, will help those suffering from a range of maladies, including Behcet's disease, a severe inflammatory disorder, and oral warts in HIV patients; the company has received orphan drug status for IFNa for both indications. Other potential disease targets for the drug include Sjogren's syndrome (an autoimmune condition that results in dryness of the eyes and mouth), chronic cough associated with idiopathic pulmonary fibrosis, and avian flu.

	Annual Growth	12/03	12/04	12/05	12/06	12/07
Sales ($ mil.)	0.0%	0.1	0.1	0.2	0.1	0.1
Net income ($ mil.)	—	0.2	(0.6)	(0.7)	(2.8)	(2.5)
Market value ($ mil.)	17.9%	4.4	4.7	8.5	15.9	8.5
Employees	—	—	—	—	—	—

A-MARK PRECIOUS METALS, INC.

429 Santa Monica Blvd., Ste. 230
Santa Monica, CA 90401
Phone: 310-587-1436
Fax: 310-319-0310
Web: www.amark.com

CEO: Gregory N. (Greg) Roberts
CFO: Dennis Lautzenheiser
HR: –
FYE: July 31
Type: Subsidiary

Calling all gold bugs: A-Mark Precious Metals trades, markets, and finances rare coins, precious metals, and collectibles. A-Mark Precious Metals deals in gold, silver, platinum, and palladium coins, bars, wafers, and grain for central banks, manufacturers, jewelers, and individuals around the world. A-Mark Precious Metals distributes coins for government mints, including those of Australia, Canada, South Africa, and the US. Former chairman Steven Markoff founded the company in 1965; in 2005 it was sold to Greg Manning Auctions (now Escala Group).

AMAZON.COM, INC.

NASDAQ (GS): AMZN

1200 12th Ave. South, Ste. 1200
Seattle, WA 98144
Phone: 206-266-1000
Fax: –
Web: www.amazon.com

CEO: Jeffrey P. (Jeff) Bezos
CFO: Thomas J. (Tom) Szkutak
HR: –
FYE: December 31
Type: Public

What started as Earth's biggest bookstore has rapidly become Earth's biggest anything store. Expansion has propelled Amazon.com in innumerable directions. The firm's main Web site offers millions of books, music, DVDs, and videos (which still account for the majority, more than 60%, of the firm's sales), not to mention auto parts, toys, tools, electronics, home furnishings, apparel, health and beauty goods, prescription drugs, groceries, and services including film processing. Long a model for Internet companies that put market share ahead of profits, Amazon.com also made acquisitions funded by meteoric market capitalization and is now focused on profits. Founder Jeff Bezos owns about 24% of the firm.

	Annual Growth	12/03	12/04	12/05	12/06	12/07
Sales ($ mil.)	29.6%	5,263.7	6,921.1	8,490.0	10,711.0	14,835.0
Net income ($ mil.)	91.6%	35.3	588.5	359.0	190.0	476.0
Market value ($ mil.)	16.1%	21,224.5	18,146.1	19,614.4	16,336.4	38,538.2
Employees	19.0%	—	—	12,000	13,900	17,000

AMB FINANCIAL CORP.

OTC: AMFC

8230 Hohman Ave.
Munster, IN 46321
Phone: 219-836-5870
Fax: 219-836-5883
Web: www.ambfinancial.com

CEO: Michael J. (Mike) Mellon
CFO: Steven A. Bohn
HR: –
FYE: December 31
Type: Public

AMB Financial is the holding company for American Savings, a thrift serving Lake County, Indiana, near the southern tip of Lake Michigan. Catering to families and local businesses, the bank offers checking and savings accounts, money market accounts, certificates of deposit, and IRAs. It mainly uses these deposit funds to originate real estate, construction, consumer, commercial, land, credit card, and other loans. One- to four-family residential mortgages account for approximately two-thirds of its loan portfolio. American Savings also offers investment services. It operates three offices in Dyer, Hammond, and Munster, Indiana and opened a fourth location in nearby Schererville in 2007.

	Annual Growth	12/03	12/04	12/05	12/06	12/07
Assets ($ mil.)	4.6%	146.0	157.1	170.5	182.3	174.8
Net income ($ mil.)	(46.3%)	1.2	0.9	0.9	0.6	0.1
Market value ($ mil.)	(1.0%)	13.6	13.8	13.3	16.4	13.1
Employees	1.4%	35	35	39	39	37

AMB PROPERTY CORPORATION

NYSE: AMB

Pier 1, Bay 1
San Francisco, CA 94111
Phone: 415-394-9000
Fax: 415-394-9001
Web: www.amb.com

CEO: Hamid R. Moghadam
CFO: Thomas S. Olinger
HR: –
FYE: December 31
Type: Public

AMB Property knows the ABCs about property management. The company invests primarily in industrial properties in North America, Europe, and Asia. The real estate investment trust (REIT) owns, operates, and manages about 1,000 industrial buildings (and a handful of retail properties) totaling more than 145 million sq. ft. in some 45 major metropolitan areas. The company focuses on fast-paced, high-volume warehouse distribution facilities tied to global trade near ports, airports, and highways. Its portfolio is concentrated in and around Los Angeles, San Francisco, New York, Chicago, and Seattle. The US government, Deutsche Post, and powerhouse parcel handler FedEx are the REIT's largest tenants.

	Annual Growth	12/03	12/04	12/05	12/06	12/07
Sales ($ mil.)	2.2%	615.0	665.7	676.2	729.9	669.7
Net income ($ mil.)	24.9%	129.1	125.5	257.8	224.1	314.3
Market value ($ mil.)	20.7%	2,691.2	3,362.4	4,305.4	5,255.1	5,710.6
Employees	34.6%	—	—	309	416	—

AMBAC FINANCIAL GROUP, INC.

NYSE: ABK

1 State Street Plaza
New York, NY 10004
Phone: 212-668-0340
Fax: 212-509-9190
Web: www.ambac.com

CEO: Michael A. (Mike) Callen
CFO: Sean T. Leonard
HR: Gregg L. Bienstock
FYE: December 31
Type: Public

Ambac Financial Group gives an A+ to those school bonds. Ambac Assurance, the holding company's primary subsidiary, sells financial guarantee insurance and other credit enhancement products for municipal bonds in the US market. In the international market the company insures high-quality infrastructure, structured finance, and utility finance transactions. Its financial services segment, through Ambac Financial Services, offers investment contracts, interest rate swaps, credit swaps, and investment management primarily to states and municipal authorities in connection with their bond financing.

	Annual Growth	12/02	12/03	12/04	12/05	*12/06
Assets ($ mil.)	7.2%	15,355.5	16,747.3	18,585.3	19,725.1	20,267.8
Net income ($ mil.)	19.3%	432.6	618.9	724.5	751.0	875.9
Market value ($ mil.)	13.0%	5,965.3	7,434.7	8,945.3	8,414.4	9,725.8
Employees	(2.1%)	391	—	—	354	359

*Most recent year available

An in-depth profile of this company is available to Hoover's Online members at hoovers.com.

107

AMBASSADORS GROUP, INC.

NASDAQ (GS): EPAX

Dwight D. Eisenhower Bldg., 1956 Ambassador Way
Spokane, WA 99224
Phone: 509-568-7000
Fax: –
Web: www.ambassadorsgroup.com

CEO: Jeffrey D. (Jeff) Thomas
CFO: Chadwick J. Byrd
HR: –
FYE: December 31
Type: Public

Ambassadors Group's educational travel programs provide students and professionals with opportunities to meet their counterparts overseas. Most trips are organized under contracts with the People to People organization, which was founded by President Eisenhower in 1956 as a way to promote world peace. Ambassadors Group markets trips using the People to People name and makes travel arrangements for participants. Specialized People to People offerings allow student athletes to participate in international sports programs and enable student leaders to meet one another. The organization's Professional Ambassador trips offer meetings and seminars involving people from different countries who work in similar fields.

	Annual Growth	12/03	12/04	12/05	12/06	12/07
Sales ($ mil.)	32.0%	37.7	51.8	69.3	89.0	114.5
Net income ($ mil.)	32.4%	10.1	15.6	22.4	26.7	31.0
Market value ($ mil.)	31.7%	117.6	180.3	472.8	625.2	354.2
Employees	16.7%	—	—	234	273	

AMBASSADORS INTERNATIONAL, INC.

NASDAQ (GM): AMIE

1071 Camelback St.
Newport Beach, CA 92660
Phone: 949-759-5900
Fax: 949-759-5901
Web: www.ambassadors.com

CEO: Joseph J. (Joe) Ueberroth
CFO: Blake T. Barnett
HR: Tricia Mora
FYE: December 31
Type: Public

Ambassadors International represents itself around the world in the cruise, marina, and travel and events businesses. The company provides river and coastal cruises in North America via its seven-vessel Majestic America Line, which it plans to sell. Ambassadors International's Windstar Cruises unit operates three vessels in the Mediterranean and the Caribbean. In addition, Ambassadors International designs and builds marinas worldwide and operates marinas in the US and Japan. The company's travel and events businesses focus on making arrangements for conventions and trade shows. Ambassadors International also helps companies develop performance improvement programs that use travel awards as incentives.

	Annual Growth	12/03	12/04	12/05	12/06	12/07
Sales ($ mil.)	113.9%	13.7	18.7	26.9	144.4	287.0
Net income ($ mil.)	—	(1.0)	(1.9)	3.1	5.6	(26.9)
Market value ($ mil.)	6.1%	125.1	156.9	163.0	494.4	158.8
Employees	98.9%	—	132	157	765	1,038

AMBIENT CORPORATION

OTC: ABTG

79 Chapel St.
Newton, MA 02458
Phone: 617-332-0004
Fax: 617-332-7260
Web: www.ambientcorp.com

CEO: John J. Joyce
CFO: John J. Joyce
HR: –
FYE: December 31
Type: Public

Ambient switched from smart cards to smarter networks. The development-stage company, which was founded in 1996 to create smart card technologies, switched gears and is now working to speed up your Internet connection. Looking for an alternative to high-speed data transmission technologies that use phone lines (DSL) or television cable networks, Ambient develops broadband-over-power-line (BPL) couplers for providing Internet access over electrical power lines. Ambient has partnerships with utilities such as Con Ed and Duke Energy to develop its technology.

	Annual Growth	12/03	12/04	12/05	12/06	12/07
Sales ($ mil.)	239.1%	—	—	0.2	2.3	2.3
Net income ($ mil.)	—	—	—	(11.2)	(12.7)	(15.8)
Market value ($ mil.)	(33.3%)	—	—	16.6	16.9	7.4
Employees	—	—	—	—	—	—

◫ AMC ENTERTAINMENT HOLDINGS, INC.

920 Main St.
Kansas City, MO 64105
Phone: 816-221-4000
Fax: 816-480-4617
Web: www.amctheatres.com

CEO: Peter C. Brown
CFO: Craig R. Ramsey
HR: Andy Traub
FYE: Thursday nearest March 31
Type: Private

AMC Entertainment shines when the lights go down. The #2 movie theater chain in the US (behind Regal), the company owns more than 375 theaters housing some 5,300 screens, most of which are in megaplexes (units with more than 14 screens and stadium seating). Its theaters can be found throughout the US, Canada, Europe, Mexico, and Latin America. The firm is part owner (more than 25%) of MovieTickets.com, along with Hollywood Media and rivals Cineplex Entertainmant and National Amusements, among others. The company bought rival Loews Cineplex in 2006, significantly boosting its holdings. After flirting with going public only to reconsider, AMC in 2007 again filed an IPO.

	Annual Growth	3/03	3/04	3/05	3/06	3/07
Sales ($ mil.)	20.4%	—	—	1,698.7	1,686.9	2,461.6
Net income ($ mil.)	—	—	—	(80.3)	(216.2)	116.9
Employees	1.6%	—	—	22,200	21,400	22,900

AMC, INC.

240 Peachtree St., Ste. 2200
Atlanta, GA 30303
Phone: 404-220-3000
Fax: 404-220-3030
Web: www.americasmart.com

CEO: John C. Portman Jr.
CFO: –
HR: Bob Brush
FYE: August 31
Type: Private

AMC owns and manages the AmericasMart Atlanta trade show center, one of the largest such facilities in the world. The firm also organizes and runs 17 wholesale markets every year and six markets — including an apparel market and a gift products market. AmericasMart Atlanta consists of three buildings that house permanent showroom space, exhibit halls, convention space, and meeting rooms all focused on bringing retailers and wholesalers together. It was established in 1957 by architect John Portman.

	Annual Growth	8/03	8/04	8/05	8/06	8/07
Est. sales ($ mil.)	—	—	—	—	—	127.6
Employees	—	—	—	—	—	240

AMCOL INTERNATIONAL CORPORATION

NYSE: ACO

1 North Arlington, 1500 W. Shure Dr., Ste. 500
Arlington Heights, IL 60004
Phone: 847-394-8730
Fax: 847-506-6199
Web: www.amcol.com

CEO: Lawrence E. (Larry) Washow
CFO: Donald W. Pearson
HR: –
FYE: December 31
Type: Public

AMCOL International is the cat owner's meow. Its minerals segment (about half of the company's sales) mines and processes bentonite clay that is used in cat litter, cosmetics, metal castings, and pharmaceuticals, as well as to produce iron ore and to drill wells. The company's environmental segment makes and distributes bentonite products used for sealing landfills and waterproofing construction sites. AMCOL's Oilfield Services unit processes wastewater produced in oil fields. The company's transportation business provides long-haul trucking and freight brokerage services to AMCOL units and third parties in the US.

	Annual Growth	12/03	12/04	12/05	12/06	12/07
Sales ($ mil.)	19.6%	364.0	459.1	535.9	611.6	744.3
Net income ($ mil.)	18.4%	28.9	31.6	41.0	50.3	56.7
Market value ($ mil.)	16.4%	590.9	593.1	611.2	830.4	1,084.3
Employees	(64.2%)	—	—	15,742	1,759	2,017

AMCOMP INCORPORATED

NASDAQ (GM): AMCP

701 US Hwy. 1
North Palm Beach, FL 33408
Phone: 561-840-7171
Fax: 800-226-1805
Web: www.amcomp.com

CEO: Fred R. Lowe
CFO: Kumar Gursahaney
HR: Laura Newstead
FYE: December 31
Type: Public

AmCOMP helps make on-the-job injuries less painful for employers. The holding company's subsidiaries specialize in all aspects of workers' compensation insurance operations, including underwriting, claims management, premium collection, loss control and prevention, employer education, and provision of network providers. Client industries include construction contracting, manufacturing, and retail merchandising. The company markets its products through independent agencies in the Southeast, Southwest, Midwest, and Mid-Atlantic regions. AmCOMP is registered in more than 20 states and writes policies in about 17. AmCOMP has agreed to be acquired by Employers Holdings.

	Annual Growth	12/03	12/04	12/05	12/06	12/07
Assets ($ mil.)	10.0%	457.4	543.8	589.7	684.5	669.2
Net income ($ mil.)	113.8%	0.9	5.0	16.8	16.6	18.8
Market value ($ mil.)	(17.4%)	—	—	—	173.2	143.0
Employees	7.4%	—	432	454	498	—

AMCON DISTRIBUTING COMPANY

AMEX: DIT

7405 Irvington Rd.
Omaha, NE 68122
Phone: 402-331-3727
Fax: 402-331-4834
Web: www.amcon.com

CEO: Christopher H. Atayan
CFO: Andrew C. Plummer
HR: –
FYE: September 30
Type: Public

AMCON Distributing enjoys a healthy meal, but it's not without its vices. The company's a wholesale distributor of consumer products, including cigarettes, and a retailer of health and natural foods. AMCON serves some 4,000 convenience stores, supermarkets, and institutional customers in the Great Plains and Rocky Mountain regions. It also distributes candy, beverages, groceries, paper products, and health and beauty care products. AMCON operates about a dozen regional health food stores run under the Chamberlin's and Akin's banners. In 2006 the firm scrapped plans to sell those stores (operating under unit The Healthy Edge) to director and former chairman William Wright, who owns a 26% stake in AMCON.

	Annual Growth	9/03	9/04	9/05	9/06	9/07
Sales ($ mil.)	2.5%	772.1	821.8	845.9	839.5	853.6
Net income ($ mil.)	44.8%	1.0	(4.1)	(12.7)	(1.1)	4.4
Market value ($ mil.)	(36.5%)	89.4	10.9	11.3	7.0	14.6
Employees	(3.0%)	—	—	—	901	874

AMCOR PET PACKAGING

935 Technology Dr., Ste. 100
Ann Arbor, MI 48108
Phone: 734-428-9741
Fax: 734-302-2298
Web: www.amcor.com/businesses/pet

CEO: William J. (Bill) Long
CFO: Larry Weber
HR: –
FYE: June 30
Type: Business segment

You think those handy plastic soft drink bottles grow on trees? A business unit of Amcor Limited, Amcor PET lays claim to being the world's #1 manufacturer of polyethylene terephthalate (PET) containers. Primary customers include food (condiments, dressings, edible oils, sauces and salsas, fruit and nut spreads) and beverage (soft drinks, water, juices, sports drinks, dairy, beer) producers. Non-food applications include household cleaner, liquid soap and lotion, hair care, pharmaceutical, automotive, and agro-chemical offerings. Amcor PET operates worldwide through nearly 50 manufacturing facilities in more than 20 countries; it also recycles about 100 million pounds of PET a year.

	Annual Growth	6/03	6/04	6/05	6/06	6/07
Est. sales ($ mil.)	—	—	—	—	—	150.8
Employees	—	—	—	—	—	2,000

AMCORE FINANCIAL, INC.

NASDAQ (GS): AMFI

501 7th St.
Rockford, IL 61104
Phone: 815-968-2241
Fax: 815-961-7544
Web: www.amcore.com

CEO: William R. McManaman
CFO: Judith Carré Sutfin
HR: –
FYE: December 31
Type: Public

In the country's heartland, AMCORE Financial gets to the crux of financial matters. The holding company for AMCORE Bank operates around 80 branches in northern Illinois and southern Wisconsin, offering consumer, commercial, and mortgage banking services. It also offers online banking and brokerage services. Subsidiary AMCORE Investment Group provides trust, wealth management, and employee benefit plan administration services, while AMCORE Investment Services offers mutual funds, annuities, stocks, bonds, and insurance. AMCORE Bank is expanding by opening new branches in its market area.

	Annual Growth	12/03	12/04	12/05	12/06	12/07
Assets ($ mil.)	3.4%	4,543.6	4,940.5	5,344.9	5,292.4	5,192.8
Net income ($ mil.)	(10.3%)	43.5	45.7	44.9	47.3	28.2
Market value ($ mil.)	(7.5%)	680.2	798.7	754.5	777.3	498.0
Employees	(3.1%)	—	—	1,595	1,545	—

AMDL, INC.

AMEX: ADL

2492 Walnut Ave., Ste. 100
Tustin, CA 92780
Phone: 714-505-4460
Fax: 714-505-4464
Web: www.amdl.com

CEO: Gary L. Dreher
CFO: Akio Ariura
HR: –
FYE: December 31
Type: Public

Detecting cancer is AMDL's game. The company's DR-70 kit can detect more than a dozen different types of the disease, including breast, lung, colon, and liver cancers. The firm's primary markets for the diagnostic kit are Europe and Asia, but it also sells the product in Canada and Australia. The company had hoped to launch DR-70 in the US, but in mid-2005 the FDA ruled the test is not equivalent to other colorectal tests already approved in the US and denied it marketing clearance. AMDL also makes Pylori-Probe, which can detect *H. pylori*, a bacterium that is a leading cause of stomach ulcers. Strips to help diabetics monitor ketone levels are among the 300 OEM diagnostics the firm makes.

	Annual Growth	12/03	12/04	12/05	12/06	12/07
Sales ($ mil.)	147.5%	0.4	0.2	0.1	2.1	15.0
Net income ($ mil.)	—	(2.9)	(2.6)	(2.5)	(5.9)	(2.3)
Market value ($ mil.)	32.3%	19.8	18.3	8.2	41.1	60.8
Employees	—	—	—	3	—	—

AMEDISYS, INC.

NASDAQ (GS): AMED

5959 S. Sherwood Forest Blvd.
Baton Rouge, LA 70816
Phone: 225-292-2031
Fax: 225-292-8163
Web: www.amedisys.com

CEO: William F. (Bill) Borne
CFO: Dale E. Redman
HR: Cindy L Phillips
FYE: December 31
Type: Public

Because the last thing you want to do when you're sick is drive to a doctor's office, Amedisys has decided to bring health care to you. Through its hundreds of home health care agencies located across the US, the company provides skilled nursing and home health aide services to primarily geriatric patients covered by Medicare. Its range of services includes disease-specific programs that help patients recovering from stroke, for instance, or assist those coping with emphysema or diabetes. In addition to its home health services, Amedisys owns or manages dozens of hospice agencies that offer palliative care to terminally ill patients.

	Annual Growth	12/03	12/04	12/05	12/06	12/07
Sales ($ mil.)	48.8%	142.5	227.1	381.6	541.2	697.9
Net income ($ mil.)	66.8%	8.4	20.5	30.1	38.3	65.1
Market value ($ mil.)	75.3%	135.4	371.9	503.1	848.0	1,279.4
Employees	19.8%	—	—	6,206	6,892	8,900

An in-depth profile of this company is available to Hoover's Online members at hoovers.com.

109

AMEGY CORPORATION

4400 Post Oak Pkwy.
Houston, TX 77027
Phone: 713-235-8800
Fax: 713-439-5949
Web: www.amegybank.com

CEO: Paul B. Murphy Jr.
CFO: Randall E. Meyer
HR: Kim Zabin
FYE: December 31
Type: Subsidiary

Amegy knows banking from "A" to "Z." Amegy Corporation, parent of Amegy Bank of Texas (also known by its one-letter nickname), was purchased by Zions Bancorporation. Amegy's more than 80 branches, primarily in Houston but also in Dallas and San Antonio (through its acquisition of Intercontinental Bank Shares), offer commercial and private banking services such as deposit accounts, financial planning, and investment management, the latter through Amegy Investments, Inc. Subsidiary Amegy Mortgage originates and purchases commercial, residential, and construction mortgages.

	Annual Growth	12/03	12/04	12/05	12/06	12/07
Est. sales ($ mil.)	—	—	—	—	—	518.4
Employees	—	—	—	—	—	1,500

AMEN PROPERTIES, INC.

NASDAQ (CM): AMEN

303 W. Wall St., Ste. 2300
Midland, TX 79701
Phone: 432-684-3821
Fax: 432-685-3143
Web: amenproperties.com

CEO: Jon M. Morgan
CFO: Kris Oliver
HR: –
FYE: December 31
Type: Public

AMEN Properties' prayers are being answered with power. Subsidiary W Power, formed in 2004, provides retail electricity services in West Texas. W Power (a venture made possible when Texas deregulated the wholesale electricity market) now accounts for the bulk of AMEN Properties' sales. Its Priority Power subsidiary (acquired in 2006) has current or previous business activities in 22 states including Texas. These activities include electricity load aggregation, natural gas and electricity procurement, energy risk management, and energy consulting. AMEN Properties' Amen Delaware subsidiary invests in commercial real estate in secondary markets; Amen Minerals invests in oil and gas royalties.

	Annual Growth	12/03	12/04	12/05	12/06	12/07
Sales ($ mil.)	35.0%	4.3	2.5	10.2	15.1	14.3
Net income ($ mil.)	34.3%	0.4	0.8	(0.7)	2.2	1.3
Employees	56.7%	—	—	11	11	27

AMERCO

NASDAQ (GS): UHAL

1325 Airmotive Way, Ste. 100
Reno, NV 89502
Phone: 775-688-6300
Fax: 775-688-6338
Web: www.amerco.com

CEO: Edward J. (Joe) Shoen
CFO: Jason A. Berg
HR: –
FYE: March 31
Type: Public

U-Haul, u-work, u-strain, u-hurt . . . u-sure you don't want to spend the extra money for movers? If not, there's AMERCO, whose principal subsidiary, U-Haul International, rents its orange-and-white trucks, trailers, and vehicle tow devices and sells packing supplies to do-it-yourself movers through some 14,200 independent dealers and about 1,450 company-owned centers in the US and Canada. In addition, U-Haul is a leading operator of self-storage facilities. It maintains some 1,075 storage locations in the US and Canada, consisting of more than 385,000 rooms with about 34 million sq. ft. of space. Members of the founding Shoen family, led by chairman and president Edward "Joe" Shoen, still run the company.

	Annual Growth	3/04	3/05	3/06	3/07	3/08
Sales ($ mil.)	(1.4%)	2,167.5	2,008.1	2,106.6	2,085.6	2,049.2
Net income ($ mil.)	—	(2.8)	89.4	121.2	90.6	67.8
Market value ($ mil.)	32.0%	368.7	813.4	1,738.7	1,438.0	1,120.8
Employees	2.9%	—	—	17,500	18,000	—

☐ AMEREN CORPORATION

NYSE: AEE

1901 Chouteau Ave.
St. Louis, MO 63103
Phone: 314-621-3222
Fax: 314-554-3801
Web: www.ameren.com

CEO: Gary L. Rainwater
CFO: Warner L. Baxter
HR: Donna K. Martin
FYE: December 31
Type: Public

Ameren might be considered amorous when it comes to courting and acquiring midwestern utilities. The holding company, which has been focused on growing its core energy operations, distributes electricity to 2.4 million customers and natural gas to almost 1 million customers in Missouri and Illinois through utility subsidiaries AmerenUE, AmerenCIPS, AmerenCILCO, and AmerenIP. Ameren has a generating capacity of more than 16,200 MW (primarily coal-fired), most of which is controlled by utility AmerenUE and nonregulated subsidiary AmerenEnergy Resources Generating Company. Other nonutility operations include energy marketing and trading and management and consulting services.

	Annual Growth	12/03	12/04	12/05	12/06	12/07
Sales ($ mil.)	13.2%	4,593.0	5,160.0	6,780.0	6,880.0	7,546.0
Net income ($ mil.)	4.2%	524.0	530.0	606.0	547.0	618.0
Market value ($ mil.)	10.8%	7,493.4	9,787.3	10,488.8	11,100.6	11,291.9
Employees	(1.1%)	—	9,388	9,136	8,988	9,069

AMEREX GROUP INC.

512 7th Ave., 9th Fl.
New York, NY 10118
Phone: 212-609-3000
Fax: 212-575-1940
Web: www.amerexgroup.com

CEO: Ira Ganger
CFO: –
HR: –
FYE: December 31
Type: Private

The people at Amerex know that when "it's raining, it's pouring," their profits are soaring. Amerex makes outerwear for men, women, and children. Founded in 1946, it has licensing agreements with brands such as Jones New York, London Fog, OshKosh, and Mudd. Amerex also sells outerwear under its own labels (Static and Weather Tamer) and sports-oriented outdoor wear through subsidiary Gerry (Bombshell and Mambosok). Amerex began to make and market swimwear in 2008 under the London Fog, Isababies, Mambosok, and Bombshell labels. Amerex sells to department stores and mass merchandisers in the US and Canada. Chairman and president Ira Ganger bought out retiring partner Fred Shvetz in early 2006.

	Annual Growth	12/03	12/04	12/05	12/06	12/07
Est. sales ($ mil.)	—	—	—	—	—	69.3
Employees	—	—	—	—	—	500

AMERIANA BANCORP

NASDAQ (GM): ASBI

2118 Bundy Ave.
New Castle, IN 47362
Phone: 765-529-2230
Fax: 765-529-2232
Web: www.ameriana.com

CEO: Jerome J. (Jerry) Gassen
CFO: John J. Letter
HR: Jane K. Moyer
FYE: December 31
Type: Public

Ameriana Bancorp may sound merry, but it takes business seriously. It's the parent of Ameriana Bank, which has about a dozen offices in central Indiana. The bank offers standard deposit products, including checking, savings, and money market accounts, CDs, and IRAs. It focuses on real estate lending: residential mortgages account for about half of its loan portfolio and commercial real estate loans are about 30%. The company sells auto, home, life, health, and business coverage through its Ameriana Insurance Agency subsidiary. Another unit, Ameriana Investment Management, provides brokerage and investment services through an agreement with LPL Financial.

	Annual Growth	12/03	12/04	12/05	12/06	12/07
Assets ($ mil.)	1.5%	402.5	428.5	449.4	437.3	426.8
Net income ($ mil.)	(15.9%)	2.4	1.4	2.1	(1.0)	1.2
Market value ($ mil.)	(13.6%)	45.7	50.5	41.1	42.0	25.4
Employees	—	—	—	—	—	—

AMERICA FIRST CREDIT UNION

1344 W. 4675 South
Riverdale, UT 84405
Phone: 801-627-0900
Fax: 801-778-8079
Web: www.americafirst.com

CEO: Rick Craig
CFO: –
HR: –
FYE: December 31
Type: Not-for-profit

If saving your money makes you feel like doing a little flag-waving, could there be a more appropriate place for it than America First Credit Union? Founded in 1939, the institution offers deposit, lending, investments, and other financial services to both business and consumer customers through some 70 branches in Utah and Nevada. With more than 441,000 members, America First Credit Union ranks among the nation's top 10 credit unions by membership. With more than $3.6 billion in assets, the credit union ranks among the top 20 by that measure.

	Annual Growth	12/03	12/04	12/05	12/06	12/07
Est. sales ($ mil.)	—	—	—	—	—	205.0
Employees	—	—	—	—	—	970

AMERICA SERVICE GROUP INC.

NASDAQ (GS): ASGR

105 Westpark Dr., Ste. 200
Brentwood, TN 37027
Phone: 615-373-3100
Fax: 615-376-1350
Web: www.asgr.com

CEO: Michael Catalano
CFO: Michael W. Taylor
HR: T. Scott Hoffman
FYE: December 31
Type: Public

Talk about capturing your clients. America Service Group's subsidiaries provide managed health care services to prisoners in state, county, and local correctional facilities throughout the US. Through Correctional Health Services, EMSA, and Prison Health Services, the company contracts with government agencies to provide physical and mental health screenings and treatment, as well as dental care and medication administration. America Service Group also oversees off-site services including outpatient testing and care, emergency room care, surgery, and hospitalization.

	Annual Growth	12/03	12/04	12/05	12/06	12/07
Sales ($ mil.)	(2.9%)	549.3	665.1	562.7	569.4	489.1
Net income ($ mil.)	(30.4%)	11.9	9.0	4.4	(3.4)	2.8
Market value ($ mil.)	(17.2%)	145.2	289.4	170.7	160.5	68.3
Employees	(1.5%)	—	—	4,230	5,030	4,100

AMERICALL GROUP, INC.

550 E. Diehl Rd.
Naperville, IL 60563
Phone: 630-955-9100
Fax: 630-955-9955
Web: www.americallgroup.com

CEO: George Kestler
CFO: Stephen (Steve) Oscarson
HR: –
FYE: December 31
Type: Subsidiary

Americall would have no problem fulfilling Blondie's request to "Call Me." The company, a unit of French call-center behemoth Teleperformance, specializes in outbound teleservices for companies in the financial services and insurance industries. Other customers include membership organizations and telecommunications companies. Americall handles functions such as customer acquisition, customer care, and technical support from about half a dozen facilities in the US and Latin America. The company was founded by CEO George Kestler in 1984 and acquired by Teleperformance in 1998.

	Annual Growth	12/02	12/03	12/04	12/05	12/06
Est. sales ($ mil.)	—	—	—	—	—	312.7
Employees	—	—	—	—	—	10,000

AMERICAN AIR LIQUIDE HOLDINGS, INC.

2700 Post Oak Blvd., Ste. 1800
Houston, TX 77056
Phone: 713-624-8000
Fax: 713-624-8085
Web: www.us.airliquide.com

CEO: Pierre DuFour
CFO: –
HR: –
FYE: December 31
Type: Subsidiary

Break out the Tums, because things are awfully gassy over at American Air Liquide. The company supplies industrial gases (oxygen, nitrogen, CO2, argon, etc.) to companies in the automotive, chemicals, food and beverage, and health care industries. The US distribution arm of industrial gas provider Air Liquide, the company grew a lot bigger when its parent acquired Messer Griesheim's North American business. Depending on its customer's needs, American Air Liquide can ship its product in cylinders or by pipelines, or it can manufacture it on site. Moving forward the company hopes to depend more and more on onsite manufacturing projects.

AMERICAN AIRLINES FEDERAL CREDIT UNION

4151 Amon Carter Blvd.
Fort Worth, TX 76155
Phone: 817-963-6000
Fax: 817-963-6108
Web: www.aacreditunion.org

CEO: John M. Tippets
CFO: Eli Vazquez
HR: –
FYE: December 31
Type: Not-for-profit

American Airlines Federal Credit Union won't hassle you about the position of your tray table. The company, which operates branches in or near airports in about 20 cities in the US and Puerto Rico, provides standard financial services such as checking and savings accounts and credit cards to more than 200,000 members. It also sells investments and insurance. Its lending program consists of home mortgages and vehicle loans, education loans, and other personal loans. American Airlines Federal Credit Union was founded in 1936 by employees of American Airlines (now part of AMR Corporation) at Chicago's Midway Airport.

	Annual Growth	12/02	12/03	12/04	12/05	12/06
Est. sales ($ mil.)	—	—	—	—	—	244.1
Employees	—	—	—	—	—	454

AMERICAN AMMUNITION, INC.

Pink Sheets: AAMU

3545 NW 71st St.
Miami, FL 33147
Phone: 305-835-7400
Fax: 305-694-0037
Web: www.a-merc.com

CEO: Andres F. Fernandez
CFO: Andres F. Fernandez
HR: –
FYE: December 31
Type: Public

Apple pie and ammo. American Ammunition makes small arms ammunition for commercial, law enforcement, and military use. The company is a contractor for the US Department of Defense and sells its products to both domestic and international governmental agencies. The majority of components used in its assembly of finished pieces are made in-house. American Ammunition plans to boost production capacity over the next several years.

	Annual Growth	12/02	12/03	12/04	12/05	*12/06
Sales ($ mil.)	12.0%	1.4	2.0	3.3	3.2	2.2
Net income ($ mil.)	—	(1.9)	(2.9)	(3.3)	(6.1)	(8.6)
Employees	—	—	—	—	—	45

*Most recent year available

An in-depth profile of this company is available to Hoover's Online members at hoovers.com.

111

AMERICAN APPAREL, INC.
AMEX: APP

747 Warehouse St.
Los Angeles, CA 90021
Phone: 213-488-0226
Fax: 213-488-0334
Web: www.americanapparel.net

CEO: Dov Charney
CFO: William T. Gochnauer
HR: Kristina Moreno
FYE: December 31
Type: Public

American Apparel wants you to be comfortable inside and out. It designs and makes logo-free T-shirts, tank tops, yoga pants, and other items for men, women, and children — and does it all from its California-based factory, rather than exporting labor overseas. Its brands include Classic Girl, Standard American, Classic Baby, and Sustainable Edition, among others. American Apparel boasts some 190 stores located in about 15 countries. Riding the casual loungewear trend, the company is known for its no-sweat factory and the fair treatment of its workers, including up to $19 an hour pay for manufacturers. Founder Dov Charney owns a 55% stake in the firm, which was bought by Endeavor Acquisition Corporation.

	Annual Growth	12/03	12/04	12/05	12/06	12/07
Est. sales ($ mil.)	—	—	—	—	—	387.0
Net income ($ mil.)	—	—	—	—	—	15.5
Market value ($ mil.)	—	—	—	—	—	1,066.7
Employees	—	—	—	—	—	—

AMERICAN AUTOMOBILE ASSOCIATION

1000 AAA Dr.
Heathrow, FL 32746
Phone: 407-444-7000
Fax: 407-444-7380
Web: www.aaa.com

CEO: Robert L. Darbelnet
CFO: John Schaffer
HR: Carol Droessler
FYE: December 31
Type: Not-for-profit

This isn't your great-grandfather's American Automobile Association (AAA). The not-for-profit organization is best known as providing emergency roadside assistance to its members. AAA has extended its reach into other areas, however, such as offering a variety of financial and travel-arrangement services (foreign currency exchange and travelers checks), as well. The organization offers its members credit cards, insurance, and vehicle financing. AAA operates travel agencies and publishes maps and travel guides, to boot. AAA and its affiliated auto clubs maintain about 1,100 facilities to serve more than 50 million members that span the US and Canada. AAA was founded in 1902.

	Annual Growth	12/03	12/04	12/05	12/06	12/07
Est. sales ($ mil.)	—	—	—	—	—	39.5
Employees	—	—	—	—	—	850

AMERICAN AXLE & MANUFACTURING HOLDINGS, INC.
NYSE: AXL

1 Dauch Dr.
Detroit, MI 48211
Phone: 313-758-2000
Fax: 313-758-4257
Web: www.aam.com

CEO: Richard E. Dauch
CFO: Michael K. Simonte
HR: John E. Jerge
FYE: December 31
Type: Public

American Axle & Manufacturing (AAM) is GM's right-hand man for driveline systems and forged products. AAM manufactures axles, driveshafts, and chassis components, mainly for light trucks and SUVs, but also for cars and crossover vehicles. Axles and driveshafts account for about 85% of AAM's sales; chassis components, forged products, and other components account for the rest. The Tier 1 supplier gets more than 75% of its business from GM; other customers include PACCAR, Magna International, Chrysler, and Ford. AAM sells most of its products in the US.

	Annual Growth	12/03	12/04	12/05	12/06	12/07
Sales ($ mil.)	(3.1%)	3,682.7	3,599.6	3,387.3	3,191.7	3,248.2
Net income ($ mil.)	(34.2%)	197.1	159.5	56.0	(222.5)	37.0
Market value ($ mil.)	(16.4%)	2,166.5	1,523.8	922.0	959.0	1,055.8
Employees	(5.6%)	—	—	11,000	10,000	9,800

AMERICAN BANCORP OF NEW JERSEY, INC.
NASDAQ (GM): ABNJ

365 Broad St.
Bloomfield, NJ 07003
Phone: 973-748-3600
Fax: 973-748-2047
Web: www.americansavingsnj.com

CEO: Joseph Kliminski
CFO: Eric B. Heyer
HR: Carol Ricciardelli
FYE: September 30
Type: Public

American Bancorp of New Jersey was established in 2005 to be the holding company for American Bank of New Jersey, which operates about five branches serving Essex and Passaic counties. The bank offers standard products and services, including checking and savings accounts, CDs, money market accounts, and IRAs. It uses funds from deposits to mainly originate real estate loans: Single-family residential mortgages account for approximately 60% of its loan portfolio; multifamily and commercial real estate loans make up more than 20%. The bank sells fixed-rate annuities through its ASB Investment subsidiary.

	Annual Growth	9/03	9/04	9/05	9/06	9/07
Assets ($ mil.)	7.7%	427.1	424.9	555.9	514.3	573.7
Net income ($ mil.)	(19.1%)	1.4	2.2	2.0	2.1	0.6
Market value ($ mil.)	(8.6%)	—	—	155.4	172.2	129.9
Employees	(14.5%)	—	69	59	—	—

AMERICAN BANK INCORPORATED
OTC: AMBK

4029 W. Tilghman St.
Allentown, PA 18104
Phone: 610-366-1800
Fax: 610-289-3326
Web: www.pcbanker.com

CEO: Mark W. Jaindl
CFO: Harry C. Birkhimer
HR: –
FYE: December 31
Type: Public

American Bank Incorporated is the holding company for American Bank, which serves eastern Pennsylvania from a single branch in Allentown as well as customers throughout the US via its banking Web site. The bank's deposit products and services include checking and savings accounts, credit cards, and discount brokerage. It primarily originates real estate loans, with commercial mortgages and residential mortgages accounting for nearly 50% and 25% of the company's lending portfolio, respectively. The Jaindl family, including company CEO Mark, owns a majority of American Bank Incorporated.

	Annual Growth	12/03	12/04	12/05	12/06	12/07
Assets ($ mil.)	1.1%	482.0	503.4	529.1	504.6	504.1
Net income ($ mil.)	10.7%	2.6	3.2	3.5	2.8	3.9
Employees	6.3%	—	—	46	51	52

AMERICAN BANKNOTE CORPORATION

2200 Fletcher Ave.
Fort Lee, NJ 07024
Phone: 201-592-3400
Fax: 201-224-2762
Web: www.americanbanknote.com

CEO: Steven G. Singer
CFO: Patrick J. Gentile
HR: –
FYE: December 31
Type: Private

Take note — American Banknote aims to foil counterfeiters. The company, through its subsidiaries, prints secure financial- and identification-related documents, such as stock certificates and passports. It also makes smart cards and ID cards, including driver's licenses, and offers document distribution services. Outside the US, American Banknote has operations in Argentina, Brazil, and France. The company reorganized under Chapter 11 bankruptcy protection in 2005.

An in-depth profile of this company is available to Hoover's Online members at hoovers.com.

AMERICAN BAR ASSOCIATION

321 N. Clark St.
Chicago, IL 60610
Phone: 312-988-5000
Fax: 312-988-5177
Web: www.abanet.org

CEO: William H. Neukom
CFO: Kenneth J. Widelka
HR: –
FYE: August 31
Type: Association

The American Bar Association (ABA) doesn't have anything to do with alcohol, except maybe defending drunk drivers. The ABA seeks to promote improvements in the American justice system and develop guidelines for the advancement of the legal profession and legal education. It provides law school accreditation, continuing legal education, legal information, and other services to assist legal professionals. Its roster of more than 400,000 members includes judges, court administrators, law professors, and nonpracticing lawyers. All lawyers in good standing with any US state or territory bar are eligible for membership. The ABA cannot discipline lawyers, nor can it enforce its rules; it can only develop guidelines.

	Annual Growth	8/03	8/04	8/05	8/06	8/07
Est. sales ($ mil.)	—	—	—	—	—	191.4
Employees	—	—	—	—	—	900

AMERICAN BEVERAGE CORPORATION

1 Daily Way
Verona, PA 15147
Phone: 412-828-9020
Fax: 412-828-8876
Web: www.ambev.com

CEO: Antonio Battaglia
CFO: Peter J. Chiappa
HR: –
FYE: December 31
Type: Subsidiary

American Beverage Corporation produces bottled cocktail mixes, fruit drinks, and bottled water. The company is made up of two divisions: Daily's (fruit drinks and mixers) and Twin Mountain (bottled water). Its fruit-drink brand names include Hugs, Too Tarts, Liquid Lizard, Big Burst, Big Juicy, and Fruit Stand; its water brands include Glacial Ice and Twin Mountain. American Beverage also produces Sauza cocktail mixers, as well as a licensed brand-name mixer for Carlson Restaurants Worldwide's T.G.I. Friday's. American is a subsidiary of Dutch food giant Koninklijke Wessanen and has operations in New Hampshire and Pennsylvania.

AMERICAN BILTRITE INC.

AMEX: ABL

57 River St.
Wellesley Hills, MA 02481
Phone: 781-237-6655
Fax: 781-237-6880
Web: www.americanbiltriteinc.com

CEO: Roger S. Marcus
CFO: Howard N. Feist III
HR: Bonnie Posnak
FYE: December 31
Type: Public

American Biltrite has its hand in several different pots, some of which are sticky. Its tape division manufactures adhesive-coated, pressure-sensitive tapes and films used to protect materials during handling and storage, as well as for applications in the heating, ventilation, and air conditioning (HVAC), automotive, and electrical industries. The company also designs and distributes wholesale jewelry and accessories to specialty and department stores through its K&M subsidiary, while its AB Canada subsidiary makes floor tile and rubber products. Its Congoleum unit, which makes resilient sheet and tile flooring, filed for Chapter 11 bankruptcy protection amidst a large number of asbestos-related lawsuits.

	Annual Growth	12/03	12/04	12/05	12/06	12/07
Sales ($ mil.)	0.0%	420.1	433.9	445.2	435.5	420.7
Net income ($ mil.)	—	(14.2)	2.0	(17.6)	0.7	(2.0)
Market value ($ mil.)	(10.2%)	26.5	39.2	37.3	31.6	17.2
Employees	(3.6%)	—	—	1,650	1,590	—

AMERICAN BIO MEDICA CORPORATION

NASDAQ (CM): ABMC

122 Smith Rd.
Kinderhook, NY 12106
Phone: 518-758-8158
Fax: 518-758-8171
Web: www.americanbiomedica.com

CEO: Stan Cipkowski
CFO: Stefan Parker
HR: –
FYE: December 31
Type: Public

There's a thin line between employment and unemployment, and that line might just be on one of American Bio Medica's drug-testing kits. The company's Rapid Drug Screen products indicate within minutes the presence in a urine sample of such illegal substances as marijuana, cocaine, amphetamines, and opiates. Used by employers, law enforcement agencies, hospitals, schools, and other institutions, the tests offer up to 10-panel options (each panel tests for different substances). The company's Rapid One is a line of single-drug specific tests; its Rapid Tec and Rapid TOX products detect multiple drug classes on one panel. American Bio Medica also offers saliva-based tests for law enforcement customers.

	Annual Growth	12/03	12/04	12/05	12/06	12/07
Sales ($ mil.)	2.7%	12.5	12.2	13.0	13.8	13.9
Net income ($ mil.)	—	1.0	0.3	(0.4)	0.2	(1.0)
Market value ($ mil.)	(9.1%)	31.2	23.0	23.7	19.5	21.3
Employees	—	—	—	115	—	—

AMERICAN BRIDGE COMPANY

1000 American Bridge Way
Coraopolis, PA 15108
Phone: 412-631-1000
Fax: 412-631-2000
Web: www.americanbridge.net

CEO: Robert H. (Bob) Luffy
CFO: Pamela A. Bena
HR: Tonilynn Parks
FYE: December 31
Type: Private

American Bridge Company has been connecting one body of land with another for more than a century. The bridges and structures that the general contractor and subcontractor builds span the nation's modern industrial age, from New York's landmark Chrysler Building to the San Francisco Bay Bridge. American Bridge Company manufactures fabricated structural steel and provides construction, engineering, and design-build services to clients in the US, Canada, and South America. Its specialty lies in the erection and rehabilitation of complex bridge structures, with growing capabilities in port and military building construction. The company was a subsidiary of US Steel Corp. until 1987, when it became privately owned.

	Annual Growth	12/03	12/04	12/05	12/06	12/07
Est. sales ($ mil.)	—	—	—	—	—	44.8
Employees	—	—	—	—	—	500

AMERICAN BUILDERS & CONTRACTORS SUPPLY CO., INC.

1 ABC Pkwy.
Beloit, WI 53511
Phone: 608-362-7777
Fax: 608-362-2717
Web: www.abc-supply.com

CEO: David A. Luck
CFO: Kendra A. Story
HR: –
FYE: December 31
Type: Private

American Builders & Contractors Supply Co. (better known as ABC Supply) has put roofs over millions of heads. A leading supplier of roofing, siding, windows, gutters, doors, and related builder's supplies, ABC Supply operates about 380 outlets throughout the US. It carries its own brand of products under the Amcraft name, as well as offering products from outside vendors. The company, which markets its products mostly to small and medium-sized professional contractors, was founded in 1982 by former chairman and CEO the late Ken Hendricks, the son of a roofer.

	Annual Growth	12/02	12/03	12/04	12/05	12/06
Sales ($ mil.)	20.4%	1,424.7	1,792.5	2,042.0	2,597.0	2,990.0
Employees	10.0%	3,711	4,128	4,128	5,144	5,431

An in-depth profile of this company is available to Hoover's Online members at hoovers.com.

AMERICAN BUILDINGS COMPANY

1150 State Docks Rd.
Eufaula, AL 36027
Phone: 334-687-2032
Fax: 334-688-2185
Web: www.americanbuildings.com

CEO: Robert T. (Bob) Ammerman
CFO: Anne Savage
HR: Jan Spitzer
FYE: December 31
Type: Subsidiary

American Buildings Company can put a roof over your head, quite literally. It manufactures metal buildings and roofing products for industrial, institutional, and commercial construction applications. From multi-story buildings to customized self-storage units to metal roof and wall panels, the company's buildings and components are marketed through a network of more than 1,000 authorized builders and dealers in the US and Canada. Its heavy fabrication capabilities include building custom-engineered steel mills, sports stadiums, and large aircraft maintenance hangars. American Buildings Company and its former parent, MAGNATRAX, were acquired by Nucor Corporation in 2007.

	Annual Growth	12/03	12/04	12/05	12/06	12/07
Est. sales ($ mil.)	—	—	—	—	—	202.3
Employees	—	—	—	—	—	1,800

AMERICAN BUREAU OF SHIPPING

16855 Northchase Dr.
Houston, TX 77060
Phone: 281-877-5800
Fax: 281-877-5803
Web: www.eagle.org

CEO: Robert D. (Bob) Somerville
CFO: Jeff Weiner
HR: –
FYE: December 31
Type: Not-for-profit

Founded in 1862, American Bureau of Shipping (ABS) is one of the world's largest ship classification societies, offering inspection and analysis services to verify that vessels are mechanically and structurally fit. The not-for-profit company's surveyors examine ships in major ports throughout the world, assessing whether the vessels comply with ABS rules for design, construction, and maintenance. Additionally, its engineers consult with shipbuilders on proposed designs and repairs. The not-for-profit company operates about 150 offices in 70 countries, primarily serving fleet owners and government agencies. Through its for-profit ABS Group subsidiary, ABS offers risk management consulting services.

	Annual Growth	12/03	12/04	12/05	12/06	12/07
Est. sales ($ mil.)	—	—	—	—	—	117.1
Employees	—	—	—	—	—	2,300

AMERICAN BUSINESS BANK

OTC: AMBZ

523 W. 6th St., Ste. 900
Los Angeles, CA 90014
Phone: 213-430-4000
Fax: 213-627-2784
Web: www.americanbusinessbank.com

CEO: Donald P. (Don) Johnson
CFO: Wesley E. (Wes) Schaefer
HR: –
FYE: December 31
Type: Public

What's a "middle-market," privately owned business gotta do to get *FORTUNE 500* treatment from a bank? American Business Bank caters to private companies with sales between $5 and $145 million in sales, with an emphasis on manufacturers, service businesses, and not-for-profit organizations. It has offices in Irvine, Los Angeles, and Woodland Hills, and provides remote banking services throughout Southern California via courier and the Web. The bank offers deposit services including CDs, and checking, savings, and money market accounts. Lending products include commercial, real estate, and construction loans; lines-of-credit; and equipment financing.

	Annual Growth	12/03	12/04	12/05	12/06	12/07
Assets ($ mil.)	14.2%	360.7	458.0	508.5	537.2	613.6
Net income ($ mil.)	—	—	—	—	—	5.2
Employees	—	—	—	—	—	72

AMERICAN CAMPUS COMMUNITIES, INC.

NYSE: ACC

805 Las Cimas Pkwy., Ste. 400
Austin, TX 78746
Phone: 512-732-1000
Fax: 512-732-2450
Web: www.studenthousing.com

CEO: William C. Bayless Jr.
CFO: Jonathan A. Graf
HR: –
FYE: December 31
Type: Public

American Campus Communities (ACC) actually does most of its business off campus. The self-managed real estate investment trust (REIT) owns and operates more than 40 student housing properties in more than 15 states. Its holdings are located on or near colleges and universities. It leases the ground for on-campus properties from the schools, which in turn receive half of the net cash flow from these properties. Additionally, ACC provides leasing and management services for other student housing owners. In all, the REIT manages more than 60 properties containing more than 15,000 units with some 44,000 beds. It also works with schools to develop and renovate student housing.

	Annual Growth	12/03	12/04	12/05	12/06	12/07
Sales ($ mil.)	25.2%	59.9	60.8	87.5	118.9	147.1
Net income ($ mil.)	—	(0.9)	(1.3)	9.7	22.6	(1.7)
Market value ($ mil.)	37.2%	—	283.7	426.3	652.1	732.3
Employees	8.3%	—	—	828	897	—

AMERICAN CANCER SOCIETY, INC.

1599 Clifton Rd. NE
Atlanta, GA 30329
Phone: 404-320-3333
Fax: 404-982-3677
Web: www.cancer.org

CEO: John R. Seffrin
CFO: –
HR: –
FYE: August 31
Type: Not-for-profit

The American Cancer Society (ACS) works as a firefighter for your lungs. Dedicated to the elimination of cancer, the not-for-profit organization is staffed by professionals and more than 2 million volunteers at some 3,400 local units across the country. ACS is the largest source of private cancer research funds in the US. Recipients of the society's funding include 42 Nobel Prize laureates. In addition to research, the ACS supports detection, treatment, and education programs. The organization encourages prevention efforts with programs such as the Great American Smokeout. Patient services include moral support, transportation to and from treatment, and camps for children who have cancer.

	Annual Growth	8/02	8/03	8/04	8/05	8/06
Sales ($ mil.)	6.1%	—	—	—	977.9	1,037.7
Employees	—	—	—	—	—	—

AMERICAN CAPITAL STRATEGIES, LTD.

NASDAQ (GS): ACAS

2 Bethesda Metro Center, 14th Fl.
Bethesda, MD 20814
Phone: 301-951-6122
Fax: 301-654-6714
Web: www.american-capital.com

CEO: Malon Wilkus
CFO: John R. Erickson
HR: Ira J. Wagner
FYE: December 31
Type: Public

Whether you make musical instruments or mints, salon appliances or safes, this company has a strategy for you. Founded in 1986, American Capital Strategies invests in middle-market companies through about a dozen offices in the US and Europe. It typically provides up to $800 million per transaction for management and employee buyouts, private equity firm buyouts, acquisitions, and restructurings. American Capital's portfolio consists of stakes in more than 200 companies, with holdings in such sectors as commercial services, consumer goods, financial services, food, electrical equipment, health care, oil and gas, packaging, real estate, retail, and technology.

	Annual Growth	12/03	12/04	12/05	12/06	12/07
Sales ($ mil.)	56.6%	206.3	435.3	554.5	1,330.0	1,240.0
Net income ($ mil.)	56.1%	118.0	281.4	364.9	896.0	700.0
Market value ($ mil.)	34.7%	1,960.7	2,958.3	4,305.8	6,828.0	6,456.9
Employees	44.8%	132	191	308	484	580

An in-depth profile of this company is available to Hoover's Online members at hoovers.com.

AMERICAN CAST IRON PIPE COMPANY

1501 31st Ave. North
Birmingham, AL 35207
Phone: 205-325-7701
Fax: 205-325-8014
Web: www.acipco.com

CEO: Van L. Richey
CFO: J. M. Cook
HR: Leann Barr
FYE: December 31
Type: Private

American Cast Iron Pipe Co. (ACIPCO) operates one of the largest ductile iron pipe casting plants in the world. Its divisions — including American Centrifugal, American Ductile Iron Pipe, American Flow Control, and American Steel Pipe — make ductile iron pipe and fittings, cast steel tubes, electric resistance welded steel pipes, fire hydrants and fire truck pumps, and valves for water treatment and energy production. Other ACIPCO units make molded rubber products for the water utility industry and spiral-welded steel pipe. John Joseph Eagan founded ACIPCO in 1905 and in 1922 placed all of the company's stock into a trust for employees.

	Annual Growth	12/03	12/04	12/05	12/06	12/07
Est. sales ($ mil.)	—	—	—	—	—	267.5
Employees	—	—	—	—	—	2,500

AMERICAN CENTURY COMPANIES, INC.

4500 Main St., Ste. 1500
Kansas City, MO 64111
Phone: 816-340-4200
Fax: 816-340-7962
Web: www.americancentury.com

CEO: Jonathan S. Thomas
CFO: –
HR: –
FYE: December 31
Type: Private

American Century Companies is actually closer to the half-century mark, but who's counting? The company, through subsidiary American Century Investment Management, oversees mutual funds covering a range of styles including fixed income, value, quantitative, US growth, and international growth. It even has series of funds that support cancer research. The company's brokerage services offer investors access to additional mutual funds from other firms. American Century manages more than $100 billion of client assets in accounts for individuals, corporations, charitable organizations, and retirement plans.

	Annual Growth	12/03	12/04	12/05	12/06	12/07
Est. sales ($ mil.)	—	—	—	—	—	249.6
Employees	—	—	—	—	—	1,837

AMERICAN CHEMICAL SOCIETY

1155 16th St. Northwest
Washington, DC 20036
Phone: 202-872-4600
Fax: 202-872-4615
Web: www.acs.org

CEO: Madeleine Jacobs
CFO: Brian A. Bernstein
HR: –
FYE: December 31
Type: Not-for-profit

This group has a lot of chemistry. With some 160,000 members, the American Chemical Society (ACS) is one of the world's largest scientific organizations. It provides information, career development, and educational resources to member chemists, chemical engineers, and technicians. ACS also publishes dozens of magazines, journals, and books, and its Chemical Abstracts Service provides access to an online database of more than 25 million literature and research summaries from around the world. ACS also serves as an advocate for its members on public policy issues. The not-for-profit organization was founded in 1876 and chartered by Congress in 1937.

	Annual Growth	12/03	12/04	12/05	12/06	12/07
Est. sales ($ mil.)	—	—	—	—	—	411.7
Employees	—	—	—	—	—	2,000

AMERICAN CITY BUSINESS JOURNALS, INC.

120 W. Morehead St., Ste. 400
Charlotte, NC 28202
Phone: 704-973-1000
Fax: 704-973-1001
Web: www.acbj.com

CEO: Ray Shaw
CFO: George Guthinger
HR: –
FYE: December 31
Type: Subsidiary

Both big and small cities can turn to this company for coverage of business news. American City Business Journals (ACBJ) is a leading newspaper publisher that serves more than 500,000 subscribers in more than 40 cities with local business news. Through subsidiary bizjournals, it also publishes news and information online for more than 3 million registered users. ACBJ also owns *The Sporting News*, one of the top sports magazines in the US, and Hemmings Motor News, a publisher of collectible-car books and magazines. Its Street & Smith's Sports Group publishes several sports publications including *SportsBusiness Journal*. ACBJ is a unit of newspaper and magazine publisher Advance Publications.

	Annual Growth	12/03	12/04	12/05	12/06	12/07
Est. sales ($ mil.)	—	—	—	—	—	87.8
Employees	—	—	—	—	—	1,500

AMERICAN CIVIL LIBERTIES UNION

125 Broad St., 18th Fl.
New York, NY 10004
Phone: 212-549-2500
Fax: 212-549-2646
Web: www.aclu.org

CEO: Anthony D. Romero
CFO: –
HR: –
FYE: March 31
Type: Not-for-profit

The philosopher Socrates once said, "I am that gadfly which God has given the state." While the American Civil Liberties Union (ACLU) might have a quarrel with the "God" part, the group has at times proved a stinging critic in its efforts to defend individual rights. It acts as a legal and legislative advocate in matters related to civil liberties and the Bill of Rights. The ACLU has participated in such cases as the 1925 Scopes trial (challenged a ban on teaching evolution), *Brown v. Board of Education* (school desegregation), *Roe v. Wade* (abortion rights), and *Romer v. Evans* (gay and lesbian rights). The group, which has more than 500,000 members, maintains offices throughout the US. It was founded in 1920.

	Annual Growth	3/03	3/04	3/05	3/06	3/07
Est. sales ($ mil.)	—	—	—	—	—	48.0
Employees	—	—	—	—	—	170

AMERICAN CLAIMS EVALUATION, INC.

NASDAQ (CM): AMCE

1 Jericho Plaza
Jericho, NY 11753
Phone: 516-938-8000
Fax: 516-938-0405
Web: www.rpmconsultants.net

CEO: Gary Gelman
CFO: Gary J. Knauer
HR: –
FYE: March 31
Type: Public

When safety doesn't come first, there's American Claims Evaluation. Through its RPM Rehabilitation & Associates subsidiary, the firm helps employers in Washington State resolve disability claims and get their injured workers back on the job ASAP. Its consultants work with all the parties involved — the injured worker, the employer, and medical personnel — to coordinate treatment, devise modified job descriptions, and monitor progress — with the aim of returning employees to work quickly. The company also provides consulting in areas such as ergonomics, and it supplies expert testimony should cases go to trial. Chairman, president, and CEO Gary Gelman owns about two-thirds of the company.

	Annual Growth	3/03	3/04	3/05	3/06	3/07
Sales ($ mil.)	(6.9%)	1.2	1.2	1.1	1.1	0.9
Net income ($ mil.)	—	(0.7)	(0.5)	(0.5)	(0.3)	(0.3)
Market value ($ mil.)	7.6%	6.9	14.3	9.2	11.8	9.2
Employees	(35.7%)	—	—	28	18	

An in-depth profile of this company is available to Hoover's Online members at hoovers.com.

AMERICAN COMMERCE SOLUTIONS, INC.

OTC: AACS

1400 Chamber Dr.
Bartow, FL 33830
Phone: 863-533-0326
Fax: 863-533-0327
Web: www.aacssymbol.com

CEO: Daniel L. (Dan) Hefner
CFO: Frank D. Puissegur
HR: –
FYE: February 28
Type: Public

Holding company American Commerce Solutions (ACS), through its International Machine and Welding subsidiary, provides specialized machining and repair services for heavy equipment used in the agricultural, construction, forestry, mining, and scrap industries. Its Chariot Manufacturing Company subsidiary (which includes Chariot Trailers) manufactures open and enclosed trailers to carry motorcycles. ACS also sells aftermarket repair parts. The company also has a strategic relationship with American Fiber Green Products. The Mosaic Company generates about 36% of sales.

	Annual Growth	2/04	2/05	2/06	2/07	2/08
Sales ($ mil.)	7.5%	2.1	2.8	2.3	2.3	2.8
Net income ($ mil.)	—	(1.6)	(1.3)	(0.9)	(1.5)	(1.0)
Market value ($ mil.)	(17.5%)	3.8	4.4	3.8	3.3	1.8
Employees	8.3%	24	26	33	26	33

AMERICAN COMMERCIAL LINES INC.

NASDAQ (GS): ACLI

1701 E. Market St.
Jeffersonville, IN 47130
Phone: 812-288-0100
Fax: 812-288-1766
Web: www.aclines.com

CEO: Michael P. (Mike) Ryan
CFO: Thomas R. Pilholski
HR: Nick C. Fletcher
FYE: Last Friday in December
Type: Public

One of the mightiest on the mighty Mississippi, barge operator American Commercial Lines (ACL) navigates the inland waterways of the US. ACL is a leading barge transporter of dry bulk commodities, including alumina, cement, fertilizers, and salt, as well as coal, grain, and steel. The company also transports liquid bulk cargo such as chemicals, ethanol, and petroleum products. ACL's fleet consists of about 2,070 covered dry cargo barges, 370 open dry cargo barges, and 390 tank barges, powered by about 160 towboats. In addition to transportation, the company engages in manufacturing: Its Jeffboat subsidiary builds barges for ACL and other customers.

	Annual Growth	12/03	12/04	12/05	12/06	12/07
Sales ($ mil.)	14.1%	620.1	632.3	741.4	942.5	1,050.4
Net income ($ mil.)	—	(61.6)	4.4	11.8	92.3	44.4
Market value ($ mil.)	47.6%	—	—	466.2	2,027.0	1,015.8
Employees	0.0%	3,000	2,630	2,689	2,795	3,000

AMERICAN COMMUNITY BANCSHARES, INC.

NASDAQ (CM): ACBA

4500 Cameron Valley Pkwy., Ste. 150
Charlotte, NC 28211
Phone: 704-225-8444
Fax: 704-225-8445
Web: www.americancommunitybank.com

CEO: Randy P. Helton
CFO: Dan R. Ellis Jr.
HR: –
FYE: December 31
Type: Public

American Community Bancshares is the holding company for American Community Bank, which serves individuals and small to midsized businesses through about a dozen branches in North and South Carolina. The bank offers standard products such as checking, savings, and money market accounts; certificates of deposit; and IRAs. Its loan portfolio is made up of construction and development loans (some 35% of the total) and commercial mortgages (more than 25%), as well as business, consumer, home equity, and residential mortgage loans. The bank also offers vehicle and equipment leasing services.

	Annual Growth	12/03	12/04	12/05	12/06	12/07
Assets ($ mil.)	15.8%	281.3	399.5	436.7	494.7	505.6
Net income ($ mil.)	37.5%	1.4	2.7	4.5	4.3	5.0
Market value ($ mil.)	26.9%	24.0	38.7	57.1	77.4	62.4
Employees	3.6%	—	—	109	—	117

AMERICAN COMMUNITY MUTUAL INSURANCE COMPANY

39201 Seven Mile Rd.
Livonia, MI 48152
Phone: 734-591-9000
Fax: 734-591-4628
Web: www.american-community.com

CEO: Michael E. Tobin
CFO: David A. (Dave) Skup
HR: Leslie J. Gola
FYE: December 31
Type: Mutual company

American Community Mutual would like to maintain the health and well-being of America's entire community. American Community provides group and individual health care plans and life insurance plans in nine states throughout the Midwest. The company's offerings include PPO, short-term health, dental, vision, and prescription plans. American Community also offers a high-deductible health program compatible with federal health savings accounts. Focusing largely on the small to midsized group market, the company insures more than 150,000 individuals. American Community was founded in 1938; it was the first health care insurance provider in Michigan.

	Annual Growth	12/03	12/04	12/05	12/06	12/07
Est. sales ($ mil.)	—	—	—	—	—	343.2
Employees	—	—	—	—	—	335

AMERICAN COMMUNITY NEWSPAPERS INC.

AMEX: ANE

14875 Landmark Blvd., Ste. 110
Dallas, TX 75254
Phone: 972-628-4080
Fax: 972-801-3496
Web: www.americancommunitynewspapers.com

CEO: Eugene M. (Gene) Carr
CFO: Richard D. Hendrickson
HR: Pamela J. Dahl
FYE: Sunday nearest December 31
Type: Public

American Community Newspapers is a leading publisher of weekly and niche papers serving small communities in Minnesota, Ohio, Texas, and Virginia. Its estate includes three dailies serving markets around Dallas and Minneapolis, along with more than 80 community weeklies serving mostly suburban markets. American Community Newspapers also runs more than a dozen niche publications, including free alternative weekly *The Other Paper* (Columbus, Ohio) and magazine *Columbus Monthly*. Together, the company's publications boast a circulation of more than 1.3 million.

	Annual Growth	12/03	12/04	12/05	12/06	12/07
Sales ($ mil.)	1.9%	—	34.2	0.7	2.0	36.2
Net income ($ mil.)	—	—	1.8	0.4	1.0	(4.6)
Employees	—	—	—	—	—	—

AMERICAN COMMUNITY PROPERTIES TRUST

AMEX: APO

222 Smallwood Village Center
St. Charles, MD 20602
Phone: 301-843-8600
Fax: 301-870-8481
Web: www.acptrust.com

CEO: J. Michael Wilson
CFO: Cynthia L. Hedrick
HR: –
FYE: December 31
Type: Public

American Community Properties Trust (ACPT) develops, builds, owns, and manages primarily residential real estate in Washington, DC, Maryland, Virginia, and Puerto Rico. The self-managed real estate investment trust (REIT) has ownership in more than 20 multi-family apartment communities (about 3,300 units) and 4,000 acres of undeveloped land in a planned residential community in St. Charles, Maryland. It also holds interests in about a dozen Puerto Rico apartment communities. More than half of its apartment units participate in low-income housing programs. Subsidiary American Rental Management Company manages apartments for ACPT and third parties.

	Annual Growth	12/03	12/04	12/05	12/06	12/07
Sales ($ mil.)	9.8%	58.7	49.0	62.3	98.2	85.4
Net income ($ mil.)	—	5.0	2.8	7.5	4.6	(0.5)
Market value ($ mil.)	24.5%	42.5	63.1	101.3	101.4	102.0
Employees	(3.6%)	—	—	271	—	252

AMERICAN CRYSTAL SUGAR COMPANY

101 N. Third St.
Moorhead, MN 56560
Phone: 218-236-4400
Fax: 218-236-4422
Web: www.crystalsugar.com

CEO: David A. Berg
CFO: Thomas S. Astrup
HR: Sharon Connell
FYE: August 31
Type: Cooperative

Call it saccharine, but for American Crystal Sugar, business is all about sharing. This sugar-beet cooperative is owned by some 2,900 growers in the Red River Valley of North Dakota and Minnesota, farming more than one-half million owned and contracted acres of cropland. American Crystal, formed in 1899 and converted into a co-op in 1973, divides the 35-mile-wide valley into five districts, each served by a processing plant. The plants produce sugar, molasses, and beet pulp. American Crystal's products are sold internationally to industrial users and to retail and wholesale customers under the Crystal name, as well as under private labels through marketing co-ops United Sugars and Midwest Agri-Commodities.

	Annual Growth	8/02	8/03	8/04	8/05	8/06
Sales ($ mil.)	6.7%	775.3	829.2	1,033.1	965.5	1,005.7
Net income ($ mil.)	2.8%	398.6	361.9	473.1	373.3	445.1
Employees	1.2%	1,243	1,231	1,359	1,337	1,306

AMERICAN DENTAL PARTNERS, INC.

NASDAQ (GS): ADPI

201 Edgewater Dr., Ste. 285
Wakefield, MA 01880
Phone: 781-224-0880
Fax: 781-224-4216
Web: www.amdpi.com

CEO: Gregory A. Serrao
CFO: Breht T. Feigh
HR: George R. Sullivan
FYE: December 31
Type: Public

Helping dentists focus on drilling, not billing is the mission of American Dental Partners. The company provides management services for the growing dental group practice segment of the dental care industry. Through long-term service agreements, the company manages more than 25 general and specialty dental practice groups operating more than 250 dental facilities in 18 states; its services include planning and budgeting, facilities development and management, scheduling, training, recruiting, economic analysis, financial reporting, and quality assurance.

	Annual Growth	12/03	12/04	12/05	12/06	12/07
Sales ($ mil.)	14.2%	163.7	178.6	196.9	217.9	278.8
Net income ($ mil.)	—	6.2	8.5	10.3	11.1	(7.7)
Market value ($ mil.)	23.3%	55.6	99.7	221.6	234.4	128.5
Employees	—	—	—	2,197	—	—

AMERICAN DERRINGER CORPORATION

127 N. Lacy Dr.
Waco, TX 76715
Phone: 254-799-9111
Fax: 254-799-7935
Web: www.amderringer.com

CEO: Elizabeth Saunders
CFO: Elizabeth Saunders
HR: Elizabeth Saunders
FYE: December 31
Type: Private

American Derringer owner Elizabeth Saunders is a real pistol. She stars in her own ads clad in a bustier while brandishing her signature handgun and the company's best-seller, the Lady Derringer. The tiny pistol of Wild West fame fits a petite palm with its faux ivory grip engraved with the image of a Victorian lady. American Derringer also offers a variety of pistols and accessories such as holsters, perfume, scarves, and ties. The company targets women in need of a shooting iron and collectors in need of an item. American Derringer is the only US gunsmith owned by a woman. Company founder Robert Saunders hired Elizabeth for his sales staff. They married, and when he died in 1993, she took over the company.

AMERICAN EAGLE OUTFITTERS, INC.

NYSE: AEO

77 Hot Metal St.
Pittsburgh, PA 15203
Phone: 412-432-3300
Fax: 412-432-3955
Web: www.ae.com

CEO: James V. (Jim) O'Donnell
CFO: Joan Holstein Hilson
HR: Thomas (Tom) DiDonato
FYE: Saturday nearest January 31
Type: Public

It was once a purveyor of outdoor gear, but American Eagle Outfitters now feathers its nest with polos and khakis. The mall-based retailer sells casual apparel and accessories (shirts, jeans, shorts, sweaters, skirts, footwear, belts, bags) aimed at men and women ages 15-25. Virtually all of the company's products bear its private-label brand names: American Eagle Outfitters and AE. It operates about 990 American Eagle stores in the US and Canada and plans to open more. Direct sales come from the company's Web site and its AE Magazine, a lifestyle magazine which doubles as a catalog. The Schottenstein family (which has interests in Value City department and furniture stores) owns 15% of American Eagle.

	Annual Growth	1/04	1/05	1/06	1/07	1/08
Sales ($ mil.)	19.1%	1,520.0	1,881.2	2,309.4	2,794.4	3,055.4
Net income ($ mil.)	60.7%	60.0	213.3	294.1	387.4	400.0
Market value ($ mil.)	81.6%	441.9	2,466.6	2,568.1	7,143.0	4,809.4
Employees	20.0%	—	—	23,000	27,600	—

AMERICAN EAGLE WHEEL CORPORATION

5780 Soestern Court
Chino, CA 91710
Phone: 909-590-8828
Fax: 909-628-6341
Web: www.americaneaglewheel.com

CEO: Maria Furcolow
CFO: –
HR: –
FYE: December 31
Type: Private

American Eagle Wheel takes flight when the rubber meets the road. The company makes aluminum aftermarket car and truck wheels under the BOSS, Eagle and MSR brands. American Eagle Wheel helped develop counter-pressure casting and it has exclusive use of precision CNC machine tools for making its wheels. It also has its own coating facilities to create finishes. Operating a factory in California and another in South Carolina, the company additionally makes wheel accessories, such as caps and lugs. American Eagle Wheel distributes its products through wholesale outlets in the US, Canada, Mexico, and the Caribbean.

	Annual Growth	12/03	12/04	12/05	12/06	12/07
Est. sales ($ mil.)	—	—	—	—	—	108.3
Employees	—	—	—	—	—	850

AMERICAN ECOLOGY CORPORATION

NASDAQ (GS): ECOL

300 E. Mallard Dr., Ste. 300
Boise, ID 83706
Phone: 208-331-8400
Fax: 208-331-7900
Web: www.americanecology.com

CEO: Stephen A. Romano
CFO: Jeffrey R. (Jeff) Feeler
HR: Betsy Sterk
FYE: December 31
Type: Public

American Ecology and its US Ecology subsidiary help keep a lid on hazardous waste, industrial waste, and low-level radioactive waste. The company handles hazardous and nonhazardous waste at sites in Texas, Nevada, and Idaho, and it operates a low-level radioactive waste facility in Washington state. In 2007 Honeywell International and the US Army Corps of Engineers accounted for 41% and 6% of sales, respectively. Other customers include nuclear plants, steel mills, petrochemical facilities, and academic and medical institutions. American Ecology retains interests in several nonoperating waste disposal facilities.

	Annual Growth	12/03	12/04	12/05	12/06	12/07
Sales ($ mil.)	30.5%	57.0	54.2	79.4	116.8	165.5
Net income ($ mil.)	—	(8.6)	23.4	15.4	15.9	19.4
Market value ($ mil.)	32.3%	139.7	208.4	256.0	336.4	428.4
Employees	5.6%	—	—	214	226	—

An in-depth profile of this company is available to Hoover's Online members at hoovers.com.

117

AMERICAN ELECTRIC POWER COMPANY, INC.

NYSE: AEP

1 Riverside Plaza
Columbus, OH 43215
Phone: 614-716-1000
Fax: 614-716-1823
Web: www.aep.com

CEO: Michael G. (Mike) Morris
CFO: Holly K. Koeppel
HR: Stephen P. Smith
FYE: December 31
Type: Public

American Electric Power (AEP) takes its slice of the US power pie out of Middle America. The holding company is one of the largest power generators and distributors in the US. AEP owns the nation's largest electricity transmission system, a network of almost 39,000 miles. Its electric utilities serve more than 5 million customers in 11 states and have more than 38,000 MW of largely coal-fired generating capacity. AEP is a top wholesale energy company; it markets and trades electricity, natural gas, and other commodities and has stakes in independent power plants. Other operations include natural gas transportation, storage, and processing, and barge transportation services.

	Annual Growth	12/03	12/04	12/05	12/06	12/07
Sales ($ mil.)	(2.1%)	14,545.0	14,057.0	12,111.0	12,622.0	13,380.0
Net income ($ mil.)	77.4%	110.0	1,089.0	814.0	1,002.0	1,089.0
Market value ($ mil.)	11.5%	12,052.0	13,593.8	14,603.0	16,890.4	18,643.9
Employees	3.1%	—	—	19,630	20,442	20,861

AMERICAN ELECTRIC TECHNOLOGIES, INC.

NASDAQ (CM): AETI

6410 Long Dr.
Houston, TX 77087
Phone: 713-644-8182
Fax: 713-644-7805
Web: www.aeti.com

CEO: Arthur G. Dauber
CFO: John H. Untereker
HR: Rachel Acree
FYE: December 31
Type: Public

American Electric Technologies (formerly American Access Technologies) tames wild and woolly wiring. The company makes power-delivery distribution systems that control the flow of electricity, primarily to the oil and gas industry. American Electric is looking to expand to the alternative energy market. The company also makes zone-cabling cabinets that streamline the distribution of telephone lines, data networking, security systems, and other cable and wire. The company merged with M&I Electric Industries in 2007. Its Omega Metals subsidiary fabricates precision sheet metal and provides assembling and packaging for the company.

	Annual Growth	12/03	12/04	12/05	12/06	12/07
Sales ($ mil.)	78.4%	5.5	6.7	8.4	8.4	55.7
Net income ($ mil.)	—	(0.8)	(1.0)	(0.2)	0.0	0.6
Market value ($ mil.)	—	—	—	—	—	30.6
Employees	138.5%	—	—	100	100	569

AMERICAN ENTERPRISE DEVELOPMENT

Pink Sheets: AEND

2544 Tarpley, Ste. 104
Carrollton, TX 75006
Phone: 972-266-0225
Fax: 972-418-8558
Web: www.havocenergy.com

CEO: Carey K. Williams
CFO: –
HR: –
FYE: December 31
Type: Public

American Enterprise Development Corporation (formerly A Time to Grow) is still developing. After a reverse merger with Havoc Distribution, the company has gone from a development-stage company that provided job placement services catering to hospital nurses to one that develops and markets energy drinks. The company has licensing agreements with professional sports teams, including NHL teams (Dallas Stars, St. Louis Blues, and New York Islanders) and NBA teams (Houston Rockets, Sacramento Kings), as well as collegiate sports conferences (including the Atlantic 10, Big South, Big West, and Conference USA). The company has plans to add water and iced tea to its list of products.

	Annual Growth	12/02	12/03	12/04	12/05	*12/06
Sales ($ mil.)	—	—	—	0.5	0.2	0.0
Net income ($ mil.)	—	—	—	0.2	(0.3)	(2.3)
Employees	144.9%	—	—	1	—	6

*Most recent year available

AMERICAN EQUITY INVESTMENT LIFE

NYSE: AEL

5000 Westown Pkwy., Ste. 440
West Des Moines, IA 50266
Phone: 515-221-0002
Fax: 515-221-9947
Web: www.american-equity.com

CEO: David J. (D.J.) Noble
CFO: Wendy L. Carlson
HR: –
FYE: December 31
Type: Public

Seeking to save? American Equity Investment Life Holding Company issues and administers fixed rate and index annuities through subsidiaries American Equity Investment Life Insurance and American Equity Investment Life Insurance Company of New York. Licensed in 50 states and the District of Columbia, the company sells its products through more than 52,000 independent agents and 70 national marketing associations. American Equity Investment Life targets individuals between the ages of 45 to 75. The company also offers a variety of whole, term, and universal life insurance products.

	Annual Growth	12/03	12/04	12/05	12/06	12/07
Assets ($ mil.)	16.2%	8,989.2	11,087.3	14,042.8	14,990.1	16,394.4
Net income ($ mil.)	3.4%	25.4	29.3	43.0	75.5	29.0
Market value ($ mil.)	6.0%	351.9	413.1	724.6	697.1	444.0
Employees	3.7%	—	—	270	280	—

AMERICAN EXPRESS COMPANY

NYSE: AXP

World Financial Center, 200 Vesey St.
New York, NY 10285
Phone: 212-640-2000
Fax: –
Web: www.americanexpress.com

CEO: Kenneth I. (Ken) Chenault
CFO: Daniel T. (Dan) Henry
HR: L. Kevin Cox
FYE: December 31
Type: Public

American Express makes money even if you do leave home without it. The company is one of the world's largest travel agencies, but it is equally well known for its charge cards and revolving credit cards. And yes, the company still issues traveler's checks and publishes such magazines as *Food & Wine* and *Travel & Leisure* through its American Express Publishing unit. Its travel agency operations have more than 2,200 locations worldwide and its Travelers Cheque Group is the world's largest issuer of traveler's checks (it also issues gift cards). But the company's charge and credit cards are its bread and butter; American Express has issued more than 86 million cards worldwide.

	Annual Growth	12/03	12/04	12/05	12/06	12/07
Assets ($ mil.)	(3.8%)	175,001.0	192,638.0	113,960.0	127,853.0	149,830.0
Net income ($ mil.)	7.7%	2,987.0	3,445.0	3,734.0	3,707.0	4,012.0
Market value ($ mil.)	2.4%	54,706.1	62,196.5	63,861.9	72,743.3	60,239.2
Employees	1.4%	—	—	65,800	65,400	67,700

AMERICAN FAMILY INSURANCE GROUP

6000 American Pkwy.
Madison, WI 53783
Phone: 608-249-2111
Fax: 608-243-4921
Web: www.amfam.com

CEO: David R. Anderson
CFO: Daniel R. Schultz
HR: Steven G. Maxwell
FYE: December 31
Type: Mutual company

Even confirmed bachelors can get insured through American Family Insurance. The company specializes in property/casualty insurance, but also offers life, health, and homeowners coverage, as well as investment and retirement-planning products. It is among the largest US mutual companies that concentrates on auto insurance (State Farm is the biggest). American Family Insurance also provides coverage for apartment owners, restaurants, contractors, and other businesses. Through the company's consumer finance division, agents can also offer their customers home equity and personal lines of credit.

	Annual Growth	12/02	12/03	12/04	12/05	12/06
Assets ($ mil.)	9.3%	10,840.2	12,238.6	13,641.2	14,636.6	15,477.0
Net income ($ mil.)	(19.5%)	58.2	155.4	564.4	671.5	24.4
Employees	2.4%	7,500	8,100	8,238	8,135	8,237

AMERICAN FIDELITY ASSURANCE COMPANY

2000 N. Classen Blvd.
Oklahoma City, OK 73106
Phone: 405-523-2000
Fax: 405-523-5421
Web: www.afadvantage.com

CEO: William M. (Bill) Cameron
CFO: Robert Brearton
HR: –
FYE: December 31
Type: Private

American Fidelity Assurance Company provides voluntary supplemental life and health insurance products and related services to nearly 1.5 million customers across the US and in 20 countries. The company's insurance plans include cancer, disability, life, long term care, and hospitalization insurance. The company also provides tax deferred annuity and flexible spending programs. American Fidelity Assurance Company targets primary and secondary education employees and trade association members. Products and services are sold via worksite marketing by the company's salaried sales force and a network of insurance brokers. The company is a subsidiary of family-owned American Fidelity Corporation.

	Annual Growth	12/03	12/04	12/05	12/06	12/07
Est. sales ($ mil.)	—	—	—	—	—	360.6
Employees	—	—	—	—	—	1,250

[H] AMERICAN FINANCIAL GROUP, INC.

NYSE: AFG

1 E. 4th St.
Cincinnati, OH 45202
Phone: 513-579-2121
Fax: 513-579-2113
Web: www.amfnl.com

CEO: S. Craig Lindner
CFO: Keith A. Jensen
HR: Scott H. Beeken
FYE: December 31
Type: Public

American Financial Group (AFG) insures American businesses in pursuit of the great American Dream. Through the Great American Insurance Group of companies and its flagship Great American Insurance Company, AFG offers commercial property/casualty insurance focused on specialties such as workers' compensation, professional liability, ocean and inland marine, and multiperil crop insurance. The company also provides surety coverage for contractors and risk management services. For individuals and employers AFG provides supplemental medical insurance products, and a wide range of annuities sold through its Great American Financial Resources (GAFRI) subsidiary. Chairman Carl Lindner and his sons own 30% of AFG.

	Annual Growth	12/03	12/04	12/05	12/06	12/07
Assets ($ mil.)	6.3%	20,197.3	22,559.5	22,816.0	25,101.1	25,807.5
Net income ($ mil.)	6.9%	293.8	359.9	206.6	453.4	383.2
Market value ($ mil.)	26.3%	1,288.7	1,599.6	1,993.8	4,284.2	3,277.9
Employees	(71.4%)	—	—	6,100	5,200	500

AMERICAN FOODS GROUP, LLC

2209 Jefferson St., Ste. 301
Alexandria, MN 56308
Phone: 320-759-5900
Fax: 320-159-5910
Web: www.americanfoodsgroup.com

CEO: Carl W. Kuehne
CFO: Robert Hovde
HR: Trudy Kamps
FYE: June 30
Type: Private

American Foods Group is a bona fide Green Bay packer. It slaughters cattle and produces branded and private-label beef products for the grocery and foodservice industries. Products include fresh, frozen, and cooked meats, such as ground beef, bacon, beef cuts, deli meats, and sausage. The company also has a pet treat business, Performance Pet Products. Co-CEO Carl Kuehne purchased American Foods in 1985 and grew it through acquisitions and product development. In 2005 American Foods merged with meat processor Rosen's Diversified. Rosen's agricultural chemical and fertilizer businesses were not included in the transaction. The company's meat products are available throughout the US, as well as overseas.

AMERICAN FURNITURE COMPANY

3535 Menaul Blvd. NE
Albuquerque, NM 87107
Phone: 505-883-2211
Fax: 505-883-2310
Web: www.americanhome.com

CEO: Kenton Van Harten
CFO: Scott McIntosh
HR: –
FYE: Last Saturday in January
Type: Private

Bring the look of the Southwest into your home. American Furniture Company operates about a dozen furniture and housewares stores in Arizona and New Mexico under the names American Home, American Home Design Store, and American Warehouse Plus. Its products include mid-priced to upscale home furnishings (Kemp, Hillcraft, Natuzzi, DeCoro), lamps, bedding (Sealy, Simmons, Tempur-Pedic), rugs, dinnerware, related accessories, and gift registry and interior design services. The company expanded in Arizona with new stores in Mesa and Sahuarita in 2006.

	Annual Growth	1/03	1/04	1/05	1/06	1/07
Est. sales ($ mil.)	—	—	—	—	—	119.5
Employees	—	—	—	—	—	1,200

AMERICAN FURNITURE MANUFACTURING, INC.

604 Pontotoc County Industrial Park Rd.
Ecru, MS 38841
Phone: 662-489-2633
Fax: 662-488-9558
Web: www.americanscans.com

CEO: Michael (Mike) Thomas
CFO: Blair Taylor
HR: –
FYE: December 31
Type: Private

American Furniture Manufacturing makes upholstered home furnishings including sofas, chairs, and recliners. The company distributes products to most major furniture stores in the US and Canada. One of its most popular products is its sofa priced under $300. American Furniture Manufacturing operates by having stock on hand and can ship most furniture within 48 hours. The company sources some fabrics from China, which has also helped to keep down costs. In 2004 an investor group led by Hampshire Equity Partners and Hunt Private Equity Group, and including the company's senior management, purchased American Furniture Manufacturing.

	Annual Growth	12/03	12/04	12/05	12/06	12/07
Est. sales ($ mil.)	—	—	—	—	—	42.7
Employees	—	—	—	—	—	800

AMERICAN FURNITURE WAREHOUSE CO., INC.

8820 American Way
Englewood, CO 80112
Phone: 303-799-9044
Fax: 720-873-8600
Web: www.afwonline.com

CEO: Jacob (Jake) Jabs
CFO: Bob Schwartz
HR: Crystal Hayes
FYE: March 31
Type: Private

Tony the Tiger hawking home furnishings might give some marketers pause, but the combination seems to work for American Furniture Warehouse. The company sells furniture at discounted prices throughout the state of Colorado through a dozen retail locations and its Web site, which also features a bridal registry for its customers. American Furniture's television commercials often feature white-haired president and CEO Jake Jabs (who has become a well known television personality in the state, as well as in the home furnishings industry) accompanied by baby exotic animals, mostly tigers. Jabs bought the struggling company in 1975.

	Annual Growth	3/03	3/04	3/05	3/06	3/07
Est. sales ($ mil.)	—	—	—	—	—	339.4
Employees	—	—	—	—	—	1,900

[H] An in-depth profile of this company is available to Hoover's Online members at hoovers.com.

AMERICAN GENERAL FINANCE CORPORATION

601 NW 2nd St.
Evansville, IN 47708
Phone: 812-424-8031
Fax: 812-468-5560
Web: www.agfinance.com

CEO: Frederick W. (Rick) Geissinger
CFO: Donald R. (Don) Breivogel Jr.
HR: –
FYE: December 31
Type: Subsidiary

American General Finance is a slice of a much bigger American pie. A subsidiary of insurance giant American International Group (AIG), the consumer finance company originates and services first and second mortgages and loans for automobiles and other consumer goods. Two units, Wilmington Finance and MorEquity, originate non-conforming residential real estate loans for sale into the secondary market. In the UK, subsidiary Ocean Finance and Mortgages (acquired in 2007) offers home owner loans, mortgages, refis, and consumer loans. American General also provides credit life, credit-related property/casualty, and other insurance products through its Merit Life Insurance and Yosemite Insurance subsidiaries.

	Annual Growth	12/02	12/03	12/04	12/05	12/06
Sales ($ mil.)	9.9%	1,981.0	2,162.4	2,420.5	2,898.5	2,890.8
Employees	6.4%	7,400	8,400	8,900	—	9,500

AMERICAN GIRL BRANDS, LLC

8400 Fairway Place
Middleton, WI 53562
Phone: 608-836-4848
Fax: 608-836-1999
Web: www.americangirl.com

CEO: Ellen L. Brothers
CFO: Tony Simms
HR: Ray Greger
FYE: December 31
Type: Subsidiary

Pleasant Rowland introduced American Girl dolls in 1986 as a historically themed alternative to Barbie and the Cabbage Patch Kids. Since 1998 her firm has been owned by the maker of both rival dolls, #1 toy maker Mattel. American Girl (formerly Pleasant Company) makes the American Girls Collection of 18-inch, high-dollar dolls, including Kirsten (the plucky pioneer) and Molly (WWII-era). It also publishes *American Girl* magazine and American Girl books (more than 110 million copies sold) and sells room décor, clothing, and accessories, including items that match the dolls. Items are sold through catalogs, its Web site, at American Girl Place stores, and an outlet store in Wisconsin.

AMERICAN GOLF CORPORATION

2951 28th St.
Santa Monica, CA 90405
Phone: 310-664-4000
Fax: 310-664-4386
Web: www.americangolf.com

CEO: Tom Ferguson
CFO: Mike Moecker
HR: Joe Stegman
FYE: December 31
Type: Private

In the golf business, it's important to stay out of the rough. American Golf Corporation (AGC) is one of the largest golf course management firms in the world with more than 120 public, private, and resort properties in more than 25 states. Its portfolio of courses includes such country clubs as The Golf Course at Mansion Ridge (Monroe, New York), Oakhurst Country Club (Clayton, California), and Palm Valley Country Club (Palm Desert, California). AGC also runs the American Golf Foundation, which helps promote the game through charity and education. It is owned by investment firms Goldman Sachs and Starwood Capital.

	Annual Growth	12/03	12/04	12/05	12/06	12/07
Est. sales ($ mil.)	—	—	—	—	—	266.7
Employees	—	—	—	—	—	10,000

AMERICAN GREETINGS CORPORATION

NYSE: AM

1 American Rd.
Cleveland, OH 44144
Phone: 216-252-7300
Fax: 216-252-6778
Web: corporate.americangreetings.com

CEO: Zev Weiss
CFO: Stephen J. Smith
HR: Brian T. McGrath
FYE: Last day in February
Type: Public

American Greetings has been building its sturdy house of cards for more than a century. The #2 US maker of greeting cards (behind Hallmark), the company makes American Greetings, Carlton Cards, and Gibson Greetings brand missives. While greeting cards make up more than 60% of sales, the company also produces DesignWare party goods, Plus Mark gift wrap, and DateWorks calendars. The company operates more than 400 retail outlets under the Carlton banner in North America, while its AG Interactive subsidiary distributes online greeting cards and other interactive media. American Greetings' products are sold in 125,000 retail stores worldwide. The family of chairman Morry Weiss controls more than 45% of the company.

	Annual Growth	2/04	2/05	2/06	2/07	2/08
Sales ($ mil.)	(3.0%)	2,008.9	1,902.7	1,885.7	1,744.6	1,776.4
Net income ($ mil.)	(5.6%)	104.7	95.3	84.4	42.4	83.0
Market value ($ mil.)	(12.0%)	1,425.5	1,597.7	1,177.6	1,188.6	853.0
Employees	(68.1%)	—	—	29,500	9,400	—

AMERICAN HEART ASSOCIATION, INC.

7272 Greenville Ave.
Dallas, TX 75231
Phone: 214-373-6300
Fax: 214-706-1191
Web: www.americanheart.org

CEO: M. Cass Wheeler
CFO: Sunder Joshi
HR: –
FYE: June 30
Type: Not-for-profit

The American Heart Association (AHA) is a nonprofit organization devoted to the fight against heart disease and stroke (the nation's #1 and #3 killers, respectively), and other cardiovascular illnesses. In addition to conducting research, it serves as a clearinghouse for information on heart-related diseases and conditions and acts as an advocate on public policy issues related to its mission. The organization has affiliate offices throughout the US and in Puerto Rico. The AHA was founded in 1924 by six cardiologists, who recognized the need to widely share their heart disease education and research.

AMERICAN HOME FOOD PRODUCTS, INC.

OTC: AHFP

500 W. 37th St.
New York, NY 10018
Phone: 212-239-1200
Fax: –

CEO: Daniel W. Dowe
CFO: –
HR: –
FYE: May 31
Type: Public

American Home Food Products aspires to be the big cheese. The company, a building supply marketing firm, is considering operations in the a private-label food manufacturing sector. In 2007 it acquired specialty food company Artisanal Premium Cheese for about $4.5 million. At the same time the company sold its building material assets for approximately $1 million. While it continues to explore the private-label food manufacturing options, the company's revenues are generated through the marketing of building materials. Artisinal Premium Cheese markets and sells specialty and handmade cheeses and other food products to upscale restaurants and retailers.

	Annual Growth	5/03	5/04	5/05	5/06	5/07
Sales ($ mil.)	(26.0%)	1.0	0.2	0.2	0.2	0.3
Net income ($ mil.)	—	(1.6)	0.2	(0.4)	(0.3)	(0.4)
Market value ($ mil.)	3.1%	2.6	2.7	—	—	—
Employees	—	—	—	—	—	—

AMERICAN HOME SHIELD CORPORATION

889 Ridgelake Blvd.	CEO: J. Patrick (Pat) Spainhour
Memphis, TN 38120	CFO: –
Phone: 901-537-8000	HR: –
Fax: –	FYE: December 31
Web: www.americanhomeshield.com	Type: Subsidiary

Protecting you against those pesky domestic disasters, American Home Shield (AHS), a subsidiary of The ServiceMaster Company, provides homeowners with home warranty plans. These cover home repairs; the replacement of electrical, plumbing, and heating and cooling systems; and the breakdown of major home appliances. It administers more than 1.2 million contracts in 49 states and the District of Columbia; AHS serves clients from four call centers across the nation. The company also performs home inspections throughout the US and Canada under the AmeriSpec name via some 350 locations (almost all of which are franchises).

	Annual Growth	12/02	12/03	12/04	12/05	12/06
Sales ($ mil.)	—	—	—	—	—	528.7
Employees	—	—	—	—	—	—

[H] AMERICAN HOMEPATIENT, INC.

OTC: AHOM

5200 Maryland Way, Ste. 400	CEO: Joseph F. Furlong III
Brentwood, TN 37027	CFO: Stephen L. Clanton
Phone: 615-221-8884	HR: Sandy Irvin
Fax: 615-373-9932	FYE: December 31
Web: www.ahom.com	Type: Public

American HomePatient is making sure no one is home alone when it comes to health care. American HomePatient provides home health services from about 250 locations in more than 30 states. The company provides respiratory therapy and equipment, including oxygen therapy and nebulizers. It also offers home infusion therapy services, including parenteral and enteral feeding and the intravenous administration of pain drugs and antibiotics. Additionally, American HomePatient rents and sells durable hospital equipment, including beds, wheelchairs, and other aids. Though the company operates mainly through its wholly owned locations, it provides home care in a few areas through joint ventures with hospitals.

	Annual Growth	12/03	12/04	12/05	12/06	12/07
Sales ($ mil.)	(3.4%)	336.2	335.8	328.4	328.1	293.0
Net income ($ mil.)	—	14.0	13.2	7.7	(2.6)	(5.5)
Market value ($ mil.)	(2.6%)	20.5	61.7	57.5	24.6	18.5
Employees	0.4%	—	—	—	2,576	2,586

[H] AMERICAN HOMESTAR CORPORATION

Pink Sheets: AHMS

2450 South Shore Blvd., Ste. 300	CEO: Finis F. (Buck) Teeter
League City, TX 77573	CFO: Craig A. Reynolds
Phone: 281-334-9700	HR: –
Fax: 281-334-9737	FYE: Friday nearest June 30
Web: www.americanhomestar.com	Type: Public

Stormy weather in the manufactured housing market hasn't snowed American Homestar. Out of bankruptcy and reorganized, it produces factory-built, modular and multi-section and single-section manufactured homes that sell for about half the price of comparable site-built homes. Its modular homes range from 1,200 to 2,600 sq. ft; its multi-section homes can have as many as six bedrooms. The company sells its homes through company-owned retail centers in Louisiana, Oklahoma, and Texas; independent dealers; and through sales centers in manufactured housing communities. Other operations include insurance and mortgage services.

	Annual Growth	6/03	6/04	6/05	6/06	6/07
Sales ($ mil.)	2.3%	92.1	72.4	79.4	116.7	100.8
Net income ($ mil.)	—	(2.2)	(1.1)	(2.0)	10.4	1.2
Employees	1.0%	672	568	637	675	700

AMERICAN HONDA MOTOR CO., INC.

1919 Torrance Blvd.	CEO: Tetsuo Iwamura
Torrance, CA 90501	CFO: Kohei Takeuchi
Phone: 310-783-2000	HR: Gary Kessler
Fax: 310-783-2110	FYE: March 31
Web: www.honda.com	Type: Subsidiary

Its cars might not be as American as apple pie, but American Honda Motor Co. keeps the US appetite for Hondas sated. A subsidiary of Honda Motor Co., Ltd. (Japan), American Honda makes Accord, Civic, and Acura cars, and Gold Wing, Shadow, and Valkyrie motorcycles. American Honda's best-selling cars include the Odyssey minivan and the CR-V sport utility vehicle (SUV). American Honda has also rolled out hybrid versions of its Accord and Civic sedans. The company, started in 1959 as a small motorcycle store in Los Angeles, has grown to include car, motorcycle, and lawnmower manufacturing plants that export throughout the Americas.

AMERICAN HOSPITAL ASSOCIATION

1 N. Franklin	CEO: Richard J. (Rich) Umbdenstock
Chicago, IL 60606	CFO: –
Phone: 312-422-3000	HR: –
Fax: 312-422-4796	FYE: December 31
Web: www.aha.org	Type: Not-for-profit

American Hospital Association (AHA) represents 5,000 hospitals and other care providers and 37,000 individuals from various health care fields. The AHA acts as an advocate in national health care policy development and provides services to its members, such as helping hospitals and other health care providers form networks for patient care, conducting research and development projects on the structuring and delivery of health care services, and producing educational programs and publications. The AHA Resource Center maintains an extensive collection of books and documents relating to hospitals and health care. AHA was founded in 1898.

	Annual Growth	12/03	12/04	12/05	12/06	12/07
Est. sales ($ mil.)	—	—	—	—	—	31.0
Employees	—	—	—	—	—	450

AMERICAN HOTEL REGISTER COMPANY

100 S. Milwaukee Ave.	CEO: James F. (Jim) Leahy
Vernon Hills, IL 60061	CFO: Bob Schmidt
Phone: 847-564-4000	HR: Julie Baker
Fax: 847-743-2098	FYE: December 31
Web: www.americanhotel.com	Type: Private

Intrigued by embossed soaps and other sundries enjoyed during your hotel visits? Thank American Hotel Register. The company supplies hotels of all sizes with more than 50,000 products, including toiletries, cleaning products, furniture, carpeting, drapery, linens, and embossed items. It also caters to funeral homes, health care facilities, government offices, and military institutions. American Hotel Register sells its products through its 2,000-page catalog and its Web site. The company was founded in 1865 to sell hotel guest registers. It was acquired by Thomas Leahy in the early 1900s and his descendants still own and operate the company.

[H] An in-depth profile of this company is available to Hoover's Online members at hoovers.com.

121

AMERICAN INDEPENDENCE CORP.

NASDAQ (GM): AMIC

485 Madison Ave.	CEO: Roy T. K. Thung
New York, NY 10022	CFO: Teresa A. Herbert
Phone: 212-355-4141	HR: –
Fax: 212-644-7450	FYE: December 31
Web: www.americanindependencecorp.com	Type: Public

Since the name American Independence tells you nothing about the company, we'll help you out. What sounds like a lone, bold ideal, is really a holding company which, through its subsidiaries, provides reinsurance, specializing in medical stop-loss insurance for self-insured employers. It also offers group and individual health and short-term medical insurance. Subsidiary Independence American is licensed to provide property/casualty insurance in more than 40 states and Washington, DC. Independence Holding, which also owns Madison National Life Insurance and Standard Security Life Insurance, owns nearly half of American Independence.

	Annual Growth	12/03	12/04	12/05	12/06	12/07
Assets ($ mil.)	6.8%	112.1	124.4	129.7	134.8	146.1
Net income ($ mil.)	(45.8%)	12.7	5.9	5.5	1.5	1.1
Market value ($ mil.)	(6.2%)	99.5	123.3	97.1	91.3	77.0
Employees	(17.0%)	—	—	77	—	53

AMERICAN INFRASTRUCTURE, INC.

1805 Berks Rd.	CEO: A. Ross Myers
Worcester, PA 19490	CFO: William Murdock III
Phone: 610-222-8800	HR: –
Fax: 610-222-4810	FYE: December 31
Web: www.americaninfrastructure.com	Type: Private

Like any good parent, American Infrastructure provides balance and structure. Through subsidiaries Allan A. Myers and American Infrastructure-Virginia (formerly R.G. Griffith), the firm provides heavy civil construction services for projects in the Mid-Atlantic. It builds and reconstructs federal highways, water treatment plants, medical facilities, and shopping centers, and offers site development for homebuilders. Its Independence Construction Materials subsidiary supplies aggregates, asphalt, and ready-mixed concrete to its construction companies. American Infrastructure consistently ranks in the top half of *Engineering News-Record* magazine's annual Top 400 US Contractors.

	Annual Growth	12/03	12/04	12/05	12/06	12/07
Est. sales ($ mil.)	—	—	—	—	—	234.9
Employees	—	—	—	—	—	2,045

AMERICAN INSTITUTES FOR RESEARCH

1000 Thomas Jefferson St., NW	CEO: Sol H. Pelavin
Washington, DC 20007	CFO: Robert M. Bussjaeger
Phone: 202-403-5000	HR: Mark S. Fanning
Fax: 202-403-5001	FYE: September 30
Web: www.air.org	Type: Not-for-profit

The American Institutes for Research (AIR) lives and breathes to enhance human performance. The not-for-profit organization conducts behavorial and social science research on topics related to education, health research and communication, individual and organizational performance, and usability. Clients, including several federal agencies, use AIR's research to help develop policies. The organization has an ongoing major initiative to provide tools to improve education both in the US and internationally, particularly in disadvantaged areas. John Flanagan, who developed the Critical Incident Technique personnel-selection tool to identify human success indicators in the workplace, founded the company in 1946.

	Annual Growth	9/03	9/04	9/05	9/06	9/07
Est. sales ($ mil.)	—	—	—	—	—	228.8
Employees	—	—	—	—	—	1,175

AMERICAN INTERNATIONAL GROUP, INC.

NYSE: AIG

70 Pine St.	CEO: Robert B. (Bob) Willumstad
New York, NY 10270	CFO: Steve Bensinger
Phone: 212-770-7000	HR: Andrew J. Kaslow
Fax: 212-509-9705	FYE: December 31
Web: www.aigcorporate.com	Type: Public

American International Group (AIG) is one of the world's largest insurance firms. Domestically the company is known as a leading provider of property/casualty, life, and specialty insurance to commercial, institutional, and individual customers. Internationally, AIG provides reinsurance, life insurance and retirement services, asset management, and financial services (including financing commercial aircraft leasing) in more than 130 countries. Acquisitions have brought in leading annuities firm AIG Retirement Services, life insurer AIG American General, and other companies specializing in retail financial markets.

	Annual Growth	12/03	12/04	12/05	12/06	12/07
Assets ($ mil.)	11.8%	678,346.0	801,145.0	853,370.0	979,414.0	1,060,505.0
Net income ($ mil.)	(9.6%)	9,274.0	9,839.0	10,477.0	14,048.0	6,200.0
Market value ($ mil.)	(3.9%)	172,887.9	170,507.1	177,169.2	186,401.7	147,474.7
Employees	9.4%	—	—	97,000	106,000	116,000

AMERICAN INTERNATIONAL INDUSTRIES, INC.

OTC: AMIN

601 Cien St., Ste. 235	CEO: Daniel Dror
Kemah, TX 77565	CFO: Sherry Couturier
Phone: 281-334-9479	HR: –
Fax: 281-334-9508	FYE: December 31
Web: www.americanii.com	Type: Public

Nothing says "Texas" like oil and real estate. American International Industries covers those bases — and more — from its home in the Houston metro area. The company typically takes a controlling interest in undervalued companies; it holds investments in oil wells, real estate, and various industrial manufacturers. American International Industries holds a majority stake in well servicing contractor Delta Seaboard Well Service. It also owns 48% of Hammonds Industries, which owns Hammonds Technical Services, Hammonds Fuel Additives, and Hammonds Water Treatment Systems. Its Northeastern Plastics subsidiary makes automotive after-market products.

	Annual Growth	12/03	12/04	12/05	12/06	12/07
Sales ($ mil.)	45.0%	7.9	16.7	25.5	33.4	34.9
Net income ($ mil.)	—	(0.9)	1.0	(4.5)	1.6	(1.8)
Market value ($ mil.)	22.7%	—	—	17.7	18.4	26.7
Employees	(6.0%)	—	—	—	50	47

AMERICAN ITALIAN PASTA COMPANY

Pink Sheets: AITP

4100 N. Mulberry Dr., Ste. 200	CEO: Jack Kelly
Kansas City, MO 64116	CFO: Paul R. Geist
Phone: 816-584-5000	HR: Robert W. (Bob) Schuller
Fax: 816-584-5100	FYE: Friday nearest September 30
Web: www.aipc.com	Type: Public

American Italian Pasta Company (AIPC) uses its noodle in many different ways. The company is the largest maker of dry pasta in North America, offering some 200 different pasta shapes, everything from angel hair to ziti. Its consumer brands, such as Mueller's, Golden Grain, Heartland, R&R, and Mrs. Grass, are staples on supermarket shelves throughout the US, as well as overseas. The Kansas City Missouri company's private-label and ingredient customers include most major US grocers and club stores, as well as foodservice operators and food processors.

	Annual Growth	9/03	9/04	9/05	9/06	9/07
Sales ($ mil.)	(2.4%)	438.8	417.4	364.2	367.0	398.1
Net income ($ mil.)	(40.6%)	42.6	3.0	(100.3)	(30.4)	5.3
Employees	—	—	—	—	—	—

An in-depth profile of this company is available to Hoover's Online members at hoovers.com.

THE AMERICAN KENNEL CLUB, INCORPORATED

260 Madison Ave.	CEO: Dennis B. Sprung
New York, NY 10016	CFO: James T. Stevens
Phone: 212-696-8200	HR: James T. Stevens
Fax: 212-696-8217	FYE: December 31
Web: www.akc.org	Type: Not-for-profit

Dog lovers unite! The American Kennel Club (AKC) maintains a registry of purebred canines from more than 150 breeds. In addition, the group stages dog shows and publishes magazines (*AKC Gazette, AKC Family Dog*) on dog ownership. It sponsors the Canine Health Foundation, Companion Animal Recovery (microchip-implanted dog recovery), the Museum of the Dog, and a pet insurance program. The AKC's Compliance division inspects dog kennels and breeders to ensure the animals receive proper care. More than 590 member clubs make up the AKC, which recognizes another 4,100-plus clubs. The organization was founded in 1884 by a group of men who ran sporting dog clubs.

	Annual Growth	12/03	12/04	12/05	12/06	12/07
Est. sales ($ mil.)	—	—	—	—	—	72.7
Employees	—	—	—	—	—	450

AMERICAN LAFRANCE, LLC

8500 Palmetto Commerce Pkwy.	CEO: A. Matthew Karmel
Ladson, SC 29456	CFO: Ronald P. Stewart
Phone: 843-486-7400	HR: –
Fax: 843-486-7417	FYE: December 31
Web: www.americanlafrance.com	Type: Private

The flashing lights in your rear-view mirror just might be an American LaFrance product. The company manufactures a variety of emergency vehicle equipment, including fire trucks, tankers, ambulances, aerial ladders, fire pumps, and fire rescue boats. It serves markets in the US and Canada through six regional sales offices. Once a subsidiary of DaimlerChrysler's Freightliner (now Daimler Trucks North America), DaimlerChrysler sold American LaFrance to private equity firm Patriarch Partners for an undisclosed sum late in 2005. Citing inventory problems and a lackluster market for emergency vehicles, the company filed for Chapter 11 bankruptcy protection in January 2008 and exited the following May.

	Annual Growth	12/03	12/04	12/05	12/06	12/07
Est. sales ($ mil.)	—	—	—	—	—	166.6
Employees	—	—	—	—	—	1,200

AMERICAN LAND LEASE, INC.   NYSE: ANL

29399 US Hwy. 19 North, Ste. 320	CEO: Terry Considine
Clearwater, FL 33761	CFO: Shannon E. Smith
Phone: 727-726-8868	HR: Jerry Deese
Fax: 727-725-4391	FYE: December 31
Web: www.americanlandlease.com	Type: Public

American Land Lease wants to make the American Dream an American Reality, especially during the golden years. A self-managed real estate investment trust (REIT), American Land Lease owns, develops, renovates, and manages manufactured housing communities. It owns about 30 communities in Alabama, Arizona, and Florida; properties include some 11,000 leased, developed, and undeveloped homesites and RV parks. In light of growing senior demographics, American Land Lease operates its properties primarily as retirement communities. The REIT's communities often feature swimming pools, golf courses, and clubhouses. Through a subsidiary, American Land Lease also sells manufactured homes.

	Annual Growth	12/03	12/04	12/05	12/06	12/07
Sales ($ mil.)	0.4%	65.2	70.2	84.0	83.9	66.2
Net income ($ mil.)	13.1%	8.8	8.7	11.9	11.7	14.4
Market value ($ mil.)	1.4%	141.7	165.8	180.6	203.2	149.8
Employees	—	—	—	204	—	—

AMERICAN LAWYER MEDIA HOLDINGS, INC.

345 Park Ave. South	CEO: William L. (Bill) Pollak
New York, NY 10010	CFO: Eric F. Lundberg
Phone: 212-779-9200	HR: –
Fax: 212-696-4514	FYE: December 31
Web: www.americanlawyermedia.com	Type: Subsidiary

American Lawyer Media (ALM) pleads guilty to committing legal journalism. Publisher of more than 30 national and regional legal magazines (*The American Lawyer*) and newspapers (*New York Law Journal, The National Law Journal*) and more than 120 legal books, ALM scours the legal landscape to keep attorneys abreast of events in the world of law. The firm also publishes newsletters, offers research services through its ALM Research unit, and hosts legal seminars, conferences, and trade shows. It additionally operates Law.com, a site devoted to legal issues. The company is a subsidiary of UK-based business information provider Incisive Media.

	Annual Growth	12/03	12/04	12/05	12/06	12/07
Est. sales ($ mil.)	—	—	—	—	—	167.1
Employees	—	—	—	—	—	777

AMERICAN LEATHER

4501 Mountain Creek Pkwy.	CEO: Bob Duncan
Dallas, TX 75236	CFO: Bruce Weinberg
Phone: 972-296-9599	HR: –
Fax: 972-296-8859	FYE: December 31
Web: www.americanleather.com	Type: Private

It may not be as American as apple pie, but American Leather hopes to make itself into a household name. The company, a manufacturer of custom-made leather furniture, offers furnishing pieces such as sofas, loveseats, sectionals, chairs, sleepers, beds, and ottomans in more than a dozen styles (including traditional, transitional, and contemporary) and more than 70 colors. American Leather sells its products through independent retailers located throughout the US and has showrooms in Dallas; High Point, North Carolina; and San Francisco. It also makes exclusive styles for Crate & Barrel, Design Within Reach, and Room & Board.

	Annual Growth	12/03	12/04	12/05	12/06	12/07
Est. sales ($ mil.)	—	—	—	—	—	71.0
Employees	—	—	—	—	—	353

AMERICAN LEISURE HOLDINGS, INC.   OTC: AMLH

2460 Sand Lake Rd.	CEO: Malcolm J. Wright
Orlando, FL 32809	CFO: Omar Jimenez
Phone: 407-251-2240	HR: –
Fax: 407-251-8455	FYE: December 31
Web: www.americanleisureholdings.com	Type: Public

American Leisure Holdings (AMLH) runs the gamut in the travel and leisure industry through its travel, resort development, and communications divisions. Across its nearly 40 subsidiaries, AMLH offers travel services while also developing, constructing, and operating vacation homes and resorts. The strategy allows it to market memberships in its vacation properties to affinity clubs while also renting those properties out to guests looking for a vacation stay, generating two major streams of income. The company operates in the US (primarily in Florida) and the Caribbean. Roger Maddock, former head of an acquired company, and president and CEO Malcolm Wright each own about 50% of its voting rights.

	Annual Growth	12/02	12/03	12/04	12/05	*12/06
Sales ($ mil.)	—	0.0	3.3	6.4	38.6	38.9
Net income ($ mil.)	—	(0.6)	(2.1)	(6.6)	(4.1)	(8.1)
Employees	57.9%	—	75	—	—	295
					*Most recent year available	

AMERICAN LICORICE CO. INC.

595 SW Bluff Dr., Ste. B
Bend, OR 97702
Phone: 541-617-0800
Fax: 541-617-0224
Web: www.americanlicorice.com

CEO: John Kretchmer
CFO: Kate Dunning
HR: Susan (Sue) Jones
FYE: October 31
Type: Private

American Licorice makes candy concoctions using one of America's favorite flavorings — licorice. The company manufactures licorice twists, pieces, and ropes in various flavors (including original red, original black, strawberry, and cherry). It also makes sour hard candies. American's brand names include RedVines, Snaps, Super Ropes, Sour Punch, and Twisty Punch. The company's products can be purchased at retail food outlets, grocery chains, club stores, and specialty venues throughout the US as well as online through its CandyCabinet.com division.

	Annual Growth	10/03	10/04	10/05	10/06	10/07
Est. sales ($ mil.)	—	—	—	—	—	86.6
Employees	—	—	—	—	—	950

AMERICAN LOCKER GROUP INCORPORATED

Pink Sheets: ALGI

815 S. Main St.
Grapevine, TX 76051
Phone: 817-329-1600
Fax: 817-329-1600
Web: www.americanlocker.com

CEO: Allen E. Tilley
CFO: Paul M. Zaidins
HR: Patricia Calanni
FYE: December 31
Type: Public

American Locker Group can no longer count on the check being in the mail. The company, which had pinned its hopes on the plastic clusters of mailboxes it sold to the United States Postal Service (USPS) for use in housing developments and apartment complexes, lost its contract in early 2005 and is still feeling the effects. American Locker also sells and rents coin-, key-, and electronically controlled lockers used by the recreation and transportation industries, as well as by bookstores and libraries. It also makes a coin- and credit card-operated baggage cart system for use in airports. The firm, founded in 1958, has assembly and maintenance operations in the US and Canada.

	Annual Growth	12/03	12/04	12/05	12/06	12/07
Sales ($ mil.)	(15.3%)	39.3	49.0	32.3	25.1	20.2
Net income ($ mil.)	—	2.2	2.7	(8.1)	0.6	(1.9)
Employees	(4.9%)	154	149	132	147	126

AMERICAN LUNG ASSOCIATION

61 Broadway, 6th Fl.
New York, NY 10006
Phone: 212-315-8700
Fax: 212-315-8870
Web: www.lungusa.org

CEO: Bernadette A. Toomey
CFO: Kim Schwartz
HR: Susan Cutter
FYE: June 30
Type: Not-for-profit

Many Americans breathe easier because of the American Lung Association. Dedicated to the prevention and cure of lung disease, the group focuses on asthma management, air quality, and tobacco control. It funds research, develops public education materials, sponsors conferences, and lobbies for legislation. It operates through a network of about 200 local offices throughout the US and in Puerto Rico and the US Virgin Islands. Most of the American Lung Association's support comes in response to direct-mail solicitations, including the annual Christmas Seals drive. It also receives grants from companies, foundations, and government agencies. The group was founded in 1904 to fight tuberculosis.

	Annual Growth	6/03	6/04	6/05	6/06	6/07
Est. sales ($ mil.)	—	—	—	—	—	50.3
Employees	—	—	—	—	—	500

AMERICAN MANAGEMENT ASSOCIATION

1601 Broadway
New York, NY 10019
Phone: 212-586-8100
Fax: 212-903-8168
Web: www.amanet.org

CEO: Edward T. Reilly
CFO: Vivianna Guzman
HR: Manny Avramidis
FYE: December 31
Type: Not-for-profit

If you need a little bit of assistance managing your association, you might consider giving American Management Association a call. American Management Association (AMA) provides a variety of educational and management development services to businesses, government agencies, and individuals. The not-for-profit membership organization offers business courses in areas such as communication, leadership, sales and marketing, human resources, and finance and accounting. AMA was founded in 1913 as the National Association of Corporation Schools; it became the American Management Association in 1923.

	Annual Growth	12/03	12/04	12/05	12/06	12/07
Est. sales ($ mil.)	—	—	—	—	—	23.6
Employees	—	—	—	—	—	700

AMERICAN MANAGEMENT SERVICES COMPANY LLC

Pier 70, 2801 Alaskan Way, Ste. 200
Seattle, WA 98121
Phone: 206-215-9700
Fax: 206-215-9777
Web: www.pinnaclerealty.com

CEO: Stan Harrelson
CFO: –
HR: –
FYE: December 31
Type: Private

With some help from American Management Services (operating as Pinnacle), real estate investors ensure their assets are in top form. Pinnacle provides property management and brokerage services for clients, which include financial institutions, foreign investors, government housing agencies, pension funds, and private partnerships. Its portfolio of properties — worth more than $12 billion — spans 260 cities across the US, as well as Asia and Canada. Its assets under management include about 140,000 apartment units and nearly 20 million sq. ft. of industrial, retail, and office space. Pinnacle also offers such services as customized financial reporting, risk management, recruitment, and technology planning.

	Annual Growth	12/03	12/04	12/05	12/06	12/07
Est. sales ($ mil.)	—	—	—	—	—	48.8
Employees	—	—	—	—	—	2,400

⊞ AMERICAN MEDIA, INC.

1000 American Media Way
Boca Raton, FL 33431
Phone: 561-997-7733
Fax: –
Web: www.americanmediainc.com

CEO: David J. Pecker
CFO: Dean D. Durbin
HR: Ken Slivken
FYE: March 31
Type: Private

If you've sighted Elvis or Bigfoot recently, or better yet Paris Hilton, you might want to contact one of these papers. American Media is the nation's top publisher of tabloid newspapers and magazines, including *National Enquirer* and *Star*. It also publishes women's health magazine *Shape*, as well as a number of other magazines such as *Flex*, *Men's Fitness*, and *Natural Health*. In addition to publishing, American Media offers distribution services to other publishers to get their periodicals in the racks at supermarkets throughout the US and Canada. American Media is owned by EMP Group LLC, a holding company controlled by private equity firms Evercore Partners and Thomas H. Lee.

	Annual Growth	3/02	3/03	3/04	3/05	3/06
Sales ($ mil.)	7.8%	368.1	399.7	515.7	536.6	496.2
Employees	(9.5%)	2,122	2,316	2,363	2,181	1,421

AMERICAN MEDICAL ALERT CORP.

NASDAQ (CM): AMAC

3265 Lawson Blvd.
Oceanside, NY 11572
Phone: 516-536-5850
Fax: 516-536-5276
Web: www.amacalert.com

CEO: Jack Rhian
CFO: Richard Rallo
HR: –
FYE: December 31
Type: Public

It's like having a guardian angel hovering above, but without the wings. American Medical Alert Corp provides health care communication and monitoring services. The company's Health Safety and Monitoring Services (HSMS) unit markets remote patient monitoring systems, including personal emergency response systems, health management and medication management systems, and safety monitoring systems. Its Telephony Based Communication Services (TBCS) unit provides telephone answering services and operates clinical trial recruitment call centers. Products are sold to consumers and health care facilities such as home care, hospice, pharmacy, managed care, and other health care organizations.

	Annual Growth	12/03	12/04	12/05	12/06	12/07
Sales ($ mil.)	21.1%	16.6	19.1	22.5	30.8	35.7
Net income ($ mil.)	25.7%	0.6	0.4	0.9	1.3	1.5
Market value ($ mil.)	22.8%	28.8	41.9	54.1	61.5	65.7
Employees	36.5%	—	—	389	531	—

AMERICAN MEDICAL ASSOCIATION

515 N. State St.
Chicago, IL 60610
Phone: 312-464-5000
Fax: 312-464-4184
Web: www.ama-assn.org

CEO: Michael D. Maves
CFO: Denise Hagerty
HR: Robert W. (Bob) Davis
FYE: December 31
Type: Association

The AMA knows whether there's a doctor in the house. The American Medical Association (AMA) prescribes the standards for the medical profession. The membership organization's activities include advocacy for physicians, promoting ethics standards in the medical community, and improving health care education. Policies are set by the AMA's House of Delegates, which is made up mainly of elected representatives. The AMA also publishes books and products for physicians, is a partner in the Medem online physician network, sells medical malpractice insurance, and helps doctors fight legal claims. The organization was founded in 1847 to establish a code of medical ethics. The AMA has about 240,000 members.

	Annual Growth	12/02	12/03	12/04	12/05	12/06
Sales ($ mil.)	3.4%	250.5	256.4	269.9	280.1	286.0
Employees	—	—	—	—	—	—

AMERICAN MEDICAL SYSTEMS HOLDINGS, INC.

NASDAQ (GS): AMMD

10700 Bren Rd. West
Minnetonka, MN 55343
Phone: 952-930-6000
Fax: 952-930-6373
Web: www.americanmedicalsystems.com

CEO: Anthony P. (Tony) Bihl III
CFO: Mark A. Heggestad
HR: Janet L. Dick
FYE: December 31
Type: Public

American Medical Systems (AMS) aims to make life better for millions of patients afflicted with pelvic disorders. A leading maker of urological devices, AMS makes erectile dysfunction products such as inflatable penile implants, as well as urinary incontinence devices for men and women. Its other products treat such conditions as menorrhagia (excessive uterine bleeding), enlarged prostate, and fecal incontinence. AMS has around 70 international distributors in addition to a direct sales force of some 500 employees. Marketing efforts target urologists, gynecologists, colorectal surgeons, and other specialty physicians.

	Annual Growth	12/03	12/04	12/05	12/06	12/07
Sales ($ mil.)	28.9%	168.3	208.8	262.6	358.3	463.9
Net income ($ mil.)	(18.3%)	29.0	(3.1)	39.3	(49.3)	12.9
Market value ($ mil.)	30.4%	362.3	1,410.6	1,244.7	1,316.0	1,049.2
Employees	31.2%	—	—	720	1,095	1,239

AMERICAN MEDICAL TECHNOLOGIES, INC.

OTC: ADLI

5655 Bear Ln.
Corpus Christi, TX 78405
Phone: 361-289-1145
Fax: 361-289-5554
Web: www.americanmedicaltech.com

CEO: Judd D. Hoffman
CFO: Barbara D. Woody
HR: –
FYE: December 31
Type: Public

American Medical Technologies (AMT) can get you a good deal on dental products. The company makes the Hydro Jet system, which removes tooth decay with a stream of tiny particles and water propelled by compressed air. However, as the market for the system has softened, AMT is increasingly focused on its role as a distributor or broker for products made by others. It uses its worldwide network of dealers and sales representatives to distribute the tooth-whitening products of Spectrum Dental, for instance, as well as crowns, bridges, dental head light systems, and other oral care products made by third parties.

	Annual Growth	12/03	12/04	12/05	12/06	12/07
Sales ($ mil.)	1.6%	3.0	2.3	2.2	2.8	3.2
Net income ($ mil.)	—	0.1	0.0	(1.5)	(1.4)	(0.9)
Market value ($ mil.)	(18.5%)	4.1	3.6	1.4	1.3	1.8
Employees	(16.4%)	—	24	20	17	14

AMERICAN MORTGAGE ACCEPTANCE COMPANY

AMEX: AMC

625 Madison Ave.
New York, NY 10022
Phone: 212-317-5700
Fax: 212-751-3550
Web: www.americanmortgageco.com

CEO: James L. Duggins
CFO: Robert L. (Rob) Levy
HR: –
FYE: December 31
Type: Public

American Mortgage Acceptance Company has been hit hard by the subprime mortgage crisis of 2007. The firm is a real estate investment trust (REIT) that makes multi-family residential mortgages and bridge and mezzanine loans. Centerline/AMAC Manager, an affiliate of Centerline, formerly CharterMac, manages the REIT's operations. Besides mortgages, the company's portfolio includes investments including collateralized debt obligations and commercial-backed mortgage securities. American Mortgage Acceptance divested its government-insured mortgages, leaving it vulnerable to the subprime mortgage crisis. As a result, the company has halted its investment activities and may have to jettison assets.

	Annual Growth	12/03	12/04	12/05	12/06	12/07
Sales ($ mil.)	40.3%	15.5	15.9	39.2	38.6	60.1
Net income ($ mil.)	—	11.9	11.3	15.2	2.7	(58.6)
Market value ($ mil.)	(48.9%)	135.9	136.9	121.2	141.8	9.3
Employees	—	—	—	0	—	0

AMERICAN MUSEUM OF NATURAL HISTORY

Central Park West at 79th St.
New York, NY 10024
Phone: 212-769-5000
Fax: 212-769-5006
Web: www.amnh.org

CEO: Ellen V. Futter
CFO: –
HR: –
FYE: June 30
Type: Not-for-profit

The American Museum of Natural History is one of the world's foremost scientific museums. Its landmark building on New York's Central Park West showcases parts of its immense collections of anthropological and zoological specimens, along with meteorites, gemstones, dinosaur fossils, and a butterfly conservatory. The museum, which is also home to the Hayden Planetarium and a top-flight research library, conducts many educational programs, offers an IMAX theater, and publishes *Natural History* magazine. The American Museum of Natural History is part of the University of the State of New York. The museum was chartered by the New York legislature in 1869.

	Annual Growth	6/03	6/04	6/05	6/06	6/07
Est. sales ($ mil.)	—	—	—	—	—	122.5
Employees	—	—	—	—	—	1,262

An in-depth profile of this company is available to Hoover's Online members at hoovers.com.

125

AMERICAN NATIONAL BANKSHARES INC.

NASDAQ (GS): AMNB

628 Main St.
Danville, VA 24541
Phone: 434-792-5111
Fax: 434-792-1582
Web: www.amnb.com

CEO: Charles H. (Charlie) Majors
CFO: Neal A. Petrovich
HR: Jeffrey V. Haley
FYE: December 31
Type: Public

American National Bankshares wants to carry the deposits of its customers back to old Virginny and its American National Bank and Trust subsidiary. Founded in 1909, the bank operates about 20 branches and a loan office serving southern and central Virginia and north central North Carolina. It offers checking and savings accounts, CDs, IRAs, trust and investment services, and insurance. Its lending activities primarily consist of real estate loans: Commercial mortgages account for about one-third of the company's loan portfolio; residential mortgages, another quarter. The bank also originates construction, consumer, business, home equity, and land development loans.

	Annual Growth	12/03	12/04	12/05	12/06	12/07
Assets ($ mil.)	4.6%	644.3	619.1	623.5	777.7	772.3
Net income ($ mil.)	4.7%	9.5	8.0	10.0	11.4	11.4
Market value ($ mil.)	(4.6%)	147.6	133.7	126.5	143.7	122.2
Employees	—	—	—	220	—	—

AMERICAN NATIONAL INSURANCE COMPANY

NASDAQ (GS): ANAT

1 Moody Plaza
Galveston, TX 77550
Phone: 409-763-4661
Fax: 409-766-6663
Web: www.anico.com

CEO: Robert L. Moody
CFO: Stephen Pavlicek
HR: Carol Ann Kratz
FYE: December 31
Type: Public

You can't get much more American than this. Through subsidiaries, American National offers personal life insurance, as well as property and casualty insurance, annuities, group health insurance, and other types of insurance throughout the US, Puerto Rico, and other territories. It also provides policies for US military personnel in Western Europe. The company's subsidiaries include Garden State Life Insurance, Standard Life and Accident Insurance, and Farm Family Holdings. The Securities Management and Research subsidiary provides investment advisory and manages mutual funds. American National offers insurance in Mexico through American National de México (ANMEX).

	Annual Growth	12/03	12/04	12/05	12/06	12/07
Sales ($ mil.)	3.4%	2,684.5	2,879.3	3,045.5	3,114.4	3,071.0
Net income ($ mil.)	7.2%	182.2	255.6	235.9	273.2	240.8
Employees	—	—	—	—	—	—

THE AMERICAN NATIONAL RED CROSS

2025 E St. NW
Washington, DC 20006
Phone: 202-303-4498
Fax: –
Web: www.redcross.org

CEO: Mary S. Elcano
CFO: Robert P. (Bob) McDonald
HR: D. Eric (Rick) Pogue
FYE: June 30
Type: Not-for-profit

A specialist in dealing with events beyond its control, The American Red Cross offers disaster relief and other humanitarian services through more than 700 chapters nationwide. Although it was chartered by Congress in 1905, the American Red Cross isn't a government agency. The not-for-profit organization relies on the efforts of about 1 million volunteers. Aside from helping victims of about 70,000 disasters large and small each year, the American Red Cross teaches CPR and first aid courses; provides counseling for US military personnel; and maintains some of the largest blood and plasma banks nationwide. The group is a member of the International Red Cross and Red Crescent Movement.

	Annual Growth	6/03	6/04	6/05	6/06	6/07
Sales ($ mil.)	2.5%	3,033.8	3,091.5	3,919.3	5,747.4	3,347.8
Employees	(3.3%)	40,000	—	35,000	35,000	35,000

AMERICAN OIL & GAS, INC.

AMEX: AEZ

1050 17th St., Ste. 2400
Denver, CO 80265
Phone: 303-991-0173
Fax: 303-595-0709
Web: www.americanoilandgasinc.com

CEO: Patrick D. (Pat) O'Brien
CFO: Joseph B. Feiten
HR: –
FYE: December 31
Type: Public

Deep in the heart of the North American continent lie untapped natural gas deposits, and American Oil & Gas is searching for them. The exploration and production company is focusing on Montana, North Dakota, and Wyoming, a region with one of the largest undeveloped natural gas fields in the US. American Oil & Gas has acquired stakes in more than 421,140 gross undeveloped acres in its five core project areas, and has estimated proved reserves of 91,850 barrels of oil and 809.8 million cu. ft. of natural gas. The company was formed via a strategic alliance between North Finn LLC and Tower Colombia Corporation. In 2005 American Oil & Gas acquired Tower Colombia Corp.

	Annual Growth	12/03	12/04	12/05	12/06	12/07
Sales ($ mil.)	111.5%	0.1	0.8	4.7	3.8	2.0
Net income ($ mil.)	—	(0.8)	(0.4)	1.0	1.2	(2.7)
Market value ($ mil.)	99.3%	17.1	80.2	147.7	253.4	269.3
Employees	36.9%	—	—	8	13	15

AMERICAN PACIFIC CORPORATION

NASDAQ (GM): APFC

3770 Howard Hughes Pkwy., Ste. 300
Las Vegas, NV 89169
Phone: 702-735-2200
Fax: 702-735-4876
Web: www.apfc.com

CEO: John R. Gibson
CFO: Dana M. Kelley
HR: Linda G. Ferguson
FYE: September 30
Type: Public

American Pacific knows how to have a blast. The company's products launch rockets, propel missiles, deploy airbags, and suppress fires. Its largest unit also makes active pharmaceutical ingredients. American Pacific's specialty chemicals include ammonium perchlorate (AP), a rocket fuel oxidizer; sodium azide, an airbag deployment chemical also used in pharmaceuticals; and Halotron, an ozone-friendly fire suppressant. The company also makes commercial packaged explosives, aerospace propulsion equipment for satellites, and environmental protection products. American Pacific relies heavily on a few customers, with its five largest accounting for more than two-thirds of sales; Alliant Techsystems accounts for 15%.

	Annual Growth	9/03	9/04	9/05	9/06	9/07
Sales ($ mil.)	27.8%	68.9	59.5	83.3	141.9	183.9
Net income ($ mil.)	(14.6%)	9.4	(0.4)	(9.7)	(3.9)	5.0
Market value ($ mil.)	17.2%	61.4	54.5	43.2	56.1	116.0
Employees	38.5%	—	—	254	—	487

AMERICAN PAD & PAPER LLC

3101 E. George Bush Hwy., Ste. 200
Richardson, TX 75082
Phone: 972-578-2000
Fax: 972-424-7493
Web: www.ampad.com

CEO: Donald Meltzer
CFO: Ed Byrne
HR: Janine Adamski
FYE: December 31
Type: Private

Pssst! Wanna buy a pad? It's legal. American Pad & Paper (AMPAD) has been in the legal pad business for more than a century. Credited with designing the first legal pad in 1888, AMPAD manufactures more than 1,700 quality, paper-based office supply products, including easel pads, flip charts, filing products (such as file folders, tabs and inserts, portfolios, index cards, and report covers), envelopes, and specialty papers (such as wedding invitations, certificates, and note cards). Prominent brand names include AMPAD, Gold Fibre, Evidence, Peel & Seal, and EnviroTech.

	Annual Growth	12/03	12/04	12/05	12/06	12/07
Est. sales ($ mil.)	—	—	—	—	—	126.2
Employees	—	—	—	—	—	860

AMERICAN PHYSICIANS CAPITAL, INC.

NASDAQ (GS): ACAP

1301 N. Hagadorn Rd.
East Lansing, MI 48823
Phone: 517-351-1150
Fax: 517-351-7866
Web: www.apcapital.com

CEO: R. Kevin Clinton
CFO: Frank H. Freund
HR: Nancy Axtell
FYE: December 31
Type: Public

American Physicians Capital (APCapital) helps doctors sleep more soundly at night. The company writes medical professional-liability insurance through subsidiary American Physicians Assurance Corporation. Operating principally in a handful of states in the Midwest, it concentrates on individual and small-group practices and has more than 9,000 policies in force. Other subsidiaries deal with income portfolio management, health care consulting, and physician and medical staff credential verification and review. Founded in 1975, the company was known as Mutual Insurance Corporation until 2000, when it was demutualized.

	Annual Growth	12/03	12/04	12/05	12/06	12/07
Assets ($ mil.)	(0.1%)	1,063.1	1,069.9	1,109.3	1,095.8	1,057.5
Net income ($ mil.)	—	(76.8)	20.0	72.4	43.2	52.8
Market value ($ mil.)	41.7%	104.1	208.2	254.4	462.7	419.9
Employees	(7.1%)	224	169	162	164	167

AMERICAN PHYSICIANS SERVICE GROUP, INC.

NASDAQ (CM): AMPH

1301 Capital of Texas Hwy., Ste. C300
Austin, TX 78746
Phone: 512-328-0888
Fax: 512-314-4398
Web: www.amph.com

CEO: Kenneth S. (Ken) Shifrin
CFO: Mark J. Zimmerman
HR: –
FYE: December 31
Type: Public

Medical claims are nothing new; neither is the need for doctors to protect themselves against lawsuits. American Physicians Service Group is a liability insurance writer and provider for medical professionals through its wholly owned subsidiary American Physicians Insurance Company (API). It insures about 5,000 individual doctors and group practices primarily in Texas, but also in Arkansas and Oklahoma. Approximately 99% of its premiums are written through purchasing groups. The group sells its insurance products through independent agents and reinsurance brokers. About one-fifth of its premiums come from selling directly to policyholders.

	Annual Growth	12/03	12/04	12/05	12/06	12/07
Assets ($ mil.)	82.3%	25.6	30.4	33.5	36.3	282.8
Net income ($ mil.)	69.8%	2.8	2.2	5.5	3.2	23.3
Market value ($ mil.)	53.7%	25.9	27.0	36.8	45.0	144.6
Employees	—	—	—	—	112	—

AMERICAN PUBLIC EDUCATION, INC.

NASDAQ (GM): APEI

111 W. Congress St.
Charles Town, WV 25414
Phone: 304-724-3700
Fax: 304-724-3780
Web: www.apus.edu

CEO: Wallace E. Boston Jr.
CFO: Harry T. Wilkins
HR: –
FYE: December 31
Type: Public

American Public Education promotes military intelligence. The company offers online postsecondary education to those in the military and public service (law enforcement) sectors through American Military University and American Public University. Together these two schools make up the American Public University System, which offers more than 50 degree programs and nearly as many certificate programs in such disciplines as business administration, criminal justice, intelligence, liberal arts, and national security. Enrollment consists of about 30,000 part-time students hailing from all 50 states and about 130 foreign countries, more than 80% of whom serve in the US military.

	Annual Growth	12/03	12/04	12/05	12/06	12/07
Sales ($ mil.)	44.1%	—	23.1	28.2	40.0	69.1
Net income ($ mil.)	56.4%	—	2.3	1.1	1.8	8.8
Market value ($ mil.)	—	—	—	—	—	739.0
Employees	—	—	—	—	660	—

AMERICAN RAILCAR INDUSTRIES, INC.

NASDAQ (GS): ARII

100 Clark St.
St. Charles, MO 63301
Phone: 636-940-6000
Fax: 636-940-6030
Web: www.americanrailcar.com

CEO: James J. Unger
CFO: William P. Benac
HR: –
FYE: December 31
Type: Public

American Railcar Industries doesn't make the little engine that could or the little red caboose — just the cars that go in between. The company is a leading manufacturer of covered hopper cars, used for dry bulk commodities, and tank cars, used for liquid and compressed bulk commodities. American Railcar Industries also makes railcar components and offers railcar maintenance and fleet management services. It operates two manufacturing facilities in Arkansas; manufacturing operations account for more than 90% of the company's sales. The company's main customers are railcar leasing companies, rail shippers, and railroads. Financier Carl Icahn controls about a 54% stake in American Railcar Industries.

	Annual Growth	12/03	12/04	12/05	12/06	12/07
Sales ($ mil.)	33.8%	218.0	355.1	608.2	646.0	698.1
Net income ($ mil.)	141.3%	1.1	1.9	14.8	35.2	37.3
Market value ($ mil.)	(43.2%)	—	—	—	721.9	410.1
Employees	(1.9%)	—	2,372	2,425	2,575	2,238

AMERICAN REALTY INVESTORS, INC.

NYSE: ARL

1800 Valley View Ln., Ste. 300
Dallas, TX 75234
Phone: 469-522-4200
Fax: 469-522-4299
Web: www.amrealtytrust.com

CEO: Daniel J. (Danny) Moos
CFO: David R. Fletcher
HR: Michael K. Lane
FYE: December 31
Type: Public

American Realty Investors (ARI) invests in, develops, and operates commercial properties and land in growing suburban markets. The company's portfolio includes about 50 apartment communities, about 20 office, retail, and industrial properties, and a half-dozen hotel properties. ARI has properties in about 20 states, but most are located in Texas. (It also owns a stake in a hotel in Poland, as well as undeveloped land throughout the US.) ARI is part of a complex web of ownership that includes Prime Income Asset Management, which manages ARI and owns about 15% of it. Through various entities, Texas real estate mogul Gene Phillips and his family control more than 75% of ARI.

	Annual Growth	12/03	12/04	12/05	12/06	12/07
Sales ($ mil.)	(11.4%)	287.2	239.9	202.6	182.3	176.9
Net income ($ mil.)	25.6%	10.7	33.2	47.4	13.1	26.6
Market value ($ mil.)	1.3%	97.2	9.5	81.4	79.9	102.5
Employees	—	—	—	895	—	—

AMERICAN REPROGRAPHICS COMPANY

NYSE: ARP

700 N. Central Ave., Ste. 550
Glendale, CA 91203
Phone: 818-500-0225
Fax: 818-500-0195
Web: www.e-arc.com

CEO: Kumarakulasingam (Suri) Suriyakumar
CFO: Jonathan R. Mather
HR: –
FYE: December 31
Type: Public

This "arc" keeps builders from being flooded with too much paper. American Reprographics Company (ARC) provides large-format document reproduction services, mainly to architectural, engineering, and construction firms. It operates about 300 facilities under a variety of local brands and offers on-site document management services at some 4,600 customer locations. In addition, the company sells reprographics equipment and supplies and licenses its proprietary PlanWell document management software to independent reprographers. Although ARC's network of facilities extends across some 40 states and into Canada and Mexico, operations in California account for more than 40% of the company's sales.

	Annual Growth	12/03	12/04	12/05	12/06	12/07
Sales ($ mil.)	13.4%	416.0	443.9	494.2	591.8	688.3
Net income ($ mil.)	110.8%	3.5	29.5	60.5	51.4	69.1
Market value ($ mil.)	(18.8%)	—	—	1,133.3	1,510.5	747.3
Employees	15.8%	—	—	3,800	4,400	—

An in-depth profile of this company is available to Hoover's Online members at hoovers.com.

127

AMERICAN RESIDENTIAL SERVICES L.L.C.

965 Ridge Lake Blvd., Ste. 201
Memphis, TN 38120
Phone: 901-271-9700
Fax: –
Web: www.ars.com

CEO: Donald K. (Don) Karnes
CFO: Jim McMahon
HR: Bill Young
FYE: December 31
Type: Private

For those whose home maintenance skills don't rival Bob Vila's, there's American Residential Services (ARS). The company is an amalgamation of some 100 firms combined to create a national home improvement services company specializing in heating, ventilation, air-conditioning, plumbing, and electricity, as well as major home appliance installation, maintenance, repair, and replacement. Under the ARS Service Express and Rescue Rooter brand names, it services homes as well as small commercial buildings. ARS has some 55 locations across the US. It was a subsidiary of home services giant ServiceMaster until late 2006, when it was acquired by two private equity firms for $100 million.

	Annual Growth	12/03	12/04	12/05	12/06	12/07
Est. sales ($ mil.)	—	—	—	—	—	1,662.0
Employees	—	—	—	—	—	7,500

AMERICAN RESTAURANT GROUP, INC.

4410 El Camino Real, Ste. 201
Los Altos, CA 94022
Phone: 650-949-6400
Fax: 650-917-9207
Web: www.stuartandersons.com

CEO: Bruce MacDiarmid
CFO: Ronald (Ron) Maccarone
HR: Doug Gammon
FYE: Last Monday in December
Type: Private

As far as this company is concerned, Angus beef is as American as apple pie. American Restaurant Group owns and operates the Black Angus Steakhouse chain with more than 80 locations in 10 Western states. The upscale casual diners offer a menu of steaks and prime rib, along with chicken, seafood, and pasta dishes. Many locations also offer drive-up take-out service in addition to dine-in seating. Rancher and entrepreneur Stuart Anderson opened his first Black Angus restaurant in Seattle in 1964. American Restaurant Group emerged from Chapter 11 bankruptcy in 2005 with creditors controlling more than 98% of the company.

	Annual Growth	12/03	12/04	12/05	12/06	12/07
Est. sales ($ mil.)	—	—	—	—	—	276.6
Employees	—	—	—	—	—	6,600

AMERICAN RIVER BANKSHARES

NASDAQ (GS): AMRB

3100 Zinfandel Dr., Ste. 450
Rancho Cordova, CA 95670
Phone: 916-851-0123
Fax: 916-641-1262
Web: www.amrb.com

CEO: David T. Taber
CFO: Mitchell A. (Mitch) Derenzo
HR: Anneliese Hein
FYE: December 31
Type: Public

American River Bankshares' family is growing. The holding company is the parent of American River Bank, which has about a dozen branches in Central California. About half of the bank's offices are operating under the North Coast Bank or Bank of Amador names. The bank serves area small to midsized businesses and individuals, offering traditional deposit products such as checking and savings accounts and CDs. It offers commercial and residential mortgages, as well as business, construction, and consumer loans, and lease financing for business equipment.

	Annual Growth	12/03	12/04	12/05	12/06	12/07
Assets ($ mil.)	9.6%	397.4	586.7	612.8	604.0	573.7
Net income ($ mil.)	16.0%	4.7	5.8	9.2	9.1	8.5
Market value ($ mil.)	9.1%	67.7	102.7	111.7	129.3	95.8
Employees	0.8%	—	—	122	—	124

AMERICAN SAFETY RAZOR COMPANY

240 Cedar Knolls Rd.
Cedar Knolls, NJ 07927
Phone: 973-753-3000
Fax: 973-326-9004
Web: www.asrco.com

CEO: Mario Soussou
CFO: J. Andrew (Andy) Bolt
HR: Doug Decker
FYE: December 31
Type: Private

There's nothing dull about American Safety Razor (ASR). The company is a leading maker of shaving razors and blades. American Safety Razor's primary products include value-priced brand-name and private-label shaving razors and blades. It also makes shaving cream, aftershave, and soap; bladed hand tools (carpet knives, paint and window scrapers); bar soap; and specialty industrial and medical blades. ASR sells its wares under such brands as Bump Fighter, Burma-Shave, Personna, and others. Investment firm J. W. Childs bought ASR in 1999. London's Lion Capital, a private equity firm, acquired ASR in mid-2006.

	Annual Growth	12/03	12/04	12/05	12/06	12/07
Est. sales ($ mil.)	—	—	—	—	—	297.5
Employees	—	—	—	—	—	1,522

AMERICAN SCIENCE AND ENGINEERING, INC.

NASDAQ (GS): ASEI

829 Middlesex Tpke.
Billerica, MA 01821
Phone: 978-262-8700
Fax: 978-262-8804
Web: www.as-e.com

CEO: –
CFO: –
HR: George M. Peterman
FYE: Friday nearest March 31
Type: Public

You can't hide from American Science and Engineering (AS&E). The company makes X-ray detection systems for inspection and security applications at airports, border control sites, shipping ports, and special events. Unlike ordinary X-rays, AS&E's backscatter technology detects organic materials such as illegal drugs, plastic explosives, and plastic weapons; its Z Backscatter Van features an X-ray system built into a delivery van. AS&E also makes scanning equipment for detecting contraband on persons and in luggage and packages. Customers include the Department of Homeland Security. About 55% of sales are to the US government and its contractors.

	Annual Growth	3/04	3/05	3/06	3/07	3/08
Sales ($ mil.)	21.6%	76.3	88.3	163.6	153.2	166.7
Net income ($ mil.)	74.2%	1.9	11.2	29.8	24.6	17.5
Market value ($ mil.)	41.3%	122.4	372.9	847.2	483.9	488.2
Employees	1.7%	324	286	288	299	346

AMERICAN SEAFOODS GROUP LLC

Marketplace Tower, 2025 1st Ave., Ste. 900
Seattle, WA 98121
Phone: 206-374-1515
Fax: 206-374-1516
Web: www.americanseafoods.com

CEO: Bernt O. Bodal
CFO: Brad D. Bodenman
HR: Tammy French
FYE: December 31
Type: Private

With operations in the northern Pacific and Atlantic oceans as well as catfish processing in the southern US, American Seafoods Group has cast a wide net. The company offers frozen and processed fish such as Alaska pollock, Pacific whiting, Pacific cod, sea scallops, and farm- raised catfish. It operates its own fleet of ships that process and freeze the catch while at sea, as well as a fleet of transport trucks. The company's land-based processing is done in Alabama and Massachusetts. American Seafoods sells its fish under the American Pride, Frionor, and Southern Pride brand names. Its value-added products include surimi, breaded and battered filets, and nuggets.

AMERICAN SHARED HOSPITAL SERVICES

AMEX: AMS

4 Embarcadero Center, Ste. 3700
San Francisco, CA 94111
Phone: 415-788-5300
Fax: 415-788-5660
Web: www.ashs.com

CEO: Ernest A. Bates
CFO: Craig K. Tagawa
HR: –
FYE: December 31
Type: Public

Business *is* brain surgery for American Shared Hospital Services (ASHS). The company owns 81% of GK Financing (GKF), which installs, finances, and services the Leksell Gamma Knife, a noninvasive surgical device that uses gamma rays to destroy brain tumors without harming surrounding tissue. Sweden-based Elekta, which makes the Gamma Knife, owns the other 19% of GKF. GKF usually leases the Gamma Knife units on a per-use basis to major urban medical centers; it has contracts for units installed in about 20 hospitals in the US; it markets the product in the US and Brazil.

	Annual Growth	12/03	12/04	12/05	12/06	12/07
Sales ($ mil.)	8.7%	16.2	16.4	18.2	20.4	22.6
Net income ($ mil.)	(10.5%)	1.4	2.0	1.8	1.7	0.9
Market value ($ mil.)	(18.7%)	23.7	28.4	31.5	33.4	10.4
Employees	0.0%	—	—	12	12	—

[Ⓗ] THE AMERICAN SOCIETY OF COMPOSERS, AUTHORS & PUBLISHERS

1 Lincoln Plaza
New York, NY 10023
Phone: 212-621-6000
Fax: 212-724-9064
Web: www.ascap.com

CEO: John LoFrumento
CFO: Bob Candela
HR: Carolyn Jensen
FYE: December 31
Type: Association

While Frank Sinatra got the glory, songwriter Johnny Mercer got some of the money, and his estate still does, thanks to the American Society of Composers, Authors and Publishers (ASCAP). ASCAP is the top performance rights organization in the world. The group protects the rights of composers, songwriters, lyricists, and music publishers by licensing their copyrighted works for public performances and distributing royalties. Be they played in a stadium, on the radio or Internet, on an airplane, or in a bar, songs of more than 300,000 members are covered. ASCAP also lobbies Congress on behalf of its members. The organization was founded in 1914.

	Annual Growth	12/03	12/04	12/05	12/06	12/07
Est. sales ($ mil.)	—	—	—	—	—	49.8
Employees	—	—	—	—	—	630

[Ⓗ] AMERICAN SOFTWARE, INC.

NASDAQ (GS): AMSWA

470 E. Paces Ferry Rd.
Atlanta, GA 30305
Phone: 404-264-5296
Fax: 404-264-5206
Web: www.amsoftware.com

CEO: James C. Edenfield
CFO: Vincent C. (Vince) Klinges
HR: –
FYE: April 30
Type: Public

American Software sells supply chain management software from sea to shining sea. The company offers its e-Intelliprise suite as a way to connect departments within an organization so they can collaborate on the various aspects of bringing goods to market. Its products are used by manufacturers and distributors to manage back-office operations, including global supply chain, warehouse, and transportation operations. Its 88%-owned Logility unit makes collaborative applications that connect buyers with suppliers and help in planning transportation and logistics. Co-founders James Edenfield (CEO) and Thomas Newberry (chairman) together control 70% of the voting power of the company.

	Annual Growth	4/04	4/05	4/06	4/07	4/08
Sales ($ mil.)	12.9%	54.7	64.5	76.6	84.4	89.0
Net income ($ mil.)	3.3%	5.7	3.3	5.0	8.4	6.5
Employees	5.6%	—	304	321	—	—

AMERICAN SOIL TECHNOLOGIES, INC.

OTC: SOYL

12224 Montague St.
Pacoima, CA 91331
Phone: 818-899-4686
Fax: 818-899-4670
Web: www.americansoiltech.com

CEO: Carl P. Ranno
CFO: Carl P. Ranno
HR: –
FYE: September 30
Type: Public

American Soil Technologies works to make sure your farmland isn't dirt poor. The company manufactures agricultural chemicals that help retain water in soil, the direct benefit of which is manifold. In addition to minimizing the frequency of irrigation, the chemicals also decrease the likelihood of erosion and reduce other environmental damage. Its Agriblend product is used by agricultural clients, and its Nutrimoist product is used for residential and recreational applications. In early 2007 the company acquired Smart World Organics, allowing American Soil to enter the organic turf and horticultural markets for the first time. Chairman Louie Visco controls 48% of the company.

	Annual Growth	12/03	12/04	12/05	12/06	*9/07
Sales ($ mil.)	68.2%	0.1	0.6	0.6	0.6	0.8
Net income ($ mil.)	—	(2.9)	(1.6)	(2.1)	(2.3)	(3.1)
Employees	—	—	—	—	19	—

*Fiscal year change

AMERICAN SPECTRUM REALTY, INC.

AMEX: AQQ

5850 San Felipe, Ste. 450
Houston, TX 77057
Phone: 713-706-6200
Fax: 713-706-6201
Web: www.americanspectrum.com

CEO: William J. Carden
CFO: G. Anthony Eppolito
HR: –
FYE: December 31
Type: Public

American Spectrum Realty has narrowed the spectrum of property types in which it invests. The company owns and manages commercial real estate, primarily office and industrial space in a half-dozen states, with the majority of its property in Texas. American Spectrum Realty owns about 25 properties with some 2 million sq. ft. of leasable space. Since 2002, it has sold more than 20 noncore properties (apartment communities, shopping centers, land parcels, office properties in the Midwest); it has also acquired several Houston office buildings. American Spectrum Realty determined in 2006 it would not seek status as a real estate investment trust (REIT). CEO William Carden controls about a third of the company.

	Annual Growth	12/03	12/04	12/05	12/06	12/07
Sales ($ mil.)	4.2%	25.9	27.2	20.3	26.0	30.5
Net income ($ mil.)	—	(14.4)	(9.1)	(2.3)	6.5	(8.8)
Market value ($ mil.)	8.8%	22.1	14.8	22.2	32.6	31.0
Employees	—	—	—	28	—	—

AMERICAN STATES WATER COMPANY

NYSE: AWR

630 E. Foothill Blvd.
San Dimas, CA 91773
Phone: 909-394-3600
Fax: 909-394-1382
Web: www.aswater.com

CEO: Floyd E. Wicks
CFO: Robert J. Sprowls
HR: Kris O'Connor
FYE: December 31
Type: Public

American States Water holds the essence of life for Californians and Arizonans. Its main subsidiary, regulated public utility Golden State Water Company (GSWC), which was formerly known as Southern California Water Company, supplies water to about 254,550 customers in 75 communities, primarily in Los Angeles, San Bernardino, and Orange counties. GSWC's Bear Valley Electric subsidiary distributes electricity to more than 23,270 Californians. American States Water's Chaparral City Water unit serves about 13,500 customers in Fountain Hills and Scottsdale, Arizona.

	Annual Growth	12/03	12/04	12/05	12/06	12/07
Sales ($ mil.)	9.1%	212.7	228.0	236.2	268.6	301.4
Net income ($ mil.)	23.9%	11.9	18.5	26.8	23.1	28.0
Market value ($ mil.)	14.3%	380.1	435.6	517.4	658.4	649.3
Employees	—	—	—	—	—	—

[Ⓗ] An in-depth profile of this company is available to Hoover's Online members at hoovers.com.

129

AMERICAN STOCK EXCHANGE LLC

86 Trinity Place
New York, NY 10006
Phone: 212-306-1000
Fax: 212-306-1218
Web: www.amex.com

CEO: Neal L. Wolkoff
CFO: Paul M. Warner
HR: Ivonne L. Natal
FYE: December 31
Type: Not-for-profit

Don't confuse AMEX (The American Stock Exchange) with that credit card in your wallet. The exchange provides a floor-based auction market that specializes in stocks, bonds, and exchange-traded funds (ETFs). AMEX lists primarily small and midsized companies and newer issues, and is the US's second-largest options exchange (behind the Chicago Board Options Exchange). It also has a growing business in listing structured products and closed-end funds and has begun trading in select Nasdaq stocks. AMEX announced plans in 2006 to demutualize and convert to a for-profit organization.

AMERICAN SUPERCONDUCTOR

NASDAQ (GM): AMSC

68 Jackson Rd.
Devens, MA 01434
Phone: 978-842-3000
Fax: 978-842-3024
Web: www.amsuper.com

CEO: Gregory J. (Greg) Yurek
CFO: David A. (Dave) Henry
HR: Susan DiCecco
FYE: March 31
Type: Public

American Superconductor Corporation (AMSC) gets a charge out of carrying a heavy load. The company has two units — AMSC Superconductors, which combined AMSC Wires and SuperMachines (prototype electric motors and synchronous condensers), and AMSC Power Systems. In early 2007 AMSC acquired a company that previously was a customer, Windtec Consulting, to expand into the alternative energy market. The Austrian firm develops and licenses wind turbine system designs, and sells wind turbine electrical systems. Windtec became part of AMSC Power Systems. Customers in the Asia/Pacific region account for about two-thirds of sales.

	Annual Growth	3/04	3/05	3/06	3/07	3/08
Sales ($ mil.)	28.4%	41.3	58.3	50.9	52.2	112.4
Net income ($ mil.)	—	(26.7)	(19.7)	(30.9)	(34.7)	(25.5)
Market value ($ mil.)	28.4%	354.6	324.8	373.3	471.7	963.3
Employees	9.4%	267	264	241	263	382

AMERICAN SUZUKI MOTOR CORPORATION

3251 E. Imperial Hwy.
Brea, CA 92821
Phone: 714-996-7040
Fax: 714-524-8499
Web: www.suzuki.com

CEO: Motoo Murakami
CFO: Shawn Suzuki
HR: Hideaki Tanaka
FYE: December 31
Type: Subsidiary

Predictably enough, American Suzuki Motor (ASMC) is the US subsidiary of Japan's Suzuki Motor. ASMC markets Suzuki cars, motorcycles, ATVs, and marine engines in the US. ASMC's automotive offerings include the Forenza (sedan and wagon), Grand Vitara (SUV), Reno (5-door hatchback) and XL7 (seven-passenger luxury SUV). The company markets Suzuki cars through a network of more than 500 dealerships all across the US. ASMC hoped to leverage the decades-long success of its motorcycles and marine engines to rev up US car sales, but the company fell short of the five-year plan instituted in 2003. President Rick Suzuki, the grandson of Suzuki Motor founder Michio Suzuki, announced in early 2008 that he would step down.

	Annual Growth	12/03	12/04	12/05	12/06	12/07
Est. sales ($ mil.)	—	—	—	—	—	178.9
Employees	—	—	—	—	—	540

AMERICAN TECHNICAL CERAMICS CORP.

1 Norden Ln.
Huntington Station, NY 11746
Phone: 631-622-4700
Fax: 631-622-4748
Web: www.atceramics.com

CEO: John S. Gilbertson
CFO: Andrew R. Perz
HR: Pam Reese
FYE: June 30
Type: Subsidiary

American Technical Ceramics (ATC) isn't into pottery. The company makes ceramic and porcelain single- and multilayer capacitors that store and discharge precise amounts of electrical current. The company's radio-frequency (RF), microwave, and millimeter-wave capacitors are key components in mobile phones, instruments, radar and navigation systems, and broadcast satellites. Its high-reliability products are used in critically sensitive military and aerospace applications. ATC also makes resistors, as well as custom thin-film substrates for microwave and fiber-optic telecommunications devices. Rival AVX has acquired ATC for about $231 million in cash.

	Annual Growth	6/02	6/03	6/04	6/05	6/06
Sales ($ mil.)	14.1%	49.6	49.0	61.2	73.0	84.1
Net income ($ mil.)	—	(4.2)	(0.5)	2.2	4.3	6.0
Employees	13.0%	479	—	—	760	782

AMERICAN TECHNOLOGIES GROUP, INC.

OTC: ATGR

P.O. Box 90
Monrovia, CA 91016
Phone: 626-357-5000
Fax: 626-357-4464

CEO: Thomas E. Durkin III
CFO: –
HR: –
FYE: July 31
Type: Public

Before moving into the steel products industry in 2005, American Technologies Group had been a shell company with no significant operations. The company had been seeking markets for its catalyst technology in the automotive aftermarket and water purification industries and its vacuum distiller technology for consumer applications. American Technologies Group expanded in September 2005 by buying North Texas Steel, a fabricator of structural steel components for commercial, institutional, and civil construction projects. In 2006 the company bought Whitco Company, a maker of steel and aluminum light poles.

	Annual Growth	7/03	7/04	7/05	7/06	7/07
Sales ($ mil.)	—	0.0	0.0	0.0	22.0	32.3
Net income ($ mil.)	—	(0.5)	(0.5)	(0.5)	(16.9)	(3.9)
Market value ($ mil.)	(58.7%)	60.0	179.8	149.9	10.5	1.7
Employees	178.9%	2	2	95	115	121

AMERICAN TECHNOLOGY CORPORATION

NASDAQ (CM): ATCO

15378 Avenue of Science, Ste. 100
San Diego, CA 92128
Phone: 858-676-1112
Fax: 858-676-1120
Web: www.atcsd.com

CEO: Thomas R. (Tom) Brown
CFO: Katherine H. (Kathy) McDermott
HR: –
FYE: September 30
Type: Public

High-tech sound technology may drive American Technology's development, but the firm is banking on it driving its bottom line. American Technology Corporation (ATC), whose sales in the past largely came from its portable radios, discontinued the entirety of its portable consumer products division and is focusing on enhancing its sound technologies. It's also busy supplying the US armed forces with its products through resellers. The firm is seeking manufacturers to license its sound technology, including its Stratified Field speaker technology. ATC licenses its HyperSonic sound and NeoPlanar technologies, which allow sound to travel farther with less distortion, and its PureBass extended range bass woofer.

	Annual Growth	9/03	9/04	9/05	9/06	9/07
Sales ($ mil.)	66.1%	1.3	5.8	10.2	8.9	9.9
Net income ($ mil.)	—	(8.2)	(6.0)	(9.1)	(7.7)	(5.6)
Market value ($ mil.)	(0.4%)	117.7	113.9	124.9	115.0	116.0
Employees	—	—	—	46	—	—

AMERICAN TELECOM SERVICES, INC.

Pink Sheets: ATEL

6 Concourse Pkwy. NE, Ste. 1525
Atlanta, GA 30328
Phone: 404-261-7466
Fax: 404-237-7466
Web: www.atsphone.com

CEO: Bruce Hahn
CFO: August J. Liguori
HR: –
FYE: June 30
Type: Public

American Telecom Services resells phone service bundled with its own telephones through major retailers such as Staples, Best Buy, Wal-Mart, and Amazon.com. The company offers a cordless broadband phone, sold along with Voice over Internet Protocol (VoIP) service from SunRocket. It also sells a bundled phone and prepaid long-distance product, branded as Pay N' Talk, through a partnership with IDT Corporation. CEO and founder Bruce Hahn and manufacturing president Yu Wen Ching hold stakes in the company of about 12% and 10%, respectively.

	Annual Growth	6/02	6/03	6/04	6/05	*6/06
Sales ($ mil.)	—	—	—	—	—	3.1
Net income ($ mil.)	—	—	—	—	—	(5.7)
Employees	—	—	—	—	—	—

*Most recent year available

AMERICAN TIRE DISTRIBUTORS HOLDINGS, INC.

12200 Herbert Wayne Ct., Ste. 150
Huntersville, NC 28078
Phone: 704-992-2000
Fax: 704-992-1384
Web: www.americantiredistributors.com

CEO: Richard P. (Dick) Johnson
CFO: David L. Dyckman
HR: –
FYE: December 31
Type: Private

American Tire Distributors Holdings' business starts where the rubber meets the road. The company, through its American Tire Distributors unit, is one of the largest tire wholesalers in the US. Offerings include the flagship brands of industry leaders Bridgestone, Continental, Goodyear, and Michelin, as well as budget brands and private-label tires. Tires account for about 90% of the company's sales; American Tire Distributors also distributes custom wheels and tire service equipment. It maintains about 85 distribution centers that serve independent tire dealers, retail chains, and auto service facilities in more than 35 states. Investment firm Investcorp owns the company.

	Annual Growth	12/02	12/03	12/04	12/05	12/06
Sales ($ mil.)	10.4%	1,060.4	1,112.5	1,282.1	1,150.9	1,578.0
Net income ($ mil.)	—	37.4	16.0	25.0	(1.6)	(4.6)
Employees	2.3%	1,915	1,894	2,071	2,127	2,100

AMERICAN TOWER CORPORATION

NYSE: AMT

116 Huntington Ave.
Boston, MA 02116
Phone: 617-375-7500
Fax: 617-375-7575
Web: www.americantower.com

CEO: James D. (Jim) Taiclet Jr.
CFO: Bradley E. (Brad) Singer
HR: Allen Todres
FYE: December 31
Type: Public

American Tower's business is all about getting high. The tower management firm (formerly American Tower Systems) operates about 22,500 broadcast and communications towers in the US, Brazil, and Mexico. The company rents space on multi-tenant towers and rooftops to wireless carriers and radio and TV broadcasters. American Tower also offers some network development services to third parties: It provides site acquisition for new tower construction and performs structural analyses for carriers to determine if a tower can support additional equipment. The company has sold off its other network development businesses, including its tower construction unit.

	Annual Growth	12/03	12/04	12/05	12/06	12/07
Sales ($ mil.)	19.5%	715.1	706.7	944.8	1,317.4	1,456.6
Net income ($ mil.)	—	(325.3)	(247.6)	(181.4)	27.5	56.3
Market value ($ mil.)	65.1%	2,290.7	4,224.6	11,182.9	15,831.8	17,019.5
Employees	11.5%	—	—	904	995	1,124

AMERICAN TRANSMISSION COMPANY LLC

N19 W23993 Ridgeview Pkwy. West
Waukesha, WI 53187
Phone: 262-506-6700
Fax: 262-506-6710
Web: www.atcllc.com

CEO: José M. Delgado
CFO: Daniel A. (Dan) Doyle
HR: Maureen Hogan
FYE: December 31
Type: Private

American Transmission Company is an entrepreneur in the US power grid business. Connecting electricity producers to distributors, American Transmission owns, operates, monitors, and maintains more than 9,100 miles of high-voltage electric transmission lines and 480 substations in portions of Illinois, Michigan, Minnesota, and Wisconsin. Created in 2001, American Transmission is one of the first for-profit transmission companies formed in the deregulating US marketplace. The company operates the former transmission assets of some of its shareholders. About 30 utilities, municipalities, municipal electric companies, and electric cooperatives in its service area have an ownership stake in American Transmission.

	Annual Growth	12/03	12/04	12/05	12/06	12/07
Est. sales ($ mil.)	—	—	—	—	—	340.7
Employees	—	—	—	—	—	450

AMERICAN TRIM, LLC

1005 W. Grand Ave.
Lima, OH 45801
Phone: 419-228-1145
Fax: 419-996-4850
Web: www.amtrim.com

CEO: Jeffrey A (Jeff) Hawk
CFO: –
HR: Bob Stead
FYE: December 31
Type: Private

American Trim is not a new fad diet, but a company that manufactures metal components for the automotive, appliance, and furniture industries. American Trim's automotive products include bumper beams, frame members, and interior and exterior trim. Other products include office furniture doors and shelves, appliance handles and hinges, support members, and decorative metal tiles. The company also provides services such as product design, tooling and process development, metal forming, metal finishing, and assembly. Founded in 1951, the company has manufacturing facilities in Alabama, Ohio, and Pennsylvania, as well as in Mexico.

	Annual Growth	12/03	12/04	12/05	12/06	12/07
Est. sales ($ mil.)	—	—	—	—	—	230.0
Employees	—	—	—	—	—	1,500

AMERICAN TRUCKING ASSOCIATIONS

950 N. Glebe Rd., Ste. 210
Alexandria, VA 22203
Phone: 703-838-1700
Fax: 703-836-5880
Web: www.truckline.com

CEO: Bill Graves
CFO: –
HR: –
FYE: December 31
Type: Not-for-profit

American Trucking Associations (ATA) aims to be heard over the roar of diesel engines on the interstate as the unified voice of the trucking industry. The group seeks to represent the national interests of truckers in legislation, regulation, the courts, and the media. It works closely with state trucking associations and with groups concerned with segments of the trucking business and key industry issues, such as safety. ATA produces several publications and hosts seminars, meetings, and conventions. The organization was formed in 1933 and in 1944 adopted a federation structure comprising national, state and local, and special affiliated interests.

	Annual Growth	12/03	12/04	12/05	12/06	12/07
Est. sales ($ mil.)	—	—	—	—	—	74.5
Employees	—	—	—	—	—	280

An in-depth profile of this company is available to Hoover's Online members at hoovers.com.

AMERICAN TV & APPLIANCE OF MADISON, INC.

2404 W. Beltline Hwy.
Madison, WI 53713
Phone: 608-271-1000
Fax: 608-275-7339
Web: www.americantv.com

CEO: Douglas G. (Doug) Reuhl
CFO: Steve Mixtacki
HR: —
FYE: June 30
Type: Private

Of course, if they only sold American television sets, they wouldn't have anything to stock. American TV & Appliance of Madison sells appliances, electronics, and furniture in Illinois, Iowa, Michigan, Missouri, and Wisconsin. Its 15 retail outlets generate annual sales of about $450 million and offer such products as recliners, dining room sets, mattresses, car stereos, CD players, dishwashers, refrigerators, personal computers, digital cameras, plasma and LCD TVs, and DVD players. The company also has two distribution centers and a service center offering parts and repairs. American TV even makes house calls to fix large appliances, regardless of where they were purchased. Ferd Mattioli founded the company in 1954.

	Annual Growth	6/03	6/04	6/05	6/06	6/07
Est. sales ($ mil.)	—	—	—	—	—	343.6
Employees	—	—	—	—	—	1,700

AMERICAN UNITED MUTUAL INSURANCE HOLDING COMPANY

1 American Sq.
Indianapolis, IN 46206
Phone: 317-285-1111
Fax: 317-285-1728
Web: www.aul.com

CEO: Dayton H. Molendorp
CFO: J. Scott Davison
HR: Mark C. Roller
FYE: December 31
Type: Mutual company

There are 50 states, but only OneAmerica. American United Mutual Insurance Holding Company, whose operating units do business under the OneAmerica Financial Partners banner, specializes in annuities and individual and group life insurance and disability coverage throughout the US. Its subsidiaries include American United Life Insurance, The State Life Insurance Company, and OneAmerica Securities. The insurer restructured into mutual holding company ownership in 2000, a move that has not only given it a more favorable tax status, but has allowed it to form and acquire stock subsidiaries. The company operates in 49 states and Washington, DC.

	Annual Growth	12/02	12/03	12/04	12/05	12/06
Sales ($ mil.)	(1.2%)	1,182.8	1,004.4	1,004.8	1,064.2	1,126.4
Net income ($ mil.)	65.2%	9.1	61.5	56.3	62.1	67.7
Employees	2.9%	1,700	1,730	1,800	—	—

AMERICAN VANGUARD CORPORATION

NYSE: AVD

4695 MacArthur Ct.
Newport Beach, CA 92660
Phone: 949-260-1200
Fax: 949-260-1201
Web: www.american-vanguard.com

CEO: Eric G. Wintemute
CFO: David T. Johnson
HR: Teresa Chavez
FYE: December 31
Type: Public

American Vanguard Corporation (AMVAC) bugs bugs, roots out weeds, and helps people take care of their person. The company makes specialty chemicals designed to protect the health of animals, crops, and people. Products made by its AMVAC Chemical subsidiary include pesticides, plant-growth regulators, herbicides, and soil fumigants. Its GemChem subsidiary distributes the company's chemicals nationally to the cosmetic, nutritional, and pharmaceutical industries. American Vanguard also has marketing subsidiaries in the UK, Switzerland, and Mexico. UAP, now a part of Agrium, is its largest customer with almost 20% of sales. Co-chairmen Herbert Kraft and Glenn Wintemute together own 22% of American Vanguard.

	Annual Growth	12/03	12/04	12/05	12/06	12/07
Sales ($ mil.)	14.8%	124.9	150.9	189.8	193.8	216.7
Net income ($ mil.)	16.1%	10.3	14.5	19.0	15.4	18.7
Market value ($ mil.)	53.0%	83.7	125.5	322.4	415.4	458.5
Employees	1.5%	—	—	300	—	309

AMERICAN VANTAGE COMPANIES

Pink Sheets: AVCS

4735 S. Durango Dr., Ste. 105
Las Vegas, NV 89147
Phone: 702-227-9800
Fax: 702-227-8525
Web: www.americanvantage.com

CEO: Ronald J. Tassinari
CFO: Anna M. Morrison
HR: —
FYE: December 31
Type: Public

This company can understand the advantage of owning a couple of different businesses. American Vantage Companies is a holding company that operates through subsidiaries in the gaming industry and the corporate staffing business. Its majority-owned subsidiary Brownstone provides consulting and development services to clients in the casino gaming industry, as well as to those clients trying to get in. It also owns Candidates on Demand Group, a New York City-based recruiting and temporary placement company with offices in Florida, New Jersey, and New York.

	Annual Growth	7/03	*12/04	12/05	12/06	12/07
Sales ($ mil.)	57.6%	0.6	17.8	0.3	2.0	3.7
Net income ($ mil.)	—	(0.9)	(4.0)	(4.8)	(0.4)	1.3
Employees	—	—	—	—		

*Fiscal year change

AMERICAN WAGERING, INC.

OTC: BETM

675 Grier Dr.
Las Vegas, NV 89119
Phone: 702-735-5529
Fax: 702-735-0142
Web: www.americanwagering.com

CEO: Victor J. (Vic) Salerno
CFO: Melody Sullivan
HR: Elaine Elliot
FYE: January 31
Type: Public

This company lets you play the ponies without being there. American Wagering owns and operates Leroy's Horse and Sports Place, a chain of more than 60 race and sports books located in Nevada. Patrons can place bets on horse races and a variety of other sporting events. The company also markets sports wagering equipment, kiosks, and software to other gaming operators through its subsidiaries AWI Manufacturing and Computerized Bookmaking Systems. In addition, American Wagering owns and operates Sturgeon's Inn & Casino in Lovelock, Nevada. CEO Victor Salerno owns about 30% of the company.

	Annual Growth	1/04	1/05	1/06	1/07	1/08
Sales ($ mil.)	14.4%	10.9	11.1	12.5	19.4	18.7
Net income ($ mil.)	—	(0.5)	(1.1)	0.4	1.8	(0.8)
Market value ($ mil.)	(28.2%)	—	—	—	8.9	6.4
Employees	—	—	—	—	224	—

AMERICAN WATER WORKS COMPANY, INC.

NYSE: AWK

1025 Laurel Oak Rd.
Voorhees, NJ 08043
Phone: 856-346-8200
Fax: 856-346-8360
Web: www.amwater.com

CEO: Donald L. (Don) Correll
CFO: Ellen C. Wolf
HR: —
FYE: December 31
Type: Public

Water, water, everywhere — and American Water Works wants to own it. The company (formerly American Water), a subsidiary of German utility giant RWE, is one of the largest water utility holding companies in the US. Through its regulated utilities and its contract services division, American Water Works serves more than 16.2 million consumers in 32 US states, Canada, and Puerto Rico. The company also provides wastewater treatment in some of its service areas. Nonregulated subsidiary American Water Works Service provides contract management services for water and wastewater systems. In 2007 RWE filed to spin off American Water Works via an IPO.

	Annual Growth	12/03	12/04	12/05	12/06	12/07
Sales ($ mil.)	3.1%	—	2,017.9	2,136.7	2,093.1	2,214.2
Net income ($ mil.)	—	—	(64.9)	(325.0)	(162.2)	(342.8)
Employees	5.2%	—	6,009	6,194	6,900	7,000

AMERICAN WOODMARK CORPORATION

NASDAQ (GS): AMWD

3102 Shawnee Dr.	CEO: Kent B. Guichard
Winchester, VA 22601	CFO: Jonathan H. (Jon) Wolk
Phone: 540-665-9100	HR: Rick Hardy
Fax: 540-665-9176	FYE: April 30
Web: www.americanwoodmark.com	Type: Public

American Woodmark has more cabinet selections than the prime minister of Russia. A top maker of kitchen cabinets in the US and Canada, the company makes more than 350 lines of low- to mid-priced kitchen cabinets and vanities in oak, cherry, hickory, and maple. The company offers stock cabinetry with about 80 door designs. Brands include American Woodmark, Shenandoah Cabinetry, Potomac, and Timberlake. American Woodmark markets its products to remodeling and new home construction markets and sells through home centers, major builders, and independent dealer/distributors; Lowe's and The Home Depot account for 66% of sales. Co-founder and former chairman William Brandt and his family own about 23% of the company.

	Annual Growth	4/04	4/05	4/06	4/07	4/08
Sales ($ mil.)	(2.5%)	667.5	777.0	837.7	760.9	602.4
Net income ($ mil.)	(39.3%)	31.7	35.6	33.2	32.6	4.3
Market value ($ mil.)	0.3%	264.2	522.1	554.7	514.9	267.0
Employees	(19.1%)	—	—	6,360	5,148	—

AMERICANWEST BANCORPORATION

NASDAQ (GS): AWBC

41 W. Riverside Ave., Ste. 400	CEO: Robert M. (Bob) Daugherty
Spokane, WA 99201	CFO: Patrick J. (Pat) Rusnak
Phone: 509-467-6993	HR: Larry Arnold
Fax: 509-465-9681	FYE: December 31
Web: www.awbank.net	Type: Public

If you rustle up some cash, AmericanWest will help you ride herd on it. AmericanWest Bancorporation is the holding company for AmericanWest Bank, which has more than 45 branches in eastern and central Washington and northern Idaho, and about 15 more in Utah, where it operates as Far West Bank. The banks serve consumers and small to mid-sized businesses, offering standard services such as checking and savings accounts, CDs, and ATM and debit cards. The company's loan portfolio is dominated by commercial real estate, construction, land, and business loans. The bank also originates agricultural, consumer, and residential mortgage loans.

	Annual Growth	12/03	12/04	12/05	12/06	12/07
Assets ($ mil.)	20.0%	1,023.6	1,049.0	1,109.1	1,416.5	2,120.2
Net income ($ mil.)	(11.7%)	14.0	9.5	13.9	7.6	8.5
Market value ($ mil.)	12.3%	190.8	209.7	247.9	275.8	303.2
Employees	27.0%	—	—	436	—	703

AMERICA'S CAR-MART, INC.

NASDAQ (GS): CRMT

802 SE Plaza Ave., Ste. 200	CEO: Tilman J. (Skip) Falgout III
Bentonville, AR 72712	CFO: Jeffrey A. Williams
Phone: 479-464-9944	HR: –
Fax: 479-273-7556	FYE: April 30
Web: www.car-mart.com	Type: Public

No Credit? Bad Credit? No problem. America's Car-Mart targets car buyers with poor or limited credit histories. Car-Mart's subsidiaries operate 90-plus used-car dealerships in about 10 states, primarily in smaller urban and rural markets throughout the South-Central region of the US. The dealerships focus on selling basic, affordable transportation (average selling price about $8,100). The company is expanding primarily in Alabama, Oklahoma, and Missouri. While its traditional business plan has focused on cities of 20,000 to 50,000 in population, the company has begun opening dealerships in more populous cities, including Tulsa, Oklahoma. America's Car-Mart was founded in 1981 as the Crown Group.

	Annual Growth	4/04	4/05	4/06	4/07	4/08
Sales ($ mil.)	11.7%	176.2	204.8	234.2	240.3	274.6
Net income ($ mil.)	(1.3%)	15.8	18.0	16.7	4.2	15.0
Market value ($ mil.)	5.8%	134.4	250.4	241.1	152.2	168.2
Employees	9.0%	—	715	779	—	—

AMERICA'S HOME PLACE, INC.

2144 Hilton Dr.	CEO: Barry G. Conner
Gainesville, GA 30501	CFO: Claudette Bragg
Phone: 770-532-1128	HR: –
Fax: –	FYE: December 31
Web: www.americashomeplace.com	Type: Private

America's Home Place builds custom homes on its customers' land. The company builds single-family, detached houses with more than 90 custom floor plans and designs. Its two- to five-bedroom cabin, chalet, ranch, two-story, and split-level houses range in price from about $80,000 to more than $300,000, and in size from about 900 sq. ft. to 4,000 sq. ft. America's Home Place operates roughly 50 building centers and showrooms in the Southeast US. Buyers typically already own their land, from a single lot to many acres. The company also assists buyers who are not landowners in locating available property. President Barry Conner owns the company he founded in 1972.

	Annual Growth	12/03	12/04	12/05	12/06	12/07
Est. sales ($ mil.)	—	—	—	—	—	184.8
Employees	—	—	—	—	—	350

AMERICHOICE CORPORATION

8045 Leesburg Pike, 6th Fl.	CEO: Rick Jelenik
Vienna, VA 22182	CFO: Steve Swift
Phone: 703-506-3555	HR: –
Fax: 703-506-3556	FYE: December 31
Web: www.americhoice.com	Type: Subsidiary

AmeriChoice offers health care for those who don't have much choice. Specializing in the federal health care market, the company operates managed health care plans for Medicaid, Medicare, and Children's Health Insurance Program (CHIP) recipients. AmeriChoice has more than 1.7 million members in 16 states. The company also provides managed care information technology services such as medical and dental claims processing and member databases, as well as clinical care and consulting services, to government agencies and medical practices. AmeriChoice is a subsidiary of UnitedHealth Group.

	Annual Growth	12/03	12/04	12/05	12/06	12/07
Est. sales ($ mil.)	—	—	—	—	—	7.7
Employees	—	—	—	—	—	165

AMERICO LIFE, INC.

1055 Broadway	CEO: Gary L. Muller
Kansas City, MO 64105	CFO: Mark K. Fallon
Phone: 816-391-2000	HR: –
Fax: 816-391-2083	FYE: December 31
Web: www.americo.com	Type: Private

Americo Life is a holding company for subsidiaries that primarily sell life insurance and annuities. The company sells its products mainly through Americo Financial Life and Annuity Insurance. Americo Life companies also offer insurance policies that cover funeral expenses and mortgages. Other business interests include real estate ventures in Texas and Missouri, and a 50% stake in Argus Health Systems, a processor of prescription drug claims. The firm is a wholly owned subsidiary of Financial Holding Corporation, which the family of chairman Michael Merriman controls.

	Annual Growth	12/03	12/04	12/05	12/06	12/07
Est. sales ($ mil.)	—	—	—	—	—	248.7
Employees	—	—	—	—	—	766

An in-depth profile of this company is available to Hoover's Online members at hoovers.com.

AMERICOLD LOGISTICS, LLC

10 Glenlake Pkwy., Ste. 800, S. Tower
Atlanta, GA 30328
Phone: 678-441-1400
Fax: 678-441-6824
Web: www.americold.net

CEO: Tony Schnug
CFO: Ronald B. Hutchison
HR: Jim Romine
FYE: December 31
Type: Private

In business to keep cool, AmeriCold Logistics is a leading provider of temperature-controlled warehousing and distribution services. The company offers some 545 million cu. ft. of storage space for refrigerated, frozen, and dry merchandise in about 100 facilities throughout the US, including 10 regional distribution centers. Major customers have included Heinz and ConAgra. AmeriCold Logistics is owned by Americold Realty Trust, which in turn is owned by Vornado Realty Trust, which owns 47.6%; Crescent Real Estate Equities, which owns 31.7%; and investment firm Yucaipa, which owns 20.7%.

	Annual Growth	12/03	12/04	12/05	12/06	12/07
Est. sales ($ mil.)	—	—	—	—	—	314.7
Employees	—	—	—	—	—	5,900

AMERICREDIT CORP.

NYSE: ACF

801 Cherry St., Ste. 3900
Fort Worth, TX 76102
Phone: 817-302-7000
Fax: 817-302-7101
Web: www.americredit.com

CEO: Daniel E. (Dan) Berce
CFO: Chris A. Choate
HR: Nancy Smart
FYE: June 30
Type: Public

Credit is the American way, according to AmeriCredit. The company purchases loans made by more than 19,000 franchised and selected independent auto dealers primarily to consumers with less-than-ideal credit histories. It typically finances low-mileage, late-model used cars (about 80% of all loans), and the occasional new automobile. The company securitizes and sells most of its loans, retains the servicing, and reinvests the proceeds in new loans. The lender has more than 1 million customers and approximately $16 billion in managed auto receivables. It operates about 65 branches in the US and two more in Canada. Investment firm Leucadia owns more than 20% of AmeriCredit.

	Annual Growth	6/03	6/04	6/05	6/06	6/07
Assets ($ mil.)	21.7%	8,108.0	8,824.6	10,947.0	13,067.9	17,811.0
Net income ($ mil.)	103.0%	21.2	227.0	285.9	306.2	360.3
Market value ($ mil.)	23.9%	1,337.7	3,078.2	3,713.5	3,555.1	3,150.3
Employees	10.2%	—	—	3,653	4,025	—

AMERIGAS PARTNERS, L.P.

NYSE: APU

460 N. Gulph Rd.
King of Prussia, PA 19406
Phone: 610-337-7000
Fax: 610-992-3259
Web: www.amerigas.com

CEO: Eugene V. N. Bissell
CFO: Jerry E. Sheridan
HR: William D. Katz
FYE: September 30
Type: Public

America has a gas with AmeriGas Partners. Purveying propane has propelled the company to its position as one of the top two US retail propane marketers (rivaling Ferrellgas for the #1 slot). It serves 1.3 million residential, commercial, industrial, agricultural, motor fuel, and wholesale customers from about 650 locations in 46 states. AmeriGas also sells propane-related supplies and equipment and exchanges prefilled portable tanks for empty ones. The company stores propane in Arizona, California, and Virginia and distributes its products through an interstate carrier structure that runs through 48 states in the US and in Canada. Utility holding company UGI owns 44% of AmeriGas.

	Annual Growth	9/03	9/04	9/05	9/06	9/07
Sales ($ mil.)	8.7%	1,628.4	1,775.9	1,963.3	2,119.3	2,277.4
Net income ($ mil.)	27.6%	72.0	91.8	60.8	91.2	190.8
Market value ($ mil.)	11.6%	1,313.6	1,608.6	1,827.6	1,752.8	2,034.5
Employees	1.7%	—	—	6,000	5,900	6,200

AMERIGON INCORPORATED

NASDAQ (GM): ARGN

21680 Haggerty Rd., Ste. 101
Northville, MI 48167
Phone: 248-504-0500
Fax: 248-348-9735
Web: amerigon.com

CEO: Daniel R. Coker
CFO: Barry G. Steele
HR: Janice Garcia
FYE: December 31
Type: Public

Amerigon wants to put you in the hot seat — or the cool seat, depending on the season. The company's climate-control seat (CCS) allows year-round temperature control of car seats on vehicles available in North America and Asia that are made by Ford, General Motors, and Toyota, among others. Amerigon provides the CCS under contracts with auto industry suppliers such as Lear, Johnson Controls, and NHK Spring; NHK and Lear each account for about 30% of the company's sales. In 2007 Amerigon introduced its first non-automotive climate control device. Dubbed the C2, it regulates climates in personal workspaces, such as offices or cubicles. The C2 is offered exclusively through office furniture maker Herman Miller.

	Annual Growth	12/03	12/04	12/05	12/06	12/07
Sales ($ mil.)	21.7%	29.0	32.7	35.7	50.6	63.6
Net income ($ mil.)	—	(1.4)	1.1	16.5	3.5	7.4
Market value ($ mil.)	71.5%	53.6	55.0	92.7	206.1	463.3
Employees	10.6%	—	—	58	—	71

AMERIGROUP CORPORATION

NYSE: AGP

4425 Corporation Ln.
Virginia Beach, VA 23462
Phone: 757-490-6900
Fax: 757-222-2330
Web: www.amerigroupcorp.com

CEO: James G. (Jim) Carlson
CFO: James W. (Jim) Truess
HR: –
FYE: December 31
Type: Public

AMERIGROUP looks after the health of America's needy. The managed health care provider targets people eligible for Medicaid, FamilyCare, the State Children's Health Insurance Program (SCHIP), and Special Needs Plans. Plans include AMERICAID, a Medicaid product for families receiving temporary assistance to needy families (TANF) benefits; AMERIKIDS for uninsured kids ineligible for Medicaid; AMERIPLUS for low-income elderly or disabled persons receiving supplemental income; and AMERIFAM for uninsured parents of government-insured children. The company contracts with some 80,000 primary care doctors and specialists to serve more than 1.7 million members in about a dozen states.

	Annual Growth	12/03	12/04	12/05	12/06	12/07
Sales ($ mil.)	24.9%	1,622.2	1,823.7	2,329.9	2,835.1	3,945.5
Net income ($ mil.)	14.7%	67.3	86.0	53.7	107.1	116.4
Market value ($ mil.)	38.8%	521.3	1,911.5	1,003.5	1,876.1	1,936.6
Employees	24.7%	—	—	2,700	3,500	4,200

AMERIMARK DIRECT LLC

6864 Engle Rd.
Cleveland, OH 44130
Phone: 440-325-2000
Fax: –
Web: www.amerimark.com

CEO: Gareth Giesler
CFO: –
HR: Carolyn Offutt
FYE: December 31
Type: Private

Women looking to make their mark on fashion without leaving the house shop AmeriMark Direct. The company is a catalog and online retailer of women's apparel, shoes, cosmetics, jewelry and other accessories, as well as health-related merchandise. AmeriMark Direct sells its wares through about a half a dozen catalog titles: Anthony Richards, Beauty Boutique, Complements by Anthony Richards, Essentials by Anthony Richards, Healthy Living, and Windsor Collection. The firm was founded in 1969; it began selling products online at amerimark.com in 2000.

	Annual Growth	12/03	12/04	12/05	12/06	12/07
Est. sales ($ mil.)	—	—	—	—	—	97.0
Employees	—	—	—	—	—	575

AMERIPATH, INC.

7111 Fairway Dr., Ste. 400
Palm Beach Gardens, FL 33418
Phone: 561-712-6200
Fax: 561-845-0129
Web: www.ameripath.com

CEO: David L. Redmond
CFO: David L. Redmond
HR: –
FYE: December 31
Type: Subsidiary

Pickled organs and preserved tissues are AmeriPath's favorite things. The firm provides anatomic pathology and esoteric testing services to hospitals, doctors, clinics, and clinical laboratories in more than 20 states. Some 400 pathologists in AmeriPath's network diagnose diseases by examining tissue samples; work is performed in more than 40 outpatients labs and in about 220 hospitals. The company enhanced its esoteric testing capabilities with the 2006 acquisition of Specialty Laboratories; esoteric testing involves complex, specialized clinical tests (including DNA analysis and molecular diagnostics) that doctors use to diagnose and treat disease. Quest Diagnostics acquired AmeriPath in 2007.

	Annual Growth	12/02	12/03	12/04	12/05	12/06
Sales ($ mil.)	12.0%	478.8	485.0	507.3	563.6	752.3
Net income ($ mil.)	(30.3%)	44.6	23.4	1.5	9.2	10.5
Employees	7.8%	2,945	2,685	2,729	2,885	3,979

AMERIPRIDE SERVICES INC.

10801 Wayzata Blvd.
Minnetonka, MN 55305
Phone: 952-738-4200
Fax: 952-738-4252
Web: www.ameripride.com

CEO: Bruce Steiner
CFO: Kay Barber
HR: –
FYE: December 31
Type: Private

Keeping its customers covered is AmeriPride's business. From business-casual clothing to protective apparel, AmeriPride Services offers work uniforms and apparel to companies in the maintenance, foodservice, health care, and technology industries. The company rents, sells, and maintains such garments as shirts, pants, scrubs, hospital gowns, aprons, clean room coveralls, and jackets. AmeriPride also supplies floor mats, mops, and a variety of towels, as well as restroom products including hand soap, room deodorizer, and paper towels. More than 115 years old and family-owned, AmeriPride has more than 190 offices and more than 2,000 trucks in the US and Canada.

AMERIPRISE FINANCIAL, INC.

NYSE: AMP

707 2nd Ave. South
Minneapolis, MN 55402
Phone: 612-671-3131
Fax: 612-671-5112
Web: www.ameriprise.com

CEO: James M. (Jim) Cracchiolo
CFO: Walter S. Berman
HR: Kelli A. Hunter
FYE: December 31
Type: Public

It's no surprise that Ameriprise Financial is a leading provider of financial advice. Formerly known as American Express Financial, the company offers financial planning, products, and services to individual and institutional investors, primarily in the US. Through Ameriprise Financial Services and other affiliates, the company sells insurance, mutual funds, college savings plans, personal trust services, retail brokerage, and other products and services. Its Ameriprise Bank subsidiary offers deposits and loans. Ameriprise distributes its products primarily through around 12,000 financial advisors (including employees, franchisees, affiliates, and the Securities America broker-dealer subsidiary).

	Annual Growth	12/03	12/04	12/05	12/06	12/07
Assets ($ mil.)	8.3%	—	—	93,121.0	104,172.0	109,230.0
Net income ($ mil.)	19.1%	—	—	574.0	631.0	814.0
Market value ($ mil.)	10.7%	—	—	10,245.9	13,155.8	12,551.2
Employees	(14.3%)	—	—	11,900	11,858	8,750

AMERIRESOURCE TECHNOLOGIES, INC.

OTC: AMRE

3440 E. Russell Rd., Ste. 217
Las Vegas, NV 89120
Phone: 702-214-4249
Fax: 702-214-4221
Web: www.ameriresourcetechnologies.com

CEO: Delmar A. Janovec
CFO: Delmar A. Janovec
HR: –
FYE: December 31
Type: Public

AmeriResource Technologies is resourceful when it comes to finding business opportunities. The company operates through wholly owned and minority-owned subsidiaries including RoboServer Systems (point-of-sale restaurant management systems), Net2Auction (online auction drop-off locations), and VoIPCOM USA. Its RoboServer self-serve kiosk applications have been installed in an Angelo's Fast-Food in Encinitas, California, as well as in a Dairy Queen in Oceanside, California.

	Annual Growth	12/03	12/04	12/05	12/06	12/07
Sales ($ mil.)	136.0%	0.1	0.1	0.2	0.9	3.1
Net income ($ mil.)	—	(0.7)	(2.5)	(2.0)	(2.3)	(1.4)
Market value ($ mil.)	(83.8%)	—	19,376.9	25,923.2	33,791.0	82.8
Employees	—	—	—	—	20	—

AMERIS BANCORP

NASDAQ (GS): ABCB

24 2nd Ave. SE
Moultrie, GA 31768
Phone: 229-890-1111
Fax: 229-890-2235
Web: www.amerisbank.com

CEO: Edwin W. (Ed) Hortman Jr.
CFO: Dennis J. Zember Jr.
HR: –
FYE: December 31
Type: Public

Ameris Bancorp (formerly ABC Bancorp) enjoys the financial climate of the deep south. The institution is the holding company of Ameris, a community bank serving Alabama, Georgia, South Carolina, and northern Florida from some 45 branch locations. Ameris offers standard deposit products and services, including checking and savings accounts, money market accounts, and NOW accounts; it also provides credit card, trust, and brokerage services. Commercial real estate mortgages make up about 55% of its loan portfolio, while residential real estate mortgages and construction loans each account for about 10%.

	Annual Growth	12/03	12/04	12/05	12/06	12/07
Assets ($ mil.)	16.0%	1,168.0	1,268.0	1,697.2	2,047.5	2,112.1
Net income ($ mil.)	5.9%	12.0	13.1	13.7	22.1	15.1
Market value ($ mil.)	9.7%	157.5	246.0	257.0	381.2	228.1
Employees	2.6%	—	—	585	600	—

AMERISAFE, INC.

NASDAQ (GS): AMSF

2301 Hwy. 190 West
DeRidder, LA 70634
Phone: 337-463-9052
Fax: 337-463-7298
Web: www.amerisafe.com

CEO: C. Allen Bradley Jr.
CFO: Geoffrey R. (Geoff) Banta
HR: Cynthia P. Harris
FYE: December 31
Type: Public

AMERISAFE has what it takes to insure roughnecks and truckers. AMERISAFE specializes in providing workers' compensation insurance for businesses in hazardous industries including agriculture, manufacturing, construction, logging, oil and gas, and trucking. Through its subsidiaries, American Interstate Insurance, Silver Oak Casualty, and American Interstate Insurance of Texas, the company writes coverage for more than 7,000 employers (mainly small and midsized firms). In addition, AMERISAFE offers worksite safety reviews, loss prevention, and claims management services. AMERISAFE sells its products in more than 30 states and the District of Columbia.

	Annual Growth	12/03	12/04	12/05	12/06	12/07
Assets ($ mil.)	11.8%	678.6	754.2	892.3	994.2	1,061.8
Net income ($ mil.)	55.4%	8.6	10.6	5.9	37.4	50.2
Market value ($ mil.)	29.0%	—	—	175.5	289.2	291.8
Employees	—	—	—	435	—	—

An in-depth profile of this company is available to Hoover's Online members at hoovers.com.

135

AMERISERV FINANCIAL, INC.

NASDAQ (GM): ASRV

216 Franklin St.
Johnstown, PA 15907
Phone: 814-533-5300
Fax: 814-533-5427
Web: www.ameriservfinancial.com

CEO: Allan R. Dennison
CFO: Jeffrey A. Stopko
HR: –
FYE: December 31
Type: Public

AmeriServ Financial offers up a smorgasbord of banking services for Pennsylvanians. The company owns AmeriServ Financial Bank, which primarily serves the southwestern portion of the state through some 20 branches. Targeting individuals and local businesses, the bank offers such retail services as deposit accounts and loans. Commercial mortgages account for about 45% of its loan portfolio; residential real estate accounts for more than 35%. Additional offerings include investment management, brokerage, trust, and financial planning services. One of a handful of unionized banks in the US, AmeriServ also manages union pension funds.

	Annual Growth	12/03	12/04	12/05	12/06	12/07
Assets ($ mil.)	(5.8%)	1,147.9	1,010.0	880.2	896.0	904.9
Net income ($ mil.)	49.5%	0.6	(9.7)	(9.1)	2.3	3.0
Market value ($ mil.)	(3.1%)	69.8	101.9	96.9	109.2	61.5
Employees	(18.1%)	—	—	428	—	287

AMERISOURCEBERGEN CORPORATION

NYSE: ABC

1300 Morris Dr., Ste. 100
Chesterbrook, PA 19087
Phone: 610-727-7000
Fax: 610-727-3600
Web: www.amerisourcebergen.com

CEO: R. David (Dave) Yost
CFO: Michael D. DiCandilo
HR: Jeanne B. Fisher
FYE: September 30
Type: Public

AmerisourceBergen is *the* source for many of North America's pharmacies and health care providers. The company serves as a go-between for drugmakers and the pharmacies, doctors' offices, hospitals, and other health care providers who dispense drugs. Operating primarily in the US and Canada, it distributes generic, branded, and over-the-counter pharmaceuticals, as well as some medical supplies and other products, using its network of about 25 facilities. Its specialty distribution unit focuses on sensitive and complex biopharmaceuticals, such as cancer drugs, vaccines, and plasma products. And its PMSI unit provides workers' compensation services to insurance companies and other health care payors.

	Annual Growth	9/03	9/04	9/05	9/06	9/07
Sales ($ mil.)	7.4%	49,657.3	53,178.9	54,577.3	61,203.1	66,074.3
Net income ($ mil.)	1.6%	441.2	468.4	264.6	467.7	469.2
Market value ($ mil.)	25.7%	3,074.8	2,992.5	4,117.7	9,015.6	7,682.4
Employees	(8.2%)	—	—	13,400	14,700	11,300

AMERISTAR CASINOS, INC.

NASDAQ (GS): ASCA

3773 Howard Hughes Pkwy., Ste. 490 South
Las Vegas, NV 89109
Phone: 702-567-7000
Fax: 702-369-8860
Web: www.ameristarcasinos.com

CEO: Gordon R. Kanofsky
CFO: Thomas M. (Tom) Steinbauer
HR: Scott Sell
FYE: December 31
Type: Public

When you wish upon Ameristar, you can hit the jackpot on land or on boat. Ameristar Casinos owns six casino hotels and two casinos, including Ameristar St. Charles and Ameristar Kansas City (both in Missouri), Ameristar Black Hawk (Colorado), and The Jackpot Properties (Nevada). Ameristar Casino Vicksburg in Mississippi is a permanently docked riverboat casino on the Mississippi River, and Ameristar Casinos' Council Bluffs (Iowa) riverboat casino sits on the Missouri River. Ameristar's casinos offer slot machines (about 75% of gaming sales), blackjack, craps, roulette, and poker. Properties also include movie theaters, shops, entertainment arenas, restaurants, bars, and private clubs.

	Annual Growth	12/03	12/04	12/05	12/06	12/07
Sales ($ mil.)	8.4%	782.0	854.7	961.4	1,000.3	1,080.5
Net income ($ mil.)	9.9%	47.6	62.0	66.3	59.6	69.4
Market value ($ mil.)	48.3%	325.6	591.5	1,270.3	1,737.6	1,574.2
Employees	9.8%	—	—	7,460	7,200	9,000

AMERISURE MUTUAL INSURANCE COMPANY

26777 Halsted Rd.
Farmington Hills, MI 48331
Phone: 248-615-9000
Fax: 248-615-8548
Web: www.amerisure.com

CEO: Richard F. Russell
CFO: R. Douglas Kinnan
HR: Derick W. Adams
FYE: December 31
Type: Mutual company

This company wants to help all businesses rest Amerisured. Amerisure provides a range of commercial property & casualty products; it specializes in workers' compensation programs, primarily for the manufacturing and contracting industries. Coverage includes general and employee benefits liability, property, auto, inland marine, and equipment insurance. Amerisure also sells commercial property policies and provides reinsurance through a Bermuda-based subsidiary. The company operates out of about a dozen offices in the southern and midwestern parts of the US. Amerisure was founded as Michigan Workmen's Compensation Mutual Insurance in 1912.

	Annual Growth	12/03	12/04	12/05	12/06	12/07
Est. sales ($ mil.)	—	—	—	—	—	430.8
Employees	—	—	—	—	—	700

AMERITRANS CAPITAL CORPORATION

NASDAQ (CM): AMTC

747 3rd Ave., 4th Fl.
New York, NY 10017
Phone: 212-355-2449
Fax: 212-759-3338
Web: www.ameritranscapital.com

CEO: Gary C. Granoff
CFO: Gary C. Granoff
HR: –
FYE: June 30
Type: Public

When cabbies need a loan, they hail Ameritrans Capital. The firm owns Elk Associates Funding, a small business investment company (SBIC) that makes loans primarily to Boston, Chicago, Miami, and New York taxicab owners who require financing to buy medallions (city-granted operating licenses). Such loans, which account for about 60% of the firm's portfolio, have low down payments and long payment terms. Elk Associates also issues commercial loans and mortgages to operators of businesses such as laundromats and restaurants in the New York metropolitan area.

	Annual Growth	6/03	6/04	6/05	6/06	6/07
Assets ($ mil.)	1.5%	60.1	57.1	57.9	56.0	63.9
Net income ($ mil.)	—	0.4	(0.4)	0.1	(0.2)	0.0
Market value ($ mil.)	14.8%	10.2	10.2	12.0	17.2	17.7
Employees	0.0%	—	—	10	—	10

AMERON INTERNATIONAL CORPORATION

NYSE: AMN

245 S. Los Robles Ave.
Pasadena, CA 91101
Phone: 626-683-4000
Fax: 626-683-4060
Web: www.ameron.com

CEO: James S. Marlen
CFO: James R. (Jim) McLaughlin
HR: Terrence P. (Terry) O'Shea
FYE: November 30
Type: Public

When Ameron talks business, it talks corrosion prevention and fluids transmission. The company designs, makes, and markets corrosion-resistant fiberglass-composite pipe and pipe fittings for industrial, chemical, petrochemical, and petroleum customers. Ameron also makes and sells concrete pipe for water transmission and sewage and waste water collection; clients include municipalities, builders, and developers. Additionally, the company supplies ready-mix concrete and aggregates, box culverts, and dune sand (mainly to projects in Hawaii) and manufactures various construction products (concrete light poles) for infrastructure projects.

	Annual Growth	11/03	11/04	11/05	11/06	11/07
Sales ($ mil.)	1.2%	600.5	605.8	704.6	549.2	631.0
Net income ($ mil.)	22.4%	29.9	13.5	32.6	52.2	67.2
Market value ($ mil.)	37.4%	271.1	320.2	392.9	682.5	966.7
Employees	(6.9%)	—	—	3,000	—	2,600

AMES CONSTRUCTION, INC.

2000 Ames Dr.
Burnsville, MN 55306
Phone: 952-435-7106
Fax: 952-435-7142
Web: www.amesconstruction.com

CEO: Richard J. (Dick) Ames
CFO: Dennis D. McGill
HR: –
FYE: November 30
Type: Private

Ames aims right for the heart of the heavy construction industry. Ames Construction is primarily a general contractor, providing heavy civil and industrial construction services to the transportation, mining, and power industries, primarily in the West and Midwest. It works on highways, airports, bridges, pipelines, power plants, and other infrastructure projects. It also performs flood control, environmental remediation, reclamation, and landfill work. Additionally, the firm builds golf courses and undertakes other commercial and residential site development projects. It typically partners with other companies to perform the engineering and design portion of its construction jobs.

	Annual Growth	11/03	11/04	11/05	11/06	11/07
Est. sales ($ mil.)	—	—	—	—	—	189.2
Employees	—	—	—	—	—	1,500

AMES NATIONAL CORPORATION

NASDAQ (CM): ATLO

405 5th St.
Ames, IA 50010
Phone: 515-232-6251
Fax: 515-663-3033
Web: www.amesnational.com

CEO: Thomas H. Pohlman
CFO: John P. Nelson
HR: Jennifer J. Thompson
FYE: December 31
Type: Public

This company wants you to take Ames . . . Ames and the rest of Iowa, that is. Ames National Corporation is the multi-bank holding company for flagship subsidiary First National Bank, Ames, Iowa, as well as Boone Bank & Trust, Randall-Story State Bank, State Bank & Trust, and United Bank & Trust. With about a dozen branches, the banks provide area individuals and businesses with deposit products including checking and savings accounts, CDs, and debit cards. They also offer mortgage, home equity, and other consumer and commercial loans. Additionally, Ames National Corporation offers trust, cash management, and investment services.

	Annual Growth	12/03	12/04	12/05	12/06	12/07
Assets ($ mil.)	3.4%	752.8	839.8	819.4	838.8	861.6
Net income ($ mil.)	(1.3%)	11.6	12.4	11.6	10.9	11.0
Market value ($ mil.)	31.9%	60.8	84.2	242.2	197.9	183.9
Employees	(27.8%)	—	—	182	—	95

AMETEK, INC.

NYSE: AME

37 N. Valley Rd., Bldg. 4
Paoli, PA 19301
Phone: 610-647-2121
Fax: 610-323-9337
Web: www.ametek.com

CEO: Frank S. Hermance
CFO: John J. Molinelli
HR: John J. Weaver
FYE: December 31
Type: Public

You might say that AMETEK is *instrument*al when it comes to monitoring equipment and electric motors. The company's Electronic Instruments Group (56% of sales) makes monitoring, calibration, and display devices for the aerospace, heavy equipment, power generation, and other industrial markets. AMETEK's Electromechanical Group (44% of sales) makes air-moving electric motors for vacuum cleaners and other floor-care equipment, and brushless air-moving motors for the aerospace, mass transit, medical, and computer markets. The group also makes specialty metals for the telecommunications, electronics, consumer, and automotive industries. AMETEK gets about half of its sales in the US.

	Annual Growth	12/03	12/04	12/05	12/06	12/07
Sales ($ mil.)	18.3%	1,091.6	1,232.3	1,434.5	1,819.3	2,136.9
Net income ($ mil.)	26.9%	87.8	112.7	140.6	181.9	228.0
Market value ($ mil.)	47.0%	1,077.5	1,642.0	1,998.7	3,376.9	5,029.1
Employees	7.4%	—	—	9,800	10,400	11,300

AMEXDRUG CORPORATION

OTC: AXRX

8909 W. Olympic Blvd., Ste. 208
Beverly Hills, CA 90211
Phone: 310-855-0475
Fax: 888-325-2499
Web: www.amexdrug.com

CEO: Jack Amin
CFO: –
HR: –
FYE: December 31
Type: Public

Amexdrug, through subsidiaries Allied Med and Dermagen, is a wholesale distributor of pharmaceuticals, nutritional supplements, and beauty products to pharmacies and other retailers. The company allows small pharmacies to get the lower prices that large pharmaceutical chains such as Walgreen and CVS enjoy. Its customers are primarily located in California. Part of Allied Med's growth strategy includes increasing its online traffic, so it is increasing its name recognition and branding efforts. Top executive Jack Amin and his wife own more than 90% of the company.

	Annual Growth	12/03	12/04	12/05	12/06	12/07
Sales ($ mil.)	(15.0%)	11.7	6.5	4.9	4.7	6.1
Net income ($ mil.)	—	0.0	0.0	0.0	0.0	0.0
Market value ($ mil.)	(14.8%)	19.3	1.3	16.9	17.4	10.2
Employees	—	—	—	—	6	—

⊞ AMF BOWLING WORLDWIDE, INC.

Pink Sheets: AMBWQ

8100 AMF Dr.
Richmond, VA 23111
Phone: 804-730-4000
Fax: 804-559-6276
Web: www.amf.com

CEO: Frederick R. (Fred) Hipp
CFO: William A. (Bill) McDonnell
HR: Anthony (Tony) Ponsiglione
FYE: June 30
Type: Public

If you're a fan of knocking down pins, this company is right down your alley. AMF Bowling Worldwide is a leading operator of bowling centers, with more than 340 locations in the US. The centers offer league and non-league bowling, along with video games, billiards, and other amusements. AMF's locations also offer food and beverage services and sell bowling gear. In addition to its bowling centers, the company owns 50% of QubicaAMF Worldwide, a joint venture with Italian manufacturer Qubica that sells a variety of bowling center equipment, including bowling pins, refurbished pinsetters, and scoring systems. AMF Bowling is controlled by investment firm Code Hennessy.

	Annual Growth	6/02	6/03	6/04	6/05	*6/06
Sales ($ mil.)	9.9%	341.9	667.6	678.8	568.6	499.1
Employees	(10.4%)	14,500	15,361	13,800	9,845	9,362

*Most recent year available

⊞ AMGEN INC.

NASDAQ (GS): AMGN

1 Amgen Center Dr.
Thousand Oaks, CA 91320
Phone: 805-447-1000
Fax: 805-447-1010
Web: www.amgen.com

CEO: Kevin W. Sharer
CFO: Robert (Bob) Bradway
HR: Brian M. McNamee
FYE: December 31
Type: Public

Amgen is among the biggest of the biotech big'uns. And it's determined to get even bigger. The company uses cellular biology and medicinal chemistry to target cancers, kidney ailments, inflammatory disorders, and metabolic diseases. Anti-anemia drugs Epogen and Aranesp account for more than one-third of its sales. Enbrel, another leading drug, treats rheumatoid arthritis and is one of the best-selling drugs in this multi-billion-dollar market. The company has a promising drug pipeline and marketing alliances with Hoffmann-La Roche, Japanese brewer and drugmaker Kirin, and other pharmas. Amgen sells its products primarily through wholesale distributors in North America and Europe.

	Annual Growth	12/03	12/04	12/05	12/06	12/07
Sales ($ mil.)	15.3%	8,356.0	10,550.0	12,430.0	14,268.0	14,771.0
Net income ($ mil.)	8.8%	2,259.5	2,363.0	3,674.0	2,950.0	3,166.0
Market value ($ mil.)	(10.7%)	79,319.8	80,829.0	96,524.6	79,649.5	50,480.3
Employees	3.0%	—	—	16,500	20,100	17,500

⊞ An in-depth profile of this company is available to Hoover's Online members at hoovers.com.

137

AMICAS, INC.

NASDAQ (GM): AMCS

20 Guest St., Ste. 200
Boston, MA 02135
Phone: 617-779-7878
Fax: 617-779-7879
Web: www.amicas.com

CEO: Stephen N. Kahane
CFO: Kevin C. Burns
HR: –
FYE: December 31
Type: Public

The local radiologist is one of AMICAS's favorite people — so much so that the company is tying its future to its radiology friends. Formerly VitalWorks, AMICAS changed its name in 2005, when it sold off its Medical division (which provided software for doctors' offices and hospitals) to Cerner for about $100 million. The company has refocused entirely on developing medical image and information management software for radiology departments. Targeting ambulatory and acute care radiology markets, AMICAS offers radiology information systems, picture archiving and communications (PACS) systems, Web-based and wireless image and report distribution tools, and billing systems, among other products and services.

	Annual Growth	12/03	12/04	12/05	12/06	12/07
Sales ($ mil.)	(18.2%)	111.5	42.3	52.8	49.4	49.9
Net income ($ mil.)	—	8.0	(12.5)	44.2	(1.0)	(0.9)
Market value ($ mil.)	(11.3%)	191.4	197.4	239.9	131.0	118.3
Employees	(29.6%)	—	724	246	247	253

AMICUS THERAPEUTICS, INC.

NASDAQ (GM): FOLD

6 Cedar Brook Dr.
Cranbury, NJ 08512
Phone: 609-662-2000
Fax: 609-662-2001
Web: www.amicustherapeutics.com

CEO: John F. Crowley
CFO: James E. (Jim) Dentzer
HR: S. Nicole Schaeffer
FYE: December 31
Type: Public

Amicus Therapeutics develops drugs that treat rare genetic diseases known as lysosomal storage disorders. The company's enzyme replacement therapies are designed to target defective proteins and restore their functions. Its lead drug candidate, Amigal, is aimed at aiding patients with Fabry disease, whose symptoms include skin rashes, impaired sweating, and gastrointestinal, heart, and kidney problems that vary in severity. Amicus is also developing drugs to treat Gaucher disease, a disorder that can cause anemia and skeletal lesions, and Pompe disease, which causes muscle weakness and impairs breathing, mobility, and heart function.

	Annual Growth	12/03	12/04	12/05	12/06	12/07
Sales ($ mil.)	—	—	—	—	—	1.8
Net income ($ mil.)	—	—	—	—	—	(41.2)
Market value ($ mil.)	—	—	—	—	—	240.9
Employees	—	—	—	—	—	—

AMKOR TECHNOLOGY, INC.

NASDAQ (GS): AMKR

1900 S. Price Rd.
Chandler, AZ 85248
Phone: 480-821-5000
Fax: 480-821-8276
Web: www.amkor.com

CEO: James J. Kim
CFO: Joanne Solomon
HR: Gil C. Tilly
FYE: December 31
Type: Public

Amkor Technology is more than amicable about lending a hand with chip packaging. Amkor is a top provider of semiconductor packaging and test services. Packaging includes dicing semiconductor wafers into separate chips, die bonding, wire bonding, and encapsulating chips in protective plastic. Amkor's testing procedures verify function, current, timing, and voltage. Amkor has hundreds of customers worldwide, including such industry leaders as Altera, Atmel, Infineon Technologies, Intel, IBM, LSI Corp., QUALCOMM, Samsung Electronics, STMicroelectronics, Texas Instruments, and Toshiba. The company gets nearly two-thirds of its sales outside of the US.

	Annual Growth	12/03	12/04	12/05	12/06	12/07
Sales ($ mil.)	14.3%	1,603.8	1,901.3	2,099.9	2,728.6	2,739.4
Net income ($ mil.)	216.2%	2.2	(37.5)	(137.2)	170.1	219.9
Market value ($ mil.)	(16.3%)	3,165.6	1,173.8	989.7	1,675.8	1,550.7
Employees	1.6%	20,261	22,033	24,000	22,700	21,600

AML COMMUNICATIONS, INC.

OTC: AMLJ

1000 Avenida Acaso
Camarillo, CA 93012
Phone: 805-388-1345
Fax: 805-484-2191
Web: www.amlj.com

CEO: Jacob Inbar
CFO: Heera Lee
HR: –
FYE: March 31
Type: Public

AML Communications wants to pump up the volume — and its sales — with its microwave amplifiers for wireless communications. The amplifiers support defense-related radar, satellite, and surveillance systems, as well as commercial wireless applications. AML also makes higher power microwave amplifiers for the defense market through subsidiary Microwave Power. AML's customers include defense equipment manufacturers (such as Raytheon and Boeing), systems integrators, and commercial wireless operators (AT&T Mobility and Verizon Wireless).

	Annual Growth	3/03	3/04	3/05	3/06	3/07
Sales ($ mil.)	18.6%	4.5	7.0	8.6	9.5	8.9
Net income ($ mil.)	—	(1.2)	1.0	0.9	2.2	1.6
Market value ($ mil.)	85.6%	1.2	12.5	12.2	12.5	13.9
Employees	1.4%	—	—	70	71	—

AMLI RESIDENTIAL

200 W. Monroe St., Ste. 2200
Chicago, IL 60606
Phone: 312-283-4700
Fax: 312-283-4720
Web: www.amli.com

CEO: Gregory T. Mutz
CFO: –
HR: Leslie S. Silverman
FYE: December 31
Type: Subsidiary

AMLI can provide your FAMLI with the swankiest of pads. AMLI Residential invests in, develops, and manages multifamily residential properties. It has interests in more than 60 upscale apartment complexes containing more than 22,000 units. The company also has several properties under development. The firm concentrates its investments in about 10 metropolitan markets, including the Atlanta, Chicago, and Dallas/Fort Worth areas. Morgan Stanley Real Estate's Prime Property Fund acquired AMLI in an all-cash transaction valued at approximately $2.1 billion in 2006.

	Annual Growth	12/03	12/04	12/05	12/06	12/07
Est. sales ($ mil.)	—	—	—	—	—	174.8
Employees	—	—	—	—	—	850

AMN HEALTHCARE SERVICES, INC.

NYSE: AHS

12400 High Bluff Dr., Ste. 100
San Diego, CA 92130
Phone: 866-871-8519
Fax: 800-282-0328
Web: www.amnhealthcare.com

CEO: Susan R. Nowakowski
CFO: David C. Dreyer
HR: Beth L. Machado
FYE: December 31
Type: Public

Understaffed hospitals say "amen" for AMN Healthcare Services. Operating as American Mobile Healthcare, Medical Express, NurseChoice, NursesRx, Preferred Healthcare Staffing, and O'Grady-Peyton International, the firm is one of the leading temporary health care staffing companies in the world. It places nurses, technicians, and therapists for 13-week stints at hospitals, clinics, and schools nationwide. With professionals recruited from Australia, Canada, South Africa, the UK, and the US, AMN provides travel reimbursement and housing for its 6,500 nurse and health care workers on assignment. The majority of temporary assignments for its 2,000-plus clients are at acute-care hospitals in the US.

	Annual Growth	12/03	12/04	12/05	12/06	12/07
Sales ($ mil.)	13.0%	714.2	629.0	705.8	1,081.7	1,164.0
Net income ($ mil.)	(0.9%)	37.8	17.4	22.2	35.1	36.5
Market value ($ mil.)	4.7%	482.5	451.0	617.1	952.4	580.9
Employees	(50.6%)	—	—	8,200	9,000	2,000

An in-depth profile of this company is available to Hoover's Online members at hoovers.com.

AMPAC PACKAGING, LLC

12025 Tricon Rd.
Cincinnati, OH 45246
Phone: 513-671-1777
Fax: 513-671-2920
Web: www.ampaconline.com

CEO: John Q. Baumann
CFO: Jon Dill
HR: –
FYE: December 31
Type: Private

Ampac Packaging packs a lot into its products. The company serves the retail, restaurant, grocery, convenience store, and gaming industries through the manufacture of plastic and paper bags for food, garments, and other retail merchandise, as well as mail, coin, and currency. Ampac also makes security products such as cash transfer and deposit bags. The company has manufacturing and sales office scattered across the US as well as in China, Germany, India, and the UK. An investor group that includes Prudential Capital, Falcon Investment Advisors, and Ampac executives owns the company.

	Annual Growth	12/03	12/04	12/05	12/06	12/07
Est. sales ($ mil.)	—	—	—	—	—	109.4
Employees	—	—	—	—	—	847

AMPACET CORPORATION

660 White Plains Rd.
Tarrytown, NY 10591
Phone: 914-631-6600
Fax: 914-631-7197
Web: www.ampacet.com

CEO: Robert A. DeFalco
CFO: Joel Slutsky
HR: Robert K. (Bob) Oakes
FYE: December 31
Type: Private

Ampacet helps manufacturers of plastic products show their true hues with its custom color and additive concentrates. Using polyethylene, polypropylene, polystyrene, polyamide, and polyester resins, Ampacet makes compounds, concentrates, and masterbatches that enable plastics manufacturers to produce consistent colors and chemical characteristics for their extruded and molded products. Globally, the company is #2 behind Ciba Specialty Chemicals in the market for color concentrates. The company's additives are used in food and industrial packaging, pipe and conduit, wire and cable, and other plastic products. Ampacet was founded in 1937, and Norman Alexander, chairman of Sequa Corporation, owns the firm.

AMPCO-PITTSBURGH CORPORATION

NYSE: AP

600 Grant St., Ste. 4600
Pittsburgh, PA 15219
Phone: 412-456-4400
Fax: 412-456-4404
Web: www.ampcopgh.com

CEO: Robert A. Paul
CFO: Marliss D. (Dee Ann) Johnson
HR: –
FYE: December 31
Type: Public

All amped up to make some financial noise, Ampco-Pittsburgh, operating in two business units, manufactures a variety of metal products. Its forged and cast steel rolls unit (Union Electric Steel, Davy Roll Co.) makes hardened-steel rolls for the steel and aluminum industries. The air and liquid processing segment includes Buffalo Pumps (centrifugal pumps for the refrigeration, marine defense, and power generation industries); Aerofin (finned-tube heat-exchange coils used in the construction and utility industries); and Buffalo Air Handling (custom air-handling systems used in commercial, industrial, and institutional buildings). Chairman Louis Berkman owns 16% of the company.

	Annual Growth	12/03	12/04	12/05	12/06	12/07
Sales ($ mil.)	17.8%	180.2	202.9	247.0	301.8	346.8
Net income ($ mil.)	—	(2.2)	(2.6)	15.0	16.6	39.2
Market value ($ mil.)	30.9%	132.0	142.3	141.7	329.3	388.0
Employees	—	—	—	1,234	—	—

AMPEX CORPORATION

NASDAQ (CM): AMPX

1228 Douglas Ave.
Redwood City, CA 94063
Phone: 650-367-2011
Fax: 650-367-4669
Web: www.ampex.com

CEO: D. Gordon Strickland
CFO: Craig L. McKibben
HR: Sharon M. Genberg
FYE: December 31
Type: Public

Ampex has recorded quite a history of data storage. The company that invented the videocassette recorder (VCR) now specializes in instrumentation recorders used in commercial and military aircraft, satellite surveillance systems, and other aerospace and industrial applications. In addition to its magnetic disk and solid-state memory-based recorders, the company offers tape-based products including instrumentation recorders, as well as drives and library systems. Ampex also generates revenues from licensing its patents, with its technology going into digital still cameras, camera phones, digital video camcorders, and DVD recorders.

	Annual Growth	12/03	12/04	12/05	12/06	12/07
Sales ($ mil.)	(1.1%)	43.4	101.4	53.2	35.9	41.5
Net income ($ mil.)	—	(1.8)	46.4	6.7	(4.0)	0.9
Employees	0.0%	—	127	127	—	—

AMPHASTAR PHARMACEUTICALS, INC.

11570 6th St.
Rancho Cucamonga, CA 91730
Phone: 909-980-9484
Fax: 909-980-8296
Web: www.amphastar.com

CEO: Jack Y. Zhang
CFO: John Webber
HR: –
FYE: December 31
Type: Private

Amphastar Pharmaceuticals wants to help drugs help themselves. A maker of injectable and inhalant drugs and drug delivery systems, the company focuses on drugs that are difficult to manufacture or administer, or suffer from deficiencies. Amphastar's products include Amphadase (increases absorption and dispersion of injected drugs), Duocaine (anesthetic for eye surgery), Cortrosyn (tests for adrenal gland disorders), and Prefilled Disposable Pipette (single-dose dispenser for liquids, creams, and other forms). The company also offers contract manufacturing services, including labeling and packaging, cold storage, and aseptic filling. President and CEO Jack Zhang controls 27% of Amphastar.

	Annual Growth	12/03	12/04	12/05	12/06	12/07
Est. sales ($ mil.)	—	—	—	—	—	61.0
Employees	—	—	—	—	—	720

AMPHENOL CORPORATION

NYSE: APH

358 Hall Ave.
Wallingford, CT 06492
Phone: 203-265-8900
Fax: 203-265-8516
Web: www.amphenol.com

CEO: Martin H. Loeffler
CFO: Diana G. Reardon
HR: Jerome Monteith
FYE: December 31
Type: Public

Amphenol knows it's all about connections. The company makes cable and connectors for the communications, industrial, medical, and military markets. Amphenol's interconnect products, which account for 90% of sales, are used in computers, wired and wireless communications and networking equipment, medical instruments, office equipment, aircraft and spacecraft, and energy applications. Its Times Fiber subsidiary is a leading maker of coaxial cable for the cable TV industry and flat-ribbon cable for computer and telecommunications products. Amphenol ships products to more than 10,000 customer locations around the world, and it has a diverse customer base. More than half of sales are outside of the US.

	Annual Growth	12/03	12/04	12/05	12/06	12/07
Sales ($ mil.)	23.2%	1,239.5	1,530.4	1,808.2	2,471.4	2,851.0
Net income ($ mil.)	35.8%	104.0	163.3	206.3	255.7	353.2
Market value ($ mil.)	85.5%	700.7	1,614.6	1,976.5	2,766.7	8,292.8
Employees	23.2%	13,900	16,100	22,700	25,600	32,000

An in-depth profile of this company is available to Hoover's Online members at hoovers.com.

139

AMR CORPORATION

NYSE: AMR

4333 Amon Carter Blvd.
Fort Worth, TX 76155
Phone: 817-963-1234
Fax: 817-967-4162
Web: www.aa.com

CEO: Gerard J. Arpey
CFO: Thomas W. Horton
HR: Jeffery J. Brundage
FYE: December 31
Type: Public

AMR knows America's spacious skies — and lots of others. Its main subsidiary is American Airlines, the #1 airline in the US (UAL's United Airlines is #2) and one of the largest in the world. Together with sister company American Eagle and regional carriers that operate as American Connection, American Airlines serves some 250 destinations in about 40 countries in the Americas, Europe, and the Asia/Pacific region. The overall fleet exceeds 1,000 aircraft; American Airlines operates about 650 jets. The carrier extends its geographic reach through code-sharing arrangements. It is part of the Oneworld global marketing alliance, along with British Airways, Cathay Pacific, Qantas, and other airlines.

	Annual Growth	12/03	12/04	12/05	12/06	12/07
Sales ($ mil.)	7.1%	17,440.0	18,645.0	20,712.0	22,563.0	22,935.0
Net income ($ mil.)	—	(1,228.0)	(761.0)	(861.0)	231.0	504.0
Market value ($ mil.)	14.1%	2,066.6	1,764.7	4,137.4	6,717.8	3,499.1
Employees	(1.7%)	—	—	88,400	86,600	85,500

AMR RESEARCH, INC.

125 Summer St., 4th Fl.
Boston, MA 02110
Phone: 617-542-6600
Fax: 617-542-5670
Web: www.amrresearch.com

CEO: Anthony J. (Tony) Friscia
CFO: Robert B. (Bob) Blakely
HR: Lisa Lawton
FYE: December 31
Type: Private

If CRM, ERP, and SCM software decisions are making you dizzy, call AMR Research. The company offers analytical research reports covering a broad range of information technologies, such as enterprise resource planning (ERP), customer relationship management (CRM), and supply chain management (SCM) software, and their application to business enterprises. Its experts and analysts also offer business leaders technology evaluation reports and strategic white papers. AMR Research provides contract negotiation services, hosts executive conferences, and provides market statistics and forecasts. The company was founded by CEO Tony J. Friscia in 1986.

	Annual Growth	12/03	12/04	12/05	12/06	12/07
Est. sales ($ mil.)	—	—	—	—	—	7.3
Employees	—	—	—	—	—	210

AMREIT

AMEX: AMY

8 Greenway Plaza, Ste. 1000
Houston, TX 77046
Phone: 713-850-1400
Fax: 713-850-0498
Web: www.amreitinc.com

CEO: H. Kerr Taylor
CFO: Chad C. Braun
HR: –
FYE: December 31
Type: Public

AmREIT is tuned in to its own shopping network. A self-managed real estate investment trust (REIT), the company invests in, develops, and manages retail properties — primarily lifestyle centers, grocery store-anchored strip centers, and single-tenant retail properties. It owns some 50 properties in about 15 states; more than half are located in Texas. The company's preferred assets are located in dense, high-traffic areas in the suburbs of such metropolises as Houston, Dallas, and San Antonio. The REIT's largest tenants are Kroger, DineEquity (formerly IHOP), and CVS Pharmacy. Subsidiary AmREIT Securities, a registered broker/dealer, raises capital for the company by managing its own offerings.

	Annual Growth	12/03	12/04	12/05	12/06	12/07
Sales ($ mil.)	40.9%	12.6	21.8	34.7	59.3	49.6
Net income ($ mil.)	27.6%	2.0	0.6	10.1	7.6	5.3
Market value ($ mil.)	25.8%	18.0	27.8	44.2	52.1	45.0
Employees	15.8%	—	—	50	64	67

AMREP CORPORATION

NYSE: AXR

300 Alexander Park, Ste. 204
Princeton, NJ 08540
Phone: 609-716-8200
Fax: 609-716-8255
Web: amrepcorp.com

CEO: James H. Wall
CFO: Peter M. Pizza
HR: Nancy Headley
FYE: April 30
Type: Public

Mailing magazines and developing land in New Mexico keep AMREP hopping. Nearly 50% of the company's sales come from the distribution and subscription fulfillment services it provides through its Kable Media subsidiary. Kable serves more than 200 publishing clients, managing subscriptions and mailing over 700 magazine titles. AMREP continues to develop its Rio Rancho property (nearly 22,000 acres) outside Albuquerque, New Mexico. The company dropped its homebuilding operations outside of New Mexico in the late 1990s, and after restructuring its real estate segment exited homebuilding all together. Company director and publishing and real estate executive Nicholas Karabots owns about 55% of AMREP.

	Annual Growth	4/03	4/04	4/05	4/06	4/07
Sales ($ mil.)	29.1%	73.8	131.1	134.5	148.3	204.8
Net income ($ mil.)	63.6%	6.3	11.7	15.5	26.0	45.1
Market value ($ mil.)	59.5%	61.9	114.3	161.0	310.6	400.9
Employees	(5.1%)	—	—	1,365	1,295	—

AMS HEALTH SCIENCES, INC.

OTC: AMSI

711 NE 39th St.
Oklahoma City, OK 73105
Phone: 405-842-0131
Fax: 405-843-4935
Web: www.amsonline.com

CEO: Jerry W. Grizzle
CFO: Sarah Nemlowill
HR: –
FYE: December 31
Type: Public

Combine green algae, ionized silver, shark cartilage, and pomegranate juice and you might find the fountain of youth, or at least the ingredients for a multi-level marketing company like AMS Health Sciences. The company's 60 products consist of dietary supplements, weight management products, and hair and skin care products — all of which are manufactured by third parties. A network of 11,000 independent distributors sell the products in Canada, Puerto Rico, and the US. Its products are sold under the Advantage, AMS, Prime One, and ToppFast brands. The company also markets and sells promotional material to its distributors. AMS has filed for Chapter 11 bankruptcy protection.

	Annual Growth	12/02	12/03	12/04	12/05	*12/06
Sales ($ mil.)	(18.8%)	22.3	18.5	18.2	13.7	9.7
Net income ($ mil.)	—	(3.2)	(2.6)	(6.3)	(3.8)	(2.2)
Employees	(21.9%)	78	69	75	38	29

*Most recent year available

AMSCAN HOLDINGS, INC.

80 Grasslands Rd.
Elmsford, NY 10523
Phone: 914-345-2020
Fax: 914-345-3884
Web: www.amscan.com

CEO: Gerald C. (Jerry) Rittenberg
CFO: Michael A. Correale
HR: Laura Bucci
FYE: December 31
Type: Private

Amscan caters to the party animal in all of us. The company designs, makes, and distributes party goods, including balloons, invitations, piñatas, stationery, and tableware to party superstores and other retailers worldwide. On the retail side of the business Amscan owns or franchises about 955 party supply stores in the US, Puerto Rico, and Dubai under the Party City, Party America, and Factory Card & Party Outlet banners, among others. Amscan makes party items and buys the rest from other manufacturers, primarily in Asia. It has production and distribution facilities in Asia, Australia, Europe, and North America.

	Annual Growth	12/02	12/03	12/04	12/05	12/06
Sales ($ mil.)	27.4%	385.6	402.8	399.2	417.7	1,015.1
Net income ($ mil.)	(21.1%)	16.5	17.2	7.7	12.3	6.4
Employees	20.3%	2,000	1,900	1,750	3,550	4,194

AMSEC LLC

2829 Guardian Ln.
Virginia Beach, VA 23452
Phone: 757-463-6666
Fax: 757-463-9110
Web: amsec.com

CEO: Harris Leonard
CFO: Michael Helpinstill
HR: Kelly J. Carlan
FYE: January 31
Type: Subsidiary

AMSEC allows the navy to run a tight ship. The company supplies naval architecture and marine engineering services to commercial companies and the US Navy. With more than 20 locations near domestic US naval and marine industrial bases, AMSEC's technical staff provides engineering, logistics, technical support, and maintenance services for virtually any shipboard system on a variety of ships, including aircraft carriers and submarines. AMSEC was founded in 1981 and was a joint venture between SAIC and Northrop Grumman Newport News Shipbuilding until 2007 when it was restructured — its operations split between its two owners — and it became a wholly owned subsidiary of Northrop Grumman.

	Annual Growth	1/03	1/04	1/05	1/06	1/07
Est. sales ($ mil.)	—	—	—	—	—	473.2
Employees	—	—	—	—	—	4,500

AMSTED INDUSTRIES INCORPORATED

2 Prudential Plaza, 180 N. Stetson St., Ste. 1800
Chicago, IL 60601
Phone: 312-645-1700
Fax: 312-819-8494
Web: www.amsted.com

CEO: W. Robert Reum
CFO: Stephen Gregory
HR: Shirley J. Whitesell
FYE: September 30
Type: Private

Wilbur and Orville Wright's first flight might never have succeeded without an assist from Amsted Industries' Diamond Chain subsidiary. A maker of roller chains for a variety of equipment and machinery, Diamond Chain also produced the propeller chain for the Wright brothers' aircraft. The company has three main segments, selling its products to industrial distributors, locomotive and railcar manufacturers, and automotive OEMs. Employee-owned Amsted Industries has nearly 50 plants worldwide. North American customers account for 85% of the company's sales.

	Annual Growth	9/02	9/03	9/04	9/05	9/06
Sales ($ mil.)	22.4%	1,360.0	2,000.0	1,600.0	2,500.0	3,050.0
Employees	2.4%	9,000	9,200	9,100	9,600	9,884

AMSURG CORP.

NASDAQ (GS): AMSG

20 Burton Hills Blvd.
Nashville, TN 37215
Phone: 615-665-1283
Fax: 615-665-0755
Web: www.amsurg.com

CEO: Christopher A. Holden
CFO: Claire M. Gulmi
HR: Julie Farris
FYE: December 31
Type: Public

AmSurg serves only certain cuts, but it's not a pricey steakhouse — the company operates specialty ambulatory surgery centers that focus on a narrow range of high-volume, low-risk procedures in such specialties as gastroenterology (colonoscopy and endoscopy), orthopedics (knee scopes and carpal tunnel repair), and ophthalmology (cataracts and laser eye surgery). AmSurg promotes its centers, which are each affiliated with a physicians practice group, to patients and doctors, as well as managed care organizations and employers. AmSurg owns a majority interest in some 180 outpatient centers, mainly gastroenterology centers, in 32 states and the District of Columbia.

	Annual Growth	12/03	12/04	12/05	12/06	12/07
Sales ($ mil.)	15.2%	301.4	334.3	391.8	464.6	531.1
Net income ($ mil.)	10.1%	30.1	39.7	35.2	37.7	44.2
Market value ($ mil.)	13.6%	507.8	869.1	678.7	688.5	844.3
Employees	—	—	—	1,705	—	—

AMTECH SYSTEMS, INC.

NASDAQ (GM): ASYS

131 S. Clark Dr.
Tempe, AZ 85281
Phone: 480-967-5146
Fax: 480-968-3763
Web: www.amtechsystems.com

CEO: Jong S. Whang
CFO: Bradley C. Anderson
HR: Katherine Burgess
FYE: September 30
Type: Public

Amtech Systems furnishes fabs with furnaces and more. The company's Tempress Systems subsidiary makes diffusion furnaces for semiconductor fabrication and for precision thermal processing — including annealing, brazing, silvering, sealing, and soldering — of electronic devices, including optical components and solar cells. Its P.R. Hoffman Machine Products subsidiary makes equipment used to polish items, including silicon wafers, precision optics, ceramic components, and disk media. Amtech Systems gets about half of its sales from the Asia/Pacific region, primarily from China and Taiwan.

	Annual Growth	9/03	9/04	9/05	9/06	9/07
Sales ($ mil.)	24.1%	19.4	19.3	27.9	40.4	46.0
Net income ($ mil.)	—	(0.1)	(3.2)	(0.3)	1.3	2.4
Market value ($ mil.)	56.2%	14.0	11.6	15.6	23.1	83.6
Employees	11.7%	106	132	144	153	165

AMTROL, INC.

1400 Division Rd.
West Warwick, RI 02893
Phone: 401-884-6300
Fax: 401-884-4773
Web: www.amtrol.com

CEO: Larry T. Guillemette
CFO: Joseph L. (Joe) DePaula
HR: Michael Montigny
FYE: December 31
Type: Private

AMTROL will help you to not sweat the small stuff. A maker of HVAC (heating/ventilation/air conditioning) expansion and pressure control products used in water systems, the company's products include well water accumulators, hot water expansion controls, and indirect-fired water heaters. Its brands include CHAMPION, EXTROL, Therm-X-Trol, Water Worker, and Well-X-Trol. AMTROL's distribution network of independent dealers reaches 1,600 customers in North America alone — which is not to mention AMTROL's extensive reach in Europe. Investment firm The Cypress Group owns the company. Late in 2006, AMTROL filed for Chapter 11 bankruptcy protection.

AMTRUST BANK

1801 E. 9th St., Ste. 200
Cleveland, OH 44114
Phone: 216-696-2222
Fax: 216-622-4417
Web: www.amtrust.com

CEO: Robert Goldberg
CFO: –
HR: –
FYE: September 30
Type: Private

AmTrust Bank has more than 50 branches and loan offices in the Buckeye State, concentrated in and around Cleveland, Akron, and Columbus. Not content to stay in just one state, AmTrust moved into southeastern Florida in the late 1980s and Arizona in 2000. To better reflect its expansion, the bank's name was changed from Ohio Savings to AmTrust Bank in 2007. The company provides traditional retail services such as checking and savings accounts, credit cards, and CDs. Its banks concentrate on residential lending, primarily one- to four-family residential mortgages. The company traces its roots to Ohio Savings' founding in 1889.

	Annual Growth	9/03	9/04	9/05	9/06	9/07
Est. sales ($ mil.)	—	—	—	—	—	1,083.6
Employees	—	—	—	—	—	1,600

An in-depth profile of this company is available to Hoover's Online members at hoovers.com.

141

AMTRUST FINANCIAL SERVICES, INC.

NASDAQ (GM): AFSI

59 Maiden Ln., 6th Fl.
New York, NY 10038
Phone: 212-220-7120
Fax: –
Web: www.amtrustgroup.com

CEO: Barry D. Zyskind
CFO: Ronald E. Pipoly Jr.
HR: –
FYE: December 31
Type: Public

Catering specifically to small businesses (with an average of six employees), AmTrust offers specialty property/casualty insurance, workers' compensation, and extended service and warranty coverage. Its seven subsidiaries, which operate in the US, Bermuda, Ireland, and England, underwrite insurance policies that are then distributed through brokers, agents, and claims administrators. Its customers include such businesses as restaurants, retail stores, physicians' offices, auto and consumer electronics manufacturers, and non-profit organizations. Chairman Michael Karfunkel holds 30% of the company, his brother George Karfunkel holds 30%, and his son-in-law CEO Barry Zyskind holds 10%.

	Annual Growth	12/03	12/04	12/05	12/06	12/07
Assets ($ mil.)	67.1%	—	497.5	611.3	1,185.4	2,322.8
Net income ($ mil.)	85.6%	—	14.1	37.6	48.9	90.1
Market value ($ mil.)	61.0%	—	—	—	512.6	825.5
Employees	—	—	—	—	325	—

AMWINS GROUP, INC.

4064 Colony Rd., Ste. 450
Charlotte, NC 28211
Phone: 704-943-2000
Fax: 704-943-9000
Web: www.amwins.com

CEO: M. Steven (Steve) DeCarlo
CFO: Scott M. Purviance
HR: Kristin L. Downey
FYE: December 31
Type: Private

AmWINS is rarely at a loss when it comes to insurance. The company is among the largest wholesale insurance brokers in the US (along with Swett & Crawford and Crump). The group sells insurance products — including property/casualty, group benefits, and specialty coverage — to retail brokers across the country. It also provides underwriting of specialty insurance products for niches including armored cars, broadcasters, and Domino's franchise owners. The company also offers additional services such as administration and actuarial services for some products. Private equity firm Parthenon Capital acquired a majority stake in AmWINS in 2005.

	Annual Growth	12/02	12/03	12/04	12/05	12/06
Sales ($ mil.)	47.1%	—	58.2	84.6	142.3	185.3
Employees	18.5%	—	—	695	976	976

AMX CORPORATION

3000 Research Dr.
Richardson, TX 75082
Phone: 469-624-8000
Fax: 469-624-7153
Web: www.amxcorp.com

CEO: Rashid M. Skaf
CFO: Chris Apple
HR: Steve H. Byars
FYE: December 31
Type: Subsidiary

Like a football fan on Sunday, AMX knows how to work the remote control. The company designs and sells systems that control devices such as lights, audio and video equipment, and security cameras from a common remote interface. Its systems are used in corporate, educational, entertainment, industrial, and government settings. AMX also offers residential systems that control security systems, lighting, and electronic devices in the home. The firm sells its products through manufacturers and distributors. Founded in 1982, AMX was acquired by Duchossois Industries for about $315 million in early 2005.

	Annual Growth	12/03	12/04	12/05	12/06	12/07
Est. sales ($ mil.)	—	—	—	—	—	25.5
Employees	—	—	—	—	—	346

AMYLIN PHARMACEUTICALS, INC.

NASDAQ (GS): AMLN

9360 Towne Centre Dr.
San Diego, CA 92121
Phone: 858-552-2200
Fax: 858-552-2212
Web: www.amylin.com

CEO: Daniel M. (Dan) Bradbury
CFO: Mark G. Foletta
HR: Roger Marchetti
FYE: December 31
Type: Public

Amylin Pharmaceuticals helps diabetics gain the upper hand in their battle with the disease. The company makes and markets two injectable diabetes drugs, Byetta and Symlin, that are approved as adjunct therapies to other diabetes treatments such as metformin and insulin. Development partner Eli Lilly markets Byetta worldwide and is responsible for the development of Byetta in international markets. Amylin's US-based sales force co-promotes the drug and markets Symlin on its own. The company is working on other diabetes drugs, including a once-weekly version of Byetta, as well as treatments for obesity.

	Annual Growth	12/03	12/04	12/05	12/06	12/07
Sales ($ mil.)	73.7%	85.7	34.3	140.5	510.9	781.0
Net income ($ mil.)	—	(122.8)	(157.2)	(206.8)	(218.9)	(211.1)
Market value ($ mil.)	24.4%	2,089.2	2,207.3	4,450.6	4,705.6	4,996.6
Employees	28.5%	—	—	1,150	1,550	1,900

AMY'S KITCHEN, INC.

2227 Capricorn Way, Ste. 201
Santa Rosa, CA 95407
Phone: 707-578-7188
Fax: 707-578-7995
Web: www.amyskitchen.com

CEO: Andy Berliner
CFO: Don Watts
HR: –
FYE: June 30
Type: Private

Amy's Kitchen is an answer to the prayers of vegetarians scouring the frozen-dinner and packaged-food aisles of their supermarkets. The company, which makes some 150 different frozen and pre-packaged vegetarian items using all-natural and organic ingredients, is also a popular option for non-vegetarian, health-conscious consumers. Its products include frozen entrees, pocket sandwiches, pizzas, pot pies, toaster pops, veggie burgers, canned soups, beans, and chili, along with jarred pasta sauces and salsa. Amy's distributes its specialty meals through leading supermarkets, natural foods and grocery stores, and warehouse and club stores throughout the US and Canada.

	Annual Growth	6/03	6/04	6/05	6/06	6/07
Est. sales ($ mil.)	—	—	—	—	—	80.3
Employees	—	—	—	—	—	860

⊞ ANACOMP, INC.

Pink Sheets: ANCPA

15378 Avenue of Science
San Diego, CA 92128
Phone: 858-716-3400
Fax: 858-716-3775
Web: www.anacomp.com

CEO: Howard Dratler
CFO: Jeffrey S. (Jeff) Cartwright
HR: Joette Briggs
FYE: September 30
Type: Public

Forget *The X-Files*, Anacomp has the e-files. The company's electronic information management services and products are used by companies throughout the banking, insurance, investment, telecommunications, and transportation industries. Anacomp provides document management services and technology for clients throughout North America and Western Europe. Its docHarbor suite of products prepares, scans, stores, and manipulates documents for online conversion. In 2006, Anacomp acquired Virginia-based Imaging Acceptance Corporation (IAC), a fellow document services specialist serving the federal government sector. The company, which was founded in 1968, takes its name from the combination of "ANAlyse" and "COMpute."

	Annual Growth	9/03	9/04	9/05	9/06	9/07
Sales ($ mil.)	(7.9%)	204.0	184.4	168.3	151.7	147.0
Employees	10.0%	—	—	—	1,000	1,100

ANADARKO PETROLEUM CORPORATION

NYSE: APC

1201 Lake Robbins Dr.
The Woodlands, TX 77380
Phone: 832-636-1000
Fax: 832-636-8220
Web: www.anadarko.com

CEO: James T. (Jim) Hackett
CFO: R. A. (Al) Walker
HR: Preston H. Johnson Jr.
FYE: December 31
Type: Public

Anadarko Petroleum has ventured beyond its original area of operation — the Anadarko Basin — to explore for, develop, produce, and market oil, natural gas, natural gas liquids, and related products worldwide. The large independent company has proved reserves of 1 billion barrels of crude oil and 8.5 trillion cu. ft. of natural gas, more than 70% of which are located in the Continental US. Other activities include coal, trona, and mineral mining. Anadarko operates seven gas-gathering systems in the mid-continent. Internationally, the company has substantial oil and gas interests in Algeria's Sahara Desert, Venezuela, and western Canada.

	Annual Growth	12/03	12/04	12/05	12/06	12/07
Sales ($ mil.)	32.7%	5,122.0	6,067.0	7,100.0	10,187.0	15,892.0
Net income ($ mil.)	30.8%	1,292.0	1,606.0	2,471.0	4,854.0	3,781.0
Market value ($ mil.)	47.5%	6,503.8	7,767.5	10,986.3	20,323.8	30,742.9
Employees	57.6%	—	—	3,300	5,200	—

ANADIGICS, INC.

NASDAQ (GM): ANAD

141 Mt. Bethel Rd.
Warren, NJ 07059
Phone: 908-668-5000
Fax: 908-668-5068
Web: www.anadigics.com

CEO: Bami Bastani
CFO: Thomas C. Shields
HR: –
FYE: December 31
Type: Public

ANADIGICS makes chips that cook with GaAs. The company makes gallium arsenide (GaAs) and indium phosphide (InP) radio-frequency integrated circuits for cable television systems, wireless communications devices, and fiber-optic equipment. GaAs and InP are costlier than silicon, but their physical properties allow the compound materials to be used for chips that are smaller and faster or more energy-efficient than silicon chips. ANADIGICS' power amplifiers, switches, and other chips can be found in the cell phones, cable modems, set-top boxes, and other gear of Intel (22% of sales), Kyocera, LG Electronics (10%), Motorola, Samsung Electronics (13%), Huawei Technologies (also 10%), and Cisco Systems (also 10%).

	Annual Growth	12/03	12/04	12/05	12/06	12/07
Sales ($ mil.)	32.3%	75.2	91.3	108.3	169.9	230.6
Net income ($ mil.)	—	(50.8)	(43.1)	(31.2)	(8.9)	5.9
Market value ($ mil.)	39.7%	186.1	124.0	209.4	434.9	707.8
Employees	6.8%	480	424	439	508	625

ANADYS PHARMACEUTICALS, INC.

NASDAQ (GM): ANDS

3115 Merrifield Row
San Diego, CA 92121
Phone: 858-530-3600
Fax: 858-527-1540
Web: www.anadyspharma.com

CEO: Stephen T. Worland
CFO: James T. (Jim) Glover
HR: Mary Yaroshevsky-Glanville
FYE: December 31
Type: Public

Anadys Pharmaceuticals has hepatitis and cancer in the crosshairs. The biotechnology company is developing new therapeutic treatments for those infected with hepatitis C (HCV) and other bacterial infections, as well as for applications in oncology. Anadys is exploring compounds that either act as direct antivirals or stimulate the body's immune system responses to fight disease. Anadys Pharmaceuticals seeks out strategic alliances with other pharmaceutical firms for development and licensing arrangements. The company has licensed its drug discovery technologies to such firms as Daiichi Sankyo, Roche, and Amgen.

	Annual Growth	12/03	12/04	12/05	12/06	12/07
Sales ($ mil.)	79.9%	2.3	1.8	4.9	5.4	24.1
Net income ($ mil.)	—	(24.0)	(33.0)	(21.9)	(26.8)	(9.2)
Market value ($ mil.)	(34.9%)	—	167.3	249.7	140.7	46.2
Employees	—	—	—	92	—	—

ANALEX CORPORATION

2677 Prosperity Ave., Ste. 400
Fairfax, VA 22031
Phone: 703-852-4000
Fax: 703-852-2200
Web: www.analex.com

CEO: Michael G. Stolarik
CFO: Kathryn JohnBull
HR: Elisa Rivera
FYE: December 31
Type: Subsidiary

Analex brings together science and security. Formerly Hadron, the company provides a range of research, science, and technology services for homeland security and defense-related projects. Its homeland security and systems engineering units provide engineering, program management, and systems integration services to the US Department of Defense, US intelligence agencies, NASA, and aerospace contractors. In 2006 the company sold its SyCom Services subsidiary to Florida-based staffing firm Ameri-Force Craft Services. A year later Analex merged with QinetiQ North America, a subsidiary of British firm QinetiQ Group.

ANALOG DEVICES, INC.

NYSE: ADI

1 Technology Way
Norwood, MA 02062
Phone: 781-329-4700
Fax: 781-461-4482
Web: www.analog.com

CEO: Jerald G. (Jerry) Fishman
CFO: Joseph E. McDonough
HR: William (Bill) Matson
FYE: Saturday nearest October 31
Type: Public

Analog Devices, Inc. (ADI) is fluent in both analog and digital. The company is a leading maker of analog (linear and mixed-signal) and digital integrated circuits (ICs), including digital signal processors (DSPs). Its linear ICs translate real-world phenomena such as pressure, temperature, and sound into digital signals. ADI's thousands of chip designs are used in industrial applications, medical and scientific instrumentation, communications equipment, computers, and consumer electronics devices. ADI's chips are used in high-tech goods from companies such as Alcatel-Lucent, Dell, Ericsson, Philips, Siemens, and Sony. Customers outside the US account for about three-quarters of ADI's sales.

	Annual Growth	10/03	10/04	10/05	10/06	10/07
Sales ($ mil.)	5.6%	2,047.3	2,633.8	2,388.8	2,573.2	2,546.1
Net income ($ mil.)	13.6%	298.3	570.7	414.8	549.5	496.9
Market value ($ mil.)	(11.7%)	16,412.5	15,131.3	12,696.0	10,646.5	9,980.4
Employees	3.4%	8,400	8,900	8,800	9,800	9,600

ANALOGIC CORPORATION

NASDAQ (GS): ALOG

8 Centennial Dr.
Peabody, MA 01960
Phone: 978-326-4000
Fax: 978-977-6810
Web: www.analogic.com

CEO: James W. (Jim) Green
CFO: John J. Millerick
HR: Douglas B. Rosenfeld
FYE: July 31
Type: Public

Analogic uses data logically. The company's data acquisition, conversion, and signal processing gear converts analog signals such as pressure, temperature, and X-rays into digital computer data. Its medical image processing systems, digital signal processors, and security imaging products are used in equipment including CAT and MRI scanners, luggage inspection systems, semiconductor test equipment, and industrial weighing gear. Top customers include Toshiba (18% of sales), L-3 Communications (11%), Siemens, GE, and Philips. About half of the company's sales come from the US. Analogic also owns a Boston-area hotel.

	Annual Growth	7/03	7/04	7/05	7/06	7/07
Sales ($ mil.)	(7.8%)	471.5	355.6	364.6	351.4	340.8
Net income ($ mil.)	(25.3%)	49.5	8.4	28.9	25.1	15.4
Market value ($ mil.)	7.9%	653.4	568.6	709.1	637.9	886.3
Employees	(4.5%)	1,800	1,700	1,725	1,500	1,500

An in-depth profile of this company is available to Hoover's Online members at hoovers.com.

ANALYSTS INTERNATIONAL CORPORATION

NASDAQ (GM): ANLY

3601 W. 76th St.
Minneapolis, MN 55435
Phone: 952-835-5900
Fax: 952-897-4555
Web: www.analysts.com

CEO: Elmer Baldwin
CFO: Walter P. (Mic) Michels
HR: Angelia Smith-Brekke
FYE: Saturday nearest December 31
Type: Public

These analysts will put your technology on the couch. Analysts International provides a wide range of information technology (IT) and business consulting services, including mainframe migrations, network analysis and design, custom programming, project management, and Internet/intranet development. The company's customers come from industries such as oil and gas, manufacturing, telecommunications, and retail. Its Managed Services division provides help desk, software engineering, and other outsourced technical staffing primarily to large corporations.

	Annual Growth	12/03	12/04	12/05	12/06	12/07
Sales ($ mil.)	2.0%	331.9	341.6	322.3	347.0	359.7
Net income ($ mil.)	—	(1.5)	3.8	(17.7)	(1.1)	(16.2)
Market value ($ mil.)	(18.1%)	77.0	96.8	59.0	46.2	34.6
Employees	(11.5%)	—	3,015	3,095	2,397	2,093

ANALYTICAL SURVEYS, INC.

OTC: ANLT

4040 Broadway, Ste. 103
San Antonio, TX 78209
Phone: 210-657-1500
Fax: –
Web: www.asienergy.com

CEO: James Kerstein
CFO: Michael W. Johnson
HR: –
FYE: September 30
Type: Public

Analytical Surveys, Inc. (ASI) has surveyed the landscape and decided to shift into a new line of business. ASI's traditional business line had involved providing data conversion, data management, and technical services for the geographic information systems (GIS) industry. The company also digitized paper maps and aerial photographs and added related information, such as utility rights-of-way, property lines, and roads. Facing increased competition and unable to secure new clients, the company shifted its focus to the oil and gas industry. In 2007 ASI announced yet another shift in plans, this time to merge with Axion International, a licensee of advanced technology regarding plastic composition.

	Annual Growth	9/03	9/04	9/05	9/06	9/07
Sales ($ mil.)	(55.3%)	15.0	11.6	6.1	4.3	0.6
Net income ($ mil.)	—	(3.3)	(1.3)	(3.3)	(0.3)	(4.5)
Market value ($ mil.)	28.6%	1.2	1.4	3.9	2.6	—
Employees	(66.8%)	—	109	82	9	4

ANAREN, INC.

NASDAQ (GM): ANEN

6635 Kirkville Rd.
East Syracuse, NY 13057
Phone: 315-432-8909
Fax: 315-432-9121
Web: www.anaren.com

CEO: Lawrence A. Sala
CFO: Joseph E. Porcello
HR: Amy B. Tewksbury
FYE: June 30
Type: Public

Anaren is hot for things wireless. The company makes microwave components, assemblies, and subsystems used in signal processing devices for wireless communications, satellite communications, and defense electronics. Its products include signal splitters, combiners, and microwave backplanes that wireless equipment makers incorporate into their amplifiers, receivers, and cellular base station gear. Anaren also custom builds subassemblies and components for satellite and military applications. The company counts Boeing, Ericsson, Motorola, Nokia (about 16% of sales), and Raytheon (13%) among its customers. Anaren gets more than half of its sales in the US.

	Annual Growth	6/03	6/04	6/05	6/06	6/07
Sales ($ mil.)	12.7%	79.9	85.1	94.5	105.5	129.0
Net income ($ mil.)	—	(3.8)	8.0	7.4	11.1	15.4
Market value ($ mil.)	8.5%	208.1	335.8	230.4	360.8	288.4
Employees	—	—	—	587	—	—

ANCHIN, BLOCK & ANCHIN LLP

1375 Broadway
New York, NY 10018
Phone: 212-840-3456
Fax: 212-840-7066
Web: www.anchin.com

CEO: James Anchin
CFO: –
HR: David Finkelstein
FYE: September 30
Type: Partnership

Anchin, Block & Anchin is good with numbers. The accounting and consulting firm concentrates on privately held businesses. Industry specializations include construction, real estate, and law firms. Anchin, Block & Anchin partners also serve wealthy clients with investment, family office, and other services. Anchin, Block & Anchin, which was founded in 1923, provides services outside the US through its affiliation with HLB International. Subsidiaries and affiliates specialize in such areas as mergers and acquisitions, workers compensation premium reduction, and cost reduction.

	Annual Growth	9/03	9/04	9/05	9/06	9/07
Est. sales ($ mil.)	—	—	—	—	—	18.2
Employees	—	—	—	—	—	300

ANCHOR BANCORP WISCONSIN INC.

NASDAQ (GS): ABCW

25 W. Main St.
Madison, WI 53703
Phone: 608-252-8700
Fax: 608-252-8976
Web: www.anchorbank.com

CEO: Douglas J. Timmerman
CFO: Dale C. Ringgenberg
HR: –
FYE: March 31
Type: Public

Anchor BanCorp Wisconsin is the holding company for AnchorBank, which has about 75 branches across the Badger State and in parts of Illinois, Iowa, and Minnesota. The thrift targets individuals and local businesses, offering checking and savings accounts, money market accounts, CDs, and IRAs, as well as insurance and investment products. Single-family residential mortgages account for more than 20% of the bank's loan book; commercial real estate loans make up about 25%. Other loans include construction loans, second mortgages, home equity loans, and student loans. Subsidiary Investment Directions participates in partnerships that develop and sell real estate.

	Annual Growth	3/04	3/05	3/06	3/07	3/08
Assets ($ mil.)	7.8%	3,810.4	4,050.5	4,275.1	4,539.7	5,149.6
Net income ($ mil.)	(10.0%)	47.4	48.3	44.7	39.0	31.1
Market value ($ mil.)	(8.6%)	580.5	627.4	662.4	614.3	405.0
Employees	0.5%	—	967	988	976	—

ANCHOR GLASS CONTAINER CORPORATION

3101 W. M.L. King Jr. Blvd., Ste. 301
Tampa, FL 33607
Phone: 813-884-0000
Fax: –
Web: www.anchorglass.com

CEO: Brian N. Bussell
CFO: James (Jim) Fredlake
HR: –
FYE: December 31
Type: Private

In a sea of packaging companies, Anchor Glass Container has established its position as one of the leading glass container manufacturers in the US, behind Owens-Illinois and Saint-Gobain Containers. Anchor Glass Container serves companies in the beverage and food industries, including producers of beer and liquor. It produces clear and colored glass containers through several US facilities. Once a subsidiary of the bankrupt Consumers Packaging of Canada, Anchor Glass Container filed for Chapter 11 bankruptcy protection in 2002 and emerged in 2003 before going public that year. It filed for bankruptcy protection again in 2005; it emerged from Chapter 11 as it went private the next year.

	Annual Growth	12/03	12/04	12/05	12/06	12/07
Est. sales ($ mil.)	—	—	—	—	—	290.5
Employees	—	—	—	—	—	2,840

ANCHOR HOCKING COMPANY

519 Pierce Ave.
Lancaster, OH 43130
Phone: 740-681-6478
Fax: 740-681-6040
Web: www.anchorhocking.com

CEO: Mark R. Eichhorn
CFO: –
HR: –
FYE: December 31
Type: Private

The Anchor Hocking name is nearly synonymous with glassware. The Anchor Hocking Company, in existence for more than a century, manufactures beverageware (glasses, pitchers), cookware (pans, casserole dishes), servingware (platters, cake sets, punch bowls), storage items (canisters), and giftware (vases). It also serves as a third-party manufacturer for other companies. Anchor Hocking products are sold through US retailers, such as Wal-Mart and Target, as well as directly to foodservice and specialty markets. Private equity firm Monomoy Capital Partners, which focuses on middle market investments, bought Anchor Hocking in March 2007 for $75 million.

	Annual Growth	12/03	12/04	12/05	12/06	12/07
Est. sales ($ mil.)	—	—	—	—	—	610.9
Employees	—	—	—	—	—	8,900

ANCIRA

6111 Bandera Rd.
San Antonio, TX 78238
Phone: 210-681-4900
Fax: 210-681-9413
Web: www.ancira.com

CEO: Ernesto Ancira Jr.
CFO: Betty Ferguson
HR: –
FYE: December 31
Type: Private

ANCIRA wants to help Texans hit the road: It sells cars, trucks, and recreational vehicles from more than a dozen dealerships all located in the Lone Star State. The company's dealerships feature new vehicles under the Buick, Chevrolet, Chrysler, Ford, GMC, Jeep, Kia, Nissan, Pontiac, and Volkswagen brands, as well as used cars and trucks. ANCIRA also sells new and used campers, motor homes, and recreational vehicles under the Fleetwood and Winnebago names, among others. The company operates on-site parts and service departments. ANCIRA, which was founded in 1972, is owned by president Ernesto Ancira.

	Annual Growth	12/03	12/04	12/05	12/06	12/07
Est. sales ($ mil.)	—	—	—	—	—	232.5
Employees	—	—	—	—	—	701

ANDERSEN CORPORATION

100 4th Ave. North
Bayport, MN 55003
Phone: 651-264-5150
Fax: 651-264-5107
Web: www.andersenwindows.com

CEO: James E. (Jim) Humphrey
CFO: Philip (Phil) Donaldson
HR: Mary D. Carter
FYE: December 31
Type: Private

Windows of opportunity open daily for Andersen, a leading and well-known maker of wood-clad windows and patio doors in the US. Andersen offers window designs from hinged, bay, and double-hung to skylight, gliding, and picture windows. It operates more than 100 Renewal by Andersen window replacement stores in around 35 states. Andersen's EMCO Doors subsidiary makes storm and screen doors. Through independent and company-owned distributorships (including its Andersen Logistics division), Andersen sells to homeowners, architects, builders, designers, and remodelers. The company is owned by the Andersen family, the Andersen Foundation, and company employees.

	Annual Growth	12/02	12/03	12/04	12/05	12/06
Est. sales ($ mil.)	10.7%	2,000.0	2,000.0	2,500.0	3,000.0	3,000.0
Employees	15.0%	8,000	8,000	8,500	16,000	14,000

ANDERSON NEWS, LLC

6016 Brookvale Ln., Ste. 151
Knoxville, TN 37919
Phone: 865-584-9765
Fax: 865-584-7769
Web: www.andersonnews.com

CEO: Charles (Charlie) Anderson
CFO: John Campbell
HR: Carl Boley
FYE: December 31
Type: Private

Anderson News is the cover girl of the magazine wholesale industry. The company is one of the top US magazine distributors. It distributes thousands of magazine titles to about 40,000 outlets in 45 states, including bookstores, mass merchants, grocery stores, discount retailers, and just about any place that sells books and magazines. The company distributes best-selling books and comics as well. Anderson News also owns Liquid Digital Music, an online music download service used by retailers like Wal-Mart and Amazon.com. Anderson News was founded in 1917 by CEO Charles Anderson's grandfather; it is still family owned. The founding Anderson family also runs the #3 US bookstore chain, Books-A-Million.

	Annual Growth	12/02	12/03	12/04	12/05	12/06
Est. sales ($ mil.)	20.9%	1,100.0	1,100.0	1,300.0	2,696.0	2,350.0
Employees	9.3%	7,000	7,000	8,400	12,100	10,000

THE ANDERSONS, INC.

NASDAQ (GS): ANDE

480 W. Dussel Dr.
Maumee, OH 43537
Phone: 419-893-5050
Fax: 419-891-6670
Web: www.andersonsinc.com

CEO: Michael J. Anderson
CFO: Gary L. Smith
HR: Charles E. Gallagher
FYE: December 31
Type: Public

The Andersons earns its daily bread on a mix of grains, trains, and corncobs. Founded in 1947, the agricultural firm buys, conditions, and resells corn, soybeans, and wheat through elevators and terminals located in the Midwest. The Andersons also runs six retail home-center stores in Ohio that sell home-improvement products, nursery stock, groceries, and other items. Its turf and specialty unit shreds corncobs into animal bedding, pet litter, and turf materials. The company's rail group sells, leases, repairs, and reconfigures railcars and locomotives.

	Annual Growth	12/03	12/04	12/05	12/06	12/07
Sales ($ mil.)	17.5%	1,247.0	1,275.3	1,296.7	1,458.1	2,379.1
Net income ($ mil.)	55.7%	11.7	19.1	26.1	36.3	68.8
Market value ($ mil.)	93.5%	57.5	93.8	163.7	750.6	806.5
Employees	3.6%	—	—	2,750	2,862	2,953

ANDREA ELECTRONICS CORPORATION

OTC: ANDR

65 Orville Dr., Ste. 1
Bohemia, NY 11716
Phone: 631-719-1800
Fax: 631-719-1998
Web: www.andreaelectronics.com

CEO: Douglas J. Andrea
CFO: Corisa L. Guiffre
HR: –
FYE: December 31
Type: Public

Andrea Electronics wants to make a big noise with its Anti-Noise technology. The company's Anti-Noise products include software that increases voice clarity and reduces background noise, plus headsets that enhance audio in high-noise environments. Andrea Electronics also offers voice recognition products for voice-activated computing applications such as word processing. The company designs its products for audio and video conferencing, call centers, in-vehicle communications, and personal computing. Andrea sells directly and through distributors, software publishers, Internet software providers, and other resellers.

	Annual Growth	12/03	12/04	12/05	12/06	12/07
Sales ($ mil.)	0.0%	5.1	5.6	4.2	5.7	5.1
Net income ($ mil.)	—	(4.3)	(1.7)	(0.6)	0.0	(0.4)
Market value ($ mil.)	(2.8%)	—	3.6	2.1	8.0	3.3
Employees	—	—	—	—	—	16

An in-depth profile of this company is available to Hoover's Online members at hoovers.com.

145

ANDREW CORPORATION

3 Westbrook Corporate Center, Ste. 900
Westchester, IL 60154
Phone: 708-236-6600
Fax: 708-349-5444
Web: www.andrew.com

CEO: Ralph E. Faison
CFO: Marty R. Kittrell
HR: Robert J. (Bob) Hudzik
FYE: September 30
Type: Subsidiary

Andrew Corporation puts the "structure" in global wireless communications infrastructure. The company's microwave networking equipment and systems include cellular base stations and antennas, antenna towers, transmitters, and receivers. Its equipment is used to build cell phone and other wireless communications networks. Other products include transmission line cable used to connect wireless components and radar antennas. Andrew serves distributors of telecommunications equipment, wireless network operators such as AT&T Mobility and Verizon Wireless, and industrial manufacturers like Siemens. The company is a subsidiary of CommScope.

	Annual Growth	9/03	9/04	9/05	9/06	9/07
Sales ($ mil.)	21.3%	1,014.5	1,838.8	1,961.2	2,146.1	2,195.1
Net income ($ mil.)	—	15.5	33.0	38.9	(34.3)	(162.8)
Employees	6.1%	—	9,408	11,318	11,778	11,251

ANESIVA, INC.

NASDAQ (GM): ANSV

650 Gateway Blvd.
South San Francisco, CA 94080
Phone: 650-624-9600
Fax: 650-624-7540
Web: www.anesiva.com

CEO: John P. McLaughlin
CFO: Jean-Frederic Viret
HR: –
FYE: December 31
Type: Public

Anesiva wants to keep pain at bay. The biopharmaceutical firm is developing treatments for pain management with product candidates that include Zingo, a fast-acting, needle-free local anesthetic designed to reduce the pain of IV insertion, and Adlea, an analgesic for post-surgical pain after orthopedic surgery and osteoarthritis treatment. Zingo has been approved by the FDA for blood draws in children ages three to 18; it has also filed for approval in the adult population. Anesiva has a co-promotion agreement with Sagent Pharmaceuticals to distribute Zingo to US hospitals. It also has marketing and distribution agreements with Medical Futures in Canada and Sigma-Tau in several countries in Europe.

	Annual Growth	12/03	12/04	12/05	12/06	12/07
Sales ($ mil.)	0.0%	—	—	—	0.1	0.1
Net income ($ mil.)	—	—	—	—	(55.6)	(59.3)
Market value ($ mil.)	6.4%	—	—	—	189.7	201.9
Employees	—	—	—	—	—	—

ANGEION CORPORATION

NASDAQ (CM): ANGN

350 Oak Grove Pkwy.
St. Paul, MN 55127
Phone: 651-484-4874
Fax: 651-379-8227
Web: www.angeion.com

CEO: Rodney A. Young
CFO: William J. (Bill) Kullback
HR: –
FYE: October 31
Type: Public

Every breath you take, Angeion is watching you. The company designs and sells cardiorespiratory diagnostic systems that analyze lung function and diagnose disease. Its MedGraphics-branded systems are aimed at health care providers and life sciences researchers; they are non-invasive devices that analyze a patient's inhaled and exhaled breath and can help detect emphysema, asthma, and heart disease, among other things. Angeion sells one of its diagnostic systems to the health and fitness market under the brand name New Leaf; fitness professionals can help users design personalized training regimens based on the metabolic data gleaned from the New Leaf device.

	Annual Growth	10/03	10/04	10/05	10/06	10/07
Sales ($ mil.)	19.9%	18.7	20.7	23.8	33.7	38.6
Net income ($ mil.)	—	(2.8)	(2.3)	(0.9)	1.4	1.1
Market value ($ mil.)	42.0%	7.9	5.2	8.2	40.5	32.1
Employees	5.0%	—	—	127	155	140

ANGELICA CORPORATION

NYSE: AGL

424 S. Woods Mill Rd.
Chesterfield, MO 63017
Phone: 314-854-3800
Fax: 314-854-3890
Web: www.angelica.com

CEO: Stephen M. O'Hara
CFO: James W. (Jim) Shaffer
HR: Robert C. Shell
FYE: Last Saturday in January
Type: Public

Hospitals don't have to move heaven and earth to get clean sheets — Angelica will do it for them. Founded in 1878, the firm provides laundry services and rents linens to dental offices, hospitals, medical clinics, and nursing homes. Angelica rents and cleans scrubs, bed sheets, towels, gowns, and surgical linens. It also provides mops, mats, sterile surgical packs, and onsite linen room management. The company, which operates about 30 laundry service centers across more than 20 US states, has been growing through acquisitions. Investor Steel Partners, represented on the company's board, owns about 20% of Angelica. The company agreed in May 2008 to be acquired by Lehman Brothers Merchant Banking Partners.

	Annual Growth	1/04	1/05	1/06	1/07	1/08
Sales ($ mil.)	3.5%	374.3	316.1	418.4	425.7	430.0
Net income ($ mil.)	(19.3%)	9.2	6.4	0.3	3.6	3.9
Market value ($ mil.)	(2.4%)	195.5	260.0	155.6	242.5	177.3
Employees	2.2%	—	6,130	6,600	6,400	—

ANGELO, GORDON & CO.

245 Park Ave.
New York, NY 10167
Phone: 212-692-2000
Fax: 212-867-9328
Web: www.angelogordon.com

CEO: John M. Angelo
CFO: Joseph (Joe) Wekselblatt
HR: –
FYE: December 31
Type: Private

For Angelo, Gordon, bucking tradition goes hand-in-hand with making money. The hedge fund firm specializes in so-called "non-traditional" investments, such as distressed assets (bankrupt and other troubled companies), merger arbitrage (mergers, reorganizations, or liquidations), and convertible arbitrage (trading strategies-based convertible securities). Angelo, Gordon has expanded its investment activities into utility markets, real estate, and credit arbitrage. The company gives clients the choice of focusing their investments on just one of the company's strategies, or diversifying across several. Angelo, Gordon, which was founded in 1988, has about $11 billion in assets under management.

	Annual Growth	12/03	12/04	12/05	12/06	12/07
Est. sales ($ mil.)	—	—	—	—	—	364.9
Employees	—	—	—	—	—	2,683

ANGIODYNAMICS, INC.

NASDAQ (GS): ANGO

603 Queensbury Ave.
Queensbury, NY 12804
Phone: 518-798-1215
Fax: 518-798-3625
Web: www.angiodynamics.com

CEO: Eamonn P. Hobbs
CFO: D. Joseph (Joe) Gersuk
HR: –
FYE: Saturday nearest May 31
Type: Public

AngioDynamics gets your blood flowing, and flowing easier if need be. The company makes medical devices for the treatment of peripheral vascular disease (PVD), where arteries or veins in the arms or legs become blocked or restricted by plaque. AngioDynamics' interventional product line includes catheters for angiography, dialysis, and angioplasty; image-guided vascular access products; laser venous systems to treat varicose veins; and drainage products. The company also offers tools and systems for minimally invasive oncological treatments. AngioDynamics' direct sales force sells to doctors in the US; internationally, distributors sell the products in more than 30 countries.

	Annual Growth	5/03	5/04	5/05	5/06	5/07
Sales ($ mil.)	30.7%	38.4	49.1	60.3	78.4	112.2
Net income ($ mil.)	—	1.2	3.1	4.6	6.9	(9.1)
Market value ($ mil.)	35.1%	—	158.1	245.7	455.5	390.1
Employees	—	—	—	—	306	—

⊞ ANHEUSER-BUSCH COMPANIES, INC. NYSE: BUD

1 Busch Place	CEO: August A. Busch IV
St. Louis, MO 63118	CFO: W. Randolph Baker
Phone: 314-577-2000	HR: John T. (Tim) Farrell
Fax: 314-577-2900	FYE: December 31
Web: www.anheuser-busch.com	Type: Public

Anheuser-Busch Companies (A-B) wants to be the life of every party, whether with its brews or its theme parks. One of the world's largest brewers, the company is best known for Budweiser and Bud Light, as well as such labels as Busch and Michelob. Its beers lead the US with a market share of some 48%. A-B also owns a 50% stake in Mexico's top brewer, GRUPO MODLEO, maker of Corona and Negra Modelo. In addition to beer, Anheuser-Busch produces energy drinks and non-alcoholic malt beverages. The company has several operations outside of brewing as well, including its Busch Entertainment theme-park business. A-B received an unsolicited takeover offer in 2008 from Belgium brewer InBev.

	Annual Growth	12/03	12/04	12/05	12/06	12/07
Sales ($ mil.)	4.2%	14,146.7	14,934.2	15,035.7	15,717.1	16,685.7
Net income ($ mil.)	0.5%	2,075.9	2,240.3	1,839.2	1,965.2	2,115.3
Market value ($ mil.)	(3.2%)	42,706.9	39,415.1	33,352.5	37,534.0	37,430.7
Employees	(1.0%)	—	—	31,485	30,183	30,849

ANIKA THERAPEUTICS, INC. NASDAQ (GS): ANIK

160 New Boston St.	CEO: Charles H. Sherwood
Woburn, MA 01801	CFO: Kevin W. Quinlan
Phone: 781-932-6616	HR: William J. Mrachek
Fax: 781-935-7803	FYE: December 31
Web: www.anikatherapeutics.com	Type: Public

Anika Therapeutics is roosterrific. The company uses hyaluronic acid, a natural polymer extracted from rooster combs and other sources, to make products that treat bone, cartilage, and soft tissue. Anika's OrthoVisc treats osteoarthritis of the knee and is available in the US and overseas. DePuy Mitek sells the product in the US. A unit of Boehringer Ingelheim sells Anika's osteoarthritis treatment for racehorses, Hyvisc. Bausch & Lomb sells two of the company's products that maintain eye shape and protect tissue during eye surgery. Other products include surgical anti-adhesives and aesthetic dermatology products.

	Annual Growth	12/03	12/04	12/05	12/06	12/07
Sales ($ mil.)	18.9%	15.4	26.5	29.8	26.8	30.8
Net income ($ mil.)	65.5%	0.8	11.2	5.9	4.6	6.0
Market value ($ mil.)	13.8%	97.3	93.9	122.7	143.0	163.3
Employees	(1.5%)	—	—	65	64	—

ANIMAL HEALTH INTERNATIONAL, INC. NASDAQ (GM): AHII

7 Village Circle, Ste. 200	CEO: James C. Robison
Westlake, TX 76262	CFO: William F. Lacey
Phone: 817-859-3000	HR: Kathy C. Hassenpflug
Fax: 817-859-3099	FYE: June 30
Web: www.ahii.com	Type: Public

If dog is man's best friend, then perhaps Animal Health International (AHI) is dog's best friend. As one of the largest distributors of veterinary products in the US, AHI operates through several subsidiaries, including Walco International, RXV Products, and Agripharm Products. Its companies sell more than 40,000 prescription and OTC pharmaceuticals, nutritional supplements, vaccines, and other products to customers in the US and Canada. Other products include capital equipment, devices and supplies, diagnostics, parasiticides, and sanitizers. Its primary customers are livestock operations (dairy farms, feedlots, poultry producers), retailers, and veterinarians.

	Annual Growth	6/03	6/04	6/05	6/06	6/07
Sales ($ mil.)	7.8%	—	502.7	535.7	571.2	629.5
Net income ($ mil.)	(20.1%)	—	10.2	7.3	7.4	5.2
Market value ($ mil.)	—	—	—	—	—	352.5
Employees	—	—	—	—	—	—

⊞ ANIXTER INTERNATIONAL INC. NYSE: AXE

2301 Patriot Blvd.	CEO: Robert W. Grubbs Jr.
Glenview, IL 60026	CFO: Dennis J. Letham
Phone: 224-521-8000	HR: Rodney A. Smith
Fax: 224-521-8100	FYE: Friday nearest December 31
Web: www.anixter.com	Type: Public

Psssst — need wiring products? Anixter International has got connections. The company is a major global distributor of wiring systems, networking products, and fasteners. Anixter sells more than 350,000 different items — including copper and fiber-optic transmission cable, electrical wiring systems, and security system components — through a worldwide network of sales and distribution centers. The company obtains products from more than 5,000 suppliers and sells worldwide to more than 100,000 active customers, including resellers such as contractors, installers, engineers, and wholesale distributors. Anixter International does more than half of its sales in the US.

	Annual Growth	12/03	12/04	12/05	12/06	12/07
Sales ($ mil.)	22.2%	2,625.2	3,275.2	3,847.4	4,938.6	5,852.9
Net income ($ mil.)	56.8%	41.9	77.7	90.0	209.3	253.5
Market value ($ mil.)	24.6%	939.6	1,350.2	1,501.4	2,144.9	2,262.6
Employees	8.5%	—	—	6,800	7,500	8,000

ANNALY CAPITAL MANAGEMENT, INC. NYSE: NLY

1211 Avenue of the Americas, Ste. 2902	CEO: Michael A. J. Farrell
New York, NY 10036	CFO: Kathryn F. Fagan
Phone: 212-696-0100	HR: –
Fax: 212-696-9809	FYE: December 31
Web: www.annaly.com	Type: Public

Annaly Capital Management, a real estate investment trust (REIT), owns and manages mortgage-backed securities. Among its investments are mortgage pass-through certificates, collateralized mortgage obligations, and agency callable debentures. Certificates are issued or guaranteed by third-party issuers like Freddie Mac, Fannie Mae, and Ginnie Mae. At least 75% of its assets are high-quality, mortgage-backed securities or short-term investments. All of the REIT's assets are agency certificates with implied AAA ratings backed by single-family residential mortgages. Annaly subsidiary Fixed Income Discount Advisory Company (FIDAC) is its taxable REIT subsidiary and provides investment advisory services.

	Annual Growth	12/03	12/04	12/05	12/06	12/07
Sales ($ mil.)	59.0%	378.3	550.1	740.7	1,258.9	2,417.9
Net income ($ mil.)	23.2%	180.1	248.6	(9.3)	93.8	414.4
Market value ($ mil.)	42.6%	1,767.8	2,379.2	1,353.1	2,856.4	7,305.1
Employees	12.2%	—	—	31	34	39

ANNAPOLIS BANCORP, INC. NASDAQ (CM): ANNB

1000 Bestgate Rd., Ste. 400	CEO: Richard M. (Rick) Lerner
Annapolis, MD 21401	CFO: Margaret T. (Peg) Faison
Phone: 410-224-4455	HR: Bonnie L. Beck
Fax: 410-224-3132	FYE: December 31
Web: www.bankannapolis.com	Type: Public

You don't have to attend "Canoe U" to bank with Annapolis Bancorp. It's the holding company for BankAnnapolis, which serves individual and small business customers through about 10 branches in and around the Maryland capital. The bank offers such retail services as checking, savings, and money market accounts; IRAs; and CDs. It also provides private business banking, including cash management and credit products. Its lending activities comprise commercial mortgages (about 30% of its total loan portfolio), one- to four-family real estate loans (more than 25%), business loans (some 20%), and to a lesser extent, construction and consumer loans.

	Annual Growth	12/03	12/04	12/05	12/06	12/07
Assets ($ mil.)	11.8%	231.3	284.2	304.9	351.9	361.9
Net income ($ mil.)	9.0%	1.7	2.2	3.0	3.0	2.4
Market value ($ mil.)	9.5%	21.3	37.2	36.6	39.0	30.6
Employees	—	—	—	—	79	—

⊞ An in-depth profile of this company is available to Hoover's Online members at hoovers.com.

ANNA'S LINENS

3550 Hyland Ave.
Costa Mesa, CA 92626
Phone: 714-850-0504
Fax: 714-850-9170
Web: www.annaslinens.com

CEO: Alan Gladstone
CFO: Neil T. Watanabe
HR: Linda Norton Wendt
FYE: Sunday nearest January 31
Type: Private

Motherly devotion paid off for entrepreneur and company founder Alan Gladstone. Anna's Linens is a specialty retailer of discounted home furnishings, including bed linens, window coverings, and bath accessories, featuring brand names such as Wamsutta and Grand Patrician. Its some 250 retail locations in more than 20 states have expanded their offerings to include additional home décor items such as area rugs, decorative pillows, housewares, and kitchen textiles. Chairman, president, and CEO Gladstone (who named the company after his mother, Anna, whose picture graces its direct mail advertising, Web site, and store marketing materials) envisions Anna's Linens eventually growing to 1,000 storefronts nationwide.

ANNETT HOLDINGS, INC.

6115 SW Leland Ave.
Des Moines, IA 50321
Phone: 515-287-6380
Fax: 515-287-3249
Web: www.annettholdings.com

CEO: Harrold Annett
CFO: Larry Clark
HR: Glen McCravy
FYE: September 30
Type: Private

Freight that travels on flatbed trailers might travel with TLC from TMC. Through its main subsidiary, TMC Transportation, Annett Holdings hauls freight such as steel and building materials throughout the US on flatbed trailers. TMC offers both regional and long-haul service with a fleet of some 2,800 tractors and 3,300 trailers. The company also provides logistics services, such as freight transportation arrangement, and dedicated fleet services, in which drivers and equipment are assigned to a customer long-term. Chairman and CEO Harrold Annett founded the company in 1972.

	Annual Growth	9/03	9/04	9/05	9/06	9/07
Est. sales ($ mil.)	—	—	—	—	—	196.4
Employees	—	—	—	—	—	2,750

ANNIE'S INC.

564 Gateway Dr.
Napa, CA 94558
Phone: 707-254-3700
Fax: 707-259-0219
Web: www.anniesinc.com

CEO: John Foraker
CFO: Steve Jackson
HR: Amy Barberi
FYE: March 31
Type: Private

With Annie's you don't have to boil and shred, you just shake the box. We're talking macaroni and cheese here. Under its Annie's Homegrown label, and with its *rabbit* of approval, the company makes boxed natural macaroni and cheese mixes for the kiddies, as well as more sophisticated pasta and sauce meals for more mature taste buds. Annie's also offers Fantastic World Foods (vegetarian convenience meals, soup cups) and Annie's Naturals (organic salad dressings, oils, marinades, and other condiments). The company's products are available throughout the US at food retailers such as Whole Foods.

	Annual Growth	3/03	3/04	3/05	3/06	3/07
Est. sales ($ mil.)	—	—	—	—	—	78.6
Employees	—	—	—	—	—	50

ANNTAYLOR STORES CORPORATION

NYSE: ANN

7 Times Sq., 15th Fl.
New York, NY 10036
Phone: 212-541-3300
Fax: 212-541-3379
Web: www.anntaylor.com

CEO: Katherine (Kay) Lawther Krill
CFO: Michael J. (Mike) Nicholson
HR: Mark Morrison
FYE: Saturday nearest January 31
Type: Public

At AnnTaylor, basic black is as appreciated by its customers as its classic styles. The company (named for a fictional person) is a national retailer of upscale women's clothing designed exclusively for its stores. Its AnnTaylor and AnnTaylor LOFT shops offer apparel, shoes, and accessories. Targeting fashion-conscious career women, AnnTaylor operates about 930 stores (more than half are LOFT outlets) in some 45 US states, the District of Columbia, and Puerto Rico. Most are located in malls or upscale retail centers. AnnTaylor LOFT stores offer their own label of mid-priced apparel, while AnnTaylor Factory Stores sell clearance merchandise. AnnTaylor also has its own e-commerce Web site.

	Annual Growth	1/04	1/05	1/06	1/07	1/08
Sales ($ mil.)	10.8%	1,587.7	1,853.6	2,073.1	2,342.9	2,396.5
Net income ($ mil.)	(0.9%)	100.9	63.3	81.9	143.0	97.2
Market value ($ mil.)	5.8%	1,225.2	1,505.2	2,482.1	2,451.0	1,537.8
Employees	4.7%	—	—	16,900	17,700	—

ANR PIPELINE COMPANY

El Paso Bldg., 1001 Louisiana St.
Houston, TX 77002
Phone: 713-420-2600
Fax: 713-420-6969
Web: www.anrpl.com

CEO: Stephen C. Beasley
CFO: John R. (J. R.) Sult
HR: John W. Richards
FYE: December 31
Type: Subsidiary

ANR Pipeline keeps natural gas in line, a pipeline that is. The company operates one of the largest interstate natural gas pipeline systems in the US. A subsidiary of TransCanada Corp., ANR controls more than 10,600 miles of pipeline and delivers more than a trillion cu. ft. of natural gas per year. The company primarily serves customers in the Midwest, but through its network is capable of connecting to all major gas basins in North America. Through its ANR Storage subsidiary, the company also provides natural gas storage services and has ownership interests in more than 200 billion cu. ft. of underground natural gas storage capacity. El Paso Corp. sold ANR Pipeline to TransCanada in 2007.

	Annual Growth	12/02	12/03	12/04	12/05	12/06
Sales ($ mil.)	(0.2%)	544.0	554.0	470.0	548.0	540.0
Net income ($ mil.)	(1.7%)	163.0	130.0	117.0	147.0	152.0
Employees	18.5%	390	390	390	390	770

ANSCHUTZ COMPANY

555 17th St., Ste. 2400
Denver, CO 80202
Phone: 303-298-1000
Fax: 303-298-8881

CEO: Philip F. Anschutz
CFO: Wayne A. Barnes
HR: Mariette Van Engelen
FYE: December 31
Type: Private

You might say that Denver multibillionaire Philip Anschutz is on a Qwest. His holding company includes a stable of entertainment, media, and sports businesses. Through Anschutz Entertainment Group, Anschutz owns sports and entertainment centers throughout the US, as well as hockey, soccer, and other pro sports teams in the US and Europe. It promotes concerts and other events as well. Other Anschutz holdings include movie chain Regal Entertainment Group, newspaper companies *The San Francisco Examiner* and *The Washington Examiner,* and film interest Walden Media. Anschutz, who founded his eponymous firm in 1958, made his first fortune from oil on his Utah/Wyoming ranch. He also founded Qwest Communications.

	Annual Growth	12/03	12/04	12/05	12/06	12/07
Est. sales ($ mil.)	—	—	—	—	—	1,066.2
Employees	—	—	—	—	—	27,205

ANSOFT CORPORATION

NASDAQ (GS): ANST

225 W. Station Square Dr., Ste. 200
Pittsburgh, PA 15219
Phone: 412-261-3200
Fax: 412-471-9427
Web: www.ansoft.com

CEO: Nicholas (Nick) Csendes
CFO: Shane Emswiler
HR: Jennifer Arnold
FYE: April 30
Type: Public

Ansoft has answers for engineers who design electrical hardware, including high-performance devices and systems like cellular phones, satellite communications equipment, computer circuit boards, and motors. The company's electronic design automation (EDA) software analyzes electromagnetic interaction and helps design and test devices such as integrated circuits, antenna and radar systems, and microwave components. Ansoft sells worldwide to more than 2,000 clients in a wide range of industries; customers have included Boeing, Intel, Ford, and Motorola. The company was founded in 1989. Ansoft agreed to be acquired by rival ANSYS for $832 million in 2008.

	Annual Growth	4/04	4/05	4/06	4/07	4/08
Sales ($ mil.)	17.2%	54.7	67.7	77.2	89.1	103.3
Net income ($ mil.)	74.5%	2.6	9.4	17.8	20.2	24.1
Market value ($ mil.)	75.6%	82.0	140.2	524.9	773.5	778.9
Employees	2.2%	—	287	298	300	—

ANSWER FINANCIAL INC.

15910 Ventura Blvd.
Encino, CA 91436
Phone: 818-644-4000
Fax: 818-644-4410
Web: www.answerfinancial.com

CEO: Robert J. Slingerland
CFO: –
HR: –
FYE: December 31
Type: Private

There are no dumb questions, and Answer Financial will be the first to tell you there are no dumb answers, either. The Web- and telephone-based insurance brokerage assists consumers in selecting various types of insurance, including auto, home, life, health, long-term care, and pet insurance. Other products include annuities, dental care, and online banking. The company's Web site offers side-by-side competitive quotes for more than 200 insurance providers across the US. Chairman Alan Snyder founded Answer Financial in 1997.

	Annual Growth	12/03	12/04	12/05	12/06	12/07
Est. sales ($ mil.)	—	—	—	—	—	8.2
Employees	—	—	—	—	—	250

ANSYS, INC.

NASDAQ (GS): ANSS

275 Technology Dr.
Canonsburg, PA 15317
Phone: 724-746-3304
Fax: 724-514-9494
Web: www.ansys.com

CEO: James E. (Jim) Cashman III
CFO: Maria T. Shields
HR: Elaine Keim
FYE: December 31
Type: Public

ANSYS helps designers and engineers around the world really visualize their ideas. With the company's software, developers and engineers can see a simulation of their design concept on their desktop computer before a prototype is built. The computerized models are analyzed for their response to combinations of such physical variables as stress, pressure, impact, temperature, and velocity. Customers come from a number of different industries and have included Boeing, Cummins, and Motorola. ANSYS sells its products through independent distributors in about 40 countries. The company was founded in 1970 as Swanson Analysis Systems, when ANSYS was the name of the simulation software program.

	Annual Growth	12/03	12/04	12/05	12/06	12/07
Sales ($ mil.)	35.7%	113.5	134.5	158.0	263.6	385.3
Net income ($ mil.)	40.2%	21.3	34.6	43.9	14.2	82.4
Market value ($ mil.)	115.1%	151.5	503.6	688.8	839.2	3,242.1
Employees	36.5%	—	550	600	1,400	1,400

ANTARES PHARMA, INC.

AMEX: AIS

250 Phillips Blvd., Ste. 290
Ewing, NJ 08618
Phone: 609-359-3020
Fax: 609-359-3015
Web: www.antarespharma.com

CEO: Jack E. Stover
CFO: Robert F. (Bob) Apple
HR: –
FYE: December 31
Type: Public

Antares Pharma understands antagonism towards needles. The company develops needle-free systems for administering injectable drugs. Its Medi-Jector Vision system, for instance, injects a thin, high-pressure stream of liquid, eliminating the need for a needle. The Vision system is used primarily for the delivery of insulin and of human growth hormones; it is available over-the-counter and by prescription in the US and is also sold overseas. In addition to its needle-free systems, the company develops other drug delivery platforms, including topical gels, orally administered disintegrating tablets, and mini-needle injection systems.

	Annual Growth	12/03	12/04	12/05	12/06	12/07
Sales ($ mil.)	20.1%	3.8	2.8	2.2	4.3	7.9
Net income ($ mil.)	—	(32.8)	(8.4)	(8.5)	(8.1)	(8.6)
Market value ($ mil.)	13.2%	39.1	54.6	81.7	64.0	64.2
Employees	—	—	—	24	—	—

ANTHONY & SYLVAN POOLS CORPORATION

Mt. Vernon Sq., 6690 Beta Dr., Ste. 300
Mayfield Village, OH 44143
Phone: 440-720-3301
Fax: 440-720-3303
Web: www.anthonysylvan.com

CEO: Stuart D. Neidus
CFO: William J. (Bill) Evanson
HR: Ken F. Sloan
FYE: December 31
Type: Private

Pooling resources is second nature to Anthony & Sylvan Pools Corporation. The company, created through the 1996 union of industry leaders Anthony Pools and Sylvan Pools, installs custom in-ground concrete swimming pools for private residences. It operates a network of more than 35 company-owned locations, consisting of sales and design centers, pool and spa renovation centers, and retail service centers that sell pool accessories such as chemicals, heaters, filters, pumps, and toys. The company is active in California, Texas, Nevada, and 10 East Coast states.

ANTHRACITE CAPITAL, INC.

NYSE: AHR

40 E. 52nd St.
New York City, NY 10022
Phone: 212-409-3333
Fax: 212-754-8760
Web: www.anthracitecapital.com

CEO: Christopher A. (Chris) Milner
CFO: James J. Lillis
HR: –
FYE: December 31
Type: Public

Anthracite Capital doesn't invest in coal mines, but it does hope its real estate investments will turn into gold. The real estate investment trust (REIT) focuses on non-investment-grade commercial mortgage loans, commercial mortgage-backed securities, and other real estate assets in the US and in international markets. It also provides mezzanine loan financing for commercial real estate transactions, generally partnering with fund manager Carbon Capital (of which it owns approximately 20%). Anthracite is externally managed by investment management firm BlackRock.

	Annual Growth	12/03	12/04	12/05	12/06	12/07
Sales ($ mil.)	21.6%	163.8	203.9	260.5	303.4	358.5
Net income ($ mil.)	—	(8.6)	43.2	70.6	80.5	84.0
Market value ($ mil.)	(4.4%)	547.6	658.7	593.2	736.2	458.0
Employees	—	—	—	—	—	—

An in-depth profile of this company is available to Hoover's Online members at hoovers.com.

149

ANTIGENICS INC.

NASDAQ (GM): AGEN

162 5th Ave., Ste. 900
New York, NY 10111
Phone: 212-994-8200
Fax: 212-994-8299
Web: www.antigenics.com

CEO: Garo H. Armen
CFO: Shalini Sharp
HR: John Cerio
FYE: December 31
Type: Public

Cancer and other diseases had better beware — Antigenics is packing heat. The firm develops heat shock proteins, which are related to the immune system's response to disease. Its patient-specific vaccines work on the theory that each person's cancer has a unique signature and are derived from the tumor after it has been removed. Lead drug candidate Oncophage is the first personalized cancer vaccine to receive FDA fast track status; it has this designation for kidney and skin cancers. Another cancer vaccine candidate in the firm's pipeline targets genital herpes.

	Annual Growth	12/03	12/04	12/05	12/06	12/07
Sales ($ mil.)	6.2%	4.4	0.7	0.6	0.7	5.6
Net income ($ mil.)	—	(65.9)	(56.2)	(74.1)	(51.9)	(36.8)
Market value ($ mil.)	(28.8%)	448.2	460.8	217.0	83.9	115.4
Employees	—	—	—	171	—	—

ANTS SOFTWARE INC.

OTC: ANTS

700 Airport Blvd., Ste. 300
Burlingame, CA 94010
Phone: 650-931-0500
Fax: 650-931-0510
Web: www.ants.com

CEO: Joseph M. Kozak
CFO: Kenneth (Ken) Ruotolo
HR: –
FYE: December 31
Type: Public

ANTs software hopes to help your data march about in perfect order, with no locking up. The company develops and markets software used to improve the performance of database-driven enterprise applications. ANTs' technology is designed to process and manipulate data with no database locking. The company's primary product is its ANTs Data Server, which is a relational database management system (RDBMS). ANTs markets its products to information technology departments, application developers, and database architects. The company also provides professional services such as consulting, training, support, implementation, and maintenance. In May 2008 the company acquired Inventa Technologies.

	Annual Growth	12/03	12/04	12/05	12/06	12/07
Sales ($ mil.)	(10.6%)	—	—	0.5	0.3	0.4
Net income ($ mil.)	—	—	—	(8.7)	(15.1)	(16.3)
Market value ($ mil.)	(33.9%)	—	—	93.3	135.1	40.8
Employees	—	—	—	—	—	49

ANVIL HOLDINGS, INC.

228 E. 45th St.
New York, NY 10017
Phone: 212-476-0300
Fax: 212-476-0323
Web: www.anvilknitwear.com

CEO: Anthony Corsano
CFO: Frank Ferramosca
HR: –
FYE: Saturday nearest January 31
Type: Private

Despite its name, it likely won't require metal shaping to get this imprinting job done. Anvil Holdings, which operates primarily through its subsidiary Anvil Knitwear, makes and markets activewear for men, women, and children that it sells to screen printers, private label brand owners, and distributors in the US. In addition to its apparel offerings (primarily short- and long-sleeve T-shirts), Anvil also makes bags, caps, robes, and towels. Before they're purchased, Anvil's products are typically embellished with characters, designs, or logos. The company's brands include Anvil Logo, Anvil, Cotton Deluxe, chromaZONE, and Towels Plus by Anvil, as well as private labels manufactured for other companies.

	Annual Growth	1/02	1/03	1/04	1/05	1/06
Sales ($ mil.)	(2.6%)	199.7	224.3	191.2	192.4	179.9
Net income ($ mil.)	—	4.4	10.6	(18.2)	(8.6)	(28.5)
Employees	(10.3%)	—	5,169	4,612	3,832	3,734

ANWORTH MORTGAGE ASSET CORPORATION

NYSE: ANH

1299 Ocean Ave., Ste. 250
Santa Monica, CA 90401
Phone: 310-255-4493
Fax: 310-434-0070
Web: www.anworth.com

CEO: Lloyd McAdams
CFO: Thad M. Brown
HR: Kathryn Pellman
FYE: December 31
Type: Public

Anworth Mortgage ain't worth mere peanuts. A self-managed real estate investment trust (REIT), Anworth Mortgage invests in mortgage assets, including mortgage pass-through certificates, collateralized mortgage obligations, mortgage loans, and other real estate securities. Its asset portfolio includes $4.7 billion in agency mortgage-backed securities (securities issued or guaranteed by the government and its agencies) and other investment-grade mortgage securities, including those highly rated by Standard & Poor's or Moody's. Remaining assets include securities rated below investment grade, leveraged mortgage derivative securities, and shares of other REITs or mortgage-related firms.

	Annual Growth	12/03	12/04	12/05	12/06	12/07
Sales ($ mil.)	24.5%	103.6	163.6	281.9	312.0	248.8
Net income ($ mil.)	—	50.2	55.8	28.9	(14.2)	(156.5)
Market value ($ mil.)	(6.2%)	612.3	498.0	331.4	433.8	473.2
Employees	0.0%	—	—	12	—	12

A. O. SMITH CORPORATION

NYSE: AOS

11270 W. Park Place
Milwaukee, WI 53224
Phone: 414-359-4000
Fax: 414-359-4180
Web: www.aosmith.com

CEO: Paul W. Jones
CFO: Terry M. Murphy
HR: Mark A. Petrarca
FYE: December 31
Type: Public

Aerosmith has a lot of fans — A. O. Smith has a lot of fan motors. The company makes electric motors and water heaters. Its Electrical Products segment makes pump motors for home water systems, swimming pools, and hot tubs; fan motors for furnaces and air conditioners; and hermetic motors for compressors and commercial refrigeration units. The company's Water Products segment makes residential gas and electric water heaters and commercial water-heating systems. A. O. Smith customers include Lowe's and Sears. Customers in the US account for about three-quarters of A. O. Smith's sales. Members of the founding Smith family control the company.

	Annual Growth	12/03	12/04	12/05	12/06	12/07
Sales ($ mil.)	10.9%	1,530.7	1,653.1	1,689.2	2,161.3	2,312.1
Net income ($ mil.)	14.0%	52.2	35.4	46.5	76.5	88.2
Market value ($ mil.)	0.3%	841.8	634.0	844.1	841.7	850.5
Employees	(0.3%)	17,000	16,600	17,650	18,000	16,800

AOL LLC

770 Broadway
New York, NY 10003
Phone: 212-652-6400
Fax: –
Web: www.corp.aol.com

CEO: Randel A. (Randy) Falco
CFO: Nisha Kumar
HR: Lance Miyamoto
FYE: December 31
Type: Subsidiary

This Internet pioneer is still serving America — and other countries — online. AOL is one of the world's leading online content providers, serving more than 100 million users with a vast portal of news, sports, and information. Its advertising-supported content also includes games, music, and video, as well as e-mail, instant messaging, and other interactive services. AOL also sells and distributes online advertising through such subsidiaries as Advertising.com and search marketing firm Quigo Technologies. In addition, the company still offers online access services to more than 8.5 million subscribers. AOL is a subsidiary of media behemoth Time Warner.

AON CORPORATION

NYSE: AOC

Aon Center, 200 E. Randolph St.
Chicago, IL 60601
Phone: 312-381-1000
Fax: 312-381-6032
Web: www.aon.com

CEO: Gregory C. (Greg) Case
CFO: Christa Davies
HR: Jeremy G.O. Farmer
FYE: December 31
Type: Public

Aon (the name means "oneness" in Gaelic) is one of the world's leading insurance brokerages, as well as a top reinsurance broker. The company operates in three major segments: commercial brokerage, consulting services, and consumer insurance underwriting. The company's brokerage unit, Aon Risk Services, provides retail property/casualty, liability, and other insurance products for groups and businesses, as well as risk management services. Aon Re Global handles reinsurance brokerage services for aviation, marine, energy, professional liability, and other niche and specialty business lines. Its consulting unit, Aon Consulting Worldwide, specializes in employee benefits administration.

	Annual Growth	12/03	12/04	12/05	12/06	12/07
Sales ($ mil.)	(6.6%)	9,810.0	10,172.0	9,837.0	8,954.0	7,471.0
Net income ($ mil.)	8.3%	628.0	546.0	737.0	720.0	864.0
Market value ($ mil.)	17.8%	7,534.4	7,574.7	11,547.1	10,544.6	14,512.1
Employees	(4.5%)	—	—	46,600	43,100	42,500

A.P. PHARMA, INC.

NASDAQ (GM): APPA

123 Saginaw Dr.
Redwood City, CA 94063
Phone: 650-366-2626
Fax: 650-365-6490
Web: www.appharma.com

CEO: Gregory H. Turnbull
CFO: Gregory H. Turnbull
HR: Sandra Squires
FYE: December 31
Type: Public

A.P. Pharma wants to hit you where it hurts. The firm develops bioerodible polymers for injectable and implantable drug delivery. Its Biochronomer technology delivers medication directly to the site where the drug is needed. A.P. Pharma's leading drug candidate, APF530, could ease chemotherapy-induced nausea and vomiting. A second candidate in clinical trials is a post-surgical pain management product that delivers pain relief right to the surgical site. A.P. Pharma is also developing therapies for inflammation and chronic pain using its Biochronomer technology. Its drug candidates combine approved therapeutics with its bioerodible polymers.

	Annual Growth	12/03	12/04	12/05	12/06	12/07
Sales ($ mil.)	—	—	—	—	—	0.4
Net income ($ mil.)	—	—	—	—	—	(20.2)
Market value ($ mil.)	—	—	—	—	—	48.7
Employees	—	—	—	—	—	—

APAC CUSTOMER SERVICES INC.

NASDAQ (GM): APAC

6 Parkway North
Deerfield, IL 60015
Phone: 847-374-4980
Fax: 847-236-5453
Web: www.apaccustomerservices.com

CEO: Michael P. (Mike) Marrow
CFO: Andrew B. Szafran
HR: Michael V. Hoehne
FYE: Sunday nearest December 31
Type: Public

The telephone isn't the instrument of choice for APAC Customer Services anymore. The company, formerly APAC TeleServices, provides outsourced customer-management and acquisition services using the telephone and the Internet. It operates eight customer interaction centers (they aren't just call centers anymore) in the US and the Philippines. APAC's customer management services include customer retention, help-line information, direct mail response, and order entry services. Clients include companies in the parcel delivery, pharmaceutical, telecommunications, retail, and financial industries.

	Annual Growth	12/03	12/04	12/05	12/06	12/07
Sales ($ mil.)	(8.7%)	322.9	273.2	239.8	224.3	224.7
Net income ($ mil.)	4.4%	4.3	(6.5)	(22.4)	(30.5)	5.1
Market value ($ mil.)	(17.5%)	128.1	86.1	90.9	187.0	59.4
Employees	(2.3%)	—	10,200	8,500	7,900	9,500

APAC, INC.

900 Ashwood Pkwy., Ste. 700
Atlanta, GA 30338
Phone: 770-392-5300
Fax: 770-392-5393
Web: apac.com

CEO: Robert K. (Kirk) Randolph
CFO: John Connolly
HR: −
FYE: September 30
Type: Business segment

If you hit the road, Jack, APAC (formerly Ashland Paving and Construction) can pave your way. APAC, once a subsidiary of Ashland, is now a part of Oldcastle Materials. The company provides highway construction services, as well as excavation, grading, and other specialty services. It also supplies the materials to make roads, including asphalt, ready-mix concrete, and crushed stone. APAC operates quarries, aggregate production facilities, ready-mix concrete plants, hot-mix asphalt plants, and a large fleet of mobile equipment. The company was formed in 1879 when it supplied asphalt for the first commercial asphalt road in the US.

	Annual Growth	9/03	9/04	9/05	9/06	9/07
Est. sales ($ mil.)	—	—	—	—	—	1,199.2
Employees	—	—	—	—	—	9,500

APACHE CORPORATION

NYSE: APA

2000 Post Oak Blvd., Ste. 100
Houston, TX 77056
Phone: 713-296-6000
Fax: 713-296-6496
Web: www.apachecorp.com

CEO: G. Steven (Steve) Farris
CFO: Roger B. Plank
HR: Margery M. (Margie) Harris
FYE: December 31
Type: Public

There's more than a patch of oil in Apache's portfolio. Apache is an oil and gas exploration and production company with onshore and offshore operations in North America and in Argentina, Australia, Egypt, and the UK. The company has estimated proved reserves of 2.4 billion barrels of oil equivalent, mostly from North American regions: the Gulf of Mexico, the Gulf Coast of Texas and Louisiana, the Permian Basin in West Texas, the Anadarko Basin in Oklahoma, and Canada's Western Sedimentary Basin. In 2007 Anadarko Petroleum agreed to sell its interests in 28 crude oil fields in West Texas to Apache for about $1 billion.

	Annual Growth	12/03	12/04	12/05	12/06	12/07
Sales ($ mil.)	24.2%	4,190.3	5,332.6	7,584.2	8,288.8	9,977.9
Net income ($ mil.)	25.8%	1,121.9	1,668.8	2,623.7	2,552.4	2,812.4
Market value ($ mil.)	28.4%	13,180.2	16,559.5	22,619.9	21,997.3	35,803.0
Employees	10.6%	2,353	2,642	2,805	3,150	3,521

APARTMENT INVESTMENT AND MANAGEMENT

NYSE: AIV

4582 S. Ulster Street Pkwy., Ste. 1100
Denver, CO 80237
Phone: 303-757-8101
Fax: 303-759-3226
Web: www.aimco.com

CEO: Terry Considine
CFO: Thomas M. (Tom) Herzog
HR: James G. (Jim) Purvis
FYE: December 31
Type: Public

Apartment Investment and Management Company (AIMCO) is the REIT with the mostest — apartment units, that is. The REIT (real estate investment trust) owns or manages about 200,000 apartment units, making it #1 in that category, although that comprises only a small fraction of a very fragmented market. Sam Zell's Equity Residential is the only apartment REIT that surpasses AIMCO's sales. Through subsidiary AIMCO Properties, the company has interests in about 1,180 properties in 46 states, Puerto Rico, and the District of Columbia. The company's apartment portfolio consists of garden style, midrise, and high-rise properties.

	Annual Growth	12/03	12/04	12/05	12/06	12/07
Sales ($ mil.)	3.2%	1,516.3	1,468.9	1,521.5	1,691.0	1,721.2
Net income ($ mil.)	(34.1%)	158.9	263.5	71.0	176.8	29.9
Market value ($ mil.)	0.8%	3,239.1	3,655.7	3,625.4	5,423.9	3,338.6
Employees	(17.1%)	—	—	6,400	6,000	4,400

An in-depth profile of this company is available to Hoover's Online members at hoovers.com.

151

APAX PARTNERS, INC.

153 E. 53rd St., 53rd Fl.
New York, NY 10022
Phone: 212-753-6300
Fax: 212-319-6155
Web: www.apax.com

CEO: Martin Halusa
CFO: –
HR: –
FYE: December 31
Type: Private

Founded in 1969 by Alan Patricof, investment firm Apax Partners (formerly Patricof & Co.) provides financing to companies in the high-tech, media, retail, health care, communications, and financial and business services industries. The company, which had a hand in the startup of such ventures as Apple and Office Depot, announced it has ceased venture capital investing. It closed its latest fund, which raised some $13 billion and will focus on leveraged buyouts, in 2007. Apax Partners bought clothing designer Tommy Hilfiger in 2006, and teamed up with Morgan Stanley to buy insurance brokerage Hub International in 2007.

	Annual Growth	12/03	12/04	12/05	12/06	12/07
Est. sales ($ mil.)	—	—	—	—	—	35.7
Employees	—	—	—	—	—	7,750

APCO ARGENTINA INC.

NASDAQ (CM): APAGF

One Williams Center, Mail Drop 26-4
Tulsa, OK 74172
Phone: 918-573-2164
Fax: –
Web: www.williams.com/productservices/exploration/argentina.asp

CEO: Ralph A. Hill
CFO: –
HR: –
FYE: December 31
Type: Public

Aptly named, Apco Argentina exploits oil and gas resources in Argentina. Deregulation gave Apco Argentina's joint venture with Petrobras Energia and Petrolera Entre Lomas the right to pump oil from the Entre Lomas concession in southwestern Argentina until 2026. The exploration and production company (69%-owned by US powerhouse The Williams Companies) holds a 53% stake in the Entre Lomas joint venture. In 2007 Apco Argentina, which also holds interests in other oil and gas concessions in Argentina, reported consolidated proved reserves of 11 million barrels of oil and 24.1 billion cu. ft. of gas.

	Annual Growth	12/03	12/04	12/05	12/06	12/07
Sales ($ mil.)	14.6%	35.8	41.6	41.7	58.0	61.7
Net income ($ mil.)	26.1%	12.4	15.5	29.9	40.1	31.4
Market value ($ mil.)	101.7%	49.0	68.0	95.0	161.5	810.2
Employees	24.3%	—	—	11	—	17

APCO WORLDWIDE INC.

700 12th St. NW, Ste. 800
Washington, DC 20005
Phone: 202-778-1000
Fax: 202-466-6002
Web: www.apcoworldwide.com

CEO: Margery Kraus
CFO: Denise Teeling
HR: Stacy Reyan
FYE: December 31
Type: Private

Public affairs and strategic communications put APCO Worldwide on the map. The company's expert services include corporate, investor, employee communication, crisis management, litigation communication, and government relations. Clients have included *FORTUNE* 500 companies, governments, and industry associations such as Bristol-Myers Squibb, Dow Corning, Microsoft, The Restaurant Association, and World Wrestling Entertainment. The company has offices in North America, Europe, and Africa and has been aggressively expanding into Asia. APCO, a majority women-owned business, was established in 1984.

	Annual Growth	12/03	12/04	12/05	12/06	12/07
Est. sales ($ mil.)	—	—	—	—	—	74.0
Employees	—	—	—	—	—	450

APERTO NETWORKS, INC.

598 Gibraltar Dr.
Milpitas, CA 95035
Phone: 408-719-9977
Fax: 408-719-9970
Web: www.apertonet.com

CEO: Michael K. (Mike) Pratt
CFO: Kenneth E. Elmer
HR: Glenda Dubsky
FYE: December 31
Type: Private

Aperto Networks is not tethered to its work. The company manufactures wireless networking equipment used to connect service providers to broadband customers over the last mile. Its PacketWave and PacketMAX product lines (the latter using WiMAX technology) include radio frequency base stations, antennas, and customer premise equipment. The company's products have been used by service providers in more than 60 countries to deliver converged voice, data, and video services to hundreds of thousands of end users. Aperto Networks has received equity financing from Alliance Ventures, Canaan Partners, Stratex Networks, and Innovacom, among others.

	Annual Growth	12/03	12/04	12/05	12/06	12/07
Est. sales ($ mil.)	—	—	—	—	—	12.6
Employees	—	—	—	—	—	90

APEX COVANTAGE

198 Van Buren St., 200 Presidents Plaza
Herndon, VA 20170
Phone: 703-709-3000
Fax: 703-709-0333
Web: www.apexinc.com

CEO: Shashikant (Shashi) Gupta
CFO: –
HR: –
FYE: December 31
Type: Private

Apex CoVantage provides outsourced project management and consulting services in a number of areas such as engineering design and back office processes. Its Apex Publishing unit provides digital content services (building digital libraries and databases); Apex also handles print production for publishing companies and offers in-bound and out-bound teleservices. The company serves clients in a number of industries, including transportation, technology, publishing, manufacturing, education, and aerospace. Owning more than 10 offices throughout India, Apex was established in 1988.

	Annual Growth	12/03	12/04	12/05	12/06	12/07
Est. sales ($ mil.)	—	—	—	—	—	214.3
Employees	—	—	—	—	—	2,500

APEX OIL COMPANY, INC.

8235 Forsyth Blvd., Ste. 400
Clayton, MO 63105
Phone: 314-889-9600
Fax: 314-854-8539
Web: www.apexoil.com

CEO: P. Anthony (Tony) Novelly
CFO: John L. Hank Jr.
HR: Julie Cook
FYE: September 30
Type: Private

At the top of its game, Apex Oil is engaged in the wholesale sales, storage, and distribution of petroleum products. Its range of refined products includes asphalt, kerosene, fuel oil, diesel fuel, heavy oil, gasoline, and bunker fuels. The company's terminals are located on the East Coast and Gulf Coast, in California, and in the Midwest. Internationally, Apex Oil has a terminal in Caracas, Venezuela, and has additional activities in Bermuda, Monaco, and the Netherlands. The company is also engaged in a tug boat and barge business and has a storage and truck rack operation. Apex Oil is controlled by CEO Tony Novelly.

	Annual Growth	9/02	9/03	9/04	9/05	9/06
Est. sales ($ mil.)	0.0%	—	—	—	1,020.0	1,020.0
Employees	180.0%	—	—	—	250	700

APEX RESTAURANT GROUP LP

6340 International Pkwy., Ste. 300
Plano, TX 75093
Phone: 972-220-0200
Fax: 972-588-5901
Web: www.apexrestaurants.com

CEO: Mark L. Bromberg
CFO: Andrew Hamme
HR: Jenna Doughty
FYE: –
Type: Private

APEX Restaurant Group manages a handful of casual dining restaurant chains with about a dozen locations operating under such banners as Blue Chalk Cafe, Dakota Steakhouse, Left at Albuquerque, and The Sirloin Saloon. It also provides marketing, consulting, and administrative support services to third-party restaurant chains. CEO Mark Bromberg, formerly chairman of Bennigan's operator Metromedia Restaurant Group, and partner John Todd formed the company in 2002.

API GROUP, INC.

2366 Rose Place
St. Paul, MN 55113
Phone: 651-636-4320
Fax: 651-636-0312
Web: www.apigroupinc.com

CEO: Russell (Russ) Becker
CFO: –
HR: –
FYE: December 31
Type: Private

Holding company APi Group has a piece of the action in five business sectors: construction services, fire protection, special systems, manufacturing, and materials distribution. APi has more than 25 subsidiaries, which operate as independent companies. Services provided by the company's construction subsidiaries include energy conservation; electrical, industrial, and mechanical contracting; industrial insulation; and overhead door installation. Other units install fire protection systems, fabricate structural steel, and distribute building materials. The family-owned company was founded by Reuben Anderson, father of chairman Lee Anderson.

	Annual Growth	12/02	12/03	12/04	12/05	12/06
Est. sales ($ mil.)	—	—	—	—	—	900.0
Employees	—	—	—	—	—	5,000

APL LIMITED

1111 Broadway
Oakland, CA 94607
Phone: 510-272-8000
Fax: –
Web: www.apl.com

CEO: Ronald D. (Ron) Widdows
CFO: Cedric Foo
HR: –
FYE: December 31
Type: Subsidiary

It's full steam ahead for APL. The company, a subsidiary of Singapore's Neptune Orient Lines, is one of the largest US-based container shipping companies. The company's fleet of about 125 containerships serves more than 90 ports in the Americas, the Asia/Pacific region, Europe, the Middle East, and Africa. APL deploys containers and chassis worldwide, and partnerships enable the company to offer intermodal transportation — movement of freight through combinations of ship, train, and truck. The liner operator coordinates its offerings with those of a sister company, APL Logistics, which provides supply chain management services.

	Annual Growth	12/03	12/04	12/05	12/06	12/07
Est. sales ($ mil.)	—	—	—	—	—	1,195.5
Employees	—	—	—	—	—	4,782

APL LOGISTICS, LTD.

1111 Broadway
Oakland, CA 94607
Phone: 510-272-8000
Fax: 510-272-7011
Web: www.apllogistics.com

CEO: Brian T. Lutt
CFO: Cedric Foo
HR: –
FYE: December 31
Type: Subsidiary

APL Logistics, the logistics arm of Singapore-based marine transportation giant Neptune Orient Lines, offers a wide range of supply chain management services, including freight forwarding, warehousing and distribution, manufacturing support, and merchandise consolidation. It targets customers in the automotive, consumer goods, retail, and technology sectors. APL Logistics operates from more than 300 offices that serve more than 100 countries in Africa, the Americas, Asia and the Middle East, and Europe. A sister company, APL, offers ocean container transportation services.

APOGEE ENTERPRISES, INC.

NASDAQ (GS): APOG

7900 Xerxes Ave. South, Ste. 1800
Minneapolis, MN 55431
Phone: 952-835-1874
Fax: 952-487-7565
Web: www.apog.com

CEO: Russell Huffer
CFO: James S. Porter
HR: Warren Planitzer
FYE: Saturday nearest February 28
Type: Public

Apogee Enterprises goes to great panes for its glass business customers. The company focuses on two core segments within the industry. Its architectural products and services unit, which accounts for most of the company's sales, makes and installs energy-efficient windows for high-rises and other commercial and institutional buildings. Customers include construction contractors, building owners, and architects. Apogee's large-scale optical technologies segment makes specialized glass primarily for the picture-framing market and optical thin-film coatings for consumer electronics displays. The company has exited its auto glass segment, which made aftermarket car windshields through Viracon/Curvlite.

	Annual Growth	2/04	2/05	2/06	2/07	2/08
Sales ($ mil.)	13.3%	535.3	628.8	696.7	778.8	881.8
Net income ($ mil.)	—	(5.6)	16.6	23.8	31.6	48.5
Market value ($ mil.)	6.6%	342.0	388.6	481.9	553.6	442.4
Employees	4.0%	—	—	4,465	4,645	—

APOGEE TECHNOLOGY, INC.

OTC: ATCS

129 Morgan Dr.
Norwood, MA 02062
Phone: 781-551-9450
Fax: 781-440-9528
Web: www.apogeemems.com

CEO: Herbert M. Stein
CFO: Paul Murphy
HR: –
FYE: December 31
Type: Public

Apogee Technology listened to the footsteps of competition in the audio-chip business and didn't like what it heard. In 2005 the company sold its audio division to SigmaTel to focus on developing a new, different line of chips. Apogee acquired a portfolio of microelectromechanical systems (MEMS) intellectual property from Standard MEMS, Inc. in 2004 and has established a MEMS division in order to develop system-on-chip (SoC) products, such as automotive sensors, disposable medical products, and headsets, that combine microphones with Apogee's audio amplification technology.

	Annual Growth	12/03	12/04	12/05	12/06	12/07
Sales ($ mil.)	(63.4%)	11.1	6.2	5.2	1.9	0.2
Net income ($ mil.)	—	0.8	(3.4)	3.0	(3.0)	(3.2)
Employees	(19.3%)	33	35	12	12	14

An in-depth profile of this company is available to Hoover's Online members at hoovers.com.

153

APOGEN TECHNOLOGIES, INC.

7918 Jones Branch Dr., Ste. 400
McLean, VA 22102
Phone: 703-752-6500
Fax: 703-821-3598
Web: www.apogentech.com

CEO: Paul G. Leslie
CFO: Thomas W. (Tom) Weston Jr.
HR: Ilene R. Colina
FYE: September 30
Type: Subsidiary

They're not a Mission Impossible team, but when the mission is critical, Apogen Technologies takes the call. The company provides a variety of information technology (IT) services to government agencies. Clients include the departments of Defense, Energy, and Homeland Security; the IRS; the US Navy; and the Census Bureau. Apogen also provides IT outsourcing services to the City of New Orleans and others. The company's vision of "Aiming Higher" is reflected in its name: the melding of "apogee" (the highest point of an orbit) and "genesis." Apogen was acquired by the QinetiQ Group for about $300 million in 2005.

	Annual Growth	9/03	9/04	9/05	9/06	9/07
Est. sales ($ mil.)	—	—	—	—	—	181.9
Employees	—	—	—	—	—	1,294

APOLLO GOLD CORPORATION

AMEX: AGT

5655 S. Yosemite St., Ste. 200
Greenwood Village, CO 80111
Phone: 720-886-9656
Fax: 720-482-0957
Web: www.apollogold.com

CEO: R. David Russell
CFO: Melvyn Williams
HR: –
FYE: December 31
Type: Public

Apollo Gold is not something you might find on Mount Olympus, but rather a mining company operating in Canada and the US. The company has gold, silver, lead, and zinc mine operations in Montana and Ontario; it also operates an exploration project in Chihuahua, Mexico. The company's Montana Tunnels facility accounts for the majority of the company's silver, lead, and zinc production. In 2006 it ceased activity at its Montana gold milling facility, but the company re-started production there the next year. In the near term, Apollo is primarily focused on developing its Black Fox Project gold mine operation in Ontario.

	Annual Growth	12/03	12/04	12/05	12/06	12/07
Sales ($ mil.)	(12.9%)	66.8	64.7	43.3	10.2	38.5
Net income ($ mil.)	—	(10.4)	(25.1)	(22.2)	(12.2)	(13.9)
Market value ($ mil.)	(14.1%)	172.6	78.0	25.6	65.4	93.7
Employees	33.5%	—	—	129	165	230

APOLLO ADVISORS, L.P.

2 Manhattanville Rd.
Purchase, NY 10577
Phone: 914-694-8000
Fax: 914-694-8067

CEO: Leon D. Black
CFO: –
HR: –
FYE: December 31
Type: Private

In Greek and Roman mythology, Apollo is the god of light, medicine, arts, and archery, but Apollo Advisors is even more diverse. Also known as Apollo Management, the private equity firm owns stakes in companies in a range of industries. Its portfolio holdings include movie theater chain AMC Entertainment, home products retailer Linens 'n Things, Covalence Specialty Materials, Jacuzzi Brands (acquired in 2007), and Hexion Specialty Chemicals, which is buying Huntsman Corporation for some $10.5 billion. Apollo joined forces with TPG to purchase gaming company Harrah's Entertainment for nearly $28 billion in early 2008.

	Annual Growth	12/03	12/04	12/05	12/06	12/07
Est. sales ($ mil.)	—	—	—	—	—	13.3
Employees	—	—	—	—	—	81

APOLLO GROUP, INC.

NASDAQ (GS): APOL

4615 E. Elwood St.
Phoenix, AZ 85040
Phone: 480-966-5394
Fax: 480-379-3503
Web: www.apollogrp.edu

CEO: Brian Mueller
CFO: Joseph L. D'Amico
HR: Diane Thompson
FYE: August 31
Type: Public

Even the sun god needs a college degree these days. Apollo Group is a for-profit education company that provides programs tailored to working adults. The company has more than 160 learning centers and 100 campuses (including an online campus). Its University of Phoenix is the US's largest private university with more than 300,000 students; its other subsidiaries include Institute for Professional Development, Inc. (develops working student curricula for other colleges), The College for Financial Planning Institutes (financial services and retirement planning training), Western International University, Inc. (BA and MA degree programs), and Insight Schools, Inc. (online high school programs).

	Annual Growth	8/03	8/04	8/05	8/06	8/07
Sales ($ mil.)	19.4%	1,339.5	1,798.4	2,251.5	2,477.5	2,723.8
Net income ($ mil.)	13.4%	247.0	277.8	444.7	414.8	408.8
Market value ($ mil.)	(3.5%)	11,230.6	14,630.2	14,094.6	8,664.0	9,730.1
Employees	5.6%	—	—	32,666	36,416	36,418

APOLLO INVESTMENT CORPORATION

NASDAQ (GS): AINV

9 W. 57th St., 41st Fl.
New York, NY 10019
Phone: 212-515-3450
Fax: –
Web: www.apolloic.com

CEO: John J. Hannan
CFO: Richard L. Peteka
HR: –
FYE: March 31
Type: Public

Private equity investor Apollo Investment shines its light on the world of middle-market corporate finance. Through its advisor Apollo Investment Management, it specializes in subordinated debt and equity capital. As a business development company (BDC) it provides middle-market companies with mezzanine or senior subordinated loans, as well as direct equity investments in likely companies. The company invests between $20 million and $250 million. Apollo Investment has stakes in about 70 portfolio companies, including financial services behemoth First Data and vinyl and building products company Associated Materials. Apollo Investment is affiliated with Apollo Advisors (also known as Apollo Management).

	Annual Growth	3/04	3/05	3/06	3/07	3/08
Sales ($ mil.)	105.1%	—	47.8	152.8	453.0	412.2
Net income ($ mil.)	—	—	44.1	120.4	312.2	(33.4)
Market value ($ mil.)	21.8%	—	1,049.7	1,453.4	2,215.1	1,897.9
Employees	—	—	—	—	—	—

APP PHARMACEUTICALS, INC.

NASDAQ (GS): APPX

1501 E. Woodfield Rd., Ste. 300 E
Schaumburg, IL 60173
Phone: 847-969-2700
Fax: –
Web: www.appdrugs.com

CEO: Thomas H. Silberg
CFO: Richard J. Tajak
HR: James Callanan
FYE: December 31
Type: Public

Because brand names are less important when you're sedated, APP Pharmaceuticals could save you some money. The company manufactures generic injectable drugs for use in hospitals, care facilities, and clinics in North America. The company's products include anti-infectives, and anesthetic and analgesic products, as well as drugs used in the treatment of cancer and a number of specialty drugs. APP Pharmaceuticals markets its products through its own sales force; distribution is handled through group purchasing organizations and specialty distributors. The company has offices in the US and Canada and manufacturing facilities in Illinois, New York, and Puerto Rico.

	Annual Growth	12/03	12/04	12/05	12/06	12/07
Sales ($ mil.)	16.5%	351.3	405.0	518.8	765.5	647.4
Net income ($ mil.)	(16.8%)	71.7	56.7	86.4	(46.9)	34.4
Market value ($ mil.)	—	—	—	—	—	1,644.1
Employees	—	—	—	—	1,400	—

APPALACHIAN BANCSHARES, INC.

NASDAQ (GM): APAB

822 Industrial Blvd.
Ellijay, GA 30540
Phone: 706-276-8000
Fax: 706-276-8010
Web: www.appalachianbank.com

CEO: Tracy R. Newton
CFO: Danny F. Dukes
HR: –
FYE: December 31
Type: Public

Appalachian Bancshares doesn't make mountains out of molehills, but it does make money at banking. The holding company owns Appalachian Community Bank, which serves several north Georgia counties, as well as nearby areas in North Carolina and Tennessee, from about a dozen locations. The bank, which operates as Gilmer County Bank in some locations, offers such products and services as checking and savings accounts, credit and debit cards, money market accounts, and loans. The company's lending activities are focused on real estate; construction loans make up about half of the portfolio and other real estate loans contribute more than 40%. The bank also originates business loans and consumer loans.

	Annual Growth	12/03	12/04	12/05	12/06	12/07
Assets ($ mil.)	27.1%	—	472.8	592.6	758.2	971.2
Net income ($ mil.)	11.0%	—	4.1	5.1	6.0	5.6
Market value ($ mil.)	(25.3%)	—	—	93.3	100.2	52.1
Employees	34.3%	—	—	157	262	283

APPALACHIAN POWER COMPANY

1 Riverside Plaza
Columbus, OH 43215
Phone: 614-716-1000
Fax: 614-716-1823
Web: www.apcocustomer.com

CEO: Michael G. (Mike) Morris
CFO: Holly Koeppel
HR: –
FYE: December 31
Type: Subsidiary

When they're not out enjoying the scenery, Virginians and West Virginians count on Appalachian Power to keep indoor temperatures stable. A subsidiary of American Electric Power, Appalachian Power serves 956,000 residential and business customers in southwestern Virginia and southern West Virginia, and a small portion of northwestern Tennessee. The electric utility operates more than 52,560 miles of transmission and distribution wires. It also has stakes in coal-fired and hydroelectric power plants that give it about 6,300 MW of capacity, and it markets power to wholesale customers in the region.

	Annual Growth	12/03	12/04	12/05	12/06	12/07
Est. sales ($ mil.)	—	—	—	—	—	2,607.3
Net income ($ mil.)	—	—	—	—	—	54.7
Employees	—	—	—	—	—	—

APPAREL VENTURES INC.

13809 S. Figueroa St.
Los Angeles, CA 90061
Phone: 310-538-4980
Fax: 310-538-0515

CEO: Marvin Goodman
CFO: William (Bill) Singletary
HR: Betty Rodriguez
FYE: June 30
Type: Private

Apparel Ventures wants your beach experience to be an adventure in the sun. The company manufactures women's swimwear and beach accessories under its own Playa by La Blanca and Sessa names, as well as for companies such as Anne Klein, Ocean Pacific, Polo Ralph Lauren, and Rampage. The firm further enhanced its portfolio with the late 2004 purchase of Los Angeles-based swimwear maker Waterfront Design Group, which it renamed Blue Water Design Co. Apparel Ventures distributes its products through department stores (such as J.C. Penney and Bergdorf), mass retailers, and specialty swimwear stores nationwide.

	Annual Growth	6/03	6/04	6/05	6/06	6/07
Est. sales ($ mil.)	—	—	—	—	—	88.7
Employees	—	—	—	—	—	235

APPIAN CORPORATION

8000 Towers Crescent Dr., 16th Fl.
Vienna, VA 22182
Phone: 703-442-8844
Fax: 703-442-8919
Web: www.appian.com

CEO: Matthew W. (Matt) Calkins
CFO: Bob Kramer
HR: –
FYE: December 31
Type: Private

Appian wants its clients to be walking down the same path when it comes to crucial information. Founded in 1999, Appian provides business process management (BPM) software that helps corporate, government, and non-governmental organization clients with process management, knowledge management, and analytics functions. The company's software platform includes tools for workflow management, collaboration, and business intelligence, addressing business functions such as compliance, operations, finance, purchasing, sales and marketing, and human resources.

	Annual Growth	12/03	12/04	12/05	12/06	12/07
Est. sales ($ mil.)	—	—	—	—	—	10.1
Employees	—	—	—	—	—	160

APPLE AMERICAN GROUP LLC

6200 Oak Tree Blvd., Ste. 250
Independence, OH 44131
Phone: 216-525-2775
Fax: 216-328-1956
Web: www.appleamerican.com

CEO: Gregory G. (Greg) Flynn
CFO: Lorin M. Cortina
HR: Sharon DellaFave
FYE: December 31
Type: Private

Apple American Group is a leading franchisee of Applebee's International, with more than 140 Applebee's Neighborhood Grill & Bar locations in Indiana, Ohio, and a half dozen other states. Applebee's is the largest casual dining chain in the US, and is especially popular for its selection of appetizers. The chain also offers a full-service menu of beef, chicken, and pork entrees. Apple American was founded in 1998 by CEO Greg Flynn. Private equity firm Weston Presidio Service acquired control of the business in 2005.

	Annual Growth	12/03	12/04	12/05	12/06	12/07
Est. sales ($ mil.)	—	—	—	—	—	119.3
Employees	—	—	—	—	—	5,500

APPLE BANK FOR SAVINGS

122 E. 42nd St., 9th Fl.
New York, NY 10168
Phone: 212-224-6400
Fax: 212-224-6589
Web: www.theapplebank.com

CEO: Alan Shamoon
CFO: Louis Rawden
HR: Susan B. Goro
FYE: December 31
Type: Private

Helping customers manage their money is at the core of Apple Bank for Savings. Apple Bank is a full-service financial institution serving residents of the Greater New York metropolitan area from about 50 branches throughout New York City, Long Island, and Westchester County. The bank offers private and commercial customers savings, checking, money market, and investment accounts; credit cards, student, and mortgage loans; and personal and business lines of credit. Services are also available via telephone and the Internet. Subsidiary ABS Associates provides term and life insurance products and fixed annuities. Apple Bank traces its roots back to 1863.

An in-depth profile of this company is available to Hoover's Online members at hoovers.com.

155

APPLE INC.

NASDAQ (GS): AAPL

1 Infinite Loop
Cupertino, CA 95014
Phone: 408-996-1010
Fax: 408-974-2113
Web: www.apple.com

CEO: Steven P. (Steve) Jobs
CFO: Peter Oppenheimer
HR: –
FYE: Last Friday in September
Type: Public

Computers are still an important part of its mix, but these days music-related products are at the top of Apple's playlist. The company scored a runaway hit with its digital music players (iPod) and online music store (iTunes). Apple's desktop and laptop computers — all of which feature its OS X operating system — include its Mac mini, iMac, and MacBook for the consumer and education markets, and more powerful Mac Pro and MacBook Pro for high-end consumers and professionals involved in design and publishing. Other products include mobile phones (iPhone), servers (Xserve), wireless networking equipment (Airport), and publishing and multimedia software. Its FileMaker subsidiary provides database software.

	Annual Growth	9/03	9/04	9/05	9/06	9/07
Sales ($ mil.)	40.2%	6,207.0	8,279.0	13,931.0	19,315.0	24,006.0
Net income ($ mil.)	166.8%	69.0	276.0	1,335.0	1,989.0	3,496.0
Market value ($ mil.)	143.7%	3,793.8	7,298.5	44,423.0	65,838.1	133,876.3
Employees	17.2%	—	13,426	16,820	17,787	21,600

APPLEBEE'S INTERNATIONAL, INC.

4551 W. 107th St., Ste. 100
Overland Park, KS 66207
Phone: 913-967-4000
Fax: 913-341-1694
Web: www.applebees.com

CEO: Michael J. (Mike) Archer
CFO: Beverly O. (Bev) Elving
HR: John Prutsman
FYE: Last Sunday in December
Type: Subsidiary

Applebee's International makes sure that even far-flung suburbs can have a neighborhood bar. The company operates the largest casual-dining chain with more than 1,970 of its signature Applebee's Neighborhood Grill & Bar locations across the US and in almost 20 other countries. Its eateries are primarily freestanding units and sport interiors festooned with local memorabilia to give each location an indigenous feel. The menu features beef, chicken, and pork items, as well as burgers, pasta, and seafood. The chain is known for its selection of appetizers. More than 500 locations are company-owned, while the rest are franchised. Applebee's was acquired by family dining operator IHOP (now DineEquity) in 2007.

	Annual Growth	12/02	12/03	12/04	12/05	12/06
Sales ($ mil.)	12.8%	826.8	990.1	1,111.6	1,216.7	1,337.9
Net income ($ mil.)	(0.6%)	83.0	93.6	110.9	101.8	80.9
Employees	8.5%	23,500	—	—	32,260	32,600

APPLERA CORPORATION

301 Merritt 7
Norwalk, CT 06856
Phone: 203-840-2000
Fax: 203-840-2312
Web: www.applera.com

CEO: Tony L. White
CFO: Dennis L. Winger
HR: Barbara J. Kerr
FYE: June 30
Type: Holding company

If you are exploring the latest scientific frontiers, Applera has some tools for your journey. Its Applied Biosystems unit makes instrumentation systems, along with related consumables, software, and services, that let life sciences researchers analyze nucleic acids, proteins, and small molecules. In addition to their usefulness in pharmaceutical and biotechnology research, the systems can also be used by organizations that perform forensic, biosecurity, and food safety testing. Applera's Celera unit is primarily engaged in genomics and proteomics research, seeking out diagnostic markers and developing molecular diagnostic products. In 2008 Applera announced that Invitrogen would acquire Applied Biosystems.

	Annual Growth	6/03	6/04	6/05	6/06	6/07
Est. sales ($ mil.)	—	—	—	—	—	2,132.5
Net income ($ mil.)	—	—	—	—	—	159.3
Employees	—	—	—	—	—	—

APPLETON MEDICAL CENTER

1818 N. Meade St.
Appleton, WI 54911
Phone: 920-731-4101
Fax: 920-738-6319
Web: www.thedacare.org

CEO: Dean Gruner
CFO: –
HR: Maureen Pistone
FYE: December 31
Type: Not-for-profit

Appleton Medical Center serves residents of northeastern Wisconsin with general and specialized health services. Its specialties include cardiac, cancer, and orthopedic care. Appleton Medical Center is one of four regional hospitals operated by ThedaCare. Established in 1958, the not-for-profit hospital started the first fertility program in the region.

	Annual Growth	12/03	12/04	12/05	12/06	12/07
Est. sales ($ mil.)	—	—	—	—	—	429.8
Employees	—	—	—	—	—	1,230

APPLETON PAPERS INC.

825 E. Wisconsin Ave.
Appleton, WI 54912
Phone: 920-734-9841
Fax: 920-991-7365
Web: www.appletonideas.com

CEO: Mark R. Richards
CFO: Thomas J. Ferree
HR: Paul J. Karch
FYE: Saturday nearest December 31
Type: Private

Appleton Papers hasn't fallen far from the tree. The company manufactures and distributes a variety of specialty paper products. Its top product is carbonless paper (sold under the NCR Paper brand), which is used for business forms. Appleton also makes thermal paper and related products that are used in point-of-sale receipts and coupons, tickets (including event, lottery, and transportation tickets), and labels. Other units make security products (checks, security-printed vouchers, and counterfeit-resistant documents) and plastic packaging films for use in the food processing, household goods, and industrial products industries. Appleton is owned by its employees.

	Annual Growth	12/02	12/03	12/04	12/05	12/06
Sales ($ mil.)	4.9%	898.0	861.5	989.5	1,046.5	1,087.4
Net income ($ mil.)	2.8%	10.1	11.2	(25.0)	(3.0)	11.3
Employees	5.9%	2,500	3,348	3,406	3,238	3,144

APPLIANCE RECYCLING CENTERS

NASDAQ (CM): ARCI

7400 Excelsior Blvd.
Minneapolis, MN 55426
Phone: 952-930-9000
Fax: 952-930-1800
Web: www.arcainc.com

CEO: Edward R. (Jack) Cameron
CFO: Peter P. Hausback
HR: Cindy Janzig
FYE: Saturday nearest December 31
Type: Public

Appliance Recycling Centers of America, Inc. (ARCA) retrieves, recycles, repairs, and resells household appliances. The company collects used appliances and reconditions them for resale at about 15 ApplianceSmart retail stores in Georgia, Minnesota, Ohio, and Texas. ARCA also sells "special-buy appliances" — returned, exchanged, or discontinued units, "scratch-and-dent" units, and factory overruns from manufacturers (mainly GE, Frigidaire, and Whirlpool). Additionally, the company collects fees for appliance disposal, sells scrap metal and reclaimed chlorofluorocarbons (CFCs) from processed appliances, and recycles household appliances for energy conservation programs of electric utilities.

	Annual Growth	12/03	12/04	12/05	12/06	12/07
Sales ($ mil.)	23.3%	43.6	52.8	74.9	77.8	100.8
Net income ($ mil.)	—	(1.5)	(1.3)	(0.9)	(1.4)	2.5
Market value ($ mil.)	56.0%	6.5	19.0	21.2	9.3	38.5
Employees	—	—	—	294	—	—

APPLICA INCORPORATED

3633 Flamingo Rd.
Miramar, FL 33027
Phone: 954-883-1000
Fax: –
Web: www.applicainc.com

CEO: Terry L. Polistina
CFO: –
HR: –
FYE: December 31
Type: Subsidiary

Applica can curl your hair and toast your bread. The company markets and distributes small appliances (coffee makers, toaster ovens, irons) and personal care products (curling irons, hair dryers). Its cupboard is filled with company-owned and licensed brands, including Black & Decker and Windmere. Applica also markets pet (Litter Maid self-cleaning cat boxes) and pest control products. Applica's wares are sold through specialty retailers, appliance distributors, and mass merchants worldwide. The company ceased its manufacturing operations in 2005. In early 2007 Applica was acquired by investment firm Harbinger Capital Partners, its largest shareholder, and became part of Salton later that year.

APPLIED BIOSYSTEMS GROUP

NYSE: ABI

850 Lincoln Centre Dr.
Foster City, CA 94404
Phone: 650-570-6667
Fax: 650-572-2743
Web: www.appliedbiosystems.com

CEO: Mark P. Stevenson
CFO: Dennis L. Winger
HR: Joan Cronin
FYE: June 30
Type: Public

Applied Biosystems Group, a tracking-stock unit of Applera, makes the big machines for life scientists to peer into the details of DNA and proteins and chart the future of medicine. Its product line includes systems that detect the polymerase chain reactions used to identify DNA sequences. The unit also provides gene expression assays for various species, specialized enzymes called reagents, and disposable plastic devices to hold DNA samples. Its customers include biotech and drug firms, as well as research institutes, that are studying how drugs interact with the body's systems (pharmacokinetics) and its genetic makeup (pharmacogenomics). In 2008 the unit agreed to be acquired by Invitrogen.

	Annual Growth	6/03	6/04	6/05	6/06	6/07
Sales ($ mil.)	5.6%	1,682.9	1,741.1	1,787.1	1,911.2	2,093.5
Employees	2.4%	4,540	4,400	4,030	4,570	5,000

APPLIED CARD SYSTEMS

50 Applied Card Way
Glen Mills, PA 19342
Phone: 484-840-1700
Fax: 484-840-2758
Web: www.appliedcard.com

CEO: Rocco A. Abessinio
CFO: –
HR: Dan Taylor
FYE: December 31
Type: Private

Applied Card Systems is the servicing arm for Applied Bank (formerly Cross Country Bank), a subprime consumer lender that issues secured and unsecured credit cards to customers with dubious or limited credit histories. Applied Card Systems processes payments from and provides customer service to holders of subprime Visa and MasterCard accounts from offices in Florida and Pennsylvania. Applied Card Systems also services credit card accounts for third-party issuers. Chairman Rocco Abessinio is the founder of both Applied Card Bank and Applied Card Systems, which was formed in 1987.

APPLIED DIGITAL SOLUTIONS, INC.

NASDAQ (CM): DIGA

1690 S. Congress Ave., Ste. 200
Delray Beach, FL 33445
Phone: 561-805-8000
Fax: 561-805-8001
Web: www.digitalangel.com

CEO: Joseph J. (Joe) Grillo
CFO: Lorraine M. Breece
HR: Carlos Botero
FYE: December 31
Type: Public

Applied Digital Solutions can get under your skin. The company, doing business as Digital Angel, is best known for its VeriChip technology — computer chips that can be embedded under the skin and read by a remote sensor to check vital signs and diagnose medical problems. Its VeriChip subsidiary markets the technology for medical use in humans. Applied Digital is also involved in network integration services through subsidiary Computer Equity Corporation, and its Thermo Life Energy business develops thermoelectric generators. In addition, the company owns nearly half of IFTH Acquisition (formerly InfoTech USA and SysComm International). Applied Digital gets about two-thirds of its sales in North America.

	Annual Growth	12/03	12/04	12/05	12/06	12/07
Sales ($ mil.)	6.0%	93.0	112.0	113.7	122.7	117.4
Net income ($ mil.)	—	3.1	(17.3)	(10.2)	(27.2)	(32.0)
Market value ($ mil.)	(31.0%)	193.3	381.0	191.7	121.2	43.9
Employees	1.0%	403	404	582	622	419

APPLIED DNA SCIENCES, INC.

OTC: APDN

25 Health Sciences Dr., Ste. 113
Stony Brook, NY 11790
Phone: 631-444-6862
Fax: 631-444-8848
Web: www.adnas.com

CEO: James A. Hayward
CFO: Kurt Jensen
HR: –
FYE: September 30
Type: Public

Applied DNA Sciences makes products encoded with botanical DNA sequences that can distinguish counterfeits from the genuine article. The DNA markers (which hold the SigNature brand) can be employed in ink, glue, holograms, microchips, and paint and then used to tag documents, currency, event tickets, and clothing labels. The company is focused on applying its SigNature markers to art and collectibles, fine wine, consumer products, digital recording media, pharmaceuticals, and homeland security products. In 2005, Taiwan-based Biowell, a maker of DNA-based fraud-prevention technology, swapped its intellectual property for a 40% stake in Applied DNA Sciences.

	Annual Growth	9/03	9/04	9/05	9/06	9/07
Sales ($ mil.)	—	—	—	—	0.0	0.1
Net income ($ mil.)	—	—	—	—	(2.4)	(13.3)
Market value ($ mil.)	49.0%	—	—	—	12.1	18.0
Employees	—	—	—	—	—	—

APPLIED ENERGETICS, INC.

NASDAQ (GM): AERG

3590 E. Columbia
Tucson, AZ 85714
Phone: 520-628-7415
Fax: 520-622-3835
Web: www.ionatron.com

CEO: Dana A. Marshall
CFO: Kenneth M. Wallace
HR: –
FYE: December 31
Type: Public

Bullets?!! We don't need no stinkin' bullets — not with the Buck Rogers technology of Applied Energetics (formerly Ionatron). The company is developing Laser Guided Energy (LGE) and Laser Induced Plasma Channel (LIPC) directed-energy weapons for sale to the US government. In plain English? Laser-guided, man-made lightning! Applied Energetics is developing more compact laser sources and field testing its technology for mobile platforms such as tanks, Humvees, and personnel carriers. Depending on the military situation, the charge can be set to stun or kill people, or to disable vehicles. Applied Energetics also develops technology for neutralizing car bombs.

	Annual Growth	6/03	*12/04	12/05	12/06	12/07
Sales ($ mil.)	(36.5%)	76.2	10.9	18.9	10.0	12.4
Net income ($ mil.)	—	(9.1)	(3.3)	(3.6)	(17.5)	(13.7)
Market value ($ mil.)	(34.1%)	—	802.7	727.9	320.5	229.5
Employees	(18.4%)	178	67	104	83	79

*Fiscal year change

An in-depth profile of this company is available to Hoover's Online members at hoovers.com.

157

APPLIED EXTRUSION TECHNOLOGIES, INC.

15 Read's Way
New Castle, DE 19720
Phone: 302-326-5500
Fax: 302-326-5501
Web: www.appliedextrusion.com

CEO: Thomas M. Mohr
CFO: Brian P. Crescenzo
HR: –
FYE: September 30
Type: Private

Soft drinks, candy, and potato chips are the major food groups for Applied Extrusion Technologies (AET). The company produces oriented polypropylene (OPP) films used to make labels for plastic soft drink containers and packages for snack foods. AET sells its OPP films to converters (companies that print text and graphics on the films) and to end users in the food and beverage industries. The company also makes apertured, or porous, films used as facing material for products such as adhesive bandages. AET's films can be found on products such as Pepsi and Coke soft drinks, and British American Tobacco cigarette boxes.

APPLIED INDUSTRIAL TECHNOLOGIES, INC.

NYSE: AIT

1 Applied Plaza
Cleveland, OH 44115
Phone: 216-426-4000
Fax: 216-426-4845
Web: www.appliedindustrial.com

CEO: David L. Pugh
CFO: Mark O. Eisele
HR: Barbara D. Emery
FYE: June 30
Type: Public

Just imagine getting lost in *that* warehouse. Applied Industrial Technologies distributes literally millions of parts made by thousands of manufacturers. The short list of products includes bearings, power transmission components, hydraulic and pneumatic components, fabricated rubber products, and linear motion systems. It primarily sells these items through about 450 service centers throughout the US (including Puerto Rico), Canada, and Mexico. Customers include both the maintenance repair operations (MRO) and original equipment manufacturing (OEM) markets. Applied also operates regional mechanical, rubber, and fluid power shops that perform services such as engineering design and conveyor belt repair.

	Annual Growth	6/03	6/04	6/05	6/06	6/07
Sales ($ mil.)	8.3%	1,464.4	1,517.0	1,717.1	1,900.8	2,014.1
Net income ($ mil.)	44.4%	19.8	31.5	55.3	72.3	86.0
Market value ($ mil.)	63.4%	178.4	261.1	645.8	1,071.3	1,271.9
Employees	6.1%	—	—	4,415	4,683	—

APPLIED MATERIALS, INC.

NASDAQ (GS): AMAT

3050 Bowers Ave.
Santa Clara, CA 95054
Phone: 408-727-5555
Fax: 408-748-9943
Web: www.appliedmaterials.com

CEO: Michael R. (Mike) Splinter
CFO: George S. Davis
HR: Menachem Erad
FYE: Last Sunday in October
Type: Public

Today, semiconductor manufacturing; tomorrow, the world — of alternative energy sources. Applied Materials is, by far, the world's largest maker of semiconductor production equipment. With its acquisition of Applied Films, the company moved into the market for equipment used in making solar power cells. Applied's machines vie for supremacy in many segments of the chip-making process, including deposition (layering film on wafers), etching (removing portions of chip material to allow precise construction of circuits), and semiconductor metrology and inspection equipment. More than two-thirds of Applied's sales come from the Asia/Pacific region, with Taiwan leading the way.

	Annual Growth	10/03	10/04	10/05	10/06	10/07
Sales ($ mil.)	21.4%	4,477.3	8,013.0	6,991.8	9,167.0	9,734.9
Net income ($ mil.)	—	(149.1)	1,351.3	1,209.9	1,516.7	1,710.2
Market value ($ mil.)	(6.8%)	34,638.3	27,052.3	26,285.5	24,021.3	26,134.5
Employees	6.2%	12,050	12,960	12,576	14,072	15,328

APPLIED MICRO CIRCUITS CORPORATION

NASDAQ (GS): AMCC

215 Moffett Dr.
Sunnyvale, CA 94089
Phone: 408-542-8600
Fax: 858-450-9885
Web: www.amcc.com

CEO: Kambiz Y. Hooshmand
CFO: Robert G. (Bob) Gargus
HR: Michael (Mike) Major
FYE: March 31
Type: Public

Applied Micro Circuits Corporation (AMCC) applies most of its microchip expertise to communications, but does more than a micro business in storage, as well. Customers use AMCC's chips — which include controllers, host bus adapters, network processors, and switch fabrics — to control the flow of voice and data transmissions in LANs, WANs, and storage networks. Having shut down its own wafer fabrication plant (or fab), the fabless semiconductor company outsources manufacturing to IBM Microelectronics, TSMC, and UMC. Its top customers include Alcatel-Lucent, Avnet (22% of sales), Cisco, Hitachi, Nortel Networks, Sanmina-SCI, and Siemens. AMCC gets more than half of its sales outside of North America.

	Annual Growth	3/04	3/05	3/06	3/07	3/08
Sales ($ mil.)	17.0%	131.2	253.8	261.8	292.9	246.1
Net income ($ mil.)	—	(104.9)	(127.4)	(148.4)	(24.2)	(115.1)
Market value ($ mil.)	(28.5%)	1,775.7	1,011.3	1,202.4	1,032.9	465.1
Employees	(5.2%)	723	755	602	619	583

APPLIED NANOTECH HOLDINGS, INC.

OTC: NNPP

3006 Longhorn Blvd., Ste. 107
Austin, TX 78758
Phone: 512-339-5020
Fax: 512-339-5021
Web: www.appliednanotech.net

CEO: Thomas F. Bijou
CFO: Douglas P. (Doug) Baker
HR: –
FYE: December 31
Type: Public

Applied Nanotech Holdings hopes to make it big by thinking small. The company, formerly known as Nano-Proprietary, conducts research on carbon nanotubes — molecular-sized cylindrical structures that the company uses in making electronic displays. Applied Nanotech derives nearly 60% of its sales from agencies of the US government. The company's Electronic Billboard Technology (EBT) subsidiary sold its intellectual property to Novus Communications Technologies in 2006 and received royalties from Novus Partners, a unit of Novus Communications. As part of the consideration, EBT received a 25% equity stake in Novus Displays, a new entity formed by Novus Communications.

	Annual Growth	12/03	12/04	12/05	12/06	12/07
Sales ($ mil.)	49.5%	0.8	0.4	0.6	1.1	4.0
Net income ($ mil.)	—	(4.2)	(4.6)	(4.7)	(6.6)	(4.3)
Market value ($ mil.)	(18.4%)	261.0	211.0	214.5	146.0	115.7
Employees	16.0%	21	26	29	35	38

APPLIED SIGNAL TECHNOLOGY, INC.

NASDAQ (GS): APSG

400 W. California Ave.
Sunnyvale, CA 94086
Phone: 408-749-1888
Fax: 408-738-1928
Web: www.appsig.com

CEO: William B. Van Vleet III
CFO: James E. Doyle
HR: –
FYE: October 31
Type: Public

Eavesdropping is no accident at Applied Signal Technology. The company makes reconnaissance equipment — including receivers, processors, and software — used by the US government and its contractors to collect and process electronic communications and other electronic signals. Applied Signal's products are used to scan and filter cell phone, ship-to-shore, microwave, and military transmissions and evaluate them for relevant information. Other products are designed to collect and process radar signals for weapons systems. The company sells primarily to intelligence agencies, with military customers accounting for most of the rest of its business.

	Annual Growth	10/03	10/04	10/05	10/06	10/07
Sales ($ mil.)	15.6%	95.4	142.8	156.1	161.9	170.4
Net income ($ mil.)	(6.0%)	8.7	12.0	9.2	4.3	6.8
Market value ($ mil.)	(5.5%)	222.9	339.6	197.8	176.9	178.0
Employees	8.4%	—	498	677	647	635

APPLIED SYSTEMS, INC.

200 Applied Pkwy.
University Park, IL 60466
Phone: 708-534-5575
Fax: 708-534-8016
Web: www.appliedsystems.com

CEO: James P. Kellner
CFO: Colleen Mikuce
HR: —
FYE: December 31
Type: Private

Applied Systems applies technology to automate the insurance industry — from lone agent to large agency. Founded in 1981, the company helps independent insurance agents become more efficient by minimizing paperwork, streamlining workflows, and improving access to information. Applied Systems' main product, the Agency Manager system, assists with client management, policy pricing, electronic data interchange, policy and claims servicing, and office administration. Its Vision systems provide large carriers with automated billing, policy and claims processing, and reports. Applied Systems, which focuses on property and casualty agencies, also provides customer support, training, and consulting services.

	Annual Growth	12/03	12/04	12/05	12/06	12/07
Est. sales ($ mil.)	—	—	—	—	—	55.7
Employees	—	—	—	—	—	716

APPLIX, INC.

289 Turnpike Rd.
Westborough, MA 01581
Phone: 508-870-0300
Fax: 508-366-2278
Web: www.applix.com

CEO: David C. Mahoney
CFO: Milton A. (Milt) Alpern
HR: Mary Murphy
FYE: December 31
Type: Subsidiary

Applix knows the value of good business planning. The company provides business intelligence and business performance management software that helps large enterprises manage such tasks as budgeting, forecasting, and financial reporting, as well as strategic planning, sales and product profitability analysis, collaboration, and creating performance metrics such as dashboards and scorecards. Applix also offers a variety of professional services, including training, support, and consulting services. In late 2007 the company was acquired by Cognos for about $306 million.

	Annual Growth	12/02	12/03	12/04	12/05	12/06
Sales ($ mil.)	9.3%	36.6	27.4	30.9	37.0	52.2
Net income ($ mil.)	—	(5.8)	0.0	4.7	6.7	9.3
Employees	10.3%	142	—	123	147	210

APPROACH RESOURCES INC.

NASDAQ (GM): AREX

6300 Ridglea Place, Ste. 1107
Fort Worth, TX 76116
Phone: 817-989-9000
Fax: 817-989-9001
Web: www.approachresources.com

CEO: J. Ross Craft
CFO: Steven P. Smart
HR: —
FYE: December 31
Type: Public

Approach Resources takes a different approach to natural gas and oil exploration, development, and production. Specializing in finding and exploiting unconventional reservoirs, the company operates primarily in West Texas' Ozona Northeast field, while developing its operations in western Kentucky and northern New Mexico. The company's unconventional designation results from a focus on developing natural gas reserves in tight gas sands and shale areas, necessitating a reliance on advanced completion, fracturing, and drilling techniques. Approach Resources has proved reserves of approximately 149 billion cu. ft. of oil equivalent, with a reserve life index of about 19 years.

	Annual Growth	12/03	12/04	12/05	12/06	12/07
Sales ($ mil.)	90.0%	—	5.7	43.3	46.7	39.1
Net income ($ mil.)	—	—	(0.3)	12.1	21.2	2.7
Market value ($ mil.)	—	—	—	—	—	265.2
Employees	—	—	—	—	—	—

APPROVA CORPORATION

1950 Roland Clark Place, Ste. 300
Reston, VA 20191
Phone: 703-956-8300
Fax: 703-956-8350
Web: www.approva.net

CEO: Prashanth V. (PV) Boccasam
CFO: Lenn Kurtzman
HR: —
FYE: December 31
Type: Private

Approva hopes to get a nod of approval when you're looking to gain control of your enterprise. The company is an enterprise controls management software developer. Its applications address financial and operational business processes, including audits, customer fulfillment, payroll, procurement, and sales. Approva serves clients in industries such as health care, financial services, manufacturing, and retail. The company was founded in 2002. Investors have included Columbia Capital, Hyperion Solutions, New Enterprise Associates, Novak Biddle Venture Partners, and Sierra Ventures.

	Annual Growth	12/03	12/04	12/05	12/06	12/07
Est. sales ($ mil.)	—	—	—	—	—	12.9
Employees	—	—	—	—	—	140

APPTIS, INC.

14155 Newbrook Dr.
Chantilly, VA 20151
Phone: 703-279-3000
Fax: 703-691-4911
Web: www.apptis.com

CEO: Albert A. (Bert) Notini
CFO: Patrick (Rick) Attilio
HR: Sharon Palmeter
FYE: December 31
Type: Private

The company formerly known as PlanetGov now wants to be called Apptis. A major provider of information technology (IT) services to the government sector, Apptis wants to expand its client base which in part explains the name change. The company provides a wide range of IT services, including network engineering, software development, and systems integration, for agencies of the federal government and commercial clients. It also builds custom computer systems and resells equipment from such vendors as Cisco, Dell, and Hewlett-Packard. Other services include maintenance, support, and training. Clients include the FAA, the DoD, and the Veterans Health Administration.

	Annual Growth	12/03	12/04	12/05	12/06	12/07
Est. sales ($ mil.)	—	—	—	—	—	240.9
Employees	—	—	—	—	—	700

APRIA HEALTHCARE GROUP INC.

NYSE: AHG

26220 Enterprise Ct.
Lake Forest, CA 92630
Phone: 949-639-2000
Fax: 949-587-9363
Web: www.apria.com

CEO: Lawrence M. Higby
CFO: Chris A. Karkenny
HR: Howard Derman
FYE: December 31
Type: Public

With about 550 branches nationwide, Apria Healthcare Group is one of the country's largest home health firms and provides services and equipment to patients in all 50 states. Its nurses and home health aids provide supplemental oxygen, ventilators, nebulizers, and sleep monitoring to patients with emphysema, sleep apnea, and other respiratory conditions. Its infusion therapy nurses administer intravenous or injectable therapies — including pain drugs, chemotherapy, and parenteral nutrition — at home or in one of the company's 50 outpatient infusion clinics. Apria also delivers home medical equipment such as walkers and hospital beds. In 2007 Apria added to its holdings with the acquisition of Coram.

	Annual Growth	12/03	12/04	12/05	12/06	12/07
Sales ($ mil.)	4.3%	1,380.9	1,451.4	1,474.1	1,517.3	1,631.8
Net income ($ mil.)	(7.2%)	116.0	114.0	66.9	75.0	86.0
Market value ($ mil.)	(10.2%)	1,455.0	1,601.7	1,018.7	1,140.3	944.6
Employees	9.2%	—	—	11,136	11,258	13,276

An in-depth profile of this company is available to Hoover's Online members at hoovers.com.

159

APRIMO, INCORPORATED

900 E. 96th St., Ste. 400
Indianapolis, IN 46240
Phone: 317-803-4300
Fax: 317-803-4251
Web: www.aprimo.com

CEO: William M. (Bill) Godfrey
CFO: Michael W. Nelson
HR: –
FYE: December 31
Type: Private

Aprimo understands that successful marketing is a prime concern of most businesses. The company provides software that customers use to manage marketing efforts, including applications to automate and analyze marketing campaigns. Aprimo's products are used for tasks such as planning, budgeting, and campaign analysis. It also offers services such as consulting, maintenance, support, installation, and training. Aprimo's customers come from a wide range of industries and have included Bank of America, Sony, Home Depot, Intel, and Toyota. The company was founded in 1998.

	Annual Growth	12/02	12/03	12/04	12/05	12/06
Sales ($ mil.)	61.0%	—	—	19.9	30.5	51.6
Net income ($ mil.)	—	—	—	(1.1)	(4.8)	2.1
Employees	—	—	—	—	—	355

APS HEALTHCARE, INC.

8403 Colesville Rd., Ste. 1600
Silver Spring, MD 20910
Phone: 301-563-5633
Fax: 301-563-7338
Web: www.apshealthcare.com

CEO: Gregory W. (Greg) Scott
CFO: John McDonough
HR: –
FYE: December 31
Type: Private

APS Healthcare manages specialty health care services for commercial health plans, large employers, and state Medicaid programs. APS provides case management and behavioral health programs for private employers, health plans, and public health services. The firm serves over 20 million plan members. Offerings include case management and disease management programs; employee assistance programs; health and wellness tools; and consulting services. In 2006 APS sold its physical medicine review business to MedRisk, a managed care services provider.

	Annual Growth	12/03	12/04	12/05	12/06	12/07
Est. sales ($ mil.)	—	—	—	—	—	464.8
Employees	—	—	—	—	—	1,200

APTARGROUP, INC.

NYSE: ATR

475 W. Terra Cotta Ave., Ste. E
Crystal Lake, IL 60014
Phone: 815-477-0424
Fax: 815-477-0481
Web: www.aptar.com

CEO: Peter H. Pfeiffer
CFO: Stephen J. Hagge
HR: Lawrence Lowrimore
FYE: December 31
Type: Public

AptarGroup hopes its dispensers are indispensable. The company's main products are pump dispensers used for fragrances and cosmetics, pharmaceuticals, and other personal care products. AptarGroup also makes dispensing closures, primarily for plastic-capped squeezable containers of personal care products, but also for the food and beverage and household products markets. The company makes its aerosol valves in continuous-spray and metered-dose varieties. AptarGroup, which operates on five continents, sells its products worldwide, primarily through an in-house sales network.

	Annual Growth	12/03	12/04	12/05	12/06	12/07
Sales ($ mil.)	14.1%	1,114.7	1,296.6	1,380.0	1,601.4	1,892.2
Net income ($ mil.)	15.5%	79.7	93.3	100.0	102.9	141.7
Market value ($ mil.)	39.6%	735.2	1,008.1	910.9	1,021.4	2,790.1
Employees	8.0%	—	—	7,200	8,200	8,400

APTIMUS, INC.

199 Fremont St., Ste. 1800
San Francisco, CA 94105
Phone: 415-896-2123
Fax: 415-896-2561
Web: www.aptimus.com

CEO: Robert W. (Rob) Wrubel
CFO: John A. Wade
HR: David H. (Dave) Davis
FYE: December 31
Type: Subsidiary

Aptimus thinks it's the most qualified to bring you online shopping deals. The company, whose name is derived from the Latin words *aptus* (unusually qualified) and *optimus* (most beneficial), operates an ad network that showcases free, trial, and promotional offers from a variety of corporate clients. Aptimus provides banner ads, hyper-links, and pop-ups across its network of sites as part of its clients' marketing campaigns and coordinates mailings using its database of e-mail addresses of people who have opted to receive promotional offers. Clients have included Procter & Gamble, Advertising.com, and Quinstreet. Aptimus is a subsidiary of education services company Apollo Group.

	Annual Growth	12/02	12/03	12/04	12/05	12/06
Sales ($ mil.)	51.3%	2.9	4.6	14.0	15.9	15.2
Net income ($ mil.)	—	(5.5)	(1.5)	2.1	1.4	(3.8)
Employees	30.6%	—	—	34	48	58

AQUA AMERICA, INC.

NYSE: WTR

762 W. Lancaster Ave.
Bryn Mawr, PA 19010
Phone: 610-527-8000
Fax: 610-525-7658
Web: www.aquaamerica.com

CEO: Nicholas DeBenedictis
CFO: David P. Smeltzer
HR: –
FYE: December 31
Type: Public

Aqua America is all wet and proud of it. The utility holding company provides water and wastewater services through its operating subsidiaries to about 2.8 million residents in more than a dozen states, including Florida, New Jersey, New York, and Pennsylvania. The state of Pennsylvania is the company's most important market. Aqua America provides water or wastewater services to Philadelphia and in 23 other counties in Pennsylvania, or about half of the company's total customers. It contracts with municipalities to operate their water and wastewater systems. The company has grown through more than 120 acquisitions since the early 1990s.

	Annual Growth	12/03	12/04	12/05	12/06	12/07
Sales ($ mil.)	13.2%	367.2	442.0	496.8	533.5	602.5
Net income ($ mil.)	7.6%	70.8	80.0	91.2	92.0	95.0
Market value ($ mil.)	16.5%	1,534.7	1,759.2	3,520.9	3,014.4	2,828.1
Employees	3.2%	—	—	1,489	1,540	1,585

AQUANTIVE, INC.

821 2nd Ave., Ste. 1800
Seattle, WA 98104
Phone: 206-816-8700
Fax: 206-816-8808
Web: www.aquantive.com

CEO: Brian P. McAndrews
CFO: M. Wayne Wisehart
HR: –
FYE: December 31
Type: Subsidiary

Online advertising won't take you to Easy Street anymore, but it might lead you to Avenue A. aQuantive, through its Avenue A/Razorfish subsidiary, offers digital marketing services to help clients make the most of their online ad budgets. Services include online media buying and planning, ad campaign management, e-mail direct marketing, search engine optimization, and data warehousing and analysis. Its Atlas unit provides marketing software which allows clients to manage digital campaigns. Through subsidiaries such as DRIVEpm and Mediabrokers, aQuantive's third business line buys blocks of online media advertising to resell on a targeted basis. In August 2007, Microsoft acquired aQuantive for $6 billion.

	Annual Growth	12/02	12/03	12/04	12/05	12/06
Sales ($ mil.)	35.1%	132.6	222.0	157.9	308.4	442.2
Net income ($ mil.)	—	(4.6)	11.8	42.9	35.2	54.0
Employees	64.9%	285	376	1,130	1,463	2,106

AQUENT

711 Boylston St.	CEO: John H. Chuang
Boston, MA 02116	CFO: Nunzio Domilici
Phone: 617-535-5000	HR: −
Fax: 617-535-5005	FYE: December 31
Web: www.aquent.com	Type: Private

Aquent can help quench the thirst of firms in need of good employees. The staffing and consulting agency places contract workers with specialized creative, technical, and Web skills such as graphic design, writing and editing, and print production. In addition to temporary services, Aquent offers permanent staffing, executive search, and creative and IT outsourcing. It also offers financial services to small businesses, as well as recruiting help to health care organizations. Aquent operates from 70 offices in more than 15 countries across Europe, North America, and the Asia/Pacific region. CEO John Chuang controls Aquent.

AQUILA, INC.
NYSE: ILA

20 W. 9th St.	CEO: Richard C. (Rick) Green Jr.
Kansas City, MO 64105	CFO: Beth A. Armstrong
Phone: 816-421-6600	HR: −
Fax: 816-467-3591	FYE: December 31
Web: www.aquila.com	Type: Public

Having been buffeted by industry turbulence, Aquila (Latin for eagle, pronounced ah-KWIL-uh), once a global high flier in the merchant energy industry, is reducing the breadth of its wingspan, and staying close to home. The company is focusing on its regulated US utility division, which serves more than 519,620 natural gas customers in Colorado and Kansas, and more than 400,800 electricity customers in Colorado, Iowa, Kansas, and Nebraska. Aquila also generates 1,849 MW of capacity and sells excess power to other utilities and energy marketers. Other operations include independent power production and telecommunications services.

	Annual Growth	12/03	12/04	12/05	12/06	12/07
Sales ($ mil.)	(3.3%)	1,674.0	1,711.0	1,314.2	1,369.6	1,466.6
Net income ($ mil.)	—	(336.4)	(292.5)	(230.0)	23.9	(5.4)
Market value ($ mil.)	20.6%	661.9	892.0	1,345.0	1,760.2	1,402.1
Employees	(16.9%)	—	—	3,204	2,456	2,213

AQUILEX CORPORATION

3339 Peachtree Rd. NE	CEO: L. William (Bill) Varner Jr.
Atlanta, GA 30326	CFO: Jay W. Ferguson
Phone: 404-869-6677	HR: Greg Losh
Fax: 404-869-6678	FYE: December 31
Web: www.aquilex.com	Type: Private

Through its Welding Services unit, Aquilex provides maintenance and repair services for power generation facilities and other industrial plants, including cement, petrochemical, pulp and paper, and steel manufacturing operations. In 2005 Aquilex sold its equipment business, Wheelabrator Air Pollution Control, to Siemens Power Generation. The company is controlled by private equity firm Harvest Partners, (which bought the company from First Reserve in 2007). That year Aquilex agreed to acquire HydroChem Industrial Services, a US-based provider of industrial cleaning services.

	Annual Growth	12/03	12/04	12/05	12/06	12/07
Est. sales ($ mil.)	—	—	—	—	—	256.3
Employees	—	—	—	—	—	916

ARABIAN AMERICAN DEVELOPMENT COMPANY
NASDAQ (GS): ARSD

10830 N. Central Expwy., Ste. 175	CEO: Hatem El Khalidi
Dallas, TX 75231	CFO: Hatem El Khalidi
Phone: 214-692-7872	HR: −
Fax: 214-692-7874	FYE: December 31
	Type: Public

Arabian American Development may dream of making a fortune exploring for precious minerals in Saudi Arabia, but it generates most of its bread-and-butter income as an independent refiner in Texas. Through US subsidiary American Shield Refining, it operates a specialty petrochemical product refinery that primarily produces high purity solvents used in the plastics and foam industries. Subsidiary Gulf State Pipe Line owns and operates three pipelines. In addition, Arabian American holds a mining lease (for copper, gold, silver, and zinc) in southwestern Saudi Arabia's Al Masane area and has mining claims in Nevada. Arabian American Development was formed in 1967.

	Annual Growth	12/03	12/04	12/05	12/06	12/07
Sales ($ mil.)	28.7%	39.6	59.8	80.4	98.5	108.6
Net income ($ mil.)	—	(3.5)	(2.5)	16.6	7.9	7.8
Market value ($ mil.)	285.2%	—	3.1	32.8	71.1	179.6
Employees	5.3%	122	—	—	133	150

ARADIGM CORPORATION
OTC: ARDM

3929 Point Eden Way	CEO: Igor Gonda
Hayward, CA 94545	CFO: Norman L. Halleen
Phone: 510-265-9000	HR: −
Fax: 510-265-0277	FYE: December 31
Web: www.aradigm.com	Type: Public

Aradigm helps the medicine go down for people who swoon at the sight of a needle. Aradigm develops orally-inhaled drug delivery systems that treat respiratory diseases. Its lead delivery technology, AERx (an aerosol created from liquid drug formulations), had been in clinical testing as an inhalable insulin product for patients with diabetes until 2008, when partner Novo Nordisk announced that it was halting development following the failure of similar products to gain traction in the market. Aradigm has since refocused its efforts on developing respiratory treatments for cystic fibrosis, bronchiectasis, inhalation anthrax, smoking cessation, pulmonary arterial hypertension, and asthma.

	Annual Growth	12/03	12/04	12/05	12/06	12/07
Sales ($ mil.)	(58.6%)	33.9	28.0	10.5	4.8	1.0
Net income ($ mil.)	—	(26.0)	(30.2)	(29.2)	(13.0)	(24.2)
Market value ($ mil.)	(33.6%)	429.2	500.3	42.5	13.3	83.3
Employees	—	—	—	103	—	—

ARAMARK CORPORATION

ARAMARK Tower, 1101 Market St.	CEO: Joseph (Joe) Neubauer
Philadelphia, PA 19107	CFO: L. Frederick Sutherland
Phone: 215-238-3000	HR: Lynn B. McKee
Fax: 215-238-3333	FYE: Friday nearest September 30
Web: www.aramark.com	Type: Private

Keeping employees fed and clothed is one mark of this company. ARAMARK is the world's #3 foodservice provider (behind Compass Group and Sodexo) and the #2 uniform supplier (behind Cintas) in the US. It offers corporate dining services and operates concessions at many sports arenas and other entertainment venues, while its ARAMARK Refreshment Services unit is a leading provider of vending and beverage services. The company also provides facilities management services. Through ARAMARK Uniform and Career Apparel, the company supplies uniforms for health care, public safety, and technology workers. Founded in 1959, ARAMARK is owned by an investment group led by chairman and CEO Joseph Neubauer.

	Annual Growth	9/03	9/04	9/05	9/06	9/07
Sales ($ mil.)	7.0%	9,447.8	10,192.2	10,963.4	11,621.2	12,384.3
Net income ($ mil.)	(43.4%)	301.1	263.1	288.5	261.1	30.9
Employees	5.7%	200,000	242,500	240,000	240,000	250,000

ARAMARK REFRESHMENT SERVICES, INC.

ARAMARK Tower, 1101 Market St.	CEO: Bill Wilson
Philadelphia, PA 19107	CFO: David Luckner
Phone: 215-238-3000	HR: –
Fax: 215-238-3333	FYE: Friday nearest September 30
Web: www.aramarkrefreshments.com	Type: Subsidiary

This company is ready to meet you in the break room. ARAMARK Refreshment Services is a leading provider of corporate beverage and dining services serving more than 100,000 North American locations through nearly 90 distribution facilities. It is also one of the country's leading operators and suppliers of vending machines. It offers a variety of coffees, sandwiches, snacks, and soft drinks, as well as drinking water dispensers and other refreshment equipment and supplies. ARAMARK Refreshment Services is a subsidiary of food services provider ARAMARK.

	Annual Growth	9/03	9/04	9/05	9/06	9/07
Est. sales ($ mil.)	—	—	—	—	—	80.7
Employees	—	—	—	—	—	4,500

ARB, INC.

26000 Commercentre Dr.	CEO: Brian L. Pratt
Lake Forest, CA 92630	CFO: Alfons Theeuwes
Phone: 949-598-9242	HR: Lauren Liu
Fax: 949-454-7190	FYE: December 31
Web: www.arbinc.com	Type: Private

Power shortages generate sales for ARB. The pipeline and industrial construction services company has benefited from power plant construction booms in low-supply regions of the Western US, particularly in California, where it maintains the majority of its offices. ARB also stays busy building underground pipelines. Other services include cable and conduit installation, structural steel fabrication and installation, water treatment plant construction, and horizontal directional drilling. Customers include companies in the manufacturing, mining, oil and gas, and utilities industries. ARB is owned by Primoris Corporation, which agreed to merge with Rhapsody Acquisition Corp. in 2008.

	Annual Growth	12/03	12/04	12/05	12/06	12/07
Est. sales ($ mil.)	—	—	—	—	—	343.6
Employees	—	—	—	—	—	1,200

ARBELLA INSURANCE GROUP

1100 Crown Colony Dr.	CEO: John F. Donohue
Quincy, MA 02169	CFO: Robert P. Medwid
Phone: 617-328-2800	HR: Gayle O'Connell
Fax: 617-328-2970	FYE: December 31
Web: www.arbella.com	Type: Private

A safe road and home is a beautiful thing for Arbella Insurance and the people it covers. The New England company was founded in 1988 to provide consumer auto and homeowners insurance in Massachusetts and has become the state's #3 auto insurer. Its primary operating unit is Arbella Mutual, which underwrites auto, homeowners, and other personal insurance products in Massachusetts. The group has expanded its offerings to other lines and states, however. It also provides business insurance products (auto fleet coverage and workers' compensation, for instance) in its home state and Rhode Island. And its Covenant Insurance subsidiary writes personal insurance policies in Connecticut.

	Annual Growth	12/02	12/03	12/04	12/05	12/06
Est. sales ($ mil.)	—	—	—	—	—	686.2
Employees	—	—	—	—	—	—

ARBINET-THEXCHANGE, INC.

NASDAQ (GM): ARBX

120 Albany St., Tower II, Ste. 450	CEO: William M. (Bill) Freeman
New Brunswick, NJ 08901	CFO: John (Jack) Wynne Jr.
Phone: 732-509-9100	HR: –
Fax: 732-509-9101	FYE: December 31
Web: www.arbinet.com	Type: Public

Arbinet-thexchange helps make communications capacity a tradable commodity. The company created and operates the leading electronic marketplace for communications trading. Used by its roughly 1,000 members, primarily communications services providers, the Arbinet automated platform offers anonymous buying and selling of voice and data traffic capacity. Arbinet also offers credit risk management, billing, and commercial settlement of these transactions. Utilizing a direct sales force, the company targets customers in the Americas, Asia, Europe, and the Middle East.

	Annual Growth	12/03	12/04	12/05	12/06	12/07
Sales ($ mil.)	7.2%	404.0	520.0	530.5	543.0	534.0
Net income ($ mil.)	—	0.0	7.9	9.7	(0.4)	(6.9)
Market value ($ mil.)	(36.6%)	—	608.7	177.7	141.3	155.4
Employees	10.6%	—	—	112	—	137

ARBITRON INC.

NYSE: ARB

142 W. 57th St.	CEO: Stephen B. (Steve) Morris
New York, NY 10019	CFO: Sean R. Creamer
Phone: 212-887-1300	HR: Mary Lou Legge
Fax: 212-887-1390	FYE: December 31
Web: www.arbitron.com	Type: Public

Arbitron watches radio listeners. The leading provider of radio station audience ratings in the US, Arbitron surveys radio listeners in some 300 local markets throughout the country. Its survey reports measure not only what stations people are listening to but also demographic information about those listeners, including income, lifestyles, and shopping habits. More than 4,500 radio stations and 2,200 advertising agencies subscribe to its services. In addition to radio ratings data, Arbitron offers market research for cable TV, Internet, and outdoor advertising customers.

	Annual Growth	12/03	12/04	12/05	12/06	12/07
Sales ($ mil.)	5.5%	273.5	296.5	310.0	329.3	338.5
Net income ($ mil.)	(5.3%)	49.9	60.6	67.3	50.7	40.2
Market value ($ mil.)	(2.1%)	1,281.2	1,213.0	1,179.1	1,289.8	1,176.8
Employees	(3.6%)	—	—	1,742	1,908	1,620

ARBOR NETWORKS, INC.

430 Bedford St.	CEO: John J. (Jack) Boyle III
Lexington, MA 02420	CFO: Thomas A. Austin
Phone: 781-684-0900	HR: –
Fax: 781-768-3299	FYE: December 31
Web: www.arbornetworks.com	Type: Private

Arbor Networks can help you grow a healthy, secure network. The company provides network security products for recognizing and responding to network anomalies, including denial of service attacks. Arbor's products are used for tasks such as network traffic monitoring, routing, and detection. Customers come from industries such as financial services, telecommunications service providers, education, and health care. The company was founded in 2000 and has received funding from Battery Ventures, Thomas Weisel Venture Partners, and Cisco Systems.

ARBOR REALTY TRUST, INC.

NYSE: ABR

333 Earle Ovington Blvd., Ste. 900
Uniondale, NY 11553
Phone: 516-832-8002
Fax: 516-832-8045
Web: www.arborrealtytrust.com

CEO: Ivan Kaufman
CFO: Paul Elenio
HR: —
FYE: December 31
Type: Public

Investing wisely can be a real ART . . . Arbor Realty Trust, that is. The real estate investment trust (REIT) invests in real estate-related bridge (short term financing) and mezzanine loans (large and usually unsecured loans), mortgage-related securities, and interests in first mortgages and preferred and direct equity. To a lesser extent, it also invests in discounted mortgage notes and other real estate-related assets. The REIT targets lending and investment opportunities with borrowers seeking interim financing until permanent financing is attained.

	Annual Growth	12/03	12/04	12/05	12/06	12/07
Sales ($ mil.)	67.8%	—	58.0	121.6	173.7	274.0
Net income ($ mil.)	49.9%	—	25.1	50.4	50.4	84.5
Market value ($ mil.)	(6.5%)	—	404.1	442.0	514.8	330.6
Employees	—	—	—	—	—	—

ARC INTERNATIONAL NORTH AMERICA INC.

Box 5001, Wade Blvd.
Millville, NJ 08332
Phone: 856-825-5620
Fax: 856-696-3442

CEO: Susan Saideman
CFO: Ken Bell
HR: —
FYE: December 31
Type: Subsidiary

Clumsy friends aren't a friend of ARC International North America. The US subsidiary for the world's #1 crystal and glassware maker, the company distributes glassware and tableware for the North American market and sells to discount retailers, mass merchants, and specialty chains. The firm's most recognized brand name is Mikasa, which has about 130 stores in the US. Other brands include Luminarc, Studio Nova, Crystal D' Arques, and Salviata. Fellow New Jersey-based glass maker Durand Glass Manufacturing Company acts as a sister company (and manufacturing arm) to ARC International North America.

	Annual Growth	12/03	12/04	12/05	12/06	12/07
Est. sales ($ mil.)	—	—	—	—	—	39.7
Employees	—	—	—	—	—	170

ARC WIRELESS SOLUTIONS, INC.

NASDAQ (CM): ARCW

10601 W. 48th Ave.
Wheat Ridge, CO 80033
Phone: 303-421-4063
Fax: 303-424-5085
Web: www.arcwireless.net

CEO: Randall P. Marx
CFO: Monty R. Lamirato
HR: —
FYE: December 31
Type: Public

ARC Wireless Solutions fits a boatload of wireless technology under its umbrella of products and services. Its Wireless Communications Solutions division manufactures wireless communications equipment — including cellular base station, mobile, cellular, conformal, and flat-panel antennas — which it sells directly to wireless carriers and through third-party distributors. Subsidiary Starworks Wireless makes coaxial cable products for satellite television and other wireless applications. Antenna manufacturing comprises the bulk of ARC's annual revenue.

	Annual Growth	12/03	12/04	12/05	12/06	12/07
Sales ($ mil.)	(28.3%)	30.6	37.4	39.7	6.5	8.1
Net income ($ mil.)	—	(0.3)	0.7	1.3	(0.7)	(0.7)
Market value ($ mil.)	(66.6%)	1,231.0	1,077.3	771.5	15.6	15.3
Employees	—	—	—	—	—	—

ARCADIA RESOURCES, INC.

AMEX: KAD

26777 Central Park Blvd., Ste. 200
Southfield, MI 48076
Phone: 248-352-7530
Fax: 248-352-7534
Web: www.arcadiaresourcesinc.com

CEO: Marvin Richardson
CFO: Matthew R. Middendorf
HR: —
FYE: March 31
Type: Public

Arcadia Resources, which operates under the trade name Arcadia HealthCare, offers mail order pharmacy, home health care, and staffing services, as well as durable medical equipment (DME) such as home respiratory therapy products. Its home care services include nursing and help with daily activities, including walking and exercise, bathing and dressing, and light housework. The company offers staffing services in areas such as health care, light industrial, office and technical support, and skilled trades. Additionally, Arcadia runs a mail order pharmacy and provides a specialty packaging service called DailyMed, which is designed to help customers comply with their medication regimens.

	Annual Growth	3/04	3/05	3/06	3/07	3/08
Sales ($ mil.)	(4.7%)	—	—	—	158.4	151.0
Net income ($ mil.)	—	—	—	—	(43.8)	(23.4)
Market value ($ mil.)	(52.2%)	—	—	—	239.7	114.5
Employees	—	—	—	—	—	—

ARCADIS US INC.

630 Plaza Dr., Ste. 200
Highlands Ranch, CO 80129
Phone: 720-344-3500
Fax: 720-344-3535
Web: www.arcadis-us.com

CEO: Steven B. (Steve) Blake
CFO: John J. Chouinard
HR: James Barrett
FYE: December 31
Type: Subsidiary

ARCADIS US is the US-based arm of Netherlands environmental and engineering services company ARCADIS. It provides consulting, design, and project management services related to infrastructure, environment, and facilities. Services include designing groundwater monitoring and treatment systems, feasibility studies, construction management, and operation and maintenance of remedial technologies. The group also offers risk evaluation and assessment services, bioremediation services, regulatory compliance support, and testing and sampling services. The US accounts for more than one-third of parent ARCADIS' sales and is its largest geographic market.

	Annual Growth	12/03	12/04	12/05	12/06	12/07
Est. sales ($ mil.)	—	—	—	—	—	288.9
Employees	—	—	—	—	—	3,400

ARCELORMITTAL USA INC.

1 S. Dearborn St.
Chicago, IL 60603
Phone: 312-899-3440
Fax: 312-899-3504
Web: www.arcelormittal.com

CEO: Michael G. (Mike) Rippey
CFO: John L. Brett
HR: Thomas F. (Tom) Wood
FYE: December 31
Type: Subsidiary

First the world and then the US. ArcelorMittal became the world's largest steel company in 2004 with the merger of Ispat and LNM Holdings, and the following year it chose to dominate the US market with the acquisition of International Steel Group (ISG). ArcelorMittal USA ranks as the nation's top steel producer, ahead of U.S. Steel and Nucor, and maintains facilities (including integrated plants, electric arc furnace plants, and finishing facilities) in about 10 states, mostly in the Midwest. Its primary market is the automotive industry, but it also serves makers of appliances, industrial machinery, and packaging products. In addition to straight steel, ArcelorMittal USA also makes tinplate and wire rod.

	Annual Growth	12/03	12/04	12/05	12/06	12/07
Est. sales ($ mil.)	—	—	—	—	—	2,147.5
Employees	—	—	—	—	—	20,500

An in-depth profile of this company is available to Hoover's Online members at hoovers.com.

163

ARCH CHEMICALS, INC.

NYSE: ARJ

501 Merritt 7
Norwalk, CT 06851
Phone: 203-229-2900
Fax: 203-229-3652
Web: www.archchemicals.com

CEO: Michael E. Campbell
CFO: Steven C. (Steve) Guiliano
HR: Hayes Anderson
FYE: December 31
Type: Public

Arch Chemicals and its HTH brand of pool cleaners make it safe to go back in the water. The company operates two primary business segments: treatment products and performance products. Its treatment products include water sanitizers (sold under the HTH brand, a leader in hypochlorite swimming pool cleaners), biocides (for paints and coatings, among other uses), personal care product ingredients, and wood preservatives. Arch's performance products include specialty polyols (used in coatings and adhesives), glycols (used in cleaners, personal care products, and antifreeze), and hydrazine products (for chemical products and propellants).

	Annual Growth	12/03	12/04	12/05	12/06	12/07
Sales ($ mil.)	10.2%	1,009.1	1,120.9	1,305.1	1,434.7	1,487.6
Net income ($ mil.)	6.5%	27.4	19.9	40.5	14.2	35.3
Market value ($ mil.)	10.9%	600.7	679.0	705.6	802.8	907.7
Employees	(6.1%)	—	—	3,025	3,000	2,670

ARCH COAL, INC.

NYSE: ACI

1 CityPlace Dr., Ste. 300
St. Louis, MO 63141
Phone: 314-994-2700
Fax: 314-994-2878
Web: www.archcoal.com

CEO: Steven F. Leer
CFO: John T. Drexler
HR: Sheila B. Feldman
FYE: December 31
Type: Public

What powers your power company? Perhaps Arch Coal. About half of the electricity generated in the US comes from coal, and Arch Coal is one of the country's largest coal producers, behind industry leader Peabody Energy. Arch Coal produces about 130 million tons of coal a year from about 20 mines in the western US and Central Appalachia; the company has proved and probable reserves of 2.9 billion tons. Steam coal — low-ash coal used by electric utilities to produce steam in boilers — accounts for the vast majority of the company's sales. To store and ship its Appalachian coal, the company operates the Arch Coal Terminal near the Ohio River.

	Annual Growth	12/03	12/04	12/05	12/06	12/07
Sales ($ mil.)	11.6%	1,557.8	1,907.2	2,508.8	2,500.4	2,413.6
Net income ($ mil.)	79.9%	16.7	113.7	38.1	260.9	174.9
Market value ($ mil.)	66.9%	829.2	1,104.3	2,833.6	4,269.6	6,432.1
Employees	4.4%	—	—	3,700	4,050	4,030

ARCHER DANIELS MIDLAND COMPANY

NYSE: ADM

4666 Faries Pkwy.
Decatur, IL 62525
Phone: 217-424-5200
Fax: 217-424-6196
Web: www.admworld.com

CEO: Patricia A. (Pat) Woertz
CFO: Steven R. Mills
HR: Michael (Mike) D'Ambrose
FYE: June 30
Type: Public

Archer Daniels Midland (ADM) knows how to grind and squeeze a fortune out of humble plants. It is one of the world's largest processors of oilseeds, corn, and wheat. Its main offerings include soybean, peanut, and other oilseed products. From corn, it produces syrups, sweeteners, citric and lactic acids, and ethanol, among other items. ADM also produces wheat and durum flour for bakeries and pasta makers. It processes cocoa beans and has a variety of other business interests, ranging from fish farming to banking and insurance. Archer Daniels Midland has interests in food processors in Asia, Canada, Europe, South America, and the US.

	Annual Growth	6/03	6/04	6/05	6/06	6/07
Sales ($ mil.)	9.4%	30,708.0	36,151.4	35,943.8	36,596.1	44,018.0
Net income ($ mil.)	48.0%	451.1	494.7	1,044.4	1,312.1	2,162.0
Market value ($ mil.)	26.5%	8,299.3	10,919.6	13,905.5	27,066.7	21,276.9
Employees	1.9%	—	—	—	26,800	27,300

ARCHON CORPORATION

OTC: ARHN

4336 Losee Rd., Ste. 5
North Las Vegas, NV 89030
Phone: 702-732-9120
Fax: 702-658-4331

CEO: Paul W. Lowden
CFO: Grant L. Siler
HR: –
FYE: September 30
Type: Public

Archon is banking on gamblers to follow the trail of the Pioneer. Formerly Santa Fe Gaming, the embattled company owns and operates one casino, the Pioneer Hotel & Gambling Hall, in Laughlin, Nevada. The Pioneer features some 400 guest rooms and gaming operations that consist of approximately 730 slot machines, eight blackjack tables, one craps table, one roulette wheel, and five other gaming tables. The hotel includes two restaurants and bars, a special events area, banquet rooms, and a swimming pool and spa. Gaming accounts for more than half of revenues. Chairman and CEO Paul Lowden owns 75% of the company.

	Annual Growth	9/03	9/04	9/05	9/06	9/07
Sales ($ mil.)	(3.9%)	53.0	53.5	43.7	45.2	45.2
Net income ($ mil.)	—	(7.8)	(1.9)	(4.9)	(3.4)	0.6
Employees	—	—	—	—	—	556

ARCHSTONE

9200 E. Panorama Cir., Ste. 400
Englewood, CO 80112
Phone: 303-708-5959
Fax: 303-708-5999
Web: www.archstoneapartments.com

CEO: R. Scot Sellers
CFO: Gerald R. (Gerry) Morgan
HR: –
FYE: December 31
Type: Private

Archstone (formerly Archstone-Smith Trust) is the cornerstone of Tishman Speyer and Lehman Brothers' real estate partnership. Acquired by Tishman and Lehman in 2007, the firm is one of the largest apartment investment companies in the US, behind Equity Residential and AIMCO. It owns about 57,000 apartment units in desirable locations including Washington, DC (about 40% of its portfolio); Southern California; New York City; and Boston. Archstone operates under the Archstone brand name (garden-stye units) and the Charles E. Smith brand name (high-rises). The company also offers extended-stay properties through Oakwood Worldwide. The 2007 Tishman and Lehman acquisition was priced at some $22 billion.

	Annual Growth	12/02	12/03	12/04	12/05	12/06
Sales ($ mil.)	1.2%	1,082.3	900.4	873.3	946.9	1,133.6
Net income ($ mil.)	23.3%	315.1	433.7	542.3	616.2	727.4
Employees	(6.2%)	3,450	—	—	2,703	2,666

ARCSIGHT, INC.

NASDAQ (GM): ARST

5 Results Way
Cupertino, CA 95014
Phone: 408-864-2600
Fax: 408-342-1615
Web: www.arcsight.com

CEO: Robert W. Shaw
CFO: Stewart Grierson
HR: –
FYE: April 30
Type: Public

ArcSight keeps a watchful eye on business risk. The company provides security and compliance management software to customers in the enterprise and government sectors. Its applications handle functions such as risk correlation, threat management, compliance reporting, incident investigation, and security analysis. It sells its products directly and through resellers and systems integrators. The company counts Cisco Systems, IBM, and McAfee among its strategic partners. ArcSight's largest shareholders include Kleiner Perkins Caufield & Byers (19%) and Institutional Venture Partners (10%).

	Annual Growth	4/04	4/05	4/06	4/07	4/08
Sales ($ mil.)	45.7%	—	32.8	39.4	69.8	101.5
Net income ($ mil.)	—	—	(2.8)	(16.8)	(0.3)	(2.0)
Market value ($ mil.)	—	—	—	—	—	238.6
Employees	—	—	—	—	287	—

ARCTIC CAT INC.

NASDAQ (GS): ACAT

601 Brooks Ave. South	CEO: Christopher A. Twomey
Thief River Falls, MN 56701	CFO: Timothy C. Delmore
Phone: 218-681-8558	HR: Terry J. Blount
Fax: 218-681-3162	FYE: March 31
Web: www.arctic-cat.com	Type: Public

On hard ground or snow, Arctic Cat growls with speed. The company manufactures and markets all-terrain vehicles (ATVs), snowmobiles, and related products and accessories. The company sells its four-wheel model ATVs under the Arctic Cat name for uses ranging from commercial to recreation. Artic Cat categorizes its snowmobiles as Mountain, Performance, Hybrid, Touring, and Utility models. The company also makes replacement parts and branded clothing and accessories. Arctic Cat's products are sold through a network of independent dealers throughout the US and Canada and distributed worldwide. Suzuki, Arctic Cat's snowmobile engine maker, owns nearly 35% of the company.

	Annual Growth	3/04	3/05	3/06	3/07	3/08
Sales ($ mil.)	(1.1%)	649.6	689.1	732.8	782.4	621.6
Net income ($ mil.)	—	30.4	28.3	23.8	22.1	(3.3)
Market value ($ mil.)	(30.0%)	362.6	362.0	305.8	238.9	87.2
Employees	6.2%	—	1,631	1,802	1,840	—

ARCTIC SLOPE REGIONAL CORPORATION

3900 C St., Ste. 801	CEO: Roberta (Bobbi) Quintavell
Anchorage, AK 99503	CFO: Kristin Mellinger
Phone: 907-339-6000	HR: David White
Fax: 907-339-6028	FYE: December 31
Web: www.asrc.com	Type: Private

The Inupiat people have survived the Arctic for centuries, and now they're surviving in the business world. The Inupiat-owned Arctic Slope Regional Corporation (ASRC) was set up to manage 5 million acres on Alaska's North Slope after the Alaska Native Claims Settlement Act in 1971 cleared the way for oil development in the area. ASRC gets more than two-thirds of sales from its energy services subsidiary (ASRC Energy Services) and its petroleum refining and marketing unit (Petro Star). Other operations include construction, engineering, and governmental services.

	Annual Growth	12/02	12/03	12/04	12/05	12/06
Sales ($ mil.)	15.0%	973.7	1,029.2	1,200.6	1,566.5	1,700.5
Net income ($ mil.)	87.2%	16.8	4.9	(17.0)	127.5	206.3
Employees	(1.6%)	6,400	6,458	6,500	6,000	6,000

ARDEN GROUP, INC.

NASDAQ (GM): ARDNA

2020 S. Central Ave.	CEO: Bernard Briskin
Compton, CA 90220	CFO: Laura J. Neumann
Phone: 310-638-2842	HR: Brenda McDaniel
Fax: 310-631-0950	FYE: Saturday nearest December 31
Web: www.gelsons.com	Type: Public

Glitz meets groceries at Arden Group's 18 supermarkets in Southern California (primarily in the Los Angeles area). Through its wholly owned subsidiary Arden-Mayfair, the company operates 17 Gelson's Markets and a single Mayfair supermarket. Gelson's upscale stores average between 18,000 and 40,000 sq. ft. and carry traditional grocery items, as well as imported foods and unusual deli selections. Most also feature coffee bars, fresh pizza, and bakeries. The company's Mayfair Markets store (about 25,000 sq. ft.) offers a more limited selection of goods. Chairman, president, and CEO Bernard Briskin controls about 60% of the company's stock.

	Annual Growth	12/03	12/04	12/05	12/06	12/07
Sales ($ mil.)	(0.2%)	489.7	502.9	470.4	482.7	485.9
Net income ($ mil.)	15.2%	16.6	22.7	19.9	23.2	29.2
Market value ($ mil.)	31.2%	154.7	334.3	307.5	391.4	457.6
Employees	(2.6%)	—	—	2,430	2,368	—

ARDENT HEALTH SERVICES LLC

1 Burton Hills Blvd., Ste. 250	CEO: David T. Vandewater
Nashville, TN 37215	CFO: Kerry Gillespie
Phone: 615-296-3000	HR: Neil Hemphill
Fax: 615-296-6351	FYE: December 31
Web: www.ardenthealth.com	Type: Private

Ardent Health Services is opting to heal just the body, not the mind. The company sold off its 20 behavioral health care facilities to Psychiatric Solutions in order to focus on the dozen or so acute care hospitals it owns. Those acute care hospitals are primarily located in New Mexico, operating as the Lovelace Sandia Health System, and in Oklahoma, operating as the Hillcrest Healthcare System. Lovelace Sandia also operates a health plan that serves some 193,000 members in New Mexico. Welsh, Carson, Anderson & Stowe owns Ardent Health Services.

	Annual Growth	12/02	12/03	12/04	12/05	12/06
Sales ($ mil.)	42.2%	408.0	1,319.7	1,607.0	1,731.0	1,670.0
Employees	(0.5%)	—	10,100	15,900	8,800	9,942

ARDMORE HOLDING CORPORATION

Pink Sheets: AHLN

1608 W. 2225 South	CEO: Li Liu
Woods Cross, UT 84087	CFO: Tong Li
Phone: 801-295-3400	HR: –
Fax: 801-294-2772	FYE: December 31
Web: www.inetmi.com	Type: Public

Ardmore Holding (formerly I/NET) is looking for new opportunities. The company previously provided Web access and e-commerce software and support, primarily for IBM's midrange AS/400 and iSeries systems. It also developed conversational interface software. Its conversational interface systems for the automotive and telematics industries let manufacturers incorporate voice recognition technology. The company counted IBM and NASA among its customers, but contracts with those businesses were terminated in 2002 and 2004, respectively. I/NET was acquired by Tryant, an entity controlled by then-CEO Jeff Jenson, in 2006. Renamed Ardmore in 2007, the company is pursuing unspecified business opportunities.

	Annual Growth	12/02	12/03	12/04	12/05	*12/06
Sales ($ mil.)	—	—	—	—	0.0	0.0
Net income ($ mil.)	—	—	—	—	0.0	0.0
Market value ($ mil.)	185.1%	—	—	—	56.1	160.0
Employees	—	—	—	—	—	—

*Most recent year available

ARENA FOOTBALL LEAGUE, LLC

105 Madison Ave., 9th Fl.	CEO: C. David Baker
New York, NY 10016	CFO: Laura Skarnulis
Phone: 212-252-8100	HR: –
Fax: 212-252-8030	FYE: December 31
Web: www.arenafootball.com	Type: Association

Here's a league for sports fans who think football should always be played indoors. The Arena Football League (AFL) is the main proponent of indoor football in the US, overseeing a conference of 17 teams that play from February to June. The game follows the basic rules of traditional football but with a few twists: The field is only 50 yards long, there is no punting, and only eight players per team are on the field at a time (playing both offense and defense). The AFL regulates franchise ownership, promotes its teams, and generates revenue from sponsorships and broadcasting rights. The league, which also runs a minor league called arenafootball2, was founded with just four franchises in 1987.

	Annual Growth	12/03	12/04	12/05	12/06	12/07
Est. sales ($ mil.)	—	—	—	—	—	5.4
Employees	—	—	—	—	—	50

An in-depth profile of this company is available to Hoover's Online members at hoovers.com.

165

ARENA PHARMACEUTICALS, INC.

NASDAQ (GM): ARNA

6166 Nancy Ridge Dr.
San Diego, CA 92121
Phone: 858-453-7200
Fax: 858-453-7210
Web: www.arenapharm.com

CEO: Jack (Jackie) Lief
CFO: Robert E. Hoffman
HR: —
FYE: December 31
Type: Public

Though not a football team, Arena Pharmaceuticals likes the end-around. The firm's CART technology discovers drugs without first identifying ligands, the molecules that bind to a drug's potential target and trigger a biological response. The technology mimics the behavior of ligands to identify chemical compounds that alter biological responses, facilitating faster drug discovery. Arena's focus is on treatments for metabolic, cardiovascular, and central nervous system diseases. Lead drug candidate lorcaserin could help obese people control body fat. Arena earns most of its revenues from R&D partnerships, including one with Ortho-McNeil Pharmaceutical to develop a treatment for type 2 diabetes.

	Annual Growth	12/03	12/04	12/05	12/06	12/07
Sales ($ mil.)	10.8%	12.8	13.7	23.2	30.6	19.3
Net income ($ mil.)	—	(47.1)	(58.0)	(67.9)	(86.3)	(143.2)
Market value ($ mil.)	37.5%	158.4	178.0	504.3	784.6	565.8
Employees	—	—	—	323	—	—

ARENA RESOURCES, INC.

NYSE: ARD

6555 S. Lewis
Tulsa, OK 74136
Phone: 918-747-6060
Fax: 918-747-7620
Web: www.arenaresourcesinc.com

CEO: Phillip (Phil) Terry
CFO: William Randall (Randy) Broaddrick
HR: —
FYE: December 31
Type: Public

Independent energy company Arena Resources battles with the big boys in the arena of oil and gas exploration and production. The company operates in Kansas, New Mexico, Oklahoma, and Texas, and has proved reserves of 55.4 million barrels of oil equivalent. Its assets in Oklahoma and Texas account for the bulk of the company's proved reserves. About 30% of its reserves depend upon secondary recovery techniques to make them productive. Arena Resources had an average daily production of 5,565 barrels of oil equivalent in 2007. That year Navajo Refining and DCP Midstream accounted for most of the company's oil and gas sales.

	Annual Growth	12/03	12/04	12/05	12/06	12/07
Sales ($ mil.)	128.1%	3.7	8.5	25.8	59.8	100.1
Net income ($ mil.)	156.1%	0.8	2.5	9.5	23.3	34.4
Market value ($ mil.)	185.0%	21.7	38.8	180.8	313.3	1,429.8
Employees	97.7%	—	—	22	52	86

ARES MANAGEMENT LLC

1999 Avenue of the Stars, Ste. 1900
Los Angeles, CA 90067
Phone: 310-201-4100
Fax: 310-201-4170
Web: www.aresmgmt.com

CEO: Antony P. Ressler
CFO: Daniel Nguyen
HR: Alison Sternberg
FYE: —
Type: Private

Ares Management invests in companies through private equity investments (through the Ares Corporate Opportunities fund), recapitalizations, and leveraged buyouts. The firm typically invests $25 million to $75 million per transaction. Portfolio companies include Maidenform, Serta, Orchard Supply Hardware, Kinetic Systems, AmeriQual (a provider of ready-to-eat meals for the military), and ethanol producer White Energy. Ares Management was founded in 1997 by several executives affiliated with Apollo Management; it now has some $16 billion of capital under management.

AREVA T&D

1 International Plaza, Ste. 300
Philadelphia, PA 19113
Phone: 484-766-8100
Fax: 484-766-8150
Web: www.areva-td.com

CEO: Philippe Guillemot
CFO: Karim Vissandjee
HR: Laurent Mareschal
FYE: December 31
Type: Subsidiary

AREVA T&D knows how to keep the juices flowing. The manufacturer provides industrial equipment and services for companies engaged in electric power production and distribution. Products include circuit breakers, transformers, rectifiers, surge arresters, and switchgear. The company also offers a wide range of services, including asset and operation management, consulting, diagnostics, maintenance, repair, customer support, retrofits and refurbishments, training, and turnkey construction. Europe is AREVA T&D's largest market, followed by Asia/Pacific.

	Annual Growth	12/03	12/04	12/05	12/06	12/07
Est. sales ($ mil.)	—	—	—	—	—	53.1
Employees	—	—	—	—	—	975

ARGAN, INC.

AMEX: AGX

1 Church St., Ste. 401
Rockville, MD 20850
Phone: 301-315-0027
Fax: 301-315-0064
Web: www.arganinc.com

CEO: Rainer H. Bosselmann
CFO: Arthur F. Trudel Jr.
HR: —
FYE: January 31
Type: Public

Argan makes sure its customers stay all juiced up. Its Gemma Power Systems division designs and builds power plants including traditional and alternate fuel plants. Argan's Southern Maryland Cable (SMC) unit provides inside premise wiring and also performs splicing and underground and aerial telecom infrastructure construction services to carriers, government entities, service providers, and electric utilities. SMC's three largest customers are Southern Maryland Electrical Cooperative, Verizon, and Electronic Data Systems. The holding company's Vitarich Laboratories subsidiary makes and distributes private-label dietary supplements and other nutraceuticals and personal health-care products.

	Annual Growth	1/04	1/05	1/06	1/07	1/08
Sales ($ mil.)	134.8%	6.8	14.5	28.5	68.9	206.8
Net income ($ mil.)	—	(0.6)	(3.2)	(9.5)	(0.1)	(3.2)
Market value ($ mil.)	83.2%	—	—	—	68.8	126.0
Employees	—	—	—	—	525	—

ARGON ST, INC.

NASDAQ (GS): STST

12701 Fair Lakes Cir., Ste. 800
Fairfax, VA 22033
Phone: 703-322-0881
Fax: 703-322-0885
Web: www.argonst.com

CEO: Terry L. Collins
CFO: Aaron N. Daniels
HR: Abbey Flowers
FYE: September 30
Type: Public

Argon ST makes electronic intelligence, communications, and imaging systems. Offerings include electronic intelligence systems that intercept, interpret, and track microwave signals from hostile radar and weapons; systems that intercept and locate the source of communications signals and radar; acoustic systems used to detect undersea threats; secure communications and networking systems; and imaging systems used to survey geographic areas of interest. The US Navy accounts for more than 60% of the company's sales; other US government entities account for another 33%.

	Annual Growth	9/03	9/04	9/05	9/06	9/07
Sales ($ mil.)	51.8%	53.2	129.2	271.8	258.8	282.2
Net income ($ mil.)	37.6%	4.1	9.9	21.8	19.4	14.7
Market value ($ mil.)	(7.5%)	—	547.1	587.6	531.8	433.4
Employees	23.4%	—	—	637	840	970

⊞ ARGOSY GAMING COMPANY

219 Piasa St.	CEO: Richard J. Glasier
Alton, IL 62002	CFO: Dick Banner
Phone: 618-474-7500	HR: –
Fax: 618-474-7636	FYE: December 31
Web: www.argosy.com/corporate/contactargosy.asp	Type: Subsidiary

Odds are Mark Twain would find Argosy Gaming's riverboats more likable than those he worked on. The company operates riverboat casinos such as Argosy Casino Alton (serving St. Louis); Argosy Casino Kansas City; Argosy Casino Sioux City; and Argosy Casino Lawrenceburg (near Cincinnati). Argosy's gargantuan (74,300 sq. ft.) Lawrenceburg casino is one of the nation's most successful riverboat casinos. The company was acquired by Penn National Gaming in 2005 for some $2.3 billion. Penn sold Argosy's Casino Baton Rouge and is divesting Argosy's Empress Casino Hotel in Joliet, Illinois.

ARGO-TECH CORPORATION

23555 Euclid Ave.	CEO: Bradley Morton
Cleveland, OH 44117	CFO: –
Phone: 216-692-6000	HR: –
Fax: 216-692-5293	FYE: Last Saturday in October
Web: www.argo-tech.com	Type: Subsidiary

Argo-Tech helps keep commercial and military aircraft aloft with its fuel-flow devices. The company makes main engine fuel pumps and airframe fuel pumps and fuel distribution products. Argo-Tech also makes ground refueling equipment through its Carter Ground Fueling division. Customers have included engine and airframe makers such as Airbus, Boeing, GE Aircraft Engines, Lockheed Martin, Rolls-Royce, and aerospace distributor Upsilon International. Argo-Tech was sold by investment concerns Greenbriar Equity Group and Vestar Capital Partners to Eaton in early 2007.

	Annual Growth	10/02	10/03	10/04	10/05	10/06
Sales ($ mil.)	10.4%	155.3	160.7	187.3	212.6	230.9
Net income ($ mil.)	—	5.9	4.5	(0.5)	(6.2)	(16.8)
Employees	2.6%	664	654	690	729	736

ARI NETWORK SERVICES, INC.

OTC: ARIS

11425 W. Lake Park Dr., Ste. 900	CEO: Roy W. Olivier
Milwaukee, WI 53224	CFO: Brian E. Dearing
Phone: 414-973-4300	HR: –
Fax: 414-973-4618	FYE: July 31
Web: www.arinet.com	Type: Public

The sum of all parts results in ARI Network Services. The company provides software and technical support services for creating electronic parts catalogs in various industries including construction, farm, and marine equipment. More than 20,000 dealers and distributors in some 100 countries use ARI's catalogs. Its PartSmart application allows companies to collect, organize, and maintain product information for their suppliers and dealers, who can access and search the database using ARI's EMPART tools suite. In addition, the company's TradeRoute e-commerce and communication application processes orders, product registrations, and warranty claims.

	Annual Growth	7/03	7/04	7/05	7/06	7/07
Sales ($ mil.)	5.1%	12.6	13.4	13.7	14.0	15.4
Net income ($ mil.)	—	(1.4)	1.1	2.8	3.2	0.1
Market value ($ mil.)	40.0%	2.7	8.6	17.0	14.0	10.5
Employees	—	—	—	—	—	103

ARIAD PHARMACEUTICALS, INC.

NASDAQ (GM): ARIA

26 Landsdowne St.	CEO: Harvey J. Berger
Cambridge, MA 02139	CFO: Edward M. (Ed) Fitzgerald
Phone: 617-494-0400	HR: Kathy Lawton
Fax: 617-494-8144	FYE: December 31
Web: www.ariad.com	Type: Public

ARIAD Pharmaceuticals is exploring the myriad possibilities for new cancer treatments. The firm's lead drug candidate deforolimus targets solid tumors and hematological cancers. The drug blocks the cellular functions essential to the disease process by basically starving cancerous cells. The development-stage biotech is developing the drug in partnership with Merck. Deforolimus has also shown promise in preventing blockage in blood vessels, so the company has partnered with medical device firms Icon Medical and Medinol to develop drug-eluting stents. ARIAD is researching another compound, AP24534, as a possible treatment for chronic myeloid leukemia and other malignancies.

	Annual Growth	12/03	12/04	12/05	12/06	12/07
Sales ($ mil.)	50.6%	0.7	0.7	1.2	0.9	3.6
Net income ($ mil.)	—	(19.7)	(35.6)	(55.5)	(61.9)	(58.5)
Market value ($ mil.)	(4.2%)	348.8	392.5	360.9	336.1	294.3
Employees	3.6%	—	—	108	—	116

⊞ ARIBA, INC.

NASDAQ (GM): ARBA

807 11th Ave.	CEO: Robert M. (Bob) Calderoni
Sunnyvale, CA 94089	CFO: James W. (Jim) Frankola
Phone: 650-390-1000	HR: –
Fax: 650-390-1100	FYE: September 30
Web: www.ariba.com	Type: Public

Ariba helps ensure that your supplies arrive in a timely fashion. The company provides procurement software and consulting services used by manufacturers, retailers, and distributors to connect with suppliers and manage procurement. Its applications automate buying, help target preferred suppliers, and manage enterprise sourcing. Companies use the applications to procure such services as equipment repair, temporary workers, and travel. Ariba has partnered with more than 150,000 suppliers to make their wares available through its supplier network. The company offers its customers technical support services, as well as consulting, implementation, and training.

	Annual Growth	9/03	9/04	9/05	9/06	9/07
Sales ($ mil.)	6.3%	236.7	245.8	323.0	296.0	301.7
Net income ($ mil.)	—	(106.3)	(25.2)	(349.6)	(47.8)	(15.0)
Market value ($ mil.)	(35.2%)	4,929.2	612.1	408.9	564.8	867.4
Employees	(0.3%)	—	1,686	1,506	—	1,669

ARIEL WAY, INC.

OTC: AWYI

8000 Towers Crescent Dr., Ste. 1220	CEO: Arne Dunhem
Vienna, VA 22182	CFO: –
Phone: 703-624-8042	HR: –
Fax: –	FYE: September 30
Web: www.arielway.com	Type: Public

Ariel Way keeps finding new ways to do business. The company develops digital signage and interactive media products for delivery over satellite, terrestrial, and wireless networks. Formerly called Netfran Development, the company franchised Web development and consulting services under the name Netspace, providing Web site design, hosting, maintenance, and administration services for small and midsized businesses. A 2005 reverse merger with communications technology provider Ariel Way resulted in the company ditching its Web services franchise operations in favor of Ariel Way's name, operations, and executives. The new company provided business communication services, but it exited that business in 2006.

	Annual Growth	12/03	12/04	*9/05	9/06	9/07
Sales ($ mil.)	0.0%	0.9	0.3	1.0	2.5	0.9
Net income ($ mil.)	—	(0.2)	(0.5)	(2.6)	(3.1)	0.6
Market value ($ mil.)	—	3.9	—	—	—	—
Employees	—	7	0	18	7	0

*Fiscal year change

⊞ An in-depth profile of this company is available to Hoover's Online members at hoovers.com.

167

ARINC INCORPORATED

2551 Riva Rd.
Annapolis, MD 21401
Phone: 410-266-4000
Fax: 410-266-2020
Web: www.arinc.com

CEO: John M. Belcher
CFO: Richard F. (Dick) Jones
HR: Robert E. Manigold Jr.
FYE: December 31
Type: Private

ARINC provides a variety of information and communications systems and services for companies and government agencies involved with airports, aviation, defense, and surface transportation. ARINC's offerings include air traffic management systems, aircraft testing equipment, baggage systems, intrusion detection devices, satellite testing equipment, and specialized radios and communication networks, as well as engineering and network design services. ARINC — originally Aeronautical Radio, Inc. — was founded in 1929 to provide radio communications services for airlines. ARINC was acquired by the Carlyle Group in 2007.

	Annual Growth	12/03	12/04	12/05	12/06	12/07
Est. sales ($ mil.)	—	—	—	—	—	918.8
Employees	—	—	—	—	—	3,000

ARISTOCRAT TECHNOLOGIES, INC.

7230 Amigo St.
Las Vegas, NV 89119
Phone: 702-270-1000
Fax: 702-270-1001
Web: www.aristocratgaming.com/usa/corp_home.aspx

CEO: Timothy J. (Tim) Parrott
CFO: Simon Ashley
HR: –
FYE: December 31
Type: Subsidiary

Aristocrat Technologies helps casino managers tell if the house is ahead. The company designs, manufactures, and markets casino management tools and software called OASIS, which monitors gaming machine use and controls payouts. Additional features — from monitoring table games and security surveillance to marketing and accounting — can be added with software modules. OASIS systems are used in such North American casinos as the Golden Nugget in Las Vegas. Aristocrat Technologies also sells gaming machines and casino signage. Owned by Australian gaming machine manufacturer Aristocrat Leisure, the company serves as regional arm of Aristocrat Leisure responsible for North America and Latin America.

THE ARISTOTLE CORPORATION

96 Cummings Point Rd.
Stamford, CT 06902
Phone: 203-358-8000
Fax: 203-358-0179
Web: www.aristotlecorp.net

NASDAQ (CM): ARTL
CEO: Steven B. Lapin
CFO: Dean T. Johnson
HR: –
FYE: December 31
Type: Public

Aristotle helps students learn a wide range of skills from CPR to sewing to geometry. The company makes educational products for grades K-12, as well as medical teaching aids including CPR mannequins and simulation kits. Aristotle sells more than 80,000 items bearing brands such as Simulaids, Haan Crafts, and Hubbard Scientific primarily through catalogs. The company also makes products for the agricultural (hand tools and equipment), senior care (materials for nursing home activities), and food industries (sampling bags and containers). Aristotle president Steven Lapin and director Edward Netter own more than 88% of the company through Geneve Corporation.

	Annual Growth	12/03	12/04	12/05	12/06	12/07
Sales ($ mil.)	6.7%	163.2	175.1	188.8	203.0	211.6
Net income ($ mil.)	18.3%	12.0	17.6	17.9	23.8	23.5
Market value ($ mil.)	29.0%	88.8	120.4	130.5	156.1	246.1
Employees	—	—	—	850	—	—

ARIZONA CHEMICAL COMPANY

4600 Touchton Rd. East, Ste. 500
Jacksonville, FL 32246
Phone: 904-928-8700
Fax: 904-928-8779
Web: www.arizonachemical.com

CEO: Gerald C. Marterer
CFO: Charles Nelson
HR: Dave Cowfer
FYE: December 31
Type: Private

Arizona Chemical is always pining for more business. The company is among the world's largest fractionators (separators) of crude tall oil (from the Swedish word *talloja*, or pine oil). It manufactures such pine tree-based chemicals as fatty acids, rosin esters, and terpenes. These chemicals are used to manufacture a wide variety of products, including adhesives, household cleaners, hydraulic fluids, inks, paints, personal care products, and plastics. Arizona Chemical was formed in 1930 by paper products maker International Paper (IP) and American Cyanamid and now is owned by private equity group Rhone Capital after being sold in early 2007 by IP. Tall oil is a by-product of paper making.

	Annual Growth	12/02	12/03	12/04	12/05	12/06
Sales ($ mil.)	6.6%	595.0	625.0	672.0	692.0	769.0
Employees	(4.4%)	—	1,600	1,600	1,600	1,400

ARIZONA PUBLIC SERVICE COMPANY

400 N. 5th St.
Phoenix, AZ 85072
Phone: 602-250-1000
Fax: 602-250-3007
Web: www.aps.com

CEO: Donald E. (Don) Brandt
CFO: –
HR: Lori S. Sundberg
FYE: December 31
Type: Subsidiary

Arizona Public Service is a grand provider of energy in the Grand Canyon state. Arizona Public Service, a subsidiary of Pinnacle West Capital, distributes power to more than 1 million customers in 11 of 15 Arizona counties, making it the largest electric utility in the state. It operates 5,760 miles of transmission lines and 28,680 miles of distribution lines; it also generates 6,160 MW of capacity at mainly fossil-fueled and nuclear power plants. Arizona Public Service's marketing and trading division sells excess energy from the utility's power plants, as well as power generated by Pinnacle West Energy, to wholesale customers in the western US.

	Annual Growth	12/02	12/03	12/04	12/05	12/06
Sales ($ mil.)	8.2%	1,936.2	2,104.9	2,197.1	2,270.8	2,658.5
Net income ($ mil.)	7.9%	199.3	180.9	199.6	170.5	269.7
Employees	3.2%	—	6,000	6,100	6,400	6,600

ARIZONA TILE SUPPLY, INC.

8829 S. Priest Dr.
Tempe, AZ 85284
Phone: 480-893-9393
Fax: 480-893-9390
Web: www.arizonatile.com

CEO: John G. Huarte
CFO: Gary Skarsten
HR: –
FYE: December 31
Type: Private

Arizona Tile has a soft spot for hard floors. The company imports and distributes ceramic and porcelain tile and natural stone for use by builders, designers, and architects in residential and commercial installations. Natural stone products include granite, onyx, limestone, marble, slate, travertine, and tumbled stone. It also offers installation and maintenance materials as well as decorative accent tiles. The company sells its wares through more than 20 branches in Arizona and California, as well as five other southwestern states. Former Heisman Trophy winner and pro football player John Huarte founded Arizona Tile in 1977.

	Annual Growth	12/03	12/04	12/05	12/06	12/07
Est. sales ($ mil.)	—	—	—	—	—	134.3
Employees	—	—	—	—	—	950

ARK RESTAURANTS CORP.

NASDAQ (GM): ARKR

85 Fifth Ave., 14th Fl.
New York, NY 10003
Phone: 212-206-8800
Fax: 212-206-8845
Web: www.arkrestaurants.com

CEO: Michael Weinstein
CFO: Robert J. Stewart
HR: Marilyn Guy
FYE: Saturday nearest September 30
Type: Public

You might say this company floats the boat of fine dining fans. Ark Restaurants owns and manages about two dozen chic eateries in New York, Las Vegas, and Washington, DC, including the Bryant Park Grill and Center Café. Its Las Vegas operations include three restaurants in the New York-New York Hotel & Casino (owned by MGM MIRAGE); the company also operates the casino's room service and banquet facilities, as well as multiple food courts. In addition, it has restaurants, bars, and food service operations in the Venetian Casino Resort (Las Vegas Sands) and Caesars Palace (Harrah's Entertainment). Founder and CEO Michael Weinstein owns nearly 30% of Ark Restaurants.

	Annual Growth	9/03	9/04	9/05	9/06	9/07
Sales ($ mil.)	1.6%	116.6	115.7	115.6	116.0	124.2
Net income ($ mil.)	40.9%	3.3	6.7	6.6	5.2	13.0
Market value ($ mil.)	38.5%	36.0	91.8	108.2	94.3	132.5
Employees	4.0%	—	—	1,990	2,117	2,151

ARKANSAS BEST CORPORATION

NASDAQ (GS): ABFS

3801 Old Greenwood Rd.
Fort Smith, AR 72903
Phone: 479-785-6000
Fax: 479-785-6004
Web: www.arkbest.com

CEO: Robert A. (Bob) Davidson
CFO: Judy R. McReynolds
HR: –
FYE: December 31
Type: Public

Arkansas Best puts its best efforts on the road to provide freight transportation services in its home state — and the rest of North America. Specializing in long-haul, less-than-truckload (LTL) shipments of general commodities, subsidiary ABF Freight System accounts for nearly all of the company's sales. (LTL carriers combine freight from multiple shippers into a single truckload.) ABF Freight System operates a fleet of about 4,000 tractors and 20,000 trailers from about 290 terminals in the US, Canada, and Puerto Rico; it offers service into Mexico via alliances. Freight carried by the company includes food, textiles, apparel, and furniture.

	Annual Growth	12/03	12/04	12/05	12/06	12/07
Sales ($ mil.)	4.7%	1,527.5	1,715.8	1,860.3	1,860.5	1,836.9
Net income ($ mil.)	5.4%	46.1	75.5	104.6	84.1	56.8
Market value ($ mil.)	(8.8%)	787.6	1,134.6	1,108.5	894.8	545.7
Employees	(0.8%)	—	12,174	12,327	12,665	11,895

ARKANSAS CHILDREN'S HOSPITAL

800 Marshall St.
Little Rock, AR 72202
Phone: 501-364-1100
Fax: 501-364-7219
Web: www.archildrens.org

CEO: Jonathan R. (Jon) Bates
CFO: Gena Wingfield
HR: Andre Trosclair
FYE: June 30
Type: Not-for-profit

As the only pediatric medical center in the state, Arkansas Children's Hospital serves the youngest Razorbacks, from birth to age 21. The hospital has more than 280 beds and a medical staff of 500 physicans, and it provides care in numerous specialties including childhood cancer, pediatric orthopedics, and neonatology. In addition to its acute care services, it operates specialty clinics and outpatient centers. The hospital is also engaged in teaching and medical research through its affiliation with the University of Arkansas for Medical Sciences, the academic medical center of the University of Arkansas System.

ARKEMA INC.

2000 Market St.
Philadelphia, PA 19103
Phone: 215-419-7000
Fax: 215-419-5394
Web: www.arkema-inc.com

CEO: George Cornelius
CFO: Patricia McCarthy
HR: Christopher Giangrasso
FYE: December 31
Type: Subsidiary

Arkema's into vinyl, but not in a weird way. Arkema manufactures a number of vinyl products such as PVC, chlorochemicals, and assorted vinyl compounds. Its other products include industrial chemicals and plastics like acrylics, hydrogen peroxide, and fluorochemicals and performance products such as additives, agrochemicals, organic peroxides, and technical polymers. Arkema operates about 20 manufacturing facilities in North America and accounts for about a quarter of its parent's total sales. The company was created in 2004 when TOTAL broke up its former chemicals subsidiary, ATOFINA, into two units: Arkema and TOTAL Petrochemicals.

ARMSTRONG WORLD INDUSTRIES, INC.

NYSE: AWI

2500 Columbia Ave.
Lancaster, PA 17604
Phone: 717-397-0611
Fax: 717-396-6133
Web: www.armstrong.com

CEO: Michael D. (Mike) Lockhart
CFO: F. Nicholas (Nick) Grasberger III
HR: Donald A. McCunniff
FYE: December 31
Type: Public

People the world over have walked all over Armstrong World Industries (AWI) for years, and the company is ready for more. AWI's Armstrong Floor Products unit produces vinyl sheet and tile, linoleum, specialty carpet, and hardwood flooring (Hartco, Bruce, and Robbins brands). Its Armstrong Building Products unit produces acoustical ceilings and suspension systems (mainly commercial) both on its own and through a joint venture, WAVE. Its Armstrong Cabinet Products makes hardwood, kitchen, and bathroom cabinets. The company sells primarily through wholesale distributors and home improvement chains. AWI emerged from Chapter 11 bankruptcy protection in 2006 and dissolved ties with former parent Armstrong Holdings.

	Annual Growth	12/03	12/04	12/05	12/06	12/07
Sales ($ mil.)	2.2%	3,259.0	3,497.3	3,558.4	3,425.9	3,549.7
Net income ($ mil.)	—	(39.3)	(79.7)	111.1	1,358.0	145.3
Market value ($ mil.)	(4.1%)	—	—	—	2,377.7	2,279.4
Employees	(1.6%)	15,200	15,500	14,900	14,500	—

ARMY AND AIR FORCE EXCHANGE SERVICE

3911 S. Walton Walker Blvd.
Dallas, TX 75236
Phone: 214-312-2011
Fax: 214-312-3000
Web: www.aafes.com

CEO: Keith L. Thurgood
CFO: Harold Lavender
HR: Ronnie D. Compton
FYE: Saturday nearest January 31
Type: Government agency

Be all that you can be and buy all that you can buy at the PX (Post Exchange). The Army and Air Force Exchange Service (AAFES) runs more than 3,100 facilities — including PXs and BXs (Base Exchanges) — at US Army and Air Force bases in about 30 countries (including Iraq), 49 US states, and five US territories. Its outlets range from tents to shopping centers that have retail stores, fast-food outlets (brand names like Burger King and Taco Bell), movie theaters, beauty shops, and gas stations. AAFES serves active-duty military personnel, reservists, retirees, and their family members. Although it is a government agency under the DOD, it receives less than 5% of its funding from the department.

	Annual Growth	1/03	1/04	1/05	1/06	1/07
Sales ($ mil.)	5.1%	7,323.4	7,905.3	8,351.7	8,667.3	8,921.4
Net income ($ mil.)	0.7%	415.5	485.0	474.1	378.4	427.5
Employees	(2.5%)	49,861	47,323	48,000	45,000	45,000

An in-depth profile of this company is available to Hoover's Online members at hoovers.com.

169

ARNHOLD AND S. BLEICHROEDER ADVISERS, LLC

1345 Avenue of the Americas, 44th Fl.
New York, NY 10105
Phone: 212-698-3000
Fax: 212-299-4360
Web: www.asbai.com

CEO: John P. Arnhold
CFO: –
HR: –
FYE: December 31
Type: Private

Arnhold and S. Bleichroeder Advisers wants to make investing money a bit easier than saying its name. The firm offers asset management services to institutional and high net-worth individual investors. Through First Eagle Funds, it invests in domestic and international companies, including companies undergoing major structural changes such as mergers and reorganizations. The company prides itself on conducting extensive research into the firms in which it invests, including visiting prospective companies, and holding those investments for the long-term. Founded in Germany in 1803, the company moved to New York City in 1937, and now has more than $45 billion under management.

	Annual Growth	12/03	12/04	12/05	12/06	12/07
Est. sales ($ mil.)	—	—	—	—	—	21.4
Employees	—	—	—	—	—	226

ARNOLD & PORTER LLP

555 12th St. NW
Washington, DC 20004
Phone: 202-942-5000
Fax: 202-942-5999
Web: www.arnoldporter.com

CEO: Thomas H. Milch
CFO: –
HR: Elizabeth C. Respess
FYE: December 31
Type: Partnership

A tourist might go to Washington, DC, to see the Smithsonian's museums, but an executive's agenda might include a visit to Arnold & Porter. The law firm's wide-ranging practice areas center on business transactions and public policy; its specialties include antitrust, intellectual property, and litigation. General Electric and Xerox have been among the firm's clients. Arnold & Porter has more than 600 lawyers at six offices in the US and two in Europe. The firm was established in 1946 as Arnold, Fortas & Porter; Abe Fortas, later a Supreme Court justice, was a founding partner.

	Annual Growth	12/03	12/04	12/05	12/06	12/07
Est. sales ($ mil.)	—	—	—	—	—	129.9
Employees	—	—	—	—	—	1,500

ARNOLD LOGISTICS LLC

4410 Industrial Park Rd.
Camp Hill, PA 17011
Phone: 717-731-4374
Fax: 717-761-6688
Web: www.arnoldlogistics.com

CEO: Douglas B. (Doug) Enck
CFO: Eugene Kostelac
HR: –
FYE: December 31
Type: Private

Arnold Logistics dreams of logistical nightmares. The company provides warehousing, distribution, order fulfillment, contract packaging, and reverse logistics services (handling of merchandise returned to retailers). Customers have included Hershey, Quaker Oats, Coors, and Simon & Schuster. Arnold Logistics operates from facilities in California, Illinois, Nevada, Ohio, Pennsylvania, and Texas. Investment firm Oak Hill Capital Partners, which owns a majority stake in Arnold Logistics, intends to combine the company with Iowa-based logistics provider Jacobson, which Oak Hill has agreed to buy.

	Annual Growth	12/03	12/04	12/05	12/06	12/07
Est. sales ($ mil.)	—	—	—	—	—	94.8
Employees	—	—	—	—	—	1,000

ARNOLD TRANSPORTATION SERVICES, INC.

9523 Florida Mining Blvd.
Jacksonville, FL 32257
Phone: 904-262-4285
Fax: 904-260-0628
Web: www.arnoldtrans.com

CEO: Michael S. Walters
CFO: Erik Samartino
HR: –
FYE: December 31
Type: Subsidiary

Arnold Transportation Services specializes in regional truckload freight transportation services. The company operates a fleet of about 1,650 tractors in several regions, including the mid-Atlantic, northeastern, southeastern, and southwestern US. Besides its regional service, Arnold Transportation offers medium-haul (800-1,200 mile) freight transportation. In addition, the company provides dedicated contract carriage, in which drivers and equipment are assigned to customers long-term. Nationwide truckload transportation company U.S. Xpress Enterprises owns a controlling stake in Arnold Transportation.

	Annual Growth	12/03	12/04	12/05	12/06	12/07
Est. sales ($ mil.)	—	—	—	—	—	121.4
Employees	—	—	—	—	—	1,700

ARNOLD WORLDWIDE PARTNERS

101 Huntington Ave.
Boston, MA 02199
Phone: 617-587-8000
Fax: 617-587-8004
Web: www.arnoldworldwidepartners.com

CEO: Francis J. (Fran) Kelly III
CFO: –
HR: Melissa Morgante
FYE: December 31
Type: Business segment

Far from being terminated, a partnership with this Arnold will get your brand promoted. Arnold Worldwide Partners operates a global advertising agency network with offices in about 10 countries. In the US it operates across six offices serving such clients as RadioShack, McDonald's, Levi's, and Volvo. The full-service agency offers creative ad development, campaign planning, and brand management. Arnold also has a strong presence in France through such agencies as Devarrieuxvillaret and W&Cie. Arnold Worldwide is a unit of Paris-based advertising conglomerate Havas.

AROTECH CORPORATION

NASDAQ (GM): ARTX

1229 Oak Valley Dr.
Ann Arbor, MI 48108
Phone: 800-281-0356
Fax: 734-761-5368
Web: www.arotech.com

CEO: Robert S. Ehrlich
CFO: Thomas J. Paup
HR: –
FYE: December 31
Type: Public

It's no longer all about batteries for Arotech. The company has broadened its horizons to include use-of-force simulators and vehicle armor in addition to its line of zinc-air batteries and fuel cells. Arotech's FAAC and IES Interactive Training subsidiaries provide simulators, related software, and training for law enforcement and military entities. Arotech's majority-owned MDT Protective Industries and MDT Armor units make lightweight ceramic armor and ballistic glass for military and passenger vehicles; Armour of America makes shielding for aircraft and for people. Arotech still makes batteries and charging systems, mainly for the military and homeland security markets.

	Annual Growth	12/03	12/04	12/05	12/06	12/07
Sales ($ mil.)	35.1%	17.3	50.0	49.0	43.1	57.7
Net income ($ mil.)	—	(9.2)	(9.0)	(24.0)	(15.6)	(3.1)
Market value ($ mil.)	(60.8%)	1,208.1	1,814.9	32.0	36.5	28.6
Employees	—	—	—	277	—	—

ARQULE, INC.

NASDAQ (GM): ARQL

19 Presidential Way
Woburn, MA 01801
Phone: 781-994-0300
Fax: 781-376-6019
Web: www.arqule.com

CEO: Paolo Pucci
CFO: Robert Weiskopf
HR: Anthony S. (Tony) Messina
FYE: December 31
Type: Public

Even though it was doing okay in Chemistry, ArQule has decided to major in Molecular Biology. The biotechnology firm had been providing chemistry services to help drugmakers discover new potential drug compounds. However, it has switched from being a helper to becoming a doer. Now ArQule is developing its own portfolio of oncology drugs, with a handful of anti-cancer compounds undergoing clinical trials. It is testing its most advanced candidate, ARQ 197, as a treatment for a variety of tumor types; and it is working with partner Roche on a handful of other anti-cancer compounds that reactivate the cellular functions that kill cancer cells.

	Annual Growth	12/03	12/04	12/05	12/06	12/07
Sales ($ mil.)	(38.8%)	65.5	54.5	52.9	6.6	9.2
Net income ($ mil.)	—	(34.8)	(4.9)	(7.5)	(31.4)	(53.4)
Market value ($ mil.)	16.0%	140.2	167.8	216.0	212.0	253.8
Employees	—	—	—	246	—	—

ARRAY BIOPHARMA INC.

NASDAQ (GM): ARRY

3200 Walnut St.
Boulder, CO 80301
Phone: 303-381-6600
Fax: 303-386-1390
Web: www.arraybiopharma.com

CEO: Robert E. (Bob) Conway
CFO: R. Michael Carruthers
HR: Sherri A. Norland
FYE: June 30
Type: Public

Array BioPharma is discovering it's best to be your own boss. Once devoted to discovering drug candidates for other firms, the company is increasingly focused on its own drug development efforts in the areas of cancer and inflammatory disease. Candidates in early clinical trials include potential therapies for breast cancer (ARRY-543) and rheumatoid arthritis (ARRY-162). Array has also out-licensed some cancer programs to AstraZeneca and Genentech; ARRY-886, developed with AstraZeneca, is in clinical trials for melanoma. Drug discovery services for third-parties still account for a big chunk of business; Array has R&D agreements with InterMune, Ono Pharmaceutical, Amgen, and others.

	Annual Growth	6/03	6/04	6/05	6/06	6/07
Sales ($ mil.)	1.3%	35.1	34.8	45.5	45.0	37.0
Net income ($ mil.)	—	(19.6)	(26.0)	(23.2)	(39.6)	(55.4)
Market value ($ mil.)	57.9%	88.5	229.5	242.3	336.5	549.4
Employees	—	—	—	269	—	—

ARRHYTHMIA RESEARCH TECHNOLOGY, INC.

AMEX: HRT

25 Sawyer Passway
Fitchburg, MA 01420
Phone: 978-345-5000
Fax: 978-342-0168
Web: www.arthrt.com

CEO: James E. Rouse
CFO: David A. Garrison
HR: –
FYE: December 31
Type: Public

It's all about heart for Arrhythmia Research Technology (ART). The company offers signal-averaging electrocardiographic (SAECG) software that collects data and analyzes electrical impulses of the heart in an effort to detect potentially lethal heart arrhythmias. The company plans to sell the products through licensing agreements with equipment makers. Until it finds a marketing partner, however, ART is relying on sales from its Micron Products subsidiary, which makes snaps and sensors used in the manufacture and operation of disposable electrodes for electrocardiographic (ECG) equipment. Micron Products has acquired assets of several companies that enhance its metal and plastics molding capabilities.

	Annual Growth	12/03	12/04	12/05	12/06	12/07
Sales ($ mil.)	26.1%	7.7	11.1	12.9	19.3	19.5
Net income ($ mil.)	0.0%	1.3	1.6	1.6	2.2	1.3
Employees	14.3%	—	63	75	100	94

☐ ARRIS GROUP, INC.

NASDAQ (GS): ARRS

3871 Lakefield Dr.
Suwanee, GA 30024
Phone: 678-473-2000
Fax: 678-473-8470
Web: www.arrisi.com

CEO: Robert J. (Bob) Stanzione
CFO: David B. (Dave) Potts
HR: –
FYE: December 31
Type: Public

ARRIS brings the idea of broadband home. The company makes communications equipment and components used to enable voice and data transmission in high-speed networks and to build television broadcast networks. ARRIS' products include cable network headend gear, IP switching systems, modems and other consumer premises products, and associated software. The company also sells such related hardware as cable, connectors, and other supplies used for mounting and installation. ARRIS primarily serves cable operators; other clients include local and long distance carriers.

	Annual Growth	12/03	12/04	12/05	12/06	12/07
Sales ($ mil.)	23.0%	434.0	490.0	680.4	891.5	992.2
Net income ($ mil.)	—	(47.3)	(28.4)	51.5	142.3	98.3
Market value ($ mil.)	20.5%	627.7	617.4	1,000.0	1,349.8	1,321.4
Employees	39.9%	—	728	732	781	1,992

☐ ARROW ELECTRONICS, INC.

NYSE: ARW

50 Marcus Dr.
Melville, NY 11747
Phone: 631-847-2000
Fax: 631-847-2222
Web: www.arrow.com

CEO: William E. (Bill) Mitchell
CFO: Paul J. Reilly
HR: John P. McMahon
FYE: December 31
Type: Public

Arrow Electronics knows its target market. The company is one of the world's largest distributors of electronic components and computer products, alongside rival Avnet. Arrow sells semiconductors, computer peripherals, passive components, and interconnect products from about 700 suppliers to more than 140,000 computer manufacturers and commercial customers worldwide. The company distributes products made by such manufacturers as 3Com, CA, Hitachi, Intel, Motorola, and Texas Instruments. Arrow also provides value-added services, such as component design, inventory management, and contract manufacturing. The company gets half of its sales in the US.

	Annual Growth	12/03	12/04	12/05	12/06	12/07
Sales ($ mil.)	16.5%	8,679.3	10,646.1	11,164.2	13,577.1	15,985.0
Net income ($ mil.)	99.6%	25.7	207.5	253.6	388.3	407.8
Market value ($ mil.)	19.8%	2,339.0	2,826.1	3,844.0	3,862.3	4,824.6
Employees	5.1%	—	—	11,400	12,000	12,600

ARROW FINANCIAL CORPORATION

NASDAQ (GS): AROW

250 Glen St.
Glens Falls, NY 12801
Phone: 518-745-1000
Fax: 518-761-0843
Web: www.arrowfinancial.com

CEO: Thomas L. Hoy
CFO: Terry R. Goodemote
HR: –
FYE: December 31
Type: Public

Arrow Financial has more than one shaft in its quiver. It's the holding company for two banks: Glens Falls National Bank and Trust Company and Saratoga National Bank and Trust Company, which together operate more than 30 branches in five upstate New York counties. Targeting individuals and area businesses, the banks offer checking, savings, and money market accounts, CDs, and IRAs. They also provide retirement, trust, and estate planning services and employee benefit plan administration. Residential mortgages make up the largest segment (about 40%) of Arrow Financial's loan book; indirect loans account for more than 30%. Other loans include commercial real estate, agricultural, and construction.

	Annual Growth	12/03	12/04	12/05	12/06	12/07
Assets ($ mil.)	3.6%	1,373.9	1,377.9	1,519.6	1,520.2	1,584.8
Net income ($ mil.)	(2.2%)	18.9	19.5	18.6	16.9	17.3
Market value ($ mil.)	(1.4%)	244.1	288.9	257.5	256.1	230.7
Employees	—	—	—	—	—	448

☐ An in-depth profile of this company is available to Hoover's Online members at hoovers.com.

171

ARROW INTERNATIONAL, INC.

2400 Bernville Rd.
Reading, PA 19605
Phone: 610-378-0131
Fax: 610-374-5360
Web: www.arrowintl.com

CEO: Philip B. (Phil) Fleck
CFO: Frederick J. Hirt
HR: Carl W. Staples
FYE: August 31
Type: Subsidiary

When it comes to healing patients, Arrow International makes its point. The company makes vascular access and cardiac assist products used in a variety of diagnostic and therapeutic procedures. Its critical care segment makes disposable catheters used to administer dialysis treatments, monitor arterial blood pressure, and deliver drugs and fluids. Many of its catheters are treated with its ARROWg+ard antiseptic coating to reduce infection risk. Arrow also makes cardiac care products, including balloon pumps and catheters that help the heart to pump properly following surgery, heart attack, or angioplasty. The firm was acquired in 2007 by diversified manufacturer Teleflex for about $2 billion.

	Annual Growth	8/02	8/03	8/04	8/05	8/06
Sales ($ mil.)	9.0%	340.8	380.4	433.1	454.3	481.6
Net income ($ mil.)	9.5%	39.0	45.7	55.9	39.5	56.0
Employees	—	3,005	—	—	—	—

ARROW-MAGNOLIA INTERNATIONAL LP

2646 Rodney Ln.
Dallas, TX 75229
Phone: 972-247-7111
Fax: 972-484-2896
Web: www.arrowmagnolia.com

CEO: David J. Tippeconnic
CFO: James Barry
HR: –
FYE: December 31
Type: Private

Whether it flies, bulldozes, or hauls golfers, Arrow-Magnolia International has something that cleans it. The company makes about 400 chemical cleaners that it sells under its own brands; it also distributes nonchemical janitorial supplies. Its products include chemicals used in construction (concrete and rust removers), government engineering (street and equipment cleaners), aviation (carbon and dirt removers), and golf course maintenance. Arrow-Magnolia makes more than half of its products in-house and sells them through independent representatives and a dozen distributors. An investment group led by Tanya Tippeconnic-Shaw bought Arrow-Magnolia in 2005, a transaction that took the company private.

	Annual Growth	12/03	12/04	12/05	12/06	12/07
Est. sales ($ mil.)	—	—	—	—	—	2,147.5
Employees	—	—	—	—	—	56

ARROW TRUCKING COMPANY

4230 S. Elwood Ave.
Tulsa, OK 74107
Phone: 918-446-1441
Fax: 918-445-5702
Web: www.arrowtrucking.com

CEO: James D. (Doug) Pielsticker
CFO: Bob Fitzgerald
HR: Trena Appleby
FYE: December 31
Type: Private

Aiming to deliver the goods on target, Arrow Trucking specializes in hauling freight such as construction materials and oil field equipment on flatbed trailers. The company offers long-haul and regional flatbed service; it also transports oversize and overweight loads. In addition, Arrow provides logistics services, including freight brokerage. The company operates throughout the US and in Canada. Its fleet includes some 1,400 tractors and 2,300 trailers. Carol Pielsticker, widow of company founder Jim Pielsticker and mother of CEO Doug Pielsticker, owns Arrow. Jim Pielsticker bought Arrow with a partner in 1968 and became sole owner in 1987.

	Annual Growth	12/03	12/04	12/05	12/06	12/07
Est. sales ($ mil.)	—	—	—	—	—	121.4
Employees	—	—	—	—	—	1,700

ARROWHEAD RESEARCH CORPORATION

NASDAQ (GM): ARWR

201 S. Lake Ave., Ste. 703
Pasadena, CA 91101
Phone: 626-304-3400
Fax: 626-304-3401
Web: www.arrowres.com

CEO: Christopher (Chris) Anzalone
CFO: Paul McDonnel
HR: –
FYE: September 30
Type: Public

Arrowhead Research is a development-stage company with several subsidiaries focused on developing and commercializing nanotechnologies. Its Aaonex unit is working on a process for making semiconductor nanomaterials that could be used in LEDs, high-frequency power amplifiers, and solar cells. Insert Therapeutics has developed a polymer for drug delivery, and Unidym focuses on the commercialization of nanotube-based properties. In addition, Calando Pharmaceuticals develops and commercializes therapeutics. Arrowhead also funds nanoscience research at universities (including the California Institute of Technology and Duke University) in exchange for the right to commercialize the resulting intellectual property.

	Annual Growth	9/03	9/04	9/05	9/06	9/07
Sales ($ mil.)	81.7%	—	0.2	0.6	0.6	1.2
Net income ($ mil.)	—	—	(2.5)	(6.6)	(19.0)	(29.9)
Market value ($ mil.)	37.5%	—	75.0	83.7	170.4	195.0
Employees	42.6%	—	20	32	—	58

ARROWPOINT CAPITAL CORPORATION

Whitehall Corporate Center 3, 3600 Arco Corporate Dr.
Charlotte, NC 28273
Phone: 704-522-2000
Fax: –
Web: www.arrowpointcapitalcorp.com

CEO: John Tighe
CFO: Sean Beatty
HR: Bob Dixon
FYE: December 31
Type: Private

Even though its former parent company no longer wanted it, Arrowpoint Capital (formerly Royal & SunAlliance USA) has the will to live and sell insurance. The company was a subsidiary of UK-based insurer Royal & Sun Alliance but suffered from relentless trimmings when its business was deemed to be non-core. The business was acquired in early 2007 by a group of its management and outside directors. It was renamed Arrowpoint Capital and operates through its Royal Indemnity, Royal Surplus Lines Insurance, and Security Insurance Company of Hartford subsidiaries. The company continues to offer individual and commercial property/casualty coverage under the Royal Care brand.

ARSENAL CAPITAL PARTNERS, INC.

320 Park Ave., 30th Fl.
New York, NY 10022
Phone: 212-771-1717
Fax: 212-771-1718
Web: www.arsenalcapital.com

CEO: Terrence Mullen
CFO: Joseph Croasdale
HR: Joelle Marquis
FYE: December 31
Type: Private

Arsenal Capital Partners keeps its armory stocked with both manufacturing and service companies. The private equity firm takes aim at acquiring middle-market companies in a variety of sectors, including industrial chemicals, automotive aftermarket, HVAC servicing, drug distribution, and medical devices. Other sector focuses include specialty manufacturing, transportation and logistics, and process industry components and services. Portfolio companies include printer manufacturer TallyGenicom and speciality chemicals concern Velsicol Chemical. In 2008 the company opened an office in China to provide Asia logistical support to its portfolio companies.

	Annual Growth	12/03	12/04	12/05	12/06	12/07
Est. sales ($ mil.)	—	—	—	—	—	221.1
Employees	—	—	—	—	—	2,933

ART TECHNOLOGY GROUP, INC.

NASDAQ (GM): ARTG

1 Main St.
Cambridge, MA 02142
Phone: 617-386-1000
Fax: 617-386-1111
Web: www.atg.com

CEO: Robert D. (Bob) Burke
CFO: Julia M.B. Bradley
HR: Patricia (Pat) O'Neill
FYE: December 31
Type: Public

Art Technology Group (ATG) knows there's a fine art to managing customers. The company's products include software and online systems for developing and deploying e-commerce applications. ATG's software helps companies offer personalized customer services on their Web sites, enabling them to target specific content and data (including catalog content and merchandising programs) to individual customers and Web site visitors. ATG's software can be used for functions such as customer self-service, marketing, and managing online sales. The company also provides design, consulting, custom application development, and support services. Clients have included Best Buy, Citibank, J. Crew, Hyatt, Target, and Wells Fargo.

	Annual Growth	12/03	12/04	12/05	12/06	12/07
Sales ($ mil.)	17.3%	72.5	69.2	90.7	103.2	137.1
Net income ($ mil.)	—	4.2	(9.5)	5.8	9.7	(4.2)
Market value ($ mil.)	49.6%	111.6	162.2	216.8	296.0	558.5
Employees	19.6%	—	—	309	378	442

ART VAN FURNITURE, INC.

6500 14 Mile Rd.
Warren, MI 48092
Phone: 586-939-0800
Fax: 586-939-3055
Web: www.artvan.com

CEO: Art Van Elslander
CFO: Michael Bolton
HR: Gary Van Elslander
FYE: September 30
Type: Private

Family-owned Art Van Furniture ought to be family friendly. The firm — Michigan's #1 furniture seller — offers mid-priced home furniture in some 30 Michigan stores. The chain has undergone a renovation, adding more upscale furniture (it sells Sealy, Simmons, and Broyhill brands) and perks such as children's play areas. The company is known for its aggressive sales and service. (Employees have been known to greet patrons carside with umbrellas on rainy days.) CEO Art Van Elslander, who has 10 children himself (some active in the business), founded the firm with a single East Detroit store in 1959. Upscale-furniture retailer Scott Shuptrine, purchased by Art Van in 1986, closed its three stores in 2002.

ARTEL, INC.

1893 Preston White Dr.
Reston, VA 20191
Phone: 703-620-1700
Fax: 703-620-4262
Web: www.artelinc.com

CEO: Abbas Yazdani
CFO: Steven Mansouri
HR: Andrea Zeman
FYE: December 31
Type: Private

Information technology is the name of the game for ARTEL, Inc. The company is a global provider of a full range of managed network services, solutions integration, e-government solutions, and information assurance and homeland security services for its government and corporate clients throughout the world. ARTEL's full life-cycle process solutions provide strategic business analysis and planning through to full implementation. President and CEO Abbas Yazdani founded ARTEL in 1986.

	Annual Growth	12/03	12/04	12/05	12/06	12/07
Est. sales ($ mil.)	—	—	—	—	—	149.8
Employees	—	—	—	—	—	200

ARTEMIS INTERNATIONAL SOLUTIONS CORPORATION

6011 W. Courtyard Dr.
Austin, TX 78730
Phone: 512-874-3030
Fax: 512-874-8900
Web: www.aisc.com

CEO: Randall (Randy) Jacops
CFO: Sean Fallon
HR: –
FYE: December 31
Type: Subsidiary

Artemis International Solutions helps the arrow find its mark for project, portfolio, and resource managers. The company provides investment planning and control software that helps organizations manage their information technology resources, product development, assets, and investment portfolios through a collaborative workflow management and analytics system. Its software enables companies to plan, budget, and share information about projects or resources through Web-based portals. Artemis targets customers in the aerospace and defense, energy, pharmaceuticals, government, and financial services industries. In July 2006 the company was acquired by Versata.

ARTES MEDICAL, INC.

NASDAQ (GM): ARTE

5870 Pacific Center Blvd.
San Diego, CA 92121
Phone: 858-550-9999
Fax: 858-550-9997
Web: www.artesmedical.com

CEO: Christopher J. Reinhard
CFO: Michael K. (Mike) Green
HR: –
FYE: December 31
Type: Public

Artes Medical wants to fill the gap in substances dermatologists and cosmetic surgeons use to fill "smile lines" with its new product, ArteFill. The micro-injectable product combines bovine collagen and synthetic microspheres of polymethylmethacrylate (PMMA). The combination is intended to provide a longer-lasting remedy to nasolabial folds (smile lines) than competing absorbable products, such as Botox and temporary dermal fillers (including hyaluronic acid and human or bovine collagen). Artes Medical believes the nonabsorbable PMMA microspheres stimulate patients' natural collagen growth in the treated area. ArteFill is sold through a direct sales force to dermatologists and plastic surgeons.

	Annual Growth	12/03	12/04	12/05	12/06	12/07
Sales ($ mil.)	—	—	—	—	—	13.3
Net income ($ mil.)	—	—	—	—	—	(26.9)
Market value ($ mil.)	—	—	—	—	—	37.5
Employees	—	—	—	—	—	—

ARTESIAN RESOURCES CORPORATION

NASDAQ (GM): ARTNA

664 Churchmans Rd.
Newark, DE 19702
Phone: 302-453-6900
Fax: 302-453-6957
Web: www.artesianwater.com

CEO: Dian C. Taylor
CFO: David B. Spacht
HR: Patti Cumpston
FYE: December 31
Type: Public

Well, well, well. This Artesian peddles its water wares in New Castle, Kent, and Sussex. Holding company Artesian Resources operates primarily through regulated utility Artesian Water, which provides water in all three Delaware counties. Its 73,800 customer accounts represent about 243,000 Delaware residents, about 29% of the state's population; residential customers account for 94% of the utility's sales. Artesian pumps about 17.5 million gallons of water daily from its wells, then sends it to customers through 1,050 miles of mains. The company operates a wastewater facility in New Castle County.

	Annual Growth	12/03	12/04	12/05	12/06	12/07
Sales ($ mil.)	9.7%	36.3	39.6	45.3	48.6	52.5
Net income ($ mil.)	12.7%	3.9	4.4	5.0	6.1	6.3
Market value ($ mil.)	18.4%	61.9	63.4	67.6	102.3	121.8
Employees	—	—	—	189	—	—

An in-depth profile of this company is available to Hoover's Online members at hoovers.com.

173

ARTHREX, INC.

1370 Creekside Blvd.
Naples, FL 34108
Phone: 239-643-5553
Fax: 239-598-5521
Web: www.arthrex.com

CEO: Reinhold D. Schmieding
CFO: Jon Check
HR: Kathy Sparrow
FYE: December 31
Type: Private

You might notice a common trait among Arthrex customers — steady hands. The company designs and makes products used for arthroscopic and orthopedic surgery. Arthrex distributes more than 2,000 products to hospitals and surgeons throughout the US and in 60 other countries. Established in 1984, the company operates from 13 locations in the Americas, Europe, and in Korea. Arthrex also offers training in a variety of surgical skills from facilities in Arizona, California, and Florida.

	Annual Growth	12/03	12/04	12/05	12/06	12/07
Est. sales ($ mil.)	—	—	—	—	—	400.0
Employees	—	—	—	—	—	400

ARTHROCARE CORPORATION

NASDAQ (GS): ARTC

7500 Rialto Blvd., Bldg. 2, Ste. 100
Austin, TX 78735
Phone: 512-391-3900
Fax: 512-391-3901
Web: www.arthrocare.com

CEO: Michael A. Baker
CFO: Michael Gluk
HR: –
FYE: Saturday nearest December 31
Type: Public

With the wave of a wand, ArthroCare makes tissue disappear. The company's proprietary Coblation technology uses radio frequency energy to remove soft tissue from the body. With its minimally invasive surgery systems, surgeons use specialized wands to focus the energy and minimize damage to nearby healthy tissue, simultaneously sealing small, bleeding vessels. First used in arthroscopic procedures to repair joints, the electrosurgery system product line now includes equipment used in minimally invasive ear, nose, and throat procedures (such as tonsillectomies) and spinal surgeries.

	Annual Growth	12/03	12/04	12/05	12/06	12/07
Sales ($ mil.)	28.0%	118.8	154.1	214.3	263.0	319.2
Net income ($ mil.)	54.9%	7.5	(26.2)	23.5	31.7	43.2
Market value ($ mil.)	25.6%	518.0	772.2	1,064.2	1,093.6	1,288.1
Employees	(44.1%)	—	—	1,324	881	413

ARTHUR J. GALLAGHER & CO.

NYSE: AJG

The Gallagher Centre, 2 Pierce Place
Itasca, IL 60143
Phone: 630-773-3800
Fax: 630-285-4000
Web: www.ajg.com

CEO: J. Patrick Gallagher Jr.
CFO: Douglas K. (Doug) Howell
HR: Susan E. McGrath
FYE: December 31
Type: Public

Arthur J. Gallagher knows all about risky business. The company provides insurance brokerage and risk management services through a network of subsidiaries. It places property/casualty and surplus lines in addition to offering retirement solutions and managing employee benefits programs. Risk management services include claims management, loss control consulting, and workers' compensation investigations. Gallagher UK places insurance and reinsurance with the Lloyd's of London exchange. The global company has sales and service operations in about a dozen nations and, through correspondent brokers and consultants, does business in more than 100 countries.

	Annual Growth	12/03	12/04	12/05	12/06	12/07
Sales ($ mil.)	5.1%	1,329.0	1,521.6	1,483.9	1,534.0	1,623.3
Net income ($ mil.)	(1.3%)	146.2	188.5	30.8	128.5	138.8
Market value ($ mil.)	(6.6%)	2,924.0	2,994.1	2,955.9	2,906.4	2,226.7
Employees	7.2%	—	—	8,100	8,750	9,300

ARTISTDIRECT, INC.

OTC: ARTDE

1601 Cloverfield Blvd., Ste. 400 South
Santa Monica, CA 90404
Phone: 310-956-3300
Fax: 310-956-3301
Web: www.artistdirect.com

CEO: Dimitri Villard
CFO: René Rousselet
HR: –
FYE: December 31
Type: Public

Are you an artist fearful of pirates? Head for ARTISTdirect. The company's MediaDefender subsidiary offers Internet piracy prevention (IPP) services that prevent unauthorized downloads of customer-specified content. The company additionally operates the ARTISTdirect Network, a collection of Web sites featuring music-related content, including music news and information and an online database covering more than 100,000 artists. The ARTISTdirect Network is classified under the company's media segment, which earns money through online advertising and marketing fees. ARTISTdirect's e-commerce operations offer a selection of music recordings and other music-related merchandise.

	Annual Growth	12/03	12/04	12/05	12/06	12/07
Sales ($ mil.)	41.7%	6.0	5.1	14.0	24.1	24.2
Net income ($ mil.)	—	(21.7)	(3.3)	(12.1)	(4.9)	11.5
Market value ($ mil.)	(50.5%)	—	—	16.0	23.9	3.9
Employees	—	—	—	—	74	—

ART'S-WAY MANUFACTURING CO., INC.

NASDAQ (CM): ARTW

5556 Hwy. 9
Armstrong, IA 50514
Phone: 712-864-3131
Fax: 712-864-3154
Web: www.artsway-mfg.com

CEO: Carrie L. Majeski
CFO: –
HR: Jean Stensland
FYE: November 30
Type: Public

Sinatra did it his way, but farmers are able to do it Art's way since 1956. Art's-Way Manufacturing makes an assortment of machinery under its own label and private labels. The company's equipment includes custom animal-feed processing machines, high-bulk mixing wagons, mowers and stalk shredders, and equipment for harvesting sugar beets and potatoes. Its private-label customers include CNH Global, for which the company makes feed-processing products, service parts, and tillage equipment. Equipment dealers throughout the US sell Art's-Way products. Steel truck bodies are manufactured under the Cherokee Truck Bodies name. Chairman J. Ward McConnell Jr. owns roughly 40% of the company.

	Annual Growth	11/03	11/04	11/05	11/06	11/07
Sales ($ mil.)	22.3%	11.4	12.8	14.6	19.9	25.5
Net income ($ mil.)	6.7%	1.7	1.4	1.0	0.9	2.2
Market value ($ mil.)	49.0%	9.5	11.8	9.5	12.6	46.8
Employees	(4.0%)	—	—	116	102	107

ARUBA NETWORKS, INC.

NASDAQ (GM): ARUN

1322 Crossman Ave.
Sunnyvale, CA 94089
Phone: 408-227-4500
Fax: 408-227-4550
Web: www.arubanetworks.com

CEO: Dominic P. Orr
CFO: Steffan Tomlinson
HR: Aaron Bean
FYE: July 31
Type: Public

Aruba Networks wants to turn your business into a wireless paradise. The company designs equipment used to build wireless LANs. Its products include controllers, access points, and concentrators, as well as operating system and management software. Aruba also provides professional and support services. The company targets the corporate, education, and government sectors, selling directly and through distributors, resellers, and OEMs. Its customers include Google, NTT DATA, The Ohio State University, and The United States Air Force. Aruba outsources the manufacturing of its products to Flextronics.

	Annual Growth	7/03	7/04	7/05	7/06	7/07
Est. sales ($ mil.)	—	—	—	—	—	72.5
Employees	—	—	—	—	—	350

ARVINMERITOR, INC.   NYSE: ARM

2135 W. Maple Rd.
Troy, MI 48084
Phone: 248-435-1000
Fax: 248-435-1393
Web: www.arvinmeritor.com

CEO: Charles G. (Chip) McClure Jr.
CFO: Jeffrey A. (Jay) Craig
HR: —
FYE: September 30
Type: Public

Whether it's building axles for big rigs or steel wheels for passenger cars, ArvinMeritor's actions are always meritorious. Once known as Meritor Automotive, ArvinMeritor was formed in 2000 when Meritor acquired Arvin Industries. It makes components for commercial vehicles (axles, transmissions, and braking systems) as well as for light vehicles (door, roof, wheels, and suspension systems). ArvinMeritor has divested its light vehicle aftermarket product businesses, including aftermarket exhaust (North American and European operations), filters, and motion control operations. In 2008 ArvinMeritor announced that it would separate its Light Vehicle Systems (LVS) and Commercial Vehicle Systems (CVS) divisions.

	Annual Growth	9/03	9/04	9/05	9/06	9/07
Sales ($ mil.)	(4.6%)	7,788.0	8,033.0	8,903.0	9,195.0	6,449.0
Net income ($ mil.)	—	136.0	(42.0)	12.0	(175.0)	(219.0)
Market value ($ mil.)	0.4%	1,220.0	1,303.1	1,175.4	1,005.3	1,239.3
Employees	(5.2%)	—	—	29,000	27,500	—

ARYX THERAPEUTICS   NASDAQ (GM): ARYX

6300 Dumbarton Cir.
Fremont, CA 94555
Phone: 510-585-2200
Fax: 510-585-2202
Web: www.aryx.com

CEO: Paul Goddard
CFO: John Varian
HR: David Nagler
FYE: December 31
Type: Public

Everything's retro these days, including drugs. ARYx Therapeutics is developing drugs using its "retrometabolic design", a process which examines the chemical properties of existing drugs, and attempts to improve them. These improvements focus on reducing the possible danger of side effects when the drugs are metabolized in the liver. ARYx's lead drug candidates are analogs of drugs approved for treatment of gastroesophageal reflux disease, a heart irregularity known as atrial fibrillation, and dangerous blood clots. ARYx Therapeutics holds the rights to two of its candidates, and shares the development rights for its ATI-7505 candidate with Procter & Gamble.

	Annual Growth	12/03	12/04	12/05	12/06	12/07
Sales ($ mil.)	(10.6%)	—	—	—	4.7	4.2
Net income ($ mil.)	—	—	—	—	(27.3)	(27.6)
Market value ($ mil.)	—	—	—	—	—	136.8
Employees	—	—	—	—	70	—

ASA INTERNATIONAL LTD.   Pink Sheets: ASAL

10 Speen St.
Framingham, MA 01701
Phone: 508-626-2727
Fax: 508-626-0645
Web: www.asaint.com

CEO: Alfred C. Angelone
CFO: Terrence C. McCarthy
HR: —
FYE: December 31
Type: Public

ASA International treads a path through a variety of industries. Through its operating divisions, the company provides software, systems, and services to tire dealers and retreaders, systems integrators, law firms, and manufacturing and distribution companies. ASA Tire Systems builds network systems for the tire and automotive aftermarket industries and operates online marketplace eTireLink. Khameleon Software provides e-business management tools for systems integrators. ASA's Rainmaker Software division develops accounting and practice management applications for law firms, and Verticent offers enterprise software for manufacturers and distributors.

	Annual Growth	12/03	12/04	12/05	12/06	12/07
Est. sales ($ mil.)	—	—	—	—	—	19.8
Employees	—	—	—	—	—	110

ASARCO LLC

1150 N. 7th Ave.
Tucson, AZ 85705
Phone: 520-798-7500
Fax: 520-798-7780
Web: www.asarco.com

CEO: Joseph F. Lapinsky
CFO: Don Mills
HR: Donna Lane
FYE: December 31
Type: Subsidiary

A subsidiary of diversified mining firm Grupo México, ASARCO operates mining and copper smelting activities primarily in the southwestern US. Each year it produces around 600 million pounds of copper, 300 million pounds of zinc, and 20 million ounces of silver. The company also produces copper rod and billet and sulfuric acid as a by-product of the smelting process. Some of ASARCO's assets, including its majority stake in Southern Copper Corp., were sold to Grupo México in 2003 in an effort to improve ASARCO's financial picture. It didn't work; the company filed for Chapter 11 bankruptcy in 2005. Three years later, UK miner Vedanta used its Indian subsidiary Sterlite Industries to buy ASARCO for $2.6 billion.

ASB FINANCIAL CORP.   Pink Sheets: ASBN

503 Chillicothe St.
Portsmouth, OH 45662
Phone: 740-354-3177
Fax: 740-355-1142
Web: www.asbfinancialcorp.com

CEO: Robert M. Smith
CFO: Michael L. Gampp
HR: —
FYE: June 30
Type: Public

ASB Financial is the holding company for American Savings Bank. Operating since 1892, the bank serves Scioto and Pike counties in southern Ohio, as well as communities across the Ohio River in northern Kentucky. American Savings' products include IRAs; CDs; and NOW, money market, savings, and checking accounts. From a handful of offices, the thrift originates a variety of loans, more than half of which are one- to four-family mortgages. Other products include commercial real estate, construction, home equity, business, and consumer loans. In 2005 ASB Financial completed a reverse stock split and shareholder buyout that took the company private.

	Annual Growth	6/03	6/04	6/05	6/06	6/07
Assets ($ mil.)	8.5%	152.8	166.4	184.8	198.5	211.7
Net income ($ mil.)	(8.1%)	2.1	2.0	2.2	1.7	1.5
Employees	—	—	—	—	—	—

ASBURY AUTOMOTIVE GROUP, INC.   NYSE: ABG

622 Third Ave., 37th Fl.
New York, NY 10017
Phone: 212-885-2500
Fax: 212-297-2649
Web: www.asburyauto.com

CEO: Charles R. Oglesby
CFO: Craig T. Monaghan
HR: Philip R. (Phil) Johnson
FYE: December 31
Type: Public

Asbury Automotive Group has forfeited its title — as the largest privately owned dealership group in the US — by going public. The company, which has grown through acquisitions, operates about 125 auto franchises that sell some 35 US and foreign brands of new and used vehicles at more than 90 dealership locations in a dozen states, including California, Florida, New Jersey, and Texas. Asbury dealerships also offer parts, service, and collision repair as well as financing and insurance. The company is shifting its focus from buying large multi-location dealerships with established independent brands to acquiring single dealerships, which it re-brands and folds into the existing local group.

	Annual Growth	12/03	12/04	12/05	12/06	12/07
Sales ($ mil.)	4.6%	4,776.5	4,971.9	5,540.7	5,748.3	5,713.0
Net income ($ mil.)	35.3%	15.2	50.1	61.1	60.8	51.0
Market value ($ mil.)	(4.9%)	580.9	448.9	540.7	790.1	475.3
Employees	(2.9%)	—	—	8,800	8,300	8,300

ASC INCORPORATED

1 ASC Center	CEO: Paul B. Wilbur
Southgate, MI 48195	CFO: John Carson
Phone: 734-285-4911	HR: –
Fax: –	FYE: December 31
Web: www.ascglobal.com	Type: Private

When it comes to developing new car models, ASC and ye shall receive. Formerly a simple sunroof maker, ASC — the name now stands for American Specialty Cars — works with carmakers to deliver entire specialty vehicles. Models ASC has helped bring to life include the Chevrolet SSR, Pontiac Vibe GTR, and the Porsche 968 convertible. With its unique approach, ASC can help a car company reinvigorate a tired brand. The company operates mainly in Michigan. An affiliate of investment firm Questor Management owns ASC. The company filed for Chapter 11 backruptcy protection in 2007.

ASCENDANT SOLUTIONS, INC.

OTC: ASDS

16250 Dallas Pkwy., Ste. 111	CEO: David E. Bowe
Dallas, TX 75248	CFO: Mark S. Heil
Phone: 972-250-0945	HR: –
Fax: 972-250-0934	FYE: December 31
Web: www.ascendantsolutions.com	Type: Public

Ascendant Solutions holds stakes in companies in health care, real estate, and other industries. Its investments include Dallas-based specialty pharmacy Dougherty's; CRESA Partners, which provides tenant representation and lease management services; and CRESA Capital Markets, a provider of strategic real estate advice to corporate clients. Ascendant Solutions also owns stakes in Ampco Safety Tools and Dallas-area mixed-use real estate development Frisco Square. Chairman James Leslie holds almost 20% of Ascendant Solutions; CLB Partners (with which directors Jonathan Bloch and Will Cureton are affiliated) owns more than 15%.

	Annual Growth	12/03	12/04	12/05	12/06	12/07
Sales ($ mil.)	217.5%	0.5	39.3	43.8	55.4	50.8
Net income ($ mil.)	—	(0.8)	0.3	0.1	1.0	4.5
Employees	(11.1%)	—	196	180	155	—

ASCENDIA BRANDS, INC.

AMEX: ASB

100 American Metro Blvd., Ste. 108	CEO: Steven R. Scheyer
Hamilton, NJ 08619	CFO: Keith S. Daniels
Phone: 609-219-0930	HR: –
Fax: 609-219-1238	FYE: Last day in February
Web: www.ascendiabrands.com	Type: Public

Ascendia Brands is making a name for itself in the health and beauty sector. It markets health and beauty care products typically sold in value-focused retailers, such as Wal-Mart, Kmart, and Dollar General. In May 2005 the company, then a wireless technology development firm called Cenuco, merged with consumer products maker Lander. It changed its name to Ascendia Brands in 2006. Ascendia still operates a Cenuco wireless division; the unit provides software used for streaming video (mostly for security monitoring) to handheld devices, cell phones, and the Internet. Its MobileMonitor lets families and small business owners remotely monitor their property.

	Annual Growth	6/02	6/03	6/04	*2/06	†2/07
Sales ($ mil.)	138.1%	3.1	1.6	1.5	79.6	99.6
Net income ($ mil.)	—	(0.1)	(1.3)	(3.6)	(48.9)	(103.6)
Employees	—	—	—	—	—	—

*Fiscal year change   †Most recent year available

ASCENSION HEALTH

4600 Edmundson Rd.	CEO: Anthony R. (Tony) Tersigni
St. Louis, MO 63134	CFO: Anthony J. (Tony) Speranzo
Phone: 314-733-8000	HR: –
Fax: 314-733-8013	FYE: June 30
Web: www.ascensionhealth.org	Type: Not-for-profit

Ascension Health has ascended to the pinnacle of not-for-profit health care. As the largest Catholic hospital system in the US, and thus one of the top providers of charity care in the nation, the organization's health care network consists of more than 60 general hospitals along with a dozen long-term care acute care, rehabilitation, and psychiatric hospitals. Ascension Health also operates nursing homes, community clinics, and other health care providers. Its network of medical facilities spans 19 states and the District of Columbia. The organization's facilities have more than 16,700 licensed beds.

	Annual Growth	6/03	6/04	6/05	6/06	6/07
Sales ($ mil.)	8.0%	9,054.3	10,046.4	10,861.0	11,263.0	12,322.0
Employees	4.9%	87,469	—	107,000	—	106,000

ASCENT HEALTHCARE SOLUTIONS, INC.

10232 S. 51st St.	CEO: John Grotting
Phoenix, AZ 85044	CFO: Tim Einwechter
Phone: 480-763-5300	HR: John Sabat
Fax: 480-763-0101	FYE: December 31
Web: ascenths.com	Type: Private

Ascent Healthcare Solutions (formed through the 2006 merger of Alliance Medical Corporation and Vanguard Medical Concepts) is banking on the idea that one man's trash could be another man's treasure. The company serves an important environmental need in the medical community as it helps hospitals with the three "R"s — reduce, reuse, and recycle. Ascent focuses on the reprocessing of disposable medical devices for health care facilities. Its OR-based systems permit the collection of approximately 7,000 tons of devices, as well as other recyclable materials. After collecting the used devices, it cleans, sterilizes, tests, and then returns them from its centers in Lakeland, Florida and Phoenix.

	Annual Growth	12/03	12/04	12/05	12/06	12/07
Est. sales ($ mil.)	—	—	—	—	—	70.0
Employees	—	—	—	—	—	808

ASCENT MEDIA GROUP, INC.

520 Broadway, 5th Fl.	CEO: Jose A. Royo
Santa Monica, CA 90401	CFO: George C. Platisa
Phone: 310-434-7000	HR: –
Fax: 310-434-7001	FYE: December 31
Web: www.ascentmedia.com	Type: Subsidiary

While Ascent Media Group may be no *American Beauty*, it has won its fair share of Oscars. A leading provider of postproduction services for the television and film industries, the company has brought home the gold about 15 times, winning Academy Awards for best sound and technical achievement. Its sound services include music recording, sound editing, and the mixing of dialogue, music, and sound effects. Its video services include film-to-video transfer, visual effects and graphics, videotape editing, and mastering and duplication of videotape and DVD formats. Parent Discovery Holding, controlled by Liberty Media chairman John Malone, plans to spin-off Ascent Media as a publicly-traded company.

ASCENT SOLAR TECHNOLOGIES, INC.

NASDAQ (CM): ASTI

8120 Shaffer Pkwy.
Littleton, CO 80127
Phone: 303-285-9885
Fax: 303-285-9882
Web: www.ascentsolartech.com

CEO: Matthew Foster
CFO: Gary Gatchell
HR: –
FYE: December 31
Type: Public

As long as that sun keeps ascending in the eastern skies every day, there will be ventures trying to tap its enormous energy resources. Ascent Solar Technologies is a development-stage company working on photovoltaic modules for use in satellites and spacecraft. The firm aspires to make such gear smaller, lighter, and more flexible than existing solar cells for use in space by utilizing a thin-film absorbing layer on top of a polyimide substrate. The thin-film layer on top of the high-temperature plastic is made up of copper, indium, gallium, and selenium, which is why the technology is called CIGS. Norsk Hydro has a 35% stake in the company.

	Annual Growth	12/03	12/04	12/05	12/06	12/07
Sales ($ mil.)	—	—	—	—	—	1.0
Net income ($ mil.)	—	—	—	—	—	(6.5)
Market value ($ mil.)	—	—	—	—	—	284.3
Employees	—	—	—	—	—	35

ASH GROVE CEMENT COMPANY

11011 Cody St.
Overland Park, KS 66210
Phone: 913-451-8900
Fax: 913-451-8324
Web: www.ashgrove.com

CEO: Charles T. Sunderland
CFO: John H. Woodfill
HR: Dave Ezell
FYE: December 31
Type: Private

Ash Grove Cement is a pioneer in the US cement industry. Tracing its roots back to 1882, the company is one of the largest cement manufacturers in North America. Ash Grove Cement's products include portland and masonry cements used in roads, bridges, and buildings, as well as ready-mix concrete. The company operates nine plants with an annual capacity of some 9 million tons of cement; it also operates aggregate quarries in the US and Canada and a lime plant in Oregon. Other operations include Ash Grove Packaging (packaged materials), Permanent Paving (concrete paving services), and Cedar Creek Properties (real estate). Lester T. Sunderland joined Ash Grove Cement in 1909; his heirs own the company.

	Annual Growth	12/02	12/03	12/04	12/05	12/06
Est. sales ($ mil.)	—	—	—	—	—	1,190.2
Employees	—	—	—	—	—	2,600

ASHFORD HOSPITALITY TRUST, INC.

NYSE: AHT

14185 Dallas Pkwy., Ste. 1100
Dallas, TX 75254
Phone: 972-490-9600
Fax: 972-980-2705
Web: www.ahtreit.com

CEO: Montgomery J. (Monty) Bennett
CFO: –
HR: Donald J. (Don) Denzin
FYE: December 31
Type: Public

Ashford Hospitality is in with the inn crowd. A self-administered real estate investment trust (REIT), Ashford owns and has interests in more than 110 upscale and upper upscale hotels in the US and one in Canada, which operate under such brands as Hyatt, Marriott, Radisson, and Starwood. More than one-third of Ashford's properties are managed by Remington Lodging, with the rest overseen by third-party management companies. The REIT also offers mezzanine financing, first mortgages, construction loans, and sale-leasebacks.

	Annual Growth	12/03	12/04	12/05	12/06	12/07
Sales ($ mil.)	127.3%	42.3	116.9	331.6	480.4	1,128.8
Net income ($ mil.)	—	(3.9)	1.4	9.4	37.8	30.2
Market value ($ mil.)	37.6%	241.6	393.1	459.8	908.1	865.5
Employees	26.9%	—	—	41	—	66

ASHLAND INC.

NYSE: ASH

50 E. RiverCenter Blvd.
Covington, KY 41012
Phone: 859-815-3333
Fax: 859-815-5053
Web: www.ashland.com

CEO: James J. (Jim) O'Brien Jr.
CFO: Lamar M. Chambers
HR: Susan B. Esler
FYE: September 30
Type: Public

Ashland is built on chemicals and cars. The company consists of four business units. Ashland Distribution buys chemicals and plastics and then blends and repackages them for distribution in Europe and North America. Ashland Performance Materials makes specialty resins, polymers, and adhesives. Ashland Water Technologies provides both chemical and non-chemical products for commercial, industrial, and municipal water treatment facilities. The company's Valvoline unit operates an oil-change chain and markets Valvoline motor oil and Zerex antifreeze. Ashland sold construction unit APAC (which supplies highway materials, builds bridges, and paves streets) in 2006 to Oldcastle Materials for $1.3 billion.

	Annual Growth	9/03	9/04	9/05	9/06	9/07
Sales ($ mil.)	(0.1%)	7,865.0	8,781.0	9,860.0	7,277.0	7,834.0
Net income ($ mil.)	32.3%	75.0	378.0	2,004.0	407.0	230.0
Market value ($ mil.)	13.9%	2,253.6	4,037.8	3,928.6	4,273.3	3,793.2
Employees	(25.2%)	—	—	20,900	11,700	11,700

ASHLAND PERFORMANCE MATERIALS

5200 Blazer Pkwy.
Dublin, OH 43017
Phone: 614-790-3333
Fax: 614-790-4119
Web: www.ashland.com/businesses/apm

CEO: Frank L. (Hank) Waters
CFO: –
HR: Dwight King
FYE: September 30
Type: Business segment

Adhesives are the glue that holds Ashland Performance Materials together. The division of Ashland makes a variety of specialty chemicals used primarily by the auto, packaging, metal castings, and construction markets. Among its offerings are adhesives, composite polymers, binders, and catalysts for casting systems. Ashland Performance Materials also makes polyester and vinyl ester resins and gelcoats for plastics makers. Sister company Ashland Distribution distributes chemicals from Ashland and from other chemical firms. When Ashland completed its sale of APAC to Oldcastle Materials, the parent company split up the former Ashland Specialty Chemicals into Performance Materials and Ashland Water Technologies.

ASHLEY FURNITURE INDUSTRIES, INC.

1 Ashley Way
Arcadia, WI 54612
Phone: 608-323-3377
Fax: 608-323-6008
Web: www.ashleyfurniture.com

CEO: Todd Wanek
CFO: –
HR: Jim Dotta
FYE: December 31
Type: Private

Not to be confused with Laura Ashley, this Ashley is more interested in peddling leather, hardwood, and bedding than toile and chenille. Ashley Furniture Industries, one of the nation's largest furniture manufacturers, makes and imports upholstered furniture, as well as leather and hardwood pieces. It has manufacturing plants and distribution centers throughout the country and overseas. Ashley licenses its name to about 300 Ashley Furniture HomeStores located in the US, Canada, and Japan. These stores are independently owned and sell only Ashley Furniture-branded products. Founded by Carlyle Weinberger in 1945, Ashley Furniture is owned by father-and-son duos Ron and Todd Wanek and Chuck and Ben Vogel.

	Annual Growth	12/02	12/03	12/04	12/05	12/06
Est. sales ($ mil.)	22.2%	1,400.0	1,700.0	2,000.0	2,550.0	3,120.0
Employees	16.2%	8,000	9,300	11,000	13,400	14,600

An in-depth profile of this company is available to Hoover's Online members at hoovers.com.

177

ASHWORTH, INC.

NASDAQ (GM): ASHW

2765 Loker Ave. West
Carlsbad, CA 92010
Phone: 760-438-6610
Fax: 760-476-8417
Web: www.ashworthinc.com

CEO: Allan Fletcher
CFO: Greg W. Slack
HR: Donna Fenn
FYE: October 31
Type: Public

Offering more earth tones and less madras, Ashworth makes golf garb that's on par with typical fashions. As a leading designer of golf apparel, Ashworth offers men's and women's sportswear and accessories under the Ashworth, Callaway Golf (under license), Kudzu, and The Game brand names. Most of Ashworth's clothing is made in Asian countries. Ashworth markets its products primarily in the US, Canada, and Europe in golf pro shops and upscale department and specialty stores, such as Nordstrom. Its primary customers are resorts and golf courses. The manufacturer also sells its clothing and accessories through nearly 20 Ashworth retail outlets. Ashworth was founded in 1987 by Gerald Montiel and John Ashworth.

	Annual Growth	10/03	10/04	10/05	10/06	10/07
Sales ($ mil.)	7.9%	149.4	173.1	204.8	209.6	202.2
Net income ($ mil.)	—	7.3	8.2	(0.7)	0.9	(14.1)
Market value ($ mil.)	(7.5%)	111.6	115.1	100.3	101.9	81.8
Employees	(4.0%)	—	—	755	625	696

ASI COMPUTER TECHNOLOGIES, INC.

48289 Fremont Blvd.
Fremont, CA 94538
Phone: 510-226-8000
Fax: 510-226-8858
Web: www.asipartner.com

CEO: Marcel Liang
CFO: –
HR: –
FYE: December 31
Type: Private

ASI Computer Technologies is a wholesale distributor of computer software, hardware, and accessories. It offers more than 8,000 products, including PCs, modems, monitors, networking equipment, and storage devices. ASI sells to more than 20,000 resellers throughout North America. The company's vendor partners include such companies as AMD, Intel, Microsoft, Samsung, and Western Digital. Its services include custom systems integration and contract assembly. The company also markets a line of computer devices and configures custom computer systems under its own Nspire brand.

	Annual Growth	12/02	12/03	12/04	12/05	12/06
Sales ($ mil.)	6.4%	865.6	1,200.0	1,060.0	1,110.0	1,110.0
Employees	12.5%	530	550	500	600	850

ASI TECHNOLOGY CORPORATION

OTC: ASIT

980 American Pacific Dr., Ste. 111
Henderson, NV 89014
Phone: 702-734-1888
Fax: 702-737-6900
Web: www.asiplasma.com

CEO: Jerry E. Polis
CFO: Eric M. Polis
HR: –
FYE: September 30
Type: Public

ASI Technology is developing products based on plasma technologies, including a noise modulator for commercial jet engines and cold plasma decontamination and sterilization instruments. In 2003 the company sold its plasma antenna technology, along with related government contract rights and intellectual property, to Markland Technologies. ASI is branching out into specialty finance, making loans to affiliates of Concordia Homes of Nevada, a residential builder in the Las Vegas area. President Jerry Polis owns 41% of ASI Technology, including options and warrants.

	Annual Growth	9/03	9/04	9/05	9/06	9/07
Sales ($ mil.)	100.0%	—	—	—	0.3	0.6
Net income ($ mil.)	—	—	—	—	0.0	0.1
Market value ($ mil.)	166.3%	—	—	—	2.8	7.5
Employees	—	—	—	—	0	0

ASICS AMERICA CORPORATION

16275 Lagna Canyon Rd.
Irvine, CA 92618
Phone: 949-453-8888
Fax: 949-453-0292
Web: www.asicsamerica.com

CEO: Seiho Gohashi
CFO: –
HR: Eileen Schaaf
FYE: March 31
Type: Subsidiary

With ASICS America you don't have to *earn* your stripes, you just have to *purchase* them. ASICS America is the North American sales and marketing arm of Japanese athletic footwear, apparel, and accessories maker ASICS Corporation. The company's shoe collection — featuring its trademarked stripe design — includes footwear for basketball, cheerleading, court and training, running, track and field, volleyball, walking, and wrestling. Its Budokan label represents one of its "sportstyle" products that targets a hip crowd. ASICS products, which were introduced in the US in 1977, are sold at regional and national retailers throughout the country, as well as through online vendors.

	Annual Growth	3/03	3/04	3/05	3/06	3/07
Est. sales ($ mil.)	—	—	—	—	—	19.5
Employees	—	—	—	—	—	195

ASKMENOW, INC.

OTC: AKMN

26 Executive Park, Ste. 250
Irvine, CA 92614
Phone: 949-861-2590
Fax: 949-861-2591
Web: www.askmenow.com

CEO: Darryl R. Cohen
CFO: Dennis Bergquist
HR: –
FYE: December 31
Type: Public

Ask and ye shall receive a text message answer. AskMeNow is a mobile content provider that offers information services to users of mobile phones and other handheld devices. By sending a text message or e-mail, those who need to know now can get answers to almost any question, including driving directions, directory information, sports scores, and weather. Information comes from such content licensing partners as Maps.com, Astrology.com, Hotels.com, and Shopping.com. The company generates revenue through charging a fee per question answered, or a basic monthly fee for unlimited use. It also sells advertising and sponsorships.

	Annual Growth	9/03	9/04	*12/05	12/06	12/07
Sales ($ mil.)	(70.5%)	13.2	6.9	0.0	0.0	0.1
Net income ($ mil.)	—	0.3	(2.9)	(8.8)	(12.6)	(20.4)
Employees	—	—	—	—	121	—

*Fiscal year change

ASPECT MEDICAL SYSTEMS, INC.

NASDAQ (GM): ASPM

1 Upland Rd.
Norwood, MA 02062
Phone: 617-559-7000
Fax: 617-559-7400
Web: www.aspectms.com

CEO: Nassib G. Chamoun
CFO: Michael Falvey
HR: Margery Ahearn
FYE: December 31
Type: Public

"Frère Jacques. Frère Jacques. Dormez-vous?" Aspect Medical Systems can give you the answer. The company makes the BIS System, which can assess consciousness levels during surgery. The system is based on its Bispectral Index technology, which measures the effects of anesthetics on the brain. The BIS is designed to prevent surgical awareness, wherein patients become conscious during surgery though they appear anesthetized and are unable to communicate, as well as to improve recovery processes. Aspect Medical Systems markets the system, which includes monitors, module kits, and sensors, in the US and abroad through direct sales and distribution agreements.

	Annual Growth	12/03	12/04	12/05	12/06	12/07
Sales ($ mil.)	21.9%	44.1	55.6	77.0	91.3	97.3
Net income ($ mil.)	—	(6.5)	0.3	8.5	37.1	2.3
Market value ($ mil.)	1.8%	222.9	509.7	765.4	421.7	239.7
Employees	11.6%	—	—	258	288	—

ASPEN EDUCATION GROUP INC.

17777 Center Court Dr., Ste. 300
Cerritos, CA 90703
Phone: 562-467-5500
Fax: 562-402-7036
Web: www.aspeneducation.com

CEO: James M. (Jim) Dredge
CFO: Thomas Hopkins
HR: –
FYE: December 31
Type: Private

Aspen Education Group helps youth struggling with behavioral, emotional, learning, and motivational issues make positive life changes. The company provides services — which it says exist at the intersection of therapy and education — in traditional classrooms, through experiential outdoor learning, and on the Internet. The company operates more than 35 programs in about a dozen states and the UK. Offerings include boarding schools, residential treatment, weight-loss programs, and wilderness therapy that target kids fighting to overcome challenges such as academic underachievement, anger, anxiety, depression, family conflict, obesity, and substance abuse.

	Annual Growth	12/03	12/04	12/05	12/06	12/07
Est. sales ($ mil.)	—	—	—	—	—	64.9
Employees	—	—	—	—	—	1,913

ASPEN EXPLORATION CORPORATION

OTC: ASPN

2050 S. Oneida St., Ste. 208
Denver, CO 80224
Phone: 303-639-9860
Fax: 303-639-9863
Web: www.aspenexploration.com

CEO: R. V. Bailey
CFO: Kevan B. Hensman
HR: –
FYE: June 30
Type: Public

Aspen Exploration's aspiration is to explore for and produce oil and gas in northern California. The company operates 56 gas wells and also holds non-operating interests in a further 20. Between 2001 and 2006 the oil and gas independent successfully completed 39 gas wells out of 46 attempts, including a number of wildcat wells. Aspen Exploration has estimated proved reserves of 1,838 barrels of oil and 2.8 billion cu. ft. of natural gas and has more than 5,360 net acres of leasehold property. Enserco Energy and Calpine accounted for 73% and 27%, respectively, of Aspen Exploration's oil and gas sales in fiscal 2006. Chairman R.V. Bailey owns about 19% of the company; director Robert Cohan, 10%.

	Annual Growth	6/03	6/04	6/05	6/06	6/07
Sales ($ mil.)	35.6%	1.3	1.8	4.1	6.0	4.4
Net income ($ mil.)	73.2%	0.1	0.2	1.5	3.0	0.9
Market value ($ mil.)	52.5%	5.0	5.9	22.9	33.7	26.9
Employees	—	—	—	—	—	—

ASPEN MARKETING SERVICES, INC.

1240 North Ave.
West Chicago, IL 60185
Phone: 630-293-9600
Fax: 630-293-7584
Web: www.aspenms.com

CEO: Patrick J. O'Rahilly
CFO: Don Danner
HR: Cathy Horn
FYE: –
Type: Private

As the largest privately-held marketing firm in the US, Aspen Marketing Services provides integrated marketing services to clients such as Georgia-Pacific, General Motors, Omaha Steaks, and the American Cancer Society. The company blends strategic planning, public relations, brand promotion, as well as event and direct marketing, to provide clients in a wide range of industries unified marketing for greater results. Its digital marketing capabilities utilize web design, e-mail marketing, database processing, and online loyalty marketing services. Aspen was founded in 1986 and operates about 10 offices spanning the US. The company's growth has been attributed to a steady stream of acquisitions.

ASPEN TECHNOLOGY, INC.

Pink Sheets: AZPN

200 Wheeler Road
Burlington, MA 01803
Phone: 781-221-6400
Fax: 617-949-1030
Web: www.aspentec.com

CEO: Mark E. Fusco
CFO: Bradley T. Miller
HR: Hedwig Veith (Hedy) Whitney
FYE: June 30
Type: Public

Aspen Technology (AspenTech) helps its customers scale mountains of supply chain and engineering challenges. The company provides supply chain management, plant operations, and engineering software for companies in the oil and gas, petrochemicals, and pharmaceuticals industries. Its software combines supplier collaboration, inventory management, and production planning functions to help manage the supply chain from start to finish. The company's engineering software offerings include collaborative engineering applications for manufacturing plant design and simulation. AspenTech sells directly and through systems integrators such as Accenture, Intergraph, Microsoft, and Schlumberger.

	Annual Growth	6/03	6/04	6/05	6/06	6/07
Sales ($ mil.)	1.4%	322.7	333.0	269.6	293.1	341.0
Net income ($ mil.)	—	(160.8)	(21.8)	(69.4)	12.8	45.5
Employees	(14.9%)	—	1,550	1,319	—	—

ASPENBIO PHARMA, INC.

NASDAQ (CM): APPY

1585 S. Perry St.
Castle Rock, CO 80104
Phone: 303-794-2000
Fax: 303-798-8332
Web: www.aspenbioinc.com

CEO: Richard G. Donnelly
CFO: Jeffrey G. (Jeff) McGonegal
HR: –
FYE: December 31
Type: Public

Is Bessie "in the family way"? AspenBio Pharma can assist you in settling this all-important question. The company has four animal reproductive drugs for cows and horses in late stage development. BoviPure FSH and EquiPure FSH are fertility enhancers, EquiPure LT is for timed ovulation in horses, and StayBred helps reduce pregnancy loss in cows. AspenBio Pharma doesn't just make products for animals. It's making the first blood test for appendicitis, called AppyScore, and a sister product, AppyScreen. The company also makes some 30 antigens and tumor markers used in human diagnostics. It also produces about 10 human hormones, including a growth hormone and a thyroid stimulating hormone.

	Annual Growth	12/03	12/04	12/05	12/06	12/07
Sales ($ mil.)	10.7%	0.6	0.8	0.9	1.2	0.9
Net income ($ mil.)	—	(1.7)	(2.1)	(2.1)	(3.1)	(6.2)
Market value ($ mil.)	121.8%	11.1	7.6	16.1	59.0	269.1
Employees	—	—	—	—	—	—

ASPLUNDH TREE EXPERT CO.

708 Blair Mill Rd.
Willow Grove, PA 19090
Phone: 215-784-4200
Fax: 215-784-4493
Web: www.asplundh.com

CEO: Christopher B. Asplundh
CFO: Joseph P. Dwyer
HR: Ryan Swier
FYE: December 31
Type: Private

How much wood would a woodchuck chuck, if a woodchuck could chuck wood? A lot, if the woodchuck were named Asplundh. One of the world's leading tree-trimming businesses, Asplundh clears tree limbs from power lines for utilities and municipalities throughout the US and in Canada, Australia, and New Zealand. Asplundh also offers utility-related services such as line construction, meter reading, and pole maintenance; in addition, the company has branched out into fields such as billboard maintenance, traffic signal and highway lighting construction, and vegetation control for railroads and pipelines. The Asplundh family owns and manages the company, which was founded in 1928.

	Annual Growth	12/02	12/03	12/04	12/05	12/06
Sales ($ mil.)	9.4%	1,678.0	1,800.0	2,080.0	2,366.0	2,400.0
Employees	0.8%	27,978	28,948	28,638	24,000	28,831

An in-depth profile of this company is available to Hoover's Online members at hoovers.com.

179

ASPYRA, INC.

AMEX: APY

26115-A Mureau Rd.
Calabasas, CA 91302
Phone: 818-880-6700
Fax: 818-880-4398
Web: www.aspyra.com

CEO: James (Jim) Zierick
CFO: Anahita (Ana) Villafane
HR: –
FYE: December 31
Type: Public

Aspyra aspires to keep folks around the globe healthy. The company, a provider of clinical and diagnostic information solutions for the health care industry, specializes in enterprise-wide systems for hospitals, multi-specialty clinics, clinical laboratories, imaging departments and centers, orthopedic environments, and pharmacies. Aspyra was formed from the merger of Creative Computer Applications (CCA), a provider of clinical information systems, and StorCOMM, a provider of clinical image management systems, in November 2005.

	Annual Growth	8/03	8/04	*12/05	12/06	12/07
Sales ($ mil.)	8.6%	7.4	7.7	7.2	12.7	10.3
Net income ($ mil.)	—	0.1	0.2	(2.5)	(3.6)	(4.2)
Market value ($ mil.)	0.3%	—	—	21.6	19.6	21.8
Employees	—	—	—	—	101	—

*Fiscal year change

ASSET ACCEPTANCE CAPITAL CORP.

NASDAQ (GS): AACC

28405 Van Dyke Ave.
Warren, MI 48093
Phone: 586-939-9600
Fax: 586-446-7837
Web: www.assetacceptance.com

CEO: Nathaniel F. (Brad) Bradley IV
CFO: Mark A. Redman
HR: Deanna S. Hatmaker
FYE: December 31
Type: Public

Asset Acceptance Capital tries to help creditors accept the things they cannot change and to have the courage to pay off the debt they can. The company buys portfolios of written-off consumer debt (credit cards, consumer loans, utilities) at a deep discount, then attempts to collect on them. Purchased receivables of Visa, MasterCard, and Discover cards make up about 50% of the company's portfolio. The company focuses on debt in the primary, secondary, and tertiary markets, which means typically between one and three collection agencies have already had a go at them; these portfolios are often the cheapest to acquire but are the hardest to collect on.

	Annual Growth	12/03	12/04	12/05	12/06	12/07
Sales ($ mil.)	11.5%	160.2	214.8	252.7	254.9	248.0
Net income ($ mil.)	(14.2%)	37.7	0.8	51.3	45.5	20.4
Market value ($ mil.)	(26.2%)	—	792.9	836.1	626.1	318.2
Employees	(13.7%)	—	—	1,980	1,708	—

⊞ ASSISTED LIVING CONCEPTS, INC.

NYSE: ALC

W140 N8981 Lilly Rd.
Menomonee Falls, WI 53051
Phone: 262-257-8888
Fax: –
Web: www.alcco.com

CEO: Laurie A. Bebo
CFO: John Buono
HR: –
FYE: December 31
Type: Public

Assisted Living Concepts (ALC) helps its residents to live large. The company, formerly a subsidiary of Extendicare, runs more than 200 assisted living centers in the US. The company's facilities enable residents to maintain fairly independent lifestyles but provide assistance with activities such as eating, bathing, medication management, and laundry. The communities also offer social activities, arts and crafts, and the like. In addition to providing full-time housing for residents, some of ALC's communities offer the option of short-term stays. Extendicare spun off the firm in 2006 after having acquired it the previous year.

	Annual Growth	12/03	12/04	12/05	12/06	12/07
Sales ($ mil.)	(0.7%)	—	—	—	231.1	229.4
Net income ($ mil.)	91.1%	—	—	—	9.0	17.2
Market value ($ mil.)	(28.5%)	—	—	—	588.5	421.0
Employees	—	—	—	—	4,600	—

ASSOCIATED BANC-CORP

NASDAQ (GS): ASBC

1200 Hansen Rd.
Green Bay, WI 54304
Phone: 920-491-7000
Fax: 920-491-7090
Web: www.associatedbank.com

CEO: Paul S. Beideman
CFO: Joseph B. (Joe) Selner
HR: Judith M. Docter
FYE: December 31
Type: Public

A lot of Midwesterners are associated with Associated Banc-Corp, the holding company for Associated Bank, which operates some 300 banking offices in communities in Illinois, Minnesota, and Wisconsin. Targeting individuals and local businesses, the bank offers deposit accounts, credit and debit cards, and asset management services. Other activities include insurance, brokerage, mortgage banking, and leasing. It also administers pension, profit-sharing, and employee benefits plans and trusts. Commercial loans, including agricultural, construction, and real estate loans, make up about two-thirds of the bank's loan portfolio, which also includes residential mortgages, consumer loans, and home equity loans.

	Annual Growth	12/03	12/04	12/05	12/06	12/07
Assets ($ mil.)	9.1%	15,247.9	20,520.1	22,100.1	20,861.4	21,592.1
Net income ($ mil.)	5.7%	228.7	258.3	320.2	316.6	285.8
Market value ($ mil.)	13.3%	2,093.2	4,312.3	4,416.2	4,495.1	3,449.2
Employees	(0.4%)	—	—	5,146	5,101	5,110

ASSOCIATED CATHOLIC CHARITIES, INC.

320 Cathedral St.
Baltimore, MD 21201
Phone: 410-261-5800
Fax: 410-889-9243
Web: www.catholiccharities-md.org

CEO: Harold A. (Hal) Smith
CFO: Terry Tanner-Hill
HR: Kathleen Mills
FYE: June 30
Type: Not-for-profit

Associated Catholic Charities provides people in the greater Baltimore area, including nine Maryland counties, with a wide variety of social services. The group focuses on children and families, the elderly, and people with developmental disabilities; offerings include adoption services, child abuse prevention, food, immigration assistance, residential facilities, and services for homeless people. Associated Catholic Charities serves more than 160,000 people of all religions each year. Money for the group's operations comes mainly from government contracts and grants. In addition, the group relies on a network of about 10,000 volunteers. Associated Catholic Charities was founded in 1923.

	Annual Growth	6/03	6/04	6/05	6/06	6/07
Est. sales ($ mil.)	—	—	—	—	—	108.6
Employees	—	—	—	—	—	2,000

ASSOCIATED ESTATES REALTY CORPORATION

NYSE: AEC

1 AEC Pkwy.
Richmond Heights, OH 44143
Phone: 216-261-5000
Fax: 216-289-9600
Web: www.aecrealty.com

CEO: Jeffrey I. Friedman
CFO: Lou Fatica
HR: Kara Florack
FYE: December 31
Type: Public

Associated Estates Realty no longer prefers to associate itself with affordable housing. The self-administered real estate investment trust (REIT) is in the process of exiting that market to focus on multifamily apartment properties, which it acquires, develops, and operates in eight states. Ohio, Michigan, Georgia, and Florida represent its largest markets. The REIT's portfolio consists of about 70 apartment communities (including more than 15,000 units) that it either wholly owns, manages for third parties, or asset manages. Subsidiary MIG Realty Advisors provides real estate investment and management services to both its parent and other companies.

	Annual Growth	12/03	12/04	12/05	12/06	12/07
Sales ($ mil.)	(1.0%)	157.3	160.4	150.4	145.8	151.4
Net income ($ mil.)	—	(10.9)	3.3	36.2	27.0	10.2
Market value ($ mil.)	2.0%	142.4	200.9	162.3	237.2	154.4
Employees	(10.7%)	—	—	728	650	—

ASSOCIATED FOOD STORES, INC.

1850 W. 2100 South	CEO: Richard A. (Rich) Parkinson
Salt Lake City, UT 84119	CFO: Robert (Bob) Obray
Phone: 801-973-4400	HR: Dave Jonckowski
Fax: 801-978-8551	FYE: Saturday nearest March 31
Web: www.afstores.com	Type: Cooperative

This business makes sure there's plenty of grub for the Wild West. Associated Food Stores is a leading regional cooperative wholesale distributor that supplies groceries and other products to about 600 independent supermarkets in eight Western states. It also offers a variety of support services for its member-owners, including market research, real estate analysis, store design, technology procurement, and training. In addition, Associated Food Stores owns about 20% of Western Family Foods, a grocery wholesalers' partnership that produces Western Family private-label goods. The co-op was formed in 1940 by Donald Lloyd, then president of the Utah Retail Grocers Association, and 34 other retailers.

	Annual Growth	3/03	3/04	3/05	3/06	3/07
Est. sales ($ mil.)	—	—	—	—	—	1,522.5
Employees	—	—	—	—	—	2,000

ASSOCIATED GROCERS OF FLORIDA, INC.

1411 SW 12th Ave.	CEO: Calvin J. Miller
Pompano Beach, FL 33069	CFO: Allan C. Sutherland
Phone: 954-876-3000	HR: Iris Cerullo
Fax: 954-876-3003	FYE: July 31
Web: www.agfla.com	Type: Private

You might say this company helps keep grocery store associates busy stocking shelves. Associated Grocers of Florida (AGFL) is a leading wholesale food distributor serving independent retailers and foodservice operators in the Southeast and in international markets. The company supplies more than 22,000 products including such brands as IGA, Surefine, and Top Care. AGFL operates two distribution facilities in Florida. In addition to wholesale distribution, the member-owned cooperative offers a variety of business support services, including advertising planning, merchandising, and technology procurement. The company was formed in 1945.

	Annual Growth	7/03	7/04	7/05	7/06	7/07
Est. sales ($ mil.)	—	—	—	—	—	588.1
Employees	—	—	—	—	—	500

ASSOCIATED GROCERS OF NEW ENGLAND, INC.

11 Cooperative Way	CEO: Michael C. (Mike) Bourgoine
Pembroke, NH 03275	CFO: Steven (Steve) Murphy
Phone: 603-223-6710	HR: –
Fax: –	FYE: March 31
Web: www.agne.com	Type: Cooperative

Associated Grocers of New England (AGNE) distributes more than 26,000 grocery products to more than 400 independent retailers throughout the New England states of Connecticut, Massachusetts, New Hampshire, Rhode Island, and Vermont, as well as in parts of Maine and New York. It supplies customers with bakery goods, fresh produce, and meat, as well as general grocery items and other merchandise. AGNE also offers such retail support services as advertising, marketing, and merchandising. In addition, it operates a small number of stores under the banners Harvest Market, Riverview Market, and Vista Foods. The cooperative was formed as New Hampshire Wholesale Grocers in 1946.

	Annual Growth	3/03	3/04	3/05	3/06	3/07
Est. sales ($ mil.)	—	—	—	—	—	266.8
Employees	—	—	—	—	—	600

ASSOCIATED MATERIALS INCORPORATED

3773 State Rd.	CEO: Thomas N. (Tom) Chieffe
Cuyahoga Falls, OH 44223	CFO: Cynthia L. (Cyndi) Sobe
Phone: 330-929-1811	HR: John F. Haumesser
Fax: 330-922-2354	FYE: Saturday nearest December 31
Web: www.associatedmaterials.com	Type: Private

Vinyl has never gone out of style at Associated Materials Incorporated (AMI). AMI makes and distributes vinyl siding and windows, as well as aluminum and steel siding, aluminum trim coil, and accessories. Products are sold primarily in the US and Canada, and bear such brand names as Alside, Gentek, and Revere. The home repair and remodeling markets make up about 65% of sales; the rest is new construction sales. AMI's approximately 125 supply centers generate 70% of sales, primarily to contractors. AMI also distributes building products made by other OEMs, and makes UltraGuard-branded vinyl fencing and railing. AMI is indirectly owned by AMH Holdings, which is controlled by Investcorp and Harvest Partners.

	Annual Growth	12/02	12/03	12/04	12/05	12/06
Sales ($ mil.)	18.7%	629.6	779.8	1,094.0	1,173.6	1,250.1
Net income ($ mil.)	51.0%	6.4	24.5	(10.9)	22.4	33.3
Employees	18.4%	2,550	3,173	3,137	3,872	5,009

⊞ ASSOCIATED MILK PRODUCERS INC.

315 N. Broadway	CEO: Mark Furth
New Ulm, MN 56073	CFO: –
Phone: 507-354-8295	HR: Jeff Davies
Fax: 507-359-8651	FYE: December 31
Web: www.ampi.com	Type: Cooperative

Associated Milk Producers Inc. (AMPI) might wear a cheesy grin, but it churns up solid sales. The dairy cooperative transforms more than 5 billion pounds of milk into butter, cheese, and fluid milk and other dairy products each and every year. A regional co-op with some 4,000 member/farmers from Iowa, Minnesota, Missouri, Nebraska, North and South Dakota, and Wisconsin, AMPI operates 12 manufacturing plants. Aside from its own AMPI and State brands, Associated Milk Producers makes private-label products for food retailers and foodservice companies. It also makes dairy ingredients for food manufacturers.

⊞ THE ASSOCIATED PRESS

450 W. 33rd St.	CEO: Thomas (Tom) Curley
New York, NY 10001	CFO: Kenneth J. (Ken) Dale
Phone: 212-621-1500	HR: Jessica Bruce
Fax: 212-621-5447	FYE: December 31
Web: www.ap.org	Type: Cooperative

This just in: The Associated Press (AP) is reporting tonight and every night wherever news is breaking. AP is one of the world's largest newsgathering organizations, with about 240 news bureaus in nearly 100 countries. It provides news, photos, graphics, and audiovisual services that reach people daily through print, radio, television, and the Web. In addition to traditional news services, it operates international television news service APTN (AP Television News), photo archives, and an interactive news service (AP Digital). It also offers advertising management and distribution services. The not-for-profit cooperative was founded in 1846 and is owned by 1,500 US daily newspaper members.

⊞ An in-depth profile of this company is available to Hoover's Online members at hoovers.com.

181

ASSOCIATED WHOLESALE GROCERS, INC.

5000 Kansas Ave.	CEO: Gary A. Phillips
Kansas City, KS 66106	CFO: Robert C. (Bob) Walker
Phone: 913-288-1000	HR: Frank Tricamo
Fax: 913-288-1587	FYE: Last Saturday in December
Web: www.awginc.com	Type: Cooperative

Associated Wholesale Grocers (AWG) knows its customers can't live by bread and milk alone. One of the largest US retailer-owned cooperatives, AWG supplies more than 1,900 member-stores in 21 states from eight distribution centers with a wide array of grocery items, produce, and fresh meats, along with other retail merchandise and specialty services for in-store delis and bakeries. AWG has also developed its own grocery store concepts, including Country Mart and Homeland. In addition, the co-op offers a variety of business services to its members, including advertising and marketing programs, insurance, retail systems support, and store design. AWG was founded by a group of independent grocers in 1924.

ASSOCIATED WHOLESALERS, INC.

Route 422	CEO: J. Christopher (Chris) Michael
Robesonia, PA 19551	CFO: Thomas C. Teeter
Phone: 610-693-3161	HR: Audrey Schein
Fax: 610-693-3171	FYE: July 31
Web: www.awiweb.com	Type: Cooperative

Grocery stores can profit from an association with this business. Associated Wholesalers, Inc., (AWI) is a retailer-owned cooperative that supplies a wide array of food and non-food products to independent grocers and convenience stores along the eastern seaboard from distribution centers in Pennsylvania and New Jersey. It distributes broadline grocery products, bakery goods, meat and dairy items, fresh produce, and frozen foods, as well as a full line of general merchandise products. Its White Rose Foods unit serves supermarkets and grocers in the New York City area, as well as in New Jersey and New England. AWI also operates nine supermarkets under the Shurefine Markets banner.

ASSURANCEAMERICA CORPORATION

OTC: ASAM

5500 Interstate N. Pkwy., Ste. 600	CEO: Lawrence (Bud) Stumbaugh
Atlanta, GA 30328	CFO: Gregory D. (Greg) Woods
Phone: 770-952-0200	HR: –
Fax: 770-952-0258	FYE: December 31
Web: www.assuranceamerica.com	Type: Public

AssuranceAmerica will assure you that they meant to leave out the space between its names. Through its three operating subsidiaries the company writes and markets nonstandard (high-risk) auto insurance to customers in the Southeast. Its AssuranceAmerica Insurance subsidiary writes the policies while its Managing General Agency markets the products and provides services through a network of 1,800 independent agencies. Its TrustWay Insurance Agencies operates retail agencies in Florida, Alabama, and Georgia, which sell nonstandard auto insurance underwritten by AssuranceAmerica and other unaffiliated carriers. Chairman Guy Millner controls nearly half of the company.

	Annual Growth	12/03	12/04	12/05	12/06	12/07
Assets ($ mil.)	52.0%	23.5	36.3	69.0	95.7	125.3
Net income ($ mil.)	—	(1.2)	(0.1)	2.3	4.7	0.3
Market value ($ mil.)	—	—	—	—	—	40.8
Employees	5.2%	—	—	—	268	282

ASSURANT, INC.

NYSE: AIZ

1 Chase Manhattan Plaza, 41st Fl.	CEO: Robert B. Pollock
New York, NY 10005	CFO: Michael J. (Mike) Peninger
Phone: 212-859-7000	HR: –
Fax: 212-859-7010	FYE: December 31
Web: www.assurant.com	Type: Public

From credit cards to trailer parks, Assurant provides a range of specialty insurance products. Through Assurant Solutions and Assurant Specialty Property, the company offers such products as credit insurance, manufactured home coverage, creditor-placed homeowners insurance, pre-need funeral policies, and extended warranties for electronics, appliances, and vehicles. Individuals and small employer groups can choose from several types of health coverage offered by Assurant Health, while group life, dental, and disability products are available through the Assurant Employee Benefits segment. Assurant's products are distributed through sales offices and independent agents across the US and abroad.

	Annual Growth	12/03	12/04	12/05	12/06	12/07
Assets ($ mil.)	3.0%	23,728.3	24,503.9	25,365.4	25,165.2	26,750.3
Net income ($ mil.)	37.0%	185.6	350.6	479.4	717.4	653.8
Market value ($ mil.)	22.7%	—	4,269.9	5,679.4	6,774.7	7,881.4
Employees	8.0%	—	—	12,000	13,400	14,000

ASTA FUNDING, INC.

NASDAQ (GS): ASFI

210 Sylvan Ave.	CEO: Gary Stern
Englewood Cliffs, NJ 07632	CFO: Mitchell M. Cohen
Phone: 201-567-5648	HR: Gihan Elsmira
Fax: 201-569-4595	FYE: September 30
Web: www.astafunding.com	Type: Public

Say "hasta luego" to unpaid receivables. Asta Funding buys, sells, services, and collects unpaid credit card debts and consumer loans. The company buys discount, primarily delinquent accounts directly from the credit grantors as well as indirectly through auctions and brokers. It buys credit card charge-offs from Visa, MasterCard, private labels, and banks in addition to telecom and other industry charge-offs. The company then collects on its debt balances either internally or with an outsourced agency. Asta Funding also invests in semi-performing and non-deliquent receivables. Chairman Arthur Stern and his family control some 47% of the company.

	Annual Growth	9/03	9/04	9/05	9/06	9/07
Sales ($ mil.)	41.7%	34.9	51.2	69.5	102.0	140.8
Net income ($ mil.)	45.7%	11.6	22.2	31.0	45.8	52.3
Market value ($ mil.)	57.5%	86.7	217.5	412.8	515.7	533.3
Employees	3.6%	—	—	—	166	172

ASTEA INTERNATIONAL INC.

NASDAQ (CM): ATEA

240 Gibraltar Rd., Ste. 300	CEO: Zack B. Bergreen
Horsham, PA 19044	CFO: Frederic (Rick) Etskovitz
Phone: 215-682-2500	HR: –
Fax: 215-682-2515	FYE: December 31
Web: www.astea.com	Type: Public

Astea International aspires to serve a wide field of customers. The company's customer relationship management (CRM) software is used to automate sales and service processes, manage contracts and warranties, and distribute information to employees, customers, and suppliers. Astea's customers (primarily professional services firms or organizations that sell and service equipment) come from a variety of industries, including health care, medical devices, controls and instrumentation, information technology, facilities management, and telecommunications. The company also offers services such as consulting, implementation, and maintenance. Founder and CEO Zack Bergreen owns about 45% of Astea.

	Annual Growth	12/03	12/04	12/05	12/06	12/07
Sales ($ mil.)	24.1%	12.8	19.3	22.8	20.3	30.4
Net income ($ mil.)	—	(5.5)	2.1	1.8	(5.0)	2.8
Market value ($ mil.)	23.4%	8.8	20.0	50.2	24.0	20.4
Employees	40.3%	—	—	139	195	—

An in-depth profile of this company is available to Hoover's Online members at hoovers.com.

ASTEC INDUSTRIES, INC.

NASDAQ (GS): ASTE

1725 Shepherd Rd.
Chattanooga, TN 37421
Phone: 423-899-5898
Fax: 423-899-4456
Web: www.astecindustries.com

CEO: J. Don Brock
CFO: Fred McKamy Hall
HR: –
FYE: December 31
Type: Public

"On the Road Again" isn't just a Willie Nelson song to Astec Industries, it's a way of life. The company makes equipment for every phase of road building, such as aggregate crushers, pavers, and portable hot-mix asphalt plants. Its 170 products are auger boring, impact crusher, trenching, directional drilling, and heat-transfer equipment for the construction, demolition, mining, recycling, and oil and gas industries. Founded in 1972, the company also sells replacement parts for its equipment. Astec Industries provides equipment for both government and private clients, including asphalt road paving contractors, utility and pipeline contractors, and open mine and quarry operators.

	Annual Growth	12/03	12/04	12/05	12/06	12/07
Sales ($ mil.)	19.5%	426.6	504.5	616.1	710.6	869.0
Net income ($ mil.)	—	(29.0)	19.0	28.1	39.6	56.8
Market value ($ mil.)	35.9%	242.8	344.0	691.7	761.5	829.3
Employees	5.9%	—	—	826	875	—

ASTELLAS PHARMA US, INC.

3 Pkwy. North
Deerfield, IL 60015
Phone: 847-317-8800
Fax: –
Web: www.astellas.us

CEO: Yoshihiko Hatanaka
CFO: Shinichiro (Shin) Katayanagi
HR: Collette Taylor
FYE: March 31
Type: Subsidiary

Astellas Pharma US pilots pharma efforts that are really outta this world. The company's primary products include the antifungal Mycamine, the vascular dilator Andenoscan, enlarged prostate treatment Flomax, and the organ transplant immunosuppressant Prograf. It is focusing its efforts on the following therapeutic areas: cardiology, dermatology, immunology, infectious diseases, and urology. The company's other products include overactive bladder treatment VESIcare and dermatological products Protopic and Amevive. Astellas Pharma US is a subsidiary of Astellas Pharma, which was formed in 2005 with the merger of Japan-based pharmaceutical companies Yamanouchi and Fujisawa.

	Annual Growth	3/03	3/04	3/05	3/06	3/07
Est. sales ($ mil.)	—	—	—	—	—	101.6
Employees	—	—	—	—	—	800

ASTENJOHNSON INC.

4399 Corporate Rd.
Charleston, SC 29405
Phone: 843-747-7800
Fax: 843-747-3856
Web: www.astenjohnson.com

CEO: Dan Cappell
CFO: David Meek
HR: –
FYE: December 31
Type: Private

Formed through the 1999 merger of two venerable paper machine clothing makers with European origins, AstenJohnson makes specialty textiles (paper machine clothing, specialty fabrics, and filaments) for the printing and papermaking industries. The company also produces monofilaments used in making paper machine clothing, and specialty fabrics for pulp mills and manufacturers in non-paper industries. It also makes specialty drainage equipment for paper machines. AstenJohnson operates 12 manufacturing plants in North America and sells its products to end users worldwide.

	Annual Growth	12/03	12/04	12/05	12/06	12/07
Est. sales ($ mil.)	—	—	—	—	—	115.8
Employees	—	—	—	—	—	1,500

ASTORIA FINANCIAL CORPORATION

NYSE: AF

1 Astoria Federal Plaza
Lake Success, NY 11042
Phone: 516-327-3000
Fax: 516-327-7461
Web: www.astoriafederal.com

CEO: George L. Engelke Jr.
CFO: Frank E. Fusco
HR: Arnold K. Greenberg
FYE: December 31
Type: Public

Astoria Financial is the holding company for Astoria Federal Savings and Loan, one of the largest thrifts in the US. The bank has about 90 branches in and around New York City (Brooklyn, Queens, and Nassau, Soffolk, and Westchester counties), as well as a mortgage broker network spanning about a dozen states and Washington, DC. It attracts deposits from individuals and area businesses by offering CDs and checking, savings, and retirement accounts. With these funds, it primarily writes loans and invests in mortgage-backed securities. Subsidiary AF Insurance Agency sells annuities and life and property/casualty coverage.

	Annual Growth	12/03	12/04	12/05	12/06	12/07
Assets ($ mil.)	(0.8%)	22,457.7	23,415.9	22,380.3	21,554.5	21,719.4
Net income ($ mil.)	(10.8%)	196.9	219.5	233.8	174.9	124.8
Market value ($ mil.)	3.4%	1,951.0	2,939.3	3,086.0	2,960.7	2,227.6
Employees	(8.1%)	—	—	1,770	1,626	—

ASTRAZENECA PHARMACEUTICALS LP

1800 Concord Pike
Wilmington, DE 19850
Phone: 302-886-3000
Fax: 302-886-2972
Web: www.astrazeneca-us.com

CEO: Tony P. Zook
CFO: David V. Elkins
HR: Penny Stoker
FYE: December 31
Type: Subsidiary

Whether you've got heartburn or high cholesterol from your addiction to chili cheese dogs, AstraZeneca Pharmaceuticals (which does business as AstraZeneca US) can help. The company, a subsidiary of global druggernaut AstraZeneca, is the fifth-largest drug company in the US. Its sales represent about 5% of all the drugs sold in the US and 45% of its parent company's revenues. AstraZeneca US' treatments focus on five therapeutic areas: cardiovascular and metabolic, gastrointestinal, infection, neuroscience, oncology, and respiratory. Its best-known products include Nexium (acid reflux), Seroquel (anti-psychotic), Toprol XL (high blood pressure), and Crestor (high cholesterol).

ASTRO-MED, INC.

NASDAQ (GM): ALOT

600 E. Greenwich Ave.
West Warwick, RI 02893
Phone: 401-828-4000
Fax: 401-822-2430
Web: www.astro-medinc.com

CEO: Albert W. Ondis
CFO: Joseph P. O'Connell
HR: Marcia Ryter
FYE: January 31
Type: Public

Astro-Med holds a high-tech trident. The company operates three divisions: QuickLabel Systems, Test and Measurement, and Grass-Telefactor. Astro-Med's QuickLabel Systems division makes digital color label printers, bar code printers, automatic labelers, and printer consumables. The company's Grass-Telefactor Group makes EEG equipment, instruments for monitoring such conditions as epilepsy and sleep disorders, and biomedical research supplies. Its Test and Measurement division makes products that record and monitor data for customers in the aerospace, automotive, power, and telecommunications industries. Chairman and CEO Albert Ondis owns about 30% of Astro-Med.

	Annual Growth	1/04	1/05	1/06	1/07	1/08
Sales ($ mil.)	6.7%	55.8	56.0	59.3	65.5	72.4
Net income ($ mil.)	7.7%	3.2	2.7	2.5	6.1	4.3
Market value ($ mil.)	7.1%	51.6	40.0	43.8	70.7	67.8
Employees	5.3%	—	361	375	400	—

An in-depth profile of this company is available to Hoover's Online members at hoovers.com.

ASTRONAUTICS CORPORATION OF AMERICA

4115 N. Teutonia Ave.
Milwaukee, WI 53209
Phone: 414-449-4000
Fax: 414-447-8231
Web: www.astronautics.com

CEO: Ronald E. Zelazo
CFO: Steven Givant
HR: –
FYE: May 31
Type: Private

Sometimes it's hard to know which end is up when you're in an airplane or spacecraft. That's where Astronautics Corporation of America comes in. The company makes, maintains, and repairs electronic components and systems that enable users — whether in airplanes, ships, land vehicles, or spacecraft — to orient themselves in time and space. Products include attitude director indicators, horizontal situation indicators, electronic flight instruments, mission and display processors, and inertial navigation systems (through subsidiary Kearfott Guidance & Navigation Corp.). Astronautics was founded in 1959.

	Annual Growth	5/03	5/04	5/05	5/06	5/07
Est. sales ($ mil.)	—	—	—	—	—	201.2
Employees	—	—	—	—	—	2,160

ASTRONICS CORPORATION

NASDAQ (GM): ATRO

130 Commerce Way
East Aurora, NY 14052
Phone: 716-805-1599
Fax: 716-805-1286
Web: www.astronics.com

CEO: Peter J. Gundermann
CFO: David C. Burney
HR: Jill Draper
FYE: December 31
Type: Public

Lights in the sky that aren't UFOs or shooting stars may well be the work of Astronics. The company makes external and internal lighting systems, as well as power generation and distribution technology, for commercial, general aviation, and military aircraft. Products include cabin emergency lighting systems (floor and seat escape path markers, exit locators), cockpit lighting systems (avionics keyboards, ambient light sensors, annunciator panels, electronic dimmers), and formation lighting systems (external lights). Astronics' lighting systems are made by the company's Luminescent Systems unit.

	Annual Growth	12/03	12/04	12/05	12/06	12/07
Sales ($ mil.)	47.7%	33.2	34.7	74.3	110.8	158.2
Net income ($ mil.)	93.4%	1.1	(0.7)	2.2	5.7	15.4
Market value ($ mil.)	78.2%	28.3	29.8	67.7	111.8	285.9
Employees	12.4%	—	—	700	787	

ASURION

648 Grassmere Park Dr., Ste. 300
Nashville, TN 37211
Phone: 615-837-3000
Fax: 615-837-3001
Web: www.asurion.com

CEO: Bret Comolli
CFO: Gerald Risk
HR: Vijay Velamoor
FYE: –
Type: Private

Dead battery? Empty tank? Asurion assures that you won't be stranded. The company provides customer contact and support services, including roadside assistance to stranded motorists, for the wireless phone industry. It also offers wireless equipment leasing and insurance services, as well as inventory management programs. Asurion serves about 45 million end users through its partnerships with such wireless carriers as ALLTEL, T-Mobile, and Cingular Wireless (now AT&T Mobility). In 2006, Asurion merged with former DST subsidiary lock/line, which processes warranty claims for telecom companies.

A.S.V., INC.

840 Lily Ln.
Grand Rapids, MN 55744
Phone: 218-327-3434
Fax: 218-327-9122
Web: asvi.com

CEO: Richard A. (Dick) Benson
CFO: Thomas R. Karges
HR: –
FYE: December 31
Type: Subsidiary

To everything there is a season, and A.S.V. has a vehicle for all seasons. The company uses rubber track suspension systems that make its vehicles operable in mud and snow and on slippery slopes and rough terrain. Its Posi-Track crawler/trailer models can be used instead of skid-steer vehicles and small dozers for construction needs, and in agricultural uses as small tractors. A.S.V. also makes loaders; its Loegering subsidiary makes bolt on/bolt off track systems that can convert most skid-steers from wheels to rubber tracks. Early in 2008 the company was acquired by mining equipment manufacturer Terex in a deal valued at about $488 million.

	Annual Growth	12/02	12/03	12/04	12/05	12/06
Sales ($ mil.)	53.6%	44.2	96.4	160.9	245.1	246.1
Net income ($ mil.)	99.1%	1.4	8.7	17.2	27.9	22.0
Employees	26.2%	112	151	224	264	284

ASYST TECHNOLOGIES, INC.

NASDAQ (GM): ASYT

46897 Bayside Pkwy.
Fremont, CA 94538
Phone: 510-661-5000
Fax: 510-661-5166
Web: www.asyst.com

CEO: Stephen S. (Steve) Schwartz
CFO: Michael A. Sicuro
HR: –
FYE: March 31
Type: Public

Whether or not cleanliness is next to godliness, it's non-negotiable for manufacturers of LCDs, semiconductors, and other precision components. Asyst Technologies is a top maker of automation and isolation systems that help chip factories run smoothly and keep semiconductor wafers ultraclean during processing. Its standard mechanical interface (SMIF) systems isolate semiconductor wafers during the manufacturing process. The company's SMART-Traveler Systems track wafers with radio-frequency tags and software. Asyst gets about four-fifths of its sales from customers outside the US.

	Annual Growth	3/04	3/05	3/06	3/07	3/08
Sales ($ mil.)	11.0%	301.6	613.0	459.2	492.5	457.2
Net income ($ mil.)	—	(83.4)	(17.5)	(0.1)	0.0	(13.7)
Market value ($ mil.)	(18.8%)	403.3	228.9	504.5	346.6	175.2
Employees	25.2%	556	894	1,042	1,218	1,367

A.T. CROSS COMPANY

AMEX: ATX

1 Albion Rd.
Lincoln, RI 02865
Phone: 401-333-1200
Fax: 401-334-2861
Web: www.cross.com

CEO: David G. (Dave) Whalen
CFO: Kevin F. Mahoney
HR: Tina C. Benik
FYE: December 31
Type: Public

Other than a diploma, what marks a high school graduation better than the gift of a Cross pen? Known for its tasteful writing instruments since 1846, A.T. Cross makes ball-point, rolling ball, and fountain pens, as well as mechanical pencils. Its writing instruments are made from high-quality metals (brass, gold, and silver) and other finishes (lacquer, onyx, wood, and marble). Cross also makes desk sets, watches, and accessories (key rings, letter openers, money clips). Its products are sold throughout the US in retail stores (gift stores, department stores, jewelers, and office supply stores) and through its Web site. Cross also operates an optical segment, Costa Del Mar Sunglasses, acquired in 2003.

	Annual Growth	12/03	12/04	12/05	12/06	12/07
Sales ($ mil.)	4.9%	125.3	129.5	129.1	139.3	151.9
Net income ($ mil.)	38.9%	1.8	(0.9)	0.4	3.3	6.7
Market value ($ mil.)	7.5%	88.3	65.2	53.0	101.8	118.1
Employees	13.1%	—	—	704	900	900

A.T. KEARNEY, INC.

222 W. Adams St.
Chicago, IL 60606
Phone: 312-648-0111
Fax: 312-223-6200
Web: www.atkearney.com

CEO: Paul A. Laudicina
CFO: Dan A. DeCanniere
HR: Peter (Pete) Pesce
FYE: December 31
Type: Private

With roots going back to the founding of McKinsey & Company in 1926, A.T. Kearney has established a place for itself in the management consulting pantheon. Today's A.T. Kearney operates from offices in more than 30 countries around the world. It offers consulting in a variety of areas, including growth strategies, IT strategies, and supply chain management. Clients have come from a wide range of industries, including automotive, financial services, health care, and utilities. A.T. Kearney is owned by its management team. The consulting firm took its current name in 1946 from that of Andrew T. Kearney, one of McKinsey's first partners.

	Annual Growth	12/02	12/03	12/04	12/05	12/06
Sales ($ mil.)	(5.6%)	1,005.0	846.0	806.0	700.0	798.0
Employees	(15.9%)	5,000	4,000	—	2,500	2,500

AT&T INC.

NYSE: T

175 E. Houston
San Antonio, TX 78205
Phone: 210-821-4105
Fax: 210-351-2071
Web: www.att.com

CEO: Randall L. Stephenson
CFO: Richard G. (Rick) Lindner
HR: William A. (Bill) Blase Jr.
FYE: December 31
Type: Public

AT&T is the industry-leading provider of voice, IP-voice, video, and data communications services. Its network spans the globe reaching every major country and metropolitan area through its subsidiaries and affliates. In the US AT&T provides telephone service to 22 US states; key markets include California, Illinois, and Texas. In addition to serving millions of consumers with phone and Internet service, the company's client list includes all of the FORTUNE 1000. AT&T is also the nation's leading wireless carrier. AT&T Mobility (formerly Cingular Wireless) provides cell phone and mobile data services to about 70 million subscribers in the US.

	Annual Growth	12/03	12/04	12/05	12/06	12/07
Sales ($ mil.)	30.6%	40,843.0	40,787.0	43,862.0	63,055.0	118,928.0
Net income ($ mil.)	8.9%	8,505.0	5,887.0	4,786.0	7,356.0	11,951.0
Market value ($ mil.)	30.7%	86,167.5	85,064.5	94,944.9	223,035.2	251,169.7
Employees	28.1%	—	—	189,000	302,000	310,000

AT&T MOBILITY LLC

Glenridge Highlands Two, 5565 Glenridge Connector
Atlanta, GA 30342
Phone: 404-236-6000
Fax: 404-236-6005
Web: www.wireless.att.com

CEO: Ralph de la Vega
CFO: Peter A. (Pete) Ritcher
HR: Rickford D. (Rick) Bradley
FYE: December 31
Type: Subsidiary

The leading wireless voice and data carrier in the US, AT&T Mobility has more than 70 million subscribers via its ALLOVER-branded network. The company, which accounts for more than one-third of parent company AT&T's business, provides a full range of wireless voice, messaging, and data services to consumer and enterprise customers. AT&T Mobility's business services include high-speed wireless Internet access through its BroadbandConnect service. AT&T Mobility provides extensive international network coverage for its subscribers in about 190 countries across the seven continents.

	Annual Growth	12/02	12/03	12/04	12/05	12/06
Sales ($ mil.)	26.3%	14,727.0	15,483.0	19,436.0	34,433.0	37,500.0
Employees	23.7%	33,800	39,400	70,300	64,000	—

ATARI, INC.

NASDAQ (GM): ATAR

417 5th Ave.
New York, NY 10016
Phone: 212-726-6500
Fax: –
Web: www.atari.com

CEO: Jim Wilson
CFO: Arturo Rodriguez
HR: –
FYE: March 31
Type: Public

Atari, Inc. — formerly Infogrames, Inc., and currently the US division of French software maker Infogrames Entertainment (IESA) — hopes to recapture magic from the past. The company adopted the classic Atari moniker in 2003 with hopes of boosting brand recognition and reviving slumping sales. Atari publishes titles such as *Dragonball Z, Alone in the Dark, Asteroids, Neverwinter Nights, Godzilla, Dungeons and Dragons, Rollercoaster Tycoon,* and *Enter the Matrix,* as well as other titles. The company's games are played on PCs, as well as Sony, Nintendo, and Microsoft gaming consoles. IESA owns 51% of Atari.

	Annual Growth	3/04	3/05	3/06	3/07	3/08
Sales ($ mil.)	(35.7%)	468.9	395.2	218.7	122.3	80.1
Net income ($ mil.)	—	0.8	5.7	(69.0)	(69.7)	(23.6)
Employees	—	—	—	329	—	—

ATC GROUP SERVICES INC.

600 W. Cummings Park, Ste. 5500
Woburn, MA 01801
Phone: 781-932-9400
Fax: 781-932-6211
Web: www.atcassociates.com

CEO: Robert (Bobby) Toups
CFO: Paul J. Grillo
HR: Staci Landress
FYE: Last day in February
Type: Private

ATC Group Services cleans up other companies' messes. The firm, which does business as ATC Associates, offers environmental, health and safety, and construction testing and engineering services (including lead-based paint and asbestos management) to clients in the petroleum, health care, construction, retail, and government sectors, among others. ATC Associates also provides environmental and health and safety training courses, standard or customized, to help students identify, assess, and mitigate environmental hazards. The company operates from some 65 offices in nearly 40 states in the US. ATC Associates was founded in 1982.

	Annual Growth	2/03	2/04	2/05	2/06	2/07
Est. sales ($ mil.)	—	—	—	—	—	126.0
Employees	—	—	—	—	—	1,738

ATC HEALTHCARE, INC.

AMEX: AHN

1983 Marcus Ave.
Lake Success, NY 11042
Phone: 516-750-1600
Fax: 516-750-1755
Web: www.atchealthcare.com

CEO: David Savitsky
CFO: David Kimbell
HR: –
FYE: February 28
Type: Public

ATC Healthcare helps keep hospitals staffed around the clock. The company provides temporary medical personnel to hospitals, nursing homes, and managed care facilities, as well as insurance companies, schools, and community health centers. Its employees include nurses, physical therapists, radiology technicians, and phlebotomists, as well as medical administrative staff. Through its Travel Nurse Program, the company recruits nurses and other health care professionals worldwide for long-term assignments in the US. Established in 1978, ATC operates through a network of more than 50 offices across about 30 US states.

	Annual Growth	2/03	2/04	2/05	2/06	*2/07
Sales ($ mil.)	(11.9%)	148.7	130.4	67.9	71.5	89.4
Net income ($ mil.)	—	(2.8)	(6.2)	(10.4)	(2.3)	(2.2)
Employees	(16.4%)	—	—	10,122	—	7,074

*Most recent year available

ATCO RUBBER PRODUCTS, INC.

7101 Atco Dr.
Fort Worth, TX 76118
Phone: 817-595-2894
Fax: 800-366-3539
Web: www.atcoflex.com

CEO: Ramesh Bhatia
CFO: –
HR: Bill Lightsey
FYE: December 31
Type: Private

Even when things heat up, ATCO Rubber Products can keep its cool and remain flexible. The company makes flexible ducts used in commercial and residential heating, cooling, and ventilation systems. It operates about 15 manufacturing sites in the US and international sites in the Netherlands, the United Arab Emirates, and India. ATCO Rubber Products was founded in 1961.

	Annual Growth	12/03	12/04	12/05	12/06	12/07
Est. sales ($ mil.)	—	—	—	—	—	112.5
Employees	—	—	—	—	—	1,200

ATHENAHEALTH, INC.

NASDAQ (GM): ATHN

311 Arsenal St.
Watertown, MA 02472
Phone: 888-652-8200
Fax: 617-402-1099
Web: www.athenahealth.com

CEO: Jonathan S. Bush
CFO: Carl B. Byers
HR: Amy Pooser
FYE: December 31
Type: Public

athenahealth knows that managing physician practices can result in a splitting headache, especially when patients are late paying bills. The company provides health care organizations with Web-based software and services (athenaCollector) that streamline practice management, workflow routing, revenue management, patient information management, billing and collection, and other health care management tasks. athenahealth also offers a clinical cycle management service (athenaClinicals) that automates and manages medical record-related functions for physician practices.

	Annual Growth	12/03	12/04	12/05	12/06	12/07
Sales ($ mil.)	37.4%	—	38.9	53.5	75.8	100.8
Net income ($ mil.)	—	—	(3.6)	(11.4)	(9.2)	(3.5)
Market value ($ mil.)	—	—	—	—	—	1,164.1
Employees	2.1%	—	357	—	—	380

ATHEROGENICS, INC.

NASDAQ (GM): AGIX

8995 Westside Pkwy.
Alpharetta, GA 30004
Phone: 678-336-2500
Fax: 678-336-2501
Web: www.atherogenics.com

CEO: Russell M. Medford
CFO: Mark P. Colonnese
HR: Jody Farmer
FYE: December 31
Type: Public

AtheroGenics is all about taming the inflamed beast. The pharmaceutical company develops drug candidates for the treatment of chronic inflammatory diseases, including diabetes and coronary heart disease. Its lead candidate, AGI-1067, is an oral drug being evaluated for its ability to improve blood sugar levels. Development of the therapeutic compound is ongoing despite disappointing results from a major AGI-1067 clinical trial, which led to the termination of a licensing agreement with AstraZeneca and an organizational restructuring that cut AtheroGenics' workforce in half in 2007. The company's alliance with Astellas Pharma on a second anti-inflammatory candidate, organ transplant drug AGI-1096, also ended.

	Annual Growth	12/03	12/04	12/05	12/06	12/07
Sales ($ mil.)	65.0%	—	—	—	31.7	52.3
Net income ($ mil.)	—	—	—	—	(67.3)	(49.5)
Market value ($ mil.)	(96.2%)	—	—	—	391.0	15.0
Employees	—	—	—	—	—	—

ATHEROS COMMUNICATIONS, INC.

NASDAQ (GS): ATHR

5480 Great America Pkwy.
Santa Clara, CA 95054
Phone: 408-773-5200
Fax: 408-773-9940
Web: www.atheros.com

CEO: Craig H. Barratt
CFO: Jack R. Lazar
HR: Edward L. Martin
FYE: December 31
Type: Public

Atheros Communications builds high-speed connections right through the ether. Its radio-frequency transceiver chipsets combine features such as a radio, power amplifier, low-noise amplifier, and a media access control (MAC) processor onto just two or three chips, eliminating the need for bulkier components in wireless networking equipment. The company's customers include Apple, Cisco Systems, Dell, Fujitsu, Hewlett-Packard, Hon Hai Precision Industry (25% of sales), IBM, Microsoft, QUALCOMM, Sony, Toshiba, and UTStarcom. The fabless semiconductor company was started by faculty members from Stanford and Berkeley. Nearly all sales are to customers in Asia, principally in Taiwan and China.

	Annual Growth	12/03	12/04	12/05	12/06	12/07
Sales ($ mil.)	47.8%	87.4	169.6	183.5	301.7	417.0
Net income ($ mil.)	—	(13.2)	10.8	16.7	18.7	40.0
Market value ($ mil.)	54.0%	—	491.5	647.3	1,157.8	1,793.6
Employees	47.8%	184	260	327	660	878

ATHLETA CORPORATION

1450 Technology Ln., Ste. 150
Petaluma, CA 94954
Phone: 707-559-2200
Fax: 707-769-2610
Web: www.athleta.com

CEO: Joseph E. Teno Jr.
CFO: Will Dargie
HR: –
FYE: December 31
Type: Private

Athleta Corporation is all about being comfortable while you work up a sweat. The company makes and sells women's athletic wear (tops, pants, sports bras, swimwear, hoodies and jackets, shoes) and related accessories (fitness gear bags, socks, hats) through its catalog and Web site. As the company has grown, Athleta has debuted more sportswear including dresses as well as extensive lines of accessories and lifestyle items, such as CamelBak hydration gear and sports watches. The company was founded in 1997 and more than 90% of the staff are women.

	Annual Growth	12/03	12/04	12/05	12/06	12/07
Est. sales ($ mil.)	—	—	—	—	—	37.0
Employees	—	—	—	—	—	110

ATKINS NUTRITIONALS, INC.

105 Maxess Rd.
Melville, NY 11747
Phone: 631-953-4000
Fax: 631-953-4001
Web: atkins.com

CEO: Christopher H. (Toby) Smith
CFO: James J. (Jim) Allwein
HR: Joseph J. Conklin
FYE: December 31
Type: Private

Atkins pushed beef off its plate in favor of a protein shake. Atkins Nutritionals, which once touted the meat-heavy Atkins diet, makes about 60 nutrition bars, shakes, ice creams, and candies. This number is down from the more than 300 items the company offered at the height of the low-carbohydrate diet craze. Atkins no longer offers low-carb dieting advice but instead focuses on "nutrition" on its Web site. The company's Atkins Advantage food products are sold nationwide. They can be found at some 30,000 US retail outlets, including Wal-Mart, Target, and Walgreens, as well as in many grocery stores and chains.

ATKINSON, MULLEN & ROSSO

7 Campus Blvd.
Newtown Square, PA 19073
Phone: 610-359-5992
Fax: 610-359-5990
Web: www.aandmtravel.com

CEO: John J. Mullen
CFO: –
HR: –
FYE: December 31
Type: Partnership

Atkinson, Mullen & Rosso provides travel arrangements for groups going by land as well as by sea. The company books resorts in Bermuda; Branson, Missouri; the Caribbean; Costa Rica; Hawaii; and cruises aboard Carnival and Norwegian lines as well as river cruises in Europe. It partners with Apple Vacations (which it owns), USA 3000, Secrets Resorts, and Sunscape Resorts to offer families, companies, churches, and other groups deals on travel packages throughout the world. The company is a joint partnership between Atkinson & Mullen Travel and Alessandro Rosso Incentive.

	Annual Growth	12/03	12/04	12/05	12/06	12/07
Est. sales ($ mil.)	—	—	—	—	—	58.8
Employees	—	—	—	—	—	375

ATLANTA NATIONAL LEAGUE BASEBALL CLUB, INC.

755 Hank Aaron Dr. SW
Atlanta, GA 30315
Phone: 404-522-7630
Fax: 404-614-7391
Web: atlanta.braves.mlb.com

CEO: Terence F. (Terry) McGuirk
CFO: –
HR: –
FYE: December 31
Type: Subsidiary

America may be the land of the free, but Atlanta is the home of the Braves. Atlanta National League Baseball Club operates the Atlanta Braves professional baseball franchise, winner of three World Series championships. A charter member of the National League, the team was formed as the Boston Red Stockings in 1871 (it became the Braves in 1912) and moved to Milwaukee in the 1950s before settling in Atlanta in 1966. Under the ownership of media mogul Ted Turner, the Braves won five pennants during the 1990s and cemented a place in the hearts of Atlanta sports fans. Liberty Media, through Liberty Capital Group, acquired the team from Time Warner's Turner Broadcasting unit in 2007.

	Annual Growth	12/02	12/03	12/04	12/05	12/06
Sales ($ mil.)	—	—	—	—	—	183.0
Employees	—	—	—	—	—	—

ATLANTIC AMERICAN CORPORATION

NASDAQ (GM): AAME

4370 Peachtree Rd., NE
Atlanta, GA 30319
Phone: 404-266-5500
Fax: 404-266-5702
Web: www.atlam.com

CEO: Hilton H. Howell Jr.
CFO: John G. Sample Jr.
HR: Barbara B. Snyder
FYE: December 31
Type: Public

Atlantic American can get you a peach of an insurance deal. Through its subsidiaries, the company sells a mix of property/casualty, health, and life insurance in the southern US. Its Bankers Fidelity Life Insurance subsidiary provides life and supplemental health insurance. Medicare supplement products account for more than 80% of the division's premiums. Its American Southern subsidiary offer personal and commercial automobile and property coverage. It also provides general commercial liability insurance. Its products are targeted at large motor pools and fleets owned by local governments. Chairman Mack Robinson and his family hold about two-thirds of the company's stock.

	Annual Growth	12/03	12/04	12/05	12/06	12/07
Assets ($ mil.)	0.8%	443.5	470.5	460.4	458.6	458.3
Net income ($ mil.)	1.8%	6.8	5.0	(3.2)	8.9	7.3
Market value ($ mil.)	(16.8%)	63.6	65.8	57.7	63.6	30.5
Employees	—	—	—	275	—	—

ATLANTIC AUTOMOTIVE CORP.

23 Walker Ave.
Baltimore, MD 21208
Phone: 410-602-6177
Fax: 410-602-2074
Web: www.mileone.com

CEO: Steven B. Fader
CFO: Louis S. (Lou) Richards
HR: –
FYE: December 31
Type: Private

Atlantic Automotive is counting on Mile One to carry it far. Founded in 1996, the company has unified its businesses under the Mile One banner. The company sells about 30 auto brands at about 70 locations in the Baltimore-Washington, DC, area that operate as the Heritage, Herb Gordon, Hall, and Tischer auto groups, as well as the Baltimore Area Saturn Dealers and MotorWorld Automotive Group in Wilkes-Barre, Pennsylvania. In the Baltimore area, Atlantic Automotive also operates six collision-repair centers. The company rents cars through Allstate at nine locations in the vicinity.

	Annual Growth	12/03	12/04	12/05	12/06	12/07
Est. sales ($ mil.)	—	—	—	—	—	598.6
Employees	—	—	—	—	—	1,800

ATLANTIC BANCGROUP, INC.

NASDAQ (CM): ATBC

1315 S. 3rd St.
Jacksonville Beach, FL 32250
Phone: 904-247-9494
Fax: 904-247-9402
Web: www.oceansidebank.com

CEO: Barry W. Chandler
CFO: David L. Young
HR: –
FYE: December 31
Type: Public

Even in Florida you can't always bank on sunshine, so Atlantic BancGroup can help you save for a rainy day. Atlantic BancGroup is the holding company for Oceanside Bank, a community bank with about five branches in and around Jacksonville. The locally operated institution targets individuals and small to midsized businesses, offering deposit products such as checking and savings accounts, IRAs, and CDs. Loans include real estate mortgages, commercial loans, and consumer loans. More than 90% of Oceanside Bank's loan portfolio is secured by real estate mortgages.

	Annual Growth	12/03	12/04	12/05	12/06	12/07
Assets ($ mil.)	15.8%	145.6	184.3	213.9	243.5	261.4
Net income ($ mil.)	8.8%	1.0	1.2	1.5	1.9	1.4
Market value ($ mil.)	(1.5%)	23.1	33.8	36.2	41.6	21.7
Employees	9.2%	—	—	47	51	56

ATLANTIC CITY ELECTRIC COMPANY

5100 Harding Hwy.
Mays Landing, NJ 08330
Phone: 800-375-7117
Fax: 302-283-6090
Web: www.atlanticcityelectric.com

CEO: Kenneth J. (Ken) Parker
CFO: Joseph M. (Joe) Rigby
HR: Ernest L. Jenkins
FYE: December 31
Type: Subsidiary

Atlantic City Electric makes America's favorite playground shine in the nighttime. The Pepco Holdings' utility generates, transmits, and distributes electricity to 544,000 homes and businesses in southern New Jersey. Atlantic City Electric operates more than 11,000 miles of transmission and distribution lines. The utility has sold most of its power generation assets, but it still has interests in selected fossil-fueled power plants. Atlantic City Electric's electricity delivery operations are regulated by the New Jersey Board of Public Utilities.

	Annual Growth	12/03	12/04	12/05	12/06	12/07
Est. sales ($ mil.)	—	—	—	—	—	1,373.3
Employees	—	—	—	—	—	588

An in-depth profile of this company is available to Hoover's Online members at hoovers.com.

187

ATLANTIC COAST FEDERAL CORPORATION

NASDAQ (GM): ACFC

505 Haines Ave.
Waycross, GA 31501
Phone: 912-283-4711
Fax: 912-284-2284
Web: www.acfederal.net

CEO: Robert J. Larison Jr.
CFO: Dawna R. Miller
HR: –
FYE: December 31
Type: Public

Not happy simply coasting, Atlantic Coast Federal Corporation works hard as the holding company for Atlantic Coast Bank (formerly Atlantic Coast Federal), a savings bank with more than a dozen branches in southeastern Georgia and the Jacksonville, Florida, metro area. Funds from deposits are used to make loans. The lending portfolio is dominated by mortgage loans (more than 50%); it also includes other real estate and construction loans, as well as consumer and business loans. Atlantic Coast Bank was established in 1939 as a credit union that served Atlantic Coast Line Railroad employees.

	Annual Growth	12/03	12/04	12/05	12/06	12/07
Assets ($ mil.)	16.9%	498.4	637.7	743.8	843.1	931.0
Net income ($ mil.)	(29.3%)	4.4	3.2	4.7	5.1	1.1
Market value ($ mil.)	(6.7%)	—	200.3	198.8	270.0	162.5
Employees	6.9%	—	—	160	—	183

ATLANTIC EXPRESS TRANSPORTATION CORP.

7 North St.
Staten Island, NY 10302
Phone: 718-442-7000
Fax: 718-442-7672
Web: www.atlanticexpress.com

CEO: Domenic Gatto
CFO: Nathan Schlenker
HR: –
FYE: July 30*
Type: Private

Driving with thousands of schoolchildren in the back seat, or rows of seats, doesn't bother Atlantic Express Transportation. The company serves about 115 school districts throughout the US with a fleet of some 5,200 vehicles. School bus services account for about 90% of the company's sales. In addition, Atlantic Express provides paratransit services (transportation of people with disabilities) in New York City and offers charter, express, and fixed-route bus services, mainly as a contractor for New York's Metropolitan Transportation Authority. Investment firm Greenwich Street Capital owns a controlling stake in Atlantic Express, which was founded in 1968.

	Annual Growth	6/03	6/04	6/05	6/06	6/07
Sales ($ mil.)	5.3%	349.0	363.5	363.7	414.1	428.8
Net income ($ mil.)	—	(20.5)	56.8	(42.4)	(30.0)	(17.1)
Employees	(2.2%)	8,300	—	—	8,100	7,600

*Fiscal year change

ATLANTIC HEALTH SYSTEM, INC.

325 Columbia Tpke., 2nd Fl.
Florham Park, NJ 07932
Phone: 973-660-3100
Fax: 973-660-9065
Web: www.atlantichealth.org

CEO: Joseph A. (Joe) Trunfio
CFO: Kevin Shanley
HR: Andrew L. Kovach
FYE: December 31
Type: Not-for-profit

Atlantic Health System (AHS) manages two acute care hospitals providing general medical and surgical services in northern New Jersey. Its Morristown Memorial Hospital has some 600 beds, serves as a regional trauma center, and provides specialty care in a number of areas, including cancer (through the Carol G. Simon Cancer Center); pediatric care (through Goryeb Children's Hospital); and cardiac care (through Gagnon Heart Hospital). A second facility, Overlook Hospital, has about 500 beds. In 2007 the not-for-profit system sold its money-losing Mountainside Hospital to Merit Health Systems, a Kentucky-based for-profit hospital operator.

	Annual Growth	12/03	12/04	12/05	12/06	12/07
Est. sales ($ mil.)	—	—	—	—	—	883.0
Employees	—	—	—	—	—	8,000

ATLANTIC METHANOL PRODUCTION COMPANY LLC

12600 Northborough Dr., Ste. 150
Houston, TX 77067
Phone: 281-872-8324
Fax: 281-872-1084
Web: www.atlanticmethanol.com

CEO: Paul Moschell
CFO: Larry Seidel
HR: Budd Buschmann
FYE: December 31
Type: Joint venture

Atlantic Methanol Production Company must like to think proverbially, because "Waste not, want not" seems to be its motto. The company tries not to waste the natural gas that is a by-product of parent company Samedan Oil's production process. Atlantic Methanol was founded in 1997 as a vehicle to make use of the nearly 100 million cubic feet of natural gas being expent each day off the coast of Equitorial Guinea. It began production four years later. Samedan (a subsidiary of Noble Energy) and Marathon Oil own 45% each, with the state-controlled Guinea Equatorial Oil & Gas owning the remaining 10%.

ATLANTIC RECORDS GROUP

1290 Avenue of the Americas
New York, NY 10104
Phone: 212-707-2000
Fax: 212-405-5475
Web: www.atlanticrecords.com

CEO: Craig Kallman
CFO: –
HR: –
FYE: September 30
Type: Business segment

This record company makes sure there's music to please fans from sea to shinning sea. Atlantic Records Group is one of the top purveyors of pop music in the US, promoting such artists as Diddy, Missy Elliott, Jason Mraz, and Rob Thomas. It distributes such imprints as Bad Boy Records (50%-owned with Bad Boy Worldwide Entertainment) and Elektra Records, as well as the venerable Atlantic Records label. A 2005 restructuring plan included the consolidation of the Elektra Records and Atlantic Records labels. Music industry mogul Ahmet Ertegun and partner Herb Abramson started Atlantic in 1947. Today it is one of the flagship label divisions of Warner Music Group. Ertegun died in late 2006.

	Annual Growth	9/03	9/04	9/05	9/06	9/07
Est. sales ($ mil.)	—	—	—	—	—	47.9
Employees	—	—	—	—	—	400

ATLANTIC SOUTHEAST AIRLINES, INC.

100 Hartsfield Centre Pkwy., Ste. 800
Atlanta, GA 30354
Phone: 404-766-1400
Fax: 404-209-0162
Web: www.flyasa.com

CEO: Jerry C. Atkin
CFO: Bradford R. Rich
HR: Kevin Wade
FYE: December 31
Type: Subsidiary

It's all about connections for Atlantic Southeast Airlines (ASA). Operating as a Delta Connection regional carrier, the company flies to smaller markets on behalf of Delta Air Lines, primarily from Delta's hubs in Atlanta and Cincinnati. The carrier serves about 145 destinations, mainly east of the Mississippi in the US, but also in western states and in Canada, Mexico, and the Caribbean. It maintains a fleet of about 160 aircraft, nearly all of which are Canadair regional jets (CRJs), made by Bombardier. ASA is a subsidiary of SkyWest, which bought the company from Delta in 2005.

ATLANTIC TELE-NETWORK, INC.

NASDAQ (GM): ATNI

10 Derby Sq.	CEO: Michael T. Prior
Salem, MA 01970	CFO: Justin D. Benincasa
Phone: 978-619-1300	HR: –
Fax: 978-744-3951	FYE: December 31
Web: www.atni.com	Type: Public

The Big Banana in Guyana's rain forests is Atlantic Tele-Network (ATN). The company owns 80% of incumbent carrier Guyana Telephone & Telegraph (GT&T). GT&T operates more than 120,000 fixed access lines and has about 270,000 cellular subscribers. About 16% of the company's revenue comes from international traffic from US-based carrier Verizon Communications; GT&T has agreements with other carriers including IDT Corporation. ATN also owns Choice Communications, which provides Internet access and wireless cable TV services in the US Virgin Islands. In 2006 ATN purchased Vermont-based communications provider SoVerNet. Chairman Cornelius Prior owns 40% of the firm.

	Annual Growth	12/03	12/04	12/05	12/06	12/07
Sales ($ mil.)	22.4%	83.3	89.3	102.3	155.4	186.7
Net income ($ mil.)	32.8%	12.2	12.1	13.6	23.5	37.9
Market value ($ mil.)	74.0%	56.1	65.1	208.9	444.5	514.2
Employees	10.3%	—	700	853	852	—

ATLANTIC TOOL & DIE CO., INC.

19963 Progress Dr.	CEO: Frank Mehwald
Strongsville, OH 44149	CFO: –
Phone: 440-238-6931	HR: –
Fax: 440-238-2210	FYE: December 31
	Type: Private

Atlantic Tool & Die found a company to die for when it hooked up with Honda in the late 1980s. The metal stamping company serves major automakers, including Honda of America Manufacturing in Marysville, Ohio. Founded in 1937, Atlantic Tool & Die manufactures metal stampings and assemblies from its five facilities in Alabama, Ohio, and Texas. The company established its main facility in Strongsville, Ohio in 1967. Atlantic Tool & Die supplies automotive parts worldwide on the just-in-time delivery system. Under the leadership of Frank Mehwald, the company has grown from a small-time die maker into a major parts supplier.

	Annual Growth	12/03	12/04	12/05	12/06	12/07
Est. sales ($ mil.)	—	—	—	—	—	40.8
Employees	—	—	—	—	—	476

ATLANTIS PLASTICS, INC.

NASDAQ (GM): ATPL

1870 The Exchange, Ste. 200	CEO: V.M. (Bud) Philbrook
Atlanta, GA 30339	CFO: Paul G. Saari
Phone: 770-953-4567	HR: Robert W. (Bob) Henson
Fax: 770-618-7080	FYE: December 31
Web: www.atlantisplastics.com	Type: Public

When fingered as a maker of quality films, Atlantis Plastics willingly takes the wrap. The company's plastic films division makes stretch film used to wrap pallets of goods. It also makes laminating, converted, and embossed films used to make packaging and institutional products such as aprons and tablecloths. Another division, which sells to customers such as Whirlpool, makes injection-molded thermoplastic parts used in appliances and cars. The company's profile extrusion unit produces custom-extruded parts for recreational vehicles, residential windows, and other trim applications. Atlantis Plastics announced in early 2008 that it would evaluate its options, which could possibly include a sale of the company.

	Annual Growth	12/02	12/03	12/04	12/05	*12/06
Sales ($ mil.)	13.9%	248.6	289.1	347.8	424.3	418.7
Net income ($ mil.)	—	2.4	8.2	11.5	6.7	(4.2)
Employees	0.1%	1,374	—	—	1,461	1,381

*Most recent year available

ATLAS AIR WORLDWIDE HOLDINGS, INC.

NASDAQ (GS): AAWW

2000 Westchester Ave.	CEO: William J. (Bill) Flynn
Purchase, NY 10577	CFO: Jason Grant
Phone: 914-701-8000	HR: James R. (Jim) Cato
Fax: 914-701-8444	FYE: December 31
Web: www.atlasair.com	Type: Public

Atlas carried the weight of the world, and Atlas Air Worldwide Holdings carries the freight of the world. Subsidiaries Atlas Air and Polar Air Cargo provide scheduled international freight services, mainly from the Asia/Pacific region, for leading freight forwarders, including DHL and Expeditors International. In addition, Atlas and Polar provide chartered freight services to commercial clients and the US military. Combined, the carriers maintain a fleet of about 40 Boeing 747 freighters. Atlas Air Worldwide Holdings also leases cargo planes to customers, mainly airlines, under aircraft, crew, maintenance, and insurance (ACMI) contracts. Its top ACMI client, Emirates, accounts for about 11% of overall sales.

	Annual Growth	12/03	12/04	12/05	12/06	12/07
Sales ($ mil.)	3.1%	1,383.7	1,414.7	1,617.9	1,476.3	1,562.7
Net income ($ mil.)	—	(101.0)	51.0	73.9	59.8	132.4
Market value ($ mil.)	35.4%	—	472.5	891.7	917.1	1,173.1
Employees	(6.3%)	—	—	—	1,840	1,725

ATLAS AMERICA, INC.

NASDAQ (GS): ATLS

Westpointe Corporate Ctr. 1, 1550 Coraopolis Heights Rd., 2nd Fl.	CEO: Edward E. Cohen
Moon Township, PA 15108	CFO: Matthew A. Jones
Phone: 412-262-2830	HR: –
Fax: 412-262-7430	FYE: December 31
Web: www.atlasamerica.com	Type: Public

Atlas America's production map can be found on the page titled Appalachia. The independent energy company is engaged in the development, production, and transportation of natural gas (and some oil) primarily in the Appalachian Basin. The company, which drills through partnerships, has proved reserves of 180.9 billion cu. ft. of natural gas equivalent. Atlas America has interests in 7,252 gross producing wells. Its natural gas transportation business is conducted through 15%-owned Atlas Pipeline Partners, which operates 3,265 miles of intrastate natural gas gathering systems in New York, Ohio, Oklahoma, Pennsylvania, and Texas. In 2007 the company agreed to buy DTE Gas & Oil for $1.2 billion.

	Annual Growth	9/03	9/04	9/05	*12/06	12/07
Sales ($ mil.)	83.9%	105.7	180.9	474.5	749.3	1,207.7
Net income ($ mil.)	26.2%	13.9	21.2	32.9	45.8	35.3
Market value ($ mil.)	131.0%	—	86.0	193.0	438.3	1,060.4
Employees	53.5%	—	—	340	517	801

*Fiscal year change

ATLAS COPCO NORTH AMERICA INC.

34 Maple Ave.	CEO: Mark Cohen
Pine Brook, NJ 07058	CFO: –
Phone: 973-439-3400	HR: –
Fax: 973-439-9455	FYE: May 31
Web: www.atlascopco.com	Type: Subsidiary

When you hear the phrase *Swedish American* you probably don't think construction and mining equipment, but maybe you should. Atlas Copco North America operates throughout the US, Canada, and Mexico for Swedish manufacturing giant Atlas Copco AG. The company's business includes manufacturing compressors and generators, construction and mining equipment, and power tools. Its line of power tools features air assembly tools, grinders, drills, air motors, hoists and trolleys, and related services. Demolition equipment, rock drills, blast hole drilling rigs, and exploration drilling tools comprise a list of its mining and construction products.

	Annual Growth	5/03	5/04	5/05	5/06	5/07
Est. sales ($ mil.)	—	—	—	—	—	499.3
Employees	—	—	—	—	—	5,114

ATLAS ENERGY RESOURCES, LLC

NYSE: ATN

Westpointe Corporate Center 1, 1550 Coraopolis Heights Rd.
Moon Township, PA 15108
Phone: 412-262-2830
Fax: 412-262-7430
Web: www.atlasenergyresources.com

CEO: Edward E. Cohen
CFO: Matthew A. Jones
HR: –
FYE: December 31
Type: Public

Atlas Energy Resources has its fingers in lots of oily pies. The company, through interests in more than 90 investment partnerships, drills for and produces natural gas and oil in the Appalachian Basin, which is known for its high yields that require little or no processing. It has a nearly 100% success rate with its more than 7,720 wells on about 697,300 net acres; about 72% of the acreage is undeveloped. In 2007 Atlas Energy reported estimated proved reserves of 896.7 billion cu. ft. of natural gas equivalent, the bulk of which is in Michigan. The company manages the natural gas and oil holdings of Atlas America, which retains an 48% interest in the company.

	Annual Growth	9/03	9/04	9/05	*12/06	12/07
Sales ($ mil.)	53.9%	103.1	148.0	212.0	321.0	577.9
Net income ($ mil.)	64.9%	15.9	27.6	41.4	51.8	117.5
Market value ($ mil.)	127.3%	—	—	—	830.3	1,887.5
Employees	—	—	—	—	0	0	467

*Fiscal year change

ATLAS MINING COMPANY

Pink Sheets: ALMI

1221 Yellowstone
Osburn, ID 83849
Phone: 208-556-1181
Fax: 208-556-6741
Web: www.atlasmining.com

CEO: Robert Dumont
CFO: Barbara S. Suveg
HR: –
FYE: December 31
Type: Public

Through its Atlas Fausett Contracting (AFC) unit, mineral exploration company Atlas Mining provides underground mining-related services for mine operators, other exploration companies, and companies in the construction and natural resource industries. Companies AFC has provided services to include Hecla Mining, Stillwater Mining, and Kinross Gold. Atlas Mining also is working to develop its Dragon Mine property in Utah, which contains a deposit of halloysite clay, a substance used to make bone china, fine china, and porcelain. In addition to its mining operations, Atlas harvests timber from land it controls in northern Idaho.

	Annual Growth	12/02	12/03	12/04	12/05	*12/06
Sales ($ mil.)	75.6%	0.4	0.3	1.0	0.6	3.8
Net income ($ mil.)	—	(0.7)	(1.4)	(0.9)	(3.8)	(2.0)
Employees	—	—	—	—	—	58

*Most recent year available

ATLAS PIPELINE HOLDINGS, L.P.

NYSE: AHD

311 Rouser Rd.
Moon Township, PA 15108
Phone: 412-262-2830
Fax: 412-262-2820
Web: www.atlaspipelineholdings.com

CEO: Edward E. Cohen
CFO: Matthew A. Jones
HR: –
FYE: December 31
Type: Public

Atlas may have carried the world on his shoulders, but the Atlas group of companies is more into sharing the heavy load across a number of related companies. In 2006 Atlas America filed an IPO for subsidiary Atlas Pipeline Holdings to hold its ownership stake in the general partner of Atlas Pipeline Partners, and increase distributions to its unitholders. Atlas Pipeline Partners operates 3,265 miles of natural gas gathering systems in eastern Ohio, southern Oklahoma, western New York, western Pennsylvania, and northern Texas. In 2007 Atlas America owned 83% of Atlas Pipeline Holdings.

	Annual Growth	12/03	12/04	12/05	12/06	12/07
Sales ($ mil.)	43.8%	—	—	—	465.1	668.8
Net income ($ mil.)	—	—	—	—	18.5	(15.6)
Market value ($ mil.)	47.2%	—	—	—	504.1	742.0
Employees						

ATLAS PIPELINE PARTNERS, L.P.

NYSE: APL

311 Rouser Rd.
Moon Township, PA 15108
Phone: 412-262-2830
Fax: 412-262-2820
Web: www.atlaspipelinepartners.com

CEO: Edward E. Cohen
CFO: Matthew A. Jones
HR: –
FYE: December 31
Type: Public

Atlas Pipeline Partners shoulders the burden of getting natural gas from wellheads to major gas utilities such as Peoples Natural Gas, National Fuel Gas, and East Ohio Gas. Atlas Pipeline operates about 3,265 miles of natural gas gathering systems in Arkansas, southeastern Missouri, eastern Ohio, southern Oklahoma, western New York, western Pennsylvania, and northern Texas. The company was formed to buy the gas gathering systems of its former owners Atlas America and Resource Energy. In 2006 Atlas America filed an IPO for subsidiary Atlas Pipeline Holdings L.P. to hold its ownership stake in the general partner of Atlas Pipeline.

	Annual Growth	12/03	12/04	12/05	12/06	12/07
Sales ($ mil.)	170.3%	15.8	91.3	371.5	464.7	842.9
Net income ($ mil.)	—	9.6	18.3	25.8	33.7	(144.3)
Market value ($ mil.)	97.8%	108.5	233.1	509.5	627.9	1,660.8
Employees	(10.5%)	—	—	210	188	—

ATLAS TECHNOLOGY GROUP, INC.

OTC: ATYG

2001 152nd Ave. NE
Redmond, WA 98052
Phone: 425-458-2360
Fax: 425-458-2361
Web: www.atlastg.com

CEO: Peter B. Jacobson
CFO: Byran S.P. (Paddy) Marra
HR: –
FYE: December 31
Type: Public

Atlas Technology Group offers IT support all over the map. The company provides outsourced software support services for custom applications. Its service capabilities range from supporting single applications to the management of entire networks. Formerly a provider of multimedia authoring tools, the company sold its iShell division and its Tribeworks Development Corporation subsidiary in 2006. The company now operates through its Atlas Technology Group subsidiary, which specializes in remote support of applications from its data centers in Malta, New Zealand, and the US.

	Annual Growth	12/03	12/04	12/05	12/06	12/07
Sales ($ mil.)	(15.9%)	1.2	0.8	0.6	0.0	0.6
Net income ($ mil.)	—	0.0	(0.2)	(0.2)	(2.0)	(12.4)
Market value ($ mil.)	(4.4%)	—	—	36.7	25.1	33.6
Employees	—	—	—	—	—	—

ATLAS WORLD GROUP, INC.

1212 St. George Rd.
Evansville, IN 47711
Phone: 812-424-2222
Fax: 812-421-7125
Web: www.atlasworldgroup.com

CEO: James A. Stamm
CFO: Richard J. (Rick) Olson
HR: –
FYE: December 31
Type: Private

Willing to carry the weight of a moving world, Atlas World Group is the holding company for Atlas Van Lines, one of the largest moving companies in the US. Atlas Van Lines transports household goods throughout the US and between the US and Canada; the company also offers specialized transportation of items such as trade show exhibits, fine art, and electronics. Other Atlas World Group companies provides international corporate relocation and freight forwarding services. The company's Atlas Canada unit moves household goods in that country. Atlas Van Lines was formed in 1948 by a group of 33 local movers; Atlas World Group was formed in 1994. The company is owned by its agents.

	Annual Growth	12/03	12/04	12/05	12/06	12/07
Est. sales ($ mil.)	—	—	—	—	—	985.6
Employees	—	—	—	—	—	450

ATMEL CORPORATION

NASDAQ (GS): ATML

2325 Orchard Pkwy.
San Jose, CA 95131
Phone: 408-441-0311
Fax: 408-436-4314
Web: www.atmel.com

CEO: Steven A. (Steve) Laub
CFO: Robert (Bob) Avery
HR: John Klinestiver
FYE: December 31
Type: Public

At the very least, Atmel offers a diverse lineup of chips. The semiconductor maker's product lines include non-volatile memory devices, such as flash memory and ROMs, as well as programmable logic chips, microcontrollers, application-specific integrated circuits, and application-specific standard products. Atmel's chips are used in consumer electronics, communications, military, industrial, and networking products, including cellular phones and base stations, along with avionics systems, networking switches and routers, digital still cameras, smart credit cards, and television set-top boxes. More than 85% of the company's sales come from customers outside North America.

	Annual Growth	12/03	12/04	12/05	12/06	12/07
Sales ($ mil.)	5.4%	1,330.6	1,649.7	1,675.7	1,670.9	1,639.2
Net income ($ mil.)	—	(118.0)	(2.4)	(32.9)	14.6	47.9
Market value ($ mil.)	(9.4%)	2,843.0	1,873.5	1,493.6	2,957.5	1,917.4
Employees	(1.6%)	7,900	8,800	8,080	7,992	7,400

ATMI, INC.

NASDAQ (GS): ATMI

7 Commerce Dr.
Danbury, CT 06810
Phone: 203-794-1100
Fax: 203-792-8040
Web: www.atmi.com

CEO: Douglas A. (Doug) Neugold
CFO: Timothy C. (Tim) Carlson
HR: Thomas J. McGowan
FYE: December 31
Type: Public

ATMI's original name — Advanced Technology Materials, Inc. — contains a pretty good summary of its business. The company furnishes semiconductor makers with ultrapure materials and related packaging and delivery systems used during chip production. ATMI has formed strategic alliances with the likes of IBM, Infineon, and Texas Instruments to develop new materials and processes. As part of its move into serving the life sciences market, the company has acquired LevTech, a provider of disposable mixing systems to the biotechnology and pharmaceutical industries, for $27 million in cash. Customers in Asia/Pacific account for about two-thirds of sales, while the US provides around one-quarter of sales.

	Annual Growth	12/03	12/04	12/05	12/06	12/07
Sales ($ mil.)	20.7%	171.6	246.3	281.8	325.9	364.1
Net income ($ mil.)	—	(9.9)	31.5	30.7	40.0	40.5
Market value ($ mil.)	10.4%	718.9	709.2	1,047.4	1,059.7	1,069.5
Employees	6.7%	—	—	711	806	809

ATMOS ENERGY CORPORATION

NYSE: ATO

3 Lincoln Centre, Ste. 1800, 5430 LBJ Fwy.
Dallas, TX 75240
Phone: 972-934-9227
Fax: 972-855-3040
Web: www.atmosenergy.com

CEO: Robert W. (Bob) Best
CFO: John Patrick (Pat) Reddy
HR: Wynn D. McGregor
FYE: September 30
Type: Public

Atmos Energy wants, at most, to be known as the largest gas-only utility company in the US. Through its utility units, which operate under the Atmos Energy brand, the holding company distributes natural gas to approximately 3.2 million residential, commercial, and industrial customers in more than 1,600 communities in 12 midwestern and southern states. Atmos Energy has expanded its operations in Texas through the acquisition of TXU Gas. Non-regulated subsidiary Atmos Energy Marketing sells natural gas and offers energy management services to utilities and industrial customers in 22 states. The company also has power generation and gas transportation and storage operations.

	Annual Growth	9/03	9/04	9/05	9/06	9/07
Sales ($ mil.)	16.1%	3,244.2	2,920.0	4,973.3	6,152.4	5,898.4
Net income ($ mil.)	23.8%	71.7	86.2	135.8	147.7	168.5
Market value ($ mil.)	19.7%	1,232.3	1,581.9	2,275.2	2,333.7	2,529.7
Employees	1.2%	—	—	4,543	4,402	4,653

ATP OIL & GAS CORPORATION

NASDAQ (GS): ATPG

4600 Post Oak Place, Ste. 200
Houston, TX 77027
Phone: 713-622-3311
Fax: 713-622-5101
Web: www.atpog.com

CEO: T. Paul Bulmahn
CFO: Albert L. Reese Jr.
HR: –
FYE: December 31
Type: Public

ATP Oil & Gas looks for its revenues where others have shelved their operations. The company's strategy is to exploit continental shelf assets that are being sold by larger oil companies searching for higher returns in deeper waters. It explores and develops natural gas and oil properties primarily on the outer continental shelf of the Gulf of Mexico (where it has interests in 76 offshore blocks, 40 platforms, and 127 wells) and in the Southern Gas Basin of the UK's North Sea. Its proved reserves total 715.6 billion cu. ft. of natural gas equivalent; natural gas makes up the bulk of the reserves. Founder and CEO Paul Bulmahn owns about 19% of ATP Oil & Gas.

	Annual Growth	12/03	12/04	12/05	12/06	12/07
Sales ($ mil.)	71.5%	70.2	116.1	146.7	419.8	607.9
Net income ($ mil.)	—	(50.8)	1.4	(2.7)	6.9	48.6
Market value ($ mil.)	85.2%	153.5	538.5	1,102.6	1,194.9	1,805.9
Employees	22.9%	—	—	48	59	—

ATRIA SENIOR LIVING GROUP, INC.

401 S. 4th St., Ste. 1900
Louisville, KY 40202
Phone: 502-779-4700
Fax: 502-779-4701
Web: www.atriaseniorliving.com

CEO: John A. Moore
CFO: Mark Jesse
HR: Anne Pinter
FYE: December 31
Type: Private

Atria Senior Living Group knows that for seniors, dignity and independence don't come in one-size-fits-all living arrangements. The company operates retirement and assisted-living centers for the elderly who may need assistance with routine daily tasks but not skilled nursing care. Its services range from independent living units in a private apartment setting to more specialized care facilities for residents suffering from Alzheimer's disease or requiring respite care. Atria Senior Living Group owns or manages more than 120 facilities in 27 states.

	Annual Growth	12/03	12/04	12/05	12/06	12/07
Est. sales ($ mil.)	—	—	—	—	—	183.6
Employees	—	—	—	—	—	7,500

ATRICURE, INC.

NASDAQ (GM): ATRC

6033 Schumacher Park Dr.
West Chester, OH 45069
Phone: 513-755-4100
Fax: 513-755-4108
Web: www.atricure.com

CEO: David J. (Dave) Drachman
CFO: Julie A. Piton
HR: –
FYE: December 31
Type: Public

If your heart thumps to the beat of a different drummer, AtriCure wants to clamp down on that activity. The medical device maker has developed a system used in the treatment of atrial fibrillation (AF), a common type of heart arrhythmia. Its primary product, the Isolator bipolar ablation system, allows surgeons to manipulate clamps designed for both open-heart and minimally-invasive procedures. Although the FDA has cleared Isolator for the ablation of cardiac tissue, none of AtriCure's products have received approval specifically for the treatment of AF. Nevertheless, cardiothoracic surgeons have adopted the system to create lesions in the tissue to block electrical impulses that cause quivering in the heart.

	Annual Growth	12/03	12/04	12/05	12/06	12/07
Sales ($ mil.)	49.0%	9.8	19.2	31.0	38.2	48.3
Net income ($ mil.)	—	(7.1)	(9.4)	(12.7)	(13.7)	(11.3)
Market value ($ mil.)	20.0%	—	—	128.7	109.0	185.3
Employees	—	—	—	160	—	—

An in-depth profile of this company is available to Hoover's Online members at hoovers.com.

ATRINSIC, INC.

NASDAQ (GM): NWMO

42 Corporate Park, Ste. 250
Irvine, CA 92606
Phone: 949-777-3700
Fax: 949-777-3707
Web: www.atrinsic.com

CEO: Burton Katz
CFO: Daniel Harvey
HR: –
FYE: December 31
Type: Public

Atrinsic (formerly New Motion) puts all the entertainment at your fingertips, even when you're on the move. The company distributes digital entertainment — including music, games, sports, shopping, and dating services — to mobile phones throughout North America. Atrinsic operates four brands: Altnet (music downloads); Bid4Prizes (auction services); GatorArcade (gaming); and iMatchup (online dating). The company maintains technology partnerships with Internet companies such as AOL and Yahoo!, and telecommunication firms such as T-Mobile and Verizon. Atrinsic acquired marketing firm Traffix in 2008 in order to expand into digital advertising.

	Annual Growth	12/03	12/04	12/05	12/06	12/07
Sales ($ mil.)	150.4%	—	—	5.9	18.7	37.0
Net income ($ mil.)	—	—	—	0.4	0.7	(4.2)
Market value ($ mil.)	(31.1%)	—	—	—	458.1	315.4
Employees	—	—	—	—	38	—

ATRION CORPORATION

NASDAQ (GM): ATRI

1 Allentown Pkwy.
Allen, TX 75002
Phone: 972-390-9800
Fax: 972-396-7581
Web: www.atrioncorp.com

CEO: Emile A. Battat
CFO: Jeffery Strickland
HR: –
FYE: December 31
Type: Public

Atrion is only a little bit gassy. The company owns a 22-mile pipeline that transports gaseous oxygen in Alabama, but its primary focus is on the health care market. Its Atrion Medical Products subsidiary makes ophthalmic, diagnostic, and cardiovascular equipment. Key products include the LacriCATH line of balloon catheters for opening blocked tear ducts. Subsidiary Halkey-Roberts makes fluid and gas valves and clamps for health care equipment, marine and airplane safety devices, toys, and other inflatable products. Another subsidiary, Quest Medical, makes cardiovascular and intravenous fluid delivery products; its MPS Myocardial Protection System manages fluid delivery to the heart during open-heart surgery.

	Annual Growth	12/03	12/04	12/05	12/06	12/07
Sales ($ mil.)	9.0%	62.8	66.1	72.1	81.0	88.5
Net income ($ mil.)	28.7%	5.1	6.5	9.0	10.8	14.0
Market value ($ mil.)	32.6%	77.2	79.3	127.3	145.7	238.9
Employees	7.5%	427	456	493	—	—

ATRIUM COMPANIES, INC.

3890 W. Northwest Hwy., Ste. 500
Dallas, TX 75220
Phone: 214-630-5757
Fax: 214-630-5001
Web: home.atrium.com

CEO: Gregory T. (Greg) Faherty
CFO: Madhusudan A. (Sudan) Dewan
HR: D. D. (Gus) Agostinelli
FYE: December 31
Type: Private

Atrium Companies produces aluminum and vinyl windows and patio doors, and "woodn't" have it any other way — not after selling its wood window and door business. The company's customers include retail centers, lumberyards, builders, and wholesalers for both new construction and remodeling markets. Atrium also offers installation and repair services. Since its founding in 1948, the company has grown to include window- and door-making facilities and distribution centers, vinyl and aluminum extrusion operations, and other operations throughout the US and Canada. The company's acquisition of Canada-based North Star Vinyl Windows and Doors in 2007 expanded its product line.

	Annual Growth	12/02	12/03	12/04	12/05	12/06
Sales ($ mil.)	11.9%	536.3	597.8	800.0	800.0	840.0
Employees	7.9%	4,420	6,100	6,300	7,000	6,000

@ROAD, INC.

NASDAQ (GM): —

47071 Bayside Pkwy.
Fremont, CA 94538
Phone: 510-668-1638
Fax: 510-445-1377
Web: www.road.com

CEO: Kenneth Colby
CFO: Eric Verity
HR: –
FYE: December 31
Type: Subsidiary

Truckers still ride the lonely highways, but @Road makes sure the home office knows exactly where they are. @Road's so-called mobile resource management (MRM) system includes fleet tracking applications, field service management (dynamic scheduling), and field asset management (vehicle diagnostics and maintenance). Using GPS technology to fix a vehicle's geographic position, the company collects the data at a service center via wireless data transmissions made over the cellular networks of partner telecom companies. @Road serves customers in the transportation, distribution, field service, telecommunications, utilities, cable, and construction industries. The company is a subsidiary of Trimble Navigation.

ATS CORPORATION

OTC: ATCT

7915 Jones Branch Dr.
McLean, VA 22102
Phone: 703-506-0088
Fax: 703-903-0415
Web: www.atsva.com

CEO: Edward H. (Ed) Bersoff
CFO: Pamela A. Little
HR: Thomas W. Sanderson
FYE: December 31
Type: Public

ATS Corporation (formerly Advanced Technology Systems) knows that the key to technological success lies in the right mix of services. The company provides a variety of IT services to the federal government, including consulting, systems integration, network design, and support. Its Appix subsidiary is an IT consulting services provider to the mortgage lending and other financial services industries. ATS markets security products and services for government, schools, and corporations through its ATS International subsidiary. The company also develops software used for managing public safety operations (Pyramid), Homeland Security responses (HLS-RAM), and law enforcement activities (Voyager).

	Annual Growth	12/03	12/04	12/05	12/06	12/07
Sales ($ mil.)	—	—	—	—	—	106.9
Net income ($ mil.)	—	—	—	—	—	(6.6)
Market value ($ mil.)	—	—	—	—	—	69.1
Employees	—	—	—	—	—	—

ATS MEDICAL, INC.

NASDAQ (GM): ATSI

3905 Annapolis Ln., Ste. 105
Minneapolis, MN 55447
Phone: 763-553-7736
Fax: 763-557-2244
Web: www.atsmedical.com

CEO: Michael D. Dale
CFO: Michael (Mike) Kramer
HR: Barbara (Barb) Searle
FYE: December 31
Type: Public

ATS Medical keeps its products close to the heart. The company's main product is its ATS Open Pivot mechanical heart valve, which has been implanted in more than 140,000 patients worldwide. The valve was designed to lower the risk of blood clotting, reduce noise levels, and make the implantation procedure easier. ATS Medical sells the valve through a direct sales force in the US and some key international markets and through distributors elsewhere. The firm is diversifying its product offerings through acquisitions and marketing agreements. In 2006 it purchased medical device company 3F Therapeutics, a developer of biological tissue heart valves.

	Annual Growth	12/03	12/04	12/05	12/06	12/07
Sales ($ mil.)	28.0%	18.5	28.0	34.6	40.5	49.6
Net income ($ mil.)	—	(13.3)	(16.6)	(14.4)	(27.7)	(23.0)
Market value ($ mil.)	4.9%	108.5	144.3	85.9	83.5	131.5
Employees	61.5%	87	178	227	—	—

ATSI COMMUNICATIONS, INC.

OTC: ATSX

8600 Wurzbach Rd., Ste. 700W
San Antonio, TX 78240
Phone: 210-614-7240
Fax: 210-614-7264
Web: www.atsi.net

CEO: Arthur L. (Art) Smith
CFO: Antonio Estrada
HR: Kathleen Keller
FYE: July 31
Type: Public

VoIP via ATSI. ATSI Communications provides telecommunications services using Voice over Internet protocol (VoIP), primarily international call termination for US and Latin American carriers and telecom resellers for traffic terminating in Asia, Latin America (especially Mexico), and the Middle East (these carrier services account for more than 99% of its revenue). The company also offers private line communications service to Latin American and multinational companies needing to connect to their US offices. ATSI Communications formed a new subsidiary in 2006, called Digerati Networks, which markets VoIP service primarily in Mexico.

	Annual Growth	7/03	7/04	7/05	7/06	7/07
Sales ($ mil.)	46.4%	6.9	1.3	6.0	14.7	31.7
Net income ($ mil.)	—	(12.6)	(8.5)	10.4	0.9	(0.3)
Market value ($ mil.)	69.1%	—	1.8	1.9	3.5	8.5
Employees	—	4	—	—	—	—

ATSI HOLDINGS, INC.

25 Tri-State International, Ste. 200
Lincolnshire, IL 60069
Phone: 847-383-7900
Fax: 847-383-7949
Web: www.tpgprinters.com

CEO: Lindsey Allen
CFO: Robert Morris
HR: –
FYE: December 31
Type: Private

ATSI Holdings doesn't have a license to print money, but it can help you print a receipt. The company, formerly known as Axiohm Transaction Solutions, operates through two units: Transaction Printer Group (TPG) and Cognitive Solutions. TPG makes thermal and impact printers and supplies for the banking, gaming, hospitality, and retail markets. Cognitive Solutions supplies thermal printers, software, and supplies used to create barcode labels. The company, which has closed plants and reduced its workforce since emerging from bankruptcy in 2000, utilizes contract manufacturers in China and Mexico to supplement the output of its remaining US plants.

	Annual Growth	12/03	12/04	12/05	12/06	12/07
Est. sales ($ mil.)	—	—	—	—	—	37.8
Employees	—	—	—	—	—	351

ATT HOLDING CO.

465 Railroad Ave.
Camp Hill, PA 17011
Phone: 717-737-1500
Fax: 717-730-2552
Web: www.ames.com

CEO: Richard C. Dell
CFO: David M. (Dave) Nuti
HR: Chris Ebling
FYE: September 30
Type: Private

ATT Holding is not that mother of all phone companies, Ma Bell. Rather it could be said to be the founding father of all US lawn and garden tool manufacturing companies. ATT operates through Ames True Temper, which traces its history to 1774 and a shovel-making business founded by Captain John Ames. It's the largest maker and marketer of non-powered lawn and garden tools in the US. Its products include long- and short-handle tools, lawn carts, pruning tools, wheelbarrows, hose reels, snow tools, and striking tools, as well as decorative items. ATT sells through large retailers (Home Depot, Sears), wholesale chains (Ace, True Value), and industrial distributors (Grainger).

	Annual Growth	9/02	9/03	9/04	9/05	9/06
Sales ($ mil.)	7.3%	—	—	—	450.6	483.6
Net income ($ mil.)	—	—	—	—	(125.2)	(4.6)
Employees	—	—	—	—	—	2,048

ATTORNEYS' TITLE INSURANCE FUND, INC.

6545 Corporate Centre Blvd.
Orlando, FL 32822
Phone: 407-240-3863
Fax: 407-240-0750
Web: www.thefund.com

CEO: Charles J. Kovaleski
CFO: Jimmy R. Jones
HR: B. Gwen Geier
FYE: December 31
Type: Private

Sunshine State attorneys know where to go for title insurance services. Attorneys' Title Insurance Fund (The Fund) provides title insurance-related products to its 6,000 member attorneys throughout Florida and in several other states. The Fund is owned by a business trust created in 1947. Membership in the trust is limited to Florida attorneys, although The Fund serves non-member customers as well. Products include property information, property ownership verification, real estate closing software, and a variety of industry-related marketing tools.

	Annual Growth	12/02	12/03	12/04	12/05	12/06
Assets ($ mil.)	18.8%	183.5	243.3	282.4	332.5	365.9
Net income ($ mil.)	27.0%	10.0	26.3	32.9	31.0	26.0
Employees	(3.2%)	900	875	844	—	—

ATWOOD MOBILE PRODUCTS

1120 N. Main St.
Elkhart, IN 46514
Phone: 574-264-2131
Fax: –
Web: www.atwoodmobile.com

CEO: Timothy C. Stephens
CFO: Scott Miller
HR: –
FYE: December 31
Type: Private

Roughing it can be smooth sailing as long as you have Atwood Mobile Products along on your adventure. The company manufactures components and accessories for the recreational vehicle, heavy-duty truck, manufactured housing, residential, and marine markets. Products include heating and cooking appliances and chassis components for RVs, jacks, brakes, slide-out systems, doors and windows for trucks and RVs, and other fabricated glass products. Atwood's other markets include equipment manufacturers of agricultural, industrial, and mass transit vehicles. In 2007 Dura Automotive Systems sold Atwood to Insight Equity for about $160 million.

	Annual Growth	12/03	12/04	12/05	12/06	12/07
Est. sales ($ mil.)	—	—	—	—	—	256.5
Employees	—	—	—	—	—	2,750

ATWOOD OCEANICS, INC.

NYSE: ATW

15835 Park Ten Place Dr.
Houston, TX 77084
Phone: 281-749-7800
Fax: 281-492-7871
Web: www.atwd.com

CEO: John R. Irwin
CFO: James M. (Jim) Holland
HR: James E. Gillenwater
FYE: September 30
Type: Public

Atwood Oceanics is at work at sea all over the world. An offshore oil and gas drilling contractor, the firm owns eight drilling rigs, including four semisubmersible rigs, two jack-ups, one submersible, and one semisubmersible tender assist vessel (which places drilling equipment on permanent platforms). In 2007 some 93% of sales came from international operation. Its customers include Woodside Energy (17% of sales), BHP Billiton Petroleum Pty (13%), and Sarawak Shell Bhd. (13%). The company, which also operates in the Gulf of Mexico, is expanding its operations to include offshore Japan. Fellow drilling contractor Helmerich & Payne owns 13% of Atwood Oceanics.

	Annual Growth	9/03	9/04	9/05	9/06	9/07
Sales ($ mil.)	29.2%	144.8	163.4	176.2	276.6	403.0
Net income ($ mil.)	—	(12.8)	7.6	26.0	86.1	139.0
Market value ($ mil.)	95.5%	166.2	329.8	645.9	1,396.1	2,425.0
Employees	(9.5%)	—	—	1,100	—	900

An in-depth profile of this company is available to Hoover's Online members at hoovers.com.

193

ATX GROUP, INC.

8550 Freeport Pkwy.
Irving, TX 75063
Phone: 972-753-6200
Fax: 972-753-6226
Web: www.atxg.com

CEO: Steven A. (Steve) Millstein
CFO: Michael J. Briskey
HR: Oda-Carina Braunfeld
FYE: December 31
Type: Private

Even men can feel comfortable asking ATX Group for directions. The company provides telematics — location-based voice and data communication services that include emergency response, stolen vehicle tracking, and navigation help. ATX Group, which acts as a holding company and operates through its ATX Technologies subsidiary, contracts with car manufacturers and arranges to serve their customers. Subscribers to the company's services primarily include buyers of Mercedes-Benz, BMW, and Rolls-Royce automobiles. The company operates in Europe through Germany-based ATX Europe. Wireless carrier Vodafone Group owns 75% of ATX Group, which was founded in 1994 by chairman Steven Riebel.

	Annual Growth	12/03	12/04	12/05	12/06	12/07
Est. sales ($ mil.)	—	—	—	—	—	28.1
Employees	—	—	—	—	—	395

AUBURN NATIONAL BANCORPORATION, INC.

NASDAQ (CM): AUBN

100 N. Gay St.
Auburn, AL 36830
Phone: 334-821-9200
Fax: 334-887-2772
Web: www.auburnbank.com

CEO: E. L. Spencer Jr.
CFO: David A. Hedges
HR: Laura Carrington
FYE: December 31
Type: Public

War Eagle! Auburn National Bancorporation is the holding company for AuburnBank, which operates about 10 branches and a handful of loan offices in and around its headquarters in the eastern Alabama home of Auburn University. Formed in 1907, AuburnBank offers traditional retail banking services such as checking and savings accounts and CDs. Commercial real estate loans make up slightly more than half of the bank's loan portfolio, which also includes business loans and leases, residential mortgages, and consumer installment loans. CEO E. L. Spencer owns nearly 20% of Auburn National; vice chairman Emil Wright owns more than 10%.

	Annual Growth	12/03	12/04	12/05	12/06	12/07
Assets ($ mil.)	3.9%	590.1	591.2	608.2	635.1	688.7
Net income ($ mil.)	6.3%	5.4	6.5	6.5	6.6	6.9
Market value ($ mil.)	1.4%	76.6	79.5	84.0	108.2	80.8
Employees	—	—	—	133	—	—

AUDI OF AMERICA INC.

3800 Hamlin Rd.
Auburn Hills, MI 48326
Phone: 248-754-5000
Fax: –
Web: www.audiusa.com

CEO: Johan de Nysschen
CFO: –
HR: –
FYE: December 31
Type: Business segment

Audi of America is the US sales and marketing arm of Volkswagen's Audi brand. Models available in the US include the A3, A4, A5, A6, and A8, as well as S/RS Series, the TT coupe and roadster, and the allroad quattro SUV. Audi launched its first SUV, the Q7, in 2006. Its newest model, the R8 high-performance sports car, debuted in the fall of 2007. Audi of America also offers a range of financial services for leasing and purchasing options through Audi Financial Services and Audi Bank USA.

AUDIBLE, INC.

1 Washington Park
Newark, NJ 07102
Phone: 973-820-0400
Fax: 973-820-0505
Web: www.audible.com

CEO: Donald R. Katz
CFO: William H. (Bill) Mitchell
HR: –
FYE: December 31
Type: Subsidiary

Audible has a story to tell. It sells downloadable audio versions of books, as well as radio broadcasts, speeches, and other spoken word performances. All total, the company has some 90,000 titles available for sale via Audible Web sites in the US, the UK, France, and Germany. Users can buy individual titles or subscribe to AudibleListener to download content. Users can listen to programs on their computer, or via an MP3 player or PDA. Subscribers to a recurring title (newspaper, magazine, radio program) can have it automatically delivered to their PC, or wirelessly to their handheld device. Audible also offers a CD burning feature for listening on CD players. Amazon.com bought the company in 2008.

	Annual Growth	12/02	12/03	12/04	12/05	12/06
Sales ($ mil.)	60.5%	12.4	19.3	34.3	64.2	82.3
Net income ($ mil.)	—	(17.2)	(3.6)	2.0	(0.6)	(8.7)
Employees	(21.2%)	—	—	—	193	152

AUDIO VISUAL SERVICES CORPORATION

111 W. Ocean Blvd., Ste. 1110
Long Beach, CA 90802
Phone: 562-366-0620
Fax: 562-366-0628
Web: www.psav.com

CEO: Digby J. Davies
CFO: –
HR: Kate Daly
FYE: September 30
Type: Cooperative

This company puts a little show biz into business. Audio Visual Services Corporation, which does business as PSAV Presentation Services, rents and sells audiovisual equipment and provides staging services and related technology support for events and meetings. It offers onsite lighting, sound, and projection equipment for meetings and seminars, as well as video recording and broadcasting equipment and services. For tradeshows, PSAV provides staging and exhibit displays, in addition to planning and consulting services. The company, which traces its roots to the late 1980s, serves customers in more than 700 locations worldwide.

	Annual Growth	9/03	9/04	9/05	9/06	9/07
Est. sales ($ mil.)	—	—	—	—	—	62.8
Employees	—	—	—	—	—	2,000

AUDIOVOX CORPORATION

NASDAQ (GM): VOXX

180 Marcus Blvd.
Hauppauge, NY 11788
Phone: 631-231-7750
Fax: 631-434-3995
Web: www.audiovox.com

CEO: Patrick M. Lavelle
CFO: Charles M. Stoehr
HR: Liz O'Connell
FYE: February 28
Type: Public

Audiovox answers the call for electronics. The company sells primarily consumer electronics for communications, mobile, and home use and acts as an original equipment manufacturer (OEM) for car makers. Its products include cordless telephones, mobile video products, auto security systems, radios, CD players, and home and portable stereos. Audiovox's satellite antenna can be used to bring live TV into automobiles. The company's goods are marketed under such brand names as Acoustic Research, Advent, Audiovox, Heco, Jensen, Mac Audio, Road Gear, Movies2Go, and Magnate, among others. Founded by its chairman John Shalam in 1960, Audiovox went public in 1987.

	Annual Growth	11/03	11/04	11/05	*2/07	2/08
Sales ($ mil.)	(18.2%)	1,323.9	567.1	539.7	456.7	591.4
Net income ($ mil.)	(6.7%)	11.2	77.2	(9.6)	2.9	8.5
Market value ($ mil.)	(9.4%)	274.6	295.8	280.8	306.7	185.3
Employees	12.0%	—	—	750	840	—

*Fiscal year change

AUNTIE ANNE'S, INC.

160-A Rte. 41
Gap, PA 17527
Phone: 717-442-4766
Fax: 717-442-4139
Web: www.auntieannes.com

CEO: Samuel R. (Sam) Beiler
CFO: Grant S. Markley
HR: Gerard G. (Jere) Wiegand
FYE: December 31
Type: Private

You don't have to be twisted to enjoy one of these pretzels. Auntie Anne's is a leading franchisor of snack outlets with more than 900 pretzel stores located in some 45 states and 10 other countries. The stores offer a variety of pretzel flavors, including original, almond, whole wheat, and parmesan herb. They are primarily found in high-traffic areas, such as malls, airports, train stations, and stadiums. Anne Beiler started the company in 1988 to help fund a faith-based family assistance foundation. Sam Beiler, a cousin, bought the company in 2005.

AURORA CAPITAL GROUP

10877 Wilshire Blvd., Ste. 2100
Los Angeles, CA 90024
Phone: 310-551-0101
Fax: 310-277-5591
Web: www.auroracap.com

CEO: Gerald L. (Gerry) Parsky
CFO: –
HR: –
FYE: December 31
Type: Private

Aurora Capital Group focuses on buyouts of midsized industrial manufacturers, distributors, and service businesses. Employing a "buy and build" strategy, the private equity firm works with existing management to create organic growth, then adds on other purchases to increase the value of its portfolio companies. Its holdings include United Plastics Group, packaging company Impaxx, and ADCO Global, a manufacturer of adhesives, sealants, and coatings. Aurora Capital acquired insurance claims software company Mitchell International in 2007. The company, which is investing its third private equity fund, has some $2 billion of assets under management.

	Annual Growth	12/03	12/04	12/05	12/06	12/07
Est. sales ($ mil.)	—	—	—	—	—	244.2
Employees	—	—	—	—	—	7,808

AURA SYSTEMS, INC.

OTC: AUSI

2330 Utah Ave.
El Segundo, CA 90245
Phone: 310-643-5300
Fax: 310-643-7457
Web: www.aurasystems.com

CEO: Melvin Gagerman
CFO: Melvin Gagerman
HR: Melinda Mason
FYE: Last day in February
Type: Public

Aura Systems is charging ahead with its AuraGen electric generator, which can produce 8,500 watts of power from an idling car engine. Companies in the telecommunications, utilities, and oil and gas industries use the AuraGen to generate mobile power; the military version of the AuraGen is marketed as the VIPER. RV maker Country Coach announced plans in 2004 to install the AuraGen on its Prevost model. Aura Systems also is entitled to royalties from Daewoo Electronics for use of electro-optical technology found in projection TVs. The company gets about 80% of its sales in the US.

	Annual Growth	2/04	2/05	2/06	2/07	2/08
Sales ($ mil.)	10.2%	1.9	2.5	1.8	1.6	2.8
Net income ($ mil.)	—	(13.6)	(28.3)	6.9	(6.2)	(9.0)
Market value ($ mil.)	(7.2%)	—	—	78.9	47.3	68.0
Employees	4.8%	49	46	29	47	59

AURORA OIL & GAS CORPORATION

AMEX: AOG

4110 Copper Ridge Dr., Ste. 100
Traverse City, MI 49684
Phone: 231-941-0073
Fax: 231-933-0757
Web: www.auroraogc.com

CEO: William W. Deneau
CFO: Barbara E. Lawson
HR: –
FYE: December 31
Type: Public

The drilling of oil and gas wells has an aura of profitability for independent Aurora Oil & Gas (formerly Cadence Resources), which has exploration and production projects primarily in Indiana, Kentucky, and Michigan. The company focuses on developing unconventional gas reservoirs such as black shales, coal seams, and tight sands, including the black shales of Michigan and Indiana. Aurora Oil & Gas has estimated net proved reserves of 153 billion cu. ft. of natural gas equivalent. The company expanded in 2005 by acquiring Aurora Energy, which drilled for natural gas in unconventional reservoirs such as black shales, coal seams, and tight sands in Indiana, Kentucky, and Michigan.

	Annual Growth	9/04	9/05	*12/05	12/06	12/07
Sales ($ mil.)	83.7%	2.5	2.5	7.4	23.1	28.5
Net income ($ mil.)	—	(5.2)	(4.8)	(0.5)	(1.9)	(4.4)
Market value ($ mil.)	75.8%	16.5	—	279.4	325.5	157.7
Employees	20.3%	—	—	47		68

*Fiscal year change

AURIGA LABORATORIES, INC.

OTC: ARGA

5555 Triangle Pkwy., Ste. 300
Norcross, GA 30092
Phone: 678-282-1600
Fax: 678-282-1700
Web: www.aurigalabs.com

CEO: Frank R. Greico
CFO: Frank R. Greico
HR: –
FYE: December 31
Type: Public

Auriga Laboratories is looking for a reversal of fortune. The company, once a provider of messaging systems and other telecommunications services called Multi-Link, completed a reverse merger with Auriga Laboratories in 2006. Auriga, through its Auriga Pharmaceuticals division, markets a line of treatments for cold and allergy symptoms, as well as skin care products. Its exploratory division, Auriga Development, acquires development-stage drugs and finds new applications for them. Its most successful line of acute respiratory products sell under the brand name Extendryl. The company markets its products directly to general and specialty physicians, as well as through retailers and wholesale distributors.

	Annual Growth	12/03	12/04	12/05	12/06	12/07
Sales ($ mil.)	290.6%	—	—	—	3.2	12.5
Net income ($ mil.)	—	—	—	—	(11.7)	(21.7)
Market value ($ mil.)	(93.2%)	—	—	—	37.0	2.5
Employees	—	—	—	—	—	—

AUSTIN INDUSTRIES, INC.

3535 Travis, Ste. 300
Dallas, TX 75204
Phone: 214-443-5500
Fax: –
Web: www.austin-ind.com

CEO: Ronald J. (Ron) Gafford
CFO: Paul W. Hill
HR: James (Jim) Schranz
FYE: December 31
Type: Private

Belying its name, Austin Industries is actually based in Dallas. The company provides civil, commercial, and industrial construction services in the South and Southwest. Its oldest subsidiary, Austin Bridge & Road, provides road, bridge, and parking lot construction across Texas. (It built the longest bridge in Texas, the Port Isabella Causeway.) Subsidiary Austin Commercial builds office buildings, technology sites, hospitals, and other commercial construction. The group's Austin Industrial provides construction, maintenance, and electrical services for the chemical, refining, power, and manufacturing industries. The employee-owned company, which prides itself on its employee relations, was founded in 1918.

	Annual Growth	12/02	12/03	12/04	12/05	12/06
Sales ($ mil.)	5.5%	1,056.0	1,200.0	1,230.0	1,359.0	1,310.0
Employees	0.0%	6,000	6,000	5,300	6,000	6,000

AUSTIN VENTURES, L.P.

300 W. 6th St., Ste. 2300	CEO: John Dirvin
Austin, TX 78701	CFO: Kevin Kunz
Phone: 512-485-1900	HR: Jeff Browning
Fax: 512-476-3952	FYE: December 31
Web: www.austinventures.com	Type: Private

Texas ranches are known for longhorns, but Austin Ventures has corralled themselves a heapin' helpin' of a whole different breed — the nerd herd. The venture capital firm offers funding mainly to software, computer hardware, semiconductor, communications, and business services startups. Focused on investment opportunities in the Southwest (and still with a heavy Texas concentration despite looking outward), Austin Ventures invests from $100,000 to $20 million per transaction, usually holds its investments long-term, and almost always takes a seat on the acquired firm's board. Austin Ventures also assists clients in hiring management, setting up compensation plans, and going public.

	Annual Growth	12/03	12/04	12/05	12/06	12/07
Est. sales ($ mil.)	—	—	—	—	—	44.3
Employees	—	—	—	—	—	612

AUSTRALIAN-CANADIAN OIL ROYALTIES LTD.

OTC: AUCAF

1301 Ave. M	CEO: Andre Sakhai
Cisco, TX 76437	CFO: Bernard Lipton
Phone: 254-442-2638	HR: –
Fax: 254-442-3843	FYE: December 31
Web: www.aussieoil.com	Type: Public

There is less royalty in this Commonwealth connection than there used to be. Australian-Canadian Oil Royalties explores for and produces oil and natural gas from properties located in Australia. Originally formed as a trust, the company did not operate or control any of its properties until 2005, when Australian-Canadian Oil Royalties decided to become an oil and gas explorer as well. The company's principal assets are 15.4 million gross acres of royalty interest in Australia's Cooper-Eromanga and Gippsland Basins. It also has minor oil and gas assets in the US. Secretary and director Robert Kamon controls about 23% of Australian-Canadian Oil Royalties; president Ely Sakhai also owns about 23%.

	Annual Growth	12/03	12/04	12/05	12/06	12/07
Sales ($ mil.)	—	0.0	0.0	0.0	0.0	0.1
Net income ($ mil.)	—	(0.1)	(0.4)	(0.6)	(0.6)	(0.3)
Market value ($ mil.)	45.5%	1.5	18.3	3.0	4.0	6.6
Employees	0.0%	—	—	—	3	3

AUTHENTEC, INC.

NASDAQ (GM): AUTH

100 Rialto Rd., Ste. 400	CEO: F. Scott Moody
Melbourne, FL 32901	CFO: Gary Larsen
Phone: 321-308-1300	HR: –
Fax: 321-308-1430	FYE: December 31
Web: www.authentec.com	Type: Public

AuthenTec is good at fingering out who's using your electronic gear. The company designs biometric fingerprint sensor chips, a high-tech way to authenticate identity and to allow only authorized users to utilize the equipment. Electronics makers incorporate AuthenTec's TruePrint devices into a variety of goods, such as PCs, PDAs, and automotive subsystems, with customers including Fujitsu (about 23% of sales), Fujitsu Siemens, Hewlett-Packard, Lenovo, Samsung, and Toshiba. The technology was originally developed within Harris Semiconductor, and AuthenTec was spun out of Harris Corporation. The company gets more than 90% of sales from the Asia/Pacific region.

	Annual Growth	12/03	12/04	12/05	12/06	12/07
Sales ($ mil.)	32.6%	16.9	13.8	19.2	33.2	52.3
Net income ($ mil.)	—	—	(4.6)	(11.1)	(9.8)	(10.9)
Market value ($ mil.)	—	—	—	—	—	419.8
Employees	20.8%	54	—	—	97	115

AUTHENTIDATE HOLDING CORP.

NASDAQ (GM): ADAT

Connell Corporate Center, 3 Connell Dr.	CEO: O'Connell (Ben) Benjamin
Berkeley Heights, NJ 07922	CFO: William A. (Bill) Marshall
Phone: 908-787-1700	HR: Sean Nelson
Fax: 908-673-9920	FYE: June 30
Web: authentidate.com	Type: Public

AuthentiDate Holding puts its stamp on time-sensitive documents. The company provides secure workflow management services such as electronic signing, identity management, and content authentication. In 2007 AuthentiDate sold its document management and systems integration businesses to a group headed by VP Tom Franceski and Gregg Laird (senior manager) for approximately $7.3 million. The deal enabled the company to better focus on its health-care, e-billing, and other security application development. AuthentiDate's Web-based authentication services are utilized for digital documents, including receipts and e-mails.

	Annual Growth	6/03	6/04	6/05	6/06	6/07
Sales ($ mil.)	(33.3%)	25.3	19.2	17.5	16.6	5.0
Net income ($ mil.)	—	(9.8)	(15.7)	(19.2)	(17.8)	(15.1)
Market value ($ mil.)	(7.2%)	71.6	360.5	91.5	91.2	53.0
Employees	7.0%	—	115	123	—	—

AUTHORIA, INC.

300 5th Ave.	CEO: Tod Loofbourrow
Waltham, MA 02451	CFO: Paul J. Pedevillano
Phone: 781-530-2000	HR: Michelle D. Roccia
Fax: 781-530-2001	FYE: December 31
Web: www.authoria.com	Type: Private

Authoria has an authoritative view when it comes to human resources. The company provides human capital management software that combines communications, compensation and performance management, succession planning, recruiting, and benefits plan administration applications. Its customers have included Aetna, Bank of America, Carlson, Pepsi, Pfizer, Royal Caribbean Cruises, and Sears. Founded in 1997 by CEO Tod Loofbourrow, the company counts Capital Z Financial Services, Van Wagoner Capital Management, Dain Rauscher Wessels, and Aflac among its investors.

	Annual Growth	12/03	12/04	12/05	12/06	12/07
Est. sales ($ mil.)	—	—	—	—	—	16.5
Employees	—	—	—	—	—	210

AUTHORIZE.NET HOLDINGS, INC.

293 Boston Post Rd. West, Ste. 220	CEO: Robert E. (Bob) Donahue
Marlborough, MA 01752	CFO: Timothy C. O'Brien
Phone: 508-229-3200	HR: Kathleen A. Harris
Fax: 508-229-3255	FYE: December 31
Web: www.authorize.net	Type: Subsidiary

Authorize.Net Holdings (formerly Lightbridge) makes it A-OK to use that plastic online. The company provides secure transmission of credit card and electronic check payments via Web sites, retail stores, mail and telephone, and mobile devices. It serves more than 200,000 small-business merchant customers in the communications, education, food, government, and sports industries. Authorize.Net also offers credit qualification, fraud prevention, and billing services. The company in 2007 sold its Telecom Decisioning Services unit, which formerly accounted for more than one-third of the company's sales, to focus on payment processing services. CyberSource acquired Authorize.Net for more than $660 million in 2007.

	Annual Growth	12/02	12/03	12/04	12/05	12/06
Sales ($ mil.)	(8.0%)	133.4	120.0	133.1	108.3	95.7
Net income ($ mil.)	62.0%	3.6	(1.5)	(15.4)	19.0	24.8
Employees	(27.8%)	738	—	—	629	201

AUTOBYTEL INC.
NASDAQ (GM): ABTL

18872 MacArthur Blvd.
Irvine, CA 92612
Phone: 949-225-4500
Fax: 949-225-4557
Web: www.autobytel.com

CEO: James E. (Jim) Riesenbach
CFO: Monty A. Houdeshell
HR: Lorna Larson
FYE: December 31
Type: Public

Autobytel puts cars on the information superhighway. Using the Autobytel.com Web site, a potential car buyer can complete an online request form for the desired new or used car. The form is forwarded to a local dealer, who contacts the shopper within 24 hours with a "no-haggle" price. The company also operates sites such as Autoweb.com (Internet car buying), CarSmart.com (vehicle data), AutoSite.com (resource for entry level buyers), Car.com (consumer auto portal), and CarTV.com (multimedia content). Autobytel generates most of its revenue through lead referral fees it charges dealers (car buyers pay no fees). The company launched its new flagship consumer-driven auto site MyRide.com in 2007.

	Annual Growth	12/03	12/04	12/05	12/06	12/07
Sales ($ mil.)	(1.3%)	88.9	122.2	125.3	111.1	84.4
Net income ($ mil.)	—	7.4	5.8	(6.3)	(31.5)	(5.4)
Market value ($ mil.)	(23.1%)	344.2	253.1	208.1	149.3	120.4
Employees	(14.6%)	—	—	426	364	—

AUTOCAM CORPORATION

4436 Broadmoor SE
Kentwood, MI 49512
Phone: 616-698-0707
Fax: 616-698-6876
Web: www.autocam.com

CEO: John C. Kennedy
CFO: Warren A. Veltman
HR: Jim Wojczynski
FYE: December 31
Type: Private

Members of both the UAW and the AMA use Autocam's products. The company makes precision components for the automotive and medical device industries. Autocam makes parts used in automotive air bags, brake systems, electric motors, fuel systems, and power steering systems. The company's medical components are used in the manufacture of stents, joint implants, DNA testing equipment, and ophthalmic and surgical devices. Autocam also offers machined components for power tools. Investment firm Aurora Capital Group sold Autocam in 2004 to investors including GS Capital, Roger Penske, and Autocam CEO John Kennedy.

AUTODESK, INC.
NASDAQ (GS): ADSK

111 McInnis Pkwy.
San Rafael, CA 94903
Phone: 415-507-5000
Fax: 415-507-5100
Web: usa.autodesk.com

CEO: Carl Bass
CFO: Alfred J. (Al) Castino
HR: Jan Becker
FYE: January 31
Type: Public

Autodesk has creative designs on moving past the desks of architects. The company is a provider of computer-aided design (CAD) software. Its flagship AutoCAD product is used primarily by architects and engineers to design, draft, and model products and buildings. Autodesk's other products include geographic information systems (GIS) packages for mapping and precision drawing software for drafting. The company also develops multimedia tools for digital content creation, including applications for animation, film editing, and creating special effects. In addition, Autodesk offers professional consulting and training services.

	Annual Growth	1/04	1/05	1/06	1/07	1/08
Sales ($ mil.)	22.9%	951.6	1,233.8	1,523.2	1,839.8	2,171.9
Net income ($ mil.)	31.2%	120.3	221.5	328.9	289.7	356.2
Market value ($ mil.)	60.3%	1,435.0	6,684.9	9,319.5	10,103.7	9,464.5
Employees	21.9%	—	3,477	4,813	5,169	—

AUTOIMMUNE INC.
OTC: AIMM

1199 Madia St.
Pasadena, CA 91103
Phone: 626-792-1235
Fax: 626-792-1236
Web: www.autoimmuneinc.com

CEO: Robert C. (Bob) Bishop
CFO: Diane M. McClintock
HR: –
FYE: December 31
Type: Public

AutoImmune develops drugs to treat immune system and inflammatory diseases — or at least it would like to. It believes delivering therapeutic proteins through mucous membranes (e.g., oral drugs) prevents them from being attacked by the body as foreign invaders. Drug candidate Colloral failed to win FDA approval to treat rheumatoid arthritis, so AutoImmune sells it as a nutraceutical through a joint venture with Deseret Laboratories (Colloral LLC). The company licenses its mucosal tolerance technology to other drugmakers such as Teva Pharmaceutical, Eli Lilly, and BioMS Medical.

	Annual Growth	12/03	12/04	12/05	12/06	12/07
Sales ($ mil.)	(32.0%)	1.4	0.1	0.2	0.4	0.3
Net income ($ mil.)	—	0.6	(0.8)	(0.7)	(0.5)	(0.1)
Employees	—	—	—	—	—	2

AUTOINFO, INC.
OTC: AUTO

6413 Congress Ave., Ste. 260
Boca Raton, FL 33487
Phone: 561-988-9456
Fax: 561-994-8033
Web: www.suntecktransport.com

CEO: Harry M. Wachtel
CFO: William I. (Bill) Wunderlich
HR: –
FYE: December 31
Type: Public

Once an automobile financing company, AutoInfo is still focused on transportation — but of goods, not people. Through its subsidiary Sunteck Transport, the company acts as a freight broker, arranging the transportation of freight for customers in the US and Canada through alliances with both truckload and less-than-truckload carriers, along with air, rail, and ocean transportation providers. Separately, Sunteck Transport acts as a contract carrier, generating business through a network of sales agents and contracting with truck owner-operators to haul customers' freight. Sunteck Transport doesn't own any transportation equipment of its own.

	Annual Growth	12/03	12/04	12/05	12/06	12/07
Sales ($ mil.)	41.9%	27.2	46.5	68.0	84.1	110.3
Net income ($ mil.)	5.3%	1.3	1.5	3.6	3.6	1.6
Market value ($ mil.)	29.2%	7.9	19.0	18.3	33.1	22.2
Employees	—	—	—	—	—	52

AUTOLIV ASP, INC.

1320 Pacific Dr.
Auburn Hills, MI 48326
Phone: 248-475-9000
Fax: –
Web: www.autoliv.com

CEO: Michael Ward
CFO: –
HR: Kris Bessinger
FYE: December 31
Type: Subsidiary

Autoliv ASP, Inc., the North American subsidiary of Sweden-based Autoliv Inc., designs and manufactures automobile safety restraint systems. The subsidiary manufactures airbag inflators (the largest cost item in making an airbag module), seatbelts, cushions, steering wheels, electronics, seat subsystems, and other automotive products. It also provides testing of automotive safety products for vehicle manufacturers. In addition to providing engineering design of products, the company is involved in research and development of driver and passenger airbag inflators, side impact airbag inflators, and inflatable curtain airbags. Autoliv ASP, with about a dozen locations across the US, was founded in 1996.

	Annual Growth	12/03	12/04	12/05	12/06	12/07
Est. sales ($ mil.)	—	—	—	—	—	1,705.7
Employees	—	—	—	—	—	7,500

An in-depth profile of this company is available to Hoover's Online members at hoovers.com.

AUTOMATIC DATA PROCESSING, INC.

NYSE: ADP

1 ADP Blvd.	CEO: Gary C. Butler
Roseland, NJ 07068	CFO: Christopher R. (Chris) Reidy
Phone: 973-974-5000	HR: Benito Cachinero
Fax: 973-974-3334	FYE: June 30
Web: www.adp.com	Type: Public

The original outsourcer, Automatic Data Processing (ADP) has still got it. ADP is one of the largest payroll and tax filing processors in the world, serving more than 585,000 clients. Employer services account for the majority of the company's sales; ADP also provides inventory and other computing and data services to more than 25,000 auto and truck dealers. Other offerings include accounting, auto collision estimates for insurers, employment background checks, desktop applications support, and business development training services. In 2007 ADP spun off its brokerage services division (investor communications and securities transaction processing) to shareholders as Broadridge Financial Solutions.

	Annual Growth	6/03	6/04	6/05	6/06	6/07
Sales ($ mil.)	2.2%	7,147.0	7,754.9	8,499.1	8,881.5	7,800.0
Net income ($ mil.)	2.8%	1,018.2	935.6	1,055.4	1,554.0	1,138.7
Market value ($ mil.)	9.1%	18,352.0	22,403.7	22,187.4	23,197.6	25,970.2
Employees	2.2%	—	—	44,000	46,000	46,000

AUTOMOBILE CLUB OF SOUTHERN CALIFORNIA

2601 S. Figueroa St.	CEO: Thomas V. McKernan
Los Angeles, CA 90007	CFO: John F. Boyle
Phone: 213-741-3686	HR: James Philipp
Fax: 213-741-4890	FYE: December 31
Web: www.aaa-calif.com	Type: Not-for-profit

Ready to ride to the rescue for cars that have gone south in the Southland is the Automobile Club of Southern California. One of the largest US affiliates of the American Automobile Association (AAA), the Auto Club of Southern California is a not-for-profit that serves about 6 million members from more than 70 offices in 13 counties. The club provides 24-hour roadside assistance, travel planning, auto pricing, buying, and maintenance services, as well as a host of insurance plans. In addition, members can renew vehicle registrations, plates, and stickers at club offices. The club also publishes *Westways* magazine, which offers travel tips and discounts. Ten auto enthusiasts founded the club in 1900.

	Annual Growth	12/03	12/04	12/05	12/06	12/07
Est. sales ($ mil.)	—	—	—	—	—	544.5
Employees	—	—	—	—	—	8,051

AUTOMOBILE PROTECTION CORPORATION

6010 Atlantic Blvd.	CEO: Larry I. Dorfman
Norcross, GA 30071	CFO: –
Phone: 678-225-1000	HR: –
Fax: 770-246-2468	FYE: December 31
Web: www.easycare.com	Type: Private

For those sweet cars that turn out to be sour lemons, Automobile Protection Corporation (APCO) sells lemon aid. The company offers extended-care warranties (under the EasyCare brand) and service contracts for new and used vehicles, including cars, pickups, and recreational vehicles. The warranties provide bumper-to-bumper mechanical coverage and offer rental car and towing reimbursements. The company has agreements with auto manufacturers such as Honda, Jaguar, Land Rover, Mazda, and Volvo. It sells its contracts through car dealers in the US and Canada.

	Annual Growth	12/03	12/04	12/05	12/06	12/07
Est. sales ($ mil.)	—	—	—	—	—	49.3
Employees	—	—	—	—	—	280

AUTONATION, INC.

NYSE: AN

110 SE 6th St.	CEO: Michael J. (Mike) Jackson
Fort Lauderdale, FL 33301	CFO: Michael J. (Mike) Short
Phone: 954-769-6000	HR: Julie Staub
Fax: 954-769-6537	FYE: December 31
Web: corp.autonation.com	Type: Public

AutoNation wants to instill patriotic fervor in the fickle car-buying public. The brainchild of entrepreneur and ex-chairman Wayne Huizenga (Waste Management, Blockbuster Video), AutoNation is the largest car dealer in the US (ahead of Penske Automotive Group and Group 1 Automotive). Formerly known as Republic Industries, the firm owns about 320 new vehicle franchises in some 15 states and online sales through AutoNation.com and individual dealer Web sites. AutoNation operates under different brands (including Mike Shad in Jacksonville, Florida and Go in Denver) in local markets. In addition to auto sales, AutoNation provides maintenance and repair services, sells auto parts, and finances and insures vehicles.

	Annual Growth	12/03	12/04	12/05	12/06	12/07
Sales ($ mil.)	(2.3%)	19,381.1	19,424.7	19,253.4	18,988.6	17,691.5
Net income ($ mil.)	(12.7%)	479.2	433.6	496.5	316.9	278.7
Market value ($ mil.)	(13.1%)	4,954.6	5,076.5	5,698.3	4,408.0	2,824.4
Employees	(3.8%)	—	—	27,000	26,000	25,000

AUTO-OWNERS INSURANCE GROUP

6101 Anacapri Blvd.	CEO: Roger L. Looyenga
Lansing, MI 48917	CFO: –
Phone: 517-323-1200	HR: –
Fax: 517-323-8796	FYE: December 31
Web: www.auto-owners.com	Type: Private

There's more to Auto-Owners Insurance Group than the name implies. In addition to auto coverage, the company provides a range of personal property/casualty and life insurance products including disability and annuities. The company operates through its aptly named subsidiaries (including Auto-Owners Life Insurance, Home-Owners Insurance Company, and Property-Owners Insurance Company). Its Southern-Owners Insurance subsidiary offers property/casualty insurance in Florida. Auto-Owners Insurance Group also sells commercial auto, liability, and workers' compensation policies. Established in 1916, the company operates in some 25 states nationwide and is represented by nearly 6,000 independent agents.

	Annual Growth	12/02	12/03	12/04	12/05	12/06
Sales ($ mil.)	—	—	—	—	—	5,001.1
Employees	—	—	—	—	—	

AUTOTRADER.COM, L.L.C.

5775 Peachtree Dunwoody Rd., Ste. A-200	CEO: Victor A. (Chip) Perry III
Atlanta, GA 30342	CFO: Dave Amundsen
Phone: 404-843-5000	HR: Sylvia Taylor
Fax: 404-568-3060	FYE: December 31
Web: www.autotrader.com	Type: Subsidiary

AutoTrader.com gives the Internet its very own Motor Mile. The company operates the largest used vehicle Web site, with more than 3 million listings from both private owners and dealers. It draws about 13 million visitors a month to browse through its extensive site, which also features related content, such as vehicle reviews, warranty information, insurance, and financing. In addition to used cars and trucks, the site offers listings for motorcycles, boats, and collectors cars, as well as some new cars. AutoTrader.com generates revenue from its paid listings and from other advertising. Cox Auto Trader, a subsidiary of Cox Enterprises, owns a majority stake in AutoTrader.com.

	Annual Growth	12/03	12/04	12/05	12/06	12/07
Est. sales ($ mil.)	—	—	—	—	—	392.0
Employees	—	—	—	—	—	1,315

AUTOZONE, INC.

NYSE: AZO

123 S. Front St.
Memphis, TN 38103
Phone: 901-495-6500
Fax: 901-495-8300
Web: www.autozone.com

CEO: William C. (Bill) Rhodes III
CFO: William T. (Bill) Giles
HR: Timothy W. Briggs
FYE: Last Saturday in August
Type: Public

Imagine that you are in your garage making some weekend car repairs. The wheel cylinders are leaking . . . the brake shoe adjuster nut is rusted solid . . . you're about to enter . . . the AutoZone. With some 4,000 stores in the US and Puerto Rico, AutoZone is the nation's #1 auto parts chain and has made inroads abroad with about 120 stores are located in Mexico. AutoZone stores sell hard parts (alternators, engines, batteries), maintenance items (oil, antifreeze), accessories (car stereos, floor mats), and other merchandise under brand names as well as under private labels, including Duralast and Valucraft. It also loans tools. ESL Partners, controlled by Edward S. Lampert, owns about 36% of the company.

	Annual Growth	8/03	8/04	8/05	8/06	8/07
Sales ($ mil.)	3.1%	5,457.1	5,637.0	5,710.9	5,948.4	6,169.8
Net income ($ mil.)	3.6%	517.6	566.2	571.0	569.3	595.7
Market value ($ mil.)	(0.0%)	8,143.4	6,000.8	7,319.3	6,199.1	8,130.2
Employees	2.8%	—	—	52,000	53,000	55,000

AUXILIO, INC.

OTC: AUXO

27401 Los Altos, Ste. 100
Mission Viejo, CA 92691
Phone: 949-614-0700
Fax: 949-614-0701
Web: www.auxilioinc.com

CEO: Etienne Weidemann
CFO: Paul T. Anthony
HR: –
FYE: December 31
Type: Public

Auxilio believes that imaging is everything. The company offers document image management and related services for the health care industry. It assists hospitals and health care systems in reducing expenses and increasing efficiency by improving image management for finance, IT, and purchasing departments. The company's services include vendor monitoring, management, and contract negotiation, training, information systems integration, and strategic consulting. Auxilio provides a detailed financial analysis onsite before creating document image management programs for clients, which include such companies as California Pacific Medical Center, Catholic Healthcare West, and Memorial Health Services.

	Annual Growth	12/03	12/04	12/05	12/06	12/07
Sales ($ mil.)	93.4%	1.4	7.3	4.3	10.3	19.6
Net income ($ mil.)	—	(3.4)	1.0	(3.4)	(3.9)	(0.1)
Market value ($ mil.)	(7.9%)	36.1	47.1	23.9	6.9	26.0
Employees	—	—	—	—	60	—

AUXILIUM PHARMACEUTICALS, INC.

NASDAQ (GM): AUXL

40 Valley Stream Pkwy.
Malvern, PA 19355
Phone: 484-321-5900
Fax: 484-321-5999
Web: www.auxilium.com

CEO: Armando Anido
CFO: James E. (Jim) Fickenscher
HR: Jennifer Evans-Stacey
FYE: December 31
Type: Public

Auxilium Pharmaceuticals is supplementing men's manliness. The company is focused on developing treatments for urological and sexual health. Auxilium's lone marketed product is Testim, a transdermal gel testosterone replacement treatment for hypogonadism (low or decreased testosterone production). To increase Testim's market penetration, Auxilium has entered into partnerships to disseminate its product abroad. Paladin Labs will market Testim in Canada, while Ipsen is marketing it in Europe. DPT Laboratories manufactures Testim for Auxilium which is also researching drugs for other conditions related to scarring and pain.

	Annual Growth	12/03	12/04	12/05	12/06	12/07
Sales ($ mil.)	81.6%	8.8	27.0	42.8	68.5	95.7
Net income ($ mil.)	—	(28.9)	(28.5)	(38.3)	(46.0)	(40.7)
Market value ($ mil.)	88.4%	—	182.7	160.8	523.9	1,221.9
Employees	31.3%	—	—	174	—	300

AVALON CORRECTIONAL SERVICES, INC.

Pink Sheets: CITY

13401 Railway Dr.
Oklahoma City, OK 73114
Phone: 405-752-8802
Fax: 405-752-8852
Web: www.avaloncorrections.com

CEO: Donald E. Smith
CFO: Michael C. Bradley
HR: –
FYE: December 31
Type: Public

Avalon Correctional Services benefits from its captive market. The company manages nearly 15 community corrections facilities in Colorado, Oklahoma, Texas, and Wyoming that have a total capacity of some 2,600 beds. Avalon Correctional Services facilities provide a variety of programs for offenders, who usually are within a few months of freedom. The company's services include drug abuse treatment, work release programs, and educational and vocational training.

	Annual Growth	12/03	12/04	12/05	12/06	12/07
Est. sales ($ mil.)	—	—	—	—	—	27.3
Employees	—	—	—	—	—	430

AVALON HOLDINGS CORPORATION

AMEX: AWX

1 American Way
Warren, OH 44484
Phone: 330-856-8800
Fax: 330-856-8480
Web: www.avalonholdings.com

CEO: Ronald E. Klingle
CFO: Timothy C. Coxson
HR: –
FYE: December 31
Type: Public

The magical promise of this Avalon is waste management services and golf courses. Through its American Waste Management Services subsidiary, Avalon Holdings helps customers manage and dispose of waste. Services include hazardous and nonhazardous waste brokerage and management services and captive landfill management services — management of landfills used exclusively by their owners. The company also operates two golf courses near its headquarters. The golf operations include the management of dining and banquet facilities and a travel agency. Chairman and CEO Ronald Klingle controls a 67% voting stake in Avalon Holdings.

	Annual Growth	12/03	12/04	12/05	12/06	12/07
Sales ($ mil.)	(4.0%)	53.5	30.0	34.2	39.3	45.4
Net income ($ mil.)	—	(3.6)	(2.7)	0.4	1.3	1.5
Market value ($ mil.)	19.8%	8.4	10.1	14.9	23.0	17.2
Employees	—	—	—	143	—	—

AVALON OIL & GAS, INC.

OTC: AOGN

310 4th Ave. South
Minneapolis, MN 55415
Phone: 612-359-9020
Fax: 612-359-9017
Web: www.avalonoilinc.com

CEO: Kent A. Rodriguez
CFO: Kent A. Rodriguez
HR: –
FYE: March 31
Type: Public

Avalon Oil & Gas is looking for that legendary prize — making consistent profits in the oil business. The company focuses on acquiring mature oil and gas wells in Kansas, Louisiana, Oklahoma, and Texas and in 2007 had proved reserves of 28,772 barrels of oil equivalent. In addition, its technology group acquires oil production enhancing technologies. In 2006 Avalon acquired paraffin wax deposition mitigator Ultrasonic Mitigation Technologies. In 2007 the company and a partner jointly acquired a six-well production property located in Grant Parish, Louisiana from a Lafayette-based company. It also acquired a 15% stake in an oil field in Texas. CEO Kent Rodriguez owns about 43% of Avalon Oil & Gas.

	Annual Growth	3/03	3/04	3/05	3/06	3/07
Sales ($ mil.)	—	—	—	—	—	0.1
Net income ($ mil.)	—	—	—	—	—	(3.4)
Market value ($ mil.)	—	—	—	—	—	13.3
Employees	—	—	—	—	—	—

An in-depth profile of this company is available to Hoover's Online members at hoovers.com.

199

AVALON PHARMACEUTICALS, INC.

NASDAQ (GM): AVRX

20358 Seneca Meadows Pkwy.
Germantown, MD 20876
Phone: 301-556-9900
Fax: 301-556-9910
Web: www.avalonrx.com

CEO: Kenneth C. Carter
CFO: C. Eric Winzer
HR: –
FYE: December 31
Type: Public

Avalon Pharmaceuticals doesn't mind if genes express themselves — but they should know that anything they express can and will be used against them if they lead to cancer. The biopharmaceutical firm develops cancer therapeutics based on its AvalonRx platform, which identifies compounds that would be best suited to advance in clinical drug development. Lead product AVN944, an inhibitor of hematologic (leukemia, lymphoma, and myeloma) and solid tumor cancers, is an oral drug now in clinical trials. Avalon also has preclinical programs to develop inhibitors through partnerships with AstraZeneca, ChemDiv, Medarex, Merck, and Novartis. AVN944 was licensed from Vertex Pharmaceuticals.

	Annual Growth	12/03	12/04	12/05	12/06	12/07
Sales ($ mil.)	68.2%	0.1	1.9	1.5	2.7	0.8
Net income ($ mil.)	—	(17.1)	(13.7)	(19.3)	(17.1)	(21.7)
Market value ($ mil.)	20.9%	—	—	37.8	39.5	55.3
Employees	—	—	—	43	—	—

AVALONBAY COMMUNITIES, INC.

NYSE: AVB

2900 Eisenhower Ave., Ste. 300
Alexandria, VA 22314
Phone: 703-329-6300
Fax: 703-329-1459
Web: www.avalonbay.com

CEO: Bryce Blair
CFO: Thomas J. (Tom) Sargeant
HR: Charlene Rothkopf
FYE: December 31
Type: Public

AvalonBay Communities likes to go where the living is easy but the rules are strict. AvalonBay develops, acquires, refurbishes, leases, and manages apartment complexes. The real estate investment trust (REIT) focuses on upscale areas where restrictive municipal-development curbs have driven up demand and rents. AvalonBay owns about 160 apartment complexes containing more than 45,000 apartments in 10 states and Washington, DC. Most are branded under the Avalon name. Key markets include Boston and San Jose, California. Apartments are typically upscale and offer such amenities as swimming pools, tennis courts, and patios; most are garden-style, but about three dozen are mid- or high-rise communities.

	Annual Growth	12/03	12/04	12/05	12/06	12/07
Sales ($ mil.)	7.4%	609.7	648.5	670.7	737.3	812.7
Net income ($ mil.)	7.2%	271.5	219.7	322.4	266.5	358.2
Market value ($ mil.)	21.0%	3,390.8	5,465.4	6,574.4	9,710.6	7,278.8
Employees	9.9%	—	—	1,647	1,767	1,989

AVANEX CORPORATION

NASDAQ (GM): AVNX

40919 Encyclopedia Circle
Fremont, CA 94538
Phone: 510-897-4188
Fax: 510-897-4189
Web: www.avanex.com

CEO: Jo S. Major Jr.
CFO: Marla Sanchez
HR: Jing Liao
FYE: June 30
Type: Public

Avanex is light on its feet, and may need that flexibility to survive. The company's miniature photonic components help increase the speed and capacity of fiber-optic communications networks, in part by compensating for signal degradation during transmission. Its optical multiplexing products separate the light pulses traveling through optical fiber into individual wavelengths and control their power to boost the range of transmissions. The company sells its products directly in the US and Europe and through distributors in Japan, primarily to manufacturers of optical networking equipment.

	Annual Growth	6/03	6/04	6/05	6/06	6/07
Sales ($ mil.)	77.6%	21.4	106.9	160.7	162.9	212.8
Net income ($ mil.)	—	(102.9)	(124.1)	(108.4)	(54.7)	(30.6)
Market value ($ mil.)	10.4%	274.4	557.6	130.4	359.7	407.1
Employees	26.3%	212	963	792	610	539

AVANIR PHARMACEUTICALS

NASDAQ (GM): AVNR

101 Enterprise, Ste. 300
Aliso Viejo, CA 92656
Phone: 949-389-6700
Fax: 949-643-6800
Web: www.avanir.com

CEO: Keith A. Katkin
CFO: Christine G. Ocampo
HR: –
FYE: September 30
Type: Public

Baseball players and AVANIR Pharmaceuticals know: A sacrifice is sometimes the only way to get ahead. The drug development firm in 2007 opted to sacrifice its marketed schizophrenia drug, FazaClo, in order to advance lead candidate Zenvia in clinical trials. It sold FazaClo, which it had bought just the year before with the acquisition of Alamo Pharmaceuticals, to Irish drug developer Azur Pharma; it is using the proceeds to continue developing Zenvia as a treatment for pseudobulbar affect, the involuntary crying or laughing experienced by some people with such neurological disorders as Lou Gehrig's disease and multiple sclerosis. Zenvia is also in late-stage trials for diabetic neuropathic pain.

	Annual Growth	9/03	9/04	9/05	9/06	9/07
Sales ($ mil.)	39.9%	2.4	3.6	16.7	15.2	9.2
Net income ($ mil.)	—	(23.2)	(28.1)	(30.6)	(62.5)	(20.9)
Market value ($ mil.)	(57.9%)	—	—	—	219.4	92.3
Employees	—	—	—	76	—	—

AVANT IMMUNOTHERAPEUTICS, INC.

NASDAQ (GM): AVAN

119 4th Ave.
Needham, MA 02494
Phone: 781-433-0771
Fax: 781-433-0262
Web: www.avantimmune.com

CEO: Anthony S. Marucci
CFO: Avery W. (Chip) Catlin
HR: –
FYE: December 31
Type: Public

AVANT Immunotherapeutics wishes travelers "bon voyage" by helping them stay healthy on holiday. The biotech firm is developing oral vaccines for travelers to protect them from such maladies as *E. coli* and dysentery, and it is also working on other antibacterial vaccines to prevent cholera and typhoid. The company developed Rotarix, a vaccine that combats rotavirus infection, which causes diarrhea and vomiting in infants; partner GlaxoSmithKline sells the product worldwide and received FDA approval to market it in the US in 2008. Also in 2008, AVANT merged with privately held biotech Celldex Therapeutics, adding investigational products that may fight cancer and other diseases.

	Annual Growth	12/03	12/04	12/05	12/06	12/07
Sales ($ mil.)	2.6%	4.6	6.9	3.1	4.9	5.1
Net income ($ mil.)	—	(12.7)	(13.2)	(18.1)	(20.4)	(21.6)
Market value ($ mil.)	—	—	—	—	—	3.1
Employees	(21.0%)	—	—	85	—	53

AVATAR HOLDINGS INC.

NASDAQ (GS): AVTR

201 Alhambra Cir.
Coral Gables, FL 33134
Phone: 305-442-7000
Fax: 305-448-9927
Web: www.avatarhomes.com

CEO: Gerald D. Kelfer
CFO: Randy L. Kotler
HR: –
FYE: December 31
Type: Public

Avatar aspires to be the embodiment of retirement living. The company develops residential communities in the popular retirement destinations of central Florida and Arizona; amenities include golf courses, restaurants, and fitness centers. The company owns some 32,000 acres in Florida and Arizona of developed and developable land as well as wetlands and other open space. To focus on its core operations, Avatar Holdings has sold its cable TV holdings, mini-storage, and shopping center in Poinciana, Florida; its Harbor Island marina in Hollywood, Florida; and its utility operations in Arizona. The company also continues to purchase more land in Florida with an eye on future developments.

	Annual Growth	12/03	12/04	12/05	12/06	12/07
Sales ($ mil.)	3.6%	253.0	337.4	516.8	835.1	291.4
Net income ($ mil.)	3.7%	18.5	29.6	63.1	174.7	21.4
Market value ($ mil.)	0.7%	346.8	387.6	449.2	662.5	356.5
Employees	(25.9%)	—	—	585	483	321

AVATAR SYSTEMS, INC.

OTC: AVSYE

2801 Network Blvd., Ste. 210
Frisco, TX 75034
Phone: 972-720-1800
Fax: 972-720-1900
Web: www.avatarsystems.net

CEO: Robert C. (Chuck) Shreve Jr.
CFO: Robert C. (Chuck) Shreve Jr.
HR: –
FYE: December 31
Type: Public

Avatar Systems hopes to help you drill down to a more profitable bottom line. The company provides enterprise resource planning software for companies engaged in the petroleum exploration and production industries. The company's products and services are used to automate and integrate data and workflows across businesses, share information with external partners and suppliers, manage accounting and inventory, and handle payroll and billing. Avatar's professional services include consulting, implementation, integration, support, and maintenance.

	Annual Growth	12/03	12/04	12/05	12/06	12/07
Sales ($ mil.)	23.6%	2.1	2.7	2.3	3.7	4.9
Net income ($ mil.)	10.7%	0.2	0.2	0.2	0.3	0.3
Employees	—	—	—	—	23	—

AVATECH SOLUTIONS, INC.

OTC: AVSO

10715 Red Run Blvd., Ste. 101
Owings Mills, MD 21117
Phone: 410-581-8080
Fax: 410-581-8088
Web: www.avatechsolutions.com

CEO: George M. Davis
CFO: Lawrence (Larry) Rychlak
HR: –
FYE: June 30
Type: Public

Avatech Solutions wants to help make the design process automatic. The company resells and services third-party CAD/CAM software. One of the world's largest integrators of Autodesk software, it generates about 90% of its revenues from AutoCAD and other Autodesk packages. Avatech targets customers involved in architectural, mechanical, surveying, and civil engineering. The company's services include application development, document management, support, and training. Avatech Solutions was formed in 1997 with the merger of four Autodesk resellers.

	Annual Growth	6/03	6/04	6/05	6/06	6/07
Sales ($ mil.)	21.7%	23.0	28.0	34.1	39.6	50.5
Net income ($ mil.)	—	(3.8)	(0.9)	1.9	2.2	(0.6)
Market value ($ mil.)	84.8%	1.5	8.6	6.0	29.3	17.8
Employees	—	—	—	—	—	231

AVAX TECHNOLOGIES, INC.

OTC: AVXT

2000 Hamilton St., Ste. 204
Philadelphia, PA 19130
Phone: 215-241-9760
Fax: 215-241-9684
Web: www.avax-tech.com

CEO: François Martelet
CFO: Richard P. (Rich) Rainey
HR: –
FYE: December 31
Type: Public

AVAX Technologies wants to turn cancer cells into cancer fighters. The company is developing vaccines created by extracting a patient's own cancer cells and chemically treating them to induce an immune system response. The technology used to create the vaccines (called AC Vaccine) is licensed from Thomas Jefferson University. AVAX's lead vaccine candidate M-Vax is intended as a post-surgical treatment for late-stage melanoma, but the company is also developing vaccine candidates to fight ovarian cancer (O-Vax) and non-small cell lung cancer (L-Vax). The company also offers contract manufacturing services to other biotech and pharmaceutical companies.

	Annual Growth	12/03	12/04	12/05	12/06	12/07
Sales ($ mil.)	(9.6%)	0.9	1.7	1.6	0.7	0.6
Net income ($ mil.)	—	(3.3)	(3.5)	(3.7)	(5.4)	(6.4)
Employees	14.3%	17	20	22	24	29

AVAYA INC.

OTC: AVSYE

211 Mount Airy Rd.
Basking Ridge, NJ 07920
Phone: 908-953-6000
Fax: 908-953-7609
Web: www.avaya.com

CEO: Louis J. (Lou) D'Ambrosio
CFO: Edwin J. (Ed) Gillis
HR: Roger C. Gaston
FYE: September 30
Type: Private

Avaya helps to tie the corporate world together. The company's communication equipment and software integrates voice and data services for customers including large corporations, government agencies, and small businesses. Avaya's office phone systems incorporate IP telephony, messaging, Web access, and interactive voice response. The company offers a wide array of consulting, integration, and managed services through its Avaya Global Services unit. It sells directly and through distributors, resellers, systems integrators, and telecom service providers. Avaya was acquired by Silver Lake Partners and TPG Capital for $8.2 billion in 2007.

	Annual Growth	9/02	9/03	9/04	9/05	9/06
Sales ($ mil.)	1.0%	4,956.0	4,338.0	4,069.0	4,902.0	5,148.0
Net income ($ mil.)	—	(666.0)	(88.0)	296.0	921.0	201.0
Employees	(0.4%)	18,800	—	—	19,100	18,525

AVENTINE RENEWABLE ENERGY HOLDINGS, INC.

NYSE: AVR

120 N. Parkway
Pekin, IL 61554
Phone: 309-347-9200
Fax: 309-346-0742
Web: www.aventinerei.com

CEO: Ronald H. Miller
CFO: Ajay Sabherwal
HR: Roger E. Bushue
FYE: December 31
Type: Public

Aventine Renewable Energy Holdings is a leading US producer and marketer of ethanol, a grain alcohol mainly used as a fuel additive in gasoline to reduce vehicle emissions and enhance engine performance. Through its production facilities in Illinois and Nebraska and through purchase and resale operations and marketing alliances with other producers, the company distributes approximately 700 million gallons of ethanol. Major customers include BP, ConocoPhillips, Chevron Corporation, Royal Dutch Shell, Marathon Oil, and Valero. In 2006 the company began to trade publicly.

	Annual Growth	12/03	12/04	12/05	12/06	12/07
Sales ($ mil.)	23.5%	675.8	858.9	935.5	1,592.4	1,571.6
Net income ($ mil.)	53.4%	6.1	29.2	32.2	54.9	33.8
Market value ($ mil.)	(45.9%)	—	—	—	984.4	532.5
Employees	3.1%	—	—	—	321	331

AVENUE ENTERTAINMENT GROUP, INC.

Pink Sheets: PIXG

10 W. 66th St.
New York, NY 10023
Phone: 212-769-3814
Fax: –

CEO: Michael D. Feldman
CFO: Jerome I. (Jerry) Feldman
HR: –
FYE: December 31
Type: Public

Avenue Entertainment formerly brought entertainment to the street where you live. The company produced films such as *Closer* and *The Merchant of Venice*, and made-for-TV and cable movies, including *Angels in America* and *Path To Paradise: The Untold Story of the World Trade Center Bombing*, both for HBO. Its Wombat Productions created one-hour profiles of Hollywood celebrities, shown on networks such as PBS, A&E, and Bravo. Avenue Entertainment halted production activities and sold its assets in 2007. The company is seeking another business to acquire.

	Annual Growth	12/03	12/04	12/05	12/06	12/07
Sales ($ mil.)	—	—	—	—	0.0	0.0
Net income ($ mil.)	—	—	—	—	0.7	(0.1)
Employees	—	—	—	—	—	—

AVENUE GROUP, INC.

OTC: AVNU

405 Lexington Ave., 26th Floor
New York, NY 10174
Phone: 888-612-4188
Fax: 347-952-3683
Web: www.avenuegroupinc.com

CEO: Levi Mochkin
CFO: –
HR: –
FYE: December 31
Type: Public

Avenue Group, once solely located in the world of cyberspace, is now traveling along the narrower pathway of the US oil and gas industry. Chairman and CEO Levi Mochkin formed the company in 1999 to invest in Internet, e-commerce, and related IT ventures, but the company is now focusing on the oil and gas sector though the formation of its Avenue Energy subsidiary, which explores for oil and gas in the Appalachian Basin through its Avenue Appalachia unit. Avenue Group acquired a 50.1% stake in Stampville.com (an inactive business) in 2005. Mochkin owns 22.2% of Avenue Group.

	Annual Growth	12/03	12/04	12/05	12/06	12/07
Sales ($ mil.)	—	0.5	0.1	0.0	0.1	0.0
Net income ($ mil.)	—	(4.7)	(12.5)	(6.0)	(0.5)	(1.5)
Market value ($ mil.)	—	—	—	—	—	3.8
Employees	(15.9%)	8	7	5	5	4

AVERITT EXPRESS, INC.

1415 Neal St.
Cookeville, TN 38501
Phone: 931-526-3306
Fax: 931-520-5603
Web: www.averittexpress.com

CEO: Gary D. Sasser
CFO: George Johnson
HR: –
FYE: December 31
Type: Private

Averitt Express provides less-than-truckload (LTL) freight transportation service. (LTL carriers combine freight from multiple shippers into a single trailer.) The company operates a fleet of about 4,000 tractors and 11,250 trailers from a network of some 80 terminals. Averitt Express directly serves the southern US and selected major cities outside the region, and it provides service elsewhere in North America through partnerships with other carriers. The company also offers truckload and expedited freight transportation, along with logistics, warehousing, and international freight forwarding. CEO Gary Sasser owns Averitt Express, which was founded by Thurman Averitt as Livingston Merchants Co-op in 1958.

	Annual Growth	12/03	12/04	12/05	12/06	12/07
Est. sales ($ mil.)	—	—	—	—	—	921.3
Employees	—	—	—	—	—	7,675

⊞ AVERY DENNISON CORPORATION

NYSE: AVY

150 N. Orange Grove Blvd.
Pasadena, CA 91103
Phone: 626-304-2000
Fax: 626-792-7312
Web: www.averydennison.com

CEO: Dean A. Scarborough
CFO: Daniel R. O'Bryant
HR: Anne Hill
FYE: Saturday nearest December 31
Type: Public

Avery Dennison is easy to label: It's a global leader in the making of adhesive labels used on packaging, mailers, and other items. Pressure-sensitive adhesives and materials account for more than half of the company's sales. Under the Avery Dennison and Fasson brands, the company makes papers, films, and foils coated with adhesive and sold in rolls to printers. The company also makes school and office products (Avery, Marks-A-Lot, HI-LITER) such as notebooks, three-ring binders, markers, fasteners, business forms, tickets, tags, and imprinting equipment. Perhaps its most widely used products are the self-adhesive stamps used by the US Postal Service since 1974.

	Annual Growth	12/03	12/04	12/05	12/06	12/07
Sales ($ mil.)	7.3%	4,762.6	5,340.9	5,473.5	5,575.9	6,307.8
Net income ($ mil.)	3.2%	267.9	279.7	226.4	367.2	303.5
Market value ($ mil.)	(0.9%)	5,447.4	6,003.8	5,511.9	6,678.4	5,254.8
Employees	64.3%	—	—	—	22,700	37,300

AVERY WEIGH-TRONIX, LLC

1000 Armstrong Dr.
Fairmont, MN 56031
Phone: 507-238-4461
Fax: 507-238-8258
Web: www.wtxweb.com

CEO: Gerald (Jerry) Bowe
CFO: Ross Hunwardsen
HR: Len Bakken
FYE: March 31
Type: Private

Avery Weigh-Tronix makes a variety of industrial and retail weighing systems, including bench scales, conveyor scales, counting scales, floor scales, truck scales, and weigh bars. The company also makes accessories, such as printers, remote displays, signal processors, and wireless transceivers. Some of Avery Weigh-Tronix's predecessor companies, such as Avery and Salter, date back to the 18th century. Avery Weigh-Tronix was formed in 2000 when Weigh-Tronix, which was incorporated in 1971, acquired Avery Berkel from Marconi (now telent). The company has offices and distributors worldwide.

	Annual Growth	3/03	3/04	3/05	3/06	3/07
Est. sales ($ mil.)	—	—	—	—	—	1,016.7
Employees	—	—	—	—	—	5,500

AVI BIOPHARMA, INC.

NASDAQ (GM): AVII

1 SW Columbia, Ste. 1105
Portland, OR 97258
Phone: 503-227-0554
Fax: 503-227-0751
Web: www.avibio.com

CEO: Leslie Hudson
CFO: Mark M. Webber
HR: –
FYE: December 31
Type: Public

AVI BioPharma has a sixth sense about antisense. A developer of biopharmaceutical compounds, AVI's investigational therapies are based on its NeuGene antisense drug technology, which blocks the function of certain genetic sequences that are part of disease processes. Its lead candidate, Resten-NG, is undergoing clinical testing as a treatment for restenosis, or narrowing of the arteries. Additionally, Cook Group is using the drug to develop drug-eluting stents that prop open clogged arteries. AVI BioPharma is developing other antisense drugs for a wide range of diseases, including hepatitis C, Dengue Fever, cancer, and genetic diseases.

	Annual Growth	12/03	12/04	12/05	12/06	12/07
Sales ($ mil.)	82.1%	1.0	0.4	4.8	0.1	11.0
Net income ($ mil.)	—	(14.6)	(24.8)	(16.7)	(28.7)	(27.2)
Market value ($ mil.)	(10.3%)	140.3	84.9	176.6	169.1	90.9
Employees	—	—	—	123	—	—

AVIALL, INC.

2750 Regent Blvd.
Dallas Fort Worth Airport, TX 75261
Phone: 972-586-1000
Fax: 972-586-1361
Web: www.aviall.com

CEO: Paul E. Fulchino
CFO: Colin M. Cohen
HR: Jeffrey J. (Jeff) Murphy
FYE: December 31
Type: Subsidiary

Aviall has it all when it comes to aviation — the company is one of the world's largest distributors of commercial and general aftermarket aviation parts. Its Aviall Services business unit distributes new aviation parts, components, and supplies from about 225 OEMs to commercial airlines, military and government aircraft operators, and general aviation markets. Aviall Services also provides repair and assembly and supply chain management services. Rolls-Royce is the unit's largest customer. Aviall's Inventory Locator Service offers online inventory and service capabilities information to the aviation, marine, and defense industries. Aviall is a subsidiary of Boeing.

	Annual Growth	12/03	12/04	12/05	12/06	12/07
Est. sales ($ mil.)	—	—	—	—	—	143.0
Employees	—	—	—	—	—	1,009

AVICI SYSTEMS INC.

NASDAQ (GM): AVCI

101 Billerica Ave., Bldg. 2
North Billerica, MA 01862
Phone: 978-964-2000
Fax: 978-964-2100
Web: www.avici.com

CEO: William J. Leighton
CFO: William J. (Bill) Stuart
HR: –
FYE: December 31
Type: Public

Avici has chosen a new route. The company develops network management software for telecom carriers and enterprises through its Soapstone Networks unit. Avici traditionally developed core network routers. Its Terabit Switch Router (TSR), which was designed to prioritize, manage, and transmit large volumes of data over core fiber-optic communications networks, made a small dent in the high-end market dominated by Cisco Systems and Juniper Networks. In 2007 the company announced plans to phase out development of its core router products in order to focus on its Soapstone business. Avici plans to adopt the Soapstone name.

	Annual Growth	12/03	12/04	12/05	12/06	12/07
Sales ($ mil.)	33.3%	39.4	24.5	35.1	82.2	124.3
Net income ($ mil.)	—	(37.0)	(35.4)	(24.6)	8.3	62.3
Market value ($ mil.)	4.8%	97.3	121.6	51.5	107.6	117.2
Employees	(17.5%)	—	—	206	170	—

AVID TECHNOLOGY, INC.

NASDAQ (GS): AVID

Avid Technology Park, 1 Park West
Tewksbury, MA 01876
Phone: 978-640-6789
Fax: 978-640-3366
Web: www.avid.com

CEO: Gary G. Greenfield
CFO: Joel E. Legon
HR: Ed Raine
FYE: December 31
Type: Public

Media professionals are keen on Avid Technology. The company provides digital editing and professional audio systems for the film, music, and television industries. Its products, including Film Composer, Symphony, and Avid Xpress, are used by music and film studios, postproduction facilities, radio broadcasters, and television stations including the BBC, CBS, and NBC. Its Digidesign unit markets the ProTools line of sound editing systems. Avid also makes animation design software, newsroom automation systems, and digital storage systems. The company provides a line of video editing products for the consumer market through its Pinnacle Systems division.

	Annual Growth	12/03	12/04	12/05	12/06	12/07
Sales ($ mil.)	18.5%	471.9	589.6	775.4	910.6	929.6
Net income ($ mil.)	—	40.9	71.7	34.0	(42.9)	(8.0)
Market value ($ mil.)	(6.0%)	1,491.0	2,170.8	2,305.1	1,531.2	1,164.6
Employees	2.2%	—	—	2,613	2,792	2,731

AVIGEN, INC.

NASDAQ (GM): AVGN

1301 Harbor Bay Pkwy.
Alameda, CA 94502
Phone: 510-748-7150
Fax: 510-748-7155
Web: www.avigen.com

CEO: Kenneth G. (Ken) Chahine
CFO: Andrew A. (Andy) Sauter
HR: Janice (Jan) Linver
FYE: December 31
Type: Public

Avigen has decided to go back to pharmaceutical basics. While the company had focused its development efforts on gene therapies for Parkinson's disease and hemophilia, it has shifted its focus to small-molecule drugs. Avigen is investing its energy (and dollars) in traditional pharmaceuticals aimed at controlling chronic severe pain and other neurological and neuromuscular disorders. Its most promising candidates in the pipeline are AV650, a treatment for severe muscle spasm and spasticity, and AV411 for neuropathic pain. It has sought and found independent funding for its gene therapies in a deal with Genzyme, giving the biotech firm development and commercialization rights to those product candidates.

	Annual Growth	12/02	12/03	12/04	12/05	*12/06
Sales ($ mil.)	0.0%	0.1	0.5	2.2	12.0	0.1
Net income ($ mil.)	—	(27.7)	(25.8)	(23.9)	(14.7)	(24.3)
Market value ($ mil.)	3.7%	114.8	119.4	66.4	63.3	132.6
Employees	(24.6%)	102	—	—	32	33

*Most recent year available

AVIS BUDGET GROUP, INC.

NYSE: CAR

6 Sylvan Way
Parsippany, NJ 07054
Phone: 973-496-3500
Fax: 888-304-2315
Web: www.avisbudgetgroup.com

CEO: Ronald L. (Ron) Nelson
CFO: David B. Wyshner
HR: Mark J. Servodidio
FYE: December 31
Type: Public

Whether you're a business traveler on an expense account or you're on a family vacation and you're counting every penny, Avis Budget Group has a car rental brand for you. The company's Avis Rent A Car unit, which targets corporate and leisure travelers at the high end of the market, has 2,200 locations in the Americas and the Asia/Pacific region. Budget Rent A Car, marketed to those who watch costs closely, rents cars from 1,900 locations in the same regions and trucks from 2,800 dealers in the US. Avis Budget Group, formerly known as Cendant, changed its name in 2006 after spinning off its hotel operations (Wyndham Worldwide) and its real estate division (Realogy) and selling its travel unit (Travelport).

	Annual Growth	12/03	12/04	12/05	12/06	12/07
Sales ($ mil.)	(24.3%)	18,192.0	19,785.0	18,236.0	5,689.0	5,986.0
Net income ($ mil.)	—	1,172.0	2,082.0	1,341.0	(1,994.0)	(916.0)
Market value ($ mil.)	(38.4%)	—	—	—	2,194.8	1,351.8
Employees	(23.4%)	87,000	87,000	84,800	30,000	30,000

AVIS RENT A CAR SYSTEM, LLC

6 Sylvan Way
Parsippany, NJ 07054
Phone: 973-496-3500
Fax: 888-304-2315
Web: www.avis.com

CEO: F. Robert (Bob) Salerno
CFO: Toby Ippolito
HR: Mark J. Servodidio
FYE: December 31
Type: Subsidiary

A major player in the car rental industry, Avis Rent A Car System maintains some 2,100 locations, primarily in the US and Canada but also in Australia, New Zealand, Latin America, and the Caribbean. The company owns about 1,300 of its locations; franchisees operate the rest. A separate company with rights to the Avis name, Avis Europe, operates in Europe, Africa, the Middle East, and parts of Asia. Together with sister company Budget Rent A Car System, Avis Rent A Car System has a fleet of more than 380,000 rental cars. The company is a subsidiary of Avis Budget Group, the remaining unit of the former Cendant conglomerate.

	Annual Growth	12/03	12/04	12/05	12/06	12/07
Est. sales ($ mil.)	—	—	—	—	—	1,677.0
Employees	—	—	—	—	—	18,000

AVISTA CORPORATION

NYSE: AVA

1411 E. Mission Ave.
Spokane, WA 99202
Phone: 509-489-0500
Fax: 509-495-8725
Web: www.avistacorp.com

CEO: Scott L. Morris
CFO: Malyn K. Malquist
HR: Karen S. Feltes
FYE: December 31
Type: Public

It is no shock that Avista is a leading utility serving the northwestern US. The firm's regulated utility unit generates more than 1,770 MW of electricity, which is distributed to 352,000 customers in Idaho and Washington. It also supplies natural gas to about 311,000 customers in Idaho, Oregon, and Washington. In an effort to concentrate on its strength, Avista has sold its fuel cell development division, most of its communications operations, and most of the holdings of its nonregulated Avista Energy unit. The company continues to operate Advantage IQ, which manages energy expenses for clients.

	Annual Growth	12/03	12/04	12/05	12/06	12/07
Sales ($ mil.)	6.0%	1,123.4	1,151.6	1,359.6	1,506.3	1,417.8
Net income ($ mil.)	(3.6%)	44.5	35.2	45.2	73.1	38.5
Market value ($ mil.)	6.8%	876.0	856.5	860.6	1,329.1	1,139.7
Employees	21.5%	—	—	1,435	1,995	2,117

An in-depth profile of this company is available to Hoover's Online members at hoovers.com.

203

AVISTAR COMMUNICATIONS CORPORATION

NASDAQ (CM): AVSR

1875 S. Grant St., 10th Fl.
San Mateo, CA 94402
Phone: 650-525-3300
Fax: 650-525-1360
Web: www.avistar.com

CEO: Simon B. Moss
CFO: Robert J. Habig
HR: –
FYE: December 31
Type: Public

If geography prevents you from concluding business with a firm handshake, Avistar Communications is ready to furnish the next-best thing. The company provides communication software and hardware used to equip communications networks with video capabilities. Its systems enable videoconferencing, content creation, video broadcasting, and data sharing between users over telephony networks and the Internet. Avistar markets its products primarily to corporations in the financial services industry, including UBS Investment Bank, Deutsche Bank, and JP Morgan Chase. Chairman Gerald Burnett owns about 43% of the company.

	Annual Growth	12/03	12/04	12/05	12/06	12/07
Sales ($ mil.)	16.1%	6.6	6.9	6.9	13.2	12.0
Net income ($ mil.)	—	(8.6)	(8.7)	(5.2)	(8.1)	(2.9)
Market value ($ mil.)	(27.9%)	45.9	44.4	52.0	61.6	12.4
Employees	—	—	—	77	—	—

AVITAR, INC.

OTC: AVTIE

65 Dan Rd.
Canton, MA 02021
Phone: 781-821-2440
Fax: 781-821-4458
Web: www.avitarinc.com

CEO: Peter P. Phildius
CFO: Jay C. Leatherman Jr.
HR: –
FYE: September 30
Type: Public

Avitar is foaming at the mouth to promote a drug-free society. Literally: through its Avitar Technologies subsidiary, Avitar makes disposable polyurethane foam products for medical, dental, and diagnostic purposes. Avitar's best-sellers are diagnostic test products including drug-abuse test kits that use saliva (ORALScreen). The company also makes wound dressings and custom foam products (molded dental applicators, dressings for orthopedic braces). Products are sold through a direct sales force and through such distributors as Smith & Nephew and Quest Diagnostics. Avitar also offers contraband detection services through subsidiary BJR Security. Among its clients are NASA and CCA Industries.

	Annual Growth	9/03	9/04	9/05	9/06	9/07
Sales ($ mil.)	(9.4%)	4.6	4.1	4.5	4.9	3.1
Net income ($ mil.)	—	(6.5)	(3.0)	(2.4)	(3.7)	(2.3)
Employees	—	—	—	—	—	—

AVIZA TECHNOLOGY, INC.

NASDAQ (GM): AVZA

440 Kings Village Rd.
Scotts Valley, CA 95066
Phone: 831-438-2100
Fax: 831-439-6223
Web: www.avizatechnology.com

CEO: Jerauld J. (Jerry) Cutini
CFO: Patrick C. O'Connor
HR: Ted Washington
FYE: Last Friday in September
Type: Public

Here's an advisory on Aviza Technology: the company makes semiconductor production equipment. Aviza offers atomic layer deposition (ALD), chemical vapor deposition (CVD), and physical vapor deposition (PVD) gear. These machines deposit semiconductor materials in precise layers onto microchip wafers. Aviza also makes equipment that etches circuit patterns on wafers, as well as specialized furnaces used in microchip production. Customers include Infineon Technologies, Inotera Memories (29% of sales), Nanya Technology (12%), and Winbond Electronics. Customers in the Asia/Pacific region account for more than 60% of sales.

	Annual Growth	9/03	9/04	9/05	9/06	9/07
Sales ($ mil.)	16.3%	—	—	171.2	160.9	231.4
Net income ($ mil.)	—	—	—	(16.0)	(14.7)	0.4
Market value ($ mil.)	17.2%	—	—	—	61.4	71.9
Employees	26.8%	—	—	417	675	670

AVMED HEALTH PLANS

4300 NW 89th Blvd.
Gainesville, FL 32606
Phone: 352-372-8400
Fax: 352-337-8521
Web: www.avmed.com

CEO: Douglas G. (Doug) Cueny
CFO: Mike Gallagher
HR: Maryanne Divita
FYE: December 31
Type: Not-for-profit

AvMed Health Plans is flying high in the Florida HMO world. The not-for-profit company is one of the state's leading HMO providers (serving more than 200,000 members). AvMed designs policies for both small group and large employers throughout Florida; it also provides Medicare health plans in Miami-Dade and Broward counties in South Florida. Founded in 1969 as a health care system for pilots in the Miami area, AvMed (short for "aviation medicine") has broadened both its customer base and its product offering, introducing point-of-service (POS) plans and high-deductible plans with health savings accounts.

	Annual Growth	12/03	12/04	12/05	12/06	12/07
Est. sales ($ mil.)	—	—	—	—	—	884.9
Employees	—	—	—	—	—	850

AVNET, INC.

NYSE: AVT

2211 S. 47th St.
Phoenix, AZ 85034
Phone: 480-643-2000
Fax: 480-643-7370
Web: www.avnet.com

CEO: Roy A. Vallee
CFO: Raymond (Ray) Sadowski
HR: Steven C. (Steve) Church
FYE: Friday nearest June 30
Type: Public

If you're after an electronic component, Avnet probably has it. The company is one of the world's largest distributors of electronic components and computer products, alongside rival Arrow Electronics. Avnet's suppliers include 300-plus component and systems makers; the company distributes these suppliers' products to more than 100,000 manufacturers and resellers. Avnet Electronics Marketing handles semiconductors and other components. Avnet Technology Solutions provides computer products and services for resellers and large end-users, with system-level components, such as motherboards. The company distributes products in some 70 countries; customers located in the Americas account for about half of sales.

	Annual Growth	6/03	6/04	6/05	6/06	6/07
Sales ($ mil.)	14.7%	9,048.4	10,244.7	11,066.8	14,253.6	15,681.1
Net income ($ mil.)	—	(46.1)	72.9	168.2	204.6	393.1
Market value ($ mil.)	41.5%	1,481.1	2,518.0	2,742.6	2,936.0	5,938.3
Employees	9.3%	—	—	9,800	10,900	11,700

AVOCENT CORPORATION

NASDAQ (GS): AVCT

4991 Corporate Dr.
Huntsville, AL 35805
Phone: 256-430-4000
Fax: 256-430-4030
Web: www.avocent.com

CEO: Edwin L. (Ed) Harper
CFO: Edward H. (Teddy) Blankenship
HR: Julie Yarbrough
FYE: December 31
Type: Public

Avocent tries to give network administrators what they really need — the ability to be in multiple places at once. The company makes analog and digital KVM (keyboard, video, mouse) switching systems used to manage multiple servers. Its LongView extension products let computer users locate their mouse, monitor, keyboard, and other peripherals up to 500 feet away from their CPU. The company also provides systems management software through its LANDesk division. Avocent primarily sells its products to manufacturers such as Dell (13% of sales in 2007), Hewlett-Packard (12%), and IBM, and through distributors including Tech Data (11%) and Ingram Micro.

	Annual Growth	12/03	12/04	12/05	12/06	12/07
Sales ($ mil.)	18.6%	304.2	365.3	369.9	519.2	600.9
Net income ($ mil.)	4.5%	38.5	18.0	48.3	45.5	45.9
Market value ($ mil.)	(10.2%)	1,729.2	2,039.9	1,327.9	1,714.2	1,125.5
Employees	80.2%	—	—	—	997	1,797

⊞ AVON PRODUCTS, INC.   NYSE: AVP

1345 Avenue of the Americas	CEO: Andrea Jung
New York, NY 10105	CFO: Charles W. (Chuck) Cramb
Phone: 212-282-5000	HR: Lucien Alziari
Fax: 212-282-6049	FYE: December 31
Web: www.avoncompany.com	Type: Public

"Avon calling" — calling for a younger crowd and improved global operational efficiencies. Avon Products, the world's largest direct seller of cosmetics and beauty-related items, is busy building a global brand and enticing younger customers (while retaining its core base of middle-aged buyers). Direct selling remains the firm's *modus operandi*, but sales also come from catalogs, mall kiosks, and a Web site. Its products include cosmetics, fragrances, toiletries, jewelry, apparel, home furnishings, and more. Avon boasts about 5.4 million independent representatives. The firm, which has sales operations in 66 countries and territories, is in the final stages of a multiyear turnaround plan launched in late 2005.

	Annual Growth	12/03	12/04	12/05	12/06	12/07
Sales ($ mil.)	9.6%	6,876.0	7,747.8	8,149.6	8,763.9	9,938.7
Net income ($ mil.)	(5.5%)	664.8	846.1	847.6	477.6	530.7
Market value ($ mil.)	20.8%	7,940.1	18,248.2	12,889.8	14,580.6	16,907.0
Employees	(7.4%)	—	—	49,000	40,300	42,000

AVX CORPORATION   NYSE: AVX

801 17th Ave. South	CEO: John S. Gilbertson
Myrtle Beach, SC 29578	CFO: Kurt P. Cummings
Phone: 843-448-9411	HR: –
Fax: 843-916-7751	FYE: March 31
Web: www.avx.com	Type: Public

AVX proves that tiny parts can add up to big business. The company makes passive electronic components for products such as automotive braking systems, cell phones, copiers, hearing aids, and locomotives. AVX specializes in ceramic and tantalum capacitors, which store, filter, or regulate electrical energy in electronic devices. The company also makes a variety of electrical connectors, and it distributes components made by Japanese semiconductor packager Kyocera, AVX's majority shareholder and most important strategic partner. Customers include Flextronics, Motorola, Nokia, and Robert Bosch. About half of the company's sales are made in Asia.

	Annual Growth	3/04	3/05	3/06	3/07	3/08
Sales ($ mil.)	9.3%	1,136.6	1,283.2	1,333.2	1,498.5	1,619.3
Net income ($ mil.)	—	(107.6)	55.7	81.8	153.9	149.5
Market value ($ mil.)	(6.5%)	2,863.5	2,118.7	3,048.2	2,609.4	2,191.4
Employees	1.6%	13,150	12,000	12,100	13,000	14,000

AWARE, INC.   NASDAQ (GM): AWRE

40 Middlesex Tpke.	CEO: Michael A. Tzannes
Bedford, MA 01730	CFO: Richard P. (Rick) Moberg
Phone: 781-276-4000	HR: –
Fax: 781-276-4001	FYE: December 31
Web: www.aware.com	Type: Public

Aware takes an intellectual approach to the DSL market. The company, which sells hardware and software used to make asymmetric DSL equipment, derives some of its revenue from contract design services and licensing fees for its ADSL semiconductor intellectual property designs. Aware's products help telephone companies upgrade their systems without replacing transmission lines; they also help reduce download time for Internet users. Aware additionally develops compression software for video, image, and data transmission. The company sells to the likes of Infineon Technologies (about 26% of sales), Spirent Communications (16%), and Alcatel-Lucent (10%). Aware gets more than half of its sales in the US.

	Annual Growth	12/03	12/04	12/05	12/06	12/07
Sales ($ mil.)	25.0%	10.8	16.5	15.7	24.1	26.4
Net income ($ mil.)	—	(8.0)	(1.4)	(2.5)	1.0	0.2
Market value ($ mil.)	10.9%	66.2	111.1	103.6	126.0	100.2
Employees	6.1%	—	—	112	—	126

⊞ AXA FINANCIAL, INC.

1290 Avenue of the Americas	CEO: Christopher M. (Kip) Condron
New York, NY 10104	CFO: Richard S. Dziadzio
Phone: 212-554-1234	HR: Jennifer L. Blevins
Fax: 212-314-4480	FYE: December 31
Web: www.axa-financial.com	Type: Subsidiary

Have a financial planning question? Ask an AXA Financial financial planner. The subsidiary of French insurance giant AXA operates in two segments: financial advisory/insurance is the bailiwick of AXA Equitable, AXA Advisors, AXA Distributors, and the MONY Companies. They offer traditional, and variable insurance products, annuities, and other investment products to individuals, small businesses and trade organizations. Its investment management business is led by AllianceBernstein (63%-owned) and serves institutional and retail clients, including high-net-worth individuals. AXA Financial and its subsidiaries have approximately $900 billion in assets under management (most of it at AllianceBernstein).

AXA ROSENBERG GROUP LLC

4 Orinda Way, Bldg E.	CEO: Stéphane Prunet
Orinda, CA 94563	CFO: James Young
Phone: 925-254-6464	HR: Martha Clark
Fax: 925-253-0141	FYE: December 31
Web: www.axarosenberg.com	Type: Subsidiary

No need for rose-colored glasses; AXA Rosenberg Group prefers a more analytical approach to equity investing. The unit of insurance giant AXA manages stock portfolios for such institutional investors as corporations, pension funds, endowments, and foundations. It also acts as a manager or subadvisor for several mutual funds with holdings in global equities. AXA Rosenberg operates nearly 10 offices in financial centers around the world and has more than $140 billion of assets under management. Established in 1985, the company became part of AXA in 1999.

AXCELIS TECHNOLOGIES, INC.   NASDAQ (GM): ACLS

108 Cherry Hill Dr.	CEO: Mary G. Puma
Beverly, MA 01915	CFO: Stephen G. (Steve) Bassett
Phone: 978-787-4000	HR: Lynnette C. Fallon
Fax: 978-787-3000	FYE: December 31
Web: www.axcelis.com	Type: Public

Ion implantation devices are axial to Axcelis Technologies' business. Semiconductor makers use these implanters to insert ions into silicon wafers to change their conductive properties. Axcelis' other offerings include systems for dry strip, photostabilization, and rapid thermal processing of wafers. The company, which was spun off from industrial manufacturer Eaton, operates in Japan through SEN Corp., its joint venture with Sumitomo Heavy Industries (SHI), which pays royalties on Axcelis designs. Axcelis draws about three-quarters of revenues from customers in the US. Sumitomo Heavy Industries made an unsolicited offer to buy the company, a bid that Axcelis rejected.

	Annual Growth	12/03	12/04	12/05	12/06	12/07
Sales ($ mil.)	5.9%	322.0	508.0	372.5	461.7	404.8
Net income ($ mil.)	—	(113.9)	74.2	(3.9)	40.8	(11.4)
Market value ($ mil.)	(17.6%)	1,021.3	814.5	481.7	592.0	471.2
Employees	0.7%	1,593	1,658	1,615	1,755	1,638

AXCESS INTERNATIONAL INC.

OTC: AXSI

3208 Commander Dr.
Carrollton, TX 75006
Phone: 972-407-6080
Fax: 972-407-9085
Web: www.axcessinc.com

CEO: Allan Griebenow
CFO: Allan L. Frank
HR: –
FYE: December 31
Type: Public

Axcess International can watch the door and mind the store. The company's ActiveTag radio-frequency identification (RFID) system is for tracking people, vehicles, inventory, and equipment. Axcess International's Onlinesupervisor system integrates RFID data and digital video to a standard Web browser. The company has also developed a micro-wireless technology platform called Dot, a small, low-cost battery powered wireless computer for the automatic identification, locating, tracking, protecting, and monitoring of personnel, physical assets, and vehicles. Customers include security systems integrators and distributors in the US.

	Annual Growth	12/03	12/04	12/05	12/06	12/07
Sales ($ mil.)	39.4%	0.9	0.9	1.1	1.5	3.4
Net income ($ mil.)	—	(9.6)	(3.4)	(3.3)	(3.4)	(4.9)
Market value ($ mil.)	(3.8%)	43.8	42.8	22.5	33.5	37.5
Employees	—	—	—	—	—	—

AXESSTEL, INC.

AMEX: AFT

6815 Flanders Dr., Ste. 210
San Diego, CA 92121
Phone: 858-625-2100
Fax: 858-625-2110
Web: www.axesstel.com

CEO: H. Clark Hickock
CFO: Patrick C. Gray
HR: –
FYE: December 31
Type: Public

Axesstel can soup up that old phone on your desk. The company designs and manufactures fixed wireless voice and broadband data systems that link stationary office phones to the communications network via cellular connections. Axesstel's products include fixed wireless telephones, transmission terminals, and wireless modems. The company mostly sells its products to telecommunications companies in developing countries who then resell the products to consumers. Principal clients include India's Bharat Sanchar Nigam Limited and the Latin American operations of Telefónica Móviles and Telecommunications Movilnet.

	Annual Growth	12/03	12/04	12/05	12/06	12/07
Sales ($ mil.)	64.0%	11.4	62.6	94.7	95.5	82.4
Net income ($ mil.)	—	(2.2)	(8.3)	(10.2)	(6.6)	(9.0)
Market value ($ mil.)	(20.4%)	16.7	36.6	25.5	44.6	6.7
Employees	5.6%	—	78	97	87	—

AXM PHARMA, INC.

Pink Sheets: AXMP

20955 Pathfinder Rd., Ste. 100
Diamond Bar, CA 91765
Phone: 909-843-6338
Fax: 909-843-6350
Web: www.axmpharma.com

CEO: Wang Wei Shi
CFO: Harry Zhang
HR: –
FYE: December 31
Type: Public

Don't look for products from AXM Pharma at your local pharmacy. The company produces and sells prescription and OTC products in China through its AXM Pharma (Shenyang) subsidiary. It has more than 40 licenses to products but so far has only commercialized about half a dozen products, including LiveComf for dermatitis and other skin conditions; Bodyward, an alternative to penicillin for treating a variety of infectious illnesses; and Asarone, an anti-inflammatory for asthma and coughs that may also be useful in treating SARS. AXM Pharma also makes about half a dozen Sunkist-branded vitamins and supplements. Chairman Wang Wei Shi owns nearly 30% of the company.

	Annual Growth	12/01	12/02	12/03	12/04	*12/05
Sales ($ mil.)	(55.3%)	—	—	10.0	2.1	2.0
Net income ($ mil.)	—	—	—	(3.7)	(14.0)	(11.1)
Employees	—	—	—	—	—	150

*Most recent year available

AXS-ONE INC.

AMEX: AXO

301 Rte. 17 North
Rutherford, NJ 07070
Phone: 201-935-3400
Fax: 201-935-4088
Web: www.axsone.com

CEO: William P. (Bill) Lyons
CFO: Joseph P. (Joe) Dwyer
HR: –
FYE: December 31
Type: Public

AXS-One's first priority is to help customers get right down to business. The company offers Web-based applications that are used to manage and integrate a variety of back-office functions. Clients use AXS-One's software to manage tasks including data processing, asset management, and the delivery of Web-based content, as well as budgeting, forecasting, and revenue lifecycle management. The company also offers services such as consulting, training, and support. Customers come from fields such as manufacturing, telecommunications, and financial services.

	Annual Growth	12/03	12/04	12/05	12/06	12/07
Sales ($ mil.)	(26.0%)	39.7	38.4	32.8	10.3	11.9
Net income ($ mil.)	—	2.3	(5.2)	(9.0)	5.5	(14.9)
Market value ($ mil.)	—	—	—	—	—	15.9
Employees	—	—	—	209	—	—

AXSYS TECHNOLOGIES, INC.

NASDAQ (GS): AXYS

175 Capital Blvd., Ste. 103
Rocky Hill, CT 06067
Phone: 860-257-0200
Fax: 860-594-5750
Web: www.axsys.com

CEO: Stephen W. Bershad
CFO: David A. Almeida
HR: Lynn Kerley
FYE: December 31
Type: Public

Precision products are precisely Axsys Technologies' business. The company makes optical systems used in fighter planes, tanks, and other military and commercial applications. Offerings include precision metal optical, infrared optical, and motion control products, along with precision machined lightweight structures. The aerospace and defense market accounts for a majority of the company's sales; BAE SYSTEMS accounts for about 16%. Other customers include companies in the graphic arts, medical imaging, and semiconductor equipment industries. Axsys has divested its business that distributed precision ball bearings, spherical bearings, and bushings.

	Annual Growth	12/03	12/04	12/05	12/06	12/07
Sales ($ mil.)	19.2%	85.1	103.5	133.5	156.4	171.6
Net income ($ mil.)	35.4%	5.0	8.7	7.3	10.3	16.8
Market value ($ mil.)	73.8%	43.5	123.6	190.6	187.0	397.0
Employees	4.8%	—	—	749	765	822

AXT, INC.

NASDAQ (GM): AXTI

4281 Technology Dr.
Fremont, CA 94538
Phone: 510-683-5900
Fax: 510-353-0668
Web: www.axt.com

CEO: Philip C. S. (Phil) Yin
CFO: Wilson W. Cheung
HR: –
FYE: December 31
Type: Public

For applications in which plain silicon would get the ax, AXT offers fancier fare. AXT makes semiconductor substrates from compounds such as gallium arsenide (GaAs) and indium phosphide (InP), and from single elements such as germanium. Manufacturers use AXT's substrates to make high-performance semiconductors for products — including cell phones, fiber-optic devices, and satellite solar cells — for which standard silicon microchips are not adequate. AXT's customers include Avago, Bookham, Freescale, IQE, Kopin, and Samsung Electronics. Most of its employees are in China. Nearly two-thirds of sales are to customers in Asia.

	Annual Growth	12/03	12/04	12/05	12/06	12/07
Sales ($ mil.)	13.8%	34.7	35.5	26.5	44.4	58.2
Net income ($ mil.)	—	(26.7)	(13.6)	(12.2)	0.9	5.3
Market value ($ mil.)	27.4%	71.4	36.5	49.2	136.9	188.2
Employees	2.1%	972	1,010	842	1,022	1,057

AZ3, INC.

2761 Fruitland Ave.	CEO: Max Azria
Vernon, CA 90058	CFO: Brian Fleming
Phone: 323-589-2224	HR: Debra Parent
Fax: 323-277-5461	FYE: December 31
Web: www.bcbg.com	Type: Private

Its dba name may come from Parisian slang ("bon chic, bon genre," meaning "good style, good attitude"), but fashion firm AZ3 (better known as BCBG Max Azria) is rooted in America. French designer Max Azria started BCBG in Los Angeles, making his name with the novel baby-doll dress — which flew off the racks — and now sells his BCBG women's collection in some 100 company-owned stores (including outlets) in the US, as well as through in-store shops in department stores. The company operates about 30 stores in Canada, France, and Japan. AZ3 also boasts men's and plus-size lines, as well as accessories. Azria owns the company, which purchased the bankrupt G+G Retail in February 2006.

	Annual Growth	12/03	12/04	12/05	12/06	12/07
Est. sales ($ mil.)	—	—	—	—	—	465.8
Employees	—	—	—	—	—	2,918

AZTAR CORPORATION

2390 E. Camelback Rd., Ste. 400	CEO: Robert M. Haddock
Phoenix, AZ 85016	CFO: Neil A. Ciarfalia
Phone: 602-381-4100	HR: Sandi Whitford
Fax: 602-381-4108	FYE: Thursday nearest December 31
Web: www.aztar.com	Type: Subsidiary

Aztar wants a full house at its casino hotels and riverboats. The company's handful of properties include the Tropicana Express Hotel and Casino in Laughlin, Nevada; and the Tropicana Resort in Las Vegas (one of the last big redevelopment opportunities on the Vegas Strip). The Tropicana Atlantic City was seized by the state after losing its license; Aztar owner Tropicana Entertainment LLC subsequently filed for bankruptcy in 2008. Aztar found itself in the middle of a takeover fight in 2006; Columbia Sussex gaming affiliate Wimar Tahoe Corp. (doing business as Columbia Entertainment) acquired the firm in 2007 for about $2 billion. After the deal, Wimar Tahoe began operating as Tropicana Entertainment LLC.

AZZ INCORPORATED

NYSE: AZZ

1300 S. University Dr., University Centre 1, Ste. 200	CEO: David H. Dingus
Fort Worth, TX 76107	CFO: Dana L. Perry
Phone: 817-810-0095	HR: Robert D. Ruffin
Fax: 817-336-5354	FYE: Last day in February
Web: www.azzincorporated.com	Type: Public

When companies need to power up or get that "zinc-ing" feeling, they call AZZ incorporated (formerly Aztec Manufacturing). The company has two business segments: electrical and industrial products and galvanizing services. Through its subsidiaries, AZZ makes lighting fixtures, bus duct electrical distribution systems, and electrical power distribution centers and assemblies. Industrial, petrochemical, and power-generation and -transmission industries use the company's products. To protect steel from corrosion, the galvanizing services unit dips it into baths of molten zinc for companies in the highway construction, electrical utility, transportation, and water-treatment industries.

	Annual Growth	2/04	2/05	2/06	2/07	2/08
Sales ($ mil.)	23.8%	136.2	152.4	187.2	260.3	320.2
Net income ($ mil.)	59.3%	4.3	4.8	7.8	21.6	27.7
Market value ($ mil.)	77.4%	43.3	44.6	65.4	236.0	429.6
Employees	10.3%	959	965	1,019	1,301	1,422

B. BRAUN MEDICAL INC.

824 12th Ave.	CEO: Caroll H. Neubauer
Bethlehem, PA 18018	CFO: Bruce A. Heugel
Phone: 610-691-5400	HR: Charles (Chuck) DiNardo
Fax: 610-691-6249	FYE: December 31
Web: www.bbraunusa.com	Type: Subsidiary

B. Braun Medical is the US arm of German medical supply firm B. Braun Melsungen. The company's products and services include a wide range of IV systems and accessories, pharmaceutical devices, critical care products, and vascular access and interventional product lines, as well as outsourced pharmacy services and continuing education programs. B. Braun's customers include hospitals, outpatient surgery centers, and home care services. Its network of CAPS (Central Admixture Pharmacy Services) compounding pharmacies provides IV admixtures and solutions for more than 400 hospitals and home care providers throughout the US.

	Annual Growth	12/03	12/04	12/05	12/06	12/07
Est. sales ($ mil.)	—	—	—	—	—	345.2
Employees	—	—	—	—	—	4,099

BA MERCHANT SERVICES LLC

1231 Durrett Ln.	CEO: Dave Wood
Louisville, KY 40213	CFO: –
Phone: 502-315-2000	HR: –
Fax: 502-315-3535	FYE: December 31
Web: corp.bankofamerica.com/public/merchant	Type: Subsidiary

The next time you swipe your card and it clears, you might thank BA Merchant Services. A unit of Bank of America, it is one of the largest processors of electronic payments in the US. BA Merchant Services handles more than seven million check and credit, debit, stored value, and electronic benefits transfer (EBT) card transactions annually. Its clients include retailers, restaurants, supermarkets, utilities, gas stations, convenience stores, and government entities. BA Merchant Services was created when Bank of America acquired National Processing from National City in 2004 and combined it with its Merchant Card Services division.

	Annual Growth	12/03	12/04	12/05	12/06	12/07
Est. sales ($ mil.)	—	—	—	—	—	108.1
Employees	—	—	—	—	—	1,700

BAB, INC.

OTC: BABB

500 Lake Cook Rd., Ste. 475	CEO: Michael W. Evans
Deerfield, IL 60015	CFO: Jeffrey M. Gorden
Phone: 847-948-7520	HR: –
Fax: 847-405-8140	FYE: November 30
Web: www.babcorp.com	Type: Public

Bagels, muffins, and coffee are fueling this company. BAB operates a chain of about 130 franchised coffee and baked goods outlets under the brand names Big Apple Bagels and My Favorite Muffin. The stores offer several varieties of bagels and spreads, muffins, sandwiches, soups, salads, and gourmet coffee. The company also markets a proprietary java brand, Brewster's Coffee. BAB has coffee shops in more than 25 states, and in the United Arab Emirates. An investment group controlled by CEO Michael Evans and VP Michael Murtaugh owns nearly 40% of the company.

	Annual Growth	11/03	11/04	11/05	11/06	11/07
Sales ($ mil.)	(13.7%)	7.2	5.7	5.1	3.9	4.0
Net income ($ mil.)	18.9%	0.6	0.6	0.7	0.7	1.2
Market value ($ mil.)	23.5%	3.1	6.7	8.7	7.2	7.1
Employees	0.0%	—	—	—	33	33

An in-depth profile of this company is available to Hoover's Online members at hoovers.com.

207

THE BABCOCK & WILCOX COMPANY

20 S. Van Buren Ave.
Barberton, OH 44203
Phone: 330-753-4511
Fax: 330-860-1886
Web: www.babcock.com

CEO: John A. Fees
CFO: –
HR: Michael J. McCann
FYE: December 31
Type: Subsidiary

New York's first subway was powered by The Babcock & Wilcox Company (B&W), but don't blame the company if your train was running late this morning. B&W designs, supplies, and services power generation systems and equipment such as boilers and nuclear steam generators. The company provides about 25% of the world's boiler-powered electricity, and it has made nearly half of the process recovery boilers used in paper mills in the US. Founded in 1867, Babcock & Wilcox became a subsidiary of manufacturing and engineering company McDermott International in 1978. It entered Chapter 11 bankruptcy protection in 2000. The company emerged from Chapter 11 early in 2006.

BABIES "R" US

1 Geoffrey Way
Wayne, NJ 07470
Phone: 973-617-3500
Fax: 973-617-4006
Web: www1.toysrus.com/our/bru

CEO: Deborah M. (Deb) Derby
CFO: –
HR: –
FYE: Saturday nearest January 31
Type: Business segment

Babies may not be able to do their own shopping, but their parents can shop for them at Babies "R" Us. The company, a division of the giant toy seller Toys "R" Us, operates some 260 stores across the US as well as an online store. It offers toys, clothing, and accessories for newborns and toddlers, as well as guest services, such as a Mother's room, gift registry, and a special order department. Product offerings range from feeding, bathing, and potty-training supplies to baby furniture, strollers, car seats, high chairs, and organic/natural baby products. Founded in 1996, Babies "R" Us was taken private in 2005 when its parent company was purchased by a pair of private equity firms and a real estate concern.

	Annual Growth	1/02	1/03	1/04	1/05	1/06
Sales ($ mil.)	10.0%	1,421.0	1,595.0	1,763.0	1,863.0	2,078.0
Employees	—					

THE BABY'S ROOM, INC.

793 Springer Dr.
Lombard, IL 60148
Phone: 630-652-0600
Fax: 630-652-9080
Web: www.usababy.com

CEO: Ron Eriksen
CFO: –
HR: –
FYE: –
Type: Private

Make room for baby! Back in the 1970s, The Baby's Room founder Alan Levine sold baby furniture door to door. Recognizing an untapped market largely ignored by manufacturers, Levine started opening up his own retail stores in suburban Chicago in 1975. Today, The Baby's Room does business (primarily under the USA Baby name) through some 60 franchised stores in about 25 US states, as well as through a handful of locations in Mexico. The stores sell baby and children's furniture (cribs, dressers), linens, and strollers made by a variety of manufacturers.

BACARDI U.S.A., INC.

2100 Biscayne Blvd.
Miami, FL 33137
Phone: 305-573-8511
Fax: 305-573-7507
Web: www.bacardi.com

CEO: John P. Esposito
CFO: –
HR: –
FYE: March 31
Type: Subsidiary

Bacardi U.S.A. is truly a story of liquid assets — in more than one way. The company is the US import, sales, and marketing arm of privately owned Bacardi Limited, one of the leading wine and spirits producers in the world. Bacardi U.S.A. markets Bacardi rums (the #1 rum in the world) and Martini & Rossi wines and spirits, including vermouth. It also sells other liquid assets such as Dewar's Scotch whisky, Bombay gins, DiSaronno Amaretto, and Grey Goose vodka. The company changed its name from Bacardi-Martini U.S.A. to Bacardi U.S.A. in 1999.

	Annual Growth	3/03	3/04	3/05	3/06	3/07
Est. sales ($ mil.)	—	—	—	—	—	104.9
Employees	—	—	—	—	—	325

BACK BAY RESTAURANT GROUP, INC.

284 Newbury St.
Boston, MA 02115
Phone: 617-536-2800
Fax: 617-236-4175
Web: www.backbayrestaurantgroup.com

CEO: Charles F. Sarkis
CFO: Richard P. (Dick) Dalton
HR: Christine Bradley
FYE: Sunday nearest December 31
Type: Private

From the Maine lobster to the Charles River pie, Back Bay Restaurant Group wants its patrons to nibble on New England. The company owns and operates some 35 thematic eateries with a variety of menus. Its Papa Razzi trattorias offer Italian cuisine, while Joe's American Bar & Grill serves up steak, burgers, and more in a saloon setting. Its other restaurants include Charley's, Coach Grill, Atlantic Fish Company, and upscale steakhouse Abe & Louie's. The company's dining establishments are located in six eastern states and Washington, DC. CEO and majority owner Charles Sarkis opened his first restaurant in 1963 and formed Back Bay in 1983.

	Annual Growth	12/03	12/04	12/05	12/06	12/07
Est. sales ($ mil.)	—	—	—	—	—	69.4
Employees	—	—	—	—	—	3,200

BACK YARD BURGERS, INC.

500 Church St., Ste. 200
Nashville, TN 37219
Phone: 615-620-2300
Fax: 615-620-2301
Web: www.backyardburgers.com

CEO: C. Stephen (Steve) Lynn
CFO: Michael G. (Mike) Webb
HR: Charlotte Brown
FYE: Saturday nearest December 31
Type: Private

Back Yard Burgers offers diners the chance to eat a charbroiled burger without having to slave over hot coals. The company operates and franchises more than 170 of its signature fast food restaurants in 20 southern and Midwestern states. The eateries are known for their made-to-order charbroiled hamburgers made from 100% Black Angus beef. Back Yard Burgers' menu also includes chicken sandwiches, chili, milkshakes, salads, and cobbler. Most of the company's restaurants offer both dine-in and drive-through service. Founded by Lattimore Michael in 1987, the company is controlled by an investment group led by CEO Steve Lynn.

	Annual Growth	12/02	12/03	12/04	12/05	12/06
Sales ($ mil.)	6.5%	34.7	38.8	40.2	41.0	44.7
Net income ($ mil.)	(12.0%)	1.5	1.3	1.3	0.0	0.9
Employees	0.0%	1,000	—	—	1,000	—

☐ BACTOLAC PHARMACEUTICAL, INC.

7 Oser Ave., Unit 14
Hauppauge, NY 11788
Phone: 631-951-4908
Fax: 631-951-4749
Web: www.bactolac.com

CEO: Pailla M. Reddy
CFO: Renee Reynolds
HR: —
FYE: September 30
Type: Private

Bactolac Pharmaceutical (formerly Advanced Nutraceuticals) makes private-label vitamins, minerals, herbs, and other over-the-counter nutritional supplement products. The company's encapsulated and tablet-based products are available already packaged and branded, or sold in bulk to customers who repackage them for private-label sale. Customers include distributors, retailers, and multi-level marketing companies. Its services include product formulation, sample runs, and product testing. Chairman and CEO Pailla Reddy holds a majority of the company.

BAD BOY WORLDWIDE ENTERTAINMENT GROUP

1710 Broadway
New York, NY 10019
Phone: 212-381-1540
Fax: 212-381-1599
Web: www.badboyonline.com

CEO: Sean (Diddy) Combs
CFO: Derek Ferguson
HR: —
FYE: December 31
Type: Private

From music to fashion to food, Bad Boy Worldwide Entertainment Group sells attitude and image. The company oversees the business interests of its founder, owner, and CEO Sean "Diddy" Combs, a music impresario, fashion designer, and business mogul. Combs' core business is Bad Boy Records, founded in 1994 with Craig Mack and the late Notorious B.I.G., which produces such artists as Yung Joc, Danity Kane, and Cassie, as well as the music of Diddy himself. The label is 50% owned by Warner Music Group (WMG). Combs also markets branded clothing through Sean John Clothing and operates two upscale restaurants called Justin's (named after Combs' oldest son) in New York City and Atlanta.

BADGER METER, INC.

AMEX: BMI

4545 W. Brown Deer Rd.
Milwaukee, WI 53223
Phone: 414-355-0400
Fax: 414-371-5956
Web: www.badgermeter.com

CEO: Richard A. Meeusen
CFO: Richard E. Johnson
HR: —
FYE: December 31
Type: Public

Badger Meter does not measure the frequency of the appearance of a certain nocturnal carnivorous mammal. Instead, it provides water utilities and industrial customers with instruments that measure and control the flow of liquids. Badger, which was established in 1905, makes meters, valves, flow tubes, and other measurement devices for original equipment manufacturers, water and wastewater utilities, and companies in the pharmaceutical, chemical, concrete, and food and beverage industries. Its utility meters come with manual or automatic reading technology systems. Badger also makes a handheld device that dispenses and monitors oil and other fluids for the automotive market.

	Annual Growth	12/03	12/04	12/05	12/06	12/07
Sales ($ mil.)	6.3%	184.0	205.0	216.6	229.8	234.8
Net income ($ mil.)	21.4%	7.6	9.6	13.3	7.6	16.5
Market value ($ mil.)	113.5%	31.4	100.7	134.4	392.1	652.6
Employees	—	—	—	1,052		

BADGER STATE ETHANOL, LLC

820 W. 17th St.
Monroe, WI 53566
Phone: 608-329-3900
Fax: 608-329-3866
Web: www.badgerstateethanol.com

CEO: Gary L. Kramer
CFO: James (Jim) Leitzinger
HR: —
FYE: December 31
Type: Private

Badger State Ethanol hopes to badger gasoline consumers into using its ethanol. The company manufactures fuel-grade ethanol (a performance-enhancing gasoline additive derived from processing corn into ethyl alcohol) at the rate of 40 million gallons per year at its plant in Monroe, Wisconsin. Its ethanol is marketed through distributor Murex; the firm has also opened a retail fuel station. Badger State Ethanol also sells 128,000 tons a year of distiller's grains (an animal feed supplement) and carbon dioxide, two by-products of ethanol production. The company was formed in 2000 and opened its ethanol plant in 2002.

BAE SYSTEMS, INC.

1601 Research Blvd.
Rockville, MD 20850
Phone: 301-838-6000
Fax: 301-838-6925
Web: www.baesystems.com

CEO: Walter P. (Walt) Havenstein
CFO: Robert T. (Bob) Murphy
HR: Curtis L. (Curt) Gray
FYE: December 31
Type: Subsidiary

Subsidiary BAE Systems, Inc. takes care of business in North America for parent BAE SYSTEMS plc — the largest foreign player in the US defense market. Operations include the design, manufacture, and maintenance of military aircraft, submarines, surface ships, avionics, radar, electronics, and weapons systems. BAE Systems Inc. also provides IT services. Taken alone, BAE Systems Inc. has operations in 30 states and is a top five supplier to the US DoD. In 2004 the company acquired Boeing's commercial electronics business and government IT services company DigitalNet Holdings. BAE acquired United Defense Industries, maker of the Bradley Fighting Vehicle, in 2005.

	Annual Growth	12/03	12/04	12/05	12/06	12/07
Est. sales ($ mil.)	—	—	—	—	—	2,147.5
Employees	—	—	—	—	—	32,328

BAE SYSTEMS LAND AND ARMAMENTS

1525 Wilson Blvd., Ste. 700
Arlington, VA 22209
Phone: 703-312-6100
Fax: 703-312-6111
Web: www.uniteddefense.com

CEO: Linda P. Hudson
CFO: Gary Slack
HR: Debbie Sallis
FYE: December 31
Type: Subsidiary

Need to storm a beach? BAE Systems Land and Armaments has been making landing craft and armored vehicles since WWII. The company, formerly United Defense Industries, has an arsenal that includes combat vehicles (Bradley armored infantry vehicle), fire support equipment (self-propelled howitzers), combat support vehicles, weapons delivery systems (missile launchers, artillery systems), and amphibious assault vehicles. The US government is a major customer. BAE Systems Land and Armaments was formed in June 2005 when BAE Systems completed its acquisition of United Defense.

	Annual Growth	12/03	12/04	12/05	12/06	12/07
Est. sales ($ mil.)	—	—	—	—	—	513.0
Employees	—	—	—	—	—	5,130

☐ An in-depth profile of this company is available to Hoover's Online members at hoovers.com.

209

BAER'S FURNITURE CO INC

1589 NW 12th Ave.
Pompano Beach, FL 33069
Phone: 954-946-8001
Fax: 954-946-8006
Web: www.baersfurniture.com

CEO: Robert M. (Bobby) Baer
CFO: Ira Baer
HR: Sue Scovin
FYE: December 31
Type: Private

Family-owned Baer's Furniture operates about 15 retail furniture showrooms throughout Florida. The company offers furnishings (living room, dining room, bedroom, and office furniture), bedding, rugs, and accessories made by popular manufacturers that is designed to fit the budgets of shoppers with mid-level incomes and above. The chain was founded in 1945 by Melvin and Lucile Baer in South Bend, Indiana. Their sons Robert, now the company's CEO, and Allan, company president, moved the business to Florida in 1968.

	Annual Growth	12/03	12/04	12/05	12/06	12/07
Est. sales ($ mil.)	—	—	—	—	—	169.8
Employees	—	—	—	—	—	437

BAG'N BAGGAGE LTD.

11067 Petal St.
Dallas, TX 75238
Phone: 214-349-1800
Fax: 214-342-4301
Web: www.bagnbaggage.com

CEO: Patrick Sullivan
CFO: Rob Kuppens
HR: –
FYE: December 31
Type: Partnership

Shopping for new luggage is part and parcel of the offerings from Bag'n Baggage. The company stocks luggage from such manufacturers as Hartmann, Kenneth Cole, Lewis N. Clark, and Timberland, among others. Bag'n Baggage also sells backpacks, business and travel accessories, business cases, luggage racks, travel organizers, and wallets from its Web portal and its about 80 retail stores in nearly a dozen states. The company, which also does business as Houston Trunk Factory and Malm Luggage, offers repair services for luggage and leather goods, as well. Bag'n Baggage dates back to 1972. The company filed for Chapter 11 protection from creditors in 2003; its Chapter 11 reorganization plan was implemented in 2004.

	Annual Growth	12/03	12/04	12/05	12/06	12/07
Est. sales ($ mil.)	—	—	—	—	—	50.0
Employees	—	—	—	—	—	500

BAIN & COMPANY, INC.

131 Dartmouth St.
Boston, MA 02116
Phone: 617-572-2000
Fax: 617-572-2427
Web: www.bain.com

CEO: Steve Ellis
CFO: Leonard C. Banos
HR: Elizabeth Corcoran
FYE: December 31
Type: Private

Bain aims to be ready when corporate titans need a little direction. One of the world's leading management consulting firms, Bain & Company offers a wide array of services aimed at increasing efficiency and streamlining business processes. The firm also consults on strategic business issues, such as potential mergers and acquisitions and private equity investments; services include due-diligence preparation. In addition, Bain consultants address topics such as information technology, marketing, and performance improvement. The firm operates from more than 35 offices in about two dozen countries. It was founded in 1973 by Boston Consulting Group alumnus Bill Bain.

	Annual Growth	12/02	12/03	12/04	12/05	12/06
Est. sales ($ mil.)	15.9%	—	—	—	1,130.0	1,310.0
Employees	10.9%	—	—	—	3,200	3,550

BAIN CAPITAL, LLC

111 Huntington Ave.
Boston, MA 02199
Phone: 617-516-2000
Fax: 617-516-2010
Web: www.baincapital.com

CEO: Joshua (Josh) Bekenstein
CFO: Mike Goss
HR: Judy Frodigh
FYE: December 31
Type: Private

If you want to make a big deal out of it, chances are Bain Capital will be there. The private equity and venture capital firm invests in companies in the retail and consumer products, information technology, communications, health care, and manufacturing industries. Its holdings include stakes in Domino's Pizza, pharmaceutical group Warner Chilcott, Toys "R" Us, sportswear distributor Broder Bros., and SunGard Data Systems. The firm has made private equity investments in more than 200 companies since its 1984 founding. Bain Capital joined Thomas H. Lee Partners in a nearly $20 billion offer for broadcasting giant Clear Channel, and is part of a group that bought HCA for approximately $33 billion.

BAIRD & WARNER HOLDING COMPANY

120 S. LaSalle
Chicago, IL 60603
Phone: 312-368-1855
Fax: 312-368-1490
Web: www.bairdwarner.com

CEO: Stephen W. Baird
CFO: Martin Bozarth
HR: Wendy A. Adametz
FYE: December 31
Type: Private

Baird & Warner knows its Chicago history. Whether it be the Great Fire in 1871 or the last time the Cubbies won the Series, the venerable Baird & Warner touts itself as the nation's oldest and Illinois' largest independent real estate broker. It offers primarily residential real estate services to Chicago-area communities through a network of some 2,000 agents at more than 30 offices. Services include financing, title, and relocation offerings; it also provides a home services directory of cleaning, repair, landscaping, and other vendors that have been approved by the company.

ROBERT W. BAIRD & CO. INCORPORATED

777 E. Wisconsin Ave.
Milwaukee, WI 53201
Phone: 414-765-3500
Fax: –
Web: www.rwbaird.com

CEO: Paul E. Purcell
CFO: Leonard M. (Len) Rush
HR: Leslie H. Dixon
FYE: December 31
Type: Private

Employee-owned Robert W. Baird & Co. brings midwestern sensibility to the high-flying world of investment banking. The company offers wealth management, asset management, and middle-market investment banking services to corporate, institutional, and wealthy individual clients throughout the US, as well as in Europe and Asia. The company operates in three segments: private wealth management (about 45% of revenues), capital markets, and asset management. Baird has some $71 billion in assets under management.

	Annual Growth	12/02	12/03	12/04	12/05	12/06
Assets ($ mil.)	18.3%	857.6	1,129.9	1,331.6	1,311.5	1,681.4
Employees	(2.3%)	2,264	2,168	2,177	2,094	2,061

BAIRNCO CORPORATION

300 Primera Blvd., Ste. 432
Lake Mary, FL 32746
Phone: 407-875-2222
Fax: 407-875-3398

CEO: John J. Quicke
CFO: Lawrence C. Maingot
HR: –
FYE: December 31
Type: Subsidiary

Bairnco is on the cutting edge of chemistry and band saw blades. The company makes engineered materials and components through subsidiary Arlon and replacement blade products through Kasco. Arlon produces materials for printed circuit boards, substrates for commercial and military electronics, and materials for microwave applications. The subsidiary also makes cast and calendered vinyl films, custom-engineered laminates, and silicone rubber insulation products. Kasco makes replacement band saw blades (for cutting meat, poultry, fish, and wood). WHX Corp. owns Bairnco.

	Annual Growth	12/02	12/03	12/04	12/05	12/06
Sales ($ mil.)	3.7%	154.4	152.7	165.5	165.9	178.8
Net income ($ mil.)	37.5%	1.4	2.7	30.8	3.6	5.0
Employees	7.7%	757	761	738	836	1,020

BAKEMARK USA LLC

7351 Crider Ave.
Pico Rivera, CA 90660
Phone: 562-949-1054
Fax: 562-949-1257
Web: www.bakemarkusa.com

CEO: William (Bill) Day
CFO: Bruce D. Reynolds
HR: –
FYE: December 31
Type: Subsidiary

BakeMark helps bakers reach their mark. The company offers bakery ingredients such as cake and cookie mixes, pie and pastry fillings, and specialty prebaked products along with paper goods. Its brand names include BakeMark (mixes, bases, fillings, icings, glazes, flavors), Produits Marguerite (nut pastes, mousses, custards for French pastries), Trigal Dorado (mixes, margarines, fillings, frozen toppings for Mexican pastries), and Westco (fillings, bases, icings, glazes). With 18 locations, its customer includes retail, wholesale, and in-store bakeries, including bakery chains throughout the US. BakeMark USA is a subsidiary of Netherlands-based ingredient maker CSM, the world's largest bakery supplier.

	Annual Growth	12/03	12/04	12/05	12/06	12/07
Est. sales ($ mil.)	—	—	—	—	—	950.0
Employees	—	—	—	—	—	850

BAKE'N JOY FOODS, INC.

351 Willow St. South
North Andover, MA 01845
Phone: 978-683-1414
Fax: 978-683-1713
Web: www.bakingbusiness.com/images/ads/bnj.asp

CEO: Robert Ogan
CFO: Alice Shepherd
HR: Walter (Walt) Prior
FYE: –
Type: Private

Bake'n Joy Foods hopes its customers will enjoy bakin' with its shakin' mixes. The company manufactures premixed bases, batters, icings, dough, and dough conditioners for the baking industry. It also provides frozen ready-to-bake muffins and cakes. Bake'n Joy's products are sold at bakery counters in grocery stores, as well as in specialty stores and restaurants. The company was formed in 1940.

[L] BAKER & MCKENZIE

1 Prudential Plaza, 130 E. Randolph Dr., Ste. 2500
Chicago, IL 60601
Phone: 312-861-8800
Fax: 312-861-2899
Web: www.bakernet.com

CEO: John J. Conroy Jr.
CFO: Robert S. Spencer
HR: Greg Walters
FYE: June 30
Type: Private

Baker & McKenzie believes big is good and bigger is better. One of the world's largest law firms, it has about 3,600 attorneys practicing from some 70 offices — from Bangkok to Berlin to Buenos Aires — in almost 40 countries. It offers expertise in a wide range of practice areas, including antitrust, intellectual property, international trade, mergers and acquisitions, project finance, and tax law. Baker & McKenzie's client list includes big companies from numerous industries, including banking and finance, construction, and technology, as well as smaller enterprises. The firm was founded in 1949.

	Annual Growth	6/02	6/03	6/04	6/05	6/06
Sales ($ mil.)	9.5%	1,060.0	1,134.0	1,228.0	1,352.0	1,522.0
Employees	4.4%	8,000	8,401	8,400	8,500	9,503

[L] BAKER & TAYLOR, INC.

2550 W. Tyvola Rd., Ste. 300
Charlotte, NC 28217
Phone: 704-998-3100
Fax: 704-998-3316
Web: www.btol.com

CEO: Marshall A. (Arnie) Wight
CFO: James C. Melton
HR: –
FYE: Last Friday in June
Type: Private

If you've strolled through a library recently, you likely saw a lot of Baker & Taylor (B&T) without knowing it. The #1 book supplier to libraries, B&T primarily serves two types of markets. Its core business distributes books, calendars, music, and DVDs to thousands of school, public, and specialty libraries worldwide. The firm's retail unit supplies storefront and Internet retailers, as well as independent booksellers, with a million book titles and about 311,000 DVD, and CD titles. On the Internet (which formerly operated as Informata.com), B&T offers B2B e-commerce fulfillment services. Investment firm Willis Stein & Partners sold the company to Castle Harlan.

	Annual Growth	6/02	6/03	6/04	6/05	6/06
Sales ($ mil.)	18.3%	1,122.0	1,203.0	1,300.0	1,700.0	2,200.0
Employees	8.1%	2,750	2,850	2,700	2,600	3,750

BAKER BOTTS L.L.P.

1 Shell Plaza, 910 Louisiana St.
Houston, TX 77002
Phone: 713-229-1234
Fax: 713-229-1522
Web: www.bakerbotts.com

CEO: Walter J. (Walt) Smith
CFO: Lydia Companion
HR: Terry Mulchahey
FYE: December 31
Type: Partnership

Baker Botts is a Lone Star legal legend. The law firm's history stretches back to 1840, when founding partner Peter Gray was admitted to the bar of the Republic of Texas. The firm became Baker & Botts after Walter Browne Botts and James Addison Baker, great-grandfather of former US secretary of state and current partner James A. Baker III, joined the partnership. Today, the firm has some 750 lawyers in about 10 offices. Over the years Baker Botts has represented numerous clients from the energy industry, including Exxon Mobil and Halliburton. The firm practices in such areas as corporate, intellectual property, and tax law.

	Annual Growth	12/02	12/03	12/04	12/05	12/06
Sales ($ mil.)	8.3%	365.0	394.0	420.2	365.0	502.5
Employees	1.2%	—	1,582	1,601	—	—

An in-depth profile of this company is available to Hoover's Online members at hoovers.com.

211

BAKER BOYER BANCORP

OTC: BBBK

7 W. Main St.
Walla Walla, WA 99362
Phone: 509-525-2000
Fax: 509-525-1034
Web: www.bakerboyer.com

CEO: Megan Clubb
CFO: –
HR: –
FYE: December 31
Type: Public

For Baker Boyer Bancorp, it *is* personal. The holding company for Baker Boyer National Bank takes pride in the personal touch it applies to its services, which include standard deposit products, loans, financial planning, and insurance services. Through Baker Boyer Wealth Management Services, the company offers investments, private banking, brokerage, and trust services. Baker Boyer National Bank serves individual and business customers through about 10 branches in southern Washington and northern Oregon. Founded in 1869, the family-owned company is the oldest bank in Washington State.

	Annual Growth	12/03	12/04	12/05	12/06	12/07
Sales ($ mil.)	5.8%	—	26.6	27.1	29.3	31.5
Net income ($ mil.)	0.8%	—	4.3	4.3	4.4	4.4
Employees	(0.9%)	—	180	173	179	175

BAKER COMMODITIES, INC.

4020 Bandini Blvd.
Los Angeles, CA 90023
Phone: 323-268-2801
Fax: 323-268-5166
Web: www.bakercommodities.com

CEO: James Andreoli
CFO: Robert Alves
HR: Maxine Taylor
FYE: December 31
Type: Private

This Baker is somewhere between a butcher and a candlestick maker. Baker Commodities, Inc., is a rendering company that takes unused animal by-products from processing plants, supermarkets, and butcher shops and produces animal fats and oils, poultry and bone meal, and tallow, which can be used to make candles, animal feed, and ingredients. It is one of the nation's largest rendering companies with some 30 plants in a dozen US states, including four in California and one in Hawaii. It has one overseas plant, located in South Korea. The company also offers such services as grease collection, interceptor services, raw-material procurement, and storage-terminal operations.

	Annual Growth	12/03	12/04	12/05	12/06	12/07
Est. sales ($ mil.)	—	—	—	—	—	67.3
Employees	—	—	—	—	—	650

BAKER HUGHES INCORPORATED

NYSE: BHI

2929 Allen Pkwy., Ste. 2100
Houston, TX 77019
Phone: 713-439-8600
Fax: 713-439-8699
Web: www.bakerhughes.com

CEO: Chad C. Deaton
CFO: –
HR: Didier Charreton
FYE: December 31
Type: Public

Baker Hughes cooks up a baker's dozen of products and services for the global petroleum market. Through its Drilling and Evaluation segment, Baker Hughes makes products and services used to drill oil and natural gas wells. Through its Completion and Production segment, the company provides equipment and services used from the completion phase through the productive life of oil and natural gas wells. The company tests potential well sites and drills and operates the wells; it also makes bits and drilling fluids, makes submersible pumps, and provides equipment and well services. Baker Hughes' revenue is fairly evenly split between its Drilling and Evaluation and Completion and Production segments.

	Annual Growth	12/03	12/04	12/05	12/06	12/07
Sales ($ mil.)	18.5%	5,292.8	6,103.8	7,185.5	9,027.4	10,428.2
Net income ($ mil.)	85.1%	128.9	528.6	878.4	2,419.0	1,513.9
Market value ($ mil.)	24.4%	10,677.1	14,362.7	20,756.4	23,883.7	25,578.9
Employees	10.9%	—	—	29,100	34,600	35,800

BAKERS FOOTWEAR GROUP, INC.

NASDAQ (GM): BKRS

2815 Scott Ave.
St. Louis, MO 63103
Phone: 314-621-0699
Fax: 314-621-0708
Web: www.bakersshoes.com

CEO: Peter A. Edison
CFO: Charles R. Daniel III
HR: Vicky Williams
FYE: January 31
Type: Public

Mall rats in need of new shoes might step into Bakers Footwear. The mall-based vendor of women's shoes and accessories operates about 250 stores in 38 states, with more than 25 stores doing business under the Wild Pair banner. Wild Pair shops offer edgier fashion footwear to tempt women ages 17 to 29. Bakers Footwear sells dress, casual, and sport shoes, as well as boots, sandals, and accessories, targeting women ages 16 to 35. Private labels account for more than 70% of company sales. Bakers Footwear acquired 33 Sam & Libby shoe stores in 2002. The company also operates an online shoe store and in 2006 launched its first catalog. Chairman and CEO Peter Edison currently owns about 10% of Bakers Footwear.

	Annual Growth	12/04	12/05	*1/06	1/07	1/08
Sales ($ mil.)	5.5%	150.5	150.5	194.8	204.8	186.3
Net income ($ mil.)	—	1.4	1.4	6.6	(1.5)	(17.7)
Market value ($ mil.)	(21.4%)	51.8	78.5	125.0	74.7	19.8
Employees	8.9%	—	—	2,250	2,450	—

*Fiscal year change

BALCHEM CORPORATION

AMEX: BCPC

52 Sunrise Park Rd.
New Hampton, NY 10958
Phone: 845-326-5600
Fax: 845-326-5742
Web: www.balchem.com

CEO: Dino A. Rossi
CFO: Francis J. (Frank) Fitzpatrick
HR: Robert T. (Bob) Miniger
FYE: December 31
Type: Public

Believe Balchem when they say they have it covered. The company has developed a technology that covers or encapsulates ingredients used in food and animal health products; the encapsulation improves nutritional value and shelf life and allows for controlled time release. Balchem also distributes specialty gases such as ethylene oxide (used to sterilize medical instruments), propylene oxide (used to reduce bacteria in spice treating and chemical processing), and methyl chloride. The company's unencapsulated feed ingredients segment supplies the nutrient choline chloride to poultry and swine farmers. Reashure, an encapsulated choline product, increases milk production in dairy cows.

	Annual Growth	12/03	12/04	12/05	12/06	12/07
Sales ($ mil.)	29.9%	61.9	67.4	83.1	100.9	176.2
Net income ($ mil.)	30.2%	5.6	8.0	10.9	12.3	16.1
Market value ($ mil.)	87.1%	32.8	78.3	153.4	303.6	402.4
Employees	—	—	—	200		

BALDOR ELECTRIC COMPANY

NYSE: BEZ

5711 R. S. Boreham, Jr. St.
Fort Smith, AR 72901
Phone: 479-646-4711
Fax: 479-648-5792
Web: www.baldor.com

CEO: John A. McFarland
CFO: George Moschner
HR: Jason W. Green
FYE: Saturday nearest December 31
Type: Public

Electricity drives Baldor Electric's sales — and its products. The company manufactures industrial electric motors, controls, and drives that power products ranging from giant rock tumblers to industrial pumps. Baldor manufactures AC and DC motors that supply from 1/12 horsepower up to 1,500hp. Other products include speed reducers, industrial grinders, and polishing lathes. Baldor Electric sells primarily to OEMs in the agricultural and semiconductor equipment industries and to independent distributors for resale as replacement parts. The company has more than 8,000 customers in some 160 industries. The US (including export customers) accounts for about 90% of sales.

	Annual Growth	12/03	12/04	12/05	12/06	12/07
Sales ($ mil.)	34.2%	563.3	650.1	721.6	811.3	1,824.9
Net income ($ mil.)	39.6%	24.8	35.0	43.0	48.1	94.1
Market value ($ mil.)	20.1%	762.0	911.5	848.3	1,082.1	1,584.1
Employees	21.6%	3,696	3,814	3,841	3,950	8,083

BALDWIN & LYONS, INC.

NASDAQ (GM): BWINB

1099 N. Meridian St.	CEO: Gary W. Miller
Indianapolis, IN 46204	CFO: G. Patrick Corydon
Phone: 317-636-9800	HR: Hugh Cameron
Fax: 317-632-9444	FYE: December 31
Web: www.baldwinandlyons.com	Type: Public

Baldwin & Lyons insures truckers and the bad car drivers who terrorize them. The company's Protective Insurance subsidiary, licensed throughout the US and Canada, writes property and casualty insurance for large trucking fleets with substantial self-insurance and for medium-sized trucking companies with small deductibles. Baldwin & Lyons' Sagamore Insurance unit specializes in providing insurance to high-risk private auto drivers through a network of independent agents in some 30 states. Sagamore also sells physical-damage insurance and liability insurance for small trucking fleets.

	Annual Growth	12/03	12/04	12/05	12/06	12/07
Assets ($ mil.)	2.5%	763.2	868.6	860.4	853.7	842.8
Net income ($ mil.)	13.6%	33.1	30.3	34.2	38.2	55.1
Market value ($ mil.)	3.3%	61.5	70.7	68.0	67.3	70.0
Employees	(0.8%)	293	275	276	279	284

BALDWIN PIANO INC.

309 Plus Park Blvd.	CEO: Henry E. Juszkiewicz
Nashville, TN 37217	CFO: –
Phone: 615-871-4500	HR: –
Fax: 615-889-5509	FYE: December 31
Web: www.baldwinpiano.com	Type: Subsidiary

The keys to success for Baldwin alternate in color — black and white. One of the top piano manufacturers in the US, Baldwin is best known for making concert and upright pianos under the Baldwin, Howard, Hamilton, Chickering, and Wurlitzer names. The company also makes ConcertMaster computerized player pianos. Its custom models include the Goldtop (fashioned after the classic Les Paul guitar) and the Elvis Presley Signature vertical style. Gibson Guitar, which has been working to breath new life into Baldwin, bought the ailing piano maker from GE Capital. Dwight Hamilton Baldwin established the company as Baldwin Piano & Organ in 1862.

	Annual Growth	12/03	12/04	12/05	12/06	12/07
Est. sales ($ mil.)	—	—	—	—	—	39.6
Employees	—	—	—	—	—	1,000

BALDWIN TECHNOLOGY COMPANY, INC.

AMEX: BLD

2 Trap Falls Rd., Ste. 402	CEO: Karl S. Puehringer
Shelton, CT 06484	CFO: John P. Jordan
Phone: 203-402-1000	HR: John Lawlor
Fax: 203-402-5500	FYE: June 30
Web: www.baldwintech.com	Type: Public

Baldwin Technology always has pressing business at hand. The company manufactures printing press equipment, with more than 100 products including press-cleaning systems, fountain solution control systems that regulate water use, web-handling systems that control the flow of paper, and ink control systems. Baldwin's products are primarily used for offset (lithographic) printing, which, in turn, is used for printing books, magazines, greeting cards, business forms, catalogs, newspapers, and packaging. The company believes offset printing has become the dominant technology in the international printing industry and plans to expand its presence in this field internationally.

	Annual Growth	6/03	6/04	6/05	6/06	6/07
Sales ($ mil.)	10.7%	134.2	158.1	173.2	179.4	201.5
Net income ($ mil.)	—	(11.1)	7.0	5.0	6.3	6.6
Market value ($ mil.)	79.8%	8.2	46.2	40.1	74.2	85.9
Employees	7.0%	548	540	534	551	717

BALL CORPORATION

NYSE: BLL

10 Longs Peak Dr.	CEO: R. David Hoover
Broomfield, CO 80021	CFO: Raymond J. Seabrook
Phone: 303-469-3131	HR: –
Fax: 303-460-2127	FYE: December 31
Web: www.ball.com	Type: Public

The well-rounded Ball Corporation makes cans and containers for the food and beverage industries as well as products for the space and defense industries. Ball's food and beverage packaging products include aluminum, steel, and polyethylene terephthalate (PET) plastic containers. The company's high-tech operations are handled through its Ball Aerospace & Technologies subsidiary, which makes imaging, communications, and information components (antennas, sensors), and offers engineering and manufacturing services. As a result of Ball's mixed operations, its primary customers include PepsiCo, Coca-Cola Enterprises, SABMiller plc (brewer), Pepsi and Coke bottlers, and aerospace and defense contractors.

	Annual Growth	12/03	12/04	12/05	12/06	12/07
Sales ($ mil.)	10.7%	4,977.0	5,440.2	5,751.2	6,621.5	7,475.3
Net income ($ mil.)	5.2%	229.9	295.6	261.5	329.6	281.3
Market value ($ mil.)	28.0%	1,679.6	4,956.2	4,138.8	4,540.4	4,510.1
Employees	8.8%	—	—	13,100	15,500	15,500

BALL HORTICULTURAL COMPANY

622 Town Rd.	CEO: Anna C. Ball
West Chicago, IL 60185	CFO: Todd Billings
Phone: 630-231-3600	HR: Mike Williams
Fax: 630-231-3605	FYE: June 30
Web: www.ballhort.com	Type: Private

Flower power still reigns at Ball Horticultural. One of the nation's largest sellers of commercial seed for flowers and ornamental crops, Ball Horticultural develops, produces, and distributes seeds, young plants, and cuttings to professional growers, wholesalers, and retailers. It operates in some 20 countries through subsidiaries and joint ventures, including PanAmerican Seed and Ball Seed. The firm sells through its own sales force and online. It also publishes *FloraCulture International, Green Profit,* and *GrowerTalks* magazines. Founded in 1905 by George Ball, Ball Horticultural remains family owned. The Ball clan also owns W. Atlee Burpee, major seed seller to home gardeners.

	Annual Growth	6/03	6/04	6/05	6/06	6/07
Est. sales ($ mil.)	—	—	—	—	—	132.5
Employees	—	—	—	—	—	3,000

BALLANTYNE OF OMAHA, INC.

AMEX: BTN

4350 McKinley St.	CEO: John P. Wilmers
Omaha, NE 68112	CFO: Kevin S. Herrmann
Phone: 402-453-4444	HR: –
Fax: 402-453-7238	FYE: December 31
Web: www.ballantyne-omaha.com	Type: Public

Ballantyne of Omaha projects a lot of images. The company is an international supplier of motion picture theater equipment used by major theater chains such as AMC Entertainment and Regal Entertainment. Primary offerings include its Strong brand of film and digital projectors and accessories. Ballantyne of Omaha's Strong Entertainment lighting division manufactures lighting systems. Its spotlights and searchlights are used by movie and TV producers, hotels, sporting arenas, and amusement parks, including Walt Disney World and Universal Studios.

	Annual Growth	12/03	12/04	12/05	12/06	12/07
Sales ($ mil.)	8.3%	37.4	49.1	53.9	49.7	51.5
Net income ($ mil.)	(24.0%)	0.6	5.1	4.3	1.6	0.2
Market value ($ mil.)	21.8%	36.9	58.5	65.5	72.6	81.1
Employees	—	—	—	—	197	—

An in-depth profile of this company is available to Hoover's Online members at hoovers.com.

213

BALLISTIC RECOVERY SYSTEMS, INC.

Pink Sheets: BRSI

300 Airport Rd.
South St. Paul, MN 55075
Phone: 651-457-7491
Fax: 651-457-8651
Web: www.brsparachutes.com

CEO: Larry E. Williams
CFO: –
HR: –
FYE: September 30
Type: Public

With a Ballistic Recovery Systems (BRS) parachute system, you *and* your plane can "hit the silk" to survive an emergency and fly again. BRS manufactures emergency parachute recovery systems that lower the entire aircraft to the ground in case of emergency. Although its systems were originally designed only for ultralight aircraft, BRS has also developed parachute systems for planes used in general aviation, including models made by Cessna, Cirrus, and Symphony Aircraft. Cirrus accounts for about three-quarters of the company's sales.

	Annual Growth	9/03	9/04	9/05	9/06	9/07
Sales ($ mil.)	9.2%	6.6	6.6	8.1	9.2	9.4
Net income ($ mil.)	—	0.6	0.3	(1.1)	0.0	(1.7)
Employees	—	—	—	—	—	—

BALL'S FOOD STORES INC.

5300 Speaker Rd.
Kansas City, KS 66106
Phone: 913-573-1200
Fax: 913-551-8500
Web: www.henhouse.com

CEO: Fred Ball
CFO: Michael (Mike) Beal
HR: –
FYE: December 31
Type: Private

Ball's Food Stores operates nearly 30 supermarkets in the Kansas City area under the Ball's Price Chopper and Hen House Markets banners. Hen House Markets are upscale, service-oriented establishments, while Price Chopper is the company's price-impact supermarket format. Ball's Food Stores and rival Hy-Vee are leaders in the Kansas City market, but both grocery chains are facing increased pressure from supercenters operator Wal-Mart Stores, which is now the largest seller of groceries in the US. Founded in 1923 by Sidney and Mollie Ball, the grocery company is run by their son Chairman Fred Ball and grandson David. The grocery chain is a member of Associated Wholesale Grocers.

	Annual Growth	12/03	12/04	12/05	12/06	12/07
Est. sales ($ mil.)	—	—	—	—	—	433.7
Employees	—	—	—	—	—	4,000

BALLY TECHNOLOGIES, INC.

NYSE: BYI

6601 S. Bermuda Rd.
Las Vegas, NV 89119
Phone: 702-584-7700
Fax: 702-584-7710
Web: www.ballytech.com

CEO: Richard M. (Dick) Haddrill
CFO: Robert C. Caller
HR: –
FYE: June 30
Type: Public

This company helps keep the casinos buzzing. Bally Technologies is a leading manufacturer and supplier of casino gaming machines and information systems. Its Bally Gaming and Systems subsidiary makes slot machines, video gaming machines, and enterprise computer systems used by casinos to monitor their gaming operations. Bally Technologies also develops systems for linking slot machines together so that players can gamble for the same progressively increasing jackpot. In addition to its gaming machines and systems business, Bally owns the Rainbow Hotel Casino in Vicksburg, Mississippi.

	Annual Growth	6/03	6/04	6/05	6/06	6/07
Sales ($ mil.)	13.7%	407.6	488.9	483.1	547.1	682.3
Net income ($ mil.)	3.4%	19.5	84.5	(22.6)	(46.1)	22.3
Market value ($ mil.)	11.5%	934.5	875.9	738.1	862.3	1,444.5
Employees	17.4%	—	—	1,640	2,020	2,262

BALLY TOTAL FITNESS

Pink Sheets: BFTH

8700 W. Bryn Mawr Ave.
Chicago, IL 60631
Phone: 773-380-3000
Fax: 773-693-2982
Web: www.ballyfitness.com

CEO: Don R. Kornstein
CFO: William G. (Bill) Fanelli
HR: Harold Morgan
FYE: December 31
Type: Public

Business is working out for Bally Total Fitness Holding Corporation. The company is one of the largest fitness center operators in the US, with about 400 facilities located in the US, Mexico, South Korea, China, and the Caribbean. The clubs operate under the Bally Total Fitness and Bally Sports Clubs brands. Bally's members have access to pools, aerobic programs, running tracks, and racquet courts, as well as personal trainers and sports medicine services. Bally also markets private-label nutritional products and sells health-related products in most of its clubs, as well as in retail outlets. The company filed for Chapter 11 in 2007; it emerged from bankruptcy later that year.

	Annual Growth	12/02	12/03	12/04	12/05	*12/06
Sales ($ mil.)	2.3%	968.1	953.5	1,048.0	1,071.0	1,059.1
Net income ($ mil.)	87.3%	3.5	(646.0)	(30.3)	(9.6)	43.1
Employees	(4.4%)	23,000	—	23,200	21,600	19,200

*Most recent year available

BALTIMORE GAS AND ELECTRIC COMPANY

750 E. Pratt St.
Baltimore, MD 21202
Phone: 410-783-2800
Fax: –
Web: www.bge.com

CEO: Kenneth W. (Ken) DeFontes Jr.
CFO: John Collins
HR: Pat Walls
FYE: December 31
Type: Subsidiary

Baltimore Gas and Electric (BGE) provides electricity and natural gas services without having to pull anyone's finger. The company not only provides services in Baltimore, but to all or parts of 10 surrounding central Maryland counties as well in a service area of 2,300 square miles. The company's regulated power transmission and distribution system consists of 24,000 circuit miles of distribution lines, and 1,300 circuit miles of transmission lines, and serves more than 1.2 million customers; its gas system serves 646,200 homes and businesses in an 800-square-mile service area. BGE is a subsidiary of Constellation Energy Group.

	Annual Growth	12/03	12/04	12/05	12/06	12/07
Est. sales ($ mil.)	—	—	—	—	—	3,418.5
Net income ($ mil.)	—	—	—	—	—	139.8
Employees	—	—	—	—	—	—

THE BAMA COMPANIES, INC.

2727 E. 11th St.
Tulsa, OK 74104
Phone: 918-592-0778
Fax: 918-732-2950
Web: www.bama.com

CEO: Paula Marshall
CFO: Bill Chew
HR: –
FYE: December 31
Type: Private

Eating a cherry pie at McDonald's gives you an idea of the business that Bama is wrapped up in. The Bama Companies manufactures hand-held pies, whole pies, biscuits, cookies, crumb crusts, and frozen dough for the food service and vending machine industries. It also produces frozen cakes, donuts, and dessert items. The company, which does business in more than 20 countries, counts McDonald's, Pizza Hut, and Taco Bell among its customers. Bama has manufacturing facilities in Tulsa, Oklahoma, and in Beijing. The family-owned company was formed by Cornillia Alabama "Bama" Marshall in 1927.

	Annual Growth	12/03	12/04	12/05	12/06	12/07
Est. sales ($ mil.)	—	—	—	—	—	150.0
Employees	—	—	—	—	—	850

BANANA REPUBLIC INC.

2 Folsom St.
San Francisco, CA 94105
Phone: 650-952-4400
Fax: 415-427-2553
Web: www.bananarepublic.com

CEO: Jack Calhoun
CFO: Sabrina Simmons
HR: –
FYE: Saturday nearest January 31
Type: Subsidiary

Banana Republic has grown from its original two-store wannabe safari outfitter to an empire in its own right, though no pith hats or fake palm trees can be found now at its stores. Instead, the well-known retailer of men's and women's mid-scale (not high-dollar, but far from discount) casual and tailored apparel has a sprawling territory of 575 stores in North American and Asia, and a Web site, through all of which it distributes its well-put-together look. A division of ailing retail giant Gap Inc. since 1983, at one point it was dangerously close to cannibalizing its parent's customers. In contrast to Gap, however, the company buys up historic landmarks and refurbishes them (as opposed to paving paradise).

	Annual Growth	1/02	1/03	1/04	1/05	1/06
Sales ($ mil.)	6.1%	—	1,928.0	2,090.0	2,269.0	2,301.0
Employees	—	—	—	—	—	—

BANCFIRST CORPORATION

NASDAQ (GS): BANF

101 N. Broadway, Ste. 200
Oklahoma City, OK 73102
Phone: 405-270-1086
Fax: 405-270-1089
Web: www.bancfirst.com

CEO: David E. Rainbolt
CFO: Joe T. Shockley Jr.
HR: J. Michael Rogers
FYE: December 31
Type: Public

This Oklahoma bank wants to be more than OK. It wants to be *super*. BancFirst Corporation is the holding company for BancFirst, a super-community bank that emphasizes decentralized management and centralized support. BancFirst operates about 90 locations in more than 40 Oklahoma communities. It targets small to midsized businesses and individuals, offering a full range of traditional deposit products, including checking, savings, NOW, and money market accounts, as well as CDs and IRAs. Real estate lending (including residential and commercial property loans) makes up more than half of the bank's loan portfolio, which also includes business loans (more than 25%), and consumer and construction loans.

	Annual Growth	12/03	12/04	12/05	12/06	12/07
Assets ($ mil.)	6.4%	2,921.4	3,047.0	3,223.0	3,418.6	3,743.0
Net income ($ mil.)	13.6%	31.9	37.2	42.8	49.3	53.1
Market value ($ mil.)	30.3%	225.9	309.6	617.7	851.3	652.1
Employees	—	—	—	1,400	—	—

BANCINSURANCE CORPORATION

OTC: BCIS

250 E. Broad St., 10th Fl.
Columbus, OH 43215
Phone: 614-220-5200
Fax: 614-228-5552
Web: www.bancins.com

CEO: John S. Sokol
CFO: Matthew C. Nolan
HR: –
FYE: December 31
Type: Public

Insurance holding company Bancinsurance Corporation underwrites niche products through its subsidiary, Ohio Indemnity Company. Operating throughout most of the US, it provides coverage to protect automobile lenders and dealers by insuring collateralized personal property against damage and theft. It also bonds employers that elect not to pay unemployment taxes. Subsidiary Ultimate Services Agency offers property/casualty insurance to lenders in the Northeast. Chairman and CEO John Sokol and his family own half of the firm which his father founded.

	Annual Growth	12/03	12/04	12/05	12/06	12/07
Assets ($ mil.)	7.4%	115.9	117.1	128.3	122.3	154.3
Net income ($ mil.)	(6.3%)	3.9	(8.5)	6.3	5.5	3.0
Market value ($ mil.)	(8.9%)	37.7	36.4	22.4	30.1	26.0
Employees	—	—	—	—	—	—

BANCO POPULAR NORTH AMERICA

9600 W. Bryn Mawr Ave.
Rosemont, IL 60018
Phone: 847-994-5400
Fax: 847-994-6969
Web: www.bancopopular.com

CEO: Richard L. Carrión
CFO: Chris McFadden
HR: Kimberly Mooring
FYE: December 31
Type: Subsidiary

A full-service bank owned by Puerto Rico-based Popular, Banco Popular North America (BPNA) provides checking and savings accounts, CDs, credit cards, mortgages, business and personal loans, and investment products to consumer and business clients. Commercial real estate loans and residential mortgages make up most of the lending activities of the company, which is one of the nation's leading SBA lenders. BPNA has about 140 branches in California, Florida, Illinois, New York, New Jersey, and Texas. The company also provides leasing programs for medical, commercial, and industrial equipment through subsidiary Popular Equipment Finance and operates online lender E-LOAN.

THE BANCORP, INC.

NASDAQ (GM): TBBK

405 Silverside Rd.
Wilmington, DE 19809
Phone: 302-385-5000
Fax: 302-385-5194
Web: www.thebancorp.com

CEO: Betsy Z. Cohen
CFO: Martin F. (Marty) Egan
HR: –
FYE: December 31
Type: Public

The Bancorp is — what else? — the holding company for The Bancorp Bank, which provides financial services in the virtual world. On its home turf of the Philadelphia-Wilmington metropolitan area, The Bancorp Bank offers deposit, lending, and similar services, targeting the wealthy individuals and small to midsized businesses it believes are underserved by larger banks in the market. It also operates auto lease business Mears Leasing. Nationally, The Bancorp provides private-label online banking services for affinity groups and performs merchant card-processing services. The Bancorp's services are provided via the Internet. Commercial real estate and business loans dominate The Bancorp's loan portfolio.

	Annual Growth	12/03	12/04	12/05	12/06	12/07
Assets ($ mil.)	39.6%	—	576.3	917.5	1,334.8	1,568.4
Net income ($ mil.)	56.9%	—	3.7	7.4	12.5	14.3
Market value ($ mil.)	1.0%	—	190.2	231.9	406.2	196.0
Employees	42.8%	—	—	150	181	306

BANCORP RHODE ISLAND, INC.

NASDAQ (GS): BARI

1 Turks Head Place
Providence, RI 02903
Phone: 401-456-5000
Fax: 401-456-5059
Web: www.bankri.com

CEO: Merrill W. Sherman
CFO: Linda H. Simmons
HR: –
FYE: December 31
Type: Public

Bancorp Rhode Island is the holding company for Bank Rhode Island, which serves individuals and small businesses through about 15 branches in the state's Providence, Kent, and Washington counties. The community bank provides traditional banking products and services including checking and savings accounts, mortgages and other loans, cash management services, and investment services. Bank Rhode Island was formed in 1996 as the result of the acquisition of branches divested in the merger between FleetBoston and Shawmut Financial, which are now part of Bank of America.

	Annual Growth	12/03	12/04	12/05	12/06	12/07
Assets ($ mil.)	7.8%	1,094.0	1,239.1	1,442.3	1,479.1	1,477.1
Net income ($ mil.)	5.7%	7.2	8.6	9.6	7.7	9.0
Market value ($ mil.)	5.0%	128.1	159.2	157.1	207.3	155.7
Employees	(6.9%)	—	—	309	—	268

An in-depth profile of this company is available to Hoover's Online members at hoovers.com.

BANCORPSOUTH, INC.

NYSE: BXS

1 Mississippi Plaza, 201 S. Spring St.	CEO: Aubrey B. Patterson Jr.
Tupelo, MS 38804	CFO: L. Nash Allen Jr.
Phone: 662-680-2000	HR: W. O. Jones
Fax: 662-678-7299	FYE: December 31
Web: www.bancorpsouth.com	Type: Public

Elvis Presley may be the Boy from Tupelo, but BancorpSouth is the Bank from Tupelo. It's the holding company for BancorpSouth Bank, which operates nearly 300 branches in eight southern states. The bank offers checking and savings accounts, loans, credit cards, and commercial banking services. BancorpSouth also sells insurance and provides brokerage and asset management services throughout most of its market area. Real estate mortgages represent more than three-quarters of its loan portfolio. BancorpSouth has been expanding through acquisitions of banks and insurance agencies, as well as opening new branches.

	Annual Growth	12/03	12/04	12/05	12/06	12/07
Assets ($ mil.)	6.4%	10,305.0	10,848.2	11,768.7	12,040.5	13,189.8
Net income ($ mil.)	1.3%	131.1	110.6	115.2	125.2	137.9
Market value ($ mil.)	1.3%	1,848.4	1,901.8	1,748.8	2,121.7	1,943.1
Employees	2.3%	—	—	4,008	4,100	—

BANCTEC, INC.

2701 E. Grauwyler Rd.	CEO: J. Coley Clark
Irving, TX 75061	CFO: Jeffrey D. (Jeff) Cushman
Phone: 972-821-4000	HR: Lin M. Held
Fax: 972-821-4823	FYE: December 31
Web: www.banctec.com	Type: Private

BancTec keeps tabs on all sorts of financial transactions. The company offers electronic processing systems, software, and services for government agencies, banks, utility and telecommunications companies, and other organizations that do high-volume financial transactions. BancTec's systems and software capture and process checks, bills, and other documents; products include digital archiving systems, workflow software, and scanners. BancTec's services include cost estimates and contingency planning, resource use, systems integration, and maintenance. Founded in 1972, BancTec is owned by investment firm Welsh, Carson, Anderson & Stowe, which took BancTec private in 1999.

	Annual Growth	12/02	12/03	12/04	12/05	12/06
Sales ($ mil.)	0.0%	379.4	378.9	360.7	344.9	379.5
Net income ($ mil.)	—	—	17.8	(17.2)	(7.3)	(0.8)
Employees	(4.4%)	3,200	3,100	3,000	2,750	2,670

BANCTRUST FINANCIAL GROUP, INC.

NASDAQ (GS): BTFG

100 St. Joseph St.	CEO: W. Bibb Lamar Jr.
Mobile, AL 36602	CFO: F. Michael Johnson
Phone: 251-431-7800	HR: Diane Hollingsworth
Fax: 251-431-7851	FYE: December 31
Web: www.banctrustfinancialgroupinc.com	Type: Public

BancTrust Financial makes its sweet home in Alabama, but also spends a little time in the Florida panhandle. It is the holding company for two banks that operate as BankTrust throughout southern Alabama and neighboring parts of Florida. Through more than 50 branch offices, the banks offer such deposit products as CDs and checking, savings, and retirement accounts. The company's lending activities include mortgages (more than 40% of its loan portfolio), construction loans (nearly 30%), and commercial, agricultural, and consumer loans. Subsidiaries offer insurance, trust, and investment services. BancTrust Financial bought fellow Alabama bank holding company The Peoples BancTrust Company in 2007.

	Annual Growth	12/03	12/04	12/05	12/06	12/07
Assets ($ mil.)	20.1%	1,076.9	1,191.2	1,305.5	1,353.4	2,240.1
Net income ($ mil.)	(0.4%)	6.3	11.3	15.1	13.3	6.2
Market value ($ mil.)	4.9%	175.1	271.2	223.9	285.0	211.7
Employees	31.6%	—	—	396	—	686

BANCWEST CORPORATION

180 Montgomery St.	CEO: Don J. McGrath
San Francisco, CA 94104	CFO: Thibault Fulconis
Phone: 514-765-4884	HR: –
Fax: –	FYE: December 31
Web: www.bancwestcorp.com	Type: Subsidiary

BancWest knows which direction it's heading. The subsidiary of French banking group BNP Paribas is the holding company for Bank of the West and First Hawaiian Bank. On the US mainland, Bank of the West (founded in 1874) has more than 700 branches in some 20 states west of the Mississippi River. Founded in 1858, First Hawaiian has about 60 branches in Hawaii, Guam, and Saipan. In addition, BancWest has a representative office in New York City, as well as ones in Tokyo and Taipei, Taiwan. Subsidiary banks specialize in such activities as home and auto lending; commercial banking; and private banking and investments. BancWest is owned by BNP Paribas, which acquired it in 2001.

BANDAG, INCORPORATED

2905 N. Hwy. 61	CEO: Saul A. Solomon
Muscatine, IA 52761	CFO: –
Phone: 563-262-1400	HR: –
Fax: 563-262-1069	FYE: December 31
Web: www.bandag.com	Type: Subsidiary

It might be a tired cliché to say that Bandag is on a roll, but the company does deal in tires. Bandag makes precured tread rubber, as well as equipment and supplies for retreading tires for trucks, buses, cars, and industrial and off-road vehicles. The company also sells new and retreaded tires to commercial and industrial customers. The company's integrated dealer network includes more than 1,600 North American sales and service locations. Subsidiary Speedco is a lube service chain for heavy duty trucks. Bandag is owned by Bridgestone Americas Holding.

	Annual Growth	12/02	12/03	12/04	12/05	12/06
Sales ($ mil.)	1.9%	912.0	828.2	868.0	920.9	984.1
Net income ($ mil.)	63.5%	2.8	60.2	66.9	49.5	20.0
Employees	(2.5%)	3,715	3,002	3,384	3,788	3,362

BANDAI AMERICA INCORPORATED

5551 Katella Ave.	CEO: Masaaki (Mark) Tsuji
Cypress, CA 90630	CFO: Kunio Ikoma
Phone: 714-816-9500	HR: –
Fax: 714-816-6710	FYE: March 31
Web: www.bandai.com	Type: Subsidiary

Confused as to who Sword Strike Gundam and Astro Boy are? Bandai America, the North American marketing arm of Japanese toy maker Namco Bandai, can help clear up any action figure confusion you may have. Licensed product lines include Power Rangers, Gundam, Teen Titans, Tamagotchi, and Hello Kitty. The company also makes a number of original products to supplement its licensed toys and games. Bandai America's operations consist of candy and toy distribution, Japanese animation home video distribution (through Bandai Entertainment), video game production, and the development of wireless technology and content that works with existing mobile phones.

	Annual Growth	3/03	3/04	3/05	3/06	3/07
Est. sales ($ mil.)	—	—	—	—	—	7.1
Employees	—	—	—	—	—	60

B&G FOODS, INC.

NYSE: BGF

4 Gatehall Dr., Ste. 110
Parsippany, NJ 07054
Phone: 973-401-6500
Fax: 973-364-1037
Web: www.bgfoods.com

CEO: David L. Wenner
CFO: Robert C. Cantwell
HR: Cynthia Wojcik
FYE: Saturday nearest December 31
Type: Public

Peter Piper can pick more than a peck of peppers or pickles from B&G Foods. There's jalapenos, beans, sandwich spreads, and an array of other products sold regionally and nationally through B&G's network of subsidiaries. B&G brands its pickles, peppers, and hot sauces under the B&G and Trappey labels. Other key brands include Ac'cent meat flavoring, Emeril's seasonings (under license), Ortega Mexican products, Cream of Wheat hot cereal, and Underwood meat spreads. Products are sold to grocery retailers, mass merchandisers, warehouse clubs, wholesalers, and foodservice companies.

	Annual Growth	12/03	12/04	12/05	12/06	12/07
Sales ($ mil.)	9.5%	328.4	372.8	379.3	411.3	471.3
Net income ($ mil.)	4.0%	15.2	3.3	8.0	11.6	17.8
Market value ($ mil.)	10.7%	—	260.5	290.4	400.4	353.4
Employees	3.9%	—	—	—	721	749

THE BANK HOLDINGS

NASDAQ (CM): TBHS

9990 Double R Blvd.
Reno, NV 89521
Phone: 775-853-8600
Fax: 775-853-2068
Web: www.thebankholdings.com

CEO: Harold G. (Hal) Giomi
CFO: Jack B. Buchold
HR: –
FYE: December 31
Type: Public

You can probably guess what The Bank Holdings does. Where they do it is out west. As the holding company for Nevada Security Bank, the company operates branches in the northern portion of the state. Nevada Security Bank offers typical deposit products, such as checking and savings accounts, as well as CDs and IRAs. Commercial real estate loans make up about 40% of the bank's loan portfolio, which also includes construction/development loans, consumer loans, residential mortgages, and business loans (including SBA loans). The Bank Holdings moved into California through its 2004 purchase of CNA Trust Corporation of Costa Mesa. The California branch (now located in Roseville) operates as Silverado Bank.

	Annual Growth	12/03	12/04	12/05	12/06	12/07
Assets ($ mil.)	39.4%	166.1	246.8	384.6	651.5	626.6
Net income ($ mil.)	—	(0.6)	0.3	1.4	2.1	1.7
Market value ($ mil.)	(2.0%)	—	55.8	56.1	105.5	52.5
Employees	105.1%	—	—	59	121	

BANK LEUMI USA

579 5th Ave.
New York, NY 10017
Phone: 917-542-2343
Fax: 917-542-2254
Web: www.leumiusa.com

CEO: Uzi Rosen
CFO: Benjamin Naveh
HR: John P. McGann
FYE: December 31
Type: Subsidiary

Bank Leumi USA is a subsidiary of Bank Leumi le-Israel, one of Israel's leading banks. It provides commercial and international banking services to large and midsized corporations, specializing in import and export lending, as well as lending to businesses in such industries as textiles and apparel, real estate, diamonds, and entertainment. The bank, which also acts as an intermediary for American firms and individuals with investments in Israel, has more than a dozen offices in California, Florida, Illinois, and New York. Some of Bank Leumi USA's other services for individuals include private banking and wealth management.

	Annual Growth	12/03	12/04	12/05	12/06	12/07
Assets ($ mil.)	2.1%	5,347.0	5,703.8	6,129.1	5,750.7	5,814.2
Net income ($ mil.)	(0.3%)	30.9	33.0	24.3	25.8	30.5
Employees	2.7%	450	454	451	465	500

BANK MUTUAL CORPORATION

NASDAQ (GS): BKMU

4949 W. Brown Deer Rd.
Milwaukee, WI 53223
Phone: 414-354-1500
Fax: 414-354-5450
Web: www.bankmutualcorp.com

CEO: Michael T. Crowley Jr.
CFO: Eugene H. Maurer Jr.
HR: Diane Selfworth
FYE: December 31
Type: Public

Bank Mutual Corporation is the holding company for Bank Mutual, which offers consumer and business banking through around 80 branches in Wisconsin and one in Minnesota. Deposit products include CDs and checking, money market, and savings accounts. The company mainly uses funds gathered to originate a variety of loans and to invest in mortgage-backed securities. Residential mortgages and consumer loans dominate the bank's loan portfolio (representing about 50% and 20% respectively), which also includes commercial real estate, construction, and business loans. Bank subsidiary BancMutual Financial and Insurance Services offers mutual funds, annuities, insurance, and brokerage and wealth management services.

	Annual Growth	12/03	12/04	12/05	12/06	12/07
Assets ($ mil.)	2.9%	3,108.5	3,445.3	3,431.4	3,451.4	3,488.1
Net income ($ mil.)	(6.7%)	22.6	29.5	28.0	20.6	17.1
Market value ($ mil.)	(13.0%)	897.3	894.3	660.6	730.0	513.8
Employees	(5.6%)	829	800	792	781	657

BANK OF AMERICA CORPORATION

NYSE: BAC

100 N. Tryon St., Bank of America Corporate Center
Charlotte, NC 28255
Phone: 704-386-5681
Fax: 704-386-6699
Web: www.bankofamerica.com

CEO: Kenneth D. (Ken) Lewis
CFO: Joe L. Price
HR: –
FYE: December 31
Type: Public

Welcome to the machine. The second-largest bank in the US by assets (behind Citigroup), Bank of America boasts the country's most extensive branch network, with more than 6,100 locations covering some 30 states from coast to coast. Its core services include consumer and small business banking, credit cards, investment banking and brokerage, and asset management. In 2007 Bank of America bought U.S. Trust from Charles Schwab for more than $3 billion and acquired Chicago-based LaSalle Bank from Netherlands-based ABN AMRO for some $21 billion. Also that year the company made a $2 billion investment in Countrywide Financial, and in early 2008 agreed to buy the troubled company for some $4 billion in stock.

	Annual Growth	12/03	12/04	12/05	12/06	12/07
Assets ($ mil.)	23.5%	736,445.0	1,110,457.0	1,291,803.0	1,459,737.0	1,715,746.0
Net income ($ mil.)	8.5%	10,810.0	14,143.0	16,465.0	21,133.0	14,982.0
Market value ($ mil.)	33.3%	57,955.6	190,147.2	184,585.6	238,020.7	183,107.1
Employees	12.0%	133,549	175,742	176,638	203,425	210,000

BANK OF COMMERCE HOLDINGS

NASDAQ (GM): BOCH

1951 Churn Creek Rd.
Redding, CA 96002
Phone: 530-224-3333
Fax: 530-224-3337
Web: www.reddingbankofcommerce.com

CEO: Patrick J. (Pat) Moty
CFO: Linda J. Miles
HR: Donna Moore
FYE: December 31
Type: Public

Bank of Commerce Holdings is where Northern California commerce banks. Formerly Redding Bancorp, Bank of Commerce Holdings provides traditional banking services through subsidiary Redding Bank of Commerce and its divisions, Roseville Bank of Commerce and Sutter Bank of Commerce. It targets small to midsized businesses and medium to high net worth individuals in the California counties of El Dorado, Placer, Sacramento, and Shasta. Through its handful of branches the company provides savings accounts, deposit accounts, and loans. It provides single- and multifamily residential financing, refinancing, and equity lines of credit through subsidiary Bank of Commerce Mortgage (formerly RBC Mortgage Services).

	Annual Growth	12/03	12/04	12/05	12/06	12/07
Assets ($ mil.)	11.4%	401.2	438.5	511.6	583.4	618.3
Net income ($ mil.)	9.8%	4.2	5.0	6.3	6.6	6.1
Market value ($ mil.)	35.4%	22.8	105.0	87.4	106.1	76.6
Employees	(4.5%)	—	—	125	115	114

An in-depth profile of this company is available to Hoover's Online members at hoovers.com.

217

BANK OF FLORIDA CORPORATION

NASDAQ (GM): BOFL

1185 Immokalee Rd.
Naples, FL 34103
Phone: 239-254-2100
Fax: 239-254-2107
Web: www.bankoffloridaonline.com

CEO: Michael L. McMullan
CFO: Tracy L. Keegan
HR: –
FYE: December 31
Type: Public

Bank of Florida (formerly Bancshares of Florida) is the holding company for its eponymous Bank of Florida subsidiaries, which operate about a dozen branches in southeastern and southwestern portions of the state, as well as in the Tampa Bay area. Subsidiary Bank of Florida Trust offers trust, estate planning, and investment management services. Both the bank and the trust company cater to professionals, entrepreneurs, and small to midsized businesses, providing personalized deposit, lending, and investment services that larger banks in their market often do not. In 2007 Bank of Florida bought Old Florida Bankshares, the holding company for Old Florida Bank, expanding its presence in Lee County.

	Annual Growth	12/03	12/04	12/05	12/06	12/07
Assets ($ mil.)	55.8%	222.6	420.8	569.8	883.1	1,310.5
Net income ($ mil.)	—	(2.7)	(2.9)	4.9	2.3	2.7
Market value ($ mil.)	34.1%	45.4	77.9	134.9	196.2	147.0
Employees	29.6%	—	—	153	200	257

BANK OF GRANITE CORPORATION

NASDAQ (GS): GRAN

23 N. Main St.
Granite Falls, NC 28630
Phone: 828-496-2027
Fax: 828-496-2077
Web: www.bankofgranite.com

CEO: R. Scott Anderson
CFO: Kirby A. Tyndall
HR: Karen Warlick
FYE: December 31
Type: Public

This company doesn't take its customers for granite. Bank of Granite Corporation is the holding company for a community bank of the same name that serves individuals and small businesses in nearly 10 west-central North Carolina counties. From about two dozen branches, Bank of Granite offers traditional demand and time deposit products. Through Granite Mortgage, it originates and underwrites mortgage loans, offering mostly government-guaranteed mortgages (first-time buyers, FHA, VA loans). Mortgages make up more than half of Bank of Granite's loan portfolio, which also consists of agricultural, business, construction, and consumer loans. The bank was founded in 1906.

	Annual Growth	12/03	12/04	12/05	12/06	12/07
Assets ($ mil.)	5.8%	971.4	1,032.2	1,106.7	1,199.8	1,219.2
Net income ($ mil.)	—	15.3	12.7	15.0	18.0	(15.3)
Market value ($ mil.)	(8.9%)	236.9	222.6	191.4	303.9	163.2
Employees	3.7%	—	—	333	—	358

🏛 BANK OF HAWAII CORPORATION

NYSE: BOH

130 Merchant St.
Honolulu, HI 96813
Phone: 888-643-3888
Fax: 808-537-8440
Web: www.boh.com

CEO: Allan R. (Al) Landon
CFO: Kent T. Lucien
HR: Jean Hamakawa
FYE: December 31
Type: Public

Bank of Hawaii knows there's no place like home. The holding company felt its empire was stretched too thin after years of international expansion and a foray to the US mainland, so it divested most of its far-flung holdings to focus on its home state and its Bank of Hawaii (familiarly known as Bankoh). Bank of Hawaii operates in four segments: retail banking for consumers and small businesses; commercial banking, including property/casualty insurance; investment services, including trust and private banking; and treasury, which performs corporate asset and liability management services. The bank operates through about 90 offices in Hawaii, and another two dozen in American Samoa, the Marianas, Guam, and Palau.

	Annual Growth	12/03	12/04	12/05	12/06	12/07
Assets ($ mil.)	2.6%	9,461.7	9,766.2	10,187.0	10,571.8	10,472.9
Net income ($ mil.)	8.0%	135.2	173.3	181.6	180.4	183.7
Market value ($ mil.)	1.5%	2,318.0	2,788.7	2,642.8	2,685.5	2,464.8
Employees	0.0%	—	—	2,600	2,600	2,600

THE BANK OF KENTUCKY FINANCIAL CORPORATION

OTC: BKYF

111 Lookout Farm Dr.
Crestview Hills, KY 41017
Phone: 859-371-2340
Fax: 859-578-2487
Web: www.bankofky.com

CEO: Robert W. (Bob) Zapp
CFO: Martin J. Gerrety
HR: –
FYE: December 31
Type: Public

The Bank of Kentucky Financial Corporation is the holding company for The Bank of Kentucky, which provides a variety of personal and commercial banking services from more than 25 branches in northern portions of the Bluegrass State. It attracts deposits by offering checking and savings accounts, CDs, and IRAs. Commercial real estate loans make up about 40% of the bank's loan portfolio, while residential mortgage loans account for more than 20%. The bank also offers business, consumer, and consumer loans, as well as credit cards, investments, and trust services.

	Annual Growth	12/03	12/04	12/05	12/06	12/07
Assets ($ mil.)	10.9%	816.0	878.1	957.3	1,051.6	1,232.7
Net income ($ mil.)	4.2%	9.4	10.1	10.1	10.4	11.1
Market value ($ mil.)	(5.9%)	181.3	154.1	153.0	152.1	142.1
Employees	—	—	—	—	—	332

BANK OF MARIN BANCORP

NASDAQ (CM): BMRC

Pell Plaza, 504 Redwood Blvd., Ste. 100
Novato, CA 94947
Phone: 415-763-7781
Fax: –
Web: www.bankofmarin.com

CEO: Russell A. (Russ) Colombo
CFO: Christina J. Cook
HR: –
FYE: December 31
Type: Public

Bank of Marin Bancorp was formed in 2007 to be the holding company for community-oriented Bank of Marin, which operates a loan production office in San Francisco and about a dozen branches in the posh California counties of Marin and Sonoma in the hills north of the city. Targeting area residents and small to midsized businesses, the bank offers such standard retail products as checking and savings accounts, CDs, credit cards, and loans. Commercial real estate mortgages account for the largest portion of the company's loan portfolio, followed by business loans and construction loans. The bank's Wealth Management unit provides investment advice, financial products, private banking, and trust services.

	Annual Growth	12/03	12/04	12/05	12/06	12/07
Assets ($ mil.)	9.8%	642.6	737.1	840.5	876.6	933.9
Net income ($ mil.)	13.2%	7.5	9.5	11.7	11.9	12.3
Market value ($ mil.)	19.0%	74.8	164.4	168.5	193.5	149.8
Employees	4.9%	—	—	185	194	—

BANK OF MCKENNEY

NASDAQ (CM): BOMK

20718 1st St.
McKenney, VA 23872
Phone: 804-478-4433
Fax: 804-478-4704
Web: www.bankofmckenney.com

CEO: Richard M. Liles
CFO: James B. Neville Jr.
HR: Ruth Wray
FYE: December 31
Type: Public

This company can help you make the most of your McKenney penny or your Dinwiddie dollar. The Bank of McKenney is a community thrift serving central Virginia's Dinwiddie and Chesterfield counties, the independent city of Colonial Heights, and surrounding areas. The bank's six branches offer traditional deposit products including savings and checking accounts, NOW accounts, money markets, and CDs. Commercial real estate loans make up about half of the company's lending portfolio; residential mortgages and trusts make up about 35%. Subsidiary McKenney Group provides investment services, insurance products, and business management services.

	Annual Growth	12/02	12/03	12/04	12/05	*12/06
Assets ($ mil.)	9.6%	105.3	124.3	132.3	142.2	151.9
Net income ($ mil.)	(33.1%)	6.5	6.6	1.2	1.3	1.3
Employees	—	—	—	—	—	61

*Most recent year available

An in-depth profile of this company is available to Hoover's Online members at hoovers.com. 🏛

THE BANK OF NEW YORK MELLON CORPORATION

NYSE: BK

1 Wall St., 10th Fl.	CEO: Robert P. (Bob) Kelly
New York, NY 10286	CFO: Bruce W. Van Saun
Phone: 212-495-1784	HR: Lisa B. Peters
Fax: 212-809-9528	FYE: December 31
Web: www.bnymellon.com	Type: Public

Big Apple, meet Iron City. The Bank of New York cemented its status as one of the world's largest asset administration firms with the 2007 acquisition of Pittsburgh-based Mellon Financial. The merger also fits in with the company's other areas of focus, asset management and corporate trust services. It was The Bank of New York's third attempt to acquire Mellon. Now known as The Bank of New York Mellon (BNY Mellon), the firm has about $20 trillion in assets under custody and more than $1 trillion of assets under management. The company has a presence in about 35 countries, including more than 80 wealth management offices in the US and the UK. Its Pershing subsidiary is a leading securities clearing firm.

	Annual Growth	12/03	12/04	12/05	12/06	12/07
Assets ($ mil.)	20.9%	92,397.0	94,529.0	102,074.0	103,370.0	197,656.0
Net income ($ mil.)	15.2%	1,157.0	1,440.0	1,571.0	3,011.0	2,039.0
Employees	16.4%	22,901	23,363	23,451	22,961	42,100

BANK OF SOUTH CAROLINA CORPORATION

NASDAQ (CM): BKSC

256 Meeting St.	CEO: Hugh C. Lane Jr.
Charleston, SC 29401	CFO: William L. (Bill) Hiott Jr.
Phone: 843-724-1500	HR: Mindy Buhrmaster
Fax: 843-724-1513	FYE: December 31
Web: www.banksc.com	Type: Public

What, were you expecting something different? The Bank of South Carolina Corporation is the holding company for The Bank of South Carolina. It operates four branches in and around Charleston. Targeting individuals and small to midsized business customers, the bank offers such standard retail services as checking and savings accounts, credit cards, and money market and NOW accounts. Real estate loans make up more than 60% of the The Bank of South Carolina's loan portfolio, which also includes commercial loans (around one-third) and to a lesser extent, personal loans.

	Annual Growth	12/03	12/04	12/05	12/06	12/07
Assets ($ mil.)	4.7%	187.3	201.2	222.5	243.5	225.2
Net income ($ mil.)	18.9%	1.9	1.9	3.2	3.9	3.8
Market value ($ mil.)	18.4%	28.6	27.3	47.1	61.9	56.1
Employees	3.8%	—	—	65	69	70

BANK OF THE CAROLINAS CORPORATION

NASDAQ (GM): BCAR

135 Boxwood Village Dr.	CEO: Robert E. Marziano
Mocksville, NC 27028	CFO: Michelle L. Clodfelter
Phone: 336-751-5755	HR: –
Fax: 336-751-4222	FYE: December 31
Web: www.bankofthecarolinas.com	Type: Public

It would be more accurate to call it Bank of the North Carolina. Bank of the Carolinas Corporation was formed in 2006 to be the holding company for Bank of the Carolinas, which provides traditional deposit and lending services to individuals and businesses through about 10 branches in central North Carolina. Deposit services include checking, savings, and money market accounts; IRAs; and CDs. The bank's lending activities include credit cards, business and consumer loans, mortgages, equity lines of credit, and overdraft checking credit. However, commercial real estate loans account for the largest portion of the company's loan portfolio.

	Annual Growth	12/03	12/04	12/05	12/06	12/07
Assets ($ mil.)	20.1%	—	292.1	390.2	454.6	506.0
Net income ($ mil.)	10.1%	—	1.5	2.3	3.5	2.0
Market value ($ mil.)	(3.8%)	—	46.1	62.4	56.5	41.1
Employees	18.4%	—	72	—	101	—

BANK OF THE JAMES FINANCIAL GROUP, INC.

OTC: BOJF

828 Main St.	CEO: Robert R. Chapman III
Lynchburg, VA 24504	CFO: J. Todd Scruggs
Phone: 434-846-2000	HR: –
Fax: 434-846-4450	FYE: December 31
Web: www.bankofthejames.com	Type: Public

Whether you're a Tom, a Dick, or a Harry, there's no disputing that Bank of the James Financial Group is the holding company for Bank of the James, a financial institution serving central Virginia. Bank of the James targets individuals and smaller businesses from about 10 branch locations. The bank offers standard retail products and services including checking and savings accounts, CDs, and IRAs. Funds from deposits are used to originate commercial, consumer, and real estate loans. Residential mortgages make up about half of the bank's loan portfolio.

	Annual Growth	12/03	12/04	12/05	12/06	12/07
Assets ($ mil.)	17.4%	—	—	195.9	232.7	270.1
Net income ($ mil.)	8.0%	—	—	1.8	1.8	2.1
Market value ($ mil.)	12.3%	—	—	25.8	36.0	32.5
Employees	—	—	—	—	—	108

BANK OF THE OZARKS, INC.

NASDAQ (GS): OZRK

12615 Chenal Pkwy.	CEO: George G. Gleason
Little Rock, AR 72231	CFO: Paul Moore
Phone: 501-978-2265	HR: Diane Hilburn
Fax: 501-978-2350	FYE: December 31
Web: www.bankozarks.com	Type: Public

Bank of the Ozarks is the holding company for the bank of the same name, which has around 65 branches in Arkansas. It also has about five locations in Texas and a loan production office in North Carolina. Serving individuals and small to midsized businesses, the bank offers traditional deposit and loan services, in addition to trust services, retirement planning, cash management, and equipment leasing. Mutual funds, annuities, insurance, and other investment products and services are available through a third-party provider. Construction and land development loans make up the largest portion of Bank of the Ozarks' loan portfolio, followed by commercial real estate loans and residential mortgages.

	Annual Growth	12/03	12/04	12/05	12/06	12/07
Assets ($ mil.)	18.2%	1,386.5	1,726.8	2,134.9	2,529.4	2,710.9
Net income ($ mil.)	12.0%	20.2	25.9	31.5	31.7	31.8
Market value ($ mil.)	4.8%	365.7	561.3	614.9	553.6	440.6
Employees	4.7%	—	—	629	699	689

BANK OF THE WEST

180 Montgomery St.	CEO: J. Michael Shepherd
San Francisco, CA 94104	CFO: Kevin F. Ames
Phone: 925-942-8300	HR: Donald R. Ward
Fax: 925-943-1224	FYE: December 31
Web: www.bankofthewest.com	Type: Subsidiary

Bank of the West can't "bear" the thought of customers banking elsewhere. The bank (which has a bear as its logo) has nearly 700 banking offices in about 20 western and Midwestern states. Bank of the West targets consumers and small to mid-market companies with such offerings as checking, savings, and money market accounts and CDs; as well as credit cards, insurance, investment products, trusts, and financial planning. Business banking targets such sectors as agribusiness, commercial real estate, financial services, health care, religious groups, and the public sector. Lending is focused on mortgages, consumer finance, and equipment leases. Parent company BancWest is owned by French bank BNP Paribas.

	Annual Growth	12/03	12/04	12/05	12/06	12/07
Sales ($ mil.)	25.1%	1,545.3	1,692.3	2,447.5	3,520.9	3,782.2
Employees	38.9%	5,281	7,336	—	—	—

An in-depth profile of this company is available to Hoover's Online members at hoovers.com.

219

BANK OF VIRGINIA

NASDAQ (CM): BOVA

11730 Hull Street Rd.
Midlothian, VA 23112
Phone: 804-774-7576
Fax: 804-774-2306
Web: www.bankofva.com

CEO: Frank Bell III
CFO: Kenneth P. Mulkey
HR: Nancy R. Coffman
FYE: December 31
Type: Public

Bank of Virginia helps put the Rich in Richmond. The company serves Chesterfield County from a handful of banking branches in Midlothian, Richmond, and Chester. Bank of Virginia offers standard retail and commercial services including checking and savings accounts, CDs, IRAs, and money market accounts. Commercial mortgages account for about a third of the company's lending portfolio, which also includes business loans, single-family mortgages, and construction loans. (Consumer lending accounts for less than 5% of its portfolio.) The bank opened its doors in 2004 and is using funds from its 2005 initial public offering to expand its commercial business and open new branches.

	Annual Growth	12/02	12/03	12/04	12/05	*12/06
Assets ($ mil.)	82.1%	—	—	41.4	85.7	137.3
Net income ($ mil.)	—	—	—	(2.7)	(1.8)	99.0
Employees	6.1%	—	—	32	31	36

*Most recent year available

BANKATLANTIC BANCORP, INC.

NYSE: BBX

2100 W. Cypress Creek Rd.
Fort Lauderdale, FL 33309
Phone: 954-940-5000
Fax: 954-940-5250
Web: www.bankatlanticbancorp.com

CEO: Alan B. Levan
CFO: Valerie C. Toalson
HR: Susan D. McGregor
FYE: December 31
Type: Public

BankAtlantic Bancorp has an ocean of ideas about what you should do with your money. The company owns BankAtlantic, which operates more than 90 branches in Florida, with a focus on the Miami and Tampa metropolitan areas. Residential real estate loans make up more than 45% of BankAtlantic's loan portfolio; commercial real estate loans add nearly 20% more. The bank also makes a variety of business and personal loans. Holding company BFC Financial, headed by BankAtlantic Bancorp chairman Alan Levan and vice chairman John Abdo, controls the company; BFC Financial also controls Woodbridge Holdings (formerly Levitt Corporation) and, indirectly, Bluegreen.

	Annual Growth	12/03	12/04	12/05	12/06	12/07
Assets ($ mil.)	7.2%	4,831.5	6,356.8	6,471.4	6,495.7	6,378.8
Net income ($ mil.)	—	67.7	70.8	59.2	15.4	(22.2)
Market value ($ mil.)	(27.8%)	775.4	1,098.8	782.4	775.5	210.7
Employees	(6.2%)	—	—	2,921	2,819	2,569

BANKERS FINANCIAL CORPORATION

360 Central Ave.
St. Petersburg, FL 33701
Phone: 727-823-4000
Fax: 727-823-6518
Web: www.bankersfinancialcorp.com

CEO: David K. Meehan
CFO: Edwin C. Hussemann
HR: –
FYE: December 31
Type: Private

Bankers Financial Corporation has more to do with extended warranties and hurricanes than it does with checking accounts. The holding company owns Bankers Insurance Group, which provides personal and commercial property/casualty coverage and life insurance products through its carrier subsidiaries. These include Bankers Insurance Company (personal and commercial lines in more than 40 states); First Community Insurance (homeowners, excess, and flood insurance in Florida); Bankers Specialty Insurance Company (property insurance in Louisiana); and Bankers Life Insurance (annuities). Bankers Insurance will begin offering federal flood insurance in 2008, working through its BinTech Partners, an outsourcing provider.

	Annual Growth	12/03	12/04	12/05	12/06	12/07
Est. sales ($ mil.)	—	—	—	—	—	279.0
Employees	—	—	—	—	—	955

THE BANKER'S STORE, INC.

OTC: BSTR

1535 Memphis Junction Rd.
Bowling Green, KY 42101
Phone: 270-781-8453
Fax: 270-782-9639
Web: www.bankstore.com

CEO: Vincent C. (Vince) Buckman
CFO: Vincent C. (Vince) Buckman
HR: –
FYE: May 31
Type: Public

The Banker's Store sells and services drive-up and walk-up teller systems, automated teller machines (ATMs), vaults, and safe deposit boxes. In addition, the company offers used office furniture, along with gun safes and other security equipment. It also provides locksmith services. Primarily serving Kentucky, Tennessee, and surrounding states, the company counts banks, pharmacies, drug stores, and hospitals among its customers. Chairman Paul Clark and company secretary Roberta Clark, husband and wife, together own about 84% of the company.

	Annual Growth	5/03	5/04	5/05	5/06	5/07
Sales ($ mil.)	0.0%	2.6	2.5	2.9	2.5	2.6
Net income ($ mil.)	—	0.0	0.0	0.1	0.1	(0.2)
Market value ($ mil.)	9.3%	1.0	—	1.9	1.2	1.5
Employees	—	—	—	—	19	—

BANKFINANCIAL CORPORATION

NASDAQ (GM): BFIN

15W060 N. Frontage Rd.
Burr Ridge, IL 60527
Phone: 630-242-7700
Fax: 708-675-6699
Web: www.bankfinancial.com

CEO: F. Morgan Gasior
CFO: Paul A. Cloutier
HR: Patricia M. Smith
FYE: December 31
Type: Public

If you need a BankNow to handle all your BankBusiness, try BankFinancial. The holding company's subsidiary BankFinancial, F.S.B. provides banking and financial services to individuals and businesses through about 20 branches in the northeastern Illinois counties of Cook, DuPage, Lake, and Will. It offers such products as savings, money market, demand, and NOW accounts, as well as loans. Nonresidential real estate loans account for more than 25% of the bank's loan portfolio; one- to four-family residential mortgages account for more than 20%. The bank also offers business, construction, and consumer loans.

	Annual Growth	12/03	12/04	12/05	12/06	12/07
Assets ($ mil.)	(4.2%)	—	—	1,614.4	1,613.1	1,480.5
Net income ($ mil.)	(19.5%)	—	—	11.1	10.1	7.2
Market value ($ mil.)	(1.6%)	—	—	359.2	412.7	347.9
Employees	(3.0%)	—	—	418	—	393

BANKRATE, INC.

NASDAQ (GS): RATE

11760 U.S. Hwy. 1, Ste. 200
North Palm Beach, FL 33408
Phone: 561-630-2400
Fax: 561-625-4540
Web: www.bankrate.com

CEO: Thomas R. Evans
CFO: Edward J. (Ed) DiMaria
HR: –
FYE: December 31
Type: Public

Bankrate knows there's life after budget-cutting. The firm's Bankrate.com provides personal finance information on more than 300 products including mortgages, credit cards, money market accounts, certificates of deposit, and home equity loans. Its Interest.com publishes financial rates and information connecting consumers with lenders, and its FastFind sells consumer leads to lenders for mortgages, home-equity loans, auto financing, and online education. Bankrate also has print publications, such as its *Mortgage Guide*, a weekly newspaper-advertising table consisting of product and rate information from local mortgage companies and financial institutions.

	Annual Growth	12/03	12/04	12/05	12/06	12/07
Sales ($ mil.)	27.1%	36.6	39.2	49.0	79.7	95.6
Net income ($ mil.)	13.4%	12.1	13.4	9.7	10.0	20.0
Market value ($ mil.)	48.4%	187.1	218.6	468.8	691.6	907.8
Employees	2.5%	—	—	159	163	—

BANKUNITED FINANCIAL CORPORATION
NASDAQ (GS): BKUNA

255 Alhambra Cir.
Coral Gables, FL 33134
Phone: 305-569-2000
Fax: 305-569-2057
Web: www.bankunited.com

CEO: Alfred R. Camner
CFO: Humberto L. (Bert) Lopez
HR: Roberta R. Kressel
FYE: September 30
Type: Public

BankUnited Financial is keeping it all together. The financial institution is the holding company for BankUnited, one of Florida's largest banking institutions with some 90 branches. The federal savings bank's deposit options include CDs and checking, NOW, and money market accounts. One- to four-family residential mortgages account for around 85% of BankUnited's loan portfolio. The bank's other loan offerings include commercial and multifamily mortgages and construction and land loans. BankUnited sells some of the mortgages it originates on the secondary market, often retaining the loan servicing functions.

	Annual Growth	9/03	9/04	9/05	9/06	9/07
Assets ($ mil.)	20.5%	7,145.1	8,710.4	10,667.7	13,570.9	15,046.3
Net income ($ mil.)	20.1%	39.1	50.7	27.5	83.9	81.4
Market value ($ mil.)	(3.2%)	617.7	860.6	685.8	942.2	542.5
Employees	15.0%	—	—	1,137	1,350	1,504

BANNER CORPORATION
NASDAQ (GS): BANR

10 S. First Ave.
Walla Walla, WA 99362
Phone: 509-527-3636
Fax: 509-526-8898
Web: www.banrbank.com

CEO: D. Michael Jones
CFO: Lloyd W. Baker
HR: Debi Sapp
FYE: December 31
Type: Public

Flagging bank accounts? See Banner Corporation. Banner is the holding company for Banner Bank, which serves the Pacific Northwest through some 80 branches and about a dozen loan production offices in nearly 30 Washington, Oregon, and Idaho counties. The company offers traditional retail banking products, as well as business, consumer, and agriculture loans. Construction and land loans make up about one-third of the company's loan portfolio; commercial real estate loans account for around a quarter. Bank subsidiary Community Financial writes residential mortgage and construction loans. As of 2007, Banner is also parent to Islanders Bank, which operates three branches in Washington's San Juan Islands.

	Annual Growth	12/03	12/04	12/05	12/06	12/07
Assets ($ mil.)	14.3%	2,635.3	2,897.1	3,040.6	3,495.6	4,492.7
Net income ($ mil.)	23.0%	16.1	19.3	12.4	32.2	36.9
Market value ($ mil.)	12.4%	288.6	369.8	367.6	535.4	460.4
Employees	19.8%	—	—	821	—	1,178

BANNER HEALTH

1441 N. 12th St.
Phoenix, AZ 85006
Phone: 602-495-4000
Fax: —
Web: www.bannerhealth.com

CEO: Peter S. Fine
CFO: Ron Bunnell
HR: Gerri Twomey
FYE: December 31
Type: Not-for-profit

Hoist this Banner high! Banner Health is one of the largest secular not-for-profit health systems in the US. The organization operates 20 hospitals (about 3,100 beds), half a dozen long-term care centers, and family clinics in seven states. Banner Health provides a variety of additional health services, including home and hospice care, pediatrics, and rehabilitation. Banner Health also participates in medical research in areas such as Alzheimer's disease and spinal cord injuries. The health system plans to spend $14 million to expand its Banner Estrella Medical Center, as well as build a cancer center with some 150 beds.

	Annual Growth	12/03	12/04	12/05	12/06	12/07
Est. sales ($ mil.)	—	—	—	—	—	2,147.5
Employees	—	—	—	—	—	25,000

BANYAN CORPORATION
OTC: BNYN

1925 Century Park East, Ste. 500
Los Angeles, CA 90067
Phone: 800-808-0899
Fax: 403-287-8804
Web: www.chiropracticusa.net

CEO: Michael J. Gelmon
CFO: Cory H. Gelmon
HR: —
FYE: December 31
Type: Public

Banyan Corporation banishes bad backs. Banyan is developing a national chain of franchised chiropractic clinics under the Chiropractic USA brand. The company provides consulting, corporate identity and marketing materials, operating formats, and other related support services to its franchisees. Banyan also offers diagnostic testing services to doctors and chiropractors through subsidiary Premier Medical Group. Its diagnostic tests help detect nervous system disorders. Another division, Virtual Medical Systems, markets the VT3000 electro-diagnostic nerve testing machine.

	Annual Growth	12/03	12/04	12/05	12/06	12/07
Sales ($ mil.)	29.1%	1.8	0.5	1.1	5.4	5.0
Net income ($ mil.)	—	(3.9)	(2.5)	(4.7)	(4.1)	(5.5)
Market value ($ mil.)	(36.3%)	—	645.3	86.3	262.1	—
Employees	—	—	—	—	48	—

BAPTIST HEALTH SOUTH FLORIDA

6855 Red Rd.
Coral Gables, FL 33143
Phone: 786-662-7000
Fax: 786-662-7334
Web: www.baptisthealth.net

CEO: Brian E. Keeley
CFO: Ralph E. Lawson
HR: —
FYE: September 30
Type: Not-for-profit

Baptist Health South Florida is a not-for-profit health care organization composed of six Miami-area hospitals and a cardiovascular care institute. Baptist Health, which is a provider for about 40 health plans, offers a wide range of services including a comprehensive cancer program, pediatric services, addiction treatment, outpatient services, rehabilitation, and home care. Baptist Health has more than 1,400 hospital beds. The system includes a children's hospital, outpatient diagnostic and treatment facilities, and a home health care agency. Baptist Health South Florida, established in 1990, provides treatment for more than 100,000 patients each year.

	Annual Growth	9/03	9/04	9/05	9/06	9/07
Est. sales ($ mil.)	—	—	—	—	—	1,517.6
Employees	—	—	—	—	—	9,374

BAPTIST HEALTH SYSTEM, INC.

800 Prudential Dr.
Jacksonville, FL 32207
Phone: 904-202-2000
Fax: 904-202-2833
Web: www.e-baptisthealth.com

CEO: A. Hugh Greene
CFO: Michael Lukaszewski
HR: —
FYE: September 30
Type: Not-for-profit

Even if you don't root for the Jacksonville Jaguars, you can still seek care from Baptist Health System. The health care system serves the Jacksonville, Florida area through four hospitals. Baptist Medical Center, its flagship facility, is a full-service medical center. Across the street, Wolfson Children's Hospital cares for the city's youngest residents. Baptist Medical Center Beaches, an acute care facility, operates with more than 120 beds; its Baptist Medical Center Nassau hospital has more than 50 beds. Baptist Health Systems offers centers for specialties such as cardiac care, cancer treatment, and emergency medicine.

	Annual Growth	9/03	9/04	9/05	9/06	9/07
Est. sales ($ mil.)	—	—	—	—	—	736.9
Employees	—	—	—	—	—	7,000

An in-depth profile of this company is available to Hoover's Online members at hoovers.com.

221

BAR HARBOR BANKSHARES

AMEX: BHB

82 Main St.
Bar Harbor, ME 04609
Phone: 207-288-3314
Fax: 207-288-2626
Web: www.bhbt.com

CEO: Joseph M. Murphy
CFO: Gerald Shencavitz
HR: Marsha C. Sawyer
FYE: December 31
Type: Public

Bar Harbor Bankshares is a *Maine*-stay for communities in the Pine Tree State's Hancock, Knox, and Washington counties. Through about a dozen branches, subsidiary Bar Harbor Bank & Trust offers such deposit products as checking, savings, and money market accounts; NOW accounts; IRAs; and CDs. Real estate mortgages make up some 80% of the bank's loan portfolio, which also includes consumer, commercial, and agricultural loans. About 10% of the bank's lending is focused on the tourist industry associated with nearby Acadia National Park. Bar Harbor Trust Services, a subsidiary of the bank, offers trust and estate planning services.

	Annual Growth	12/03	12/04	12/05	12/06	12/07
Assets ($ mil.)	11.1%	583.8	666.8	747.9	824.9	889.5
Net income ($ mil.)	8.5%	5.2	5.7	6.4	6.9	7.2
Market value ($ mil.)	2.8%	83.8	89.2	80.5	96.8	93.5
Employees	—	—	—	154	—	—

BARCLAYS BANK DELAWARE

100 S. West St.
Wilmington, DE 19801
Phone: 302-888-1400
Fax: 302-888-0405
Web: www.juniperfinancial.com

CEO: Lloyd M. Wirshba
CFO: Lloyd M. Wirshba
HR: Kathleen (Kathy) Kreusch Cobb
FYE: December 31
Type: Subsidiary

Fill 'er up and receive gasoline rebates at the same time! Co-branded gas cards are just one of the offerings from Barclays Bank Delaware, formerly Juniper Financial. The company issues Visa and MasterCard credit cards, and has about 40 card partnerships specializing in private-label cards for such partners as Gulf, TiVo, Carnival Cruise Lines, and Harvard. The company was founded in 2000; UK-based Barclays PLC entered the US credit card market when it acquired Juniper Financial in December 2004.

	Annual Growth	12/03	12/04	12/05	12/06	12/07
Est. sales ($ mil.)	—	—	—	—	—	11.3
Employees	—	—	—	—	—	350

BARCLAYS GLOBAL INVESTORS

45 Fremont St.
San Francisco, CA 94105
Phone: 415-597-2000
Fax: 415-597-2140
Web: www.barclaysglobal.com

CEO: Blake R. Grossman
CFO: Frank Ryan
HR: Chris McCrum
FYE: December 31
Type: Subsidiary

Barclays Global Investors has no trouble with trillions. With more than $1.8 trillion under management, the company is one of the world's largest administrators of institutional assets, serving more than 2,800 corporations, pension plans, unions, not-for-profits and other clients in more than 50 countries. It offers approximately 200 mutual funds, including its LifePath family of funds and iShares, the company's proprietary exchange-traded funds (ETFs). Barclays Global Investors also performs securities lending, currency management, and portfolio transaction management services. The company is a subsidiary of one of the largest banks in the world, Barclays.

	Annual Growth	12/03	12/04	12/05	12/06	12/07
Est. sales ($ mil.)	—	—	—	—	—	31.7
Employees	—	—	—	—	—	800

BARE ESCENTUALS, INC.

NASDAQ (GS): BARE

71 Stevenson St., 22nd Fl.
San Francisco, CA 94105
Phone: 415-489-5000
Fax: 877-963-3329
Web: www.bareescentuals.com

CEO: Leslie A. Blodgett
CFO: Myles B. McCormick
HR: –
FYE: Sunday nearest December 31
Type: Public

When it comes to keeping its customers looking naturally pretty, Bare Escentuals has a mineral interest. The company, which rolled out its bareMinerals makeup brand in 1976 along with its first retail store, develops, markets, and sells natural cosmetics, skin care, and body care items. Brand names include RareMinerals, i.d. bareMinerals, md formulations, and its namesake line, among others. Formerly STB Beauty, Bare Escentuals sells its products through its more than 50 company-owned US boutiques, about 500 retailers, some 1,200 spas and salons, infomercials, and several Web sites.

	Annual Growth	12/03	12/04	12/05	12/06	12/07
Sales ($ mil.)	52.4%	94.7	141.8	259.3	394.5	511.0
Net income ($ mil.)	65.3%	11.8	4.0	23.9	50.2	88.1
Market value ($ mil.)	(19.7%)	—	—	—	2,775.0	2,227.0
Employees	65.1%	—	—	576	863	1,571

BARNES & NOBLE COLLEGE BOOKSTORES, INC.

120 Mountain View Blvd.
Basking Ridge, NJ 07920
Phone: 908-991-2665
Fax: 908-991-2846
Web: www.bkstore.com

CEO: Max J. Roberts
CFO: Jack A. Dill
HR: –
FYE: April 30
Type: Private

Barnes & Noble College Bookstores is the scholastic sister company of Barnes & Noble (B&N), the US's largest bookseller. Started in 1873, the company operates more than 600 campus bookstores nationwide, selling textbooks, trade books, school supplies, collegiate clothing, and emblematic merchandise. Universities, medical and law schools, and community colleges hire Barnes & Noble College Bookstores to replace traditional campus cooperatives. (The schools get a cut of the sales.) Its College Marketing Network division offers on-campus marketing opportunities to businesses. B&N's chairman, Leonard Riggio, owns a controlling interest in the company.

	Annual Growth	4/02	4/03	4/04	4/05	4/06
Est. sales ($ mil.)	6.2%	1,250.0	1,300.0	1,300.0	1,540.0	1,590.0
Employees	6.0%	9,500	9,700	9,900	13,900	12,000

BARNES & NOBLE, INC.

NYSE: BKS

122 5th Ave.
New York, NY 10011
Phone: 212-633-3300
Fax: 212-675-0413
Web: www.barnesandnobleinc.com

CEO: Stephen (Steve) Riggio
CFO: Joseph J. Lombardi
HR: Michelle Smith
FYE: Saturday nearest January 31
Type: Public

Barnes & Noble does business — big business — by the book. As the #1 bookseller in the US, it operates more than 700 Barnes & Noble superstores (selling books, music, movies, and gifts) throughout all 50 US states and the District of Columbia. It also owns about 85 mostly mall-based B. Dalton bookstores. In cyberspace, the firm conducts sales through subsidiary Barnes & Noble.com (accounting for about 10% of total sales). Barnes & Noble's remaining businesses include leading general trade book publisher Sterling Publishing Co., and a 74% interest in seasonal kiosk retailer Calendar Club.

	Annual Growth	1/04	1/05	1/06	1/07	1/08
Sales ($ mil.)	(2.4%)	5,951.0	4,873.6	5,103.0	5,261.3	5,410.8
Net income ($ mil.)	(2.8%)	151.9	143.4	146.7	150.5	135.8
Market value ($ mil.)	5.5%	1,658.3	2,227.5	2,770.6	2,631.5	2,051.8
Employees	(1.6%)	—	42,000	39,000	39,000	40,000

BARNES GROUP INC.

NYSE: B

123 Main St.	CEO: Gregory F. Milzcik
Bristol, CT 06011	CFO: Francis C. Boyle Jr.
Phone: 860-583-7070	HR: John R. Arrington
Fax: 860-589-3507	FYE: December 31
Web: www.barnesgroupinc.com	Type: Public

Barnes Group keeps the financial spring in its step by making springs. The company produces precision mechanical and nitrogen gas springs through its Barnes Industrial segment (formerly Associated Spring). Its Barnes Distribution business sells maintenance, repair, and operating supplies such as fasteners, adhesives, and sealants (generally sourced from outside the company) as well as automotive key-making equipment. Through Barnes Aerospace, the company makes machined parts for jet engines, airframes, and turbines. Customers include manufacturers of industrial and textile machinery, appliances, electronics, and vehicles. US customers account for 61% of sales; General Electric accounts for around 18%.

	Annual Growth	12/03	12/04	12/05	12/06	12/07
Sales ($ mil.)	12.7%	890.8	994.7	1,102.2	1,259.7	1,439.5
Net income ($ mil.)	32.4%	33.0	33.4	60.5	73.8	101.3
Market value ($ mil.)	48.7%	369.4	307.9	398.6	1,139.9	1,805.4
Employees	2.5%	—	—	6,205	6,666	6,523

BARNESANDNOBLE.COM LLC

76 9th Ave., 9th Fl.	CEO: Marie J. Toulantis
New York, NY 10011	CFO: Kevin M. Frain
Phone: 212-414-6000	HR: Michelle Smith
Fax: 212-414-6140	FYE: January 31
Web: www.barnesandnoble.com	Type: Subsidiary

barnesandnoble.com wants to be the Internet bookshelf's best-seller, but it's a distant #2 behind top online bookseller Amazon.com. A subsidiary of Barnes & Noble, the online retailer sells books, magazines, music, software, DVDs, videocassettes, and more. barnesandnoble.com also offers author biographies and book reviews from in-house editors, customers, and sources such as *The New Yorker, Kirkus Reviews,* and *Publisher's Weekly.* Other offerings include rare and out-of-print books and online book clubs. The company's online portals attract bookworms from more than 230 countries.

BARNEYS NEW YORK, INC.

575 5th Ave.	CEO: –
New York, NY 10017	CFO: Steven M. Feldman
Phone: 212-339-7300	HR: Marc H. Perlowitz
Fax: 212-450-8489	FYE: December 31
Web: www.barneys.com	Type: Private

Barneys New York is no purple dinosaur, even if it did have a brush with extinction. The luxury department store chain sells designer apparel for men, women, and children; shoes; accessories; and home furnishings. It operates about 35 stores including full-size flagship shops in New York City, Beverly Hills, Boston, and Chicago; smaller Barneys New York Co-Op locations; and outlet stores. Barney Pressman founded the firm in 1923. Former owner Jones Apparel Group, which acquired Barneys in 2004 for about $400 million, sold the company in 2007 for $945 million to an affiliate of Istithmar PJSC, an investment firm owned by the Dubai government.

	Annual Growth	12/03	12/04	12/05	12/06	12/07
Est. sales ($ mil.)	—	—	—	—	—	104.2
Employees	—	—	—	—	—	1,400

BARNWELL INDUSTRIES, INC.

AMEX: BRN

1100 Alakea St., Ste. 2900	CEO: Morton H. Kinzler
Honolulu, HI 96813	CFO: Russell M. Gifford
Phone: 808-531-8400	HR: –
Fax: 808-531-7181	FYE: September 30
Web: www.brninc.com	Type: Public

Barnwell Industries has more than a barnful of assets, which range from oil and gas production, contract well drilling, and Hawaiian land and housing investments. Barnwell Industries explores for and produces oil and natural gas primarily in Alberta. It has proved reserves of 1.4 million barrels of oil and 24 billion cu. ft. of gas. Subsidiary Water Resources International drills water and geothermal wells and installs and repairs water pump systems in Hawaii. The company also owns a 78% interest in Kaupulehu Developments, which owns leasehold rights to more than 1,000 acres in Hawaii. In 2007 Barnwell Industries established a real estate development segment to acquire house lots and build single-family homes.

	Annual Growth	9/03	9/04	9/05	9/06	9/07
Sales ($ mil.)	18.9%	23.7	38.0	44.2	58.0	47.4
Net income ($ mil.)	11.1%	2.3	8.7	6.0	14.6	3.5
Market value ($ mil.)	124.0%	5.5	10.3	174.2	159.3	137.6
Employees	23.6%	—	—	—	55	68

BARR PHARMACEUTICALS, INC.

NYSE: BRL

223 Quaker Rd.	CEO: Bruce L. Downey
Pomona, NY 10970	CFO: William T. (Bill) McKee
Phone: 845-362-1100	HR: Jane F. Greenman
Fax: 845-362-2774	FYE: December 31
Web: www.barrlabs.com	Type: Public

Barr Pharmaceuticals is raising the bar and lowering the prices for many medications. The company is one of the world's largest makers of generic drugs, the cheaper knock-offs of off-patent branded pharmaceuticals. Through its Barr Laboratories subsidiary, the firm makes more than 100 generics for the North American market, with a particular emphasis on oral contraceptives. Barr's PLIVA subsidiary, acquired in 2006, makes and sells hundreds of generic drugs, as well as active pharmaceutical ingredients, primarily in Germany and Eastern Europe. Barr Pharmaceuticals also develops branded drugs through its Duramed unit; its brand-name products include contraceptives such as Seasonale and Plan B.

	Annual Growth	6/04	6/05	6/06	*12/06	12/07
Sales ($ mil.)	17.6%	1,309.1	1,047.4	1,314.5	916.4	2,500.6
Net income ($ mil.)	1.1%	123.1	215.0	336.5	(338.2)	128.4
Market value ($ mil.)	12.9%	3,521.5	5,038.1	5,065.0	5,341.0	5,724.7
Employees	67.3%	—	1,900	2,040	—	8,900
					*Fiscal year change	

BARRACUDA NETWORKS, INC.

3175 S. Winchester Blvd.	CEO: Dean Drako
Campbell, CA 95008	CFO: David Faugno
Phone: 408-342-5400	HR: –
Fax: 408-342-1061	FYE: December 31
Web: www.barracudanetworks.com	Type: Private

Barracuda Networks provides firewalls that protect enterprises from e-mail spam, viruses, and spyware. Barracuda serves small, midsized, and large businesses in industries such as financial services, manufacturing, technology, consumer goods, utilities, and retail. The company also provides professional services such as support, consulting, and implementation. Barracuda was founded in 2002.

	Annual Growth	12/03	12/04	12/05	12/06	12/07
Est. sales ($ mil.)	—	—	—	—	—	18.1
Employees	—	—	—	—	—	200

An in-depth profile of this company is available to Hoover's Online members at hoovers.com.

223

BARRETT BUSINESS SERVICES, INC.

NASDAQ (GS): BBSI

8100 NE Parkway Dr., Ste. 200
Vancouver, WA 98662
Phone: 360-828-0700
Fax: 360-828-0701
Web: www.barrettbusiness.com

CEO: William W. Sherertz
CFO: James D. Miller
HR: –
FYE: December 31
Type: Public

Barrett Business Services really puts people to work. The company offers both temporary and long-term staffing to some 2,300 small and midsized businesses. Its staffing services focus on light industrial, clerical, and technical businesses. Barrett also does business as a professional employment organization (PEO), providing outsourced human resource services, such as payroll management, benefits administration, risk management, recruiting, and placement for about 1,200 clients. Barrett operates through about 45 branch offices across 10 US states.

	Annual Growth	12/03	12/04	12/05	12/06	12/07
Sales ($ mil.)	23.9%	122.7	195.0	231.4	259.2	289.2
Net income ($ mil.)	68.2%	2.1	7.4	12.5	16.3	16.8
Market value ($ mil.)	42.0%	49.3	52.9	276.1	263.5	200.4
Employees	—	—	—	27,400	—	—

BARRICK GOLDSTRIKE MINES INC.

P.O. Box 29
Elko, NV 89803
Phone: 702-738-8043
Fax: –
Web: www.barrick.com

CEO: Gregory A. Lang
CFO: –
HR: –
FYE: December 31
Type: Subsidiary

Barrick Goldstrike Mines is the mother lode for Barrick Gold. The company operates three producing mines (the open pit Betze-Post and the underground Meikle and Rodeo) on property totaling some 9,900 acres, located on the prolific Carlin Trend in Nevada. Goldstrike produces about 2 million ounces of gold annually and has reserves of about 15 million ounces. It's the largest gold producing operation for Canadian mining company Barrick Gold, the largest gold miner in the world. There are two processing plants located on the property which separate the gold from the recovered ore. Barrick is actively exploring other areas of the Goldstrike property for development.

BARRIER THERAPEUTICS, INC.

NASDAQ (GM): BTRX

600 College Rd. East, Ste. 3200
Princeton, NJ 08540
Phone: 609-945-1200
Fax: 609-945-1212
Web: www.barriertherapeutics.com

CEO: Alfred (Al) Altomari
CFO: Dennis P. Reilly
HR: –
FYE: December 31
Type: Public

Barrier Therapeutics wants to come between you and some nasty fungi. The company's diaper rash cream, sold in the US as Vusion, is its top product; the same treatment is marketed as Zimycan in Europe. Other key products include solar lentigines treatment Solagé (solar lentigines is the fancy name for skin blemishes known as "liver spots" or "sun spots") and seborrheic dermatitis (recurring skin rash) treatment Xolegel. Barrier's drug candidates include antifungal tablet Hyphanox for nail fungus and Rambazole for psoriasis and acne. The company acquires and in-licenses development-stage pharmaceuticals in order to complete the development process. It sells its products through an internal sales force.

	Annual Growth	12/03	12/04	12/05	12/06	12/07
Sales ($ mil.)	178.6%	0.4	0.9	2.5	6.7	24.1
Net income ($ mil.)	—	(20.2)	(39.7)	(45.2)	(52.7)	(53.7)
Market value ($ mil.)	(8.8%)	—	181.7	197.6	220.2	137.9
Employees	—	—	—	89	—	—

BAR-S FOODS CO.

3838 N. Central Ave., Ste. 1900
Phoenix, AZ 85012
Phone: 602-264-7272
Fax: 602-285-5252
Web: www.bar-s.com

CEO: Timothy T. (Tim) Day
CFO: James S. (Jim) Kuykendall
HR: Martin (Marty) Thompson
FYE: September 30
Type: Private

Bar-S Foods hopes to raise the bar in the processed meat industry. The company manufactures hot dogs, corn dogs, bacon, lunch meats, hams, turkey breasts, and other processed deli meats under brands including Bar-S, Extra Lean, Old World Premium, Jumbo Jumbos, President's Pride, and Chuck Wagon. Its more than 100 meat products are sold to deli, retail grocery, warehouse club, and military customers throughout the US; Bar-S also exports its meat products. The company operates three production facilities and a distribution center in Oklahoma. Bar-S was founded in 1981 subsequent to acquiring the assets of Cudahy Company.

BARTLETT AND COMPANY

4800 Main St., Ste. 1200
Kansas City, MO 64112
Phone: 816-753-6300
Fax: 816-753-0062
Web: www.bartlettandco.com

CEO: James B. Hebenstreit
CFO: Arnie Wheeler
HR: Bill Webster
FYE: December 31
Type: Private

When the cows come home, Bartlett and Company will be ready. The company's primary business is grain merchandising, but it also runs cattle feedlots, mills flour, and sells feed and fertilizer. Bartlett operates grain storage facilities, terminal elevators, and country elevators in the midwestern US, including locations in Kansas, Iowa, Missouri, and Nebraska. Bartlett also operates flour mills and feed stores in the Midwest and along the East Coast; its cattle operations are based in Texas. The Bartlett and Company Grain Charitable Foundation makes financial gifts to local causes. Founded in 1907 as Bartlett Agri Enterprises, the company is still owned by the founding Bartlett family.

	Annual Growth	12/02	12/03	12/04	12/05	12/06
Sales ($ mil.)	—	—	—	—	—	1,100.0
Employees	—	—	—	—	—	750

BARTON MALOW COMPANY

26500 American Dr.
Southfield, MI 48034
Phone: 248-436-5000
Fax: 248-436-5001
Web: www.bmco.com

CEO: Ben C. Maibach III
CFO: Lori R. Howlett
HR: Cheryl Bowlson
FYE: March 31
Type: Private

Barton Malow scores by building end zones and home plates. The construction management and general contracting firm also makes points for its schools, hospitals, offices, and plants. It is a top automotive contractor. Its services range from planning to completion on projects in 37 states and Washington, DC. These include Atlanta's Phillips Arena, Boston's Shriners Hospital, and General Motors' Truck Product Center. Barton Malow Design provides architecture and engineering services, and the Barton Malow Rigging unit installs process equipment and machinery. President Ben Maibach III and his family own a majority stake in the company, which Carl Osborn Barton began as C.O. Barton Company in Detroit in 1924.

	Annual Growth	3/02	3/03	3/04	3/05	3/06
Sales ($ mil.)	2.5%	1,251.0	1,350.0	1,100.0	1,080.0	1,380.0
Employees	0.7%	1,264	1,550	1,250	1,280	1,300

BASF CATALYSTS LLC

25 Middlesex/Essex Tpke.
Iselin, NJ 08830
Phone: 732-205-5000
Fax: 732-321-1161
Web: www.catalysts.basf.com

CEO: Kurt W. Bock
CFO: Fried-Walter Münstermann
HR: −
FYE: December 31
Type: Subsidiary

BASF Catalysts converts base materials into wealth — but no alchemy is involved. The company makes chemical catalysts and adsorbents, used in manufacturing pharmaceutical, steel, and packaging products as well as other chemicals. BASF Catalysts' environmental technologies segment makes catalysts used in emission-control systems, such as catalytic converters for automobiles. It also provides precious and base metals as raw materials for manufacturers through its material services segment. In 2006, chemicals giant BASF acquired the company, then called Engelhard, for nearly $5 billion and made it a wholly owned subsidiary, changing its name later that year.

	Annual Growth	12/03	12/04	12/05	12/06	12/07
Est. sales ($ mil.)	—	—	—	—	—	1,017.3
Employees	—	—	—	—	—	6,284

BASF CORPORATION

100 Campus Dr.
Florham Park, NJ 07932
Phone: 973-245-6000
Fax: 973-245-6714
Web: www.basf.com

CEO: Kurt W. Bock
CFO: Fried-Walter Muenstermann
HR: Andre D. Becker
FYE: December 31
Type: Subsidiary

If you're a North American chemical company, BASF might strike you as a four-letter word. BASF Corporation — the North American subsidiary of the world's largest chemicals company, BASF SE — makes nearly every chemical under the sun. The company has six business segments: chemicals (basic, intermediate, and performance), plastics (thermoplastics, foams, and urethanes), coatings (automotive and coil coatings), fine chemicals (vitamins, feed supplements, and raw materials for pharmaceuticals), agricultural chemicals (herbicides, insecticides), and BASF Plant Science (biotechnology). The company is BASF's NAFTA region representative and is responsible for about a fifth of its parent's total sales.

BASHAS' INC.

22402 S. Basha Rd.
Chandler, AZ 85248
Phone: 480-895-9350
Fax: 480-895-5371
Web: www.bashas.com

CEO: Edward N. (Eddie) Basha Jr.
CFO: James (Jim) Buhr
HR: Michael Gantt
FYE: December 31
Type: Private

Bashas' has blossomed in the Arizona desert. The food retailer has grown to about 165 stores located primarily in Arizona, as well as a few stores in California and New Mexico. Its holdings include Bashas' traditional supermarkets, AJ's Fine Foods (gourmet-style supermarkets), and about a dozen Food City supermarkets (which cater to Hispanics in southern Arizona). It also operates a handful of Dine Markets in the Navajo Nation ("dine" means "the people" in Navajo) and offers natural and organic items through 50 Natural Choice instore departments. The company was founded in 1932 and is still owned by the Basha family.

	Annual Growth	12/02	12/03	12/04	12/05	12/06
Sales ($ mil.)	6.8%	1,600.0	1,800.0	2,000.0	2,500.0	2,080.0
Employees	3.4%	12,500	13,200	14,100	14,300	14,299

BASIC AMERICAN FOODS, INC.

2999 Oak Rd.
Walnut Creek, CA 94597
Phone: 925-472-4000
Fax: 925-472-4360
Web: www.baf.com

CEO: Loren Kimura
CFO: John Argent
HR: Sandy Makamura
FYE: December 31
Type: Private

Basic American Foods caters to your basic meat-and-potatoes type of guy. The company makes dehydrated potato products (varieties include au gratin, hash brown, mashed, and scalloped) for the foodservice industry under such brands as Potato Pearls, Nature's Own, and Naturally Potatoes. It also produces refried and black beans (under the Santiago label) and Quick-Start chili mixes. Basic American Foods has processing and sales facilities in the US and international marketing offices in Mexico City and Hong Kong. The company's customers include foodservice distributors and operators, industrial food manufacturers, and wholesale club and retail food operations.

	Annual Growth	12/03	12/04	12/05	12/06	12/07
Est. sales ($ mil.)	—	—	—	—	—	161.0
Employees	—	—	—	—	—	1,500

BASIC EARTH SCIENCE SYSTEMS, INC.

OTC: BSIC

1801 Broadway, Ste. 620
Denver, CO 80202
Phone: 303-296-3076
Fax: 303-773-8099

CEO: Ray Singleton
CFO: Joseph B. Young
HR: −
FYE: March 31
Type: Public

You don't have to be an earth scientist to know that Basic Earth Science Systems gets down to the basics — oil and gas. It is involved in exploration, production, operation, and development activities, exploiting crude oil and natural gas assets in Colorado's Denver-Julesburg Basin, the Williston Basin of Montana, North Dakota, and Saskatchewan, and South Texas and the Gulf Coast. The company operates some 93 gross wells and has proved developed reserves of 995,000 barrels of oil and 1.1 billion cu. ft. of gas. Basic Earth Science Systems' president and CEO Ray Singleton controls 26% of the company.

	Annual Growth	3/04	3/05	3/06	3/07	3/08
Sales ($ mil.)	25.3%	3.0	4.9	6.6	7.2	7.4
Net income ($ mil.)	8.5%	1.3	1.8	2.8	2.5	1.8
Market value ($ mil.)	33.9%	6.0	25.0	38.6	27.6	19.2
Employees	—	—	—	8	—	—

BASIC ENERGY SERVICES, INC.

NYSE: BAS

500 W. Illinios, Ste. 800
Midland, TX 79701
Phone: 432-620-5500
Fax: 432-620-5501
Web: www.basicenergyservices.com

CEO: Kenneth V. (Ken) Huseman
CFO: Alan Krenek
HR: James E. Tyner
FYE: December 31
Type: Public

Oil and gas producers turn to Basic Energy Services for the fundamentals. The company provides well site services with its fleet of well-servicing rigs (at about 390, the third-largest in the US behind Key Energy Services and Nabors Industries), 645 fluid service trucks, and related equipment. These services include acidizing, cementing, fluid handling, fracing, well construction, well maintenance, and workover. Basic Energy Services serves producers operating in Louisiana, New Mexico, Oklahoma, and Texas. It is a consolidator in the fragmented well services industry. Investment firm DLJ Merchant Banking Partners III, L.P., controls the company. In 2008 Basic Energy Services agreed to be acquired by Grey Wolf.

	Annual Growth	12/03	12/04	12/05	12/06	12/07
Sales ($ mil.)	48.4%	180.9	311.5	459.8	730.2	877.2
Net income ($ mil.)	136.6%	2.8	12.9	44.8	98.8	87.7
Market value ($ mil.)	15.4%	—	—	674.0	944.0	898.3
Employees	17.1%	—	—	3,280	4,000	4,500

An in-depth profile of this company is available to Hoover's Online members at hoovers.com.

225

BASIN ELECTRIC POWER COOPERATIVE

1717 E. Interstate Ave.
Bismarck, ND 58503
Phone: 701-223-0441
Fax: 701-224-5336
Web: www.basinelectric.com

CEO: Ronald R. (Ron) Harper
CFO: Clifton T. Hudgins
HR: –
FYE: December 31
Type: Cooperative

Ranges at home on the range depend on Basin Electric Power Cooperative, as do other electric-powered items in nine states from Montana to Iowa to New Mexico. The regional, consumer-owned power generation and transmission co-op generates about 2,600 MW of capacity (mostly coal-fired) for some 120 rural electric member systems, which serve about 2.5 million people. It generates an additional 1,000 MW for participants in the Missouri Basin Power Project. Basin Electric's subsidiaries include Dakota Gasification (produces natural gas from coal), Dakota Coal (markets lignite and limestone), Basin Telecommunications (Internet access), and Basin Cooperative Services (property management).

	Annual Growth	12/03	12/04	12/05	12/06	12/07
Est. sales ($ mil.)	—	—	—	—	—	628.7
Employees	—	—	—	—	—	1,800

BASIN WATER, INC.

NASDAQ (GM): BWTR

8731 Prestige Ct.
Rancho Cucamonga, CA 91730
Phone: 909-481-6800
Fax: 909-481-6801
Web: www.basinwater.com

CEO: Michael M. (Mike) Stark
CFO: Thomas C. (Tom) Tekulve
HR: Thomas C. (Tom) Tekulve
FYE: December 31
Type: Public

If you want clean water in your basin, you want Basin Water. The company designs and builds water treatment systems that remove chemicals like arsenic and chromium. City utilities and other water suppliers buy the systems; Basin Water has about 80 installations in Arizona, California, and New Jersey. Customers include American Water, California Water Service, and American States Water Company. The company has sales and marketing alliances with The Shaw Group and Aqua America. It is focusing on the western US, where rapid population growth and dwindling clean water supplies have created a strong demand for groundwater purification.

	Annual Growth	12/03	12/04	12/05	12/06	12/07
Sales ($ mil.)	63.5%	—	4.3	12.2	17.1	18.8
Net income ($ mil.)	—	—	(0.6)	0.6	(11.2)	(15.3)
Market value ($ mil.)	34.8%	—	—	—	134.6	181.5
Employees	51.7%	—	29	44	—	—

BASS PRO SHOPS, INC.

2500 E. Kearney
Springfield, MO 65898
Phone: 417-873-5000
Fax: 417-873-4672
Web: www.basspro.com

CEO: John L. (Johnny) Morris
CFO: Toni Miller
HR: Mike Roland
FYE: December 31
Type: Private

Bass Pro Shops (BPS) knows how to reel in shoppers. Each of more than 40 Outdoor World stores in the US and Canada covers about 280,000 sq. ft. The cavernous outlets sell boats, campers, equipment, and apparel for most outdoor activities and offer features such as archery ranges, fish tanks, snack bars, and video arcades. The first Outdoor World store (in Missouri) has been one of the state's biggest tourist attractions since it opened in 1981. It owns Tracker Marine (boat manufacturing) and American Rod & Gun (sporting goods wholesale) and runs an 850-acre resort in the Ozark Mountains. Founder John Morris owns BPS.

	Annual Growth	12/02	12/03	12/04	12/05	12/06
Est. sales ($ mil.)	17.4%	1,400.0	1,600.0	2,050.0	1,915.0	2,660.0
Employees	3.3%	11,400	10,700	11,300	12,500	13,000

BASSETT FURNITURE INDUSTRIES

NASDAQ (GS): BSET

3525 Fairystone Park Hwy.
Bassett, VA 24055
Phone: 276-629-6000
Fax: 276-629-6333
Web: www.bassettfurniture.com

CEO: Robert H. (Rob) Spilman Jr.
CFO: Barry C. Safrit
HR: Eddie White
FYE: Last Saturday in November
Type: Public

Bassett Furniture Industries, Incorporated, tries to get a leg up on competing furniture makers. The firm makes wooden and upholstered furniture for the home, featuring bedroom and dining suites, sofas, chairs, love seats, and home office furniture. Bassett sells its products primarily through more than 130 Bassett Furniture Direct stores (most of which are licensed), and also through some 800 multi-line furniture and department stores across the US. Dogged by years of dismal sales, Bassett has reduced its number of manufacturing, warehouse, and showroom facilities from 13 to three and cut its workforce from 4,200 to 1,450 employees in the last seven years.

	Annual Growth	11/03	11/04	11/05	11/06	11/07
Sales ($ mil.)	(1.7%)	316.9	315.6	335.2	328.2	295.4
Net income ($ mil.)	—	(0.5)	8.2	7.6	5.4	(9.9)
Market value ($ mil.)	(11.9%)	189.9	232.0	217.1	205.1	114.4
Employees	(18.2%)	—	—	2,200	1,800	—

BATH & BODY WORKS, INC.

7 Limited Pkwy.
Reynoldsburg, OH 43068
Phone: 614-856-6000
Fax: 614-856-6013
Web: www.bathandbodyworks.com

CEO: Diane L. Neal
CFO: Andrew Meslow
HR: –
FYE: Saturday nearest January 31
Type: Subsidiary

Women turn to Bath & Body Works (BBW) to help wash away the daily stresses of life. A subsidiary of Intimate Brands, which is owned by Limited Brands, BBW operates about 1,600 stores throughout the US, as well as an online store. The company sells natural body and hair care products as well as personal care products and fragrances. Customers in need of rejuvenation can also find a line of aromatherapy and at-home spa treatments, and in some stores, extra indulgences such as massages and pedicures. The BBW brand had an image makeover; from country-inspired to a modern-day apothecary of beauty.

	Annual Growth	1/03	1/04	1/05	1/06	1/07
Sales ($ mil.)	9.5%	1,781.0	1,934.0	2,169.0	2,285.0	2,556.0
Employees	—	—	—	—	—	—

BATTELLE MEMORIAL INSTITUTE

505 King Ave.
Columbus, OH 43201
Phone: 614-424-6424
Fax: 614-424-5263
Web: www.battelle.org

CEO: Carl F. Kohrt
CFO: I. Martin Inglis
HR: Demetrai Mitchell
FYE: September 30
Type: Not-for-profit

When you use a copier, hit a golf ball, or listen to a CD, you're using technologies developed by Battelle Memorial Institute. The not-for-profit trust operates one of the world's largest research enterprises, with more than 20,000 scientists, engineers, and staff serving some 1,100 corporate and government customers each year. Owning its own research facilities in the US and Switzerland, Battelle also manages or co-manages several Department of Energy-sponsored labs, including Brookhaven National Laboratory, Oak Ridge National Laboratory, Idaho National Laboratory, and Pacific Northwest National Laboratory. The family of Gordon Battelle, an early leader in the steel industry, established the institute in 1929.

	Annual Growth	9/02	9/03	9/04	9/05	9/06
Sales ($ mil.)	34.8%	1,157.0	1,316.8	2,863.8	3,481.8	3,815.1
Net income ($ mil.)	(8.4%)	59.6	9.5	21.1	29.5	42.0
Employees	1.9%	8,700	8,900	9,034	—	—

BATTERY VENTURES

930 Winter St., Ste. 2500
Waltham, MA 02451
Phone: 781-478-6600
Fax: 781-478-6601
Web: www.battery.com

CEO: Richard D. (Rick) Frisbie
CFO: Christopher (Chris) Schiavo
HR: –
FYE: December 31
Type: Private

Battery Ventures gives emerging technology companies the juice they need to keep running. A venture capital firm specializing in such high-tech fields as communications, software, and e-commerce, the company has invested in more than 200 businesses around the world. It invests as little as several hundred thousand dollars to seed small ventures on up to $50 million for late-stage expansion; it also takes equity stakes in companies through its private equity operations. Battery Ventures manages more than $3 billion in committed capital; notable past investments include Akamai Technologies, Allegiance Telecom, Focal Communications, and Chordiant Software.

	Annual Growth	12/03	12/04	12/05	12/06	12/07
Est. sales ($ mil.)	—	—	—	—	—	3.2
Employees	—	—	—	—	—	54

BAUER PUBLISHING USA

270 Sylvan Ave.
Englewood Cliffs, NJ 07632
Phone: 201-569-6699
Fax: 201-569-5303
Web: www.baueradsales.com

CEO: Hubert Boehle
CFO: Richard (Rich) Teehan
HR: –
FYE: December 31
Type: Subsidiary

Feeling out of touch? Turn to Bauer Publishing USA, publisher of celebrity and style magazines *In Touch Weekly* and *Life & Style Weekly*, women's magazines *First for Women* and *Woman's World*, soap magazine *Soaps in Depth*, and teen magazines *TWIST*, *M*, and *J-14*. Bauer Publishing USA uses a European approach to publishing, which includes a focus on newsstand, not subscription, sales. The company is owned by German parent company Bauer Verlagsgruppe (also known as The Bauer Publishing Group).

	Annual Growth	12/03	12/04	12/05	12/06	12/07
Est. sales ($ mil.)	—	—	—	—	—	33.4
Employees	—	—	—	—	—	300

⊞ BAUSCH & LOMB INCORPORATED

1 Bausch & Lomb Place
Rochester, NY 14604
Phone: 585-338-6000
Fax: 585-338-6007
Web: www.bausch.com

CEO: Gerald M. Ostrov
CFO: Efrain Rivera
HR: Clayton Osborne
FYE: Last Saturday in December
Type: Private

Eyes are the windows to profit for Bausch & Lomb. The eye care company is best known as a leading maker of contact lenses and lens care solutions (including the PureVision and ReNu brands). In addition to its lens products, Bausch & Lomb makes prescription and over-the-counter ophthalmic drugs through its pharmaceuticals division, while its surgical unit makes equipment for cataract, refractive, and other ophthalmic surgeries. Bausch & Lomb markets its products in more than 100 countries worldwide. The company was acquired by private equity firm Warburg Pincus in 2007, in a deal worth about $3.7 billion plus assumption of debt.

	Annual Growth	12/02	12/03	12/04	12/05	12/06
Sales ($ mil.)	6.0%	1,816.7	2,019.5	2,232.3	2,353.8	2,292.4
Net income ($ mil.)	(32.7%)	72.5	125.5	159.6	19.2	14.9
Employees	3.1%	11,500	—	—	—	13,000

BAX GLOBAL INC.

440 Exchange
Irvine, CA 92602
Phone: 714-442-4500
Fax: 714-442-2900
Web: www.baxglobal.com

CEO: Joseph L. (Joey) Carnes
CFO: Stephen Mattessich
HR: Jay Arnold
FYE: December 31
Type: Subsidiary

Freight forwarder BAX Global makes tracks across the globe. The company arranges the transportation of air, ocean, and surface freight worldwide and acts as a customs broker. (As a freight forwarder, the company buys transportation capacity from carriers and resells it to customers.) It operates from some 500 facilities in more than 130 countries. BAX Global also offers supply chain management services; customers include companies in the aerospace, automotive, health care, retail, and technology industries. It specializes in handling heavyweight shipments. BAX Global is a subsidiary of German rail transportation and logistics giant Deutsche Bahn.

⊞ BAXTER INTERNATIONAL INC.

NYSE: BAX

1 Baxter Pkwy.
Deerfield, IL 60015
Phone: 847-948-2000
Fax: 847-948-2016
Web: www.baxter.com

CEO: Robert L. Parkinson Jr.
CFO: Robert M. Davis
HR: Jeanne K. Mason
FYE: December 31
Type: Public

Why choose between making drugs and making medical equipment? Baxter International does it all. The company makes a wide variety of medical products across its three divisions, including drugs and vaccines, dialysis equipment, and IV supplies. Its BioScience segment makes protein and plasma therapies to treat hemophilia and immune disorders, as well as vaccines and biological sealants used to close surgical wounds. Baxter is a leading maker of intravenous (IV) supplies and systems via its Medication Delivery segment; the segment also makes infusion pumps and inhaled anesthetics. Baxter's Renal division makes dialyzers and other products for the treatment of end-stage renal disease (ESRD).

	Annual Growth	12/03	12/04	12/05	12/06	12/07
Sales ($ mil.)	6.1%	8,904.0	9,509.0	9,849.0	10,378.0	11,263.0
Net income ($ mil.)	18.5%	866.0	388.0	956.0	1,397.0	1,707.0
Market value ($ mil.)	18.5%	18,656.9	21,343.1	23,527.4	30,175.7	36,782.7
Employees	(1.1%)	—	—	47,000	48,000	46,000

BAY NATIONAL CORPORATION

NASDAQ (GM): BAYN

2328 W. Joppa Rd.
Lutherville, MD 21093
Phone: 410-494-2580
Fax: 410-494-2589
Web: www.baynational.com

CEO: Hugh W. Mohler
CFO: Mark A. Semanie
HR: –
FYE: December 31
Type: Public

Bay National Corporation is staying afloat in the banking waters. The institution is a holding company for Bay National Bank, which operates two banking locations in Baltimore and Salisbury, Maryland. Targeting small to midsized businesses and individuals (primarily those associated with business customers as well as professionals and high-net-worth individuals), Bay National Bank offers traditional banking products including checking and savings accounts, CDs, and loans. (Commercial loans and real estate construction, combined, account for about 75% of its lending portfolio.) The company partners with other firms to provide its clients with investment advisory, risk management, and employee benefit services.

	Annual Growth	12/03	12/04	12/05	12/06	12/07
Assets ($ mil.)	20.3%	122.3	170.8	210.0	254.8	256.5
Net income ($ mil.)	—	0.0	0.8	2.7	2.4	0.9
Market value ($ mil.)	5.1%	17.1	23.1	36.7	33.8	20.8
Employees	13.4%	—	—	56	57	72

⊞ An in-depth profile of this company is available to Hoover's Online members at hoovers.com.

227

BAYER CORPORATION

100 Bayer Rd.
Pittsburgh, PA 15205
Phone: 412-777-2000
Fax: 412-777-2034
Web: www.bayerus.com

CEO: Attila Molnar
CFO: Daniel J. (Dan) Apel
HR: Susanna Wayt
FYE: December 31
Type: Subsidiary

For when you can't "bayer" the pain, Bayer Corporation makes your medicine. The US subsidiary of pharmaceuticals and materials giant Bayer AG (or Bayer Group), the company operates through three divisions and an internal services company. Bayer Corporation handles Bayer Group's US operations in three segments: Bayer HealthCare (pharmaceuticals, animal health, and over-the-counter medicines), MaterialScience (plastics, coatings, and polyurethanes), and Bayer CropScience (herbicides, fungicides, and insecticides). The internal services unit, Bayer Corporate and Business Services, handles administrative, technology, human resources, legal, and procurement functions for the Bayer Group's US operations.

	Annual Growth	12/02	12/03	12/04	12/05	12/06
Sales ($ mil.)	2.2%	9,424.5	10,999.3	11,504.0	8,747.2	10,262.8
Employees	(8.6%)	24,600	23,300	22,300	16,200	17,200

BAYER HEALTHCARE PHARMACEUTICALS INC.

6 W. Belt
Wayne, NJ 07470
Phone: 973-305-5000
Fax: 973-487-2003
Web: pharma.bayer.com

CEO: Reinhart Franzen
CFO: –
HR: –
FYE: December 31
Type: Subsidiary

Take a pinch of Bayer, add a dash of Schering, put it in the oven of the US pharmaceuticals market, and you've got the recipe for Bayer HealthCare Pharmaceuticals. The US-based pharmaceuticals unit of Bayer Healthcare, the company was formed by combining the former Schering AG's Berlex subsidiary with the US prescription drug operations of Bayer. (Schering AG is now Bayer Schering Pharma.) The company is focused on specialty therapeutics in the areas of diagnostic imaging, hematology and cardiology, cancer, women's health, and several other serious chronic diseases such as multiple sclerosis and Parkinson's disease.

BAYLAKE CORP.

OTC: BYLK

217 N. 4th Ave.
Sturgeon Bay, WI 54235
Phone: 920-743-5551
Fax: 920-746-3984
Web: www.baylake.com

CEO: Thomas L. Herlache
CFO: Kevin L. LaLuzerne
HR: Sharon A. Haines
FYE: December 31
Type: Public

In need of a loan? Just row, row, row your boat all the way to Baylake Corporation. The institution is the holding company for Baylake Bank, which provides financial services to individuals and small businesses from more than 25 offices in northeastern Wisconsin. The bank offers standard products and services including checking and savings accounts, IRAs, CDs, credit card services, and personal and business loans. It also offers trust and financial planning services. Additionally, Baylake Bank owns an insurance agency and holds a 49.8%-stake in United Financial Services (ATM and data processing services).

	Annual Growth	12/03	12/04	12/05	12/06	12/07
Assets ($ mil.)	3.2%	975.2	1,047.8	1,089.4	1,111.7	1,106.6
Net income ($ mil.)	(60.2%)	8.0	10.8	8.9	7.4	0.2
Employees	0.0%	—	—	—	327	327

BAYLOR HEALTH CARE SYSTEM

3500 Gaston Ave.
Dallas, TX 75246
Phone: 214-820-0111
Fax: 214-820-7499
Web: www.bhcs.com

CEO: Joel T. Allison
CFO: Lydia W. Jumonville
HR: Marshal Mills
FYE: June 30
Type: Not-for-profit

It's not a veterinary health system, but they do treat injured Bears from time to time. The Baylor Health Care System (BHCS) offers a bundle of services. Founded in 1981, it was governed by Baylor University until establishing autonomy in 1997. The not-for-profit medical network serves seven counties in the Dallas-Fort Worth metroplex through more than a dozen hospitals and medical centers, including the Baylor University Medical Center complex, one of the state's major teaching and referral facilities. Other system members include rehabilitation facilities and primary care, senior health, and family health centers. The system also provides home health care and specialized pediatric services.

BAYOU CITY EXPLORATION, INC.

OTC: BYCX

10777 Westheimer, Ste. 170
Houston, TX 77042
Phone: 832-358-3900
Fax: 832-358-3903
Web: www.bcexploration.com

CEO: Robert D. Burr
CFO: –
HR: –
FYE: December 31
Type: Public

Reflecting the shift in its exploration focus from Appalachia to the Gulf Coast, in 2005 Blue Ridge Energy renamed itself Bayou City Exploration. An affiliate of the Blue Ridge Group, the company is engaged in oil and gas exploration primarily in Texas and Louisiana. Bayou City Exploration conducts its activities through partnerships and the acquisition of direct stakes in oil and gas properties, and in exploratory and development wells. The company has four projects in Aransas, Willacy, and Kenedy counties in coastal and south Texas, with estimated project reserves totalling 54.5 billion cu. ft. of natural gas equivalent. The Blue Ridge Group owns 14% of Bayou City Exploration.

	Annual Growth	12/03	12/04	12/05	12/06	12/07
Sales ($ mil.)	(51.5%)	1.8	0.6	0.6	0.3	0.1
Net income ($ mil.)	—	(0.4)	(1.3)	(1.8)	(3.9)	(1.5)
Market value ($ mil.)	22.2%	2.6	10.6	48.9	23.9	5.9
Employees	—	—	—	—	5	—

BAYSTATE HEALTH

280 Chestnut St.
Springfield, MA 01199
Phone: 413-794-0000
Fax: 413-794-8274
Web: baystatehealth.com

CEO: Mark R. Tolosky
CFO: Keith C. McLean-Shinaman
HR: Ann Marie Szmyt
FYE: September 30
Type: Not-for-profit

Patients in need of medical care can dock at this bay. Not-for-profit Baystate Health is the largest health care services provider in western Massachusetts. The system operates four acute-care hospitals with a total of more than 750 beds, and a specialized children's hospital with nearly 60 bassinets. Baystate Health offers ancillary medical services, including cancer care, respiratory care, infusion therapy, visiting nurse, and hospice services. Baystate Health holds a majority of Health New England, a for-profit HMO with some 100,000 members in western Massachusetts.

	Annual Growth	9/03	9/04	9/05	9/06	9/07
Est. sales ($ mil.)	—	—	—	—	—	168.5
Employees	—	—	—	—	—	5,000

BAYWOOD INTERNATIONAL, INC.

OTC: BAYW

14950 N. 83rd Place, Ste. 1
Scottsdale, AZ 85260
Phone: 480-951-3956
Fax: 480-483-2168
Web: www.bywd.com

CEO: Neil Reithinger
CFO: Neil Reithinger
HR: –
FYE: December 31
Type: Public

Baywood International develops, distributes and markets blended dietary supplements. Its products include blends of botanicals, enzymes, herbs, minerals, and vitamins in pill and cosmetic forms to address a range of ailments and conditions including allergies, high cholesterol, joint pains, snoring, thin lips, and weight loss. The firm distributes its products through health food stores, pharmacies, and grocery stores. Its four main product lines are marketed under the Baywood Purechoice, Solutions, Complete Le Femme, and Evolution brands. Third-party manufacturers produce and package the company's products.

	Annual Growth	12/03	12/04	12/05	12/06	12/07
Sales ($ mil.)	35.7%	2.8	2.9	1.2	1.1	9.5
Net income ($ mil.)	—	(0.4)	(0.7)	(0.4)	(0.6)	(1.7)
Market value ($ mil.)	(37.7%)	32.8	51.2	18.1	42.7	4.9
Employees	—	—	—	—	9	—

BB&T CORPORATION

NYSE: BBT

200 W. 2nd St.
Winston-Salem, NC 27101
Phone: 336-733-2000
Fax: 336-733-2470
Web: www.bbt.com

CEO: John A. Allison IV
CFO: Christopher L. (Chris) Henson
HR: –
FYE: December 31
Type: Public

Big, Bold & Temerarious? That might be an apt description of BB&T, the wildly acquisitive banking company that's been spreading across the Southeast like kudzu. The company serves consumers, small to midsized businesses, and government entities through about 1,500 branches. Its flagship subsidiary, Branch Banking and Trust (aka BB&T), is one of North Carolina's oldest banks and a leading originator of residential mortgages in the Southeast. In addition to deposit accounts and loans, the company offers insurance, mutual funds, discount brokerage, wealth management, and financial planning services. Business services include leasing, factoring, and investment banking (through Scott & Stringfellow).

	Annual Growth	12/03	12/04	12/05	12/06	12/07
Assets ($ mil.)	10.0%	90,466.6	100,508.6	109,169.8	121,351.0	132,618.0
Net income ($ mil.)	13.0%	1,064.9	1,558.4	1,653.8	1,528.0	1,734.0
Market value ($ mil.)	(5.4%)	20,940.7	23,144.6	22,761.4	23,787.0	16,744.4
Employees	3.0%	—	—	27,700	29,300	29,400

BBDO WORLDWIDE

1285 Avenue of the Americas
New York, NY 10019
Phone: 212-459-5000
Fax: 212-459-6645
Web: www.bbdo.com

CEO: Andrew Robertson
CFO: James A. (Jim) Cannon
HR: –
FYE: December 31
Type: Subsidiary

This alphabet soup of advertising hopes to spell success for its clients. As the flagship agency of media conglomerate Omnicom Group, BBDO Worldwide offers creative development services for some of the world's top brands using television, print, and other media. BBDO Worldwide also provides campaign planning and management services, as well as other brand promotion services. The firm's Atmosphere BBDO unit offers interactive marketing services in North America. BBDO's clients have included Chrysler, FedEx, and PepsiCo. The company operates through some 290 offices in more than 75 countries, featuring outposts such as Abbott Mead Vickers, Proximity London, and BBDO Detroit.

BCB BANCORP, INC.

NASDAQ (GM): BCBP

104-110 Ave. C
Bayonne, NJ 07002
Phone: 201-823-0700
Fax: 201-339-0403
Web: bayonnecommunitybank.com

CEO: Donald Mindiak
CFO: Donald Mindiak
HR: –
FYE: December 31
Type: Public

BCB Bancorp *be* the holding company for Bayonne Community Bank, a relative newcomer on the scene which opened its doors in late 2000. The independent bank serves Hudson County and the surrounding area from its offices in Bayonne, New Jersey. The bank offers traditional deposit products and services, including savings accounts, money market accounts, CDs, and IRAs. Funds from deposits are used to originate mortgages and loans, primarily commercial real estate and multi-family property loans (which together account for more than half of the bank's loan portfolio).

	Annual Growth	12/03	12/04	12/05	12/06	12/07
Assets ($ mil.)	17.0%	300.7	378.3	466.2	510.8	563.5
Net income ($ mil.)	16.4%	2.4	3.6	4.7	5.6	4.4
Market value ($ mil.)	25.0%	32.3	45.9	78.0	83.9	79.0
Employees	—	—	—	63	—	—

BCSB BANCORP, INC.

NASDAQ (GM): BCSB

4111 E. Joppa Rd., Ste. 300
Baltimore, MD 21236
Phone: 410-256-5000
Fax: 410-256-0261
Web: www.baltcosavings.com

CEO: Joseph J. Bouffard
CFO: Anthony (Tony) Cole
HR: –
FYE: September 30
Type: Public

BCSB Bancorp (formerly BCSB Bankcorp) is the holding company for Baltimore County Savings Bank, which has about 20 branches in the Baltimore metropolitan area. Serving individuals and local businesses, the community-oriented bank offers such standard retail products as CDs, IRAs, and checking, savings, and money market accounts. Single-family residential mortgages make up nearly 40% of the bank's loan portfolio, which also includes commercial real estate loans (more than 25%), home equity lines of credit, and construction, business, and automobile loans.

	Annual Growth	9/03	9/04	9/05	9/06	9/07
Assets ($ mil.)	(1.0%)	668.2	773.6	812.7	785.9	642.4
Net income ($ mil.)	—	1.3	0.9	0.6	(7.4)	(2.9)
Employees	(5.3%)	—	—	173	—	155

BD BIOSCIENCES

2350 Qume Dr.
San Jose, CA 95131
Phone: 877-232-8995
Fax: 800-325-9637
Web: www.bdbiosciences.com

CEO: William A. Kozy
CFO: –
HR: –
FYE: September 30
Type: Business segment

BD Biosciences helps scientists get into your genes. One of the three business segments of Becton, Dickinson, it serves the life sciences research market through three units: Discovery Labware, Immunocytometry Systems, and Pharmingen. Products include cell imaging, sample preparation and automation systems, flow cytometers, reagents, diagnostic assays, labware, and software. In addition to researchers and drug developers, BD Biosciences counts among its customers blood banks, hospitals, and clinical labs. The business segment sells its goods around the world through its own sales force and through independent distributors.

	Annual Growth	9/03	9/04	9/05	9/06	9/07
Est. sales ($ mil.)	—	—	—	—	—	1,034.0
Employees	—	—	—	—	—	—

An in-depth profile of this company is available to Hoover's Online members at hoovers.com.

229

BDO SEIDMAN, LLP

130 E. Randolph, Ste. 2800, 1 Prudential Plaza
Chicago, IL 60601
Phone: 312-240-1236
Fax: 312-240-3311
Web: www.bdo.com

CEO: Jack Weisbaum
CFO: Howard B. Allenberg
HR: Patrick Lloyd
FYE: June 30
Type: Partnership

BDO knows accounting. BDO Seidman is the US arm of BDO International, one of the largest accounting firms outside of the Big Four (Deloitte Touche Tohmatsu, Ernst & Young, KPMG, and PricewaterhouseCoopers). The firm, which has more than 30 locations, offers midsized companies a broad range of accounting, consulting, and related services, including auditing, tax planning, strategic financial advising, litigation consulting, and appraisals and valuations. More than 300 additional offices are operated by independent US firms that are members of the BDO Seidman Alliance. The firm was founded in 1910.

	Annual Growth	6/03	6/04	6/05	6/06	6/07
Sales ($ mil.)	13.9%	350.0	365.0	440.0	558.0	589.0
Employees	—		1,972	—	—	—

BDP INTERNATIONAL, INC.

210 Walnut St.
Philadelphia, PA 19106
Phone: 215-629-8900
Fax: 215-629-8940
Web: www.bdpinternational.com

CEO: Richard J. Bolte Jr.
CFO: Frank P. Osusky
HR: Doug Waitzman
FYE: December 31
Type: Private

Be it by air, ground, or ocean, BDP International is in the business of moving raw materials and finished products around the globe. The company provides logistics services such as customs brokerage, freight forwarding, and warehousing and distribution for customers in a variety of industries, including chemicals and retail. Clients have included Dow Chemical, Cargill, and Trek Bicycle. BDP International and its subsidiaries (including Elite Group) have about 20 offices in the US; internationally, the company operates through subsidiaries, joint ventures, and agents in more than 120 countries. President and CEO Richard Bolte Jr. and his family own the company, which was founded by his father in 1966.

	Annual Growth	12/03	12/04	12/05	12/06	12/07
Est. sales ($ mil.)	—	—	—	—	—	104.2
Employees	—	—	—	—	—	1,100

☐ BE AEROSPACE, INC.   NASDAQ (GS): BEAV

1400 Corporate Center Way
Wellington, FL 33414
Phone: 561-791-5000
Fax: 561-791-7900
Web: www.beaerospace.com

CEO: Amin J. Khoury
CFO: Thomas P. McCaffrey
HR: RJ Landry
FYE: December 31
Type: Public

BE Aerospace (B/E) ensures that travelers have a place to sit and enjoy a cup of coffee. A leading maker of cabin components for commercial passenger aircraft and business jets, B/E's offerings include aircraft seats, coffee makers, refrigeration equipment, galley structures, and emergency oxygen systems. It also provides maintenance and repair services for cabin interior products, converts passenger aircraft into freighters, and distributes aerospace fasteners. B/E sells its products to most major airlines and to manufacturers of aviation equipment. In mid-2008 the company agreed to acquire the assets of Honeywell's Consumable Solutions distribution business for $1.05 billion in cash and stock.

	Annual Growth	12/03	12/04	12/05	12/06	12/07
Sales ($ mil.)	28.0%	624.4	733.5	844.1	1,128.2	1,677.7
Net income ($ mil.)	—	(53.5)	(22.0)	84.6	85.6	147.3
Market value ($ mil.)	123.3%	198.2	658.8	1,634.6	2,041.6	4,923.6
Employees	17.5%	3,300	3,500	3,980	5,058	6,298

☐ BEA SYSTEMS, INC.

2315 N. 1st St.
San Jose, CA 95131
Phone: 408-570-8000
Fax: 408-570-8901
Web: www.bea.com

CEO: Alfred S. Chuang
CFO: Mark P. Dentinger
HR: –
FYE: January 31
Type: Subsidiary

BEA Systems knows that if one is provided the right platform, success is simply a matter of applying oneself. The company is a leading provider of application server software and middleware used by software developers to establish platforms (which span mainframe, client-server, and Web-based environments) upon which software applications run. Its products support functions such as transaction processing, billing, customer service, provisioning, and securities trading. In late 2007 the company received a $6.7 billion acquisition offer from Oracle; BEA rejected that bid but accepted a second offer of $8.5 billion and the deal closed in April 2008.

	Annual Growth	1/04	1/05	1/06	1/07	1/08
Sales ($ mil.)	11.0%	1,012.5	1,080.1	1,199.8	1,402.3	1,535.8
Net income ($ mil.)	15.1%	118.7	131.1	142.7	4.5	208.2
Employees	10.3%	—	—	3,878	4,278	—

BEACH FIRST NATIONAL BANCSHARES, INC.   NASDAQ (GM): BFNB

3751 Robert M. Grissom Pkwy., Ste. 100
Myrtle Beach, SC 29577
Phone: 843-626-2265
Fax: 843-916-7818
Web: www.beachfirst.com

CEO: Walter E. (Walt) Standish III
CFO: Gary S. Austin
HR: Lorie Y. Runion
FYE: December 31
Type: Public

Locals call the area The Grand Strand but it could also be called The Millions Strand. Beach First National Bancshares is the holding company for Beach First National Bank, a community bank serving South Carolina's Myrtle Beach and Hilton Head Island. Targeting commercial customers in the community, the bank has about a half-dozen branches and provides traditional deposit services, including checking and savings accounts, money markets, IRAs, and CDs. Mortgage loans — mostly commercial — make up about 75% of the bank's loan portfolio. The bank also writes business loans and consumer loans. Beach First National Bank was established in 1996.

	Annual Growth	12/03	12/04	12/05	12/06	12/07
Assets ($ mil.)	38.4%	165.1	242.1	397.4	520.2	606.0
Net income ($ mil.)	55.9%	1.0	1.4	3.4	6.2	5.9
Market value ($ mil.)	61.1%	11.3	27.5	51.8	91.2	76.3
Employees	56.6%	—	—	62	125	152

BEACON POWER CORPORATION   NASDAQ (CM): BCON

65 Middlesex Rd.
Tyngsboro, MA 01879
Phone: 978-694-9121
Fax: 978-694-9127
Web: www.beaconpower.com

CEO: F. William (Bill) Capp
CFO: James M. Spiezio
HR: –
FYE: December 31
Type: Public

Beacon Power is a beacon of hope for companies seeking backup power. The development-stage company's flywheel energy storage systems provide uninterruptible electric power for communications networks, computers, industrial manufacturing, and other generation applications. Beacon Power's flywheel systems draw electrical energy from a power source, such as an electric power grid or a fuel cell, and then store it. The power can then be delivered as needed when a primary energy source either fails or is disrupted. Beacon Power also makes photovoltaic power conversion systems (solar inverters).

	Annual Growth	12/03	12/04	12/05	12/06	12/07
Sales ($ mil.)	67.1%	—	0.3	1.5	1.0	1.4
Net income ($ mil.)	—	—	(5.3)	(9.3)	(12.2)	(12.9)
Market value ($ mil.)	49.6%	—	40.3	105.5	70.6	134.8
Employees	17.5%	—	29	30	49	47

BEACON ROOFING SUPPLY, INC.

NASDAQ (GS): BECN

1 Lakeland Park Dr.
Peabody, MA 01960
Phone: 978-535-7668
Fax: 978-535-7358
Web: www.beaconroofingsupply.net

CEO: Robert R. (Bob) Buck
CFO: David R. (Dave) Grace
HR: Thomas R. Miller
FYE: Last Saturday of September
Type: Public

Not all products from Beacon Roofing Supply (BRS) are over your head. One of North America's largest roofing materials distributors, the company operates more than 175 branches in about 35 US states and three Canadian provinces. BRS distributes some 10,000 stock keeping units (SKUs) to about 40,000 customers. Besides roofing products, it distributes related materials such as siding, windows, and waterproofing systems. Customers include contractors, home builders, building owners, and other resellers. BRS was formed in 1997 when investment firm Code Hennessy & Simmons acquired a controlling interest in Beacon Sales, a commercial roofer founded in 1928. The company is growing rapidly through acquisitions.

	Annual Growth	9/03	9/04	9/05	9/06	9/07
Sales ($ mil.)	31.0%	559.5	652.9	850.9	1,500.6	1,645.8
Net income ($ mil.)	37.4%	7.1	(15.4)	32.9	49.3	25.3
Market value ($ mil.)	17.3%	—	280.3	564.9	887.9	452.5
Employees	12.0%	—	—	2,157	2,641	2,708

BEAM GLOBAL SPIRITS & WINE, INC.

510 Lake Cook Rd.
Deerfield, IL 60015
Phone: 847-948-8888
Fax: 847-948-8610
Web: www.beamglobal.com

CEO: Thomas J. (Tom) Flocco
CFO: Ronald G. Kapolnek
HR: Florence Pramberger
FYE: December 31
Type: Subsidiary

At Beam Global Spirits & Wine (formerly Jim Beam Brands Worldwide), the spotlight is on bourbon. Jim Beam is the #1 selling bourbon in the world, hanging out on liquor store shelves with drinking buddies such as Old Crow and Old Grand Dad and small batch bourbons such as Knob Creek. Gilbey's Gin, Lord Calvert Canadian whiskey, and Vox vodka are among the other brands that show up for Christmas parties at Fortune Brands, of which Beam Global Spirits & Wine is a subsidiary. The company also sells DeKuyper, the #1 cordial brand in the US.

BE&K, INC.

2000 International Park Dr.
Birmingham, AL 35243
Phone: 205-972-6000
Fax: 205-972-6651
Web: www.bek.com

CEO: T. Michael (Mike) Goodrich
CFO: Clyde M. Smith
HR: Kimberly S. Patterson
FYE: March 31
Type: Private

A busy bee in the power plant industry, BE&K is a top US engineering and construction contractor. Through a network of subsidiaries, BE&K provides engineering, procurement, and construction and maintenance services worldwide for power plants and other facilities in the cement, chemical, petrochemical, pharmaceutical, and pulp and paper industries. It also serves the telecommunications, manufacturing, environmental, and commercial sectors, and offers technical staffing services through Allstates Technical Services. Houston-based construction giant KBR announced plans to buy BE&K for some $550 million in 2008.

	Annual Growth	3/02	3/03	3/04	3/05	3/06
Sales ($ mil.)	0.9%	1,478.0	1,098.0	1,000.0	1,339.0	1,530.0
Employees	(1.6%)	8,822	8,212	7,700	7,283	8,256

BEAR, STEARNS & CO. INC.

383 Madison Ave.
New York, NY 10179
Phone: 212-272-2000
Fax: 212-272-4785
Web: www.bearstearns.com

CEO: Alan D. Schwartz
CFO: Samuel L. (Sam) Molinaro Jr.
HR: –
FYE: November 30
Type: Subsidiary

You'll just have to grin and bear the fact that Bear Stearns & Co. is one of the primary operating subsidiaries of bulge-bracket investment bank The Bear Stearns Companies. The company provides brokerage, investment advisory, and corporate advisory services. It is designated as a primary dealer in US government securities by the Federal Reserve Bank of New York. The company's client roster includes corporations, institutional investors, government entities, and wealthy individual investors. Bear Stearns has about 10 domestic offices and more than 10 others overseas. Parent Bear Stearns is being acquired by rival JPMorgan Chase after it collapsed from the weight of its subprime mortgage investments.

BEARINGPOINT, INC.

NYSE: BE

1676 International Dr.
McLean, VA 22102
Phone: 703-747-3000
Fax: 703-747-8500
Web: www.bearingpoint.com

CEO: F. Edwin (Ed) Harbach
CFO: Eddie R. Munson
HR: Rick Martino
FYE: December 31
Type: Public

In the uncharted seas of modern business and technology, management consulting and systems integration firm BearingPoint wants to help its clients navigate their way to success. The firm provides a variety of consulting services to large and medium-sized businesses, as well as to government agencies and other enterprises. The US Department of Defense generates about 11% of BearingPoint's sales; overall, US government agencies account for nearly 30%. BearingPoint's private-sector practices focus on clients in such industries as communications, consumer goods, financial services, and technology. The firm operates in about 60 countries worldwide.

	Annual Growth	12/03	12/04	12/05	12/06	12/07
Sales ($ mil.)	22.1%	1,554.4	3,375.8	3,388.9	3,444.0	3,455.6
Net income ($ mil.)	—	(165.8)	(546.2)	(721.6)	(213.4)	(362.7)
Market value ($ mil.)	(25.4%)	1,962.3	1,600.5	1,584.1	1,586.5	608.9
Employees	(2.3%)	—	—	—	17,500	17,100

BEASLEY BROADCAST GROUP, INC.

NASDAQ (GM): BBGI

3033 Riviera Dr., Ste. 200
Naples, FL 34103
Phone: 239-263-5000
Fax: 239-263-8191
Web: www.beasleybroadcasting.com

CEO: George G. Beasley
CFO: B. Caroline Beasley
HR: Patricia (Pat) Russell
FYE: December 31
Type: Public

Beasley Broadcast Group is a leading radio broadcaster with more than 40 stations operating in about a dozen markets in six states, primarily Florida, Georgia, and North Carolina. The company's stations broadcast a variety of formats, including news, sports, and talk radio, as well as several music formats. Most of its stations are clustered within markets, allowing the company to combine certain business functions and achieve greater operating efficiencies. Chairman and CEO George Beasley holds about 80% voting control in the company.

	Annual Growth	12/03	12/04	12/05	12/06	12/07
Sales ($ mil.)	4.0%	114.5	122.2	124.3	125.2	133.9
Net income ($ mil.)	(21.7%)	12.8	12.0	10.7	10.1	4.8
Market value ($ mil.)	(26.1%)	123.1	129.7	103.5	71.2	36.7
Employees	—	—	—	662	—	—

An in-depth profile of this company is available to Hoover's Online members at hoovers.com.

231

BEAULIEU GROUP, L.L.C.

1502 Coronet Dr.
Dalton, GA 30720
Phone: 706-695-4624
Fax: 706-695-6237
Web: www.beaulieugroup.com

CEO: Carl M. Bouckaert
CFO: Tom Weisser
HR: Bernadette Martin
FYE: December 31
Type: Private

Beaulieu of America is rolling into a room near you with products that primarily include berber, commercial, and indoor/outdoor (nonwoven, turf) carpet. Chances are you may have had Beaulieu underfoot at some point; the company is the third-largest carpet manufacturer in the world. Major customers for its carpets include home improvement chains The Home Depot and Lowe's Companies. Consumer brands include Beaulieu, Coronet, and Hollytex; the company markets commercial products under the Bolyu (high-end), Cambridge (value), and Aqua (hospitality) brands.

	Annual Growth	12/02	12/03	12/04	12/05	12/06
Est. sales ($ mil.)	9.1%	—	—	—	1,100.0	1,200.0
Employees	(21.7%)	—	—	—	8,300	6,500

BEAUTICONTROL, INC.

2121 Midway Rd.
Carrollton, TX 75006
Phone: 972-458-0601
Fax: 972-341-3071
Web: www.beauticontrol.com

CEO: Kristi L. Hubbard
CFO: Kristi L. Hubbard
HR: –
FYE: December 31
Type: Subsidiary

BeautiControl has a firm grip on the business of aesthetics and enjoys calling Texas home, alongside direct-selling rival Mary Kay. A unit of household products maker Tupperware Brands Corporation, BeautiControl sells its beauty care items to its 1.1 million independent sales consultants, who in turn sell to consumers in 23 markets worldwide. Consultants provide computer-assisted, head-to-toe makeup advice through in-home demos. The company's products include skin and nail care, fragrances, cosmetics, toiletries, nutritional and weight-management food supplements, and in-home spa retreats. Tupperware purchased BeautiControl in 2000; in 2005 Tupperware executive David Halversen took control of BeautiControl.

	Annual Growth	12/03	12/04	12/05	12/06	12/07
Est. sales ($ mil.)	—	—	—	—	—	38.0
Employees	—	—	—	—	—	325

BEAUTY BRANDS, INC.

4600 Madison Ave., Ste. 400
Kansas City, MO 64112
Phone: 816-960-5000
Fax: 816-960-5890
Web: www.beautybrands.com

CEO: Robert (Bob) Bernstein
CFO: Charlotte Kerner
HR: Billie Sue Power
FYE: December 31
Type: Private

Beauty Brands is into the idea of one-stop shopping and primping. The company combines its retail superstores (which measure between 5,000 and 8,000 sq. ft.) with full-service salons and spas and currently operates 50 locations in more than 10 US states. In addition to selling thousands of beauty products, Beauty Brands offers services including facials, haircuts and highlights, hair removal, manicures and pedicures, and massage therapy. The company was founded in 1995 by Bob Bernstein.

	Annual Growth	12/03	12/04	12/05	12/06	12/07
Est. sales ($ mil.)	—	—	—	—	—	65.5
Employees	—	—	—	—	—	1,000

BEAVEX, INC.

2970 Peachtree Rd. NE, Ste. 275
Atlanta, GA 30305
Phone: 404-260-0961
Fax: 404-260-0962
Web: www.beavex.com

CEO: Mark Tuchmann
CFO: Tad Selby
HR: Sandra Foster
FYE: December 31
Type: Private

Just as 10X Beaver is a mark of a good hat, BeavEx wants to be the mark of a courier service its customers can hang their hats on. BeavEx provides courier services in more than 25 states and the District of Columbia. The company operates primarily in the eastern US; it also maintains facilities in southwestern and western states. Services include scheduled same-day delivery, management of customers' interoffice mail systems, and logistics consulting. Banks and health care companies are among BeavEx's major customers. CEO Mark Tuchmann founded the company in 1989.

	Annual Growth	12/03	12/04	12/05	12/06	12/07
Est. sales ($ mil.)	—	—	—	—	—	110.0
Employees	—	—	—	—	—	300

BEAZER HOMES USA, INC.

NYSE: BZH

1000 Abernathy Rd., Ste. 1200
Atlanta, GA 30328
Phone: 770-829-3700
Fax: 770-481-2808
Web: www.beazer.com

CEO: Ian J. McCarthy
CFO: Allan P. Merrill
HR: Fred Fratto
FYE: September 30
Type: Public

Beazer Homes USA builds for the middle-class buyer who's ready to make the move into the white-picket-fence scene. Building homes with an average price of about $277,000, the company courts the entry-level, move-up, and active adult markets. Beazer Homes USA focuses on high-growth regions in the Southeast, Mid-Atlantic, and West; it closed on some 12,000 homes in 2007 (down from an average of 18,000 homes). It also provides title insurance services in some markets. Company design centers offer homebuyers limited customization for such features as appliances, cabinetry, flooring, fixtures, and wall coverings. Like most large homebuilders, Beazer subcontracts to build its homes.

	Annual Growth	9/03	9/04	9/05	9/06	9/07
Sales ($ mil.)	2.4%	3,177.4	3,907.1	4,995.4	5,462.0	3,490.8
Net income ($ mil.)	—	172.7	235.8	262.5	388.8	(411.1)
Market value ($ mil.)	(4.0%)	381.0	489.2	2,446.7	1,518.2	323.9
Employees	(3.2%)	2,986	3,428	4,578	4,234	2,619

BEBE STORES, INC.

NASDAQ (GS): BEBE

400 Valley Dr.
Brisbane, CA 94005
Phone: 415-715-3900
Fax: 415-715-3939
Web: www.bebe.com

CEO: Gregory (Greg) Scott
CFO: Walter J. Parks
HR: Louis Leidelmeyer
FYE: July 31
Type: Public

Retailer bebe stores offers apparel in two main sizes: slim and none. bebe (pronounced "beebee") designs and sells contemporary women's clothing and accessories under the bebe, BEBE SPORT, and bebe O brands through 270-plus stores in the US, Canada, and Puerto Rico; abroad through licensees; and online. The company targets hip, body-conscious (some say "skinny") 21- to 35-year-olds. bebe dropped its bbsp line in favor of the casual BEBE SPORT. The company licenses its name for items such as eyewear and swimwear. The majority of bebe's products are designed in-house and produced by contract manufacturers. Chairman Manny Mashouf founded bebe in 1976 and, with his wife, Neda Mashouf, owns about 73% of the company.

	Annual Growth	6/03	6/04	6/05	6/06	*7/07
Sales ($ mil.)	20.0%	323.5	372.3	509.5	579.1	670.9
Net income ($ mil.)	41.5%	19.3	33.8	66.3	73.8	77.3
Market value ($ mil.)	80.8%	145.4	348.6	2,485.1	1,414.7	1,553.8
Employees	—	—	—	3,400		

*Fiscal year change

BECHTEL GROUP, INC.

50 Beale St.
San Francisco, CA 94105
Phone: 415-768-1234
Fax: 415-768-9038
Web: www.bechtel.com

CEO: Riley P. Bechtel
CFO: Peter Dawson
HR: Mary Moreton
FYE: December 31
Type: Private

Whether the job is raising an entire city or razing a nuclear power plant, you can bet the Bechtel Group will be there to bid on the business. The engineering, construction, and project management firm is the US's #1 contractor (ahead of Fluor) per *Engineering News-Record*. It operates worldwide and has participated in such historic projects as the construction of Hoover Dam and the cleanup of the Chernobyl nuclear plant. Bechtel's Oil, Gas & Chemical business unit and Bechtel National, its government contracts group, are its leading revenue producers. The group is in its fourth generation of leadership by the Bechtel family, with chairman and CEO Riley Bechtel at the helm.

	Annual Growth	12/03	12/04	12/05	12/06	12/07
Sales ($ mil.)	13.4%	16,337.0	17,378.0	18,100.0	20,500.0	27,000.0
Employees	(0.9%)	44,000	40,000	40,000	40,000	42,500

THE BECK GROUP

1807 Ross Ave., Ste. 500
Dallas, TX 75201
Phone: 214-303-6200
Fax: 214-303-6300
Web: www.beckgroup.com

CEO: Henry C. (Peter) Beck III
CFO: –
HR: Joe Flores
FYE: December 31
Type: Private

At the beck and call of commercial developers, The Beck Group has built everything from racetracks to runways, retail centers, hotels, and hospitals. The firm provides design/build, general contracting, and construction management services in the US and Mexico. Focusing on commercial and institutional building, Beck offers services such as project management and outsourcing of facilities construction. The company also provides real estate development services. Projects include Dallas' Cotton Bowl, the Texas Motor Speedway outside Fort Worth, the Museum of Contemporary Art in Los Angeles, and California's Beverly Hills Hotel. The company, founded in 1912 by Henry Beck, is owned by the group's managing directors.

	Annual Growth	12/03	12/04	12/05	12/06	12/07
Est. sales ($ mil.)	—	—	—	—	—	126.3
Employees	—	—	—	—	—	575

BECKMAN COULTER, INC.

NYSE: BEC

4300 N. Harbor Blvd.
Fullerton, CA 92834
Phone: 714-871-4848
Fax: 714-773-8283
Web: www.beckmancoulter.com

CEO: Scott Garrett
CFO: Charles P. (Charlie) Slacik
HR: J. Robert Hurley
FYE: December 31
Type: Public

Like the nerdiest kid in school, Beckman Coulter never saw a test it didn't love. The company makes all kinds of diagnostic testing systems, from simple blood tests to complicated genetic diagnostic tools used by hospital-based and other clinical laboratories to suss out diseases and monitor their progression. Its clinical products include immunoassay, clinical chemistry, and hematology systems, as well as products in the growing field of molecular diagnostics. In addition to its systems for diagnosing patients, Beckman Coulter makes products used by life sciences researchers, including those at academic research centers and drug companies, to understand disease and develop new therapies.

	Annual Growth	12/03	12/04	12/05	12/06	12/07
Sales ($ mil.)	5.9%	2,192.5	2,408.3	2,443.8	2,528.5	2,761.3
Net income ($ mil.)	0.5%	207.2	210.9	150.6	186.9	211.3
Market value ($ mil.)	9.6%	3,151.5	4,126.6	3,591.9	3,647.8	4,550.0
Employees	0.4%	—	—	10,416	10,340	10,500

BECTON, DICKINSON AND COMPANY

NYSE: BDX

1 Becton Dr.
Franklin Lakes, NJ 07417
Phone: 201-847-6800
Fax: 201-847-6475
Web: www.bd.com

CEO: Edward J. (Ed) Ludwig
CFO: John R. Considine
HR: Donna M. Boles
FYE: September 30
Type: Public

Don't worry, you'll only feel a slight prick if Becton, Dickinson (BD) is at work. The company's BD Medical segment is one of the top manufacturers of syringes and other injection and infusion devices. BD Medical also makes IV catheters and syringes, self-injection devices for diabetes patients, surgical instruments (scalpels and anesthesia trays, for instance), and ACE brand elastic bandages. BD's Diagnostics segment offers tools for collecting specimens and the equipment and reagents to detect diseases in them. Finally, Becton Dickinson caters to researchers through its BD Biosciences unit, which makes reagents, antibodies, imaging systems, and labware used in basic and clinical research.

	Annual Growth	9/03	9/04	9/05	9/06	9/07
Sales ($ mil.)	8.9%	4,527.9	4,934.7	5,414.7	5,834.8	6,359.7
Net income ($ mil.)	12.9%	547.1	467.4	722.3	752.3	890.0
Market value ($ mil.)	21.9%	9,070.9	12,890.6	12,986.1	17,347.2	20,012.0
Employees	5.5%	—	—	25,571	26,990	—

BED BATH & BEYOND INC.

NASDAQ (GS): BBBY

650 Liberty Ave.
Union, NJ 07083
Phone: 908-688-0888
Fax: 908-688-6483
Web: www.bedbathandbeyond.com

CEO: Steven H. (Steve) Temares
CFO: Eugene A. (Gene) Castagna
HR: Concetta Van Dyke
FYE: Saturday nearest February 28
Type: Public

Bed Bath & Beyond (BBB) has everything you need to play "house" for real. It's the #1 superstore domestics retailer in the US (ahead of Linens 'n Things), with more than 880 BBB stores throughout the US and a single location in Ontario, Canada. The stores' floor-to-ceiling shelves stock better-quality (brand-name and private-label) goods in two main categories: domestics (bed linens, bathroom and kitchen items) and home furnishings (cookware and cutlery, small household appliances, picture frames, and more). BBB relies exclusively on circulars, mailings, and word-of-mouth for advertising. The company also operates three smaller specialty chains — including some 40 Christmas Tree Shops — in the eastern US.

	Annual Growth	2/04	2/05	2/06	2/07	2/08
Sales ($ mil.)	12.0%	4,478.0	5,147.7	5,809.6	6,617.4	7,048.9
Net income ($ mil.)	8.9%	399.5	505.0	572.8	594.2	562.8
Market value ($ mil.)	(12.1%)	12,290.4	10,998.0	10,037.0	10,958.3	7,337.8
Employees	8.0%	—	31,000	33,000	35,000	39,000

BEECH-NUT NUTRITION CORPORATION

100 S. Fourth St., Ste. 1010
St. Louis, MO 63102
Phone: 314-436-7667
Fax: 314-436-7679
Web: www.beechnut.com

CEO: Christoph Rudolf
CFO: Alain Souligny
HR: John Garvaglia
FYE: June 30
Type: Private

Peas and applesauce — Beech-Nut Nutrition puts them in jars for lunch or finger-painting. As the #2 US baby food maker (trailing Nestlé's #1 Gerber), Beech-Nut Nutrition hopes baby will open up ever wider for the airplane. In addition to jars of pureed fruits, vegetables, meats, and meals, the company produces cereals, jarred fruits, vegetables, meals, juices, and water for the youngest palates. It offers more than150 different baby and toddler food products. The company introduced a new line of baby food in 2007. Named Good Morning and Good Evening, the line was created as a result of research showing the benefits of time-of-day feeding. Beech-Nut is owned by Swiss branded consumer-goods manufacturer Hero.

	Annual Growth	6/03	6/04	6/05	6/06	6/07
Est. sales ($ mil.)	—	—	—	—	—	68.0
Employees	—	—	—	—	—	500

An in-depth profile of this company is available to Hoover's Online members at hoovers.com.

BEHRMAN CAPITAL L.P.

126 E. 56th St., 27th Fl.
New York, NY 10022
Phone: 212-980-6500
Fax: 212-980-7024
Web: www.behrmancap.com

CEO: Grant G. Behrman
CFO: Gary K. Dieber
HR: Jacqui Shurslep
FYE: December 31
Type: Private

Private equity firm Behrman Capital engages in management buyouts, recapitalizations, acquisitions, and consolidations within fragmented industries. Targeting established firms with revenues from $50 million to $500 million, the company typically makes equity investments from $25 million to $100 million. It prefers to be the lead investor on transactions and takes an active role in the management of the companies in which it acquires stakes. Behrman Capital focuses on the defense, health care, information technology, manufacturing, and telecommunications sectors. It has more than $2 billion of assets under management.

	Annual Growth	12/03	12/04	12/05	12/06	12/07
Est. sales ($ mil.)	—	—	—	—	—	387.9
Employees	—	—	—	—	—	4,490

BEIERSDORF, INC.

187 Danbury Rd., Ste. 7
Wilton, CT 06897
Phone: 203-563-5800
Fax: 203-563-5893
Web: www.bdfusa.com

CEO: Ian Holding
CFO: –
HR: –
FYE: December 31
Type: Subsidiary

Beiersdorf loves the skin you're in and wants to improve it one product at a time. A subsidiary of Beiersdorf AG, the firm makes and markets skin care brands NIVEA, Curad, Basis, Eucerin, Futuro, and Aquaphor. Beiersdorf's products are sold in approximately 150 countries. NIVEA, developed and named in 1911 from the Latin word "nivius" meaning "snow-white," marked the beginning of Beiersdorf's portfolio of brands. The company discovered Eucerit, the industry's first water-in-oil emulsifier, at the turn of the century. Beiersdorf products are available worldwide through grocery stores and mass merchant retailers such as Target.

BEKINS HOLDING CORP.

330 S. Mannheim Rd.
Hillside, IL 60162
Phone: 708-547-2000
Fax: 708-547-3228
Web: www.bekins.com

CEO: Michael Petersen
CFO: –
HR: –
FYE: December 31
Type: Private

Bekins would like to be a beacon of help to families and businesses on the move. Through its Bekins Van Lines subsidiary, the company provides household and corporate relocation services in North America, as well as tradeshow logistics services and transportation of high-value items. In addition, Bekins handles international moves through a network of partners around the world; specialties include service to government and military clients. The company is owned by its agents, who bought it from former parent GeoLogistics in 2002. Bekins was founded in 1891.

	Annual Growth	12/03	12/04	12/05	12/06	12/07
Est. sales ($ mil.)	—	—	—	—	—	39.3
Employees	—	—	—	—	—	550

BEL FUSE INC.

NASDAQ (GS): BELFA

206 Van Vorst St.
Jersey City, NJ 07302
Phone: 201-432-0463
Fax: 201-432-9542
Web: www.belfuse.com

CEO: Daniel (Dan) Bernstein
CFO: Colin Dunn
HR: Miriam Martinez
FYE: December 31
Type: Public

Manufacturers worldwide can choose to use more than a Bel Fuse fuse. Bel makes electronic components for networking, telecommunications, automotive, and consumer electronics applications. Its magnetic components include transformers, filters, chokes, and delay lines, and the MagJack brand of connector modules. Bel's miniature and micro fuses provide supplementary circuit protection in TVs, VCRs, computers, telephones, and other devices. The company also makes DC/DC converters, jacks, plugs, cable assemblies, and custom modules. Customers in the Asia/Pacific region provide more than half of Bel Fuse's sales.

	Annual Growth	12/03	12/04	12/05	12/06	12/07
Sales ($ mil.)	13.1%	158.5	190.0	215.9	254.9	259.1
Net income ($ mil.)	17.5%	13.8	24.7	20.2	25.2	26.3
Market value ($ mil.)	1.7%	80.8	79.2	68.9	81.5	86.6
Employees	7.1%	1,479	1,969	1,851	1,956	1,948

BELCAN CORPORATION

10200 Anderson Way
Cincinnati, OH 45242
Phone: 513-891-0972
Fax: 513-985-7276
Web: www.belcan.com

CEO: Ralph G. Anderson
CFO: Michael J. Wirth
HR: –
FYE: December 31
Type: Private

From engineering to information technology to multimedia, Belcan takes care of the technical stuff. The company's Advanced Engineering & Technology Division (AETD) provides such services as product design, vibration analysis, procurement, and computer modeling. Its multimedia division produces videos and interactive presentations and provides desktop publishing services for corporate, industrial, and business communications. Belcan also offers technical and general staffing services and, through its IT division, provides planning, networking, systems integration, and other services. Founded in 1958, the company serves clients across the US and abroad.

	Annual Growth	12/03	12/04	12/05	12/06	12/07
Est. sales ($ mil.)	—	—	—	—	—	419.4
Employees	—	—	—	—	—	6,000

BELDEN & BLAKE CORPORATION

1001 Fannin St., Ste. 800
Houston, TX 77002
Phone: 713-659-3500
Fax: –

CEO: Mark A. Houser
CFO: James M. Vanderhider
HR: –
FYE: December 31
Type: Private

It may sound like a law firm, but Belden & Blake is in fact an energy company that obeys the laws of supply and demand in the oil and gas market. It acquires properties, explores for and develops oil and gas reserves, and gathers and markets natural gas in the Appalachian and Michigan basins. In 2007 Belden & Blake reported interests in 4,470 wells, leases on 571,141 net acres, and it owned and operated 1,620 miles of gas gathering lines. The company had estimated proved reserves of 258.1 billion cu. ft. of gas equivalent. Belden & Blake is controlled by Capital C Energy Operations, itself controlled by EnerVest Ltd.

	Annual Growth	12/02	12/03	12/04	12/05	12/06
Sales ($ mil.)	8.7%	113.9	109.1	101.8	154.8	159.1
Net income ($ mil.)	113.8%	2.5	(2.3)	12.7	17.2	52.2
Employees	—	301	305	180	134	0

BELDEN INC.

NYSE: BDC

7701 Forsyth Blvd., Ste. 800	CEO: John S. Stroup
St. Louis, MO 63105	CFO: Gray Benoist
Phone: 314-854-8000	HR: Cathy Odom Staples
Fax: 314-854-8001	FYE: December 31
Web: www.beldencdt.com	Type: Public

Belden (formerly Belden CDT) belts out cable and wire in bunches. The company makes many different cable and wire products for use in the broadcasting, computer, entertainment, security, instrumentation, and networking industries. Its products include fiber optic, coaxial, and multiconductor cables, as well as lead and hookup wires and connectivity and management products. The company's specialty products division makes high-performance and specialized cable for networking, transportation, and defense industries. Belden garners some sales directly from OEMs and systems integrators, but also uses distributors. Belden was founded in Chicago more than a hundred years ago by Joseph C. Belden.

	Annual Growth	7/03	*12/04	12/05	12/06	12/07
Sales ($ mil.)	43.1%	484.7	966.2	1,352.1	1,495.8	2,032.8
Net income ($ mil.)	—	(71.6)	15.2	47.6	65.9	137.1
Market value ($ mil.)	38.6%	537.6	1,095.1	1,034.3	1,725.9	1,984.4
Employees	26.3%	—	—	5,200	4,650	8,300

*Fiscal year change

BELK, INC.

2801 W. Tyvola Rd.	CEO: Thomas M. (Tim) Belk Jr.
Charlotte, NC 28217	CFO: Brian T. Marley
Phone: 704-357-1000	HR: Stephen J. (Steve) Pernotto
Fax: 704-357-1876	FYE: Saturday nearest January 31
Web: www.belk.com	Type: Private

Belk is busy bulking up. Already the nation's largest privately-owned department store chain, Belk now operates about 300 stores in some 15 states, following its 2006 purchase of the Parisian chain from Saks. Previously, Belk acquired Saks' McRae's and Proffitt's divisions. Belk stores are located primarily in the Southeast and Mid-Atlantic (the Carolinas and Georgia) states and offer mid-priced brand-name and private-label apparel, shoes, jewelry, cosmetics, gifts, and home furnishings. Its stores usually anchor malls or shopping centers in small to medium-sized markets and target 35-to-54-year-old middle- and upper-income women. The Belk family runs the show and owns most of the company.

	Annual Growth	1/04	1/05	1/06	1/07	1/08
Sales ($ mil.)	14.0%	2,264.9	2,446.8	2,968.8	3,684.8	3,824.8
Net income ($ mil.)	(3.7%)	111.5	124.1	136.9	181.9	95.7
Employees	18.9%	17,200	17,900	23,200	28,900	—

BELKIN INTERNATIONAL, INC.

501 W. Walnut St.	CEO: Mark Reynoso
Compton, CA 90220	CFO: Elvira Yankiv
Phone: 310-898-1100	HR: Donna Van Gundy
Fax: 310-898-1111	FYE: December 31
Web: www.belkin.com	Type: Private

Can't find your portable music player? There's a good chance it's attached to an accessory from Belkin. The company makes a variety of connectivity and power products. A leading manufacturer of Universal Serial Bus (USB) devices, Belkin also provides surge protectors, uninterruptible power supplies, and computer cables. Other products include FireWire digital video editing and connectivity products, LAN cabling and networking hardware, and accessories for cell phones and personal digital assistants. The company, which was founded in 1983, sells its products worldwide, primarily through resellers and distributors.

	Annual Growth	12/03	12/04	12/05	12/06	12/07
Est. sales ($ mil.)	—	—	—	—	—	116.1
Employees	—	—	—	—	—	550

BELL HELICOPTER TEXTRON INC.

600 E. Hurst Blvd.	CEO: Richard J. (Dick) Millman
Hurst, TX 76053	CFO: –
Phone: 817-280-2011	HR: Martha May
Fax: 817-280-2321	FYE: December 31
Web: www.bellhelicopter.com	Type: Subsidiary

Bell Helicopter Textron is betting on tilting. A subsidiary of Textron, the company makes commercial and military helicopters and tiltrotor aircraft. Bell's commercial helicopters seat up to 15 passengers and include models designed for transport, emergency medical services, and search and rescue operations. Military models include the venerable UH-1Y "Huey," a utility helicopter used for personnel and medical transportation; the AH-1Z Super Cobra reconnaissance/attack helicopter; the Eagle Eye Unmanned Aerial Vehicle (UAV); and the V-22 Osprey tiltrotor (with Boeing). Bell also makes tiltrotor aircraft through joint venture Bell/Agusta Aerospace and provides repair, maintenance, and overhaul services.

	Annual Growth	12/03	12/04	12/05	12/06	12/07
Est. sales ($ mil.)	—	—	—	—	—	599.2
Employees	—	—	—	—	—	8,172

BELL INDUSTRIES, INC.

AMEX: BI

8888 Keystone Crossing, Ste. 1700	CEO: Clinton J. Coleman
Indianapolis, IN 46240	CFO: Kevin J. Thimjon
Phone: 317-704-6000	HR: Fred Parker
Fax: 317-704-0064	FYE: December 31
Web: www.bellind.com	Type: Public

Bell Industries brings a distinctive ring to technology consulting and puts the buzz in snowmobiles. Specializing in computer systems integration services through its Bell Tech.logix division, the company offers network engineering, project management, support, software development, and training services in the eastern and midwestern US. Other offerings include product and technology lifecycle management, maintenance, and integration. Bell's Recreational Products Group division distributes aftermarket parts for motorcycles, boats, snowmobiles, and recreational vehicles.

	Annual Growth	12/03	12/04	12/05	12/06	12/07
Sales ($ mil.)	(4.1%)	141.9	143.9	130.9	120.3	119.9
Net income ($ mil.)	—	(3.8)	(0.9)	(0.8)	(2.9)	(15.3)
Employees	4.9%	—	—	850	1,150	936

BELL MICROPRODUCTS INC.

NASDAQ (GM): BELM

1941 Ringwood Ave.	CEO: W. Donald (Don) Bell
San Jose, CA 95131	CFO: William E. (Bill) Meyer
Phone: 408-451-9400	HR: Richard J. (Dick) Jacquet
Fax: 408-451-1600	FYE: December 31
Web: www.bellmicro.com	Type: Public

Bell Microproducts aims to be ahead of the curve in its industry. The company distributes network storage, semiconductor, and other computer products, primarily to computer makers and resellers. It sells products from more than 150 suppliers, including Advanced Micro Devices, EMC, IBM, NEC, Quantum, Seagate Technology, Sony, and Toshiba. Specializing in data storage products, Bell Micro offers services such as subsystems integration and kitting (providing materials in kit form, ready for assembly). The company markets its own storage devices through its Hammer Storage subsidiary, while reselling and supporting storage products from vendors including Brocade Communications, HP, Hitachi, and StorageTek.

	Annual Growth	12/01	12/02	12/03	12/04	*12/05
Sales ($ mil.)	12.3%	2,007.1	2,104.9	2,230.3	2,827.8	3,193.8
Net income ($ mil.)	—	(22.1)	(7.1)	(4.5)	11.3	0.5
Employees	5.5%	1,476	1,344	—	—	1,827

*Most recent year available

An in-depth profile of this company is available to Hoover's Online members at hoovers.com.

235

BELLE TIRE DISTRIBUTORS

1000 Enterprise Dr.
Allen Park, MI 48101
Phone: 313-271-9400
Fax: 313-271-6793
Web: www.belletire.com

CEO: Donald L. Barnes Jr.
CFO: –
HR: –
FYE: December 31
Type: Private

Even black rubber can be beautiful at Belle Tire. The company operates about 75 tire stores and automotive service centers throughout Michigan and in Cleveland and Toledo, Ohio. Tire brands include BF Goodrich, Continental, Kelly, and Michelin. Services include air conditioning, brakes, wheel alignment, and shocks and struts. Belle Tire also offers custom wheels, Dynomax exhaust systems, and Eibach springs and lowering kits. The company sponsors the Belle Tire junior hockey club. Founded in 1922 as a single location, Belle Tire has been busy expanding its business in recent years.

	Annual Growth	12/03	12/04	12/05	12/06	12/07
Est. sales ($ mil.)	—	—	—	—	—	100.1
Employees	—	—	—	—	—	1,100

BELLSOUTH CORPORATION

1155 Peachtree St. NE
Atlanta, GA 30309
Phone: 404-249-2000
Fax: 404-249-2071
Web: www.bellsouth.com

CEO: Rod D. Odom Jr.
CFO: –
HR: –
FYE: December 31
Type: Subsidiary

The original Southern Bell, BellSouth is the incumbent local exchange carrier (ILEC) for nine states from Louisiana to Kentucky. In spite of a decrease in demand for local wireline services, the Baby Bell has more than 20 million access lines in service. In late 2006 BellSouth was acquired by AT&T (formerly SBC Communications) in a deal valued at $86 billion, making it the world's largest telecom operator by market capitalization. Prior to the acquisition, BellSouth owned 40% of Cingular Wireless (now AT&T Mobility), the #1 mobile phone operator in the US; the deal gave AT&T complete control of the wireless carrier. BellSouth, now also known as AT&T Southeast, expects to incur 10,000 job cuts by 2009.

BELO CORP.

NYSE: BLC

400 S. Record St.
Dallas, TX 75202
Phone: 214-977-6606
Fax: 214-977-6603
Web: www.belo.com

CEO: Dunia A. Shive
CFO: Dennis A. Williamson
HR: Marian Spitzberg
FYE: December 31
Type: Public

You might say this company has a starring role in the lives of small-screen fans. Belo Corp. is a leading TV broadcaster with more than 20 television stations serving markets in 10 states, mostly Texas and Washington. Its portfolio includes affiliate stations of all four major broadcast networks, as well as a few independent stations and affiliates of mini-networks The CW and MyNetworkTV. Belo also operates some local and regional cable news outlets, including NWCN (NorthWest Cable News) and TXCN (Texas Cable News). The company spun off its newspaper publishing operations as A. H. Belo Corporation in 2008. Chairman Robert Decherd and his family have nearly 65% voting control over Belo.

	Annual Growth	12/03	12/04	12/05	12/06	12/07
Sales ($ mil.)	1.4%	1,436.0	1,510.2	1,521.2	1,588.3	1,515.6
Net income ($ mil.)	—	128.5	132.5	127.7	130.5	(262.8)
Market value ($ mil.)	(13.9%)	2,243.4	2,071.9	1,583.1	1,293.1	1,232.0
Employees	(4.6%)	—	—	7,800	7,100	7,100

BELRON US INC.

2400 Farmers Dr., 5th Fl.
Columbus, OH 43235
Phone: 614-210-9000
Fax: 614-210-9451
Web: www.safelite.com

CEO: Dan Wilson
CFO: Douglas A. (Doug) Herron
HR: –
FYE: Saturday nearest March 31
Type: Subsidiary

Belron US (formerly Safelite Group) has the answer to what blew into your windshield. The company, one of the US's largest auto glass repair providers and an operating segment of global auto glass repair giant Belron, fixes and replaces windshields through a network of facilities in all 50 states. Operating under the Safelite name, Belron US makes its own replacement windshields at a factory in North Carolina and distributes materials and tools to other auto glass repair companies as well. Acquired by Belron in mid-2007, it operates two national call centers for auto glass service scheduling and claims processing for insurance companies. The company was founded in 1947 as Safelite AutoGlass.

BEMIS COMPANY, INC.

NYSE: BMS

1 Neenah Center, 4th Fl.
Neenah, WI 54957
Phone: 920-727-4100
Fax: 920-527-7600
Web: www.bemis.com

CEO: Henry J. Theisen
CFO: Gene C. Wulf
HR: Eugene H. (Gene) Seashore Jr.
FYE: December 31
Type: Public

Thanks to companies like Bemis, modern delectables such as potato chips and snack cakes have longer shelf lives than most marriages. Bemis makes a broad line of flexible packaging materials, including polymer films, barrier laminates, and paper-bag packaging that customers in the food industry use to package all manner of edibles. In addition to bags, Bemis also produces pressure-sensitive products ranging from label paper and graphic films to thin-film adhesives. Although Bemis' primary market is the food industry, the company also sells to the agricultural, chemical, medical, personal care, and printing industries. The US accounts for about two-thirds of sales.

	Annual Growth	12/03	12/04	12/05	12/06	12/07
Sales ($ mil.)	8.5%	2,635.0	2,834.4	3,473.9	3,639.4	3,649.3
Net income ($ mil.)	5.4%	147.1	180.0	162.5	176.3	181.6
Market value ($ mil.)	0.9%	2,656.1	3,111.1	2,934.9	3,562.5	2,752.2
Employees	(1.3%)	—	—	15,900	15,700	—

BEMIS MANUFACTURING COMPANY

300 Mill St.
Sheboygan Falls, WI 53085
Phone: 920-467-4621
Fax: 920-467-8573
Web: www.bemismfg.com

CEO: Richard (Dick) Bemis
CFO: Frank Poja
HR: Joe Hilke
FYE: December 31
Type: Private

Staying focused on the water closet has led to Bemis Manufacturing being flushed with success, as one of the world's largest manufacturers of toilet seats. But far from sitting on its laurels, the company also makes molded and extruded plastic products for the health care industry, as well as humidifiers and air purifiers. In addition, Bemis provides contract manufacturing services, producing a range of industrial products. The company's brand names include Carrara, Church, Mayfair, and PlastExport. Bemis has operations throughout Asia, North America, Latin America, and Europe.

	Annual Growth	12/03	12/04	12/05	12/06	12/07
Est. sales ($ mil.)	—	—	—	—	—	135.7
Employees	—	—	—	—	—	1,800

BEN & JERRY'S HOMEMADE INC.

30 Community Dr.
South Burlington, VT 05403
Phone: 802-846-1500
Fax: 802-846-1610
Web: www.benjerry.com

CEO: Walt Freese
CFO: Michael Graning
HR: Jane Bowman
FYE: Last Saturday in December
Type: Subsidiary

Not yet ready for a scoop of Multinational Mocha? Don't worry, Ben & Jerry's is still Ben & Jerry's Homemade: A top maker of super premium ice cream (along with rival Nestlé's Häagen-Dazs). The quirky company was bought by consumer products giant Unilever in 2000 but it still marches to the beat of its own ice cream scoops on the tops of its own ice cream drums. The company sells its colorfully named ice cream, ice-cream novelties, and frozen yogurt under such monikers as Chunky Monkey, Phish Food, and Cherry Garcia. It also franchises some 580 Ben & Jerry's SCOOP SHOPS worldwide. Ben & Jerry's donates a minimum of $1.1 million of pretax profits to philanthropic causes yearly.

BEN VENUE LABORATORIES, INC.

300 Northfield Rd.
Bedford, OH 44146
Phone: 440-232-3320
Fax: 440-439-6398
Web: www.benvenue.com

CEO: Thomas Murphy
CFO: Thomas Murphy
HR: –
FYE: December 31
Type: Subsidiary

Ben Venue Laboratories prides itself on having products that are clean, clear, and cold. A subsidiary of German drug firm Boehringer Ingelheim, the company provides contract manufacturing services, including product and process development and regulatory compliance services. The company specializes in manufacturing liquid and lyophilized (freeze-dried in a high vacuum) pharmaceuticals. Ben Venue's Bedford Laboratories division provides contract manufacturing of injectable pharmaceuticals and active pharmaceutical ingredients (APIs). Customers include multinational drugmakers with hundreds of products on the market and small biotechs working to get their first drug approved.

BEN BRIDGE JEWELER INC.

2901 3rd Ave., Ste. 200
Seattle, WA 98111
Phone: 206-448-8800
Fax: 206-448-7456
Web: www.benbridge.com

CEO: Jonathan L. (Jon) Bridge
CFO: Jerry Gronfein
HR: Orley Solomon
FYE: December 31
Type: Subsidiary

Founded by Samuel Silverman in 1912, today jewelry chain Ben Bridge Jeweler operates about 80 stores in a dozen mostly western states, including Alaska and Hawaii. The company sells platinum, 14 and 18 karat gold jewelry, diamonds, watches, and bridal and anniversary fare from its mall-based stores and Web site. Ben Bridge Jeweler opened its first stores in Minnesota in mid-2005. Ben Bridge married Silverman's daughter in 1922, bought out his father-in-law, and renamed the company after himself. Still run by the Bridge family, the company became a subsidiary of billionaire investor Warren Buffett's Berkshire Hathaway in 2000.

	Annual Growth	12/03	12/04	12/05	12/06	12/07
Est. sales ($ mil.)	—	—	—	—	—	60.2
Employees	—	—	—	—	—	700

BENCHMARK CAPITAL MANAGEMENT CO., L.L.C.

2480 Sand Hill Rd., Ste. 200
Menlo Park, CA 94025
Phone: 650-854-8180
Fax: 650-854-8183
Web: www.benchmark.com

CEO: Steve Spurlock
CFO: Jill Jarrett
HR: –
FYE: December 31
Type: Private

Benchmark Capital is trying to set the standard in the world of venture capital. The company focuses on startup investments typically ranging from $3 million to $5 million with later investments reaching up to $15 million. These funds go to companies in the US and Israel that are involved in enterprise software and services, communications, semiconductors, and other high-tech sectors, as well as consumer and financial services. The firm's corporate network includes executives from a range of industries, who help foster growth in Benchmark's portfolio companies with their expertise and strategic partnerships. Founded in 1995, Benchmark manages more than $2.5 billion of committed capital.

	Annual Growth	12/03	12/04	12/05	12/06	12/07
Est. sales ($ mil.)	—	—	—	—	—	3.9
Employees	—	—	—	—	—	29

BEN E. KEITH COMPANY

601 E. 7th St.
Fort Worth, TX 76102
Phone: 817-877-5700
Fax: 817-338-1701
Web: www.benekeith.com

CEO: Robert Hallam
CFO: Mel Cockrell
HR: Sam Reeves
FYE: June 30
Type: Private

Ben E. Keith is your bud if you like eating out and drinking brew. A leading food and beverage distributor, the company supplies restaurants, hotels, schools, and other institutional foodservice operators in six Southern states with more than 20,000 food and non-food products from its six distribution centers. Ben E. Keith is also one of the largest Anheuser-Busch distributors, delivering beer to customers in some 60 Texas counties. Founded in 1906 as Harkrider-Morrison, the company assumed its current name in 1931 in honor of Benjamin Ellington Keith, who served as the firm's president until 1959. It is controlled by Robert and Howard Hallam.

	Annual Growth	6/02	6/03	6/04	6/05	6/06
Sales ($ mil.)	16.3%	1,185.0	1,335.0	1,500.0	2,000.0	2,170.0
Employees	7.7%	2,526	2,618	2,800	3,200	3,400

BENCHMARK ELECTRONICS, INC.

NYSE: BHE

3000 Technology Dr.
Angleton, TX 77515
Phone: 979-849-6550
Fax: 979-848-5270
Web: www.bench.com

CEO: Cary T. Fu
CFO: Donald F. Adam
HR: Gail Combs
FYE: December 31
Type: Public

Benchmark Electronics is setting a benchmark for electronics manufacturing services (EMS). The company, which provides contract manufacturing services to electronics makers, produces complex printed circuit boards and related electronics systems and subsystems. Its customers include manufacturers of computers, medical devices, telecommunications and industrial control equipment, and test instruments. Benchmark also offers design, engineering, materials management, testing, distribution, and other services. Sun Microsystems (22% of sales) is the company's biggest customer. Benchmark Electronics gets about three-quarters of its revenues in the US.

	Annual Growth	12/03	12/04	12/05	12/06	12/07
Sales ($ mil.)	12.2%	1,839.8	2,001.3	2,257.2	2,907.3	2,915.9
Net income ($ mil.)	13.9%	55.4	71.0	80.6	111.7	93.3
Market value ($ mil.)	7.2%	949.2	945.7	945.4	1,577.3	1,251.3
Employees	14.9%	6,274	7,393	8,972	9,548	10,920

An in-depth profile of this company is available to Hoover's Online members at hoovers.com.

237

BENCHMARK HOSPITALITY INTERNATIONAL

2170 Buckthorne Place, Ste. 400
The Woodlands, TX 77380
Phone: 281-367-5757
Fax: 281-367-1407
Web: www.benchmarkhospitality.com

CEO: Burt Cabañas
CFO: Dennis Blyshak
HR: Eileen Santoli
FYE: December 31
Type: Private

You never know what Benchmark Hospitality is going to resort to — but it will be nice. The company operates about 25 conference hotels and resorts across the US, and one location in Tokyo. Its portfolio includes Scottsdale Resort and Conference Center (Scottsdale, Arizona), Cheyenne Mountain Resort (Colorado Springs, Colorado), Turtle Bay Resort (Oahu, Hawaii), and Montauk Yaht Club (Long Island, New York). Many of Benchmark Hospitality's resorts include luxury spas and golf courses.

	Annual Growth	12/03	12/04	12/05	12/06	12/07
Est. sales ($ mil.)	—	—	—	—	—	212.1
Employees	—	—	—	—	—	6,300

BENDIX COMMERCIAL VEHICLE SYSTEMS LLC

901 Cleveland St.
Elyria, OH 44035
Phone: 440-329-9000
Fax: 440-329-9557
Web: www.bendix.com

CEO: Joseph J. (Joe) McAleese
CFO: Rick Nork
HR: Diane Shields
FYE: December 31
Type: Subsidiary

If you slow down on the interstate and notice an 18-wheeler in your rearview mirror, you may be more grateful for Bendix Commercial Vehicle Systems than you realize. The company makes air brake control systems and related components for heavy- and medium-duty trucks, trailers, tractors, buses, and other commercial vehicles. Other products include night vision systems, adaptive cruise control, and fan clutches. Customers include Blue Bird, Caterpillar, Mack Trucks, International Truck and Engine, and PACCAR. Bendix operates plants in the US and Mexico. The company is a unit of German brake manufacturing giant Knorr-Bremse.

	Annual Growth	12/03	12/04	12/05	12/06	12/07
Est. sales ($ mil.)	—	—	—	—	—	269.6
Employees	—	—	—	—	—	2,110

BENEFICIAL MUTUAL BANCORP, INC.

NASDAQ (GS): BNCL

510 Walnut St., 19th Fl.
Philadelphia, PA 19106
Phone: 215-864-6000
Fax: 215-864-6177
Web: www.beneficialsavings.com

CEO: Gerard P. Cuddy
CFO: Joseph F. Conners
HR: –
FYE: December 31
Type: Public

You would expect something beneficial from the city of brotherly love. Beneficial Mutual Bancorp is the holding company for Beneficial Bank, which serves the greater Philadelphia area and southern New Jersey through more than 70 branches. Founded in 1853 as Beneficial Mutual Savings Bank, the bank provides traditional deposit products such as checking, savings, and money market accounts; IRAs; and CDs. Commercial real estate loans account for nearly a third of the company's loan portfolio; residential mortgages are almost a quarter. Beneficial Bank also offers investment consulting, mutual funds, and annuities.

	Annual Growth	12/03	12/04	12/05	12/06	12/07
Assets ($ mil.)	21.9%	—	—	2,392.4	2,300.2	3,557.8
Net income ($ mil.)	—	—	11.6	13.2	11.6	(1.5)
Market value ($ mil.)	—	—	—	—	—	799.6
Employees	—	—	—	—	577	

BENEFIT COSMETICS LLC

685 Market St., 7th Fl.
San Francisco, CA 94105
Phone: 415-781-8153
Fax: 415-781-3930
Web: www.benefitcosmetics.com

CEO: Jean-André Rougeot
CFO: –
HR: –
FYE: December 31
Type: Subsidiary

Give them the benefit of the doubt. BeneFit Cosmetics will make you look lovely, and it's for a good cause. BeneFit's products have a madcap glamour-girl sensibility. Clever names ("ooh la lift") and pin-up lasses are found on nearly every package. BeneFit sells its lines through more than 600 counters (called "Beauty Bars") in department store locations worldwide, at beauty specialty store Sephora, and about 20 dedicated boutiques. BeneFit Cosmetics, whose celebrity-endorsed Benetint product brought the fledgling company into the mainstream, was founded in 1976 in San Francisco by sisters Jean Ann and Jane Ann Ford as The Face Place. Glamour leviathan LVMH holds a 70% stake.

	Annual Growth	12/03	12/04	12/05	12/06	12/07
Est. sales ($ mil.)	—	—	—	—	—	14.7
Employees	—	—	—	—	—	220

BENIHANA INC.

NASDAQ (GS): BNHN

8685 NW 53rd Terrace
Miami, FL 33166
Phone: 305-593-0770
Fax: 305-592-6371
Web: www.benihana.com

CEO: Joel A. Schwartz
CFO: Jose I. Ortega
HR: Laurie Casey
FYE: Sunday nearest March 31
Type: Public

The main course at Benihana comes with an appetizer of culinary entertainment. The company's flagship chain of teppanyaki-style Asian restaurants offers a dining experience that is part theater as wisecracking, fast-chopping chefs prepare the meals on a grill that is part of the table. Benihana owns and operates about 60 Benihana and Benihana Grill locations in about 20 states and has nearly 20 franchised restaurants in a dozen other countries. In addition, the company operates about 30 other restaurants doing business as Haru and RA Sushi. Benihana of Tokyo, a company controlled by the family of founder Rocky Aoki, owns about 25% of Benihana.

	Annual Growth	3/04	3/05	3/06	3/07	3/08
Sales ($ mil.)	10.0%	203.0	218.3	245.6	272.6	297.0
Net income ($ mil.)	9.2%	9.0	7.8	14.6	14.5	12.8
Market value ($ mil.)	19.5%	35.0	29.0	47.8	39.6	71.5
Employees	8.8%	—	4,226	4,600		

BENJAMIN FRANKLIN BANCORP, INC.

NASDAQ (GM): BFBC

58 Main St.
Franklin, MA 02038
Phone: 508-528-7000
Fax: 508-520-8364
Web: www.benfranklinbank.com

CEO: Thomas R. Venables
CFO: Claire S. Bean
HR: Kathleen P. (Kathy) Sawyer
FYE: December 31
Type: Public

Benjamin Franklin Bancorp would *never* say neither a borrower nor a lender be (that was Polonius). The holding company operates through Benjamin Franklin Bank, which has around a dozen branches southwest of Boston in the Massachusetts counties of Middlesex, Norfolk, and Worcester. It offers traditional deposit products to individual and small to midsized business customers. Residential mortgages and home equity loans make up around 36% of Benjamin Franklin's total loan portfolio. Commercial mortgage loans account for about 35%. The remainder of its portfolio consists of business, construction, and consumer loans.

	Annual Growth	12/03	12/04	12/05	12/06	12/07
Assets ($ mil.)	18.5%	458.8	517.4	867.1	913.7	903.3
Net income ($ mil.)	20.6%	1.7	1.7	0.4	4.7	3.6
Market value ($ mil.)	(8.2%)	—	—	119.4	134.5	100.7
Employees	7.5%	—	133	140	169	165

BENJAMIN MOORE & CO.

101 Paragon Dr.	CEO: Yvan Dupuy
Montvale, NJ 07645	CFO: Donald E. Devine II
Phone: 201-573-9600	HR: Bart Finnegan
Fax: 201-573-0046	FYE: December 31
Web: www.benjaminmoore.com	Type: Subsidiary

Not only can you paint the town red with Benjamin Moore paints, you can stain and finish it as well. In addition to ready-mixed colors — sold under such brands as Benjamin Moore Paints, Moorcraft, and Benwood — the company can match almost any shade with roughly 3,300 colors. Benjamin Moore also makes industrial coatings and coatings for manufacturers of furniture and roof decking. The company sells its paints through a dealer network of about 4,000 independent paint and decorating stores, most of which are in North America. Benjamin Moore became a subsidiary of Warren Buffett's Berkshire Hathaway in 2000.

BENTELER AUTOMOTIVE CORPORATION

1780 Pond Run	CEO: Nick N. Ghoussaini
Auburn Hills, MI 48326	CFO: –
Phone: 248-377-9999	HR: –
Fax: 248-364-7001	FYE: December 31
Web: www.benteler.de/english/automotive	Type: Subsidiary

Benteler Automotive is the US automotive parts manufacturing outpost of Germany's Benteler Group. Benteler Automotive, the largest of the family-owned Benteler Group's segments, manufactures auto parts including chassis components (such as crossmembers and suspension modules), structural safety components (bumper and door beams, pillar reinforcements, roof and side rails), exhaust manifolds and complete exhaust systems, and fuel components. The company also offers engineering services. The Benteler Group's automotive operations include about 70 locations in 22 countries. Benteler Automotive got its start in 1935 after its first order of exhaust pipes for the Ford Eifel.

	Annual Growth	12/03	12/04	12/05	12/06	12/07
Est. sales ($ mil.)	—	—	—	—	—	233.1
Employees	—	—	—	—	—	2,500

BENTLEY PHARMACEUTICALS, INC.

NYSE: BNT

2 Holland Way	CEO: James R. Murphy
Exeter, NH 03833	CFO: Richard P. Lindsay
Phone: 603-658-6100	HR: –
Fax: 603-658-6101	FYE: December 31
Web: www.bentleypharm.com	Type: Public

Bentley Pharmaceuticals has a dual personality. In the US, the company develops drug delivery systems, but nearly all of Bentley's revenues come from its Spanish subsidiaries (Laboratorios Belmac, Laboratorios Davur, and Laboratorios Rimafar) which make and sell generic pharmaceuticals and active pharmaceutical ingredients, primarily in Spain. Their products target four therapeutic areas: cardiovascular, gastrointestinal, neurological, and infectious disease. The company has announced plans to spin off its drug delivery business into a separate, publicly traded company called CPEX Pharmaceuticals. In 2008 it agreed to sell its Spanish generics businesses (what remains of itself following the spin-off) to Teva.

	Annual Growth	12/03	12/04	12/05	12/06	12/07
Sales ($ mil.)	17.8%	64.7	73.4	97.7	109.5	124.7
Net income ($ mil.)	(18.4%)	6.1	5.7	10.9	1.0	2.7
Employees	—	—	—	420	—	—

BENTLEY SYSTEMS, INCORPORATED

685 Stockton Dr.	CEO: Gregory S. (Greg) Bentley
Exton, PA 19341	CFO: –
Phone: 610-458-5000	HR: David G. Nation
Fax: 610-458-1060	FYE: December 31
Web: www.bentley.com	Type: Private

Bentley Systems moves ideas from inception to groundbreaking to ribbon cutting. Engineers use the company's computer-aided design software to design and build such large-scale projects as airports, transit and utilities systems, manufacturing plants, and buildings. Bentley's software (available on both a perpetual license and subscription basis) lets architects, engineers, builders, and property owners collaborate over the Web to develop and maintain their projects. The company also provides content management applications, as well as consulting, integration, and training services. Mapping and design systems maker Intergraph owns about one-quarter of the company.

BERBEE INFORMATION NETWORKS CORPORATION

5520 Research Park Dr.	CEO: Paul S. Shain
Madison, WI 53711	CFO: Brett M. Rimkus
Phone: 608-288-3000	HR: Diane Rivers
Fax: 608-288-3007	FYE: July 31
Web: www.berbee.com	Type: Subsidiary

Berbee Information Networks has staked its reputation on engineering and advanced information technologies. It specializes in such managed services as network infrastructure and unified communications, productivity applications, security, and systems and storage. The company's customers include companies of all sizes and come from fields such as financial services, manufacturing, telecommunications, and retail. Berbee Information Networks is a certified vendor for products by Cisco, IBM, and Microsoft. Founded in 1993 by former IBM systems engineer Jim Berbee, the company was acquired in 2006 by CDW.

	Annual Growth	7/02	7/03	7/04	7/05	7/06
Sales ($ mil.)	—	—	—	—	—	390.0
Employees	—	—	—	—	—	800

BERETTA USA, CORP.

17601 Beretta Dr.	CEO: Ugo Gussalli Beretta
Accokeek, MD 20607	CFO: Steve Biondi
Phone: 301-283-2191	HR: Paola Bonifonti
Fax: 301-283-0435	FYE: December 31
Web: www.berettausa.com	Type: Subsidiary

Beretta USA is right on target. The firm is the North American manufacturing and marketing arm of the oldest gunsmith company in the world. Products include handguns, rifles, and shotguns, as well as knives, accessories, and sporting apparel. Beretta USA sells to law enforcement agencies, through exclusive distributors, and at its high-end retail galleries. It also supplies the US military with weapons. Galleries in the US are located in Dallas and New York City. The manufacturer also offers hand-finished firearms, specialty books, gift items, and custom-made hunting apparel. The company's guns are showcased in a TV show broadcast on cable channel Versus called *The World of Beretta*. Beretta USA was established in 1977.

	Annual Growth	12/03	12/04	12/05	12/06	12/07
Est. sales ($ mil.)	—	—	—	—	—	72.7
Employees	—	—	—	—	—	325

An in-depth profile of this company is available to Hoover's Online members at hoovers.com.

239

BERKLINE/BENCHCRAFT HOLDINGS, INC.

1 Berkline Dr.
Morristown, TN 37813
Phone: 423-585-1500
Fax: 423-585-4420
Web: www.berkline.com

CEO: C. William (Bill) Wittenberg Jr.
CFO: Steven M. Smith
HR: Dennis Carper
FYE: December 31
Type: Private

Berkline/BenchCraft would be tickled for you to kick back, slip off your tired loafers, and recline in one of its upholstered chairs. The company, comprising firms Berkline and BenchCraft, makes mid-priced upholstered furniture for home use. Berkline makes specialty motion upholstery and reclining chairs, while BenchCraft primarily makes stationary fabric and leather pieces. In addition to its upholstered offerings, the firm also makes occasional tables and complementary pieces including its Lyndon line. With manufacturing facilities in Tennessee, Mississippi, and Montreal, it sells through independent, regional, and national furniture retailers.

BERKSHIRE BANCORP INC.

NASDAQ (GM): BERK

160 Broadway
New York, NY 10038
Phone: 212-791-5362
Fax: 212-791-5367
Web: www.berkbank.com

CEO: Steven Rosenberg
CFO: Steven Rosenberg
HR: –
FYE: December 31
Type: Public

This company may not win a Tony Award, but it is on Broadway. Headquartered on this famous Manhattan street, Berkshire Bancorp is the holding company for The Berkshire Bank, which operates about a dozen branches mostly in New York, but also in New Jersey. The bank's products and services include individual and business checking and savings accounts, money market accounts, and CDs. Lending activities consist mostly of non-residential mortgages (about half of the company's total loan portfolio) and one- to four-family real estate loans (more than 30%). Through subsidiaries, the bank offers title insurance and property investment services.

	Annual Growth	12/03	12/04	12/05	12/06	12/07
Assets ($ mil.)	5.5%	905.7	972.7	977.5	948.7	1,120.5
Net income ($ mil.)	(8.0%)	7.4	7.5	5.5	4.9	5.3
Market value ($ mil.)	32.4%	36.8	138.3	117.5	113.8	112.9
Employees	(0.5%)	—	—	107		106

⊞ BERKSHIRE HATHAWAY INC.

NYSE: BRK

1440 Kiewit Plaza
Omaha, NE 68131
Phone: 402-346-1400
Fax: 402-346-3375
Web: www.berkshirehathaway.com

CEO: Warren E. Buffett
CFO: Marc D. Hamburg
HR: –
FYE: December 31
Type: Public

Berkshire Hathaway is where Warren Buffett, the world's richest man, spreads his risk by investing in a variety of companies, from insurance and building materials to apparel and furniture retailers. Insurance subsidiaries include National Indemnity, GEICO Corporation, and reinsurance giant General Re. The company also owns McLane Company, Dairy Queen, Clayton Homes, and MidAmerican Energy Holdings. In 2006 it bought press release distributor Business Wire, sportswear company Russell, and 80% of ISCAR Metalworking, an Israel-based maker of metal-cutting tools and the first foreign company in which Berkshire has a controlling stake. Buffett owns about a third of Berkshire Hathaway.

	Annual Growth	12/03	12/04	12/05	12/06	12/07
Sales ($ mil.)	16.7%	63,859.0	74,382.0	82,451.0	98,539.0	118,245.0
Net income ($ mil.)	12.8%	8,151.0	7,308.0	8,528.0	11,015.0	13,213.0
Market value ($ mil.)	9.2%	107,708.6	111,525.8	111,742.7	122,921.5	153,122.0
Employees	10.2%	—	—	192,000	217,000	233,000

BERKSHIRE HILLS BANCORP, INC.

NASDAQ (GS): BHLB

24 North St.
Pittsfield, MA 01201
Phone: 413-443-5601
Fax: 413-443-3587
Web: www.berkshirebank.com

CEO: Michael P. Daly
CFO: John S. Millet
HR: Linda A. Johnston
FYE: December 31
Type: Public

Berkshire Hills Bancorp is the holding company for Berkshire Bank, which serves individuals and small businesses through about 40 branches in western Massachusetts, eastern New York, and southern Vermont. Established in 1846, the bank provides an array of deposit products such as savings, checking, and money market accounts; CDs; and IRAs. It also offers credit cards, insurance, investments, private banking, and wealth management services. Berkshire Hills Bancorp also owns Berkshire Bank Municipal Bank, which collects deposits from municipalities and other government entities in New York.

	Annual Growth	12/03	12/04	12/05	12/06	12/07
Assets ($ mil.)	19.8%	1,218.6	1,310.1	2,035.6	2,149.6	2,513.4
Net income ($ mil.)	10.7%	9.0	11.5	8.2	11.3	13.5
Market value ($ mil.)	6.3%	213.7	218.2	286.1	291.6	272.8
Employees	18.5%	—	—	399	522	560

BERKSHIRE INCOME REALTY, INC.

AMEX: BIR-PA

1 Beacon St., Ste. 1500
Boston, MA 02108
Phone: 617-523-7722
Fax: 617-646-2375
Web: www.berkshireincomerealty.com

CEO: David C. Quade
CFO: David C. Quade
HR: –
FYE: December 31
Type: Public

If you enjoy attractive landscaping and swimming pools, but can't stand the upkeep and maintenance, Berkshire Income Realty might have just the spot for you. The real estate investment trust (REIT) invests in apartment communities; it owns more than 25 properties comprising some 7,800 units in Austin, Dallas, and Houston; Chicago; and the Washington, DC, metropolitan area. The company focuses on properties that have been neglected and improves its portfolio through property renovations and aggressive refinancing. Affiliate Berkshire Property Advisors provides day-to-day management and business operations services to the company.

	Annual Growth	12/03	12/04	12/05	12/06	12/07
Sales ($ mil.)	29.6%	30.2	40.5	59.7	72.4	85.3
Net income ($ mil.)	(5.3%)	3.6	(7.8)	6.4	(20.0)	2.9
Employees	—	0	0	0	0	0

BERKSHIRE PARTNERS LLC

1 Boston Place, Ste. 3300
Boston, MA 02108
Phone: 617-227-0050
Fax: 617-227-6105
Web: www.berkshirepartners.com

CEO: Bradley M. (Brad) Bloom
CFO: Kenneth Bring
HR: Elizabeth (Liz) Liacos
FYE: December 31
Type: Private

No, not *that* Berkshire — the other one. Berkshire Partners is a private equity firm that targets established companies worth $200 million to $2 billion in varied industries, including industrial manufacturing, consumer products, transportation, communication, business services, and retailing. The firm generally avoids investing in high-tech firms. Its typical transactions are buyouts, recapitalizations, privatizations, and growth capital investments. The company's portfolio includes Masai Group International (footwear), Amscan Holdings (balloons and party goods), and English Welsh & Scottish Railway (UK freight rail). Berkshire Partners has about $6.5 billion in assets under management.

	Annual Growth	12/03	12/04	12/05	12/06	12/07
Est. sales ($ mil.)	—	—	—	—	—	3.8
Employees	—	—	—	—	—	36

BERLIN PACKAGING

111 N. Canal St., Ste. 300
Chicago, IL 60606
Phone: 312-876-9292
Fax: 312-876-9290
Web: www.berlinpackaging.com

CEO: Andrew T. Berlin
CFO: Neil R. Schwab
HR: Jim Sollenberger
FYE: December 31
Type: Private

Berlin is found in the heart of the continent . . . of North America. Chicago-based Berlin Packaging, a leading US distributor of rigid packaging, stocks glass, plastic, and metal cans, closures, and other components for use in the personal care, chemical, food and beverage, and pharmaceutical industries. Each year the company buys billions of containers and closures, including jars, cylinders, decanters, cans, caps, and bottles with dispensers, from hundreds of suppliers. In addition, it offers packaging design, inventory management, delivery, and financing services. Berlin has about 25 sales and supply facilities across the US. Equity group Investcorp is acquiring a majority stake in the family-owned company.

BERLITZ INTERNATIONAL, INC.

400 Alexander Park
Princeton, NJ 08540
Phone: 609-514-3400
Fax: 609-514-3405
Web: www.berlitz.com

CEO: Mark Harris
CFO: –
HR: Kimiko Kunimasa
FYE: March 31
Type: Subsidiary

Do you speak Dansk, Deutsch, Español, Magyar, or Português? If not, Berlitz can teach you. Berlitz International owns or franchises about 500 language centers in more than 60 countries. It also offers courses through study-abroad programs, books, videotape, audio cassettes, CDs, and over the Web. While Berlitz originally focused on teaching languages to pleasure travelers, it has broadened its scope to include related business services such as cultural-awareness programs. The company offers language classes for adults, teenagers, and children. Founded in 1878, Berlitz International is a subsidiary of Benesse Corporation.

	Annual Growth	3/03	3/04	3/05	3/06	3/07
Est. sales ($ mil.)	—	—	—	—	—	190.4
Employees	—	—	—	—	—	5,594

BERNARD CHAUS, INC.

OTC: CHBD

530 7th Ave.
New York, NY 10018
Phone: 212-354-1280
Fax: 201-863-6307
Web: www.bernardchaus.com

CEO: Josephine Chaus
CFO: Barton (Bart) Heminover
HR: Tanya Banner
FYE: June 30
Type: Public

Bernard Chaus' clothes are made for the days when a woman has *nothing* to wear. The company designs and sells upscale women's career and casual sportswear, primarily under the Josephine Chaus and Cynthia Steffe trademarks. Its jackets, skirts, pants, blouses, sweaters, and accessories are coordinated by style, color, and fabric. Bernard Chaus' clothing is sold in about 5,000 US department and specialty stores and is manufactured mostly in Asia and South America. The company also manufactures private label apparel. Chairwoman and CEO Josephine Chaus, widow of Bernard Chaus' namesake founder, owns about 45% of the company; Kenneth Cole Productions holds a 16% stake.

	Annual Growth	6/03	6/04	6/05	6/06	6/07
Sales ($ mil.)	1.2%	140.2	157.1	143.3	136.8	146.8
Net income ($ mil.)	(42.9%)	4.7	3.1	(1.2)	(4.9)	0.5
Market value ($ mil.)	3.9%	26.0	26.5	38.1	34.5	30.3
Employees	2.2%	—	—	—	223	228

BERNIE'S AUDIO VIDEO TV APPLIANCE CO., INC.

1559 King St.
Enfield, CT 06082
Phone: 860-741-1200
Fax: 860-741-1324
Web: www.bernies.com

CEO: Milton Rosenberg
CFO: David Sullivan
HR: –
FYE: December 31
Type: Private

Bernie's Audio Video TV Appliance wants you to have more than a weekend of fun with its products. The company operates about 15 stores in Connecticut, Massachusetts, and Rhode Island selling a variety of brand-name electronics and appliances, including home theater and stereo systems, telephones, refrigerators, washers and dryers, microwave ovens, vacuums, mattresses, and digital cameras. Bernie's was founded by Bernard ("Bernie") Rosenberg in 1947 when he sold returning war vets TVs and radios from his gas station. The first Bernie's TV and Appliance store opened in 1953. Bernie's son, Milton, is the company president.

	Annual Growth	12/02	12/03	12/04	12/05	12/06
Est. sales ($ mil.)	—	—	—	—	—	52.6
Employees	—	—	—	—	—	350

BERRY PETROLEUM COMPANY

NYSE: BRY

5201 Truxtun Ave., Ste. 300
Bakersfield, CA 93309
Phone: 661-616-3900
Fax: 661-616-3881
Web: www.bry.com

CEO: Robert F. Heinemann
CFO: Shawn M. Canaday
HR: Walter B. Ayers
FYE: December 31
Type: Public

It may be small fruit in the giant petroleum industry, but Berry Petroleum delivers the juice. The company buys properties with heavy crude oil reserves for exploitation and sale to refining companies. Berry Petroleum's core properties are in California's Kern, Los Angeles, and Ventura counties; it has proved reserves of 169 million barrels of oil equivalent. The company squeezes the most from its assets by using thermal recovery: Steam is injected into heavy crude oil reserves to reduce oil viscosity and allow it to flow to the surface. Berry Petroleum also owns three gas-fired cogeneration facilities.

	Annual Growth	12/03	12/04	12/05	12/06	12/07
Sales ($ mil.)	34.0%	180.9	275.0	406.7	486.3	583.5
Net income ($ mil.)	41.5%	32.4	69.2	112.4	107.9	129.9
Market value ($ mil.)	72.9%	211.7	502.3	603.5	1,305.5	1,892.8
Employees	16.3%	—	—	209	243	—

BERRY PLASTICS GROUP, INC.

101 Oakley St.
Evansville, IN 47710
Phone: 812-424-2904
Fax: 812-424-0128
Web: www.berryplastics.com

CEO: Ira G. Boots
CFO: James M. Kratochvil
HR: –
FYE: Last Saturday in December
Type: Private

Berry Plastics Group makes bunches and bunches of plastic products. Its operating subsidiary, Berry Plastics Corporation, is a leading maker of injection-molded plastic products. The company makes containers, closures, and consumer products such as plastic drink cups and housewares. Its containers are made to hold items ranging from dairy products and chemicals to prescriptions and personal care products. Apollo Management and Graham Partners acquired Berry Plastics from Goldman Sachs and J.P. Morgan for $2.25 billion in September 2006. The company then moved into the flexible packaging industry by merging with another Apollo-controlled company, Covalence Specialty Materials.

	Annual Growth	12/02	12/03	12/04	12/05	12/06
Sales ($ mil.)	30.5%	494.3	551.9	814.2	1,169.7	1,431.8
Net income ($ mil.)	—	(32.6)	13.0	22.9	19.8	(75.2)
Employees	19.4%	3,250	4,700	4,550	6,800	6,600

An in-depth profile of this company is available to Hoover's Online members at hoovers.com.

241

BERTUCCI'S CORPORATION

155 Otis St.
Northborough, MA 01532
Phone: 508-351-2500
Fax: 508-393-8046
Web: www.bertuccis.com

CEO: Stephen V. Clark
CFO: David G. Lloyd
HR: Bryan Schwanke
FYE: Wednesday nearest December 31
Type: Private

New Englanders in need of a taste of Italy can turn to Bertucci's. The company owns and operates more than 90 Italian casual-dining establishments operating under the Bertucci's Brick Oven Ristorante banner. The restaurants, located in about a dozen states primarily in the Northeast, feature a wide array of Tuscan-style dishes, including pasta, chicken, and seafood dishes, as well as appetizers and desserts. It also offers premium, brick oven pizza. In addition to its flagship chain, Bertucci's operates about a half dozen Vinny T's of Boston casual dining spots in Massachusetts. Chairman Benjamin Jacobson controls the company through his Jacobson Partners holding company.

	Annual Growth	12/02	12/03	12/04	12/05	12/06
Sales ($ mil.)	8.7%	162.3	186.2	200.4	204.8	226.4
Employees	6.0%	6,060	6,275	6,307	6,546	7,645

BERWIND CORPORATION

3000 Centre Sq. West, 1500 Market St.
Philadelphia, PA 19102
Phone: 215-563-2800
Fax: 215-575-2314
Web: www.berwind.com

CEO: Michael McClelland
CFO: Van Billet
HR: –
FYE: December 31
Type: Holding company

Berwind Corporation isn't workin' in a coal mine anymore. Founded in 1886 to mine Appalachian coal, the firm began leasing its mining operations in 1962 to fund investments in new ventures. Berwind Corporation gives autonomy to the management teams of its portfolio companies while adding investment fuel to their financial fires. The company's portfolio includes Elmer's Products, maker of Elmer's Glue, Krazy Glue, and other products; specialty chemicals companies CRC and Colorcon; and promotional products firm National Pen. The Berwind family owns Berwind Corporation.

	Annual Growth	12/02	12/03	12/04	12/05	12/06
Est. sales ($ mil.)	5.0%	–	–	–	1,629.0	1,710.0
Employees	0.0%	–	–	–	3,500	3,500

THE BESSEMER GROUP, INCORPORATED

630 5th Ave.
New York, NY 10111
Phone: 212-708-9100
Fax: 212-265-5826
Web: www.bessemer.com

CEO: John A. Hilton Jr.
CFO: John G. MacDonald
HR: Stephen A. Baxley
FYE: December 31
Type: Private

Forget the cold, hard steel and think cold, hard cash. The Bessemer Group manages more than $50 billion in assets for wealthy individuals and families. Main subsidiary Bessemer Trust administers portfolios with holdings in domestic and international equities and bonds, as well as such alternative assets as hedge funds, real estate, and private equity funds of funds. The group also provides trust, custody, tax and estate planning, strategic philanthropy, and financial advisory services. Steel magnate Henry Phipps (a partner of Andrew Carnegie) founded Bessemer Trust in 1907; more than six decades later, the trust began accepting clients outside the Phipps family.

	Annual Growth	12/03	12/04	12/05	12/06	12/07
Est. sales ($ mil.)	–	–	–	–	–	202.1
Employees	–	–	–	–	–	170

BEST BRANDS CORP.

111 Cheshire Ln., Ste. 100
Minnetonka, MN 55305
Phone: 952-404-7500
Fax: –
Web: www.bestbrandscorp.com

CEO: Scott Humphrey
CFO: Jody Anderson
HR: –
FYE: December 31
Type: Private

Best Brands believes it can be the best in the baking industry. The Minnesota company makes more than 4,500 fillings, frozen doughs and batters, icings, baked goods, and baking ingredients. Its brands include Best Brands, Multifoods, Fantasia, and Gourmet Baker. The company's Horizon Equipment subsidiary manufactures commercial baking equipment and parts. Best Brands serves customers in the food retail, foodservice, and wholesale food and baking industries throughout North America. The company was founded in 1971 and is owned by investment firm Value Creation Partners.

	Annual Growth	12/03	12/04	12/05	12/06	12/07
Est. sales ($ mil.)	–	–	–	–	–	77.4
Employees	–	–	–	–	–	500

BEST BUY CO., INC.

NYSE: BBY

7601 Penn Ave. South
Richfield, MN 55423
Phone: 612-291-1000
Fax: 612-292-4001
Web: www.bestbuy.com

CEO: Bradbury H. (Brad) Anderson
CFO: James L. (Jim) Muehlbauer
HR: John Pershing
FYE: Saturday nearest last day in February
Type: Public

The biggest consumer electronics outlet in the US is also the best — Best Buy, that is. The company operates a chain of about 1,300 stores in the US, Canada, and now China offering a wide variety of electronic gadgets, movies, music, computers, and appliances. In addition to selling products, the stores offer installation and maintenance services, technical support, and subscriptions for cell phone and Internet services. Covering an average of about 40,000 sq. ft., the big box stores are located in 49 states and all Canadian provinces. In addition to the Best Buy brand, the company operates the Pacific Sales (about 20 stores in California) and Future Shop (130 stores in Canada) banners, among others.

	Annual Growth	2/04	2/05	2/06	2/07	2/08
Sales ($ mil.)	13.0%	24,547.0	27,433.0	30,848.0	35,934.0	40,023.0
Net income ($ mil.)	18.9%	705.0	984.0	1,140.0	1,377.0	1,407.0
Market value ($ mil.)	11.3%	11,525.0	11,314.7	26,214.7	22,278.4	17,659.0
Employees	11.2%	–	109,000	128,000	140,000	150,000

BEST WESTERN INTERNATIONAL, INC.

6201 N. 24th Pkwy.
Phoenix, AZ 85016
Phone: 602-957-4200
Fax: 602-957-5641
Web: www.bestwestern.com

CEO: David T. Kong
CFO: Thomas R. (Tom) Johnson
HR: Barbara Bras
FYE: November 30
Type: Association

Western hospitality has really spread. Begun in 1946 by hotelier M. K. Guertin and named for its California origins, Best Western has more than 4,000 independently owned and operated hotels (including 2,200-plus in the US, Canada, and the Caribbean), making it the world's largest hotel brand (by number of rooms). Hotels sport its flag in about 80 countries; Australia and the UK have the most outside the US. Best Western is organized as a not-for-profit membership association, with most of its sales coming from monthly fees and annual dues.

	Annual Growth	11/02	11/03	11/04	11/05	11/06
Sales ($ mil.)	5.6%	165.4	178.6	190.1	198.8	205.5
Net income ($ mil.)	92.3%	0.3	4.0	(3.5)	(2.1)	4.1
Employees	(2.7%)	1,200	1,200	1,200	1,066	1,076

BET HOLDINGS, INC.

One BET Plaza, 1235 W St., NE
Washington, DC 20018
Phone: 202-608-2000
Fax: 202-608-2484
Web: www.bet.com

CEO: Debra L. Lee
CFO: Michael Pickrum
HR: –
FYE: December 31
Type: Subsidiary

This company broadcasts an urban vibe all across the nation. BET Holdings operates several cable outlets targeting African-American audiences under the BET Networks banner. Its flagship BET (Black Entertainment Television) reaches more than 83 million US homes with a mix of entertainment, music, and news programming, including reality show *Baldwin Hills*, music video show *106 & Park*, and current events show *Meet the Faith*. Other channels include BET Gospel, BET Hip Hop, and BET J (jazz and R&B programming). In addition to television, BET Holdings produces live events and radio programming, and operates Internet destinations (BET Digital Media). The company is a unit of media giant Viacom.

	Annual Growth	12/03	12/04	12/05	12/06	12/07
Est. sales ($ mil.)	—	—	—	—	—	91.5
Employees	—	—	—	—	—	683

BETTER BUSINESS BUREAUS, INC.

4200 Wilson Blvd., Ste. 800
Arlington, VA 22203
Phone: 703-276-0100
Fax: 703-525-8277
Web: www.bbb.org

CEO: Steven J. Cole
CFO: Joseph E. Dillion
HR: Anaise Schroeder
FYE: December 31
Type: Not-for-profit

The Council of Better Business Bureaus, Inc. (BBB), helps consumers and businesses know who's on the up-and-up. The group is made up of independent BBBs and branches in more than 150 locations throughout the US, as well as some 300 national companies that have shown a commitment to business ethics. More than 300,000 companies that have demonstrated a similar commitment belong to local BBBs. The companies can promote their adherence to BBB standards; in return, they are subject to "reliability reports" that consist of any complaints clients or partners have had about them. BBBs work to resolve disputes between consumers and businesses and review companies' advertising.

	Annual Growth	12/03	12/04	12/05	12/06	12/07
Est. sales ($ mil.)	—	—	—	—	—	21.9
Employees	—	—	—	—	—	133

THE BETTY FORD CENTER

39000 Bob Hope Dr.
Rancho Mirage, CA 92270
Phone: 760-773-4100
Fax: 760-773-4141
Web: www.bettyfordcenter.org

CEO: John T. Schwarzlose
CFO: Dennie Jagger
HR: Charlene Montgomery
FYE: June 30
Type: Not-for-profit

The health care center with a lengthy list of euphemisms for its name, The Betty Ford Center provides a variety of drug and alcohol rehabilitation services for all members of a family system affected by addiction. Services include a children's program, outpatient and inpatient support, a 90-day treatment program, a clinical diagnostic evaluation, and a program for licensed professionals. The not-for-profit organization also offers professional education programs for helping professionals. Its primary facility is in California on the grounds of the Eisenhower Medical Center; the children's center is in Texas. Betty Ford, the wife of the late President Gerald Ford, started the center in 1982.

	Annual Growth	6/03	6/04	6/05	6/06	6/07
Est. sales ($ mil.)	—	—	—	—	—	30.0
Employees	—	—	—	—	—	220

BEVERLY HILLS BANCORP INC.

NASDAQ (GS): BHBC

23901 Calabasas Rd., Ste. 1050
Calabasas, CA 91302
Phone: 818-223-8084
Fax: 818-223-9531
Web: www.fbbh.com

CEO: Larry B. Faigin
CFO: Takeo K. Sasaki
HR: Linda Runyan
FYE: December 31
Type: Public

If Californy is the place you oughta be, load up your cash and deposit it in Beverly . . . Beverly Hills Bancorp, that is. The holding company owns First Bank of Beverly Hills, which conducts wholesale banking operations and has one retail branch in Calabasas in Southern California. As a wholesale bank the company attracts deposits such as checking and savings accounts and CDs through third parties like trust companies and investment managers, and originates loans through independent brokers. It focuses on adjustable-rate construction loans and real estate loans secured by commercial (about half of the bank's loan portfolio) and multifamily residential (more than 30%) properties.

	Annual Growth	12/03	12/04	12/05	12/06	12/07
Assets ($ mil.)	11.4%	975.3	1,338.9	1,403.7	1,623.8	1,500.1
Net income ($ mil.)	(48.1%)	6.9	25.6	15.1	14.8	0.5
Market value ($ mil.)	(3.9%)	113.2	213.5	221.2	155.2	96.6
Employees	(9.6%)	—	—	52	47	—

BEVERLY NATIONAL CORPORATION

AMEX: BNV

240 Cabot St.
Beverly, MA 01915
Phone: 978-922-2100
Fax: 978-524-7858
Web: www.bevbank.com

CEO: Donat A. Fournier
CFO: Michael O. Gilles
HR: Ellen M. Morrison
FYE: December 31
Type: Public

Don't expect to see bank prez Milburn Drysdale or his efficient secretary Jane Hathaway in the halls of Beverly National Corporation. The financial institution is the holding company for Beverly National Bank, which provides a range of financial services to residents and businesses of Beverly, Massachusetts, and surrounding North Shore communities. Deposit services include savings, checking, money market, and NOW accounts; IRAs; and CDs. Lending activities include residential and commercial real estate loans (each account for about 40% of the company's overall loan portfolio), as well as agricultural, business, construction, and consumer loans. Two of the bank's 10 branches are located in area high schools.

	Annual Growth	12/03	12/04	12/05	12/06	12/07
Assets ($ mil.)	8.0%	347.2	378.1	412.5	467.1	472.8
Net income ($ mil.)	13.1%	2.2	2.5	2.4	2.5	3.6
Market value ($ mil.)	2.7%	48.0	50.0	47.4	63.8	53.5
Employees	—	—	—	—	—	120

BEXIL CORPORATION

Pink Sheets: BXLC

11 Hanover Sq.
New York, NY 10005
Phone: 212-785-0400
Fax: 212-363-1101
Web: www.bexil.com

CEO: Thomas B. Winmill
CFO: Thomas O'Malley
HR: Richard O'Brien
FYE: December 31
Type: Public

Bexil Corporation is leaving the insurance business behind and moving on to new ventures. The holding company's primary operation since 2002 had been a 50% stake in York Insurance Services Group, which provided independent adjustment and third-party administration services to insurance companies and self-insured groups. In 2006, however, Bexil sold its stake in York to Odyssey Investment Partners and is seeking other opportunities for investment. Investment firm Winmill & Co., which is controlled by chairman Basset Winmill, owns about a quarter of Bexil.

	Annual Growth	12/03	12/04	12/05	12/06	12/07
Sales ($ mil.)	—	5.4	0.2	0.3	0.0	0.0
Net income ($ mil.)	(41.1%)	2.5	2.2	1.4	22.3	0.3
Employees	0.0%	—	—	11	11	—

An in-depth profile of this company is available to Hoover's Online members at hoovers.com.

243

BFC FINANCIAL CORPORATION

NYSE Arca: BFF

2100 W. Cypress Creek Rd.
Fort Lauderdale, FL 33309
Phone: 954-940-4900
Fax: 954-940-4910
Web: www.bfcfinancial.com

CEO: Alan B. Levan
CFO: John K. Grelle
HR: –
FYE: December 31
Type: Public

Holding company BFC Financial controls publicly traded Florida-based bank BankAtlantic Bancorp and Woodbridge Holdings, formerly Levitt Corporation, which was famous for constructing Levittown, New York, widely regarded as the first planned community in the US. BankAtlantic spun off the former Levitt Corporation at the beginning of 2004, but BFC has retained voting control in each firm through ownership of their common stock and Class B stock. BFC also owns stakes in resort operator Bluegreen Corporation and Asian-themed restaurant chain Benihana and has investments in real estate and venture capital.

	Annual Growth	12/03	12/04	12/05	12/06	12/07
Sales ($ mil.)	(12.9%)	—	—	—	1,094.6	953.9
Net income ($ mil.)	—	—	—	—	(2.2)	(30.5)
Market value ($ mil.)	(77.8%)	—	—	—	46.4	10.3
Employees	(98.7%)	—	—	—	3,559	48

BGC PARTNERS, INC.

NASDAQ (GS): BGCP

499 Park Ave.
New York, NY 10022
Phone: 212-938-5000
Fax: 212-829-4866
Web: www.bgcpartners.com

CEO: Howard W. Lutnick
CFO: Frank V. Saracino
HR: –
FYE: December 31
Type: Public

BGC Partners (formerly eSpeed) specializes in electronic, integrated voice, and hybrid trading, clearing, and settlement services for banks, investment firms, and brokerages. Its software and services help institutional traders make real-time transactions in US treasuries, foreign government securities, Eurobonds, corporate and municipal bonds, futures, options, and other instruments. Active in the Americas, Europe, and Asia, the company also provides information and analytics products. BGC Partners is closely allied with former parent Cantor Fitzgerald. (It's named after Cantor founder B. Gerald Cantor.) In 2008 Cantor merged its brokerage affiliates eSpeed and BGC Partners into a single entity.

	Annual Growth	12/03	12/04	12/05	12/06	12/07
Sales ($ mil.)	0.4%	156.6	166.5	152.9	164.7	159.2
Net income ($ mil.)	—	36.1	25.9	2.0	4.7	(32.5)
Market value ($ mil.)	(17.0%)	722.4	386.0	215.1	317.8	342.3
Employees	—	—	—	380		

BIDZ.COM, INC.

NASDAQ (CM): BIDZ

3562 Eastham Dr.
Culver City, CA 90232
Phone: 310-280-7373
Fax: 310-280-7375
Web: www.bidz.com

CEO: David Zinberg
CFO: Lawrence Y. Kong
HR: –
FYE: December 31
Type: Public

Bidz.com combines the markdowns of a dollar store, the format of an auction house, and the convenience of the Internet to bring sparkling deals to shoppers. The company buys closeout merchandise and sells it using a live-auction format, with no reserve prices and $1 opening bids, even on items that might retail for more than $20,000. It mostly sells jewelry, including gold, platinum, and silver items set with diamonds, and other precious and semi-precious stones, but visitors will also find deals on electronics and collectibles such as art and antiques, coins, and sports cards. Chairman and CEO David Zinberg and his sister, VP Marina Zinberg, together own about a third of the company's stock.

	Annual Growth	12/03	12/04	12/05	12/06	12/07
Sales ($ mil.)	40.7%	47.7	65.3	90.6	131.8	187.1
Net income ($ mil.)	—	(5.8)	0.8	2.6	5.4	18.1
Market value ($ mil.)	—	—	—	—	—	220.3
Employees	16.5%	—	—	170	198	—

BIG 5 SPORTING GOODS CORPORATION

NASDAQ (GS): BGFV

2525 E. El Segundo Blvd.
El Segundo, CA 90245
Phone: 310-536-0611
Fax: 310-297-7585
Web: www.big5sportinggoods.com

CEO: Steven G. Miller
CFO: Barry D. Emerson
HR: Jeffrey L. (Jeff) Fraley
FYE: Sunday nearest December 31
Type: Public

Big 5 Sporting Goods has outgrown its name. The company, which started out with five army surplus shops in 1955, is now a leading sporting goods retailer with about 360 stores in more than 10 mostly Western states including California, Washington, and Arizona.. The company sells brand-name equipment and clothing for indoor and outdoor activities including camping, hunting, fishing, tennis, golf, snowboarding, and more. Big 5 has stuck with a neighborhood-store format rather than opening large superstores. The company plans to add about 15 stores per year. The family of co-founder and chairman emeritus Robert W. Miller and his son, chairman and CEO Steven, own about 7% of Big 5 Sporting Goods.

	Annual Growth	12/03	12/04	12/05	12/06	12/07
Sales ($ mil.)	6.1%	709.7	782.2	814.0	876.8	898.3
Net income ($ mil.)	1.7%	26.3	33.5	27.5	30.8	28.1
Market value ($ mil.)	(9.8%)	474.4	660.8	496.7	553.6	313.7
Employees	9.9%	—	7,166	7,500	8,100	9,500

BIG BOY RESTAURANTS INTERNATIONAL, LLC

One Big Boy Dr.
Warren, MI 48091
Phone: 586-759-6000
Fax: 586-757-4737
Web: www.bigboy.com

CEO: Anthony T. (Tony) Michaels
CFO: –
HR: Debra Murphy
FYE: December 31
Type: Private

This restaurant chain has been feeding boys big and small for more than 70 years. Big Boy Restaurants International operates and franchises more than 450 of its signature family-dining spots in the US and Japan. Known for their hamburgers (and the iconic Big Boy figure holding a plate-sized sandwich), the restaurants also offer a full menu of breakfast options along with such home-style dinner favorites as meat loaf, pork chops, and chicken fried steak. About 20 locations are company-owned, while the rest are franchised. Founded by Bob Wian in 1936, the Big Boy chain is owned by Robert Liggett.

	Annual Growth	12/03	12/04	12/05	12/06	12/07
Est. sales ($ mil.)	—	—	—	—	—	57.8
Employees	—	—	—	—	—	1,500

BIG LOTS, INC.

NYSE: BIG

300 Phillipi Rd.
Columbus, OH 43228
Phone: 614-278-6800
Fax: 614-278-6676
Web: www.biglots.com

CEO: Steven S. (Steve) Fishman
CFO: Joe R. Cooper
HR: Brad A. Waite
FYE: Saturday nearest January 31
Type: Public

Big Lots believes that a product's shelf life depends solely on which shelf it's on. The company is the nation's #1 closeout retailer, with some 1,350 Big Lots stores (down from a high of 1,500 in 2005) in 47 states. (More than one-third of its stores are located in California, Florida, Ohio, and Texas.) It sells a variety of brand-name products that have been overproduced or discontinued, typically at 20% to 40% below discounters' prices, as well as private-label items and furniture. Its wholesale division, Big Lots Wholesale, sells its discounted merchandise to a variety of retailers, manufacturers, distributors, and other wholesalers.

	Annual Growth	1/04	1/05	1/06	1/07	1/08
Sales ($ mil.)	2.8%	4,174.4	4,375.1	4,429.9	4,743.0	4,656.3
Net income ($ mil.)	18.2%	81.2	23.8	(10.1)	124.0	158.5
Market value ($ mil.)	(50.0%)	—	—	—	2,850.5	1,424.8
Employees	(6.9%)	—	—	43,985	38,738	38,153

BIG M INC.

12 Vreeland Ave.
Totowa, NJ 07512
Phone: 973-890-0021
Fax: 973-890-5994
Web: www.mandee.com

CEO: Lawrence (Larry) Mandelbaum
CFO: Robert Edmond
HR: Michael Bush
FYE: January 31
Type: Private

Annie says that savings start with a Big M. Big M Inc. operates about 50 Annie Sez off-price women's apparel shops, 10 Afaze accessory shops, and 120-plus Mandee shops (mostly in New Jersey and New York) targeting young women and teens. Its stores are also located in Connecticut, Delaware, Florida, Illinois, Maryland, Michigan, Pennsylvania, and Virginia. Mandee shops account for nearly two-thirds of the company's sales, with Annie Sez stores contributing about 30%. Mandee also sells through its Web site and offers store credit cards. The family-owned and -operated company was founded in Brooklyn in 1948 by the Mandelbaum brothers (Leon, Max, and Bernard) and today is run by their descendants.

	Annual Growth	1/03	1/04	1/05	1/06	1/07
Est. sales ($ mil.)	—	—	—	—	—	191.4
Employees	—	—	—	—	—	3,500

BIG RED, LTD.

720 Jewell Dr.
Waco, TX 76712
Phone: 254-772-7791
Fax: 254-772-2441
Web: www.bigredltd.com

CEO: Donal S. (Don) Sharp
CFO: Ginger Combs
HR: –
FYE: December 31
Type: Private

While the cola wars may leave the ground littered with empty Coke and Pepsi bottles, Big Red proves that niche soft drinks can still win over followers one gulp at a time. The company bottles and markets the Big Red strawberry-bubble-gum-flavored soft drink in about 30 states in the US. Other flavors offered by the company include Big Red Float, Big Peach, and Big Pineapple. Distribution is handled through the bottling operations of Dr Pepper Snapple Group. The company also offers the Honey Lemonade and NuGrape labels through its North American Beverages operations.

	Annual Growth	12/03	12/04	12/05	12/06	12/07
Est. sales ($ mil.)	—	—	—	—	—	2.6
Employees	—	—	—	—	—	25

BIG Y FOODS, INC.

2145 Roosevelt Ave.
Springfield, MA 01102
Phone: 413-784-0600
Fax: –
Web: www.bigy.com

CEO: Donald H. D'Amour
CFO: Herbert T. (Herb) Dotterer
HR: Jack Henry
FYE: June 30
Type: Private

Why call it Big Y? Big Y Foods began as a 900-sq.-ft. grocery at a Y intersection in Chicopee, Massachusetts. It now operates about 55 supermarkets throughout Massachusetts and Connecticut. Most of its stores are Big Y World Class Markets, offering specialty areas such as bakeries and floral shops, as well as banking. The rest consist of Big Y Supermarkets and two gourmet food and liquor stores (Table & Vine, Town & Country). Some Big Y stores provide child care, dry cleaning, photo processing, and even propane sales, and their delis and Food Courts offer to-go foods. Big Y is owned and run by the D'Amour family and is one of New England's largest independent supermarket chains.

	Annual Growth	6/02	6/03	6/04	6/05	6/06
Sales ($ mil.)	2.0%	1,200.0	1,190.0	1,210.0	1,250.0	1,300.0
Employees	4.0%	7,850	8,500	8,600	8,700	9,200

BIGBAND NETWORKS, INC.

NASDAQ (GM): BBND

475 Broadway St.
Redwood City, CA 94063
Phone: 650-995-5000
Fax: 650-995-0060
Web: www.bigbandnet.com

CEO: Amir Bassan-Eskenazi
CFO: Maurice L. (Moe) Castonguay
HR: –
FYE: December 31
Type: Public

BigBand Networks helps cable and telephone service providers keep the broadband beat. Companies use its routing and switching systems to offer data, video, and voice services. BigBand's hardware and software products support digital broadcast television, high-definition television (HDTV), high-speed data services, video on demand (VOD), and voice over Internet protocol (VoIP). The company's systems also help customers manage service quality and insert tailored advertising based on geography. BigBand counts Comcast, Cox Communications, and Time Warner Cable among its customers.

	Annual Growth	12/03	12/04	12/05	12/06	12/07
Est. sales ($ mil.)	—	—	—	—	—	176.5
Net income ($ mil.)	—	—	—	—	—	(25.4)
Market value ($ mil.)	—	—	—	—	—	318.2
Employees	—	—	—	—	—	—

BILL & MELINDA GATES FOUNDATION

1551 Eastlake Ave. East
Seattle, WA 98102
Phone: 206-709-3100
Fax: 206-709-3180
Web: www.gatesfoundation.org

CEO: Patricia Q. (Patty) Stonesifer
CFO: Alexander S. Friedman
HR: –
FYE: December 31
Type: Foundation

You don't have to be one of the world's richest men to make a difference with your charitable gifts — but it helps. Established by the chairman of Microsoft and his wife, the Bill & Melinda Gates Foundation works in developing countries to improve health and reduce poverty and in the US to support education and libraries nationwide and children and families in the Pacific Northwest. With an endowment of about $38 billion, the foundation is the largest in the US, and it's getting bigger. Investor Warren Buffett has announced plans to give the Bill & Melinda Gates Foundation about $30 billion worth of Berkshire Hathaway stock.

	Annual Growth	12/02	12/03	12/04	12/05	12/06
Sales ($ mil.)	29.2%	2,047.9	4,010.1	3,343.5	1,864.0	5,703.6
Employees	35.4%	—	184	234	270	457

BILL BARRETT CORPORATION

NYSE: BBG

1099 18th St., Ste. 2300
Denver, CO 80202
Phone: 303-293-9100
Fax: 303-291-0420
Web: www.billbarrettcorp.com

CEO: Fredrick J. (Fred) Barrett
CFO: Bob Howard
HR: –
FYE: December 31
Type: Public

Bill Barrett Corp. (named after a veteran oil industry wildcatter) is hoping for a Rocky Mountain high as it digs down deep for oil and gas. The company focuses its exploration and development activities in the Green River, Wind River, Uinta, Powder River, Denver-Julesburg, Big Horn, and Paradox Basins and the Montana and Utah Overthrusts. Bill Barrett holds about 1.2 million net undeveloped leasehold acres. In 2007 the oil and gas firm had working interests in 950 drilling locations and had estimated net proved reserves of 557.6 billion cu. ft. of natural gas equivalent.

	Annual Growth	12/03	12/04	12/05	12/06	12/07
Sales ($ mil.)	50.8%	75.4	170.0	288.8	375.3	390.3
Net income ($ mil.)	—	(4.0)	(5.3)	23.8	62.0	26.8
Market value ($ mil.)	10.6%	—	1,385.9	1,682.3	1,201.1	1,874.1
Employees	15.2%	—	—	190	216	252

An in-depth profile of this company is available to Hoover's Online members at hoovers.com.

245

BILL BLASS HOLDING CO., INC.

550 7th Ave., 12th Fl.
New York, NY 10018
Phone: 212-221-6660
Fax: 212-398-5545
Web: www.billblass.com

CEO: Michael Groveman
CFO: Ronald (Ron) Fetzer
HR: –
FYE: December 31
Type: Subsidiary

In business for some three decades, Bill Blass has reached ubiquity status as a licensor. His namesake company makes tailored men's and women's clothing known to adorn noteworthy clients from Barbara Bush to Barbra Streisand. William Ralph "Bill" Blass made a name for himself with tailored designs. Never yielding to trendy looks, such as disco or grunge, the Bill Blass name has earned a loyal fashion following. Most sales come from some 30 licenses for items such as furniture, eyewear, and accessories. Blass, who retired in 2000 and died in 2002, sold the firm in 1999 to its jeanswear licensee, The Resource Club, and CEO Michael Groveman. NexCen Brands acquired Bill Blass for about $54 million in early 2007.

BILL HEARD ENTERPRISES, INC.

200 Brookstone Center Pkwy., Ste. 205
Columbus, GA 31904
Phone: 706-323-1111
Fax: 706-321-9488
Web: www.billheard.com

CEO: William T. (Bill) Heard
CFO: Ronald A. (Ron) Feldner
HR: Jim Matthews
FYE: December 31
Type: Private

The Southern hills (and Western deserts) are alive with the sound of Chevys — music to the ears of Bill Heard Enterprises. The nation's leading chain of Chevrolet franchises, Bill Heard has about 15 dealerships in Alabama, Arizona, Florida, Georgia, Nevada, Tennessee, and Texas. The dealer sells both new and used vehicles and auto supplies and offers repair services and financing. The company also sells used Cadillac and Saab vehicles at a dealership in Georgia. William Heard Sr. opened his first dealership in 1919. He switched to selling Chevrolets exclusively in 1932, and his son and grandsons, who now run the family-owned business, continue to focus on Chevy sales.

	Annual Growth	12/03	12/04	12/05	12/06	12/07
Est. sales ($ mil.)	—	—	—	—	—	2,147.5
Employees	—	—	—	—	—	4,700

BI-LO, LLC

208 BI-LO Blvd.
Greenville, SC 29607
Phone: 864-213-2500
Fax: 864-234-6999
Web: www.bi-lo.com

CEO: Brian W. Hotarek
CFO: Brian P. Carney
HR: Susan Warzecka
FYE: December 31
Type: Private

To buy low, try BI-LO. BI-LO operates about 225 supermarkets in North and South Carolina, Georgia, and Tennessee. Many of BI-LO's stores house pharmacies and some boast Starbucks Café kiosks. Brands include national names, the BI-LO private-label banner, Finast health and beauty products, Southern Hearth Bakery items, and Vince's deli meats and meals-to-go. The firm was founded in 1961 by Frank Outlaw. Dutch grocery giant Royal Ahold, which entered the US market with its 1977 buy of BI-LO, sold the regional grocery chain and its smaller sister supermarket chain Bruno's Supermarkets to Dallas-based investment firm Lone Star Funds in 2005.

	Annual Growth	12/02	12/03	12/04	12/05	12/06
Sales ($ mil.)	11.4%	—	—	—	4,263.5	4,749.5
Employees	(2.1%)	—	—	—	23,500	23,000

BI-MART CORPORATION

220 S. Seneca Rd.
Eugene, OR 97402
Phone: 541-344-0681
Fax: 541-342-4241
Web: www.bimart.com

CEO: Marty W. Smith
CFO: David (Dave) Zientara
HR: Dennis Down
FYE: December 31
Type: Private

Bi-Mart wants you to join the club. The company operates a chain of about 65 general merchandise membership stores in the Pacific Northwest. Just $5 buys a lifetime membership to the deep-discount chain, which has enrolled more than 1,000,000 members to date. Stores offer automotive departments, clothing and shoes, food and alcohol, housewares, full-service pharmacies, and photo departments. Bi-Mart, which was started by a group of investors in Yakima, Washington, in 1955, was bought by CEO Marty Smith and other senior managers from Rite Aid Corporation in 1997. Today, the company is employee-owned.

	Annual Growth	12/03	12/04	12/05	12/06	12/07
Est. sales ($ mil.)	—	—	—	—	—	690.0
Employees	—	—	—	—	—	3,000

BIMBO BAKERIES USA

14401 Statler Blvd.
Fort Worth, TX 76155
Phone: 817-864-2500
Fax: 817-615-3186
Web: www.bimbobakeriesusa.com

CEO: Renaldo Reyna
CFO: H. Darrell Miller
HR: Maria Wong
FYE: December 31
Type: Subsidiary

No snickering — Bimbo Bakeries USA (BBU) is serious about making breads, cakes, and cookies. The US subsidiary of Mexico's baking giant, Grupo Bimbo S.A. ("bimbo" is a shortened version of the Spanish word "bambino" — or "small child"), BBU operates bakeries in California, Colorado, Oregon, and Texas. The company also manufactures tortillas, bagels, snack cakes, muffins, and pizza crust, as well as sweet and salty snacks. It manufactures and distributes products under the Bimbo, Boboli, Bohemian Hearth, Mrs Baird's, Oroweat, Francisco, Tia Rosa, and Marinela brands.

BIMINI CAPITAL MANAGEMENT, INC.

Pink Sheets: BMNM

3305 Flamingo Dr.
Vero Beach, FL 32963
Phone: 772-231-1400
Fax: 772-231-8896
Web: www.biminireit.com

CEO: Robert E. Cauley
CFO: G. Hunter Haas IV
HR: –
FYE: December 31
Type: Public

Bimini Capital Management (formerly Opteum) invests in residential mortgage-backed securities issued by Fannie Mae, Freddie Mac, and Ginnie Mae. The real estate investment trust (REIT) manages an approximately $3 billion portfolio of mortgage-related securities, most of them backed by adjustable-rate mortgages. Bimini Capital also invests in fixed-rate, hybrid adjustable-rate, and balloon maturity mortgage-backed securities. The company sold its residential mortgage origination business, which consisted of about 25 offices in five states, to Prospect Mortgage in 2007. It has also ceased conduit and wholesale lending.

	Annual Growth	12/03	12/04	12/05	12/06	12/07
Sales ($ mil.)	465.8%	0.1	50.4	164.9	262.5	102.5
Net income ($ mil.)	—	(0.3)	22.9	24.3	(49.5)	(247.6)
Employees	464.8%	5	6	1,066	901	—

BING HOLDINGS INC.

11500 Oakland Ave.
Detroit, MI 48211
Phone: 313-867-3700
Fax: 313-867-3897
Web: www.binggroup.com

CEO: David (Dave) Bing
CFO: Kirk Lewis
HR: Germaine Carter
FYE: December 31
Type: Private

What do the NBA's Detroit Pistons and a multimillion-dollar auto supplier have in common? Dave Bing — a retired pro basketball player, Hall of Famer, and founder and owner of Bing Holdings. The group's automotive activities include the production of steel blanks and welded sections, and stamping services. The company sells its services to auto parts manufacturers and metal furniture and appliance makers. Bing is considered to be one of the largest black-owned businesses in Michigan. In 2006 the company sold its 51% stake in Bing Assembly Systems to industry veteran Jim Comer.

BINGHAM MCCUTCHEN LLP

1 Federal St.
Boston, MA 02110
Phone: 617-951-8000
Fax: 617-951-8736
Web: www.bingham.com

CEO: Jay S. Zimmerman
CFO: Joseph J. Hinderhofer
HR: Lynn Carroll
FYE: December 31
Type: Partnership

Big and steadily getting bigger, Bingham McCutchen has about 1,000 lawyers overall. Bingham has grown over the years by absorbing other law firms — more than half a dozen since 1997. It maintains about 15 offices that span the US, Europe, and the Asia/Pacific region, with concentrations in California and New England. Bingham's wide range of practice areas is divided into major groups such as corporate, finance, litigation, and securities. Along with its law practices, the firm offers consulting services through subsidiaries. Bingham was established in 1891.

	Annual Growth	12/03	12/04	12/05	12/06	12/07
Est. sales ($ mil.)	—	—	—	—	—	74.8
Employees	—	—	—	—	—	867

BIO-IMAGING TECHNOLOGIES, INC.

NASDAQ (GM): BITI

826 Newtown-Yardley Rd.
Newtown, PA 18940
Phone: 267-757-3000
Fax: 267-757-3010
Web: www.bioimaging.com

CEO: Mark L. Weinstein
CFO: Ted I. Kaminer
HR: Carmella Miller
FYE: December 31
Type: Public

Bio-Imaging Technologies helps drug developers keep track of their X-rays, MRIs, and other forms of medical imaging collected during clinical drug and medical device trials. The company provides medical imaging support services including image processing and analysis, archival services, and database maintenance. Its proprietary software systems, including Bio/ImageBase, let clients and regulatory officials electronically review images and related data. Bio-Imaging Technologies serves clients, including Roche and Novartis, primarily in the US and Europe; its European operations are based in the Netherlands.

	Annual Growth	12/03	12/04	12/05	12/06	12/07
Sales ($ mil.)	17.7%	25.0	29.7	30.5	40.5	47.9
Net income ($ mil.)	0.0%	2.3	0.9	(2.5)	1.0	2.3
Market value ($ mil.)	9.3%	66.7	60.4	36.1	91.2	95.1
Employees	—	—	—	264	—	—

BIOANALYTICAL SYSTEMS, INC.

NASDAQ (GM): BASI

2701 Kent Ave.
West Lafayette, IN 47906
Phone: 765-463-4527
Fax: 765-497-1102
Web: www.bioanalytical.com

CEO: Richard M. Shepperd
CFO: Michael R. Cox
HR: Lina L. Reeves-Kerner
FYE: September 30
Type: Public

Analyze this! Bioanalytical Systems, Inc. (BASi) provides contract research and development services for the pharmaceutical, medical device, and biotechnology industries. In addition to conducting preclinical and Phase I clinical trials, the firm's research services include product purity tests, characterization analysis of compounds, and *in vivo* testing to measure how drugs are metabolized in living systems. BASi also sells analytical instruments and other products including bioanalytical separation instrumentation, chemical analyzers, diagnostic kits, and miniaturized *in vivo* sampling devices.

	Annual Growth	9/03	9/04	9/05	9/06	9/07
Sales ($ mil.)	11.0%	29.8	37.2	42.4	43.0	45.2
Net income ($ mil.)	73.2%	0.1	(0.2)	(0.1)	(2.6)	0.9
Market value ($ mil.)	13.0%	20.9	26.7	26.5	25.7	34.2
Employees	(9.1%)	—	—	370	—	306

BIOCRYST PHARMACEUTICALS, INC.

NASDAQ (GM): BCRX

2190 Parkway Lake Dr.
Birmingham, AL 35244
Phone: 205-444-4600
Fax: 205-444-4640
Web: www.biocryst.com

CEO: Jon P. Stonehouse
CFO: Stuart Grant
HR: Mike Richardson
FYE: December 31
Type: Public

BioCryst Pharmaceuticals is tackling the bad enzymes that spread disease. The firm creates small molecule compounds that inhibit enzymes associated with viral diseases, autoimmune conditions, and cancer. BioCryst's lead product candidate fodosine HCl may treat T-cell cancers, including T-cell lymphomas and leukemias, by preventing T-cells from wildly multiplying and harming the body. With funding from the Department of Health and Human Services, it is developing peramavir, a potential treatment for various strains of influenza, including the much-discussed avian flu. A third clinical-stage candidate may treat autoimmune conditions.

	Annual Growth	12/03	12/04	12/05	12/06	12/07
Sales ($ mil.)	158.3%	1.6	0.3	0.2	6.2	71.2
Net income ($ mil.)	—	(12.7)	(21.1)	(26.1)	(43.6)	(29.1)
Market value ($ mil.)	17.7%	122.4	125.8	482.6	338.1	234.6
Employees	42.8%	—	—	52	—	106

BIODEL INC.

NASDAQ (GM): BIOD

100 Saw Mill Rd.
Danbury, CT 06810
Phone: 203-796-5000
Fax: 203-796-5001
Web: www.biodel.com

CEO: Solomon S. Steiner
CFO: Gerard J. (Gerry) Michel
HR: –
FYE: September 30
Type: Public

Biodel delves into the development of viable treatments for endocrine disorders. The company uses its VIAdel biological technology to reformulate and administer existing peptide drugs. Its two main product candidates are in clinical trials for treating diabetes. Biodel's VIAject insulin formula is designed to be rapidly absorbed into the bloodstream following injection, while its VIAtab insulin tablets are administered orally. Two additional products aimed at treating osteoporosis, VIAmass and VIAcal, are in preclinical development. Members of Biodel's board of directors together own more than 50% of the company; prior to its 2007 IPO board members controlled over 80% of Biodel.

	Annual Growth	9/00	9/01	9/02	9/03	*9/04
Sales ($ mil.)	—	—	—	—	—	0.0
Net income ($ mil.)	—	—	—	—	—	(0.8)
Employees	—	—	—	—	—	—

*Most recent year available

An in-depth profile of this company is available to Hoover's Online members at hoovers.com.

247

BIODELIVERY SCIENCES INTERNATIONAL, INC.

NASDAQ (CM): BDSI

801 Corporate Center Drive, Ste. 210
Raleigh, NC 27607
Phone: 919-582-9050
Fax: 919-582-9051
Web: www.bdsinternational.com

CEO: Mark A. Sirgo
CFO: James A. (Jim) McNulty
HR: –
FYE: December 31
Type: Public

BioDelivery Sciences International isn't inventing new drugs, but it is looking for better ways to administer them. The development-stage firm takes already-approved drugs that are normally delivered intravenously and reformulates them into buccal (absorbed by the inner cheek) and oral treatments. Drugs delivered via its BEMA and Bioral systems are being studied to treat acute pain and fungal infections, respectively. BioDelivery Sciences is awaiting FDA approval of its BEMA Fentanyl candidate, which consists of a dissolving disc that delivers the cancer pain drug buccally. Swedish partner Meda AB has commercial rights to this product in the US, Canada, Europe, and Mexico.

	Annual Growth	12/03	12/04	12/05	12/06	12/07
Sales ($ mil.)	(48.8%)	2.9	1.8	0.9	0.3	0.2
Net income ($ mil.)	—	(2.5)	(2.8)	(10.1)	(22.4)	(25.2)
Market value ($ mil.)	31.2%	18.9	25.2	29.3	44.8	56.1
Employees	—	—	—	13	—	—

BIOFIELD CORP.

Pink Sheets: BZET

1025 North Nine Dr., Ste. M
Alpharetta, GA 30004
Phone: 770-740-8180
Fax: 770-740-9366
Web: www.biofield.com

CEO: Michael J. Antonoplos
CFO: –
HR: –
FYE: December 31
Type: Public

Biofield Corp. is trying to blaze a trail in the diagnostic equipment market with its Biofield Diagnostic System, which employs single-use sensors to detect and examine changes associated with breast cancer. The system, which is approved in Europe but not yet in the US, is based on the belief that epithelial cancers are characterized by changes in the electrical charge of the affected tissue; the sensors analyze these changes and identify if a lesion is malignant or benign. The process requires less than 20 minutes, and has possible applications to cancers of the ovaries, skin, prostate, and colon. Chairman James MacKay, through the MacKay Group, owns a controlling interest in Biofield.

	Annual Growth	12/03	12/04	12/05	12/06	12/07
Sales ($ mil.)	—	—	—	—	—	0.1
Net income ($ mil.)	—	—	—	—	—	(1.3)
Employees	—	—	—	—	—	—

BIOFORM MEDICAL, INC.

NASDAQ (GM): BFRM

1875 S. Grant St., Ste. 110
San Mateo, CA 94402
Phone: 650-286-4000
Fax: 650-286-4090
Web: www.bioformmedical.com

CEO: Steven L. (Steve) Basta
CFO: Derek A. Bertocci
HR: –
FYE: June 30
Type: Public

Some people believe that wrinkles are a sign, not only of age, but of wisdom and experience. BioForm Medical caters to a different clientele. The company's Radiesse product, a dermal filler used mainly for cosmetic reasons, is injected underneath a patient's facial skin to temporarily mask wrinkles brought on by aging or loss of fat; other uses include the marking of tissue for radiographic purposes. Radiesse is sold directly to physicians in the US and Europe and through distributors in other regions. BioForm's other injectable product, Coaptite, is used to treat abnormalities of the urinary tract in women and children; it is sold primarily in the US through a partnership with distributor Boston Scientific.

	Annual Growth	6/03	6/04	6/05	6/06	6/07
Sales ($ mil.)	71.1%	—	—	16.2	22.6	47.4
Net income ($ mil.)	—	—	—	(10.7)	(11.4)	(13.6)
Employees	—	—	—	—	—	292

BIOFUEL ENERGY CORP.

NASDAQ (GM): BIOF

1801 Broadway, Ste. 1060
Denver, CO 80202
Phone: 303-592-8110
Fax: 303-592-8117
Web: www.bfenergy.com

CEO: Scott H. Pearce
CFO: Kelly G. Maguire
HR: –
FYE: December 31
Type: Public

BioFuel Energy has climbed aboard the ethanol bandwagon. Construction on the company's first two plants is under way and should be completed in the first half of 2008. BioFuel holds options on land to build three more plants but has put off those plans due to the slowdown in the marketplace, wherein high corn prices have led to low ethanol prices. The company is partnering with agribusiness giant Cargill, which gives it reliable corn supplies, an established logistics/transportation network, and marketing expertise. BioFuel Energy went public in 2007, using the proceeds to repay outstanding debts, as well as to fund construction of its ethanol facilities. Greenlight Capital still owns a third of the company.

	Annual Growth	12/02	12/03	12/04	12/05	*12/06
Sales ($ mil.)	—	—	—	—	1.0	0.0
Net income ($ mil.)	—	—	—	—	0.4	(2.3)
Employees	83.3%	—	—	—	12	22

*Most recent year available

BIOGEN IDEC INC.

NASDAQ (GS): BIIB

14 Cambridge Center
Cambridge, MA 02142
Phone: 617-679-2000
Fax: 617-679-2617
Web: www.biogenidec.com

CEO: James C. (Jim) Mullen
CFO: Paul J. Clancy
HR: Craig E. Schneier
FYE: December 31
Type: Public

When it comes to developing new and better biotech drugs, Biogen Idec believes two heads are better than one. The biotech giant, formed from the merger of IDEC Pharmaceuticals and Biogen, is focused on developing treatments in the areas of oncology, immunology, and neurology. Its product roster includes best-selling Avonex, the most popular drug for the treatment of relapsing multiple sclerosis; Rituxan, a monoclonal antibody developed with Genentech that treats B-cell non-Hodgkin's lymphoma (NHL); multiple sclerosis drug Tysabri; and Fumaderm, a psoriasis drug marketed in Germany.

	Annual Growth	12/03	12/04	12/05	12/06	12/07
Sales ($ mil.)	47.0%	679.2	2,211.6	2,422.5	2,683.1	3,171.6
Net income ($ mil.)	—	(875.1)	25.1	160.7	217.5	638.2
Market value ($ mil.)	8.7%	12,126.0	22,427.6	15,393.4	16,634.8	16,948.0
Employees	13.5%	—	—	3,340	3,750	4,300

BIOHEART, INC.

NASDAQ (GM): BHRT

13794 NW 4th St., Ste. 212
Sunrise, FL 33325
Phone: 954-835-1500
Fax: 954-845-9976
Web: www.bioheartinc.com

CEO: William M. Pinon
CFO: William H. Kline
HR: Catherine Sulawske-Guck
FYE: December 31
Type: Public

Broken hearts are no fun, but damaged hearts are worse and Bioheart aims to help. The biotech company is focused on the discovery, development, and commercialization of therapies treating heart damage. Because the heart does not have cells to naturally repair itself, Bioheart is exploring the use of cells derived from the patient's own thigh muscle to improve cardiac function after a heart has been damaged by a heart attack. Its lead candidate, MyoCell, uses precursor muscle cells called myoblasts to strengthen scar tissue with living muscle tissue. The company is also developing a number of proprietary techniques and processes used to obtain and inject MyoCell.

	Annual Growth	12/03	12/04	12/05	12/06	12/07
Sales ($ mil.)	—	0.0	0.1	0.1	0.1	0.3
Net income ($ mil.)	—	(6.0)	(5.5)	(7.3)	(13.2)	(18.1)
Employees	—	—	—	22	—	—

BIOJECT MEDICAL TECHNOLOGIES INC.

NASDAQ (CM): BJCT

20245 SW 95th Ave.
Tualatin, OR 97062
Phone: 503-692-8001
Fax: 503-692-6698
Web: www.bioject.com

CEO: Ralph Makar
CFO: –
HR: –
FYE: December 31
Type: Public

Bioject Medical Technologies wants to give the medical community a shot in the arm. Its Biojector 2000 jet injection system delivers injectable medication without a needle (and thus without needle-associated risks) by using a fine, high-pressure stream that goes through the skin. The accompanying Vial Adapter device allows the Biojector syringe to be filled without a needle. The company also markets Vitajet, a needle-free self-injection device that has been cleared for administering injections of insulin and Merck Serono's human growth hormone Saizen. Bioject has additional collaborative agreements with veterinary drugmaker Merial and with Vical.

	Annual Growth	12/03	12/04	12/05	12/06	12/07
Sales ($ mil.)	7.5%	6.3	9.5	12.3	10.8	8.4
Net income ($ mil.)	—	(9.3)	(9.1)	(6.6)	(7.0)	(4.0)
Market value ($ mil.)	(28.5%)	32.5	21.4	18.0	13.8	8.5
Employees	—	—	—	84	—	—

BIO-KEY INTERNATIONAL, INC.

OTC: BKYI

3349 Hwy. 138, Bldg. D, Ste. B
Wall, NJ 07719
Phone: 732-359-1100
Fax: 732-359-1101
Web: www.bio-key.com

CEO: Michael W. (Mike) DePasquale
CFO: Francis J. (Frank) Cusick
HR: –
FYE: December 31
Type: Public

BIO-key International has its finger securely on the pulse of biometrics. The company develops biometric security software and hardware designed to secure access to networks and buildings, as well as to mobile devices. The company's products incorporate biometric technology to scan and analyze fingerprints in order to grant or deny user access. BIO-key also offers wireless information retrieval systems used by law enforcement agencies to access motor vehicle, warrant, and criminal history data. The company licenses its technology to original equipment manufacturers, systems integrators, and application developers.

	Annual Growth	12/03	12/04	12/05	12/06	12/07
Sales ($ mil.)	111.5%	0.5	5.6	14.2	15.2	10.0
Net income ($ mil.)	—	(3.8)	(7.2)	(3.7)	(11.1)	(1.1)
Market value ($ mil.)	(28.2%)	25.3	65.1	32.0	18.2	6.7
Employees	—	—	—	—	—	—

BIOLARGO, INC.

OTC: BLGO

2603 Main St., Ste. 1155
Irvine, CA 92614
Phone: 949-235-8062
Fax: 949-625-9819
Web: www.biolargolifetechnologies.com

CEO: Dennis Calvert
CFO: Charles K. Dargan II
HR: –
FYE: December 31
Type: Public

After morphing identities several times, BioLargo (formerly NuWay Medical) hopes that it has found its way. The company went from car dealership and casino ownership to being a medical device maker and application service provider (ASP). It has found a new future in designing specialty packaging for shipping blood, biohazardous materials, meat and poultry, and other items requiring sanitary containment. The company believes that its BioLargo technology, which combines an iodine-based disinfecting process with highly absorbent materials, can also be used for additional applications such as medical product design and environmental cleanup.

	Annual Growth	12/03	12/04	12/05	12/06	12/07
Sales ($ mil.)	—	—	—	—	—	0.1
Net income ($ mil.)	—	—	—	—	—	(5.3)
Market value ($ mil.)	—	—	—	—	—	38.4
Employees	—	—	—	—	—	—

BIOLASE TECHNOLOGY, INC.

NASDAQ (GM): BLTI

4 Cromwell
Irvine, CA 92618
Phone: 949-361-1200
Fax: 949-273-6677
Web: www.biolase.com

CEO: Jake St. Philip
CFO: David M. (Dave) Mulder
HR: Jodie Saundersen
FYE: December 31
Type: Public

BioLase Technology is causing dentists to drop the knife and pick up the laser — it makes laser-based systems for use primarily in dental applications. BioLase's surgical cutting system, Waterlase, uses laser pulses to turn water droplets into high-speed particles that can cut both hard and soft tissues and bones in the mouth. Waterlase is used in procedures traditionally performed with dental drills and scalpels. The company's DioLase system is used to perform soft tissue and cosmetic procedures, including its LaserSmile teeth whitening procedure. BioLase markets its products in the US through distributor Henry Schein, as well as through international representatives in more than 50 countries.

	Annual Growth	12/03	12/04	12/05	12/06	12/07
Sales ($ mil.)	8.0%	49.2	60.7	62.1	69.7	66.9
Net income ($ mil.)	—	19.1	(23.2)	(17.5)	(4.7)	(7.3)
Market value ($ mil.)	(36.9%)	357.9	244.8	185.8	208.0	56.6
Employees	(4.8%)	—	—	209	199	—

BIOLIFE SOLUTIONS, INC.

OTC: BLFS

171 Front St.
Owego, NY 13827
Phone: 607-687-4487
Fax: 607-687-6683
Web: www.biolifesolutions.com

CEO: Michael (Mike) Rice
CFO: Roderick (Rod) de Greef
HR: –
FYE: Sunday before December 31
Type: Public

BioLife Solutions makes sure your tissues and organs don't get freezer burn. The company has designed liquid media technologies for frozen (cryogenic) storage and cold (hypothermic) storage of biological products including cells, tissues, and organs. Its HypoThermosol and CryoStor products minimize the damage done to these biological products during refrigeration and freezing, making them viable for transplant or experimentation for longer periods. The company sells its products directly to academic institutions, companies, and laboratories conducting clinical research.

	Annual Growth	12/03	12/04	12/05	12/06	12/07
Sales ($ mil.)	13.6%	0.6	0.6	0.6	0.6	1.0
Net income ($ mil.)	—	(1.3)	(0.7)	(0.6)	(1.1)	(2.8)
Market value ($ mil.)	32.2%	1.4	1.1	1.4	4.5	4.2
Employees	—	—	—	—	—	—

BIOMARIN PHARMACEUTICAL INC.

NASDAQ (GM): BMRN

105 Digital Dr.
Novato, CA 94949
Phone: 415-506-6700
Fax: 415-382-7889
Web: www.biomarinpharm.com

CEO: Jean-Jacques (J.J.) Bienaimé
CFO: Jeffrey H. (Jeff) Cooper
HR: Mark Wood
FYE: December 31
Type: Public

If spawning orphans makes for success in the drug world, then BioMarin Pharmaceutical takes the prize. The company has developed three FDA-approved drugs that qualify for orphan drug status, a financial incentive that encourages companies to create drugs for rare diseases by giving the compounds a period of market exclusivity. BioMarin's Aldurazyme (co-developed with Genzyme) treats the life-threatening inherited condition MPS I, caused by a rare enzyme deficiency. Its Naglazyme is approved in the US and Europe to treat another rare genetic disease called MPS VI. And Kuvan, which won FDA approval in 2007, treats another enzyme deficiency called PKU, which prevents patients from metabolizing certain proteins.

	Annual Growth	12/03	12/04	12/05	12/06	12/07
Sales ($ mil.)	78.0%	12.1	18.6	25.7	84.2	121.6
Net income ($ mil.)	—	(75.8)	(187.4)	(74.3)	(28.5)	(15.8)
Market value ($ mil.)	62.1%	497.9	412.2	805.8	1,567.6	3,437.8
Employees	—	—	—	314	—	—

BIOMED REALTY TRUST, INC.

NYSE: BMR

17140 Bernardo Center Dr., Ste. 222
San Diego, CA 92128
Phone: 858-485-9840
Fax: 858-485-9843
Web: www.biomedrealty.com

CEO: Alan D. Gold
CFO: R. Kent Griffin Jr.
HR: –
FYE: December 31
Type: Public

BioMed Realty knows its niche. A self-administered real estate investment trust (REIT), the company acquires, develops, leases, and manages research laboratories and offices for biotechnology companies, pharmaceutical firms, research institutions, and other life science tenants. BioMed owns more than 65 properties in about a dozen states; they contain more than 100 buildings and total approximately 12 million sq. ft. of rentable space. The REIT's preferred markets include research and development hubs such as Boston, New York, San Diego, San Francisco, and Seattle. Its largest tenants include Human Genome Sciences (20% of sales), Vertex Pharmaceuticals, Genzyme, and Centocor.

	Annual Growth	12/03	12/04	12/05	12/06	12/07
Sales ($ mil.)	109.9%	13.7	32.4	138.9	221.4	266.1
Net income ($ mil.)	155.5%	1.7	5.8	17.0	35.0	72.5
Market value ($ mil.)	29.7%	—	697.1	1,140.6	1,871.2	1,519.3
Employees	11.8%	40	—	50	—	—

BIOMERICA, INC.

OTC: BMRA

1533 Monrovia Ave.
Newport Beach, CA 92663
Phone: 949-645-2111
Fax: 949-722-6674
Web: www.biomerica.com

CEO: Zackary S. Irani
CFO: Janet Moore
HR: –
FYE: May 31
Type: Public

God bless Biomerica. The company makes diagnostic tests for use worldwide in hospitals, clinics, research laboratories, physicians' offices, and pharmacies, as well as testing kits that are sold over-the-counter. Biomerica's tests detect and monitor medical problems including allergies, cancer, infectious disease, diabetes, and other chronic diseases. Prior to 2006 Biomerica had a controlling interest in Lancer Orthodontics, which makes orthodontic products including arch wires, lingual attachments, and buccal tubes. The company lost its control of Lancer in 2005, however, and no longer counts the company's income as its own. Biomerica has manufacturing facilities in California and Mexico.

	Annual Growth	5/03	5/04	5/05	5/06	5/07
Sales ($ mil.)	(10.6%)	9.1	9.2	9.3	7.2	5.8
Net income ($ mil.)	—	(0.3)	(0.2)	0.2	0.2	0.5
Market value ($ mil.)	17.6%	2.5	3.2	2.5	2.4	4.8
Employees	—	—	—	62	—	—

BIOMET, INC.

56 E. Bell Dr.
Warsaw, IN 46582
Phone: 574-267-6639
Fax: 574-267-8137
Web: www.biomet.com

CEO: Jeffrey R. Binder
CFO: Daniel P. (Dan) Florin
HR: Darlene K. Whaley
FYE: May 31
Type: Private

When the leg bone and the knee bone don't connect so well anymore, Biomet may have a solution. Orthopedic specialists use the medical devices made by Biomet, whose wares include reconstructive products (hips, knees, and shoulders), fixation devices (bone screws and pins), orthopedic support devices, dental implants, and operating-room supplies. Through its EBI subsidiary, the firm also sells electrical bone-growth stimulators and external devices, which are attached to bone and protrude from the skin. Subsidiary Biomet Microfixation markets implants and bone substitute material for craniomaxillofacial surgery. In 2007 Biomet was acquired by a group of private equity firms for more than $11 billion.

	Annual Growth	5/03	5/04	5/05	5/06	5/07
Sales ($ mil.)	11.0%	1,390.3	1,615.3	1,879.9	2,025.7	2,107.4
Net income ($ mil.)	4.0%	286.7	325.6	351.6	405.9	335.9
Employees	3.3%	—	—	6,100	4,075	6,506

BIOMIMETIC THERAPEUTICS, INC.

NASDAQ (GM): BMTI

389-A Nichol Mill Ln.
Franklin, TN 37067
Phone: 615-844-1280
Fax: 615-844-1281
Web: www.biomimetics.com

CEO: Samuel E. Lynch
CFO: Lawrence E. (Larry) Bullock
HR: –
FYE: December 31
Type: Public

BioMimetic Therapeutics' GEM might not attract the attention of admirers, but it does attract cells promoting tissue and bone growth when it is applied to damaged tissue or a bone fracture. The company's lead product candidates, orthopedic bone grafts GEM OS1 and GEM OS2, are combination drug and medical devices that contain a human tissue growth factor with a synthetic bone matrix. BioMimetic Therapeutics is hoping to develop the GEM technology as a treatment for various fractures, where its bone matrix can be used to repair, reinforce, or fuse broken bones. The company is focused on orthopedic, spine, and sports injuries. The company has sold its commercial GEM 21S dental product.

	Annual Growth	12/03	12/04	12/05	12/06	12/07
Sales ($ mil.)	84.8%	0.6	5.6	4.5	4.1	7.0
Net income ($ mil.)	—	(4.0)	(1.0)	(11.7)	(17.1)	(24.6)
Market value ($ mil.)	54.4%	—	—	—	206.4	318.8
Employees	—	—	—	—	—	—

BIOPHAN TECHNOLOGIES, INC.

OTC: BIPH

15 Schoen Pl.
Pittsford, NY 14534
Phone: 585-267-4800
Fax: –
Web: www.biophan.com

CEO: John F. Lanzafame
CFO: Robert J. Wood
HR: –
FYE: February 28
Type: Public

Biophan Technologies appreciates high visibility and smooth circulation. The firm develops blood circulation support systems and technologies to help make medical devices compatible with MRI (magnetic resonance imaging) equipment. The company's majority-owned Myotech unit is developing a system to restore and sustain blood flow in patients with acute heart failure. The system is based on a device that even a general surgeon can fit directly on a patient's heart to restart its pumping. Biophan's other technologies improve the visibility of coronary stents and vena cava filters in MRIs.

	Annual Growth	2/04	2/05	2/06	2/07	2/08
Sales ($ mil.)	242.1%	—	—	1.0	1.0	11.7
Net income ($ mil.)	—	—	—	(14.5)	(17.7)	(5.2)
Market value ($ mil.)	(77.3%)	—	—	126.1	32.3	6.5
Employees	(4.3%)	—	—	23	22	—

BIOPURE CORPORATION

NASDAQ (GM): BPUR

11 Hurley St.
Cambridge, MA 02141
Phone: 617-234-6500
Fax: 617-234-6505
Web: www.biopure.com

CEO: Zafiris G. Zafirelis
CFO: David A. Butler
HR: –
FYE: October 31
Type: Public

We don't need no stinkin' transfusions! Biopure eliminates that need through its products, dubbed oxygen therapeutics, which are designed to deliver oxygen to cells via the bloodstream. Its Hemopure, for humans, and FDA-approved Oxyglobin, for dogs, release more oxygen to tissues than a blood transfusion, due to the fact that the molecules are 1,000 times smaller than red blood cells, the normal carriers of oxygen. The products are made of purified and processed cow blood, can be stored at room temperature for three years, do not require blood typing, and are screened for potential pathogens such as those related to HIV, hepatitis, and mad cow disease.

	Annual Growth	10/03	10/04	10/05	10/06	10/07
Sales ($ mil.)	(10.2%)	4.0	3.8	2.1	1.7	2.6
Net income ($ mil.)	—	(47.0)	(41.7)	(28.7)	(26.5)	(36.3)
Market value ($ mil.)	(63.3%)	923.7	155.3	24.4	40.0	16.7
Employees	13.3%	—	—	67	—	86

BIO-RAD LABORATORIES, INC.

AMEX: BIO

1000 Alfred Nobel Dr.
Hercules, CA 94547
Phone: 510-724-7000
Fax: 510-741-5815
Web: www.bio-rad.com

CEO: Norman Schwartz
CFO: Christine A. Tsingos
HR: Colleen Corey
FYE: December 31
Type: Public

Bio-Rad Laboratories makes a most excellent array of diagnostic testing systems and life science research instruments. Among its more than 8,000 products are equipment and reagents used in monitoring diabetes, detecting antibiotic-resistant infections in hospital patients, and diagnosing autoimmune disease. It sells these diagnostic products primarily to hospital and reference laboratories. Its life sciences segment makes laboratory equipment — including tools used for imaging, gene transfer, and chromatography — used by medical researchers at drug companies, university labs, and government research facilities. The Schwartz family owns about a third of the company.

	Annual Growth	12/03	12/04	12/05	12/06	12/07
Sales ($ mil.)	9.9%	1,003.4	1,090.0	1,181.0	1,273.9	1,461.1
Net income ($ mil.)	5.1%	76.2	68.2	81.6	103.3	93.0
Market value ($ mil.)	17.4%	1,194.3	1,204.6	1,395.0	1,782.0	2,267.0
Employees	10.9%	—	—	5,200	5,400	6,400

BIO-REFERENCE LABORATORIES, INC.

NASDAQ (GS): BRLI

481 Edward H. Ross Dr.
Elmwood Park, NJ 07407
Phone: 201-791-2600
Fax: 201-791-1941
Web: www.bioreference.com

CEO: Marc D. Grodman
CFO: Sam Singer Sr.
HR: –
FYE: October 31
Type: Public

Bio-Reference Laboratories has tested positive as the lab of choice for many in the Northeast. Primarily serving the greater New York Metropolitan Area, the company offers routine clinical tests, including Pap smears, pregnancy tests, cholesterol checks, and blood cell counts. Through its GenPath business unit, it also performs more sophisticated "esoteric" testing in areas such as cancer pathology and molecular diagnostics. It gets most of its orders (about 3.5 million per year) from doctors' offices, collecting specimens at about 50 patient centers scattered throughout its service area in New York and New Jersey. It also does some business in Connecticut and Pennsylvania.

	Annual Growth	10/03	10/04	10/05	10/06	10/07
Sales ($ mil.)	23.1%	109.0	136.2	163.9	193.1	250.4
Net income ($ mil.)	21.1%	6.5	8.5	7.6	11.3	14.0
Market value ($ mil.)	23.3%	190.0	178.1	246.1	320.3	439.3
Employees	13.6%	—	—	1,276	1,551	1,648

BIOSANTE PHARMACEUTICALS, INC.

NASDAQ (GM): BPAX

111 Barclay Blvd.
Lincolnshire, IL 60069
Phone: 847-478-0500
Fax: 847-478-9152
Web: www.biosantepharma.com

CEO: Stephen M. Simes
CFO: Phillip B. Donenberg
HR: –
FYE: December 31
Type: Public

BioSante Pharmaceuticals wants to be the patron saint of hormonal ups and downs. The firm is developing topical hormone therapy gels to deliver supplemental estradiol, progestogen, or testosterone. Lead product Elestrin has received its FDA approval to treat menopausal symptoms in women. The company's other product candidates still in development include gels that treat female sexual dysfunction (LibiGel) and testosterone deficiency in men (Bio-T-Gel). BioSante has licensed to Solvay Pharmaceuticals its Bio-E/P-Gel, a combination of estrogen and progestogen to help menopausal women.

	Annual Growth	12/03	12/04	12/05	12/06	12/07
Sales ($ mil.)	49.5%	0.1	0.1	0.3	14.4	0.5
Net income ($ mil.)	—	(6.0)	(12.0)	(9.6)	2.8	(7.6)
Market value ($ mil.)	15.9%	56.1	103.9	69.4	63.6	101.3
Employees	(42.9%)	—	—	14	8	—

BIOSCRIP, INC.

NASDAQ (GM): BIOS

100 Clearbrook Rd.
Elmsford, NY 10523
Phone: 914-460-1600
Fax: 914-460-1660
Web: www.bioscrip.com

CEO: Richard H. Friedman
CFO: Stanley G. Rosenbaum
HR: –
FYE: December 31
Type: Public

By land, by mail, or at the pharmacy counter, BioScrip gets medications to the people who need them. The company distributes biotech and other high-cost drugs (including injectable and intravenous drugs) to patients with chronic and life-threatening diseases such as HIV, multiple sclerosis, and cancer. It distributes the medicines through its own community pharmacies, home delivery services, and a specialty mail order pharmacy. Additionally, BioScrip offers pharmacy benefit management (PBM) services for such customers as managed care organizations, government agencies, and self-funded employer groups.

	Annual Growth	12/03	12/04	12/05	12/06	12/07
Sales ($ mil.)	19.4%	588.8	630.5	1,073.2	1,152.5	1,197.7
Net income ($ mil.)	(22.4%)	9.1	7.0	(23.9)	(38.3)	3.3
Market value ($ mil.)	17.5%	155.4	141.9	279.7	129.7	295.7
Employees	(3.7%)	—	—	974	867	904

BIOSITE INCORPORATED

9975 Summers Ridge Rd.
San Diego, CA 92121
Phone: 858-805-2000
Fax: 858-455-4815
Web: www.biosite.com

CEO: Kim D. Blickenstaff
CFO: Christopher J. (Chris) Twomey
HR: –
FYE: December 31
Type: Private

Biosite makes truth serum for specimen cups. The company's diagnostic products include its Triage Drugs of Abuse Panel and Triage TOX Drug Screen, single-sample urine tests that indicate illegal drug use, including amphetamines, cocaine, marijuana, and opiates. The firm's Triage *C. difficile* and Triage Parasite Panels detect intestinal parasites and other pathogens. Its Triage BNP Test helps to diagnose congestive heart failure. The Biosite Discovery program is a collaborative research effort to identify protein markers for a variety of ailments. Medical diagnostics firm Inverness Medical Innovations acquired Biosite in 2007.

	Annual Growth	12/02	12/03	12/04	12/05	12/06
Sales ($ mil.)	30.9%	105.2	173.4	244.9	287.7	308.6
Net income ($ mil.)	31.4%	13.4	24.8	41.5	54.0	40.0
Employees	19.2%	513	817	905	1,003	1,036

BIO-SOLUTIONS MANUFACTURING, INC.

OTC: BSLM

4440 Arville St., Ste. 6
Las Vegas, NV 89103
Phone: 702-222-9532
Fax: –

CEO: David S. Bennett
CFO: –
HR: –
FYE: October 31
Type: Public

Clogged drains? Nothing at all! Backed up pipes? P'shaw! Grease traps full-to-bursting? No problem for the guys at Bio-Solutions Manufacturing (BSM). The company's products make use of microbes and enzymes that can be used to treat sites contaminated by such pollutants as hydrocarbons, grease, hydrogen sulfide, and ammonia. In addition to waste remediation, Bio-Solutions' micro-organisms can clean up oil spills and contaminated groundwater by literally eating away at the contaminants. The company's customers include municipalities and restaurants throughout the US. It also hopes to begin producing biodiesel at some point in the future. BSM distributes its products through subsidiary Bio-Solutions Franchise.

	Annual Growth	10/03	10/04	10/05	10/06	10/07
Sales ($ mil.)	0.0%	—	0.2	0.2	0.1	0.2
Net income ($ mil.)	—	—	(0.7)	(1.0)	(2.7)	(2.5)
Market value ($ mil.)	(29.9%)	—	14.8	10.8	7.0	5.1
Employees	—	—	—	—	—	7

An in-depth profile of this company is available to Hoover's Online members at hoovers.com.

251

BIOSPECIFICS TECHNOLOGIES CORP.

OTC: BSTC

35 Wilbur St.	CEO: Thomas L. Wegman
Lynbrook, NY 11563	CFO: Thomas L. Wegman
Phone: 516-593-7000	HR: —
Fax: 516-593-7039	FYE: December 31
Web: www.biospecifics.com	Type: Public

BioSpecifics Technologies previously made the active pharmaceutical ingredient collagenase for a topical ointment used to treat severe burns and skin ulcers; the Ross Products unit of Abbott Laboratories was its primary customer. However, because of steadily declining demand for the ointment, BioSpecifics sold the business in 2006 to DFB Biotech. It is instead developing an injectable collagenase as a treatment for a number of conditions, including skin-thickening disorders Dupuytren's disease and Peyronie's disease. The company is working with Auxilium Pharmaceuticals on these indications. The family of founder Edwin Wegman owns about 40% of BioSpecifics; Wegman died in 2007.

	Annual Growth	12/03	12/04	12/05	12/06	12/07
Sales ($ mil.)	(47.8%)	—	—	5.5	1.9	1.5
Net income ($ mil.)	—	—	—	(1.3)	(0.8)	(4.5)
Employees	—	—	—	—	—	—

BIOSPHERE MEDICAL, INC.

NASDAQ (GM): BSMD

1050 Hingham St.	CEO: Richard J. (Rick) Faleschini
Rockland, MA 02370	CFO: Martin J. (Marty) Joyce
Phone: 781-681-7900	HR: —
Fax: 781-792-2745	FYE: December 31
Web: www.biospheremed.com	Type: Public

BioSphere Medical's products are extremely well-rounded. The firm makes bioengineered polymer beads called microspheres for use in embolotherapy, a process in which materials are injected into a blood vessel to cut blood flow to tumors and other vascular abnormalities, such as uterine fibroids. Interventional radiologists inject the company's Embosphere Microspheres (approved in the US, Europe, and other international markets) in a minimally invasive, catheter-based procedure. BioSphere Medical has also developed microspheres to treat liver cancer; its cancer-fighting HepaSphere Microspheres are approved in the European Union. Sepracor owns nearly 25% of the company.

	Annual Growth	12/03	12/04	12/05	12/06	12/07
Sales ($ mil.)	20.4%	12.8	14.2	18.5	22.9	26.9
Net income ($ mil.)	—	(7.3)	(6.8)	(2.8)	(2.3)	(1.9)
Market value ($ mil.)	14.5%	54.7	55.6	121.5	120.0	93.8
Employees	7.7%	—	—	69	—	80

BIOSYNERGY, INC.

Pink Sheets: BSYN

1940 E. Devon Ave.	CEO: Fred K. Suzuki Jr.
Elk Grove Village, IL 60007	CFO: Laurence C. Mead
Phone: 847-956-0471	HR: —
Fax: 847-956-6050	FYE: April 30
Web: www.biosynergyinc.com	Type: Public

Biosynergy does its part to keep the good blood good. Biosynergy makes disposable laboratory, medical, and industrial thermometric and thermographic cholesteric liquid crystal devices, most of which are used in blood banks to keep blood healthy and at the right temperature. The company also distributes blood bank and laboratory products made by third parties. In addition, Biosynergy is developing antibacterial compounds for use in food and other products. The company sells its products to hospitals, laboratories, product dealers, and clinical end-users. Chairman, president, and CEO Fred Suzuki controls about 35% of the company.

	Annual Growth	4/03	4/04	4/05	4/06	4/07
Sales ($ mil.)	9.3%	0.7	0.7	0.8	0.8	1.0
Net income ($ mil.)	—	0.0	0.0	0.0	0.0	0.1
Employees	11.9%	5	6	—	7	—

BIOTEL, INC.

OTC: BTEL

11481 Rupp Drive	CEO: B. Steven (Steve) Springrose
Burnsville, MN 55337	CFO: Judy E. Naus
Phone: 952-890-5135	HR: —
Fax: 952-882-6550	FYE: June 30
Web: www.biotelinc.com	Type: Public

Biotel can tell you how your body is doing by reading your vital signs. Through its subsidiaries, such as Advanced Biosensor, Biotel manufactures and distributes various medical devices and patient monitoring systems along with custom-built software that is needed to operate such medical equipment. Subsidiary Braemar is a leading maker of portable electrocardiogram (ECG) devices such as Holter recorders and also makes liposuction and ultrasound components. Most of the company's products are made for and marketed through other medical device makers; customers also include hospitals and clinics. Biotel provides data management services for clinical trials through Agility Centralized Research.

	Annual Growth	6/03	6/04	6/05	6/06	6/07
Sales ($ mil.)	7.5%	8.4	9.3	10.2	10.2	11.2
Net income ($ mil.)	(13.7%)	0.9	1.1	0.4	0.4	0.5
Market value ($ mil.)	30.4%	—	—	5.3	5.0	9.0
Employees	—	—	48	—	—	—

BIOTIME, INC.

OTC: BTIM

6121 Hollis St.	CEO: Michael D. West
Emeryville, CA 94608	CFO: Hal Sternberg
Phone: 510-350-2940	HR: —
Fax: 510-350-2948	FYE: December 31
Web: www.biotimeinc.com	Type: Public

After a long day in surgery, it's BioTime. Actually, BioTime is more useful *during* a long day of surgery, with its water-based solutions to prevent massive blood loss after traumatic injury, preserve organs for transplant, and replace blood during such procedures as cardiac bypass. BioTime's Hextend has received FDA approval to maintain blood volume during surgery. The firm is also developing PentaLyte, a version of the blood volume replacement product that metabolizes more quickly, and HetaCool, intended to replace blood volume in cryosurgery and preserve donated organs. Hospira distributes Hextend in the US and Canada, and CJ markets the drug in South Korea.

	Annual Growth	12/03	12/04	12/05	12/06	12/07
Sales ($ mil.)	13.6%	0.6	0.7	0.9	1.2	1.0
Net income ($ mil.)	—	(1.7)	(3.1)	(2.1)	(1.9)	(1.4)
Market value ($ mil.)	(15.9%)	18.8	26.9	6.9	6.0	9.4
Employees	—	—	—	—	—	—

BIRCH TELECOM, INC.

2300 Main St., 6th Fl.	CEO: Stephen Dubé
Kansas City, MO 64108	CFO: Thomas A. Peterson
Phone: 816-300-3000	HR: —
Fax: 816-300-3291	FYE: December 31
Web: www.birch.com	Type: Subsidiary

Birch Telecom's bark has been worse than its bite. Operating in the back yards of two Baby Bells — BellSouth and AT&T Inc. (formerly SBC Communications) — Birch Telecom offers alternative local access and long-distance voice services as well as Internet access primarily to small and midsized businesses. The carrier has struggled under regulations passed by the Federal Communications Commission in 2005 which restricted access to local phone lines. As a result, Birch Telecom in early 2006 emerged for the second time from Chapter 11 bankruptcy protection (it previously reorganized under Chapter 11 in 2002). In 2008 the company was acquired by Access Integrated Networks.

An in-depth profile of this company is available to Hoover's Online members at hoovers.com.

BIRDS EYE FOODS, INC.

90 Linden Oaks
Rochester, NY 14625
Phone: 585-383-1850
Fax: 585-385-2857
Web: www.birdseyefoods.com

CEO: Neil Harrison
CFO: Earl L. Powers
HR: –
FYE: Last Saturday in June
Type: Private

Whether from a bird's eye or with eyes on the bottom line, the view is excellent at Birds Eye Foods. As the #1 US maker of frozen vegetables, the company's namesake brand is the market leader, offering some 500 different products. The company also makes pie fillings (Comstock, Wilderness), chili and chili ingredients (Brooks, Nalley), salad dressings (Bernstein's, Nalley), and salty snacks (Husman's, Snyder of Berlin, Tim's). In addition to the retail food sector, the company also supplies foodservice and industrial-market customers. Birds Eye is owned by investment firm Vestar Capital Partners.

	Annual Growth	6/02	6/03	6/04	6/05	6/06
Sales ($ mil.)	(2.1%)	1,010.5	878.3	843.4	858.7	927.8
Net income ($ mil.)	—	(130.7)	20.8	31.9	18.6	14.7
Employees	(9.7%)	4,000	3,200	2,750	2,730	2,660

BIRKENSTOCK DISTRIBUTION USA, INC.

6 Hamilton Landing
Novato, CA 94949
Phone: 415-884-3200
Fax: 888-937-2475
Web: www.birkenstockusa.com

CEO: Gene Kunde
CFO: Desiree Hartdidker
HR: –
FYE: September 30
Type: Private

You can walk from Woodstock to the stock market in your Birkenstocks. Birkenstock USA (formerly Birkenstock Distribution USA) is the exclusive US importer and distributor of the German-made footwear that was transformed from cult status to mainstream hip as the look of the 1970s re-emerged. The company's high-comfort products include more than 400 styles of shoes, sandals, clogs, and arch supports for men, women, and children, all designed around the concept that the shape of the shoe should follow the shape of the foot. Birkenstock sells shoes through more than 1,800 retailers and more than 200 licensed specialty shops. Birkenstock employees own 100% of the company.

	Annual Growth	9/03	9/04	9/05	9/06	9/07
Est. sales ($ mil.)	—	—	—	—	—	56.3
Employees	—	—	—	—	—	200

BIRLASOFT INC.

2035 Lincoln Hwy., 2nd Fl.
Edison, NJ 08817
Phone: 732-287-5000
Fax: 732-287-5559
Web: www.birlasoft.com

CEO: Kamal Mansharamani
CFO: K. S. (Ananth) Ananthanarayanan
HR: Narendra (Naren) Puppala
FYE: March 31
Type: Private

Birlasoft is more than willing to handle all of the heavy information technology lifting, so that you can focus on more important business matters. The company is an IT outsourcing company for customers in the financial services, retail, health care, software, and manufacturing industries. It offers consulting, project management, systems integration, network design, application development, support, and training. The company has development centers in Australia, India, Singapore, Europe, and the US. Birlasoft is the technology services division of the $1.2 billion CK Birla Group and has received funding from GE Equity.

	Annual Growth	3/03	3/04	3/05	3/06	3/07
Est. sales ($ mil.)	—	—	—	—	—	104.0
Employees	—	—	—	—	—	3,500

BIRNER DENTAL MANAGEMENT SERVICES, INC.

NASDAQ (CM): BDMS

3801 E. Florida Ave., Ste. 508
Denver, CO 80210
Phone: 303-691-0680
Fax: 303-691-0889
Web: www.bdms-perfectteeth.com

CEO: Frederic W. J. Birner
CFO: Dennis N. Genty
HR: Laura Marshall
FYE: December 31
Type: Public

Birner Dental Management Services hopes to leave its customers smiling. The company acquires, develops, and manages dental practice networks, freeing dentists of their administrative duties by providing management services such as billing, accounting, and marketing. Birner Dental manages about 60 offices under the Perfect Teeth brand name; more than 40 of the practices are located in Colorado, and the rest are in Arizona and New Mexico. Some locations offer special services such as orthodontics, oral surgery, and periodontics. Brothers and co-founders Frederic (chairman and CEO) and Mark (president) Birner together own more than one-quarter of the company.

	Annual Growth	12/03	12/04	12/05	12/06	12/07
Sales ($ mil.)	7.7%	30.3	32.2	36.7	39.4	40.8
Net income ($ mil.)	18.9%	1.2	1.4	2.2	2.3	2.4
Market value ($ mil.)	55.1%	7.9	11.9	47.5	40.4	45.5
Employees	—	—	—	531	—	—

BISON BUILDING MATERIALS, LTD.

1445 W. Sam Houston Pkwy. North
Houston, TX 77043
Phone: 713-467-6700
Fax: 713-935-1223
Web: www.bisonbuilding.com

CEO: Tom Tolleson
CFO: Gary Turner
HR: –
FYE: April 30
Type: Private

As its name implies, Bison Building Materials is a company with both bison and building materials. It provides lumber and building materials to primarily residential contractors and remodelers through nearly 20 locations in the Houston area and Central Texas, as well as Arizona, Colorado, Nevada, and New Mexico. Besides lumber and plywood, Bison Building Materials specializes in engineered wood products, such as flooring and structural beams, fiberglass insulation, and millwork. Affiliated with the company is a ranch at Frio Canyon, Texas, with up to 100 buffalo. Founded in 1962 by Roy W. Bierschwale, Bison Building Materials is still owned by the Bierschwale family.

	Annual Growth	4/03	4/04	4/05	4/06	4/07
Est. sales ($ mil.)	—	—	—	—	—	401.4
Employees	—	—	—	—	—	600

BISSELL HOMECARE, INC.

2345 Walker St. NW
Grand Rapids, MI 49544
Phone: 616-453-4451
Fax: 616-453-1383
Web: www.bissell.com

CEO: Mark J. Bissell
CFO: Daniel T. Caldon
HR: Daniel Jones
FYE: December 31
Type: Private

BISSELL's in the business of seeing spots and taking care of dust bunnies. A pioneer in the carpet-cleaning industry, BISSELL Homecare makes a full line of vacuum cleaners, sweepers, steam cleaners, deep cleaners, and cleaning chemicals for home use. Its models include the Powersteamer, Little Green, and Spotlifter machines. The firm sells its products worldwide under the BISSELL brand name, through mass merchandisers (Best Buy, Target, Wal-Mart), home centers (Lowe's, Home Depot), and hardware stores (Ace Hardware). Its product also are sold online at BISSELL.com. Founded in 1876 by Melville and Anna Bissell, the company is still owned and operated by the Bissell family.

An in-depth profile of this company is available to Hoover's Online members at hoovers.com.

253

BITSTREAM INC.

NASDAQ (CM): BITS

245 1st St., 17th Fl.
Cambridge, MA 02142
Phone: 617-497-6222
Fax: 617-868-0784
Web: www.bitstream.com

CEO: Anna M. Chagnon
CFO: James P. (Jim) Dore
HR: –
FYE: December 31
Type: Public

Bitstream counts on its fonts to keep business flowing. The company develops software that creates and manages typefaces. It has a library of more than 500 fonts and develops technology for delivering typographic capabilities to hardware, software, and Web applications. Bitstream also develops browser software for mobile handsets. Its products include the ThunderHawk browser, as well as text distribution applications (TrueDoc). Subsidiary Pageflex offers publishing software that designs and creates custom business documents based on customer profiles. Bitstream's MyFonts.com subsidiary offers a Web site for locating, testing, and purchasing different fonts.

	Annual Growth	12/03	12/04	12/05	12/06	12/07
Sales ($ mil.)	24.9%	9.7	11.6	15.6	20.3	23.6
Net income ($ mil.)	—	(1.2)	(0.6)	1.0	3.2	4.0
Market value ($ mil.)	24.7%	26.3	23.2	32.7	80.9	63.6
Employees	8.1%	—	—	62	67	—

BIW LIMITED

AMEX: BIW

230 Beaver St.
Ansonia, CT 06401
Phone: 203-735-1888
Fax: 203-732-2616
Web: www.buiweb.com

CEO: David Silverstone
CFO: Anthony DiSalvo
HR: –
FYE: December 31
Type: Public

Holding company BIW (formerly Birmingham Utilities) helps keep people and plants alive in south central Connecticut, including the towns of Ansonia, Derby, and Seymour, and in eastern Connecticut. Nonregulated subsidiary Birmingham H2O Services contracts to provide water-related services for other utilities. The company supplies water to about 11,500 residential and business customers through its Birmingham Utilities unit, which in 2007 it agreed to sell to the South Central Connecticut Regional Water Authority for $40 million.

	Annual Growth	12/02	12/03	12/04	12/05	*12/06
Sales ($ mil.)	18.0%	4.8	6.4	9.9	9.1	9.3
Net income ($ mil.)	(6.9%)	0.8	0.8	0.5	0.7	0.6
Employees	29.1%	20	—	—	43	—

*Most recent year available

⊞ BJ SERVICES COMPANY

NYSE: BJS

4601 Westway Park Blvd.
Houston, TX 77092
Phone: 713-462-4239
Fax: 713-895-5851
Web: www.bjservices.com

CEO: James W. Stewart
CFO: Jeffrey E. (Jeff) Smith
HR: Susan E. Douget
FYE: September 30
Type: Public

BJ Services keeps the pressure on oil production. Along with Halliburton and Schlumberger, the company is one of the top providers of pressure-pumping services used to protect the oil formation. BJ Services stimulates production through acidizing, cementing, coiled tubing, fracturing, and sand control. Its oilfield services include casing and tubular services, process and pipeline services, production chemicals, completion tools, and completion fluids services. The company operates onshore and offshore in most of the world's major oil and gas producing regions. In 2007 BJ Services began operation of stimulation vessels in India and began fracturing work in Australia.

	Annual Growth	9/03	9/04	9/05	9/06	9/07
Sales ($ mil.)	22.4%	2,142.9	2,601.0	3,243.2	4,367.9	4,802.4
Net income ($ mil.)	41.5%	188.2	361.0	453.0	804.6	753.6
Market value ($ mil.)	30.2%	2,704.7	4,241.8	11,639.6	8,833.9	7,774.5
Employees	10.8%	—	—	13,600	16,000	16,700

B.J. TIDWELL INDUSTRIES, INC.

3215 N. Panam Expwy.
San Antonio, TX 78219
Phone: 210-225-0290
Fax: 210-212-5823

CEO: Bryan W. Tidwell
CFO: Kim James
HR: Richard Serrano
FYE: December 31
Type: Private

B.J. Tidwell Industries manufactures and distributes bath and kitchen cabinets through its Cardell Kitchen & Bath division, doing business as Cardell Cabinetry. The company offers a wide range of cabinet styles made from cherry, oak, hickory, and maple woods, for custom design flexibility. Product lines include the Coventry series, the Odyssey Collection, and the 360 series. The company primarily sells to customers in the new home construction market and in the repair and remodel markets throughout the US. It operates plants in San Antonio and El Campo, Texas. President Bill Tidwell established B.J. Tidwell in 1965.

	Annual Growth	12/03	12/04	12/05	12/06	12/07
Est. sales ($ mil.)	—	—	—	—	—	254.9
Employees	—	—	—	—	—	2,711

B.J. VINES, INC.

498 7th Ave., 21st Fl.
New York, NY 10018
Phone: 212-244-0843
Fax: 212-244-0855
Web: www.betseyjohnson.com

CEO: Betsey Johnson
CFO: John Freidman
HR: –
FYE: December 31
Type: Private

B.J. Vines, aka Betsey Johnson, is a perennial favorite among women who are funky and consider themselves eclectic, and after some 30 years in the business, the eccentric designer and her company namesake are still going strong. Betsey Johnson clothes, shoes, fragrance, makeup, lingerie, legwear, and accessories are distributed through about 50 specialty stores of the same name and department stores worldwide. B.J. Vines has expanded its product offerings and operations through about a dozen licensing agreements. Having owned a majority of the firm, Johnson sold a controlling stake to Boston-based private equity firm Castanea Partners in August 2007.

	Annual Growth	12/03	12/04	12/05	12/06	12/07
Est. sales ($ mil.)	—	—	—	—	—	13.5
Employees	—	—	—	—	—	200

BJC HEALTHCARE

4444 Forest Park Ave.
St. Louis, MO 63108
Phone: 314-286-2000
Fax: 314-286-2060
Web: www.bjc.org

CEO: Steven H. Lipstein
CFO: Kevin V. Roberts
HR: Carlos Perea
FYE: December 31
Type: Not-for-profit

BJC HealthCare operates about a dozen hospitals — including Barnes-Jewish Hospital, Boone Hospital Center, and Christian Hospital — and about 100 primary care and home health facilities in and around St. Louis. BJC HealthCare's facilities all together have more than 3,500 beds. Specialized services include hospice care, behavioral health care, and outpatient services, along with long-term care at a handful of nursing facilities. The company's BarnesCare and OccuMed subsidiaries offer occupational health care and workers' compensation services. BJC HealthCare has several hospitals affiliated with Washington University School of Medicine.

BJ'S RESTAURANTS, INC.

NASDAQ (GS): BJRI

7755 Center Ave., Ste. 300
Huntington Beach, CA 92647
Phone: 714-500-2400
Fax: —
Web: www.bjsbrewhouse.com

CEO: Gerald W. (Jerry) Deitchle
CFO: Gregory S. (Greg) Levin
HR: Thomas F. (Tom) Norton
FYE: Tuesday nearest December 31
Type: Public

The Windy City inspires the food and drink at BJ's. BJ's Restaurants owns and operates about 70 restaurants in California and about 10 other mostly Western states under the names BJ's Restaurant & Brewery, BJ's Pizza & Grill, and BJ's Restaurant & Brewhouse. The casual-dining eateries offer Chicago-style pizza, salads, sandwiches, pasta, and the company's own hand-crafted beers. Its dozen Restaurant & Brewery locations, which feature an onsite microbrewery, help supply beer to the rest of the chain. California food service distributor (and BJ's supplier) Jacmar owns more than 15% of the company.

	Annual Growth	12/03	12/04	12/05	12/06	12/07
Sales ($ mil.)	32.4%	103.0	129.1	178.2	238.9	316.1
Net income ($ mil.)	34.3%	3.6	6.3	8.4	9.8	11.7
Market value ($ mil.)	11.1%	281.0	277.4	528.5	526.7	428.6
Employees	0.0%	—	—	5,341	5,341	—

BJ'S WHOLESALE CLUB, INC.

NYSE: BJ

1 Mercer Rd.
Natick, MA 01760
Phone: 508-651-7400
Fax: 508-651-6114
Web: www.bjswholesale.com

CEO: Herbert J. (Herb) Zarkin
CFO: Frank D. Forward
HR: Thomas Davis III
FYE: Saturday nearest January 31
Type: Public

"Exclusive membership" has never been as common as it is at BJ's Wholesale Club. The firm is the nation's #3 membership warehouse club (behind leaders Costco and SAM'S CLUB) and #1 in New England, with more than 8.5 million members and about 180 locations in some 16 states, mostly in the Northeast. BJ's stores sell some 7,300 products, including canned, fresh, and frozen foods (food accounts for about 60% of sales). It also sells general merchandise, including apparel, housewares, office equipment, small appliances, and gas. Unlike its major rivals, BJ's targets individual retail customers rather than small businesses. More than half of BJ's stores sell discounted gas to members.

	Annual Growth	1/04	1/05	1/06	1/07	1/08
Sales ($ mil.)	7.6%	6,724.2	7,375.3	7,949.9	8,480.3	9,005.0
Net income ($ mil.)	4.5%	102.9	114.4	128.5	72.0	122.9
Market value ($ mil.)	7.5%	1,510.9	1,919.3	2,157.2	2,030.9	2,018.0
Employees	1.2%	—	—	20,300	21,200	20,800

BKD, LLP

901 E. St. Louis St., Ste. 1800, Hammons Tower
Springfield, MO 65801
Phone: 417-831-7283
Fax: 417-831-4763
Web: www.bkd.com

CEO: Neal D. Spencer
CFO: Brad Buehler
HR: Randy L. Hultz
FYE: May 31
Type: Partnership

BKD wants to make sure your company is AOK. The firm has offices throughout the heartland states, offering individuals and businesses a variety of accounting, consulting, financial planning, and related services. Subsidiaries include BKD Corporate Finance, which offers mergers & acquisitions, leverage buyouts, employee tax plans, and other services. Its BKD Wealth Advisors provides clients with wealth and estate planning. BKD Insurance offers asset-liability risk assessment and other services. BKD also serves clients through its affiliation with Praxity, an association of independent accounting practices in more than 65 countries.

	Annual Growth	5/03	5/04	5/05	5/06	5/07
Sales ($ mil.)	10.8%	—	—	—	287.0	318.0
Employees	18.8%	—	—	—	1,600	1,900

BKF CAPITAL GROUP, INC.

Pink Sheets: BKFG

1 Rockefeller Plaza, 19th Fl.
New York, NY 10020
Phone: 212-332-8400
Fax: 212-332-8459
Web: www.bkfcapital.com

CEO: Harvey J. Bazaar
CFO: J. Clarke Gray
HR: Susan Shanklin
FYE: December 31
Type: Public

Wanted: business opportunity for former investment firm. Contact BKF Capital Group. BKF is evaluating strategic alternatives (either a merger or liquidation). The company has no operations and only a small revenue stream (more like a trickle) from its days as an asset manager and broker dealer; it is no longer a registered investment advisor and has also surrendered its broker license. The company's primary subsidiary is BKF Asset Management, but as the company itself points out, it has no operations either. BKF Capital's search for a new *raison d'etre* was put on hold when it was named in a class action shareholder lawsuit, but the suit was dropped in 2007 and the search resumed.

	Annual Growth	12/03	12/04	12/05	12/06	12/07
Sales ($ mil.)	(56.7%)	102.7	123.5	123.2	24.5	3.6
Net income ($ mil.)	—	(8.4)	(1.8)	(15.9)	(47.0)	(5.7)
Employees	—	—	—	99	—	—

THE BLACK & DECKER CORPORATION

NYSE: BDK

701 E. Joppa Rd.
Towson, MD 21286
Phone: 410-716-3900
Fax: 410-716-2933
Web: www.bdk.com

CEO: Nolan D. Archibald
CFO: Michael D. Mangan
HR: Paul F. McBride
FYE: December 31
Type: Public

Other toolmakers would like to borrow the power tools, hardware, and home improvement products that Black & Decker has in its shed. Black & Decker is the nation's #1 maker of power tools and accessories, mainly under the DEWALT and Black & Decker names. It also makes electric lawn and garden tools, plumbing products (Price Pfister), specialty fastening and assembly systems, security hardware (Kwikset), and cleaning and lighting products (Dustbuster, SnakeLight, Scumbuster). Its largest customers include Home Depot and Lowe's, which together account for more than 10% of sales. It purchased power products maker Vector Products in 2006 for $160 million.

	Annual Growth	12/03	12/04	12/05	12/06	12/07
Sales ($ mil.)	10.0%	4,482.7	5,398.4	6,523.7	6,447.3	6,563.2
Net income ($ mil.)	15.3%	293.0	456.0	543.9	486.1	518.1
Market value ($ mil.)	3.3%	3,843.7	7,251.5	6,727.0	5,336.8	4,382.6
Employees	(4.1%)	—	—	27,200	25,500	25,000

BLACK & VEATCH HOLDING COMPANY

8400 Ward Pkwy.
Kansas City, MO 64114
Phone: 913-458-2000
Fax: 913-458-2934
Web: www.bv.com

CEO: Leonard C. (Len) Rodman
CFO: Karen L. Daniel
HR: Shirley Gaufin
FYE: December 31
Type: Private

From Argentina to Zimbabwe, Black & Veatch provides the ABCs of construction, engineering, and consulting. The international group is one of the largest private companies in the US. Targeting infrastructure development for the energy, water, services, and telecommunications markets, the group engages in all phases of building projects, including design and engineering, financing and procurement, and construction. Among its services are environmental consulting, operations and maintenance, security design and consulting, management consulting, and IT services. Projects include coal, nuclear, and combustion turbine plants; drinking water and coastal water operations; and wireless and broadband installation.

	Annual Growth	12/02	12/03	12/04	12/05	12/06
Sales ($ mil.)	2.4%	2,000.0	1,400.0	1,400.0	1,573.0	2,200.0
Employees	4.8%	7,124	6,200	6,800	7,500	8,600

An in-depth profile of this company is available to Hoover's Online members at hoovers.com.

255

BLACK BOX CORPORATION

NASDAQ (GS): BBOX

1000 Park Dr.
Lawrence, PA 15055
Phone: 724-746-5500
Fax: 724-746-0746
Web: www.blackbox.com

CEO: R. Terry Blakemore
CFO: Michael (Mike) McAndrew
HR: −
FYE: March 31
Type: Public

Black Box establishes a lot of connections. The company distributes and supports voice and data networking infrastructure. Its offerings include modems, routers, switches, and testing equipment, as well as cabinets, cables, and training materials. Black Box primarily distributes third-party equipment, some of which carries the Black Box brand, but it also manufactures select products. In addition, the company maintains technical support hotlines and provides services such as on-site design, installation, and maintenance. Black Box sells its products to corporations, schools, and government agencies worldwide.

	Annual Growth	3/04	3/05	3/06	3/07	3/08
Sales ($ mil.)	18.2%	520.4	535.1	721.3	1,016.3	1,016.7
Net income ($ mil.)	(4.5%)	47.2	29.9	37.4	35.6	39.2
Market value ($ mil.)	(13.3%)	954.4	630.0	845.3	640.4	540.4
Employees	—	—	—	—	3,300	—	—

BLACK HILLS CORPORATION

NYSE: BKH

625 9th St.
Rapid City, SD 57701
Phone: 605-721-1700
Fax: 605-721-2599
Web: www.blackhillscorp.com

CEO: David R. Emery
CFO: −
HR: −
FYE: December 31
Type: Public

Black Hills is alive with the sound of energy. The integrated energy company generates electricity; produces natural gas, oil, and coal; and markets energy. Its Black Hills Power utility distributes electricity to about 65,100 customers in Montana, South Dakota, and Wyoming and owns generating capacity of 435 MW. Its electric and gas utility, Cheyenne Light, Fuel & Power, serves approximately 72,400 electric and natural gas customers in Cheyenne, Wyoming, and surrounding areas. The company's Black Hills Energy wholesale segment is engaged in coal mining, power generation, oil and gas production (it has proved reserves of 207.8 billion cu. ft. of gas equivalent), and energy marketing.

	Annual Growth	12/03	12/04	12/05	12/06	12/07
Sales ($ mil.)	(13.6%)	1,250.1	1,121.7	1,391.6	656.9	695.9
Net income ($ mil.)	12.7%	61.2	58.0	33.4	81.0	98.8
Market value ($ mil.)	14.7%	963.4	996.4	1,147.5	1,232.7	1,666.8
Employees	11.5%	—	—	803	819	998

BLACKBAUD, INC.

NASDAQ (GS): BLKB

2000 Daniel Island Dr.
Charleston, SC 29492
Phone: 843-216-6200
Fax: 843-216-6111
Web: www.blackbaud.com

CEO: Marc E. Chardon
CFO: Timothy V. (Tim) Williams
HR: Timothy V. (Tim) Williams
FYE: December 31
Type: Public

Blackbaud's customers aren't in it for the cash, but that doesn't mean they can't use some financial help. Blackbaud provides financial, fundraising, and administrative software for not-for-profit organizations and educational institutions. Software offerings include The Raiser's Edge for fundraising management; The Financial Edge for accounting, and The Education Edge for managing school admissions, registration, and billing. Private equity firm Hellman & Friedman (controlled by director David Tunnell) owns 68% of Blackbaud.

	Annual Growth	12/03	12/04	12/05	12/06	12/07
Sales ($ mil.)	21.5%	118.1	138.7	166.3	191.4	257.0
Net income ($ mil.)	—	(0.5)	12.6	33.3	30.1	31.7
Market value ($ mil.)	26.5%	—	622.9	738.9	1,156.0	1,262.3
Employees	27.8%	—	—	1,014	1,165	1,655

BLACKBOARD INC.

NASDAQ (GS): BBBB

1899 L St. NW, 11th Fl.
Washington, DC 20036
Phone: 202-463-4860
Fax: 202-463-4863
Web: www.blackboard.com

CEO: Michael L. Chasen
CFO: Michael J. Beach
HR: −
FYE: December 31
Type: Public

Chalk up Blackboard's success to the Internet. Blackboard develops software that enables schools to create Internet-based learning programs and communities. The company's Academic Suite and Commerce Suite connect teachers, students, parents, and administrators via the Web, enabling Internet-based assignments, class Web sites, and online collaboration with classmates. The software also assists instructors with course administration and includes a content management system for creating and managing digital course content. Blackboard's software includes transaction, community, and payment management tools that enable students to use their college IDs for meal plans, event access, and tuition payments.

	Annual Growth	12/03	12/04	12/05	12/06	12/07
Sales ($ mil.)	26.8%	92.5	111.4	135.7	183.1	239.4
Net income ($ mil.)	—	(1.4)	10.1	41.8	(10.7)	12.9
Market value ($ mil.)	45.1%	—	384.7	796.4	848.6	1,175.2
Employees	27.3%	—	—	549	765	890

BLACKMAN PLUMBING SUPPLY CO., INC.

120 Hicksville Rd.
Bethpage, NY 11714
Phone: 516-579-2000
Fax: 516-579-2012
Web: www.blackman.com

CEO: Richard Blackman
CFO: −
HR: Sue Cook
FYE: December 31
Type: Private

Blackman Plumbing has everything for the kitchen — and bathroom — sinks. The company emphasizes personal appointments at its dozen or so designer showrooms located in Manhattan, Queens, and throughout Long Island, New York. Blackman stores feature kitchen and bathroom products including cabinets, countertops, faucets, hardware, showers, sinks, and toilets from manufacturers such as Delta Faucet, Grohe, and Moen. Blackman Plumbing was founded in 1921 by Sam Blackman. It is now owned by president Richard Blackman. In 2006 the company acquired family-owned Pilot Plumbing of Rocky Point, New York.

	Annual Growth	12/03	12/04	12/05	12/06	12/07
Est. sales ($ mil.)	—	—	—	—	—	70.2
Employees	—	—	—	—	—	320

BLACKROCK, INC.

NYSE: BLK

40 E. 52nd St.
New York, NY 10022
Phone: 212-810-5300
Fax: 212-935-1370
Web: www.blackrock.com

CEO: Laurence D. Fink
CFO: Paul L. Audet
HR: −
FYE: December 31
Type: Public

Now this is the kind of coal you want in your stocking. BlackRock has some $1 trillion in assets under management, making it one of the world's largest money managers. The company, which merged with Merrill Lynch Investment Managers (MLIM), specializes in fixed-income products and money market instruments for mostly institutional clients worldwide. Clients include pension plans, insurance companies, mutual funds, and endowments, foundations, and charities. With the merger, BlackRock incorporated MLIM's expertise in mutual funds and equity products. BlackRock also manages hedge funds and oversees the daily operations of publicly traded real estate investment trust Anthracite Capital.

	Annual Growth	12/03	12/04	12/05	12/06	12/07
Sales ($ mil.)	68.7%	598.2	725.3	1,191.4	2,098.0	4,844.7
Net income ($ mil.)	59.1%	155.4	143.1	233.9	322.6	995.3
Employees	54.2%	973	1,020	2,151	—	5,500

THE BLACKSTONE GROUP, INC.

360 N. Michigan Ave., Ste. 1500
Chicago, IL 60601
Phone: 312-419-0400
Fax: 312-419-8419
Web: www.bgglobal.com

CEO: Ashref Hashim
CFO: Michael Kondourajian
HR: –
FYE: December 31
Type: Private

The Blackstone Group provides custom market research and consulting services, helping clients make sense of customer behavior and attitudes as well as market trends. Not to be confused with leading US private equity firm The Blackstone Group, this research company serves clients in the US, Europe, and Asia with expertise in such industries as consumer packaged goods, financial services, health care, and technology. The group's studies encompass such topics as branding, customer satisfaction and loyalty, multicultural markets, new product evaluation, and segmentation. Clients have included the American Medical Association, Chicago Tribune, eBay, and Pfizer.

THE BLACKSTONE GROUP L.P.

NYSE: BX

345 Park Ave.
New York, NY 10154
Phone: 212-583-5000
Fax: 212-583-5712
Web: www.blackstone.com

CEO: Stephen A. Schwarzman
CFO: Michael A. Puglisi
HR: –
FYE: December 31
Type: Public

The Blackstone Group knows how to make a scene. Founded in 1985 by industry veterans Peter Peterson and Stephen Schwarzman, the once-reclusive company underwent one of the largest IPOs in the history of mankind in 2007. The massive private equity firm owns stakes in more than 40 companies, manages hedge funds and other funds, and provides mergers and acquisitions and restructuring advice to corporate clients. Blackstone closed its latest private equity fund — worth more than $21 billion — after going public. The firm made one of the largest private equity transactions ever when it acquired Equity Office Properties Trust for some $39 billion in 2007.

	Annual Growth	12/03	12/04	12/05	12/06	12/07
Sales ($ mil.)	82.3%	—	503.5	496.7	1,120.3	3,050.1
Net income ($ mil.)	2.1%	—	1,523.3	1,330.7	2,266.2	1,623.2
Market value ($ mil.)	—	—	—	—	—	5,750.0
Employees	16.6%	—	—	750	770	1,020

BLAIR CORPORATION

220 Hickory St.
Warren, PA 16366
Phone: 814-723-3600
Fax: 814-726-6376
Web: www.blair.com

CEO: Adelmo S. (Al) Lopez
CFO: Larry J. Pitorak
HR: Daniel R. Blair
FYE: December 31
Type: Private

Before you get engrossed in that new issue of *Modern Maturity*, Blair hopes you'll give some attention to its latest mailing. Through its Web site, catalogs, and letter-style pitches, Blair sells men's and women's clothing (most of its sales) to middle-aged and elderly low- to middle-income customers. It also sells home products, such as bath items, bedspreads, collectibles, drapes, kitchenware, and rugs. Most of its merchandise is made to its specifications by independent suppliers. Blair also operates a retail store and a factory outlet in Pennsylvania and one factory outlet in Delaware. Apparel marketer Appleseed's Topco (now Orchard Brands), owned by Golden Gate Capital, acquired Blair in May 2007.

	Annual Growth	12/02	12/03	12/04	12/05	12/06
Sales ($ mil.)	(8.2%)	609.2	625.5	540.8	492.7	433.3
Net income ($ mil.)	(68.0%)	19.1	14.5	14.9	31.5	0.2
Employees	(11.1%)	2,700	2,600	2,000	1,900	—

BLANK ROME LLP

1 Logan Sq.
Philadelphia, PA 19103
Phone: 215-569-5500
Fax: 215-569-5555
Web: www.blankrome.com

CEO: Carl M. Buchholz
CFO: John Seifarth
HR: Nathaniel R. Jones
FYE: December 31
Type: Partnership

Blank Rome has about 500 lawyers in about a dozen offices in the eastern US and one in Hong Kong. The firm practices in such areas as bankruptcy, intellectual property, litigation, maritime, real estate, and tax. Blank Rome beefed up its maritime practice and gained its Hong Kong office in 2006 by combining with Healy & Baillie, a firm with about 30 lawyers that also had offices in the eastern US. Through its Blank Rome Government Relations affiliate, the firm provides advocacy and communications services. Blank Rome was established in 1946.

	Annual Growth	12/03	12/04	12/05	12/06	12/07
Est. sales ($ mil.)	—	—	—	—	—	44.2
Employees	—	—	—	—	—	515

BLAST ENERGY SERVICES, INC.

OTC: BESV

14550 Torrey Chase Blvd., Ste. 330
Houston, TX 77014
Phone: 281-453-2888
Fax: 281-453-2899
Web: www.blastenergyservices.com

CEO: John O'Keefe
CFO: John MacDonald
HR: –
FYE: December 31
Type: Public

Despite some financial struggles, Blast Energy Services (formerly Verdisys) is having a blast helping its customers keep pumping out oil from mature fields. Using specially fabricated mobile drilling rigs, the company provides a range of oil and gas services, including lateral drilling and well production enhancement. It also provides satellite telecommunications services to oil and gas companies operating throughout North America. The company, which revamped its management organization following an investigation of its accounting practices, filed for Chapter 11 bankrutcy protection in 2007.

	Annual Growth	12/03	12/04	12/05	12/06	12/07
Sales ($ mil.)	(18.4%)	0.9	1.5	1.2	3.2	0.4
Net income ($ mil.)	—	(7.4)	(8.8)	(2.9)	(38.1)	(9.9)
Market value ($ mil.)	(22.6%)	—	19.1	32.8	25.2	8.8
Employees	—	10	—	—	—	—

BLISTEX INC.

1800 Swift Dr.
Oak Brook, IL 60523
Phone: 630-571-2870
Fax: 630-571-3437
Web: www.blistex.com

CEO: David C. Arch
CFO: Phillip (Phil) Hoolehan
HR: Dawn Naydenoff
FYE: June 30
Type: Private

As one of the largest lip-care product makers in the US, Blistex would like to gloss over its competition. The company's Blistex lip-care products include ointments, balms, and medicated items. To grow its brand portfolio, Blistex added new products to its existing brands and acquired new product lines — such as Stri-Dex acne treatments, Kank-A for mouth pain, Foille first aid spray, and Ivarest for poison ivy itch — in an effort to grow its business. Blistex sells its products mostly through supermarkets and drugstores worldwide. The Arch family has owned and operated Blistex since founding it in 1947.

	Annual Growth	6/03	6/04	6/05	6/06	6/07
Est. sales ($ mil.)	—	—	—	—	—	100.0
Employees	—	—	—	—	—	185

An in-depth profile of this company is available to Hoover's Online members at hoovers.com.

257

BLIZZARD ENTERTAINMENT, INC.

P.O. Box 18979
Irvine, CA 92623
Phone: 949-955-1380
Fax: 949-737-2000
Web: www.blizzard.com

CEO: Michael (Mike) Morhaime
CFO: –
HR: –
FYE: December 31
Type: Subsidiary

Blizzard Entertainment hopes to continue to produce a flurry of hit games. The company (part of the Vivendi Games group) develops and publishes video game software, including the popular *Warcraft*, *Starcraft*, and *Diablo* series available for play on PCs and console systems. Its highly anticipated massively multiplayer online roleplaying game (MMORPG) *World of Warcraft* debuted in North America to record-breaking sales in late 2004 and has since surpassed the 7 million worldwide player mark, making it one of the most popular MMORPGs.

BLOCK COMMUNICATIONS, INC.

6450 Monroe St.
Sylvania, OH 43560
Phone: 419-724-6212
Fax: 419-724-6167
Web: www.blockcommunications.com

CEO: Gary J. Blair
CFO: Jodi L. Miehls
HR: Barbara F. Gessel
FYE: December 31
Type: Private

If your block happens to be in Toledo, Ohio, or Pittsburgh, you can thank this company for delivering the daily news. Block Communications (BCI) is a family-owned regional media company that operates two major newspapers, *The Blade* (Toledo) and the *Pittsburgh Post-Gazette*. It also owns and operates five broadcast TV stations in Idaho, Illinois, Indiana, Ohio, and Kentucky, as well as cable television systems serving subscribers in Toledo and Sandusky, Ohio. Other subsidiaries provide construction and telephony services. Block family patriarch Paul Block started the family fortune when he acquired *The Blade* in 1926.

BLOCKBUSTER INC.

NYSE: BBI

1201 Elm St.
Dallas, TX 75270
Phone: 214-854-3000
Fax: 214-854-3677
Web: www.blockbuster.com

CEO: James W. (Jim) Keyes
CFO: Thomas M. Casey
HR: Dan Satterthwaite
FYE: December 31
Type: Public

When it comes to renting movies, this company is a Blockbuster. Blockbuster is the world's largest video rental chain, with more than 7,800 company-owned or franchised stores in more than 20 countries (about 60% are in the US). The chain rents more than 1 billion videos, DVDs, and video games at its Blockbuster Video outlets each year. Customers can also make rentals through its Web site, Blockbuster Online, which has taken on a more prominent role as the company attempts to fend off competitors such as Netflix. The company is closing struggling stores and has announced plans to divest its foreign operations and focus on its business in North America.

	Annual Growth	12/03	12/04	12/05	12/06	12/07
Sales ($ mil.)	(1.6%)	5,911.7	6,053.2	5,864.4	5,523.5	5,542.4
Net income ($ mil.)	—	(983.9)	(1,248.8)	(588.1)	54.7	(73.8)
Market value ($ mil.)	(11.1%)	662.4	1,065.6	429.8	620.5	414.5
Employees	(9.4%)	—	—	72,600	67,300	59,643

BLONDER TONGUE LABORATORIES, INC.

AMEX: BDR

1 Jake Brown Rd.
Old Bridge, NJ 08857
Phone: 732-679-4000
Fax: 732-679-4353
Web: www.blondertongue.com

CEO: James A. Luksch
CFO: Eric S. Skolnik
HR: –
FYE: December 31
Type: Public

Blonder Tongue Laboratories isn't involved in genetic research — the company makes equipment for acquiring and distributing cable TV signals. Its headend system wares include satellite receivers, antennas, and other signal processing devices. Blonder also makes products that distribute signals to TV sets, control subscriber access to programming, and convert microwave signals. It offers a line of concentrators and multiplexers designed for deploying telephony service. Blonder sells to distributors, private cable operators, and systems integrators that build and operate cable systems for hotels and other multi-unit buildings.

	Annual Growth	12/03	12/04	12/05	12/06	12/07
Sales ($ mil.)	(1.6%)	35.4	39.2	36.5	35.8	33.2
Net income ($ mil.)	—	(3.1)	(3.1)	(5.5)	0.3	(0.6)
Market value ($ mil.)	(19.9%)	25.7	34.5	15.6	10.6	10.6
Employees	(7.5%)	—	—	271	—	232

BLOOD SYSTEMS

6210 E. Oak St.
Scottsdale, AZ 85257
Phone: 480-946-4201
Fax: 480-675-5767
Web: www.bloodsystems.org

CEO: J. Daniel Connor
CFO: Susan L. Barnes
HR: –
FYE: December 31
Type: Not-for-profit

Blood Systems is a not-for-profit health care service company which operates a network of blood bank facilities that provide blood products and services to more than 500 hospitals in about 20 states. Blood Systems also provides blood donor testing services through its Blood Systems Laboratories facilities. Its BioCARE division distributes plasma derivative products. The company was founded in 1943 as the Salt River Valley Blood Bank.

	Annual Growth	12/03	12/04	12/05	12/06	12/07
Est. sales ($ mil.)	—	—	—	—	—	434.9
Employees	—	—	—	—	—	3,700

BLOOMBERG L.P.

731 Lexington Ave.
New York, NY 10022
Phone: 212-318-2000
Fax: 917-369-5000
Web: www.bloomberg.com

CEO: Alexius (Lex) Fenwick
CFO: –
HR: –
FYE: December 31
Type: Private

What do you do when you've conquered Wall Street? You become mayor of the city the famous financial district calls home. After leading his financial news and information company to success, Michael Bloomberg left to lead the Big Apple in 2002. The company's core product is the Bloomberg Professional, a service terminal that provides real-time, around-the-clock financial news, market data, and analysis. (Bloomberg is among the world's largest providers of such devices). The company also has a syndicated news service, publishes books and magazines, and disseminates business information via TV (Bloomberg Television), radio, and the Web. Michael Bloomberg founded the company in 1981; he owns about 70% of the firm.

	Annual Growth	12/02	12/03	12/04	12/05	12/06
Sales ($ mil.)	11.9%	3,000.0	3,250.0	3,500.0	4,100.0	4,700.0
Employees	3.7%	8,200	8,200	8,000	8,200	9,500

BLOUNT INTERNATIONAL, INC.

NYSE: BLT

4909 SE International Way	CEO: James S. Osterman
Portland, OR 97222	CFO: Calvin E. Jenness
Phone: 503-653-4573	HR: Dale C. Johnson Jr.
Fax: 503-653-4612	FYE: December 31
Web: www.blount.com	Type: Public

When you have your work cut out for you, Blount International is the one to see. The company manufactures products and accessories that can cut wood, brush, and concrete. Operating through Blount, Inc., the company manufactures chainsaws, saw bars, and concrete cutting products at facilities in Brazil, Canada, China, and the US. Customers include the farming, construction, marine, and utility industries. More than 60% of the company's products are exported outside of North America. US-based investment banking concern director E. Daniel James owns about 19% of the company on behalf of Lehman Brothers Holdings.

	Annual Growth	12/03	12/04	12/05	12/06	12/07
Sales ($ mil.)	(2.0%)	559.1	692.6	756.6	651.1	515.5
Net income ($ mil.)	—	(30.1)	6.3	106.6	42.5	42.9
Market value ($ mil.)	24.5%	242.6	783.4	748.8	635.9	582.2
Employees	(8.2%)	—	—	3,800	3,400	3,200

BLUE BELL CREAMERIES, L.P.

1101 S. Blue Bell Rd.	CEO: Paul W. Kruse
Brenham, TX 77833	CFO: William J. (Bill) Rankin
Phone: 979-836-7977	HR: Becky Plagens
Fax: 979-830-2198	FYE: December 31
Web: www.bluebell.com	Type: Private

Despite its bucolic trademark of a barefoot country girl leading a milk cow, ice cream maker Blue Bell Creameries means big business. It offers some 50 different ice cream flavors. Although Blue Bell is still a regional brand (with distribution in fewer than 20 mainly southern US states), it is one of the most popular ice cream brands in the country. In addition to ice cream, the company sells yogurt, frozen treats, sherbet, and low-fat and sugar-free ice creams. Blue Bell is slowly expanding from its strong regional base surrounding Texas, but retains total control of production and distribution.

BLUE BIRD CORPORATION

402 Blue Bird Blvd.	CEO: William (Bill) Cooper
Fort Valley, GA 31030	CFO: Keith Romundo
Phone: 478-825-2021	HR: Mike McCurdy
Fax: 478-822-2457	FYE: December 31
Web: www.blue-bird.com	Type: Private

Blue Bird is from the "old school" of bus manufacturers. The US's largest school bus maker, Blue Bird also produces commercial and specialty buses. Blue Bird's line of school buses has models for carrying as few as 10 to as many as 100 kids. A network of independent distributors sells the company's buses to school districts, churches, businesses, and non-profit organizations. Blue Bird specialty division makes security buses, shell buses that are finished out by customers, and buses for export. The company also provides financing services. In 2006 Blue Bird was acquired by Cerberus Capital Management L.P.

	Annual Growth	12/03	12/04	12/05	12/06	12/07
Est. sales ($ mil.)	—	—	—	—	—	201.5
Employees	—	—	—	—	—	1,950

BLUE COAT SYSTEMS, INC.

NASDAQ (GM): BCSI

420 N. Mary Ave.	CEO: Brian M. NeSmith
Sunnyvale, CA 94085	CFO: Kevin S. Royal
Phone: 408-220-2200	HR: –
Fax: 408-220-2250	FYE: April 30
Web: www.bluecoat.com	Type: Public

Blue Coat Systems protects and serves corporate networks. Enterprises use its proxy appliances to protect their networks from viruses and other security threats and improve network performance. Blue Coat appliances guard against inappropriate Web surfing and activities such as peer-to-peer file sharing and video streaming that tax network resources, and provide application acceleration. Its WinProxy software helps small organizations share Internet resources. Blue Coat customers have included CompUSA, the Green Bay Packers, Maxtor, Merck, the National Institutes of Health, PlainsCapital Bank, and the US Air Force. Blue Coat markets directly and through resellers and distributors such as Westcon.

	Annual Growth	4/04	4/05	4/06	4/07	4/08
Sales ($ mil.)	46.6%	66.1	96.2	141.7	177.7	305.4
Net income ($ mil.)	—	(0.3)	5.4	2.9	(7.2)	32.6
Market value ($ mil.)	34.3%	248.1	89.5	159.5	264.9	807.8
Employees	45.4%	—	336	572	—	1,033

🏢 BLUE CROSS AND BLUE SHIELD ASSOCIATION

225 N. Michigan Ave.	CEO: Scott P. Serota
Chicago, IL 60601	CFO: Kathryn M. Sullivan
Phone: 312-297-6000	HR: William (Bill) Colbourne
Fax: 312-297-6609	FYE: December 31
Web: www.bcbs.com	Type: Association

The rise of managed health care has had some of its members singing the blues, but the Blues — with nearly 100 million members nationwide — aren't complaining. The Blue Cross and Blue Shield Association is a federation of independent health insurance companies who license the Blue Cross and Blue Shield brand names. Member companies — of which there are about 40 — own the rights to sell Blue-branded health plans within defined regions. The Association coordinates some national programs such as BlueCard, which allows members of one franchisee to have coverage in other service areas, and the Federal Employee Program, which covers more than half of federal government employees, retirees, and their families.

BLUE CROSS AND BLUE SHIELD OF ALABAMA

450 Riverchase Pkwy. East	CEO: Gary Phillip Pope
Birmingham, AL 35244	CFO: Sherrie LeMier
Phone: 205-220-2100	HR: –
Fax: 205-220-6477	FYE: December 31
Web: www.bcbsal.com	Type: Not-for-profit

Blue Cross and Blue Shield of Alabama provides health insurance products and related services to individuals and employees of small and large companies who do business in Alabama. Its products include managed care plans and major medical coverage, as well as a nationwide PPO for multi-state employers. It also provides long-term care insurance and a Medicare Advantage PPO, as well as disease management services and wellness programs. The largest health insurer in Alabama, the company serves about 30,000 companies and has more than 3.5 million health plan members. It is a licensee of the Blue Cross and Blue Shield Association.

	Annual Growth	12/03	12/04	12/05	12/06	12/07
Est. sales ($ mil.)	—	—	—	—	—	984.5
Employees	—	—	—	—	—	2,533

🏢 An in-depth profile of this company is available to Hoover's Online members at hoovers.com.

259

BLUE CROSS AND BLUE SHIELD OF FLORIDA, INC.

4800 Deerwood Campus Pkwy.
Jacksonville, FL 32246
Phone: 904-791-6111
Fax: 904-905-6638
Web: www.bcbsfl.com

CEO: Robert I. Lufrano
CFO: R. Chris Doerr
HR: Robert Wall
FYE: December 31
Type: Not-for-profit

Blue Cross and Blue Shield of Florida is the state's largest and oldest health insurance provider. The company provides a wide range of health insurance products and related services to more than 8 million members in Florida. The company's health insurance products include HMO, PPO, traditional indemnity, and supplemental Medicare. Blue Cross and Blue Shield of Florida also provides accident and dismemberment, dental, disability, and workers' compensation insurance. Long-term care insurance is provided through the company's for-profit subsidiary, Florida Combined Life.

	Annual Growth	12/02	12/03	12/04	12/05	12/06
Sales ($ mil.)	—	—	—	—	—	7,470.0
Employees	—	—	—	—	—	8,500

BLUE CROSS AND BLUE SHIELD OF KANSAS CITY

1 Pershing Sq., 2301 Main St.
Kansas City, MO 64108
Phone: 816-395-2222
Fax: 816-395-2726
Web: www.bcbskc.com

CEO: Tom E. Bowser
CFO: Marilyn T. Tromans
HR: Sherri L. Enright
FYE: December 31
Type: Not-for-profit

Blue Cross and Blue Shield of Kansas City provides health care insurance and related services for about 880,000 members in 32 counties in Kansas and Missouri. Its Good Health HMO subsidiary is a for-profit health maintenance organization that serves more than 58,000 members. Another for-profit subsidiary, Blue-Advantage Plus of Kansas City, provides HMO services as an alternative to Medicaid to customers in nine counties in the Kansas City area. Blue Cross and Blue Shield of Kansas City, which was founded in 1932, is the largest not-for-profit health insurance provider in the state.

	Annual Growth	12/03	12/04	12/05	12/06	12/07
Est. sales ($ mil.)	—	—	—	—	—	1,562.0
Employees	—	—	—	—	—	1,000

BLUE CROSS AND BLUE SHIELD OF KANSAS, INC.

1133 SW Topeka Blvd.
Topeka, KS 66629
Phone: 785-291-7000
Fax: 785-290-0711
Web: www.bcbsks.com

CEO: Andrew C. (Andy) Corbin
CFO: Beryl (Bebo) Lowery-Born
HR: Beryl (Bebo) Lowery-Born
FYE: December 31
Type: Mutual company

Blue Cross and Blue Shield of Kansas provides health insurance products and related services to about 850,000 Kansas customers. The company also processes Medicare claims for the states of Kansas, Missouri (northwestern), and Nebraska. Founded in 1942, Blue Cross and Blue Shield of Kansas is an independent member of the Blue Cross and Blue Shield Association.

	Annual Growth	12/03	12/04	12/05	12/06	12/07
Est. sales ($ mil.)	—	—	—	—	—	782.9
Employees	—	—	—	—	—	2,016

BLUE CROSS AND BLUE SHIELD OF LOUISIANA

5525 Reitz Ave.
Baton Rouge, LA 70809
Phone: 225-295-3307
Fax: 225-295-2054
Web: www.bcbsla.com

CEO: Gery J. Barry
CFO: Peggy B. Scott
HR: Todd G. Schexnayder
FYE: December 31
Type: Not-for-profit

The Bayou State's largest health insurer, Blue Cross and Blue Shield of Louisiana provides health insurance products and related services to more than 1 million members across Louisiana. Established in 1934, the company is an independent licensee of the Blue Cross and Blue Shield Association and has offices throughout the state. Blue Cross and Blue Shield of Louisiana offers point-of-service, PPO, supplemental Medicare, and traditional health care plans, as well as the Blue*Saver* high-deductible plan with a health savings account. Its HMO Louisiana subsidiary offers an HMO plan that provides some out-of-network benefits. Customers include both individuals and employer groups.

	Annual Growth	12/02	12/03	12/04	12/05	12/06
Sales ($ mil.)	9.5%	1,226.9	1,351.0	1,497.0	1,626.0	1,764.0
Net income ($ mil.)	10.4%	—	58.0	81.0	111.0	78.0
Employees	1.3%	1,475	—	—	—	1,555

⊞ BLUE CROSS AND BLUE SHIELD OF MASSACHUSETTS, INC.

LandMark Center, 401 Park Dr.
Boston, MA 02215
Phone: 617-246-5000
Fax: 617-246-4832
Web: www.bcbsma.com

CEO: Cleve L. Killingsworth Jr.
CFO: Allen P. Maltz
HR: Ann S. Anderson
FYE: December 31
Type: Not-for-profit

Hobbled by its past, Blue Cross and Blue Shield of Massachusetts has worked its way back into the race. Serving nearly 3 million members, it offers indemnity insurance, HMOs, preferred provider organizations, and Medicare extension programs. The not-for-profit organization runs HMO Blue, HMO Blue New England, and Blue Choice New England (POS), as well as Medex, a Medicare supplemental plan. Blue Cross and Blue Shield of Massachusetts also teams up with other regional Blues to offer plans HMO Blue New England and Blue Choice New England, which feature discounts at some health clubs.

	Annual Growth	12/02	12/03	12/04	12/05	12/06
Sales ($ mil.)	(15.1%)	4,043.0	4,496.6	4,927.6	1,976.8	2,097.5
Net income ($ mil.)	10.9%	104.0	264.8	242.8	127.7	157.3
Employees	3.9%	3,424	3,545	—	4,038	3,983

BLUE CROSS AND BLUE SHIELD OF MINNESOTA

3535 Blue Cross Rd.
Eagan, MN 55122
Phone: 651-662-8000
Fax: 651-662-2777
Web: www.bluecrossmn.com

CEO: Mark W. Banks
CFO: Michael J. Morrow
HR: Roger W. Kleppe
FYE: December 31
Type: Not-for-profit

Blue Cross and Blue Shield of Minnesota is the state's oldest and largest not-for-profit health insurer, serving some 2.7 million members, including employees for General Mills and Northwest Airlines. The company's insurance plans include traditional indemnity coverage, HMOs (Blue Plus and Preferred Gold), PPOs (Aware), and major medical plans. Blue Cross Blue Shield of Minnesota also offers Medicare Advantage PPOs and other products aimed at seniors. Additionally, its BluePrint for Health program offers disease management assistance for those with chronic conditions, as well as other health improvement programs such as fitness center discounts and work-site flu shot programs.

	Annual Growth	12/03	12/04	12/05	12/06	12/07
Est. sales ($ mil.)	—	—	—	—	—	1,420.0
Employees	—	—	—	—	—	3,650

BLUE CROSS AND BLUE SHIELD OF NORTH CAROLINA

5901 Chapel Hill Rd.	CEO: Robert (Bob) Greczyn Jr.
Chapel Hill, NC 27707	CFO: Daniel E. (Dan) Glaser
Phone: 919-489-7431	HR: Fara Palumbo
Fax: 919-765-7818	FYE: December 31
Web: www.bcbsnc.com	Type: Not-for-profit

Blue Cross and Blue Shield of North Carolina (BCBSNC) provides health care insurance products and related services to more than 3.4 million members in North Carolina. The company's health plans include Blue Care (HMO), Blue Options (PPO), Blue Choice (POS), and Classic Blue (traditional indemnity). BCBSNC also provides dental, life, disability, long-term care, and Medicare supplemental insurance, as well as prescription drug and pharmacy services. The company's Partners National Health Plans subsidiary offers Medicare Advantage health plans. BCBSNC is a licensee of the Blue Cross and Blue Shield Association.

BLUE CROSS AND BLUE SHIELD OF TEXAS

901 S. Central Expwy.	CEO: Darren Rodgers
Richardson, TX 75080	CFO: Sherman M. Wolff
Phone: 972-766-6900	HR: –
Fax: 972-766-6234	FYE: December 31
Web: www.bcbstx.com	Type: Subsidiary

If an apple a day kept the doctor away, Blue Cross and Blue Shield of Texas (BCBS Texas) would stock up on apples for its more than 4 million customers. The reason? The not-for-profit insurer emphasizes preventive medicine to hold down the costs of operating its HMO, PPO, point-of-service, and indemnity insurance health care plans in Texas. The company's network has more than 35,000 doctors and 400 hospitals. A division of Chicago-based Health Care Service Corporation, BCBS Texas counts among its customers Continental Airlines, the University of Texas System, and Halliburton.

BLUE CROSS & BLUE SHIELD OF RHODE ISLAND

444 Westminster St.	CEO: James E. Purcell
Providence, RI 02903	CFO: James J. Joy
Phone: 401-459-1000	HR: Eric Gasbarro
Fax: 401-459-1333	FYE: December 31
Web: www.bcbsri.com	Type: Not-for-profit

Blue Cross & Blue Shield of Rhode Island (BCBSRI) provides health insurance products and related services to more than 670,000 people in Rhode Island, primarily through their employers. Rhode Island's largest health insurer, the company offers a variety of plan types, including PPO (HealthMate Coast-to-Coast), HMO (BlueCHiP), traditional indemnity (Classic Blue), and high deductible (BlueSolutions) plans. It also sells Medicare Advantage and Medicare supplemental coverage, as well as Medicaid managed care plans (known as Rite Care in Rhode Island). A not-for-profit licensee of the Blue Cross and Blue Shield Association, BCBSRI was founded in 1939.

	Annual Growth	12/03	12/04	12/05	12/06	12/07
Est. sales ($ mil.)	—	—	—	—	—	1,800.0
Employees	—	—	—	—	—	1,100

BLUE CROSS BLUE SHIELD OF ARIZONA

2444 W. Las Palmaritas Dr.	CEO: Richard L. Boals
Phoenix, AZ 85021	CFO: Tony M. Astorga
Phone: 602-864-4400	HR: Deanna Salazar
Fax: –	FYE: December 31
Web: www.bcbsaz.com	Type: Not-for-profit

Blue Cross Blue Shield of Arizona provides health insurance products and services to more than one million Arizonans each year. The not-for-profit company's insurance plans consist of BluePreferred (PPO), Blue Select (HMO), and BlueClassic (traditional indemnity). Blue Cross Blue Shield of Arizona also offers dental, vision, and prescription management plans and services, as well as supplemental plans for Medicare beneficiaries. Through its affiliate, Healthyroads, the company offers its members online health information, discounts on health care products and services, and other health and wellness programs.

	Annual Growth	12/03	12/04	12/05	12/06	12/07
Est. sales ($ mil.)	—	—	—	—	—	1,055.2
Employees	—	—	—	—	—	1,278

BLUE CROSS AND BLUE SHIELD OF SOUTH CAROLINA

2501 Faraway Dr.	CEO: M. Edward Sellers
Columbia, SC 29219	CFO: Robert Leichtle
Phone: 803-788-0222	HR: –
Fax: 803-264-8077	FYE: December 31
Web: www.southcarolinablues.com	Type: Not-for-profit

Blue Cross and Blue Shield of South Carolina provides health insurance and related services to about 1 million members in South Carolina. Its BlueChoice HealthPlan is an HMO offering managed care plans to about 200,000 members. Other group offerings include PPO plans (Preferred Blue), traditional indemnity coverage (Simply Blue), and a consumer-driven plan (Blue-by-Design). For individual buyers, the firm provides Personal BluePlans, Medicare supplemental coverage, and Medicare Advantage PPO and private-fee-for-service plans. Under the name Palmetto Government Benefit Solutions, the company administers managed care contracts for Medicare, Medicaid, and TRICARE (for military families).

BLUE CROSS BLUE SHIELD OF MICHIGAN

600 E. Lafayette Blvd.	CEO: Daniel J. Loepp
Detroit, MI 48226	CFO: Mark R. Bartlett
Phone: 313-225-9000	HR: Kathryn Elston
Fax: 313-225-5629	FYE: December 31
Web: www.bcbsm.com	Type: Not-for-profit

Blue Cross Blue Shield of Michigan is Michigan's leading health benefits organization, serving more than 4.6 million members residing in the state or employed by companies headquartered there. The company's insurance offerings include traditional indemnity, PPO, and POS plans, in addition to its Blue Care Network HMO plans. It also offers consumer-directed Flexible Blue plans paired with health savings accounts, as well as options for individual buyers and Medicare beneficiaries. The not-for-profit organization is an independent licensee of the Blue Cross and Blue Shield Association.

	Annual Growth	12/03	12/04	12/05	12/06	12/07
Sales ($ mil.)	(7.9%)	13,716.0	8,044.2	8,150.6	8,686.5	9,849.0
Net income ($ mil.)	(16.7%)	367.7	411.0	294.9	243.0	177.3
Employees	1.3%	8,500	—	—	—	8,945

An in-depth profile of this company is available to Hoover's Online members at hoovers.com.

261

BLUE CROSS & BLUE SHIELD OF MISSISSIPPI

3545 Lakeland Dr.
Flowood, MS 39232
Phone: 601-932-3704
Fax: 601-939-7035
Web: www.bcbsms.com

CEO: Richard J. (Rick) Hale
CFO: Jeff Leber
HR: John Proctor
FYE: December 31
Type: Mutual company

Blue Cross and Blue Shield of Mississippi provides health insurance products and related services to members in Mississippi. The company is the largest health plan provider in Mississippi and is an independent licensee of the Blue Cross and Blue Shield Association. Blue Cross and Blue Shield of Mississippi's managed care offerings include group (Network Blue), individual (Blue Care), and supplemental Medicare (Blue 65) health plans. Additionally, the company's Bluebonnet Life Insurance subsidiary sells non-Blue products, including life and accident insurance.

	Annual Growth	12/03	12/04	12/05	12/06	12/07
Est. sales ($ mil.)	—	—	—	—	—	386.8
Employees	—	—	—	—	—	1,000

BLUE CROSS OF NORTHEASTERN PENNSYLVANIA

19 N. Main St.
Wilkes-Barre, PA 18711
Phone: 570-200-4300
Fax: 570-200-6640
Web: www.bcnepa.com

CEO: Denise S. Cesare
CFO: J. Ken Suchoski
HR: −
FYE: December 31
Type: Not-for-profit

A licensee of the Blue Cross and Blue Shield Association, Blue Cross of Northeastern Pennsylvania provides heath insurance to some 600,000 people in 13 northeastern and north central Pennsylvania counties. The company's health insurance plans include BlueCare-branded HMO, PPO, point-of-service, and traditional indemnity plans, as well as consumer-directed offerings and Medicare supplemental coverage. The insurer sells to employer groups and individuals mainly through its First Priority Health and First Priority Life Insurance affiliates. Its dental and vision benefit packages are underwritten by United Concordia and HM Insurance, respectively, both subsidiaries of Pennsylvania insurer Highmark.

	Annual Growth	12/03	12/04	12/05	12/06	12/07
Est. sales ($ mil.)	—	—	—	—	—	408.0
Employees	—	—	—	—	—	1,000

BLUE DIAMOND GROWERS

1802 C St.
Sacramento, CA 95814
Phone: 916-442-0771
Fax: 916-446-8461
Web: bluediamond.com

CEO: Douglas D. Youngdahl
CFO: Robert S. Donovan
HR: Sheryl Guzman
FYE: Last Friday in August
Type: Cooperative

Blue Diamond Growers is one nutty business. Some 3,000 California almond growers belong to the cooperative, which is a top global player in the tree nut market. The company sells almonds and almond products, hazelnuts, and macadamia, pistachio, and other nuts to food and candy makers, the foodservice industry, and food retailers. Blue Diamond Growers has developed products such as Almond Breeze, an almond-based, lactose-free milk substitute; Nut Thins crackers; and special cuts and flavored varieties of the nuts. The co-op, formed in 1910, sells its products throughout the US and in more than 90 other countries. It operates processing plants, receiving stations, and retail nut stores in California and Oregon.

BLUE DOLPHIN ENERGY COMPANY

NASDAQ (CM): BDCO

801 Travis, Ste. 2100
Houston, TX 77002
Phone: 713-227-7660
Fax: 713-227-7626
Web: www.blue-dolphin.com

CEO: Ivar Siem
CFO: Michael J. (Mike) Jacobson
HR: −
FYE: December 31
Type: Public

Blue Dolphin Energy is trying to stay afloat in the waters of the Gulf of Mexico. Blue Dolphin Energy explores for and acquires, develops, and operates oil and gas properties in the Gulf of Mexico and along the Texas Gulf Coast. The company also owns offshore pipeline operations. Blue Dolphin Energy swam in choppy waters in 2003 and 2004, running up heavy debts in its exploration and production activities. Rising oil prices helped to improve its lot in 2005 and 2006. It reported proved reserves in 2006 of 200 barrels of oil and 108 million cu. ft. of natural gas.

	Annual Growth	12/03	12/04	12/05	12/06	12/07
Sales ($ mil.)	4.7%	2.5	1.4	4.5	4.3	3.0
Net income ($ mil.)	—	(0.8)	(2.5)	0.5	0.9	(1.6)
Market value ($ mil.)	12.6%	11.3	6.7	21.5	35.4	18.1
Employees	5.4%	—	—	9	—	10

BLUE HOLDINGS, INC.

NASDAQ (CM): BLUE

5804 E. Slauson Ave.
Commerce, CA 90040
Phone: 323-725-5555
Fax: 323-725-5504
Web: www.blueholdings.com

CEO: Glenn S. Palmer
CFO: Eric R. Hohl
HR: −
FYE: December 31
Type: Public

If you don't mind paying a premium for premium denim, Blue Holdings has some jeans for you. The firm designs, makes, and sells high-end fashion jeans, jackets, T-shirts, footwear, and accessories under the Antik Denim, Taverniti So Jeans, Faith Connexion, and Yanuk brands. The men's and women's lines are sold in upscale department stores (Bloomingdale's, Neiman Marcus, Saks Fifth Avenue) and some 1,300 boutiques nationwide, as well as in Canada, France, Hong Kong, Japan, and the UK. Blue Holdings also operates a store on Melrose Avenue in Los Angeles. Denim products account for 75% of sales. Chairman Paul Guez and his wife own about 72% of Blue Holdings' shares.

	Annual Growth	12/03	12/04	12/05	12/06	12/07
Sales ($ mil.)	(3.6%)	—	—	36.4	49.0	33.8
Net income ($ mil.)	—	—	—	5.1	(4.8)	(5.6)
Market value ($ mil.)	(64.6%)	—	—	134.2	39.1	16.8
Employees	—	—	—	134	—	—

BLUE NILE, INC.

NASDAQ (GS): NILE

705 5th Ave. South, Ste. 900
Seattle, WA 98104
Phone: 206-336-6700
Fax: 206-336-6750
Web: www.bluenile.com

CEO: Diane Irvine
CFO: Marc D. Stolzman
HR: −
FYE: December 31
Type: Public

Blue Nile helps tech-savvy Marc Antonys bejewel their Cleopatras. The company, which offers luxury-grade jewelry online at bluenile.com, sells loose diamonds, settings, engagement rings, and other jewelry made of gold, platinum, and silver set with diamonds, pearls, emeralds, rubies, and sapphires. The e-tailer, offering over 1,000 styles of jewelry, also sells men's and women's watches and accessories. Blue Nile also operates Canadian and UK Web sites. CEO Mark Vadon, a discouraged engagement-ring shopper, and Ben Elowitz, formerly of Fatbrain.com, founded the site in 1999 as RockShop.com and, briefly, Internet Diamonds Inc., before adopting the Blue Nile brand name later that year.

	Annual Growth	12/03	12/04	12/05	12/06	12/07
Sales ($ mil.)	25.5%	128.9	169.2	203.2	251.6	319.3
Net income ($ mil.)	(10.3%)	27.0	10.0	13.1	13.1	17.5
Market value ($ mil.)	32.1%	—	489.6	698.6	589.2	1,128.3
Employees	16.5%	—	—	146	161	198

BLUE RHINO

470 West Hanes Mill Rd., Ste. 200
Winston-Salem, NC 27105
Phone: 336-659-6900
Fax: 336-659-6726
Web: www.bluerhino.com

CEO: Tod D. Brown
CFO: William M. Dull
HR: Jillian Robbins
FYE: July 31
Type: Business segment

You don't have to travel far to see a Blue Rhino — the cerulean rhinoceros with a flaming snout is displayed across all 50 states in the US and Puerto Rico. Blue Rhino exchanges propane cylinders (the ones used for gas grills). Customers exchange empty cylinders for prefilled ones at hardware and convenience stores, including Home Depot, Lowe's, Wal-Mart, and Circle K. In an effort to gain greater control over distribution, the company has acquired additional independent propane distributors that deliver the cylinders to stores. The company also serves the paintball market through Rhino Power, which provides a retail-based CO2 tank exchange program. Blue Rhino is a unit of propane powerhouse Ferrellgas.

BLUE RIDGE PAPER PRODUCTS INC.

41 Main St.
Canton, NC 28716
Phone: 828-454-0679
Fax: 828-646-6102
Web: www.blueridgepaper.com

CEO: Thomas J. (Tom) Degnan
CFO: Ricardo Alvergue
HR: –
FYE: December 31
Type: Private

From its corporate headquarters and original manufacturing base in the Blue Ridge Mountains of North Carolina, Blue Ridge Paper Products makes a wide range of paper, board, and packaging products. Its paper products include envelope, form, offset, and specialty papers. The company's paperboard includes polycoated and uncoated versions, primarily for food service packaging applications. Its DairyPak unit makes gable top cartons for liquid and dry goods. Blue Ridge was acquired by New Zealand-based Rank Group for $338 million in 2007. The paper manufacturer was previously 45%-owned by its employees through an employee stock ownership plan (ESOP), and KPS Special Situations Fund owned the balance.

	Annual Growth	12/03	12/04	12/05	12/06	12/07
Est. sales ($ mil.)	—	—	—	—	—	509.9
Employees	—	—	—	—	—	2,066

BLUE RIVER BANCSHARES, INC.

OTC: BRBI

29 E. Washington St.
Shelbyville, IN 46176
Phone: 317-398-9721
Fax: 317-835-0306
Web: www.shelbycountybank.com

CEO: Russell Breeden III
CFO: Sarita S. Grace
HR: –
FYE: December 31
Type: Public

Linda Ronstadt took "Blue Bayou" to the bank, but the folks in the Hoosier State take their green to Blue River Bancshares. The firm is the holding company for SBC Bank (also known as Shelby County Bank), which has a handful of branches in Shelby County, Indiana. The banks offer a variety of deposit products such as checking, savings, NOW, and money market accounts, certificates of deposit, and individual retirement accounts. With these funds, they primarily originate one- to four-family residential mortgage loans, commercial mortgages, home equity and other consumer loans, and business loans. Blue River sold the Paramount Bank division of SBC Bank in Lexington, Kentucky to Porter Bancorp in 2008.

	Annual Growth	12/02	12/03	12/04	12/05	*12/06
Assets ($ mil.)	24.2%	95.1	198.8	206.6	221.2	226.5
Net income ($ mil.)	—	(4.5)	0.1	(0.3)	1.6	0.6
Market value ($ mil.)	—	—	—	—	—	21.4
Employees	13.0%	43	63	68	64	70
						*Most recent year available

BLUE SHIELD OF CALIFORNIA

50 Beale St.
San Francisco, CA 94105
Phone: 415-229-5000
Fax: 415-229-5070
Web: www.blueshieldca.com

CEO: Bruce G. Bodaken
CFO: Heidi Kunz
HR: Marianne Jackson
FYE: December 31
Type: Not-for-profit

Blue Shield Of California (a.k.a. California Physicians' Service) provides health insurance products and related services to more than 3 million members in the state of California. The not-for-profit organization's health insurance products include HMO, preferred provider organization (PPO), dental, and a Medicare supplemental plan. Accidental death and dismemberment, executive medical reimbursement, life insurance, vision, and short-term health plans are provided by the company's Blue Shield of California Life & Health Insurance subsidiary. Blue Shield of California has more than 20 locations across California.

	Annual Growth	12/02	12/03	12/04	12/05	12/06
Sales ($ mil.)	15.2%	4,624.4	6,202.7	6,846.2	7,518.9	8,150.0
Net income ($ mil.)	6.7%	—	314.2	334.2	329.5	382.0
Employees	1.7%	4,200	4,200	—	4,300	4,500

BLUE STAR JETS, INC.

805 3rd Ave., 28th Fl.
New York, NY 10022
Phone: 212-446-9037
Fax: 212-446-9061
Web: www.bluestarjets.com

CEO: Richard Sitomer
CFO: –
HR: –
FYE: December 31
Type: Private

Blue Star Jets doesn't do the flying itself, but the company will make sure you can fly to the destination of your choice in the type of aircraft you like best. Blue Star Jets acts as a brokerage firm, purchasing seats from other private jet companies and reselling them to customers. The company has access to thousands of aircraft from numerous manufacturers, ranging from turboprops to jumbo jets. Blue Star Jets markets its services to small and medium-sized companies and individuals. Along with arranging flights, Blue Star Jets can provide catering, concierge, and ground transportation services.

	Annual Growth	12/03	12/04	12/05	12/06	12/07
Est. sales ($ mil.)	—	—	—	—	—	6.3
Employees	—	—	—	—	—	140

BLUE TEE CORP.

250 Park Ave. South
New York, NY 10003
Phone: 212-598-0880
Fax: 212-598-0896
Web: www.bluetee.com

CEO: Richard A. Secrist
CFO: David P. Alldian
HR: –
FYE: December 31
Type: Private

Blue Tee has stayed out of the rough through diversification. The company, operating through its subsidiaries, distributes steel and scrap metal and manufactures a variety of industrial equipment. Blue Tee's Brown-Strauss Steel subsidiary is a leading distributor of steel products (beams, pipe, tubing) in the western US. Other operations include AZCON (scrap metal sales and rail cars and parts), GEFCO (portable drilling rigs), Standard Alloys (pump parts), and Steco (dump-truck trailers). Union Tractor provides replacement parts for construction and transportation equipment in western Canada. Blue Tee is owned by its employees.

	Annual Growth	12/02	12/03	12/04	12/05	12/06
Est. sales ($ mil.)	29.8%	300.0	379.2	740.7	698.8	852.4
Net income ($ mil.)	97.3%	—	4.7	36.2	22.8	36.1
Employees	—	870	—	—	—	—

An in-depth profile of this company is available to Hoover's Online members at hoovers.com.

263

BLUE VALLEY BAN CORP.

OTC: BVBC

11935 Riley
Overland Park, KS 66225
Phone: 913-338-1000
Fax: 913-338-2801
Web: www.bankbv.com

CEO: Robert D. (Bob) Regnier
CFO: Mark A. Fortino
HR: Jill Krizek
FYE: December 31
Type: Public

Protect your green at Blue Valley Ban Corp, the holding company of Bank of Blue Valley. Founded in 1989, the bank targets closely held small to midsized businesses and their owners, plus professionals and residents in Johnson County, Kansas. Through about a half dozen branches located within the Kansas City metropolitan area, the bank provides traditional deposit products, cash management services, investment brokerage, and trust services. Its lending activities are focused on construction loans, which account for about 30% of its portfolio, as well as business and commercial real estate loans, which each account for about a quarter.

	Annual Growth	12/03	12/04	12/05	12/06	12/07
Assets ($ mil.)	4.1%	626.5	672.7	689.6	692.2	736.2
Net income ($ mil.)	(5.3%)	5.6	1.9	4.6	6.9	4.5
Market value ($ mil.)	7.2%	57.4	55.9	71.5	81.9	75.6
Employees	(8.4%)	—	278	265	—	214

BLUEARC CORPORATION

50 Rio Robles Dr.
San Jose, CA 95134
Phone: 408-576-6600
Fax: 408-576-6601
Web: www.bluearc.com

CEO: Michael B. (Mike) Gustafson
CFO: Michael S. Hasley
HR: Robert A. (Bob) Harvey
FYE: January 31
Type: Private

BlueArc is redefining the network storage performance curve. The company provides high-end data storage systems used in network-attached storage (NAS) and storage area network (SAN) configurations. Companies involved in drug research, oil and gas exploration, financial services, high-performance computing, manufacturing, special effects, and other data-intensive tasks use its scalable Titan SiliconServers. BlueArc's servers, which are manufactured by Sanmina-SCI, utilize programmable chips designed by Altera. BlueArc has attracted backing from investors including Meritech Capital Partners, which owns almost a third of the company, Crosslink Capital (20%), and Morgenthaler Ventures (13%).

	Annual Growth	1/03	1/04	1/05	1/06	1/07
Sales ($ mil.)	35.3%	—	—	23.0	23.0	42.1
Net income ($ mil.)	—	—	—	(27.4)	(21.1)	(12.8)
Employees	—	—	—	—	—	240

BLUECROSS BLUESHIELD OF TENNESSEE, INC.

801 Pine St.
Chattanooga, TN 37402
Phone: 423-755-5600
Fax: 423-755-5792
Web: www.bcbst.com

CEO: Vicky Gregg
CFO: David Deal
HR: Vicki Cansler
FYE: December 31
Type: Not-for-profit

BlueCross BlueShield of Tennessee is the oldest and largest not-for-profit managed care provider in the state of Tennessee. Serving more than 2 million people, the company offers PPO and traditional indemnity health insurance plans. BlueCross BlueShield of Tennessee also provides Medicare supplement plans (BlueCross 65), as well as vision and dental plans. In addition, the company offers disease management services for medical conditions such as asthma, diabetes, and heart disease through its affiliate LifeMasters Supported SelfCare. The company is part of the BlueCross BlueShield Association.

	Annual Growth	12/03	12/04	12/05	12/06	12/07
Est. sales ($ mil.)	—	—	—	—	—	2,147.5
Employees	—	—	—	—	—	4,589

BLUEFLY, INC.

NASDAQ (CM): BFLY

42 W. 39th St., 9th Fl.
New York, NY 10018
Phone: 212-944-8000
Fax: 212-354-3400
Web: www.bluefly.com

CEO: Melissa Payner
CFO: Kara B. Jenny
HR: Katherine Stage
FYE: December 31
Type: Public

Bargain e-tailer Bluefly aims to fly anywhere but further into the red. The company offers excess and closeout apparel and home accessories for men, women, and teens via its Web site (Bluefly.com) at prices it claims are 30%-75% cheaper than retail. The site carries more than 50,000 styles from more than 350 brands, including Prada and Calvin Klein. Former chairman Ken Seiff founded the company in 1991 as Pivot Rules to sell golf apparel to young golfers. It discontinued its golf sportswear line and sold its Pivot Rules trademarks to make the transition to an off-price e-tailer. The Bluefly.com site was launched in 1998. Financier George Soros owns about 38% of Bluefly.

	Annual Growth	12/03	12/04	12/05	12/06	12/07
Sales ($ mil.)	24.7%	37.9	43.8	58.8	77.1	91.5
Net income ($ mil.)	—	(6.4)	(3.8)	(3.8)	(12.2)	(15.8)
Market value ($ mil.)	17.5%	522.2	353.6	213.5	1,670.2	995.7
Employees	12.9%	—	—	85	96	—

BLUEGATE CORPORATION

OTC: BGAT

701 N. Post Oak Rd., Ste. 600
Houston, TX 77024
Phone: 713-686-1100
Fax: 713-682-7402
Web: www.bluegate.com

CEO: Stephen Sperco
CFO: Charles E. (Charlie) Leibold
HR: –
FYE: December 31
Type: Public

Bluegate has worn many colors. The company provides information technology (IT) services to the health care industry. It specializes in medical-grade network and managed services that meet HIPAA (Health Insurance Portability and Accoutability Act) compliance regulations. It serves hospitals, medical practices, and other centralized health care providers. The company sold its ISP assets in 2004 to Maryland-based MobilePro; the next year it acquired Trilliant, a provider of technology services with a focus on the health care industry. Former CEO Manfred Sternberg holds a 31% stake; former director Robert Davis owns 20% of the company.

	Annual Growth	12/03	12/04	12/05	12/06	12/07
Sales ($ mil.)	27.4%	2.2	1.1	2.5	3.7	5.8
Net income ($ mil.)	—	(2.5)	(0.6)	(4.2)	(9.2)	(5.1)
Market value ($ mil.)	(63.9%)	152.0	1.3	4.4	11.5	2.6
Employees	—	—	—	—	—	—

BLUEGREEN CORPORATION

NYSE: BXG

4960 Conference Way North, Ste. 100
Boca Raton, FL 33431
Phone: 561-912-8000
Fax: 561-912-8100
Web: www.bluegreenonline.com

CEO: John M. Maloney Jr.
CFO: Anthony M. Puleo
HR: Susan J. Saturday
FYE: December 31
Type: Public

If blue-green makes you think of think sunny breezes and tropical waters, then Bluegreen has a time-share for you. Through its Bluegreen Resorts, the company operates some 40 time-share resorts (also known as "vacation ownership interests," or VOIs) in such popular vacation spots as Florida; the Carolina coast; the Smoky Mountains; Hershey, Pennsylvania; and Branson, Missouri. Through its Bluegreen Communities, the company develops upscale residential subdivisions and golf communities in Texas, Georgia, North Carolina, and Virginia. The company provides financing for land and time-share purchases. Levitt Corporation owns about 30% of Bluegreen.

	Annual Growth	12/03	12/04	12/05	12/06	12/07
Sales ($ mil.)	12.1%	438.5	601.6	684.2	673.4	691.5
Net income ($ mil.)	5.4%	25.8	36.5	46.5	29.8	31.9
Market value ($ mil.)	9.6%	155.7	599.5	482.1	395.8	224.3
Employees	11.7%	—	—	4,789	5,342	5,971

BLUELINX HOLDINGS INC.

NYSE: BXC

4300 Wildwood Pkwy.
Atlanta, GA 30339
Phone: 770-953-7000
Fax: 770-221-8902
Web: www.bluelinxco.com/home.asp

CEO: Howard S. Cohen
CFO: Douglas (Doug) Goforth
HR: Dean Adelman
FYE: Saturday nearest December 31
Type: Public

You won't find many building products missing from BlueLinx. Through 80-plus warehouses, the company distributes more than 10,000 building products to some 11,500 customers. Structural products, including plywood, oriented strand board, and lumber, account for more than half of BlueLinx's revenues. The company also distributes specialty products, such as roofing, insulation, molding, and engineered wood products. BlueLinx serves building material dealers, home improvement retailers, manufactured housing builders, and industrial users of building products. The company began as a division of Georgia-Pacific in 1954 and was sold in mid-2004 to Cerberus ABP Investor LLC. BlueLinx went public in late 2004.

	Annual Growth	12/03	12/04	12/05	12/06	12/07
Sales ($ mil.)	(2.7%)	4,271.8	3,672.8	5,622.1	4,899.4	3,833.9
Net income ($ mil.)	—	56.2	25.9	44.6	15.8	(27.9)
Market value ($ mil.)	(33.3%)	—	426.9	340.3	321.5	126.5
Employees	(11.8%)	—	—	3,600	3,300	2,800

BLYTH, INC.

NYSE: BTH

1 E. Weaver St.
Greenwich, CT 06831
Phone: 203-661-1926
Fax: 203-661-1969
Web: www.blyth.com

CEO: Robert B. Goergen Sr.
CFO: Robert H. Barghaus
HR: Tyler P. Schuessler
FYE: January 31
Type: Public

Blyth prefers to light up the party with one of its wicked products. Its portfolio of products includes unscented and scented candles and their accessories, portable heating fuels, gift bags and giftware, and other fragrance products, such as potpourri. As the largest candle maker in the US, Blyth sells its products under the Colonial Candle of Cape Cod, Miles Kimball, PartyLite, Sterno, and Handy Fuel names, among others. Its products are sold through home parties and retailers worldwide. It also supplies institutional customers, such as restaurants and hotels. Chairman and CEO Robert Goergen, Sr., owns about 31% of Blyth. It spun off its Dutch wholesale units in mid-2006 to be a new publicly traded company.

	Annual Growth	1/04	1/05	1/06	1/07	1/08
Sales ($ mil.)	(6.2%)	1,505.6	1,586.3	1,573.1	1,220.6	1,164.9
Net income ($ mil.)	(40.1%)	86.3	96.5	24.9	(103.2)	11.1
Market value ($ mil.)	(15.1%)	1,518.1	1,284.7	889.6	817.1	790.6
Employees	(23.7%)	—	—	5,500	4,000	3,200

BMC SOFTWARE, INC.

NYSE: BMC

2101 CityWest Blvd.
Houston, TX 77042
Phone: 713-918-8800
Fax: 713-918-8000
Web: www.bmc.com

CEO: Robert E. (Bob) Beauchamp
CFO: Stephen B. (Steve) Solcher
HR: –
FYE: March 31
Type: Public

BMC doesn't stand for Business Mismanagement Cure, but it could. BMC Software is a leading provider of enterprise management software used for a variety of functions, including recovery and storage management, business process scheduling and integration, service management, and application and database performance management. BMC provides tools designed to manage enterprise servers, speed up and monitor databases, eliminate unplanned outages, and recover system assets. It also provides professional services such as consulting and systems integration. BMC sells directly and through channel partners worldwide.

	Annual Growth	3/04	3/05	3/06	3/07	3/08
Sales ($ mil.)	5.1%	1,418.7	1,463.0	1,498.4	1,580.4	1,731.6
Net income ($ mil.)	—	(26.8)	75.3	102.0	215.9	313.6
Market value ($ mil.)	9.2%	4,365.5	3,310.5	5,393.3	7,666.7	6,198.3
Employees	(3.2%)	—	—	6,200	6,000	—

THE BMS ENTERPRISES, INC.

308 Arthur St.
Fort Worth, TX 76107
Phone: 817-810-9200
Fax: 817-810-9226
Web: www.blackmonmooring.com

CEO: Kirk Blackmon
CFO: Bill Blackmon
HR: –
FYE: December 31
Type: Private

The BMS (Blackmon Mooring Steamatic) Enterprises' services include air duct cleaning, carpet cleaning, fire restoration, water restoration, and mold remediation. The company has hundreds of franchise locations in the US and about two dozen other countries. BMS was founded in 1948 by Scott Mooring Jr. and Bill Blackmon Jr. In 1968 the duo formed Steamatic Inc., a cleaning process that was patented in 1974. After being run by the Blackmon family for several decades, Bill Sims, the former vice president of franchise development, acquired the business in late 2006.

	Annual Growth	12/03	12/04	12/05	12/06	12/07
Est. sales ($ mil.)	—	—	—	—	—	262.6
Employees	—	—	—	—	—	1,700

BMW MANUFACTURING CORPORATION

1400 Hwy. 101 South
Greer, SC 29651
Phone: 864-968-6000
Fax: –
Web: www.bmwebcam.com

CEO: Josef Kerscher
CFO: Sean Noonan
HR: Kathleen Wall
FYE: December 31
Type: Subsidiary

BMW Manufacturing Corporation serves up German engineering with a little Southern hospitality on the side. The company builds the Z4 roadster and coupe, M roadster and coupe, and the X5 SUV. The 2.4-million-sq.-ft. factory, BMW's first full manufacturing facility outside Germany and the only US BMW plant, delivers Ms, Z4s, and X5s all over the world, as well as to destinations in the US. In 2007 BMW announced it will introduce six new vehicles in the US over the course of several years. However, it's too early to tell if any of them will be built by BMW Manufacturing.

	Annual Growth	12/03	12/04	12/05	12/06	12/07
Est. sales ($ mil.)	—	—	—	—	—	444.6
Employees	—	—	—	—	—	4,500

BMW OF NORTH AMERICA, LLC

300 Chestnut Ridge Rd.
Woodcliff Lake, NJ 07677
Phone: 201-307-4000
Fax: 201-307-4095
Web: www.bmwusa.com

CEO: Tom Purves
CFO: Guenter Niedernhuber
HR: –
FYE: December 31
Type: Subsidiary

A subsidiary of BMW, BMW of North America imports BMW, MINI, and Rolls-Royce cars and motorcycles into the US and provides marketing, sales, and financial services for some 340 BMW dealerships, about 330 BMW Sports Activity Vehicle dealerships, some 150 BMW motorcycle retailers, about 80 MINI dealerships, and 25 Rolls-Royce dealers. BMW of North America divisions include BMW Manufacturing, industrial-design firm DesignworksUSA, a parts distribution center, and a technical training center. BMW of North America was established in 1975. BMW secured the full rights to the Rolls-Royce brand from Volkswagen in 2003.

	Annual Growth	12/02	12/03	12/04	12/05	12/06
Sales ($ mil.)	14.4%	9,500.0	14,585.4	14,523.9	13,690.5	16,274.9
Employees	—	1,700	—	—	—	—

An in-depth profile of this company is available to Hoover's Online members at hoovers.com.

265

BNC BANCORP

NASDAQ (CM): BNCN

831 Julian Ave.
Thomasville, NC 27360
Phone: 336-476-9200
Fax: 336-476-5818
Web: www.bankofnc.com

CEO: W. Swope Montgomery Jr.
CFO: David B. Spencer
HR: –
FYE: December 31
Type: Public

BNC Bancorp knows the ABCs of the financial world. The firm is the holding company for Bank of North Carolina, which has about a dozen bank branches and loan offices in central and northeastern portions of the state. The bank offers community-oriented services to local business and retail customers, providing checking, savings, and money market accounts, credit cards, and CDs. Its loan portfolio is mainly composed of residential and commercial mortgages and construction loans. Bank of North Carolina also offers insurance, retirement planning, and other investment products and services. BNC Bancorp acquired Greensboro, North Carolina-based SterlingSouth Bank & Trust in late 2006.

	Annual Growth	12/03	12/04	12/05	12/06	12/07
Assets ($ mil.)	32.0%	372.3	497.5	594.5	951.7	1,130.1
Net income ($ mil.)	21.5%	3.4	3.8	4.5	6.2	7.4
Market value ($ mil.)	30.8%	41.9	45.6	73.7	113.3	122.7
Employees	25.3%	—	—	142	193	223

BNCCORP, INC.

NASDAQ (GM): BNCC

322 E. Main Ave.
Bismarck, ND 58501
Phone: 701-250-3040
Fax: 701-222-3653
Web: www.bnccorp.com

CEO: Gregory K. Cleveland
CFO: Timothy J. Franz
HR: –
FYE: December 31
Type: Public

The high plains drifter might have banked with BNCCORP. The holding company for BNC National Bank has established its range in Arizona, North Dakota, Minnesota, Colorado, and Nevada. From nearly 30 branches the bank offers traditional retail banking services to individuals and small to midsized businesses. Mortgages account for more than 30% of the bank's loan portfolio; commercial and industrial loans account for more than 25%. BNC Bank also offers wealth management services.

	Annual Growth	12/03	12/04	12/05	12/06	12/07
Assets ($ mil.)	3.0%	621.5	673.7	740.0	692.3	699.6
Net income ($ mil.)	(14.8%)	3.8	3.4	4.1	3.6	2.0
Employees	(22.7%)	—	—	303	—	181

BNS HOLDING, INC.

Pink Sheets: BNSSA

61 E. Main St., Ste. B
Los Gatos, CA 95031
Phone: 401-848-6300
Fax: –
Web: www.bnsholding.com

CEO: Kenneth N. Kermes
CFO: Terry Gibson
HR: –
FYE: October 31
Type: Public

BNS has a new bag. Without any business operations for two years, the company acquired 80% of bus manufacturer Collins Industries in late 2006. Formerly Brown & Sharpe Manufacturing, BNS changed its name in 2001 when debt and a history of losses prompted it to sell its metrology instrument business (substantially all of its sales) to Hexagon AB. Included in the sale were BNS' Measuring Systems Group (coordinate measuring machines), its Precision Measuring Instruments Division (mechanical and electronic measuring tools), its Xygent subsidiary (metrology software), and the Brown & Sharpe brand name. BNS has also sold its remaining UK real estate. Steel Partners owns about 42% of the firm.

	Annual Growth	10/03	10/04	10/05	10/06	10/07
Sales ($ mil.)	(0.9%)	—	—	—	309.9	307.1
Net income ($ mil.)	—	—	—	—	8.1	0.0
Employees	—	—	—	—	—	—

BOARDWALK PIPELINE PARTNERS, LP

NYSE: BWP

3800 Frederica St.
Owensboro, KY 42301
Phone: 270-926-8686
Fax: 270-688-5872
Web: www.boardwalkpipelines.com

CEO: Rolf A. Gafvert
CFO: Jamie L. Buskill
HR: –
FYE: December 31
Type: Public

Boardwalk Pipeline Partners is in the business of interstate transportation, gathering, and storage of natural gas. The company operates through two subsidiaries — Texas Gas Transmission and Gulf South Pipeline Company — with a combined 13,550 miles of pipeline in 11 states. Texas Gas operates in Arkansas, Illinois, Indiana, Kentucky, Louisiana, Mississippi, Ohio, Tennessee, and Texas. Gulf South operates in Alabama, Florida, Louisiana, Mississippi, and Texas. Customers include local gas distribution companies, local governments, other interstate and intrastate pipeline companies, direct industrial users, and electric power generators. Boardwalk Pipeline Partners is owned by Loews Corporation.

	Annual Growth	12/03	12/04	12/05	12/06	12/07
Sales ($ mil.)	45.7%	142.9	263.6	560.5	607.6	643.3
Net income ($ mil.)	78.4%	22.5	48.8	100.9	197.6	227.8
Market value ($ mil.)	51.6%	—	—	1,227.2	2,316.3	2,819.4
Employees	(0.5%)	—	1,100	1,100	1,150	1,084

BOAR'S HEAD PROVISIONS CO., INC.

1819 Main St., Ste. 800
Sarasota, FL 34236
Phone: 941-955-0994
Fax: –
Web: www.boarshead.com

CEO: Robert S. Martin
CFO: Blair Waldick
HR: Scott Habermehl
FYE: August 31
Type: Private

Boar's Head Provisions is more of a ham than a bore. Under the Boar's Head brand, the company manufactures and distributes more than 300 specialty deli meats and cheeses to restaurants, grocers, and delicatessens throughout the US. The company has operations in Arkansas, Florida, Michigan, New Jersey, New York, and Virginia. Boar's Head products are distributed in distinctive refrigerated trucks owned by its sister company, Frank Brunckhorst Co. Boar's Head Provisions was founded in 1905 by Frank Brunckhorst, and is owned and operated by his descendants.

BOB EVANS FARMS, INC.

NASDAQ (GS): BOBE

3776 S. High St.
Columbus, OH 43207
Phone: 614-491-2225
Fax: 614-492-4949
Web: www.bobevans.com

CEO: Steven A. (Steve) Davis
CFO: Donald J. (Don) Radkoski
HR: Matthew J. Kimble
FYE: Last Friday in April
Type: Public

Bob Evans Farms brings home the bacon and serves it at the table. The company is well-known for its meat and pork products served at about 570 family-style restaurants in about 20 states. Popular for its breakfast menu, the chain also serves traditional American fare for lunch and dinner. The company sells its Bob Evans and Owens Country Sausage brand meat products through grocery stores, along with Bob Evans branded frozen dinners. In addition to its core brands, Bob Evans owns SWH Corporation, which operates Mimi's Café, a chain of more than 130 full-service restaurants offering American-style dishes served with a New Orleans twist.

	Annual Growth	4/04	4/05	4/06	4/07	4/08
Sales ($ mil.)	9.7%	1,198.0	1,460.2	1,584.8	1,654.5	1,737.0
Net income ($ mil.)	(2.6%)	72.0	37.0	54.8	60.5	64.9
Market value ($ mil.)	(6.0%)	1,083.0	722.2	1,040.6	1,304.5	844.0
Employees	(1.4%)	—	52,558	50,810	51,092	—

BOBCATS BASKETBALL HOLDINGS, LLC

333 E. Trade St., Ste. 700
Charlotte, NC 28202
Phone: 704-424-4120
Fax: 704-388-8734
Web: www.nba.com/bobcats

CEO: Robert L. Johnson
CFO: Michael (Mike) Behrman
HR: Kay Lowery
FYE: December 31
Type: Private

Bobcats Basketball Holdings hopes to take a bigger bite out of the North Carolina market than the city's former basketball team. The company, which does business as Bobcats Sports & Entertainment, owns and operates the Charlotte Bobcats, which joined the National Basketball Association in 2004. The league granted the new franchise to Robert Johnson, founder of BET, to replace the Hornets, which moved to New Orleans in 2002 after that team's unpopular owners George Shinn and Ray Wooldridge failed to get the city to fund a new arena. Johnson, though, was successful in courting the city, and now the Bobcats play host at the new Time Warner Cable Arena.

	Annual Growth	12/03	12/04	12/05	12/06	12/07
Est. sales ($ mil.)	—	—	—	—	—	30.0
Employees	—	—	—	—	—	100

BOB'S DISCOUNT FURNITURE, LLC.

428 Tolland Tpke.
Manchester, CT 06040
Phone: 860-645-3208
Fax: 860-645-4056
Web: www.mybobs.com

CEO: Edmond J. (Ted) English
CFO: Bill Ballou
HR: —
FYE: December 31
Type: Private

Bob's Discount Furniture operates about 30 furniture stores (featuring mini-golf courses and complimentary refreshments) in Connecticut, Massachusetts, New Hampshire, and four other eastern states. Bob's also offers several in-store "outlets" where customers can find discounted furniture that has been discontinued, returned, or slightly damaged. Following a 1976 motorcycle accident, company founder and president Bob Kaufman (who's something of a celebrity in the Northeast, thanks to his quirky television commercials) spent months recuperating in a waterbed. Fully recovered and inspired by his experience, Kaufman partnered with cousin Gene Rosenberg and opened up the first Bob's Discount Furniture shop in 1991.

BODDIE-NOELL ENTERPRISES, INC.

1021 Noell Ln.
Rocky Mount, NC 27804
Phone: 252-937-2800
Fax: 252-937-2978
Web: www.bneinc.com

CEO: William L. (Bill) Boddie
CFO: Craig Worthy
HR: Robert Crumley
FYE: December 31
Type: Private

Boddie-Noell Enterprises is a hearty competitor in the fast-food business. The company is one of the largest franchisees of Hardee's restaurants (owned by CKE Restaurants), with about 350 locations in four southeastern states. Boddie-Noell also operates its own chain of more than 30 Texas Steakhouse & Saloon restaurants, six Cafe Carolina locations, about 10 Moe's Southwest Grills, and a single Highway Diner. The company develops commercial and resort properties through BNE Land & Development, and it operates the Rose Hill Conference Center in Rocky Mount, North Carolina. Started in 1962, Boddie-Noell is owned by the family of chairman B. Mayo Boddie, who is also founder of BNP Residential Properties.

BOE FINANCIAL SERVICES OF VIRGINIA, INC.

NASDAQ (CM): BSXT

1325 Tappahannock Blvd.
Tappahannock, VA 22560
Phone: 804-443-4343
Fax: 804-443-9472
Web: www.bankofessex.com

CEO: George M. Longest Jr.
CFO: Bruce E. Thomas
HR: Suzanne S. Rennolds
FYE: December 31
Type: Public

BOE Financial Services of Virginia is the holding company for Bank of Essex. Founded in 1926, the community bank operates seven branches in the Tidewater region northeast of Richmond, Virginia. Targeting individuals and local business customers, the bank offers such standard retail deposits as checking and savings accounts, money market accounts, and CDs. Real estate and construction loans dominate the bank's lending activities. Essex Services, a subsidiary of the bank, sells title insurance and other insurance and investment products. BOE Financial Services is merging with TransCommunity Financial Corporation; the combined firm will be called Community Bankers Trust Corporation.

	Annual Growth	12/03	12/04	12/05	12/06	12/07
Assets ($ mil.)	6.9%	231.7	237.1	261.9	281.4	302.4
Net income ($ mil.)	2.0%	2.4	2.9	3.1	3.1	2.6
Employees	2.1%	—	—	93	—	97

BOEHRINGER INGELHEIM CORPORATION

900 Ridgebury Rd.
Ridgefield, CT 06877
Phone: 203-798-9988
Fax: 203-791-6234
Web: us.boehringer-ingelheim.com

CEO: Rich Pilnik
CFO: —
HR: —
FYE: December 31
Type: Subsidiary

The US headquarters of German drug company Boehringer Ingelheim, Boehringer Ingelheim Corporation oversees about half a dozen stateside subsidiaries that produce and sell drugs (both prescription and over-the-counter), animal health products, and chemicals for the US market. It sells its prescription and OTC products through its largest unit Boehringer Ingelheim Pharmaceuticals. Those products include treatments for HIV/AIDS (Viramune), enlarged prostate (Flomax), chronic obstructive pulmonary disease (Spiriva), and high blood pressure (Micardis); its OTC lineup features Dulcolax laxatives and gastrointestinal treatment Zantac. Additionally, the company's Roxane Laboratories unit makes generic drugs.

	Annual Growth	12/03	12/04	12/05	12/06	12/07
Est. sales ($ mil.)	—	—	—	—	—	771.5
Employees	—	—	—	—	—	6,000

BOEING CAPITAL CORPORATION

500 Naches Ave. SW, 3rd Fl.
Renton, WA 98057
Phone: 425-965-4000
Fax: 425-965-4085
Web: www.boeing.com/bcc

CEO: Walter E. (Walt) Skowronski
CFO: —
HR: —
FYE: December 31
Type: Subsidiary

Need financing for that 747? Boeing Capital, a subsidiary of Boeing, provides asset-backed leasing and lending services through two divisions: Aircraft Financial Services offers financing and leasing services for airlines and governmental customers interested in Boeing aircraft; Space & Defense Financial Services offers similar services for Boeing's Integrated Defense Systems customers. Until 2004 Boeing also provided financial services in non-aerospace areas, but it sold its commercial financing operations to General Electric for about $2 billion. Boeing Capital was founded in 1968 as McDonnell Douglas Finance, and changed its name when Boeing acquired McDonnell Douglas in 1997.

	Annual Growth	12/03	12/04	12/05	12/06	12/07
Sales ($ mil.)	(9.6%)	1,220.0	959.0	966.0	1,025.0	815.0
Net income ($ mil.)	11.4%	106.0	173.0	139.0	194.0	163.0
Employees	(8.2%)	241	183	186	180	171

An in-depth profile of this company is available to Hoover's Online members at hoovers.com.

THE BOEING COMPANY
NYSE: BA

100 N. Riverside Plaza
Chicago, IL 60606
Phone: 312-544-2000
Fax: 312-544-2082
Web: www.boeing.com

CEO: W. James (Jim) McNerney Jr.
CFO: James A. Bell
HR: Richard D. (Rick) Stephens
FYE: December 31
Type: Public

Boeing is the 800-pound gorilla of US aerospace. The world's largest aerospace company, Boeing is the #2 maker of large commercial jets (behind rival Airbus) and the #2 defense contractor behind Lockheed Martin. Boeing has two major segments: Commercial Airplanes and Integrated Defense Systems. Boeing's commercial aircraft include the 787 Dreamliner (due in late 2008), 767, 747, and the next-generation 737; military aircraft include the F/A-18 Hornet, the F-15 Eagle, the C-17 Globemaster III transport, and the AH-64D Apache helicopter. Boeing's space operations include communications satellites, missiles, the International Space Station, and the Space Shuttle (with Lockheed).

	Annual Growth	12/03	12/04	12/05	12/06	12/07
Sales ($ mil.)	7.1%	50,485.0	52,457.0	54,845.0	61,530.0	66,387.0
Net income ($ mil.)	54.3%	718.0	1,872.0	2,572.0	2,215.0	4,074.0
Market value ($ mil.)	18.8%	33,764.5	43,082.2	56,204.0	89,929.3	67,173.1
Employees	2.0%	—	—	153,000	154,000	159,300

BOEING EMPLOYEES' CREDIT UNION

12770 Gateway Dr.
Tukwila, WA 98168
Phone: 206-439-5700
Fax: 206-439-5804
Web: www.becu.org

CEO: Gary J. Oakland
CFO: Kathy Elser
HR: Elaine M. Terry
FYE: December 31
Type: Not-for-profit

Boeing Employees' Credit Union (BECU) initially was founded to serve . . . you guessed it . . . the employees of Boeing, which called Seattle home until 2001. Today, membership in the credit union is no longer restricted to employees of the aircraft manufacturer; in fact, all residents of Washington state are eligible. BECU has more than 40 locations in the state's Puget Sound region; many of them are in Safeway supermarkets. The credit union offers standard retail financial services, such as checking and savings accounts, credit cards, home mortgages, and other loans. Established in 1935, BECU is one of the largest credit unions in the US, boasting about 550,000 members.

	Annual Growth	12/03	12/04	12/05	12/06	12/07
Est. sales ($ mil.)	—	—	—	—	—	370.2
Employees	—	—	—	—	—	900

BOFI HOLDING, INC.
NASDAQ (GM): BOFI

12777 High Bluff Dr., Ste. 100
San Diego, CA 92130
Phone: 858-350-6200
Fax: 858-350-0443
Web: www.bofiholding.com

CEO: Gregory Garrabrants
CFO: Andrew J. Micheletti
HR: –
FYE: June 30
Type: Public

BofI Holding owns Bank of Internet USA, a savings bank that operates online in all 50 states. The bank offers checking, savings, and money market accounts, CDs, and ATM and check cards. Multifamily real estate loans account for nearly two-thirds of the company's loan portfolio although the bank only offers them in selected states; it also acquires them on the secondary market. Offered nationwide, single-family residential mortgages make up around 20% of its loan portfolio. Bank of Internet USA also issues home equity, automobile, and recreational vehicle loans. Insiders own more than 30% of BofI Holding's stock.

	Annual Growth	6/03	6/04	6/05	6/06	6/07
Assets ($ mil.)	36.4%	273.5	405.0	609.5	737.8	947.2
Net income ($ mil.)	18.0%	1.7	2.2	2.9	3.3	3.3
Market value ($ mil.)	(10.7%)	—	—	75.0	67.0	59.9
Employees	24.0%	—	—	26	26	40

BOGEN COMMUNICATIONS INTERNATIONAL, INC.
Pink Sheets: BOGN

50 Spring St.
Ramsey, NJ 07446
Phone: 201-934-8500
Fax: 201-934-9832
Web: www.bogen.com

CEO: Jonathan G. Guss
CFO: Maureen A. Flotard
HR: Jill Glatman
FYE: December 31
Type: Public

Bogen Communications knows how the soothing sounds of smooth jazz can make time fly while holding on the telephone. Through subsidiaries Bogen Communications and Speech Design, the company makes telecommunications peripherals and sound equipment. Bogen Communications sells telecom equipment including music-on-hold devices, unified messaging systems, call distributors, and voice mail systems. Speech Design sells a comparable selection of call processing and PBX products primarily in Germany. Bogen also makes audio amplifiers and speaker systems. Schools, restaurants, and stores use the company's line of intercom and paging systems for public address and background music.

	Annual Growth	12/03	12/04	12/05	12/06	12/07
Sales ($ mil.)	(0.2%)	55.5	59.8	56.0	50.8	55.1
Net income ($ mil.)	41.4%	0.4	2.4	4.3	3.2	1.6
Employees	—	240	—	—	—	—

BOINGO WIRELESS, INC.

1601 Cloverfield Blvd., Ste. 570 South
Santa Monica, CA 90404
Phone: 310-586-5180
Fax: 310-586-4060
Web: www.boingo.com

CEO: David (Dave) Hagan
CFO: Edward K. (Ed) Zinser
HR: Michael Ihde
FYE: December 31
Type: Private

Boingo Wireless looks at the fragmented Wi-Fi world and asks, "Why can't we all just get along?" The company sells access to a global Wi-Fi network of more than 100,000 public hot spots (located largely in hotels, convention centers, airports, and restaurants) through wholesale agreements with wireless network and hot spot operators. Additionally, Boingo offers its roaming network and software to ISPs and managed service providers. ALLTEL, Fiberlink, and Verizon Business are among its customers. Boingo is backed by such investors as New Enterprise Associates, Mitsui & Co., BT Infonet, Red Rock Ventures, and Sprint Nextel. Boingo was founded in 2001 by chairman and Earthlink founder Sky Dayton.

	Annual Growth	12/03	12/04	12/05	12/06	12/07
Est. sales ($ mil.)	—	—	—	—	—	4.1
Employees	—	—	—	—	—	37

BOIS D'ARC ENERGY, INC.
NYSE: BDE

600 Travis St., Ste. 5200
Houston, TX 77002
Phone: 713-228-0438
Fax: 713-228-1759
Web: www.boisdarcenergy.com

CEO: Gary W. Blackie
CFO: Roland O. Burns
HR: –
FYE: December 31
Type: Public

Like its namesake tree, Bois d'Arc Energy has strong roots and a flexible growth strategy. The oil and natural gas exploration and production independent focuses on the Gulf of Mexico shelf. Bois d'Arc Energy concentrates on this region because of its vast area of undiscovered reserves and because major oil companies have moved on to larger projects in the deepwater Gulf of Mexico. The company has proved reserves of 398 billion cu. ft. of natural gas equivalent (37% proved developed and 63% natural gas). Comstock Resources controls Bois d'Arc Energy. In 2008 the company agreed to be acquired by Stone Energy.

	Annual Growth	12/03	12/04	12/05	12/06	12/07
Sales ($ mil.)	27.8%	133.4	143.1	184.4	254.7	355.5
Net income ($ mil.)	11.0%	51.9	39.0	(51.7)	55.0	78.7
Market value ($ mil.)	13.9%	—	—	1,017.5	971.9	1,319.0
Employees	12.7%	13	14	20	23	21

An in-depth profile of this company is available to Hoover's Online members at hoovers.com.

BOISE CASCADE HOLDINGS, L.L.C.

1111 W. Jefferson St., Ste. 900
Boise, ID 83702
Phone: 208-384-6161
Fax: –
Web: www.bc.com

CEO: William Thomas (Tom) Stephens
CFO: Thomas E. Carlile
HR: –
FYE: December 31
Type: Private

Boise Cascade Holdings manufactures and distributes lumber, plywood, particleboard, and engineered products such as wood I-joists and laminated lumber. It also operates about 30 wholesale building material distribution centers throughout the US that sell a broad line of building materials, including those made by the company. To better focus on its core wood products and building materials distribution businesses, the firm has sold its paper and packaging and newsprint businesses as well as its timberland assets. Formerly part of Boise Cascade Corporation (now OfficeMax), Boise Cascade Holdings is controlled by the private investment firm Madison Dearborn Partners through Forest Products Holdings, L.L.C.

	Annual Growth	12/02	12/03	12/04	12/05	12/06
Sales ($ mil.)	7.8%	4,276.3	4,653.7	5,734.8	5,907.0	5,780.0
Net income ($ mil.)	—	(60.9)	(47.4)	94.2	121.0	72.0
Employees	(1.5%)	—	—	10,494	10,155	10,191

BOJANGLES' HOLDINGS INC.

9432 Southern Pines Blvd.
Charlotte, NC 28273
Phone: 704-527-2675
Fax: 704-523-6803
Web: www.bojangles.com

CEO: Randy Kibler
CFO: John Jordan
HR: Vickie Smith
FYE: Last Sunday in December
Type: Subsidiary

This Bojangles won't dance in worn out shoes, but it will cook some chicken for you. Bojangles' Holdings operates and franchises more than 375 quick-service eateries that specialize in Cajun-style chicken and biscuits. The restaurants also offer chicken sandwiches and Buffalo-style chicken wings, along with a breakfast menu. Located mostly in Southeastern states, the chain includes about 135 company-owned locations; the rest are operated by franchisees. Founded in 1977 by former KFC president Richard Thomas and partner Jack Fulk, Bojangles' is owned by an investor group led by Falfurrias Capital Partners.

	Annual Growth	12/03	12/04	12/05	12/06	12/07
Est. sales ($ mil.)	—	—	—	—	—	97.6
Employees	—	—	—	—	—	4,500

BOK FINANCIAL CORPORATION

NASDAQ (GS): BOKF

Bank of Oklahoma Tower
Tulsa, OK 74192
Phone: 918-588-6000
Fax: 918-588-6853
Web: www.bokf.com

CEO: Stanley A. (Stan) Lybarger
CFO: Steven E. Nell
HR: –
FYE: December 31
Type: Public

Will your money B OK? Multibank holding company BOK Financial will try to make sure it is! With seven principal banking subsidiaries operating in eight mostly southern states, BOK offers regional businesses and consumers a broad range of financial products and services. Through a combined network of about 190 branches, BOK Financial offers deposit and loan products and investment and trust services. Commercial loans (primarily to the energy, services, and wholesale/retail industries) make up nearly 60% of BOK Financial's loan portfolio; commercial real estate lending adds another 20%.

	Annual Growth	12/03	12/04	12/05	12/06	12/07
Assets ($ mil.)	11.3%	13,581.7	14,395.4	16,252.9	18,059.6	20,839.9
Net income ($ mil.)	8.3%	158.4	179.0	201.5	213.0	217.7
Market value ($ mil.)	13.7%	2,150.5	2,946.1	3,084.9	3,777.4	3,591.3
Employees	3.7%	—	—	3,825	3,958	4,110

THE BOLER COMPANY

500 Park Blvd., Ste. 1010
Itasca, IL 60143
Phone: 630-773-9111
Fax: 630-773-9121
Web: www.hendrickson-intl.com

CEO: Matthew J. Boler
CFO: –
HR: Dave Templeton
FYE: December 31
Type: Private

This Boler wants trucks to ride smoothly in their lanes. The holding company's main subsidiary, Hendrickson, makes truck and trailer suspension systems and auxiliary axle systems for the commercial heavy-duty vehicle market. Hendrickson's stamping division makes truck bumpers and stamped components, and its spring division manufactures steel flat-leaf and parabolic taper-leaf springs. Hendrickson sells to OEMs not only in North America but also in Australia, Mexico, and Europe. Boler, which acquired Hendrickson in 1978, has agreed to buy Texas-based Watson and Chalin Manufacturing, another maker of truck and trailer suspension systems.

BOLLINGER SHIPYARDS, INC.

8365 Hwy. 308 South
Lockport, LA 70374
Phone: 985-532-2554
Fax: 985-532-7225
Web: www.bollingershipyards.com

CEO: Donald T. Bollinger
CFO: Andrew J. St. Germain
HR: Doug F. Taylor
FYE: September 30
Type: Private

Bollinger Shipyards is a leading provider of shipbuilding and ship repair services along the US Gulf Coast. The company specializes in the construction, repair, and conversion of Navy and Coast Guard patrol boats, oil tankers, and supply and utility vessels such as barges and tugboats. It operates from some 13 shipyards, primarily in Louisiana. Bollinger Shipyards was founded in 1946.

	Annual Growth	9/03	9/04	9/05	9/06	9/07
Est. sales ($ mil.)	—	—	—	—	—	222.0
Employees	—	—	—	—	—	2,900

BOLT TECHNOLOGY CORPORATION

AMEX: BTJ

4 Duke Place
Norwalk, CT 06854
Phone: 203-853-0700
Fax: 203-854-9601
Web: www.bolt-technology.com

CEO: Raymond M. Soto
CFO: Joseph Espeso
HR: Jolsen Stetso
FYE: June 30
Type: Public

Bolt Technology's action is technology, the kind used to map out oil and gas discoveries. The company provides geophysical equipment to the energy industry. Its marine air guns help produce 3-D seismic maps for oil and gas exploration by firing high-pressure air into the water, producing elastic waves that penetrate deep into the earth. These waves are then used to create a "map" of the subsurface geography. Through its Custom Products subsidiary, Bolt Technology makes miniature industrial clutches and brakes used in airplane video systems, hospital beds, barcode labelers, and banking machines. The company's customers in 2006 included WesternGeco (22% of sales) and CCG-Veritas (15%).

	Annual Growth	6/03	6/04	6/05	6/06	6/07
Sales ($ mil.)	47.1%	10.8	14.8	18.8	32.6	50.5
Net income ($ mil.)	—	(0.2)	0.9	1.7	4.8	10.6
Market value ($ mil.)	91.6%	18.7	24.4	34.7	67.1	252.0
Employees	14.6%	—	—	86	100	113

An in-depth profile of this company is available to Hoover's Online members at hoovers.com.

BOMBARDIER FLEXJET

3400 Waterview Pkwy., Ste. 400
Richardson, TX 75080
Phone: 800-353-9538
Fax: 877-225-7329
Web: www.flexjet.com

CEO: Michael McQuay
CFO: –
HR: –
FYE: January 31
Type: Business segment

Bombardier Flexjet (known as Flexjet) offers fractional jet ownership services, in which customers acquire partial ownership of aircraft operated by the company. With ownership comes a specified number of flying hours — think of the arrangement as an airborne timeshare. (A one-sixteenth share of an airplane equates to 50 hours of flight time per year.) Through the Flexjet 25 program, customers can also buy flight time in 25-hour blocks without taking an ownership interest in a plane. Flexjet's fleet of more than 90 aircraft includes Learjet and Challenger business jets manufactured by the company's parent, Montreal-based Bombardier. Flexjet was established in 1995.

	Annual Growth	1/03	1/04	1/05	1/06	1/07
Est. sales ($ mil.)	—	—	—	—	—	159.8
Employees	—	—	—	—	—	1,129

THE BOMBAY COMPANY, INC.

Pink Sheets: BBAO

550 Bailey Ave.
Fort Worth, TX 76107
Phone: 817-347-8200
Fax: 817-332-7066
Web: www.bombaycompany.com

CEO: Donald V. Roach
CFO: Elaine D. Crowley
HR: James D. Johnson
FYE: January 31
Type: Public

You don't have to visit an 18th-century British colony to get 18th-century, British-styled furniture — the mall will do, old chap. The Bombay Company operates about 385 stores in the US and Canada that sell classic and traditional furniture, wall décor, and accessories for the bedroom, dining room, home office, and living room. It also operates four dozen outlet stores and 35 BombayKIDS locations, and sells items through catalogs and online. Amid a sales slump, the ailing home-furnishings retailer filed for Chapter 11 bankruptcy protection in September 2007 and was later sold at auction to two investment firms specializing in asset dispositions. The new owners plan to shutter all of the company's US stores.

	Annual Growth	1/03	1/04	1/05	1/06	*1/07
Sales ($ mil.)	2.1%	494.0	596.4	576.1	565.1	536.3
Net income ($ mil.)	—	7.2	9.9	(12.2)	(46.7)	(52.8)
Employees	(2.6%)	5,000	5,500	5,000	5,000	4,500

*Most recent year available

BON SECOURS HEALTH SYSTEM, INC.

1505 Marriottsville Rd.
Marriottsville, MD 21104
Phone: 410-442-5511
Fax: 410-442-1082
Web: www.bshsi.com

CEO: Richard J. (Rich) Statuto
CFO: Katherine Arbuckle
HR: David D. Jones
FYE: August 31
Type: Not-for-profit

Bon Secours Health System provides succor to the poor and sick. The Roman Catholic health care organization, sponsored by the Sisters of Bon Secours, set up its first hospital in Baltimore in 1919. Today, Bon Secours Health System includes nearly 20 hospitals with more than 4,000 licensed acute care beds. The organization's facilities are in seven states in the eastern US, from New York to Florida. In addition to its acute care facilities, the health care system operates numerous outpatient centers, nursing homes, assisted-living facilities, and hospices and home health care agencies.

	Annual Growth	8/03	8/04	8/05	8/06	8/07
Est. sales ($ mil.)	—	—	—	—	—	2,147.5
Employees	—	—	—	—	—	19,000

THE BON-TON STORES, INC.

NASDAQ (GS): BONT

2801 E. Market St.
York, PA 17402
Phone: 717-757-7660
Fax: 717-751-3108
Web: www.bonton.com

CEO: Byron L. (Bud) Bergren
CFO: Keith E. Plowman
HR: Dennis R. Clouser
FYE: Saturday nearest January 31
Type: Public

Fashion hounds lost in the wilds from Maine to Montana can take refuge in The Bon-Ton Stores. The company operates about 280 department stores under eight nameplates, including the Bon-Ton, Elder-Beerman, and Carson Pirie Scott banners, in some two dozen states. The stores sell branded (Calvin Klein, Estée Lauder, Liz Claiborne, Nautica, and Waterford) and private-label women's, children's, and men's clothing; accessories; cosmetics; and home furnishings. Bon-Ton acquired the 142-store Northern Department Store Group (NDSG) from Saks in 2006, doubling its store count. The Bon-Ton Stores was founded in 1898 by the Grumbacher family, and today is controlled by its chairman Tim Grumbacher.

	Annual Growth	1/04	1/05	1/06	1/07	1/08
Sales ($ mil.)	39.0%	930.0	1,319.6	1,307.6	3,455.8	3,467.7
Net income ($ mil.)	(13.4%)	20.6	20.2	26.0	46.9	11.6
Market value ($ mil.)	(8.8%)	156.9	204.4	293.5	540.0	108.6
Employees	(1.2%)	—	—	33,500	33,000	32,700

BONNE BELL, INC.

18519 Detroit Ave.
Lakewood, OH 44107
Phone: 216-221-0800
Fax: 216-221-6256
Web: www.bonnebell.com

CEO: Jess A. (Buddy) Bell Jr.
CFO: –
HR: Marion Walker
FYE: December 31
Type: Private

Bonne Bell and the teenage game of spin the bottle go hand in hand. The company's Smackers lip gloss brand (introduced in 1973) is geared toward 'tweens who want their lips berry sweet. In addition to Bonne Bell's lipsticks and glosses, the firm makes eye makeup (eye shadows, eye liners, mascara), as well as face and body products (bronzing and self-tanning products). Founded in the late 1920s by J. G. Bell, a Kansas salesman whose first factory was in the basement of his family's rented home and named after his daughter, Bonne Bell now operates globally and is in its third generation of family management.

	Annual Growth	12/03	12/04	12/05	12/06	12/07
Est. sales ($ mil.)	—	—	—	—	—	72.0
Employees	—	—	—	—	—	700

BONNEVILLE POWER ADMINISTRATION

905 NE 11th Ave.
Portland, OR 97208
Phone: 503-230-3000
Fax: 503-230-5884
Web: www.bpa.gov

CEO: Stephen J. (Steve) Wright
CFO: David J. Armstrong
HR: Godfrey Beckett
FYE: September 30
Type: Government-owned

Bonneville Power Administration (BPA) keeps the lights on in the Pacific Northwest. The US Department of Energy power marketing agency operates a 15,440-mile high-voltage transmission grid that delivers about 35% of the electrical power consumed in the region. The electricity that BPA wholesales is generated primarily by 31 federal hydroelectric plants and one private nuclear facility. BPA also purchases power from other hydroelectric, gas-fired, and wind and solar generation facilities in North America. Founded in 1937, the utility sells power primarily to public and investor-owned utilities, as well as some industrial customers.

	Annual Growth	9/02	9/03	9/04	9/05	9/06
Sales ($ mil.)	(0.8%)	3,533.7	3,612.1	3,197.9	3,268.1	3,419.4
Net income ($ mil.)	183.2%	9.5	555.4	504.4	486.9	611.1
Employees	0.4%	2,878	3,121	3,153	3,028	2,923

BONTEX, INC.

Pink Sheets: BOTX

One Bontex Dr.
Buena Vista, VA 24416
Phone: 540-261-2181
Fax: 540-261-3784
Web: www.bontex.com

CEO: James C. Kostelni
CFO: Jeffrey C. Kostelni
HR: Brenda Clark
FYE: June 30
Type: Public

C'est bon! Bontex makes fiberboard products for the footwear, headwear, luggage, and automotive industries. In addition to its fiberboard cushion insole materials for footwear, Bontex also distributes a polyurethane material with moisture transmission characteristics for use in sock linings and insoles. It touts its fiberboard products, which it makes from recycled and primary cellulose fibers, as being environmentally friendly. Bontex, which has discontinued its European operations, is controlled by the families of Dolores Kostelni (wife of chairman James Kostelni and owner of 55% of stock) and former director Patricia Surmonte Tischio, daughter of the late founder, Hugo Surmonte.

	Annual Growth	6/03	6/04	6/05	6/06	6/07
Est. sales ($ mil.)	—	—	—	—	—	25.0
Employees	—	—	—	—	—	250

BOOKHAM, INC.

NASDAQ (GM): BKHM

2584 Junction Ave.
San Jose, CA 95134
Phone: 408-383-1400
Fax: 408-919-6083
Web: www.bookham.com

CEO: Alain Couder
CFO: Stephen M. Abely
HR: –
FYE: Sunday nearest June 30
Type: Public

And you thought splitting hairs was tedious. Bookham integrates the light processing functions of optical networking components onto silicon chips, which it then puts into communications products such as transceivers, transponders, transmitters, receivers, and multiplexers. Typical devices for dividing wavelengths of light combine several components, such as tunable lasers, lenses, and filters. Bookham has shifted its emphasis away from passive optical components to active optical components. North America accounts for about half of sales. Bookham's major customers include Nortel (20% of sales).

	Annual Growth	6/03	6/04	6/05	6/06	6/07
Sales ($ mil.)	0.6%	—	—	200.3	231.6	202.8
Net income ($ mil.)	—	—	—	(248.0)	(87.5)	(82.2)
Market value ($ mil.)	32.9%	—	—	106.1	194.8	187.4
Employees	—	—	—	2,309	—	—

🔲 BOOKS-A-MILLION, INC.

NASDAQ (GS): BAMM

402 Industrial Ln.
Birmingham, AL 35211
Phone: 205-942-3737
Fax: 205-942-6601
Web: www.bamm.com

CEO: Sandra B. Cochran
CFO: Douglas Markham
HR: Chad Tice
FYE: Saturday nearest January 31
Type: Public

Books-A-Million is made for readers who aren't millionaires. The #3 US book chain (after Barnes & Noble and Borders) has 180-plus superstores in some 20 southeastern states and the District of Columbia. Most of its outlets are superstores operating under the Books-A-Million and Books & Co. names, which offer amenities including author signings, kid-related events, and Joe Muggs coffee bars in addition to discounted books, magazines, and newspapers. Books-A-Million also runs about 20 smaller-sized Bookland and Books-A-Million stores, and Joe Muggs Newsstands (with coffee bars). Other operations include book wholesaler American Wholesale Book. Chairman Clyde Anderson (and his family) own about 51% of the firm.

	Annual Growth	1/04	1/05	1/06	1/07	1/08
Sales ($ mil.)	3.8%	460.2	475.2	503.8	520.4	535.1
Net income ($ mil.)	23.5%	7.1	10.2	13.1	18.9	16.5
Market value ($ mil.)	12.1%	106.5	151.5	187.7	310.4	168.1
Employees	3.0%	—	—	5,000	5,000	5,300

BOOKSPAN

501 Franklin Avenue
Garden City, NY 11530
Phone: 516-490-4561
Fax: 516-490-4714
Web: www.bookspan.com

CEO: Stuart Goldfarb
CFO: –
HR: –
FYE: December 31
Type: Private

Spanning the globe to bring you . . . books. Bookspan is a direct marketer of book clubs, including such familiar names as the Book-of-the-Month club, Doubleday Book Club, and the Literary Guild. Book selections are chosen by editors in various categories. Bookspan operates about 40 book clubs in several categories: general interest, lifestyles, and male specialty (history, military, sci-fi). The clubs boast more than 8 million members. Bookspan also includes Yes Solutions, which provides logistics consulting to publishers. The company was created through a partnership between Bertelsmann AG and Time Warner. Time Warner sold its stake to Bertelsmann in 2007.

	Annual Growth	12/03	12/04	12/05	12/06	12/07
Est. sales ($ mil.)	—	—	—	—	—	401.9
Employees	—	—	—	—	—	2,300

BOOTS & COOTS INTERNATIONAL WELL CONTROL, INC.

AMEX: WEL

7908 N. Sam Houston Pkwy. West, Ste. 500
Houston, TX 77064
Phone: 281-931-8884
Fax: 281-931-8392
Web: www.bncg.com

CEO: Jerry L. Winchester
CFO: –
HR: Kelly Hebert
FYE: December 31
Type: Public

Boots & Coots International Well Control scoots to the rescue of oil companies faced with oil and gas well blowouts and fires. Besides being in the "hellfighting" business, the company contains oil and hazardous material spills, restores affected sites, and provides snubbing and noncritical services such as troubleshooting and contingency planning. Post-Gulf War contracts in Iraq, as well as the disposal of noncore operations, helped the company mitigate some of its earlier financial difficulties. Boots & Coots' founders, including Boots Hansen and Coots Mathews, learned their trade working for industry pioneer Red Adair. Oil States International unit Oil States Energy Services owns 15% of the company.

	Annual Growth	12/03	12/04	12/05	12/06	12/07
Sales ($ mil.)	30.9%	35.9	24.2	29.5	97.0	105.3
Net income ($ mil.)	2.7%	7.1	(0.3)	2.8	11.2	7.9
Market value ($ mil.)	37.6%	34.4	26.8	30.8	132.6	123.2
Employees	12.4%	—	—	355	399	—

🔲 BOOZ ALLEN HAMILTON INC.

8283 Greensboro Dr.
McLean, VA 22102
Phone: 703-902-5000
Fax: 703-902-3333
Web: www.boozallen.com

CEO: Ralph W. Shrader
CFO: Douglas G. (Doug) Swenson
HR: Horacio Rozanski
FYE: March 31
Type: Private

Consultants at Booz Allen Hamilton serve the needs of big business and big government through about 110 offices around the globe. The firm's commercial unit provides management consulting and technology integration services to help *FORTUNE* 500 companies and other large enterprises improve their business processes. Booz Allen's US government unit provides similar services for federal agencies, not only at home but also around the globe. The firm, founded in 1914, is owned by its officers. In 2008 Booz Allen announced plans to separate its commercial- and government-related businesses and to sell a majority stake in the government consulting unit to investment firm The Carlyle Group.

	Annual Growth	3/03	3/04	3/05	3/06	3/07
Sales ($ mil.)	15.5%	2,300.0	2,700.0	3,300.0	3,700.0	4,100.0
Employees	13.9%	11,300	14,000	16,000	17,300	19,000

🔲 An in-depth profile of this company is available to Hoover's Online members at hoovers.com.

BORAL USA

200 Mansell Ct. East, Ste. 310
Roswell, GA 30076
Phone: 770-645-4500
Fax: 770-645-2888
Web: www.boral.com.au/boral_companies/Boral_USA.asp

CEO: Emery S. Severin
CFO: Ken M. Barton
HR: Robin J. Town
FYE: June 30
Type: Business segment

Boral USA operates some of the largest brick and tile manufacturing businesses in the US. The company's operations include Boral Brick, clay roof tile maker US Tile, concrete roof tile maker MonierLifetile (a joint venture with France-based Lafarge), and fly ash marketer Boral Material Technologies Inc (BMTI). The company's Boral Brick business manufactures about 1.5 billion bricks annually through more than 20 brick plants in the southeastern and southwestern US, making it a leading domestic brick maker. Boral USA is a division of Australian building and construction materials supplier Boral Limited.

	Annual Growth	6/03	6/04	6/05	6/06	6/07
Est. sales ($ mil.)	—	—	—	—	—	128.6
Employees	—	—	—	—	—	1,900

BORDER FOODS, INC.

1750 Valley View Ln.
Farmers Branch, TX 75234
Phone: 972-406-3300
Fax: 972-406-3390
Web: www.borderfoodsinc.com

CEO: John Bowman
CFO: –
HR: –
FYE: June 30
Type: Private

Instead of hitching a ride down south and over the border for some spicy grub, pick up a can of Border Foods' peppers and make some belly-blasting food yourself. The company is a major global processor of green chili peppers and a leading US supplier of jalapeño peppers. It also offers tomatillos and banana pepper products. Located in New Mexico, Border Foods supplies the foodservice, industrial, and retail food industries throughout the US with canned, fresh, frozen and dried peppers, salsas, dips, sauces, as well as other Mexican condiments and snack products.

	Annual Growth	6/03	6/04	6/05	6/06	6/07
Est. sales ($ mil.)	—	—	—	—	—	73.5
Employees	—	—	—	—	—	784

[H] BORDERS GROUP, INC.

NYSE: BGP

100 Phoenix Dr.
Ann Arbor, MI 48108
Phone: 734-477-1100
Fax: 734-477-1285
Web: www.bordersgroupinc.com

CEO: George L. Jones
CFO: Edward W. (Ed) Wilhelm
HR: Daniel T. (Dan) Smith
FYE: Saturday nearest January 31
Type: Public

If you want John Updike or Janet Jackson to go with your java, Borders is for you. The #2 bookstore operator in the US (after Barnes & Noble), Borders Group runs more than 1,000 retail stores, which include Borders superstores and mall-based Waldenbooks stores. The chain has been divesting its international holdings, selling its Borders (UK) business in 2007 and its 30 Asia-Pacific superstores in 2008, to reduce debt and allow it to focus on domestic operations. Borders stores offer up to 200,000 book, music, and movie titles and regularly host live literary events and musician showcases to lure customers. Borders has also set up shop at select US airport and outlet mall locations.

	Annual Growth	1/04	1/05	1/06	1/07	1/08
Sales ($ mil.)	0.6%	3,731.0	3,903.0	4,079.2	4,113.5	3,820.9
Net income ($ mil.)	—	120.0	131.9	101.0	(151.3)	(157.4)
Market value ($ mil.)	(20.9%)	1,679.0	1,889.0	1,557.5	1,248.5	656.7
Employees	(8.8%)	—	—	35,500	33,600	29,500

[H] BORGWARNER INC.

NYSE: BWA

3850 Hamlin Rd.
Auburn Hills, MI 48326
Phone: 248-754-9200
Fax: 248-754-9397
Web: www.bwauto.com

CEO: Timothy M. Manganello
CFO: Robin J. Adams
HR: Angela D'Aversa
FYE: December 31
Type: Public

If suburbanites need four-wheel-drive vehicles to make it up their steep driveways, that's OK with BorgWarner (formerly Borg-Warner Automotive), a leading maker of power train products for the world's major automakers. Its largest customers include Volkswagen (15% of sales), Ford (12%), and Daimler (6%). Its power train products include four-wheel-drive and all-wheel-drive transfer cases (primarily for light trucks and sport utility vehicles), as well as automatic transmission and timing-chain systems. BorgWarner operates more than 60 manufacturing, assembly, and technical facilities worldwide.

	Annual Growth	12/03	12/04	12/05	12/06	12/07
Sales ($ mil.)	14.8%	3,069.2	3,525.3	4,293.8	4,585.4	5,328.6
Net income ($ mil.)	13.3%	174.9	218.3	239.6	211.6	288.5
Market value ($ mil.)	76.0%	586.5	1,526.4	1,732.0	1,702.5	5,621.8
Employees	0.9%	—	—	17,400	17,400	17,700

[H] BORLAND SOFTWARE CORPORATION

NASDAQ (GM): BORL

8303 N. Mopac Expressway, Ste. A-300
Austin, TX 78759
Phone: 512-340-2200
Fax: –
Web: www.borland.com

CEO: Tod Nielsen
CFO: Erik E. Prusch
HR: Jonathan T. Schoonmaker
FYE: December 31
Type: Public

Software development doesn't have to be a boring, tedious job. Borland Software offers technology used in the development, deployment, integration, and management of software applications. The company's products include programming languages, database software, and application development software. Borland, which is focusing on the Java development market, also offers Web-based application integration software that lets clients deploy online applications compatible with different platforms.

	Annual Growth	12/03	12/04	12/05	12/06	12/07
Sales ($ mil.)	(2.3%)	295.2	309.5	276.7	304.7	268.8
Net income ($ mil.)	—	(40.5)	11.4	(29.8)	(52.0)	(61.7)
Market value ($ mil.)	(33.3%)	788.1	939.9	508.1	428.2	156.0
Employees	(8.0%)	—	—	1,269	1,168	—

BOSCH REXROTH CORPORATION

5150 Prairie Stone Pkwy.
Hoffman Estates, IL 60192
Phone: 847-645-3600
Fax: 847-645-0804
Web: www.boschrexroth-us.com

CEO: Berend Bracht
CFO: Steve Roberts
HR: –
FYE: December 31
Type: Subsidiary

Bosch Rexroth is not a driver's ed. instructor, but it is something of a drive and control company. Bosch Rexroth Corporation, the US arm of the Germany-based Bosch Rexroth AG (which itself is a subsidiary of Robert Bosch GmbH), makes electric drives (servo drives and controls), hydraulic systems (industrial and mobile), bushings and shafts, and pneumatic valves and actuators. The company's products can be found in automobiles, construction vehicles (backhoes, cranes, excavators), and material handling equipment (conveyors, linear motion systems), as well as on factory production lines. Bosch Rexroth AG gets about 20% of its sales in the Americas.

	Annual Growth	12/03	12/04	12/05	12/06	12/07
Est. sales ($ mil.)	—	—	—	—	—	198.9
Employees	—	—	—	—	—	1,996

BOSCH SECURITY SYSTEMS, INC.

130 Perinton Pkwy.
Fairport, NY 14450
Phone: 585-223-4060
Fax: 585-223-9180
Web: www.boschsecurity.com

CEO: Christopher P. Gerace
CFO: Christopher P. Gerace
HR: –
FYE: December 31
Type: Subsidiary

Bosch Security Systems has a sixth sense for finding business. The company makes electronic detection and communications equipment for firms that provide security and fire protection systems and services. Its products include smoke detectors, motion detectors, closed-circuit TV systems, access control systems, and control panels. Related communications equipment sends alarm signals over telephone lines, wireless networks, and WANs. Bosch also makes personal safety systems that when activated, transmit the user's identity and location to a monitoring station. The company has sales offices and distribution centers worldwide. Bosch Security Systems is a subsidiary of German manufacturing giant Robert Bosch.

	Annual Growth	12/03	12/04	12/05	12/06	12/07
Est. sales ($ mil.)	—	—	—	—	—	99.1
Employees	—	—	—	—	—	1,229

BOSCOV'S DEPARTMENT STORE, LLC

4500 Perkiomen Ave.
Reading, PA 19606
Phone: 610-779-2000
Fax: 610-370-3495
Web: www.boscovs.com

CEO: Kenneth S. Lakin
CFO: Russell C. Diehm
HR: Ed Elko
FYE: January 31
Type: Private

Outlet mall capital Reading, Pennsylvania, has conceived more than bargain shopping. It's given us Boscov's Department Store, which operates about 50 department stores that anchor malls mainly in Pennsylvania and five other mid-Atlantic states. Boscov's increased its store count by 25% with its purchase of about 10 stores from Macy's, Inc. (formerly Federated Department Stores) in 2006. The stores sell men's, women's, and children's apparel, shoes, and accessories, as well as jewelry, cosmetics, housewares, appliances, toys, and sporting goods. It also operates an online store. Boscov's was founded by Solomon Boscov in 1911 and is owned by the families of Albert Boscov and Edwin Lakin.

	Annual Growth	1/02	1/03	1/04	1/05	1/06
Sales ($ mil.)	4.0%	1,000.0	1,016.0	1,051.0	1,072.0	1,170.0
Employees	(4.5%)	12,000	10,500	11,000	10,000	10,000

BOSE CORPORATION

The Mountain
Framingham, MA 01701
Phone: 508-879-7330
Fax: 508-766-7543
Web: www.bose.com

CEO: Amar G. Bose
CFO: Daniel A. Grady
HR: John C. Ferrie
FYE: March 31
Type: Private

Bose has been making noise in the audio products business for some time. The firm is one of the world's leading manufacturers of speakers for the home entertainment, automotive, and pro audio markets. It makes a variety of consumer models for stereo systems and home theaters, including its compact Wave radio system. For sound professionals, Bose offers loudspeakers and amplifiers, as well as products designed for musicians. Bose sells its products at 100-plus factory and showcase stores and through affiliated retailers. The company is using its expertise to branch out into other markets. Founder Amar Bose, a former professor of electrical engineering at Massachusetts Institute of Technology, owns the company.

	Annual Growth	3/02	3/03	3/04	3/05	3/06
Sales ($ mil.)	11.4%	1,300.0	1,600.0	1,700.0	1,800.0	2,000.0
Employees	3.4%	7,000	8,000	8,000	8,000	8,000

BOSS HOLDINGS, INC.

OTC: BSHI

221 W. 1st St.
Kewanee, IL 61443
Phone: 309-852-2131
Fax: 309-852-0848
Web: www.bossgloves.com

CEO: G. Louis Graziadio III
CFO: Steven G. Pont
HR: Beverley Williams
FYE: December 31
Type: Public

Boss Holdings would rather take orders (for its gloves, boots, and rainwear) than give them. Subsidiary Boss Manufacturing Company (BMC) imports and markets gloves and protective wear sold through mass merchandisers, hardware stores, and other retailers in the US and Canada. It also sells its products directly to commercial users in industries such as agriculture and automotive. The company's Warren Pet division markets pet supplies (collars, chains, pet shampoos, toys) to US retailers. The company also sells latex balloons through its Galaxy Balloons subsidiary. Boss Holdings was founded in 1893 as a manufacturer of work gloves. The company's gloves and protective gear account for about 70% of sales.

	Annual Growth	12/03	12/04	12/05	12/06	12/07
Sales ($ mil.)	11.4%	35.9	43.5	54.2	53.7	55.2
Net income ($ mil.)	23.6%	0.6	3.7	0.7	3.9	1.4
Market value ($ mil.)	16.6%	9.8	13.6	15.7	12.1	18.1
Employees	—	—	—	—	—	—

BOSTON ACOUSTICS, INC.

300 Jubilee Dr.
Peabody, MA 01960
Phone: 978-538-5000
Fax: 978-538-5199
Web: www.bostonacoustics.com

CEO: Charlie Randall
CFO: Debra A. Ricker
HR: Amelia Arruda
FYE: Last Saturday in March
Type: Subsidiary

Play "Dark Side of the Moon" on a set of Boston Acoustics' speakers and you'll see the light. The company designs and makes moderately priced and high-end loudspeaker systems for the home and auto markets. It also makes home entertainment systems, amplifiers, and ancillary speaker equipment including selectors and volume controls. Boston Acoustics mostly tunes out mass retailers, selling its products through a select group of specialty dealers. Its products are manufactured by third parties in Asia and the Pacific Rim, Canada, and Europe, as well as in the US. Former chairman and treasurer Andrew Kotsatos and former CEO Frank Reed founded the company in 1979. D&M Holdings acquired Boston Acoustics in 2005.

THE BOSTON BEER COMPANY, INC.

NYSE: SAM

1 Design Center Place, Ste. 850
Boston, MA 02110
Phone: 617-368-5000
Fax: 617-368-5500
Web: www.bostonbeer.com

CEO: Martin F. Roper
CFO: William F. Urich
HR: Amy Waryas
FYE: Last Saturday in December
Type: Public

A half-pint compared to mega-brewers such as Anheuser-Busch and Miller Brewing, The Boston Beer Company holds the distinction of being America's largest microbrewer. Boston Beer produces more than 20 seasonal and year-round varieties of craft-brewed beers at its Cincinnati and Boston breweries. Annually, it sells almost 1.4 million barrels of lager (such as its flagship Samuel Adams Boston Lager), ales (other Samuel Adams brands), HardCore brand cider, and Twisted Tea malt beverages. The company distributes its brews primarily in the US, but they are also sold in Canada, the Caribbean, Europe, Israel, and the Pacific Rim countries.

	Annual Growth	12/03	12/04	12/05	12/06	12/07
Sales ($ mil.)	13.2%	207.9	217.2	238.3	285.4	341.6
Net income ($ mil.)	20.7%	10.6	12.5	15.6	18.2	22.5
Market value ($ mil.)	20.0%	183.5	213.4	245.4	359.5	380.6
Employees	13.2%	—	—	390	433	500

An in-depth profile of this company is available to Hoover's Online members at hoovers.com.

273

THE BOSTON CONSULTING GROUP INC.

1 Exchange Place, 6th Fl.
Boston, MA 02109
Phone: 617-973-1200
Fax: 617-973-1399
Web: www.bcg.com

CEO: Hans-Paul Bürkner
CFO: Debbie Simpson
HR: –
FYE: December 31
Type: Private

Global corporations are willing to give much more than a penny for the thoughts of Boston Consulting Group (BCG). One of the world's top-ranked consulting practices, BCG operates from about 65 offices in more than 35 countries in the Americas, Europe, and the Asia/Pacific region. The firm's 3,900 consultants offer a wide array of services, mainly to large corporate clients. BCG's practice areas include branding and marketing, corporate finance, globalization, and information technology. Founded in 1963 by industry pioneer Bruce Henderson, the firm is owned by its employees.

	Annual Growth	12/02	12/03	12/04	12/05	12/06
Est. sales ($ mil.)	20.0%	—	—	—	1,500.0	1,800.0
Employees	14.0%	—	—	—	5,500	6,270

BOSTON MARKET CORPORATION

14103 Denver West Pkwy.
Golden, CO 80401
Phone: 303-278-9500
Fax: 303-216-5678
Web: www.bostonmarket.com

CEO: Richard K. (Rick) Arras
CFO: Gregory S. Uhing
HR: Juan Marcos
FYE: December 31
Type: Private

Boston Market brings home-style cooking far beyond the borders of the commonwealth. A leader in quick-casual dining, Boston Market owns and operates about 600 eateries in almost 30 states. Its menu features grilled and rotisserie chicken, ham, meat loaf, and turkey, as well as such side dishes as mashed potatoes, macaroni and cheese, and stuffing. The chain also serves soups, salads, and dessert items. Boston Market's locations feature a cafeteria-style serving line and seating for dining in, as well as drive-through and carry-out service. Fast-food leader McDonald's sold Boston Market to private equity firm Sun Capital Partners in 2007.

	Annual Growth	12/03	12/04	12/05	12/06	12/07
Est. sales ($ mil.)	—	—	—	—	—	326.1
Employees	—	—	—	—	—	15,041

BOSTON MEDICAL CENTER

1 Boston Medical Center Place
Boston, MA 02118
Phone: 617-638-8000
Fax: 617-268-6960
Web: www.bmc.org

CEO: Elaine S. Ullian
CFO: Ronald E. Bartlett
HR: –
FYE: September 30
Type: Not-for-profit

Located in Boston's South End neighborhood, Boston Medical Center offers a full spectrum of health care services, from prenatal care and obstetrics to surgery and rehabilitation. Boston Medical Center is also the city's largest provider of indigent care, spending more than a quarter of a billion dollars on care for uninsured patients and offering free screenings and other community outreach programs. The hospital boasts some 550 beds and includes a Level 1 trauma center, acute rehabilitation facilities, and neonatal and pediatric intensive care units. The center is the primary teaching hospital of Boston University's School of Medicine.

BOSTON PRIVATE FINANCIAL HOLDINGS, INC.

NASDAQ (GS): BPFH

10 Post Office Sq.
Boston, MA 02109
Phone: 617-912-1900
Fax: 617-912-4550
Web: www.bostonprivate.com

CEO: Timothy L. Vaill
CFO: David Kaye
HR: Pilar Pueyo
FYE: December 31
Type: Public

Boston Private — isn't that David Kelley's new TV series? Not exactly. The holding company owns several private banks and investment management companies that primarily serve well-to-do and institutional clients on both US coasts. Their offerings include deposit accounts, loans, trust services, and financial advice. Boston Private Bank & Trust operates about 10 branches in New England, while Gibraltar Bank serves southern Florida and New York City. In California, the company runs Borel Private Bank & Trust and First Private Bank & Trust. In 2007 it acquired Washington state-based Charter Bank, for nearly $80 million.

	Annual Growth	12/03	12/04	12/05	12/06	12/07
Assets ($ mil.)	32.7%	2,196.3	3,270.3	5,134.1	5,763.5	6,818.1
Net income ($ mil.)	(33.7%)	21.8	33.6	46.3	54.4	4.2
Market value ($ mil.)	12.9%	625.1	788.0	1,058.6	1,032.2	1,014.7
Employees	14.3%	—	—	892	1,031	1,166

BOSTON PROPERTIES, INC.

NYSE: BXP

111 Huntington Ave.
Boston, MA 02199
Phone: 617-236-3300
Fax: 617-536-5087
Web: www.bostonproperties.com

CEO: Edward H. Linde
CFO: Michael E. LaBelle
HR: Adele Schlotzhauer
FYE: December 31
Type: Public

Don't be fooled by the name. Boston Properties has holdings in Manhattan, San Francisco, and Washington, DC, too. The company builds and owns commercial real estate. It has some 130 properties, primarily office buildings as well as a few hotel and retail holdings totaling around 44 million sq. ft. (including parking). Major tenants include the US government, Lockheed Martin, and Citibank. Boston Properties, an umbrella partnership real estate investment trust (UPREIT), operates through Boston Properties LP. Boston Properties chairman and media czar Mort Zuckerman (of *U.S. News & World Report* and *New York Daily News* fame) and CEO Edward Linde each own around 7% of the company.

	Annual Growth	12/03	12/04	12/05	12/06	12/07
Sales ($ mil.)	3.1%	1,309.6	1,400.5	1,437.6	1,477.6	1,482.3
Net income ($ mil.)	38.0%	365.3	284.0	438.3	873.6	1,324.7
Market value ($ mil.)	23.4%	4,733.7	7,134.4	8,342.8	13,146.3	10,971.5
Employees	(1.0%)	—	—	673	650	660

THE BOSTON RED SOX

4 Yawkey Way
Boston, MA 02215
Phone: 617-267-9440
Fax: 617-375-0944
Web: boston.redsox.mlb.com

CEO: Larry Lucchino
CFO: Robert C. (Bob) Furbush
HR: Benjamin P. (Ben) Cherington
FYE: December 31
Type: Private

You might say this team is now a curse on the other teams in Major League Baseball. The Boston Red Sox is one of the oldest and most storied franchises in the major leagues, notable for its 86-year championship drought popularly attributed to "The Curse of the Bambino." The team broke The Curse in 2004 when it won the World Series, then won its seventh championship three years later. Throughout its struggles, though, the Sox have continued to enjoy strong support from hometown fans at venerable Fenway Park, the oldest pro baseball stadium in the country. The franchise was founded as a charter member of the American League in 1901; it has been owned by John Henry since 2002.

	Annual Growth	12/02	12/03	12/04	12/05	12/06
Sales ($ mil.)	8.2%	171.0	190.0	220.0	206.0	234.0
Employees	—	—	—	—	—	—

⊞ BOSTON SCIENTIFIC CORPORATION

NYSE: BSX

1 Boston Scientific Place
Natick, MA 01760
Phone: 508-650-8000
Fax: 508-650-8910
Web: www.bostonscientific.com

CEO: James R. (Jim) Tobin
CFO: Sam R. Leno
HR: Lucia L. Quinn
FYE: December 31
Type: Public

Boston Scientific operates under the threat of minimal invasion. The company makes medical supplies used in minimally invasive surgical procedures. Its devices are used to diagnose and treat conditions in a variety of medical fields, including cardiology, gynecology, urology, endoscopy, and neuromodulation. Products include defibrillators, catheters, coronary and ureteral stents, pacemakers, biopsy forceps and needles, and urethral slings. Boston Scientific markets in some 45 countries worldwide, primarily through its own direct sales staff.

	Annual Growth	12/03	12/04	12/05	12/06	12/07
Sales ($ mil.)	24.5%	3,476.0	5,624.0	6,283.0	7,821.0	8,357.0
Net income ($ mil.)	—	472.0	1,062.0	628.0	(3,577.0)	(495.0)
Market value ($ mil.)	(13.2%)	30,373.4	29,696.5	20,090.4	25,334.9	17,206.7
Employees	17.9%	—	—	19,800	28,600	27,500

BOTTOMLINE TECHNOLOGIES (DE), INC.

NASDAQ (GM): EPAY

325 Corporate Dr.
Portsmouth, NH 03801
Phone: 603-436-0700
Fax: 603-436-0300
Web: www.bottomline.com

CEO: Robert A. (Rob) Eberle
CFO: Kevin M. Donovan
HR: –
FYE: June 30
Type: Public

Bottomline Technologies helps you track both the bottom dollar and the bill. The company provides financial resource management software that lets financial institutions and other corporations convert from paper-based billing systems to systems that enable electronic funds transfer, banking, and bill presentment and payment. Bottomline's Purchase-to-Pay software enables corporations to electronically present bills and accept payments from external parties, while its PayBase and WebSeries products allow customers to manage and track internal billing and payment processes.

	Annual Growth	6/03	6/04	6/05	6/06	6/07
Sales ($ mil.)	13.5%	71.3	82.1	96.5	101.7	118.3
Net income ($ mil.)	—	(27.9)	(2.4)	5.9	(1.8)	(7.0)
Market value ($ mil.)	22.9%	128.8	187.2	281.2	191.7	294.1
Employees	—	—	—	475	—	—

BOURNS, INC.

1200 Columbia Ave.
Riverside, CA 92507
Phone: 951-781-5690
Fax: 951-781-5273
Web: www.bourns.com

CEO: Gordon Bourns
CFO: William P. McKenna
HR: Charles MacBeth
FYE: December 31
Type: Private

Bourns makes a broad range of electronic components, such as potentiometers, power protection devices, sensors, resistors, switches, encoders, panel controls, dials, and chip resistor arrays. The company sells primarily to the automotive, computer, portable electronics, and telecommunications markets. Bourns was established in 1947 by Marlan and Rosemary Bourns (parents of CEO Gordon Bourns) in their garage in Altadena, California. The company, incorporated in 1952, is owned by the Bourns family. Bourns has sales offices and distributors worldwide.

	Annual Growth	12/03	12/04	12/05	12/06	12/07
Est. sales ($ mil.)	—	—	—	—	—	343.5
Employees	—	—	—	—	—	4,000

BOVIE MEDICAL CORPORATION

AMEX: BVX

734 Walt Whitman Rd.
Melville, NY 11747
Phone: 631-421-5452
Fax: 631-421-5821
Web: www.boviemedical.com

CEO: Andrew Makrides
CFO: Andrew Makrides
HR: Vera MacElroy
FYE: December 31
Type: Public

Surgeons don't think about Bovie during surgery, but Bovie constantly thinks about them. Bovie Medical makes and markets electrosurgical devices and power generators primarily used for outpatient surgical procedures under its Bovie and Aaron brands and for private label clients. Its top-selling products include generators used in physicians' offices, electrodes, and other devices for cutting and cauterizing tissue in dermatology, urology, gynecology, or cosmetic procedures. Bovie also makes battery-operated cauteries (to stop bleeding), physician pen lights, other medical lighting equipment, and a nerve locator simulator used mainly to locate motor nerves in hand and facial reconstruction procedures.

	Annual Growth	12/03	12/04	12/05	12/06	12/07
Sales ($ mil.)	15.6%	16.1	20.5	20.2	26.7	28.8
Net income ($ mil.)	36.1%	0.7	1.5	0.4	2.7	2.4
Market value ($ mil.)	24.4%	41.3	35.3	41.8	138.1	98.9
Employees	7.6%	—	—	140	161	162

BOWL AMERICA INCORPORATED

AMEX: BWLA

6446 Edsall Rd.
Alexandria, VA 22312
Phone: 703-941-6300
Fax: 703-256-2430
Web: www.bowlamericainc.com

CEO: Leslie H. (Les) Goldberg
CFO: Cheryl A. Dragoo
HR: –
FYE: Sunday nearest June 30
Type: Public

This company is looking make a strike in the business of recreation. Bowl America owns and operates about 20 bowling centers in four markets, including the Baltimore-Washington, DC, area; Jacksonville and Orlando, Florida; and Richmond, Virginia. The bowling centers offer a total of more than 750 lanes for both league and non-league bowling, as well as Cosmic Bowling (with glow-in-the-dark balls and laser light shows) for younger patrons. The centers also feature game rooms, food and beverage services, and other amenities. President Leslie Goldberg and his sister Merle Fabian together own more than 50% of Bowl America.

	Annual Growth	6/03	6/04	6/05	6/06	6/07
Sales ($ mil.)	2.1%	29.4	28.4	28.6	30.3	32.0
Net income ($ mil.)	3.9%	3.6	4.7	3.8	3.6	4.2
Market value ($ mil.)	9.8%	43.1	52.3	51.3	53.4	62.5
Employees	3.5%	—	—	700	750	750

BOWLIN TRAVEL CENTERS, INC.

OTC: BWTL

150 Louisiana NE
Albuquerque, NM 87108
Phone: 505-266-5985
Fax: 505-266-7821
Web: www.bowlintc.com

CEO: Michael L. Bowlin
CFO: Nina J. Pratz
HR: Johnny Riley
FYE: January 31
Type: Public

Dotting the desert with gas pumps and gifts, Bowlin Travel Centers (BTC) operates about 10 full-service, southwestern-themed travel centers along interstates I-10 and I-40 in arid Arizona and New Mexico. Its travel centers offer snacks, souvenirs provided by Native American tribes or imported from Mexico, gas (Citgo and ExxonMobil brands), and restaurants (Dairy Queen at five locations). It also sells gasoline wholesale. BTC was spun off by Bowlin Outdoor Advertising & Travel Centers immediately before the former parent company was acquired by Louisiana-based Lamar Advertising in 2001. Chairman, president, and CEO Michael Bowlin and his family own about 61% of BTC.

	Annual Growth	1/04	1/05	1/06	1/07	1/08
Sales ($ mil.)	7.0%	21.5	23.6	27.7	27.8	28.2
Net income ($ mil.)	0.0%	0.5	0.4	0.6	0.6	0.5
Market value ($ mil.)	(1.6%)	8.3	8.7	8.0	8.0	7.7
Employees	(6.7%)	—	—	165	154	—

⊞ An in-depth profile of this company is available to Hoover's Online members at hoovers.com.

275

BOWNE & CO., INC.

55 Water St.
New York, NY 10041
Phone: 212-924-5500
Fax: 212-229-3400
Web: www.bowne.com

NYSE: BNE
CEO: David J. Shea
CFO: John J. Walker
HR: Susan W. Cummiskey
FYE: December 31
Type: Public

Savvy investors see the work of Bowne & Co. every day. The company specializes in printing financial documents, such as prospectuses, annual and interim reports, and other paperwork required by the SEC. Bowne (rhymes with "down") also handles electronic filings via the SEC's EDGAR system and provides electronic distribution and high-volume mailing services. Documents associated with transactions, such as equity and debt issuances and mergers and acquisitions generate a significant share of sales. In addition to its financial communications offerings, Bowne provides marketing and business communications services to companies in financial services, health care, and travel and leisure industries.

	Annual Growth	12/03	12/04	12/05	12/06	12/07
Sales ($ mil.)	(5.5%)	1,064.8	899.0	694.1	832.2	850.6
Net income ($ mil.)	—	(9.1)	27.5	(0.6)	(1.8)	27.1
Market value ($ mil.)	8.6%	546.9	549.4	622.0	678.0	759.7
Employees	(9.8%)	—	4,900	3,100	3,200	3,600

BOY SCOUTS OF AMERICA

1325 W. Walnut Hill Ln.
Irving, TX 75015
Phone: 972-580-2000
Fax: 972-580-7870
Web: www.scouting.org

CEO: Robert (Bob) Mazzuca
CFO: –
HR: James S. Turley
FYE: December 31
Type: Not-for-profit

Scouts enter dens as Tigers and eventually take flight as Eagles. Boy Scouts of America (BSA), one of the nation's largest youth organizations, has about 2.9 million youth members and 1.2 million adult leaders in some 122,500 units. BSA offers educational and character-building programs emphasizing leadership, citizenship, personal development, and physical fitness. In addition to traditional scouting programs (Tiger, Cub, Webelos, and Boy Scouts, ranging up to Eagle rank), it offers the Venturing program for boys and girls ages 14-20. BSA generates revenue through membership and council fees, supply and magazine sales, and contributions. The organization was founded by Chicago publisher William Boyce in 1910.

BOYD GAMING CORPORATION

3883 Howard Hughes Pkwy., 9th Fl.
Las Vegas, NV 89169
Phone: 702-792-7200
Fax: 702-792-7313
Web: www.boydgaming.com

NYSE: BYD
CEO: Keith E. Smith
CFO: Josh Hirsberg
HR: Robert Gerst
FYE: December 31
Type: Public

A key ingredient for Boyd Gaming's success is — or was — stardust. One of the country's leading casino operators, Boyd demolished the iconic Stardust Resort and Casino on the Las Vegas Strip in 2007 to make way for a new development, Echelon Place, which is set to open in 2010. Boyd's 16 properties include locations in Las Vegas, as well as in Florida, Indiana, Illinois, Louisiana, and Mississippi; together they have some 23,000 slot machines and 500 table games and typically feature multiple restaurants, lounges, and showrooms. Boyd also owns Coast Casino, as well as 50% of Atlantic City's Borgata Hotel Casino with MGM MIRAGE. Chairman William S. Boyd and his family own more than 35% of Boyd Gaming.

	Annual Growth	12/03	12/04	12/05	12/06	12/07
Sales ($ mil.)	13.5%	1,253.1	1,734.1	2,223.0	2,278.8	2,080.3
Net income ($ mil.)	65.0%	40.9	111.4	144.6	116.8	303.0
Market value ($ mil.)	29.9%	1,048.8	3,645.9	4,255.4	3,946.7	2,989.5
Employees	(21.8%)	—	—	23,400	18,300	—

THE BOYDS COLLECTION, LTD.

350 South St.
McSherrystown, PA 17344
Phone: 717-633-9898
Fax: 717-633-5511
Web: www.boydsstuff.com

Pink Sheets: BYDC
CEO: Robert Coccoluto
CFO: Joseph E. Macharsky
HR: Ruth Karabeievschy
FYE: December 31
Type: Public

In the forest of collectibles, The Boyds Collection bears are watching. The firm sells resin, porcelain, and plush renditions of bears and other animals, including its Bearstones figurines and its J.B. Bean & Associates line of fully-jointed bears and other animals. It also sells other collectibles and home décor items, such as stationery, picture frames, and furniture, as well as NASCAR- and Coca-Cola-licensed products. Products are designed to appeal to older women (although it has added items for men). Its products are sold primarily in US gift shops and department stores, as well as through catalogs and trade shows. Boyds filed for Chapter 11 bankruptcy protection in late 2005 and emerged in mid-2006.

	Annual Growth	12/01	12/02	12/03	12/04	*12/05
Sales ($ mil.)	—	—	—	—	—	78.6
Employees	—	—	—	—	—	420

*Most recent year available

BOZZUTO'S INC.

275 School House Rd.
Cheshire, CT 06410
Phone: 203-272-3511
Fax: 203-250-2954
Web: www.bozzutos.com

CEO: Michael A. Bozzuto
CFO: Robert H. (Bob) Wood
HR: Lilly Branco
FYE: September 30
Type: Private

Bozzuto's is a leading wholesale grocery distribution company that supplies food and non-food products to independent supermarkets belonging to the IGA network in Maryland, New Jersey, New York, Pennsylvania, and in New England. The company distributes a full line of grocery items, including meat products, produce, and frozen food, as well as household goods and other general merchandise. It carries goods sold under both the IGA and Hy-Top labels, in addition to national brands. Bozzuto's also owns about 10 supermarkets in Connecticut and Massachusetts operating under the Adams Super Food Stores banner. The company, founded in 1945, is owned and operated by the Bozzuto family.

	Annual Growth	9/02	9/03	9/04	9/05	9/06
Est. sales ($ mil.)	8.3%	—	—	—	1,080.0	1,170.0
Employees	0.0%	—	—	—	3,100	3,100

BP LUBRICANTS USA, INC.

1500 Valley Rd.
Wayne, NJ 07470
Phone: 973-633-2200
Fax: 973-633-0879
Web: www.castrolusa.com

CEO: Paul Waterman
CFO: –
HR: –
FYE: December 31
Type: Subsidiary

BP Lubricants USA (formerly Castrol Consumer North America) spends as much time on top of a hood as it does under them. The company, the Castrol brand sponsor of a variety of drag racing, funny car, and Formula 1 racecar drivers, is a distributor of Castrol synthetic lubricants to automotive service providers and retailers in North America. It also provides specialty lubricants, including degreasers, lubes, and transmission fluids, for boating, motorcycling, racing, and snowmobile customers. BP Lubricants USA is a regional unit of Castrol, the UK-based lubricants firm owned by global oil giant BP.

	Annual Growth	12/03	12/04	12/05	12/06	12/07
Est. sales ($ mil.)	—	—	—	—	—	108.0
Employees	—	—	—	—	—	600

BP NGL

150 W. Warrenville Rd.
Naperville, IL 60563
Phone: 630-836-5000
Fax: 630-836-6535
Web: www.ngl.com

CEO: Jeanne Johns
CFO: William A. (Bill) Spencer
HR: –
FYE: December 31
Type: Subsidiary

BP NGL is just marketing what comes natural. The company, a regional unit of oil giant BP's BP Gas Power and NGL division, is one of North America's leading natural gas producers, with extraction, fractionation, storage, transportation, and gas processing plants throughout the US and Canada. BP NGL markets more than 500,000 barrels of natural gas liquids per day. The company explores for and holds large reserves of gas in western Canada. It also operates gas gathering systems and gas plants, markets and trades gas and natural gas liquids, and is entering the petrochemicals industry.

BP PRUDHOE BAY ROYALTY TRUST

NYSE: BPT

101 Barclay St.
New York, NY 10286
Phone: 212-815-6908
Fax: 212-815-2293

CEO: Remo J. Reale
CFO: –
HR: –
FYE: December 31
Type: Public

BP Prudhoe Bay Royalty Trust may not literally be on top of the world, but it's close: It makes its money from assets at the top end of Alaska (the North Slope). The trust was set up in 1989 by The Standard Oil Company and BP Exploration (both part of BP), along with The Bank of New York to passively administer overriding royalty interests. It distributes royalties on 16% of the first 90,000 barrels of the average actual daily net production per quarter from BP's working interest in the Prudhoe Bay Field, one of the largest oil-producing areas in North America. BP Prudhoe Bay Royalty Trust owns net interests in proved remaining reserves of 97.8 million barrels of crude oil and condensate at the site.

	Annual Growth	12/03	12/04	12/05	12/06	12/07
Sales ($ mil.)	33.4%	56.0	82.7	153.0	184.9	177.4
Net income ($ mil.)	33.8%	54.8	81.7	151.9	183.9	175.7
Market value ($ mil.)	29.5%	609.7	1,033.6	1,425.2	1,647.4	1,716.3
Employees	—	—	—	0	0	0

BP SOLAR INTERNATIONAL INC.

630 Solarex Crt.
Frederick, MD 21703
Phone: 301-698-4200
Fax: –
Web: www.bpsolar.com

CEO: Lee Edwards
CFO: –
HR: –
FYE: December 31
Type: Subsidiary

BP Solar International displays a certain flair as it seeks to transform the sun's energy into power. A subsidiary of UK oil giant BP, the company designs, manufactures, supplies, and installs photovoltaic cells and modules that provide power for homes, remote villages and facilities, commercial offices, and industrial equipment. BP Solar also provides cost estimation, logistic management, remote monitoring, and training services. Customers include Ericsson, NEC, and Telstra. In an effort to expand its presence in the US, BP Solar has begun to sell its home solar power systems at Home Depot; complete installation services are also available.

	Annual Growth	12/03	12/04	12/05	12/06	12/07
Est. sales ($ mil.)	—	—	—	—	—	45.0
Employees	—	—	—	—	—	585

BPI ENERGY HOLDINGS, INC.

AMEX: BPG

30775 Bainbridge Rd., Ste. 280
Solon, OH 44139
Phone: 440-248-4200
Fax: 440-248-4240
Web: www.bpi-energy.com

CEO: James G. (Jim) Azlein
CFO: Randall L. (Randy) Elkins
HR: –
FYE: July 31
Type: Public

BPI Energy (formerly BPI Industries) spends its energy acquiring, exploring for, developing, and producing coalbed methane reserves. The Canadian company moved its headquarters to the US in 2005 to focus on its operations in the Southern and Northern Illinois Basins, where it controls 512,000 acres of coalbed methane rights. It also leases acreage in other properties within the Illinois Basin and in 2007 reported proved reserves of 16.3 billion cu. ft. of natural gas equivalent. Two major gas pipelines cross BPI's acreages, providing access to gas markets for future production.

	Annual Growth	7/03	7/04	7/05	7/06	7/07
Sales ($ mil.)	9.1%	—	—	—	1.1	1.2
Net income ($ mil.)	—	—	—	—	(8.8)	(20.6)
Market value ($ mil.)	(46.7%)	—	—	—	85.7	45.7
Employees	—	—	—	—	—	—

BPO MANAGEMENT SERVICES, INC.

OTC: BPOM

1290 N. Hancock St., Ste. 202
Anaheim, CA 92807
Phone: 714-974-2670
Fax: 714-974-4771
Web: www.bpoms.com

CEO: Patrick A. Dolan
CFO: Donald W. (Don) Rutherford
HR: –
FYE: December 31
Type: Public

BPO Management Services (formerly netGuru) isn't coy about what it does. The company offers business process outsourcing (BPO) engineering services such as custom application development, systems integration, network design, and support, training, and data migration. The company's clients have included Agilent, Ericsson, McGraw-Hill, and Tetra Tech. In 2006 netGuru completed a reverse merger agreement with San Francisco-based BPO Management Services (BPOMS). As part of the merger agreement privately held BPOMS became a subsidiary of netGuru, which then adopted the BPO Management Services name. Chairman and CEO Patrick Dolan and president James Cortens own 45% and 32% of company shares respectively.

	Annual Growth	3/04	3/05	3/06	*12/06	12/07
Sales ($ mil.)	(1.7%)	17.7	15.8	3.9	4.7	16.5
Net income ($ mil.)	—	(3.1)	(0.8)	14.7	(3.3)	(6.5)
Market value ($ mil.)	(75.3%)	—	—	—	22.1	5.4
Employees	(18.2%)	260	307	174	—	—

*Fiscal year change

BPZ ENERGY, INC.

AMEX: BZP

580 Westlake Park Blvd., Ste. 525
Houston, TX 77079
Phone: 281-556-6200
Fax: 281-556-6377
Web: www.bpzenergy.com

CEO: Manolo Pablo Zúñiga-Pflücker
CFO: Edward G. Caminos
HR: –
FYE: December 31
Type: Public

BPZ Energy (formerly Navidec) has navigated into a new line of business. The company once provided information technology services, including security and access services, application integration, and software development. In 2002 the company discontinued reselling operations that had previously offered customers third-party computer hardware and networking equipment systems; that same year it formed Navidec Capital to evaluate acquisition opportunities. In 2004 the company acquired BPZ Energy — a move intended to take the company into the oil and gas business. In 2005 the company officially changed its name to BPZ Energy. BPZ owns oil and gas properties in northwest Peru and southwest Ecuador.

	Annual Growth	12/03	12/04	12/05	12/06	12/07
Sales ($ mil.)	—	—	—	—	—	2.3
Net income ($ mil.)	—	—	—	—	—	(20.5)
Market value ($ mil.)	—	—	—	—	—	826.4
Employees	—	—	—	—	—	—

An in-depth profile of this company is available to Hoover's Online members at hoovers.com.

277

BRADCO SUPPLY CORP.

34 Englehard Ave.
Avenel, NJ 07001
Phone: 732-382-3400
Fax: 732-382-6577
Web: www.bradcosupply.com

CEO: Barry Segal
CFO: Joe Stacy
HR: Andrew Fullerton
FYE: December 31
Type: Private

Bradco Supply offers construction contractors everything they need to put a roof over their clients' heads. The company distributes roofing, siding, windows, and other building materials through about 155 locations in nearly 30 states under several names including Wickes, Bak-A-Lum, FlexMaster, and Pinnacle 7. It is one of the nation's largest distributors of roofing materials for commercial use. Bradco also exports its construction materials to the Caribbean, Europe, Latin America, and the Middle East. The company has been acquiring smaller roofing material businesses including six companies between 2000 and 2005. CEO Barry Segal owns Bradco Supply, which he founded in 1966.

	Annual Growth	12/02	12/03	12/04	12/05	12/06
Sales ($ mil.)	22.6%	850.0	995.0	1,340.0	1,760.0	1,920.0
Employees	15.0%	1,770	2,000	3,250	3,200	3,100

THE BRADFORD EXCHANGE, LTD.

9333 Milwaukee Ave.
Niles, IL 60714
Phone: 847-966-2770
Fax: 847-966-3121
Web: www.collectiblestoday.com

CEO: Richard Tinberg
CFO: −
HR: −
FYE: −
Type: Private

In need of a figurine to complete your latest collection? The Bradford Exchange can help. The company, doing business as collectiblestoday.com, is the e-commerce arm of The Bradford Group, one of the world's largest trading centers for collectibles. The company also sells products of affiliated companies such as The Bradford Editions (mini-plates and canvas prints, Christmas ornaments), Ashton-Drake Galleries (dolls), and Ardleigh Elliot (music boxes), as well as Precious Moments, Elvis memorabilia, and works from artists such as Norman Rockwell and Thomas Kinkade. The Bradford Exchange was founded by J. Roderick MacArthur in 1973.

BRADFORD WHITE CORPORATION

725 Talamore Dr.
Ambler, PA 19002
Phone: 215-641-9400
Fax: 215-641-1612
Web: www.bradfordwhite.com

CEO: A. Robert (Bob) Carnevale
CFO: Robert Hunter
HR: Herbert Foster
FYE: December 31
Type: Private

Not to be confused with Barry "the Walrus of Love" White, the Bradford White Corporation is big in its own right — the water heater industry. The company manufactures water heaters for residential, commercial, and hydronic space heating applications. The privately held company, which was founded in 1881, sells its products to wholesale distributors. It makes oil-fired products, gas power burners, and indirect-fired units. Through subsidiary Bradford White-Canada, it also manufactures products such as pool heaters, oil burners, and air handlers. Another subsidiary, Niles Steel Tank, produces custom steel tanks for companies in the automotive, petrol-chemical, pharmaceutical, and refrigeration industries.

	Annual Growth	12/03	12/04	12/05	12/06	12/07
Est. sales ($ mil.)	—	—	—	—	—	125.8
Employees	—	—	—	—	—	1,219

▥ BRADY CORPORATION

NYSE: BRC

6555 W. Good Hope Rd.
Milwaukee, WI 53223
Phone: 414-358-6600
Fax: 800-292-2289
Web: www.bradycorp.com

CEO: Frank M. Jaehnert
CFO: Frank M. Jaehnert
HR: −
FYE: July 31
Type: Public

It's the story, of a firm named Brady. Brady Corporation makes more than 50,000 industrial identification and specialty coated material products. These include industrial and facility ID products such as printable labels, wire markers, and informational signs; safety and regulatory compliance offerings, including lockout/tagout products, safety signs, and traffic control products; and such components as specialty tapes, computer application products, and die-cut tapes. Through Accidental Health & Safety and its Trafalgar First Aid unit, it supplies safety and first aid products in Australia. Trusts controlled by direct descendants of founder William H. Brady own almost all of the company.

	Annual Growth	7/03	7/04	7/05	7/06	7/07
Sales ($ mil.)	25.2%	554.9	671.2	816.5	1,018.4	1,362.6
Net income ($ mil.)	50.4%	21.4	50.9	81.9	104.2	109.4
Market value ($ mil.)	47.8%	370.6	504.2	1,563.2	1,694.4	1,770.0
Employees	77.8%	—	—	4,500	8,000	—

BRAKE PARTS, INC.

4400 Prime Pkwy.
McHenry, IL 60050
Phone: 815-363-9000
Fax: 815-363-9030
Web: www.raybestos.com

CEO: John Washbish
CFO: −
HR: −
FYE: December 31
Type: Private

Brake Parts Inc. knows how to pull out all of the stops. The company, doing business under the Raybestos brand, manufactures aftermarket motor vehicle brake systems and parts. Products include brake pads and shoes, rotors, drums, calipers, wheel cylinders, master cylinders, and hardware. Investment firm The Cypress Group took control of Brake Parts, Inc. when it bought the aftermarket automotive parts businesses of Dana Corporation late in 2004. Brake Parts is part of Cypress' Affinia Under Vehicle Group of automotive holdings, which includes AIMCO (brake parts), Spicer (chassis and steering components), and Wix (air, fuel, and oil filters).

	Annual Growth	12/03	12/04	12/05	12/06	12/07
Est. sales ($ mil.)	—	—	—	—	—	287.8
Employees	—	—	—	—	—	3,085

BRAND ENERGY & INFRASTRUCTURE SERVICES, INC.

2505 S. Main St.
Kennesaw, GA 30152
Phone: 678-285-1498
Fax: 770-514-0285
Web: www.brandscaffold.com

CEO: Paul T. Wood
CFO: Anthony A. (Tony) Rabb
HR: George Fleck
FYE: December 31
Type: Private

Unlike Superman, Brand Energy & Infrastructure Services (formerly Brand Intermediate Holdings) cannot leap tall buildings in a single bound, but it can provide a way to get you to the top of a tall building. The company, doing business as Brand Services, provides industrial construction services through more than 90 locations; most are in North America, but the company also has service offices around the world. Brand Services mainly sells, rents, and services scaffolding equipment to companies in the chemical, oil, paper, and petrochemical industries for nonresidential building construction, renovation, and maintenance. The company is a holding of energy industry private equity firm First Reserve.

	Annual Growth	12/03	12/04	12/05	12/06	12/07
Sales ($ mil.)	33.1%	347.7	334.0	491.4	811.6	1,089.7
Net income ($ mil.)	—	(5.8)	(6.8)	(14.5)	3.6	(50.4)
Employees	25.9%	4,900	5,000	6,500	—	12,300

BRANDPARTNERS GROUP, INC.
OTC: BPTR

10 Main St.
Rochester, NH 03839
Phone: 603-335-1400
Fax: 603-332-7429
Web: www.bptr.com

CEO: James F. (Jim) Brooks
CFO: James F. (Jim) Brooks
HR: –
FYE: December 31
Type: Public

From conception to construction, BrandPartners Group will help you build a better brand. Through subsidiaries BrandPartners and BrandPartners Europe, the company offers architectural design and construction services, as well as advertising, marketing, and other branding and operations consulting, primarily to the retail banking industry. Another subsidiary, Grafico Incorporated, provides advertising and marketing services, mainly to the sub-prime retail financial services sector, and the company's Building Partners unit provides general contracting services. Originally established in 1984, BrandPartners Group has offices in the US and the UK.

	Annual Growth	12/03	12/04	12/05	12/06	12/07
Sales ($ mil.)	6.8%	33.7	50.6	52.0	52.5	43.8
Net income ($ mil.)	—	(11.0)	14.2	1.9	(2.3)	(12.3)
Market value ($ mil.)	(31.2%)	11.4	30.9	15.4	3.7	2.5
Employees	—	—	—	—	—	—

BRANDYWINE REALTY TRUST
NYSE: BDN

555 E. Lancaster Ave., Ste. 100
Radnor, PA 19087
Phone: 610-325-5600
Fax: 610-325-5622
Web: www.brandywinerealty.com

CEO: Gerard H. (Jerry) Sweeney
CFO: Howard M. Sipzner
HR: Karen M. Heisler
FYE: December 31
Type: Public

If the thought of making it big in real estate intoxicates you, look into Brandywine. A real estate investment trust (REIT), Brandywine buys, leases, sells, and manages commercial properties. It owns some 220 office properties, nearly 25 industrial properties, a mixed-use property, about a dozen properties under development, and more than 400 acres of undeveloped land. Its portfolio totals roughly 29 million sq. ft. of rentable space, mainly located in the Mid-Atlantic region, as well as California and Texas. Brandywine also manages properties and offers such services as construction and redevelopment to other property owners.

	Annual Growth	12/03	12/04	12/05	12/06	12/07
Sales ($ mil.)	22.3%	305.7	323.6	391.5	662.8	684.0
Net income ($ mil.)	(10.2%)	86.7	60.3	42.8	10.5	56.5
Market value ($ mil.)	9.2%	1,098.7	1,625.1	2,535.0	2,936.9	1,560.2
Employees	36.9%	—	—	300	599	562

BRASFIELD & GORRIE, LLC

3021 7th Ave. South
Birmingham, AL 35233
Phone: 205-328-4000
Fax: 205-251-1304
Web: www.brasfieldgorrie.com

CEO: M. Miller Gorrie
CFO: Randall J. Freeman
HR: –
FYE: December 31
Type: Private

Brasfield & Gorrie has a healthy share of the health care construction market. One of the top construction companies in the US, as well as a leading regional contractor in the Southeast, Brasfield & Gorrie also works on hotels, industrial plants, multi-story offices, retail complexes, schools, and water-treatment plants. Commercial and industrial construction together account for most of its revenues. It provides general contracting, design/build, and construction management services. Founded in 1922 by Thomas C. Brasfield, the company was sold to owner Miller Gorrie (chairman and CEO) in 1964.

	Annual Growth	12/02	12/03	12/04	12/05	12/06
Sales ($ mil.)	18.3%	1,011.0	1,040.0	1,260.0	1,645.0	1,980.0
Employees	8.9%	2,088	2,301	2,267	2,743	2,939

BRAVO! DEVELOPMENT, INC.

777 Goodale Blvd., Ste. 100
Columbus, OH 43212
Phone: 614-326-7944
Fax: 614-326-7943
Web: www.bestitalianusa.com

CEO: Rick Doody
CFO: –
HR: –
FYE: December 31
Type: Private

Standing ovations are welcomed but not required at these restaurants. BRAVO! Development operates more than 50 upscale casual-dining spots specializing in Italian cooking that are located in about 20 states. Its flagship chain, Bravo! Cucina Italiana, offers a wide variety of Italian dishes, including pasta, pizza, and several Tuscan-style specialties, which are prepared in exhibition kitchens. Its other concepts include Brio Tuscan Grille, Lindey's (American cuisine), and Bon Vie Bistro (French). Private equity firms Bruckmann, Rosser, Sherrill and Castle Harlan together own 80% of BRAVO! Development; founders and brothers Chris and Rick Doody, who opened their first restaurant in 1992, own the remaining 20%.

	Annual Growth	12/03	12/04	12/05	12/06	12/07
Est. sales ($ mil.)	—	—	—	—	—	65.1
Employees	—	—	—	—	—	3,000

BRAVO RESTAURANTS, INC.

600 W. Jackson Blvd., Ste. 200
Chicago, IL 60661
Phone: 312-463-1210
Fax: 312-798-6761

CEO: Jeffrey (Jeff) Himmel
CFO: Jim Zdarsky
HR: Bob Maldonado
FYE: December 31
Type: Private

Although they didn't create the Chicago deep dish pizza, they are famous for serving it up. Bravo Restaurants operates more than two dozen casual dining spots in four states, primarily in the Chicago area. Its well-known concepts include Italian eateries Gino's East and Edwardo's Natural Pizza; its popular Ed Debevic's locations offer a 1950s-style diner menu and atmosphere. The company also sells frozen food wholesale through its Bravo Foods subsidiary. Ivan Himmel and his son Jeff formed Bravo Restaurants in 1994.

	Annual Growth	12/03	12/04	12/05	12/06	12/07
Est. sales ($ mil.)	—	—	—	—	—	10.5
Employees	—	—	—	—	—	483

BRAVOSOLUTION US

400 Chester Field Pkwy.
Malvern, PA 19355
Phone: 610-240-0600
Fax: 610-240-9470
Web: www.bravosolutionus.com

CEO: John H. McNeill Jr.
CFO: Jonathan T. Cohen
HR: –
FYE: December 31
Type: Subsidiary

BravoSolution US provides strategic sourcing and supply management software. Its suite of enterprise applications allows companies to interact with their suppliers for product sourcing, price negotiation, contract management, and shipment scheduling. The company's software includes tools for sharing product information with customers and managing inventories. It also offers spend analysis and supply chain consulting services. Formerly called Verticalnet, the company was acquired by BravoSolution, a subsidiary of Italian construction giant Italcementi, in 2007.

	Annual Growth	12/02	12/03	12/04	12/05	12/06
Sales ($ mil.)	(22.0%)	43.7	9.6	22.9	20.6	16.2
Net income ($ mil.)	—	(22.5)	(11.0)	(9.7)	(13.7)	(24.5)
Employees	27.9%	65	—	—	136	—

An in-depth profile of this company is available to Hoover's Online members at hoovers.com.

279

BRAZAURO RESOURCES CORPORATION

Pink Sheets: BZOFF

16360 Park Ten Place, Ste. 217
Houston, TX 77084
Phone: 281-579-3400
Fax: 281-579-9799
Web: www.brazauroresources.com

CEO: Mark E. Jones III
CFO: Mark E. Jones III
HR: –
FYE: January 31
Type: Public

Brazauro Resources is hunting for buried treasure in Brazil. The company focuses on acquiring, exploring, and developing properties primarily for gold. Brazauro Resources currently holds stakes in property in the Tapajos gold district in northern Brazil's Pará state. The company shifted its focus to Brazilian gold after results from its diamond mining business in Arkansas proved to be disappointing. Founded in 1986, Brazauro Resources plans to acquire more mineral properties in the Tapajos area, as well as in other regions around the globe.

	Annual Growth	1/03	1/04	1/05	1/06	*1/07
Sales ($ mil.)	—	0.0	0.3	0.0	0.2	0.2
Net income ($ mil.)	—	(2.8)	(0.6)	(3.0)	(8.1)	(5.2)
Employees	86.1%	2	3	3	—	24

*Most recent year available

BRE PROPERTIES, INC.

NYSE: BRE

525 Market St., 4th Fl.
San Francisco, CA 94105
Phone: 415-445-6530
Fax: 415-445-6505
Web: www.breproperties.com

CEO: Constance B. Moore
CFO: Henry L. Hirvela
HR: Deborah Jones
FYE: December 31
Type: Public

The huddled masses that yearn to breathe free of high housing costs turn to BRE Properties. The real estate investment trust (REIT) acquires, develops, and manages multifamily properties in the western US. It owns about 80 apartment communities with some 22,000 units in Arizona, California, and Washington. Most properties offer amenities including clubhouses, exercise facilities, business centers, and swimming pools. The REIT also has about 10 properties under development and owns stakes in about a dozen more. BRE Properties has eliminated its holdings in New Mexico and Nevada to focus on markets in California, where high housing costs and a stable occupancy rate make for an attractive environment.

	Annual Growth	12/03	12/04	12/05	12/06	12/07
Sales ($ mil.)	5.8%	275.1	280.6	298.1	330.0	345.2
Net income ($ mil.)	11.4%	83.1	73.5	80.9	120.2	128.1
Market value ($ mil.)	5.5%	1,669.7	2,032.4	2,333.7	3,282.5	2,065.8
Employees	(0.6%)	—	—	824	—	814

BREEZE-EASTERN CORPORATION

AMEX: BZC

700 Liberty Ave.
Union, NJ 07083
Phone: 908-686-4000
Fax: 908-686-9292
Web: breeze-eastern.com

CEO: Robert L.G. (Bob) White
CFO: Joseph F. Spanier
HR: –
FYE: March 31
Type: Public

Products made by Breeze-Eastern, formerly TransTechnology, don't lift aircraft into the sky, but they do lift people and cargo onto aircraft. The company makes helicopter rescue hoists, cargo winches, cargo tie-downs, external hook systems, and weapons handling systems. Its external cargo hook systems for helicopters range in capacity from 1,000 pounds to 36,000 pounds. The company's weapons-handling products include hoists to lift weapons onto carrier-based aircraft and to manipulate weapons on ground-based fighting vehicles. US government (primarily military) contracts account for more than 50% of Breeze-Eastern's sales.

	Annual Growth	3/04	3/05	3/06	3/07	3/08
Sales ($ mil.)	4.1%	64.6	62.9	64.4	73.3	76.0
Net income ($ mil.)	53.3%	1.7	(2.8)	1.3	4.0	9.4
Market value ($ mil.)	19.6%	49.7	53.6	85.4	94.8	101.8
Employees	—	—	—	—	206	—

BREITBURN ENERGY PARTNERS L.P.

NASDAQ (GM): BBEP

515 S. Flower St., Ste. 4800
Los Angeles, CA 90071
Phone: 213-225-5900
Fax: 213-225-5916
Web: www.breitburn.com

CEO: Randall H. (Randy) Breitenbach
CFO: James G. Jackson
HR: –
FYE: December 31
Type: Public

Oil and gas futures burn brightly for BreitBurn Energy Partners, one of California's largest independent exploration and production companies. With assets in Southern California, Florida, Kentucky, Michigan, Texas, and Wyoming, the company has estimated proved reserves of 142.2 million barrels of oil equivalent. BreitBurn Energy Partners' predecessor was founded in 1998 by Randall Breitenbach and Halbert Washburn. Breitenbach and Washburn serve as co-CEOs of BreitBurn Energy Partners' general partner, BreitBurn GP LLC. Canada's Provident Energy Trust acquired 92% of the predecessor company in 2004. It retains control of BreitBurn Energy Partners.

	Annual Growth	12/03	12/04	12/05	12/06	12/07
Sales ($ mil.)	15.5%	42.2	41.2	101.9	138.0	75.0
Net income ($ mil.)	—	14.6	3.3	39.0	49.9	(60.4)
Market value ($ mil.)	265.7%	—	—	—	529.6	1,936.9
Employees	2.7%	—	—	146	150	—

BREMER FINANCIAL CORPORATION

445 Minnesota St., Ste. 2000
St. Paul, MN 55101
Phone: 651-227-7621
Fax: 651-312-3550
Web: www.bremer.com

CEO: Stan K. Dardis
CFO: Robert B. Buck
HR: Carla L. Paulson
FYE: December 31
Type: Private

Bremer Financial Corporation is the holding company for Bremer Bank, which operates more than 100 branches across Minnesota, North Dakota, and Wisconsin. It offers traditional retail banking services such as checking and savings accounts, money markets, CDs, and credit cards. Commercial mortgages and business loans together account for approximately two-thirds of company's loan portfolio. In addition to deposits and loans, the bank also provides insurance, investment management, brokerage, and trust services. The not-for-profit Otto Bremer Foundation owns more than 90% of Bremer Financial; the company's employees own the rest.

BRENDAN TECHNOLOGIES, INC.

OTC: BDTE

2236 Rutherford Rd., Ste. 107
Carlsbad, CA 92008
Phone: 760-929-7500
Fax: –
Web: www.brendan.com

CEO: John R. Dunn
CFO: Lowell W. Giffhorn
HR: –
FYE: June 30
Type: Public

Omni U.S.A. has shifted gears. In January 2006 the company sold its power transmission and jack manufacturing units and acquired software company Brendan Technologies, changing its name in the process. Brendan's software is used to manage immunoassay testing in agricultural, biopharmaceutical, clinical, research, and veterinary laboratories. Applications include automating of immunoassay testing, data management, quality assurance, and regulatory compliance.

	Annual Growth	6/03	6/04	6/05	6/06	6/07
Sales ($ mil.)	(60.2%)	20.0	19.1	21.0	0.7	0.5
Net income ($ mil.)	—	0.4	0.3	(0.6)	(0.9)	(2.1)
Market value ($ mil.)	76.4%	—	1.6	1.7	6.6	9.0
Employees	—	—	—	—	—	14

BRENNTAG NORTH AMERICA, INC.

5083 Pottsville Pike
Reading, PA 19605
Phone: 610-926-6100
Fax: 610-926-0411
Web: www.brenntagnorthamerica.com

CEO: Stephen R. (Steve) Clark
CFO: H. Edward Boyadjian
HR: –
FYE: December 31
Type: Subsidiary

If you live in the US and need a chemical fix, Brenntag North America can set you up. One of the largest chemical distributors in North America, the company offers hundreds of industrial and specialty chemicals — from acetic acid to zinc oxide — and provides custom blending and packaging of chemicals in dry, liquid, or gaseous states. Customers include manufacturers in such industries as chemicals, pharmaceuticals, paints, electronics, pulp and paper, cosmetics, food and beverages, textiles, and water treatment. European private equity group BC Partners acquired Brenntag — and thus Brenntag North America — from Bain Capital in 2006 for something close to $4 billion.

BRESLER & REINER, INC.

11200 Rockville Pike, Ste. 502
Rockville, MD 20852
Phone: 301-945-4300
Fax: 301-945-4301
Web: www.breslerandreiner.com

OTC: BRER

CEO: Sidney M. Bresler
CFO: Darryl M. Edelstein
HR: –
FYE: December 31
Type: Public

Bresler & Reiner are like the bosom buddies of property development in the Mid-Atlantic region. The firm acquires and develops commercial, residential, and hospitality properties in such markets as Philadelphia, Baltimore, and Washington, DC. It owns or holds ownership interests in nearly 50 commercial office and flex warehouse buildings, totaling nearly 4 million sq. ft. of space, plus five apartment communities, one hotel, and land slated for development. Beyond the Mid-Atlantic, a good portion of its portfolio is located in Houston. The Bresler and Reiner families collectively own more than 70% of the company.

	Annual Growth	12/03	12/04	12/05	12/06	12/07
Sales ($ mil.)	31.5%	34.7	78.3	122.9	100.4	103.9
Net income ($ mil.)	—	9.6	4.4	(2.3)	15.7	(9.3)
Employees	21.6%	—	15	22	28	27

BRESNAN COMMUNICATIONS, INC.

1 Manhattanville Rd.
Purchase, NY 10577
Phone: 914-641-3300
Fax: 914-641-3301
Web: www.bresnan.com

CEO: William J. Bresnan
CFO: Andrew C. (Andy) Kober
HR: –
FYE: December 31
Type: Private

Who says there's nowhere to surf in Montana? Not Bresnan Communications — the company supplies channel and Web surfers with cable TV and broadband Internet service in Big Sky Country, as well as in Colorado, Montana, Utah, and Wyoming. Bresnan serves more than 300,000 small-market customers over its fiber-optic coaxial network. It has also begun offering digital phone service in select markets. CEO William Bresnan founded the company in 1984.

	Annual Growth	12/03	12/04	12/05	12/06	12/07
Est. sales ($ mil.)	—	—	—	—	—	147.8
Employees	—	—	—	—	—	1,100

THE BRIAD GROUP

78 Okner Pkwy.
Livingston, NJ 07039
Phone: 973-597-6433
Fax: 973-597-6422
Web: www.briad.com

CEO: Bradford L. (Brad) Honigfeld
CFO: Dave Cahill
HR: Grant Schneider
FYE: December 31
Type: Private

This hospitality company is thankful for Friday's. The Briad Group is the #1 operator of T.G.I. Friday's restaurants, with about 70 locations in six states, primarily in Arizona, California, and New Jersey. Franchised from Carlson Restaurants Worldwide, the casual dining restaurants are popular for their appetizers and bar-like atmosphere. Briad is also a leading franchisee of Wendy's International, with about 50 Wendy's fast food restaurants in New Jersey, New York, and Pennsylvania. The company also has a small number of Hilton and Marriott hotels. Founder and CEO Bradford Honigfeld leads an investment group that owns Briad.

	Annual Growth	12/02	12/03	12/04	12/05	12/06
Est. sales ($ mil.)	—	—	—	—	—	9.1
Employees	—	—	—	—	—	419

THE BRICKMAN GROUP, LTD.

18227D Flower Hill Way
Gaithersburg, MD 20879
Phone: 301-987-9200
Fax: 240-683-2030
Web: www.brickmangroup.com

CEO: Scott W. Brickman
CFO: Charlie Silcox
HR: –
FYE: December 31
Type: Private

The Brickman Group offers landscape design and maintenance services for college campuses, municipal properties, sports facilities, and retail establishments. It provides sports turf services such as field design and consulting, irrigation, mowing, and field maintenance for MLB and the Olympic Games. Serving more than 10,000 clients, the company has also taken on such special projects as repairing New Orleans City Park's irrigation system after Hurricane Katrina. Founded in 1939 by Theodore Brickman, the group has more than 100 branch offices in about 25 US states. Private equity firm Leonard Green & Partners owns a majority shareholding of the company.

	Annual Growth	12/03	12/04	12/05	12/06	12/07
Est. sales ($ mil.)	—	—	—	—	—	454.5
Employees	—	—	—	—	—	5,047

BRIDGE BANCORP, INC.

2200 Montauk Hwy.
Bridgehampton, NY 11932
Phone: 631-537-1000
Fax: 631-537-1835
Web: www.bridgenb.com

OTC: BDGE

CEO: Kevin M. O'Connor
CFO: Howard H. Nolan
HR: Deborah McGrory
FYE: December 31
Type: Public

Bridge Bancorp wants you to cross over to its subsidiary The Bridgehampton National Bank, which operates more than a dozen locations in eastern Long Island, New York. Founded in 1910, the bank offers traditional deposit services to area individuals, small businesses, and municipalities, including checking, savings, and money market accounts, and CDs. Deposits are invested primarily in mortgages, which account for some 80% of the bank's loan portfolio. Title insurance services are available through bank subsidiary Bridge Abstract; wealth management services include financial planning, estate administration, and trustee services.

	Annual Growth	12/03	12/04	12/05	12/06	12/07
Assets ($ mil.)	4.4%	511.6	547.2	533.4	573.6	607.4
Net income ($ mil.)	(3.6%)	9.6	10.4	9.6	8.2	8.3
Market value ($ mil.)	11.2%	97.0	191.4	153.3	145.9	148.5
Employees	—	—	—	—	—	157

An in-depth profile of this company is available to Hoover's Online members at hoovers.com.

281

BRIDGE CAPITAL HOLDINGS

NASDAQ (GM): BBNK

55 Almaden Blvd.	CEO: Daniel P. (Dan) Myers
San Jose, CA 95113	CFO: Thomas A. (Tom) Sa
Phone: 408-423-8500	HR: –
Fax: 408-423-8520	FYE: December 31
Web: www.bridgebank.com	Type: Public

Bridge Capital Holdings helps its business clients get from here to there. It is the holding company of Bridge Bank, which serves small, midsized, and emerging technology businesses in California's Silicon Valley. The bank has regional branches in Palo Alto and San Jose; it also has Small Business Administration (SBA) loan production offices in Redwood City, San Francisco, San Ramon, and Sacramento. Additional SBA offices are located in Southern California; Dallas, Texas; and Reston, Virginia. Bridge Bank converted to a holding company structure in 2004.

	Annual Growth	12/03	12/04	12/05	12/06	12/07
Assets ($ mil.)	24.4%	—	402.0	536.5	722.0	774.8
Net income ($ mil.)	53.7%	—	3.0	5.7	8.6	10.9
Market value ($ mil.)	12.7%	—	97.4	115.2	129.2	139.3
Employees	28.5%	—	—	103	134	170

BRIDGELINE SOFTWARE, INC.

NASDAQ (CM): BLSW

10 6th Rd.	CEO: Thomas L. Massie
Woburn, MA 01801	CFO: Gary M. Cebula
Phone: 781-376-5555	HR: Peter (Pip) Winslow
Fax: 781-376-5033	FYE: September 30
Web: www.bridgelinesw.com	Type: Public

Bridgeline Software believes the key to business optimization lies in the Web. The company develops Web service applications, including content and relationship management systems. It also offers e-commerce, usability engineering, e-training, search engine optimization, and rich media development services. Bridgeline targets financial services providers, government agencies, foundations and non-profit organizations, and companies involved in technology and life sciences. Its customers have included Depository Trust & Clearing, John Hancock, Nomura Securities, and Pfizer.

	Annual Growth	9/03	9/04	9/05	9/06	9/07
Sales ($ mil.)	—	—	—	—	—	11.1
Net income ($ mil.)	—	—	—	—	—	(1.9)
Market value ($ mil.)	—	—	—	—	—	34.9
Employees	—	—	—	—	—	138

BRIDGESTONE AMERICAS HOLDING, INC.

535 Marriott Dr.	CEO: Mark A. Emkes
Nashville, TN 37214	CFO: Shoji Mizuochi
Phone: 615-937-1000	HR: Frank R. Doman
Fax: 615-937-3621	FYE: December 31
Web: www.bridgestone-firestone.com	Type: Subsidiary

Bridgestone Americas Holding likes to deal with round numbers. The Pan American subsidiary of Bridgestone Corporation is best known for the tires bearing the Bridgestone, Firestone, or Dayton logo found on cars, trucks, motorcycles, and tractors, but also makes tires for earthmoving equipment and aircraft. Bridgestone also makes rubber building products for roofing and industrial textiles. Other products include natural rubber and synthetic polymers, air spring suspensions for heavy-duty trucks, and aftermarket performance suspensions for passenger cars.

BRIDGFORD FOODS CORPORATION

NASDAQ (GM): BRID

1308 N. Patt St.	CEO: John V. Simmons
Anaheim, CA 92801	CFO: Raymond F. Lancy
Phone: 714-526-5533	HR: Brenda Potts
Fax: 714-526-4360	FYE: Friday nearest October 31
Web: www.bridgford.com	Type: Public

Bridgford Foods is comfortable with comfort food and eschews fat-free fads to pile on what it knows customers want: rolls, cheese, and sausage (it's one of the nation's largest sellers of jerky and other meat snacks). Refrigerated and snack foods account for about 60% of its sales; the remainder comes from frozen foods. Bridgford Foods' nearly 500 products are marketed to food retailers, restaurants, and institutions across the US and Canada through its own sales network and through brokers, cooperatives, and distributors. More than one-quarter of Bridgford's products are manufactured or processed by third parties.

	Annual Growth	10/03	10/04	10/05	10/06	10/07
Sales ($ mil.)	(2.1%)	136.3	137.9	130.8	134.3	125.1
Net income ($ mil.)	—	1.2	0.0	(0.9)	1.2	(0.3)
Market value ($ mil.)	(2.3%)	75.1	84.0	71.8	61.1	68.3
Employees	(7.4%)	—	—	739	684	—

BRIGGS & STRATTON CORPORATION

NYSE: BGG

12301 W. Wirth St.	CEO: John S. Shiely
Wauwatosa, WI 53222	CFO: James E. (Jim) Brenn
Phone: 414-259-5333	HR: Jeffrey G. Mahloch
Fax: 414-259-5773	FYE: Sunday nearest June 30
Web: www.briggsandstratton.com	Type: Public

Briggs & Stratton doesn't mind getting yanked around. The company is the world's largest manufacturer of air-cooled gas engines (ranging from 3 to 31 horsepower) for use in lawn mowers and garden tillers. Through its chief subsidiary, Briggs & Stratton Power Products Group, the company also manufactures portable generators, pressure washers, switches, welders, and other related products. Lawn and garden equipment manufacturers are its biggest customers, with generator, pressure washer, and pump manufacturers following. Engine products include the Classic, I/C, Sprint, Quattro, Quantum, INTEK, and Vanguard brands. The engines are made in the US and are sold worldwide through its own sales and service centers.

	Annual Growth	6/03	6/04	6/05	6/06	6/07
Sales ($ mil.)	6.8%	1,657.6	1,947.4	2,654.9	2,542.2	2,157.2
Net income ($ mil.)	(77.7%)	80.6	136.1	136.6	102.3	0.2
Market value ($ mil.)	30.1%	547.3	1,116.3	1,820.2	1,592.8	1,566.4
Employees	(4.8%)	4,503	4,230	4,058	3,874	3,693

BRIGHAM EXPLORATION COMPANY

NASDAQ (GS): BEXP

6300 Bridge Point Pkwy., Bldg. 2, Ste. 500	CEO: Ben M. (Bud) Brigham
Austin, TX 78730	CFO: Eugene B. Shepherd Jr.
Phone: 512-427-3300	HR: –
Fax: 512-427-3400	FYE: December 31
Web: www.bexp3d.com	Type: Public

Still a young company, Brigham Exploration was one of the first small independent exploration and production firms to use 3-D seismic imaging. The company continues to rely on 3-D and other advanced technologies for onshore exploration. It explores mainly in the Anadarko Basin, the onshore Texas Gulf Coast, and West Texas. Since its founding by CEO Ben Brigham in 1990, Brigham Exploration has drilled 760 wells. In 2007 the company had 284 gross and 104 net productive wells. That year Brigham Exploration had estimated proved reserves of about 140.2 billion cu. ft. of natural gas equivalent.

	Annual Growth	12/03	12/04	12/05	12/06	12/07
Sales ($ mil.)	23.2%	51.7	72.2	97.0	106.3	119.0
Net income ($ mil.)	(13.6%)	18.3	19.6	27.4	19.8	10.2
Market value ($ mil.)	2.0%	313.9	378.3	532.7	329.0	339.9
Employees	—	—	—	64	—	—

BRIGHT HORIZONS FAMILY SOLUTIONS, INC.

200 Talcott Ave. South	CEO: David H. Lissy
Watertown, MA 02472	CFO: Elizabeth J. Boland
Phone: 617-673-8000	HR: Danroy T. (Dan) Henry
Fax: 617-673-8001	FYE: December 31
Web: www.brighthorizons.com	Type: Private

At Bright Horizons Family Solutions, kids learn while parents earn. The firm operates more than 600 workplace child-care centers in more than 40 US states, the District of Columbia, Canada, Ireland, and the UK. Bright Horizons offers day care, emergency back-up, before-and after-school, and vacation care, as well as summer camps, elementary schools, and college admissions counseling services. More than 80% of its centers are accredited by the National Association for the Education of Young Children, which generally uses more stringent standards than those required by states. In 2008 Bright Horizons was acquired by Bain Capital, a Boston-based private equity firm, for a reported $1.3 billion.

	Annual Growth	12/03	12/04	12/05	12/06	12/07
Sales ($ mil.)	13.1%	472.8	551.8	625.3	697.9	774.6
Net income ($ mil.)	18.2%	20.0	27.3	36.7	41.7	39.1
Employees	1.1%	—	—	18,000	18,000	18,400

BRIGHT NOW! DENTAL, INC.

201 E. Sandpointe, Ste. 800	CEO: Steven C. (Steve) Bilt
Santa Ana, CA 92707	CFO: Bradley E. (Brad) Schmidt
Phone: 714-668-1300	HR: Catherine R. Crow
Fax: 714-428-1300	FYE: December 31
Web: www.brightnow.com	Type: Private

Bright Now! Dental is smiling all the way to the bank. Bright Now! Dental provides dental practice management services to nearly 300 dental offices in 18 states. Bright Now! Dental provides its dental practices with accounting, information technology, marketing, and other administrative services. Bright Now! Dental's staff and affiliated dentists serve more than 2.5 million dental patients a year; and provide cosmetic, children's, orthodontics, general, preventive, and specialty dental services. Freeman Spogli & Co. is Bright Now! Dental's majority owner.

	Annual Growth	12/03	12/04	12/05	12/06	12/07
Est. sales ($ mil.)	—	—	—	—	—	138.3
Employees	—	—	—	—	—	4,100

BRIGHTPOINT, INC.

NASDAQ (GS): CELL

2601 Metropolis Pkwy., Ste. 210	CEO: Robert J. Laikin
Plainfield, IN 46168	CFO: Anthony W. Boor
Phone: 317-707-2355	HR: Annette Cyr
Fax: 317-707-2512	FYE: December 31
Web: www.brightpoint.com	Type: Public

Brightpoint makes money moving mobiles. The company is a top global distributor of mobile phones and other wireless products, acting as a middleman between manufacturers and wireless service providers. It ships the equipment to companies that sell mobile phones and accessories, including wireless carriers, dealers, and retailers; customers include Vodafone, Best Buy, and Sprint Nextel. Brightpoint also offers a range of services that includes warehousing, product fulfillment, purchasing, contract manufacturing, call center outsourcing, customized packaging, activation, and Web marketing.

	Annual Growth	12/03	12/04	12/05	12/06	12/07
Sales ($ mil.)	24.3%	1,800.4	1,859.4	2,140.2	2,425.4	4,300.3
Net income ($ mil.)	41.9%	11.7	13.8	10.4	35.6	47.4
Market value ($ mil.)	78.6%	123.1	129.5	638.9	684.0	1,251.7
Employees	39.4%	—	—	1,683	2,112	3,269

BRIGHTSTAR CORP.

9725 NW 117th Ave., Ste. 300	CEO: R. Marcelo Claure
Miami, FL 33178	CFO: Dennis Strand
Phone: 305-421-6000	HR: –
Fax: –	FYE: December 31
Web: www.brightstarcorp.com	Type: Private

Brightstar shines in the constellation of telecommunications distributors. The company distributes wireless communications products, including cell phones and accessories, wireless data equipment, and prepaid wireless products. It also offers inventory management, logistics, fulfillment, customized packaging, and assembly services. Brightstar distributes cell phones made by the likes of Motorola, Kyocera, Samsung, LG, and Sony Ericsson. Brightstar operates facilities in more than 40 countries. It sells to network operators, retailers, and resellers.

	Annual Growth	12/02	12/03	12/04	12/05	12/06
Sales ($ mil.)	59.4%	—	—	—	2,252.0	3,590.0
Employees	16.9%	—	—	—	1,441	1,684

BRILLSTEIN ENTERTAINMENT PARTNERS, LLC

9150 Wilshire Blvd., Ste. 350	CEO: Jon Liebman
Beverly Hills, CA 90212	CFO: –
Phone: 310-275-6135	HR: –
Fax: 310-275-6180	FYE: December 31
	Type: Private

Brillstein Entertainment Partners (formerly Brillstein-Grey Entertainment) has its eyes on the talent. The agency is a powerful Hollywood management firm with a talent division of some 200 clients including stars such as Jennifer Aniston and Brad Pitt. It also produces movies (*Scary Movie*) and TV shows that showcase the talents of its clients. Producer Bernie Brillstein founded the Brillstein Co. in 1969 and helped launch programs such as *Saturday Night Live* and *The Muppet Show*. Brad Grey came to work for his mentor in 1985, and the two became equal partners in 1991. Brillstein sold his ownership stake to Grey, who sold the company to longtime executives Cynthia Pett-Dante and Jon Liebman in 2005.

	Annual Growth	12/03	12/04	12/05	12/06	12/07
Est. sales ($ mil.)	—	—	—	—	—	53.3
Employees	—	—	—	—	—	290

BRINKER INTERNATIONAL, INC.

NYSE: EAT

6820 LBJ Fwy., Ste. 200	CEO: Douglas H. (Doug) Brooks
Dallas, TX 75240	CFO: Charles M. (Chuck) Sonsteby
Phone: 972-980-9917	HR: Valerie L. Davisson
Fax: 972-770-9593	FYE: Last Wednesday in June
Web: www.brinker.com	Type: Public

This company is one hot player in the restaurant industry. Brinker International is the world's #2 casual-dining restaurant operator in terms of revenue (behind Darden Restaurants), with more than 1,800 restaurant locations in some 20 countries. Its flagship Chili's Grill & Bar chain boasts about 1,300 restaurants and trails only Applebee's as the largest full-service restaurant chain. Specializing in southwestern-style dishes, Chili's menu features fajitas, margarita grilled chicken, and its popular baby back ribs. Brinker also operates the Italian-themed Romano's Macaroni Grill, with more than 240 locations, as well as such smaller chains as On The Border Mexican Grill & Cantina and Maggiano's Little Italy.

	Annual Growth	6/03	6/04	6/05	6/06	6/07
Sales ($ mil.)	7.4%	3,285.4	3,707.5	3,912.9	4,151.3	4,376.9
Net income ($ mil.)	8.1%	168.6	150.9	160.2	212.4	230.1
Market value ($ mil.)	8.3%	2,347.2	2,062.0	2,367.5	1,972.1	3,225.6
Employees	2.5%	—	—	108,500	110,800	113,900

An in-depth profile of this company is available to Hoover's Online members at hoovers.com.

283

THE BRINK'S COMPANY
NYSE: BCO

1801 Bayberry Ct.
Richmond, VA 23226
Phone: 804-289-9600
Fax: 804-289-9770
Web: www.brinkscompany.com

CEO: Michael T. Dan
CFO: Michael J. (Mike) Cazer
HR: Frank T. Lennon
FYE: December 31
Type: Public

Teetering on the brink of a security disaster? The Brink's Company can help. The company operates through two main subsidiaries: its Brink's, Inc. is a leading operator of armored cars that transport cash for banks and retailers (85% of sales), and Brink's Home Security (BHS) installs and monitors alarm systems (15% of sales). More than 90% of employees work at Brink's, Inc; the remainder are at BHS. Brink's in 2007 began reviewing shareholder proposals for alternative options for the company, and hired consulting firm Monitor Company Group to help in a re-examination of strategic moves. It has subsequently decided to spin-off BHS into a separate publicly traded company.

	Annual Growth	12/03	12/04	12/05	12/06	12/07
Sales ($ mil.)	(5.3%)	3,998.6	4,718.1	2,549.0	2,837.6	3,219.0
Net income ($ mil.)	47.0%	29.4	121.5	142.4	587.2	137.3
Market value ($ mil.)	23.9%	1,227.7	2,240.8	2,812.3	3,100.1	2,891.4
Employees	8.5%	—	—	45,800	48,700	53,900

BRISTOL COMPRESSORS INTERNATIONAL, INC.

15185 Industrial Park Rd.
Bristol, VA 24202
Phone: 276-466-4121
Fax: 276-645-7500
Web: www.bristolcompressors.com

CEO: Wayne J. Kennedy
CFO: –
HR: Lisa Phipps
FYE: December 31
Type: Private

What would air conditioners be without compressors? Probably just hunks of lifeless plastic. Fortunately, Bristol Compressors is well aware of this. The company manufactures compressors that are used inside residential and commercial air conditioning units and heat pumps. Compressors turn refrigerant (Freon) from a cool gas into a hot, high-pressure gas that is then passed on to the condenser. The company sells its products — under the Benchmark and Bristol brand names — to original equipment manufacturers and wholesale distributors in more than 50 countries worldwide. Bristol Compressors was sold to KPS Capital Partners, an affiliate of KPS Special Situations Funds, by Johnson Controls in 2007.

BRISTOL WEST HOLDINGS, INC.

5701 Stirling Rd.
Davie, FL 33314
Phone: 954-316-5200
Fax: 954-316-5275
Web: www.bristolwest.com

CEO: James R. Fisher
CFO: Robert D. Sadler
HR: Nila J. Harrison
FYE: December 31
Type: Private

Looking for auto coverage? Go West, young man. Bristol West Holdings sells non-standard private passenger insurance — that is, insurance for those who have trouble getting standard coverage because of bad driving records, age, limited financial resources, and the like. Most of Bristol West's policyholders purchase minimum liability coverage as required by the states they live in. The company operates in 22 states (it is licensed in 38 states and the District of Columbia), with nearly 65% of its gross written premiums coming from California, Florida, and Texas. Farmers Group, a unit of Zurich Financial Services, acquired Bristol West in 2007.

	Annual Growth	12/02	12/03	12/04	12/05	12/06
Assets ($ mil.)	10.5%	633.1	777.9	1,040.9	893.4	944.6
Net income ($ mil.)	38.3%	11.5	33.5	61.1	54.7	42.1
Employees	(3.5%)	—	1,285	1,288	1,205	1,154

BRISTOL-MYERS SQUIBB COMPANY
NYSE: BMY

345 Park Ave.
New York, NY 10154
Phone: 212-546-4000
Fax: 212-546-4020
Web: www.bms.com

CEO: James M. (Jim) Cornelius
CFO: Jean-Marc Huet
HR: Anthony McBride
FYE: December 31
Type: Public

Pharmaceutical giant Bristol-Myers Squibb (BMS) makes big bucks on matters of the heart. The company's blockbuster cardiovascular line-up includes heart disease drug Plavix, as well as Pravachol (which lowers cholesterol) and Avapro (for hypertension). BMS also makes antipsychotic medication Abilify and drugs in a number of other therapeutic categories, particularly oncology, virology (including HIV), and autoimmune disease. Through its Mead Johnson subsidiary, BMS makes Enfamil infant formula and other nutritional products for children. Its ConvaTec business produces ostomy supplies and wound-cleansing products.

	Annual Growth	12/03	12/04	12/05	12/06	12/07
Sales ($ mil.)	(1.9%)	20,894.0	19,380.0	19,207.0	17,914.0	19,348.0
Net income ($ mil.)	(8.6%)	3,106.0	2,388.0	3,000.0	1,585.0	2,165.0
Market value ($ mil.)	(1.4%)	55,483.5	49,882.1	44,971.9	51,639.8	52,350.5
Employees	(1.2%)	—	—	43,000	43,000	42,000

BRISTOW GROUP INC.
NYSE: BRS

2000 W. Sam Houston Pkwy. South, Ste. 1700
Houston, TX 77042
Phone: 713-267-7600
Fax: 713-267-7620
Web: www.bristowgroup.com

CEO: William E. (Bill) Chiles
CFO: Perry L. Elders
HR: Hilary Ware
FYE: March 31
Type: Public

Bristow Group takes its customers for a ride. The company offers helicopter transportation services for offshore petroleum workers and equipment. Through its Air Logistics and Bristow Helicopters units and several affiliates, Bristow Group serves oil and gas exploration and production companies in the world's major offshore oil production zones. Its main operating areas are the North Sea and the Gulf of Mexico. About 20% of the company's sales come from Shell Oil and related entities. Bristow Group operates a fleet of about 400 aircraft, which consists primarily of helicopters but also includes some fixed-wing aircraft. Affiliates operate another 140-plus aircraft.

	Annual Growth	3/04	3/05	3/06	3/07	3/08
Sales ($ mil.)	15.6%	567.6	673.7	768.9	897.9	1,012.8
Net income ($ mil.)	15.8%	57.8	51.6	57.8	74.2	104.0
Market value ($ mil.)	15.5%	722.6	776.8	722.6	859.7	1,284.0
Employees	(0.3%)	4,200	3,300	4,200	4,159	—

BRITTON & KOONTZ CAPITAL CORPORATION
NASDAQ (CM): BKBK

500 Main St.
Natchez, MS 39120
Phone: 601-445-5576
Fax: 601-445-2488
Web: www.bkbank.com

CEO: W. Page Ogden
CFO: William M. Salters
HR: –
FYE: December 31
Type: Public

You'll find this bank along the banks of the Mississippi. Britton & Koontz Capital is the holding company for Britton & Koontz First National Bank, which has about a half-dozen branches in Natchez and Vicksburg, Mississippi, and Baton Rouge, Louisiana. Targeting individual and local business customers, the bank offers such standard deposit products as checking, savings, and money market accounts; CDs; and trust services. A majority of the bank's loan portfolio consists of real estate loans; however, Britton & Koontz Capital also makes agricultural, business, and consumer loans. Brothers William and Audley Britton, along with George Koontz, established the bank in 1836.

	Annual Growth	12/03	12/04	12/05	12/06	12/07
Assets ($ mil.)	(0.4%)	374.4	377.2	389.3	369.3	368.4
Net income ($ mil.)	2.7%	2.7	2.8	3.2	3.6	3.0
Market value ($ mil.)	(2.2%)	36.5	38.6	45.0	41.9	33.4
Employees	4.7%	—	—	103	—	113

BROADCAST INTERNATIONAL, INC.
OTC: BCST

7050 Union Park Ave., Ste. 600
Salt Lake City, UT 84047
Phone: 801-562-2252
Fax: 801-562-1773
Web: www.brin.com

CEO: Rodney M. (Rod) Tiede
CFO: Randy Turner
HR: –
FYE: December 31
Type: Public

Broadcast International (BI) has traded laser vision for video vision. The company provides network integration services for large retailers and other geographically dispersed businesses, helping employees, customers, and others communicate using satellite, Internet video streaming, and Wi-Fi technologies. BI offers hosting of video streaming, as well as audio and video production capabilities. Customers include Caterpillar, Safeway, and Chevron. In 2004 BI acquired Interact Devices, which developed an encoding system (CodecSys) used to create streaming video; it has also acquired video processing technology from UTEK.

	Annual Growth	12/03	12/04	12/05	12/06	12/07
Sales ($ mil.)	(3.2%)	4.9	5.4	5.4	13.9	4.3
Net income ($ mil.)	—	(3.9)	(16.5)	(5.6)	(15.6)	(26.3)
Market value ($ mil.)	8.7%	100.0	67.1	49.2	32.0	139.8
Employees	(0.8%)	—	44	44	35	43

BROADCAST MUSIC, INC.

320 W. 57th St.
New York, NY 10019
Phone: 212-586-2000
Fax: 212-245-8986
Web: www.bmi.com

CEO: Del R. Bryant
CFO: Bruce Esworthy
HR: –
FYE: June 30
Type: Not-for-profit

If you are a composer or musician, Broadcast Music, Inc. (BMI) is here to see that your royalties are paid. The not-for-profit organization collects licensing fees from a host of outlets and venues (such as radio stations, TV programs, Web sites, restaurants, and nightclubs) and distributes them to the more than 350,000 songwriters, composers, and music publishers it represents. Its catalog of compositions includes more than 6.5 million works by a diverse range of artists including the Dixie Chicks, Marilyn Manson, Willie Nelson, Sting, and Shania Twain.

	Annual Growth	6/02	6/03	6/04	6/05	6/06
Sales ($ mil.)	7.9%	574.0	630.0	673.0	728.0	779.0
Employees	0.0%	700	700	700	—	—

BROADCASTER, INC.
OTC: BCAS

9201 Oakdale Ave., Ste. 200
Chatsworth, CA 91311
Phone: 818-206-9274
Fax: 818-206-9371
Web: www.broadcaster.com

CEO: Martin R. Wade III
CFO: Blair Mills
HR: –
FYE: June 30
Type: Public

Broadcaster (formerly International Microcomputer Software) is announcing new plans. The company had provided design and engineering software and services, but in 2006 it merged with AccessMedia Networks and changed its name to Broadcaster. Broadcaster's Social Media Network allows users to upload and view a variety of videos, including the capability to publish and access live Web cam feeds and chat with other users. CEO Martin Wade, III, and president Nolan Quan together own more than 40% of the company.

	Annual Growth	6/03	6/04	6/05	6/06	6/07
Sales ($ mil.)	(6.2%)	8.9	12.0	13.9	8.2	6.9
Net income ($ mil.)	—	10.7	0.6	(1.8)	0.9	(20.0)
Market value ($ mil.)	40.6%	32.9	66.7	73.4	200.6	128.4
Employees	—	—	—	—	—	50

BROADCOM CORPORATION
NASDAQ (GS): BRCM

5300 California Ave.
Irvine, CA 92617
Phone: 949-926-5000
Fax: 949-926-6589
Web: www.broadcom.com

CEO: Scott A. McGregor
CFO: Eric K. Brandt
HR: Dianne Dyer-Bruggeman
FYE: December 31
Type: Public

Broadcom harbors broad ambitions for its chips' impact on broadband communications: it wants them to drive every part of the high-speed networks of the future. The core applications for its integrated circuits (ICs) are digital set-top boxes, cable modems, servers, and local-area and home networking gear. Broadcom also makes ICs for carrier access, DSL, and wireless communications equipment, including mobile phones. Customers include 3Com, Apple, Cisco, Dell, Hewlett-Packard, IBM, and Motorola (about 11% of sales). The Asia/Pacific region contributes around 80% of Broadcom's sales.

	Annual Growth	12/03	12/04	12/05	12/06	12/07
Sales ($ mil.)	23.8%	1,610.1	2,400.6	2,670.8	3,667.8	3,776.4
Net income ($ mil.)	—	(959.9)	218.7	367.1	379.0	213.3
Market value ($ mil.)	22.5%	5,448.7	5,877.4	14,044.6	15,299.9	12,255.9
Employees	22.3%	2,833	3,373	4,287	5,233	6,347

BROADLANE, INC.

13727 Noel Rd., Ste. 1400
Dallas, TX 75240
Phone: 972-813-7500
Fax: 972-813-8400
Web: www.broadlane.com

CEO: Charles E. (Chuck) Saunders
CFO: Laurie Jackson
HR: –
FYE: May 31
Type: Private

Broadlane directs traffic between hospitals and medical equipment makers. The company is a group purchasing organization (GPO) that negotiates contracts on behalf of its clients, using the combined purchasing power of its client base to get good deals on medical/surgical supplies, capital equipment, drugs, information technology, and even labor. Its proprietary OnRamp portal allows clients to order from an online catalog, view contracts, track pending transactions, and obtain reports. Established in 1999, the company is a spin-off of hospital operator Tenet Healthcare, which remains a client. Broadlane serves more than 900 hospitals and thousands of non-acute care facilities and physicians practices.

	Annual Growth	5/03	5/04	5/05	5/06	5/07
Est. sales ($ mil.)	—	—	—	—	—	135.0
Employees	—	—	—	—	—	560

BROADPOINT SECURITIES GROUP, INC.
NASDAQ (GM): BPSG

1 Penn Plaza
New York, NY 10119
Phone: 212-273-7100
Fax: –
Web: www.broadpointsecurities.com

CEO: Peter J. McNierney
CFO: Robert I. (Rob) Turner
HR: –
FYE: December 31
Type: Public

Broadpoint Securities Group (formerly First Albany Companies) provides investment banking services to small and middle-market firms in the energy, health care, and technology industries, and provides equity analysis of companies in those sectors. Subsidiary FA Technology Ventures provides venture capital to high-tech firms; another subsidiary, Broadpoint Securities (formerly Descap) trades fixed-income securities. In 2007 the company sold its municipal capital markets group and the rights to the First Albany brand to Ireland's DEPFA BANK (now part of Hypo Real Estate). As a result, First Albany Companies changed its name to Broadpoint Securities Group later that year.

	Annual Growth	12/03	12/04	12/05	12/06	12/07
Sales ($ mil.)	(29.9%)	195.5	181.8	179.0	138.3	47.1
Net income ($ mil.)	—	10.6	(3.6)	(10.2)	(44.0)	(19.5)
Market value ($ mil.)	(18.5%)	154.6	144.0	113.4	37.9	68.3
Employees	(26.3%)	—	—	388	—	211

BROADRIDGE FINANCIAL SOLUTIONS, INC.
NYSE: BR

1981 Marcus Ave.
Lake Success, NY 11042
Phone: 516-472-5400
Fax: –
Web: www.broadridge.com

CEO: Richard J. Daly
CFO: Dan Sheldon
HR: Richard C. Berke
FYE: June 30
Type: Public

Broadridge Financial Solutions is fully backing the outsourcing movement. Itself a provider of technology-based outsourcing to companies in the financial services industry, it specializes in three specific areas of service: investor communications, securities processing, and clearing and outsourcing. Components of Broadridge's securities processing solutions are used by seven of the top 10 broker-dealers in the US. In 2007 business process outsourcing provider Automatic Data Processing (ADP) spun off its brokerage services division and rebranded it as Broadridge Financial Solutions.

	Annual Growth	6/03	6/04	6/05	6/06	6/07
Sales ($ mil.)	10.9%	—	—	—	1,949.5	2,162.7
Net income ($ mil.)	18.2%	—	—	—	166.7	197.1
Market value ($ mil.)	—	—	—	—	—	2,663.4
Employees	3.4%	—	—	—	4,100	4,241

BROADVIEW INSTITUTE, INC.
OTC: BVII

4455 W. 77th St.
Minneapolis, MN 55435
Phone: 952-835-4455
Fax: 952-835-0971
Web: www.broadviewmedia.com

CEO: Laurence S. (Larry) Zipkin
CFO: Kenneth J. McCarthy
HR: Stephanie Knickerbocher
FYE: March 31
Type: Public

Broadview Institute (formerly Broadview Media) isn't narrow-minded about film and video production. The company produces and edits film and video productions for cable networks, the government, ad agencies, and corporations. Productions have included commercials, broadcast programs, and infomercials, as well as government and industrial programs. Broadview has reduced its reliance on government contracts and expanded into business communications (Web design and streaming video) and educational products (multimedia for teachers and students). It also owns and operates Utah Career College (UCC) and provides services for the Minnesota School of Business (MSB). Chairman Terry Myhre owns about 65% of Broadview.

	Annual Growth	3/03	3/04	3/05	3/06	3/07
Sales ($ mil.)	14.8%	5.3	4.3	3.3	9.9	9.2
Net income ($ mil.)	—	(0.4)	(0.4)	(0.8)	(0.5)	0.2
Market value ($ mil.)	43.0%	3.3	15.0	10.9	18.6	13.8
Employees	—	—	—	—	—	124

BROADVIEW NETWORKS HOLDINGS, INC.

800 Westchester Ave., Ste. N501
Rye Brook, NY 10573
Phone: 914-922-7000
Fax: –
Web: www.broadviewnet.com

CEO: Michael K. Robinson
CFO: Corey Rinker
HR: –
FYE: December 31
Type: Private

Broadview Networks seeks to expand its customers' horizons. The company provides telecommunications services, including local and long-distance voice, DSL broadband Internet access, and Web hosting, to small and midsized businesses and residential customers in ten states in the northeastern US. Broadview is emphasizing a range of data services based on its T-1 network, including computer telephony and hosted VPNs, as its core business. The company, which has about 800,000 lines in service, serves such major metropolitan markets as Baltimore, Boston, New York, and Philadelphia. Broadview was founded in 1996.

	Annual Growth	12/02	12/03	12/04	12/05	12/06
Sales ($ mil.)	77.6%	—	—	86.5	240.4	272.7
Net income ($ mil.)	—	—	—	(17.7)	(38.9)	(41.5)
Employees	—	—	—	—	—	1,270

BROADVISION, INC.
OTC: BVSN

1600 Seaport Blvd., Ste. 550
Redwood City, CA 94063
Phone: 650-331-1000
Fax: 650-364-3425
Web: www.broadvision.com

CEO: Pehong Chen
CFO: Shin-Yuan Tzou
HR: –
FYE: December 31
Type: Public

BroadVision gives companies a peek into the world of customer self-service. The company provides software applications that enable businesses to offer their customers personalized self-service via the Internet. BroadVision's software suite includes applications for integrating business processes with self-service operations; managing the sales process, including lead generation, execution, and customer service; connecting customers to personalized online views of content; and managing content from creation through distribution. Founder and CEO Pehong Chen owns 60% of BroadVision.

	Annual Growth	12/03	12/04	12/05	12/06	12/07
Sales ($ mil.)	(13.2%)	88.1	78.0	60.1	52.0	50.0
Net income ($ mil.)	—	(35.5)	20.6	(39.0)	15.0	17.3
Market value ($ mil.)	8.2%	142.1	93.4	16.9	83.1	195.0
Employees	22.6%	—	—	—	159	195

BROADWAY FINANCIAL CORPORATION
NASDAQ (CM): BYFC

4800 Wilshire Blvd.
Los Angeles, CA 90010
Phone: 323-634-1700
Fax: 323-634-1717
Web: www.broadwayfederalbank.com

CEO: Paul C. Hudson
CFO: Sam Sarpong
HR: Kim Johnson
FYE: December 31
Type: Public

This company won't quit 'til it's a star! Broadway Financial is the holding company for Broadway Federal Bank, a savings and loan which serves the low- and moderate-income minority neighborhoods of central and south central Los Angeles and nearby Inglewood. Through about a half dozen branches and loan offices, the bank primarily originates multi-family (about 40% of its loan portfolio) and commercial real estate loans (another 40%). These loans are secured primarily by multi-family dwellings and properties used for business and religious purposes. Deposit products include savings, checking, money market, and NOW accounts, and certificates of deposit.

	Annual Growth	12/03	12/04	12/05	12/06	12/07
Assets ($ mil.)	11.6%	229.8	276.5	292.3	301.0	356.8
Net income ($ mil.)	0.0%	1.5	1.7	1.7	1.7	1.5
Market value ($ mil.)	(10.5%)	23.8	19.0	17.0	17.2	15.3
Employees	22.5%	—	—	56	—	84

BROCADE COMMUNICATIONS SYSTEMS, INC.
NASDAQ (GS): BRCD

1745 Technology Dr.
San Jose, CA 95110
Phone: 408-333-8000
Fax: 408-333-8101
Web: www.brocade.com

CEO: Michael (Mike) Klayko
CFO: Richard Deranleau
HR: Bonnie Helton
FYE: October 31
Type: Public

Brocade Communications Systems maintains silky smooth computer network operations. The company makes Fibre Channel switches and related software for connecting corporate storage systems and servers. Its products are used in storage area networks (SANs), which pool storage resources across enterprises for easier management and more efficient utilization of assets. The company's SilkWorm switches automatically reroute data upon path failure and reconfigure the SAN when new devices are added. Brocade sells its products primarily through equipment manufacturers, including EMC, Hewlett-Packard, and IBM, which together generate about 70% of revenues.

	Annual Growth	10/03	10/04	10/05	10/06	10/07
Sales ($ mil.)	23.9%	525.3	596.3	574.1	750.6	1,236.9
Net income ($ mil.)	—	(136.2)	(33.7)	43.1	67.6	76.9
Market value ($ mil.)	—	—	—	—	—	3,506.0
Employees	64.4%	—	—	—	1,440	2,368

BRODART CO.

500 Arch St.
Williamsport, PA 17701
Phone: 570-326-2461
Fax: 570-326-1479
Web: www.brodart.com

CEO: Joseph Largen
CFO: Steven (Steve) Uzupis
HR: –
FYE: December 31
Type: Private

If you're in the library business, Brodart can help you manage your books. The company provides automation software and services used by libraries to manage their collections and catalogs. Brodart also provides custom processed books, library supplies and furnishings, and custom contract furniture, as well as support, training, and consulting services. Brodart serves clients throughout North America from offices in Canada and the US. The company's roots can be traced to the 1939 invention of the plastic book jacket cover by founder and chairman Arthur Brody.

	Annual Growth	12/03	12/04	12/05	12/06	12/07
Est. sales ($ mil.)	—	—	—	—	—	134.1
Employees	—	—	—	—	—	950

BRODER BROS., CO.

6 Neshaminy Interplex, 6th Fl.
Trevose, PA 19053
Phone: 215-291-6140
Fax: 800-521-1251
Web: www.broderbros.com

CEO: Thomas Myers
CFO: Martin J. Matthews
HR: Richard Emrich
FYE: December 31
Type: Private

Selling clothes had been in the genes of sportswear distributor Broder Bros. for years. Begun as a haberdashery in 1919, it evolved from making hats and gloves to distributing imprintable sportswear, such as golf shirts, T-shirts, sweatshirts, and jerseys. The firm sells trade brands (Hanes), exclusive brands (adidas Golf), and private labels and operates under the Broder, Alpha, and NES units. Its private labels include Devon & Jones, Desert Wash, Harvard Square, and others. Customers, mostly small US retailers, order merchandise through seasonal catalogs or online. Private investment firm Bain Capital has held a majority interest of the company since May 2000, when the Broder family sold the firm.

	Annual Growth	12/02	12/03	12/04	12/05	12/06
Sales ($ mil.)	22.2%	429.7	487.8	877.4	978.4	959.3
Net income ($ mil.)	—	(1.4)	(12.5)	(1.5)	—	(7.7)
Employees	9.6%	—	—	1,498	1,571	1,799

THE BROE COMPANIES, INC.

252 Clayton St., 4th Fl.
Denver, CO 80206
Phone: 303-393-0033
Fax: 303-393-0041
Web: www.broe.com

CEO: Patrick D. (Pat) Broe
CFO: –
HR: –
FYE: December 31
Type: Private

Broe knows how to grow its dough — just don't expect it to tell you how it's done. The secretive company invests in a variety of industries in the US and Canada, largely funded by profits made in real estate investments. It focuses primarily on hard-asset-based investment opportunities, as well as distressed businesses. Broe's brotherhood of companies includes a short-line railroad owner (OmniTRAX), a pain management medical device manufacturer (McKinley Medical), and a Kentucky coal company (Century Coal). Denver property investor Pat Broe controls the company, which he founded in 1972.

	Annual Growth	12/03	12/04	12/05	12/06	12/07
Est. sales ($ mil.)	—	—	—	—	—	150.0
Employees	—	—	—	—	—	103

BRONCO DRILLING COMPANY, INC.

NASDAQ (CM): BRNC

16217 N. May Ave.
Edmond, OK 73013
Phone: 405-242-4444
Fax: 405-285-0478
Web: broncodrill.com

CEO: D. Frank Harrison
CFO: Zachary M. Graves
HR: –
FYE: December 31
Type: Public

Bronco Drilling is game to compete in that wild ride called oil and gas drilling, where the chances of getting bucked off are as likely as the chance of making a buck. The contract land driller owns a fleet of 56 land drilling rigs, of which 45 are in use. Many of its rigs, ranging from 500 to 2,000 horsepower, can drill to depths between 15,000 and 25,000 feet. The company, which serves natural gas production firms across the US, has 70 trucks to transport its rigs. In 2007 it drilled wells for 67 different customers. In 2008 Allis-Chalmers Energy agreed to buy Bronco Drilling for $437.8 million.

	Annual Growth	12/03	12/04	12/05	12/06	12/07
Sales ($ mil.)	121.2%	12.5	21.9	77.9	285.8	299.0
Net income ($ mil.)	—	(1.5)	(2.8)	5.1	59.8	37.6
Market value ($ mil.)	(14.5%)	—	—	533.0	428.7	390.1
Employees	62.7%	—	360	1,400	2,050	1,551

BRONX-LEBANON HOSPITAL CENTER

1650 Grand Concourse
Bronx, NY 10457
Phone: 718-590-1800
Fax: 718-299-5447
Web: www.bronxcare.org

CEO: Miguel A. Fuentes Jr.
CFO: Victor DeMarco
HR: Selena Griffin-Mahon
FYE: December 31
Type: Not-for-profit

Bronx-Lebanon Hospital Center cares for patients in central and south Bronx, no doubt while rooting for the Yankees a few blocks away. The health care provider has about 860 beds on its two campuses, as well as a 240-bed nursing home facility that contains a specialized AIDS unit. In addition to acute and long-term care, Bronx-Lebanon manages a network of about 70 owned and affiliated medical practices; the network — branded as BronxCare — includes primary care doctors and drug treatment clinics, as well as outpatient and rehabilitation facilities. The hospital is also a primary teaching hospital for the Albert Einstein College of Medicine.

	Annual Growth	12/03	12/04	12/05	12/06	12/07
Est. sales ($ mil.)	—	—	—	—	—	513.4
Employees	—	—	—	—	—	4,000

BROOKDALE SENIOR LIVING, INC.

NYSE: BKD

330 N. Wabash, Ste. 1400
Chicago, IL 60611
Phone: 312-977-3700
Fax: –
Web: www.brookdaleliving.com

CEO: William E. (Bill) Sheriff
CFO: Mark W. Ohlendorf
HR: Glenn Maul
FYE: December 31
Type: Public

Brookdale Senior Living's communities aim to make folks feel at home. The company operates assisted and independent living centers and retirement communities for middle- and upper-income elderly clients. Brookdale Senior Living has some 550 facilities in 35 states, offering studio, one-bedroom, and two-bedroom units, as well as meal service, 24-hour emergency response, housekeeping, concierge services, transportation, and recreational activities. The company also provides facilities designed for the treatment of Alzheimer's patients and others who require ongoing care. Chairman Wesley Edens owns about 60% of the company through Fortress Investment Group.

	Annual Growth	12/03	12/04	12/05	12/06	12/07
Sales ($ mil.)	69.5%	222.6	660.9	790.6	1,309.9	1,839.3
Net income ($ mil.)	—	(13.2)	(21.9)	(51.0)	(108.1)	(162.0)
Market value ($ mil.)	24.0%	—	—	1,937.9	4,860.5	2,982.0
Employees	46.0%	—	10,500	15,760	32,000	32,700

An in-depth profile of this company is available to Hoover's Online members at hoovers.com.

287

BROOKE CORPORATION

NASDAQ (GM): BXXX

8500 College Blvd.
Overland Park, KS 66210
Phone: 913-661-0123
Fax: 913-451-3183
Web: www.brookecorp.com

CEO: Leland G. Orr
CFO: Travis W. Vrbas
HR: –
FYE: December 31
Type: Public

Here comes the death of the (independent) insurance salesman: Brooke Corporation offers financial services and insurance policies, mainly property/casualty insurance, through its network of some 900 franchise locations across the US. The company believes its franchise system (which includes selling insurance through local owners) is more effective than regular independent agent models. Brooke also provides life insurance, consulting, banking, lending, and brokerage services through its subsidiaries. Brooke Holdings, which is controlled by brothers Robert Orr and Leland Orr (Brooke Corporation chairman and CEO, respectively), owns a controlling stake in Brooke Corporation.

	Annual Growth	12/03	12/04	12/05	12/06	12/07
Sales ($ mil.)	34.2%	66.0	101.9	145.4	179.7	214.0
Net income ($ mil.)	(21.4%)	4.2	6.7	9.7	10.7	1.6
Market value ($ mil.)	42.0%	23.6	226.7	174.8	144.4	95.9
Employees	1.8%	—	—	647	572	671

BROOKFIELD HOMES CORPORATION

NYSE: BHS

12865 Pointe Del Mar, Ste. 200
Del Mar, CA 92014
Phone: 858-481-8500
Fax: 858-794-6185
Web: www.brookfieldhomes.com

CEO: Ian G. Cockwell
CFO: Paul G. Kerrigan
HR: –
FYE: December 31
Type: Public

Brookfield Homes builds you up as the master of your own domain. A spinoff of Brookfield Properties, the land developer and homebuilder designs and constructs single- and multi-family homes for move-up and luxury buyers. Its homes average about $660,000 and are located in master-planned communities in Los Angeles, Riverside, San Diego, Sacramento, San Francisco Bay Area, and Washington, DC. The company entitles and develops land for its own properties and also sells lots to third-party homebuilders. Through Brookfield Asset Management Inc., chairman J. Bruce Flatt and president and CEO Ian Cockwell own around 60% of the company.

	Annual Growth	12/03	12/04	12/05	12/06	12/07
Sales ($ mil.)	(13.1%)	1,023.3	1,231.8	1,231.1	887.8	583.3
Net income ($ mil.)	(35.2%)	88.3	146.4	218.7	148.4	15.6
Market value ($ mil.)	(14.7%)	795.8	1,047.2	1,361.5	997.1	421.3
Employees	(7.1%)	—	—	636	591	

BROOKLINE BANCORP, INC.

NASDAQ (GS): BRKL

160 Washington St.
Brookline, MA 02447
Phone: 617-730-3500
Fax: 617-730-3552
Web: www.brooklinebank.com

CEO: Richard P. Chapman Jr.
CFO: Paul R. Bechet
HR: –
FYE: December 31
Type: Public

Brookline Bancorp wants to be one of Boston's greatest hits. It's the holding company for Brookline Bank, a community-oriented financial institution with nearly 20 branches throughout the greater Boston area. The bank offers checking, savings, NOW, and money market accounts, as well as IRAs and CDs. In 2003 it started offering indirect auto loans originated by car dealerships; they now account for the largest portion of its loan portfolio (about 30%). Commercial real estate loans account for another 20%, while one- to four-family and multifamily mortgages each account for about 15%.

	Annual Growth	12/03	12/04	12/05	12/06	12/07
Assets ($ mil.)	12.2%	1,524.0	1,694.5	2,214.7	2,373.0	2,418.5
Net income ($ mil.)	5.1%	14.5	17.8	22.0	20.8	17.7
Market value ($ mil.)	(10.1%)	902.4	965.2	872.6	811.1	589.2
Employees	17.6%	127	131	202	248	243

BROOKLYN ACADEMY OF MUSIC

30 Lafayette Ave.
Brooklyn, NY 11217
Phone: 718-636-4100
Fax: 718-857-2021
Web: www.bam.org

CEO: Karen Brooks Hopkins
CFO: –
HR: –
FYE: June 30
Type: Not-for-profit

The Brooklyn Academy of Music (better known as BAM) is famous for its progressive nature. The urban arts center is America's oldest operating performing arts center and brings international performing arts, media, and film to Brooklyn, New York. In addition, the academy annually hosts the Next Wave Festival (featuring avant-garde music, dance, theater, and opera) and houses a four-screen cineplex to draw young audiences. BAM's resident orchestra produces an annual season of concerts. BAM was founded in Brooklyn Heights in 1861.

	Annual Growth	6/03	6/04	6/05	6/06	6/07
Est. sales ($ mil.)	—	—	—	—	—	34.5
Employees	—	—	—	—	—	150

BROOKLYN FEDERAL BANCORP, INC.

NASDAQ (GM): BFSB

81 Court St.
Brooklyn, NY 11201
Phone: 718-855-8500
Fax: 718-858-5174
Web: www.brooklynbank.com

CEO: Angelo J. Di Lorenzo
CFO: Ralph Walther
HR: –
FYE: September 30
Type: Public

Brooklyn Federal Bancorp won't sell you a bridge, but it might loan you money to build one yourself. It's the holding company for Brooklyn Federal Savings Bank, which has been operating since 1887. As one might expect, the thrift operates in the New York City area, with two branches in Brooklyn and two on Long Island. It provides traditional deposit and loan services to area individuals and businesses and focuses on real estate lending; commercial mortgages make up more than 40% of the company's loan portfolio, which also includes one- to four-family home mortgages (more than 30%), multifamily residential loans (nearly 20%), and construction loans.

	Annual Growth	9/03	9/04	9/05	9/06	9/07
Assets ($ mil.)	7.0%	—	—	340.9	408.0	390.4
Net income ($ mil.)	0.0%	—	—	3.8	4.6	3.8
Market value ($ mil.)	8.8%	—	—	154.6	170.6	183.0
Employees	26.2%	—	—	59	—	94

⊞ BROOKS AUTOMATION, INC.

NASDAQ (GS): BRKS

15 Elizabeth Dr.
Chelmsford, MA 01824
Phone: 978-262-2400
Fax: 978-262-2500
Web: www.brooks.com

CEO: Robert J. (Bob) Lepofsky
CFO: Martin S. Headley
HR: –
FYE: September 30
Type: Public

Brooks Automation supplies a steady stream of production tools and factory automation products for chip makers and suppliers of chip-making equipment. The company makes tool automation products, such as vacuum robots and cluster assemblies used by semiconductor manufacturers. Brooks' wafer handling systems include vacuum cassette elevator loadlocks, transfer robots, and thermal conditioning modules and aligners. The company also makes vacuum equipment for makers of flat-panel displays and data storage devices. Customers include Lam Research, Novellus Systems, and Samsung Electronics. Brooks derives some two-thirds of its sales from customers in North America.

	Annual Growth	9/03	9/04	9/05	9/06	9/07
Sales ($ mil.)	21.3%	343.6	539.8	463.8	692.9	743.3
Net income ($ mil.)	—	(185.8)	17.7	(11.6)	25.9	151.5
Market value ($ mil.)	2.1%	924.5	632.4	993.6	984.4	1,002.8
Employees	10.6%	—	—	1,800	2,400	2,200

BROOKS BROTHERS INC.

eCommerce Department, 346 Madison Ave.
New York, NY 10017
Phone: 212-682-8800
Fax: 212-309-7273
Web: www.brooksbrothers.com

CEO: Claudio Del Vecchio
CFO: Brian Baumann
HR: –
FYE: March 31
Type: Subsidiary

Known for its classic — some would say staid — styling, Brooks Brothers has been getting men dressed for nearly two centuries. Brooks Brothers is one of America's oldest retailers, specializing in men's suits and outerwear (Abe Lincoln was wearing a Brooks Brothers suit and overcoat when he was assassinated); the company also sells women's apparel. Brooks Brothers operates about 180 upscale retail stores and outlet locations in the US. Through partnerships, Brooks Brothers has 100-plus stores in about a dozen countries including China, Japan, and Italy. The UK's Marks and Spencer sold the chain in 2001 for $225 million to Retail Brand Alliance, which is trying to return Brooks Brothers to its glory days.

	Annual Growth	3/03	3/04	3/05	3/06	3/07
Est. sales ($ mil.)	—	—	—	—	—	260.2
Employees	—	—	—	—	—	3,500

BROOKSHIRE BROTHERS, LTD.

1201 Ellen Trout Dr.
Lufkin, TX 75904
Phone: 936-634-8155
Fax: –
Web: www.brookshirebrothers.com

CEO: Jerry Johnson
CFO: –
HR: Emily Watts
FYE: April 30
Type: Private

From its roots in East Texas the Brookshire Brothers supermarket chain now has 70-plus locations stretching from Louisiana to Central Texas. The regional grocery company primarily operates under the Brookshire Brothers banner, but some of its supermarkets operate under the B&B Foods name. Nearly all of the stores feature outlets selling Conoco gasoline (the company is one of Conoco's largest distributors). Brookshire Brothers is not affiliated with Brookshire Grocery of Tyler, Texas. The companies share a common ancestry dating back to 1921, but a split between the founding brothers in the late 1930s resulted in separate grocery chains. Formerly family-owned, the grocery chain is now 100% employee-owned.

	Annual Growth	4/02	4/03	4/04	4/05	4/06
Est. sales ($ mil.)	—	—	—	—	—	1,100.0
Employees	—	—	—	—	—	5,600

BROOKSHIRE GROCERY COMPANY

1600 W. South West Loop 323
Tyler, TX 75701
Phone: 903-534-3000
Fax: 903-534-2206
Web: www.brookshires.com

CEO: Rick Rayford
CFO: Tim King
HR: –
FYE: September 30
Type: Private

By selling staples, specialties, and Southern hospitality, Brookshire Grocery Co. has grown into a chain of about 155 Brookshire's, Super 1 Food, and Olé Foods supermarkets in Texas, Arkansas, Louisiana, and Mississippi. The company also owns three distribution centers, a dairy, a fleet of some 350 trucks, and SouthWest Foods, its private-label manufacturing unit. Brookshire's stores average about 40,000 sq. ft., while its warehouse-style Super 1 Foods stores average 80,000 sq. ft. More than 40 of Brookshire Grocery's stores sell gasoline. Originally part of the Brookshire Brothers grocery chain (dating back to 1921), the company split from it in 1939. The Brookshire family is still among the company's owners.

	Annual Growth	9/02	9/03	9/04	9/05	9/06
Est. sales ($ mil.)	5.4%	1,700.0	1,900.0	1,960.0	2,000.0	2,100.0
Employees	2.1%	11,500	12,000	12,000	12,500	12,500

BROOKSTONE, INC.

1 Innovation Way
Merrimack, NH 03054
Phone: 603-880-9500
Fax: 603-577-8005
Web: www.brookstone.com

CEO: Louis (Lou) Mancini
CFO: Philip W. Roizin
HR: Carol A. Lambert
FYE: Saturday nearest December 31
Type: Private

Need an office putting green? How about an alarm clock that projects the outside temperature on the ceiling? Then Brookstone is the place for you. It sells gifts, gadgets, and other doodads targeted primarily toward men through more than 300 stores in more than 40 states, the District of Columbia, and Puerto Rico. The company's functional yet unique product categories include health and fitness, home and office, outdoor living, and travel and auto. Brookstone also sells online and through catalogs Brookstone and Hard-To-Find Tools. Because most of Brookstone's sales are gifts, it operates temporary kiosks during the busy Father's Day and December holiday seasons. The company is owned by Osim International.

	Annual Growth	1/03	1/04	1/05	*12/05	12/06
Sales ($ mil.)	8.0%	375.9	434.2	498.9	440.6	511.9
Net income ($ mil.)	(39.6%)	12.0	17.6	21.4	(3.6)	1.6
Employees	2.3%	2,992	2,905	3,016	—	3,278
					*Fiscal year change	

BROTHER INTERNATIONAL CORPORATION

100 Somerset Corporate Blvd.
Bridgewater, NJ 08807
Phone: 908-704-1700
Fax: 908-704-8235
Web: www.brother-usa.com

CEO: Tadashi Ishiguro
CFO: Anthony Melfi
HR: –
FYE: March 31
Type: Subsidiary

Brother International is a part of one big global family. Headquartered in New Jersey and serving the Americas, Brother International, a subsidiary of Japan-based Brother Industries, makes and sells fax machines, printers, sewing machines, laminators, typewriters, and the P-touch labeling system. The subsidiary operates facilities in California, Georgia, Illinois, Massachusetts, and Tennessee. Brother International also has its own subsidiaries in Ohio and in Argentina, Brazil, Canada, Chile, and Mexico. Brother International was formed in 1954.

	Annual Growth	3/03	3/04	3/05	3/06	3/07
Est. sales ($ mil.)	—	—	—	—	—	1,506.0
Employees	—	—	—	—	—	1,500

BROWN & BROWN, INC.

NYSE: BRO

220 S. Ridgewood Ave.
Daytona Beach, FL 32114
Phone: 386-252-9601
Fax: 386-239-5729
Web: www.brown-n-brown.com

CEO: J. Hyatt Brown
CFO: Cory T. Walker
HR: Linda S. Downs
FYE: December 31
Type: Public

Brown & Brown is an independent insurance agency and brokerage firm. It provides property/casualty, life and health insurance, and risk management services through its retail division, mainly to commercial clients. The company also designs customized programs for niche clients, such as dentists, lawyers, optometrists, food processors, and towing operators. Reinsurance is provided through subsidiary Axiom Re, acquired in 2006. The wholesale brokerage division distributes excess and surplus commercial insurance through independent agents. The company's services segment provides self-insured and third-party administrator services. Brown & Brown has some 200 offices in 38 states.

	Annual Growth	12/03	12/04	12/05	12/06	12/07
Sales ($ mil.)	14.9%	551.0	646.9	785.8	878.0	959.7
Net income ($ mil.)	14.7%	110.3	128.8	150.6	172.4	191.0
Market value ($ mil.)	31.1%	1,117.9	1,505.9	4,256.8	3,949.9	3,307.1
Employees	5.4%	—	—	4,540	4,733	5,047

An in-depth profile of this company is available to Hoover's Online members at hoovers.com.

289

BROWN AND CALDWELL

201 N. Civic Dr.
Walnut Creek, CA 94596
Phone: 925-937-9010
Fax: 925-937-9026
Web: www.brownandcaldwell.com

CEO: Craig A. Goehring
CFO: Angela Ferrif
HR: Susy Pepper
FYE: September 30
Type: Private

Brown and Caldwell is headed straight to the gutter — to clean it up. The employee-owned firm provides environmental consulting and engineering services to industrial, governmental, and utility clients. Brown and Caldwell designs and builds water, wastewater, and solid waste systems for clients in the paper and pulp, food processing, and chemical manufacturing industries. It offers watershed and stormwater management services, as well as pipeline engineering and repair services. The company provides soil and groundwater remediation, underground storage-tank management, risk assessment, and customized data management systems.

	Annual Growth	9/03	9/04	9/05	9/06	9/07
Est. sales ($ mil.)	—	—	—	—	—	267.0
Employees	—	—	—	—	—	1,100

BROWN BROTHERS HARRIMAN & CO.

140 Broadway
New York, NY 10005
Phone: 212-483-1818
Fax: 212-493-8545
Web: www.bbh.com

CEO: Douglas A. Donahue Jr.
CFO: Maroa C. Velez
HR: –
FYE: December 31
Type: Private

Brown Brothers Harriman is one of the largest, most prestigious private banks in the US. As a private partnership, the bank is not insured by the FDIC, and each of its some 40 partners has unlimited liability. The company provides investment management, brokerage, banking, and trust services to financial institutions, corporations, and well-off families and individuals around the world. It also provides merger and acquisition advisory, securities lending, and corporate financing services. Founded in 1818 and known for its conservative investment approach, Brown Brothers Harriman oversees some $45 billion in assets.

	Annual Growth	12/03	12/04	12/05	12/06	12/07
Est. sales ($ mil.)	—	—	—	—	—	270.0
Employees	—	—	—	—	—	3,000

BROWN JORDAN INTERNATIONAL, INC.

475 W. Town Place, Ste. 201
St. Augustine, FL 32092
Phone: 904-495-0717
Fax: –
Web: www.bji.com

CEO: Gene J. Moriarty
CFO: Vincent A. Tortorici Jr.
HR: –
FYE: December 31
Type: Private

Brown Jordan International (formerly WinsLoew Furniture) takes the cyclical nature of its industry sitting down. The firm makes indoor and outdoor chairs, tables, sofas, and love seats for home and commercial use. Major brands include Pompeii, Texacraft, Tropic Craft, and Wabash Valley, as well as Charter, Loewenstein, and Stuart Clark (for commercial customers). Residential products are sold in patio furniture stores; commercial lines are sold to hotels, restaurants, health care facilities, and schools. Brown Jordan also sells Southern Wood brand ready-to-assemble furniture through mass retailers and catalogs. Chairman Earl Powell and his investment group, Trivest Partners, acquired the company in 1999.

	Annual Growth	12/03	12/04	12/05	12/06	12/07
Est. sales ($ mil.)	—	—	—	—	—	346.3
Employees	—	—	—	—	—	2,000

BROWN SHOE COMPANY, INC.

NYSE: BWS

8300 Maryland Ave.
St. Louis, MO 63105
Phone: 314-854-4000
Fax: 314-854-4274
Web: www.brownshoe.com

CEO: Ronald A. (Ron) Fromm
CFO: Mark E. Hood
HR: Doug Koch
FYE: Saturday nearest January 31
Type: Public

There's no business like shoe business for Brown Shoe Company. Brown Shoe owns about 1,075 Famous Footwear stores in the US, about 250 Naturalizer stores in the US and Canada, and 15 F.X. LaSalle stores around Montreal, Canada, as well as shops in China. Besides its venerable Buster Brown line, its brands include Airstep, Connie, LifeStride, and Nickels; it also sells Dr. Scholl's, Power Rangers, and Disney licensed footwear. It distributes footwear worldwide through more than 2,000 retailers, including independent, chain (DSW), and department stores (Sears). Brown Shoe is opening new stores, closing underperforming ones, and updating styles to appeal to youth. In 2005 it acquired Bennett Footwear Group.

	Annual Growth	1/04	1/05	1/06	1/07	1/08
Sales ($ mil.)	6.5%	1,832.1	1,941.8	2,292.1	2,470.9	2,359.9
Net income ($ mil.)	6.5%	46.9	43.3	41.0	65.7	60.4
Employees	3.1%	11,600	12,000	12,800	12,700	13,100

BROWN-FORMAN CORPORATION

NYSE: BFB

850 Dixie Hwy.
Louisville, KY 40210
Phone: 502-585-1100
Fax: 502-774-7876
Web: www.brown-forman.com

CEO: Paul C. Varga
CFO: Donald C. Berg
HR: James S. Welch Jr.
FYE: April 30
Type: Public

Don't blame Brown-Forman (B-F) employees if the company Christmas party gets out of control; they have lots to drink on hand. B-F's products include such well-known spirits as Jack Daniel's, Canadian Mist, Early Times, Korbel, Southern Comfort, Old Forester, Finlandia, Gentleman Jack, and Pepe Lopez. Its wine labels include Bolla, Fetzer, Bel Arbor, Five Rivers, Little Black Dress, and Michel Picard. Jack Daniel's is the company's leading brand and is the largest selling American whiskey in the world (by volume). Offering 35 recognized brands of wines and spirits, the company's products are available in more than 135 countries.

	Annual Growth	4/04	4/05	4/06	4/07	4/08
Sales ($ mil.)	6.2%	2,577.0	2,729.0	2,444.0	2,806.0	3,282.0
Net income ($ mil.)	14.3%	258.0	308.0	320.0	389.0	440.0
Market value ($ mil.)	11.6%	3,034.0	3,610.1	4,888.9	4,242.8	4,706.2
Employees	17.3%	—	—	3,750	4,400	—

BROWNING ARMS COMPANY

1 Browning Place
Morgan, UT 84050
Phone: 801-876-2711
Fax: 801-876-3331
Web: www.browning.com

CEO: Charles Guevremont
CFO: Kraig Walker
HR: Arlys Johanson
FYE: December 31
Type: Subsidiary

Browning Arms Company has drawn a bead on the firearms market for more than 125 years. The company traces its roots to the late nineteenth century, when John Moses Browning established his firearms factory in Utah. Mr. Browning, who earned many patents for his gunsmithing inventions, developed designs that were manufactured by Winchester, Colt, and Fabrique Nationale. The firm, which has also operated as the J. M. & M. S. Browning Company and as Browning Industries, now makes rifles, shotguns, pistols, and accessories, along with archery and fishing equipment, knives, flashlights, outdoor apparel, footwear, and security safes.

	Annual Growth	12/03	12/04	12/05	12/06	12/07
Est. sales ($ mil.)	—	—	—	—	—	218.1
Employees	—	—	—	—	—	250

BRT REALTY TRUST

NYSE: BRT

60 Cutter Mill Rd., Ste. 303
Great Neck, NY 11021
Phone: 516-466-3100
Fax: 516-466-3132
Web: www.brtrealty.com

CEO: Jeffrey A. Gould
CFO: George E. Zweier
HR: –
FYE: September 30
Type: Public

BRT Realty is a real estate investment trust (REIT) that originates and holds senior and junior mortgage loans for income-producing commercial property. Most are high-yield short-term mortgages or bridge loans secured by shopping centers, office buildings, hotels and apartments that are being converted into condominiums, and other multifamily residential properties. The REIT also invests in real estate joint ventures and in stock of other real estate companies. BRT Realty's loan portfolio consists of approximately 50 mortgages on properties in about a dozen states, mainly New York, New Jersey, and Florida. Chairman Fredric Gould and his family control about a quarter of BRT Realty.

	Annual Growth	9/03	9/04	9/05	9/06	9/07
Sales ($ mil.)	30.5%	14.8	18.6	25.7	37.5	42.9
Net income ($ mil.)	26.5%	13.7	12.0	16.2	20.1	35.1
Market value ($ mil.)	7.7%	143.1	164.3	180.4	224.0	192.2
Employees	—	—	—	6	—	—

BRUCE FOODS CORPORATION

Hwy. 182 West
Cade, LA 70519
Phone: 337-365-8101
Fax: 337-364-3742
Web: www.brucefoods.com

CEO: Joseph S. (Si) Brown III
CFO: –
HR: Brenda Warfield
FYE: April 30
Type: Private

Hot sauce and candied yams — aaiiieeee! Bruce Foods was Cajun long before Cajun was, well, hot. The company's Original Louisiana Hot Sauce is a top-selling US hot sauce (along with rival McIlhenny's Tabasco brand hot-pepper sauce). Louisiana-brand hot peppers — for brave souls — are available, too. Bruce Foods makes less lethal offerings, including Tex-Mex products and traditional Southern favorites — canned yams and sweet potato pancake, muffin, and biscuit mixes. Cajun King seasonings, Casa Fiesta Mexican foods, and Mexene chili beans and seasonings round out the menu.

BRUCKMANN, ROSSER, SHERRILL & CO., L.L.C.

126 E. 56th St., 29th Fl.
New York, NY 10022
Phone: 212-521-3700
Fax: 212-521-3799
Web: www.brs.com

CEO: Bruce C. Bruckmann
CFO: Paul D. Kaminski
HR: –
FYE: December 31
Type: Private

Bruckmann, Rosser, Sherrill & Co. (BRS) focuses on management buyouts and recapitalizations of middle-market firms in the consumer goods and services, restaurant, specialty retail, and commercial services sectors. The private equity firm's portfolio holdings include Logan's Roadhouse, The Sheridan Group, and Things Remembered. In 2007 BRS sold Remington Arms to Cerberus Capital Management; it also divested its controlling interest in totes>>Isotoner in a sale to MidOcean Partners, but retained a minority stake. Founded in 1995, BRS manages more than $1 billion of committed capital in three private equity funds.

	Annual Growth	12/03	12/04	12/05	12/06	12/07
Est. sales ($ mil.)	—	—	—	—	—	20.0
Employees	—	—	—	—	—	7,819

BRUEGGER'S ENTERPRISES, INC.

159 Bank St.
Burlington, VT 05402
Phone: 802-660-4020
Fax: 802-652-9293
Web: www.brueggers.com

CEO: James J. Greco
CFO: Robert D. (Bob) Parette
HR: Matt Riley
FYE: December 31
Type: Private

Bagels are the focus of this dough-making enterprise. Bruegger's Enterprises operates and franchises the second-largest chain of bagel outlets in the US (behind Einstein Noah Restaurant Group's Einstein Bros. Bagels chain), with about 260 locations in more than 20 states. The eateries feature fresh, New York-style bagels that are kettle boiled and available in a variety of flavors, along with several kinds of cream cheese spreads. In addition, Bruegger's offers soups, salads, and sandwiches, as well as premium coffee. Founded by partners Nord Brue and Mike Dressell in 1983, the company was purchased in 2003 by CEO James Greco and Sun Capital Partners.

	Annual Growth	12/03	12/04	12/05	12/06	12/07
Est. sales ($ mil.)	—	—	—	—	—	43.9
Employees	—	—	—	—	—	1,600

BRUKER CORPORATION

NASDAQ (GM): BRKR

40 Manning Rd.
Billerica, MA 01821
Phone: 978-663-3660
Fax: 978-667-5993
Web: www.bruker-biosciences.com

CEO: Frank H. Laukien
CFO: William J. (Bill) Knight
HR: –
FYE: December 31
Type: Public

Bruker (formerly Bruker BioSciences) is the parent company of operating subsidiaries Bruker Daltonics, Bruker AXS, Bruker Optics, and Bruker BioSpin. The company was formed after a merger of the forerunners of Bruker Daltonics and Bruker AXS. Bruker sells X-ray technology and products from the Bruker AXS portfolio and Bruker Daltonics' life science tools based on mass spectrometry for customers such as pharmaceutical companies, biotechs, academic institutions, and government agencies. Bruker Optics develops tools based on molecular spectroscopy, and Bruker BioSpin makes research equipment using magnetic resonance technology. CEO Frank Laukien and members of the Laukien family control the company.

	Annual Growth	12/03	12/04	12/05	12/06	12/07
Sales ($ mil.)	20.4%	260.7	284.4	297.6	435.8	547.6
Net income ($ mil.)	—	(17.5)	(7.8)	3.7	18.5	31.5
Market value ($ mil.)	37.7%	391.3	360.6	437.8	770.2	1,406.0
Employees	31.5%	—	—	1,279	—	2,212

⊞ BRUNO'S SUPERMARKETS, INC.

800 Lakeshore Pkwy.
Birmingham, AL 35211
Phone: 205-916-5220
Fax: 205-916-5261
Web: www.brunos.com

CEO: Kent Moore
CFO: –
HR: Dennis Wade
FYE: December 31
Type: Private

Bruno's Supermarkets, after a series of ownership changes, is on its own again. The regional grocery chain runs about 65 stores (down from more than 150 several years ago) under the Bruno's, Food Max, and Food World banners, mostly in Alabama, but also in the Florida panhandle. The stores sell traditional grocery fare and wine, and feature Vincent's To Go prepared meals. Founded in 1932 by Joe Bruno, the chain was acquired by Ahold USA in 2000 and later sold along with its bigger sister chain BI-LO in 2005 to Dallas-based Lone Star Funds for about $660 million. In early 2007 Lone Star separated the operations of Bruno's and BI-LO prior to putting both companies up for sale.

	Annual Growth	12/03	12/04	12/05	12/06	12/07
Est. sales ($ mil.)	—	—	—	—	—	1,247.5
Employees	—	—	—	—	—	11,500

⊞ An in-depth profile of this company is available to Hoover's Online members at hoovers.com.

291

BRUNSWICK CORPORATION

NYSE: BC

1 N. Field Ct.
Lake Forest, IL 60045
Phone: 847-735-4700
Fax: 847-735-4765
Web: www.brunswick.com

CEO: Dustan E. (Dusty) McCoy
CFO: Peter G. Leemputte
HR: B. Russell (Russ) Lockridge
FYE: December 31
Type: Public

Brunswick's business is everyone else's free time. A global leader in the leisure products industry, the company's Brunswick Boat Group's pleasure boat brands include Sea Ray, Bayliner, Boston Whaler, Lund, and Hatteras, just to name a few. The company also makes marine engines ranging from 2.5 to 350 horsepower under nameplates including Mercury and Mariner. It also makes Brunswick bowling and billiards products, as well as fitness equipment (Life Fitness, ParaBody, and Hammer Strength). Brunswick owns or franchises 108 fun centers throughout Canada, Europe, and the US that feature bowling, billiards, restaurants, and "Cosmic (glow-in-the-dark) Bowling."

	Annual Growth	12/03	12/04	12/05	12/06	12/07
Sales ($ mil.)	8.3%	4,128.7	5,229.3	5,923.8	5,665.0	5,671.2
Net income ($ mil.)	(4.7%)	135.2	269.8	385.4	133.9	111.6
Market value ($ mil.)	(15.6%)	2,932.5	4,793.0	3,889.4	2,898.7	1,491.0
Employees	4.3%	—	—	27,500	28,000	29,920

BRUSH ENGINEERED MATERIALS INC.

NYSE: BW

17876 St. Clair Ave.
Cleveland, OH 44110
Phone: 216-486-4200
Fax: 216-383-4091
Web: www.beminc.com

CEO: Richard J. (Dick) Hipple
CFO: John D. Grampa
HR: Joseph Szafraniec
FYE: December 31
Type: Public

Brush Engineered Materials, through Brush Wellman and other subsidiaries, makes precious and specialty metal products for the medical, communications, and high-tech industries. It also is a supplier of beryllium, alloys such as copper beryllium, and beryllia ceramics. Its Metal Systems Group supplies beryllium products and alloys and accounts for not quite half of its sales. Beryllium's properties — high thermal conductivity, strength, hardness, and resistance to corrosion and wear — give it a wide variety of uses in the computer, telecommunications, medical, and electronics industries. The company also produces special materials such as high-temperature braze materials and precious metal preforms.

	Annual Growth	12/03	12/04	12/05	12/06	12/07
Sales ($ mil.)	24.2%	401.0	496.3	541.3	763.0	955.7
Net income ($ mil.)	—	(13.2)	15.5	17.8	49.6	53.3
Market value ($ mil.)	31.4%	254.5	355.6	305.9	678.9	757.8
Employees	5.7%	—	—	1,970	2,185	2,201

BRYAN CAVE LLP

One Metropolitan Sq., 211 N. Broadway, Ste. 3600
St. Louis, MO 63102
Phone: 314-259-2000
Fax: 314-259-2020
Web: www.bryancave.com

CEO: Don G. Lents
CFO: Michael D. Stolte
HR: Lori Johnson
FYE: December 31
Type: Partnership

With offices in regions ranging from the Midwest to the Middle East, law firm Bryan Cave is able to represent its clients' interests worldwide. The firm focuses on corporate transactions and litigation; specialties include agribusiness, entertainment, environmental, health care, intellectual property, real estate, and tax law. It has more than 800 lawyers in about 15 offices in the US, Europe, the Middle East, and the Asia/Pacific region. Two affiliates — Bryan Cave International Trade and Bryan Cave Strategies — offer consulting services. Bryan Cave was founded in St. Louis in 1873.

	Annual Growth	12/03	12/04	12/05	12/06	12/07
Est. sales ($ mil.)	—	—	—	—	—	165.0
Employees	—	—	—	—	—	1,904

BRYCE CORPORATION

4505 Old Lamar Ave.
Memphis, TN 38118
Phone: 901-369-4400
Fax: 901-369-4419
Web: www.brycecorp.com

CEO: Thomas J. Bryce
CFO: Tad Feeney
HR: Donnie Sappington
FYE: December 31
Type: Private

Sweet! Bryce Corporation makes a brace of plastic-film packaging products for snack food and candy companies. It also serves the consumer products, graphic arts, household, label, and photographic industries. The company, a leader in the film conversion and flexible packaging industry, produces films, sleeves, printing plates, and converting technologies. Bryce offers its customers flexographic printing in up to 10 colors, a range of different laminations (including solvent adhesives, multilayer barrier extrusions, and tandem laminations), and barrier, coextrusion, emulsion, and wax coatings. It also makes bags, pouches, and other customized items.

	Annual Growth	12/03	12/04	12/05	12/06	12/07
Est. sales ($ mil.)	—	—	—	—	—	137.5
Employees	—	—	—	—	—	1,100

BRYN MAWR BANK CORPORATION

NASDAQ (GM): BMTC

801 Lancaster Ave.
Bryn Mawr, PA 19010
Phone: 610-525-1700
Fax: 610-526-2450
Web: www.bmtc.com

CEO: Frederick C. (Ted) Peters II
CFO: J. Duncan Smith
HR: –
FYE: December 31
Type: Public

Unlike the college of the same name, this Bryn Mawr caters to women *and* men. Bryn Mawr Bank Corporation is the holding company for Bryn Mawr Trust, which operates approximately 15 offices (about half are limited-service branches located in retirement communities) in Pennsylvania's Chester, Delaware, and Montgomery counties, including Philadelphia's tony Main Line suburbs. In addition to such traditional services as checking and savings accounts, CDs, mortgages, and business and consumer loans, the bank also provides insurance products, investment management, retirement planning, tax planning and preparation, and trust services. Bryn Mawr Bank Corporation has some $3.3 billion of assets under management.

	Annual Growth	12/03	12/04	12/05	12/06	12/07
Assets ($ mil.)	13.5%	604.8	683.0	727.2	826.7	1,002.1
Net income ($ mil.)	9.7%	9.4	9.3	11.4	12.7	13.6
Market value ($ mil.)	(1.7%)	209.0	189.1	185.3	202.4	195.5
Employees	3.7%	—	—	255	—	274

BSD MEDICAL CORPORATION

NASDAQ (GM): BSDM

2188 W. 2200 South
Salt Lake City, UT 84119
Phone: 801-972-5555
Fax: 801-972-5930
Web: www.bsdmc.com

CEO: Hyrum A. Mead
CFO: Dennis P. Gauger
HR: –
FYE: August 31
Type: Public

BSD Medical has developed equipment to provide hyperthermia treatment, specifically for treating cancer (including melanoma, breast cancer, brain cancer, and cervical cancer) in tandem with chemotherapy and radiation therapy or as a stand-alone treatment. BSD Medical was the first to develop an approvable hyperthermia system, which uses focused radio frequencies and microwaves to heat cancer cells until they die. The company's devices are designed to target superficial tumors, as well as tumors located deep within a patient's body. Its products are sold to clinics, hospitals, and other cancer-treatment institutions.

	Annual Growth	8/03	8/04	8/05	8/06	8/07
Sales ($ mil.)	1.9%	2.6	1.6	2.0	2.9	2.8
Net income ($ mil.)	—	(0.6)	8.4	3.3	9.3	(3.3)
Employees	16.8%	—	—	33	—	45

BSH HOME APPLIANCES CORPORATION

5551 McFadden Ave.
Huntington Beach, CA 92649
Phone: 714-901-6600
Fax: 714-901-5980
Web: www.siemens-home.com

CEO: Franz Bosshard
CFO: Thorsten Rosenberg
HR: Victor Poglinco
FYE: December 31
Type: Subsidiary

BSH can help make a HSH — a home sweet home, that is. BSH Home Appliances is a subsidiary of German manufacturer BSH Bosch und Siemens Hausgeräte. The company makes and distributes a variety of home appliances under the Gaggenau, Siemens, Bosch, and Thermador brands, including dishwashers, ovens, cooktops, barbecues, washing machines, and dryers. BSH Home Appliances operates plants in North Carolina and Tennessee. In late 2006 the company established a subsidiary in Toronto that serves customers in eastern Canada. BSH products are sold directly to new homebuilders, as well as through retailers such as Home Depot and Lowe's.

BSML, INC.

NASDAQ (CM): BSML

460 N. Wiget Ln.
Walnut Creek, CA 94598
Phone: 925-941-6260
Fax: 925-941-6266
Web: www.britesmile.com

CEO: Jeff Nourse
CFO: Marc P. Applebaum
HR: Mark Murano
FYE: Saturday nearest December 31
Type: Public

If your pearly whites aren't so pearly any more, BSML (formerly BriteSmile) can help. The company's BriteSmile Professional Whitening System uses a blue gas plasma light to activate a peroxide-based whitening gel that can remove stains and other discolorations from teeth. The company targets metropolitan areas with BriteSmile Centers in nearly a dozen cities, such as Los Angeles and Houston. BSML operates nearly 20 centers in the US; it also sells whitening products such as toothpaste. The company has sold its associated centers business, which licensed the BriteSmile system to 5,000 dental offices worldwide, to Discus Dental. Former chairman Anthony Pilaro owns a controlling stake in the company.

	Annual Growth	12/03	12/04	12/05	12/06	12/07
Sales ($ mil.)	(4.6%)	—	—	—	26.2	25.0
Net income ($ mil.)	—	—	—	—	4.4	(5.2)
Market value ($ mil.)	(77.7%)	—	—	—	19.0	4.2
Employees	—	—	—	—	—	—

BSQUARE CORPORATION

NASDAQ (GM): BSQR

110 110th Ave. NE, Ste. 200
Bellevue, WA 98004
Phone: 425-519-5900
Fax: 425-519-5999
Web: www.bsquare.com

CEO: Brian T. Crowley
CFO: Scott C. Mahan
HR: –
FYE: December 31
Type: Public

BSQUARE is hip to intelligent computing devices (ICDs) and smart devices, including Internet appliances, handheld computers, TV set-top boxes, and gaming consoles. With BSQUARE's engineering and development services and software, equipment makers can integrate Microsoft's Windows operating systems into their products. Its consumer software enables handheld PCs to perform such tasks as faxing and printing. BSQUARE also resells products from assorted vendors, including Adobe Systems and Microsoft, which provides the majority of the company's revenues.

	Annual Growth	12/03	12/04	12/05	12/06	12/07
Sales ($ mil.)	12.1%	37.6	38.9	42.9	49.8	59.3
Net income ($ mil.)	—	(14.0)	(7.1)	(1.3)	(0.5)	2.8
Market value ($ mil.)	(24.8%)	211.7	227.3	31.0	27.4	67.7
Employees	6.3%	—	—	155	170	175

BT INFONET

2160 E. Grand Ave.
El Segundo, CA 90245
Phone: 310-335-2600
Fax: 310-335-4507
Web: www.infonet.com

CEO: José A. Collazo
CFO: Akbar H. Firdosy
HR: Robert A. Passaretti
FYE: March 31
Type: Subsidiary

"Global" is more than a buzzword for BT Infonet. The company, a subsidiary of BT Group, provides managed network communications services for multinational corporations using its own private network. The data carrier provides local service support in more than 70 countries and its network can be reached within more than 180 countries, serving nearly 3,000 corporations. Clients include Allergan, Bayer, and Hitachi. Cross-border services include frame relay, virtual private networks (VPNs), dedicated and dial-up Internet access, and remote access.

	Annual Growth	3/03	3/04	3/05	3/06	3/07
Est. sales ($ mil.)	—	—	—	—	—	138.8
Employees	—	—	—	—	—	1,085

BT INS, INC.

1600 Memorex Dr., Ste. 200
Santa Clara, CA 95050
Phone: 408-330-2700
Fax: 408-330-2701
Web: www.ins.com

CEO: David Butze
CFO: Julia Kellberg
HR: Bart Erwin
FYE: September 30
Type: Subsidiary

When this INS knocks, only hackers run. BT INS (formerly International Network Services) provides network consulting services, including business alignment, IT infrastructure, network and systems management, operating systems integration, project management, security consulting, storage, and strategy and planning. As part of its security consulting portfolio, INS offers ethical hacking services intended to identify potential network risks and vulnerabilities. The company also offers the Diamond IP family of networking software. Customers have included Allstate, Baxter, and Texas Christian University. BT INS is a subsidiary of UK communications firm BT Group.

	Annual Growth	9/03	9/04	9/05	9/06	9/07
Est. sales ($ mil.)	—	—	—	—	—	53.3
Employees	—	—	—	—	—	900

BT RADIANZ

575 Lexington Ave.
New York, NY 10022
Phone: 212-415-4600
Fax: 212-415-4603
Web: www.btradianz.com

CEO: Laurie Bowen
CFO: Lawrence K. (Larry) Kinsella
HR: Steve Messinger
FYE: December 31
Type: Subsidiary

BT Radianz customers looked into the light and liked what they saw. The company operates an Internet Protocol (IP)-based extranet network, RadianzNet, for providing transaction and information services to the financial services industry. The network enables subscribers such as investment banks, brokers, and stock exchanges to electronically and privately distribute information to their customers and execute trades. BT Radianz's customers include the American Stock Exchange, Standard & Poor's, and Bear Stearns. The company is a subsidiary of BT Group.

	Annual Growth	12/03	12/04	12/05	12/06	12/07
Est. sales ($ mil.)	—	—	—	—	—	127.9
Employees	—	—	—	—	—	1,000

BTU INTERNATIONAL, INC.

NASDAQ (GM): BTUI

23 Esquire Rd.
North Billerica, MA 01862
Phone: 978-667-4111
Fax: 978-667-9068
Web: www.btu.com

CEO: Paul J. van der Wansem
CFO: Thomas P. Kealy
HR: –
FYE: December 31
Type: Public

Things are heating up at BTU International. BTU makes, sells, and services thermal processing equipment and controls for the manufacture of printed circuit boards and for semiconductor packaging. The company supplies systems for solder reflow (for printed circuit boards), as well as technical ceramic sintering, electrical component brazing, and the deposition of film coatings. BTU equipment is also used to make photovoltaic solar cells and solid oxide fuel cells, and for sintering nuclear fuel. The company sells its products to manufacturers of computers, printed circuit board assemblies, and consumer electronics products throughout the world. BTU gets more than half of its sales from the Asia/Pacific region.

	Annual Growth	12/03	12/04	12/05	12/06	12/07
Sales ($ mil.)	22.3%	28.5	54.6	66.4	78.3	63.7
Net income ($ mil.)	—	(6.8)	(4.2)	4.6	9.2	2.0
Market value ($ mil.)	49.2%	25.2	22.0	112.1	90.0	124.6
Employees	13.2%	214	250	311	348	351

BUBBA GUMP SHRIMP CO. INTERNATIONAL, LLC

209 Avenida Fabricante, Ste. 200
San Clemente, CA 92672
Phone: 949-366-6260
Fax: 949-366-6261
Web: www.bubbagump.com

CEO: Scott Barnett
CFO: Daniel (Dan) Bylund
HR: –
FYE: December 31
Type: Private

Maybe for this company the restaurant business is like a box of chocolates. Bubba Gump Shrimp Co. International operates and franchises about 25 Bubba Gump Shrimp Co. Restaurant & Market casual-dining seafood restaurants in 10 states and five other countries. Inspired by the 1994 film *Forrest Gump*, the chain's menu features such items as Jenny's Peace 'n Love Veggie Plate, Lt. Dan's Drunken Shrimp, and the Run Across America Sampler. The restaurants can mostly be found at tourist destinations, such as the Mall of America and the Universal Orlando theme park. CEO Scott Barnett struck a licensing deal with Paramount Pictures in 1996 to convert units of the Rusty Pelican restaurant chain into Gump-themed eateries.

	Annual Growth	12/03	12/04	12/05	12/06	12/07
Est. sales ($ mil.)	—	—	—	—	—	5.9
Employees	—	—	—	—	—	300

BUCA, INC.

NASDAQ (GM): BUCA

1300 Nicollet Mall, Ste. 5003
Minneapolis, MN 55403
Phone: 612-225-3400
Fax: 612-225-3302
Web: www.bucainc.com

CEO: John T. Bettin
CFO: Dennis J. Goetz
HR: –
FYE: Last Sunday in December
Type: Public

Everyone's *famiglia* at these restaurants. BUCA owns and operates about 90 Buca di Beppo Italian restaurants in about 25 states and Washington, DC. Each themed eatery is an over-the-top recreation of a post-war Italian-American restaurant decked out with a hodgepodge of memorabilia. Geared for larger parties of people and event dining, the menu features Southern Italian-American cuisine served family-style to encourage sharing and conversation. Most locations of the casual-dining chain offer a lunch menu (smaller portions for single diners) in addition to its popular dinner options.

	Annual Growth	12/03	12/04	12/05	12/06	12/07
Sales ($ mil.)	(1.1%)	257.0	258.4	239.0	253.8	245.6
Net income ($ mil.)	—	(12.3)	(37.6)	(32.1)	(3.6)	(16.2)
Market value ($ mil.)	(35.0%)	112.1	149.6	107.7	100.7	20.0
Employees	(2.1%)	—	—	6,300	6,170	

BUCKEYE GP HOLDINGS L.P.

NYSE: BGH

5 TEK Park, 9999 Hamilton Blvd.
Breinigsville, PA 18031
Phone: 610-904-4000
Fax: 484-232-4543
Web: www.buckeye.com

CEO: Forrest E. Wylie
CFO: Vance E. Powers
HR: –
FYE: December 31
Type: Public

With the price of crude oil burgeoning, Buckeye GP Holdings L.P. sees no reason to buck the trend of making money from petroleum products. The company owns Buckeye GP LLC, the general partner of Buckeye Partners, L.P. The holding company makes all of its money from its general partner interests in Buckeye Partners, which is engaged in the transportation, terminalling, and storage of refined petroleum products across the US. Buckeye Partners owns and operates one of the country's largest independent refined petroleum products pipeline systems, with about 5,400 miles of pipeline, serving 17 states.

	Annual Growth	12/03	12/04	12/05	12/06	12/07
Sales ($ mil.)	17.1%	—	323.5	408.4	461.8	519.3
Net income ($ mil.)	115.1%	—	2.3	7.0	8.7	22.9
Market value ($ mil.)	77.4%	—	—	—	441.2	782.8
Employees		—	—	801	—	—

BUCKEYE PARTNERS, L.P.

NYSE: BPL

5 TEK Park, 9999 Hamilton Blvd.
Breinigsville, PA 18031
Phone: 610-904-4000
Fax: 484-232-4543
Web: www.buckeye.com

CEO: Forrest E. Wylie
CFO: Vance E. Powers
HR: –
FYE: December 31
Type: Public

Buckeye Partners serves the Buckeye State and then some. Its main subsidiary, Buckeye Pipe Line, stretches 2,643 miles from Massachusetts to Illinois. Other pipelines include Laurel Pipe Line (Pennsylvania), Everglades Pipe Line (Florida), and Wood River Pipe Lines (Illinois, Indiana, Missouri, and Ohio). The company operates a total of about 5,400 miles of pipeline, serving 17 states, and 51 storage terminals capable of holding 20 million barrels of refined petroleum. It owns a major natural gas storage facility in northern California; and markets refined petroleum products in a number of the geographic areas served by its pipeline and terminal operations.

	Annual Growth	12/03	12/04	12/05	12/06	12/07
Sales ($ mil.)	17.4%	273.0	323.5	408.5	461.8	519.3
Net income ($ mil.)	50.7%	30.1	83.0	100.0	110.2	155.4
Market value ($ mil.)	14.8%	1,302.6	1,497.5	1,601.3	1,833.8	2,258.9
Employees	—	—	—	801	867	0

BUCKEYE TECHNOLOGIES INC.

NYSE: BKI

1001 Tillman St.
Memphis, TN 38112
Phone: 901-320-8100
Fax: 901-320-8836
Web: www.bkitech.com

CEO: John B. Crowe
CFO: Steven G. Dean
HR: Terrence M. Reed
FYE: June 30
Type: Public

Buckeye Technologies isn't a course taught at Ohio State. The company produces absorbent products, chemical cellulose products (derived from wood and cotton), and customized paper. Buckeye's absorbent products, made from cellulose, fluff pulp, non-wovens, and other fibers, are used in diapers, napkins, tablecovers, baby wipes, household wipes, mops, and feminine hygiene items. Buckeye's chemical cellulose is used in coat linings, cosmetics, food casings, tire and hose reinforcement, food thickeners, pharmaceuticals, plastics, and rayon filament. Its customized paper is used in automotive air and oil filters, currency, letterhead, and stationery. Procter & Gamble is Buckeye's largest customer.

	Annual Growth	6/03	6/04	6/05	6/06	6/07
Sales ($ mil.)	4.7%	641.1	656.9	712.8	728.5	769.3
Net income ($ mil.)	—	(24.9)	(38.2)	20.2	2.0	30.1
Market value ($ mil.)	24.5%	251.4	430.6	299.6	289.6	604.0
Employees	(5.9%)	—	—	1,700	1,600	

THE BUCKLE, INC.

NYSE: BKE

2407 W. 24th St.
Kearney, NE 68845
Phone: 308-236-8491
Fax: 308-236-4493
Web: www.buckle.com

CEO: Dennis H. Nelson
CFO: Karen B. Rhoads
HR: –
FYE: Saturday nearest January 31
Type: Public

The Buckle has done away with the notion that Midwestern kids wear only overalls. With about 370 mostly mall-based stores in 38 states, The Buckle sells fashion-conscious 12- to 24-year-olds the clothes they've just got to have: mid- to higher-priced casual apparel (pants, tops, outerwear, shoes, and accessories), including brand names such as Dr. Martens, Fossil, Lucky, Polo, and Silver. Denim, which accounts for about 40% of sales, is popular with its customers. The Buckle operates under the names Buckle and The Buckle; it also has an online store. Born and raised in Nebraska, it has expanded into the South and West. Chairman Daniel Hirschfeld, the founder's son, owns more than 40% of The Buckle's shares.

	Annual Growth	1/04	1/05	1/06	1/07	1/08
Sales ($ mil.)	10.0%	422.8	470.9	501.1	530.1	619.9
Net income ($ mil.)	22.3%	33.7	43.2	51.9	55.7	75.3
Market value ($ mil.)	35.8%	368.8	408.8	444.4	996.1	1,253.9
Employees	4.8%	—	—	6,100	6,100	6,700

BUCKMAN LABORATORIES INTERNATIONAL, INC.

1256 N. McLean Blvd.
Memphis, TN 38108
Phone: 901-278-0330
Fax: 901-276-5343
Web: www.buckman.com

CEO: Edson P. Peredo
CFO: Michael Huthwaite
HR: Charles (Chip) Westbrook
FYE: December 31
Type: Private

Buckman Laboratories International defends the world against tiny invaders. The global specialty chemicals manufacturer focuses on products that control the growth of microorganisms such as mold and fungi. The company's more than 500 products are key to aqueous industrial processes used in manufacturing and treating pulp and paper, leather, paint, coatings, plastics, and wood. They include chemical intermediates, coagulants, corrosion inhibitors, defoamers, dispersants, flocculants, microbicides, polymers, and scale inhibitors. The family of founder Stanley Buckman owns the company through Bulab Holdings.

	Annual Growth	12/03	12/04	12/05	12/06	12/07
Est. sales ($ mil.)	—	—	—	—	—	82.3
Employees	—	—	—	—	—	350

BUCYRUS INTERNATIONAL, INC.

NASDAQ (GS): BUCY

1100 Milwaukee Ave.
South Milwaukee, WI 53172
Phone: 414-768-4000
Fax: 414-768-4474
Web: www.bucyrus.com

CEO: Timothy W. Sullivan
CFO: Craig R. Mackus
HR: –
FYE: December 31
Type: Public

Bucyrus International caters to those who *mine* their own business. The company (formerly Bucyrus-Erie Co.) provides replacement parts and services to the surface mining industry. Bucyrus also makes large excavation machinery used for surface mining. Its products, which include walking draglines, electric mining shovels, and blast-hole drills, are used for mining coal, gold, iron ore, oil sands, and other minerals. Equipment geared toward coal excavation was boosted in 2007 with the acquisition of DBT from Germany-based coal producer RAG. Bucyrus' customers are primarily large companies and quasi-governmental agencies operating in South America and Australia, Canada, China, India, South Africa, and the US.

	Annual Growth	12/03	12/04	12/05	12/06	12/07
Sales ($ mil.)	47.8%	337.7	454.2	575.0	738.0	1,613.4
Net income ($ mil.)	—	(3.6)	6.1	53.6	70.3	136.1
Market value ($ mil.)	90.0%	—	271.3	369.5	817.2	1,860.2
Employees	68.7%	—	—	2,125	2,400	6,050

BUDGET RENT A CAR SYSTEM, INC.

6 Sylvan Way
Parsippany, NJ 07054
Phone: 973-496-3500
Fax: 888-304-2315
Web: www.budget.com

CEO: Ronald L. (Ron) Nelson
CFO: David B. Wyshner
HR: Mark J. Servodidio
FYE: December 31
Type: Subsidiary

When your car rental budget won't allow for the fanciest car on the lot, Budget Rent A Car System might very well have a set of wheels for you. Budget rents cars through a network of about 1,900 locations, some 700 of which are company-owned, in the Americas and the Asia/Pacific region. The Budget car rental brand is pitched mainly to leisure travelers and to the cost-conscious. Together with sister company Avis Rent A Car System, the company operates a fleet of more than 380,000 rental cars. Affiliate Budget Truck Rental rents more than 30,000 trucks from about 2,900 franchised and company-owned locations in the US. Budget Rent A Car System is a unit of Avis Budget Group, formerly Cendant.

BUFFALO ROCK COMPANY

111 Oxmoor Rd.
Birmingham, AL 35209
Phone: 205-942-3435
Fax: 205-942-2601
Web: buffalorock.com

CEO: James C. (Jimmy) Lee III
CFO: Roger Barker
HR: –
FYE: December 31
Type: Private

This company has a solid place in the soft drink market. Buffalo Rock is a leading bottling and distribution company that supplies soft drinks and other beverages from PepsiCo, including such brands as AquaFina, Mountain Dew, Pepsi, and Tropicana. The company also bottles beverages from Dr Pepper Snapple Group and Kraft Foods, as well as its own brands Buffalo Rock Ginger Ale and Dr. Wham. In addition to beverages, Buffalo Rock distributes food products and supplies for the foodservice industry, and it operates a food-vending distribution business. The family-owned company has more than a dozen distribution facilities serving customers in Alabama, Florida, and Georgia.

BUFFALO WILD WINGS, INC.

NASDAQ (GS): BWLD

5500 Wayzata Blvd., Ste. 1600
Minneapolis, MN 55416
Phone: 952-593-9943
Fax: 952-593-9787
Web: www.buffalowildwings.com

CEO: Sally J. Smith
CFO: Mary J. Twinem
HR: Linda G. Traylor
FYE: Last Sunday in December
Type: Public

Hot sauce fuels the flight of this restaurateur. Buffalo Wild Wings (BWW) operates a chain of more than 500 Buffalo Wild Wings Grill & Bar quick-casual dining spots in more than 35 states that specialize in Buffalo-style chicken wings. The eateries offer more than a dozen dipping sauces to go with their spicy wings, as well as a complement of other items such as chicken tenders and legs. BWW's menu also offers appetizers, burgers, tacos, salads, and desserts, along with beer, wine, and other beverages. The company owns and operates more than 160 of the restaurants, while the rest are operated by franchisees.

	Annual Growth	12/03	12/04	12/05	12/06	12/07
Sales ($ mil.)	27.0%	126.5	171.1	209.7	278.2	329.6
Net income ($ mil.)	52.8%	3.6	7.2	8.9	16.3	19.6
Market value ($ mil.)	44.7%	94.6	146.0	145.6	234.0	415.0
Employees	25.0%	—	—	6,125	7,482	9,564

An in-depth profile of this company is available to Hoover's Online members at hoovers.com.

295

BUFFETS HOLDINGS, INC.

1460 Buffet Way
Eagan, MN 55121
Phone: 651-994-8608
Fax: 651-365-2356
Web: www.buffet.com

CEO: R. Michael Andrews Jr.
CFO: A. Keith Wall Jr.
HR: Jane L. Binzak
FYE: Wednesday nearest June 30
Type: Private

Corn bread dressing, fish patties, baked beans, hot wings . . . kneel and pray to the almighty buffet. Buffets Holdings is the largest operator of buffet-style restaurants in the US, with about 570 locations in 40 states. Its restaurants, including such chains as HomeTown Buffet, Old Country Buffet, and Ryan's, generally offer self-service buffets featuring entrees, sides, and desserts for an all-inclusive price. In addition to its company-owned locations, Buffets Holdings has about 20 franchised restaurants. Buffets Holdings filed for Chapter 11 bankruptcy in 2008. Private equity firm CI Capital Partners (formerly Caxton-Iseman Capital) owns nearly 80% of the company.

	Annual Growth	6/02	6/03	6/04	6/05	6/06
Sales ($ mil.)	27.4%	527.1	985.3	942.8	926.8	1,390.0
Employees	12.2%	24,000	23,000	23,000	22,000	38,000

BUILD-A-BEAR WORKSHOP, INC.

NYSE: BBW

1954 Innerbelt Business Center Dr.
St. Louis, MO 63114
Phone: 314-423-8000
Fax: 314-423-8188
Web: www.buildabear.com

CEO: Maxine K. Clark
CFO: Tina Klocke
HR: Darlene Elder
FYE: Saturday nearest December 31
Type: Public

The Build-A-Bear Workshop covers the "bear" necessities and much more. Located mainly in malls, the stores allow kids to design their own teddy bears and other stuffed animals complete with clothing (formal wear to western wear), shoes (including Skechers), and a barrage of accessories (eyewear, cell phones, and the like). Customers can also build bears online. Other offerings include the in-store Build-A-Party and an interactive online community, as well as online games and e-cards. The company, founded by CEO Maxine Clark in 1997, operates 320-plus stores in Canada, Europe, and the US, as well as some 50 franchised stores in international locations. Clark owns about 14% of the company.

	Annual Growth	12/03	12/04	12/05	12/06	12/07
Sales ($ mil.)	22.1%	213.7	301.7	361.8	437.1	474.4
Net income ($ mil.)	29.5%	8.0	20.0	27.3	29.5	22.5
Market value ($ mil.)	(24.1%)	—	687.5	596.4	575.5	300.2
Employees	4.2%	—	—	6,350	6,900	6,900

BUILDERS FIRSTSOURCE, INC.

NASDAQ (GS): BLDR

2001 Bryan St., Ste. 1600
Dallas, TX 75201
Phone: 214-880-3500
Fax: 214-880-3599
Web: www.buildersfirstsource.com

CEO: Floyd F. Sherman
CFO: Charles L. Horn
HR: Bobby Quinten
FYE: December 31
Type: Public

If you're a new home builder, these guys want to be your first, well, source. Builders FirstSource sells hardware and doors, windows, lumber, and other structural building products to professional homebuilders. Customers include Centex, D.R. Horton, and Hovnanian Enterprises. Builders FirstSource has grown through about 25 acquisitions to operate some 65 distribution centers and 60-plus manufacturing plants in about a dozen states. The company was founded in 1998 as BSL Holdings by a management team headed by former CEO John Roach and private investment firm JLL Partners. Affiliates of JLL and private equity firm Warburg Pincus own about 50% of Builders FirstSource's stock.

	Annual Growth	12/03	12/04	12/05	12/06	12/07
Sales ($ mil.)	(1.3%)	1,675.1	2,058.1	2,337.8	2,239.4	1,592.5
Net income ($ mil.)	—	17.6	51.6	48.6	68.9	(23.8)
Market value ($ mil.)	(39.5%)	—	—	705.2	621.1	257.8
Employees	(10.6%)	—	—	6,600	5,900	—

BUILDING MATERIALS HOLDING CORPORATION

NYSE: BLG

4 Embarcadero Center, Ste. 3200
San Francisco, CA 94111
Phone: 415-627-9100
Fax: 415-627-9119
Web: www.bmhc.com

CEO: Robert E. (Rob) Mellor
CFO: William M. (Bill) Smartt
HR: Steven H. (Steve) Pearson
FYE: December 31
Type: Public

Building Materials Holding Corporation (BMHC) goes with the pros. Its SelectBuild Construction subsidiary provides services such as project estimating and material procurement for large-volume homebuilders in key markets. Its other business, BMC West, operates about 40 distribution centers and 60 manufacturing facilities primarily in the western US, mainly targeting professional building contractors rather than do-it-yourselfers. The stores sell manufactured products (lumber, roofing materials, paint, and tools) and value-added offerings (pre-hung doors, roof and floor trusses, and wall panels) that generate greater profits. BMC West also offers services such as component manufacturing and installation.

	Annual Growth	12/03	12/04	12/05	12/06	12/07
Sales ($ mil.)	12.7%	1,415.1	2,091.0	2,912.2	3,245.2	2,285.0
Net income ($ mil.)	—	19.9	53.9	129.5	102.1	(312.7)
Market value ($ mil.)	(77.4%)	—	—	—	719.8	162.6
Employees	21.4%	8,300	12,000	21,000	17,000	18,000

BULOVA CORPORATION

1 Bulova Ave.
Woodside, NY 11377
Phone: 718-204-3300
Fax: 718-204-3546
Web: www.bulova.com

CEO: Dennis W. Perry
CFO: Janet Gunzburg
HR: Glenn M. Parker
FYE: December 31
Type: Subsidiary

Bulova is working to keep perfect time in the watch industry. It sells watches, clocks, and timepiece parts under brands such as Accutron and Wittnauer (luxury), Bulova (mid-priced), and Caravelle (lower-priced), as well as licensed Harley-Davidson and Frank Lloyd Wright styles. The firm also sells miniature collectible clocks, mostly under the Bulova name, and has expanded its licensing efforts to include items such as eyewear. Bulova peddles its products primarily through department and jewelry stores, mostly in the US. It has offices in Canada, Mexico, Switzerland, and the Far East. The Tisch brothers' holding company, Loews, bought Bulova in 1979 and sold it in 2008 to rival Citizen Watch.

BUMBLE BEE FOODS, LLC

9655 Granite Ridge Dr., Ste. 100
San Diego, CA 92123
Phone: 858-715-4000
Fax: 858-560-6045
Web: www.bumblebee.com

CEO: Christopher D. (Chris) Lischewski
CFO: Kent McNeil
HR: –
FYE: December 31
Type: Private

Nope, Bumble Bee Foods doesn't make honey. But they do make a honey of a product line. It includes canned tuna, crab, salmon, shrimp, clams, sardines, and other specialty canned seafoods. The company's brand names include Bumble Bee, of course, along with Castleberry's, Sweet Sue, Bryan, and King Oscar. The company, when combined with its Canadian operations, Clover Leaf Seafoods, outranks its arch rival StarKist as the largest canned seafood company in North America. Bumble Bee has canning operations in California and Puerto Rico. Its customers include retail food stores and foodservice providers. The company is owned by Connors Bros. Income Fund.

	Annual Growth	12/03	12/04	12/05	12/06	12/07
Est. sales ($ mil.)	—	—	—	—	—	333.4
Employees	—	—	—	—	—	3,000

BUNGE NORTH AMERICA, INC.

11720 Borman Dr.
St. Louis, MO 63146
Phone: 314-292-2000
Fax: 314-292-2110
Web: www.bungenorthamerica.com

CEO: Carl L. Hausmann
CFO: Michael M. Scharf
HR: Philip W. Staggs
FYE: December 31
Type: Subsidiary

Bunge North America is the world's main squeeze. Its milling division, which operates five mills, is the largest corn dry miller in the world. In addition to corn, the company also deals in soybeans, canola, wheat, and sorghum. Its grain division, with 80 elevators, stores the oilseed crops; its processing division operates oilseed processing plants throughout the US and Canada; its crusher/refiner facility in Iowa is one of the largest oil-extraction lines in the US. Bunge's oil division blends and sells the oil to food producers, foodservice operators, and retail food outlets throughout the North American continent.

	Annual Growth	12/03	12/04	12/05	12/06	12/07
Est. sales ($ mil.)	—	—	—	—	—	2,146.4
Employees	—	—	—	—	—	4,679

BUNZL DISTRIBUTION USA, INC.

701 Emerson Rd., Ste. 500
St. Louis, MO 63141
Phone: 314-997-5959
Fax: 314-997-1405
Web: www.bunzldistribution.com

CEO: Patrick L. (Pat) Larmon
CFO: Jane Jennewein
HR: Robin Pokoik
FYE: December 31
Type: Subsidiary

Products provided by Bunzl Distribution USA can keep your deli from getting smelly. The company supplies plastic packaging and disposable paper products used as food containers to grocery stores, convenience stores, and other food service businesses. In addition, Bunzl Distribution USA distributes a variety of cleaning supplies and safety equipment to both food and nonfood retailers in the US, Canada, Mexico, and the Caribbean. Overall, it handles some 250,000 products, obtained from numerous manufacturers, from a network of more than 90 facilities. The company is the North American arm of Bunzl plc, a leading UK-based wholesale distribution company.

	Annual Growth	12/03	12/04	12/05	12/06	12/07
Est. sales ($ mil.)	—	—	—	—	—	946.1
Employees	—	—	—	—	—	3,625

THE BUREAU OF NATIONAL AFFAIRS, INC.

1231 25th St. NW
Washington, DC 20037
Phone: 202-452-4200
Fax: 202-452-4226
Web: www.bna.com

CEO: Paul N. Wojcik
CFO: Robert P. Ambrosini
HR: Carol A. Clark
FYE: December 31
Type: Private

The Bureau of National Affairs (BNA) is a leading provider of legal and regulatory information. The company publishes advisory and research reports, books, newsletters, and other publications covering economic, health care, labor, public policy, and tax issues for professionals in business and government. It has a staff of 600 reporters, editors, and legal experts who gather information from around the country. BNA delivers its information online and through print and electronic products, some available through subscription services such as LexisNexis and Thomson Reuter's Westlaw. It also produces financial planning and tax software (BNA Software) and provides commercial printing services (McArdle Printing).

	Annual Growth	12/02	12/03	12/04	12/05	12/06
Sales ($ mil.)	2.7%	309.8	311.8	321.3	329.0	344.9
Net income ($ mil.)	7.7%	14.4	16.1	22.6	24.1	19.4
Employees	(3.6%)	1,999	1,878	1,802	1,729	1,728

BURGER KING HOLDINGS, INC.

NYSE: BKC

5505 Blue Lagoon Dr.
Miami, FL 33126
Phone: 305-378-3000
Fax: 305-378-7262
Web: www.burgerking.com

CEO: John W. Chidsey
CFO: Ben K. Wells
HR: Peter C. (Pete) Smith
FYE: June 30
Type: Public

This king rules a whopper of a fast-food empire. Burger King Holdings operates the world's #2 hamburger chain (behind McDonald's) with more than 11,400 restaurants in the US and about 70 other countries. In addition to its popular Whopper sandwich, the chain offers a variety of burgers, chicken sandwiches, salads, and breakfast items. More than 1,300 BK locations are company-owned, while the rest are owned and operated by franchisees. Burger King was founded by James McLamore and David Edgerton in 1954. Investment firms TPG Capital, Bain Capital, and Goldman Sachs each own about 30% of the company.

	Annual Growth	6/03	6/04	6/05	6/06	6/07
Sales ($ mil.)	8.4%	—	1,754.0	1,940.0	2,048.0	2,234.0
Net income ($ mil.)	209.3%	—	5.0	47.0	27.0	148.0
Market value ($ mil.)	70.0%	—	—	—	2,095.7	3,561.6
Employees	13.5%	—	—	30,300	37,000	39,000

BURKE MILLS, INC.

Pink Sheets: BMLS

191 Sterling St., NW
Valdese, NC 28690
Phone: 828-874-6341
Fax: 828-879-7188
Web: www.burkemills.com

CEO: Humayun N. Shaikh
CFO: Thomas I. Nail
HR: Maggie Simmons-Hughes
FYE: Saturday nearest December 31
Type: Public

Burke Mills hopes that the yarns it spins keep its customers in stitches. The company's primary business is the twisting, texturing, winding, dyeing, processing, and selling of filament, novelty, and spun yarns. Burke Mills also dyes and processes yarns for other manufacturers on a commission basis. The company principally serves the home furnishings, apparel, and contract upholstery markets. Customers have included fabric makers like Quaker Fabric Corporation. Burke Mills sells its products throughout Canada, the Caribbean Basin, Mexico, and the US, with revenue primarily coming from the eastern US. Chairman and CEO Humayun Shaikh owns about 53% of the company.

	Annual Growth	12/03	12/04	12/05	12/06	12/07
Sales ($ mil.)	(5.7%)	24.8	25.1	25.3	23.9	19.6
Net income ($ mil.)	—	(2.5)	(1.7)	(1.9)	(1.9)	(1.9)
Employees	—	—	—	—	—	200

BURLINGTON COAT FACTORY WAREHOUSE CORPORATION

1830 Rte. 130
Burlington, NJ 08016
Phone: 609-387-7800
Fax: 609-387-7071
Web: www.coat.com

CEO: Mark A. Nesci
CFO: Todd Weyhrich
HR: Sarah Orleck
FYE: Saturday nearest May 31
Type: Private

Burlington Coat Factory Warehouse has two de facto mottos: "not affiliated with Burlington Industries" (thanks to a 1981 trademark-infringement lawsuit settlement) and "We sell more than coats." The company operates around 400 no-frills retail stores offering current, brand-name clothing at less than standard retail price. Although it is one of the nation's largest coat sellers, it also sells children's apparel, bath items, furniture, gifts, jewelry, linens, and shoes. The business operates under the names Burlington Coat Factory, Cohoes Fashions, MJM Designer Shoes, and Super Baby Depot in nearly 45 states. Founded in 1972, Burlington was acquired by affiliates of buyout firm Bain Capital in 2006.

	Annual Growth	5/03	5/04	5/05	5/06	5/07
Sales ($ mil.)	5.7%	2,724.7	2,878.3	3,199.8	3,439.0	3,403.0
Net income ($ mil.)	(7.8%)	65.0	67.6	106.0	67.0	47.0
Employees	5.0%	23,000	24,000	25,000	26,500	28,005

An in-depth profile of this company is available to Hoover's Online members at hoovers.com.

297

BURLINGTON NORTHERN SANTA FE CORPORATION
NYSE: BNI

2650 Lou Menk Dr.
Fort Worth, TX 76131
Phone: 817-352-1000
Fax: 817-352-7171
Web: www.bnsf.com

CEO: Matthew K. (Matt) Rose
CFO: Thomas N. Hund
HR: Linda T. Longo-Kazanova
FYE: December 31
Type: Public

Over the years the number of major US railroads has dwindled, but Burlington Northern Santa Fe (BNSF) thrives as one of the survivors. Through its primary subsidiary, BNSF Railway, the company is the second-largest railroad operator in the US, behind Union Pacific. BNSF makes tracks through 28 states in the West, Midwest, and Sunbelt regions of the US and in two Canadian provinces. The company operates its trains over a system of about 32,000 route miles, consisting of 23,000 route miles owned by BNSF and 9,000 route miles of trackage rights, which allow BNSF Railway to use tracks owned by other railroads.

	Annual Growth	12/03	12/04	12/05	12/06	12/07
Sales ($ mil.)	13.8%	9,413.0	10,946.0	12,987.0	14,985.0	15,802.0
Net income ($ mil.)	22.4%	816.0	791.0	1,531.0	1,887.0	1,829.0
Market value ($ mil.)	24.6%	12,016.7	17,827.0	26,314.7	26,414.8	28,939.4
Employees	0.0%	—	—	40,000	41,000	40,000

BURLINGTON WORLDWIDE INC.

804 Green Valley Rd., Ste. 300
Greensboro, NC 27408
Phone: 336-379-6220
Fax: 336-332-0815
Web: www.burlington.com/worldwide/worldwidemain.html

CEO: Kenneth T. (Ken) Kunberger
CFO: –
HR: –
FYE: December 30
Type: Subsidiary

Burlington WorldWide has been altered more times than a see-saw dieter's tuxedo. The company, once a part of Burlington Industries, is now a division of International Textile Group, Inc. Burlington WorldWide is a maker of blended and performance synthetic fabrics, cottons and cotton-blends, and worsted wool fabrics. The company's products are used to manufacture apparel including menswear, womenswear, activewear, and uniforms (through Burlington Raeford). The company also makes barrier fabrics used in the health care, microelectronics, pharmaceutical, and food and beverage industries.

BURNES HOME ACCENTS, LLC

21 Cypress Blvd., Ste. 1010
Round Rock, TX 78729
Phone: 512-257-6500
Fax: 512-257-6530
Web: www.burnesgroup.com

CEO: Dean Childers
CFO: –
HR: Brian Stull
FYE: December 31
Type: Private

Burnes is behind the walls of frames featuring family and friends. Burnes Home Accents (formerly Burnes Group) manufactures decorative picture frames, photo albums, scrapbooks, and home accessories and sells them through distributors. The company also makes photo album refills and had a hand in creating the Level-Line, which helps customers hang its items well. Its products are available through large retailers, such as Wal-Mart, Michaels, Rite Aid, and Target. Brand names include Burnes of Boston, Carr Connoisseur, and RareWoods, among others. The company has been owned by several firms in recent years, as its former parent filed for bankruptcy protection in 2006.

	Annual Growth	12/03	12/04	12/05	12/06	12/07
Est. sales ($ mil.)	—	—	—	—	—	66.7
Employees	—	—	—	—	—	850

BURNS & MCDONNELL, INC.

9400 Ward Pkwy.
Kansas City, MO 64114
Phone: 816-333-9400
Fax: 816-822-3412
Web: www.burnsmcd.com

CEO: Greg M. Graves
CFO: Mark Taylor
HR: Melissa Wood
FYE: September 30
Type: Private

It may sound like a law firm, but Burns & McDonnell provides construction services, not legal advice. One of the leading design firms in the US, the company provides engineering, architectural, and design/build services for the aviation, defense, environmental, utilities, and other markets. The group has about 20 offices throughout the US, as well as locations in several other countries. It ranks among the top 10 designers for the power industry; more than one-third of its revenues are earned from projects for that market. In 2006 the company created its tenth business unit to offer architectural, engineering, and related services to the health care industry.

BURRIS LOGISTICS

501 SE 5th St.
Milford, DE 19963
Phone: 302-839-4531
Fax: 302-839-5175
Web: www.burrislogistics.com

CEO: Robert D. (Bob) Burris
CFO: Wayne Romanczuk
HR: Robert (Bob) Silva
FYE: May 31
Type: Private

Burris Logistics operates a network of about 15 temperature-controlled warehouse facilities in the eastern US, from Pennsylvania to Florida, with more than 60 million cu. ft. of storage space. The company transports customers' cargo with its own fleet of about 85 tractors and 200 refrigerated trailers. Burris Logistics specializes in providing logistics services for retailers of frozen foods. In addition, it arranges transportation of customers' goods from East Coast ports to their inland destinations. The company, which began operations in the 1920s, is owned and operated by members of the Burris family.

	Annual Growth	5/03	5/04	5/05	5/06	5/07
Est. sales ($ mil.)	—	—	—	—	—	284.0
Employees	—	—	—	—	—	850

BURTON SNOWBOARDS

80 Industrial Pkwy.
Burlington, VT 05401
Phone: 802-862-4500
Fax: 802-660-3250
Web: www.burton.com

CEO: Laurent Potdevin
CFO: Mike Abbott
HR: –
FYE: January 31
Type: Private

Burton Snowboards takes surfing to the slopes with its line of premium snowboards and snowboarding equipment. The company is the world's leading snowboard maker, controlling about 40% of the market. Burton Snowboards also produces and sells snowboarding apparel, boots, bindings, packs, luggage, eyewear, and outerwear. Brands include Burton snowboards; AK, Radar, and Ronin outerwear; R.E.D. protective gear; Anon opticwear; Gravis footwear; and Analog streetwear. Burton Snowboards operates a handful of factory outlet stores located in Massachusetts, Illinois, New York, Vermont (at the company's headquarters), and in Austria. The company is owned by its chairman, Jake Burton, a snowboarding enthusiast who founded the company in 1977.

	Annual Growth	1/03	1/04	1/05	1/06	1/07
Est. sales ($ mil.)	—	—	—	—	—	38.9
Employees	—	—	—	—	—	382

BURT'S BEES, INC.

633 Davis Dr., Ste. 600
Morrisville, NC 27560
Phone: 919-998-5200
Fax: 919-998-5201
Web: www.burtsbees.com

CEO: John Replogle
CFO: Doug Haensel
HR: Beth Ritter
FYE: December 31
Type: Subsidiary

Burt's Bees wants to mind its own beeswax but sting the competition. The firm produces lip balm, bath oils, soaps, and about 150 other personal care products made from beeswax, nut oils, and other natural ingredients. Its products are sold through more than 20,000 health food and grocery store locations in the US, Canada, Europe, and Taiwan, as well as through its Web site. Burt's Bees was founded in Maine in 1984 when Roxanne Quimby met reclusive beekeeper Burt Shavitz and they began making candles and lip balm from his beeswax. Clorox acquired the company for $925 million in cash in November 2007.

	Annual Growth	12/03	12/04	12/05	12/06	12/07
Est. sales ($ mil.)	—	—	—	—	—	62.6
Employees	—	—	—	—	—	530

BUSCH ENTERTAINMENT CORPORATION

231 S. Bemiston, Ste. 600
St. Louis, MO 63105
Phone: 314-577-2000
Fax: 314-613-6049
Web: www.4adventure.com

CEO: Keith M. Kasen
CFO: David J. Grabe
HR: David L. Hammer
FYE: December 31
Type: Subsidiary

Sure do hope that Clydesdale horses, killer whales, and dolphins all get along! Busch Entertainment Corporation (BEC), a subsidiary of brewer Anheuser-Busch, is one of the US's largest theme park operators, with nine locations in five states. BEC owns three SeaWorld parks in California, Florida, and Texas. The Florida location also houses Discovery Cove, where visitors can swim with dolphins and other marine life. In addition, vacationers can splish and splash at Florida's Adventure Island or Virginia's Water Country USA. The firm's traditional amusement parks featuring rides and shows include Busch Gardens Tampa and Busch Gardens Williamsburg.

	Annual Growth	12/03	12/04	12/05	12/06	12/07
Est. sales ($ mil.)	—	—	—	—	—	2,147.5
Employees	—	—	—	—	—	3,500

BUSH BROTHERS & COMPANY

1016 E. Weisgarber Rd.
Knoxville, TN 37909
Phone: 865-588-7685
Fax: 865-450-4100
Web: www.bushbeans.com

CEO: Jim Ethier
CFO: Al Williams
HR: –
FYE: March 31
Type: Private

Bush Brothers & Company's success is proof that well-spent ad money makes a difference — even when you're up against the bean "big boys" (think Campbell's baked beans, Heinz, Van Camp's baked beans, or even B&M). Not deterred, however, Bush Brothers cans one of the leading US lines of baked beans, Bush's Best, which is made from a family recipe and was first sold in 1969. The company also cans variety beans (black, garbanzos, pintos, refried), chili, greens, and hominy, all of which are sold in retail food outlets and to foodservice operators across the US. Company spokesbrother Jay Bush and his "talking" dog, Duke, are the stars of the company's popular TV commercials.

	Annual Growth	3/03	3/04	3/05	3/06	3/07
Est. sales ($ mil.)	—	—	—	—	—	135.4
Employees	—	—	—	—	—	650

BUSH INDUSTRIES, INC.

1 Mason Dr.
Jamestown, NY 14702
Phone: 716-665-2000
Fax: 716-665-2510
Web: www.bushindustries.com

CEO: James L. (Jim) Sherbert Jr.
CFO: Robert Thompson
HR: Dennis Roberts
FYE: Saturday nearest December 31
Type: Private

Bush Industries is scrambling for its seat in the ready-to-assemble (RTA) furniture industry. A leading maker of RTA furniture for homes and offices through its Bush Furniture North America and Europe divisions, Bush's products are sold worldwide through about 10,000 retail outlets, including furniture and department stores, electronics and office product retailers, and mass merchandisers. Its Bush Technologies unit concentrates on cell phone accessories. In March 2004 Bush filed for Chapter 11 bankruptcy protection. Its reorganizaton (which resulted in the firm being taken private in November of that year) has seen the ousting of the Bush family (former chairman and CEO Paul Bush and sons Douglas and Gregory).

	Annual Growth	12/03	12/04	12/05	12/06	12/07
Est. sales ($ mil.)	—	—	—	—	—	167.3
Employees	—	—	—	—	—	3,000

BUSHNELL OUTDOOR PRODUCTS

9200 Cody St.
Overland Park, KS 66214
Phone: 913-752-3400
Fax: 913-752-3550
Web: www.bushnellperformanceoptics.com

CEO: B. Joseph (Joe) Messner
CFO: Blake Lipham
HR: –
FYE: December 31
Type: Private

Bushnell Outdoor Products is one highly focused firm. It makes binoculars, telescopes, laser-guided rangefinders, night vision items, riflescopes, holographic gun sights, and other high-end optical equipment. It also sells Bollé ski goggles and sunglasses, H20Optix water sports sunglasses, and Serengeti all-purpose sunglasses. Bushnell owns the rights to the Tasco brand and has licensing agreements with Bausch & Lomb and Browning Firearms. The company, founded by Dave Bushnell in 1947, has offices in Australia, Canada, France, Germany, Hong Kong, the Netherlands, and the US. Bushnell has been owned by private equity firm Wind Point Partners since 1999. Bushnell acquired Meade's Simmons business in mid-2008.

	Annual Growth	12/03	12/04	12/05	12/06	12/07
Est. sales ($ mil.)	—	—	—	—	—	27.3
Employees	—	—	—	—	—	300

BUSY BEAVER BUILDING CENTERS, INC.

3130 William Pitt Way
Pittsburgh, PA 15238
Phone: 412-828-2323
Fax: 412-828-2430
Web: www.busybeaver.com

CEO: Frank Filmeck
CFO: Nicholas (Nick) Demayo
HR: Joyce Palmer
FYE: Last Sunday in December
Type: Private

They're busy as, well, you know what kind of animals, at Busy Beaver Building Centers. The company has more than 15 stores in Ohio, Pennsylvania, and West Virginia selling ceilings, flooring, lumber, plumbing fixtures, and other building materials, along with garden supplies, hardware, power equipment, and tools. Busy Beaver serves the professional contractor as well as the do-it-yourselfer. The regional home improvement center chain was founded in 1962. A management group led by chairman and former CEO Charles Bender acquired the company in 1988 and now owns about one-quarter of Busy Beaver, which is facing heavyweight competition from big-box chains, such as Home Depot and Lowe's.

	Annual Growth	12/03	12/04	12/05	12/06	12/07
Est. sales ($ mil.)	—	—	—	—	—	52.4
Employees	—	—	—	—	—	350

An in-depth profile of this company is available to Hoover's Online members at hoovers.com.

299

BUTERA FINER FOODS, INC.

1 Clock Tower Plaza	CEO: Paul Butera Sr.
Elgin, IL 60120	CFO: –
Phone: 847-741-1010	HR: –
Fax: 847-741-9674	FYE: April 30
Web: www.buteramarket.com	Type: Private

If you're in the Windy City *and* you're in the market for foodstuffs, find your way to Butera's. Butera Finer Foods runs about 10 full-service supermarkets under the Butera Market banner in northern Illinois. The stores specialize in produce, deli items, and international foods. Since its founding in 1968 by Paul Butera Sr. and his brother Joe, some 25 Butera Finer Foods supermarkets have been opened. Butera's twin sons Joseph and Paul Jr. currently run 10 of them. (The rest have been sold as franchises.) In 2003 Butera acquired three stores in Illinois from bankrupt Eagle Food Centers. Family-owned and -operated from its inception, Butera became an employee-owned company in the early 1990s.

BUTH-NA-BODHAIGE INC.

5036 1 World Way	CEO: Peter Ridler
Wake Forest, NC 27587	CFO: Kim Mattoon
Phone: 919-554-4900	HR: Donna McClellan
Fax: 919-554-4361	FYE: Saturday nearest February 28
Web: www.thebodyshop.com	Type: Subsidiary

Ask your Celtic friends why they smell terrific, and they're liable to answer "Buth-Na-Bodhaige." Buth-Na-Bodhaige (Gaelic for The Body Shop) does business as The Body Shop USA and oversees its UK parent company's US operations. It sells natural skin and hair care products through 300-plus company-owned and franchised US stores. It also sells its products online and at home via The Body Shop at Home. Buth-Na-Bodhaige (BNB), which bought out former joint venture partner Bellamy Retail Group, became part of L'Oréal S.A. through L'Oréal's acquisition of The Body Shop International PLC in mid-2006. BNB faces stiff competition from Intimate Brands' copycat chain, Bath & Body Works.

	Annual Growth	2/03	2/04	2/05	2/06	2/07
Est. sales ($ mil.)	—	—	—	—	—	130.7
Employees	—	—	—	—	—	2,000

BUTLER INTERNATIONAL, INC.

Pink Sheets: BUTL

The New River Center, Ste. 1730	CEO: Edward M. (Ed) Kopko
Fort Lauderdale, FL 33301	CFO: Mark Koscinski
Phone: 954-761-2200	HR: Darin Humbard
Fax: 954-761-9675	FYE: December 31
Web: www5.butler.com	Type: Public

This butler has many arms to serve you. Butler International provides engineering services, communications network installation, and information technology support primarily to the aerospace, defense, and telecommunications industries. It also has clients in the energy and financial services industries. Butler's engineering services include drafting, product design, and stress analysis; network services include equipment installation, network design, and maintenance; technology services include software development and staffing. Northrop Grumman, Sikorsky Aircraft, and Verizon are among its top clients. Butler operates from about 30 offices across the US and from research and development facilities in India.

	Annual Growth	12/03	12/04	12/05	12/06	12/07
Sales ($ mil.)	10.6%	209.0	251.3	287.3	322.0	312.8
Net income ($ mil.)	—	(15.4)	5.8	3.8	(0.5)	(2.3)
Employees	7.8%	—	3,100	—	3,600	—

BUTLER MANUFACTURING COMPANY

1540 Genessee St.	CEO: Patrick (Pat) Finan
Kansas City, MO 64102	CFO: –
Phone: 816-968-3000	HR: –
Fax: 816-968-3279	FYE: December 31
Web: www.butlermfg.com	Type: Subsidiary

Need a five-story building fast? Not a problem for Butler Manufacturing, maker of pre-engineered buildings, structural systems, and roof and wall systems for nonresidential construction worldwide. Butler, a part of Australia-based BlueScope Steel's North America Coated and Building Products division, produces pre-engineered and custom-designed steel structures used in a range of projects, from churches and schools to arenas and airplane hangars. Butler also offers real estate development and construction management services. It distributes its products throughout North America and Asia.

	Annual Growth	12/03	12/04	12/05	12/06	12/07
Est. sales ($ mil.)	—	—	—	—	—	483.7
Employees	—	—	—	—	—	4,298

BUTLER NATIONAL CORPORATION

OTC: BUKS

19920 W. 161st St.	CEO: Clark D. Stewart
Olathe, KS 66062	CFO: Angela D. Shinabargar
Phone: 913-780-9595	HR: –
Fax: 913-780-5088	FYE: April 30
Web: butlernational.com	Type: Public

This Butler is at the service of aircraft operators. Butler National's Avcon subsidiary (more than half of sales) provides aircraft modification services, including the conversion of passenger planes to freighters. The company works mainly on Learjet models; it also modifies Beechcraft, Cessna, and Dassault Falcon aircraft. It also adds aerial photography capability to aircraft and offers stability enhancements. The company's avionics unit makes airborne electronic components. Other Butler National businesses provide remote water and wastewater monitoring and offer gaming management services to Indian tribes.

	Annual Growth	4/03	4/04	4/05	4/06	4/07
Sales ($ mil.)	23.6%	6.3	10.1	23.4	15.3	14.7
Net income ($ mil.)	—	0.0	0.7	2.5	0.4	0.6
Market value ($ mil.)	27.9%	9.4	21.4	28.0	19.8	25.3
Employees	—	—	—	—	—	—

BUY.COM INC.

85 Enterprise, Ste. 100	CEO: Neel Grover
Aliso Viejo, CA 92656	CFO: –
Phone: 949-389-2000	HR: Kim Camp
Fax: –	FYE: December 31
Web: www.buy.com	Type: Private

Buy what.com you ask? E-tailer Buy.com sells books, cell phones and services, computer hardware and software, electronics, DVDs, jewelry, music, toys, and more. Founded in 1997, Buy.com initially made a splash by selling products below cost. It has since raised its prices but maintains an edge by offering to match any qualified competitor's price. In all, the company offers more than 2 million products to its 10 million customers. Buy.com also operates Yub.com, a social networking site with a retail slant. Users can buy products at Yub.com and also interact with fellow users by sharing recommendations or just chatting. The e-tailer ships to customers in Europe, North America, and the Pacific Rim.

BUZZI UNICEM USA INC.

100 Brodhead Rd.
Bethlehem, PA 18017
Phone: 610-866-4400
Fax: 610-866-9430

CEO: David A. (Dave) Nepereny
CFO: Dirk Beese
HR: Debbie Bahnick
FYE: December 31
Type: Subsidiary

Buzzi Unicem USA produces portland cement, masonry cement, and ready-mixed concrete, and controls approximately 10% of the US market. The company, a subsidiary of Italy-based BUZZI UNICEM SpA, owns about a dozen cement plants (including one grinding plant) with a total capacity of nearly 10 million tons. To distribute its products, Buzzi Unicem USA operates more than 25 distribution terminals and a fleet of river barges. Customers include ready-mix and pre-stressed concrete makers and highway builders. Buzzi Unicem reorganized its US operations in 2004, merging its RC Cement with Dyckerhoff's Lone Star Industries to form Buzzi Unicem USA.

	Annual Growth	12/03	12/04	12/05	12/06	12/07
Est. sales ($ mil.)	—	—	—	—	—	319.8
Employees	—	—	—	—	—	1,600

BWAY HOLDING COMPANY

NYSE: BWY

8607 Roberts Dr., Ste. 250
Atlanta, GA 30350
Phone: 770-645-4800
Fax: 770-645-4810
Web: www.bwaycorp.com

CEO: Kenneth M. (Ken) Roessler
CFO: Kevin C. Kern
HR: Joe Frabotta
FYE: Sunday nearest September 30
Type: Public

BWAY Holding helps keep coffee fresh and ammo dry. The company, which operates through subsidiary BWAY Corporation, manufactures steel containers such as aerosol and paint cans, pails, oblong cans, and specialty cans and boxes. It also makes plastic pails, bottles, drums, and other blow-molded containers. BWAY's products package items from paints, driveway sealants, and personal care products to food, coffee, and vegetable oil. BWAY Packaging (metal containers), ICL Industrial Containers (steel and plastic pails), and NAMPAC Packaging (plastic containers) are the company's main divisions.

	Annual Growth	9/03	9/04	9/05	9/06	9/07
Sales ($ mil.)	14.9%	551.1	611.6	829.1	918.5	959.0
Net income ($ mil.)	—	(3.2)	5.7	8.1	5.4	(3.1)
Market value ($ mil.)	—	—	—	—	—	241.5
Employees	9.4%	1,993	2,966	—	—	2,850
						*Fiscal year change

CA, INC.

NYSE: CA

1 CA Plaza
Islandia, NY 11749
Phone: 800-225-5224
Fax: 631-342-6800
Web: www.ca.com

CEO: John A. C. Swainson
CFO: Nancy E. Cooper
HR: Andrew (Andy) Goodman
FYE: March 31
Type: Public

CA wants to put your information technology under new management. One of the world's largest software companies, CA provides tools for managing networks, databases, applications, storage, security, and other systems. The company's Unicenter enterprise management software is designed to give customers centralized control over network infrastructure. Its applications work across both mainframes and distributed computing environments. The company also offers consulting, implementation, and training services. It markets worldwide to businesses, government agencies, and schools.

	Annual Growth	3/04	3/05	3/06	3/07	3/08
Sales ($ mil.)	6.9%	3,276.0	3,560.0	3,796.0	3,943.0	4,277.0
Net income ($ mil.)	111.5%	25.0	(4.0)	159.0	118.0	500.0
Market value ($ mil.)	(7.5%)	15,648.5	15,907.3	15,557.4	13,607.3	11,470.1
Employees	(2.6%)	—	15,300	16,000	14,500	—

CABELA'S INCORPORATED

NYSE: CAB

1 Cabela Dr.
Sidney, NE 69160
Phone: 308-254-5505
Fax: 308-254-4800
Web: www.cabelas.com

CEO: Dennis Highby
CFO: Ralph W. Castner
HR: Larry Hiers
FYE: Saturday nearest December 31
Type: Public

Cabela's is a hunter's and fisherman's Disneyland. The seller of outdoor sporting goods operates mainly through the 140 million-plus catalogs it mails each year, but its some 30 stores in the US and Canada are big attractions, too. Located mainly in the Midwest, the stores are as big as 250,000 sq. ft. and include such features as waterfalls, mountain replicas, aquariums, and banquet and meeting facilities. Cabela's sells footwear, clothing, and gear for fishing, hunting, camping, and other outdoor activities. The company also sells magazines and merchandise online and has an outdoors show on television. Cabela's was founded in 1961 by chairman Dick Cabela and his younger brother and vice chairman, Jim Cabela.

	Annual Growth	12/03	12/04	12/05	12/06	12/07
Sales ($ mil.)	14.0%	1,392.4	1,556.0	1,799.7	2,063.5	2,349.6
Net income ($ mil.)	14.4%	51.4	65.0	72.6	85.8	87.9
Market value ($ mil.)	(8.8%)	—	1,284.7	941.1	1,437.1	975.1
Employees	21.9%	6,800	7,830	9,800	11,700	15,000

CABELTEL INTERNATIONAL CORPORATION

AMEX: GBR

1755 Wittington Place, Ste. 340
Dallas, TX 75234
Phone: 972-407-8400
Fax: 972-407-8435
Web: www.cabeltel.us

CEO: Gene S. Bertcher
CFO: Gene S. Bertcher
HR: –
FYE: December 31
Type: Public

CabelTel International (formerly Greenbriar) is exploring what it hopes are greener pastures. The firm operates a residential community for senior citizens in Oregon, but it's looking to diversify. CabelTel International's retirement home offers programs ranging from meal preparation and housekeeping to transportation and recreational activities. The company formerly owned an outlet shopping mall, but sold that, just as it disposed of its oil and gas subsidiaries in 2006 and another oil and natural gas interest in Arkansas in 2008. CabelTel will continue to look for acquisition opportunities of existing oil and gas operations for development.

	Annual Growth	12/03	12/04	12/05	12/06	12/07
Sales ($ mil.)	(12.0%)	5.0	11.1	5.8	4.3	3.0
Net income ($ mil.)	(15.9%)	0.2	(2.2)	(1.0)	1.3	0.1
Market value ($ mil.)	(19.8%)	4.0	4.6	3.1	3.5	1.7
Employees	(86.5%)	—	—	481	65	—

CABLE NEWS NETWORK LP, LLLP

1 CNN Center
Atlanta, GA 30303
Phone: 404-827-1700
Fax: 404-827-1099
Web: www.cnn.com

CEO: Jim Walton
CFO: Brad Ferrer
HR: –
FYE: December 31
Type: Business segment

Whether it's reporting on the news or just talking about it, this network does it all day long. Cable News Network (CNN) operates one of the top 24-hour news channels, reaching more than 92 million US homes. In addition to its flagship CNN channel, the company offers CNN Headline News to more than 91 million homes, and it has an international division that keeps viewers informed in more than 200 countries. CNN has 36 news bureaus around the world, including 10 in the US. Away from the television, CNN operates a top-ranked news Web site and offers syndicated news services. Founded in 1980 by cable broadcasting pioneer Ted Turner, CNN operates as part of Time Warner's Turner Broadcasting division.

An in-depth profile of this company is available to Hoover's Online members at hoovers.com.

301

CABLE ONE, INC.

1314 N. 3rd St.
Phoenix, AZ 85004
Phone: 602-364-6000
Fax: 602-364-6010
Web: www.cableone.net

CEO: Thomas O. (Tom) Might
CFO: Patrick A. (Pat) Dolohanty
HR: Janiece St. Cyr
FYE: December 31
Type: Subsidiary

Its parent offers award-winning journalism to Beltway insiders, but Cable One gives small-town folk CNN *and* The Cartoon Network. A subsidiary of The Washington Post Company, Cable One provides cable television service to primarily non-urban, small communities in almost 20 states throughout the midwestern, southern, and western US. Its core service areas are the Gulf Coast region and western Idaho. More than 700,000 subscribers receive service, and more than one quarter of them are signed up for digital cable services. The company also offers broadband Internet access under the CableONE.net brand.

CABLEVISION SYSTEMS CORPORATION

NYSE: CVC

1111 Stewart Ave.
Bethpage, NY 11714
Phone: 516-803-2300
Fax: 516-803-3134
Web: www.cablevision.com

CEO: James L. Dolan
CFO: Michael P. Huseby
HR: Carolyn Dursi
FYE: December 31
Type: Public

There's no business like show business for Cablevision, which provides basic cable television to about 3 million customers in the New York City area. More than 2.5 million digital video viewers subscribe to its iO service. Through its Optimum unit, Cablevision serves more than 2 million broadband Internet and 1.5 million computer telephony subscribers. Subsidiary Lightpath provides business communications services. Cablevision also controls sports and entertainment venues Madison Square Garden and Radio City Music Hall, as well as New York sports teams the Knicks and the Rangers. The company owns and manages nationwide and regional cable programming networks and sports channels through Rainbow Media Holdings.

	Annual Growth	12/03	12/04	12/05	12/06	12/07
Sales ($ mil.)	11.6%	4,177.1	4,932.9	5,175.9	5,927.5	6,484.5
Net income ($ mil.)	—	(297.2)	(676.1)	89.3	(126.5)	218.5
Market value ($ mil.)	2.5%	5,136.3	5,527.5	5,287.1	6,542.0	5,659.7
Employees	8.1%	—	—	20,425	22,075	—

CABOT CORPORATION

NYSE: CBT

2 Seaport Ln., Ste. 1300
Boston, MA 02210
Phone: 617-345-0100
Fax: 617-342-6103
Web: www.cabot-corp.com

CEO: Patrick M. Prevost
CFO: Jonathan P. Mason
HR: Robby D. Sisco
FYE: September 30
Type: Public

Even if it lost money, Cabot still would be in the black. The company is the world's #1 producer of carbon black, a reinforcing and pigmenting agent used in tires, inks, cables, and coatings. It has about 25% of the world market for carbon black. Cabot also holds its own as a maker of fumed metal oxides such as fumed silica and fumed alumina, which are used as anti-caking, thickening, and reinforcing agents in adhesives and coatings. Other products include tantalum (used to make capacitors used in electronics) and specialty fluids for gas and oil drilling.

	Annual Growth	9/03	9/04	9/05	9/06	9/07
Sales ($ mil.)	9.9%	1,795.0	1,934.0	2,125.0	2,543.0	2,616.0
Net income ($ mil.)	12.7%	80.0	124.0	(48.0)	88.0	129.0
Market value ($ mil.)	6.9%	1,774.5	2,432.0	2,078.7	2,354.2	2,319.4
Employees	(1.1%)	—	—	4,400	4,300	4,300

CABOT MICROELECTRONICS CORPORATION

NASDAQ (GS): CCMP

870 N. Commons Dr.
Aurora, IL 60504
Phone: 630-375-6631
Fax: –
Web: www.cabotcmp.com

CEO: William P. (Bill) Noglows
CFO: William S. (Bill) Johnson
HR: Sally Baca
FYE: September 30
Type: Public

Cabot Microelectronics sits atop a mountain of slurry. The company is the world's top maker of slurries used in chemical mechanical planarization (CMP). CMP is a wafer polishing process that enables semiconductor manufacturers to produce smaller, faster, and more complex devices. The process is also used in data storage and precision optics products. Cabot Microelectronics' CMP slurries consist of liquids containing abrasives and chemicals that aid in the CMP process. The company also makes polishing pads for CMP, as well as slurries used to polish the substrates and magnetic heads of hard disk drives. More than two-thirds of sales are to customers in the Asia/Pacific region.

	Annual Growth	9/03	9/04	9/05	9/06	9/07
Sales ($ mil.)	7.7%	251.7	309.4	270.5	320.8	338.2
Net income ($ mil.)	(2.7%)	37.7	46.7	32.5	33.0	33.8
Market value ($ mil.)	(7.0%)	1,374.8	892.2	717.6	690.5	1,026.4
Employees	7.8%	549	585	650	742	742

CABOT OIL & GAS CORPORATION

NYSE: COG

1200 Enclave Pkwy.
Houston, TX 77077
Phone: 281-589-4600
Fax: 281-589-4828
Web: www.cabotog.com

CEO: Dan O. Dinges
CFO: Scott C. Schroeder
HR: Abraham D. Garza
FYE: December 31
Type: Public

Like a cog on a gear in a well-oiled machine, Cabot Oil & Gas (ticker symbol: COG) has engaged in the oil industry very efficiently. Cabot explores for and produces natural gas and oil, and it sells gas to industrial customers, local utilities, and gas marketers. It has estimated proved reserves of 1.6 trillion cu. ft. of natural gas equivalent. Major areas of operation include Appalachia, the Anadarko Basin (Kansas, Oklahoma, and Texas), the Rocky Mountains (Wyoming), and the Texas and Louisiana Gulf Coast. The company also has reserves in Alberta and British Columbia.

	Annual Growth	12/03	12/04	12/05	12/06	12/07
Sales ($ mil.)	9.5%	509.4	530.4	682.8	762.0	732.2
Net income ($ mil.)	67.8%	21.1	88.4	148.4	321.2	167.4
Market value ($ mil.)	90.0%	318.3	488.5	1,095.2	1,458.8	4,145.3
Employees	6.8%	—	—	354	374	404

CACHÉ, INC.

NASDAQ (GS): CACH

1440 Broadway
New York, NY 10018
Phone: 212-575-3200
Fax: 212-944-2842
Web: www.cache.com

CEO: Thomas E. Reinckens
CFO: Margaret Feeney
HR: Margarita Croasdaile
FYE: December 31
Type: Public

Caché sells fashions that bring cachet to the soirée. The upscale women's apparel retailer owns and operates about 300 specialty stores in shopping malls in 40-plus US states, Puerto Rico, and the US Virgin Islands under the Caché and Caché Luxe banners, as well as an online shopping site. Sportswear, including casual wear, collections, and separates, accounts for about 60% of apparel sales. It closed all of its Lillie Rubin shops in 2006 and launched a new format — Caché Luxe. The firm buys its merchandise primarily from domestic suppliers, but it has begun to source more overseas. Caché acquired New York-based Adrienne Victoria Designs (its largest supplier) in July 2007.

	Annual Growth	12/03	12/04	12/05	12/06	12/07
Sales ($ mil.)	6.1%	216.3	247.3	266.3	279.0	274.5
Net income ($ mil.)	(12.5%)	11.1	13.3	13.4	8.3	6.5
Market value ($ mil.)	(1.9%)	143.3	283.0	273.4	411.3	132.8
Employees	5.9%	—	—	2,700	2,860	—

CACI INTERNATIONAL INC
NYSE: CAI

1100 N. Glebe Rd., Ste. 200
Arlington, VA 22201
Phone: 703-841-7800
Fax: 703-841-7882
Web: www.caci.com

CEO: Paul M. Cofoni
CFO: Thomas A. (Tom) Mutryn
HR: H. Robert (Bob) Boehm
FYE: June 30
Type: Public

CACI International doesn't need a lot of clients — just a few with deep pockets. Deriving nearly 95% its revenues from the US government and more than 70% from the US Department of Defense (DoD), CACI is one of the largest government information technology (IT) contractors. The company, which also serves commercial clients, provides a wide range of technology services including systems integration, network management, knowledge management, and engineering and simulation. CACI also develops marketing software and databases for sales tracking, demographics reporting, and other market analysis applications, and it provides debt management and litigation support services.

	Annual Growth	6/03	6/04	6/05	6/06	6/07
Sales ($ mil.)	23.1%	843.1	1,145.8	1,623.1	1,755.3	1,938.0
Net income ($ mil.)	15.1%	44.7	63.7	85.3	84.8	78.5
Market value ($ mil.)	10.4%	985.6	1,178.5	2,387.9	2,240.0	1,464.4
Employees	8.3%	—	—	9,600	10,400	—

CACTUS FEEDERS, INC.

2209 W. 7th St.
Amarillo, TX 79106
Phone: 806-373-2333
Fax: 806-371-4767
Web: www.cactusfeeders.com

CEO: Michael J. (Mike) Engler
CFO: Brad Hastings
HR: –
FYE: October 31
Type: Private

Cactus Feeders founder Paul Engler may operate one of the world's largest cattle feedlot businesses, but he was no match for Oprah Winfrey. Cactus Feeders operates nine foodlots with a capacity of some 520,000 head of cattle, which it beefs up and sells to meat packers. The company's feedyards are located in Texas and Kansas. It also provides market analysis, marketing services, and financing for its rancher/suppliers. Oh, and about Oprah, Engler and other cattle ranchers unsuccessfully sued Winfrey and a guest after a 1996 show disparaged the beef industry.

	Annual Growth	10/03	10/04	10/05	10/06	10/07
Est. sales ($ mil.)	—	—	—	—	—	678.1
Employees	—	—	—	—	—	500

CADBURY ADAMS USA LLC

389 Interpace Pkwy.
Parsippany, NJ 07054
Phone: 973-909-2000
Fax: –
Web: www.cadburyadams.com

CEO: Bradley C. (Brad) Irwin
CFO: –
HR: –
FYE: December 31
Type: Subsidiary

Cadbury Adams USA has it all wrapped up — in thin little rectangles wrapped in foil. The US subsidiary of British candy giant Cadbury makes non-chocolate candy, chewing gum, and mints. Its brands include Bubblicious, Certs, Chiclets, Dentyne, HALLS, Sour Patch, Swedish Fish, and Trident. The company also makes retro gum brands Beeman's, Blackjack, and Clove, which it reintroduces every few years. Cadbury Adams USA was formed after Cadbury Schweppes bought the Adams chewing gum brands from Pfizer for $4.2 billion in 2003 and integrated it into its already existing US operations. (Cadbury Schweppes later spun off its beverage operations to focus solely on candy.)

	Annual Growth	12/03	12/04	12/05	12/06	12/07
Est. sales ($ mil.)	—	—	—	—	—	79.2
Employees	—	—	—	—	—	870

CADBURY SCHWEPPES BOTTLING GROUP

5301 Legacy Dr.
Plano, TX 75024
Phone: 972-673-7000
Fax: –
Web: www.dpsubg.com

CEO: Larry D. Young
CFO: Jon Stewart
HR: Kellie Defratus
FYE: December 31
Type: Subsidiary

The Cadbury Schweppes Bottling Group rings up sweet results for its parent, the Dr Pepper Snapple Group. The company is a leading bottler of soft drinks in the US, distributing beverages in about 30 US states. In addition to the Dr Pepper and 7 UP brands, it also bottles the lesser-known Big Red, RC Cola, Diet Rite, and Crush brands and other carbonated drinks, as well as Clearly Canadian, Sunkist, and other bottled waters and beverages. The bottler owns Southeast-Atlantic Beverage Corp. (SEABEV). It operates 10 manufacturing plants and more than 100 distribution centers.

	Annual Growth	12/03	12/04	12/05	12/06	12/07
Est. sales ($ mil.)	—	—	—	—	—	1,218.8
Employees	—	—	—	—	—	8,000

CADENCE DESIGN SYSTEMS, INC.
NASDAQ (GS): CDNS

2655 Seely Ave., Bldg. 5
San Jose, CA 95134
Phone: 408-943-1234
Fax: 408-428-5001
Web: www.cadence.com

CEO: Michael J. (Mike) Fister
CFO: Kevin Palatnik
HR: Tina Jones
FYE: Saturday nearest December 31
Type: Public

Cadence Design Systems has designs on enabling engineers to pick up the development tempo. A leader in the electronic design automation (EDA) market, Cadence sells and leases software and hardware products for designing integrated circuits (ICs), printed circuit boards (PCBs), and other electronic systems. Electronics companies use Cadence's products to build components used in wireless devices, computer systems, networking equipment, and other applications. The company also provides maintenance and support and offers design and methodology consulting services. In June 2008 the company offered to buy rival Mentor Graphics in a deal valued at about $1.45 billion.

	Annual Growth	12/03	12/04	12/05	12/06	12/07
Sales ($ mil.)	9.6%	1,119.5	1,197.5	1,329.2	1,483.9	1,615.0
Net income ($ mil.)	—	(17.6)	74.5	49.3	142.6	296.3
Market value ($ mil.)	(1.2%)	4,901.8	—	4,753.8	4,923.7	4,677.9
Employees	3.0%	—	—	5,000	5,200	5,300

CADENCE FINANCIAL CORPORATION
NASDAQ (GS): CADE

301 E. Main St.
Starkville, MS 39759
Phone: 662-323-1341
Fax: 662-338-5031
Web: www.cadencebanking.com

CEO: Lewis F. Mallory Jr.
CFO: Richard T. Haston
HR: Phillip D. Sprayberry
FYE: December 31
Type: Public

Holding down the northern tip of the Golden Triangle region is Cadence Financial. The Mississippi holding company owns and conducts business through Cadence Bank (the erstwhile National Bank of Commerce), which operates more than 20 branches in the area, plus another nearly 20 locations in Alabama, Florida, Georgia, and Tennessee. The community bank offers a range of banking products, including checking, savings, NOW, and money market accounts, as well as CDs and loans. It primarily originates commercial real estate mortgages (nearly half of its loan portfolio), but also makes financial, agricultural, construction, and installment loans.

	Annual Growth	12/03	12/04	12/05	12/06	12/07
Assets ($ mil.)	16.1%	1,093.2	1,439.6	1,446.1	1,899.9	1,984.2
Net income ($ mil.)	(7.7%)	13.5	12.3	13.8	14.1	9.8
Market value ($ mil.)	(5.5%)	217.9	255.5	228.8	257.6	173.6
Employees	—	—	—	419	—	—

An in-depth profile of this company is available to Hoover's Online members at hoovers.com.

303

CADENCE INNOVATION LLC

977 E. 14 Mile Rd.
Troy, MI 48084
Phone: 248-457-4400
Fax: 248-585-1686
Web: www.cadenceinnovation.com

CEO: Jerry L. Mosingo
CFO: Rajesh Shah
HR: Ronda B. Coogan
FYE: December 31
Type: Private

Auto parts maker Cadence Innovation (formerly New Venture Holdings) supplies car manufacturers with products such as cargo management systems, doors and door modules, instrument panels and cockpits, and painted exterior components. Customers include Ford, General Motors, PSA Peugeot Citroën, and Volkswagen. Cadence was formed in 2005 when Harbinger Capital Partners and The Yucaipa Companies LLC bought key assets from bankrupt Venture Holdings. The company changed its name to Cadence Innovation in November 2005. In 2008 its private equity owners decided to put Cadence up for sale in the face of diminished business from the Detroit Three and high materials costs.

	Annual Growth	12/03	12/04	12/05	12/06	12/07
Est. sales ($ mil.)	—	—	—	—	—	113.0
Employees	—	—	—	—	—	1,500

CADENCE PHARMACEUTICALS, INC.

NASDAQ (GM): CADX

12481 High Bluff Dr., Ste. 200
San Diego, CA 92130
Phone: 858-436-1400
Fax: 858-436-1401
Web: www.cadencepharm.com

CEO: Theodore R. Schroeder
CFO: William R. (Bill) LaRue
HR: Diane K. Sheehan
FYE: December 31
Type: Public

Cadence Pharmaceuticals follows the rhythm of hospitals' medical needs. The biopharmaceutical company develops drug candidates primarily for use in a hospital setting. The company licenses rights to compounds and develops them for sale in untapped markets or for new indications. Cadence's late-stage candidates include Acetavance (injectable acetaminophen), which is marketed in Europe by the Bristol-Myers Squibb Company under the name Perfalgan, for treating acute pain and fever. The company also is developing Omigard, a topical antimicrobial gel used to prevent and treat infections in surgical wounds, burns, and medical device-related wounds such as from catheters.

	Annual Growth	12/00	12/01	12/02	12/03	*12/04
Sales ($ mil.)	—	—	—	—	—	0.0
Net income ($ mil.)	—	—	—	—	—	(3.1)
Employees	—	—	—	—	—	

*Most recent year available

CADIZ INC.

NASDAQ (GM): CDZI

550 S. Hope St., Ste. 2850
Los Angeles, CA 90071
Phone: 213-271-1600
Fax: 213-271-1614
Web: www.cadizinc.com

CEO: Keith Brackpool
CFO: O'Donnell (Don) Iselin II
HR: –
FYE: December 31
Type: Public

Cadiz hopes to strike gold with water. The company owns some 45,000 acres of land and groundwater resources in eastern San Bernardino County near the Colorado River Aqueduct and in the eastern Mojave Desert. Cadiz is betting on its groundwater storage and distribution project as water supplies become increasingly scarce in Southern California. After the Metropolitan Water District of Southern California cancelled its agreement with Cadiz in 2002, the company has resumed the project with San Bernardino County. Cadiz is also looking into commercial and residential development of its land. It has some agricultural assets which are leased as lemon groves and grape vineyards.

	Annual Growth	12/03	12/04	12/05	12/06	12/07
Sales ($ mil.)	(40.5%)	3.2	0.1	1.2	0.6	0.4
Net income ($ mil.)	—	(11.5)	(16.0)	(23.0)	(13.8)	(13.6)
Market value ($ mil.)	19.3%	—	147.1	243.6	264.8	250.0
Employees	6.5%	7	—	8	—	9

CADUS CORPORATION

OTC: KDUS

767 5th Ave., 47th Fl.
New York, NY 10153
Phone: 212-702-4351
Fax: 212-750-5815

CEO: David Blitz
CFO: David Blitz
HR: –
FYE: December 31
Type: Public

Cadus Pharmaceutical had hoped to make some dough from yeast. Its drug discovery technologies used genetically engineered yeast cells, but the firm sold its discovery programs to OSI Pharmaceuticals and is looking for new opportunities. The company even dropped "Pharmaceutical" from its name to signal its interest in acquisitions outside the biotech industry. Its subsidiary Cadus Technologies still holds some assets related to its yeast cell technology and is seeking interested parties to license the intellectual properties. Investor Carl Icahn, a director and former chairman of the company, owns almost 40% of Cadus.

	Annual Growth	12/03	12/04	12/05	12/06	12/07
Sales ($ mil.)	(15.9%)	0.2	0.1	0.1	0.1	0.1
Net income ($ mil.)	—	(0.2)	(0.4)	0.0	0.4	(0.3)
Market value ($ mil.)	6.0%	19.6	20.1	21.0	21.0	24.7
Employees	—	—	—	—	—	0

CADWALADER, WICKERSHAM & TAFT LLP

One World Financial Center
New York, NY 10281
Phone: 212-504-6000
Fax: 212-504-6666
Web: www.cadwalader.com

CEO: Robert O. Link Jr.
CFO: Mitchel E. Sekler
HR: Patricia Ellis
FYE: December 31
Type: Partnership

Founded during the presidency of George Washington, Cadwalader, Wickersham & Taft is one of the oldest law firms in the US. Since 1792 the firm has grown to include more than 700 lawyers and to encompass offices not only in the US, but also in Europe and the Asia/Pacific region. Among the areas of practice for which the firm is regularly recognized are capital markets, financial restructuring, and mergers and acquisitions. Banks and other financial institutions have been prominently represented on Cadwalader's client list; in addition, the firm undertakes work for other large businesses and for government entities, health care organizations, nonprofits, and individuals.

	Annual Growth	12/03	12/04	12/05	12/06	12/07
Est. sales ($ mil.)	—	—	—	—	—	110.6
Employees	—	—	—	—	—	1,279

CAFE ENTERPRISES, INC.

4324 Wade Hampton Blvd.
Taylors, SC 29687
Phone: 864-322-1331
Fax: 864-322-1332
Web: www.fatzcafe.com

CEO: Steve Bruce
CFO: –
HR: Steve Corson
FYE: December 31
Type: Private

You might say this company runs a plus-size restaurant chain. Cafe Enterprises owns and operates more than 40 Fatz Cafe casual-dining establishments in South Carolina, North Carolina, Georgia, and Tennessee. The restaurants, known for their down-home atmosphere, offer standard American fare such as burgers, chicken, and steaks. They also serve seafood, pasta, and a selection of appetizers. Entrepreneur Jimmy Rogers opened the first Fatz Cafe in 1988; chairman Bill Burton, an industry veteran who had served at TW Services (the former parent of Denny's), bought the chain in 1999.

	Annual Growth	12/03	12/04	12/05	12/06	12/07
Est. sales ($ mil.)	—	—	—	—	—	59.0
Employees	—	—	—	—	—	2,000

CAFE RIO, INC.

527 E. 770 North
Orem, UT 84097
Phone: 801-818-2791
Fax: 801-818-2794
Web: www.caferio.com

CEO: Robert T. (Bob) Nilsen
CFO: Robert J. (Bob) Baker
HR: Tera Sunder
FYE: December 31
Type: Private

If you're feeling kind of full of Mexican food, maybe you can blame it on Rio. Cafe Rio operates more than a dozen Café Rio Mexican Grill full-service restaurant locations mostly in Utah, including six in the Salt Lake City area. The chain offers traditional Tex-Mex fare, such as burritos, enchiladas, and tacos, as well as a rotating selection of daily specials. In addition to dining, the restaurants offer to-go service for those who want to enjoy their meals at home. Steve and Patricia Stanley started the business in 1997 and sold it in 2004 to former Taco Bell executive Bob Nilsen with backing from private equity firm Saunders Karp & Megrue (which later merged with Apax Partners).

	Annual Growth	12/03	12/04	12/05	12/06	12/07
Est. sales ($ mil.)	—	—	—	—	—	17.4
Employees	—	—	—	—	—	800

CAGLE'S, INC.

AMEX: CGLA

2000 Hills Ave. NW
Atlanta, GA 30318
Phone: 404-355-2820
Fax: 404-355-9326
Web: www.cagles.net

CEO: J. Douglas (Doug) Cagle
CFO: Mark M. Ham IV
HR: Lavon Waite
FYE: Saturday nearest March 31
Type: Public

The people at Cagle's may be outnumbered, but nonetheless, the chickens never have a chance. The poultry company slaughters and processes some 2 million birds each week. Vertically integrated, Cagle's also has breeding, hatching, and feed milling operations (the birds are then raised by about 160 contract grower-farmers). The company specializes in value-added meat — most of its birds wind up deboned, quick-frozen, marinated, breaded, or otherwise processed to make cooking easier for its retail and foodservice customers. Cagle's has operations in Alabama and Georgia.

	Annual Growth	3/04	3/05	3/06	3/07	3/08
Sales ($ mil.)	4.8%	—	246.3	237.3	233.9	283.6
Net income ($ mil.)	—	—	11.5	(0.6)	0.6	(0.8)
Market value ($ mil.)	(13.1%)	—	43.6	33.1	34.9	28.7
Employees	(3.2%)	—	1,975	1,909	1,850	—

CAHILL GORDON & REINDEL LLP

80 Pine St.
New York, NY 10005
Phone: 212-701-3000
Fax: 212-269-5420
Web: www.cahill.com

CEO: Daniel J. (Dan) Zubkoff
CFO: —
HR: Patricia A. Harrison
FYE: December 31
Type: Partnership

Here's a name clients have banked on: Cahill Gordon & Reindel. The firm's roster of clients has included investment banks such as Goldman Sachs, J.P. Morgan Chase, and Merrill Lynch, as well as commercial banks and big companies from a variety of other industries. The firm maintains a broad range of practice areas; among its specialties are corporate transactions, litigation, media law, and tax. Cahill, which has about 300 lawyers, has offices in New York; Washington, DC; and London. The firm was founded in 1919.

	Annual Growth	12/03	12/04	12/05	12/06	12/07
Est. sales ($ mil.)	—	—	—	—	—	51.6
Employees	—	—	—	—	—	600

CAI INTERNATIONAL, INC.

NYSE: CAP

1 Embarcadero Ctr., Ste. 2101
San Francisco, CA 94111
Phone: 415-788-0100
Fax: 415-788-3430
Web: www.capps.com

CEO: Masaaki (John) Nishibori
CFO: Victor M. Garcia
HR: —
FYE: December 31
Type: Public

CAI International (formerly Container Applications International) is one of the world's leading lessors and managers of shipping containers. Its fleet (66%-managed; 34%-owned) has about 754,000 twenty-foot equivalent units (TEU) of capacity. Its leasing segment offers short-term, long-term, and finance (giving the lessee the option to purchase the container at the end of its term) leases. In the late 1990s CAI (which was founded by chairman Hiromitsu Ogawa as a traditional container leasing firm in 1989) shifted its focus to managing containers owned by container investors. The company primarily leases containers to container shipping lines. CAI filed for an IPO in May 2007.

	Annual Growth	12/03	12/04	12/05	12/06	12/07
Sales ($ mil.)	6.9%	—	—	—	60.7	64.9
Net income ($ mil.)	23.1%	—	—	—	15.6	19.2
Market value ($ mil.)	—	—	—	—	—	180.4
Employees	—	—	—	—	—	—

CAITHNESS CORPORATION

565 5th Ave., 29th Fl.
New York, NY 10017
Phone: 212-921-9099
Fax: 212-921-9239
Web: www.caithnessenergy.com

CEO: James D. Bishop Sr.
CFO: Christopher T. McCallion
HR: —
FYE: December 31
Type: Private

Scotland's windswept Caithness region might well serve as an inspiration for Caithness Corp., which develops renewable power plants in the US under the Caithness Energy brand. Although the company has focused on the development, acquisition, operation, and management of geothermal, hydroelectric, wind, and solar energy power projects, it also has environmentally friendly fossil-fueled plants using coal and diesel. Caithness is the largest producer of renewable energy in the US, with more than 360 MW generated by geothermal projects, 160 MW generated by solar plants, and 345 MW produced by wind turbine projects. On the non-renewable side it also produces more than 1,980 MW of gas-turbine powered generation.

	Annual Growth	12/03	12/04	12/05	12/06	12/07
Est. sales ($ mil.)	—	—	—	—	—	51.7
Employees	—	—	—	—	—	175

CAJUN INDUSTRIES, LLC

15635 Airline Hwy.
Baton Rouge, LA 70817
Phone: 225-753-5857
Fax: 225-751-9777
Web: www.cajunusa.com

CEO: Ken Jacob
CFO: Shane Recile
HR: —
FYE: June 30
Type: Private

Offering a jambalaya of services, Cajun Industries builds refineries, power plants, process plants, water-treatment plants, and other industrial and infrastructure projects, primarily in Louisiana and Texas. Subsidiary Cajun Constructors provides a full range of services from design/build to maintenance; Cajun Deep Foundations offers drilling, piles installation, and related services. Cajun Maritime focuses on marine, coastal, and oilfield services including construction, repair, and power distribution. Cajun Equipment Services manages a fleet of trucks and trailers that can transport heavy and specialized loads. Chairman and owner Lane Grigsby founded the company as Cajun Contractors and Engineers in 1973.

	Annual Growth	6/03	6/04	6/05	6/06	6/07
Est. sales ($ mil.)	—	—	—	—	—	234.1
Employees	—	—	—	—	—	1,500

An in-depth profile of this company is available to Hoover's Online members at hoovers.com.

305

CAJUN OPERATING COMPANY

980 Hammond Dr. NE, Ste. 1100
Atlanta, GA 30328
Phone: 770-350-3800
Fax: 770-512-3920
Web: www.churchs.com

CEO: Harsha V. Agadi
CFO: Louis J. (Dusty) Profumo
HR: Bonita (Bunny) Williams
FYE: December 31
Type: Private

This company has several places fried-chicken worshipers can flock to. Cajun Operating Company owns and operates Church's Chicken, one of the leading quick-service chicken chains in the world with more than 1,600 locations in more than 18 countries. The restaurants specialize in fried chicken available with such side items as biscuits, fried okra, fries, and mashed potatoes. About 270 of the locations are company-owned while the rest are franchised. Church's Chicken was started in 1952 by retired chicken incubator salesman George Church as Church's Fried Chicken to Go. Cajun Operating Company is owned by private equity firm Arcapita.

CAL DIVE INTERNATIONAL, INC.

NYSE: DVR

2500 City W. Blvd., Ste. 2200
Houston, TX 77042
Phone: 713-361-2600
Fax: 713-361-2690
Web: www.caldive.com

CEO: Quinn J. Hébert
CFO: G. Kregg Lunsford
HR: –
FYE: December 31
Type: Public

Cal Dive International may or may not be California dreaming, but its waking hours are spent beneath the waters of the Gulf of Mexico. The subsea contractor operates a fleet of 24 surface and saturation diving support vessels, six shallow water pipelay vessels, one dedicated pipebury barge, one combination pipelay/derrick barge, and two derrick barges. It installs and maintains offshore platforms, pipelines, and production systems on the Outer Continental Shelf of the Gulf of Mexico, as well as in offshore markets in the Middle East, Southeast Asia, and Trinidad. Following its 2006 IPO, the former subsidiary of Helix Energy Solutions is 58.5%-owned by that company.

	Annual Growth	12/03	12/04	12/05	12/06	12/07
Sales ($ mil.)	46.5%	135.5	125.8	224.3	509.9	623.6
Net income ($ mil.)	76.8%	10.8	7.7	37.7	119.4	105.6
Market value ($ mil.)	31.6%	—	—	—	1,057.9	1,392.3
Employees	53.8%	—	—	—	1,300	2,000

CALAMOS ASSET MANAGEMENT, INC.

NASDAQ (GS): CLMS

2020 Calamos Ct.
Naperville, IL 60563
Phone: 630-245-7200
Fax: 630-245-6335
Web: www.calamos.com

CEO: John P. Calamos Sr.
CFO: Cristina Wasiak
HR: Gary J. Felsten
FYE: December 31
Type: Public

Calamos Asset Management wants to make the most of your assets. Through its subsidiaries the company provides money management and investment advice to institutional and individual investors. The firm manages about a dozen mutual funds and five closed-end funds representing a range of investment strategies and risk levels; it also offers managed accounts and alternative investments. Calamos, which has more than $45 billion in its keep — most of it invested in equities — was founded in 1977 and went public in 2004. Chairman and CEO John Calamos and his family control the company.

	Annual Growth	12/03	12/04	12/05	12/06	12/07
Assets ($ mil.)	84.8%	104.5	516.5	665.5	795.8	1,217.7
Net income ($ mil.)	(19.9%)	67.3	106.2	29.2	34.0	27.7
Market value ($ mil.)	0.0%	—	621.0	723.4	621.4	621.6
Employees	14.8%	—	—	331	380	—

CALAMP CORP.

NASDAQ (GS): CAMP

1401 N. Rice Ave.
Oxnard, CA 93030
Phone: 805-987-9000
Fax: 805-987-8359
Web: www.calamp.com

CEO: Richard B. (Rick) Gold
CFO: Richard K. (Rick) Vitelle
HR: –
FYE: Saturday nearest last day in February
Type: Public

CalAmp adds a little boost even to the weakest of TV programs. The former military supplier makes microwave amplification and conversion components that improve reception in satellite television, wireless cable, and wireless broadband access systems. Its products include antennas, amplifiers, and transceivers and receivers for broadband wireless transmission. CalAmp made the MultiCipher cable signal-scrambling system that prevents unauthorized viewing of cable programming. The company's leading customers include DIRECTV (about 24% of sales) and DISH Network (11%). Most of CalAmp's sales are in the US.

	Annual Growth	2/04	2/05	2/06	2/07	2/08
Sales ($ mil.)	2.3%	128.6	220.0	217.5	222.3	140.9
Net income ($ mil.)	—	5.7	8.1	14.6	(31.2)	(84.2)
Market value ($ mil.)	(32.2%)	339.1	164.0	233.2	209.8	71.6
Employees	(5.0%)	515	600	480	580	420

CALAVO GROWERS, INC.

NASDAQ (GM): CVGW

1141-A Cummings Rd.
Santa Paula, CA 93060
Phone: 805-525-1245
Fax: 805-921-3223
Web: www.calavo.com

CEO: Lecil E. (Lee) Cole
CFO: Arthur J. (Art) Bruno
HR: Patricia (Pat) Vorhies
FYE: October 31
Type: Public

The avocado growers of Calavo Growers might not be a cooperative anymore, but they're still friendly folks. Calavo (the name is a combination of "California" and "avocado") began as a growers' marketing cooperative founded in 1924 in order to transform the exotic hobby crop, avocados, into a culinary staple. And the avocado has become, if not a staple, then a regular in US supermarket shopping carts. Calavo procures and processes avocados, tomatoes, and other fresh fruits grown mainly in California, Chile, and Mexico. The products are then distributed to retail food outlets and foodservice operators throughout the world.

	Annual Growth	10/03	10/04	10/05	10/06	10/07
Sales ($ mil.)	5.3%	246.8	274.2	258.8	273.9	303.0
Net income ($ mil.)	0.3%	7.2	6.2	3.3	5.8	7.3
Market value ($ mil.)	23.9%	139.6	144.5	138.2	139.4	329.2
Employees	8.8%	—	701	750	830

CALENDAR CLUB, L.L.C.

6411 Burleson Rd.
Austin, TX 78744
Phone: 512-386-7220
Fax: 512-369-6192
Web: www.calendarclub.com

CEO: Marc Winkelman
CFO: Jim Hall
HR: Sara Rodriguez
FYE: January 31
Type: Private

During the holiday season, Calendar Club transforms empty retail space in Canada and the US into Calendar Club, Christmas Corner, San Francisco Music Box, and Go! Games and Go! Toys shops. The company's temporary stores range in size from kiosks to some 6,000 square feet. Founded in 1993 with just 62 stores, Calendar Club now operates more than 900 locations in the US and 250-plus outlets in Australia, Canada, the Netherlands, New Zealand, and the UK. The company also sells merchandise year round on its Web sites, including Calendars.com and SFMusicBox.com. Bookseller Barnes & Noble owns 74% of Calendar Club.

	Annual Growth	1/03	1/04	1/05	1/06	1/07
Est. sales ($ mil.)	—	—	—	—	—	93.0
Employees	—	—	—	—	—	150

An in-depth profile of this company is available to Hoover's Online members at hoovers.com.

CALGON CARBON CORPORATION
NYSE: CCC

400 Calgon Carbon Dr.
Pittsburgh, PA 15205
Phone: 412-787-6700
Fax: 412-787-4511
Web: www.calgoncarbon.com

CEO: John S. Stanik
CFO: Leroy M. Ball
HR: Gail A. Gerono
FYE: December 31
Type: Public

With pure intentions, Calgon Carbon makes activated carbons and purification systems and offers purification, separation, and concentration services to the industrial process and environmental markets. The company provides activated, impregnated, and acid-washed carbons (about 130 million pounds annually) for use in applications such as food processing, wastewater treatment, and emissions control. Calgon Carbon also sells equipment that uses activated carbon and ion exchange resins for the purification of products in the chemical, food, and pharmaceutical industries. The company's consumer products include charcoal and carbon cloth.

	Annual Growth	12/03	12/04	12/05	12/06	12/07
Sales ($ mil.)	6.0%	278.3	336.6	290.8	316.1	351.1
Net income ($ mil.)	35.8%	4.5	5.9	(7.4)	(7.8)	15.3
Market value ($ mil.)	27.4%	242.2	355.7	225.7	246.3	639.0
Employees	(5.5%)	—	—	972	847	868

CALIBER HOLDINGS CORPORATION

17771 Cowan Ave., Ste. 100
Irvine, CA 92614
Phone: 949-224-0300
Fax: 949-224-0313
Web: www.calibernet.com

CEO: John M. Hovis
CFO: Robert (Bob) Kliewe
HR: Anne Chinarian
FYE: December 31
Type: Private

Whether cruising the Hollywood Hills of California or the Hill Country of Texas, you can get auto repair help from Caliber Holdings. The company operates about 35 body shops in Southern California and also about 30 shops in Texas, operating as Caliber Collision Centers. Its locations include a 90,000 square foot collision repair facility in Santa Monica, California. Caliber offers 24-hour customer service seven days a week and a lifetime warranty on all work. Caliber Holdings was founded in 1997 by several California body-shop owners.

	Annual Growth	12/03	12/04	12/05	12/06	12/07
Est. sales ($ mil.)	—	—	—	—	—	84.2
Employees	—	—	—	—	—	1,500

CALIFORNIA CASUALTY GROUP

1900 Alameda de las Pulgas
San Mateo, CA 94403
Phone: 650-574-4000
Fax: 650-572-4585
Web: www.calcas.com

CEO: Carl B. Brown
CFO: Michael A. Ray
HR: James F. Grady
FYE: December 31
Type: Private

California Casualty does not specialize in the protection of failed actresses or surfers. Instead, the group of four property/casualty insurance companies provides personal automobile and homeowners insurance to affiliation groups. Operating in nearly 40 states, it specializes in serving education and public safety association and credit unions. The group is managed by its attorney-in-fact, California Casualty Management. California Casualty plans to expand its operations and eventually do business throughout the US. Chairman Thomas Brown, whose grandfather founded California Casualty in 1914, controls the firm.

CALIFORNIA COASTAL COMMUNITIES, INC.
NASDAQ (GM): CALC

6 Executive Cir., Ste. 250
Irvine, CA 92614
Phone: 949-250-7700
Fax: 949-250-7705
Web: www.californiacoastalcommunities.com

CEO: Raymond J. Pacini
CFO: Sandra G. Sciutto
HR: —
FYE: December 31
Type: Public

The tide has turned for California Coastal Communities. Long wrapped up in a battle over land development rights, the company has begun development of the disputed land, some 215 acres (about half of that undevelopable land) situated on important wetlands in Bolsa Chica, the last undeveloped strip of coastal property in Orange County. Besides the controversial parcels, the company is also building houses in Riverside, Los Angeles, San Bernardino, and Ventura counties, where it has the option to buy some 170 acres. California Coastal Communities' operations include Hearthside Homes, a homebuilder in southern California; and Signal Landmark, which is in the process of developing the Bolsa Chica land.

	Annual Growth	12/03	12/04	12/05	12/06	12/07
Sales ($ mil.)	(4.2%)	55.8	76.0	129.5	95.7	47.0
Net income ($ mil.)	—	2.9	4.8	28.4	5.6	(18.9)
Market value ($ mil.)	(12.7%)	110.0	243.6	398.6	232.8	63.8
Employees	—	—	—	64	—	—

CALIFORNIA DAIRIES INC.

2000 N. Plaza Dr.
Visalia, CA 93291
Phone: 559-625-2200
Fax: 559-625-5433
Web: www.californiadairies.com

CEO: Richard Cotta
CFO: Joe Heffington
HR: Holly Misenhimer
FYE: April 30
Type: Cooperative

Herding dairies to give them greater "ag"-gregate strength has made California Dairies one of the largest dairy cooperatives in the US. California Dairies' 626 members provide the co-op with 16 billion pounds of milk a year. Its plants process milk, cheese, butter, and powdered milk. California Dairies' subsidiaries include Challenge Dairy Products (retail and foodservice butter products) and Los Banos Foods (cheddar cheese ingredients for food manufacturing). California Dairies is also a majority owner of DairyAmerica, Inc., which markets dairy products, including some 60% of all the milk powder produced in the US. The company exports its products to some 40 countries worldwide.

CALIFORNIA FIRST NATIONAL BANCORP
NASDAQ (GM): CFNB

18201 Von Karman Ave., Ste. 800
Irvine, CA 92612
Phone: 949-255-0500
Fax: 949-255-0501
Web: www.calfirstbancorp.com

CEO: Patrick E. Paddon
CFO: S. Leslie Jewett
HR: —
FYE: June 30
Type: Public

California First National Bancorp (CalFirst) wants to be first on your mind when it comes to meeting your equipment leasing needs. Through subsidiaries Amplicon and California First Leasing (CalFirst Leasing), the firm leases mainly computers and software. It also leases retail point-of-sale systems, ATMs, telecommunications equipment, office furniture, and other equipment. CalFirst also operates California First National Bank (CalFirst Bank), a branchless retail bank that accepts deposits through the mail, by phone, or over the Internet. CEO Patrick Paddon owns more than half of the company; COO Glen Tsuma owns about 12%.

	Annual Growth	6/03	6/04	6/05	6/06	6/07
Sales ($ mil.)	0.1%	35.9	35.8	34.5	35.9	36.1
Net income ($ mil.)	(1.9%)	10.7	9.8	8.2	10.7	9.9
Market value ($ mil.)	12.6%	103.8	149.0	125.3	161.1	166.5
Employees						

An in-depth profile of this company is available to Hoover's Online members at hoovers.com.

307

CALIFORNIA MICRO DEVICES CORPORATION

NASDAQ (GM): CAMD

490 N. McCarthy Blvd., Ste. 100
Milpitas, CA 95035
Phone: 408-263-3214
Fax: 408-263-7846
Web: www.calmicro.com

CEO: Robert V. Dickinson
CFO: Kevin J. Berry
HR: –
FYE: March 31
Type: Public

I wish they all could be California . . . chips? California Micro Devices (CMD) specializes in integrated passive devices (IPDs), including application-specific and customized models. IPDs are integrated circuits that combine passive components, such as capacitors and resistors, with active semiconductors. CMD also makes analog and mixed-signal semiconductors, such as operational amplifiers, power management devices, and telecommunications transceivers. Its products are used in various types of electronic gear, including wireless phones, PCs, and medical devices. Among its top clients are Motorola, Philips, Samsung Electronics, and Sony. About 90% of sales are to customers in Asia.

	Annual Growth	3/04	3/05	3/06	3/07	3/08
Sales ($ mil.)	(0.2%)	59.6	65.9	70.2	68.0	59.2
Net income ($ mil.)	—	3.6	4.0	10.0	(0.1)	(1.4)
Market value ($ mil.)	(28.7%)	265.0	109.1	180.8	108.3	68.5
Employees	(8.5%)	154	100	94	107	108

CALIFORNIA NATIONAL BANK

221 S. Figueroa St.
Los Angeles, CA 90012
Phone: 213-253-5700
Fax: 213-628-7020
Web: www.calnationalbank.com

CEO: Gregory A. (Greg) Mitchell
CFO: Karen A. Schoenbaum
HR: –
FYE: December 31
Type: Subsidiary

California National Bank wants to rule an empire. The Inland Empire (Southern California or SoCal to the locals), to be exact. Located just inland from Los Angeles, Orange, and San Diego counties, this California economic hot zone is targeted by California National Bank for serious expansion. A subsidiary of the Illinois-based multibank holding company FBOP, California National Bank operates more than 60 branches in Southern California with plans to open more. The bank offers standard personal and business banking products including deposit accounts and loans.

CALIFORNIA PIZZA KITCHEN, INC.

NASDAQ (GS): CPKI

6053 W. Century Blvd., 11th Fl.
Los Angeles, CA 90045
Phone: 310-342-5000
Fax: 310-342-4640
Web: www.cpk.com

CEO: Larry S. Flax
CFO: Susan M. Collyns
HR: –
FYE: Sunday nearest December 31
Type: Public

California Pizza Kitchen (CPK) puts a West Coast twist on an old favorite. The company operates a chain of about 240 casual-dining restaurants in 30 states and nearly 10 other countries offering pizzas with a variety of unique topping combinations, including duck, barbecued chicken, and grilled shrimp. It also serves Neapolitan pizzas from Italy, as well as American-style pies. CPK rounds out its menu with pastas, soups, salads, and desserts. The company owns about 200 of its locations, while the rest are franchised. In addition to its full-service establishments, CPK has more than two dozen quick-service kiosk locations. The company also markets a line of frozen pizzas with Kraft Foods.

	Annual Growth	12/03	12/04	12/05	12/06	12/07
Sales ($ mil.)	15.2%	359.9	422.5	479.6	554.6	632.9
Net income ($ mil.)	16.6%	8.0	17.8	19.5	21.0	14.8
Market value ($ mil.)	15.2%	247.7	294.9	419.1	428.5	435.6
Employees	7.1%	—	—	12,900	13,900	14,800

CALIFORNIA PUBLIC EMPLOYEES' RETIREMENT SYSTEM

Lincoln Plaza, 400 Q St.
Sacramento, CA 95811
Phone: 916-795-3829
Fax: 916-795-4001
Web: www.calpers.ca.gov

CEO: Fred R. Buenrostro Jr.
CFO: –
HR: Jarvio A. Grevious
FYE: June 30
Type: Government-owned

California's public-sector retirees already have a place in the sun; CalPERS gives them the money to enjoy it. CalPERS is the California Public Employees' Retirement System, one of the largest public pension systems in the US. It manages retirement and health plans for more than 1.4 million beneficiaries (employees, retirees, and their dependents) from more than 2,500 government agencies and school districts. Even though the system's beneficiaries are current or former employees of the Golden State, CalPERS brings its influence to bear in all 50 states and beyond.

	Annual Growth	6/02	6/03	6/04	6/05	6/06
Assets ($ mil.)	12.0%	162,166.6	173,332.9	198,633.0	235,759.0	254,762.7
Employees	4.5%	1,614	1,687	1,687	1,924	1,924

CALIFORNIA STATE AUTOMOBILE ASSOCIATION INTER-INSURANCE BUREAU

100 Van Ness Ave
San Francisco, CA 94102
Phone: 415-565-2141
Fax: –
Web: www.csaa.com

CEO: James R. Pouliot
CFO: Michael Day
HR: –
FYE: December 31
Type: Association

Why let a name limit the scope of a business? California State Automobile Association Inter-Insurance Bureau doesn't just stick to California, autos, or even just insurance. The California State Automobile Association (CSAA) branch provides automotive, travel, and financial services to more than 4 million members in Northern California, Nevada, and Utah and is the second-largest affiliate of AAA. The Inter-Insurance Bureau arm offers auto insurance (including for motorcycles), as well as homeowners and personal umbrella insurance to AAA members. The Inter-Insurance Bureau includes subsidiaries Western United Insurance and ACA Insurance.

	Annual Growth	12/03	12/04	12/05	12/06	12/07
Est. sales ($ mil.)	—	—	—	—	—	537.0
Employees	—	—	—	—	—	6,500

CALIFORNIA STATE LOTTERY COMMISSION

600 N. 10th St.
Sacramento, CA 95814
Phone: 916-323-7095
Fax: 916-327-0489
Web: www.calottery.com

CEO: Joan Borucki
CFO: Patt Eberhart
HR: –
FYE: June 30
Type: Government-owned

There's still a gold rush going on in the Golden State, but you won't need a pick or a shovel to get in on the action. The California State Lottery Commission offers a string of scratch-off games (Treasure Hunt, Lucky Dog) and numbers games (Fantasy 5, SuperLotto Plus) for Californians' wagering pleasure. Scratch-off and Fantasy 5 players also can win chances to spin a wheel for prizes on the *Big Spin* TV show. State law requires that at least 34% of lottery proceeds go to public education in California; since its 1985 inception, the lottery has provided more than $18 billion to that cause. Most of those funds are used to attract and retain teachers.

CALIFORNIA STATE UNIVERSITY SYSTEM

401 Golden Shore	CEO: Charles B. Reed
Long Beach, CA 90802	CFO: Richard P. West
Phone: 562-951-4000	HR: Gail E. Brooks
Fax: 562-951-4861	FYE: June 30
Web: www.calstate.edu	Type: School

California State University (CSU) turns students into teachers. The university traces its roots to the state's teaching colleges and trains about 85% of California's teachers and staff. CSU is neck-and-neck with the State University of New York (SUNY) as the nation's largest university system. With some baby boomers' children reaching college age and college participation increasing among adults, CSU's student body has grown to about 415,000. The system has campuses in about 20 cities, including Bakersfield, Los Angeles, San Francisco, and San Jose. CSU primarily awards bachelor's and master's degrees in nearly 250 subject areas, leaving higher levels of study to the University of California (UC) system.

CALIFORNIA STEEL INDUSTRIES, INC.

14000 San Bernardino Ave.	CEO: Vicente Wright
Fontana, CA 92335	CFO: Ricardo Bernandes
Phone: 909-350-6300	HR: Brett Guge
Fax: 909-350-6398	FYE: December 31
Web: www.californiasteel.com	Type: Joint venture

California Steel Industries (CSI) doesn't use forensic evidence, but its work does involve a steel slab. The company uses steel slab produced by third parties to manufacture steel products such as hot-rolled and cold-rolled steel, galvanized coils and sheets, and electric resistance weld (ERW) pipe. Its customers include aftermarket automotive manufacturers, oil and gas producers, roofing makers, tubing manufacturers, and building suppliers. CSI serves the western region of the US. The company operates slitting, shearing, coating, and single-billing services for third parties. Japan's JFE Holdings and Brazilian iron ore miner Companhia Vale do Rio Doce (Vale) each own 50% of CSI.

	Annual Growth	12/02	12/03	12/04	12/05	12/06
Sales ($ mil.)	15.8%	754.4	763.6	1,257.0	1,234.4	1,358.8
Net income ($ mil.)	32.8%	35.0	4.5	109.3	43.4	109.0
Employees	0.1%	929	921	944	938	931

CALIFORNIA WATER SERVICE GROUP

	NYSE: CWT
1720 N. 1st St.	CEO: Peter C. Nelson
San Jose, CA 95112	CFO: Martin A. (Marty) Kropelnicki
Phone: 408-367-8200	HR: Christine L. McFarlane
Fax: 408-367-8430	FYE: December 31
Web: www.calwatergroup.com	Type: Public

A big fish in California's water industry pond, California Water Service Group is in the swim in three other states, as well. The company's main subsidiary, regulated utility California Water Service Company (Cal Water), keeps water flowing in 26 systems for 463,600 customers throughout the state. Cal Water obtains its water from wells and wholesale suppliers. California Water Service Group's other water utility subsidiaries include Washington Water (15,800 customers), New Mexico Water (7,500 water and wastewater customers), and Hawaii Water (700 customers). The company's CWS Utility Services unit contracts to provide water system operation, meter reading, and billing services.

	Annual Growth	12/03	12/04	12/05	12/06	12/07
Sales ($ mil.)	7.3%	277.1	315.6	320.7	334.7	367.1
Net income ($ mil.)	12.6%	19.4	26.0	27.2	25.6	31.2
Market value ($ mil.)	13.3%	463.9	691.5	703.0	834.5	765.1
Employees	—	—	—	—	840	—	—

CALIPER LIFE SCIENCES, INC.

	NASDAQ (GM): CALP
68 Elm St.	CEO: E. Kevin Hrusovsky
Hopkinton, MA 01748	CFO: Peter F. McAree
Phone: 508-435-9500	HR: Paula J. Cassidy
Fax: 508-435-3439	FYE: December 31
Web: www.caliperls.com	Type: Public

Caliper Life Sciences helps researchers avoid teeny-tiny spills with its microfluid chips and liquid handling technologies. The firm's LabChip microchips incorporate short glass tubes (Caliper's patented "sipper" technology) to extract samples and internal channels that hold fluids for analysis and experimentation. Its Sciclone line of liquid handling systems pull up, shake, measure, and filter liquids robotically; and its IVIS imaging systems allow researchers to examine molecular interactions *in vivo* (or inside an organism). The company's tools are aimed at helping drug firms and biomedical researchers in the drug discovery and development process by increasing the speed and efficiency of screening compounds.

	Annual Growth	12/03	12/04	12/05	12/06	12/07
Sales ($ mil.)	29.9%	49.4	80.1	87.0	107.9	140.7
Net income ($ mil.)	—	(49.5)	(31.6)	(14.5)	(28.9)	(24.1)
Market value ($ mil.)	8.7%	189.0	229.6	199.3	267.8	263.8
Employees	10.7%	—	—	443	550	543

CALIX NETWORKS, INC.

1035 N. McDowell Blvd.	CEO: Carl Russo
Petaluma, CA 94954	CFO: Kelyn Brannon-Ahn
Phone: 707-766-3000	HR: –
Fax: 707-766-3100	FYE: December 31
Web: www.calix.com	Type: Private

With Calix Networks' access equipment, your bandwidth runneth over. Calix ("cup" in Latin) makes broadband access equipment for network service providers. Its products increase the capacity of fiber-optic and copper lines to deliver next-generation telecommunications services, such as Internet protocol (IP) television and voice service, as well as high-speed DSL Internet. The company also makes Web-based network management software that handles provisioning, testing, and troubleshooting. In 2006 Calix acquired fiber-to-the-premises (FTTP) equipment maker Optical Solutions.

	Annual Growth	12/03	12/04	12/05	12/06	12/07
Est. sales ($ mil.)	—	—	—	—	—	31.5
Employees	—	—	—	—	—	370

CALL NOW, INC.

	OTC: CLNWE
1 Retama Pkwy.	CEO: Thomas R. Johnson
Selma, TX 78154	CFO: Thomas R. Johnson
Phone: 210-651-7145	HR: Angela C. Cooper
Fax: –	FYE: December 31
Web: www.retamapark.com	Type: Public

Call Now operates the Retama Park horse racing facility in Selma, Texas, through its 80%-owned subsidiary, Retama Entertainment Group. The track, which opened in 1995, offers both live and simulcast thoroughbred racing. Call Now purchased rights to operate the racetrack a year later (the actual land and facility are owned by Retama Development Corporation, which is a division of the city of Selma). Retama Park's grandstand features a dining room and sports bar. Private club facilities also are on site.

	Annual Growth	12/03	12/04	12/05	12/06	12/07
Sales ($ mil.)	(2.8%)	5.5	4.7	5.2	5.3	4.9
Net income ($ mil.)	—	0.1	0.1	0.0	0.1	(0.4)
Employees	—	—	—	—	—	—

An in-depth profile of this company is available to Hoover's Online members at hoovers.com.

309

CALLAWAY GOLF COMPANY
NYSE: ELY

2180 Rutherford Rd.
Carlsbad, CA 92008
Phone: 760-931-1771
Fax: 760-930-5015
Web: www.callawaygolf.com

CEO: George Fellows
CFO: Bradley J. (Brad) Holiday
HR: Christopher O. (Chris) Carroll
FYE: December 31
Type: Public

Big Bertha gets Callaway Golf swinging. With its flagship driver named after a WWI cannon, it makes premium-priced golf clubs that are popular with amateurs and professionals alike. Its other drivers include the ERC, Hawk Eye, and Steelhead. Callaway makes fairway woods, irons, wedges, Odyssey White Hot and Dual Force putters, and high-tech golf balls (HX, HX Tour, Big Bertha). The firm, at the top of the worldwide golf market, licenses its name for apparel, shoes, and golf accessories. Callaway purchased the Top-Flite, Strata, and Ben Hogan brands from SHC's bankrupt Top-Flite Golf Company.

	Annual Growth	12/03	12/04	12/05	12/06	12/07
Sales ($ mil.)	8.4%	814.0	934.6	998.1	1,017.9	1,124.6
Net income ($ mil.)	4.7%	45.5	(10.1)	13.3	23.3	54.6
Market value ($ mil.)	(2.4%)	1,273.3	1,029.9	1,058.1	1,053.9	1,155.3
Employees	0.0%	—	—	3,000	3,000	3,000

CALLIDUS SOFTWARE INC.
NASDAQ (GM): CALD

160 W. Santa Clara St., Ste. 1500
San Jose, CA 95113
Phone: 408-808-6400
Fax: 408-271-2662
Web: www.callidussoftware.com

CEO: Leslie J. Stretch
CFO: Ronald J. (Ron) Fior
HR: –
FYE: December 31
Type: Public

Callidus Software takes good care of office overachievers. The company provides enterprise incentive management (EIM) software for managing compensation and commission programs, including salaries, options, bonuses, and sales commissions. Callidus Software targets CFOs and other executives, who use its applications to align employee incentive programs with corporate business and profit objectives. Products include TrueComp, a sales and channel incentive management suite; TrueResolution, an application for streamlining and automating disputes over incentive compensation; and TrueInformation, a Web-based compensation reporting and analytics tool. Crosspoint Venture Partners owns about 24% of Callidus.

	Annual Growth	12/03	12/04	12/05	12/06	12/07
Sales ($ mil.)	9.1%	71.7	58.7	61.5	76.1	101.7
Net income ($ mil.)	—	0.8	(25.5)	(8.6)	(8.7)	(12.4)
Market value ($ mil.)	(22.4%)	423.9	148.8	112.8	178.6	153.6
Employees	12.8%	—	—	300	355	382

CALLON PETROLEUM COMPANY
NYSE: CPE

200 N. Canal St.
Natchez, MS 39120
Phone: 601-442-1601
Fax: 601-446-1410
Web: www.callon.com

CEO: Fred L. Callon
CFO: Fred L. Callon
HR: –
FYE: December 31
Type: Public

Callon Petroleum can call on new technologies to find old petroleum resources, employing computer-aided techniques such as 3-D surveys to explore and develop oil and gas properties. It also focuses on acquiring properties. Most of the firm's holdings are in federal waters in the Gulf of Mexico, although some are onshore in Alabama and Louisiana. Callon's estimated proved reserves stand at 145.6 billion cu. ft. of natural gas equivalent. The firm owns working and/or royalty interests in about 233 producing oil wells and 246 producing gas wells. Natural gas accounts for the bulk of its daily production. The company collaborates with Murphy Oil, BP, and others in its offshore exploration.

	Annual Growth	12/03	12/04	12/05	12/06	12/07
Sales ($ mil.)	23.4%	73.7	119.8	141.3	182.3	170.8
Net income ($ mil.)	—	(18.0)	21.5	26.8	40.6	15.2
Market value ($ mil.)	24.2%	144.5	254.7	341.7	311.8	343.7
Employees	(1.1%)	—	—	87	86	—

CALLWAVE, INC.
NASDAQ (GM): CALL

136 W. Canon Perdido St., Ste. A
Santa Barbara, CA 93101
Phone: 805-690-4000
Fax: 805-690-4241
Web: www.callwave.com

CEO: Jeffrey M. (Jeff) Cavins
CFO: Mark Stubbs
HR: –
FYE: June 30
Type: Public

CallWave considers itself a lifesaver to those drowning in phone calls. The company provides call management services using VoIP technology. These call-bridging services enable consumer and business customers to redirect calls from multiple wireless, landline, or Internet phone accounts to a single number. CallWave provides services including call screening, call forwarding, and voicemail over both the telephone network and the Internet. The company's services are provided by its local-exchange carrier subsidiary Liberty Telecom, which operates a call-switching facility in Reno, Nevada.

	Annual Growth	6/03	6/04	6/05	6/06	6/07
Sales ($ mil.)	2.9%	22.5	38.9	45.5	36.6	25.2
Net income ($ mil.)	—	1.6	11.5	11.6	(2.0)	(7.5)
Market value ($ mil.)	(12.5%)	—	—	99.0	75.9	75.8
Employees	—	—	—	103	—	—

CAL-MAINE FOODS, INC.
NASDAQ (GM): CALM

3320 Woodrow Wilson Ave.
Jackson, MS 39209
Phone: 601-948-6813
Fax: 601-969-0905
Web: www.calmainefoods.com

CEO: Fred R. Adams Jr.
CFO: Timothy A. Dawson
HR: Alan Holland
FYE: Saturday nearest May 31
Type: Public

What comes first, the chicken or the egg? For Cal-Maine Foods, it's definitely the egg and some 24 million laying hens help settle the question. The company is one of the largest fresh egg producers in the US. Cal-Maine sells its eggs to supermarkets across the US. It also produces specialty eggs which it sells under the Egg-Land's Best and Farmhouse labels. The company has operations in Arkansas, Georgia, Kansas, Kentucky, Louisiana, Mississippi, New Mexico, North Carolina, Ohio, Oklahoma, South Carolina, Tennessee, Texas, and Utah and include breeding facilities, hatcheries, feed mills, shell-egg production and pullet-growing sites, and processing, packing, and wholesaling operations.

	Annual Growth	5/03	5/04	5/05	5/06	5/07
Sales ($ mil.)	11.5%	387.5	572.3	375.3	477.6	598.1
Net income ($ mil.)	31.7%	12.2	66.4	(10.4)	(1.0)	36.7
Market value ($ mil.)	79.1%	27.7	484.8	237.5	252.6	285.3
Employees	6.9%	—	—	1,400	—	1,600

CALPINE CORPORATION
NYSE: CPN

50 W. San Fernando St.
San Jose, CA 95113
Phone: 408-995-5115
Fax: 408-995-0505
Web: www.calpine.com

CEO: Robert P. (Bob) May
CFO: Zamir Rauf
HR: Casey L. Gunnell
FYE: December 31
Type: Public

Calpine may get hot, but it also knows how to blow off some steam. The independent power producer and marketer controls more than 23,800 MW of generating capacity through interests in 60 natural gas-fired power plants throughout the US and 17 geothermal power plants in California. Calpine is a top geothermal producer; it owns 90% of the plants at the largest geothermal facility in the US (the Geysers in northern California), where electricity is produced from natural steam. Calpine has 725 MW of capacity from these plants. Calpine emerged from bankruptcy in 2008. That year NRG Energy bid $11 billion to acquire Calpine, but Calpine rejected the offer.

	Annual Growth	12/03	12/04	12/05	12/06	12/07
Sales ($ mil.)	(2.8%)	8,919.5	9,229.9	10,112.7	6,705.8	7,970.0
Net income ($ mil.)	75.8%	282.0	(242.5)	(9,939.2)	(1,764.9)	2,693.0
Employees	(9.8%)	—	—	—	2,306	2,080

CALTON, INC.

OTC: CTON

2050 40th Ave., Ste. 1
Vero Beach, FL 32960
Phone: 772-794-1414
Fax: 772-794-2828
Web: www.caltoninc.com

CEO: Anthony J. Caldarone
CFO: Vicky Savage
HR: –
FYE: November 30
Type: Public

Calton develops residential communities and builds single-family residences through its Homes by Calton subsidiary. Active in coastal Florida's Vero Beach, the company offers some 15 floor plans for homes ranging in price from $425,000 to $775,000 and in size from 1,900 to 3,600 sq. ft. It also acts as a contractor for the construction of custom homes. The company delivers about 10 homes annually. Calton operates its own sales office within its development community. The company formed PrivilegeONE Networks subsidiary to develop a loyalty and co-branded credit card, but that segment has yet to begin actively operating.

	Annual Growth	11/03	11/04	11/05	11/06	11/07
Sales ($ mil.)	12.1%	3.1	12.2	13.9	6.6	4.9
Net income ($ mil.)	—	(1.7)	0.6	1.1	(1.4)	(1.0)
Market value ($ mil.)	(12.1%)	6.9	3.4	4.2	4.7	—
Employees	—	—	—	—	—	—

CALUMET SPECIALTY PRODUCTS PARTNERS

NASDAQ (GM): CLMT

2780 Waterfront Parkway East Dr., Ste. 200
Indianapolis, IN 46214
Phone: 317-328-5660
Fax: 317-328-5668
Web: www.calumetlubricants.com

CEO: F. William Grube
CFO: R. Patrick Murray II
HR: –
FYE: December 31
Type: Public

It's two-faced, but there's no calumny involved at Calumet Specialty Products Partners, L.P. The specialty hydrocarbon producer operates in two business segments — specialty products and fuel products. The specialty products unit processes crude oil into lubricating oils, solvents, waxes, and other petroleum products. It sells these items primarily to industrial customers who use them in the manufacture of basic automotive, consumer, and industrial goods. The fuel products unit processes crude oil into unleaded gasoline, diesel fuel, and jet fuel. Calumet Specialty Products Partners also produces asphalt. The company is 18.5% owned by The Heritage Group, a vehicle of the chairman Fred Fehsenfeld and his family.

	Annual Growth	12/03	12/04	12/05	12/06	12/07
Sales ($ mil.)	12.7%	—	—	1,289.1	1,641.1	1,637.8
Net income ($ mil.)	170.9%	—	—	11.3	93.9	82.9
Market value ($ mil.)	8.3%	—	—	—	655.3	709.7
Employees	35.2%	—	—	350	360	640

CALVIN B. TAYLOR BANKSHARES, INC.

OTC: TYCB

24 N. Main St.
Berlin, MD 21811
Phone: 410-641-1700
Fax: 410-641-0543
Web: www.taylorbank.com

CEO: Raymond M. Thompson
CFO: William H. Mitchell
HR: –
FYE: December 31
Type: Public

Calvin B. Taylor Bankshares *be* the holding company for Calvin B. Taylor Banking Company (aka Taylor Bank), which has branches in southeastern Maryland and another in Delaware. The bank offers standard commercial and retail services including checking and savings accounts, money market accounts, and credit cards. It also offers discount securities brokerage through an affiliation with correspondent bank M&T Securities. Residential mortgages account for about half of the bank's portfolio; commercial mortgages make up another third. Other offerings include construction, business, and consumer loans. The bank is named after its founder, who opened a predecessor to Calvin B. Taylor Banking Company in 1890.

	Annual Growth	12/03	12/04	12/05	12/06	12/07
Assets ($ mil.)	(1.1%)	386.5	393.3	389.1	367.5	369.1
Net income ($ mil.)	7.3%	5.5	5.6	6.8	7.4	7.3
Market value ($ mil.)	0.3%	119.4	117.1	120.3	112.3	121.0
Employees	—	—	—	—	—	92

CALVIN KLEIN, INC.

Subsidiary

205 W. 39th St.
New York, NY 10018
Phone: 866-214-6694
Fax: –
Web: www.pvh.com/Brand_CK_Intro.html

CEO: Paul Thomas (Tom) Murry
CFO: John Van Glahn
HR: –
FYE: Sunday nearest February 1
Type: Subsidiary

Mark Wahlberg's underwear and Brooke Shields' implied lack thereof made everyone aware of the company's Calvins. From its tighty-whitey briefs to the *haute couture* of runway fashion, Calvin Klein is known for simply elegant and pricey clothes for men, women, and children; fragrances; and accessories. The company makes its flagship ready-to-wear collection of women's clothing, but gets most of its revenue from licensing its name for items such as shoes, coats, fragrances, jeans, underwear, furnishings, hosiery, watches, bedding, and tabletop products. The firm was founded in 1968 by Barry Schwartz and Calvin Klein, who were its sole owners until clothing maker Phillips-Van Heusen (PVH) bought the company.

	Annual Growth	1/03	1/04	1/05	1/06	1/07
Est. sales ($ mil.)	—	—	—	—	—	52.2
Employees	—	—	—	—	—	700

CALYPTE BIOMEDICAL CORPORATION

OTC: CBMC

5 Centerpointe Dr., Ste. 400
Lake Oswego, OR 97035
Phone: 971-204-0282
Fax: 971-204-0284
Web: www.calypte.com

CEO: Roger I. Gale
CFO: Jerrold D. Dotson
HR: –
FYE: December 31
Type: Public

Fear of needles need not stop you from getting tested for HIV infection. Calypte Biomedical's line of HIV testing products includes several tests that use saliva rather than blood. These rapid-detection tests (sold under the Aware brand name) don't require sophisticated laboratory equipment, and Calypte hopes that such products will appeal to markets in developing countries where the incidence of HIV is high but health care infrastructure is lacking. The company has obtained regulatory approval for its Aware Rapid HIV tests in several foreign markets, including South Africa and Russia. The company has also developed an Aware HIV blood test and an over-the-counter version of its oral test.

	Annual Growth	12/03	12/04	12/05	12/06	12/07
Sales ($ mil.)	(35.7%)	3.5	3.3	0.4	0.6	0.6
Net income ($ mil.)	—	(26.4)	(17.3)	(8.8)	(13.8)	(8.3)
Market value ($ mil.)	(12.3%)	63.4	66.1	29.0	15.9	37.5
Employees	(58.6%)	70	63	12	—	—

CAM COMMERCE SOLUTIONS, INC.

NASDAQ (GM): CADA

17075 Newhope St., Ste. A
Fountain Valley, CA 92708
Phone: 714-241-9241
Fax: 714-241-9893
Web: www.camcommerce.com

CEO: Geoffrey D. (Geoff) Knapp
CFO: Paul Caceres Jr.
HR: Marita Swanson
FYE: September 30
Type: Public

CAM Commerce Solutions doesn't want you missing a single sale or losing a single inventory item. The company provides automation software that helps retailers track inventory, bill customers, and monitor sales performance. Its systems also include accounting and reporting features. CAM Commerce sells its software together with third-party point-of-sale (POS) equipment as a turnkey service. The company's CAM32 system is designed for hard goods retailers, while its Profit$ system is targeted toward apparel and shoe stores. In June 2008 the company agreed to be acquired and taken private by Great Hill Partners in a deal valued at $180 million.

	Annual Growth	9/03	9/04	9/05	9/06	9/07
Sales ($ mil.)	12.5%	20.1	23.6	24.9	27.2	32.2
Net income ($ mil.)	—	(0.1)	2.2	1.8	2.7	4.7
Market value ($ mil.)	65.8%	18.6	53.6	68.3	79.2	140.6
Employees	4.3%	—	—	180	—	196

CAMAC INTERNATIONAL CORPORATION

Four Oaks Place, 1330 Post Oak Blvd., Ste. 2200
Houston, TX 77056
Phone: 713-965-5100
Fax: 713-965-5129
Web: www.camacholdings.com

CEO: Kase L. Lawal
CFO: Kamoru A. Lawal
HR: Jeana Raines Herrington
FYE: December 31
Type: Private

It's not Carnac the Magnificent, but CAMAC International that seems to be able to look into the future and see a fortune. Its own. Arguably America's largest black-owned business, CAMAC International (the CAMAC name derives from Cameroon-American Company) is an integrated oil and gas company, engaging in a range of oil and gas exploration, production, refining, and energy trading activities. The company has major energy assets in Nigeria and South Africa. Chairman and CEO Kase Lawal also serves as vice chairman of the Port of Houston Authority Board of Commissioners. A global player, CAMAC International has offices in Houston, Johannesburg, Lagos, and London.

	Annual Growth	12/02	12/03	12/04	12/05	12/06
Est. sales ($ mil.)	—	—	—	—	—	1,490.0
Employees	—	—	—	—	—	300

CAMBREX CORPORATION

NYSE: CBM

1 Meadowlands Plaza
East Rutherford, NJ 07073
Phone: 201-804-3000
Fax: 201-804-9852
Web: www.cambrex.com

CEO: Steven M. (Steve) Klosk
CFO: Gregory P. (Greg) Sargen
HR: Melissa M. Lesko
FYE: December 31
Type: Public

Cambrex has slimmed down because it wants to focus on its health and yours. The company's lone operating unit develops products for the human health care market like active pharmaceutical ingredients (APIs) and intermediates for over-the-counter and prescription drugs. It also makes intermediates used in cosmetics and food additives. Cambrex maintains manufacturing and R&D facilities in Italy, Sweden, and the US. In 2007 the company significantly pared down its operations with the sale of two divisions to French specialty chemicals maker Lonza; Cambrex sold its former bioproducts and biopharma units for about $460 million.

	Annual Growth	12/03	12/04	12/05	12/06	12/07
Sales ($ mil.)	(11.4%)	410.6	443.7	455.1	455.5	252.5
Net income ($ mil.)	—	(54.1)	(26.9)	(110.5)	(30.1)	209.3
Market value ($ mil.)	(7.1%)	326.6	355.4	250.3	314.7	243.1
Employees	(35.7%)	—	—	2,041	1,916	844

CAMBRIDGE BANCORP

OTC: CATC

1336 Massachusetts Ave.
Cambridge, MA 02138
Phone: 617-876-5500
Fax: 617-441-1421
Web: www.cambridgetrust.com

CEO: Joseph V. (Joe) Roller II
CFO: Albert R. (Al) Rietheimer
HR: Noreen A. Briand
FYE: December 31
Type: Public

Cambridge Bancorp is the holding company for Cambridge Trust Company, a community bank serving Cambridge, Massachusetts and the Greater Boston area from about ten locations. It offers standard retail products and services including checking and savings accounts, mortgages and home equity loans, credit cards, and consumer loans. Residential mortgages, including home equity loans, account for nearly 60% of the bank's loan portfolio; commercial real estate loans make up about 30%. The company also offers wealth management and investment planning services. Cambridge Trust Company was established in 1892.

	Annual Growth	12/03	12/04	12/05	12/06	12/07
Sales ($ mil.)	10.0%	—	—	49.3	54.9	59.6
Net income ($ mil.)	9.3%	—	—	7.7	8.7	9.2
Employees	—	—	—	—	107	—

CAMBRIDGE HEART, INC.

OTC: CAMH

1 Oak Park Dr.
Bedford, MA 01730
Phone: 781-271-1200
Fax: 781-275-8431
Web: www.cambridgeheart.com

CEO: Ali Haghighi-Mood
CFO: Vincenzo LiCausi
HR: Janet Miller
FYE: December 31
Type: Public

It's not just a heart, it's a *Cambridge* heart. Cambridge Heart makes noninvasive tools for diagnosing cardiac arrest and ventricular arrhythmia. Its CH 2000 system conducts cardiac stress tests and measures extremely low levels of T-wave alternans, an irregularity in an electrocardiogram indicating the risk of sudden cardiac death. Another product, the Heartwave II System, allows T-wave alternans screenings to be performed with any stress test system. The company's Microvolt T-Wave Alternans technology can detect the smallest heartbeat variation, measuring from one-millionth of a volt. The company markets its products in the US through direct sales and representatives; it also has international distributors.

	Annual Growth	12/03	12/04	12/05	12/06	12/07
Sales ($ mil.)	10.0%	6.9	5.1	4.2	7.4	10.1
Net income ($ mil.)	—	(3.4)	(3.7)	(2.6)	(10.6)	(9.2)
Market value ($ mil.)	36.1%	19.1	22.7	34.0	175.6	65.4
Employees	—	—	—	—	—	—

CAMBRIDGE INTEGRATED SERVICES GROUP, INC.

4B Cedar Brook Dr.
Cranbury, NJ 08512
Phone: 609-655-8383
Fax: 609-655-0503
Web: www.cambridgeintegrated.com

CEO: Chris Sinclair
CFO: Pradeep Chaudhry
HR: Richard R. Gros
FYE: December 31
Type: Private

This Cambridge educates businesses on safe and efficient work practices. Cambridge Integrated Services offers risk management services including liability claims, managed care, anti-fraud investigations, and recovery services for insurance, financial services, and health care businesses. With about 90 offices throughout the US and the UK as well as operations in Asia and Australia, the company is one of the largest third-party business process outsourcing (BPO) providers. Formerly a division of brokerage giant Aon, Cambridge Integrated Services was acquired by Singapore-based technology consultant Scandent Group in 2004.

	Annual Growth	12/03	12/04	12/05	12/06	12/07
Est. sales ($ mil.)	—	—	—	—	—	120.3
Employees	—	—	—	—	—	2,200

CAMBRIDGE SOUNDWORKS, INC.

120 Water St.
Andover, MA 01845
Phone: 978-623-4400
Fax: 978-794-2903
Web: www.cambridgesoundworks.com

CEO: Robert S. (Rob) Mainiero
CFO: Rob Cardin
HR: –
FYE: June 30
Type: Subsidiary

Cambridge SoundWorks wants to be speaker of the house, the car, and the computer. It's a leading manufacturer of speaker systems for consumer use, including floor speakers and bookshelf models. It also makes home theater speaker systems, outdoor speakers, and surround sound units. Steep discounting of consumer electronics contributed to the firm's decision to close all but one of its once 30 stores to focus on online and catalog sales. The chain began to sell its private-label products in other electronics stores. Cambridge SoundWorks also sells audio and video items from such manufacturers as Samsung, Sony, and Toshiba, as well as products made by its parent company, Creative Technology.

	Annual Growth	6/03	6/04	6/05	6/06	6/07
Est. sales ($ mil.)	—	—	—	—	—	37.5
Employees	—	—	—	—	—	253

CAMCO FINANCIAL CORPORATION

NASDAQ (GM): CAFI

6901 Glenn Hwy.
Cambridge, OH 43725
Phone: 740-435-2020
Fax: 740-435-2021
Web: www.camcofinancial.com

CEO: Richard C. Baylor
CFO: –
HR: James W. (Jim) Chugg
FYE: December 31
Type: Public

Camco Financial tries to give customers a financial edge through its Advantage Bank subsidiary. The company operates about 30 branches, loan offices, and Camco Title Agency offices in Ohio, northern Kentucky, and western West Virginia. The bank primarily uses funds from deposits (checking, savings, and money market accounts; CDs; and IRAs) to originate residential mortgages, which make up about 60% of its loan portfolio; the bank also issues nonresidential real estate, consumer, and construction loans. Ohio-based First Place Financial plans to buy Camco Financial for some $97 million in cash and stock.

	Annual Growth	12/03	12/04	12/05	12/06	12/07
Assets ($ mil.)	(0.4%)	1,039.2	1,065.8	1,071.3	1,048.2	1,023.3
Net income ($ mil.)	(10.1%)	6.9	(2.5)	8.8	5.9	4.5
Market value ($ mil.)	(11.2%)	127.1	118.0	108.0	95.2	79.1
Employees	0.5%	—	—	275	—	278

CAMDEN NATIONAL CORPORATION

NASDAQ (GS): CAC

2 Elm St.
Camden, ME 04843
Phone: 207-236-8821
Fax: 207-236-6256
Web: www.camdennational.com

CEO: Robert W. (Bob) Daigle
CFO: Sean G. Daly
HR: Carolyn Crosby
FYE: December 31
Type: Public

Camden National Corporation is the holding company for Camden National Bank, which was founded in 1875 and once issued its own US currency. With about 40 branches throughout Maine, the bank provides such deposit products as checking and savings accounts, CDs, and IRAs. Business loans, including commercial mortgages, make up nearly half of the company's loan portfolio; residential mortgages account for approximately a third, and consumer and municipal loans constitute almost all of the balance. In 2008 Camden National bought bank holding company Union Bankshares, which expanded its presence along coastal portions of Maine.

	Annual Growth	12/03	12/04	12/05	12/06	12/07
Assets ($ mil.)	5.8%	1,370.4	1,489.9	1,653.3	1,769.9	1,716.8
Net income ($ mil.)	1.8%	18.9	19.5	21.4	20.3	20.3
Market value ($ mil.)	(5.9%)	235.6	300.9	247.6	305.2	184.9
Employees	(0.8%)	—	—	320	—	315

CAMDEN PROPERTY TRUST

NYSE: CPT

3 Greenway Plaza, Ste. 1300
Houston, TX 77046
Phone: 713-354-2500
Fax: 713-354-2700
Web: www.camdenliving.com

CEO: Richard J. Campo
CFO: Dennis M. Steen
HR: Cindy Scharringhausen
FYE: December 31
Type: Public

If your living tastes are more Melrose Place than Mel's Diner, Camden Property Trust just might have the spot for you. A real estate investment trust (REIT), Camden Property Trust invests in, develops, and operates luxury and middle-market apartment complexes in about a dozen states, with about one-quarter of its properties in Texas. Its portfolio (which includes both wholly owned and joint-venture holdings) is made up of approximately 180 urban and suburban properties with more than 66,000 apartment units; most communities carry the Camden brand name. Top markets include Southeast Florida, Houston, and the District of Columbia.

	Annual Growth	12/03	12/04	12/05	12/06	12/07
Sales ($ mil.)	11.1%	416.5	431.2	568.6	635.0	634.1
Net income ($ mil.)	49.9%	29.4	41.3	199.1	232.9	148.5
Market value ($ mil.)	9.2%	2,217.7	2,478.7	3,519.4	4,194.3	3,150.6
Employees	(3.5%)	—	—	2,042	1,920	1,900

CAMERA PLATFORMS INTERNATIONAL, INC.

OTC: CPFR

10909 Vanowen St.
North Hollywood, CA 91605
Phone: 818-623-1700
Fax: 818-623-1710
Web: www.shotmaker.com

CEO: Martin Perellis
CFO: Martin Perellis
HR: –
FYE: December 31
Type: Public

Camera Platforms International helps cameras move to great heights. The company, which does business as Shotmaker, leases and rents production equipment, including camera cars, dollies, cranes, and accessories, to the film and video industries. Camera Platforms International carries the Shotmaker, Pegasus, Enlouva, and Panther brand names. Its equipment has been used on films such as *Mission: Impossible III, Spider-Man 3*, and *The 40 Year Old Virgin*, and TV programs such as *My Name is Earl, Scrubs*, and *Fear Factor*. CEO Martin Perellis and director William Fleischman together own more than half of Camera Platforms International, which has announced plans to sell all of its assets to Moving Vehicular Platforms.

	Annual Growth	12/02	12/03	12/04	12/05	*12/06
Sales ($ mil.)	(21.7%)	0.8	0.7	0.6	0.3	0.3
Net income ($ mil.)	—	(0.8)	(0.2)	(0.1)	(0.1)	(0.1)
Employees	—	—	—	—	—	—

*Most recent year available

CAMERON INTERNATIONAL CORPORATION

NYSE: CAM

1333 West Loop South, Ste. 1700
Houston, TX 77027
Phone: 713-513-3300
Fax: 713-513-3456
Web: www.c-a-m.com

CEO: Jack B. Moore
CFO: Charles M. Sledge
HR: Joseph H. Mongrain
FYE: December 31
Type: Public

Cameron International (formerly Cooper Cameron) knows how to work under pressure. A manufacturer, provider, and servicer of oil and gas industry equipment, the company makes products that control pressure at oil and gas wells, including blowout preventers, chokes, controls, wellheads, and valves. It also makes integral and separable reciprocating engines and compressors used in oil and gas and power-generation applications. Cameron International sells its products, which are used for offshore, onshore, and subsea applications, under brand names such as Ajax, Cameron, Demco, Foster, Petreco, Retsco, and Willis.

	Annual Growth	12/03	12/04	12/05	12/06	12/07
Sales ($ mil.)	30.0%	1,634.3	2,092.8	2,517.9	3,742.9	4,666.4
Net income ($ mil.)	63.9%	69.4	94.4	171.1	317.8	500.9
Market value ($ mil.)	102.3%	626.8	726.8	2,393.5	2,978.5	10,492.8
Employees	12.4%	—	—	12,200	12,400	15,400

CAMINOSOFT CORP.

OTC: CMSF

600 Hampshire Rd., Ste. 105
Westlake Village, CA 91361
Phone: 805-370-3100
Fax: 805-370-3200
Web: www.caminosoft.com

CEO: Stephen Crosson
CFO: Stephen Crosson
HR: –
FYE: September 30
Type: Public

CaminoSoft helps customers navigate the road to manageable data storage. The company markets the Managed Server HSM line of computer data storage management software. Its applications are designed for use with Novell and Microsoft-based systems. CaminoSoft sells through distributors, OEMs, resellers, and systems integrators; its target markets include architectural and engineering services, banks and financial services, government agencies, health care providers, legal services, and schools. BFSUS Special Opportunities Trust, Renaissance US Growth & Income Trust, and Renaissance Capital Growth & Income Fund III collectively control a majority stake in the company.

	Annual Growth	9/03	9/04	9/05	9/06	9/07
Sales ($ mil.)	27.3%	0.8	1.3	2.6	1.8	2.1
Net income ($ mil.)	—	(2.2)	(2.1)	(0.8)	(1.7)	(0.7)
Market value ($ mil.)	(19.2%)	4.3	6.6	14.2	3.8	1.9
Employees	—	—	—	—	—	7

CAMP DRESSER & MCKEE INC.

1 Cambridge Place, 50 Hampshire St.
Cambridge, MA 02139
Phone: 617-452-6000
Fax: 617-452-8000
Web: www.cdm.com

CEO: Thomas D. Furman Jr.
CFO: Robert J. Anton
HR: Charlene P. Allen
FYE: December 31
Type: Private

Camp Dresser & McKee does not give sartorial advice, but it has fashioned a business out of providing engineering, consulting, construction, and operations services. The company, doing business as CDM, provides services worldwide. Founded in 1947 by engineers Thomas Camp, Herman Dresser, and Jack McKee, CDM has expanded from its traditional services in water-treatment technologies to services in such markets as environmental management, transportation development, and facilities design. One of the top environmental design firms, CDM is a major player in the environmental management, water treatment and supply, wastewater treatment, and hazardous waste markets.

CAMPBELL-EWALD

30400 Van Dyke Ave.
Warren, MI 48093
Phone: 586-574-3400
Fax: 586-575-9925
Web: www.campbell-ewald.com

CEO: Anthony J. (Tony) Hopp
CFO: Joseph A. (Joe) Naporano
HR: Deborah S. Osborne
FYE: December 31
Type: Subsidiary

This agency knows it takes more than a good name to make a great brand. Campbell-Ewald is one of the Midwest's leading advertising agencies, offering creative development and campaign management services for broadcast, print, and interactive media. In addition to traditional advertising, the firm provides services for direct response marketing, event marketing, and business-to-business selling. Major clients have included the American Heart Association, Carrier, Michelin, and the United States Postal Service. Its Campbell-Ewald Publishing unit offers custom publishing services for creating branded content. The agency is part of global marketing services conglomerate Interpublic Group.

CAMPBELL HAUSFELD

100 Production Dr.
Harrison, OH 45030
Phone: 513-367-4811
Fax: 513-367-3176
Web: www.chpower.com

CEO: Hilarie Meyer
CFO: Dave Kohlayer
HR: –
FYE: December 31
Type: Subsidiary

Need air-powered tools? You might want to set up camp at Campbell Hausfeld. A manufacturer of powered equipment, Campbell Hausfeld makes air compressors, air tools (air hammers, drills, screwdrivers, grinders, ratchets, valves, hoses, paint spray guns), nailers and staplers, paint sprayers, pressure washers (detergents, cleaners, garden hose attachments), and welders (flux core welders, arc welders). Its products are geared to both the professional and DIY markets. Founded in 1836, the company sells its powered equipment through its Ohio-based headquarters and is a subsidiary of diversified manufacturer The Scott Fetzer Company.

CAMPBELL SOUP COMPANY

NYSE: CPB

1 Campbell Place
Camden, NJ 08103
Phone: 856-342-4800
Fax: 856-342-3878
Web: www.campbellsoup.com

CEO: Douglas R. Conant
CFO: Robert A. (Bob) Schiffner
HR: Nancy A. Reardon
FYE: Sunday nearest July 31
Type: Public

Soup means *M'm! M'm! Money!* for the Campbell Soup Company. The company is the world's biggest soup maker; its almost 70% share in the US is led by Campbell's chicken noodle, tomato, and cream of mushroom soups. The company also makes meal kits, Franco-American sauces and canned pasta, Pace picante sauce, Pepperidge Farm baked goods (yes, the goldfish crackers you sneak at midnight), and V8 beverages. Its Australian division produces snack foods and its popular "down-under" Arnott's biscuit brand. Campbell sold its Godiva Chocolatier business in 2008.

	Annual Growth	7/03	7/04	7/05	7/06	7/07
Sales ($ mil.)	4.2%	6,678.0	7,109.0	7,548.0	7,343.0	7,867.0
Net income ($ mil.)	9.5%	595.0	647.0	707.0	766.0	854.0
Market value ($ mil.)	9.8%	9,786.7	10,440.7	12,586.8	14,781.5	14,208.7
Employees	0.0%	—	—	24,000	24,000	—

CAMPMOR, INC.

400 Corporate Dr.
Mahwah, NJ 07430
Phone: 201-825-8300
Fax: 201-236-3601
Web: www.campmor.com

CEO: Daniel Jarashow
CFO: Anna Chirico
HR: –
FYE: December 31
Type: Private

Campmor takes its name seriously and seriously implores you to take to the outdoors and *camp more*. A leading manufacturer of outdoor apparel and equipment, the company is best known through its catalogs and Web site (campmor.com), though it does operate a single retail store in Paramus, New Jersey. Products include apparel, bicycling equipment, climbing gear, footwear, and more. Campmor also sells bicycles at its bricks-and-mortar store. Founded in 1978 by chairman Morton Jarashow, the company is run by his son, Daniel (president and CEO).

	Annual Growth	12/03	12/04	12/05	12/06	12/07
Est. sales ($ mil.)	—	—	—	—	—	82.9
Employees	—	—	—	—	—	300

CANAAN PARTNERS

2765 Sand Hill Rd.
Menlo Park, CA 94025
Phone: 650-854-8092
Fax: 650-854-8127
Web: www.canaan.com

CEO: Eric A. Young
CFO: Guy M. Russo
HR: –
FYE: December 31
Type: Private

It's the land of milk and honey for start-up companies. Canaan Partners is a venture capital firm that invests primarily in early stage technology and health care companies. Canaan Partners generally invests $4 million to $20 million per investment, at any stage of growth. Notable past investments include Match.com, Advance PCS, and Commerce One; current investments include pharmaceutical developer Amicus Therapeutics and wireless broadband firm Aperto Networks. Canaan Partners has approximately $2.5 billion in capital under management and has invested in more than 250 companies since its founding in 1987.

	Annual Growth	12/03	12/04	12/05	12/06	12/07
Est. sales ($ mil.)	—	—	—	—	—	3.6
Employees	—	—	—	—	—	25

CANAL CAPITAL CORPORATION

OTC: COWP

490 Wheeler Rd., Ste. 185
Hauppauge, NY 11788
Phone: 631-234-0140
Fax: 631-234-0215

CEO: Michael E. Schultz
CFO: Reginald Schauder
HR: –
FYE: October 31
Type: Public

Just as a canal has two different sides, Canal Capital has two different businesses. The company develops, manages, leases, and sells commercial, industrial, and retail real estate in five Midwestern states: Iowa, Minnesota, Missouri, Nebraska, and South Dakota. It develops or sells vacant land and manages properties such as offices, lumber yards, car shops, and meat packing facilities. Capital also operates two public livestock stockyards. The company's stockyard operations (in Missouri and South Dakota) provide exchange markets for a variety of livestock and supplies. Chairman Asher Edelman owns some 44% of Canal Capital.

	Annual Growth	10/03	10/04	10/05	10/06	10/07
Sales ($ mil.)	(6.9%)	4.8	4.2	6.5	4.4	3.6
Net income ($ mil.)	—	(0.5)	(0.6)	0.7	(0.3)	(0.9)
Employees	—	—	—	—	—	—

CANANDAIGUA NATIONAL CORPORATION

OTC: CNND

72 S. Main St.
Canandaigua, NY 14424
Phone: 585-394-4260
Fax: 585-394-4001
Web: www.cnbank.com

CEO: George W. Hamlin IV
CFO: Lawrence A. Heilbronner
HR: Mary Ann M. Ridley
FYE: December 31
Type: Public

Canandaigua National can undoubtedly stake its claim as the holding company for Canandaigua National Bank and Trust, which operates more than 20 branches in the Finger Lakes region of upstate New York. In addition to traditional deposits and loans, the bank also offers online brokerage, insurance, and wealth management services. Its loan portfolio is composed largely of commercial mortgages (nearly 40%) and other business loans (more than 20%). Canandaigua National Bank and Trust also writes consumer loans, business loans, residential mortgages, and other loan types. Genesee Valley Trust, acquired in 2008, provides services including corporate retirement plan management and individual financial planning.

	Annual Growth	12/03	12/04	12/05	12/06	12/07
Assets ($ mil.)	8.5%	907.8	974.8	1,071.8	1,205.9	1,256.3
Net income ($ mil.)	5.0%	10.3	10.6	11.2	11.9	12.5
Market value ($ mil.)	3.6%	—	149.2	144.0	152.1	166.0
Employees	2.1%	355	—	—	—	386

CANBERRA INDUSTRIES, INC.

800 Research Pkwy.
Meriden, CT 06450
Phone: 203-238-2351
Fax: 203-235-1347
Web: www.canberra.com

CEO: Fred Heems
CFO: Jean-Paul Goslin
HR: –
FYE: December 31
Type: Subsidiary

The threat of "dirty bombs" may be bad news for big cities, but not-so-bad news for Canberra Industries, a manufacturer of radiation detection and analysis instrumentation. A business unit of nuclear power generation and electricity transmission and distribution company AREVA, Canberra Industries supplies integrated nuclear gamma and alpha spectroscopy instrumentation for the nuclear power industry. The company also serves industries engaged in fissile material production, environmental monitoring and restoration, and safeguarding special nuclear material. It operates 12 production and engineering facilities in Europe and North America.

	Annual Growth	12/03	12/04	12/05	12/06	12/07
Est. sales ($ mil.)	—	—	—	—	—	43.9
Employees	—	—	—	—	—	500

C&D TECHNOLOGIES, INC.

NYSE: CHP

1400 Union Meeting Rd.
Blue Bell, PA 19422
Phone: 215-619-2700
Fax: 215-619-7899
Web: www.cdtechno.com

CEO: Jeffrey A. (Jeff) Graves
CFO: Ian J. Harvie
HR: Debora M. (Deb) Castle
FYE: January 31
Type: Public

"Power to the people," a popular slogan often shouted in the 1960s, also works for the folks at C&D Technologies. The company makes reserve power systems and batteries, which can be found inside corporate data centers, factories, network operations centers, and nuclear power plants. Typical customers are companies in the cable, electric utility, and telecommunications industries. C&D has divested certain product lines to focus on the reserve power system market. Reserve power systems monitor electrical power usage and provide a source of backup power in the event of power failures and interruptions. C&D Technologies gets more than 85% of its business from US-based customers.

	Annual Growth	1/04	1/05	1/06	1/07	1/08
Sales ($ mil.)	1.6%	324.8	414.7	497.4	524.6	346.1
Net income ($ mil.)	—	14.9	(59.5)	(60.7)	(46.1)	(18.5)
Market value ($ mil.)	(26.4%)	516.6	385.0	211.9	138.5	151.9
Employees	(12.1%)	2,345	2,977	3,065	2,900	1,400

C&D ZODIAC, INC.

5701 Bolsa Ave.
Huntington Beach, CA 92647
Phone: 714-934-0000
Fax: 714-934-0088
Web: zodiac.com

CEO: Tom McFarland
CFO: John Maglione
HR: –
FYE: December 31
Type: Subsidiary

Without companies like C&D Zodiac, air passengers would tumble around in cavernous flying tubes. The company makes the storage bins that people insist on levering trunk-size objects into, the seats from which your invariably large and bathroom-visiting seatmates invade your space, the overhead panels that light your book and keep you cool, the phone-booth-sized lavatories, the oft-maligned (and now seldom-used) galleys, the ceiling panels you pray to in rough weather, and the sidewalls you lean your head against when weary. C&D also makes upgrade and retrofit security kits for cockpit doors. The company is a unit of France-based Zodiac.

	Annual Growth	12/03	12/04	12/05	12/06	12/07
Est. sales ($ mil.)	—	—	—	—	—	460.0
Employees	—	—	—	—	—	4,000

CANDELA CORPORATION

NASDAQ (GS): CLZR

530 Boston Post Rd.
Wayland, MA 01778
Phone: 508-358-7400
Fax: 508-358-5602
Web: www.candelalaser.com

CEO: Gerard E. Puorro
CFO: Robert E. Quinn
HR: Nancy L. Compton
FYE: Saturday nearest June 30
Type: Public

Medical laser maker Candela has the answer to those pesky alcohol-induced tattoos. The firm offers laser systems used for tattoo removal, treatment of dermal abnormalities (age spots, birthmarks), hair removal, and other aesthetic and cosmetic procedures. Products include ALEXLAZR, for removal of lesions and tattoos; Vbeam for vascular lesions and leg and facial veins; Smoothbeam, for treatment of acne and acne scarring; and the Dynamic Cooling Device, which reduces pain by cooling upper layers of the skin during treatment. Candela sells to cosmetic and surgical markets throughout the US and abroad.

	Annual Growth	6/03	6/04	6/05	6/06	6/07
Sales ($ mil.)	16.5%	80.8	104.4	123.9	149.5	148.6
Net income ($ mil.)	(1.9%)	6.8	8.1	7.3	14.9	6.3
Market value ($ mil.)	45.4%	59.5	225.6	247.9	375.3	265.8
Employees	—	—	—	312	—	—

An in-depth profile of this company is available to Hoover's Online members at hoovers.com.

315

C&F FINANCIAL CORPORATION

NASDAQ (GS): CFFI

3600 Lagrange Pkwy.
Toano, VA 23168
Phone: 804-843-2360
Fax: 757-741-2809
Web: www.cffc.com

CEO: Larry G. Dillon
CFO: Thomas F. Cherry
HR: Laura H. Shreaves
FYE: December 31
Type: Public

C&F Financial Corporation is the holding company for C&F Bank (aka Citizens and Farmers Bank), which operates about 20 branches in eastern Virginia. The bank targets individuals and local businesses, offering such products and services as checking and savings accounts, CDs, credit cards, and trust services. Commercial, industrial, and agricultural loans account for the largest portion of the company's loan portfolio (about 40%), which also includes residential mortgages, consumer auto loans, and consumer and construction loans.

	Annual Growth	12/03	12/04	12/05	12/06	12/07
Assets ($ mil.)	8.2%	573.5	609.1	672.0	734.5	785.6
Net income ($ mil.)	(9.9%)	12.9	11.2	11.8	12.1	8.5
Market value ($ mil.)	(10.7%)	143.4	142.8	117.5	126.5	91.3
Employees	5.4%	—	—	461	—	512

C&H SUGAR COMPANY, INC.

830 Loring Ave.
Crockett, CA 94525
Phone: 510-787-2121
Fax: 510-787-1791
Web: www.chsugar.com

CEO: David G. Koncelik
CFO: Robert J. Guilbault
HR: Steve L. Kowalski
FYE: April 30
Type: Private

C&H Sugar's products go hand-in-hand with baked sweets and candy treats. The company processes about 700,000 tons of cane sugar per year. It makes more than 70 types, grades, and package sizes of sugar, including baker's, dark brown, golden brown, powdered, superfine, washed raw, and white granulated. C&H Sugar serves consumer, foodservice, and industrial customers. Its products are processed, packaged, and shipped from the company's refinery in Crockett, California. Founded in 1906 as California and Hawaiian Sugar Refining, the privately held company was acquired by American Sugar Refining in 2005.

C&S WHOLESALE GROCERS, INC.

7 Corporate Dr.
Keene, NH 03431
Phone: 603-354-7000
Fax: 603-354-4690
Web: www.cswg.com

CEO: Richard B. (Rick) Cohen
CFO: Chris Kreidler
HR: Bruce Johnson
FYE: September 30
Type: Private

C&S Wholesale Grocers is at the bottom of the food chain — and likes it that way. The company is New England's largest food wholesaler and second in the US (behind SUPERVALU), delivering groceries to some 5,000 independent supermarkets, major supermarket chains (including Safeway), mass marketers, and wholesale clubs. The company distributes more than 53,000 items, including groceries, produce, and non-food items from its more than 70 distribution centers in a dozen states. Israel Cohen founded C&S Wholesale with Abraham Siegel in 1918. The company is still owned by Cohen's family, led by chairman and CEO Richard Cohen.

	Annual Growth	9/03	9/04	9/05	9/06	9/07
Sales ($ mil.)	9.6%	13,500.0	13,600.0	15,200.0	18,000.0	19,500.0
Employees	17.2%	9,000	12,000	18,000	20,000	17,000

CANEUM, INC.

Pink Sheets: CANM

170 Newport Center Dr., Ste. 220
Newport Beach, CA 92660
Phone: 949-273-4000
Fax: 949-273-4001
Web: www.caneum.com

CEO: Sukhbir Singh (Suki) Mudan
CFO: Sukhbir Singh (Suki) Mudan
HR: –
FYE: December 31
Type: Public

Caneum provides business process and information technology outsourcing (BPO) products and services, including data collection and entry, Web site development and maintenance, call center and customer support, application and systems integration, operational management, and business consulting. Providing its services on-shore and off-shore, the company targets vertical industries including education, energy, financial services, government, health care, technology, and transportation. The company counts Countrywide Financial, DIRECTV, Level 3, and Tenet Healthcare among its customers. The company has operations in the US and India.

	Annual Growth	12/03	12/04	12/05	12/06	12/07
Sales ($ mil.)	187.6%	—	0.5	2.2	7.0	11.9
Net income ($ mil.)	—	—	(1.4)	(1.3)	(2.0)	(3.0)
Employees	—	—	—	—	—	—

CANNONDALE BICYCLE CORPORATION

16 Trowbridge Dr.
Bethel, CT 06801
Phone: 203-749-7000
Fax: 203-748-4012
Web: www.cannondale.com

CEO: Matthew (Matt) Mannelly
CFO: Ron Lombardi
HR: –
FYE: Saturday nearest June 30
Type: Subsidiary

Cannondale's lightweight products are heavyweights in the high-performance bicycle market. It is a leading maker of mountain, road racing, multisport, recreational, and specialty bicycles, most of them with aluminum frames. Cannondale also makes bicycle-related items, such as apparel, accessories, and suspension forks. Cannondale sells some 80 bike models through specialty bike retailers in about 70 countries and co-sponsors bike racing teams to promote its products. It has offices in Canada, Switzerland, Holland, Japan, and Australia. Dorel Industries, juvenile products maker and owner of Pacific Cycle, acquired Cannondale in February 2008.

CANO PETROLEUM, INC.

AMEX: CFW

Burnett Plaza, 801 Cherry St., Unit 25, Ste. 3200
Fort Worth, TX 76102
Phone: 817-698-0900
Fax: 817-698-0796
Web: www.canopetro.com

CEO: S. Jeffrey (Jeff) Johnson
CFO: Morris B. (Sam) Smith
HR: –
FYE: June 30
Type: Public

Cano Petroleum is a "can do" independent crude oil and natural gas production company. The company (named after 16th century Spanish explorer Juan Sebastian del Cano), focuses on buying undervalued mature properties (primarily in Texas and Oklahoma) that still have development potential. Cano employs enhanced oil recovery operations, including water and chemical flooding, infill drilling, and well recompilations, to increase production on these acquired properties. The company has estimated proved reserves of 66.7 million barrels of oil equivalent. CEO Jeff Johnson owns about 4% of Cano; Wellington Management Company owns 12.4%.

	Annual Growth	6/03	6/04	6/05	6/06	6/07
Sales ($ mil.)	—	0.0	0.0	5.5	18.4	28.4
Net income ($ mil.)	—	3.1	(0.4)	(3.0)	(1.8)	(0.8)
Market value ($ mil.)	45.7%	—	63.4	103.7	145.8	196.1
Employees	—	—	—	24	—	—

CANON U.S.A., INC.

1 Canon Plaza
Lake Success, NY 11042
Phone: 516-328-5000
Fax: 516-328-5069
Web: www.usa.canon.com

CEO: Yoroku Adachi
CFO: Masahiro Haga
HR: –
FYE: December 31
Type: Subsidiary

Canon U.S.A. is the US arm of Japanese printer and peripherals giant Canon, accounting for about 30% of the parent company's sales. The company, which operates offices across North, South, and Central America and the Caribbean, specializes in office and consumer imaging equipment including copiers, printers, fax machines, and scanners. Other offerings include image filing systems, calculators, cameras and lenses, video cameras, semiconductor lithography equipment, and medical equipment such as eyecare cameras and radiography systems. Canon U.S.A. was founded in 1966.

CANTEL MEDICAL CORP.

150 Clove Rd., 9th Fl.
Little Falls, NJ 07424
Phone: 973-890-7220
Fax: 973-890-7270
Web: www.cantelmedical.com

NYSE: CMN
CEO: Andrew A. Krakauer
CFO: Craig A. Sheldon
HR: –
FYE: July 31
Type: Public

Cantel Medical can tell you that cleanliness is second to nothing when it comes to medical and scientific equipment. Through its subsidiaries, the firm sells infection prevention and control products to hospitals, dentists, drugmakers, researchers, and others in the health care market. Its offerings include medical device reprocessing systems and disinfectants for dialyzers and endoscopes, water purification equipment, masks and bibs used in dental offices, specialty packaging of biological and pharmaceutical products, and therapeutic filtration systems. Its principal subsidiary Minntech makes dialyzer reprocessing equipment, fluid filtration systems, and the Medivators line of endoscope reprocessing products.

	Annual Growth	7/03	7/04	7/05	7/06	7/07
Sales ($ mil.)	14.1%	129.3	170.0	197.4	192.2	219.0
Net income ($ mil.)	1.5%	7.9	10.6	15.5	23.7	8.4
Market value ($ mil.)	30.5%	80.4	166.9	262.7	221.4	233.4
Employees	0.9%	—	—	828	—	843

CANTERBURY CONSULTING GROUP, INC.

P.O. Box 109
Bordentown, NJ 08055
Phone: 609-298-3500
Fax: 609-298-3590
Web: www.canterburyconsultinggroup.com

CEO: Kevin J. McAndrew
CFO: Kevin J. McAndrew
HR: –
FYE: November 30
Type: Private

Canterbury Consulting Group keeps companies from feeling buried by new technology. The company's CALC/Canterbury subsidiary offers private technical and desktop applications training for software brands such as Adobe, Lotus, and Microsoft. Its Usertech/Canterbury operations provide customized training for enterprise resource planning and customer relations management software such as PeopleSoft, Oracle, and SAP applications. Its MSI/Canterbury subsidiary provides professional training that focuses on management and sales topics. The company went private in 2006.

	Annual Growth	11/03	11/04	11/05	11/06	11/07
Est. sales ($ mil.)	—	—	—	—	—	11.4
Employees	—	—	—	—	—	146

CANTERBURY PARK HOLDING CORPORATION

1100 Canterbury Rd.
Shakopee, MN 55379
Phone: 952-445-7223
Fax: 952-496-6400
Web: www.canterburypark.com

AMEX: ECP
CEO: Randall D. Sampson
CFO: David C. (Dave) Hansen
HR: Mary Fleming
FYE: December 31
Type: Public

The tails of this Canterbury are connected to horses running around a track. Canterbury Park Holding, the operator of the Canterbury Park racetrack in Shakopee, Minnesota, offers live pari-mutuel horse racing from May through September. The racetrack also offers year-round betting on simulcast races from racetracks such as Churchill Downs, Hollywood Park, and Belmont Park. When horses aren't dashing down the track, the company stages other events (snowmobile races, concerts, crafts shows, private parties) at Canterbury Park. Its also offers gambling for card sharks at its on-site Card Club. Chairman Curtis Sampson owns more than 20% of the company.

	Annual Growth	12/03	12/04	12/05	12/06	12/07
Sales ($ mil.)	2.6%	47.8	54.9	55.2	55.8	52.9
Net income ($ mil.)	(2.7%)	2.9	3.9	3.0	3.1	2.6
Market value ($ mil.)	(6.1%)	63.0	77.5	54.8	55.5	49.0
Employees	—	—	—	1,081	—	—

CANTEX, INC.

301 Commerce St., Ste. 2700
Fort Worth, TX 76102
Phone: 817-215-7000
Fax: 817-215-7001
Web: www.cantexinc.com

CEO: Hisayoshi Uno
CFO: Kevin Calcote
HR: Ray Gameson
FYE: March 31
Type: Subsidiary

Cantex is a conduit for PVC products in the utility and construction industries. The company manufactures PVC conduit, pipes, and fittings with electrical, communications, and utility duct applications. In addition to conduit and pipe used to house electrical and telephone wire, Cantex makes such products as couplers, junction boxes, elbows and sweeps (used to change wire direction without damaging the wire), receptacles, and switch covers, as well as the adhesives used to join pipes and connectors. Cantex, which has 10 US manufacturing facilities and three distribution locations, is a subsidiary of Sumitomo.

	Annual Growth	3/03	3/04	3/05	3/06	3/07
Est. sales ($ mil.)	—	—	—	—	—	275.0
Employees	—	—	—	—	—	700

CANTOR FITZGERALD, L.P.

110 E. 59th St.
New York, NY 10022
Phone: 212-938-5000
Fax: 212-829-5280
Web: www.cantor.com

CEO: Howard W. Lutnick
CFO: Douglas R. Barnard
HR: –
FYE: December 31
Type: Private

Although the spotlight on Cantor Fitzgerald has dimmed since the 2001 attacks on New York's World Trade Center, the firm continues to attract attention. One of the largest traders of US Treasuries, Cantor Fitzgerald also deals in equities, derivatives, and foreign stocks. It operates an electronic US Treasury futures exchange, and offers electronic trading of sovereign debt. Cantor Fitzgerald scrapped a plan to take institutional brokerage subsidiary BGC Partners public; its decision to combine that firm with electronic government bond trading platform eSpeed (now named BGC Partners) generated some controversy for Howard Lutnick, who was chairman and CEO of all three firms at the time of the merger in 2008.

	Annual Growth	12/03	12/04	12/05	12/06	12/07
Est. sales ($ mil.)	—	—	—	—	—	97.8
Employees	—	—	—	—	—	1,000

CAPE FEAR BANK CORPORATION

NASDAQ (CM): CAPE

1117 Military Cutoff Rd.
Wilmington, NC 28405
Phone: 910-509-2000
Fax: 910-509-1542
Web: www.capefearbank.com

CEO: Cameron Coburn
CFO: Betty V. Norris
HR: –
FYE: December 31
Type: Public

Cape Fear Bank Corporation doesn't want you to be afraid of losing your money. Instead, the holding company wants you to deposit it in Cape Fear Bank, which serves Wilmington and nearby North Carolina coastal communities through about 10 branches. Formerly Bank of Wilmington, it offers such standard deposit products as checking and savings accounts, CDs, credit cards, and IRAs. Through a partnership with Market Street Advisors it offers financial and wealth management services. Cape Fear Bank is mainly a real estate lender, with construction, commercial real estate, and residential mortgage loans making up about 95% of its portfolio. It also writes business and consumer loans and lines of credit.

	Annual Growth	12/03	12/04	12/05	12/06	12/07
Assets ($ mil.)	16.3%	—	—	343.3	424.9	464.3
Net income ($ mil.)	(12.6%)	—	—	1.7	2.3	1.3
Market value ($ mil.)	13.8%	—	—	33.6	37.9	43.5
Employees	32.0%	—	—	62	—	108

CAPELLA EDUCATION COMPANY

NASDAQ (GM): CPLA

225 S. 6th St., 9th Fl.
Minneapolis, MN 55402
Phone: 612-339-8650
Fax: 612-977-5060
Web: www.capellauniversity.edu

CEO: Stephen G. (Steve) Shank
CFO: Lois M. Martin
HR: Sally B. Chial
FYE: December 31
Type: Public

At Capella Education, the line to receive your cap and gown is *online*. The fast-growing company operates Capella University, an online university that offers undergraduate and graduate degree programs in business, organization and management, public safety, education, psychology, human services, and information technology. More than 22,000 students are enrolled in the school, which employs more than 1,000 faculty members (most of which are part-time employees, typically teaching one to three courses per semester). Students seeking master's or doctoral degrees account for more than 80% of enrollment. Some 75% of revenues stem from federal student financial aid programs.

	Annual Growth	12/03	12/04	12/05	12/06	12/07
Sales ($ mil.)	29.0%	81.8	117.7	149.2	179.9	226.2
Net income ($ mil.)	50.9%	4.4	18.8	10.3	13.4	22.8
Market value ($ mil.)	192.9%	—	—	—	388.0	1,136.6
Employees	23.5%	—	—	—	1,787	2,207

CAPGEMINI U.S.

623 Fifth Ave., 33rd Fl.
New York, NY 10022
Phone: 212-314-8000
Fax: 212-314-8012
Web: www.us.capgemini.com

CEO: Salil Parekh
CFO: Thierry Delaporte
HR: –
FYE: December 31
Type: Subsidiary

Vive la technologie! Capgemini U.S. oversees the North American operations of Paris-based consulting giant Capgemini. The subsidiary offers management and IT consulting services, systems integration, technology development design, and outsourcing services through offices in about two dozen states. Its consultants serve clients in a variety of industries, including automotive, energy and utilities, financial services, high-tech, manufacturing, and transportation. The unit was formed in 2000 after Cap Gemini acquired the consulting arm of accounting giant Ernst & Young.

CAPITAL ALLIANCE INCOME TRUST LTD.

AMEX: CAA

100 Pine St., Ste. 2450
San Francisco, CA 94111
Phone: 415-288-9595
Fax: 415-288-9590
Web: www.caitreit.com

CEO: Richard J. Wrensen
CFO: Richard J. Wrensen
HR: –
FYE: December 31
Type: Public

Capital Alliance Income Trust is a real estate investment trust (REIT) focused on loans rather than properties. It invests in non-conforming first and second home mortgages and home equity loans collateralized mainly by properties in California. Its portfolio consists primarily of loans that do not meet the purchasing standards set by Fannie Mae and other government housing enterprises. Its mortgage conduit business unit, operated through subsidiary Capital Alliance Funding, originates, buys, and sells single-family residential mortgage loans. The REIT's warehouse lending unit provides warehouse financing to its subsidiaries and affiliates.

	Annual Growth	12/03	12/04	12/05	12/06	12/07
Sales ($ mil.)	(19.3%)	2.6	2.1	3.8	2.5	1.1
Net income ($ mil.)	—	0.9	0.7	(0.3)	(1.6)	(2.9)
Market value ($ mil.)	(31.5%)	9.2	7.0	3.7	4.1	2.0
Employees	—	—	—	—	—	—

CAPITAL AUTOMOTIVE REAL ESTATE SERVICES, INC.

8270 Greensboro Dr., Ste. 950
McLean, VA 22102
Phone: 703-288-3075
Fax: 703-288-3375
Web: www.capitalautomotive.com

CEO: Thomas D. Eckert
CFO: David S. Kay
HR: –
FYE: December 31
Type: Private

Car dealerships are a feather in the cap of Capital Automotive Real Estate Services (formerly Capital Automotive REIT), better known as CARS. The real estate investment trust invests in properties used by automobile dealerships and other automobile-related businesses. The company usually buys the property of existing multi-franchised dealerships and then leases it back to the operator on a triple-net basis for 15 to 20 years. CARS owns properties in nearly 35 states and Canada; most are in major cities. The properties include more than 500 automobile franchises representing some 45 major brands of automobiles. CARS was acquired in 2005 by clients of DRA Advisors for a reported $3.4 billion.

	Annual Growth	12/03	12/04	12/05	12/06	12/07
Est. sales ($ mil.)	—	—	—	—	—	201.9
Employees	—	—	—	—	—	33

CAPITAL BANK CORPORATION

NASDAQ (GS): CBKN

333 Fayetteville, Ste. 700
Raleigh, NC 27601
Phone: 919-645-6400
Fax: 919-645-6435
Web: www.capitalbank-nc.com

CEO: B. Grant Yarber
CFO: Michael R. Moore
HR: Teresa White
FYE: December 31
Type: Public

Capital Bank Corporation is the holding company for Capital Bank, which capitalizes on the bustling Research Triangle area it serves. Founded in 1997, the bank has about 30 offices in central and western North Carolina. It provides a range of consumer and commercial banking services, including savings, checking, and money market accounts, as well as CDs, IRAs, and credit cards. Commercial loans, made primarily to small and midsized businesses, make up nearly 60% of the bank's loan portfolio; construction loans are around 25%. The bank also issues mortgages, home equity lines, and consumer loans. Its Capital Bank Financial Services group offers investment products and services.

	Annual Growth	12/03	12/04	12/05	12/06	12/07
Assets ($ mil.)	15.3%	857.7	882.3	960.9	1,422.4	1,517.6
Net income ($ mil.)	67.7%	1.0	5.3	6.7	12.3	7.9
Market value ($ mil.)	3.9%	101.3	121.4	180.1	197.5	117.8
Employees	6.9%	—	—	295	332	337

CAPITAL BLUECROSS

2500 Elmerton Ave.
Harrisburg, PA 17177
Phone: 717-541-7000
Fax: 717-541-6915
Web: www.capbluecross.com

CEO: Anita M. Smith
CFO: –
HR: Debra B. Cohen
FYE: December 31
Type: Not-for-profit

A licensee of the Blue Cross and Blue Shield Association, Capital BlueCross provides a variety of health insurance products to individuals and employer groups, with a total of nearly 1 million members in some 20 central Pennsylvania counties. The company offers traditional, PPO, HMO, and POS health care plans, as well as dental and vision coverage and Medicare Advantage plans. Its network includes more than 8,300 health care providers and nearly 40 hospitals. Capital BlueCross operates from offices in Allentown and Harrisburg, Pennsylvania. The company also provides benefits administration services to self-funded customers through subsidiary Capital Administrative Services (dba NCAS Pennsylvania).

	Annual Growth	12/03	12/04	12/05	12/06	12/07
Est. sales ($ mil.)	—	—	—	—	—	1,840.1
Employees	—	—	—	—	—	2,085

THE CAPITAL GROUP COMPANIES, INC.

333 S. Hope St., 53rd Fl.
Los Angeles, CA 90071
Phone: 213-486-9200
Fax: 213-486-9217
Web: www.capgroup.com

CEO: Philip de Toledo
CFO: Jim Brown
HR: –
FYE: June 30
Type: Private

If asset management companies were described like potential romantic partners in lonely hearts ads, The Capital Group Companies would definitely be marriage material. The mutual fund firm, founded in 1929, is quiet (they don't advertise or grant many interviews), conservative (known for consistent performance), and faithful (most of its investments and its executives are long-term). Among its dislikes are hierarchy, star traders, and fads. Subsidiary Capital Research and Management manages The American Funds, a family of about 30 mutual funds that ranks among the largest groups of mutual funds by assets in the US.

	Annual Growth	6/02	6/03	6/04	6/05	6/06
Est. sales ($ mil.)	41.7%	—	—	5,600.0	9,246.0	11,250.0
Employees	22.5%	—	—	6,000	8,000	9,000

CAPITAL CITY BANK GROUP, INC.

NASDAQ (GS): CCBG

217 N. Monroe St.
Tallahassee, FL 32301
Phone: 850-402-7000
Fax: 850-878-9150
Web: www.ccbg.com

CEO: William G. Smith Jr.
CFO: J. Kimbrough Davis
HR: Flecia Braswell
FYE: December 31
Type: Public

Capital City Bank Group is the holding company for Capital City Bank, which serves individuals and businesses from some 70 branches in northern Florida, plus portions of Alabama and Georgia. It offers checking, savings, money market, and NOW accounts; CDs; Internet banking; and debit and credit cards. Residential real estate mortgages account for about 35% of its loan portfolio; commercial real estate chips in about one-third. Capital City also offers trust and brokerage services, investment management, retirement plans, data processing for financial institutions, and life and long-term care insurance. President and CEO William Smith Jr. and his brother Robert own about 30% of the company.

	Annual Growth	12/03	12/04	12/05	12/06	12/07
Assets ($ mil.)	9.1%	1,846.5	2,364.0	2,625.5	2,597.9	2,616.3
Net income ($ mil.)	4.2%	25.2	29.4	30.3	33.3	29.7
Market value ($ mil.)	(0.1%)	487.0	473.4	638.9	653.7	484.9
Employees	—	—	—	1,013		

CAPITAL MERCURY APPAREL, LTD.

1359 Broadway, 19th Fl.
New York, NY 10018
Phone: 212-704-4800
Fax: 212-704-4830
Web: www.billblasspremium.com

CEO: John C. Higdon
CFO: –
HR: Cindy Young
FYE: June 30
Type: Private

Capital Mercury Apparel is playing the name game. Traditionally a maker of uniforms and private-label clothing, the employee-owned company has shifted toward more upscale, branded merchandise. Capital Mercury makes a variety of men's clothing, including shirts, sweaters, dress wear, swimwear, and sportswear. Its Robert Stock and Bill Blass brands are sold in department stores. The firm also manufactures other labels for Wal-Mart stores. Agreements with designer menswear labels Robert Stock and Wilke-Rodriguez — as well as a deal struck with Jones Apparel Group — brought the company upscale licensing deals.

	Annual Growth	6/03	6/04	6/05	6/06	6/07
Est. sales ($ mil.)	—	—	—	—	—	64.9
Employees	—	—	—	—	—	2,100

CAPITAL CORP OF THE WEST

NASDAQ (GS): CCOW

550 W. Main
Merced, CA 95340
Phone: 209-725-2269
Fax: 209-725-4550
Web: www.ccow.com

CEO: Thomas T. (Tom) Hawker
CFO: David A. Heaberlin
HR: –
FYE: December 31
Type: Public

Capital Corp of the West counts on County Bank for its capital. The holding company owns County Bank, which has more than 40 branches in California's Central Valley. Serving individuals and small to midsized businesses, the bank offers standard retail products such as savings, checking, and money market accounts, IRAs, and CDs. Real estate mortgages account for roughly half of the bank's lending portfolio, which also includes business and agricultural loans, construction loans, and consumer installment loans. In 2007 the company branched into the factoring business by acquiring Bay View Funding, which has five business development offices nationwide.

	Annual Growth	12/03	12/04	12/05	12/06	12/07
Assets ($ mil.)	14.3%	1,234.5	1,447.8	1,756.8	1,961.5	2,108.7
Net income ($ mil.)	—	13.6	12.3	21.0	22.7	(3.6)
Market value ($ mil.)	14.0%	124.3	151.3	343.2	345.8	209.9
Employees	20.7%	—	—	370	421	539

⊞ CAPITAL ONE FINANCIAL CORPORATION

NYSE: COF

1680 Capital One Dr.
McLean, VA 22102
Phone: 703-720-1000
Fax: 703-205-1755
Web: www.capitalone.com

CEO: Richard D. (Rich) Fairbank
CFO: Gary L. Perlin
HR: Matthew W. (Matt) Schuyler
FYE: December 31
Type: Public

What's in your mailbox? Probably an offer from Capital One. One of the top credit card issuers in the US, Capital One offers Visa and MasterCard plastic with a variety of rates, credit limits, finance charges, and fees. Products range from platinum and gold cards for preferred customers to secured and unsecured cards for customers with poor or limited credit histories. The company, which boasts some 50 million customer accounts, also provides auto financing, credit insurance, and other consumer lending products. It has banking operations in the Northeast and the South, and is one of the largest bank holding companies in the US with some 500 branches. The company also has operations in Canada and the UK.

	Annual Growth	12/03	12/04	12/05	12/06	12/07
Assets ($ mil.)	34.3%	46,283.7	53,747.3	88,701.4	149,739.3	150,590.4
Net income ($ mil.)	8.4%	1,135.8	1,543.5	1,809.2	2,414.5	1,570.3
Market value ($ mil.)	5.2%	14,405.7	20,815.3	26,015.6	31,490.5	17,621.1
Employees	(7.9%)	—	—	21,000	31,800	17,800

⊞ An in-depth profile of this company is available to Hoover's Online members at hoovers.com.

319

CAPITAL PACIFIC HOLDINGS, INC.

4100 MacArthur Blvd., Ste. 150
Newport Beach, CA 92660
Phone: 949-622-8400
Fax: 949-622-8404
Web: www.capitalpacifichomes.com/corp

CEO: Hadi Makarechian
CFO: Matthew C. Kern
HR: Sherry S . Irani
FYE: February 28
Type: Private

Real estate developer Capital Pacific Holdings (CPH) builds single-family homes for entry-level, move-up, and luxury buyers through its Capital Pacific Homes subsidiary. CPH builds in California, Arizona, Colorado, and Texas. Its homes range in price from $180,000 to more than $1 million. CPH builds, decorates, furnishes, and landscapes model homes for its projects and maintains on-site sales offices. Acting as general contractor, CPH subcontracts its construction jobs. CPH also operates Makar Properties LLC (mixed-use land development) and offers mortgage brokering services.

CAPITAL PROPERTIES, INC.

AMEX: CPI

100 Dexter Rd.
East Providence, RI 02914
Phone: 401-435-7171
Fax: 401-435-7179

CEO: Robert H. Eder
CFO: Barbara J. Dreyer
HR: –
FYE: December 31
Type: Public

Was it providence or clear foresight that led Capital Properties to buy land in what is now Capital Center, a downtown revitalization project in Providence, Rhode Island? The company owns and leases out about a dozen parcels of land totaling some 18 acres in the project area, making it Capital Center's largest land owner. Subsidiaries of Capital Properties own and operate a petroleum storage facility in East Providence used by Global Partners, and lease land to Lamar Advertising for roadside billboards in Rhode Island and Massachusetts.

	Annual Growth	12/03	12/04	12/05	12/06	12/07
Sales ($ mil.)	(0.7%)	6.9	7.1	6.5	5.8	6.7
Net income ($ mil.)	11.7%	0.9	1.6	1.7	1.3	1.4
Market value ($ mil.)	19.6%	38.3	—	92.2	79.3	78.2
Employees	(55.3%)	—	—	10	—	2

CAPITAL SENIOR LIVING CORPORATION

NYSE: CSU

14160 Dallas Pkwy., Ste. 300
Dallas, TX 75254
Phone: 972-770-5600
Fax: 972-770-5666
Web: www.capitalsenior.com

CEO: Lawrence A. Cohen
CFO: Ralph A. Beattie
HR: Colleen Landino
FYE: December 31
Type: Public

Capital Senior Living wants to capitalize on the growing numbers of seniors in the US. The company owns or manages about 65 senior residential properties in more than 20 states scattered across the country. Formed to consolidate the operations of several partnerships that previously owned its facilities, the company provides independent living, assisted living, and skilled nursing services. Capital Senior Living also operates a home health care agency that manages the health care needs of residents at one of its communities. Specialized care units for treatment of Alzheimer's patients are also available. Private pay sources comprise about 95% of the company's revenue.

	Annual Growth	12/03	12/04	12/05	12/06	12/07
Sales ($ mil.)	30.0%	66.3	93.3	105.2	159.1	189.1
Net income ($ mil.)	(3.1%)	5.0	(6.8)	(5.3)	(2.6)	4.4
Market value ($ mil.)	22.7%	116.7	145.8	271.8	281.2	264.1
Employees	—	—	—	2,867	—	—

CAPITAL SOUTHWEST CORPORATION

NASDAQ (GM): CSWC

12900 Preston Rd., Ste. 700
Dallas, TX 75230
Phone: 972-233-8242
Fax: 972-233-7362
Web: www.capitalsouthwest.com

CEO: Gary L. Martin
CFO: Tracy L. Morris
HR: –
FYE: March 31
Type: Public

Just don't call them a private equity company. Capital Southwest owns significant stakes in around 20 companies, many of them in Texas. The firm offers early-stage, mezzanine, and recapitalization financing, as well as funding for management buyouts to companies involved in a variety of industries. It invests anywhere from $2 million to $20 million in target companies, which do not include troubled companies, startups, oil & gas exploration companies, or other less than stable ventures. Its 12 largest holdings, including Heelys, Alamo Group, Hologic, and Palm Harbor Homes, account for more than 90% of the value of its investment portfolio.

	Annual Growth	3/04	3/05	3/06	3/07	3/08
Sales ($ mil.)	10.5%	4.7	22.7	98.6	169.6	7.0
Net income ($ mil.)	—	85.5	14.2	96.2	166.9	(139.0)
Market value ($ mil.)	13.4%	291.1	305.1	368.7	597.2	481.2
Employees	0.0%	—	—	7	7	—

CAPITAL TRUST, INC.

NYSE: CT

410 Park Ave., 14th Fl.
New York, NY 10022
Phone: 212-655-0220
Fax: 212-655-0044
Web: www.capitaltrust.com

CEO: John R. Klopp
CFO: Geoffrey G. Jervis
HR: –
FYE: December 31
Type: Public

Capital Trust originates, underwrites, and invests in commercial real estate. The real estate investment trust (REIT) focuses on mezzanine loans, collateralized mortgage-backed securities, and first mortgages secured by office, retail, hotel, multifamily, and mixed-use properties throughout the US. Its CT Investment Management subsidiary manages four private equity funds and a separate account for third parties. As of 2007, Global Realty Outsourcing, Inc., provides consulting services to Capital Trust, which has financed some $10 billion worth of loans since its founding in 1997; it made some $2.5 billion in loans during 2007.

	Annual Growth	12/03	12/04	12/05	12/06	12/07
Sales ($ mil.)	21.0%	47.8	57.2	104.8	76.6	102.5
Net income ($ mil.)	58.1%	13.5	22.0	44.1	54.1	84.4
Market value ($ mil.)	37.2%	148.5	453.6	435.4	845.6	526.1
Employees	—	—	—	28	—	—

CAPITALSOURCE INC.

NYSE: CSE

4445 Willard Ave., 12th Fl.
Chevy Chase, MD 20815
Phone: 301-841-2700
Fax: 301-841-2340
Web: www.capitalsource.com

CEO: John K. Delaney
CFO: Thomas A. Fink
HR: –
FYE: December 31
Type: Public

CapitalSource is a, well, capital source for both business loans and residential mortgage funds. The real estate investment trust (REIT) has segments devoted to commercial finance, health care leasing, and residential mortgage investing. Its commercial lending arm provides tailored financing and lending products to middle-market businesses. Its health care unit provides lease financing to skilled-nursing facilities and invests in long-term care facilities. The residential mortgage division invests in home loans backed by Fannie Mae or Freddie Mac.

	Annual Growth	12/03	12/04	12/05	12/06	12/07
Assets ($ mil.)	62.8%	2,567.1	4,736.8	6,987.1	15,210.6	18,040.3
Net income ($ mil.)	13.1%	107.8	124.8	164.7	279.3	176.3
Market value ($ mil.)	10.8%	2,575.2	3,027.2	3,145.1	4,955.5	3,882.2
Employees	4.0%	—	—	520	548	562

CAPITALSOUTH BANCORP

NASDAQ (GM): CAPB

2340 Woodcrest Place, Ste. 200
Birmingham, AL 35209
Phone: 205-870-1939
Fax: 205-879-3885
Web: www.capitalsouthbank.com

CEO: W. Dan Puckett
CFO: Carol W. Marsh
HR: —
FYE: December 31
Type: Public

CapitalSouth Bancorp is the holding company for CapitalSouth Bank, which operates about a dozen branches in the metropolitan areas of Birmingham, Huntsville, and Montgomery, Alabama, and Jacksonville, Florida. It also has two loan production offices in Georgia. The bank offers standard deposit products and services, including checking and savings accounts, money market accounts, and CDs. It focuses on real estate lending: Residential and commercial mortgages together account for about half of the company's loan portfolio. Other offerings include construction, business, and consumer loans.

	Annual Growth	12/03	12/04	12/05	12/06	12/07
Assets ($ mil.)	27.2%	293.3	337.7	423.5	482.0	767.5
Net income ($ mil.)	—	1.5	1.9	2.6	2.9	(15.3)
Market value ($ mil.)	(15.1%)	—	—	52.2	56.5	37.7
Employees	9.6%	—	—	124	124	149

CAPITOL BANCORP LTD.

NYSE: CBC

Capitol Bancorp Center, 200 Washington Sq. North
Lansing, MI 48933
Phone: 517-487-6555
Fax: 517-374-2576
Web: www.capitolbancorp.com

CEO: Joseph D. Reid
CFO: Lee W. Hendrickson
HR: Stephanie Maat
FYE: December 31
Type: Public

Most holding companies raise money and *keep* it in banks: Capitol Bancorp raises banks. The company, which owns the most bank charters in the US, has a network of more than 60 community banks (many of them start-ups) in more than 15 states. Most of the banks have only one location and are run locally. Banking services target local business customers and high net-worth individuals, offering such services as checking and savings accounts, certificates of deposit, mortgages, consumer loans, and trust and investment services. Commercial loans make up about 45% of the company's total loan portfolio. Subsidiary Capitol Wealth offers wealth management services.

	Annual Growth	12/03	12/04	12/05	12/06	12/07
Assets ($ mil.)	15.7%	2,737.1	3,091.4	3,475.7	4,065.8	4,901.8
Net income ($ mil.)	(1.6%)	23.4	26.7	35.9	42.4	21.9
Market value ($ mil.)	(3.3%)	398.4	522.3	590.7	769.5	348.4
Employees	—	—	—	—	—	1,611

CAPITOL FEDERAL FINANCIAL

NASDAQ (GS): CFFN

700 S. Kansas Ave.
Topeka, KS 66603
Phone: 785-235-1341
Fax: 785-231-6264
Web: www.capfed.com

CEO: John B. Dicus
CFO: Kent G. Townsend
HR: —
FYE: September 30
Type: Public

Dorothy and Toto may not be in Kansas anymore, but Capitol Federal Financial is. The holding company owns Capitol Federal Savings Bank, a thrift that serves metropolitan areas throughout the Sunflower State, including Kansas City, Emporia, Lawrence, Manhattan, Salina, Topeka, and Wichita. It has nearly 40 branches serving consumers and commercial customers by offering loans, CDs, and money market, checking, and savings accounts. The thrift mainly originates one- to four-family home mortgages (almost 95% of its loan portfolio), but it also writes consumer, construction, and other real estate loans.

	Annual Growth	9/03	9/04	9/05	9/06	9/07
Assets ($ mil.)	(2.8%)	8,582.5	8,541.0	8,409.7	8,199.1	7,675.9
Net income ($ mil.)	(11.2%)	52.0	(106.3)	65.1	48.1	32.3
Market value ($ mil.)	4.3%	2,148.7	2,381.0	2,542.1	2,632.6	2,539.7
Employees	(0.2%)	—	—	761	—	758

THE CAPITOL MUSIC GROUP

150 5th Ave.
New York, NY 10010
Phone: 212-786-8200
Fax: 212-786-8343
Web: www.virginrecords.com

CEO: Jason Flom
CFO: Colin Finkelstein
HR: Seth Wolk
FYE: March 31
Type: Business segment

This record label wants to be your first — and last — stop for popular music. Capital Music Group is the home of two of the top pop labels in the US — Capital and Virgin — producing music from such artists as Coldplay, Janet Jackson, Lenny Kravitz, and the Rolling Stones. Its roster of R&B and hip-hop artists includes Faith Evans, the Beastie Boys, and Jermaine Dupri. Capitol Music Group operates as part of major label EMI Group. The company was formed in 2007 by EMI to house the operations of its Virgin Records America and Virgin's sister label Capitol Records. Capitol and Virgin run as "imprints" under the North American unit of EMI Music.

	Annual Growth	3/03	3/04	3/05	3/06	3/07
Est. sales ($ mil.)	—	—	—	—	—	31.8
Employees	—	—	—	—	—	268

CAPITOL RECORDS, INC.

1750 N. Vine St.
Los Angeles, CA 90028
Phone: 323-462-6252
Fax: 323-467-5267
Web: www.capitolrecords.com

CEO: Jason Flom
CFO: Justin Morris
HR: —
FYE: March 31
Type: Subsidiary

This capitol rules over a music nation. Capitol Records is one of the leading recording labels in the US, sporting a talent roster that includes such pop artists as the Beastie Boys, Coldplay, Faith Evans, Shelby Lynne, and the Shout Out Louds. The label also distributes R&B and hip-hop albums through its Priority Records imprint, which boasts such top sellers as Ice Cube, Nelly, and Snoop Dogg, as well as newer artists such as Chingy, Houston, and Slum Village. The label is part of UK-based music giant EMI Group. It operates as part of EMI's Capitol Music Group, alongside the US operations of sister label Virgin Records.

	Annual Growth	3/03	3/04	3/05	3/06	3/07
Est. sales ($ mil.)	—	—	—	—	—	268.0
Employees	—	—	—	—	—	2,200

CAPLEASE, INC.

NYSE: LSE

1065 Avenue of the Americas
New York, NY 10018
Phone: 212-217-6300
Fax: 212-217-6301
Web: www.caplease.com

CEO: Paul H. McDowell
CFO: Shawn P. Seale
HR: Mary Kay Downey
FYE: December 31
Type: Public

CapLease prefers the net lease. Its tenants take care of their own utilities, taxes, insurance, and maintenance, while the real estate investment trust (REIT) can focus on money matters, such as property and loan investments. CapLease typically invests in single-tenant commercial (office, retail, industrial) properties in the metropolitan areas of Chicago, Dallas, New York City, Philadelphia, and Washington, DC. Its portfolio includes more than 60 properties in 26 states. The US government and Nestle Holdings account for about 10% apiece of the company's total revenue. Hotchkis and Wiley Capital Management, LLC owns a 10% interest in CapLease.

	Annual Growth	12/03	12/04	12/05	12/06	12/07
Sales ($ mil.)	73.3%	19.1	21.0	73.1	124.8	172.2
Net income ($ mil.)	—	6.6	1.4	5.1	7.3	(2.3)
Market value ($ mil.)	2.8%	—	343.6	293.5	395.5	373.4
Employees	2.4%	—	—	21	21	22

An in-depth profile of this company is available to Hoover's Online members at hoovers.com.

321

CAPMARK FINANCIAL GROUP INC.

411 Borel Ave., Ste. 320
San Mateo, CA 94402
Phone: 650-572-6600
Fax: 650-572-6634
Web: www.capmark.com

CEO: William F. (Bill) Aldinger III
CFO: Gregory J. McManus
HR: –
FYE: December 31
Type: Private

Commercial mortgages are the feather in Capmark Financial's cap. The company originates, services, and invests in mortgages for commercial real estate including retail, office, health care, hospitality, and multifamily properties. It also invests in real estate-related assets for institutional and high-net-worth investors. Capmark Financial has some 55 offices in North America, Europe, and Asia. The company originates more than $20 billion in commercial mortgages each year and its servicing portfolio is worth more than $300 billion. The investment business has more than $10.3 billion in assets under management.

	Annual Growth	12/03	12/04	12/05	12/06	12/07
Est. sales ($ mil.)	—	—	—	—	—	213.7
Employees	—	—	—	—	—	3,000

CAPRIUS, INC.

OTC: CAPS

1 University Plaza, Ste. 400
Hackensack, NJ 07601
Phone: 201-342-0900
Fax: 201-342-0991
Web: www.caprius.com

CEO: Dwight Morgan
CFO: Jonathan Joels
HR: –
FYE: September 30
Type: Public

Caprius helps doctors take out the trash. The company owns a majority interest in MCM Environmental Technologies, which provides systems for disposal of medical waste. Its SteriMed system can crush, grind, shred, and mix all types of medical waste, including metal sharps and needles, plastic tubing and IV bags, and glass items. Once this process is complete, MCM's Steri-Cid chemical process disinfects the waste, which can then be discarded as regular waste at as little as 10% of the original volume. MCM manufactures the SteriMed system in Israel; the company distributes parts and supplies from facilities in Israel. Investors Austin W. Marxe and David M. Greenhouse own a 55% stake in Caprius.

	Annual Growth	9/03	9/04	9/05	9/06	9/07
Sales ($ mil.)	45.6%	0.6	0.9	0.9	1.2	2.7
Net income ($ mil.)	—	(0.3)	(3.4)	(2.5)	(3.4)	(3.3)
Market value ($ mil.)	(61.6%)	—	45.0	8.0	2.2	2.5
Employees	(1.2%)	21	20	15	19	20

CAPROCK COMMUNICATIONS, INC.

4400 S. Sam Houston Pkwy. East
Houston, TX 77048
Phone: 832-668-2300
Fax: 832-668-2388
Web: www.caprock.com

CEO: Peter Shaper
CFO: James J. Davis
HR: Mark S. Esselman
FYE: December 31
Type: Private

CapRock Communications (formerly IWL Communications) provides satellite communications services where others fear to tread. The company offers secure voice, data, fax, and video conferencing services primarily to customers that operate in remote locations and/or harsh environments. It maintains and operates its own global communications network in cooperation with various satellite fleet operators. CapRock offers standard "off the shelf" services or it can custom develop networks to meet a customer's needs. Clients come from such industries as construction, maritime, military, mining, and oil and gas exploration. The company was founded in 1981 as IWL Communications.

	Annual Growth	12/02	12/03	12/04	12/05	12/06
Sales ($ mil.)	26.7%	46.2	50.6	91.0	104.0	119.0
Employees	28.9%	—	210	388	392	450

CAPSTEAD MORTGAGE CORPORATION

NYSE: CMO

8401 N. Central Expwy., Ste. 800
Dallas, TX 75225
Phone: 214-874-2323
Fax: 214-874-2398
Web: www.capstead.com

CEO: Andrew F. Jacobs
CFO: Phillip A. Reinsch
HR: –
FYE: December 31
Type: Public

Capstead Mortgage is holding steady in a turbulent real estate market. To stay the course, this company's strategy is to make real estate-related investments that produce returns over the long haul, with minimal sensitivity to interest rate fluctuations. The self-managed real estate investment trust (REIT) invests in single-family residential adjustable-rate mortgage securities (ARMs) issued by government agencies Fannie Mae, Freddie Mac, and Ginnie Mae; it has also held limited investments in credit-sensitive commercial mortgage assets. Capstead Mortgage was established in 1985.

	Annual Growth	12/03	12/04	12/05	12/06	12/07
Sales ($ mil.)	24.7%	129.5	102.1	131.4	243.4	312.9
Net income ($ mil.)	(20.1%)	60.7	41.8	57.2	3.8	24.7
Market value ($ mil.)	23.0%	235.2	198.9	110.6	159.8	538.4
Employees	11.8%	—	—	12	—	15

CAPSTONE TURBINE CORPORATION

NASDAQ (GM): CPST

21211 Nordhoff St.
Chatsworth, CA 91311
Phone: 818-734-5300
Fax: 818-734-5320
Web: www.microturbine.com

CEO: Darren R. Jamison
CFO: Edward Reich
HR: Larry N. Colson
FYE: March 31
Type: Public

Capstone Turbine's theme song could be "My Generation." The company makes the Capstone MicroTurbine, a power-generating system that produces environmentally friendly electricity and heat. The microturbines, which can operate on a stand-alone basis or connected to the utility grid, run on a variety of liquid and gaseous fuels, such as natural gas, diesel, kerosene, propane, and flare gases from landfills and sewage plants. Capstone markets its microturbines for use in cogeneration (using both electricity and heat), resource recovery (burning oil and gas production by-products), backup power supply, and remote power applications. Customers located in the US make up about one-third of sales.

	Annual Growth	3/04	3/05	3/06	3/07	3/08
Sales ($ mil.)	25.5%	12.6	17.0	24.1	21.0	31.3
Net income ($ mil.)	—	(47.7)	(39.5)	(47.1)	(36.7)	(36.1)
Market value ($ mil.)	10.7%	208.7	131.5	374.8	152.6	312.9
Employees	1.7%	202	225	243	195	216

CAPTAIN D'S, LLC

1717 Elm Hill Pike, Ste. A-1
Nashville, TN 37210
Phone: 615-391-5461
Fax: 615-231-2309
Web: www.captainds.com

CEO: David W. Head
CFO: Michael (Mike) Payne
HR: –
FYE: October 31
Type: Private

This Captain is hardly a proponent of catch and release. Captain D's is a leading quick-service seafood chain with more than 600 locations in two dozen states, primarily in the South. The chain's menu features fried and broiled fish, shrimp, and chicken, as well as French fries, hush puppies, and corn on the cob. Captain D's also serves fish and chicken sandwiches, salads, and menu items for kids. Ray Danner started the business as Mr. D's in 1969. Today, the chain is owned by Sagittarius Brands, a restaurant development company backed by equity firms Charlesbank Capital Partners and Grotech Capital Group.

CAPTARIS, INC.

NASDAQ (GM): CAPA

301 116th Ave. SE, Ste. 400
Bellevue, WA 98004
Phone: 425-455-6000
Fax: 425-638-1500
Web: www.captaris.com

CEO: David P. Anastasi
CFO: Peter Papano
HR: –
FYE: December 31
Type: Public

Captaris believes one should never spend time trying to guess if that fax went through. The company's software is used to manage a variety of enterprise content, including delivering large volumes of faxes and documents electronically via desktop applications such as customer relationship management, e-mail, and imaging. Captaris also offers a business process automation platform used for collaboration, productivity, and accountability purposes as well as applications for archiving and managing documents and images. Customers have included Burger King, Verizon, Microsoft, Costco, and Telus.

	Annual Growth	12/03	12/04	12/05	12/06	12/07
Sales ($ mil.)	3.3%	83.3	78.0	86.4	92.0	94.8
Net income ($ mil.)	(64.4%)	12.5	0.1	(4.0)	4.0	0.2
Market value ($ mil.)	(11.0%)	181.9	152.1	104.7	214.1	114.3
Employees	2.9%	—	413	394	399	450

CAR TOYS, INC.

20 W. Galer St.
Seattle, WA 98119
Phone: 206-443-0980
Fax: 206-443-2525
Web: www.cartoys.com

CEO: Daniel Brettler
CFO: Robert (Rob) Jensen
HR: Jan Fitzgerald
FYE: December 31
Type: Private

When you grow out of toy cars, you will find Car Toys. Car Toys sells car audio components and systems, security systems, navigation systems, radar detectors, wireless phones, and phone plans. The company sells its products at about 50 retail locations in Colorado, Oregon, Texas, and Washington, as well as through its Web site. Car Toys stores carry such brands as Alpine, Audiovox, JBL, Motorola, Panasonic, Pioneer, T-Mobile, and Verizon Wireless. As well as selling electronics, Car Toys stores offer advice and installation. CEO and president Dan Brettler founded the company in Bellevue, Washington, in 1987.

CARACO PHARMACEUTICAL LABORATORIES, LTD.

AMEX: CPD

1150 Elijah McCoy Dr.
Detroit, MI 48202
Phone: 313-871-8400
Fax: 313-871-8314
Web: www.caraco.com

CEO: Daniel H. Movens
CFO: Mukul Rathi
HR: –
FYE: March 31
Type: Public

Caraco Pharmaceutical Laboratories is cooking up cheaper versions of prescription drugs in the Motor City. The Detroit-based drug company makes generic knock-offs of a wide variety of pharmaceuticals, producing about 50 prescription products in various strengths and dosages. Its product lineup includes treatments for high blood pressure, cancer, nervous system conditions, diabetes, allergies, and pain. Indian drugmaker Sun Pharmaceutical Industries owns about 70% of the firm and licenses US marketing rights to Caraco for a number of drugs. Caraco markets its products throughout the US and Puerto Rico, selling primarily to pharmaceutical wholesalers such as McKesson, AmerisourceBergen, and Cardinal Health.

	Annual Growth	12/04	*3/05	3/06	3/07	3/08
Sales ($ mil.)	55.3%	60.3	17.3	82.8	117.0	350.4
Net income ($ mil.)	—	(0.2)	(4.3)	(10.4)	26.9	35.4
Market value ($ mil.)	23.4%	251.7	215.6	343.5	342.3	584.3
Employees	164.0%	—	—	272	718	

*Fiscal year change

CARAUSTAR INDUSTRIES, INC.

NASDAQ (GM): CSAR

5000 Austell Powder Springs Rd., Ste. 300
Austell, GA 30106
Phone: 770-948-3101
Fax: 770-732-3401
Web: www.caraustar.com

CEO: Michael J. (Mike) Keough
CFO: Ronald J. Domanico
HR: Barry A. Smedstad
FYE: December 31
Type: Public

Caraustar Industries thinks outside the box in order to make new ones. The company recycles paper products into paperboard, which is later converted into tubes, cores, cartons, and custom packaging. About half of the company's paperboard is consumed by its own converting facilities; the balance is sold to independent converters. Caraustar's converting operations make various tubes and containers for the textile, paper, and metal industries. The company's carton and packaging products are used to box a variety of consumer goods. Recovered fiber not used by Caraustar is sold to other mill operators.

	Annual Growth	12/03	12/04	12/05	12/06	12/07
Sales ($ mil.)	(3.7%)	992.2	1,060.3	862.4	989.9	854.2
Net income ($ mil.)	—	(27.0)	(4.0)	(103.4)	47.3	(24.5)
Market value ($ mil.)	(30.5%)	389.5	483.6	250.1	235.3	91.0
Employees	(23.0%)	—	—	5,440	4,190	—

CARBIZ INC.

OTC: CBZFF

7405 N. Tamiami Trail
Sarasota, FL 34243
Phone: 941-952-9255
Fax: 941-953-3580
Web: www.carbiz.com

CEO: Carl Ritter
CFO: Stanton Heintz
HR: Jennifer Halloran
FYE: January 31
Type: Public

Carbiz's business is the car biz. The company makes its way through economic potholes by providing the software and services that car dealers need to run their businesses. Carbiz's software applications cover f&i (finance and insurance), special financing, leasing, buy here-pay here, traffic management, and accounting. Related services include software training and consulting, software applications hosting, and website design.

	Annual Growth	1/04	1/05	1/06	1/07	1/08
Sales ($ mil.)	156.2%	—	—	—	3.2	8.2
Net income ($ mil.)	—	—	—	—	(4.8)	(14.2)
Market value ($ mil.)	22.8%	—	—	—	11.6	14.2
Employees	—	—	—	—	37	—

CARBO CERAMICS INC.

NYSE: CRR

6565 MacArthur Blvd., Ste. 1050
Irving, TX 75039
Phone: 972-401-0090
Fax: 972-401-0705
Web: www.carboceramics.com

CEO: Gary A. Kolstad
CFO: Paul G. Vitek
HR: Joe Ford
FYE: December 31
Type: Public

CARBO Ceramics' proppants (tiny alumina-based ceramic beads) are a welcome release for natural gas and oil well operators. To increase well production, operators often pump fluids down wells at high pressure to create fractures in the hydrocarbon-bearing rock formation (hydraulic fracturing). Proppants are suspended in the fluid to fill the channels and "prop" up the fissures so that natural gas and oil may flow to the surface. The company's products compete against sand-based proppants. CARBOS's three top customers — BJ Services, Schlumberger, and Halliburton — together account for 70% of sales; the US accounts for 66% of sales. Chairman William Morris owns 13% of CARBO Ceramics.

	Annual Growth	12/03	12/04	12/05	12/06	12/07
Sales ($ mil.)	19.0%	169.9	223.1	252.7	312.1	340.4
Net income ($ mil.)	16.2%	29.6	41.7	46.6	54.3	53.9
Market value ($ mil.)	14.1%	537.6	735.2	1,372.7	911.5	912.0
Employees	—	—	—	530	—	—

An in-depth profile of this company is available to Hoover's Online members at hoovers.com.

323

CARDENAS MARKETS, INC.

1621 E. Francis St.
Ontario, CA 91761
Phone: 909-923-7426
Fax: 909-923-5976
Web: www.cardenasmarkets.com

CEO: Jesus Cardenas Sr.
CFO: –
HR: Cecilia Solis
FYE: December 31
Type: Private

Husband and wife team Jesus and Luz Cardenas took a gamble and ended up in hog heaven. The Cardenas family got its start as hog farmers in Corona, California, but in 1979 they sold off their farm and opened their first supermarket, primarily geared towards the Hispanic population in the region. Today, Cardenas Markets operates a chain of more than 20 grocery stores in Southern California. The stores have extensive meat and produce departments and cater to Hispanic shoppers with a wide variety of brands from Mexico and Central and South America, including Mexican pastries and tortillerias. The company's newest store opened in Coachella Valley in 2007.

	Annual Growth	12/03	12/04	12/05	12/06	12/07
Est. sales ($ mil.)	—	—	—	—	—	13.0
Employees	—	—	—	—	—	100

CARDIAC SCIENCE CORPORATION

NASDAQ (GM): CSCX

3303 Monte Villa Pkwy.
Bothell, WA 98021
Phone: 425-402-2000
Fax: 425-402-2001
Web: www.cardiacscience.com

CEO: John R. Hinson
CFO: Michael K. (Mike) Matysik
HR: Barbara J. Thompson
FYE: December 31
Type: Public

Cardiac Science Corporation wants to grab hold of your heart. The company makes cardiovascular monitoring and therapeutic equipment, including automated external defibrillators and stress test systems that analyze the heart's performance under stress. Cardiac Science also offers monitoring systems for extended surveillance, ECG management systems, and telemetry devices for evaluation of the heart during rehabilitation exercise. In addition, Cardiac Science sells accessories such as lead wires and electrodes and provides product repair and technical support services. The firm uses a direct sales force in the US, the UK, and France, and distributors in about 100 other countries.

	Annual Growth	12/03	12/04	12/05	12/06	12/07
Sales ($ mil.)	26.7%	—	89.6	106.7	155.4	182.1
Net income ($ mil.)	(17.4%)	—	15.1	(1.2)	0.1	8.5
Market value ($ mil.)	(4.8%)	—	—	203.4	182.4	184.3
Employees	8.8%	—	—	511	556	—

CARDICA, INC.

NASDAQ (GM): CRDC

900 Saginaw Dr.
Redwood City, CA 94063
Phone: 650-364-9975
Fax: 650-364-3134
Web: www.cardica.com

CEO: Bernard A. Hausen
CFO: Robert Y. Newell IV
HR: –
FYE: June 30
Type: Public

Cardica wants to help surgeons treat patients with coronary heart disease. The company makes products, including the C-Port and PAS-Port systems, that are used in coronary artery bypass surgery. The automated systems connect blood vessels that restore blood flow beyond the closed sections of coronary arteries. Its products offer a less time-consuming and simpler alternative to hand-sewn suturing. Cardica markets its C-Port system in the US via direct sales. In the EU, it sells the C-Port and PAS-Port systems through distributors. Century Medical is the exclusive distributor of PAS-Port systems in Japan. The company has a co-development agreement with Cook for a vascular access closure device.

	Annual Growth	6/03	6/04	6/05	6/06	6/07
Sales ($ mil.)	—	0.0	0.8	2.1	2.1	3.5
Net income ($ mil.)	—	(9.2)	(10.7)	(10.9)	(12.4)	(13.6)
Market value ($ mil.)	6.6%	—	—	—	77.5	82.6
Employees	—	—	—	37	—	—

CARDIMA, INC.

OTC: CADM

47266 Benicia St.
Fremont, CA 94538
Phone: 510-354-0300
Fax: 510-657-4476
Web: www.cardima.com

CEO: John R. (Rob) Cheney
CFO: John R. (Rob) Cheney
HR: Pat Reid-Purt
FYE: December 31
Type: Public

They may not pick up your morning radio exercise program, but Cardima's products can still get your heart pumping. Cardima's micro-catheters diagnose life-threatening heart arrhythmia by locating or "mapping" its source. The company's products then restore normal heart rhythm by destroying the arrhythmia-causing tissue with radio frequency energy, a process called ablation. Cardima markets its products to electrophysiologists and heart surgeons directly and through distributors primarily in the US; most of the rest of its sales are made in Europe. Cardima's brand names include REVELATION, PATHFINDER, and TRACER.

	Annual Growth	12/03	12/04	12/05	12/06	12/07
Sales ($ mil.)	(14.1%)	2.2	2.4	1.9	1.5	1.2
Net income ($ mil.)	—	(13.2)	(9.8)	(8.3)	(9.5)	(42.7)
Market value ($ mil.)	(47.7%)	795.3	517.3	45.7	51.2	59.3
Employees	—	—	—	—	—	—

CARDINAL BANKSHARES CORPORATION

OTC: CDBK

101 Jacksonville Cir.
Floyd, VA 24091
Phone: 540-745-4191
Fax: 540-745-4133
Web: www.bankoffloyd.com

CEO: Ronald Leon Moore
CFO: J. Alan Dickerson
HR: –
FYE: December 31
Type: Public

Cardinal Bankshares may not answer to the Pope, but it does *pay* attention to what its shareholders have to say. The financial institution is the holding company for The Bank of Floyd, which serves southwest Virginia's Floyd County and surrounding areas. The bank offers standard retail products and services, including checking and savings accounts, CDs, IRAs, and credit cards. It uses funds from deposits to write loans, primarily real estate loans. The Bank of Floyd subsidiary FBC, Inc., has interests in two Virginia title insurance firms and an investment services company.

	Annual Growth	12/03	12/04	12/05	12/06	12/07
Assets ($ mil.)	2.9%	186.4	190.6	196.2	207.9	209.3
Net income ($ mil.)	3.6%	2.0	2.2	2.2	2.5	2.3
Market value ($ mil.)	(3.2%)	31.5	32.3	32.6	30.3	27.6
Employees	—	—	—	—	—	83

CARDINAL FINANCIAL CORPORATION

NASDAQ (GS): CFNL

8270 Greensboro Dr., Ste. 500
McLean, VA 22102
Phone: 703-584-3400
Fax: 703-584-3410
Web: www.cardinalbank.com

CEO: Bernard H. Clineburg
CFO: Mark A. Wendel
HR: Janet L. Schuchmann
FYE: December 31
Type: Public

Cardinal Financial can help you keep out of the red. The holding company owns Cardinal Bank, which operates about two dozen branches in the Washington, DC, metropolitan area. Serving commercial and retail customers, it offers checking, savings, and money market accounts; IRAs; and CDs. Commercial real estate loans make up approximately 40% of Cardinal Financial's loan portfolio; residential mortgages and construction loans are about 20% each. Subsidiary Cardinal Wealth Services provides brokerage and investment services through an alliance with Raymond James Financial.

	Annual Growth	12/03	12/04	12/05	12/06	12/07
Assets ($ mil.)	27.7%	636.3	1,211.6	1,452.3	1,638.4	1,690.0
Net income ($ mil.)	(7.7%)	6.2	3.5	9.9	7.4	4.5
Market value ($ mil.)	13.6%	135.4	205.7	268.0	250.7	225.6
Employees	(5.3%)	—	—	406	406	364

CARDINAL HEALTH, INC.

NYSE: CAH

7000 Cardinal Place	CEO: R. Kerry Clark
Dublin, OH 43017	CFO: Jeffrey Henderson
Phone: 614-757-5000	HR: Carole S. Watkins
Fax: –	FYE: June 30
Web: www.cardinal.com	Type: Public

Cardinal Health seeks to deliver medicine to all points of the compass. The company is the second-largest distributor of pharmaceuticals and other medical supplies and equipment in the US; McKesson is #1. The largest of Cardinal Health's business segments is its health care supply chain services unit, which includes the company's pharmaceutical and medical product distribution divisions. The company provides a variety of prescriptions and medical supplies to pharmacies, hospitals, doctors' offices, and other health care businesses. Cardinal Health's other segments include medical products manufacturing (equipment, supplies, and apparel) and clinical technologies (automated pharmacy equipment).

	Annual Growth	6/03	6/04	6/05	6/06	6/07
Sales ($ mil.)	11.2%	56,737.0	65,053.5	74,910.7	81,363.6	86,852.0
Net income ($ mil.)	8.3%	1,405.8	1,474.5	1,050.7	1,000.1	1,931.1
Market value ($ mil.)	(2.5%)	28,832.1	30,184.5	24,657.4	26,426.8	26,002.6
Employees	0.0%	—	—	55,000	55,000	—

CARDINAL HEALTH SYSTEM, INC.

2401 W. University Ave.	CEO: Kelly N. Stanley
Muncie, IN 47303	CFO: Robert Gildersleeve
Phone: 765-747-3111	HR: Terry Allen
Fax: 765-751-2506	FYE: June 30
Web: www.cardinalhealthsystem.org	Type: Private

Cardinal Health System aims to keep residents of East Central Indiana healthy. Cardinal Health System is a network of hospitals, physicians' offices, pharmacies, and outpatient services serving communities in east central Indiana. Its facilities include flagship Ball Memorial Hospital and the smaller 15-bed Blackford Community Hospital. It also includes Cardinal Health Partners, which consists of ten local health centers and a network of primary and post-acute care doctors. Cardinal Health System takes its name from the athletic mascot of local Ball State University and has no affiliation with the pharmaceutical distribution company Cardinal Health.

	Annual Growth	6/03	6/04	6/05	6/06	6/07
Est. sales ($ mil.)	—	—	—	—	—	118.1
Employees	—	—	—	—	—	3,500

CARDINAL LOGISTICS MANAGEMENT CORPORATION

5333 Davidson Hwy.	CEO: Tom Hostetler
Concord, NC 28027	CFO: Carl A. Texter
Phone: 704-786-6125	HR: –
Fax: 704-788-6618	FYE: December 31
Web: www.cardlog.com	Type: Private

When it comes to freight transportation, Cardinal Logistics Management has several feathers in its cap. The company's offerings include dedicated contract carriage, in which drivers and equipment are assigned to customers long-term; local delivery; supply chain consulting; and warehousing. It also offers less-than-truckload (LTL) transportation, in which freight from multiple shippers is combined into a single trailer. Overall, Cardinal operates a fleet of about 2,200 tractors and 4,800 trailers and maintains more than 1 million sq. ft. of warehouse space. Customers have included AutoZone, Office Depot, and 7-Eleven. Chicago-based investment firm GTCR Golder Rauner owns Cardinal, which was founded in 1997.

	Annual Growth	12/03	12/04	12/05	12/06	12/07
Est. sales ($ mil.)	—	—	—	—	—	107.1
Employees	—	—	—	—	—	1,500

CARDIODYNAMICS INTERNATIONAL

NASDAQ (GM): CDIC

6175 Nancy Ridge Dr., Ste. 300	CEO: Michael K. Perry
San Diego, CA 92121	CFO: Stephen P. (Steve) Loomis
Phone: 858-535-0202	HR: Michael Stewart
Fax: 858-535-0055	FYE: November 30
Web: www.cardiodynamics.com	Type: Public

Does the idea of a tube in your heart scare you? CardioDynamics International Corporation might be able to help. Its BioZ systems give doctors a noninvasive way to gather cardiac data traditionally collected with the insertion of a catheter. The digital systems measure mechanical cardiac activity, such as contraction strength and pumping capability. Doctors can use them to assess and treat patients with heart failure, high blood pressure, and shortness of breath. The firm markets its products both directly and through distributors in more than 30 countries worldwide. Customers include some hospitals, but outpatient facilities and physician practices are its primary markets.

	Annual Growth	11/03	11/04	11/05	11/06	11/07
Sales ($ mil.)	(7.8%)	30.3	41.0	37.0	30.3	21.9
Net income ($ mil.)	—	—	2.5	10.1	(14.9)	(6.7)	(16.7)
Employees	—	—	—	233	—	—

CARDIOGENESIS CORPORATION

Pink Sheets: CGCP

11 Musick	CEO: Richard P. Lanigan
Irvine, CA 92618	CFO: William R. Abbott
Phone: 949-420-1800	HR: –
Fax: 949-420-1888	FYE: December 31
Web: www.cardiogenesis.com	Type: Public

Cardiogenesis will leave a hole in your heart and not feel a pang of guilt. The company's laser and fiber-optic systems are used for transmyocardial revascularization (TMR) and percutaneous myocardial channeling (PMC), procedures that use a laser to cut channels through the heart muscle into the heart chamber to help circulation in cardiac patients. Its SolarGen 2100 system, composed of fiber-optic and laser surgical tools on a powered base unit, is FDA-approved and is marketed through Cardiogenesis' sales force in the US and through international distributors. The company's PMC system is available outside the US. The company also sells catheters and other related equipment to operate its laser systems.

	Annual Growth	12/03	12/04	12/05	12/06	12/07
Sales ($ mil.)	(2.7%)	13.5	15.4	16.3	17.1	12.1
Net income ($ mil.)	—	(0.3)	(1.3)	(1.9)	(2.0)	0.6
Employees	—	—	—	—	—	—

CARDIONET, INC.

NASDAQ (GM): BEAT

1010 Second Ave., Ste. 700	CEO: Arie Cohen
San Diego, CA 92101	CFO: Gregory A. Marsh
Phone: 619-243-7500	HR: –
Fax: 610-828-8048	FYE: December 31
Web: www.cardionet.com	Type: Public

CardioNet wants to be as close as your next heartbeat. The company provides ambulatory, real-time outpatient cardiac-monitoring services. Improving on existing monitoring technology by providing continuous heartbeat-by-heartbeat monitoring with up to 96 hours of data, the CardioNet System provides prescribing doctors with a more complete picture of heart functions when diagnosing arrhythmias (abnormal heart rhythms). The system relies on two-way wireless communication — providing mobility for the patient and remote adjustment for physicians. The CardioNet System has primarily been marketed in the mid-Atlantic, northeastern, and midwestern states, serving more than 80,000 enrolled patients.

	Annual Growth	12/03	12/04	12/05	12/06	12/07
Sales ($ mil.)	48.7%	—	22.2	30.9	33.9	73.0
Net income ($ mil.)	—	—	(20.9)	(11.1)	(7.6)	(0.4)
Employees	18.7%	—	—	—	509	604

An in-depth profile of this company is available to Hoover's Online members at hoovers.com.

325

CARDIOTECH INTERNATIONAL, INC.

AMEX: CTE

229 Andover St.
Wilmington, MA 01887
Phone: 978-657-0075
Fax: 978-657-0074
Web: www.cardiotech-inc.com

CEO: Michael F. Adams
CFO: Eric G. Walters
HR: –
FYE: March 31
Type: Public

If artificial blood becomes a reality, the manufacturers can hook up with CardioTech International, maker of synthetic blood vessels. CardioTech's products replace or bypass damaged and diseased arteries and provide access for dialysis needles in kidney disease patients undergoing hemodialysis. These man-made blood vessels, also called vascular grafts, are made of ChronoFlex, the company's polyurethane-based biomaterial. CardioPass, one product candidate, is a synthetic coronary artery bypass graft. CardioTech also makes its HydroThane polymer-based biomaterials that mimic living tissue. It is marketed for use by other medical device makers.

	Annual Growth	3/04	3/05	3/06	3/07	3/08
Sales ($ mil.)	(38.1%)	21.8	21.8	22.4	21.1	3.2
Net income ($ mil.)	—	(1.5)	(1.6)	(5.1)	(3.0)	(6.1)
Market value ($ mil.)	(40.5%)	90.9	36.6	55.0	31.2	11.4
Employees	22.6%	—	168	206	—	—

CARDIUM THERAPEUTICS, INC.

OTC: CDTP

3611 Valley Centre Dr., Ste. 525
San Diego, CA 92130
Phone: 858-436-1000
Fax: 858-436-1001
Web: www.cardiumthx.com

CEO: Christopher J. Reinhard
CFO: Dennis M. Mulroy
HR: –
FYE: December 31
Type: Public

Whether a heart goes boom-boom, pitter-patter, or is just a-flutter, Cardium Therapeutics is interested in keeping it going strong. The company's Cardium Biologics subsidiary has three growth-factor-based drug candidates aimed at treating ischemic heart disease (such as angina), and restoring heart functioning after a heart attack. Lead candidate Generx works by stimulating the growth of new blood vessels (called angiogenesis) in angina patients. Cardium Therapeutics' Innercool Therapies subsidiary makes the Celsius Control, CoolBlue, and Rapid Blue systems, which help warm or cool patients with catheters or wraps. Temperature modulation is used both to reduce fevers and to reduce cell damage during surgery.

	Annual Growth	12/03	12/04	12/05	12/06	12/07
Sales ($ mil.)	100.0%	—	—	—	0.8	1.6
Net income ($ mil.)	—	—	—	—	(18.6)	(25.3)
Market value ($ mil.)	(2.7%)	—	—	—	109.4	106.5
Employees	—	—	—	—	—	—

CARDONE INDUSTRIES INC.

5501 Whitaker Ave.
Philadelphia, PA 19124
Phone: 215-912-3000
Fax: 215-912-3700
Web: www.cardone.com

CEO: Michael Cardone Jr.
CFO: –
HR: Kenneth Mullen
FYE: December 31
Type: Private

Old car parts get a new lease on life thanks to Cardone Industries. The company is a leading remanufacturer of automotive parts for the aftermarket. Cardone focuses on six basic product lines: brakes (master cylinders, calipers), drivetrain parts (constant-velocity drive axles), electronics (climate and spark controls, fuel-display modules), motors (window-lift and wiper), pumps (water and vacuum), and steering (rack and pinion units, power-steering filters). The Cardone family, including chairman and CEO Michael Cardone Jr., controls the company, which was founded in 1970.

	Annual Growth	12/03	12/04	12/05	12/06	12/07
Est. sales ($ mil.)	—	—	—	—	—	373.3
Employees	—	—	—	—	—	4,000

CARDTRONICS, INC.

NASDAQ (GM): CATM

3110 Hayes Rd., Ste. 300
Houston, TX 77082
Phone: 281-596-9988
Fax: 281-596-9984
Web: www.cardtronics.com

CEO: Jack M. Antonini
CFO: J. Chris Brewster
HR: –
FYE: December 31
Type: Public

Cardtronics is the Godzilla of ATMs. It's big, it's bad, and it's electronically operated. Cardtronics is the #1 owner and operator of automated teller machines and related equipment in the world. It maintains more than 32,000 ATMs in the US, UK, and Mexico. More than 10,000 of those are under contracts with banks, which allow surcharge-free access to customers. The company also leases and sells machines to airports, convenience stores, supermarkets, malls, and drug stores. Merchants can take care of their own technical maintenance or have Cardtronics do it. It also provides more complex services involving transaction processing and electronic funds transfer. The company went public via an IPO in late 2007.

	Annual Growth	12/03	12/04	12/05	12/06	12/07
Sales ($ mil.)	36.1%	110.4	192.9	269.0	293.6	378.3
Net income ($ mil.)	—	2.5	5.8	(2.4)	(0.5)	(27.1)
Market value ($ mil.)	—	—	—	—	—	389.9
Employees	44.7%	108	—	—	327	—

CARE INVESTMENT TRUST INC.

NYSE: CRE

505 Fifth Ave., 6th Fl.
New York, NY 10017
Phone: 212-771-0505
Fax: –
Web: www.carereit.com

CEO: F. Scott Kellman
CFO: Robert O'Neill
HR: –
FYE: December 31
Type: Public

Care Investment Trust is interested in health and wealth. The real estate investment trust (REIT) was formed to invest in health care-related mortgage debt and real estate, including nursing homes, hospitals, outpatient centers, assisted living facilities, and medical office buildings and labs. It will provide first lien and mezzanine loans as well as construction loans. Care Investment Trust will also acquire health care providers from time to time. The company's external manager, CIT Healthcare, a subsidiary of commercial finance giant CIT Group, will feed it mortgage business. Care Investment Trust, which began operating in March 2007, will also take advantage of opportunities outside the usual scope of CIT Healthcare.

	Annual Growth	12/03	12/04	12/05	12/06	12/07
Sales ($ mil.)	—	—	—	—	—	12.9
Net income ($ mil.)	—	—	—	—	—	(1.6)
Market value ($ mil.)	—	—	—	—	—	225.7
Employees	—	—	—	—	—	—

CAREADVANTAGE, INC.

OTC: CADV

485-C Rte. 1 South
Iselin, NJ 08830
Phone: 732-362-5000
Fax: 732-362-5005
Web: www.careadvantage.com

CEO: Dennis J. Mouras
CFO: –
HR: –
FYE: December 31
Type: Public

Your health care provider will be happy for you to get a checkup, and management consulting firm CareAdvantage will be happy to give your health care provider a checkup. The firm aims to help its customers — insurance plans, hospital systems, employers, and other health care providers — serve patients as efficiently as possible. Much of its business comes from Blue Cross Blue Shield organizations. CareAdvantage operates through two main units: CareAdvantage Health Systems and Contemporary HealthCare Management. The company's signature offering is its RightPath Navigator software, which helps clients analyze the health status and care usage of member populations.

	Annual Growth	12/03	12/04	12/05	12/06	12/07
Sales ($ mil.)	5.9%	3.5	2.3	2.8	4.4	4.4
Net income ($ mil.)	—	(5.2)	(1.8)	(1.6)	(0.2)	(0.1)
Market value ($ mil.)	(17.1%)	2.0	—	—	1.1	—
Employees	—	—	—	—	—	—

CARECENTRIC, INC.

Overlook II, 2839 Paces Ferry Rd., Ste. 900
Atlanta, GA 30339
Phone: 678-264-4400
Fax: 770-384-1650
Web: www.carecentric.com

CEO: Stewart B. Reed
CFO: Stephen M. Shea
HR: –
FYE: December 31
Type: Association

CareCentric helps home health care providers spend less time managing their business operations and more paying attention to patients. Formerly Simione Central Holdings, the company offers software systems that manage financial, operational, and clinical information for hospitals, home health care providers, home medical equipment providers, respiratory therapy service providers, and government-managed organizations. An investment firm took CareCentric private in 2003.

	Annual Growth	12/03	12/04	12/05	12/06	12/07
Est. sales ($ mil.)	—	—	—	—	—	2,147.5
Employees	—	—	—	—	—	158

CAREER EDUCATION CORPORATION

NASDAQ (GS): CECO

2895 Greenspoint Pkwy., Ste. 600
Hoffman Estates, IL 60169
Phone: 847-781-3600
Fax: 847-781-3610
Web: www.careered.com

CEO: Gary E. McCullough
CFO: Michael J. (Mike) Graham
HR: Harry L. Geller
FYE: December 31
Type: Public

Career Education Corporation (CEC) will put a diploma on your wall. The for-profit company owns and operates more than 80 domestic and international campuses offering postsecondary education to approximately 90,000 students. CEC offers certificate and degree programs in areas including visual communication and design, culinary arts, information technology, business studies, and health education. Among the company's brand names are International Academy of Design & Technology, Le Cordon Bleu College of Culinary Arts, and Colorado Technical University. CEC schools offers non-degree certificates as well as associate, bachelor's, master's, and doctoral degrees. The company is closing several campuses.

	Annual Growth	12/03	12/04	12/05	12/06	12/07
Sales ($ mil.)	9.0%	1,188.6	1,728.5	2,034.6	1,785.6	1,674.9
Net income ($ mil.)	(15.9%)	119.2	179.6	233.9	46.6	59.5
Market value ($ mil.)	(13.4%)	4,032.8	4,101.5	3,308.4	2,383.7	2,273.0
Employees	(8.2%)	—	—	17,180	16,740	14,479

CAREERBUILDER LLC

200 N. LaSalle St., Ste. 1100
Chicago, IL 60631
Phone: 773-527-3600
Fax: 773-399-6313
Web: www.careerbuilder.com

CEO: Matthew W. (Matt) Ferguson
CFO: Kevin Knapp
HR: Rosemary Haefner
FYE: December 31
Type: Joint venture

CareerBuilder constructs new careers by bringing employers and potential employees together through the Web. The company's CareerBuilder Network consists of its flagship site careerbuilder.com, as well as dozens of affiliated career sites, including iVillage.com, Experience.com, and CollegeClub.com. CareerBuilder.com allows job seekers access to the Mega Job Search to peruse more than 1.6 million job openings, and more than 300,000 employers tap into its database, consisting of over 26 million resumes. The company also conducts surveys and polls through the Web paneling of its vast database. Founded in 1995, CareerBuilder is controlled by newspaper companies Gannett, Tribune, and McClatchy.

	Annual Growth	12/02	12/03	12/04	12/05	12/06
Sales ($ mil.)	61.3%	—	160.0	280.0	495.0	672.0
Employees	48.5%	—	550	900	1,500	1,800

CAREFIRST, INC.

10455 Mill Run Circle
Owings Mills, MD 21117
Phone: 410-528-7000
Fax: 410-998-5351
Web: www.carefirst.com

CEO: Chester (Chet) Burrell
CFO: G. Mark Chaney
HR: Sharon J. Vecchioni
FYE: December 31
Type: Not-for-profit

CareFirst is a not-for-profit holding company with affiliates that provide managed health services to more than 3 million members throughout the mid-Atlantic region. The company operates in Delaware through its affiliate Blue Cross Blue Shield of Delaware; in Washington, DC, through its Group Hospitalization and Medical Services subsidiary; and in Maryland through CareFirst of Maryland. CareFirst also provides life insurance, physician practice management, and third-party administration services through several of its for-profit subsidiary companies. CareFirst operates from offices in more than 20 locations.

	Annual Growth	12/03	12/04	12/05	12/06	12/07
Est. sales ($ mil.)	—	—	—	—	—	2,147.5
Employees	—	—	—	—	—	6,000

CAREGROUP, INC.

109 Brookline Ave.
Boston, MA 02215
Phone: 617-975-5000
Fax: –
Web: www.caregroup.org

CEO: John T. Szum
CFO: John T. Szum
HR: Lisa Zankman
FYE: September 30
Type: Private

Thanks to CareGroup, there's well-being in Beantown. Formed in the 1997 union of several Boston-area health care organizations, CareGroup serves Massachusetts through its flagship, the Beth Israel Deaconess, and four other hospitals. With more than 1,000 beds, the system provides comprehensive acute care as well as specialty clinics and research facilities. CareGroup is affiliated with Harvard University, the Joslin Diabetes Center, the Mind/Body Medical Institute, and the Institute for Nursing Healthcare Leadership. Its Occupational Health Network provides clinics in eastern Massachusetts.

	Annual Growth	9/03	9/04	9/05	9/06	9/07
Est. sales ($ mil.)	—	—	—	—	—	1,038.7
Employees	—	—	—	—	—	12,000

CAREGUIDE, INC.

OTC: CGDE

4401 NW 124th Ave.
Coral Springs, FL 33065
Phone: 954-796-3714
Fax: 954-796-3703
Web: www.careguide.com

CEO: Chris E. Paterson
CFO: Thomas L. Tran
HR: –
FYE: June 30
Type: Public

Like a nagging parent, CareGuide is forever reminding you to take better care of yourself. The company (formerly Patient Infosystems) offers health care management products and services designed to help health plan members maintain and improve their health and to lower health care costs for its clients. Its One Care Street offering identifies patients who will likely need care and provides them with action plans and health coaching. The company also provides a 24-hour nurse helpline for its clients' members and provides disease management services for those with chronic illnesses. CareGuide customers include self-insured employers, health plans, and third-party administrators.

	Annual Growth	12/03	12/04	12/05	12/06	12/07
Sales ($ mil.)	12.4%	—	15.7	11.1	41.3	22.3
Net income ($ mil.)	—	—	(3.6)	(5.4)	0.1	(16.6)
Employees	5.3%	—	174	208	234	203

CAREMARK PHARMACY SERVICES

211 Commerce St., Ste. 800	CEO: Howard A. McLure
Nashville, TN 37201	CFO: Peter J. Clemens IV
Phone: 615-743-6600	HR: Dennis Zeleny
Fax: 205-733-9780	FYE: December 31
Web: www.caremark.com	Type: Business segment

Caremark Pharmacy Services (formerly Caremark Rx) cares about keeping medicine affordable. The prescription benefits management division of CVS Caremark (formerly CVS), Caremark Pharmacy Services designs and administers the drug coverage programs of thousands of corporate, managed care, government, and union health plans. It operates a national network of some 60,000 retail pharmacies and mail-order offices through which health plan members buy drugs, often at discounts that Caremark negotiates with their drugmakers. The division was formed in 2007 when CVS acquired Caremark, merging Caremark's pharmacy services businesses with those of CVS subsidiary PharmaCare.

	Annual Growth	12/02	12/03	12/04	12/05	12/06
Sales ($ mil.)	52.4%	6,805.4	9,067.3	25,801.1	32,991.3	36,750.2
Net income ($ mil.)	7.9%	791.3	290.8	600.3	932.4	1,074.0
Employees	29.7%	4,723	4,870	11,133	13,628	13,360

CAREY INTERNATIONAL, INC.

4530 Wisconsin Ave. NW	CEO: Gary L. Kessler
Washington, DC 20016	CFO: Mitchell J. (Mitch) Lahr
Phone: 202-895-1200	HR: Rae D. Fawcett
Fax: 202-895-1269	FYE: November 30
Web: www.carey.com	Type: Private

In more than 540 cities in some 60 nations, Carey International carries passengers. Through its network of franchisees, the company provides chauffeured vehicle services, primarily to business travelers, through a network of subsidiaries, licensees, and affiliates. Transportation is available for airport pick-ups and drop-offs, conventions, special events, and leisure travel. The company's fleet consists of sedans, limousines, vans, minibuses, and buses. Carey links its centralized reservation system to terminals at travel agencies, corporate travel departments, and government offices. The company also offers online reservations.

	Annual Growth	11/03	11/04	11/05	11/06	11/07
Est. sales ($ mil.)	—	—	—	—	—	7.0
Employees	—	—	—	—	—	700

CARGILL, INCORPORATED

15407 McGinty Rd. West	CEO: Gregory R. (Greg) Page
Wayzata, MN 55391	CFO: David W. MacLennan
Phone: 952-742-7575	HR: Peter Vrijsen
Fax: 952-742-7393	FYE: May 31
Web: www.cargill.com	Type: Private

Cargill may be private, but it's highly visible. The US's second-largest private corporation (after Koch Industries), Cargill's diversified operations include grain, cotton, sugar, petroleum and financial trading; food processing; futures brokering; health and pharmaceutical products; agricultural services such as animal feed and crop protection; and industrial products including biofuels, oils and lubricants, starches, and salt. The company is one of the leading grain producers in the US, and its Excel unit is one of the top US meatpackers. Cargill's brands include Diamond Crystal (salt), Gerkens (cocoa), Honeysuckle White (poultry), Sterling Silver (fresh meats), and Nutrena (dog and cat food).

	Annual Growth	5/03	5/04	5/05	5/06	5/07
Sales ($ mil.)	12.9%	54,390.0	62,907.0	71,066.0	75,208.0	88,266.0
Net income ($ mil.)	16.1%	1,290.0	1,331.0	2,103.0	1,537.0	2,343.0
Employees	12.7%	98,000	101,000	124,000	149,000	158,000

CARHARTT, INC.

5750 Mercury Dr.	CEO: Mark Valade
Dearborn, MI 48126	CFO: Linda Hubbard
Phone: 313-271-8460	HR: Jennifer Piscopink
Fax: 313-271-3455	FYE: December 31
Web: www.carhartt.com	Type: Private

Real workers don't leave home without first donning their Carhartts. The clothing manufacturer offers a line of rugged overalls, flame-resistant work wear, outerwear, sweatshirts, sportswear, and work pants favored by farmers and blue-collar workers. Teens and young adults, however, have adopted Carhartt clothes as streetwear. Its clothes have shown up in such popular movies as *The Perfect Storm* and *The Horse Whisperer*. Most of Carhartt's products are manufactured in about 10 US factories; the remainder is produced in Mexico and Europe. Authorized retailers sell Carhartt's apparel in the US, Europe, and Japan. The family of founder Hamilton Carhartt owns the firm, which was founded in 1889.

	Annual Growth	12/03	12/04	12/05	12/06	12/07
Est. sales ($ mil.)	—	—	—	—	—	454.0
Employees	—	—	—	—	—	3,000

CARIBOU COFFEE COMPANY, INC.   NASDAQ (GM): CBOU

3900 Lakebreeze Ave. North	CEO: Rosalyn (Roz) Mallet
Brooklyn Center, MN 55429	CFO: Kaye R. O'Leary
Phone: 763-592-2200	HR: Karen E. McBride-Raffel
Fax: 763-592-2300	FYE: Sunday nearest December 31
Web: www.cariboucoffee.com	Type: Public

Caribou Coffee Company serves hot joe to the java herd. The company operates the second largest non-franchised coffee chain in the US (behind Starbucks), based on the number of locations, with more than 480 stores in Minnesota and more than 15 other states. The outlets, designed to resemble ski lodges and Alaskan cabins, offer a variety of coffee blends, as well as specialty coffee drinks, teas, and baked goods. The company also sells whole bean coffee and brewing supplies. More than 50 locations are operated by franchisees, about 40 of which are in international markets. Bahrain-based investment group Arcapita owns 60% of Caribou Coffee.

	Annual Growth	12/03	12/04	12/05	12/06	12/07
Sales ($ mil.)	20.0%	123.7	160.9	198.0	236.2	256.8
Net income ($ mil.)	—	(0.9)	(2.1)	(4.9)	(9.1)	(30.7)
Market value ($ mil.)	(37.8%)	—	—	193.5	164.5	75.0
Employees	7.3%	—	—	5,745	6,698	6,616

CARILION CLINIC

1906 Bellevue Ave.	CEO: Edward G. Murphy
Roanoke, VA 24014	CFO: Donald E. (Don) Lorton
Phone: 540-981-7000	HR: Brucie Boggs
Fax: 540-344-5716	FYE: September 30
Web: www.carilion.com	Type: Not-for-profit

Carilion Clinic cares for residents of southwestern Virginia. Founded in 1899 as the Roanoke Hospital Association, the system today includes hospitals, a network of local physicians, and a research partnership with Virginia Tech. In addition to the six hospitals it owns, Carilion manages another and co-owns one with Centra Health. The system (including affiliates) has more than 1,100 beds and is expanding its operations to include a new children's hospital within its Carilion Roanoke Memorial Hospital, as well as new heart treatment and women's health centers. Its Carilion Behavioral Health facilities include inpatient care.

	Annual Growth	9/03	9/04	9/05	9/06	9/07
Est. sales ($ mil.)	—	—	—	—	—	544.1
Employees	—	—	—	—	—	9,200

CARL BUDDIG & COMPANY

950 W. 175 St.
Homewood, IL 60430
Phone: 708-798-0900
Fax: 708-798-1284
Web: www.buddig.com

CEO: Robert J. Buddig
CFO: Dan Wynn
HR: Karen Noble
FYE: December 31
Type: Private

Less is more at the Carl Buddig & Company, which manufactures and markets some of the thinnest lunch meats available. The company's most popular brand, Buddig Original, is a svelte 10-15 calories per slice and comes in choices such as beef, chicken, turkey, pastrami, and corned beef. It also offers Old Wisconsin brand beef sticks, snack bites, wieners, bratwurst, and Polish sausage. Carl Buddig meats are available in the US, Puerto Rico, and Canada, and are sold at retail food outlets, including Kroger, Albertson's, Safeway, Food Lion, Giant, Roundy's, and others.

CARLISLE COMPANIES INCORPORATED

NYSE: CSL

13925 Ballantyne Corporate Place, Ste. 400
Charlotte, NC 28277
Phone: 704-501-1100
Fax: 704-501-1190
Web: www.carlisle.com

CEO: David A. Roberts
CFO: Carol P. Lowe
HR: Beverly Sharp
FYE: December 31
Type: Public

Commercial manufacturing group Carlisle Companies is nothing if not diverse. Through dozens of subsidiaries, the company makes an array of products that include construction materials, industrial components, food service equipment, and aerospace wire and cable assemblies. Representing nearly half of the group's sales, the construction materials segment includes rubber and plastic roofing system products, as well as rigid foam insulation, waterproofing, and protective coatings. Its industrial components segment primarily makes wheels and tires for lawn and garden equipment, all-terrain vehicles (ATVs), and golf carts. Carlisle sells its products globally, but the US accounts for around 90% of sales.

	Annual Growth	12/03	12/04	12/05	12/06	12/07
Sales ($ mil.)	8.1%	2,108.2	2,227.6	2,209.6	2,572.5	2,876.4
Net income ($ mil.)	24.8%	88.9	79.6	106.4	215.7	215.6
Market value ($ mil.)	24.2%	943.1	1,002.9	1,049.6	1,210.5	2,244.2
Employees	0.0%	—	—	11,000	11,000	—

CARLSON COMPANIES, INC.

701 Carlson Pkwy.
Minnetonka, MN 55305
Phone: 763-212-4000
Fax: 763-212-2219
Web: www.carlson.com

CEO: Hubert Joly
CFO: Trudy Rautio
HR: Jim Porter
FYE: December 31
Type: Private

Carlson Companies began in 1938 as the Gold Bond Stamp Company, but has evolved into a leisure services juggernaut. The company owns 55% of travel giant Carlson Wagonlit. Its Carlson Hotels Worldwide owns and operates more than 900 hotels in some 70 countries under brands such as Radisson, Country Inns & Suites By Carlson, and Park Plaza; its Carlson Restaurants Worldwide includes the T.G.I. Friday's chain. A specialist in relationship marketing, Carlson Marketing offers services such as sales promotion and customer loyalty programs. Chairman Marilyn Carlson Nelson and director Barbara Carlson Gage, daughters of founder Curtis Carlson, each own half of the company.

	Annual Growth	12/02	12/03	12/04	12/05	12/06
Sales ($ mil.)	17.0%	19,800.0	20,900.0	30,700.0	34,400.0	37,100.0
Employees	(0.6%)	180,000	—	190,000	—	176,000

CARLSON RESTAURANTS WORLDWIDE, INC.

4201 Marsh Ln.
Carrollton, TX 75007
Phone: 972-662-5400
Fax: 972-307-2822
Web: www.fridays.com

CEO: Richard T. Snead
CFO: Brad Bixby
HR: Anne Varano
FYE: December 31
Type: Subsidiary

Carlson Restaurants Worldwide (CRW) has a lot of Friday's for which to be thankful. The company operates and franchises more than 900 T.G.I. Friday's casual dining restaurants across the US and in about 60 other countries. The chain offers a menu of beef, chicken, and seafood dishes but is popular for its appetizers and bar-like atmosphere. CRW owns about 330 of its Friday's locations and franchises or licenses the rest. The company also operates more than 125 Asian-themed restaurants under the Pick Up Stix banner. The first T.G.I. Friday's was opened in 1965 in New York City. CRW is a subsidiary of travel and hospitality conglomerate Carlson Companies.

THE CARLYLE GROUP

1001 Pennsylvania Ave. NW
Washington, DC 20004
Phone: 202-729-5626
Fax: 202-347-1818
Web: www.carlyle.com

CEO: Louis V. Gerstner Jr.
CFO: Peter H. Nachtwey
HR: Lori R. Sabet
FYE: December 31
Type: Private

The Carlyle Group, with more than $80 billion under management, is one of the world's largest private investment firms. Undertakings include management-led buyouts, minority equity investments, real estate, venture capital, and leveraged finance opportunities in the aerospace and defense, automotive and transportation, consumer and retail, and energy and power industies. Other sectors it focuses on include financial services, health care, industrial, infrastructure, real estate, technology, and telecommunications and media. Since its founding in 1987, the firm has made more than 775 investments; it maintains offices in about 20 countries and oversees some 60 private equity funds.

CARMAX, INC.

NYSE: KMX

12800 Tuckahoe Creek Parkway
Richmond, VA 23238
Phone: 804-747-0422
Fax: 804-217-6819
Web: www.carmax.com

CEO: Thomas J. (Tom) Folliard
CFO: Keith D. Browning
HR: Michael K. (Mike) Dolan
FYE: February 28
Type: Public

To the greatest extent possible, CarMax helps drivers find inexpensive autos. The nation's largest specialty used-car retailer buys, reconditions, and sells cars and light trucks at about 90 retail units in about two dozen states, mainly in the Southeast and Midwest; CarMax also operates six new-car franchises (all integrated or co-located with the used-car dealers). CarMax sells cars that are generally under six years old with less than 60,000 miles. CarMax also sells used cars through its ValuMax program. ValuMax cars are older than six years or have more than 60,000 miles. The company's Web site lets customers search CarMax outlets nationwide for a particular model.

	Annual Growth	2/04	2/05	2/06	2/07	2/08
Sales ($ mil.)	15.9%	4,597.7	5,260.3	6,364.3	7,465.7	8,285.4
Net income ($ mil.)	11.8%	116.4	112.9	148.1	198.6	182.0
Market value ($ mil.)	22.8%	1,764.2	1,721.0	1,648.8	5,692.3	4,013.8
Employees	11.8%	—	11,175	12,061	13,736	15,637

An in-depth profile of this company is available to Hoover's Online members at hoovers.com.

CARMIKE CINEMAS, INC.

NASDAQ (GM): CKEC

1301 First Ave.
Columbus, GA 31901
Phone: 706-576-3400
Fax: 706-576-2812
Web: www.carmike.com

CEO: Michael W. Patrick
CFO: Richard B. Hare
HR: –
FYE: December 31
Type: Public

Movies are the star at Carmike Cinemas, and the company wants to make sure the star shines brightly in your town. Among the largest theater chains in the US, Carmike owns, operates, or has stakes in about 2,400 screens at more than 250 theaters in 36 states. Carmike's theaters are located mostly in small to midsized communities where the chain hosts the only theater in town. The company's revenues come from the sale of admission tickets and concessions. The firm also owns two Hollywood Connection family entertainment centers, which feature multiplex theaters along with skating rinks, miniature golf, and arcades. Carmike emerged from bankruptcy in 2002 after closing about 30% of its theaters.

	Annual Growth	12/03	12/04	12/05	12/06	12/07
Sales ($ mil.)	(0.2%)	493.1	494.5	468.9	495.5	489.3
Net income ($ mil.)	—	106.4	28.4	0.2	(19.4)	(126.9)
Market value ($ mil.)	(26.5%)	318.8	443.9	312.2	254.1	93.1
Employees	(7.0%)	—	—	7,908	7,383	6,838

CARNIVAL CORPORATION

NYSE: CCL

3655 NW 87th Ave.
Miami, FL 33178
Phone: 305-599-2600
Fax: 305-406-4700
Web: www.carnivalcorp.com

CEO: Micky Arison
CFO: David Bernstein
HR: Susan Herrmann
FYE: November 30
Type: Public

Carnival offers a boatload of fun. The company is the world's #1 cruise operator, with about a dozen cruise lines and about 85 ships carrying 7 million passengers. Carnival operates in North America primarily through its Princess Cruise Line, Holland America, and Seabourn luxury cruise brand, as well as its flagship Carnival Cruise Lines unit. Brands such as AIDA, P&O Cruises, and Costa Cruises offer services to passengers in Europe, and the Cunard Line operates luxury transatlantic liners. Carnival operates as a dual-listed company with UK-based Carnival plc, forming a single enterprise under a unified executive team.

	Annual Growth	11/03	11/04	11/05	11/06	11/07
Sales ($ mil.)	18.0%	6,718.0	9,727.0	11,087.0	11,839.0	13,033.0
Net income ($ mil.)	19.2%	1,194.0	1,854.0	2,257.0	2,279.0	2,408.0
Market value ($ mil.)	6.2%	22,169.7	33,608.3	34,710.1	30,520.8	28,154.9
Employees	6.8%	—	—	71,200	74,700	81,200

CAROLINA POWER & LIGHT COMPANY

410 S. Wilmington St.
Raleigh, NC 27601
Phone: 919-546-6111
Fax: 919-546-2920
Web: www.progress-energy.com

CEO: Lloyd M. Yates
CFO: Peter M. Scott III
HR: –
FYE: December 31
Type: Subsidiary

The Palmetto state and Tarheels both have Carolina Power & Light on their minds when they need some power. The company, which operates as Progress Energy Carolinas, transmits and distributes electricity to some 1.4 million homes and businesses in the Carolinas. The utility generates more than 12,400 MW of capacity from its fossil-fueled, nuclear, and hydroelectric power plants. Carolina Power & Light purchases about 5% of the power it distributes. The Progress Energy subsidiary also sells power to wholesale customers (primarily other utilities and energy marketers).

	Annual Growth	12/03	12/04	12/05	12/06	12/07
Est. sales ($ mil.)	—	—	—	—	—	9,153.0
Net income ($ mil.)	—	—	—	—	—	504.0
Employees	—	—	—	—	—	—

CAROLINA BANK HOLDINGS INC.

NASDAQ (CM): CLBH

528 College Rd.
Greensboro, NC 27410
Phone: 336-288-1898
Fax: 336-286-5553
Web: www.carolinabank.com

CEO: Robert T. Braswell
CFO: T. Allen Liles
HR: Angela J. Nowlin
FYE: December 31
Type: Public

You'll have to ask James Taylor if he's going to Carolina Bank Holdings in his mind. The firm owns Carolina Bank, which serves individuals and small to midsized businesses through six branches in north-central North Carolina. The community-oriented financial institution offers standard services such as checking and savings accounts, money market and individual retirement accounts, CDs, ATM and debit cards, and online banking and bill payment. Its lending activities primarily consist of commercial real estate loans, residential mortgages, construction and land development loans, and business loans.

	Annual Growth	12/03	12/04	12/05	12/06	12/07
Assets ($ mil.)	21.8%	226.9	311.5	365.2	411.6	500.1
Net income ($ mil.)	28.5%	1.1	1.6	2.0	2.8	3.0
Market value ($ mil.)	28.2%	13.8	18.9	21.3	29.8	37.3
Employees	22.0%	—	—	59	72	—

CAROLINA TRUST BANK

NASDAQ (CM): CART

901 E. Main St.
Lincolnton, NC 28092
Phone: 704-735-1104
Fax: 704-735-1258
Web: www.carolinatrust.com

CEO: J. Michael Cline
CFO: Donald J. Boyer
HR: Treva J. Carey
FYE: December 31
Type: Public

Carolina Trust Bank serves southwestern North Carolina's Lincoln County from four branches (two in Lincolnton, one in Vale, and a supermarket branch in Denver). It provides a variety of commercial and personal services including checking and savings accounts, IRAs, CDs, credit cards, and merchant debit cards. Residential mortgages make up approximately 40% of its lending portfolio; other offerings include construction loans, commercial mortgages (about 20% each), and consumer loans. The bank also sells annuities and mutual funds. Carolina Trust Bank was founded in 2000.

	Annual Growth	12/02	12/03	12/04	12/05	*12/06
Assets ($ mil.)	26.6%	45.5	64.6	83.0	102.9	116.7
Net income ($ mil.)	—	—	—	—	—	1.6
Employees	—	—	—	—	—	40

*Most recent year available

CAROLINAS HEALTHCARE SYSTEM

1000 Blythe Blvd.
Charlotte, NC 28203
Phone: 704-355-2000
Fax: 704-355-4084
Web: www.carolinas.org

CEO: Michael C. (Mike) Tarwater
CFO: Greg A. Gombar
HR: F. Taylor Renfro
FYE: December 31
Type: Government-owned

"Say how thy elder children bled . . . Carolina! Carolina!" isn't piping through the hallways of the Carolinas HealthCare System facilities, but the hospitals do care for the injured and infirmed. Carolinas HealthCare System owns and operates more than 15 hospitals in North and South Carolina. The company also manages about a dozen long-term care facilities, three research centers, home health agencies, physician practices, radiation therapy facilities, and other health care operations. Its health care facilities have about 4,300 beds total.

	Annual Growth	12/03	12/04	12/05	12/06	12/07
Est. sales ($ mil.)	—	—	—	—	—	1,938.8
Employees	—	—	—	—	—	12,000

CARPENTER CO.

5016 Monument Ave.	CEO: Stanley F. Pauley
Richmond, VA 23230	CFO: Michael (Mike) Lowery
Phone: 804-359-0800	HR: Rich Trownsell
Fax: 804-353-0694	FYE: December 31
Web: www.carpenter.com	Type: Private

It's a cushy job for Carpenter Co., making polyurethane foam and chemicals and polyester fiber used as cushioning by the automotive, bedding, floor covering, packaging, and furniture industries. The company started out making foam rubber; it now also manufactures air filters, expanded polystyrene building materials, and a tire fill product used as a replacement for air in off-road construction vehicles. Carpenter also sells consumer products — which include craft fiber products, mattress pads, and pillows — through retailers. The company has facilities throughout North America and Europe. Carpenter, which was founded in 1948 by E. Rhodes Carpenter, is owned by chairman and CEO Stanley Pauley.

	Annual Growth	12/02	12/03	12/04	12/05	12/06
Sales ($ mil.)	11.3%	1,114.0	1,200.0	1,300.0	1,456.0	1,710.0
Employees	(1.4%)	6,000	6,000	6,000	5,900	5,675

CARPENTER TECHNOLOGY CORPORATION

NYSE: CRS

2 Meridian Blvd.	CEO: Anne Stevens
Wyomissing, PA 19610	CFO: K. Douglas (Doug) Ralph
Phone: 610-208-2000	HR: Barry J. Chapman
Fax: 610-208-3716	FYE: June 30
Web: www.cartech.com	Type: Public

The Tin Man never would have rusted had he been built with metal from Carpenter Technology. The company makes a variety of corrosion-resistant materials; most of its sales come from stainless steel products and alloys that provide special heat- or wear-resistance or special magnetic or conductive properties. Finished products come in billet, bar, rod, wire, and other forms. Carpenter also makes titanium products, engineered ceramic products, and tool and other specialty steels. Customers include companies in the aerospace, automotive, medical, and industrial markets.

	Annual Growth	6/03	6/04	6/05	6/06	6/07
Sales ($ mil.)	22.2%	871.1	1,016.7	1,314.2	1,568.2	1,944.8
Net income ($ mil.)	—	(10.9)	36.0	135.5	211.8	227.2
Market value ($ mil.)	76.8%	174.2	392.2	645.5	1,473.8	1,702.0
Employees	1.8%	—	—	4,003	3,990	4,152

CARQUEST CORPORATION

2635 E. Millbrook Rd.	CEO: Temple Sloan III
Raleigh, NC 27604	CFO: John Gardner
Phone: 919-573-3000	HR: Scott Derrow
Fax: 919-573-2501	FYE: December 31
Web: www.carquest.com	Type: Private

Searching for a sensor, solenoid, or switches? CARQUEST can steer you in the right direction. The replacement auto parts distribution group is owned by its five member warehouse distributors (the largest is North Carolina-based General Parts). The CARQUEST group includes a network of about 40 distribution centers serving distributor-owned and independent jobbers in the US and Canada. The company sells its own line of auto parts (made by Moog Automotive, Dana, Gabriel, and others) to the jobbers, as well as wholesalers, for eventual resale to professional repair centers, service stations, dealerships, and, to a lesser degree, do-it-yourself (DIY) customers.

CARRIAGE SERVICES, INC.

NYSE: CSV

3040 Post Oak Blvd., Ste. 300	CEO: Melvin C. (Mel) Payne
Houston, TX 77056	CFO: Terry Sanford
Phone: 713-332-8400	HR: –
Fax: 713-332-8401	FYE: December 31
Web: www.carriageservices.com	Type: Public

Though it buries its customers, Carriage Services hasn't come close to burying its competition. It's a large US death care company, but it trails far behind Service Corporation International (SCI) and rivals Stewart Enterprises and StoneMor Partners. Carriage Services runs about 140 funeral homes (owned and leased) and some 30 cemeteries (owned and leased) in about 25 states, but mostly in California, Kentucky, and Texas. It removes and prepares remains, sells caskets and memorials, provides transportation services, hosts ceremonies, performs burials, and maintains cemetery grounds. Carriage Services was established in 1993. FMR owns about 15% of the company.

	Annual Growth	12/03	12/04	12/05	12/06	12/07
Sales ($ mil.)	2.7%	150.8	150.2	155.0	151.1	167.8
Net income ($ mil.)	5.9%	6.6	9.2	(21.9)	(1.4)	8.3
Market value ($ mil.)	27.0%	64.9	88.5	92.3	94.7	169.1
Employees	—	—	—	1,781	—	—

CARRIER CORPORATION

1 Carrier Place	CEO: Geraud Darnis
Farmington, CT 06034	CFO: Joe Schena
Phone: 860-674-3000	HR: Patrick Preux
Fax: 860-674-3139	FYE: December 31
Web: www.carrier.com	Type: Subsidiary

Carrier keeps its cool when the heat is on. A subsidiary of diversified manufacturer United Technologies Corporation (UTC), Carrier is the world's largest maker of heating, ventilation, and air-conditioning (HVAC) equipment and refrigeration systems; it operates around 70 manufacturing facilities and has dealers in more than 170 countries. Its HVAC equipment is used in homes and buildings ranging from hospitals to museums. Its Transicold unit makes truck/trailer and container refrigeration equipment and provides transport air-conditioning systems for bus, rail, and marine customers. Carrier, which accounts for about 27% of UTC's sales, also provides aftermarket services and components for its products.

	Annual Growth	12/03	12/04	12/05	12/06	12/07
Est. sales ($ mil.)	—	—	—	—	—	14,600.0
Employees	—	—	—	—	—	43,000

CARRINGTON LABORATORIES, INC.

OTC: CARN

2001 Walnut Hill Ln.	CEO: Carlton E. Turner
Irving, TX 75038	CFO: Robert W. Schnitzius
Phone: 972-518-1300	HR: Carol Kitchell
Fax: 972-518-1020	FYE: December 31
Web: www.carringtonlabs.com	Type: Public

Carrington Laboratories has decided that aloe vera juice would get it only so far before it was time for a boost. The firm makes medical and consumer nutritional products, and is developing a vaccine delivery system. It also manufactures personal care products, manufactures and supplies bulk aloe vera-based materials, and provides third-party manufacturing services to other companies. Carrington's Medical Services division makes wound care products for use in hospitals and medical care facilities. However, the company has now pinned its future on the development of a polymer derived from aloe vera plants for use in vaccines. Carrington Laboratories has facilities in the US and Costa Rica.

	Annual Growth	12/03	12/04	12/05	12/06	12/07
Sales ($ mil.)	(7.0%)	29.1	30.8	28.0	27.4	21.8
Net income ($ mil.)	—	(1.5)	0.0	(5.3)	(7.6)	(9.8)
Market value ($ mil.)	(58.0%)	42.8	65.7	51.1	31.0	1.3
Employees	(3.3%)	262	324	263	260	229

An in-depth profile of this company is available to Hoover's Online members at hoovers.com.

331

CARRIX, INC.

1131 SW Klickitat Way
Seattle, WA 98134
Phone: 206-382-4490
Fax: 206-623-0179
Web: www.carrix.com

CEO: Jon Hemingway
CFO: Charles (Charlie) Sadowski
HR: –
FYE: December 31
Type: Private

Holding company Carrix carries three transportation-related businesses on its books. The company's SSA Marine unit is a leading marine terminal operator. It loads and unloads ships and provides warehousing and distribution services. Overall, SSA Marine operates from about 120 locations worldwide. Other Carrix units include Rail Management Services (RMS), which operates some 45 railyards in two dozen states; and Tideworks Technology, which produces marine terminal management software. Carrix is controlled by members of the Smith and Hemingway families, including president and CEO Jon Hemingway. In 2007, Goldman Sachs acquired a 49% stake in Carrix.

	Annual Growth	12/03	12/04	12/05	12/06	12/07
Est. sales ($ mil.)	—	—	—	—	—	728.3
Employees	—	—	—	—	—	11,000

CARRIZO OIL & GAS, INC.

NASDAQ (GS): CRZO

1000 Louisiana St., Ste. 1500
Houston, TX 77002
Phone: 713-328-1000
Fax: 713-328-1035
Web: www.carrizo.cc

CEO: S. P. Johnson IV
CFO: Paul F. Boling
HR: Deborah (Debbie) Soho
FYE: December 31
Type: Public

Carrizo Oil & Gas sees its future in 3-D. An independent exploration and production company that drills in proven onshore fields along the Gulf Coast of Texas and Louisiana, Carrizo aggressively acquires 3-D seismic data and arranges land lease options in conjunction with conducting seismic surveys. As part of a new strategy, the company is exploiting deeper, over-pressured targets, which generally require higher cost. Carrizo has additional properties in North Texas, the Rockies, Alabama, Arkansas, Kentucky, New Mexico, and in the UK North Sea. In 2007 it reported proved reserves of 347.6 billion cu. ft. of natural gas equivalent. Chairman Steven Webster owns about 8% of Carrizo.

	Annual Growth	12/03	12/04	12/05	12/06	12/07
Sales ($ mil.)	34.4%	38.5	52.4	78.2	82.9	125.8
Net income ($ mil.)	18.4%	7.9	11.1	10.6	18.3	15.5
Market value ($ mil.)	95.5%	105.1	250.4	599.0	754.0	1,533.5
Employees	22.5%	—	—	50	68	75

CARROLLTON BANCORP

NASDAQ (GM): CRRB

344 N. Charles St., Ste. 300
Baltimore, MD 21201
Phone: 410-536-4600
Fax: 410-625-0355
Web: www.carrolltonbank.com

CEO: Robert A. Altieri
CFO: James M. Uveges
HR: –
FYE: December 31
Type: Public

Carrollton Bancorp can babysit your money from Babe Ruth's hometown. The institution is the holding company for Carrollton Bank, a commercial bank serving Baltimore and surrounding areas from about a dozen branches. It offers standard retail services, such as checking and savings accounts, money market accounts, and IRAs. Commercial real estate and residential mortgages account for about 45% and 20%, respectively, of the bank's loan portfolio. Bank subsidiary Carrollton Financial Services sells stocks, bonds, mutual funds, and annuities; Carrollton Mortgage Services originates and sells residential mortgages.

	Annual Growth	12/03	12/04	12/05	12/06	12/07
Assets ($ mil.)	3.9%	302.4	319.1	360.5	349.8	352.9
Net income ($ mil.)	23.6%	0.9	0.9	2.5	2.6	2.1
Market value ($ mil.)	(5.9%)	50.3	50.4	42.1	48.2	39.5
Employees	(6.6%)	—	—	157	—	137

CARROLS RESTAURANT GROUP, INC.

NASDAQ (GM): TAST

968 James St.
Syracuse, NY 13203
Phone: 315-424-0513
Fax: 315-475-9616
Web: www.carrols.com

CEO: Alan Vituli
CFO: Paul R. Flanders
HR: –
FYE: Sunday nearest December 31
Type: Public

This company has some fast food royalty in its blood. Carrols Restaurant Group is a leading quick-service restaurant operator and the #1 Burger King franchisee in the US, with more than 320 units in New York, Ohio, and about 10 other states. The company also operates two of its own quick-service chains: Taco Cabana and Pollo Tropical. Taco Cabana offers Tex-Mex and Mexican dishes through about 150 locations (mostly in Texas), while Pollo Tropical features fresh grilled chicken at more than 100 company-owned and franchised locations found primarily in Florida.

	Annual Growth	12/03	12/04	12/05	12/06	12/07
Sales ($ mil.)	5.2%	645.0	697.9	706.9	751.4	789.4
Net income ($ mil.)	58.4%	2.4	(8.1)	(4.3)	13.4	15.1
Market value ($ mil.)	(32.0%)	—	—	—	305.6	207.7
Employees	1.0%	15,900	17,000	16,300	16,400	—

CARSEY-WERNER, LLC

4024 Radford Ave., Ste. 3
Studio City, CA 91604
Phone: 818-655-5598
Fax: 818-655-6067
Web: www.cwm.com

CEO: Robert (Bob) Dubelko
CFO: Bret Sarnoff
HR: –
FYE: December 31
Type: Private

Many consider Carsey-Werner to be the king of TV comedy. During its high-point, the television production and distribution company was responsible for creating several hit TV shows, including *The Cosby Show, 3rd Rock From the Sun*, and *Roseanne*, as well as *A Different World, Grace Under Fire*, and *Cybil*. No longer active in TV production, Carsey-Werner continues to distribute shows for syndication in more than 175 countries and in 50 languages. Its films division continues to develop a small number of projects, as well. Partners Marcy Carsey and Tom Werner founded the studio in 1981.

CARTER & BURGESS, INC.

777 Main St.
Fort Worth, TX 76102
Phone: 817-735-6000
Fax: 817-735-6148
Web: www.c-b.com

CEO: Benjamin G. (Ben) Watts
CFO: David S. Johnson
HR: James (Jim) Garman
FYE: December 31
Type: Subsidiary

Carter & Burgess takes a civil approach to engineering and design. Founded in 1939 as a two-man partnership between friends Gene Carter and John Burgess, Carter & Burgess has grown into one of the largest architectural and engineering firms in the US. Expanding on its traditional offering of civil engineering and landscape architecture, Carter & Burgess provides a full portfolio of services, including strategic planning, surveying, and construction and project management. A leading "pure design" firm, Carter & Burgess serves several industry sectors, including retail, transportation, land development, and environmental. Customers include FedEx and Wal-Mart. Jacobs Engineering acquired Carter & Burgess in 2007.

	Annual Growth	12/03	12/04	12/05	12/06	12/07
Est. sales ($ mil.)	—	—	—	—	—	498.1
Employees	—	—	—	—	—	2,840

CARTER LUMBER

601 Tallmadge Rd.
Kent, OH 44240
Phone: 330-673-6100
Fax: 330-678-6134
Web: www.carterlumber.com

CEO: Neil C. Sackett
CFO: Jeffrey S. (Jeff) Donley
HR: David McCafferty
FYE: December 31
Type: Private

If new home construction has you yelling "timber!" Carter has the answer. Carter Lumber owns more than 200 lumber and home-improvement stores in 10 states from Michigan to South Carolina. The company caters to both contractors and do-it-yourselfers, supplying them with lumber, plywood, roofing, windows, doors, plumbing and electrical products, heating equipment, tools, siding, and other products. The home-improvement retailer also owns the Carter-Jones Timber Co., which owns and manages about 74,000 acres of timberland in Arkansas. Warren Carter, who founded the company in 1932, died in 2000 at the age of 101. However, Carter Lumber continues to be a family-owned business.

	Annual Growth	12/03	12/04	12/05	12/06	12/07
Est. sales ($ mil.)	—	—	—	—	—	313.5
Employees	—	—	—	—	—	120

CARTER'S, INC.

NYSE: CRI

The Proscenium, 1170 Peachtree St. NE, Ste. 900
Atlanta, GA 30309
Phone: 404-745-2700
Fax: 404-892-0968
Web: www.carters.com

CEO: Frederick J. (Fred) Rowan II
CFO: Michael D. Casey
HR: Clyde Stutts
FYE: Saturday nearest December 31
Type: Public

For babes, there's nothing quite as comforting as snuggling up to Mom or Dad while in a Carter's sleeper. In addition to producing babies' and children's sleepwear, Carter's (which operates through its The William Carter Company unit) is a leading US maker of apparel for fashionable youngsters. Its primary products include newborn layette clothing, sleepwear, and playwear. Carter's markets its items under names Carter's, Child of Mine, OshKosh B'Gosh, and Just One Year through department and specialty stores and about 390 company outlets nationwide. Berkshire Partners bought the company and took it public in 2003. Carter's bought OshKosh B'Gosh for about $312 million in 2005.

	Annual Growth	12/03	12/04	12/05	12/06	12/07
Sales ($ mil.)	19.0%	703.8	823.1	1,121.4	1,343.5	1,412.3
Net income ($ mil.)	—	23.3	49.7	47.2	87.2	(70.6)
Market value ($ mil.)	34.4%	351.8	483.2	850.7	1,502.6	1,147.5
Employees	36.7%	—	—	4,083	6,731	7,630

THE CARTOON NETWORK LP, LLLP

1050 Techwood Dr.
Atlanta, GA 30318
Phone: 404-827-1700
Fax: 404-827-2559
Web: www.cartoonnetwork.com

CEO: Stuart C. Snyder
CFO: –
HR: –
FYE: December 31
Type: Subsidiary

If you like powerpuffs or superheroes, science geniuses or martial arts, you might want to toon into The Cartoon Network. Owned by Turner Broadcasting, the television subsidiary of Time Warner, the cable channel is best known for its popular programs such as *The Powerpuff Girls, Dexter's Laboratory, Teen Titans,* and *Foster's Home for Imaginary Friends*. The network offers original, acquired, and classic animated entertainment for kids and families. In addition to children's programming, adults can also get in on the animated action with the Adult Swim late-night block of shows. The Cartoon Network is seen in more than 90 million US households, as well as in 160 countries.

CARVEL CORPORATION

200 Glenridge Point Pkwy., Ste. 200
Atlanta, GA 30342
Phone: 404-255-3250
Fax: 404-255-4978
Web: www.carvel.com

CEO: Gary Bales
CFO: Lenore L. Krentz
HR: –
FYE: December 31
Type: Subsidiary

If Fudgie the Whale and Cookie Puss conjure up childhood memories of ice cream, you're a true fan of Carvel's. The company operates a chain of more than 570 franchised ice cream outlets known for their soft-serve ice cream and other frozen treats, including character-shaped frozen ice cream cakes. Carvel locations are typically found in high-traffic areas such as airports, malls, and sports stadiums in 25 states (mostly in the Northeast), Canada, and Puerto Rico. In addition, the company sells ice cream cakes through about 8,500 supermarkets. Tom Carvel, a traveling salesman, founded the chain in 1934. It is owned by FOCUS Brands, an affiliate of Atlanta-based Roark Capital Group.

CARVER BANCORP, INC.

AMEX: CARV

75 W. 125th St.
New York, NY 10027
Phone: 212-876-4747
Fax: 212-426-6159
Web: www.carverbank.com

CEO: Deborah C. (Debbie) Wright
CFO: Roy Swan
HR: Margaret D. Roberts
FYE: March 31
Type: Public

Carver Bancorp, one of the largest minority-led financial institutions in the US, is the holding company for Carver Federal Savings Bank, which was founded in 1948 to provide community banking services to New York City's African-American and Caribbean-American population. From about 10 branches in Harlem, Brooklyn, and Queens, the thrift offers deposit accounts, insurance, and investment products. Carver Federal's lending activities are focused on housing (residential mortgages and multifamily real estate loans) and non-residential real estate (churches and commercial properties; about 35% of the loan portfolio).

	Annual Growth	3/04	3/05	3/06	3/07	3/08
Assets ($ mil.)	10.3%	538.8	626.4	661.0	740.0	796.4
Net income ($ mil.)	(4.5%)	4.8	2.7	3.8	2.6	4.0
Market value ($ mil.)	(14.4%)	53.7	47.2	42.8	41.8	28.8
Employees	(6.7%)	—	135	126	—	—

CARVER BOAT CORPORATION, LLC

790 Markham Dr.
Pulaski, WI 54162
Phone: 920-822-1600
Fax: 920-822-8820
Web: www.carveryachts.com

CEO: Robert (Bob) VanGrunsven
CFO: –
HR: –
FYE: December 31
Type: Private

Carver Boat manufactures luxury motor yachts that range in size from 36 feet to 56 feet. Models include Mariner, Super Sport, and Voyager. Carver Boat is part of the Carver Yacht Group, which is a division of pleasure boat manufacturer Genmar Holdings. Other Carver Yacht Group brands include Marquis and Nuvari by Carver. Carver Boat maintains manufacturing facilities in Wisconsin and in Fano, Italy. The company was founded in 1954.

	Annual Growth	12/03	12/04	12/05	12/06	12/07
Est. sales ($ mil.)	—	—	—	—	—	89.4
Employees	—	—	—	—	—	950

An in-depth profile of this company is available to Hoover's Online members at hoovers.com.

333

CAS MEDICAL SYSTEMS, INC.

NASDAQ (GM): CASM

44 E. Industrial Rd.
Branford, CT 06405
Phone: 203-488-6056
Fax: 203-488-9438
Web: www.casmed.com

CEO: Andrew E. Kersey
CFO: Jeffery A. Baird
HR: –
FYE: December 31
Type: Public

CAS Medical Systems (CASMED) makes blood pressure measurement devices, vital signs monitors, apnea monitors, and neonatal supplies. Major brands include the MAXNIBP blood pressure technology, the CAS 750 vital signs monitor, and the AMI and 511 cardio-respiratory monitoring system. Subsidiary Statcorp makes blood pressure cuffs, pressure infuser cuffs, and blood filter products. The company sells its products in Europe, North America, Latin America, Africa, and the Pacific Rim to hospitals and other health care professionals through specialty distributors and sales representatives.

	Annual Growth	12/03	12/04	12/05	12/06	12/07
Sales ($ mil.)	22.6%	16.9	19.9	26.9	35.2	38.2
Net income ($ mil.)	(19.1%)	0.7	1.2	1.8	1.8	0.3
Market value ($ mil.)	44.9%	13.6	22.2	86.0	84.7	59.9
Employees	6.3%	—	—	143	152	—

CASCADE BANCORP

NASDAQ (CM): CACB

1100 NW Wall St.
Bend, OR 97701
Phone: 541-385-6205
Fax: 541-382-8780
Web: www.botc.com

CEO: Patricia L. Moss
CFO: Gregory D. Newton
HR: Peggy L. Biss
FYE: December 31
Type: Public

Forget the dirty dishes. Cascade Bancorp wants to provide sparkling customer service. It's the holding company for Bank of the Cascades, which operates about 35 branches in Oregon and Idaho. Targeting individuals and small to midsized businesses, the banks offer traditional retail banking services and trust and investment services. More than two-thirds of the company's loan portfolio is composed of construction, residential mortgage, and commercial real estate loans. The bank also offers business loans; consumer loans accounted for only 2% in 2007.

	Annual Growth	12/03	12/04	12/05	12/06	12/07
Assets ($ mil.)	34.4%	734.7	1,004.8	1,269.7	2,249.3	2,394.5
Net income ($ mil.)	21.2%	13.9	16.0	22.4	35.7	30.0
Market value ($ mil.)	25.8%	155.6	270.8	312.1	879.1	390.2
Employees	29.0%	—	—	336	573	559

CASCADE CORPORATION

NYSE: CAE

2201 NE 201st Ave.
Fairview, OR 97024
Phone: 503-669-6300
Fax: 503-669-6716
Web: www.cascorp.com

CEO: Robert C. (Bob) Warren Jr.
CFO: Joseph G. Pointer
HR: Gregory S. Anderson
FYE: January 31
Type: Public

Cascade is in a rush to give you a lift. The company's two principal product lines — Cascade attachment products and Cascade-Kenhar fork products — are manufactured for the lift truck industry. Cascade's product line includes forklift attachments, forks, hydraulic cylinders, and replacement parts that help pull, rotate, tilt, side shift, clamp, and lift appliances, paper rolls, and other types of loads. Its products are sold to original equipment manufactures (OEMs) and original equipment dealers (OEDs), primarily in North America (accounting for 50% of sales), but the company has operations worldwide. Sales to OEMs make up about 45% of total revenues.

	Annual Growth	1/04	1/05	1/06	1/07	1/08
Sales ($ mil.)	17.0%	297.8	385.7	450.5	478.9	558.1
Net income ($ mil.)	34.3%	18.5	28.5	42.0	45.5	60.2
Market value ($ mil.)	21.6%	255.6	447.4	640.1	648.4	559.6
Employees	10.5%	—	—	1,900	2,100	—

CASCADE FINANCIAL CORPORATION

NASDAQ (GS): CASB

2828 Colby Ave.
Everett, WA 98201
Phone: 425-339-5500
Fax: 425-259-8512
Web: www.cascadebank.com

CEO: Carol K. Nelson
CFO: Lars H. Johnson
HR: –
FYE: December 31
Type: Public

Cascade Financial is the holding company for Cascade Bank, which operates almost 20 branches in Washington State's Puget Sound area. Founded in 1916, the bank offers such deposit products as checking, savings, and money market accounts, as well as CDs and IRAs. Funds gathered are used primarily to originate business loans (more than 40% of the company's loan portfolio), construction loans (more than 30%), commercial and residential mortgages, and consumer loans. The bank also issues Visa credit cards. It offers investment services through an agreement with Stockcross Financial Services.

	Annual Growth	12/03	12/04	12/05	12/06	12/07
Assets ($ mil.)	12.5%	885.2	1,089.0	1,211.8	1,345.3	1,417.6
Net income ($ mil.)	12.9%	9.6	10.8	13.1	13.4	15.6
Market value ($ mil.)	6.4%	127.8	144.2	136.4	206.7	163.5
Employees	1.2%	—	—	206	—	211

CASCADE MICROTECH, INC.

NASDAQ (GM): CSCD

2430 NW 206th Ave.
Beaverton, OR 97006
Phone: 503-601-1000
Fax: 503-601-1002
Web: www.cascademicrotech.com

CEO: Geoffrey (Geoff) Wild
CFO: Steven (Steve) Sipowicz
HR: Art Smith
FYE: December 31
Type: Public

In the foothills of the Cascade Range, Cascade Microtech makes test systems for microelectronics. Semiconductor makers such as Fujitsu Microelectronics, Intel, Infineon, and Texas Instruments use the company's probe cards, probe stations, and analytical probes to ensure the quality of their integrated circuits (ICs). Many of Cascade's customers use its tools to test their wireless, broadband, or other communications ICs at the wafer level, before the wafers are cut into individual chips. The company has a development alliance with test equipment giant Agilent Technologies. Cascade gets about 60% of its sales outside of the US.

	Annual Growth	12/03	12/04	12/05	12/06	12/07
Sales ($ mil.)	15.5%	50.6	64.4	73.6	84.8	89.9
Net income ($ mil.)	—	(0.4)	4.7	8.3	3.6	0.9
Market value ($ mil.)	(3.5%)	—	145.9	143.1	153.5	131.2
Employees	9.9%	243	272	287	366	354

CASCADE NATURAL GAS CORPORATION

222 Fairview Ave. North
Seattle, WA 98109
Phone: 206-624-3900
Fax: 206-624-7215
Web: www.cngc.com

CEO: David L. Goodin
CFO: James E. (Jim) Haug
HR: Larry C. Rosok
FYE: September 30
Type: Subsidiary

To 93 small communities in Washington and Oregon, Cascade Natural Gas is the main man. The gas utility transmits and distributes natural gas to 244,000 residential, commercial, and industrial customers. It also distributes gas to approximately 200 noncore customers, mostly large industrial users buying their supplies from third parties. Cascade Natural Gas owns 5,408 miles of distribution mains, 214 miles of transmission mains, and 3,681 miles of service lines. Subsidiary CGC Energy offers services to industrial natural gas customers. The utility obtains its gas mainly from Canadian suppliers. In 2007 diversified natural resources company MDU Resources acquired Cascade for $475 million.

	Annual Growth	9/02	9/03	9/04	9/05	9/06
Sales ($ mil.)	9.2%	321.0	302.8	318.1	326.5	456.0
Net income ($ mil.)	3.7%	10.8	9.1	13.3	9.3	12.5
Employees	(5.5%)	444	437	428	375	—

CASELLA WASTE SYSTEMS, INC.

NASDAQ (GS): CWST

25 Greens Hill Ln.
Rutland, VT 05701
Phone: 802-775-0325
Fax: 802-775-6198
Web: www.casella.com

CEO: John W. Casella
CFO: Richard A. Norris
HR: Gerry Gormley
FYE: April 30
Type: Public

The wasteful habits of Americans are big business for Casella Waste Systems, which operates regional waste-hauling businesses, mainly in the northeastern US, that serve commercial, industrial, and residential customers. Overall, the company owns and/or operates 38 solid waste collection businesses, 38 recycling facilities, 32 transfer stations, 11 ordinary and two sepcialized landfills, and one waste-to-energy power generation facility. In addition to its waste-related operations, Casella Waste Systems has a 50% stake in GreenFiber, a joint venture with Louisiana-Pacific that produces cellulose insulation. Investment firm Buckhead Capital Management controls 14.4% in Casella Waste Systems.

	Annual Growth	4/04	4/05	4/06	4/07	4/08
Sales ($ mil.)	7.1%	439.7	482.0	525.9	547.0	579.5
Net income ($ mil.)	—	8.1	7.3	11.1	(17.9)	(7.8)
Market value ($ mil.)	(6.5%)	340.7	281.3	376.1	226.3	260.8
Employees	(3.4%)	—	—	2,900	2,800	—

CASEY'S GENERAL STORES, INC.

NASDAQ (GS): CASY

1 Convenience Blvd.
Ankeny, IA 50021
Phone: 515-965-6100
Fax: 515-965-6160
Web: www.caseys.com

CEO: Ronald M. (Ron) Lamb
CFO: William J. (Bill) Walljasper
HR: Julie L. Jackowski
FYE: April 30
Type: Public

Casey's General Stores makes sure that small towns in the Midwest get their fill of convenient shopping. The company operates or franchises more than 1,450 convenience stores, mostly in Illinois, Iowa, and Missouri, but also in Indiana, Kansas, Minnesota, Nebraska, South Dakota, and Wisconsin, all within about 500 miles of the company's headquarters and distribution center. Casey's stores sell beverages, gasoline, groceries, and fresh prepared foods, such as donuts, pizza, and sandwiches. Casey's also sells tobacco products, automotive goods, and other nonfood items, including ammunition, housewares, and photo supplies.

	Annual Growth	4/04	4/05	4/06	4/07	4/08
Sales ($ mil.)	19.5%	2,369.1	2,810.5	3,515.1	4,024.0	4,827.1
Net income ($ mil.)	23.5%	36.5	36.8	60.5	61.9	84.9
Market value ($ mil.)	7.9%	828.3	847.2	1,077.4	1,272.4	1,122.7
Employees	8.9%	—	14,440	15,692	17,136	—

CASH AMERICA INTERNATIONAL, INC.

NYSE: CSH

1600 W. 7th St.
Fort Worth, TX 76102
Phone: 817-335-1100
Fax: 817-570-1225
Web: www.cashamerica.com

CEO: Daniel R. (Dan) Feehan
CFO: Thomas A. Bessant Jr.
HR: –
FYE: December 31
Type: Public

If cash is king, then Cash America International is king of pawns. Ruling over a kingdom of some 500 locations in 22 states, it's one of the largest providers of secured, non-recourse loans (known as pawn loans) in the nation. It operates through Cash America Pawn and SuperPawn shops; customers collateralize high-interest loans with jewelry, electronics, and other items. If the loans aren't repaid, the firm sells the collateral in its stores. Cash America also offers cash advances, check cashing, and money orders and transfers through stores operating as Cashland Financial Services and Cash America Payday Advance. Check cashing services are offered through about 130 owned and franchised Mr. Payroll stores.

	Annual Growth	12/03	12/04	12/05	12/06	12/07
Assets ($ mil.)	16.6%	489.5	555.2	598.7	776.2	904.6
Net income ($ mil.)	27.5%	30.0	56.8	45.0	60.9	79.3
Market value ($ mil.)	12.0%	597.2	871.0	680.9	1,391.5	939.9
Employees	12.9%	—	—	4,565	5,152	—

CASH SYSTEMS, INC.

NASDAQ (GM): CKNN

7350 Dean Martin Dr., Ste. 309
Las Vegas, NV 89139
Phone: 702-987-7169
Fax: 702-987-7168
Web: www.cashsystemsinc.com

CEO: Michael D. Rumbolz
CFO: Andrew J. Cashin
HR: –
FYE: December 31
Type: Public

Cash Systems helps casinos keep their customers in cash. The company provides clients in the gaming and retail industries with cash advance hardware and software systems. In addition to credit/debit cash advance machines, Cash Systems' products include automated teller machines (ATMs) and related services such as maintenance and armored car transport. It also provides check cashing products and services that it operates inside casinos. The company markets to customers across the US and in Caribbean countries. Cash Systems agreed to be acquired by rival Global Cash Access for $33 million in 2008.

	Annual Growth	12/03	12/04	12/05	12/06	12/07
Sales ($ mil.)	33.8%	32.7	48.4	63.2	96.0	104.9
Net income ($ mil.)	—	1.6	2.2	(3.8)	(10.0)	(15.4)
Market value ($ mil.)	(3.1%)	92.4	147.8	148.0	130.7	81.6
Employees	—	—	—	243	—	—

CASH TECHNOLOGIES, INC.

AMEX: TQ

1434 W. 11th St.
Los Angeles, CA 90015
Phone: 213-745-2000
Fax: 213-745-2005
Web: www.cashtechnologies.com

CEO: Bruce R. Korman
CFO: Edmund (Ed) King
HR: –
FYE: May 31
Type: Public

Cash Technologies wants to cash in on the cashless society. The company operates in two segments — health care reimbursement services and stored value cards. The company's Claim-Remedi Services offers claims collection services to the health care industry through several applications: ProIdentify (eligibility verification), Pro837 (claims editing), and ProClaimSubmit (claim forwarding). CashTechCard Systems offers a stored-value debit MasterCard for corporate expense and benefits reimbursement, Health Savings Accounts, loyalty card programs, and other uses. Cash Technologies is also developing its E-commerce Message Management Architecture (EMMA) technology, for financial network integration.

	Annual Growth	5/03	5/04	5/05	5/06	5/07
Sales ($ mil.)	—	—	—	—	—	0.3
Net income ($ mil.)	—	—	—	—	—	(3.1)
Market value ($ mil.)	—	—	—	—	—	22.8
Employees	—	—	—	—	—	—

CASIO, INC.

570 Mount Pleasant Ave.
Dover, NJ 07801
Phone: 973-361-5400
Fax: 973-537-8926
Web: www.casio.com

CEO: Hideaki Terada
CFO: –
HR: –
FYE: March 31
Type: Subsidiary

You might be (G-)shocked to learn how many products Casio, Inc., sells. As the US subsidiary of Japanese electronics giant CASIO COMPUTER, the firm manufactures products ranging from handheld computers and calculators to electronic keyboards and its popular G-Shock watch line. Established in 1957, Casio also makes and markets digital cameras, label printers, clocks, portable TVs, and other items. Going beyond the consumer market, Casio targets the retail, hospitality, and industrial markets (cash registers and industrial handheld PDAs). And to make sure that young consumers remember its name, the company also sells to the education market.

	Annual Growth	3/03	3/04	3/05	3/06	3/07
Est. sales ($ mil.)	—	—	—	—	—	22.1
Employees	—	—	—	—	—	250

An in-depth profile of this company is available to Hoover's Online members at hoovers.com.

335

CASPIAN SERVICES, INC.

OTC: CSSV

257 E. 200 South, Ste. 340
Salt Lake City, UT 84101
Phone: 801-746-3700
Fax: 801-746-3701
Web: www.caspianservicesinc.com

CEO: Laird Garrard
CFO: John Baile
HR: –
FYE: September 30
Type: Public

Caspian Services (formerly EMPS Corporation) provides geophysical and seismic data acquisition and interpretation services to the oil and gas industry operating in the Caspian Sea region. It also owns or leases a fleet of 14 shallow draft vessels that provide offshore marine services, including transportation, housing, and supplies for production personnel. Caspian Services' ships are chartered to Agip KCO, a consortium of oil companies operating in the Caspian Sea. The company operates a desalinization plant and sells purified drinking water. Caspian Services has expanded its operations through the acquisitions of Kazakhstan-based companies that provide geophysical services to the oil and gas industry.

	Annual Growth	12/03	12/04	*9/05	9/06	9/07
Sales ($ mil.)	57.7%	10.5	14.6	23.8	43.0	64.9
Net income ($ mil.)	—	(0.2)	(0.2)	2.2	(1.9)	9.5
Market value ($ mil.)	8.6%	105.0	109.2	174.9	197.7	145.9
Employees	—	—	—	—	—	560

*Fiscal year change

CASS INFORMATION SYSTEMS, INC.

NASDAQ (GM): CASS

13001 Hollenberg Dr.
Bridgeton, MO 63044
Phone: 314-506-5500
Fax: 314-506-5955
Web: www.cassinfo.com

CEO: Lawrence A. Collett
CFO: P. Stephen (Steve) Appelbaum
HR: Wayne D. Muskopf
FYE: December 31
Type: Public

Rolling, rolling, rolling . . . keep those payments rolling! Cass Information Systems provides freight payment and information processing services to large manufacturing, distributing, and retail firms in the US. Its offerings include freight bill payment, audit, and rating services, as well as outsourcing of utility bill processing and payments. The company grew out of Cass Commercial Bank (now a subsidiary), which supports the company's other operations and provides banking services to private companies and churches, as well as to consumers, in the St. Louis area and Santa Ana, California. Other major customer bases include Massachusetts, Ohio, and South Carolina.

	Annual Growth	12/03	12/04	12/05	12/06	12/07
Sales ($ mil.)	9.3%	68.3	69.9	76.9	89.9	97.6
Net income ($ mil.)	22.5%	7.9	8.0	10.9	15.1	17.8
Market value ($ mil.)	65.9%	40.6	52.1	110.7	273.9	307.7
Employees	—	—	—	716	—	—

CASTLE & COOKE, INC.

10900 Wilshire Blvd., Ste. 1600
Los Angeles, CA 90024
Phone: 310-208-3636
Fax: 310-824-7770
Web: www.castlecooke.net

CEO: David H. Murdock
CFO: Scott A. Griswold
HR: Philip M. Young
FYE: December 31
Type: Private

Say aloha to Castle & Cooke, a 150-year-old real estate company that develops residential and commercial real estate in Hawaii, California, and a handful of southwestern and southern states. It owns and manages office buildings, shopping centers, and other commercial and industrial properties. Oahu, Hawaii, and Bakersfield, California, are among its biggest residential markets. It also owns just over 75% of Lanai, Hawaii's sixth-largest island, where it has built resort hotels, golf courses, and vacation homes. Castle & Cooke was spun off from Dole Food in 1995; CEO David Murdock (who also heads Dole) owns the company.

CASTLE BRANDS INC.

AMEX: ROX

570 Lexington Ave., 29th Fl.
New York, NY 10022
Phone: 646-356-0200
Fax: 646-356-0222
Web: www.castlebrandsinc.com

CEO: Donald L. (Don) Marsh Jr.
CFO: Alfred J. Small
HR: –
FYE: March 31
Type: Public

Castle Brands hopes to earn a king's ransom selling imported distilled spirits. Among its brands are Boru vodka (35% of sales), Sea Wynde rum, and Knappogue Castle whiskey. The company also owns 60% of the Celtic Crossing brand of Irish liqueur. In addition, it has marketing and distribution rights for other brands such as Gosling's rum and Pallini liqueurs. Castle Brands does business in both the US and Europe. The company was formed in 2003 following the merger of Great Spirits Company and The Roaring Water Bay Spirits Group. The company mainly employs other firms to distill and bottle its products.

	Annual Growth	3/04	3/05	3/06	3/07	3/08
Sales ($ mil.)	54.4%	4.8	12.6	21.1	25.2	27.3
Net income ($ mil.)	—	(6.4)	(12.5)	(13.1)	(16.6)	(27.6)
Market value ($ mil.)	(80.8%)	—	—	—	83.9	16.1
Employees	4.1%	—	49	51	—	—

CASTLE DENTAL CENTERS, INC.

3701 Kirby Dr., Ste. 550
Houston, TX 77098
Phone: 800-867-6453
Fax: –
Web: www.castledental.com

CEO: Steven C. (Steve) Bilt
CFO: Bradley E. Schmidt
HR: –
FYE: December 31
Type: Subsidiary

Castle Dental Centers manages and operates dental practice networks in California, Florida, Tennessee, and Texas. The company provide non-dental management services to about 75 dental centers, which include general, orthodontic, and multispecialty practices. Castle Dental Centers' administrative management services include marketing and sales, human resources services, equipment supply, insurance services, and financial and accounting reporting and administration. Dentists contract with the company to work with patients. Castle Dental Centers is a wholly owned subsidiary of Bright Now! Dental.

	Annual Growth	12/03	12/04	12/05	12/06	12/07
Est. sales ($ mil.)	—	—	—	—	—	36.1
Employees	—	—	—	—	—	860

CASTLE HARLAN, INC.

150 E. 58th St.
New York, NY 10155
Phone: 212-644-8600
Fax: 212-207-8042
Web: www.castleharlan.com

CEO: Justin B. Wender
CFO: Howard Weiss
HR: Beverly Fox
FYE: December 31
Type: Private

Castle Harlan is a private equity firm that invests in a variety of restaurant chains, industrial and manufacturing firms, shipping and transportation support companies, and other concerns in the US and Australia. The hands-on firm sniffs out established enterprises with steady earnings; Castle Harlan often partners with the existing management of an acquired company, places directors on its board, and eventually seeks a profitable exit. Its restaurant holdings include well-known names Perkins & Marie Callender's and Morton's. The firm was co-founded in 1987 by Leonard Harlan and chairman John Castle, a former CEO of Donaldson, Lufkin & Jenrette.

	Annual Growth	12/03	12/04	12/05	12/06	12/07
Est. sales ($ mil.)	—	—	—	—	—	2,147.5
Employees	—	—	—	—	—	13,450

CASUAL MALE RETAIL GROUP, INC.

NASDAQ (GM): CMRG

555 Turnpike St.
Canton, MA 02021
Phone: 781-828-9300
Fax: 781-821-6094
Web: www.casualmalexl.com

CEO: David A. Levin
CFO: Dennis R. Hernreich
HR: Walter Sprague
FYE: Saturday nearest January 31
Type: Public

Casual Male Retail Group sells men their Friday-wear and formalwear. The company offers private-label and name-brand casual wear, dresswear, and suits for big-and-tall men through about 490 stores in some 45 US states, as well as online and through catalogs. It also operates a single Rochester Big & Tall store in London, England. Trade names include Casual Male XL (formerly Casual Male Big & Tall), Rochester Big & Tall Clothing, B&T Factory Direct, and newly launched Shoes XL and Living XL. Founded as Designs, Inc., in 1976, the company acquired Casual Male out of bankruptcy in 2002 and adopted the better-known name.

	Annual Growth	1/04	1/05	1/06	1/07	1/08
Sales ($ mil.)	2.0%	429.5	365.0	421.4	467.5	464.1
Net income ($ mil.)	—	(12.1)	1.5	10.8	42.6	0.4
Market value ($ mil.)	(3.7%)	239.6	185.0	252.5	551.3	206.1
Employees	11.6%	—	—	2,770	3,092	—

CATALINA LIGHTING, INC.

Pink Sheets: CALA

18191 NW 68th Ave.
Miami, FL 33015
Phone: 305-558-4777
Fax: 305-827-3994
Web: www.catalinaltg.com

CEO: A. Corydon Meyer
CFO: Gary Rodney
HR: –
FYE: September 30
Type: Public

Business is a particularly illuminating experience at Catalina Lighting. The company manufactures and distributes residential and commercial lighting fixtures and lamps under such brand names as Catalina, Dana, Illuminada, Tensor, and Ring. Catalina Lighting's lighting products range from table and floor lamps and ceiling fixtures to wall and vanity lights and outdoor lighting. The company markets its products primarily through retailers including home centers, hardware stores, discount department stores, warehouse clubs, and office supply chains.

	Annual Growth	9/00	9/01	9/02	9/03	*9/04
Sales ($ mil.)	0.9%	202.6	234.8	220.3	202.0	209.8
Net income ($ mil.)	—	2.8	(18.4)	0.9	5.0	(6.0)
Employees	(12.2%)	3,400	3,400	2,623	—	—

*Most recent year available

CATALINA MARKETING CORPORATION

200 Carillon Pkwy.
St. Petersburg, FL 33716
Phone: 727-579-5000
Fax: 727-556-2700
Web: www.catmktg.com

CEO: L. Dick Buell
CFO: Rick P. Frier
HR: –
FYE: December 31
Type: Private

To reach shoppers when they are shopping, consumer packaged-goods manufacturers call on Catalina Marketing. The company's network, installed at the cash registers of more than 22,000 supermarkets and drugstores throughout the US, prints out coupons and other marketing communications for consumers based on the products they have just purchased. A similar system, installed at more than 13,200 pharmacies, delivers health-related information to consumers based on the prescriptions they pick up. Outside the US, Catalina Marketing has installed its networks at about 8,000 retail locations in Europe and Japan. The company was acquired by investment firm Hellman & Friedman in October 2007.

	Annual Growth	3/03	3/04	3/05	3/06	*12/06
Sales ($ mil.)	(7.7%)	470.7	473.0	410.1	417.8	340.9
Net income ($ mil.)	(6.1%)	55.1	(19.3)	65.4	71.6	42.8
Employees	9.1%	—	—	1,100	1,200	—

*Fiscal year change

CATALINA RESTAURANT GROUP INC.

5780 Fleet St., Ste. 250
Carlsbad, CA 92008
Phone: 760-804-5750
Fax: 760-476-5141
Web: www.catalinarestaurantgroup.com

CEO: Samuel Nicholas (Sam) Borgese
CFO: –
HR: Jan Miller
FYE: December 31
Type: Subsidiary

Catalina Restaurant Group is pretty casual about dining. The company operates about 220 casual-dining restaurants under the Carrows and Coco's names. Its Carrows Restaurant chain offers family dining fare for breakfast, lunch, and dinner at more than 100 locations. Several of the eateries are open 24 hours a day. Coco's Bakery Restaurants feature fresh-baked goods, burgers, sandwiches, and breakfast items at more than 115 locations. Most of Catalina Restaurant Group's properties are found in California, with additional locations in Arizona, Colorado, Nevada, New Mexico, Oregon, and Texas. Formed in 2002, the company was acquired by Tokyo-based Zensho Co. in 2006.

	Annual Growth	12/03	12/04	12/05	12/06	12/07
Est. sales ($ mil.)	—	—	—	—	—	86.7
Employees	—	—	—	—	—	4,000

CATALYST INTERNATIONAL, INC.

8989 N. Deerwood Dr.
Milwaukee, WI 53223
Phone: 414-362-6800
Fax: 414-362-6794
Web: www.catalystinternational.com

CEO: Michael G. Eleftheriou
CFO: –
HR: Lisa DeMartimo
FYE: December 31
Type: Private

Catalyst International serves as an agent of change in supply chains. The company's supply chain execution, performance, and process management software helps clients manage inventory and fulfillment, monitor their supply chain activities, and automate a range of warehouse functions, including receiving, loading, and storage. Catalyst's software integrates with applications from software giant SAP, including logistics, warehouse management, and task and resource management systems. The company provides consulting, implementation, and maintenance services. Catalyst was acquired by ComVest Investment Partners in 2004.

	Annual Growth	12/03	12/04	12/05	12/06	12/07
Est. sales ($ mil.)	—	—	—	—	—	20.6
Employees	—	—	—	—	—	187

CATALYST PHARMACEUTICAL PARTNERS, INC.

NASDAQ (GM): CPRX

355 Alhambra Circle, Ste. 1370
Coral Gables, FL 33134
Phone: 305-529-2522
Fax: 305-529-0933
Web: www.catalystpharma.com

CEO: Patrick J. McEnany
CFO: Jack Weinstein
HR: –
FYE: December 31
Type: Public

Catalyst Pharmaceutical Partners may help some kick the habit. The development-stage company's lead candidate, CPP-109 (based on the chemical compound vigabatrin) is in clinical studies for the treatment of cocaine and methamphetamine addiction. The drug is designed to be readily absorbed into the central nervous system, preventing the perception of pleasure that results from dramatic increases in dopamine caused by cocaine and meth use. Contract manufacturer Pharmaceutics International is supplying CPP-109 for use in upcoming clinical trials and may also be contracted for future commercial supplies should the drug become approved in the US.

	Annual Growth	12/99	12/00	12/01	12/02	*12/03
Sales ($ mil.)	—	—	—	—	—	0.0
Net income ($ mil.)	—	—	—	—	—	(0.4)
Employees	—	—	—	—	—	—

*Most recent year available

An in-depth profile of this company is available to Hoover's Online members at hoovers.com.

CATALYST SEMICONDUCTOR, INC.

NASDAQ (GM): CATS

2975 Stender Way
Santa Clara, CA 95054
Phone: 408-542-1000
Fax: 408-542-1200
Web: www.catsemi.com

CEO: Gelu Voicu
CFO: David P. (Dave) Eichler
HR: –
FYE: Sunday nearest April 30
Type: Public

Catalyst Semiconductor keeps the memory moving. The company develops non-volatile memory chips, which retain data when a system's power is off. Products include EEPROMs (electronically erasable programmable read-only memories) and flash memories used in cell phones and computer peripherals, and NVRAMs (non-volatile random-access memories) used in antilock brakes and networking gear. Catalyst also designs mixed-signal chips used in a variety of applications. It outsources chip production to X-FAB, and sells to manufacturers including Hewlett-Packard, Infineon, and Samsung Electronics. Catalyst Semiconductor has more than 3,400 customers.

	Annual Growth	4/04	4/05	4/06	4/07	4/08
Sales ($ mil.)	4.6%	63.5	62.3	60.2	66.3	75.9
Net income ($ mil.)	(25.5%)	9.4	3.8	2.6	(0.4)	2.9
Market value ($ mil.)	(12.9%)	119.8	76.6	78.5	61.5	69.1
Employees	17.6%	130	139	155	169	249

CATAPULT COMMUNICATIONS

NASDAQ (GS): CATT

160 S. Whisman Rd.
Mountain View, CA 94041
Phone: 650-960-1025
Fax: 650-960-1029
Web: www.catapult.com

CEO: Richard A. (Dick) Karp
CFO: Christopher (Chris) Stephenson
HR: Kathy T. Omaye-Sosnow
FYE: September 30
Type: Public

Catapult Communications Corporation hates for network performance issues to be up in the air. Its digital communication test systems are used by telecom service providers and equipment makers to design, test, and configure network elements. Catapult's systems perform simulations, conformance testing, load testing, feature verification, and network monitoring. The company also offers services such as consulting, support, and training. Top customers include Alcatel-Lucent, Ericsson, and Nokia Siemens Networks. CEO Richard Karp owns about 22% of Catapult Communications.

	Annual Growth	9/03	9/04	9/05	9/06	9/07
Sales ($ mil.)	(3.4%)	45.2	58.0	64.9	47.4	39.3
Net income ($ mil.)	—	4.4	13.9	14.1	(10.7)	(4.4)
Market value ($ mil.)	(10.3%)	158.1	274.0	270.1	117.2	102.6
Employees	—	—	—	—	—	220

CATERPILLAR FINANCIAL SERVICES CORPORATION

2120 West End Ave.
Nashville, TN 37203
Phone: 615-341-1000
Fax: 615-341-5022
Web: finance.cat.com

CEO: Kent M. Adams
CFO: James A. Duensing
HR: Paulette Jackson
FYE: December 31
Type: Subsidiary

There's only one way to lease a Cat: Caterpillar Financial Services. Cat Financial provides loans and leases to corporate customers to buy or rent equipment and machinery manufactured by its parent company, industry giant Caterpillar. That equipment includes mining and logging equipment, off-road trucks, excavating machinery, gas turbines and engines, forklifts, backhoes, and construction equipment. Affiliate Cat Insurance offers insurance products to customers and dealers. The company has more than 40 offices in some 30 countries in North and South America, Europe, the Middle East, and the Asia/Pacific region.

	Annual Growth	12/03	12/04	12/05	12/06	12/07
Sales ($ mil.)	14.6%	1,736.0	1,924.0	2,354.0	2,763.0	2,998.0
Net income ($ mil.)	17.9%	256.0	287.0	364.0	473.0	494.0
Employees	5.8%	1,282	1,399	1,490	1,537	1,606

CATERPILLAR INC.

NYSE: CAT

100 NE Adams St.
Peoria, IL 61629
Phone: 309-675-1000
Fax: 309-675-1182
Web: www.cat.com

CEO: James W. (Jim) Owens
CFO: David B. (Dave) Burritt
HR: Sidney C. (Sid) Banwart
FYE: December 31
Type: Public

Building more than cocoons, Caterpillar is the world's #1 maker of earth moving machinery and a leading supplier of agricultural equipment. The company makes construction, mining, and logging machinery; diesel and natural gas engines; industrial gas turbines; and electrical power-generation systems. Caterpillar has plants worldwide and sells its equipment globally via a network of 3,600 locations in 180 countries. Caterpillar offers rental services through more than 1,600 outlets worldwide, and it provides financing and insurance for its dealers and customers. Cat Power Ventures invests in power projects that use Caterpillar power generation equipment. Caterpillar Logistics Services offers supply chain solutions.

	Annual Growth	12/03	12/04	12/05	12/06	12/07
Sales ($ mil.)	18.5%	22,763.0	30,251.0	36,339.0	41,517.0	44,958.0
Net income ($ mil.)	34.0%	1,099.0	2,035.0	2,854.0	3,537.0	3,541.0
Market value ($ mil.)	33.5%	14,269.6	16,719.9	38,756.0	39,607.4	45,276.4
Employees	10.0%	69,169	76,920	85,116	94,593	101,333

CATHAY GENERAL BANCORP

NASDAQ (GS): CATY

777 N. Broadway
Los Angeles, CA 90012
Phone: 626-582-7380
Fax: 213-625-1368
Web: www.cathaybank.com

CEO: Dunson K. Cheng
CFO: Heng W. Chen
HR: Jennifer Laforcarde
FYE: December 31
Type: Public

Cathay General Bancorp is the holding company for Cathay Bank, which serves Chinese and Vietnamese communities from some 30 branches in California, and about 20 more in Illinois, New Jersey, New York, Massachusetts, Washington, and Texas. It also has offices in Hong Kong, Shanghai, and Taipei. Catering to small businesses and low- to middle-income consumers, the bank offers standard deposit services and loans; commercial mortgages account for more than half of the bank's portfolio; business loans comprise more than 20%. The bank's Cathay Wealth Management unit offers online stock trading, mutual funds, and other investment products and services through an agreement with PrimeVest.

	Annual Growth	12/03	12/04	12/05	12/06	12/07
Assets ($ mil.)	17.0%	5,541.9	6,098.0	6,397.5	8,026.5	10,402.5
Net income ($ mil.)	22.6%	55.6	86.8	104.1	117.6	125.5
Market value ($ mil.)	17.1%	694.6	1,901.6	1,803.9	1,792.1	1,306.9
Employees	16.8%	—	—	900	1,051	—

CATHOLIC HEALTH EAST

3805 W. Chester Pike, Ste. 100
Newtown Square, PA 19073
Phone: 610-355-2000
Fax: 610-271-9600
Web: www.che.org

CEO: Robert V. Stanek
CFO: Peter L. (Pete) DeAngelis Jr.
HR: Kristin Kelly
FYE: December 31
Type: Not-for-profit

Catholic Health East doesn't believe prayers to St. Jude are necessary to continue providing health care to any person in need. As one of the top religious health systems in the US, Catholic Health East carries out its mission of serving the poor and the old by offering health care through more than 30 hospitals, 40 nursing homes, and 20 independent- and assisted-living facilities. Primarily serving the East Coast, the network also operates behavioral health facilities and offers adult day care, home health services, and hospice care. Catholic Health East is sponsored by 15 religious communities.

	Annual Growth	12/02	12/03	12/04	12/05	12/06
Sales ($ mil.)	(4.4%)	5,000.0	5,700.0	4,034.5	4,245.9	4,175.9
Net income ($ mil.)	(1.4%)	—	—	205.1	219.2	199.2
Employees	3.8%	43,000	43,000	43,000	43,000	50,000

An in-depth profile of this company is available to Hoover's Online members at hoovers.com.

CATHOLIC HEALTH INITIATIVES

1999 Broadway, Ste. 2600
Denver, CO 80202
Phone: 303-298-9100
Fax: 303-298-9690
Web: www.catholichealthinit.org

CEO: Kevin E. Lofton
CFO: Colleen M. Blye
HR: Herbert J. Vallier
FYE: June 30
Type: Not-for-profit

For Catholic Health Initiatives (CHI), returning sick people to good health is more than a business; it's a mission. Formed in 1996 through the merger of three Catholic hospital systems, the giant not-for-profit organization is the second-largest Catholic hospital operator in the US, just behind Ascension Health. It operates some 70 hospitals and more than 40 long-term care, assisted-living, and senior residential facilities in about 20 states from Washington to Maryland. Its hospitals range from large urban medical centers to small critical-access hospitals in rural areas. All told, the health system has more than 14,000 acute care beds. It is sponsored by a dozen different congregations of nuns.

	Annual Growth	6/03	6/04	6/05	6/06	6/07
Sales ($ mil.)	6.2%	6,071.6	6,121.1	7,091.4	7,251.7	7,731.5
Net income ($ mil.)	45.2%	202.9	770.0	460.7	604.3	902.2
Employees	4.4%	54,975	53,459	54,044	65,070	65,296

CATHOLIC HEALTHCARE PARTNERS

615 Elsinore Place
Cincinnati, OH 45202
Phone: 513-639-2800
Fax: 513-639-2700
Web: www.health-partners.org

CEO: Michael D. Connelly
CFO: William Shuttleworth
HR: John Starcher
FYE: December 31
Type: Not-for-profit

Say "Amen" to the healing powers of Catholic Healthcare Partners (CHP). One of the nation's largest not-for-profit health systems, CHP offers health care services, primarily in Ohio but also in Indiana, Kentucky, Pennsylvania, and Tennessee through some 100 organizations. Facilities include about 30 hospitals, more than a dozen long-term care facilities, housing for the elderly, and wellness centers. CHP also offers physician practices and hospice and home health care. The system is co-sponsored by the Sisters of Mercy communities of Cincinnati and Dallas, Pennsylvania; the Sisters of the Humility of Mary of Villa Maria, Pennsylvania; the Franciscan Sisters of the Poor; and Covenant Health Systems.

	Annual Growth	12/02	12/03	12/04	12/05	12/06
Sales ($ mil.)	6.6%	2,714.8	2,874.3	3,157.9	3,360.6	3,505.1
Net income ($ mil.)	—	(122.2)	—	171.0	154.2	143.1
Employees	2.9%	30,524	30,524	—	35,000	34,280

CATHOLIC HEALTHCARE WEST

185 Berry St., Ste. 300
San Francisco, CA 94107
Phone: 415-438-5500
Fax: 415-438-5724
Web: www.chwhealth.org

CEO: Lloyd H. Dean
CFO: Michael D. Blaszyk
HR: Ernest (Ernie) Urquhart
FYE: June 30
Type: Not-for-profit

Catholic Healthcare West (CHW) has found it takes a lot of nunsense to become one of the largest private, not-for-profit health care providers in the state of California. Sponsored by seven congregations of nuns, CHW operates a network of more than 40 acute care facilities located in the Golden State and, to a lesser extent, in Arizona and Nevada. Those facilities house more than 7,000 acute care beds, as well as nearly 1,000 skilled nursing beds. CHW also provides home health care and hospice services through agencies in California and Nevada. Founded in 1986, CHW is the official health care provider of the San Francisco Giants.

	Annual Growth	6/03	6/04	6/05	6/06	6/07
Sales ($ mil.)	7.8%	4,989.1	5,396.8	6,002.1	6,617.3	6,730.1
Net income ($ mil.)	71.4%	50.7	246.1	348.2	442.9	437.9
Employees	8.6%	36,000	40,000	40,000	—	50,000

THE CATO CORPORATION

NYSE: CTR

8100 Denmark Rd.
Charlotte, NC 28273
Phone: 704-554-8510
Fax: 704-551-7594
Web: www.catocorp.com

CEO: John P. Derham Cato
CFO: John Howe
HR: Robert C. Brummer
FYE: Saturday nearest January 31
Type: Public

The Cato Corporation caters to fashion-minded Southerners on a budget. The retailer operates more than 1,300 women's apparel specialty stores under the names Cato, Cato Fashions, Cato Plus, It's Fashion!, and It's Fashion Metro. Its mostly private-label merchandise includes misses', juniors', and plus-sized sportswear, career wear, coats, hosiery, shoes, and accessories priced for low- to middle-income female customers ages 18 to 50. (The company also offers clothing for girls ages 7 to 16 in some stores.) Cato's stores are currently located mainly in small-town strip centers in some 30 states, primarily in the Southeast. Founded in 1946, the company is run by John Derham Cato, the third generation of Catos in the family business.

	Annual Growth	1/04	1/05	1/06	1/07	1/08
Sales ($ mil.)	3.2%	747.3	789.6	836.4	875.9	846.4
Net income ($ mil.)	0.7%	31.4	34.8	44.8	51.5	32.3
Market value ($ mil.)	13.1%	280.9	406.2	658.8	704.0	460.3
Employees	(1.0%)	—	—	10,000	10,400	9,800

CATUITY INC.

NASDAQ (CM): CTTY

300 Preston Ave., Ste. 302
Charlottesville, VA 22902
Phone: 434-979-0724
Fax: 734-293-4213
Web: www.catuity.com

CEO: Alfred H. (John) Racine III
CFO: Debra R. (Deb) Hoopes
HR: –
FYE: December 31
Type: Public

Keeping customers purring with joy is the aim of Catuity's software. The company markets a suite of applications that help retailers set up and manage customer loyalty and incentive programs. Its software helps track customer data and manage multiple reward programs — including customized discounts, promotions, gift cards, rewards programs, and points-based programs — for both traditional and online sales. Catuity's products work with retail payment terminals, electronic cash registers, and internal store networks.

	Annual Growth	12/02	12/03	12/04	12/05	*12/06
Sales ($ mil.)	(9.6%)	3.0	5.0	0.8	1.0	2.0
Net income ($ mil.)	—	(2.8)	(0.6)	(3.6)	(3.0)	(4.2)
Employees	(2.6%)	39	—	—	36	—

*Most recent year available

CAVALIER HOMES, INC.

AMEX: CAV

32 Wilson Blvd. 100
Addison, AL 35540
Phone: 256-747-9800
Fax: 256-747-3044
Web: www.cavalierhomebuilders.com

CEO: David A. Roberson
CFO: Michael R. (Mike) Murphy
HR: Mark Hankins
FYE: December 31
Type: Public

Cavalier Homes builds castles for regular Joes. Through about a half-dozen plants the company makes manufactured single- and multi-section homes for the low- to medium-priced market in the south-central and south-Atlantic US; it sells around 4,700 homes annually. The company also manufactures cabinetry and other components and participates in joint ventures for lumber distribution and roof truss manufacturing. Cavalier Homes markets its products through a network of about 60 exclusive and about 300 non-exclusive dealers, as well as one company-owned retail center. It offers financing and insurance for its homes and is a supplier for federal disaster-relief programs.

	Annual Growth	12/03	12/04	12/05	12/06	12/07
Sales ($ mil.)	(4.0%)	247.8	234.2	272.0	227.9	210.6
Net income ($ mil.)	—	(4.6)	3.2	10.9	0.2	(8.5)
Market value ($ mil.)	(10.4%)	55.7	106.2	118.1	76.3	35.9
Employees	—	—	—	2,200	—	—

An in-depth profile of this company is available to Hoover's Online members at hoovers.com.

339

CAVALIER TELEPHONE LLC

2134 W. Laburnum Ave.
Richmond, VA 23227
Phone: 804-422-4100
Fax: 804-422-4392
Web: www.cavtel.com

CEO: Edward B. Meyercord III
CFO: David Whitt
HR: Jeff Snyder
FYE: December 31
Type: Private

Cavalier Telephone takes a serious approach to residential and business telecommunications. The facilities-based competitive local-exchange carrier (CLEC) offers local and long-distance phone services in Delaware, Maryland, southern New Jersey, Pennsylvania, and Virginia. The company also offers broadband Internet services and Voice over Internet Protocol (VoIP), as well as business data services such as private lines and colocation. Cavalier Telephone serves more than 550,000 residential and 85,000 business customers. Cavalier's investors include Bank of America, GE Capital, and MC Venture Partners. Executive chairman Brad Evans founded the company in 1998.

	Annual Growth	12/03	12/04	12/05	12/06	12/07
Est. sales ($ mil.)	—	—	—	—	—	99.3
Employees	—	—	—	—	—	778

CAVCO INDUSTRIES, INC.

NASDAQ (GS): CVCO

1001 N. Central Ave., 8th Fl.
Phoenix, AZ 85004
Phone: 602-256-6263
Fax: 602-256-6189
Web: www.cavco.com

CEO: Joseph H. (Joe) Stegmayer
CFO: Daniel L. Urness
HR: —
FYE: March 31
Type: Public

Cavco's constructs keep kinfolk covered. Cavco Industries produces some 3,300 manufactured residential homes a year (retail prices ranged from $32,000 to more than $100,000), mainly for US markets in the Southwest and West. Its products include full-sized homes (ranging from about 500 sq. ft. to 3,300 sq. ft.); park model homes (less than 400 sq. ft.) for use as recreational and retirement units; camping cabins; and commercial structures for use as portable classrooms, showrooms, and offices. It has three factories in Arizona and one in Texas. Cavco homes are available from some 360 retailers in two dozen states and seven company-owned outlets in Arizona, New Mexico, and Texas.

	Annual Growth	3/04	3/05	3/06	3/07	3/08
Sales ($ mil.)	2.4%	128.9	157.4	189.5	169.1	141.9
Net income ($ mil.)	0.4%	6.2	10.1	15.1	11.6	6.3
Market value ($ mil.)	40.6%	57.9	152.1	308.7	223.1	226.1
Employees	(18.6%)	—	—	1,320	1,075	

CAVIUM NETWORKS, INC.

NASDAQ (GM): CAVM

805 E. Middlefield Rd.
Mountain View, CA 94043
Phone: 650-623-7000
Fax: 650-625-9751
Web: www.caviumnetworks.com

CEO: Syed B. Ali
CFO: Arthur D. (Art) Chadwick
HR: —
FYE: December 31
Type: Public

Cavium Networks can help keep networks secure without hiding them in a cave somewhere. The company designs specialized microprocessors used in secure network transmissions, based on processor technology developed by MIPS Technologies. Cavium's customers include such heavy hitters as Aruba Networks, Cisco Systems (23% of sales), Citrix Systems, F5 Networks (18%), Fujitsu, Furukawa Electric, Juniper Networks, NETGEAR, Nokia, SafeNet, Samsung Electronics, SonicWALL, Sun Microsystems, Yamaha, and ZTE. Distributors generate around one-quarter of sales. Customers in the US provide about 60% of Cavium's sales.

	Annual Growth	12/03	12/04	12/05	12/06	12/07
Sales ($ mil.)	94.2%	—	7.4	19.4	34.2	54.2
Net income ($ mil.)	—	—	(11.7)	(11.7)	(9.0)	2.2
Market value ($ mil.)	—	—	—	—	—	927.9
Employees	26.4%	—	100	125	157	202

CB RICHARD ELLIS GROUP, INC.

NYSE: CBG

11150 Santa Monica Blvd., Ste. 1600
Los Angeles, CA 90025
Phone: 310-405-8900
Fax: —
Web: www.cbre.com

CEO: W. Brett White
CFO: Kenneth J. (Ken) Kay
HR: Jack Van Berkel
FYE: December 31
Type: Public

CB Richard Ellis Group (CBRE) is all about location, location, location — not to mention *ubicación, l'emplacement, posizione,* and *Standort.* The world's largest commercial real estate services company and an international powerhouse, CBRE has operations in more than 30 countries. Through subsidiaries Insignia Financial, the acquisition of which made CBRE the largest commercial-property manager in the world, and Trammell Crow, CBRE oversees real estate management, investment, property development, and related operations for top corporations that outsource their real estate requirements. It manages more than 1 billion sq. ft. of commercial space. CBRE also provides asset management and brokerage services.

	Annual Growth	12/03	12/04	12/05	12/06	12/07
Sales ($ mil.)	38.7%	1,630.1	2,365.1	2,910.6	4,032.0	6,034.3
Net income ($ mil.)	—	(34.7)	64.7	217.3	318.6	390.5
Market value ($ mil.)	76.2%	—	794.3	1,447.4	7,552.2	4,344.4
Employees	41.4%	—	—	14,500	24,000	29,000

CBC RESTAURANT CORP.

12700 Park Central Dr., Ste. 1300
Dallas, TX 75251
Phone: 972-619-4100
Fax: —
Web: www.cornerbakerycafe.com

CEO: Michael J. (Mike) Hislop
CFO: —
HR: Denise Clemens
FYE: December 31
Type: Holding company

The bakery does seem like a logical place to start looking for a sandwich. CBC Restaurant Corp. operates a chain of about 100 quick-casual eateries in eight states under the Corner Bakery Cafe banner. The restaurants offer a menu of sandwiches, soups, and salads, along with pasta dishes and a large variety of dessert items. In addition to lunch and dinner service, the chain serves breakfast, and most locations offer catering. The first Corner Bakery Cafe was opened in 1991. CBC Restaurant Corp. is owned by Il Fornaio (America), an operator of upscale Italian restaurants.

	Annual Growth	12/02	12/03	12/04	12/05	12/06
Est. sales ($ mil.)	—	—	—	—	—	215.0
Employees	—	—	—	—	—	3,000

CBEYOND, INC.

NASDAQ (GM): CBEY

320 Interstate North Pkwy. SE, Ste. 300
Atlanta, GA 30339
Phone: 678-424-2400
Fax: 678-424-2500
Web: www.cbeyond.net

CEO: James F. (Jim) Geiger
CFO: J. Robert (Bob) Fugate
HR: Joan L. Tolliver
FYE: December 31
Type: Public

Cbeyond isn't looking past the 25 million small businesses in the US to find customers for its broadband services. The Voice over Internet Protocol (VoIP) carrier provides local and long-distance services and broadband Internet access over its own private IP network, as well as mobile voice and data services. The company hopes to side-step stiff competition from incumbent carriers by focusing on the traditionally underserved small-business market. Cbeyond offers services in the Atlanta, Dallas, Denver, Houston, Chicago, Los Angeles, San Diego, Detroit, and San Francisco Bay areas.

	Annual Growth	12/03	12/04	12/05	12/06	12/07
Sales ($ mil.)	43.8%	65.5	113.3	159.1	213.9	280.0
Net income ($ mil.)	—	(29.5)	(11.5)	3.7	7.8	21.5
Market value ($ mil.)	100.1%	—	—	274.7	838.7	1,099.8
Employees	26.5%	—	586	707	905	1,187

CBIZ, INC.

NYSE: CBZ

6050 Oak Tree Blvd. South, Ste. 500
Cleveland, OH 44131
Phone: 216-447-9000
Fax: 216-447-9007
Web: www.cbiz.com

CEO: Steven L. Gerard
CFO: Ware H. Grove
HR: Robert A. O'Byrne
FYE: December 31
Type: Public

CBIZ wants its customers to see the advantages of farming out some of the tasks involved in running a business. The company provides clients with outsourced business services, including accounting and tax preparation, valuation, insurance and benefits administration, and IT consulting. Medical practice management, including billing services, is a CBIZ specialty. Overall, CBIZ has about 90,000 customers, mainly small and medium-sized businesses, but also government agencies, individuals, and not-for-profits. The company operates from more than 140 offices in about 35 states; it also does business in Canada.

	Annual Growth	12/03	12/04	12/05	12/06	12/07
Sales ($ mil.)	5.9%	512.8	520.1	559.3	601.1	643.9
Net income ($ mil.)	22.8%	15.3	16.0	18.7	24.4	34.8
Market value ($ mil.)	13.5%	381.6	329.8	444.4	469.9	634.1
Employees	3.9%	—	4,900	4,700	5,200	5,500

CBL & ASSOCIATES PROPERTIES, INC.

NYSE: CBL

2030 Hamilton Place Blvd., Ste. 500
Chattanooga, TN 37421
Phone: 423-855-0001
Fax: 423-490-8390
Web: www.cblproperties.com

CEO: Charles B. Lebovitz
CFO: John N. Foy
HR: Maggie Carrington
FYE: December 31
Type: Public

CBL & Associates Properties lives for those who love to shop. The self-managed real estate investment trust (REIT) owns, develops, manages, and finances shopping malls and other retail properties, primarily in the Southeast (57% of revenues; Nashville is its largest market) and Midwest. It owns or partially owns about 150 properties, including more than 80 malls, office buildings, and community centers. Strip malls, typically anchored by grocery or discount stores, associated centers (retail properties located adjacent to malls), and mortgage loans round out the firm's portfolio. The company's largest tenants include The Limited, The Gap, and Foot Locker.

	Annual Growth	12/03	12/04	12/05	12/06	12/07
Sales ($ mil.)	11.7%	667.5	759.2	907.5	1,002.1	1,040.6
Net income ($ mil.)	(11.3%)	144.1	121.1	162.5	117.5	89.2
Market value ($ mil.)	16.6%	856.6	1,198.7	2,469.9	2,836.0	1,582.4
Employees	—	—	—	1,483	1,511	0

CBRE REALTY FINANCE, INC.

NYSE: CBF

185 Asylum St., 37th Floor
Hartford, CT 06103
Phone: 860-275-6200
Fax: –
Web: www.cbrerealtyfinance.com

CEO: Kenneth J. Witkin
CFO: Michael A. Angerthal
HR: –
FYE: December 5
Type: Public

How *REIT* it is to be affiliated with one of the world's largest global commercial real estate services firms. CBRE Realty Finance is managed and advised by CBRE Realty Finance Management — an indirect subsidiary of commercial real estate services giant CB Richard Ellis through its wholly owned CBRE | Melody subsidiary. Set up as a real estate investment trust (REIT), CBRE Realty Finance is a specialty finance firm. It finances, invests in, and manages loans, securities, and other interests related to commercial real estate. The company's portfolio is worth some $1.7 billion and includes joint venture assets and mezzanine loans.

	Annual Growth	12/03	12/04	12/05	12/06	12/07
Sales ($ mil.)	237.2%	—	—	12.4	74.1	141.0
Net income ($ mil.)	—	—	—	1.1	13.7	(70.8)
Market value ($ mil.)	(65.7%)	—	—	—	480.7	165.1
Employees	—	—	—	26	—	—

CBRL GROUP, INC.

NASDAQ (GS): CBRL

305 Hartmann Dr.
Lebanon, TN 37088
Phone: 615-444-5533
Fax: 615-443-9476
Web: www.cbrlgroup.com

CEO: Michael A. (Mike) Woodhouse
CFO: N.B. Forrest Shoaf
HR: Robert J. Harig
FYE: Friday nearest July 31
Type: Public

CBRL Group has gotten ahead in the restaurant business by holding on to a bit of the past. The company operates more than 570 Cracker Barrel Old Country Store restaurants known for their country kitsch, rustic decor, and down-home cooking. The eateries, located in more than 40 states, offer mostly standard American fare, such as chicken, ham, and roast beef dishes but are most popular as breakfast spots. Each Cracker Barrel location features a retail area where patrons can buy hand-blown glassware, cast-iron cookware, and woodcrafts, as well as jellies and old-fashioned candies.

	Annual Growth	7/03	7/04	7/05	7/06	7/07
Sales ($ mil.)	1.7%	2,198.2	2,380.9	2,567.6	2,643.0	2,351.6
Net income ($ mil.)	11.1%	106.5	111.9	126.6	116.3	162.1
Market value ($ mil.)	(15.2%)	1,684.6	1,620.1	1,826.1	1,002.3	871.7
Employees	(13.5%)	—	—	—	74,031	64,000

CBS BROADCASTING INC.

51 W. 52nd St.
New York, NY 10019
Phone: 212-975-4321
Fax: 212-975-4516
Web: www.cbs.com

CEO: Nancy Tellem
CFO: Bruce Taub
HR: Tony Ambrosio
FYE: December 31
Type: Subsidiary

It takes less than *60 Minutes* to see that CBS is a *Survivor* in the ratings. A unit of CBS Corporation, CBS Broadcasting operates the CBS Television Network, the #2 network in the US behind FOX. Its top shows include *CSI: Crime Scene Investigation* and its two spin-offs, as well as *Survivor* and a host of prime-time comedy shows. The network boasts more than 200 affiliate stations around the nation. CBS Broadcasting also oversees 50%-owned The CW Network and production and distribution operations including CBS Television Distribution Group. In addition, CBS owns and operates about 40 TV stations across the country.

CBS CORPORATION

NYSE: CBS

51 W. 52nd St.
New York, NY 10019
Phone: 212-975-4321
Fax: 212-975-4516
Web: www.cbscorporation.com

CEO: Leslie (Les) Moonves
CFO: Frederic G. Reynolds
HR: Anthony G. Ambrosio
FYE: December 31
Type: Public

This media conglomerate has its eye focused on the TV. CBS Corporation is one of the leading television broadcasting and production companies in the world with CBS Broadcasting, the #2 network in the US behind FOX. It also operates about 40 TV stations around the country and owns 50% of The CW Network. On cable, CBS owns movie channel Showtime and sports channel CBS College Sports Network. It creates and distributes programming through CBS Television Distribution Group and CBS Paramount Network Television. In addition to TV, the company owns CBS Radio, CBS Outdoor, and book publisher Simon & Schuster. Chairman Sumner Redstone controls CBS Corp. through his National Amusements movie theater chain.

	Annual Growth	12/03	12/04	12/05	12/06	12/07
Sales ($ mil.)	(14.7%)	26,585.3	22,525.9	14,536.4	14,320.2	14,072.9
Net income ($ mil.)	(3.1%)	1,416.9	(17,462.2)	(7,089.1)	1,660.5	1,247.0
Market value ($ mil.)	(3.0%)	—	—	17,722.5	22,041.1	16,687.9
Employees	(13.7%)	—	—	32,160	23,654	23,970

An in-depth profile of this company is available to Hoover's Online members at hoovers.com.

341

⊞ CBS RADIO INC.

1515 Broadway, 46th Fl.	CEO: Daniel R. (Dan) Mason
New York, NY 10036	CFO: Anton Guitano
Phone: 212-846-3939	HR: –
Fax: 212-314-9228	FYE: December 31
Web: www.cbsradio.com	Type: Subsidiary

This company has its eye on radio listeners. CBS Radio is one of the country's leading radio broadcasters, with more than 140 stations serving about 30 major markets. Its stations, which offer a variety of programming from talk and sports to a wide range of music styles, primarily operate in regional clusters, sharing business functions such as finance, ad sales, and marketing. In addition to original programming, most of the stations are affiliates of the Westwood One radio network, which offers news, sports, and entertainment programming nationwide. (CBS Radio owns 15% of the radio content syndicator.) CBS Radio is a subsidiary of broadcasting giant CBS Corporation.

⊞ CBSSPORTS.COM

2200 W. Cypress Creek Rd.	CEO: Stephen E. (Steve) Snyder
Fort Lauderdale, FL 33309	CFO: Steven Haft
Phone: 954-489-4000	HR: –
Fax: 954-771-2807	FYE: December 31
Web: www.cbs.sportsline.com	Type: Subsidiary

You might say this Internet company has its eye on sports. CBSSports.com, formerly CBS SportsLine.com, operates a leading sports news and information Web site. In addition to providing headline news and analysis on all four major professional sports (from the NFL, NBA, MLB, and NHL), as well as college sports, golf, tennis, and auto racing, the company publishes the official sports site of the NCAA. Registered users and subscribers can also take part in a variety of fantasy sports leagues. CBSSports.com operates as part of CBS Interactive, the new media operations unit of CBS Corporation.

	Annual Growth	12/03	12/04	12/05	12/06	12/07
Est. sales ($ mil.)	—	—	—	—	—	15.5
Employees	—	—	—	—	—	250

CBT FINANCIAL CORP.   OTC: CBTC

11 N. 2nd St.	CEO: William E. Wood
Clearfield, PA 16830	CFO: Richard W. Ogden
Phone: 814-765-7551	HR: –
Fax: 814-765-2943	FYE: December 31
Web: www.cbtfinancial.com	Type: Public

CBT Financial is the holding company for Clearfield Bank & Trust Company, which operates about a dozen offices in central Pennsylvania. Targeting individuals and local businesses, the bank offers traditional deposit products, credit cards, trust and investment services, and loans. The bulk of the bank's lending portfolio is secured by residential and commercial mortgages. It also offers consumer, construction, and business loans. CBT Financial nearly doubled its operations in 2005 when it acquired six banking locations from First Commonwealth Financial.

	Annual Growth	12/02	12/03	12/04	12/05	*12/06
Assets ($ mil.)	8.7%	—	283.0	298.3	378.8	363.2
Net income ($ mil.)	—	—	—	—	—	643.0
Employees	—	—	—	—	—	136

*Most recent year available

CCA GLOBAL PARTNERS

4301 Earth City Expwy.	CEO: Howard Brodsky
St. Louis, MO 63045	CFO: Ed Muchnick
Phone: 314-506-0000	HR: Lisa Miles
Fax: 314-291-6674	FYE: September 30
Web: www.ccaglobal.com	Type: Cooperative

Business is "floor"ishing at CCA Global Partners. Formerly Carpet Co-op, the firm operates more than 3,600 retail stores in the US and abroad in floor covering and various other specialties. Many stores operate under the Carpet One name; other names include Flooring America, Flooring One, ProSource, and International Design Guild (high-end showrooms). The world's largest floor covering retailer (with stores in the US, Canada, Australia, and New Zealand), Carpet One is the exclusive US marketer of Bigelow and LEES For Living carpet brands. CCA Global has also made forays into bicycle retailing, mortgage banking, and men's formalwear. Executives Howard Brodsky and Alan Greenberg founded the co-op in 1984.

	Annual Growth	9/02	9/03	9/04	9/05	9/06
Sales ($ mil.)	14.2%	6,000.0	8,000.0	8,700.0	9,393.0	10,200.0
Employees	(36.4%)	550	350	—	—	—

CCA INDUSTRIES, INC.   AMEX: CAW

200 Murray Hill Pkwy.	CEO: David Edell
East Rutherford, NJ 07073	CFO: Stephen A. Heit
Phone: 201-330-1400	HR: –
Fax: 201-842-6014	FYE: November 30
Web: www.ccaindustries.com	Type: Public

CCA Industries curls its customers' hair and brightens their smiles. It markets health and beauty aids, including Plus+White, Bikini Zone, Sudden Change, Solar Sense, and Nutra Nail. It also sells dietary supplements (Mega-T), shampoos (Wash 'N Curl), perfumes (Cherry Vanilla), and other health and beauty items. CCA outsources its manufacturing and supplies products to some 300 accounts, including food and drug retailers, mass merchandisers, and beauty aid wholesalers. It operates its business primarily in the US, with a small portion of sales generated overseas. Several of CCA's products, such as Hair-Off, Mega-T green tea, and Kids Sense, are made and marketed through licensing agreements.

	Annual Growth	11/03	11/04	11/05	11/06	11/07
Sales ($ mil.)	2.7%	54.7	61.5	63.7	64.1	60.9
Net income ($ mil.)	0.9%	5.3	5.8	3.8	5.6	5.5
Market value ($ mil.)	5.1%	48.5	67.7	51.3	70.3	59.3
Employees	—	—	—	153	—	—

CCC INFORMATION SERVICES GROUP INC.

222 Merchandise Mart, Ste. 900	CEO: Githesh Ramamurthy
Chicago, IL 60654	CFO: Andrew G. Balbirer
Phone: 312-222-4636	HR: Gary Newman
Fax: 312-527-2298	FYE: December 31
Web: www.cccis.com	Type: Subsidiary

CCC Information Services Group helps smooth the dents in auto claims processing. The company offers computer software and services that help insurance agencies, independent appraisers, and collision repair shops process auto claims. CCC's offerings include its Pathways application for estimating collision and repair cost and its Valuescope claim settlement services application for estimating the worth of totaled vehicles. CCC Information Services was acquired by Investcorp for about $496 million in early 2006, joining a diverse group of businesses that Investcorp has purchased.

	Annual Growth	12/03	12/04	12/05	12/06	12/07
Est. sales ($ mil.)	—	—	—	—	—	80.1
Employees	—	—	—	—	—	834

An in-depth profile of this company is available to Hoover's Online members at hoovers.com. ⊞

CCF HOLDING COMPANY

NASDAQ (CM): CCFH

101 N. Main St.
Jonesboro, GA 30236
Phone: 770-478-8881
Fax: 678-284-3315
Web: www.heritage24.com

CEO: David B. Turner
CFO: Mary Jo Rogers
HR: –
FYE: December 31
Type: Public

CCF Holding Company sees green in the Peach State. The institution is the parent of Heritage Bank, which operates about a half-dozen branches in the Clayton, Fayette, and Henry counties of greater metropolitan Atlanta. Centered in the fast-growing Hartsfield International Airport region, the bank targets individuals and local businesses, offering such standard retail services as checking and savings accounts, NOW and money market accounts, CDs, and IRAs. Real estate loans, including construction and land development loans and commercial and residential mortgages, account for about 90% of the bank's lending portfolio. Heritage Bank also writes consumer and business loans.

	Annual Growth	12/03	12/04	12/05	12/06	12/07
Assets ($ mil.)	9.4%	295.7	340.1	364.2	425.9	422.8
Net income ($ mil.)	14.3%	2.4	2.8	3.3	5.2	4.1
Market value ($ mil.)	26.6%	14.7	29.9	20.4	74.1	37.7
Employees	11.3%	—	—	105	—	130

CCFNB BANCORP, INC.

OTC: CCFN

232 East St.
Bloomsburg, PA 17815
Phone: 570-784-4400
Fax: 570-387-4049
Web: www.ccfnb.com

CEO: Lance O. Diehl
CFO: Virginia D. Kocher
HR: Edwin A. (Ed) Wenner
FYE: December 31
Type: Public

CCFNB Bancorp knows the ABCs of banking. The firm is the holding company for Columbia County Farmers National Bank, a community institution serving eastern Pennsylvania's Columbia County from several branch locations. The bank offers standard products and services as well as wealth management and trust services. It uses funds from deposits to write a variety of loans; real estate loans account for more than 80% of its loan portfolio. The bank also offers consumer and construction loans. CCFNB Bancorp also owns a 50% stake in Neighborhood Group (dba Neighborhood Advisors), an insurance and financial products agency.

	Annual Growth	12/03	12/04	12/05	12/06	12/07
Assets ($ mil.)	1.3%	232.9	235.4	231.2	241.9	245.3
Net income ($ mil.)	5.3%	2.2	2.2	2.2	2.4	2.7
Market value ($ mil.)	(3.8%)	35.9	34.3	35.9	35.0	30.7
Employees	—	—	—	—	—	95

CCH INCORPORATED

2700 Lake Cook Rd.
Riverwoods, IL 60015
Phone: 847-267-7000
Fax: 773-866-3095
Web: www.cch.com

CEO: Mike Sabbatis
CFO: Douglas M. (Doug) Winterrose
HR: –
FYE: December 31
Type: Subsidiary

Tax season must be CCH's favorite time of year. A subsidiary of Dutch publisher Wolters Kluwer, CCH publishes more than 700 publications in print and electronic form primarily concerning the subjects of tax and business law. Publications are available in a variety of formats including loose-leaf reports, CD-ROMs, books, newsletters, audio cassettes, and online. The company's flagship product is *The Standard Federal Tax Reporter*. Its Tax and Accounting unit produces software used for tax preparation, audits, and office productivity. The company was founded in 1913, the same year the US federal income tax was created.

	Annual Growth	12/03	12/04	12/05	12/06	12/07
Est. sales ($ mil.)	—	—	—	—	—	537.9
Employees	—	—	—	—	—	4,743

CCMP CAPITAL ADVISORS, LLC

245 Park Ave., 16th Fl.
New York, NY 10167
Phone: 212-600-9600
Fax: 212-599-3481
Web: www.ccmpcapital.com

CEO: Stephen P. Murray
CFO: Marc Unger
HR: Julie Casella-Esposito
FYE: –
Type: Private

CCMP Capital is the former buyout and growth equity arm of venerable J.P. Morgan Partners. The firm was launched in 2006 (along with sister firm Panorama Capital) with $10 billion in assets and investments in some 375 companies. CCMP Capital focuses on five sectors: Consumer, Retail, and Services; Energy; Healthcare Infrastructure; Industrials; and Media and Telecom. Former JPMP managers are at the helm of the new company, whose investments include drug marketer Warner Chilcott's IPO and standby power generator maker Generac Power Systems, Inc. CCMP Capital also manages funds that are owned by its former parent.

CDI CORP.

NYSE: CDI

1717 Arch St., 35th Fl.
Philadelphia, PA 19103
Phone: 215-569-2200
Fax: 215-569-1300
Web: www.cdicorp.com

CEO: Roger H. Ballou
CFO: Mark A. Kerschner
HR: Cecilia J. Venglarik
FYE: December 31
Type: Public

If you want to get technical, give CDI a call. The company provides engineering and information technology (IT) staffing services to customers in such industries as aerospace, biotech, chemical, manufacturing, and pharmaceutical. Its engineering segment includes CDI Government Services, which focuses on defense-related work. Other CDI units include MRINetwork (permanent employment recruiting and temporary staffing services) and AndersElite (staffing services for the UK construction industry). To focus on its engineering- and IT-related staffing businesses, CDI in October 2007 sold its Todays Staffing subsidiary to rival Spherion for $40 million.

	Annual Growth	12/03	12/04	12/05	12/06	12/07
Sales ($ mil.)	2.9%	1,060.3	1,045.2	1,133.6	1,265.3	1,187.3
Net income ($ mil.)	11.0%	22.5	7.5	13.8	23.3	34.2
Market value ($ mil.)	(6.3%)	641.0	421.3	543.2	498.2	493.3
Employees	(72.7%)	—	—	18,800	1,700	1,400

CDW CORPORATION

200 N. Milwaukee Ave.
Vernon Hills, IL 60061
Phone: 847-465-6000
Fax: –
Web: www.cdw.com

CEO: John A. Edwardson
CFO: Ann E. Ziegler
HR: Dennis G. Berger
FYE: December 31
Type: Private

CDW Corporation takes more orders than Beetle Bailey. The firm offers some 100,000 computer products, mostly through catalogs, telesales, and the company's Internet and extranet Web sites. Brands include Adobe, Apple, Cisco, Lenovo, Samsung, ViewSonic, and others. In addition to computers, CDW also sells items such as printers, software, accessories, and networking products from companies including Hewlett-Packard, IBM, Microsoft, Sony, and Xerox. Almost all of CDW's sales come from private business and public sector customers. Founded in 1984, CDW was acquired in 2007 by private equity firm Madison Dearborn Partners for about $7.3 billion.

	Annual Growth	12/02	12/03	12/04	12/05	12/06
Sales ($ mil.)	12.3%	4,264.6	4,664.6	5,737.8	6,291.8	6,785.5
Net income ($ mil.)	9.5%	185.3	175.2	241.4	272.1	266.1
Employees	17.4%	2,900	—	—	4,300	5,500

An in-depth profile of this company is available to Hoover's Online members at hoovers.com.

343

CEC ENTERTAINMENT, INC.

NYSE: CEC

4441 W. Airport Fwy.
Irving, TX 75062
Phone: 972-258-8507
Fax: 972-258-5524
Web: www.chuckecheese.com

CEO: Richard M. Frank
CFO: –
HR: –
FYE: Friday nearest December 31
Type: Public

Don't let the mouse mascot fool you: This amusement kingdom is founded on the power of pizza. CEC Entertainment operates the Chuck E. Cheese's chain of pizza parlors, with more 530 locations throughout the US and in Canada. The restaurants, which are especially popular for birthday parties, feature dining-room entertainment provided by robotic characters, arcade games, and other activities targeting families with young children. The menu includes a variety of pizzas, sandwiches, salads, and desserts. CEC Entertainment owns about 490 of the pizza and fun joints, while the rest are franchised.

	Annual Growth	12/03	12/04	12/05	12/06	12/07
Sales ($ mil.)	4.7%	654.6	728.1	726.2	774.2	785.3
Net income ($ mil.)	(4.6%)	67.4	82.5	74.7	68.3	55.9
Market value ($ mil.)	(12.9%)	1,217.3	1,452.8	1,144.3	1,298.5	699.2
Employees	(2.4%)	—	—	19,408	18,395	18,500

CECIL BANCORP, INC.

OTC: CECB

127 North St.
Elkton, MD 21921
Phone: 410-398-1650
Fax: 410-392-3128
Web: www.cecilfederal.com

CEO: Mary B. Halsey
CFO: R. Lee Whitehead
HR: –
FYE: December 31
Type: Public

Cecil Bancorp is the holding company for Cecil Federal Bank, which serves northeastern Maryland's Cecil and Harford counties. Founded in 1959, Cecil Federal Bank offers standard deposit products and services including checking and savings accounts, money market accounts, and NOW accounts. It also offers brokerage and investment services through an agreement with UVEST. Cecil Federal focuses on real estate lending; single- to four-family mortgages make up the largest portion of the bank's loan portfolio, and real estate loans in general make up two-thirds of all loans. Chairman Charles Sposato owns about 35% of the company.

	Annual Growth	12/03	12/04	12/05	12/06	12/07
Assets ($ mil.)	28.0%	149.6	200.4	267.1	347.5	401.4
Net income ($ mil.)	29.7%	1.2	1.5	2.1	2.7	3.4
Market value ($ mil.)	37.5%	9.3	15.7	13.9	17.3	33.1
Employees	—	—	—	—	—	92

CECO ENVIRONMENTAL CORP.

NASDAQ (GM): CECE

3120 Forrer St.
Cincinnati, OH 45209
Phone: 513-458-2600
Fax: 513-458-2647
Web: www.cecoenviro.com

CEO: Phillip DeZwirek
CFO: Dennis W. Blazer
HR: –
FYE: December 31
Type: Public

CECO Environmental wants to clear the air. Through its subsidiaries, CECO Environmental makes industrial ventilation and pollution control systems, including air filters to remove airborne solid and liquid pollutants. The company serves customers in the automotive, chemical, electronics, pharmaceutical, and textile industries, among others. Customers have included General Motors, Honda, and Procter & Gamble. CECO Environmental also provides custom metal fabrication services, making components for its own ventilation systems. CEO Phillip DeZwirek and his family control CECO Environmental.

	Annual Growth	12/03	12/04	12/05	12/06	12/07
Sales ($ mil.)	36.4%	68.2	69.4	81.5	135.4	235.9
Net income ($ mil.)	—	(0.7)	(0.9)	(0.4)	3.1	6.3
Market value ($ mil.)	77.2%	16.5	34.4	57.4	103.0	162.4
Employees	46.0%	—	—	446	651	—

CEDAR FAIR, L.P.

NYSE: FUN

1 Cedar Point Dr.
Sandusky, OH 44870
Phone: 419-626-0830
Fax: 419-627-2260
Web: www.cedarfair.com

CEO: Richard L. (Dick) Kinzel
CFO: Peter J. Crage
HR: –
FYE: December 31
Type: Public

Cedar Fair wants to take you for the ride of your life. The firm owns and manages 11 amusement parks, six outdoor water parks, one indoor water park, and five hotels. Properties include Knott's Berry Farm in California, Michigan's Adventure, and Valleyfair in Minnesota. Knott's Berry Farm operates year-round, while other parks are open daily from Memorial Day through Labor Day, plus additional weekends in April, May, September, and October. Additionally, the company owns Star Trek: The Experience (themed rides, a museum, and Quark's Bar & Restaurant) in the Las Vegas Hilton. Cedar Fair bought Paramount Parks from CBS Corp. in 2006. The parks together draw more than 22 million visitors a year.

	Annual Growth	12/03	12/04	12/05	12/06	12/07
Sales ($ mil.)	17.9%	510.0	542.0	568.7	831.4	987.0
Net income ($ mil.)	—	85.9	78.3	160.9	87.5	(4.5)
Market value ($ mil.)	(7.4%)	1,558.2	1,759.5	1,535.4	1,504.8	1,146.3
Employees	96.6%	—	—	16,200	31,850	—

CEDAR SHOPPING CENTERS, INC.

NYSE: CDR

44 S. Bayles Ave., Ste. 304
Port Washington, NY 11050
Phone: 516-767-6492
Fax: 516-767-6497
Web: www.cedarshoppingcenters.com

CEO: Leo S. Ullman
CFO: Lawrence E. (Larry) Kreider Jr.
HR: –
FYE: December 31
Type: Public

Cedar Shopping Centers (formerly Cedar Income Fund) has tended its portfolio from a sapling to a full-grown evergreen. The self-managed real estate investment trust (REIT) owns, develops, and manages retail properties, mainly supermarket- or drug-store-anchored strip centers in the Northeast and Mid-Atlantic. It owns nearly 120 properties totaling 12 million sq. ft., as well as more than 200 acres of developable land. Its community shopping center portfolio spans nine states, with the largest concentration in Pennsylvania, Ohio, and Virginia. Major tenants include Giant Foods, Discount Drug Mart, CVS, and Rite Aid. The acquisitive REIT usually redevelops or expands existing properties after it buys them.

	Annual Growth	12/03	12/04	12/05	12/06	12/07
Sales ($ mil.)	55.0%	26.5	51.1	78.9	126.5	152.9
Net income ($ mil.)	—	(21.4)	7.9	13.2	15.3	22.0
Market value ($ mil.)	22.0%	204.4	276.7	416.7	696.4	452.6
Employees	13.2%	—	—	71	—	91

CEDARS-SINAI MEDICAL CENTER

8700 Beverly Blvd.
Los Angeles, CA 90048
Phone: 310-423-3277
Fax: –
Web: www.csmc.edu

CEO: Thomas M. (Tom) Priselac
CFO: Edward M. Prunchunas
HR: Jeanne Flores
FYE: June 30
Type: Not-for-profit

Many a star has been born, literally, at Cedars-Sinai Medical Center. The 875-bed teaching and research hospital is located right where Los Angeles meets Beverly Hills and West Hollywood, and it has tended to the medical needs of a number of celebrities since its inception in 1902. However, the center is also a major teaching hospital for UCLA's David Geffen School of Medicine and is engaged in some 600 research programs, in areas such as cancer, neuroscience, and genetics. Its Cedars-Sinai Medical Group is a multi-specialty physicians group consisting of about 75 doctors; the medical center is also affiliated with an Independent Physician Association with roughly 600 primary care and specialist doctors.

	Annual Growth	6/03	6/04	6/05	6/06	6/07
Est. sales ($ mil.)	—	—	—	—	—	377.0
Employees	—	—	—	—	—	8,000

CEGEDIM DENDRITE

1207 Rte. 206 South
Bedminster, NJ 07921
Phone: 908-443-2000
Fax: –
Web: www.cegedimdendrite.com/En/Pages

CEO: John E. Bailye
CFO: Brent J. Cosgrove
HR: –
FYE: December 31
Type: Subsidiary

Cegedim Dendrite helps salespeople conduct business, offering services and software that manage and analyze sales efforts for the pharmaceutical and consumer packaged goods industries. Its products include applications that help sales forces access product information and physician databases, evaluate competitors, and catalog client and prospect data. In 2006 the company purchased the assets of OPUS Health LLC, a provider of direct-to-patient persistence technologies. In May 2007 Dendrite was acquired by Cegedim for $751 million.

	Annual Growth	12/02	12/03	12/04	12/05	12/06
Sales ($ mil.)	17.1%	225.8	321.1	399.2	437.2	424.0
Net income ($ mil.)	—	15.4	21.1	29.6	21.5	(26.7)
Employees	12.9%	1,559	2,524	2,549	2,793	2,534

CELADON GROUP, INC.

NASDAQ (GS): CLDN

9503 E. 33rd St.
Indianapolis, IN 46235
Phone: 317-972-7000
Fax: 317-890-8099
Web: www.celadontrucking.com

CEO: Stephen (Steve) Russell
CFO: Paul A. Will
HR: Brett Terchila
FYE: June 30
Type: Public

As far north as Canada and as far south as Mexico, Celadon trucks go up and down the road. Celadon Group provides long-haul, dry van truckload service throughout North America through Celadon Trucking Services, Jaguar, and Celadon Canada. Celadon's subsidiaries operate from more than 15 terminals with a fleet of about 3,000 tractors and 7,800 trailers. Besides for-hire transportation, Celadon offers dedicated contract carriage, in which drivers and equipment are assigned to a customer long-term, and warehousing services. An e-commerce unit, TruckersB2B, serves as a purchasing cooperative for small and medium-sized trucking fleets and provides discounts on products such as fuel, tires, and satellite systems.

	Annual Growth	6/03	6/04	6/05	6/06	6/07
Sales ($ mil.)	8.2%	367.1	397.9	436.8	480.2	502.7
Net income ($ mil.)	57.8%	3.6	(0.3)	12.6	20.5	22.3
Market value ($ mil.)	85.7%	31.5	76.3	75.7	509.4	374.9
Employees	4.5%	—	—	3,210	3,353	—

CELANESE CORPORATION

NYSE: CE

1601 W. LBJ Fwy.
Dallas, TX 75234
Phone: 972-443-4000
Fax: 972-443-8555
Web: www.celanese.com

CEO: David N. Weidman
CFO: Steven M. (Steve) Sterin
HR: Kevin J. Rogan
FYE: December 31
Type: Public

Celanese Corporation's primary operations include the manufacture of building block chemicals like acetic acid and vinyl acetate monomers (VAM). With Canadian acetyls maker Acetex as a subsidiary, Celanese is the world's largest acetyls manufacturer. Acetyls are used in everything from paints and inks to agricultural products and chewing gum. Two-thirds of the company's sales come from the US and Germany. Celanese Corporation was created in 2004 by the Blackstone Group, which had acquired a majority share in Celanese AG, turned it private, and then flipped it in a 2005 public offering. Blackstone finally divested its remaining holdings in Celanese in 2007.

	Annual Growth	12/03	12/04	12/05	12/06	12/07
Sales ($ mil.)	8.3%	—	5,069.0	6,070.0	6,656.0	6,444.0
Net income ($ mil.)	—	—	(175.0)	277.0	406.0	426.0
Market value ($ mil.)	45.7%	—	—	3,031.7	4,106.3	6,437.0
Employees	(5.0%)	—	—	9,300	8,900	8,400

CELEBRATE EXPRESS, INC.

NASDAQ (GM): BDAY

11220 120th Ave. NE
Kirkland, WA 98033
Phone: 425-250-1064
Fax: 425-828-6252
Web: www.celebrateexpress.com

CEO: Kevin A. Green
CFO: Kristopher S. (Kris) Galvin
HR: –
FYE: May 31
Type: Public

Celebrate Express provides everything for a birthday party except the suit. Operating as Birthday Express, the company offers more than 150 themed party packages targeting families with young children through its catalog and Web site. Party packages include planning assistance (themes and activities) and supplies (paper products, balloons, favors). It produces much of its party merchandise (accounting for more than 80% of sales), offering such private-label items as crepe paper and piñatas. The direct retailer also sells children's costumes and accessories via its Costume Express Web site. Founded in 1994 as Birthday Express, the company changed its name to Celebrate Express in 2000 and went public in 2004.

	Annual Growth	5/03	5/04	5/05	5/06	5/07
Sales ($ mil.)	22.5%	37.8	51.9	69.1	87.0	85.2
Net income ($ mil.)	—	(1.6)	9.5	2.5	0.4	0.0
Market value ($ mil.)	(12.2%)	—	—	90.3	99.1	69.6
Employees	32.2%	—	—	345	456	—

CELERA GROUP

NYSE: CRA

45 W. Gude Dr.
Rockville, MD 20850
Phone: 240-453-3000
Fax: 240-453-4000
Web: www.celera.com

CEO: Kathy P. Ordoñez
CFO: Joel R. Jung
HR: –
FYE: June 30
Type: Public

Celera Group spent years unwrapping the secrets of genetics, and now it is ready to do something with all that it has learned. Celera Group (formerly Celera Genomics Group) cleared a major hurdle when it mapped the human genome, but the firm, a tracking stock of Applera, wants to turn its knowledge of proteins into a profit. Sister firm Applied Biosystems handles the marketing of Celera's genomics databases (which detail the genomes of mice, fruit flies, various bacteria, and other life forms) to life sciences companies so that Celera can focus on developing gene and protein-based diagnostics. Applera has announced that it intends to split Celera off as an independent company.

	Annual Growth	6/02	6/03	6/04	6/05	*6/06
Sales ($ mil.)	(22.2%)	120.8	86.4	57.4	28.1	44.2
Net income ($ mil.)	—	(211.8)	(81.9)	(57.5)	(77.1)	(62.7)
Employees	(22.2%)	820	540	530	480	300

*Most recent year available

CELERITY, INC.

1463 Centre Pointe Dr.
Milpitas, CA 95035
Phone: 408-946-3100
Fax: 408-935-4506
Web: www.celerity.net

CEO: Timothy D. (Tim) Harris
CFO: –
HR: Adriana Stadecker
FYE: December 31
Type: Private

Celerity speeds the flow of fluids. Formed in 1999, Celerity offers mass flow controllers and other fluid delivery instruments that makers of semiconductor manufacturing equipment incorporate into their products. Applied Materials accounts for most of the company's sales. Celerity's products also are used in equipment for manufacturing flat-panel displays, magnetic and optical storage devices, microelectromechanical systems, and photovoltaic solar cells. Texas Pacific Group (TPG) acquired Celerity through an asset purchase in late 2004. The company is not related to Celerity Solutions, a software firm.

An in-depth profile of this company is available to Hoover's Online members at hoovers.com.

345

CELGENE CORPORATION

NASDAQ (GS): CELG

86 Morris Ave.
Summit, NJ 07901
Phone: 908-673-9000
Fax: 908-673-9001
Web: www.celgene.com

CEO: Sol J. Barer
CFO: David W. Gryska
HR: Mary Weger
FYE: December 31
Type: Public

A terror from the past has provided hope in the present. Celgene's flagship products Thalomid and Revlimid are versions of the infamous thalidomide, the morning sickness remedy pulled from shelves in the 1960s after it was linked to birth defects. Revlimid, a treatment for multiple myeloma (bone marrow cancer) and a malignant blood disease called MDS, is approved in the US and Europe; Thalomid is approved in the US for multiple myeloma, and it won European approval in 2008. Celgene sells them both under strict risk management plans that ensure they are safely administered. The firm has other drugs in development that combat inflammatory diseases and cancer. In 2008 Celgene acquired Pharmion for $2.9 billion.

	Annual Growth	12/03	12/04	12/05	12/06	12/07
Sales ($ mil.)	50.8%	271.5	377.5	536.9	898.9	1,405.8
Net income ($ mil.)	102.4%	13.5	52.8	63.7	69.0	226.4
Market value ($ mil.)	112.5%	913.4	2,188.8	11,086.4	21,633.3	18,628.4
Employees	33.6%	—	—	944	1,287	1,685

CELL GENESYS, INC.

NASDAQ (GM): CEGE

500 Forbes Blvd.
South San Francisco, CA 94080
Phone: 650-266-3000
Fax: 650-266-3010
Web: www.cellgenesys.com

CEO: Stephen A. (Steve) Sherwin
CFO: Sharon E. Tetlow
HR: Christine B. (Chris) McKinley
FYE: December 31
Type: Public

Cell Genesys wants to be the beginning of the end for cancer. The development-stage company is researching biotech treatments for various forms of the disease. Its lead technology is its GVAX immunotherapy platform, which stimulates a patient's immune system to fight tumors. GVAX vaccines are in late stages of development as a treatment for prostate cancer, and may also fight pancreatic cancer, leukemia, and myelodysplastic syndrome. A second Cell Genesys program is developing viruses (including the common cold virus) that are specially engineered to fight cancer cells; it is working with druggernaut Novartis to develop viral therapies for recurrent bladder cancer.

	Annual Growth	12/03	12/04	12/05	12/06	12/07
Sales ($ mil.)	(47.3%)	18.1	11.5	4.6	1.4	1.4
Net income ($ mil.)	—	(56.4)	(97.4)	(64.9)	(82.9)	(99.3)
Market value ($ mil.)	(22.8%)	507.4	364.3	270.2	196.1	180.5
Employees	—	—	—	—	267	—

CELL THERAPEUTICS, INC.

NASDAQ (GM): CTIC

501 Elliott Ave. West, Ste. 400
Seattle, WA 98119
Phone: 206-282-7100
Fax: 206-284-6206
Web: www.cticseattle.com

CEO: James A. Bianco
CFO: Louis A. Bianco
HR: –
FYE: December 31
Type: Public

Cell Therapeutics (CTI) is a toxic avenger. The firm creates more effective and less toxic treatments for various forms of cancer. It markets FDA-approved Zevalin, a radioimmunotherapy for B-cell non-Hodgkin's lymphoma, in the US; it acquired the drug in 2007 from Biogen Idec. CTI is also developing a number of other cancer-fighting compounds, including paclitaxel poliglumex (formerly branded as Xyotax) for non-small cell lung and ovarian cancers, and pixantrone, another treatment for non-Hodgkin's lymphoma. The company's Systems Medicine subsidiary is working on a potential sarcoma-fighter called brostallicin.

	Annual Growth	12/03	12/04	12/05	12/06	12/07
Sales ($ mil.)	(74.8%)	24.8	29.6	16.1	0.1	0.1
Net income ($ mil.)	—	(130.0)	(252.3)	(102.5)	(135.8)	(138.1)
Market value ($ mil.)	(12.1%)	297.7	519.8	160.1	271.5	177.9
Employees	—	—	—	214	—	—

CELLCO PARTNERSHIP

1 Verizon Way
Basking Ridge, NJ 07920
Phone: 908-559-2000
Fax: –
Web: www.verizonwireless.com

CEO: Lowell C. McAdam
CFO: John Townsend
HR: Martha Delehanty
FYE: December 31
Type: Joint venture

Cellco Partnership, which does business as Verizon Wireless, is the #2 US wireless phone operator (after rival AT&T Mobility), serving nearly 66 million customers nationwide. The company also offers mobile voice services, including text messaging, multimedia content, and mobile Web services. Verizon Wireless began operations in 2000 when Bell Atlantic and Vodafone combined their US wireless assets. It gained GTE's US wireless operations when Bell Atlantic bought GTE to form Verizon Communications, which owns 55% of the company; Vodafone owns 45%. In June 2008 the company announced plans to purchase ALLTEL in a $28.1 billion deal that would make Verizon Wireless the top wireless provider in the US.

	Annual Growth	12/03	12/04	12/05	12/06	12/07
Sales ($ mil.)	18.2%	22,489.0	27,662.0	32,301.0	38,000.0	43,900.0
Employees	12.0%	43,900	49,800	55,700	67,000	69,000

CELLEGY PHARMACEUTICALS, INC.

OTC: CLGY

2085B Quaker Point Rd.
Quakertown, PA 18951
Phone: 215-529-6084
Fax: 215-529-6086

CEO: Richard C. Williams
CFO: Robert J. (Rob) Caso
HR: Bethany Banner
FYE: December 31
Type: Public

Cellegy Pharmaceuticals develops specialty prescription drugs, but its own well-being has come into question. After getting a disappointing response from the FDA in 2006 regarding Cellegesic (a treatment for anal fissures), the company sold the drug, as well as a number of other candidates, to Strakan International, a subsidiary of ProStrakan Group. It owns intellectual property related to a group of microbicidal gels, including Savvy, which is in late-stage trials in the US as a contraceptive. However, the company began considering strategic alternatives, including a merger or sale, and in 2008 announced plans to merge with privately held drug firm Adamis Pharmaceuticals.

	Annual Growth	12/02	12/03	12/04	12/05	*12/06
Sales ($ mil.)	17.8%	1.4	1.6	2.6	12.8	2.7
Net income ($ mil.)	—	(15.2)	(13.5)	(28.1)	(5.0)	9.7
Market value ($ mil.)	(62.1%)	79.6	62.3	75.0	16.7	1.6
Employees	(31.7%)	23	20	32	19	5

*Most recent year available

CEL-SCI CORPORATION

AMEX: CVM

8229 Boone Blvd., Ste. 802
Vienna, VA 22182
Phone: 703-506-9460
Fax: 703-506-9471
Web: www.cel-sci.com

CEO: Geert R. Kersten
CFO: Geert R. Kersten
HR: –
FYE: September 30
Type: Public

CEL-SCI hopes to make L.E.A.P.S. and bounds in preventing and treating deadly diseases. Its L.E.A.P.S. (Ligand Epitope Antigen Presentation System) technology modulates T-cells and may lead to synthetic vaccines for herpes, viral encephalitis, smallpox, and other diseases. The National Institutes of Health is testing CEL-1000 (a compound developed using L.E.A.P.S. technology) as a potential avian flu vaccine. The firm's lead drug candidate, however, is Multikine, which might make tumors more susceptible to radiation therapy and help a patient's body produce tumor-fighting antibodies; it is undergoing clinical trials for the treatment of head and neck tumors.

	Annual Growth	9/03	9/04	9/05	9/06	9/07
Sales ($ mil.)	(24.0%)	0.3	0.3	0.3	0.1	0.1
Net income ($ mil.)	—	(6.4)	(4.2)	(3.0)	(7.9)	(9.6)
Market value ($ mil.)	6.4%	56.9	41.1	35.0	51.3	72.9
Employees	17.0%	—	—	19	—	26

CELSION CORPORATION

AMEX: CLN

10220 Old Columbia Rd., Ste. L
Columbia, MD 21046
Phone: 410-290-5390
Fax: 410-290-5394
Web: www.celsion.com

CEO: Michael H. Tardugno
CFO: Paul B. Susie
HR: –
FYE: December 31
Type: Public

Celsion is trying to turn up the heat on cancer. The company is developing a heat-activated cancer therapy in the form of its lead drug, ThermoDox. ThermoDox combines a common oncology drug, doxorubicin, with a heat-activated liposome that may help deliver and release the drug more accurately. The drug is being studied as a treatment for liver cancer and breast cancer. Celsion was previously a device maker and developed the Prolieve Thermodilatation system, an FDA-approved device used to treat benign prostatic hyperplasia (prostate enlargement). Celsion sold the product line to Boston Scientific in 2007.

	Annual Growth	12/02	12/03	12/04	12/05	*12/06
Sales ($ mil.)	112.6%	—	—	2.5	12.3	11.3
Net income ($ mil.)	—	—	—	(14.0)	(8.7)	(7.6)
Employees	(6.3%)	—	—	33	29	29

*Most recent year available

CEMEX INC.

840 Gessner, Ste. 1400
Houston, TX 77024
Phone: 713-650-6200
Fax: 713-653-6815
Web: www.cemexusa.com

CEO: Gilberto Perez
CFO: –
HR: Andrew M. (Andy) Miller
FYE: December 31
Type: Subsidiary

CEMEX serves up cement with a multicultural accent. A subsidiary of Mexico-based CEMEX, S.A. de C.V., the company got a big boost — especially in terms of ready-mix capacity — when its parent acquired UK-based RMC Group in 2005. CEMEX now boasts that it's the largest cement company in the US, as well as the largest ready-mix company. In addition to cement and ready-mix, CEMEX also makes and sells concrete block and aggregates. It serves customers through some 300 ready-mix plants (up from 90 before the acquisition), 12 cement plants (with a capacity of 13 million tons per year), about 50 distribution facilities, and some 50 aggregate quarries.

	Annual Growth	12/03	12/04	12/05	12/06	12/07
Est. sales ($ mil.)	—	—	—	—	—	2,147.5
Employees	—	—	—	—	—	11,050

CENGAGE LEARNING

200 First Stamford Place, Ste. 400
Stamford, CT 06902
Phone: 203-965-8600
Fax: 800-487-8488
Web: www.cengage.com

CEO: Ronald G. (Ron) Dunn
CFO: Jerry V. Elliott
HR: Adrian Butler
FYE: December 31
Type: Private

Cengage Learning provides courseware, specialized content, and learning services for businesses, educational institutions, government agencies, and individuals. Its offerings include online reference databases, distance learning and test preparation courses, corporate training courses, and materials for specific academic disciplines. Cengage Learning offers educational products under the Wadsworth, South-Western, Course Technology, Delmar, Gale, Prometric, and NETg names. The company was acquired by Apax Partners and Omers Capital Partners in July 2007. In late 2007 the company accounced plans to purchase Houghton Mifflin Harcourt Publishing Company's College Division (HM College) for about $750 million.

CENTENE CORPORATION

NYSE: CNC

7711 Carondelet Ave., Ste. 800
St. Louis, MO 63105
Phone: 314-725-4477
Fax: 314-558-2428
Web: www.centene.com

CEO: Michael F. Neidorff
CFO: Eric R. Slusser
HR: –
FYE: December 31
Type: Public

Centene provides managed care programs and related services to individuals and families enrolled in government-assisted health programs. The company operates under the names Managed Health Services in Wisconsin and Indiana, Superior HealthPlan in Texas, Buckeye Community Health Plan in Ohio, and University Health Plans in New Jersey, among others. Centene provides services to more than 1 million low-income, elderly, and disabled people receiving Medicaid, Supplemental Security Income, and State Children's Health Insurance Program (SCHIP) benefits. Centene also offers specialty services in areas such as behavioral health, disease management, optical benefit plans, nurse triage, and pharmacy benefits management.

	Annual Growth	12/03	12/04	12/05	12/06	12/07
Sales ($ mil.)	39.6%	769.7	1,000.9	1,505.9	2,279.0	2,919.3
Net income ($ mil.)	21.8%	33.3	44.3	55.6	(43.6)	73.4
Market value ($ mil.)	20.7%	563.9	1,171.3	1,130.2	1,065.6	1,198.2
Employees	31.2%	—	—	1,800	2,600	3,100

CENTENNIAL COMMUNICATIONS CORP.

NASDAQ (GS): CYCL

3349 Rte. 138, Bldg. A
Wall, NJ 07719
Phone: 732-556-2200
Fax: 732-556-2242
Web: www.centennialwireless.com

CEO: Michael J. Small
CFO: Thomas J. Fitzpatrick
HR: –
FYE: May 31
Type: Public

Centennial Communications has high hopes for the 21st century and beyond. The company provides wireless communications in smaller markets across the central US and it offers PCS (personal communications services) in Puerto Rico, where it operates as a competitive local-exchange carrier (CLEC). Services offered in Puerto Rico include wireline and wireless broadband as well as traditional and Internet-based phone service. Centennial also provides wireless services in the US Virgin Islands and sells and leases wireless phones and accessories. Its products and services are marketed through about 180 retail outlets in the US and 75 in Puerto Rico.

	Annual Growth	5/03	5/04	5/05	5/06	5/07
Sales ($ mil.)	5.2%	745.7	828.8	882.4	945.7	911.9
Net income ($ mil.)	—	(111.9)	(22.8)	25.6	20.2	(31.6)
Market value ($ mil.)	51.7%	205.7	744.8	1,361.7	614.1	1,088.6
Employees	(7.0%)	—	—	3,350	3,400	2,900

CENTER BANCORP, INC.

NASDAQ (GS): CNBC

2455 Morris Ave.
Union, NJ 07083
Phone: 908-688-9500
Fax: 908-688-3043
Web: www.centerbancorp.com

CEO: Anthony C. (Tony) Weagley
CFO: –
HR: –
FYE: December 31
Type: Public

Center Bancorp is the holding company for Union Center National Bank, which operates about a dozen offices in northern New Jersey's Morris and Union counties. A full-service commercial bank, Union Center offers individuals and local businesses such deposit products as checking, savings, and money market accounts; CDs; and IRAs. It also offers trust services. Commercial loans account for about 50% of the bank's loan portfolio; residential mortgages account for most of the remainder. Subsidiaries offer services such as advertising, insurance (annuities, property/casualty, life, and health), wealth management, and real estate investment trust (REIT) operations.

	Annual Growth	12/03	12/04	12/05	12/06	12/07
Assets ($ mil.)	2.5%	921.8	1,009.0	1,114.8	1,051.4	1,017.6
Net income ($ mil.)	(11.6%)	6.4	7.6	7.7	3.9	3.9
Market value ($ mil.)	0.1%	144.7	118.2	140.2	199.6	145.5
Employees	(7.7%)	—	—	202	—	172

An in-depth profile of this company is available to Hoover's Online members at hoovers.com.

347

CENTER FINANCIAL CORPORATION
NASDAQ (GS): CLFC

3435 Wilshire Blvd., Ste. 700
Los Angeles, CA 90010
Phone: 213-251-2222
Fax: 213-386-6774
Web: www.centerbank.com

CEO: Jae Whan (J. W.) Yoo
CFO: Lonny D. Robinson
HR: –
FYE: December 31
Type: Public

Center Financial wants to be in the middle of your finances. Center Financial Corporation is the holding company for Center Bank, which has about 15 branches in Southern California, as well as in Chicago and Seattle. It also operates nearly 10 additional loan production offices scattered across the US mainland and Hawaii in areas heavily concentrated with Korean-American businesses and individuals, Center Financial's target market. The bank focuses on commercial lending, including mortgages, Small Business Administration loans, and short-term trade finance for importers/exporters.

	Annual Growth	12/03	12/04	12/05	12/06	12/07
Assets ($ mil.)	19.3%	1,027.4	1,338.1	1,661.0	1,843.3	2,080.7
Net income ($ mil.)	17.2%	11.6	14.2	24.6	26.2	21.9
Market value ($ mil.)	(2.0%)	218.7	326.0	413.6	398.7	201.6
Employees	6.1%	—	—	327	344	368

CENTER OIL COMPANY

600 Mason Ridge Center Dr.
St. Louis, MO 63141
Phone: 314-682-3500
Fax: 314-682-3599
Web: www.centeroil.com

CEO: Gary R. Parker
CFO: Richard I. (Rick) Powers
HR: Richard I. (Rick) Powers
FYE: December 31
Type: Private

Center Oil's core business is peddling petroleum. The company is one of the largest private wholesale distributors of gasoline and other petroleum products to customers primarily in the eastern region of the US. Center Oil owns eight storage terminals capable of storing more than 2 million barrels of petroleum products. It also has access to 36 terminals in 10 states, as well as access to the Magellan, Texas Eastern, Kinder Morgan Chicago, and Kaneb pipeline systems. Its products are also distributed through a fleet of ships, barges, and trucks.

	Annual Growth	12/02	12/03	12/04	12/05	12/06
Sales ($ mil.)	12.5%	—	—	—	4,800.0	5,400.0
Employees	(2.2%)	—	—	—	46	45

CENTERLINE HOLDING COMPANY
NYSE: CHC

625 Madison Ave.
New York, NY 10022
Phone: 212-317-5700
Fax: 212-751-3550
Web: www.centerline.com

CEO: Marc D. Schnitzer
CFO: Robert L. (Rob) Levy
HR: Katherine B. (Kelly) Schnur
FYE: December 31
Type: Public

Centerline Holding Company helps keep the multifamily housing finance market liquid. Through subsidiaries, the firm (formerly CharterMac) invests in tax-exempt multifamily mortgage bonds issued by state and municipal governments to finance the construction or rehabilitation of multifamily housing, particularly properties meeting low-income housing tax credit requirements. The company's Centerline Capital operating subsidiary (formerly CharterMac Capital) has raised some $12 billion in capital from institutional and retail investors by sponsoring real estate investment funds that are also used to finance multifamily properties.

	Annual Growth	12/03	12/04	12/05	12/06	12/07
Assets ($ mil.)	38.4%	2,583.3	5,757.4	6,978.8	9,688.5	9,491.6
Net income ($ mil.)	—	66.6	65.4	59.0	41.3	(60.1)
Market value ($ mil.)	(20.1%)	945.8	1,252.0	1,101.8	1,102.3	385.3
Employees	11.8%	—	—	400	500	500

CENTERPLATE, INC.
AMEX: CVP

201 E. Broad St.
Spartanburg, SC 29306
Phone: 864-598-8600
Fax: 864-598-8695
Web: www.centerplate.com

CEO: Janet L. Steinmayer
CFO: Kevin F. McNamara
HR: David Winarski
FYE: December 31
Type: Public

Wherever there's a sporting event, this concessions operator likes to be in the middle of the action. Centerplate is a leading provider of catering, concessions, and facilities management services in the US, serving nearly 130 stadiums, convention centers, and other venues. It operates at more than 70 sports venues, including many professional baseball and football stadiums, minor league parks, and college sports stadiums. The company also provides catering and other services at more than a dozen convention centers, including the Dallas Convention Center and the Jacob K. Javits Center in Manhattan, and at a wide range of live entertainment venues and racetracks.

	Annual Growth	12/03	12/04	12/05	12/06	12/07
Sales ($ mil.)	4.7%	616.1	607.2	643.1	681.1	740.7
Net income ($ mil.)	—	(4.4)	2.3	(4.6)	3.5	(1.9)
Market value ($ mil.)	(11.3%)	305.8	239.1	277.5	409.1	189.3
Employees	1.6%	—	—	—	28,600	29,050

CENTERPOINT ENERGY HOUSTON ELECTRIC, LLC

1111 Louisiana St.
Houston, TX 77002
Phone: 713-207-1111
Fax: 713-207-9993
Web: centerpointenergy.com

CEO: David M. McClanahan
CFO: Gary L. Whitlock
HR: –
FYE: December 31
Type: Subsidiary

Houston, we don't have a problem. CenterPoint Energy Houston Electric's glow spreads across the fourth-largest US city and surrounding areas of the Texas Gulf Coast. The utility, formerly Reliant Energy HL&P, operates the regulated power transmission and distribution systems in the Houston metropolitan area. CenterPoint Energy Houston Electric, a subsidiary of utility holding company CenterPoint Energy, serves 2 million metered customers over its more than 46,350 miles of electric distribution lines; the utility's transmission assets are managed by the Electric Reliability Council of Texas (ERCOT).

	Annual Growth	12/03	12/04	12/05	12/06	12/07
Est. sales ($ mil.)	—	—	—	—	—	1,837.0
Net income ($ mil.)	—	—	—	—	—	273.0
Employees	—	—	—	—	—	—

CENTERPOINT ENERGY, INC.
NYSE: CNP

1111 Louisiana St.
Houston, TX 77002
Phone: 713-207-1111
Fax: 713-207-3169
Web: www.centerpointenergy.com

CEO: David M. McClanahan
CFO: Gary L. Whitlock
HR: –
FYE: December 31
Type: Public

CenterPoint Energy has made a complete pivot around its core operations. The company, which had evolved from a local utility into a global power provider, has spun off most of its nonregulated operations and has returned to its roots. CenterPoint Energy's regulated utilities distribute natural gas to more than 3 million customers in six states and electricity to 1.9 million customers on the Texas Gulf Coast. CenterPoint Energy also operates 69,000 miles of gas pipeline, and it has gas gathering and storage operations. The company's main stomping ground is Texas, where it has regulated power distribution operations through subsidiary CenterPoint Energy Houston Electric.

	Annual Growth	12/03	12/04	12/05	12/06	12/07
Sales ($ mil.)	(0.4%)	9,760.1	7,999.5	9,722.0	9,319.0	9,623.0
Net income ($ mil.)	(4.7%)	483.7	(904.7)	252.0	432.0	399.0
Market value ($ mil.)	16.8%	2,968.0	3,480.9	3,983.5	5,206.1	5,533.0
Employees	(2.4%)	—	—	9,001	8,623	8,568

CENTERPOINT PROPERTIES TRUST

1808 Swift Dr.
Oak Brook, IL 60523
Phone: 630-586-8000
Fax: 630-586-8010
Web: www.centerpoint-prop.com

CEO: Michael M. Mullen
CFO: Michael J. Kraft
HR: –
FYE: December 31
Type: Private

CenterPoint wants to be at the nexus of industry in the city of big shoulders. The company invests in and develops industrial projects in greater Chicago — a transportation hub and the largest industrial market in the US. It owns more than 20 branded business parks and, with affiliates, owns around 45 million sq. ft.; the company leases to tenants in the light manufacturing, warehousing, distribution, and air freight industries. Most properties are linked to important air and rail hubs. CalEast Industrial Investors, a group which includes Jones Lang LaSalle and CalPERS, acquired CenterPoint in a $3.4 billion transaction in 2006.

	Annual Growth	12/03	12/04	12/05	12/06	12/07
Est. sales ($ mil.)	—	—	—	—	—	194.9
Employees	—	—	—	—	—	109

CENTERSTATE BANKS OF FLORIDA, INC.

NASDAQ (GM): CSFL

1101 1st St. South, Ste. 202
Winter Haven, FL 33880
Phone: 863-293-2600
Fax: 863-291-3994
Web: www.csflbanks.com

CEO: Ernest S. (Ernie) Pinner
CFO: James J. Antal
HR: –
FYE: December 31
Type: Public

CenterState Banks of Florida is a multibank holding company serving the Sunshine State from more than 35 branch locations. It owns CenterState Bank, CenterState Bank of Florida, CenterState Bank Central Florida, and Valrico State Bank (acquired in 2007). The banks offer standard retail products and services such as checking and savings accounts, money market accounts, and CDs. They focus on real estate lending, including commercial mortgages (more than 45% of the firm's total loan portfolio), residential mortgages (approximately 25%) and construction and land development loans. The banks also sell mutual funds, annuities, and other investment products.

	Annual Growth	12/03	12/04	12/05	12/06	12/07
Assets ($ mil.)	18.9%	608.9	753.8	871.5	1,077.1	1,217.4
Net income ($ mil.)	31.6%	2.6	4.4	6.3	8.5	7.8
Market value ($ mil.)	47.2%	32.0	65.1	90.6	232.6	150.5
Employees	16.2%	—	—	275	320	371

CENTEX CORPORATION

NYSE: CTX

2728 N. Harwood
Dallas, TX 75201
Phone: 214-981-5000
Fax: 214-981-6859
Web: www.centex.com

CEO: Timothy R. (Tim) Eller
CFO: Catherine R. (Cathy) Smith
HR: Joseph A. (Joe) Bosch
FYE: March 31
Type: Public

Home is at the heart of Centex Corporation. Its Centex Homes business is one of the top US home builders, along with D.R. Horton, Lennar, and Pulte Homes. Centex Homes has home-building operations in around 75 markets in more than 20 states. In fiscal 2008 the company sold more than 27,000 homes for prices ranging from $65,000 to around $3 million. It builds for the first-time, move-up, and luxury markets. The company also offers mortgages through CTX Mortgage. In the wake of the subprime mortgage crisis and residential construction downturn in 2007, Centex is moving away from holding onto a large inventory of raw land toward purchasing finished lots ready for construction.

	Annual Growth	3/04	3/05	3/06	3/07	3/08
Sales ($ mil.)	(5.5%)	10,363.4	12,859.7	14,399.7	12,014.6	8,275.6
Net income ($ mil.)	—	827.7	1,011.4	1,289.3	268.4	(2,657.5)
Market value ($ mil.)	(18.1%)	6,631.0	7,315.1	7,569.2	5,012.3	2,984.6
Employees	(40.7%)	—	—	18,544	11,418	6,530

CENTEX HOMES

2728 N. Harwood
Dallas, TX 75201
Phone: 214-981-5000
Fax: 214-981-6002
Web: www.centexhomes.com

CEO: David L. Barclay
CFO: –
HR: –
FYE: March 31
Type: Subsidiary

As everyone knows, "location, location, location" are key elements in real estate, so Centex Homes doesn't limit itself to just Texas. The company, the main home-building subsidiary of Centex Corporation, builds in nearly 700 neighborhoods in some 80 markets in more than two dozen states, operating most heavily in the South Central, Southeast, and Mid-Atlantic regions. It is one of the largest home builders in the US, building some 35,000 homes annually. The home builder's houses range in price from about $76,000 to $1.8 million, averaging about $307,000.

	Annual Growth	3/02	3/03	3/04	3/05	3/06
Sales ($ mil.)	25.3%	4,972.2	5,922.7	7,599.5	9,861.0	12,272.2
Employees	14.4%	—	—	—	8,182	9,359

CENTILLIUM COMMUNICATIONS, INC.

NASDAQ (GM): CTLM

215 Fourier Ave.
Fremont, CA 94539
Phone: 510-771-3700
Fax: 510-771-3500
Web: www.centillium.com

CEO: Faraj Aalaei
CFO: Linda Reddick
HR: –
FYE: December 31
Type: Public

Centillium Communications wants its customers to enjoy scintillating broadband speeds. The company designs and markets integrated circuits used in high-speed networking equipment. Centillium's chips are incorporated into central office switches, access multiplexers, remote terminals, and television set-top boxes. The company also targets VoIP handsets and equipment for consumers. Centillium draws most of its sales from just a few customers, including Sumitomo Electric Industries (26% of sales), the Marconi business of Ericsson (23%), Alcatel-Lucent (15%), and NEC (also 15%). The company gets more than half of sales from the Asia/Pacific region, primarily Japan.

	Annual Growth	12/03	12/04	12/05	12/06	12/07
Sales ($ mil.)	(25.2%)	125.0	71.2	76.1	64.6	39.2
Net income ($ mil.)	—	(13.4)	(43.1)	(11.3)	(10.8)	(17.6)
Market value ($ mil.)	(31.1%)	212.6	94.3	139.9	88.1	48.0
Employees	(9.2%)	361	340	286	260	245

CENTIMARK CORPORATION

12 Grandview Circle
Canonsburg, PA 15317
Phone: 724-743-7777
Fax: 724-743-7790
Web: www.centimark.com

CEO: Edward B. Dunlap
CFO: John Heisey
HR: Laura Kickbusch
FYE: April 30
Type: Private

CentiMark hit the nail right on the head when it got into the roofing business. The company has become one of the largest commercial and industrial roofing contractors in the US and Canada, providing roof inspection, repair, and emergency leak service. CentiMark typically works on flat roofs using EPDM rubber, thermoplastics, bitumen, metal, and coatings. The company counts NASA and the US Army Corps of Engineers among its customers. Its QuestMark division offers commercial, industrial, and retail flooring, do-it-yourself products, and floor maintenance and cleaning products. Chairman and CEO Edward Dunlap founded CentiMark as D&B Laboratories, an industrial cleaning business, in 1967.

	Annual Growth	4/03	4/04	4/05	4/06	4/07
Est. sales ($ mil.)	—	—	—	—	—	347.5
Employees	—	—	—	—	—	1,900

An in-depth profile of this company is available to Hoover's Online members at hoovers.com.

349

CENTIVE, INC.

1 Burlington Woods Dr.
Burlington, MA 01803
Phone: 781-852-3500
Fax: 781-852-3700
Web: www.centive.com

CEO: Michael Torto
CFO: –
HR: –
FYE: March 31
Type: Private

Centive helps businesses manage the cost of motivating their employees. The company provides sales performance management software, which tracks sales commissions, sales incentives, performance pay, variable compensation, and variable pay. Its applications are targeted to the incentive program needs of particular industries, including financial services, life sciences and medical products, technology, telecommunications, and retail. Centive's services include consulting, technical and installation support, and training. The company was founded in 1997.

	Annual Growth	3/03	3/04	3/05	3/06	3/07
Est. sales ($ mil.)	—	—	—	—	—	7.5
Employees	—	—	—	—	—	62

⊞ CENTOCOR, INC.

800/850 Ridgeview Dr.
Horsham, PA 19044
Phone: 610-651-6000
Fax: 610-651-6100
Web: www.centocor.com

CEO: –
CFO: –
HR: –
FYE: December 31
Type: Subsidiary

When the immune system fights back, Centocor is there. The Johnson & Johnson subsidiary makes the drug Remicade for autoimmune conditions like Crohn's disease (a debilitating bowel disorder), psoriasis, and rheumatoid arthritis (a multibillion-dollar market); it currently has FDA approval to treat nine different autoimmune disorders. Centocor's other major product is ReoPro, which prevents blood clots during angioplasty and is marketed primarily by Eli Lilly. Centocor sold Retavase, a clot-buster used during heart attacks, to ESP Pharma, which was acquired by Protein Design Labs.

	Annual Growth	12/03	12/04	12/05	12/06	12/07
Est. sales ($ mil.)	—	—	—	—	—	385.0
Employees	—	—	—	—	—	3,000

CENTRA, INC.

12225 Stephen Rd.
Warren, MI 48089
Phone: 586-939-7000
Fax: 586-755-5607
Web: www.centraltransportint.com

CEO: Manuel J. (Matty) Moroun
CFO: Hal Briand
HR: –
FYE: December 31
Type: Private

At the center of CenTra is Central Transport International, a less-than-truckload (LTL) carrier that operates throughout North America. (LTL carriers combine freight from multiple shippers into a single truckload.) Central Transport International and its affiliates operate from about 200 terminals, mainly in the eastern US. CenTra's CTX unit provides expedited freight transport, and its Central Global Express offers freight forwarding. The company also owns the Ambassador Bridge, a toll bridge that connects Detroit with Windsor, Ontario. CEO Manuel Moroun and his son Matthew control CenTra, which was founded by Manuel Moroun's father. The Morouns also control freight hauler Universal Truckload Services.

	Annual Growth	12/03	12/04	12/05	12/06	12/07
Est. sales ($ mil.)	—	—	—	—	—	285.7
Employees	—	—	—	—	—	4,000

CENTRAL BANCORP, INC.

NASDAQ (GM): CEBK

399 Highland Ave.
Somerville, MA 02144
Phone: 617-628-4000
Fax: 617-629-4219
Web: www.centralbk.com

CEO: John D. Doherty
CFO: Paul S. Feeley
HR: Shirley M. Tracy
FYE: March 31
Type: Public

Central Bancorp is the holding company for Central Co-operative Bank. Operating as Central Bank, it serves Middlesex County in the northwestern suburbs of Boston through about 10 bank branches and loan centers. The bank's primary business is gathering deposits by offering NOW, money market, checking, and savings accounts; CDs; and retirement savings plans. It primarily uses these funds to originate commercial mortgages (more than 50% of all loans, up from 20% in 2001). Residential mortgages have gone down from around 70% to less than 40% in that time. The bank also offers construction, home equity, business, and consumer loans.

	Annual Growth	3/04	3/05	3/06	3/07	3/08
Assets ($ mil.)	3.9%	490.9	521.1	547.3	566.1	571.2
Net income ($ mil.)	(15.2%)	2.9	2.5	2.6	1.0	1.5
Market value ($ mil.)	(16.1%)	63.3	43.0	46.1	49.2	31.4
Employees	0.7%	—	151	—	153	—

CENTRAL DUPAGE HOSPITAL

25 N. Winfield Rd.
Winfield, IL 60190
Phone: 630-933-1600
Fax: 630-933-1300
Web: www.cdh.org

CEO: Luke McGuinness
CFO: James T. Spear
HR: Jerry Lee
FYE: June 30
Type: Not-for-profit

The flagship facility of the Central DuPage health care organization, Central DuPage Hospital serves the residents of central Illinois with some 360 beds. The hospital offers specialized services such as home health care, pediatrics, cancer treatment, oncology, and behavioral health. Its emergency department receives about 50,000 visits each year. Central DuPage Hospital also provides a retirement community and a nursing and rehabilitation center, as well as independent-living and other related services for seniors. Established in 1964, the hospital has a staff of about 800 physicians.

	Annual Growth	6/03	6/04	6/05	6/06	6/07
Est. sales ($ mil.)	—	—	—	—	—	412.0
Employees	—	—	—	—	—	2,400

CENTRAL EUROPEAN DISTRIBUTION

NASDAQ (GS): CEDC

2 Bala Plaza, Ste. 300
Bala Cynwyd, PA 19004
Phone: 610-660-7817
Fax: 610-667-3308
Web: www.cedc.com.pl

CEO: William V. Carey
CFO: Christopher (Chris) Biedermann
HR: –
FYE: December 31
Type: Public

Central European Distribution Corporation (CEDC) helped Poland toast its post-Communist economy in 1991 when co-founders William O. Carey and Jeffrey Peterson introduced Foster's lager to the country. CEDC imports and distributes more than 700 brands of beer, spirits, and wines in Poland through more than 39,000 outlets. CEDC offers spirits made by Bacardi and Diageo. Other brands include Corona, Jim Beam, and E&J Gallo wines. Also a vodka distiller, the company's flagship products include Bols, Soplica, and Royal vodkas. The company owns two distilleries and operates 17 distribution centers throughout Poland and offers next-day order delivery.

	Annual Growth	12/03	12/04	12/05	12/06	12/07
Sales ($ mil.)	29.0%	429.1	580.7	749.4	944.1	1,189.8
Net income ($ mil.)	50.3%	15.1	21.8	20.3	55.5	77.1
Market value ($ mil.)	98.2%	151.7	328.0	634.8	1,141.8	2,341.8
Employees	3.4%	—	—	2,917	3,015	—

CENTRAL FEDERAL CORPORATION

NASDAQ (CM): CFBK

2923 Smith Rd.
Fairlawn, OH 44333
Phone: 330-666-7979
Fax: 330-666-7959

CEO: Mark S. Allio
CFO: Therese A. Liutkus
HR: Michele R. Guildoo
FYE: December 31
Type: Public

Central Federal Corporation is courting business. Traditionally a retail-focused savings and loan, the holding company and its CFBank have added business banking, commercial real estate, and business lending to its foundation. CFBank now serves not only local individuals, but also businesses through four branches in eastern Ohio and the state capital, Columbus. Its deposit products include checking, savings, NOW, and money market accounts, as well as CDs. While single-family residential mortgages made up about 60% of loans a few years ago, they represent less than 15% today. Over that same period, commercial and multifamily residential mortgages have increased to nearly 60% of its loan portfolio.

	Annual Growth	12/03	12/04	12/05	12/06	12/07
Assets ($ mil.)	27.1%	107.0	171.0	173.0	236.0	279.6
Net income ($ mil.)	—	(2.4)	(1.7)	(3.3)	0.0	0.0
Market value ($ mil.)	(14.9%)	32.6	29.3	17.6	33.4	17.1
Employees	—	—	—	—	—	64

CENTRAL FLORIDA INVESTMENTS, INC.

5601 Windhover Dr.
Orlando, FL 32819
Phone: 407-351-3350
Fax: 407-352-8935
Web: www.westgateresorts.com

CEO: David A. Siegel
CFO: Tom Dugan
HR: –
FYE: December 31
Type: Private

Looking for a vacation home? How about a beachside resort, a mountain lodge, a gambling pad, and rustic ranch? If you are one who wants it all, a time share from Central Florida Investments (CFI) might be the way to go. CFI subsidiary Westgate Resorts operates about 20 time-share resorts in Orlando, Florida; Williamsburg, Virginia; Park City, Utah; and seven other tourist towns. In addition to Westgate Resorts, CFI owns or has interests in magazines (*I Love Orlando, I Love Vacations*), real estate (Westgate Plaza Center retail space in Las Vegas), health spas (Papillon Spas), and restaurants (Westgate Smokehouse Grill). Chairman and CEO David Siegel founded the company in 1970.

	Annual Growth	12/03	12/04	12/05	12/06	12/07
Est. sales ($ mil.)	—	—	—	—	—	297.6
Employees	—	—	—	—	—	4,000

CENTRAL FREIGHT LINES, INC.

5601 W. Waco Dr.
Waco, TX 76710
Phone: 254-772-2120
Fax: 254-741-5370
Web: www.centralfreight.com

CEO: Robert V. (Bob) Fasso
CFO: Jeffrey A. (Jeff) Hale
HR: Jackie Guerrero
FYE: December 31
Type: Private

The Southwest, the Midwest, and the Northwest are all central to the business of Central Freight Lines, a leading regional less-than-truckload (LTL) carrier. (LTL carriers consolidate freight from multiple shippers into a single truckload.) The company focuses on next-day and second-day services within each of its regions. It operates a fleet of more than 1,900 tractors and about 8,500 trailers from a network of about 55 terminals. Central Freight Lines serves the rest of the US through alliances with other carriers. Trucking magnate Jerry Moyes owns the company.

	Annual Growth	12/03	12/04	12/05	12/06	12/07
Est. sales ($ mil.)	—	—	—	—	—	185.9
Employees	—	—	—	—	—	3,593

CENTRAL GARDEN & PET COMPANY

NASDAQ (GS): CENT

1340 Treat Blvd., Ste. 600
Walnut Creek, CA 94597
Phone: 925-948-4000
Fax: 925-287-0601
Web: www.centralgardenandpet.com

CEO: William E. Brown
CFO: Stuart W. Booth
HR: Stanley L. Bulger
FYE: Last Saturday in September
Type: Public

Central Garden & Pet is happy to help with both pets and pests. The company is among the largest US manufacturers and distributors of lawn, garden, and pet supplies, providing its products to pet supplies retailers, home improvement centers, nurseries, and mass merchandisers from approximately 40 manufacturing plants and another 40 distribution centers located throughout the US; it also has sales offices in the UK. Central Garden & Pet's proprietary brand lines include AMDRO fire ant bait, Four Paws animal products, Kaytee bird seed, Nylabone dog chews, Norcal pottery, Pennington grass seed and bird seed products, and TFH pet books. Chairman and CEO William Brown controls 45% of the company's voting rights.

	Annual Growth	9/03	9/04	9/05	9/06	9/07
Sales ($ mil.)	9.9%	1,145.0	1,266.5	1,380.6	1,621.5	1,671.1
Net income ($ mil.)	(1.7%)	34.6	41.3	53.8	65.5	32.3
Market value ($ mil.)	6.4%	154.7	197.4	293.2	359.3	198.5
Employees	0.6%	—	—	4,800	4,865	4,860

CENTRAL GROCERS, INC.

11100 Belmont Ave.
Franklin Park, IL 60131
Phone: 847-451-0660
Fax: 847-288-8710
Web: www.central-grocers.com

CEO: James (Jim) Denges
CFO: Tim Kubis
HR: Annalee Robish
FYE: Saturday nearest July 31
Type: Cooperative

In a city of big stores, Central Grocers helps neighborhood markets stay afloat. The member-owned cooperative supplies food and general merchandise to more than 200 independent retail grocery stores in the Chicago area and in parts of Indiana. It distributes products under both national brands and its own Centrella brand. The co-op also operates a number of stores under such banners as Strack & Van Til, Town & Country, Key Market, and the low-cost Ultra Foods chain. Central Grocers was founded in 1917.

	Annual Growth	7/03	7/04	7/05	7/06	7/07
Est. sales ($ mil.)	—	—	—	—	—	1,108.9
Employees	—	—	—	—	—	2,300

CENTRAL ILLINOIS LIGHT COMPANY

300 Liberty St.
Peoria, IL 61602
Phone: 309-677-5230
Fax: 309-677-5025
Web: www.ameren.com/AboutUs/ADC_AU_AmerenCILCO_Home.asp

CEO: Scott A. Cisel
CFO: Warner L. Baxter
HR: –
FYE: December 31
Type: Subsidiary

Central Illinois Light likes to be the center of attention for all this gas and electric in the Land of Lincoln. The company, which operates as AmerenCILCO, serves some 210,000 electric customers and 213,000 natural gas customers in central Illinois. The company operates 3,800 miles of gas transmission and distribution mains and two gas storage facilities. Its 300-mile power transmission system is monitored by the Midwest ISO. AmerenCILCO was acquired by Ameren from former parent AES in 2003; Ameren subsequently transferred substantially all of the utility's fossil-fueled power plants (1,100 MW of capacity) and the related wholesale marketing operations to a nonregulated affiliate.

	Annual Growth	12/03	12/04	12/05	12/06	12/07
Est. sales ($ mil.)	—	—	—	—	—	990.0
Net income ($ mil.)	—	—	—	—	—	76.0
Employees	—	—	—	—	—	—

An in-depth profile of this company is available to Hoover's Online members at hoovers.com.

351

CENTRAL ILLINOIS PUBLIC SERVICE COMPANY

607 E. Adams St.
Springfield, IL 62739
Phone: 217-523-3600
Fax: 877-226-3736
Web: www.ameren.com/AboutUs/adc_au_AmerenCIPS_Home.asp

CEO: Scott A. Cisel
CFO: Warner L. Baxter
HR: –
FYE: December 31
Type: Subsidiary

Central Illinois Public Service doesn't need Mrs. O'Leary's cow to light up the sky in Illinois. Founded in 1902, the company, which operates as AmerenCIPS, transmits and distributes electricity to almost 400,000 customers and natural gas to nearly 190,000 customers in 576 communities in Illinois. Along with Union Electric and Illinois Power Company, management of Central Illinois Public Service is handled by Midwest Independent Transmission System (MISO). Electric sales account for the bulk of sales. The firm is a subsidiary of utility holding company Ameren Corporation.

	Annual Growth	12/03	12/04	12/05	12/06	12/07
Est. sales ($ mil.)	—	—	—	—	—	1,005.0
Net income ($ mil.)	—	—	—	—	—	17.0
Employees	—	—	—	—	—	—

CENTRAL JERSEY BANCORP

NASDAQ (GM): CJBK

627 2nd Ave.
Long Branch, NJ 07740
Phone: 732-571-1300
Fax: 732-571-1037
Web: www.cjbna.com

CEO: James S. Vaccaro
CFO: Anthony Giordano III
HR: Gail Corrigan
FYE: December 31
Type: Public

Central Jersey Bancorp puts its money where its Monmouth is. The institution is the holding company for Central Jersey Bank, which operates more than a dozen branches, mostly in Monmouth County, New Jersey. The company was created by the merger of Monmouth Community Bank and Allaire Community Bank in 2005. Central Jersey Bank offers standard deposit products such as checking and savings accounts, CDs, and IRAs, as well as ancillary offerings like debit cards, wire transfers, and safe deposit boxes. Lending activities mainly consist of commercial real estate loans (about three-quarters of all loans); business, consumer, industrial, home equity, and second mortgage loans round out the bank's portfolio.

	Annual Growth	12/03	12/04	12/05	12/06	12/07
Assets ($ mil.)	22.6%	222.6	254.1	514.6	516.3	503.5
Net income ($ mil.)	12.5%	0.5	1.2	2.6	2.5	0.8
Market value ($ mil.)	44.6%	15.1	28.7	86.7	62.1	66.2
Employees	(3.3%)	—	—	152	147	—

CENTRAL MAINE POWER COMPANY

83 Edison Dr.
Augusta, ME 04336
Phone: 207-623-3521
Fax: 207-626-9571
Web: www.cmpco.com

CEO: Sara J. Burns
CFO: –
HR: –
FYE: December 31
Type: Subsidiary

Central Maine Power (CMP) has electricity pumping through its veins (and transmission lines). Incorporated in 1905, the company, a subsidiary of utility holding firm Energy East, provides regulated power services to about 599,000 residential and business customers in a 11,000-square-mile area of southern and central Maine. CMP allows nonregulated retail electric providers to supply power to customers over its 23,000-mile transmission and distribution network via 200 substations. In order to comply with Maine's deregulation law, the utility has divested its generation assets.

	Annual Growth	12/03	12/04	12/05	12/06	12/07
Est. sales ($ mil.)	—	—	—	—	—	389.2
Employees	—	—	—	—	—	1,388

CENTRAL NATIONAL-GOTTESMAN INC.

3 Manhattanville Rd.
Purchase, NY 10577
Phone: 914-696-9000
Fax: 914-696-1066
Web: www.cng-inc.com

CEO: Kenneth L. Wallach
CFO: Steven Eigen
HR: Louise Caputo
FYE: December 31
Type: Private

All the news that's fit to print (or at least some of it) shows up on a good portion of Central National-Gottesman's products. The family-owned papermaker distributes pulp, paper, paperboard, and newsprint in more than 75 countries worldwide. In addition to its North American operations, the company operates about 20 international offices in Asia, Europe, and Latin America. The Central National-Gottesman network includes the Lindenmeyr family of companies, which specialize in the distribution of fine paper as well as papers for books and magazines.

	Annual Growth	12/02	12/03	12/04	12/05	12/06
Sales ($ mil.)	17.0%	1,600.0	1,900.0	2,000.0	2,300.0	3,000.0
Employees	4.1%	850	850	775	850	1,000

CENTRAL PACIFIC FINANCIAL CORP.

NYSE: CPF

220 S. King St.
Honolulu, HI 96813
Phone: 808-544-0500
Fax: 808-531-2875
Web: www.cpbi.com

CEO: Clinton L. (Clint) Arnoldus
CFO: Dean K. Hirata
HR: –
FYE: December 31
Type: Public

When in the Central Pacific, do as the islanders do! This might include doing business with Central Pacific Financial, the holding company for Central Pacific Bank. The bank operates some 40 branch locations throughout the Hawaiian Islands. Targeting individuals and local businesses, the bank provides such standard retail banking products as checking and savings accounts, money market accounts, and CDs. Commercial real estate loans make up about a third of the bank's loan portfolio, which also includes residential mortgages (about 25%) and business, construction, and consumer loans. The company also has real estate loan production offices in California.

	Annual Growth	12/03	12/04	12/05	12/06	12/07
Assets ($ mil.)	27.2%	2,170.3	4,651.9	5,239.1	5,487.2	5,680.4
Net income ($ mil.)	(35.7%)	33.9	37.4	72.5	79.2	5.8
Market value ($ mil.)	2.4%	482.6	1,022.6	1,093.3	1,190.3	530.8
Employees	9.6%	—	—	904	1,008	1,085

CENTRAL PARKING CORPORATION

2401 21st Ave. South, Ste. 200
Nashville, TN 37212
Phone: 615-297-4255
Fax: 615-297-6240
Web: www.parking.com

CEO: Emanuel J. Eads
CFO: John I. Hill
HR: Donald N. Holmes
FYE: September 30
Type: Private

If you park your car in a central location, you might very well be doing business with Central Parking. A leading parking provider, the company oversees more than 2,800 facilities with about 1.3 million spaces, primarily in the US and Canada. Its facilities serve high-traffic locations such as airports, office buildings, and stadiums. Along with operating parking lots and garages, the company provides shuttle transportation and valet parking, plus parking meter enforcement and collection under contracts with cities. It also serves as a consultant for parking facility operators. A group of private equity firms bought Central Parking in May 2007.

	Annual Growth	9/02	9/03	9/04	9/05	9/06
Sales ($ mil.)	0.0%	1,107.3	1,136.3	1,171.5	1,133.8	1,109.4
Net income ($ mil.)	(4.7%)	33.8	(4.5)	17.0	14.3	27.9
Employees	1.1%	18,100	—	—	23,957	18,940

CENTRAL PURCHASING, INC.

3491 Mission Oaks Blvd.
Camarillo, CA 93011
Phone: 805-388-1000
Fax: 805-445-4925
Web: www.harborfreight.com

CEO: Alan Smidt
CFO: Bob Glickman
HR: –
FYE: July 31
Type: Private

Central Purchasing certainly could lay claim to the expression "the right tool for the job." The company, better recognized by its trade name, Harbor Freight Tools, is one of the country's largest tool and equipment catalog retailers. Harbor Freight Tools offers more than 7,000 tools and equipment items, including products marketed under such brands as Central Machinery, Chicago Electric, DeWalt, Makita, Pittsburgh, and Stanley. The company also sells via the Internet and through a network of more than 280 retail stores in more than 40 states. It was founded in 1968.

	Annual Growth	7/03	7/04	7/05	7/06	7/07
Est. sales ($ mil.)	—	—	—	—	—	278.9
Employees	—	—	—	—	—	1,600

CENTRAL REFRIGERATED SERVICE, INC.

5175 W. 2100 South
West Valley City, UT 84120
Phone: 801-924-7000
Fax: 801-924-7337
Web: www.centralref.com

CEO: Jon F. Isaacson
CFO: Robert T. Goates
HR: –
FYE: December 31
Type: Private

No matter the weather conditions, trucking company Central Refrigerated Service stays cool when it's on the move. The carrier provides temperature-controlled transportation services for major food suppliers and retailers across the US. Central Refrigerated Service operates a fleet of about 1,800 tractors and 2,700 refrigerated trailers, or reefers. The company is owned by Jerry Moyes, who also owns less-than-truckload carrier Central Freight Lines and truckload carrier Swift Transportation.

	Annual Growth	12/03	12/04	12/05	12/06	12/07
Est. sales ($ mil.)	—	—	—	—	—	261.5
Employees	—	—	—	—	—	1,400

CENTRAL STEEL & WIRE COMPANY

3000 W. 51st St.
Chicago, IL 60632
Phone: 773-471-3800
Fax: 800-232-9279
Web: www.centralsteel.com

CEO: Michael X. Cronin
CFO: Ronald Kazmar
HR: Daniel (Dan) Sopata
FYE: December 31
Type: Private

When it comes to metal, service center Central Steel & Wire Company (CS&W) can shape up and ship out. CS&W distributes ferrous and nonferrous metals in a variety of shapes and forms, including bars, coils, plates, sheets, structurals, tubing, and wire. Among the company's processing services are annealing, blanking, CNC laser cutting, galvanizing, and structural fabrication. CS&W's inventory includes some 15,000 items, and it ships more than 200,000 tons annually. The company distributes its products throughout North America from its facilities that are located primarily in the Midwestern US. CS&W was founded in 1909.

	Annual Growth	12/03	12/04	12/05	12/06	12/07
Est. sales ($ mil.)	—	—	—	—	—	826.3
Employees	—	—	—	—	—	1,500

CENTRAL VALLEY COMMUNITY BANCORP

NASDAQ (CM): CVCY

7100 N. Financial Dr.
Fresno, CA 93720
Phone: 559-298-1775
Fax: 559-221-4376
Web: www.cvcb.com

CEO: Daniel J. Doyle
CFO: David A. (Dave) Kinross
HR: Barbara Gillmore
FYE: December 31
Type: Public

Central Valley Community Bancorp wants to be at the very core of your banking activities. It's the holding company for Central Valley Community Bank, which offers individuals and businesses traditional banking services through about a dozen offices in the California counties of Fresno, Madera, Sacramento, and Stanislaus. Deposit products include checking, savings, and money market accounts; IRAs; and CDs. The bank offers credit card services and originates a variety of loans, including residential mortgage, business, personal, and agricultural loans. Through Central Valley Community Insurance Services, it markets health and property and casualty insurance products primarily to business customers.

	Annual Growth	12/03	12/04	12/05	12/06	12/07
Assets ($ mil.)	10.2%	327.9	368.1	483.7	500.1	483.7
Net income ($ mil.)	16.7%	3.4	3.7	6.0	6.9	6.3
Market value ($ mil.)	22.1%	29.6	30.7	88.4	89.1	65.7
Employees	(23.1%)	—	—	284	162	168

CENTRAL VERMONT PUBLIC SERVICE CORPORATION

NYSE: CV

77 Grove St.
Rutland, VT 05701
Phone: 800-649-2877
Fax: 802-747-2199
Web: www.cvps.com

CEO: Robert H. (Bob) Young
CFO: Pamela J. Keefe
HR: Joan F. Gamble
FYE: December 31
Type: Public

Moonlight in Vermont may be beautiful, but it doesn't provide any power. Vermont's largest electric utility, Central Vermont Public Service (CVPS), provides power to more than 158,000 customers in 152 communities across the state. It generates approximately 110 MW of nuclear, hydroelectric, and fossil-fueled capacity; it purchases most of its energy supply. CVPS owns 47% of state transmission company Vermont Electric Power Company (VELCO). The utility has investments in nonregulated businesses such as home maintenance contracting, real estate, and energy-related services.

	Annual Growth	12/03	12/04	12/05	12/06	12/07
Sales ($ mil.)	1.8%	306.0	302.2	311.4	325.7	329.1
Net income ($ mil.)	(5.5%)	19.8	23.8	6.3	18.4	15.8
Market value ($ mil.)	2.8%	283.2	284.1	221.6	238.6	315.9
Employees	—	—	—	529	—	—

CENTRAL VIRGINIA BANKSHARES, INC.

NASDAQ (GM): CVBK

2036 New Dorset Rd.
Powhatan, VA 23139
Phone: 804-403-2000
Fax: 804-598-5079
Web: www.centralvabank.com

CEO: Ralph L. Lyons
CFO: Charles F. Catlett III
HR: –
FYE: December 31
Type: Public

Central Virginia Bankshares is the holding company for Central Virginia Bank, which operates about 10 branches in — you guessed it — central Virginia. Targeting individuals and local business customers, the bank offers such standard retail services as checking and savings accounts, CDs, IRAs, and credit cards. Through an affiliation with The Trust Company of Virginia, the bank also provides (you guessed it again) trust services. Central Virginia Bankshares' loan portfolio consists of a mix of residential and commercial mortgages, real estate construction loans, home equity loans, and business and consumer loans.

	Annual Growth	12/03	12/04	12/05	12/06	12/07
Assets ($ mil.)	7.3%	365.8	379.3	397.4	437.5	485.2
Net income ($ mil.)	0.6%	3.9	4.4	4.9	5.2	4.0
Market value ($ mil.)	(2.8%)	47.6	58.8	57.3	59.9	42.4
Employees	9.8%	—	—	107	—	129

An in-depth profile of this company is available to Hoover's Online members at hoovers.com.

CENTRIC GROUP, L.L.C.

1260 Andes Blvd.	CEO: Jim Theiss
St. Louis, MO 63132	CFO: Vicki S. Altman
Phone: 314-214-2700	HR: Cynthia M. (Cindy) Murdoch
Fax: 314-214-2766	FYE: December 31
Web: www.centricgp.com	Type: Private

This company makes sure the world has enough balloons, baggage, and beverages. Centric Group is a holding company for several manufacturing and distribution businesses. Its Betallic unit manufactures latex and Mylar balloons sold through florist shops and other gift retailers. The company's TGR Group, meanwhile, manufactures luggage and other travel bags under such brands as Callaway Golf and Victorinox. In addition, Centric serves commissaries at correctional facilities with snacks, beverages, and other food and non-food items through its Keefe Group. The company was formed in 1974 as part of Enterprise Rent-A-Car and spun off in 1999. It is still controlled by the Taylor family.

	Annual Growth	12/02	12/03	12/04	12/05	12/06
Est. sales ($ mil.)	16.7%	—	—	—	600.0	700.0
Employees	25.0%	—	—	—	1,600	2,000

CENTURY ALUMINUM COMPANY

NASDAQ (GS): CENX

2511 Garden Rd., Bldg. A, Ste. 200	CEO: Logan W. Kruger
Monterey, CA 93940	CFO: Michael A. Bless
Phone: 831-642-9300	HR: Arline Irvine
Fax: 831-642-9399	FYE: December 31
Web: www.centuryaluminum.com	Type: Public

When the aluminum century rolls around, it'll be ready. Century Aluminum makes primary molten and ingot aluminum at facilities in Kentucky and West Virginia, as well as in Iceland; that last facility is operated by subsidiary Nordural. Century Aluminum also owns a 49.7% stake in an aluminum production facility in South Carolina (Alcoa owns the rest). Four customers — aluminum producer Rio Tinto Alcan, diversified metals company BHP Billiton, commodities trader Glencore International, and wire and cable maker Southwire — account for 85% of Century Aluminum's sales. Glencore is Century Aluminum's former parent and still has a 30% stake in the company.

	Annual Growth	12/03	12/04	12/05	12/06	12/07
Sales ($ mil.)	23.1%	782.5	1,060.8	1,132.4	1,558.6	1,798.2
Net income ($ mil.)	—	1.0	28.0	(116.3)	(41.0)	(101.3)
Market value ($ mil.)	53.0%	403.2	841.3	843.7	1,449.2	2,210.9
Employees	4.2%	—	—	1,750	1,850	1,900

CENTURY BANCORP, INC.

NASDAQ (GM): CNBKA

400 Mystic Ave.	CEO: Barry R. Sloane
Medford, MA 02155	CFO: William P. Hornby
Phone: 781-391-4000	HR: –
Fax: 781-393-4071	FYE: December 31
Web: www.century-bank.com	Type: Public

Century Bancorp is the holding company for Century Bank and Trust, which serves Boston and surrounding northeastern Massachusetts from about 20 branch locations. The bank offers standard deposit products including checking, savings, and money market accounts; CDs; and IRAs. Some 45% of the bank's loan portfolio is dedicated to commercial real estate. It also writes residential mortgages (25%), construction and development loans, business loans, and home equity loans. The company provides cash management and transaction processing services to municipalities; subsidiary Century Financial Services offers investment and brokerage services. Chairman Marshall Sloane controls the company.

	Annual Growth	12/03	12/04	12/05	12/06	12/07
Assets ($ mil.)	(0.1%)	1,688.9	1,833.7	1,728.8	1,644.3	1,680.3
Net income ($ mil.)	(9.4%)	11.7	8.9	6.9	4.7	7.9
Market value ($ mil.)	(12.5%)	120.9	101.3	101.1	95.5	70.9
Employees	(2.3%)	—	—	391		373

CENTURY CASINOS, INC.

NASDAQ (CM): CNTY

1263 Lake Plaza Dr., Ste. A	CEO: Erwin Haitzmann
Colorado Springs, CO 80906	CFO: Ray Sienko
Phone: 719-527-8300	HR: –
Fax: 719-527-8301	FYE: December 31
Web: www.cnty.com	Type: Public

In the 19th century, people rushed to Cripple Creek, Colorado, seeking their fortune in gold. Today, thanks to Century Casinos, they can do basically the same thing. Its Womacks Casino and Hotel in Cripple Creek offers some 500 slot machines and video devices, as well as a handful of gaming tables. Century Casinos also owns the Century Casino and Hotel, in Central City, Colorado. Outside the US the company owns the Caledon Hotel, Spa & Casino near Cape Town, South Africa; the Century Casino and Hotel in Edmonton, Canada; and the Casino Millennium in the Marriott hotel in Prague, Czech Republic. It is also the casino concessionaire for cruise lines Oceania, the Silver Cloud, and The World of ResidenSea.

	Annual Growth	12/03	12/04	12/05	12/06	12/07
Sales ($ mil.)	30.7%	31.4	35.8	37.4	56.3	91.7
Net income ($ mil.)	10.4%	3.3	4.7	4.5	7.6	4.9
Market value ($ mil.)	35.2%	45.6	125.0	192.5	256.7	152.4
Employees	93.4%	—	—	517	1,000	—

CENTURYTEL, INC.

NYSE: CTL

100 CenturyTel Dr.	CEO: Glen F. Post III
Monroe, LA 71203	CFO: R. Stewart Ewing Jr.
Phone: 318-388-9000	HR: –
Fax: 318-388-9064	FYE: December 31
Web: www.centurytel.com	Type: Public

Bright lights and big cities are *not* for CenturyTel. The integrated communications company primarily provides carrier and enterprise-level network access and local voice telephone services; it also offers long-distance, Internet access, and broadband services. Its rural local-exchange carrier (RLEC) subsidiaries operate in the suburbs and small towns of 25 states scattered throughout the US. The residential voice business has about 2.1 million local access lines in service. CenturyTel also provides Internet access services to more than 600,000 subscribers. The company's core service areas are located in Alabama, Arkansas, Missouri, Washington, and Wisconsin.

	Annual Growth	12/03	12/04	12/05	12/06	12/07
Sales ($ mil.)	2.8%	2,380.7	2,407.4	2,479.3	2,447.7	2,656.2
Net income ($ mil.)	5.0%	344.7	337.2	334.5	370.0	418.4
Market value ($ mil.)	(1.1%)	4,709.2	4,695.3	4,346.4	4,944.7	4,498.1
Employees	(2.2%)	—	—	6,900	6,400	6,600

CENVEO, INC.

NYSE: CVO

1 Canterbury Green, 201 Broad St.	CEO: Robert G. Burton Sr.
Stamford, CT 06901	CFO: Mark S. Hiltwein
Phone: 203-595-3000	HR: Gina Genuario
Fax: 203-595-3070	FYE: December 31
Web: www.cenveo.com	Type: Public

Commercial printer Cenveo produces not only items that go inside envelopes, but also the envelopes themselves. Among the products of the company's printing units are catalogs, journals, magazines, and marketing materials. Cenveo's envelopes and other packaging products are used for such purposes as billing, catalog distribution, and direct mail. The company also produces business forms and pressure-sensitive labels; its envelopes, forms, and labels products are sold both directly to end users and through wholesalers. Cenveo operates production, fulfillment, and distribution facilities throughout the US and Canada. In 2007 the company expanded by acquiring Cadmus Communications, a leading printer of periodicals.

	Annual Growth	12/03	12/04	12/05	12/06	12/07
Sales ($ mil.)	5.2%	1,671.7	1,742.9	1,749.4	1,511.2	2,046.7
Net income ($ mil.)	67.4%	5.2	(19.7)	(135.1)	118.7	40.8
Market value ($ mil.)	43.2%	223.0	151.0	697.8	1,134.5	938.1
Employees	15.7%	—	—	8,000	6,600	10,700

CEPHALON, INC.

NASDAQ (GS): CEPH

41 Moores Rd.
Frazer, PA 19355
Phone: 610-344-0200
Fax: 610-738-6590
Web: www.cephalon.com

CEO: Frank Baldino Jr.
CFO: J. Kevin Buchi
HR: –
FYE: December 31
Type: Public

Cephalon isn't asleep at the wheel. The company sells PROVIGIL, a treatment for the sleep disorder narcolepsy, in the US and select countries around the world. The company's other top sellers are cancer pain medications ACTIQ and FENTORA and epilepsy treatment GABITRIL (licensed from Abbott Labs and Novo Nordisk). It sells eight products in the US and has more than 20 approved drugs on the market in Europe. Cephalon's drug development activities focus on central nervous system disorders, including Parkinson's and Alzheimer's diseases, as well as cancer, addiction, and pain.

	Annual Growth	12/03	12/04	12/05	12/06	12/07
Sales ($ mil.)	25.5%	714.8	1,015.4	1,211.9	1,764.1	1,772.6
Net income ($ mil.)	—	83.9	(73.8)	(174.9)	144.8	(191.7)
Market value ($ mil.)	15.9%	2,688.4	2,932.7	3,759.6	4,618.6	4,851.3
Employees	(1.7%)	—	—	2,895	2,895	2,796

CEPHEID

NASDAQ (GM): CPHD

904 Caribbean Dr.
Sunnyvale, CA 94089
Phone: 408-541-4191
Fax: 408-541-4192
Web: www.cepheid.com

CEO: John L. Bishop
CFO: Andrew D. (Andy) Miller
HR: Laurie King
FYE: December 31
Type: Public

Cepheid sees DNA faster. The molecular diagnostics firm develops systems that automate the process of preparing and amplifying DNA in order to quickly detect diseases and harmful agents. Its two instrument platforms — SmartCycler and GeneXpert — can perform rapid molecular testing for a number of purposes, including diagnosing infectious diseases and cancer, testing food and agricultural products, and detecting biothreats such as anthrax. The company sells its products worldwide through a combination of direct sales and distributorship deals; Thermo Fisher Scientific sells the SmartCycler system in select markets in North America.

	Annual Growth	12/03	12/04	12/05	12/06	12/07
Sales ($ mil.)	62.7%	18.5	53.0	85.0	87.3	129.5
Net income ($ mil.)	—	(17.5)	(13.8)	(13.6)	(26.0)	(21.4)
Market value ($ mil.)	43.6%	344.9	418.0	375.4	467.1	1,465.4
Employees	—	—	—	265	—	—

CERADYNE, INC.

NASDAQ (GS): CRDN

3169 Red Hill Ave.
Costa Mesa, CA 92626
Phone: 714-549-0421
Fax: 714-549-5787
Web: www.ceradyne.com

CEO: Joel P. Moskowitz
CFO: Jerrold J. (Jerry) Pellizzon
HR: –
FYE: December 31
Type: Public

A bull in a china shop wouldn't stand a chance against Ceradyne's ceramics. The company's advanced technical ceramics products combine hardness with light weight and the ability to withstand high temperatures, resist corrosion, and insulate against electricity. Some uses of Ceradyne's materials include armor for military helicopters, missile nose cones, body armor for soldiers, diesel engine components, ceramic industrial products, and orthodontic brackets. The company sells to contractors and OEMs. The US government and other government agencies represent nearly three-quarters of sales.

	Annual Growth	12/03	12/04	12/05	12/06	12/07
Sales ($ mil.)	65.2%	101.5	215.6	368.3	662.9	756.8
Net income ($ mil.)	89.5%	11.2	27.6	46.8	128.4	144.3
Market value ($ mil.)	68.0%	160.9	933.6	1,173.7	1,532.2	1,282.1
Employees	49.7%	500	1,442	1,835	2,205	2,511

CERAGENIX PHARMACEUTICALS, INC.

OTC: CGXP

1444 Wazee St., Ste. 210
Denver, CO 80202
Phone: 720-946-6440
Fax: 303-534-1800
Web: www.ceragenix.com

CEO: Steven S. Porter
CFO: Jeffrey S. (Jeff) Sperber
HR: –
FYE: December 31
Type: Public

Ceragenix Pharmaceuticals wants to make sure nothing gets under your skin. The company is a development-stage biopharmaceutical company engaged in the development of dermatology, oncology, and infectious disease therapies. Its main product, Barrier Repair Technology, which mimics the barrier against infection and dehydration provided by healthy skin, is being developed in two topical creams, Epiceram and NeoCeram, for the treatment of atopic dermatitis (eczema), radiation dermatitis, actinic keratosis, and skin disorders of premature infants. The company was created in 2005 after the merger of publicly-traded shell company OnSource Corporation and Osmotics Pharma.

	Annual Growth	12/03	12/04	12/05	12/06	12/07
Est. sales ($ mil.)	—	—	—	—	—	0.0
Net income ($ mil.)	—	—	—	—	—	(6.6)
Market value ($ mil.)	—	—	—	—	—	17.2
Employees	—	—	—	—	—	—

CERBERUS CAPITAL MANAGEMENT, L.P.

299 Park Ave.
New York, NY 10171
Phone: 212-891-2100
Fax: 212-891-1540
Web: www.cerberuscapital.com

CEO: Stephen A. Feinberg
CFO: Jeffrey L. Lomasky
HR: –
FYE: December 31
Type: Partnership

Named after the mythical three-headed dog that guards the gates of hell, Cerberus Capital Management has become a *driving* force among private equity firms. One of its more recent moves is the purchase of 80% of Chrysler from Daimler in 2007. Cerberus was also the lead investor of a group that acquired 51% of GMAC, the financing arm of General Motors. The company also owns bus manufacturer Blue Bird and car parts maker TA Delaware (formerly Tower Automotive). Other holdings include a 45% stake in Japanese bank Aozora, real estate services firm LNR Property, and a 52% stake in ACE Aviation Holdings, the parent company of Air Canada.

CERIDIAN CORPORATION

3311 E. Old Shakopee Rd.
Minneapolis, MN 55425
Phone: 952-853-8100
Fax: 952-853-4430
Web: www.ceridian.com

CEO: Kathryn V. (Kathy) Marinello
CFO: Gregory J. (Greg) Macfarlane
HR: Kairus K. Tarapore
FYE: December 31
Type: Private

Problems with payroll? Trouble with taxes? Ceridian wants to help. The company's Human Resource Solutions segment provides payroll processing, tax filing, benefits administration, and other human resources services to more than 110,000 employers (and their 25 million employees), mainly in the US but also in Canada and the UK. Ceridian's other business unit, Comdata, issues and processes payments for credit, debit, and stored-value cards (gift cards and employee expense cards), primarily for companies in the trucking and retail industries. Investment firm Thomas H. Lee Partners and insurer Fidelity National Financial own Ceridian, which they acquired in November 2007 for $5.3 billion.

	Annual Growth	12/02	12/03	12/04	12/05	12/06
Sales ($ mil.)	7.1%	1,191.0	1,213.9	1,320.4	1,459.0	1,565.1
Net income ($ mil.)	17.2%	92.1	98.7	36.9	127.9	173.6
Employees	0.4%	9,411	—	—	9,433	9,579

An in-depth profile of this company is available to Hoover's Online members at hoovers.com.

355

CERNER CORPORATION

NASDAQ (GS): CERN

2800 Rockcreek Pkwy.
Kansas City, MO 64117
Phone: 816-221-1024
Fax: 816-474-1742
Web: www.cerner.com

CEO: Neal L. Patterson
CFO: Marc G. Naughton
HR: Jeffrey A. (Jeff) Townsend
FYE: Saturday nearest December 31
Type: Public

Cerner provides the IV that pumps information through a health care organization's computer network. The company's products and services combine clinical, financial, and administrative information management applications, including tools for managing electronic medical records, patient care, and health information access. Cerner's clinical and administrative information systems link emergency rooms, pharmacies, and other health care departments. The company's service offerings include implementation, data migration, maintenance, and security compliance services.

	Annual Growth	12/03	12/04	12/05	12/06	12/07
Sales ($ mil.)	16.0%	839.6	926.4	1,160.8	1,378.0	1,519.9
Net income ($ mil.)	31.3%	42.8	64.7	86.3	109.9	127.1
Market value ($ mil.)	61.1%	684.6	974.0	3,568.9	3,566.8	4,614.9
Employees	7.4%	—	—	6,830	7,419	7,873

CERTAINTEED CORPORATION

750 E. Swedesford Rd.
Valley Forge, PA 19482
Phone: 610-341-7000
Fax: 610-341-7777
Web: www.certainteed.com

CEO: Peter R. Dachowski
CFO: Robert Statile
HR: David Bomzer
FYE: December 31
Type: Subsidiary

There's no uncertainty about CertainTeed's business. A subsidiary of French industrial giant Compagnie de Saint-Gobain, CertainTeed makes building materials for both commercial and residential construction. Products include fiberglass insulation, asphalt roofing shingles, gypsum wallboard, fiber cement siding, foundations, fencing, pipes, PVC trim, and composite decking and railing. The company sells its products under the Bufftech, CertainTeed, Form-A-Drain, Prestige, and Wolverine brands. CertainTeed operates more than 60 manufacturing plants throughout the US.

	Annual Growth	12/03	12/04	12/05	12/06	12/07
Est. sales ($ mil.)	—	—	—	—	—	2,147.5
Employees	—	—	—	—	—	9,700

CERTIFIED GROCERS MIDWEST, INC.

1 Certified Dr.
Hodgkins, IL 60525
Phone: 708-579-2100
Fax: 708-354-7502
Web: www.certisaver.com

CEO: Randall D. (Randy) McMurray
CFO: −
HR: Marcy Meister
FYE: August 31
Type: Cooperative

If you shop at a Certi-Saver, you can be certain your groceries came from Certified Grocers Midwest (CGM). CGM is a leading wholesale distribution cooperative that supplies grocery items and general merchandise to member and non-member retail grocery stores in five Midwestern states. It distributes both national brands and private label (Countrys Delight and Certified Red) goods, including baked goods, fresh produce, frozen foods, and other grocery items. In addition, CGM provides business support services for its member stores, some of which operate under the Certi-Saver banner. The co-op was established in 1940.

CERUS CORPORATION

NASDAQ (GM): CERS

2411 Stanwell Dr.
Concord, CA 94520
Phone: 925-288-6000
Fax: 925-288-6001
Web: www.cerus.com

CEO: Claes Glassell
CFO: William J. Dawson
HR: Lori L. Roll
FYE: December 31
Type: Public

Cerus is no religious organization, but it does preach the power of purity. The firm develops blood purification systems (under the name INTERCEPT) that kill bacteria, viruses, and other pathogens in donated blood to improve the safety of blood transfusions. Its INTERCEPT Blood Systems for platelets and plasma are approved for sale in some European and Middle Eastern countries, where they are marketed directly to customers through subsidiary Cerus Europe. In 2007 the company spun off its immunotherapy operations, including its Listeria and KBMA vaccine platforms, to a newly formed company named Anza Therapeutics.

	Annual Growth	12/03	12/04	12/05	12/06	12/07
Sales ($ mil.)	3.2%	9.7	13.9	24.4	35.6	11.0
Net income ($ mil.)	—	(58.3)	(31.1)	13.1	(4.8)	(45.3)
Market value ($ mil.)	20.1%	100.4	65.5	227.9	186.0	209.0
Employees	—	—	—	97	—	—

CESSNA AIRCRAFT COMPANY

1 Cessna Blvd.
Wichita, KS 67215
Phone: 316-517-6000
Fax: 316-517-5669
Web: www.cessna.com

CEO: Jack J. Pelton
CFO: Mike Shonka
HR: Jim Walters
FYE: Saturday nearest December 31
Type: Subsidiary

A fly-by-night-and-day outfit, Cessna Aircraft is one of the most famous names in small planes. A subsidiary of Textron, the company manufactures business jets, utility turboprops, and small single-engine planes. Best known for its small prop planes, Cessna is also a leading maker of business jets; it makes nine variations of its popular Citation jet. Its utility turboprop plane, the Caravan, has freight, bush, amphibious, and commercial (small connecting flights) applications. Cessna's single-engine planes are typically used for personal and small-business purposes. Cessna also offers fractional ownership programs for its business jets. In 2006 Cessna accounted for 36% of Textron's sales.

	Annual Growth	12/03	12/04	12/05	12/06	12/07
Est. sales ($ mil.)	—	—	—	—	—	953.1
Employees	—	—	—	—	—	13,000

CET SERVICES, INC.

OTC: CETR

12503 E. Euclid Dr., #30
Centennial, CO 80111
Phone: 720-875-9115
Fax: 720-875-9114

CEO: Steven H. Davis
CFO: Dale W. Bleck
HR: −
FYE: December 31
Type: Public

CET Services wants to help make your city's older neighborhoods spiffy again. The company manages redevelopment projects for residential real estate including the demolition, environmental remediation, and construction of properties. It has provided services for two projects in the Denver area and has invested in land held for residential and commercial construction. In 2007, the company planned to merge with ZOI Interactive Technologies, a development-stage company that designs interactive Web content. It intended to close its real estate operations and focus on its Web activities, but the merger was called off and the company is primarily focused on its land investments.

	Annual Growth	12/03	12/04	12/05	12/06	12/07
Sales ($ mil.)	23.6%	0.9	4.0	3.2	3.0	2.1
Net income ($ mil.)	—	(0.1)	(0.3)	(0.4)	(0.3)	(1.3)
Market value ($ mil.)	(8.6%)	2.8	3.4	2.8	2.1	—
Employees	(50.0%)	—	—	4	—	1

[🔲] CEVA, INC.
NASDAQ (GM): CEVA

2033 Gateway Place, Ste. 150
San Jose, CA 95110
Phone: 408-514-2900
Fax: 408-514-2995
Web: www.ceva-dsp.com

CEO: Gideon Wertheizer
CFO: Yaniv Arieli
HR: —
FYE: December 31
Type: Public

CEVA has a fever for semiconductor design. CEVA specializes in technology — both circuit and software designs — used in cell phones, handheld computers, MP3 players, and other wireless devices. It licenses its semiconductor intellectual property (SIP) designs to such industry heavyweights as Broadcom, Freescale Semiconductor, Fujitsu, Hitachi, Infineon, NXP, National Semiconductor, Sony, STMicroelectronics, and Texas Instruments. The company derives nearly 90% of its sales from technology licensing and royalties, with the remainder coming from design and consulting services, along with maintenance and support fees from licensees. CEVA's SIP is shipped in more than 225 million devices a year.

	Annual Growth	12/03	12/04	12/05	12/06	12/07
Sales ($ mil.)	(2.5%)	36.8	37.7	35.6	32.5	33.2
Net income ($ mil.)	—	(12.0)	1.6	(2.3)	(0.1)	1.3
Market value ($ mil.)	6.6%	189.1	169.1	119.9	125.1	244.6
Employees	(1.7%)	206	227	209	196	192

CEVA LOGISTICS U.S., INC.

10751 Deerwood Park Blvd., Ste. 200
Jacksonville, FL 32256
Phone: 904-928-1400
Fax: 904-928-1410
Web: www.us.cevalogistics.com

CEO: John Pattullo
CFO: David (Dave) Siler
HR: —
FYE: December 31
Type: Subsidiary

CEVA Logistics US operates as a regional unit of global logistics giant CEVA Group. Together with its affiliates, the US company specializes in managing the supply chains of companies in industries such as automotive, consumer goods, electronics, and manufacturing. It is a leading provider of warehousing and distribution services, and it maintains about 26 million sq. ft. of warehouse space at facilities throughout North America. CEVA Logistics US and other companies in the contract logistics segment of CEVA Group coordinate their offerings with those of the parent company's freight forwarding business.

	Annual Growth	12/03	12/04	12/05	12/06	12/07
Est. sales ($ mil.)	—	—	—	—	—	97.5
Employees	—	—	—	—	—	1,365

CF INDUSTRIES HOLDINGS, INC.
NYSE: CF

4 Pkwy. North, Ste. 400
Deerfield, IL 60015
Phone: 847-405-2400
Fax: 847-267-1004
Web: www.cfindustries.com

CEO: Stephen R. Wilson
CFO: Anthony J. (Tony) Nocchiero
HR: Wendy Jablow Spertus
FYE: December 31
Type: Public

Though CF Industries wants to give you some DAP, it doesn't want to bump fists with you as an informal greeting. The company is an interregional agricultural firm that manufactures and markets nitrogenous and phosphatic fertilizers (including diammonium phosphate, or DAP). It operates a network of manufacturing and distribution facilities, primarily in the Midwest, through which it offers products worldwide. The company changed its structure from a cooperative to a holding company when it began to trade publicly in 2005. It had been owned by eight regional agricultural co-ops, including Land O'Lakes, GROWMARK, and CHS.

	Annual Growth	12/03	12/04	12/05	12/06	12/07
Sales ($ mil.)	19.1%	1,369.9	1,650.7	1,908.4	1,949.5	2,756.7
Net income ($ mil.)	—	(18.4)	67.7	(39.0)	33.3	372.7
Market value ($ mil.)	171.6%	—	—	839.2	1,414.6	6,190.4
Employees	0.0%	—	—	1,500	1,500	1,500

C.F. JORDAN L.P.

7700 C F Jordan Dr.
El Paso, TX 79912
Phone: 915-877-3333
Fax: 915-877-3999
Web: www.cfjordan.com

CEO: Darren G. Woody
CFO: J. Robert (Rob) Hutchison
HR: —
FYE: December 31
Type: Private

A high-flier in construction services, C.F. Jordan is a top US building contractor. The company has traditionally built hotels and resorts, but has diversified into military, highway, residential, and school construction. Its contracts include design/build projects for the Immigration and Naturalization Service for border patrol stations, health care centers, processing centers, and other administrative offices. Other works include Sea World in San Antonio, the Insights Science Museum in El Paso, and Hotel ZA ZA in Dallas. Chairman Charles "Paco" Jordan started the firm in 1988 after another construction company in which he was involved, Jordan and Nobles, was split between the two principal owners.

	Annual Growth	12/03	12/04	12/05	12/06	12/07
Est. sales ($ mil.)	—	—	—	—	—	260.0
Employees	—	—	—	—	—	402

CFC INTERNATIONAL, INC.

500 State St.
Chicago Heights, IL 60411
Phone: 708-891-3456
Fax: 708-758-5989
Web: www.cfcintl.com

CEO: Mike Zimmer
CFO: —
HR: —
FYE: December 31
Type: Private

At CFC International, beauty by design is only skin deep. The company makes transferable chemical coatings to beautify, protect, and add other kinds of functionality to consumer products. It makes complex functional coatings such as simulated metal used on cosmetic containers and simulated wood grain for ready-to-assemble furniture. CFC also makes holographic authentication seals (popular on tickets and software), heat transfer labels for pharmaceuticals, and magnetic strips for security and credit card uses. The company's customers include Baxter Healthcare, Intel, and Visa. Founder Roger Hruby controlled about 60% of CFC before Illinois Tool Works (ITW) acquired CFC in late 2006 for about $75 million.

	Annual Growth	12/03	12/04	12/05	12/06	12/07
Est. sales ($ mil.)	—	—	—	—	—	30.8
Employees	—	—	—	—	—	401

CFS BANCORP, INC.
NASDAQ (GM): CITZ

707 Ridge Rd.
Munster, IN 46321
Phone: 219-836-5500
Fax: 219-836-0265
Web: www.bankcfs.com

CEO: Thomas F. Prisby
CFO: Charles V. Cole
HR: —
FYE: December 31
Type: Public

CFS Bancorp is the holding company for Citizens Financial Bank, a savings and loan serving residents and businesses of northwestern Indiana and northeastern Illinois, including parts of the Chicago metropolitan area, through about two dozen branches. The bank offers standard deposit products such as checking, savings, NOW, and money market accounts, as well as certificates of deposit. It uses the funds primarily to originate commercial loans (mortgages, construction and land development loans, and business loans, which account for some two-thirds of its loan portfolio. The bank also originates residential mortgages, home equity lines of credit, and other consumer loans.

	Annual Growth	12/03	12/04	12/05	12/06	12/07
Assets ($ mil.)	(7.5%)	1,569.4	1,314.7	1,242.9	1,254.4	1,150.3
Net income ($ mil.)	21.0%	3.5	(6.6)	5.0	5.3	7.5
Market value ($ mil.)	(3.4%)	180.6	176.7	171.7	163.1	157.3
Employees	(6.6%)	—	—	347	—	303

CH ENERGY GROUP, INC.

NYSE: CHG

284 South Ave.
Poughkeepsie, NY 12601
Phone: 845-452-2000
Fax: 845-486-5465
Web: www.chenergygroup.com

CEO: Steven V. Lant
CFO: Christopher M. Capone
HR: Joseph J. DeVirgilio Jr.
FYE: December 31
Type: Public

From the bluestone houses of the Huguenots to the manufacturing plants of IBM, utility holding company CH Energy Group powers the Hudson Valley. Utility subsidiary Central Hudson Gas & Electric provides electricity to 367,000 customers in eight counties of New York State's Mid-Hudson River Valley, and delivers natural gas and electricity in a 2,600-square-mile service territory that extends from New York City to Albany. Subsidiary CHEC oversees CH Energy Group's non-regulated businesses in the Northeast and Mid-Atlantic, including petroleum product distribution (to more than 100,000 customers in nine states) and energy management services.

	Annual Growth	12/03	12/04	12/05	12/06	12/07
Sales ($ mil.)	10.4%	806.7	791.5	972.5	993.4	1,196.8
Net income ($ mil.)	(0.8%)	44.0	42.4	44.3	43.1	42.6
Market value ($ mil.)	(1.3%)	739.2	757.4	723.5	832.2	702.0
Employees	29.0%	—	843	1,398	1,402	—

C.H. GUENTHER & SON, INC.

129 E. Guenther St.
San Antonio, TX 78204
Phone: 210-227-1401
Fax: 210-227-1409
Web: www.chguenther.com

CEO: Dale W. Tremblay
CFO: Janelle M. Sykes
HR: Steve Philips
FYE: April 30
Type: Private

C.H. Guenther & Son manufactures the Pioneer brand of baking, pancake, biscuit, and gravy mixes, as well as the White Wings, Peter Pan, and Morrison branded flour, tortilla mixes, and ready-to-eat tortillas. It also makes frozen bakery products for the food service industry. In addition to food service outlets, the 150-plus-year-old company supplies the retail food sector. Guenther has manufacturing facilities in Texas, Tennessee, and South Carolina. The company also operates The Guenther House, a combination restaurant, museum, and gift shop located in San Antonio, Texas.

	Annual Growth	4/03	4/04	4/05	4/06	4/07
Est. sales ($ mil.)	—	—	—	—	—	144.6
Employees	—	—	—	—	—	750

C.H. ROBINSON WORLDWIDE, INC.

NASDAQ (GS): CHRW

14701 Charlson Rd.
Eden Prairie, MN 55347
Phone: 952-937-8500
Fax: 952-937-6714
Web: www.chrobinson.com

CEO: John P. Wiehoff
CFO: Chad M. Lindbloom
HR: Laura Gillund
FYE: December 31
Type: Public

C.H. Robinson Worldwide (CHRW) keeps merchandise moving. A leading third-party logistics provider, the company arranges freight transportation using trucks, trains, ships, and airplanes belonging to other companies. It contracts with some 48,000 carriers. CHRW handles about 6.5 million shipments per year for its 29,000-plus customers, which include companies in the food and beverage, manufacturing, and retail industries. Together with overseeing freight transportation for its customers, it offers supply chain management services. In addition, CHRW buys, sells, and transports fresh produce throughout the US, and its T-Chek unit provides fuel purchasing management services for motor carriers.

	Annual Growth	12/03	12/04	12/05	12/06	12/07
Sales ($ mil.)	19.3%	3,613.6	4,341.5	5,689.0	6,556.2	7,316.2
Net income ($ mil.)	29.8%	114.1	137.3	203.4	266.9	324.3
Market value ($ mil.)	54.6%	1,616.9	2,366.3	6,407.3	7,059.9	9,244.9
Employees	17.2%	—	—	5,776	6,768	—

CH2M HILL COMPANIES, LTD.

9191 S. Jamaica St.
Englewood, CO 80112
Phone: 303-771-0900
Fax: 720-286-9250
Web: www.ch2m.com

CEO: Ralph R. Peterson
CFO: M. Catherine Santee
HR: Robert C. (Bob) Allen
FYE: December 31
Type: Private

Catchy, no. Descriptive, yes. CH2M HILL's name is culled from its founders — Cornell, Howland, Hayes, and Merryfield — plus HILL, from its first merger. The group is organized into three divisions: civil infrastructure, industrial, and federal. Its civil infrastructure group designs and builds water and wastewater systems, airports, highways, and other transportation infrastructures. Federal services include nuclear and environmental cleanup projects and US government facility operations. Industrial operations include engineering, procurement, and construction for private-sector companies in the chemical, energy, and life sciences industries. Clients include the US Department of Defense and the US Navy.

	Annual Growth	12/03	12/04	12/05	12/06	12/07
Sales ($ mil.)	19.4%	2,154.3	2,715.4	3,152.2	4,006.9	4,376.2
Net income ($ mil.)	29.0%	23.8	32.3	81.6	38.9	66.0
Employees	12.0%	14,000	14,000	18,363	17,000	22,000

CHAD THERAPEUTICS, INC.

AMEX: CTU

21622 Plummer St.
Chatsworth, CA 91311
Phone: 818-882-0883
Fax: 818-882-1809
Web: www.chadtherapeutics.com/home.htm

CEO: Earl L. Yager
CFO: Tracy A. Kern
HR: Barbara Muskin
FYE: March 31
Type: Public

Finding the home oxygen market inhospitable, Chad Therapeutics is looking for a friendlier reception as a sleep disorder therapy company. It sold its oxygen conserver assets to Florida-based Inovo, is using the money from the sale to pay off debt and develop devices for treating sleep disorders (a therapeutic category that includes conditions such as sleep apnea). Its oxygen conserver products, which it had been making since 1986, were devices that extended the life of home oxygen supplies for patients who require supplemental oxygen, usually those who suffer from emphysema and other chronic obstructive pulmonary diseases.

	Annual Growth	3/03	3/04	3/05	3/06	3/07
Sales ($ mil.)	(0.6%)	19.5	21.5	24.3	22.4	19.0
Net income ($ mil.)	—	(0.4)	1.0	1.8	(0.7)	(3.4)
Market value ($ mil.)	(6.7%)	20.2	36.3	37.5	27.9	15.3
Employees	0.0%	—	—	130	130	—

CHAMBER OF COMMERCE OF THE UNITED STATES OF AMERICA

1615 H St. NW
Washington, DC 20062
Phone: 202-659-6000
Fax: 202-463-5836
Web: www.uschamber.com

CEO: Thomas J. Donahue
CFO: Stan M. Harrell
HR: Shannon DiBari
FYE: December 31
Type: Not-for-profit

The Chamber of Commerce of The United States of America is all business. The organization, which aims to represent the interests of US business on national issues, counts among its members some 3 million businesses, as well as thousands of state and local Chambers of Commerce and other business associations. It serves as an advocate before lawmakers, regulators, and courts; participates in public policy debates; and supports business-friendly candidates through its political arm. The US Chamber of Commerce was formed in 1912 at the behest of US President William Howard Taft.

	Annual Growth	12/03	12/04	12/05	12/06	12/07
Est. sales ($ mil.)	—	—	—	—	—	163.4
Employees	—	—	—	—	—	500

THE CHAMPAIGN TELEPHONE COMPANY

Pink Sheets: CPHT

126 Scioto St.
Urbana, OH 43078
Phone: 937-653-7605
Fax: 937-652-2777
Web: www.ctcn.net

CEO: Michael W. Conrad
CFO: –
HR: –
FYE: December 31
Type: Public

The Champaign Telephone Company and its subsidiary CT Communications provide telecommunications services to residential and business customers in Champaign County, Ohio, and in the Village of West Liberty in Logan County, Ohio. Services provided by the company include landline telephone, Internet access, and cable television; other offerings include Web hosting and managed data storage. The company's CT Wireless Service Division provides cellular phone service through a partnership with Telispire which provides access over the Sprint Nextel network.

	Annual Growth	12/03	12/04	12/05	12/06	12/07
Est. sales ($ mil.)	—	—	—	—	—	12.5
Employees	—	—	—	—	—	57

CHAMPION ENTERPRISES, INC.

NYSE: CHB

755 W. Big Beaver, Ste. 1000
Troy, MI 48084
Phone: 248-614-8200
Fax: –
Web: www.championhomes.net

CEO: William C. (Bill) Griffiths
CFO: Phyllis A. Knight
HR: Jeffrey L. Nugent
FYE: Saturday nearest December 31
Type: Public

Champion Enterprises is constantly jostling to be the #1 builder of manufactured homes in the US, along with rival Palm Harbor. The company sells about 18,000 homes annually. It mainly produces single-family ranch-style homes, but it also makes townhouses and duplexes; sizes range from 400 sq. ft. to 4,000 sq. ft. Retail prices range from $25,000 to more than $200,000 (averaging $190,000). Champion operates around 30 plants in 15 states and western Canada and sells its homes through 17 company-owned retail centers and through about 2,000 independent retailers, including 850 Champion Home Centers.

	Annual Growth	12/03	12/04	12/05	12/06	12/07
Sales ($ mil.)	2.8%	1,140.7	1,150.2	1,272.6	1,364.7	1,273.5
Net income ($ mil.)	—	(103.1)	17.0	37.8	138.3	7.2
Market value ($ mil.)	12.0%	458.9	855.3	1,035.7	715.6	723.2
Employees	(6.3%)	—	—	7,400	7,000	6,500

CHAMPION INDUSTRIES, INC.

NASDAQ (GM): CHMP

2450 1st Ave.
Huntington, WV 25728
Phone: 304-528-2700
Fax: 304-528-2765
Web: www.champion-industries.com

CEO: Marshall T. Reynolds
CFO: Todd R. Fry
HR: –
FYE: October 31
Type: Public

This Champion hopes to win business in the printing and office supply fields. Through more than a dozen operating units, Champion Industries prints books, brochures, business cards, business forms, posters, and tags, including complex four- to six-color products. Printing accounts for 70% of sales. The company also sells a wide range of office products and office furniture, which it orders from manufacturers, and provides office design services. Champion Industries operates primarily in regional markets east of the Mississippi. Chairman and CEO Marshall Reynolds controls a 42% stake in the company.

	Annual Growth	10/03	10/04	10/05	10/06	10/07
Sales ($ mil.)	4.5%	122.2	124.4	134.9	145.2	145.6
Net income ($ mil.)	35.7%	1.8	0.8	1.1	5.5	6.1
Market value ($ mil.)	11.5%	40.5	34.1	41.4	69.4	62.5
Employees	8.9%	—	—	750	—	890

CHAMPION TECHNOLOGIES, INC.

3200 Southwest Freeway, Ste. 2700
Houston, TX 77027
Phone: 713-627-3303
Fax: 713-623-8083
Web: www.champ-tech.com

CEO: Thomas N. Amonett
CFO: Chris Johnson
HR: –
FYE: December 31
Type: Subsidiary

When it comes to specialty chemicals, Champion Technologies has a crude lease on life. The firm produces specialty chemicals that help companies in the oil and gas industry withstand surface equipment problems such as internal pipe corrosion and flow assurance. The company's chemicals also are used in water-oil separation. Its manufacturing facilities are located in North America and Europe, with blending facilities located throughout the world. Special Products, a division of Champion Technologies, is a supplier of base chemicals for use in oil field production, drilling, cementing, and stimulation. The company is a subsidiary of Permian Mud Service, which is 80% owned by the John W. Johnson family.

	Annual Growth	12/03	12/04	12/05	12/06	12/07
Est. sales ($ mil.)	—	—	—	—	—	600.0
Employees	—	—	—	—	—	800

CHAMPION WINDOW MANUFACTURING INC.

12121 Champion Way
Cincinnati, OH 45241
Phone: 513-346-4600
Fax: 513-346-4614
Web: www.championwindow.com

CEO: Edward Levine
CFO: –
HR: Kathy Crawley
FYE: December 31
Type: Private

The home improvement boom has opened a window of opportunity for Champion Window Manufacturing. The company makes custom-built, vinyl-framed replacement windows and doors and sells them directly to home owners through about 60 sales and installation offices in some 30 states. It also manufactures patio rooms, porch enclosures, and vinyl siding; remodels basements; and sells patio furniture made by third-party vendors. Champion Window was founded in 1953 by Alvin Levine and Arthur Stevens as a maker of aluminum storm windows, doors, and awnings. It is owned by Chairman and CEO Edward Levine (son of Alvin) and President and COO Bernard Barbash.

	Annual Growth	12/03	12/04	12/05	12/06	12/07
Est. sales ($ mil.)	—	—	—	—	—	313.5
Employees	—	—	—	—	—	2,000

CHAMPPS ENTERTAINMENT, INC.

10375 Park Meadows Dr., Ste. 560
Littleton, CO 80124
Phone: 303-804-1333
Fax: 303-804-8477
Web: www.champps.com

CEO: Steve Johnson
CFO: James K. (Jim) Zielke
HR: –
FYE: Sunday nearest June 30
Type: Subsidiary

Champps has some choice chow for you to chomp on. Champps Entertainment operates and franchises more than 60 restaurants that offer casual-dining, as well as bar service and entertainment in Minnesota and about 20 other states. The chain's menu features a selection of appetizers, burgers, and pasta dishes. Its locations are popular spots for watching sports and other events; nighttime entertainment often includes music and karaoke. Champps typically has restaurants near shopping malls, movie megaplexes, and other high-traffic areas. About a dozen of the locations are operated by franchisees. Champps was acquired by Fox & Hound Restaurant Group in 2007.

	Annual Growth	6/03	6/04	6/05	6/06	6/07
Sales ($ mil.)	2.3%	180.7	211.5	218.4	209.6	198.1
Net income ($ mil.)	—	17.1	4.3	(0.3)	(1.6)	(7.8)
Employees	—	—	—	6,400	—	—

An in-depth profile of this company is available to Hoover's Online members at hoovers.com.

359

CHANNELL COMMERCIAL CORPORATION

NASDAQ (GM): CHNL

26040 Ynez Rd.
Temecula, CA 92591
Phone: 951-719-2600
Fax: 951-296-2322
Web: www.channellcomm.com

CEO: William H. Channell Jr.
CFO: Patrick (Pat) McCready
HR: Ginger Bejar
FYE: December 31
Type: Public

You can remove a letter or two, but Channell Commercial's products still won't make you smell nice. The company makes plastic and metal enclosures, copper wire connectors, fiber-optic cable management systems, and heat shrink products, primarily for broadband and telecommunications applications. Its products can be used for data, power, video, and voice transmissions, as well as Internet connectivity. Customers include Verizon Communications, Time Warner, Cox Communications, and Comcast. Channell Commercial also supplies water tanks through its Australian subsidiary Bushman Tanks (also known as Bushmans). Customers located in the Americas account for more than half of sales.

	Annual Growth	12/03	12/04	12/05	12/06	12/07
Sales ($ mil.)	14.9%	76.5	100.1	113.5	109.1	133.2
Net income ($ mil.)	—	(0.1)	3.6	(6.9)	(6.8)	0.3
Market value ($ mil.)	(22.9%)	38.1	78.1	47.3	28.3	13.5
Employees	10.7%	411	592	512	568	618

CHAPARRAL ENERGY, INC.

701 Cedar Lake Blvd.
Oklahoma City, OK 73114
Phone: 405-478-8770
Fax: 405-478-2906
Web: www.chaparralenergy.com

CEO: Mark A. Fischer
CFO: Joseph O. (Joe) Evans
HR: −
FYE: December 31
Type: Private

Chaparral Energy searches the scrublands of America's mid-continent and Permian Basin, looking for oil and natural gas. The exploration and production company, which also drills in Texas and the Gulf Coast, grows through exploration and acquisitions. In 2006 the company reported estimated proved reserves of some 409 billion cu. ft. of natural gas equivalent. That year the company acquired Calumet Oil for about $510 million. Chaparral Energy was founded in 1988. CEO Mark Fischer owns 42.5% of the company; Chesapeake Energy, 31.9%; and Altoma Energy — controlled by Chaparral EVP Charles Fischer, 25.6%.

	Annual Growth	12/02	12/03	12/04	12/05	12/06
Sales ($ mil.)	55.5%	41.9	62.0	92.2	133.1	245.0
Net income ($ mil.)	47.7%	5.0	10.6	17.3	12.9	23.8
Employees	24.8%	—	—	319	350	497

CHARLES & COLVARD, LTD.

NASDAQ (GS): CTHR

300 Perimeter Park Dr., Ste. A
Morrisville, NC 27560
Phone: 919-468-0399
Fax: 919-468-0486
Web: www.moissanite.com

CEO: Robert S. (Bob) Thomas
CFO: James R. (Jim) Braun
HR: Amy Wagner
FYE: December 31
Type: Public

Charles & Colvard hopes that it isn't just some shooting star. The company makes gemstones made from moissanite, a diamond substitute created in laboratories. Composed of silicon and carbon, moissanite (AKA silicon carbide or SiC) is typically found in meteorites. Charles & Colvard makes its gemstones from SiC crystals purchased primarily from Cree, Inc., and the Swedish company Norstel. Charles & Colvard markets its gemstones through two distributors (Stuller and Rio Grande) and jewelry manufacturers such as K&G Creations, Reeves Park, and Samuel Aaron International.

	Annual Growth	12/03	12/04	12/05	12/06	12/07
Sales ($ mil.)	12.8%	17.2	23.9	43.5	40.7	27.8
Net income ($ mil.)	—	1.0	1.6	5.9	6.1	0.0
Market value ($ mil.)	(1.1%)	41.6	109.5	295.7	143.8	39.8
Employees				60	—	—

CHARLES INDUSTRIES, LTD.

5600 Apollo Dr.
Rolling Meadows, IL 60008
Phone: 847-806-6300
Fax: 847-806-6231
Web: www.charlesindustries.com

CEO: Joseph T. Charles
CFO: John Sieber
HR: −
FYE: December 31
Type: Private

Charles Industries goes for cash *and* charge. Charles Industries manufactures telecommunications products, industrial chargers, and charger components, such as transformers and capacitors. It also has a joint venture with Telmax Communications to develop high-speed digital subscriber line access systems and maintains alliances with Corning Cable Systems, among other manufacturers. Although Charles Industries has sold its dockside marina products division, the company still makes marine battery chargers, power cables, and related products. Founder, president, and CEO Joseph Charles owns the company.

	Annual Growth	12/03	12/04	12/05	12/06	12/07
Est. sales ($ mil.)	—	—	—	—	—	43.1
Employees	—	—	—	—	—	450

THE CHARLES MACHINE WORKS, INC.

1959 W. Fir Ave.
Perry, OK 73077
Phone: 580-336-4402
Fax: 580-572-3527
Web: www.ditchwitch.com

CEO: Tiffany Sewell-Howard
CFO: Rick Johnson
HR: Dave Lamerton
FYE: December 31
Type: Private

Ditch Witch has cast a spell over the heavy equipment industry since 1949. The Charles Machine Works (CMW) manufactures construction equipment and parts bearing the Ditch Witch name. The company makes trenchless machines, trenchers, mini-excavators, and plows (tractors, backhoes, saws) for home construction and excavation purposes. It also makes electronic products (fault locators and beacons) for ground directional assistance and trailers (dual- and single-axle). CMW offers maintenance services on products and also sells used Ditch Witch equipment. CMW has signed a manufacturing/distribution agreement with Tu Xing Sun No-Dig Tech, a China-based horizontal drilling company. Chairman Ed Malzahn owns the company.

	Annual Growth	12/03	12/04	12/05	12/06	12/07
Est. sales ($ mil.)	—	—	—	—	—	293.0
Employees	—	—	—	—	—	1,315

CHARLES RIVER LABORATORIES INTERNATIONAL, INC.

NYSE: CRL

251 Ballardvale St.
Wilmington, MA 01887
Phone: 978-658-6000
Fax: 978-658-7132
Web: www.criver.com

CEO: James C. Foster
CFO: Thomas F. Ackerman
HR: David P. Johst
FYE: December 31
Type: Public

Charles River Laboratories International counts its chickens before they're hatched. Among other research products and services for pharmaceutical and biotech companies, Charles River Laboratories develops pathogen-free, fertilized chicken eggs used in poultry vaccines. Its Research Models and Services (RMS) unit also produces lab rats and other animals bred specifically for use in medical testing. The company provides contract research services — including toxicology studies and other kinds of testing — for drug discovery and development through its Preclinical Services segment. Customers include all the large drug firms, as well as many biotech, medical device, and animal health companies.

	Annual Growth	12/03	12/04	12/05	12/06	12/07
Sales ($ mil.)	19.0%	613.7	766.9	1,122.2	1,058.4	1,230.6
Net income ($ mil.)	17.8%	80.2	89.8	142.0	(55.8)	154.4
Market value ($ mil.)	30.6%	1,548.6	3,077.4	3,066.0	2,894.3	4,505.1
Employees	0.6%	—	—	8,400	8,000	8,500

An in-depth profile of this company is available to Hoover's Online members at hoovers.com.

CHARLES RIVER SYSTEMS, INC.

7 New England Executive Park
Burlington, MA 01803
Phone: 781-238-0099
Fax: 781-238-0088
Web: www.crd.com

CEO: Peter Lambertus
CFO: David Weber
HR: David Weber
FYE: November 30
Type: Private

The streams of global finance come flowing together in Charles River Systems' software. Founded in 1984, Charles River Systems (which does business as Charles River Development) provides software and technology consulting services for banks, fund administrators, hedge funds, insurance companies, mutual funds, and other companies in the financial services industry. The company's software offerings include applications for integrated portfolio management, investment management, trading and order management, and compliance monitoring.

	Annual Growth	11/03	11/04	11/05	11/06	11/07
Est. sales ($ mil.)	—	—	—	—	—	12.0
Employees	—	—	—	—	—	120

THE CHARLES SCHWAB CORPORATION

NASDAQ (GS): SCHW

120 Kearny St.
San Francisco, CA 94104
Phone: 415-636-7000
Fax: 415-636-9820
Web: www.schwab.com

CEO: Charles R. (Chuck) Schwab
CFO: Joseph R. Martinetto
HR: Jay L. Allen
FYE: December 31
Type: Public

The once-rebellious Charles Schwab is all grown up. The discount broker now offers the same traditional brokerage services it shunned some three decades ago. Schwab manages approximately $1.3 trillion in client assets for more than 8 million individual and institutional clients. Traders can access its services via telephone, wireless device, and the Internet, and through more than 300 US offices. Besides discount brokerage, the firm offers private banking, bond trading, annuities, and proprietary Schwab and Laudus mutual funds, as well as mortgages, CDs, and other banking products through its Charles Schwab Bank. Schwab sold U.S. Trust to Bank of America for some $3.3 billion in cash in 2007.

	Annual Growth	12/03	12/04	12/05	12/06	12/07
Sales ($ mil.)	6.7%	4,328.0	4,479.0	5,151.0	4,988.0	5,617.0
Net income ($ mil.)	50.3%	472.0	286.0	725.0	1,227.0	2,407.0
Market value ($ mil.)	16.5%	16,074.4	15,914.7	18,934.8	24,468.7	29,658.9
Employees	(2.5%)	—	—	14,000	12,400	13,300

CHARLESTON AREA MEDICAL CENTER HEALTH SYSTEM, INC.

501 Morris St.
Charleston, WV 25301
Phone: 304-388-5432
Fax: 304-341-1508
Web: www.camc.org

CEO: David L. Ramsey
CFO: Larry C. Hudson
HR: –
FYE: December 31
Type: Not-for-profit

Charleston Area Medical Center Health System, or CAMC Health System, serves as the parent corporation of several hospitals and other health care operations. Its flagship Charleston Area Medical Center is the largest hospital in West Virginia and consists of three hospitals with nearly 900 beds total. The system includes the CAMC Health Education and Research Institute which coordinates education programs for medical students from West Virginia University. The health system also operates two smaller rural hospitals, and large multi-specialty physicians practice. CAMC Health System sponsors and operates an online medical information system designed to communicate with health professionals statewide.

	Annual Growth	12/03	12/04	12/05	12/06	12/07
Est. sales ($ mil.)	—	—	—	—	—	707.3
Employees	—	—	—	—	—	4,300

CHARLOTTE PIPE & FOUNDRY COMPANY

2109 Randolph Rd.
Charlotte, NC 28207
Phone: 704-348-6450
Fax: 800-553-1605
Web: www.charlottepipe.com

CEO: Frank Dowd IV
CFO: William Hutaff
HR: Dave Magee
FYE: December 31
Type: Private

The pipe business is piping hot for Charlotte Pipe and Foundry Company, which manufactures cast-iron and plastic pipes and fittings for commercial and residential plumbing. It also produces and markets pipe and fittings for chemical waste applications under the ChemDrain brand. The company operates a foundry in Charlotte, North Carolina, and a Monroe, North Carolina, plant that produces thermoplastic pipe and fittings. It also has satellite pipe extrusion plants in Muncy, Pennsylvania; Cameron, Texas; Wildwood, Florida; and Huntsville, Alabama. The Dowd family controls Charlotte Pipe, which was founded by W. Frank Dowd in 1901.

	Annual Growth	12/03	12/04	12/05	12/06	12/07
Est. sales ($ mil.)	—	—	—	—	—	191.9
Employees	—	—	—	—	—	1,515

CHARLOTTE RUSSE HOLDING, INC.

NASDAQ (GS): CHIC

4645 Morena Blvd.
San Diego, CA 92117
Phone: 858-587-1500
Fax: 858-587-0902
Web: www.charlotte-russe.com

CEO: Mark A. Hoffman
CFO: Patricia (Patti) Johnson
HR: Jennifer L. Bolinger
FYE: Last Saturday in September
Type: Public

Charlotte Russe Holding is sweet on women's clothing. The mall-based retailer operates about 430 Charlotte Russe clothing stores in about 45 states and Puerto Rico. The stores offer established and trendy fashions for women ages 15 to 35 and priced 20% to 30% lower than competitors. Most merchandise carries the company's proprietary labels (Charlotte Russe, Refuge, and blu Chic). The company shut down its struggling 64-store Rampage chain in 2006, converting several locations to Charlotte Russe stores. Previously, the retailer had discontinued all 10 of its Charlotte's Room concept stores. Charlotte Russe Holding went public in 1999.

	Annual Growth	9/03	9/04	9/05	9/06	9/07
Sales ($ mil.)	12.9%	456.6	539.4	603.8	681.5	740.9
Net income ($ mil.)	34.8%	11.0	15.1	10.8	25.1	36.3
Market value ($ mil.)	13.0%	223.1	265.6	307.0	685.1	364.3
Employees	9.4%	—	—	7,610	8,328	—

THE CHARMER SUNBELT GROUP

60 E. 42nd St.
New York, NY 10165
Phone: 212-699-7000
Fax: 212-699-7099
Web: www.charmer-sunbelt.com

CEO: Charles (Charlie) Merinoff
CFO: Gene Luciano
HR: Ann Giambusso
FYE: March 31
Type: Private

The Charmer Sunbelt Group is one of the biggest swigs in its business sector. A leading wine and spirits wholesaler, the company operates through a number of joint ventures and subsidiaries including Charmer Industries (New York), Premier Beverage (Florida), Reliable Churchill (Maryland), and Ben Arnold-Sunbelt Beverage (South Carolina). Charmer Sunbelt also distributes non-alcoholic products such as bottled water. Division management bought the group from McKesson (drugs and sundries wholesaler) and took it private in 1988. Descendants of founder Herman Merinoff, own and operate the company.

	Annual Growth	3/02	3/03	3/04	3/05	3/06
Est. sales ($ mil.)	44.1%	950.0	2,200.0	1,700.0	2,900.0	4,100.0
Employees	40.1%	1,700	3,800	3,000	6,100	6,550

An in-depth profile of this company is available to Hoover's Online members at hoovers.com.

361

CHARMING SHOPPES, INC.

NASDAQ (GS): CHRS

450 Winks Ln.
Bensalem, PA 19020
Phone: 215-245-9100
Fax: 215-633-4640
Web: www.charmingshoppes.com

CEO: Dorrit J. Bern
CFO: Eric M. Specter
HR: Anthony A. DeSabato
FYE: Saturday nearest January 31
Type: Public

Charming Shoppes wants its shoppers to be mesmerizing. The company runs some 2,410 stores (and related Web sites) in 48 US states at three apparel chains that cater to plus-size women: 990 Fashion Bug stores that sell moderately priced apparel and accessories in girls, juniors, misses, and plus sizes; about 465 Catherines Plus Size stores; and 895 Lane Bryant and Lane Bryant Outlet stores. Across the US, Charming Shoppes serves low- to middle-income women and teens who follow fashion styles rather than set them. The company's purchase of Lane Bryant from Limited Brands in 2001 elevated Charming Shoppes to #1 in the plus-size market. The company also owns Crosstown Traders, a direct marketer of women's apparel.

	Annual Growth	1/04	1/05	1/06	1/07	1/08
Sales ($ mil.)	7.1%	2,285.7	2,332.3	2,755.7	3,067.5	3,009.9
Net income ($ mil.)	—	40.6	64.5	99.4	108.9	(83.4)
Market value ($ mil.)	4.4%	668.2	968.0	1,534.5	1,636.3	793.0
Employees	3.9%	—	—	28,000	30,000	30,200

CHART INDUSTRIES, INC.

NASDAQ (GS): GTLS

1 Infinity Corporate Centre Dr., Ste. 300
Garfield Heights, OH 44125
Phone: 440-753-1490
Fax: 440-753-1491
Web: www.chart-ind.com

CEO: Samuel F. Thomas
CFO: Michael F. Biehl
HR: Mark H. Ludwig
FYE: December 31
Type: Public

They're just chillin' at Chart Industries. The company (which was acquired by First Reserve in 2005 for $460 million) designs equipment for low-temperature uses, including cryogenic systems that can operate at temperatures near absolute zero. Chart's vessels are used to process, liquefy, store, and transport gases and are marketed to petrochemical and natural gas processors, producers of industrial gas, and satellite testing companies. The company also performs engineered bulk gas installations, and makes specialty liquid nitrogen end-use equipment used in the hydrocarbon processing and industrial gas industries. Chart's products are sold worldwide; the US accounts for about three-quarters of sales.

	Annual Growth	12/03	12/04	12/05	12/06	12/07
Sales ($ mil.)	25.9%	265.6	305.6	403.1	537.5	666.4
Net income ($ mil.)	—	(7.0)	22.6	8.4	26.9	44.2
Market value ($ mil.)	110.2%	—	—	—	414.8	871.8
Employees	15.9%	1,524	1,770	2,271	2,703	2,751

CHARTER COMMUNICATIONS, INC.

NASDAQ (GM): CHTR

12405 Powerscourt Dr., Ste. 100
St. Louis, MO 63131
Phone: 314-965-0555
Fax: 314-965-9745
Web: www.charter.com

CEO: Neil Smit
CFO: Eloise E. Schmitz
HR: Lynne F. Ramsey
FYE: December 31
Type: Public

Charter Communications is a cable television system operator with more than 5 million residential and commercial subscribers in 40 US states, making it the #4 cable company, behind Comcast, Time Warner Cable, and Cox Communications. Not just a leading cable TV player, Charter offers broadband Internet and computer telephony services (it has almost a million phone customers), as well as HDTV. Through agreements with Digeo and Oxygen Media, Charter provides interactive television services. The company also derives a portion of its revenue from the sale of local advertising on such satellite networks as MTV and CNN. Chairman Paul Allen, a co-founder of Microsoft, controls about 90% of Charter's voting power.

	Annual Growth	12/03	12/04	12/05	12/06	12/07
Sales ($ mil.)	5.6%	4,819.0	4,977.0	5,254.0	5,504.0	6,002.0
Net income ($ mil.)	—	(238.0)	(4,341.0)	(967.0)	(1,370.0)	(1,616.0)
Market value ($ mil.)	(20.8%)	1,186.1	683.7	507.8	1,248.5	465.9
Employees	(2.1%)	—	—	17,200	15,500	16,500

CHARTER FINANCIAL CORPORATION

OTC: CHFN

1233 O.G. Skinner Dr.
West Point, GA 31833
Phone: 706-645-1391
Fax: —
Web: www.charterbk.com

CEO: Robert L. Johnson
CFO: Curtis R. Kollar
HR: —
FYE: September 30
Type: Public

Charter Financial gives sound financial practices a grade of A+. The firm is the savings and loan holding company for CharterBank, which operates about 10 branches and three loan production offices in western Georgia and eastern Alabama. Deposit products include consumer and commercial checking accounts, savings and money market accounts, and CDs. The bank is focused on real estate lending, with residential and commercial mortgages each accounting for around 40% of its loan portfolio. It also makes consumer, business, and real estate construction loans. The bank gives cash awards to high school customers for making all A's. Mutual holding company First Charter MHC owns 80% of Charter Financial.

	Annual Growth	9/03	9/04	9/05	9/06	9/07
Assets ($ mil.)	0.5%	1,000.5	1,068.2	1,050.6	1,097.3	1,021.9
Net income ($ mil.)	101.3%	3.1	8.2	11.4	13.3	50.9
Employees	(1.5%)	—	181	169	179	173

CHARTER MANUFACTURING COMPANY, INC.

1212 W. Glen Oaks Ln.
Mequon, WI 53092
Phone: 262-243-4700
Fax: 262-243-4711
Web: www.chartermfg.com

CEO: John A. Mellowes
CFO: John Couper
HR: —
FYE: December 31
Type: Private

Charter Manufacturing and its divisions manufacture such steel products as special bar quality (SBQ) bar, rod, wire, and stainless steel rod. The company also supplies precision cold-rolled custom profiles and engineered components, including driveline, engine, and transmission parts, for the automotive industry. It operates from about 10 locations in the Midwest and Canada through subsidiaries Charter Specialty Steel, Charter Wire, and Milwaukee Wire Products. In early 2007 the company branched out internationally for the first time with the purchase (through Milwaukee Wire Products) of the UK company Valve Train Components Ltd. Charter Manufacturing was founded in 1936.

	Annual Growth	12/03	12/04	12/05	12/06	12/07
Est. sales ($ mil.)	—	—	—	—	—	719.6
Employees	—	—	—	—	—	1,050

CHAS. LEVY COMPANY, LLC

27500 Riverview Center Blvd.
Bonita Springs, FL 34134
Phone: 239-949-4450
Fax: 239-495-5110
Web: www.chaslevy.com

CEO: Barbara Levy Kipper
CFO: Steve Carlson
HR: —
FYE: September 30
Type: Subsidiary

Chas. Levy keeps racking up sales. The wholesaler distributes magazines and books throughout the US, primarily in several Midwestern states and the southeastern seaboard. Having grown through acquisitions of other distributors, Chas. Levy distributes books through its Levy Home Entertainment subsidiary to retail chains including Best Buy, Kmart, Meijer, ShopKo, Stop & Shop, and Wal-Mart. The company has shut down its newspaper distribution operation. Chairman Barbara Levy Kipper owned the company, which her grandfather founded in 1893, before selling it to magazine powerhouse Source Interlink in 2005.

An in-depth profile of this company is available to Hoover's Online members at hoovers.com.

CHASE CORPORATION

AMEX: CCF

26 Summer St.
Bridgewater, MA 02324
Phone: 508-279-1789
Fax: 508-697-6419
Web: www.chasecorp.com

CEO: Peter R. Chase
CFO: Kenneth L. (Ken) Dumas
HR: –
FYE: August 31
Type: Public

Duct tape is wonderful stuff, but when the situation calls for a higher-tech solution, Chase Corporation is ready for the task. The company makes tapes and protective coatings used by the electronic, public utility, and oil industries. Products include insulating and conducting materials for electrical wire; electrical repair tapes; protective pipe coatings; thermoelectric insulation for electrical equipment; and moisture protective coatings for electronics. Chase also provides circuit board manufacturing services. A trust controlled by heirs of the company's late founder, Edward Chase, owns 15% of the company; Chase's son Peter, who serves as company chairman and CEO, owns about 13% of Chase Corporation.

	Annual Growth	8/03	8/04	8/05	8/06	8/07
Sales ($ mil.)	14.3%	74.6	87.1	91.4	108.4	127.5
Net income ($ mil.)	17.8%	5.3	4.6	4.8	6.1	10.2
Market value ($ mil.)	54.4%	25.0	31.3	27.4	32.7	141.9
Employees	8.6%	—	—	325	362	383

CHASE GENERAL CORPORATION

Pink Sheets: CSGN

1307 S. 59th St.
St. Joseph, MO 64507
Phone: 816-279-1625
Fax: 816-279-1997
Web: www.cherrymash.com

CEO: Barry M. Yantis
CFO: Barry M. Yantis
HR: Brett A. Yantis
FYE: June 30
Type: Public

They not only chase but also catch the sweet life at Chase General Corporation. The company's subsidiary Dye Candy Company makes and distributes candy and confections. Using more than 15 tons of crushed maraschino cherries a year, Dye's Chase Candy division produces "Cherry Mash" candy bars, while its Poe Candy division makes Chase's brand coconut haystacks, fudge, jelly candies, peanut brittle, and peanut clusters. The company's products are distributed mainly in the Midwest. In 2006 Wal-Mart accounted for approximately 19% of Chase's sales and Associated Wholesale Grocers approximately 24%.

	Annual Growth	6/03	6/04	6/05	6/06	6/07
Sales ($ mil.)	4.9%	1.9	2.2	2.6	2.3	2.3
Net income ($ mil.)	—	0.0	0.1	0.1	(0.1)	(0.2)
Employees	0.0%	20	20	—	—	—

CHASE PAYMENTECH SOLUTIONS, LLC

14221 Dallas Pkwy., Bldg. 2
Dallas, TX 75254
Phone: 214-849-3000
Fax: 214-849-2148
Web: www.paymentech.com

CEO: Michael P. (Mike) Duffy
CFO: Kathryn (Kathy) Smith
HR: –
FYE: December 31
Type: Joint venture

Chase Paymentech Solutions keeps the wheels of commerce churning. Formerly just Paymentech, the company processes the merchant side of check and credit, debit, and pre-paid card payments, handling more than 18 billion transactions per year, both over the Internet and at the point of sale. Serving some 600,000 customers globally, Chase Paymentech Solutions assembles the authorization network and recruits new merchants into the system; it also operates merchant help desks to assist point-of-sale clients. It targets such sectors as retail, hospitality, insurance, utilities, airlines, and convenience stores and gas stations. Banking behemoth JPMorgan Chase owns 51% of the company; First Data owns the rest.

CHATTEM, INC.

NASDAQ (GS): CHTT

1715 W. 38th St.
Chattanooga, TN 37409
Phone: 423-821-4571
Fax: 423-821-0395
Web: www.chattem.com

CEO: Zan Guerry
CFO: Robert E. Bosworth
HR: –
FYE: November 30
Type: Public

Chattem's got more well-known brands than the Texas ranching industry. Over-the-counter drugs make a bundle of money for Chattem, which also makes and sells personal care products and dietary supplements. Chattem's products include pain treatments such as dental analgesic Benzodent, topical analgesic Aspercreme, Icy Hot joint and muscle pain reliever, and Pamprin menstrual symptom reliever. The company also makes the sleep aid Melatonex, medicated powder Gold Bond, Bullfrog sunscreen, and Mudd clay-based facial mask. Chattem sells its products to wholesalers and retail merchandisers. The company in 2007 acquired five brands (Balmex, Kaopectate, Unisom, Cortizone, and Act) from Johnson & Johnson.

	Annual Growth	11/03	11/04	11/05	11/06	11/07
Sales ($ mil.)	16.0%	233.8	258.2	279.3	300.5	423.4
Net income ($ mil.)	26.4%	23.4	1.6	36.0	45.1	59.7
Market value ($ mil.)	44.9%	307.0	720.1	624.9	908.2	1,353.8
Employees	2.7%	—	—	449	423	474

CHECK INTO CASH, INC.

201 Keith St. SW, Ste. 80
Cleveland, TN 37311
Phone: 423-479-2400
Fax: 423-559-1099
Web: www.checkintocash.com

CEO: W. Allan Jones
CFO: Bill Lane
HR: Scott Beck
FYE: December 31
Type: Private

If you're in need of some quick cash, you might want to check into Check Into Cash. The company offers short-term payday advances through some 1,250 Check Into Cash stores in more than 30 states. Customers issue a personal check to Check Into Cash to cover the amount borrowed (usually between $100 and $1,000), plus fees and interest. The company holds onto the check for up to two weeks until the customer's next payday, then cashes it. Customers must provide proof of ID and income, and have an active checking account. Check Into Cash markets to employed consumers who want an alternative to traditional short-term cash avenues like credit cards, consumer loans, pawn shops, or overdrafts.

	Annual Growth	12/03	12/04	12/05	12/06	12/07
Est. sales ($ mil.)	—	—	—	—	—	31.5
Employees	—	—	—	—	—	280

CHECKERS DRIVE-IN RESTAURANTS, INC.

4300 W. Cypress St., Ste. 600
Tampa, FL 33607
Phone: 813-283-7000
Fax: 813-283-7001
Web: www.checkers.com

CEO: Enrique (Rick) Silva
CFO: Todd Lindsey
HR: Wendy Harkness
FYE: Monday nearest December 31
Type: Private

You might say that this company's customers are driven to eat hamburgers. Checkers Drive-in Restaurants is the #1 operator of double drive-through fast-food restaurants, with more than 800 mostly franchised locations in about 20 states. Operating under the Checkers and Rally's Hamburgers banners, the restaurants offer a limited menu of burgers, fries, and hot dogs, as well as beverages and shakes. The restaurants are typically decorated with checkered flags and racing theme exteriors and offer no inside seating or dining areas. Checkers was taken private by Wellspring Capital in 2006.

	Annual Growth	12/03	12/04	12/05	12/06	12/07
Est. sales ($ mil.)	—	—	—	—	—	86.7
Employees	—	—	—	—	—	4,000

An in-depth profile of this company is available to Hoover's Online members at hoovers.com.

363

CHECKFREE CORPORATION

4411 E. Jones Bridge Rd.
Norcross, GA 30092
Phone: 678-375-3000
Fax: 678-375-1477
Web: www.checkfreecorp.com

CEO: Peter J. (Pete) Kight
CFO: David E. Mangum
HR: –
FYE: June 30
Type: Public

You've got bills! CheckFree provides electronic bill payment and presentment and other types of electronic commerce and payment services to consumers through numerous sources, including US banks, brokerages, Web sites, and personal financial management software. The company also offers portfolio management services to broker-dealers, money managers, and investment advisors, and makes financial application software used by large financial institutions and other corporate clients. CheckFree has expanded its technological capabilities through acquisitions; it bought financial services software developers Carreker and Corillian in 2007. Later that year Fiserv bought CheckFree for some $4.2 billion.

	Annual Growth	6/03	6/04	6/05	6/06	6/07
Sales ($ mil.)	15.2%	551.7	606.5	757.8	879.4	972.6
Net income ($ mil.)	—	(52.2)	10.5	46.8	127.3	124.4
Market value ($ mil.)	9.2%	2,499.5	2,704.9	3,074.2	4,503.4	3,548.5
Employees	13.1%	—	—	3,050	3,450	—

CHECKPOINT SYSTEMS, INC.

NYSE: CKP

101 Wolf Dr.
Thorofare, NJ 08086
Phone: 856-848-1800
Fax: 856-848-0937
Web: www.checkpointsystems.com

CEO: Robert P. (Rob) van der Merwe
CFO: Raymond D. Andrews
HR: Pablo del Amo Serrano
FYE: Sunday before December 31
Type: Public

Checkpoint Systems wants to keep shoplifters in check. The company makes electronic article surveillance systems (EAS), radio frequency identification (RFID) tags, electronic security devices, closed-circuit TV (CCTV) systems, and electronic access control systems used by retailers such as Barnes & Noble, Circuit City, Sears, Target, and Walgreen. Checkpoint's EAS units employ paper-thin disposable circuit tags attached to merchandise that are disarmed at check-out; if not disarmed, the tags trigger electronic sensors when the customer tries to leave. The company operates in about 30 countries worldwide; nearly half of its sales come from Europe.

	Annual Growth	12/03	12/04	12/05	12/06	12/07
Sales ($ mil.)	3.6%	723.3	778.7	721.0	687.8	834.2
Net income ($ mil.)	19.2%	29.1	(20.2)	39.4	35.9	58.8
Market value ($ mil.)	12.2%	668.6	683.4	968.7	793.4	1,058.7
Employees	(0.3%)	—	—	3,955	3,213	3,930

THE CHEESECAKE FACTORY INCORPORATED

NASDAQ (GS): CAKE

26901 Malibu Hills Rd.
Calabasas Hills, CA 91301
Phone: 818-871-3000
Fax: 818-871-3001
Web: www.thecheesecakefactory.com

CEO: David Overton
CFO: Michael J. Dixon
HR: Edwin T. Eynon
FYE: Tuesday nearest December 31
Type: Public

The Cheesecake Factory's vast, multipage menu is perhaps the most baroque document in the restaurant industry. The company runs about 140 casual-dining restaurants in 35 states that offer about 200 menu items ranging from sandwiches and salads to steaks and seafood. The highlight of the menu, of course, is cheesecake, which comes in about 40 varieties, including Chocolate Tuxedo Cream and Kahlua Cocoa Coffee. Each restaurant has a unique design, but all have over-the-top opulence and Las Vegas-style glitz. In addition to its flagship concept, the company operates about a dozen Grand Lux Cafes, licenses two bakery cafes, and sells its cheesecakes to grocery stores and food service operators.

	Annual Growth	12/03	12/04	12/05	12/06	12/07
Sales ($ mil.)	18.2%	773.8	969.2	1,182.1	1,315.3	1,511.6
Net income ($ mil.)	6.4%	57.8	66.5	87.9	81.3	74.0
Market value ($ mil.)	1.9%	1,520.2	2,520.4	2,933.3	1,925.2	1,639.6
Employees	9.1%	—	—	24,700	29,400	29,400

CHEF SOLUTIONS INC.

120 W. Palatine Rd.
Wheeling, IL 60090
Phone: 847-325-7500
Fax: 847-325-7594
Web: www.chefsolutions.com

CEO: Steven (Steve) Silk
CFO: Carl W. Warschausky
HR: Janie Minkin
FYE: December 31
Type: Private

Stressed-out chefs needing to round out their menus can turn to this company for the latest side dishes, salads, and bakery items. Chef Solutions is a leading supplier of fresh-prepared foods to retail and wholesale customers. Operating through its Orval Kent unit, the company supplies fresh salads, dips, and other deli-style side dishes; it operates a half-dozen manufacturing and distribution centers in California, Illinois, Kansas, Ohio, and Texas, and in Mexico. Private equity and turnaround firm Questor Management owns Chef Solutions.

	Annual Growth	12/03	12/04	12/05	12/06	12/07
Est. sales ($ mil.)	—	—	—	—	—	645.1
Employees	—	—	—	—	—	6,797

CHELSEA PROPERTY GROUP, INC.

105 Eisenhower Pkwy.
Roseland, NJ 07068
Phone: 973-228-6111
Fax: 973-228-3891
Web: www.cpgi.com

CEO: Chao Tse (Leslie) Hou
CFO: Michael J. Clarke
HR: Christina M. Casey
FYE: December 31
Type: Subsidiary

Chelsea Property Group, a subsidiary of retail giant Simon Property Group, owns, develops, leases, and manages some 50 factory outlet shopping centers. The properties are located near metropolitan areas and tourist destinations such as Disney World in Orlando, Florida; Branson, Missouri; and California's Monterey Peninsula. They feature some 750 tenants, including such high-end fashion names as Gucci and Versace. Most of its shopping centers operate under the Premium Outlet name. Through joint ventures, Chelsea Property also operates six outlet malls in Japan, one in Korea, and one in Mexico.

	Annual Growth	12/03	12/04	12/05	12/06	12/07
Est. sales ($ mil.)	—	—	—	—	—	85.3
Employees	—	—	—	—	—	853

CHELSEA & SCOTT, LTD.

75 Albrecht Dr.
Lake Bluff, IL 60044
Phone: 847-615-2110
Fax: 847-615-2290
Web: www.onestepahead.com

CEO: Karen B. Scott
CFO: –
HR: –
FYE: December 31
Type: Private

Chelsea & Scott is about babies and toddlers. The company provides educational toys and developmental products for children ages three to eight through its Leaps and Bounds catalog and Web site, and infant and toddler safety products, accessories, and toys through its One Step Ahead catalog and Web site. Offerings include innovative products, some designed by parents, like the Ride-On Carry-On, a chair that attaches to a suitcase, allowing a child to ride securely while the suitcase is being wheeled. Web site features include gift registries and guides on everything from choosing a high chair to balancing breastfeeding and work.

	Annual Growth	12/03	12/04	12/05	12/06	12/07
Sales ($ mil.)	—	—	—	—	—	76.5
Employees	—	—	—	—	—	140

CHEMCENTRAL CORPORATION

7050 W. 71st St.
Bedford Park, IL 60499
Phone: 708-594-7000
Fax: 708-594-6382
Web: www.chemcentral.com

CEO: John R. Yanney
CFO: William Wingereid
HR: Ken Krausz
FYE: December 31
Type: Subsidiary

CHEMCENTRAL is in the center of a chemically dependent world. The company is one of the top chemical distributors in North America. It carries products made by BASF, Dow Chemical, Ineos, and others. Key customers for CHEMCENTRAL's more than 8,000 chemical products include companies that manufacture adhesives, caulks, and sealants; cleaning agents; cosmetics and personal care products; inks and paint coatings; and plastic and rubber compounds. CHEMCENTRAL was established in 1926 by entrepreneurs Halbert Sampson and William Hough. In 2007 European distribution giant Univar bought CHEMCENTRAL for $650 million.

CHEMICAL LIME COMPANY

3700 Hulen St.
Fort Worth, TX 76107
Phone: 817-732-8164
Fax: 817-732-8564
Web: www.chemicallime.com

CEO: David M. Reilly
CFO: Steve Barnish
HR: Ken Cage
FYE: December 31
Type: Subsidiary

Don't put *this* lime in your gin and tonic. Chemical Lime, as its name would suggest, produces lime and lime-based products (including quicklimes and hydrated limes) for use in steelmaking, ore processing, industrial manufacturing, and construction. The company's products also serve environmental purposes such as wastewater treatment and softening drinking water, as well as roadbed stabilization. Chemical Lime provides lime slurry (hot liquid lime) to its customers from its PORTA BATCH concentrated production units. Chemical Lime's quarries and plants are primarily located in the southern and western US. Lhoist Group of Belgium owns Chemical Lime, which was founded in 1966.

CHEMED CORPORATION

NYSE: CHE

2600 Chemed Center, 255 E. 5th St.
Cincinnati, OH 45202
Phone: 513-762-6900
Fax: 513-762-6919
Web: www.chemed.com

CEO: Kevin J. McNamara
CFO: David P. Williams
HR: Jim Taylor
FYE: December 31
Type: Public

Chemed Corporation plunges right in when it comes to taking care of people. Operating through two major subsidiaries, Chemed Corporation offers care to terminally ill patients through its VITAS Healthcare subsidiary, which owns more than 40 hospice programs across about 16 US states. VITAS employs doctors, nurses, and other professionals to provide at-home and inpatient services. In addition, its famous Roto-Rooter subsidiary offers plumbing and drain-cleaning services for residential and commercial customers through company-owned, contractor-operated, and franchised locations, some 600 total. A stalwart of the industry, Roto-Rooter offers services to over 90% of the US market and nearly half of Canada.

	Annual Growth	12/03	12/04	12/05	12/06	12/07
Sales ($ mil.)	37.4%	308.9	735.3	926.5	1,018.6	1,100.1
Net income ($ mil.)	—	(3.4)	27.5	35.8	50.7	64.0
Market value ($ mil.)	55.5%	229.2	424.4	1,290.7	955.1	1,339.0
Employees	4.1%	—	—	10,881	11,621	11,783

CHEMOIL CORPORATION

4 Embarcadero Center, 34th Fl.
San Francisco, CA 94111
Phone: 415-268-2700
Fax: 415-268-2701
Web: www.chemoil.com

CEO: Clyde M. (Mike) Bandy
CFO: Jerome Lazatin Lorenzo
HR: Lucius Charles Conrad
FYE: December 31
Type: Private

Chemoil is hunkered down in the bunker fuel distribution business. The company supplies marine bunker fuels to shipping companies worldwide. Chemoil operates refineries and terminals and distributes fuel from a handful of US ports (including New York and Los Angeles), and in Colombia, the Netherlands, Panama, and Singapore. The company supplies more than 4,000 vessels a year. Fuel is delivered mostly by tankers, barges, and tugboats owned and operated by Chemoil or its affiliates, which include AFT-Chemoil (Rotterdam) and Chemoil-ITC (Singapore). Chemoil is 50%-owned by Japanese trading company ITOCHU, which helps to fund its expansion.

	Annual Growth	12/03	12/04	12/05	12/06	12/07
Est. sales ($ mil.)	—	—	—	—	—	13.7
Employees	—	—	—	—	—	45

CHEMICAL FINANCIAL CORPORATION

NASDAQ (GS): CHFC

235 E. Main St.
Midland, MI 48640
Phone: 989-839-5350
Fax: 989-839-5255
Web: www.chemicalbankmi.com

CEO: David B. Ramaker
CFO: Lori A. Gwizdala
HR: –
FYE: December 31
Type: Public

Chemical Financial has banking down to a science. The holding company for Chemical Bank (formed in 2005 from several subsidiary banks that had been operating under the Chemical Financial umbrella) provides a full range of financial services to individuals and businesses in the lower peninsula of Michigan. Through about 130 branches, the bank offers standard deposit products, including checking and savings accounts, CDs, and IRAs. The company and its subsidiaries also offer trust services, title services, data processing, and investment products.

	Annual Growth	12/03	12/04	12/05	12/06	12/07
Assets ($ mil.)	0.3%	3,708.9	3,764.1	3,749.3	3,789.3	3,754.3
Net income ($ mil.)	(8.5%)	55.7	56.7	52.9	46.8	39.0
Market value ($ mil.)	(9.0%)	824.9	1,028.8	796.5	826.8	566.6
Employees	—	—	—	1,376	—	—

CHEMTURA CORPORATION

NYSE: CEM

199 Benson Rd.
Middlebury, CT 06749
Phone: 203-573-2000
Fax: 203-573-3711
Web: www.chemtura.com

CEO: Robert L. Wood
CFO: Stephen C. Forsyth
HR: David G. Dickey
FYE: December 31
Type: Public

Chemtura would like to be the future of chemicals making. The company ranks among the top specialty chemical companies in the US, along with Rohm and Haas and Hexion, and is the #1 plastics additives maker globally. Aside from plastic additives, Chemtura holds niche-leading positions in the manufacture of petroleum additives, flame retardants, and swimming pool chemicals. Its other products include urethanes and crop protection chemicals. The company was formed in 2005 as a result of the merger of specialty chemical heavyweights Crompton Corporation and Great Lakes Chemical.

	Annual Growth	12/03	12/04	12/05	12/06	12/07
Sales ($ mil.)	14.4%	2,185.0	2,549.8	2,986.6	3,722.7	3,747.0
Net income ($ mil.)	—	19.0	(34.6)	(186.6)	(205.5)	(3.0)
Market value ($ mil.)	(21.3%)	—	—	3,047.9	2,318.8	1,888.4
Employees	(12.1%)	—	—	6,600	6,200	5,100

An in-depth profile of this company is available to Hoover's Online members at hoovers.com.

365

CHEMUNG FINANCIAL CORPORATION

OTC: CHMG

1 Chemung Canal Plaza	CEO: Ronald M. Bentley
Elmira, NY 14901	CFO: John R. Battersby Jr.
Phone: 607-737-3711	HR: Linda M. Struble
Fax: 607-735-2035	FYE: December 31
Web: www.cctc2me.com	Type: Public

Everybody Chemung Financial tonight probably wouldn't make much of a pop record. The firm is parent to Chemung Canal Trust Company, which provides bank and trust services from some 20 offices in and around southern New York's Chemung County. The trust company offers such deposit services as savings, checking, and money market accounts; IRAs; and CDs. It offers credit card services, and originates a variety of loans, including personal, small business, and residential mortgage loans. Other services include retirement and estate planning, and tax services. Another Chemung Financial subsidiary, CFS Group, offers mutual funds, discount brokerage, and other financial services.

	Annual Growth	12/03	12/04	12/05	12/06	12/07
Assets ($ mil.)	1.4%	747.2	722.5	718.0	738.2	788.9
Net income ($ mil.)	1.4%	6.9	8.7	6.6	6.6	7.3
Market value ($ mil.)	(8.0%)	137.9	119.8	111.2	113.3	98.7
Employees	—	—	—	—	—	280

CHENIERE ENERGY, INC.

AMEX: LNG

717 Texas Ave., Ste. 3100	CEO: Charif Souki
Houston, TX 77002	CFO: Don A. Turkleson
Phone: 713-659-1361	HR: Ann Raden
Fax: 713-659-5459	FYE: December 31
Web: www.cheniere.com	Type: Public

Gaseous form or liquid state are both OK with Cheniere Energy, which is engaged in the development of a liquefied natural gas (LNG) receiving-terminal business, a natural gas pipeline business, and oil and gas exploration and production. The company is building three onshore US Gulf Coast LNG receiving terminals with an aggregate regasification capacity of 10 billion cu. ft. per day, and developing pipelines to connect these to North American natural gas markets. Cheniere Energy's exploration and production unit has proved reserves of 8,869 barrels of oil and 1.3 billion cu. ft. of natural gas. The company operates along the coast of Louisiana, both onshore and in the shallow waters along the Gulf of Mexico.

	Annual Growth	12/03	12/04	12/05	12/06	12/07
Sales ($ mil.)	66.7%	0.7	2.0	3.0	2.4	5.4
Net income ($ mil.)	—	(5.3)	(24.6)	(29.8)	(145.9)	(181.8)
Market value ($ mil.)	94.4%	109.2	852.2	2,029.3	1,594.0	1,557.9
Employees	—	—	—	130	—	—

CHENIERE ENERGY PARTNERS, L.P.

AMEX: CQP

700 Milam St., Ste. 800	CEO: Charif Souki
Houston, TX 77002	CFO: Don A. Turkleson
Phone: 713-375-5000	HR: –
Fax: 713-375-6000	FYE: December 31
Web: www.cheniereenergypartners.com	Type: Public

Cheniere Energy Partners, a subsidiary of Cheniere Energy, Inc., plans to be North America's biggest gas station — natural gas, that is. Construction began on the Sabine Pass LNG (liquefied natural gas) receiving terminal in 2005 and was completed in 2008. The terminal is the largest of its kind in North America. It boasts a 4-billion-cu.-ft.-per-day regasification capacity as well as 16.8 billion cubic feet of LNG storage capacity. All of the Sabine Pass LNG receiving terminal's capacity has already been contracted to Total LNG USA (an affiliate of TOTAL S.A.), Chevron U.S.A., and Cheniere Energy Inc. subsidiary Cheniere Marketing.

CHEP

CHEP

8517 S. Park Cir.	CEO: David (Dave) Mezzanotte
Orlando, FL 32819	CFO: –
Phone: 407-370-2437	HR: –
Fax: 407-355-6211	FYE: June 30
Web: www.chep.com	Type: Subsidiary

CHEP knows it's sink or swim in the pallet and plastic container pooling services business. The company, a unit of Australia-based Brambles, manages the movement of more than 280 million pallets and containers used by companies in the automotive, consumer goods, food and beverage, home improvement, and raw materials industries. The pallets and containers are used throughout the supply chain. The company's 300,000-plus customers have included industry leaders such as General Motors, Kraft, and Procter & Gamble. CHEP operates from a network of more than 440 facilities in about 45 countries worldwide.

	Annual Growth	6/03	6/04	6/05	6/06	6/07
Sales ($ mil.)	9.2%	2,371.1	2,465.3	2,792.4	3,078.8	3,374.5
Employees	(0.1%)	7,500	7,704	7,700	7,585	7,466

CHEROKEE INC.

NASDAQ (GS): CHKE

6835 Valjean Ave.	CEO: Robert Margolis
Van Nuys, CA 91406	CFO: Russell J. Riopelle
Phone: 818-908-9868	HR: –
Fax: 818-908-9191	FYE: January 31
Web: www.cherokeegroup.com	Type: Public

Cherokee has a license to make money from clothes and shoes. The company licenses its trademarks, which include Cherokee, Sideout, and Carole Little, to retailers and wholesalers of apparel, footwear, and accessories. The main ideas behind Cherokee's business are that large retailers can source merchandise more efficiently than individual brand owners and that licensed brands can sell better for retailers than private labels. In addition to licensing its own brands, Cherokee helps other brand owners gain licensing contracts. Target, the company's largest customer, accounts for about 40% of Cherokee's revenue; other licensees include Tesco (in Europe), Zellers (in Canada), and TJX.

	Annual Growth	1/04	1/05	1/06	1/07	1/08
Sales ($ mil.)	3.5%	36.3	38.9	42.7	76.6	41.6
Net income ($ mil.)	3.7%	14.2	17.2	18.3	34.8	16.4
Market value ($ mil.)	14.3%	173.9	289.5	347.0	393.7	296.7
Employees	7.7%	—	16	17	18	20

CHEROKEE INTERNATIONAL CORPORATION

NASDAQ (GM): CHRK

2841 Dow Ave.	CEO: Jeffrey M. Frank
Tustin, CA 92780	CFO: Linster W. (Lin) Fox
Phone: 714-544-6665	HR: –
Fax: 714-838-4742	FYE: December 31
Web: www.cherokeepwr.com	Type: Public

Cherokee International feeds the need for power in electronics. The company makes custom AC/DC power supplies and rectifiers, products that convert power from alternating current (AC) wall sockets into the direct current (DC) needed for electronic devices. Cherokee also makes modified and standard power supplies, and has introduced a line of DC/DC converters. Products are used by wireless communications, enterprise networking, medical, and industrial equipment makers. The company has operations around the globe, with facilities in Belgium, China, India, and the US. About half of sales comes from customers located outside the US.

	Annual Growth	12/03	12/04	12/05	12/06	12/07
Sales ($ mil.)	3.5%	111.9	148.5	122.1	145.0	128.5
Net income ($ mil.)	—	(12.4)	10.4	(3.2)	0.1	(9.0)
Market value ($ mil.)	(38.5%)	—	184.6	88.8	77.9	43.0
Employees	—	—	—	1,484	—	—

CHERRY HILL PHOTO ENTERPRISES, INC.

1200 Haddonfield Rd.
Cherry Hill, NJ 08002
Phone: 856-663-1616
Fax: 856-663-0880
Web: www.cherryhillphoto.com

CEO: Robert C. Wolfe
CFO: Wayne Pierce
HR: Jackie Abate
FYE: September 30
Type: Private

Cherry Hill Photo Enterprises believes in Santa Claus and the Easter Bunny. The company offers holiday photography services in more than 350 malls across the US and Canada. Children can have their pictures taken with Santa (with a real beard) or the Easter Bunny at a local mall; backgrounds and foregrounds are added digitally. Services include digital, instant, and 35mm photos; snow globes and other photo merchandise; and videos of the child's visit. Non-costumed crews are available to provide a photographic record of corporate events. The company, which says its employees are trained in customer service at Disney University, also rents its Santa out for photo ops. CEO Bob Wolfe owns Cherry Hill Photo.

	Annual Growth	9/03	9/04	9/05	9/06	9/07
Est. sales ($ mil.)	—	—	—	—	—	32.0
Employees	—	—	—	—	—	35

CHESAPEAKE CORPORATION

NYSE: CSK

1021 E. Cary St., Ste. 2350
Richmond, VA 23219
Phone: 804-697-1000
Fax: 804-697-1199
Web: www.cskcorp.com

CEO: Andrew J. Kohut
CFO: Joel K. Mostrom
HR: David (Dave) Winter
FYE: Sunday nearest December 31
Type: Public

For Chesapeake, the total package is made up of paperboard and plastic specialty packaging products. The company's paperboard products, which include folding cartons, tubes, leaflets, and labels, are marketed to manufacturers in the alcoholic beverage, confectionery, cosmetics, food, household goods, health care, pharmaceutical, and tobacco industries. Paperboard products account for about 85% of the company's sales. Chesapeake's plastic packaging products include bottles, containers, and closures, mainly for companies in the agricultural and specialty chemical and food and beverage industries. Nearly all of Chesapeake's sales come from outside the US; the UK is the company's largest market.

	Annual Growth	12/03	12/04	12/05	12/06	12/07
Sales ($ mil.)	4.2%	899.3	1,031.7	1,042.0	995.4	1,059.6
Net income ($ mil.)	—	26.5	10.9	(314.3)	(39.6)	(15.5)
Market value ($ mil.)	(28.1%)	412.3	532.3	332.8	338.6	110.0
Employees	(9.4%)	—	—	6,129	5,553	—

⊞ CHESAPEAKE ENERGY CORPORATION

NYSE: CHK

6100 N. Western Ave.
Oklahoma City, OK 73118
Phone: 405-848-8000
Fax: 405-843-0573
Web: www.chkenergy.com

CEO: Aubrey K. McClendon
CFO: Marcus C. (Marc) Rowland
HR: Martha A. Burger
FYE: December 31
Type: Public

Chesapeake Energy knows the peaks and valleys of the oil and gas business. The independent exploration and production company concentrates on building natural gas reserves through acquisitions in the US midcontinent region. This region accounts for the vast majority of the company's estimated proved reserves of 10.9 trillion cu. ft. of natural gas equivalent, but Chesapeake also has assets along the Gulf Coast, in the Permian Basin, and in the Ark-La-Tex region. In 2007 it owned 38,500 producing oil and natural gas wells that produce 2.2 billion cu. ft. of natural gas equivalent per day, 92% of which was natural gas.

	Annual Growth	12/03	12/04	12/05	12/06	12/07
Sales ($ mil.)	46.0%	1,717.4	2,709.3	4,665.3	7,325.6	7,800.0
Net income ($ mil.)	46.7%	313.0	515.2	948.3	2,003.3	1,451.0
Market value ($ mil.)	61.5%	2,943.9	5,145.8	11,746.1	13,288.5	20,037.0
Employees	46.6%	—	—	2,885	4,900	6,200

CHESAPEAKE UTILITIES CORPORATION

NYSE: CPK

909 Silver Lake Blvd.
Dover, DE 19904
Phone: 302-734-6799
Fax: 302-734-6750
Web: www.chpk.com

CEO: John R. Schimkaitis
CFO: Michael P. (Mike) McMasters
HR: Richard S. Kalmas
FYE: December 31
Type: Public

Chesapeake Utilities gasses up the Chesapeake Bay, and then some. The company, through its subsidiaries, serves about 33,300 retail propane customers in Delaware, Florida, Maryland, and Virginia. Another subsidiary, Xeron, sells propane at wholesale to distributors, industrial users, and resellers throughout the US. Chesapeake's three natural gas distribution divisions serve 59,100 customers. Chesapeake's interstate pipeline company, Eastern Shore Natural Gas, transmits gas to its parent and other utilities. Through BravePoint, the company also offers data services, consulting, and software development. Other operations include real estate investment.

	Annual Growth	12/03	12/04	12/05	12/06	12/07
Sales ($ mil.)	12.3%	162.3	178.0	229.6	231.2	258.3
Net income ($ mil.)	9.1%	9.3	9.4	10.5	10.5	13.2
Market value ($ mil.)	10.0%	147.5	153.0	181.2	205.0	215.9
Employees	—	—	—	423	—	—

CHESTER BANCORP, INC.

Pink Sheets: CNBA

1112 State St.
Chester, IL 62233
Phone: 618-826-5038
Fax: 618-826-2142
Web: www.chesternationalbank.com

CEO: Michael W. Welge
CFO: Michael W. Welge
HR: –
FYE: December 31
Type: Public

Chester Bancorp didn't grow big and strong eating spinach, like Chester, Illinois, native Popeye the Sailor Man would like you to believe. Instead, the holding company garners strength from its two subsidiary banks, Chester National Bank (formed in 1919) and Chester National Bank of Missouri (founded in 1996). The banks have approximately five branches serving rural southwestern Illinois and southeastern Missouri. They provide standard retail services such as savings, checking, and money market accounts, as well as certificates of deposit. These accounts are typically used to fund residential mortgage loans, and to a lesser extent business, construction, consumer, home equity, and lot loans.

	Annual Growth	12/03	12/04	12/05	12/06	12/07
Est. sales ($ mil.)	—	—	—	—	—	4.0
Employees	—	—	—	—	—	21

CHEVIOT FINANCIAL CORP.

NASDAQ (CM): CHEV

3723 Glenmore Ave.
Cheviot, OH 45211
Phone: 513-661-0457
Fax: 513-389-3312
Web: www.cheviotsavings.com

CEO: Thomas J. Linneman
CFO: Scott T. Smith
HR: –
FYE: December 31
Type: Public

Cheviot Financial happily puts the "buck" into "Buckeye State." It is the holding company for Cheviot Savings Bank, which operates about four branch locations and one lending center in Ohio's Hamilton County, near Cincinnati. The community-oriented state savings and loan offers such traditional deposit products as savings, checking, NOW, and money market accounts. Its loan portfolio is composed largely of residential mortgages (nearly 90% of total loans); construction, consumer, and commercial loans round out its loan book. Cheviot Savings also sells loans into the secondary market. Cheviot Mutual Holding Company owns 55% of Cheviot Financial.

	Annual Growth	12/03	12/04	12/05	12/06	12/07
Assets ($ mil.)	0.1%	317.4	276.6	291.8	309.8	319.1
Net income ($ mil.)	(17.0%)	1.9	1.3	2.2	1.7	0.9
Market value ($ mil.)	(12.0%)	—	125.0	116.0	123.6	85.1
Employees	—	—	—	—	—	—

⊞ An in-depth profile of this company is available to Hoover's Online members at hoovers.com.

367

CHEVRON CORPORATION

NYSE: CVX

6001 Bollinger Canyon Rd.
San Ramon, CA 94583
Phone: 925-842-1000
Fax: 925-842-3530
Web: www.chevron.com

CEO: David J. (Dave) O'Reilly
CFO: Stephen J. (Steve) Crowe
HR: Peter J. Robertson
FYE: December 31
Type: Public

Having added Texaco's star (and subsequently Unocal's authority) to its stripes, Chevron (formerly ChevronTexaco) can pull rank on its rivals. The second-largest US integrated oil company (behind Exxon Mobil) has proved reserves of 10.8 billion barrels of oil equivalent and a daily production of 2.6 million barrels of oil equivalent, and it also owns interests in chemicals, pipelines, and power production businesses. The company, which is restructuring its refinery and retail businesses, owns or has stakes in 9,700 gas stations in the US, which operate under the Chevron and Texaco brands. Outside the US it owns or has stakes in 15,400 gas stations, which also use the Caltex brand.

	Annual Growth	12/03	12/04	12/05	12/06	12/07
Sales ($ mil.)	16.1%	121,761.0	155,300.0	198,200.0	210,118.0	220,904.0
Net income ($ mil.)	26.8%	7,230.0	13,328.0	14,099.0	17,138.0	18,688.0
Market value ($ mil.)	43.4%	46,181.8	110,644.9	126,749.6	159,160.0	195,100.2
Employees	1.4%	61,533	56,000	59,000	62,500	65,000

CHEVRON PHILLIPS CHEMICAL COMPANY LLC

10001 6 Pines Dr.
The Woodlands, TX 77380
Phone: 832-813-4100
Fax: 800-231-3890
Web: www.cpchem.com

CEO: Greg C. Garland
CFO: Greg G. Maxwell
HR: Don F. Kremer
FYE: December 31
Type: Joint venture

A coin toss determined which company's name would go first when Chevron and Phillips Petroleum (now ConocoPhillips) formed 50-50 joint venture Chevron Phillips Chemical Company in 2000. Among the largest US petrochemical firms, the company produces ethylene, propylene, polyethylene, and polypropylene — sometimes used as building blocks for the company's other products such as pipe. Chevron Phillips Chemical also produces aromatics such as benzene and styrene, specialty chemicals such as acetylene black (a form of carbon black), and mining chemicals. The company has several petrochemicals joint ventures in the Middle East, including Saudi Chevron Phillips Company (50%) and Qatar Chemical Company (roughly 50%).

	Annual Growth	12/03	12/04	12/05	12/06	12/07
Sales ($ mil.)	16.6%	7,018.0	9,558.0	11,038.0	11,839.0	12,986.0
Employees	0.2%	5,451	5,300	5,150	5,150	5,500

CHEVY CHASE BANK, F.S.B.

7501 Wisconsin Ave.
Bethesda, MD 20814
Phone: 240-497-4600
Fax: 240-497-4110
Web: www.chevychasebank.com

CEO: B. Francis Saul II
CFO: Stephen R. Halpin
HR: Russ McNish
FYE: September 30
Type: Private

Chevy Chase Bank is ready for prime time. It is one of the largest financial institutions in the greater Washington, DC, area, with a network of more than 250 branches and 1,000 ATMs. The savings bank offers traditional retail services such as checking and savings accounts, CDs, and IRAs, in addition to investment management services, insurance, credit cards, and business and private banking. CEO B. Francis Saul II, who founded the bank in 1969 and also heads retail real estate firm Saul Centers, controls Chevy Chase Bank through various entities.

	Annual Growth	9/02	9/03	9/04	9/05	9/06
Assets ($ mil.)	5.8%	11,285.6	11,795.8	13,287.4	14,261.7	14,158.1
Net income ($ mil.)	8.4%	56.6	79.6	133.7	107.8	78.2
Employees	8.6%	3,900	4,000	—	5,000	—

CHEXAR NETWORKS, INC.

623 Holcomb Bridge Rd.
Roswell, GA 30076
Phone: 770-640-0695
Fax: 678-352-1514
Web: www.nuestra.com

CEO: Drew W. Edwards
CFO: Steven Doctor
HR: −
FYE: December 31
Type: Private

Chexar Networks is undergoing *grande* changes. Formerly Banuestra Financial and before that, El Banco Financial, the company used to own El Banco de Nuestra Communidad, a community-oriented financial institution serving working-class Hispanic residents of the Atlanta area, but sold the business to Georgia-based bank holding company Peoples Holding in 2007. It is now focusing on offering consulting and technology services (including its Conexión El Banco check-cashing services) to banks and other financial institutions that want to tap the growing Latino market. As Banuestra Financial, the company registered for an IPO but scrapped those plans in 2007 because of market conditions.

	Annual Growth	12/03	12/04	12/05	12/06	12/07
Est. sales ($ mil.)	—	—	—	—	—	11.3
Employees	—	—	—	—	—	99

CHF INDUSTRIES, INC.

8701 Red Oak Blvd., Ste. 400
Charlotte, NC 28217
Phone: 704-522-5000
Fax: −
Web: www.chfindustries.com

CEO: Frank Foley
CFO: Camillo Farone
HR: −
FYE: December 31
Type: Private

CHF Industries wants its customers to sleep with the best. It's a manufacturer of fashion bedding and accessories, decorative bathroom items, and window coverings. Brand names in its portfolio include Umbra, Pcri, Donna Karan, and Hello Kitty. CHF has operations in Illinois, Massachusetts, North Carolina, South Carolina, and Texas. Its products are sold to retail stores throughout the US. CHF's Donna Karan Home division makes designer bedding and bath items in conjunction with Donna Karan International.

	Annual Growth	12/03	12/04	12/05	12/06	12/07
Est. sales ($ mil.)	—	—	—	—	—	45.6
Employees	—	—	—	—	—	810

CHG HEALTHCARE SERVICES, INC.

6440 South Millrock Dr., Ste. 175
Salt Lake City, UT 84171
Phone: 801-930-3000
Fax: 801-930-4517
Web: www.chghealthcare.com

CEO: Michael R. Weinholtz
CFO: Sean Dailey
HR: −
FYE: December 31
Type: Private

Medical practices without a doctor in the house look to CHG Healthcare Services to find them one. The company, formerly CompHealth Group, provides locum tenens (physician staffing) services, recruiting physicians in 35 specialties for temporary and permanent assignments at hospitals and medical practices throughout the US. It offers temporary placement of nurses and allied health professionals, including physician's assistants, pharmacists, and radiology technicians. CHG Healthcare operates under the names CompHealth, Weatherby Locums, Destination Healthcare Staffing, Foundation Medical Staffing, and RN Network. In December 2006, investment firm J.W. Childs acquired the company for more than $300 million.

CHICAGO BEARS FOOTBALL CLUB, INC.

1000 Football Dr.	CEO: Ted Phillips
Lake Forest, IL 60045	CFO: Karen Zust
Phone: 847-295-6600	HR: –
Fax: 847-295-8986	FYE: Last day in February
Web: www.chicagobears.com	Type: Private

These Monsters of the Midway have been scaring opponents since the very beginning. Chicago Bears Football Club operates the storied Chicago Bears professional football team, which lays claim to nine National Football League titles (its last in Super Bowl XX at the end of the 1985 season). More than 25 Hall of Fame players have graced the roster of Da Bears, including Red Grange, Dick Butkus, Gale Sayers, and Walter Payton. Loyal Chicago fans root on their team at venerable Soldier Field. The franchise, originally known as the Decatur Staleys, was a charter member of the NFL in 1920. Chairman Michael McCaskey (grandson of founder George "Papa Bear" Halas) and his family control the club.

CHICAGO BOARD OPTIONS EXCHANGE INCORPORATED

400 S. LaSalle St.	CEO: William J. (Bill) Brodsky
Chicago, IL 60605	CFO: Alan J. Dean
Phone: 312-786-5600	HR: Deborah Woods
Fax: 312-786-7409	FYE: June 30
Web: www.cboe.com	Type: Private

First there was one. The Chicago Board Options Exchange (CBOE) may no longer be the *only* options exchange, but it's still the US leader in overall volume. Member-owned and founded in 1973 by the Chicago Board of Trade (which is now part of CME Group), CBOE lists options on more than 1,900 stocks, as well as on interest rates, broad-based stock indexes (such as Standard & Poor's S&P 500 Index), and industry indexes. CBOE, which already launched the fully electronic CBOE Futures Exchange, debuted its CBOE Stock Exchange in early 2007, going head-to-head with the New York Stock Exchange and Nasdaq. CBOE also runs The Options Institute, which trains brokers and investors in all aspects of options.

	Annual Growth	6/03	6/04	6/05	6/06	6/07
Est. sales ($ mil.)	—	—	—	—	—	20.0
Employees	—	—	—	—	—	800

CHICAGO RIVET & MACHINE CO.

AMEX: CVR

901 Frontenac Rd.	CEO: John A. Morrissey
Naperville, IL 60563	CFO: –
Phone: 630-357-8500	HR: –
Fax: 630-983-9314	FYE: December 31
Web: www.chicagorivet.com	Type: Public

Rosie the Riveter might have used rivets made by Chicago Rivet & Machine. The company's main business is making fasteners, including rivets, screw machine products, and cold-formed fasteners. It also makes assembly equipment such as automatic rivet-setting equipment and rivet-working tools, and it leases rivet-setting machines. Chicago Rivet sells its products through internal and independent sales representatives to US automotive and auto parts manufacturers. Major customers include Fisher & Company (accounting for about 30% of the company's sales) and TI Automotive (14% of sales).

	Annual Growth	12/03	12/04	12/05	12/06	12/07
Sales ($ mil.)	(0.3%)	38.2	39.2	39.8	40.4	37.8
Net income ($ mil.)	12.9%	0.8	1.5	(0.4)	1.1	1.3
Market value ($ mil.)	(7.1%)	26.1	26.3	19.3	20.3	19.4
Employees	—	—	—	—	297	—

CHICK-FIL-A, INC.

5200 Buffington Rd.	CEO: Dan T. Cathy
Atlanta, GA 30349	CFO: James B. (Buck) McCabe
Phone: 404-765-8038	HR: Timothy P. (Tim) Tassopoulos
Fax: –	FYE: December 31
Web: www.chick-fil-a.com	Type: Private

Beloved by bovines, Chick-fil-A operates one of the nation's largest fast-food chains that specialize in chicken dishes. Boasting about 1,400 restaurants in almost 40 states, the chain offers chicken entrees, sandwiches, and salads, along with its popular waffle fries and fresh-squeezed lemonade. It is made up primarily of free-standing units that offer drive-through service as well as dine-in seating, but it also has a significant number of mall-based stores. Chick-fil-A also licenses its concept to food service and concessions operators. The chain was started in 1946 by chairman S. Truett Cathy; a devout Baptist, Cathy insists on a policy that all Chick-fil-A restaurants be closed on Sundays.

	Annual Growth	12/02	12/03	12/04	12/05	12/06
Est. sales ($ mil.)	15.2%	—	—	—	1,975.0	2,275.0
Employees		—	—	—	40,924	

CHICO'S FAS, INC.

NYSE: CHS

11215 Metro Pkwy.	CEO: Scott A. Edmonds
Fort Myers, FL 33966	CFO: Kent A. Kleeberger
Phone: 239-277-6200	HR: Manuel O. Jessup
Fax: 239-274-4018	FYE: Saturday nearest January 31
Web: www.chicos.com	Type: Public

Chico's FAS wants to color coordinate its customers with its chic clothes. Once a Mexican folk art shop, Chico's owns and operates more than 1,000 specialty stores in 49 states, the District of Columbia, US Virgin Islands, and Puerto Rico. Its stores are mostly located in enclosed malls and shopping centers under the banners Chico's, White House / Black Market (WH / BM), and Soma. The boutiques target middle-to-high-income women ages 25-40 with clothes made primarily from natural fabrics (cotton, linen, silk). Its casual wear includes tops, pants, shorts, skirts, and dresses, as well as jewelry and other accessories. Chico's was founded in 1983 by ex-chairman Marvin Gralnick and his wife Helene.

	Annual Growth	1/04	1/05	1/06	1/07	1/08
Sales ($ mil.)	22.2%	768.5	1,066.9	1,404.6	1,646.5	1,714.3
Net income ($ mil.)	(2.9%)	100.2	141.2	194.0	166.6	88.9
Employees	19.1%	7,100	8,800	11,000	12,500	14,300

CHIEF CONSOLIDATED MINING COMPANY

Pink Sheets: CFCM

15988 Silver Pass Rd.	CEO: Richard R. Schreiber
Eureka, UT 84628	CFO: Richard R. Schreiber
Phone: 435-433-6606	HR: –
Fax: –	FYE: December 31
Web: www.chiefmines.com	Type: Public

The chief asset of Chief Consolidated Mining is 19,000 acres of land near Eureka, Utah, that the company hopes will yield valuable minerals. The company has been working to develop the Burgin Mine (silver, plus lead and zinc) and the Trixie Mine (gold, silver, and copper). Environmental cleanup obligations associated with earlier mining operations on the property have delayed the company's progress, however. Chief Consolidated Mining also has studied the possibility of developing some of its land for commercial and residential use.

	Annual Growth	12/02	12/03	12/04	12/05	*12/06
Sales ($ mil.)	—	—	—	—	—	0.0
Net income ($ mil.)	—	—	—	—	—	(0.1)
Employees	—	—	—	—	—	—

*Most recent year available

An in-depth profile of this company is available to Hoover's Online members at hoovers.com.

369

CHIEF INDUSTRIES, INC.

3942 W. Old Hwy. 30
Grand Island, NE 68802
Phone: 308-389-7200
Fax: 308-389-7221
Web: www.chiefind.com

CEO: Robert Eihusen
CFO: Linda Berney
HR: –
FYE: June 30
Type: Private

Chief Industries' chief concern is satifying its (primarily agricultural) customers. Through its various divisions, the company makes and distributes grain-drying and storage bins, crop-drying fans, and aeration systems. Its fabrication division manufactures intermodal chassis and custom-metal fabricated parts. Chief Industries even designs and makes programmable message displays used by banks, motels, and shopping centers. Its recreational vehicle division makes RVs under the King of the Road brand name. The building division designs and constructs pre-engineered commercial and industrial buildings to customers' requests.

	Annual Growth	6/03	6/04	6/05	6/06	6/07
Est. sales ($ mil.)	—	—	—	—	—	184.8
Employees	—	—	—	—	—	1,645

CHILDREN'S HEALTHCARE OF ATLANTA

1600 Tullie Cir. NE
Atlanta, GA 30329
Phone: 404-785-7000
Fax: 404-785-7027
Web: www.choa.org

CEO: James E. Tally
CFO: Ruth Fowler
HR: Linda Matzigkeit
FYE: December 31
Type: Not-for-profit

Break your arm tumbling from a Georgia peach tree and you may end up at Children's Healthcare of Atlanta. The hospital system specializes in pediatric care, research, and education. It operates three hospitals (Children's Healthcare of Atlanta at Egleston, Hughes Spalding, and Scottish Rite) and treats more than half a million patients annually. It also operates about 20 health care facilities and contracts with some 1,400 physicians with more than 30 specialties. Children's Healthcare of Atlanta is known for its pediatric services in cardiology, cancer treatment, and neonatal care. Other specialties include orthopedics, rehabilitation, organ transplant, and general surgery.

	Annual Growth	12/03	12/04	12/05	12/06	12/07
Est. sales ($ mil.)	—	—	—	—	—	198.2
Employees	—	—	—	—	—	4,000

CHILDREN'S HOSPITAL BOSTON

300 Longwood Ave.
Boston, MA 02115
Phone: 617-355-6000
Fax: 617-730-1940
Web: www.childrenshospital.org

CEO: James Mandell
CFO: David Kirshner
HR: Inez Stewart
FYE: September 30
Type: Not-for-profit

It has a very dark exterior, but it's trying to lighten up things on the inside by helping the kiddies get better. Children's Hospital Boston is a more than 340-bed hospital that offers pediatric health care services for children from birth to age 21. It is also Harvard Medical School's main teaching hospital for children's health care and the world's largest pediatric research center. Its John F. Enders Pediatric Research facility provides research for the treatment of childhood diseases; the research center began expansion in 2003 to increase its footprint 60%. The hospital was founded in 1869.

	Annual Growth	9/03	9/04	9/05	9/06	9/07
Est. sales ($ mil.)	—	—	—	—	—	11.2
Employees	—	—	—	—	—	311

CHILDRENS HOSPITAL LOS ANGELES

4650 Sunset Blvd.
Los Angeles, CA 90027
Phone: 323-660-2450
Fax: 323-662-2713
Web: www.childrenshospitalla.org

CEO: Richard D. (Rich) Cordova
CFO: DiemLan (Lannie) Tonnu
HR: Charles B. Rooney
FYE: December 31
Type: Not-for-profit

In the City of Angels, many a patient has found an angel of mercy at Childrens Hospital Los Angeles. A pediatric hospital, Childrens Hospital of Los Angeles specializes in the treatment of seriously ill and injured children in and around L.A. County. Nearly 50 percent of its patients are under the age of 4, but its various community sites also provide adolescent medicine. The hospital offers 85 pediatric subspecialties and is affiliated with the Keck School of Medicine of the University of Southern California. It is also home to the Saban Research Institute, the largest pediatric research center in the western US, and operates about 30 outpatient clinics and diagnostic facilities in the Los Angeles area.

	Annual Growth	12/03	12/04	12/05	12/06	12/07
Est. sales ($ mil.)	—	—	—	—	—	457.0
Employees	—	—	—	—	—	3,000

THE CHILDREN'S HOSPITAL OF PHILADELPHIA

34th St. & Civic Center Blvd.
Philadelphia, PA 19104
Phone: 215-590-1000
Fax: –
Web: www.chop.edu

CEO: Steven M. Altschuler
CFO: –
HR: Meg Jones
FYE: June 30
Type: Not-for-profit

In the City of Brotherly Love, sick boys and girls have a place to go to get better. The Children's Hospital of Philadelphia is a leading pediatric hospital with one of the largest pediatric research programs in the world. The nation's first hospital devoted exclusively to the care of children, it has about 430 beds at its primary facility and operates a pediatric health care network with owned or affiliated offices, clinics, and research facilities in Delaware, New Jersey, and Pennsylvania. The hospital has been a leader in formal pediatric medical training, pediatric emergency medicine, and adolescent medicine.

	Annual Growth	6/03	6/04	6/05	6/06	6/07
Est. sales ($ mil.)	—	—	—	—	—	1,000.0
Employees	—	—	—	—	—	7,000

THE CHILDREN'S INTERNET, INC.

OTC: CITCE

110 Ryan Industrial Ct., Ste. 9
San Ramon, CA 94583
Phone: 925-743-9420
Fax: 925-743-9870
Web: www.childrensinternet.com

CEO: Tyler Wheeler
CFO: Tyler Wheeler
HR: –
FYE: December 31
Type: Public

The Children's Internet has a kindler, gentler Internet in mind. The company develops software to restrict access to Web-based content considered inappropriate for children. Its SafeZone technology also regulates e-mail. The company's business plan includes marketing and providing software to the Internet service called The Children's Internet. The service itself is owned by a third party called Two Dog Net. The company has an exclusive license to market The Children's Internet service worldwide, as well as Two Dog Net's wholesale dial-up Internet service.

	Annual Growth	12/03	12/04	12/05	12/06	12/07
Sales ($ mil.)	—	—	—	—	0.0	0.0
Net income ($ mil.)	—	—	—	—	(1.1)	(1.2)
Market value ($ mil.)	162.7%	—	—	—	2.1	5.6
Employees	—	—	—	—	5	—

CHILDREN'S MEDICAL CENTER OF DALLAS

1935 Motor St.
Dallas, TX 75235
Phone: 214-456-7000
Fax: 214-456-2197
Web: www.childrens.com

CEO: Christopher J. Durovich
CFO: Ray Dziesinski
HR: –
FYE: December 31
Type: Not-for-profit

Sick kiddos in northern Texas who need specialized care don't have to travel far to find it. Children's Medical Center of Dallas treats children from birth to age 18 with various medical needs. Specialties include craniofacial deformities, cystic fibrosis, gastroenterology, and heart disease. Children's Medical Center is also a major pediatric transplant center for bone marrow, heart, kidney, and liver. The hospital has some 410 beds and is the pediatric teaching facility for the University of Texas Southwest medical program. Children's Medical Center also operates a network of some 50 outpatient clinics in and around Dallas.

	Annual Growth	12/02	12/03	12/04	12/05	12/06
Sales ($ mil.)	13.1%	354.9	417.6	447.5	514.4	579.9
Employees	—	—	—	—	—	—

CHILDREN'S MEMORIAL HOSPITAL

2300 Children's Plaza
Chicago, IL 60614
Phone: 773-880-4000
Fax: 773-880-3697
Web: www.childrensmemorial.org

CEO: Patrick M. Magoon
CFO: Paula Noble
HR: Barbara Bowman
FYE: August 31
Type: Not-for-profit

Children's Memorial Hospital looks after the kids of Illinois. Founded in 1882, the hospital provides a full range of pediatric services, including acute and specialty care. These services are available at its main hospital campus and outpatient center in Chicago's Lincoln Park neighborhood, as well as through four suburban outpatient centers and nine outreach partner locations in the greater Chicago metropolitan area. Children's Memorial Hospital also operates a pediatric home health care agency and Children's Memorial Research Center, a national leader in pediatric research. Children's Memorial Hospital is the pediatric teaching facility of Northwestern University's Feinberg School of Medicine.

	Annual Growth	8/03	8/04	8/05	8/06	8/07
Est. sales ($ mil.)	—	—	—	—	—	403.0
Employees	—	—	—	—	—	2,800

THE CHILDREN'S MERCY HOSPITAL

2401 Gillham Rd.
Kansas City, MO 64108
Phone: 816-234-3000
Fax: 816-855-1989
Web: www.childrens-mercy.org

CEO: Randall L. O'Donnell
CFO: Sandra A.J. Lawrence
HR: Dan Wright
FYE: June 30
Type: Private

It's *never* a good thing to be at the children's mercy, but The Children's Mercy Hospital is a huge benefit to KC kiddos. The Children's Mercy Hospital offers pediatric health care in various specialties in and around Kansas City, Missouri. Services include home health care, endocrinology, genetics, heart surgery, neonatology, emergency medicine, and rehabilitation. Founded in 1897, the hospital has more than 240 beds. The Children's Mercy health care system also includes outpatient and outreach clinics and research facilities. It is a teaching hospital affiliated with University of Missouri-Kansas City Medical School, University of Kansas, the Stowers Institute, and Midwest Research Institute.

	Annual Growth	6/03	6/04	6/05	6/06	6/07
Est. sales ($ mil.)	—	—	—	—	—	425.9
Employees	—	—	—	—	—	3,000

THE CHILDREN'S PLACE RETAIL STORES, INC.

NASDAQ (GS): PLCE

915 Secaucus Rd.
Secaucus, NJ 07094
Phone: 201-558-2400
Fax: 201-558-2630
Web: www.childrensplace.com

CEO: Charles K. (Chuck) Crovitz
CFO: Richard S. (Rich) Paradise
HR: –
FYE: Saturday nearest January 31
Type: Public

If The Children's Place Retail Stores had a grandma, she'd proclaim, "My, how fast you've grown!" The clothing retailer operates about 900 Children's Place stores, primarily in malls and outlet centers in the US and Canada, and its store count is increasing by double digits. It also sells apparel online. The Children's Place outfits children from newborn to 12 years old in its own brand of apparel and accessories, most of which is produced by manufacturers in Asia. In 2008 the retailer exited the Disney Stores retail business (30% of sales), which it obtained from The Walt Disney Company in 2004. The company has put itself up for sale following a dispute with Disney and the dismissal of its CEO.

	Annual Growth	1/04	1/05	1/06	1/07	1/08
Sales ($ mil.)	28.3%	797.9	1,157.6	1,668.7	2,017.7	2,162.6
Net income ($ mil.)	—	23.0	43.3	65.6	87.4	(59.6)
Market value ($ mil.)	(5.4%)	718.9	1,007.1	1,260.4	1,695.9	576.4
Employees	5.5%	—	—	21,400	25,400	23,800

CHIMERA INVESTMENT CORPORATION

NYSE: CIM

1211 Avenue of the Americas, Ste. 2902
New York, NY 10036
Phone: 212-696-0100
Fax: 212-696-9809

CEO: Matthew Lambiase
CFO: A. Alexandra Denahan
HR: –
FYE: December 31
Type: Public

This Chimera has the body of a mortgage real estate investment trust (REIT), but its head is that of its manager, FIDAC (Fixed Income Discount Advisory Company), a wholly owned subsidiary of Annaly Capital Management. Formed in 2007, the company invests in residential mortgage loans; residential mortgage-backed securities (RMBS), such as those guaranteed by government agencies Fannie Mae and Freddie Mac; real estate-related securities; and various other asset classes, including collateralized debt obligations, or CDOs. The REIT went public in 2007, just as the subprime market went bust.

	Annual Growth	12/03	12/04	12/05	12/06	12/07
Sales ($ mil.)	—	—	—	—	—	3.5
Net income ($ mil.)	—	—	—	—	—	(2.9)
Market value ($ mil.)	—	—	—	—	—	674.2
Employees	—	—	—	—	—	—

CHINA DONGSHENG INTERNATIONAL, INC.

OTC: CDSG

1 University Plaza, Ste. 214
Hackensack, NJ 07601
Phone: 201-525-1221
Fax: 201-525-1511
Web: www.paperclip.com

CEO: Aidong Yu
CFO: Wen Jiang
HR: –
FYE: June 30
Type: Public

China DongSheng International manufactures nutritional supplements and air purifiers. Founded in 1991 as PaperClip Imaging Software, the company's original business was document management software development. After a 2006 reverse merger with American Sunrise International (the holding company of China-based Jilin Dongsheng Weiye Science & Technology Development Co.), the company changed its name to China DongSheng International and shifted its focus to natural health supplements and purifiers. Now generating the majority of its revenues from its new lines, China DongSheng plans to spin off its PaperClip operations.

	Annual Growth	12/02	12/03	12/04	12/05	*6/07
Sales ($ mil.)	117.4%	1.4	1.6	1.4	1.7	31.3
Net income ($ mil.)	172.3%	0.2	0.4	(0.3)	(0.2)	11.0
Market value ($ mil.)	60.8%	21.2	10.9	27.3	15.2	142.0
Employees	—	—	—	—	—	86

*Fiscal year change

An in-depth profile of this company is available to Hoover's Online members at hoovers.com.

371

CHINA HUAREN ORGANIC PRODUCTS, INC.

OTC: CHRN

100 Wall St., 15th Fl.
New York, NY 10005
Phone: 212-232-0120
Fax: –

CEO: Yushu Cao
CFO: Yushu Cao
HR: –
FYE: December 31
Type: Public

China Huaren Organic Products (dba Jilin Huaren) plays in a healthy arena. The company markets organic rice and organic grain products, such as corn-based cakes, wheat biscuits, and rice crackers, as well as grain sugar wafers and powders. It also makes organic nutritional supplements from ginkgo leaves and blue-green algae (spirulina). Jilin Huaren also offers organic cosmetics. All of its product-manufacturing is outsourced. Targeted at the growing urban class in China, Jilin's products are available through a multilevel distribution network, made up of 90 branch companies and 140 specialty stores, all of which are independently owned.

	Annual Growth	12/03	12/04	12/05	12/06	12/07
Sales ($ mil.)	26.4%	2.9	4.0	0.8	2.2	7.4
Net income ($ mil.)	18.9%	0.1	0.3	(5.9)	0.4	0.2
Market value ($ mil.)	—	—	—	—	—	10.3
Employees	49.5%	8	8	8	40	40

CHINA LOGISTICS GROUP, INC.

OTC: CHLO

888 East Las Olas Blvd., Ste. 710
Fort Lauderdale, FL 33301
Phone: 954-527-7780
Fax: 954-527-7772
Web: www.mediareadyinc.com

CEO: V. Jeffrey Harrell
CFO: V. Jeffrey Harrell
HR: –
FYE: December 31
Type: Public

Formerly known as MediaREADY, China Logistics Group offers international freight forwarding services through its 51%-owned Shandong Jiajia International Freight & Forwarding Co. The company serves clients in the shipping industry that want to import or export goods into or out of China. China Logistics also offers logistics management and consulting services. In addition, the company continues to offer products and services related to the distribution of broadband digital content, including its MediaREADY 4000 Internet/DVD player.

	Annual Growth	12/02	12/03	12/04	12/05	*12/06
Sales ($ mil.)	—	0.0	0.0	0.0	0.2	1.2
Net income ($ mil.)	—	(1.0)	(1.9)	(3.0)	(6.7)	(3.4)
Market value ($ mil.)	(70.5%)	—	—	—	878.9	259.6
Employees	—	—	—	—	—	9

*Most recent year available

CHINA NORTH EAST PETROLEUM HOLDINGS, LIMITED

OTC: CNEH

445 Park Ave., 10th Fl.
New York, NY 10022
Phone: 212-307-3568
Fax: 718-685-2650
Web: www.cnepetroleum.com

CEO: Hong Jun Wang
CFO: Yang Zhang
HR: –
FYE: December 31
Type: Public

China North East Petroleum Holdings, through its wholly owned subsidiary Hong Xiang, is engaged in the extraction and production of crude oil. Its current operations are focused on the Jilin Quinan Oil Field, which is located southwest of Quinan City in the Jilin Province of the Peoples Republic of China. The company's major field has an exploration area of more than 20 square kilometers — so far more than 11 kilometers have proved to be oil-bearing. It also has assets in the Hetingbao oil field. China North East Petroleum Holdings has proved reserves of 1.5 million barrels of crude oil equivalent. Large-scale commercial drilling at the Jilin Quinan Oil Field started in 1986.

	Annual Growth	12/02	12/03	12/04	12/05	*12/06
Sales ($ mil.)	—	0.0	0.0	1.4	1.4	2.7
Net income ($ mil.)	—	(0.1)	(0.5)	0.1	(0.7)	0.9
Market value ($ mil.)	83.0%	—	—	—	4.2	7.7
Employees	—	—	—	—	—	—

*Most recent year available

CHINA NUVO SOLAR ENERGY, INC.

OTC: CNUV

319 Clematis St., Ste. 703
West Palm Beach, FL 33401
Phone: 561-514-9042
Fax: –
Web: www.chinanuvosolar.com

CEO: Henry Fong
CFO: Barry S. Hollander
HR: –
FYE: July 31
Type: Public

This company is taking a gamble on solar energy. Formerly game machine manufacturer Interactive Games, China Nuvo Solar Energy is a development-stage company focused on establishing a solar technology manufacturing plant in China. The company holds the rights to a patent for a new type of solar cell that it hopes will offer lower manufacturing costs than current types of silicon-based photovoltaic solar cells. Interactive Games changed its name after acquiring Nuvo Solar Energy in 2007; it is looking to spin off its former gaming business to shareholders.

	Annual Growth	7/02	7/03	7/04	7/05	*7/06
Sales ($ mil.)	0.0%	—	—	—	0.1	0.1
Net income ($ mil.)	—	—	—	—	(0.4)	(1.1)
Market value ($ mil.)	—	—	—	—	—	3.7
Employees	—	—	—	—	6	0

*Most recent year available

CHINA WIRELESS COMMUNICATIONS, INC.

OTC: CWLC

1746 Cole Blvd., Ste. 225
Golden, CO 80401
Phone: 303-277-9968
Fax: 303-484-3794
Web: www.chinawirelesscommunications.com

CEO: Pedro E. (Pete) Racelis III
CFO: Robert Paradine
HR: –
FYE: December 31
Type: Public

China Wireless Communications has covered more ground than the Great Wall. Formerly the operator of a wireless broadband network, the company has shuttered its Internet access and VoIP operations (delivered through subsidiary Beijing In-Touch Communications) and shifted its focus to the information technology (IT) services arena. In 2005 the company acquired a majority ownership in Tianjin Create IT, a systems integration and IT company based in Tianjin, China's third-largest city. The company serves customers in banking and financial services, education, oil and gas, as well as in the government sector.

	Annual Growth	12/02	12/03	12/04	12/05	*12/06
Sales ($ mil.)	66.7%	—	—	—	0.3	0.5
Net income ($ mil.)	—	—	—	—	(2.0)	(3.2)
Employees	(13.3%)	—	—	—	15	13

*Most recent year available

CHINDEX INTERNATIONAL, INC.

NASDAQ (GM): CHDX

7201 Wisconsin Ave.
Bethesda, MD 20814
Phone: 301-215-7777
Fax: 301-215-7719
Web: www.chindex.com

CEO: Roberta Lipson
CFO: Lawrence Pemble
HR: –
FYE: March 31
Type: Public

Chindex International is good at being a go-between. The company provides Western makers of medical equipment and supplies with access to Chinese markets. Its Medical Products division distributes capital medical equipment — such as diagnostic imaging and robotic surgery systems — and other medical products to hospitals in China and Hong Kong. A second division (Healthcare Services) operates United Family Healthcare, a growing network of private hospitals and satellite medical clinics in Shanghai and Beijing. The division's two 50-bed hospitals cater to the expatriate community and to affluent Chinese customers.

	Annual Growth	3/04	3/05	3/06	3/07	3/08
Sales ($ mil.)	10.2%	88.2	100.8	90.8	105.9	130.1
Net income ($ mil.)	—	(2.0)	(5.7)	(2.9)	2.7	3.7
Market value ($ mil.)	91.9%	24.5	23.6	36.1	77.4	332.2
Employees	0.2%	—	1,003	950	1,007	—

An in-depth profile of this company is available to Hoover's Online members at hoovers.com.

CHIPOTLE MEXICAN GRILL, INC. NYSE: CMG

1543 Wazee St., Ste. 200
Denver, CO 80202
Phone: 303-595-4000
Fax: 303-595-4014
Web: www.chipotle.com

CEO: M. Steven (Steve) Ells
CFO: John R. (Jack) Hartung
HR: Ann Dowell
FYE: December 31
Type: Public

This company is spicing up the restaurant business. Chipotle Mexican Grill operates a chain of more than 700 quick-casual Mexican eateries in more than 30 states. Customers can build a 1-1/4 pound burrito or tacos from a lineup that includes chicken, steak, barbecue, or free-range pork, as well as beans, rice, guacamole, and various other veggies and salsas. The company maintains that with extras its menu offers more than 65,000 choices. Chipotle also serves chips and salsa, beer, and margaritas. Many of the eateries can be found in urban retail areas; nearly all of the restaurants are company-owned.

	Annual Growth	12/03	12/04	12/05	12/06	12/07
Sales ($ mil.)	36.2%	315.5	470.7	627.7	822.9	1,085.8
Net income ($ mil.)	—	(7.7)	6.1	37.7	41.4	70.6
Market value ($ mil.)	161.8%	—	—	—	810.7	2,122.4
Employees	20.3%	—	—	13,000	15,000	18,800

CHIQUITA BRANDS INTERNATIONAL, INC. NYSE: CQB

250 E. 5th St.
Cincinnati, OH 45202
Phone: 513-784-8000
Fax: 513-784-8030
Web: www.chiquita.com

CEO: Fernando Aguirre
CFO: Jeffrey M. Zalla
HR: Kevin R. Holland
FYE: December 31
Type: Public

As one of the world's top banana producers, Chiquita Brands International deals in big bunches. The company grows, procures, markets, and distributes bananas and other fresh fruits and vegetables under the premium Chiquita brand and other brands. Its products are sold in some 70 countries worldwide. Bananas account for approximately 43% of Chiquita's total sales and hold a 39% market share in the US. Chiquita's other products include whole citrus fruits, melons, grapes, apples, and tomatoes, as well as fresh-cut items and processed fruit ingredients. The company's Fresh Express unit is the leading seller of packaged salads in North America.

	Annual Growth	12/03	12/04	12/05	12/06	12/07
Sales ($ mil.)	15.6%	2,613.6	3,071.5	3,904.4	4,499.1	4,662.8
Net income ($ mil.)	—	99.2	55.4	131.4	(95.9)	(49.0)
Market value ($ mil.)	(3.4%)	902.0	892.9	839.0	673.2	786.0
Employees	(2.0%)	—	—	25,000	25,000	24,000

CHIRON CORPORATION

4560 Horton St.
Emeryville, CA 94608
Phone: 510-655-8730
Fax: 510-655-9910
Web: www.chiron.com

CEO: Gene W. Walther
CFO: Leone D. Patterson
HR: –
FYE: December 31
Type: Subsidiary

Chiron was a top biotech firm, but it is now a part of Novartis. Before the merger, Chiron covered several areas, including vaccines and drugs, but now it is specializing in developing screening diagnostics for blood supplies. This is nothing new for the company; it was the first to identify the hepatitis B and C viruses. It has already developed blood-testing products to detect HIV and other viruses. Novartis created a new division, Novartis Vaccines & Diagnostics, consisting of two businesses: Novartis Vaccines and a blood diagnostics business that will retain the Chiron name.

	Annual Growth	12/03	12/04	12/05	12/06	12/07
Est. sales ($ mil.)	—	—	—	—	—	707.1
Employees	—	—	—	—	—	5,500

CHOATE CONSTRUCTION COMPANY

8200 Roberts Dr., Ste. 600
Atlanta, GA 30350
Phone: 678-892-1200
Fax: 678-892-1202
Web: www.choateco.com

CEO: William Millard Choate
CFO: David A. Page
HR: Elizabeth Douglass
FYE: December 31
Type: Private

This firm has a Choate-hold on the commercial construction industry in the southeastern US. Choate Construction provides preconstruction, construction, program management, and design/build services from offices in Georgia and North and South Carolina. It builds and renovates a wide variety of commercial facilities, including automotive showrooms, churches and temples, condos, health care facilities, manufacturing plants, offices, recreational facilities, schools, shopping centers, and warehouses. Projects include a dormitory on The University of Georgia-East campus and a Crate & Barrel warehouse in North Carolina. Although the firm focuses on projects in the Southeast, it's licensed to build throughout the US.

CHOICE HOMES, INC.

1600 E. Lamar Blvd.
Arlington, TX 76011
Phone: 817-652-5100
Fax: –
Web: www.choicehomes.com

CEO: Bob Ladd
CFO: Steve Garza
HR: –
FYE: December 31
Type: Private

Choice Homes is the builder of choice primarily for first-time buyers in Texas and Georgia. The builder of affordable single-family homes (and, to a lesser extent, townhomes) is one of the largest home builders in the Dallas/Fort Worth area and one of the top 30 in the country, according to *Builder* magazine. It has built in more than 130 communities in the Lone Star State (concentrated in Amarillo, Dallas/Fort Worth, Houston, and Lubbock) and in Georgia (Atlanta, Athens, and Macon). The company, which began in 1987, builds more than 3,000 homes per year.

CHOICE HOTELS INTERNATIONAL, INC. NYSE: CHH

10750 Columbia Pike
Silver Spring, MD 20901
Phone: 301-592-5000
Fax: 301-592-6157
Web: www.choicehotels.com

CEO: Charles A. Ledsinger Jr.
CFO: David L. White
HR: Thomas L. (Tom) Mirgon
FYE: December 31
Type: Public

This company offers a lot of hospitality choices. Choice Hotels is a leading hotel franchisor with more than 5,500 locations in the US and about 40 other countries. Its flagship brands include Comfort Inn, one of the largest limited-service brands with about 2,400 properties; and Quality Inn, which serves the midscale hotel segment through more than 1,200 locations. Its Econo Lodge chain offers lodging primarily for budget-minded travelers. Other brands include the full-service Clarion chain, Rodeway Inn budget hotels, and Sleep Inn. Chairman Stewart Bainum and his family own nearly 50% of the company.

	Annual Growth	12/03	12/04	12/05	12/06	12/07
Sales ($ mil.)	12.4%	386.1	428.8	477.4	544.7	615.5
Net income ($ mil.)	11.5%	71.9	74.3	87.6	112.8	111.3
Market value ($ mil.)	35.5%	612.4	937.1	2,723.6	2,793.6	2,061.4
Employees	2.5%	—	—	1,728	1,860	1,816

CHOICEONE FINANCIAL SERVICES, INC.

OTC: COFS

109 E. Division St.
Sparta, MI 49345
Phone: 616-887-7366
Fax: 616-887-7990
Web: www.choiceone.com

CEO: James A. (Jim) Bosserd
CFO: Thomas L. (Tom) Lampen
HR: –
FYE: December 31
Type: Public

One choice for a place to park your money is ChoiceOne Financial Services. The financial institution is the holding company for ChoiceOne Bank, which has about five offices in the western part of Michigan's Lower Peninsula. The bank serves consumers and area businesses, offering checking and savings accounts, CDs, investment planning, and other services. Real estate loans, including business and consumer, constitute more than 50% of its loan portfolio. Commercial and industrial loans make up some 35%. ChoiceOne Financial Services also owns insurance agency ChoiceOne Insurance and ChoiceOne Mortgage, which originates residential mortgages.

	Annual Growth	12/03	12/04	12/05	12/06	12/07
Assets ($ mil.)	21.5%	215.5	232.3	248.1	466.6	470.2
Net income ($ mil.)	14.4%	2.1	1.9	2.2	2.1	3.6
Market value ($ mil.)	12.3%	25.4	34.4	30.5	57.5	40.4
Employees	16.0%	—	80	79	—	125

CHOICEPOINT INC.

NYSE: CPS

1000 Alderman Dr.
Alpharetta, GA 30005
Phone: 770-752-6000
Fax: 770-752-6005
Web: www.choicepointinc.com

CEO: Derek V. Smith
CFO: David E. Trine
HR: Suzanne H. Detlefts
FYE: December 31
Type: Public

ChoicePoint wants its customers to be able to make informed decisions. The company provides risk management and fraud prevention information, primarily to the insurance industry. Its insurance services division provides such underwriting and claims information as motor vehicle reports, claims histories, customized policy rating and issuance software, and property inspections and audits. ChoicePoint's screening and authentication services include pre-employment drug screening, credential verification, and background checks. The company has over 5,000 employees serving more than 50,000 customers. ChoicePoint has agreed to be acquired by publishing firm Reed Elsevier in a $4.1 billion deal.

	Annual Growth	12/03	12/04	12/05	12/06	12/07
Sales ($ mil.)	5.4%	795.8	918.7	1,057.9	1,055.0	982.0
Net income ($ mil.)	(30.9%)	142.0	148.0	140.7	16.9	32.4
Market value ($ mil.)	(6.7%)	3,296.9	4,057.8	3,855.8	2,994.7	2,493.4
Employees	(3.1%)	—	—	5,325	5,250	5,000

CHORDIANT SOFTWARE, INC.

NASDAQ (GM): CHRD

20400 Stevens Creek Blvd., Ste. 400
Cupertino, CA 95014
Phone: 408-517-6100
Fax: 408-517-0270
Web: www.chordiant.com

CEO: Steven R. Springsteel
CFO: Peter S. (Pete) Norman
HR: Jack Landers
FYE: September 30
Type: Public

Chordiant Software helps you strike a collaborative chord with customers. The company develops customer relationship management (CRM) software that links call centers, computer networks, databases, and the Internet, allowing departments and employees to share data, collaborate on projects, and retain customers while lowering their operational costs. Chordiant's other applications automate complex marketing campaigns, analyze consumer information, and provide interfaces between customers and employees. The company also offers consulting, customer support, and other services. Clients have included Barclays Bank, British Sky Broadcasting, and Canadian Imperial Bank of Commerce.

	Annual Growth	12/02	12/03	*9/05	9/06	9/07
Sales ($ mil.)	14.0%	73.8	68.3	83.7	97.5	124.6
Net income ($ mil.)	—	(32.3)	(16.4)	(19.5)	(16.0)	6.0
Market value ($ mil.)	56.6%	76.6	353.0	223.7	245.8	460.4
Employees	(3.5%)	328	—	280	325	285

*Fiscal year change

CHRISTOPHER & BANKS CORPORATION

NYSE: CBK

2400 Xenium Ln. North
Plymouth, MN 55441
Phone: 763-551-5000
Fax: 763-551-5198
Web: www.christopherandbanks.com

CEO: Lorna E. Nagler
CFO: Andrew K. Moller
HR: Kip Sassman
FYE: Saturday nearest last day in February
Type: Public

Christopher & Banks is getting pretty big for its britches. Largely mall-based, the retailer sells moderately priced private-label women's fashions. Some 850 stores cover 46 states and operate as Christopher & Banks, C.J. Banks, and Acorn shops (acquired in 2004). The Christopher & Banks and C.J. Banks brands also operate their own e-commerce sites. Sportswear accounts for about 80% of overall sales; the rest comes from sweaters and accessories. Christopher & Banks is betting big on expansion — especially in the plus-size market. Its 260-plus C.J. Banks stores offer specialty apparel in sizes 14W and up. The three chains cater to working women 40 to 60 years old with above average incomes.

	Annual Growth	2/04	2/05	2/06	2/07	2/08
Sales ($ mil.)	10.2%	390.7	438.9	490.5	547.3	575.8
Net income ($ mil.)	(18.9%)	39.3	27.0	30.4	33.7	17.0
Market value ($ mil.)	(14.1%)	699.0	592.9	761.4	651.5	380.8
Employees	10.7%	5,200	6,000	6,600	6,900	7,800

CHRISTUS HEALTH

Las Colinas Corporate Center II, 6363 N. Hwy. 161, Ste. 450
Irving, TX 75038
Phone: 214-492-8500
Fax: 214-492-8540
Web: www.christushealth.org

CEO: Thomas C. (Tom) Royer
CFO: Jay Herron
HR: Mary Lynch
FYE: June 30
Type: Not-for-profit

CHRISTUS has plenty to be merry about. The Catholic health care system operates more than 40 hospitals, including general hospitals and long-term acute care facilities (the latter under the Dubuis name). The majority of its operations are in Louisiana and Texas, but the organization also has facilities in Arkansas, Georgia, Missouri, and Utah in the US and in several states in Mexico. In addition to its acute care facilities, CHRISTUS Health runs outpatient centers, medical groups, home health and hospice agencies, and senior living facilities. Specialized services include oncology, pediatrics, rehabilitation, and women's and children's health care.

	Annual Growth	6/03	6/04	6/05	6/06	6/07
Est. sales ($ mil.)	—	—	—	—	—	2,147.5
Employees	—	—	—	—	—	25,000

CHROMALOX, INC.

103 Gamma Dr.
Pittsburgh, PA 15238
Phone: 412-967-3800
Fax: 412-967-5148
Web: www.chromalox.com

CEO: Steve Brian
CFO: –
HR: –
FYE: December 31
Type: Private

Chromalox is not part of a limerick, but its switches and electrical products are quite orthodox. The company, once a part of Emerson Electric, makes switches and electrical components for heaters, grills, hot plates, defrosters, water heaters, and other products. Its equipment has been used aboard the Space Shuttle, and on earth in the biopharmaceutical, food services, petrochemical, and power generation industries. Chromalox was founded in 1917 by inventor Edwin L. Wiegand. The company's first product was a flat-iron heating element. In 2001 Emerson sold Chromalox to an investor group led by JPMorgan Partners (now CCMP Capital Advisors) for $165 million, after owning the company for 33 years.

	Annual Growth	12/03	12/04	12/05	12/06	12/07
Est. sales ($ mil.)	—	—	—	—	—	146.4
Employees	—	—	—	—	—	1,450

An in-depth profile of this company is available to Hoover's Online members at hoovers.com.

CHROMCRAFT REVINGTON, INC.

AMEX: CRC

1330 Win Hentschel Blvd., Ste. 250
West Lafayette, IN 47906
Phone: 765-807-2640
Fax: 765-564-3722

CEO: Benjamin M. (Ben) Anderson-Ray
CFO: Frank T. Kane
HR: Anna Talbert
FYE: December 31
Type: Public

It's not hard to get an appointment with Chromcraft Revington — in fact, the company is happy to appoint you with home or office furniture. Under the Peters-Revington name, it sells mid-priced wood furniture such as bookcases, tables, and home office pieces. Its dining and commercial furniture (office chairs, conference tables) are sold under the Chromcraft name. Its Cochrane Furniture and Sumter Cabinet lines include bedroom and dining furniture, as well as upholstered sofas and ottomans. Occasional tables and entertainment centers are sold under the Silver Furniture name. Chromcraft Revington sells through US and Canadian retailers.

	Annual Growth	12/03	12/04	12/05	12/06	12/07
Sales ($ mil.)	(9.5%)	184.2	172.4	169.6	160.5	123.4
Net income ($ mil.)	—	8.1	7.7	7.2	(3.4)	(14.9)
Market value ($ mil.)	(18.7%)	67.7	73.7	80.5	53.0	29.6
Employees	—	—	—	—	1,400	—	—

CHRYSLER LLC

1000 Chrysler Dr.
Auburn Hills, MI 48326
Phone: 248-576-5741
Fax: –
Web: www.chryslerllc.com

CEO: Robert L. (Bob) Nardelli
CFO: Ronald E. Kolka
HR: John S. Franciosi
FYE: December 31
Type: Private

The divorce is final: Daimler got the Mercedes and Chrysler got the minivan. After almost a decade of trying to make the most audacious merger in automotive history work, DaimlerChrysler is now Daimler and Chrysler. In 2007 private equity concern Cerberus Capital Management bought Chrysler for about $7.4 billion — or about one-fifth of the $37 billion Daimler paid in 1998. In addition to its eponymous Chrysler brand, the company also controls the Dodge and Jeep marques. Specific models include Chrysler 300, Dodge Ram pickups, and Jeep Grand Cherokee. The company offers financing to both consumers and dealers through Chrysler Financial Services LLC.

	Annual Growth	12/03	12/04	12/05	12/06	12/07
Sales ($ mil.)	(10.1%)	—	67,515.3	59,354.7	62,160.1	49,000.0
Employees	(7.4%)	—	—	—	77,778	72,000

CHS INC.

NASDAQ (GS): CHSCP

5500 Cenex Dr.
Inver Grove Heights, MN 55077
Phone: 651-355-6000
Fax: –
Web: www.chsinc.com

CEO: John D. Johnson
CFO: John Schmitz
HR: –
FYE: August 31
Type: Public

CHS goes with the grain. As a leading US cooperative marketer of grain and oilseed, CHS represents farmers, ranchers, and cooperatives from the Great Lakes to the Pacific Northwest and from the Canadian border to Texas. CHS trades grain and sells supplies to members through its stores. It also processes soybeans for use in food and animal feeds. CHS grinds wheat into flour used in pastas and bread. Through joint ventures, the company sells soybean oil and crop nutrient and protection products, and markets grain. In addition, CHS provides insurance and financial and risk management services, and operates petroleum refineries, marketing Cenex brand fuels, lubricants, and energy products.

	Annual Growth	8/03	8/04	8/05	8/06	8/07
Sales ($ mil.)	16.3%	9,398.5	11,050.6	11,941.1	14,383.8	17,216.0
Net income ($ mil.)	56.9%	123.8	221.3	250.0	490.3	750.3
Market value ($ mil.)	12.2%	116.4	135.6	132.7	154.2	184.6
Employees	0.2%	6,820	6,800	6,370	6,540	6,885

THE CHUBB CORPORATION

NYSE: CB

15 Mountain View Rd.
Warren, NJ 07059
Phone: 908-903-2000
Fax: 908-903-2027
Web: www.chubb.com

CEO: John D. Finnegan
CFO: Michael O'Reilly
HR: –
FYE: December 31
Type: Public

Here's the skinny on Chubb: The insurer is best known for comprehensive homeowners insurance for the demographic that owns yachts (the company insures those, too). Chubb also offers commercial property/casualty insurance including multiple peril, property and marine, and worker's compensation. Its specialty insurance arm offers professional liability policies for executives across a spectrum of industries and also provides construction and commercial surety bonds. Chubb distributes its products through independent agents and brokers in the US and overseas.

	Annual Growth	12/03	12/04	12/05	12/06	12/07
Assets ($ mil.)	7.2%	38,360.6	44,260.3	48,060.7	50,277.0	50,574.0
Net income ($ mil.)	36.5%	808.8	1,548.4	1,825.9	2,528.0	2,807.0
Market value ($ mil.)	33.7%	6,400.2	7,408.4	10,206.3	21,760.7	20,448.4
Employees	(0.9%)	—	—	10,800	10,800	10,600

CHURCH & DWIGHT CO., INC.

NYSE: CHD

469 N. Harrison St.
Princeton, NJ 08543
Phone: 609-683-5900
Fax: 609-497-7269
Web: www.churchdwight.com

CEO: James R. (Jim) Craigie
CFO: Matthew T. Farrell
HR: Jacquelin J. (Jackie) Brova
FYE: December 31
Type: Public

Whether you call it saleratus (aerated salt), sodium bicarbonate, or plain old baking soda, Church & Dwight is the world's #1 maker of the powder. Church & Dwight's ARM & HAMMER baking soda is used as a deodorizer, a cleaner, a swimming pool pH stabilizer, and as leavening. The firm makes laundry detergent, bathroom cleaners, cat litter, carpet deodorizer, air fresheners, toothpaste, and antiperspirants. Church & Dwight also makes Brillo scouring pads, Trojan condoms, and industrial-grade carbonates. Its purchase of Carter-Wallace's consumer products units (alongside Kelso & Company) gave it Arrid antiperspirant and Lambert Kay brands. It also bought Procter & Gamble's SpinBrush unit for $75 million.

	Annual Growth	12/03	12/04	12/05	12/06	12/07
Sales ($ mil.)	20.4%	1,056.9	1,462.1	1,736.5	1,945.7	2,220.9
Net income ($ mil.)	20.2%	81.0	88.8	122.9	138.9	169.0
Market value ($ mil.)	35.1%	1,076.8	2,124.4	2,126.8	2,787.7	3,581.8
Employees	0.0%	—	—	3,700	3,700	3,700

CHURCHILL DOWNS INCORPORATED

NASDAQ (GS): CHDN

700 Central Ave.
Louisville, KY 40208
Phone: 502-636-4400
Fax: –
Web: www.churchilldownsincorporated.com

CEO: Robert L. (Bob) Evans
CFO: William E. (Bill) Mudd
HR: Charles G. (Chuck) Kenyon
FYE: December 31
Type: Public

You might say this company has put its money on the sport of champions to win. Churchill Downs is the leading operator of horse racing tracks in the US, with four major race courses including its namesake track that hosts the world famous Kentucky Derby. Its other tracks include Arlington Park (Illinois), Calder Race Course (Florida), and Fair Grounds Race Course (Louisiana). In addition to live horse racing, Churchill Downs operates a number of simulcast networks and off-track betting facilities, as well as a wagering deposit service (TwinSpires) that allows punters to place bets online. Richard Duchossois, who controls diversified holding company Duchossois Industries, owns about 25% of the company.

	Annual Growth	12/03	12/04	12/05	12/06	12/07
Sales ($ mil.)	(1.9%)	444.1	463.1	408.8	376.7	410.7
Net income ($ mil.)	(9.5%)	23.4	8.9	78.9	29.8	15.7
Market value ($ mil.)	11.2%	481.9	576.8	482.3	573.6	737.9
Employees	—	—	—	2,550	—	—

An in-depth profile of this company is available to Hoover's Online members at hoovers.com.

375

CHYRON CORPORATION

OTC: CYRO

5 Hub Dr.
Melville, NY 11747
Phone: 631-845-2000
Fax: 631-845-3895
Web: www.chyron.com

CEO: Michael I. Wellesley-Wesley
CFO: Jerry Kieliszak
HR: –
FYE: December 31
Type: Public

Chyron wants customers to stay tuned. The company makes software and hardware for enhancing live and pre-recorded television broadcasts with special effects and animation. Chyron's Windows-based products let journalists and producers create logos, text, and other images that can be superimposed over existing images to display sports scores, stock tickers, and weather information. Chyron's clients include ABC, ESPN, FOX News, CNN, and the BBC. In addition to broadcasters, the company markets to post-production facilities, government agencies, schools, health care providers, religious institutions, and telecom service providers.

	Annual Growth	12/03	12/04	12/05	12/06	12/07
Sales ($ mil.)	13.6%	19.4	23.2	25.1	26.3	32.3
Net income ($ mil.)	—	(0.4)	0.3	0.7	3.1	3.7
Market value ($ mil.)	21.9%	37.8	59.5	75.7	163.0	83.4
Employees	—	—	—	—	—	—

CIB MARINE BANCSHARES, INC.

Pink Sheets: CIBH

N27 W24025 Paul Ct.
Pewaukee, WI 53072
Phone: 262-695-6010
Fax: 262-695-6014
Web: www.cibmarine.com

CEO: John P. Hickey
CFO: Edwin J. Depenbrok
HR: –
FYE: December 31
Type: Public

CIB Marine Bancshares is *semper fi* to its banking strategy. The company owns Central Illinois Bank, southeastern Florida's Citrus Bank, and Marine Bank, which operates in the Milwaukee and Phoenix markets. Through some 25 branches overall, the company targets individuals and small- and midsized business customers, offering checking and savings accounts, ATM and debit cards, CDs, and IRAs. CIB Marine's loan portfolio mainly consists of commercial mortgages, business loans, and commercial real estate construction loans. The company is selling Citrus Bank to Florida-based holding company 1st United Bancorp.

	Annual Growth	12/03	12/04	12/05	12/06	12/07
Assets ($ mil.)	(25.0%)	3,186.2	1,385.9	1,138.4	997.6	1,005.8
Net income ($ mil.)	—	(137.6)	(17.4)	(11.7)	(9.3)	(13.8)
Employees	—	—	—	—	—	—

CIBA VISION CORPORATION

11460 Johns Creek Pkwy.
Duluth, GA 30097
Phone: 678-415-3937
Fax: 678-415-3001
Web: www.cibavision.com

CEO: Andrea Saia
CFO: John McKenna
HR: Martin Filippides
FYE: December 31
Type: Subsidiary

CIBA Vision is the eye care unit of Novartis. The company provides research and development and manufactures eyeglasses and contacts. CIBA Vision also offers lens care and ophthalmic surgical products and related services to customers in more than 70 countries. Its contact lens brands include AIR OPTIX, NIGHT & DAY, and Focus DAILIES. In 2005 CIBA Vision sold a couple of its soft contact lens lines — Aquaflex and Softcon — to a unit of Unilens Vision, which, as part of the agreement, pays CIBA Vision a royalty on certain sales for five years. CIBA Vision was established in 1980 by Ciba-Geigy, which merged with Sandoz in 1996 to form Novartis.

CIBER, INC.

NYSE: CBR

5251 DTC Pkwy., Ste. 1400
Greenwood Village, CO 80111
Phone: 303-220-0100
Fax: 303-220-7100
Web: www.ciber.com

CEO: Mac J. Slingerlend
CFO: Peter H. Cheesbrough
HR: David (Dave) Plisko
FYE: December 31
Type: Public

CIBER helps its customers take control of information. The company is an information technology (IT) consultancy that provides enterprise systems integration through consulting practices specializing in such software systems as Oracle, Lawson, PeopleSoft, and SAP, as well as custom software development. In addition, CIBER offers a number of support services including call center and help desk operations, data hosting, and maintenance. It serves a number of federal, state, and local government agencies and commercial customers in such industries as manufacturing, finance, and telecommunications.

	Annual Growth	12/03	12/04	12/05	12/06	12/07
Sales ($ mil.)	11.8%	692.0	843.0	956.0	995.8	1,082.0
Net income ($ mil.)	9.7%	20.0	29.7	24.7	24.7	29.0
Market value ($ mil.)	(7.5%)	507.5	602.9	409.5	418.7	371.2
Employees	2.5%	—	—	8,000	8,300	8,400

CICERO, INC.

OTC: CICN

8000 Regency Pkwy., Ste. 542
Cary, NC 27518
Phone: 919-380-5000
Fax: 919-380-5121
Web: www.level8.com

CEO: John P. Broderick
CFO: John P. Broderick
HR: –
FYE: December 31
Type: Public

Cicero takes a philosophical approach to integrating your applications. The company provides application integration software used to link a variety of enterprise applications (including mainframe, client/server, and Web-based environments), primarily for financial services firms. The company also provides services such as consulting, project management, and training. Customers have included Merrill Lynch and Bank of America. Investors Mark and Carolyn P. Landis control about 25% of the company.

	Annual Growth	12/03	12/04	12/05	12/06	12/07
Sales ($ mil.)	37.7%	0.5	0.8	0.8	1.0	1.8
Net income ($ mil.)	—	(10.0)	(9.8)	(3.7)	(3.0)	(2.0)
Employees	(10.0%)	32	29	20	18	21

CIENA CORPORATION

NASDAQ (GS): CIEN

1201 Winterson Rd.
Linthicum, MD 21090
Phone: 410-865-8500
Fax: 410-694-5750
Web: www.ciena.com

CEO: Gary B. Smith
CFO: James E. (Jim) Moylan Jr.
HR: Lynn Moore
FYE: October 31
Type: Public

Ciena doesn't limit itself to just one color of the spectrum. The company makes transport and switching equipment that increases the capacity of long-distance fiber-optic networks by transmitting multiple light signals simultaneously over the same circuit. It also sells transport systems for metro and enterprise wide-area networks, as well as broadband access products that enable communications companies to deliver Internet protocol (IP) services, such as Voice over IP (VoIP), IP video, and DSL. Ciena serves telecom service providers, cable companies, large enterprises, and government entities.

	Annual Growth	10/03	10/04	10/05	10/06	10/07
Sales ($ mil.)	28.8%	283.1	298.7	427.3	564.1	779.8
Net income ($ mil.)	—	(386.5)	(789.5)	(435.7)	0.6	82.8
Market value ($ mil.)	8.2%	3,033.3	1,412.0	1,375.4	1,995.8	4,152.0
Employees	9.6%	—	—	1,497	1,485	1,797

An in-depth profile of this company is available to Hoover's Online members at hoovers.com.

CIGNA CORPORATION
NYSE: CI

2 Liberty Place, 1601 Chestnut St.	CEO: H. Edward Hanway
Philadelphia, PA 19192	CFO: Michael W. (Mike) Bell
Phone: 215-761-1000	HR: John M. Murabito
Fax: 215-761-5515	FYE: December 31
Web: www.cigna.com	Type: Public

One of the top US health insurers, CIGNA covers more than 10 million people with its various medical plans, which include PPO, HMO, point-of-service (POS), indemnity, and consumer-directed products. CIGNA also offers specialty health coverage in the form of dental, vision, pharmacy, and behavioral health plans; and it sells group accident, life, and disability insurance. Its customers include employers, government entities, unions, Medicare recipients, and other individuals in the US and Canada. Internationally, the company sells life, accident, and supplemental health insurance in parts of Asia and the European Union, and it provides health coverage to expatriate employees of multinational companies.

	Annual Growth	12/03	12/04	12/05	12/06	12/07
Sales ($ mil.)	(1.6%)	18,808.0	18,176.0	16,684.0	16,547.0	17,623.0
Net income ($ mil.)	14.4%	650.0	1,438.0	1,625.0	1,155.0	1,115.0
Market value ($ mil.)	29.9%	5,270.9	3,589.3	4,512.3	4,326.7	15,022.3
Employees	(9.8%)	—	—	32,700	27,100	26,600

CIMAREX ENERGY CO.
NYSE: XEC

1700 Lincoln St., Ste. 1800	CEO: F. H. Merelli
Denver, CO 80203	CFO: Paul J. Korus
Phone: 303-295-3995	HR: Richard S. Dinkins
Fax: 303-295-3494	FYE: December 31
Web: www.cimarex.com	Type: Public

Cimarex Energy's energy is devoted to oil and gas exploration and production. The company was formed by the spinoff of a unit of contract driller Helmerich & Payne's Cimarex Energy subsidiary and that unit's consequent acquisition of oil and gas explorer Key Production. Cimarex Energy is focusing its operations on the Midcontinent, Gulf Coast, Permian Basin, and Gulf of Mexico. The company has proved reserves of about 1.1 trillion cu. ft. of natural gas and 58.3 million barrels of oil and natural gas liquids. Cimarex Energy participated in drilling 452 gross wells during 2007.

	Annual Growth	12/03	12/04	12/05	12/06	12/07
Sales ($ mil.)	33.2%	454.2	674.9	1,118.6	1,267.1	1,431.2
Net income ($ mil.)	38.3%	94.6	153.6	328.3	345.7	346.5
Market value ($ mil.)	33.8%	1,096.0	1,581.5	3,543.1	3,025.2	3,510.5
Employees	5.0%	—	—	689	734	760

CINCINNATI BELL INC.
NYSE: CBB

221 E. 4th St.	CEO: John F. (Jack) Cassidy
Cincinnati, OH 45202	CFO: Brian A. Ross
Phone: 513-397-9900	HR: Brian G. Keating
Fax: 513-397-5092	FYE: December 31
Web: www.cincinnatibell.com	Type: Public

Cincinnati Bell rings for Bengals and Bearcats, Musketeers, and even the Reds. The company provides local phone services through its Cincinnati Bell Telephone subsidiary to customers in southwestern Ohio, northern Kentucky, and southeastern Indiana. It has been the incumbent local-exchange carrier (ILEC) for greater Cincinnati since the 1870s and has expanded through the competitive local-exchange carrier (CLEC) operations of Cincinnati Bell Extended Territories to regions that include Dayton and Mason, Ohio. It has more than 800,000 access lines in service. Cincinnati Bell also offers regional wireless voice and data communications to more than 500,000 customers through Cincinnati Bell Wireless.

	Annual Growth	12/03	12/04	12/05	12/06	12/07
Sales ($ mil.)	(3.5%)	1,557.8	1,207.1	1,209.6	1,270.1	1,348.6
Net income ($ mil.)	(51.6%)	1,331.9	64.2	(64.5)	86.3	73.2
Market value ($ mil.)	(1.1%)	1,235.0	1,018.4	867.5	1,130.9	1,179.7
Employees	3.4%	—	—	2,900	2,950	3,100

CINCINNATI CHILDREN'S HOSPITAL MEDICAL CENTER

3333 Burnet Ave.	CEO: James M. Anderson
Cincinnati, OH 45229	CFO: –
Phone: 513-636-4200	HR: Ronald B. McKinley
Fax: 513-636-2460	FYE: June 30
Web: www.cincinnatichildrens.org	Type: Not-for-profit

Cincinnati Children's Hospital Medical Center has a special place in its heart for kids — and possibly vice versa. The pediatric health care facility offers expert care and innovative treatments in heart, liver, hematology, and oncology. Cincinnati Children's Hospital has 475 beds and operates nearly a dozen outpatient care centers. The not-for-profit hospital also serves as a Level 1 pediatric trauma center for southwestern Ohio, northern Kentucky, and southeastern Indiana. It also serves as a teaching facility for the University of Cincinnati College of Medicine. The Cincinnati Children's Research Foundation seeks new treatments for a variety of childhood diseases.

	Annual Growth	6/03	6/04	6/05	6/06	6/07
Est. sales ($ mil.)	—	—	—	—	—	912.5
Employees	—	—	—	—	—	7,700

CINCINNATI FINANCIAL CORPORATION
NASDAQ (GS): CINF

6200 S. Gilmore Rd.	CEO: John J. Schiff Jr.
Fairfield, OH 45014	CFO: Kenneth W. Stecher
Phone: 513-870-2000	HR: Greg Ziegler
Fax: 513-870-2911	FYE: December 31
Web: www.cinfin.com	Type: Public

At Skyline Chili in Cincinnati you can order your chili 3-way, 4-way, or 5-way; at Cincinnati Financial Corporation (CFC) you can order your insurance with plenty of extras as well. The company's flagship Cincinnati Insurance (with subsidiaries Cincinnati Casualty and Cincinnati Indemnity) sells commercial property, liability, auto, bond, and fire insurance; personal lines include homeowners, auto, and liability products. Cincinnati Life sells life, disability income, and annuities. The company's CFC Investment subsidiary provides commercial financing, leasing, and real estate services, and its CinFin Capital Management provides asset management services to businesses, institutions, and not-for-profits.

	Annual Growth	12/03	12/04	12/05	12/06	12/07
Assets ($ mil.)	1.8%	15,509.0	16,107.0	16,003.0	17,222.0	16,637.0
Net income ($ mil.)	23.0%	374.0	584.0	602.0	930.0	855.0
Market value ($ mil.)	2.0%	6,058.9	7,039.4	7,779.1	7,838.6	6,563.6
Employees	1.6%	—	—	3,983	4,048	—

CINCOM SYSTEMS, INC.

55 Merchant St.	CEO: Thomas M. (Tom) Nies
Cincinnati, OH 45246	CFO: Gerald L. Shawhan
Phone: 513-612-2769	HR: –
Fax: 513-612-2000	FYE: September 30
Web: www.cincom.com	Type: Private

When it comes to providing software, Cincom Systems' only sin is longevity. Since 1968, the company has developed tools for manufacturing, financial, and sales automation applications. Its software manages application development, customer support, database, call center, and manufacturing functions. Cincom sells worldwide to such customers as Coca-Cola, IBM, and Sharp. The company has used selective acquisitions to expand its offerings, including Grovewood Financial Management, a provider of financial advisory services. Thomas Nies has been CEO and owner of Cincom since he founded the company; his tenure as CEO is one of the longest in the software industry.

	Annual Growth	9/03	9/04	9/05	9/06	9/07
Est. sales ($ mil.)	—	—	—	—	—	77.3
Employees	—	—	—	—	—	900

An in-depth profile of this company is available to Hoover's Online members at hoovers.com.

377

CINEMARK HOLDINGS, INC.

NYSE: CNK

3900 Dallas Pkwy., Ste. 500
Plano, TX 75093
Phone: 972-665-1000
Fax: 972-665-1004
Web: www.cinemark.com

CEO: Alan W. Stock
CFO: Robert D. Copple
HR: –
FYE: December 31
Type: Public

Cinemark Holdings has left its mark on the cinema landscape. The third-largest movie exhibitor in the US (following Regal Entertainment and AMC) has more than 4,500 screens in some 400 theatres in the US, Canada, and Latin America. Cinemark operates its multiplex theaters in smaller cities and suburban areas of major metropolitan markets. Some larger theaters operate under the Tinseltown name; others are "discount" theaters showing no first-run films. The company prefers to build new theaters in midsized markets or in suburbs of major cities where the Cinemark theater is the only game in town. In early 2007 Cinemark filed to go public.

	Annual Growth	12/03	12/04	12/05	12/06	12/07
Sales ($ mil.)	15.1%	957.6	1,024.2	1,020.6	1,220.6	1,682.8
Net income ($ mil.)	18.8%	44.7	(14.3)	(25.4)	0.8	88.9
Market value ($ mil.)	—	—	—	—	—	1,818.7
Employees	2.3%	12,700	13,200	—	13,600	—

CINTAS CORPORATION

NASDAQ (GS): CTAS

6800 Cintas Blvd.
Cincinnati, OH 45262
Phone: 513-459-1200
Fax: 513-573-4130
Web: www.cintas.com

CEO: Scott D. Farmer
CFO: William C. Gale
HR: Michael A. Womack
FYE: May 31
Type: Public

If Cintas had its way, you'd never agonize over what to wear to work. The #1 uniform supplier in the US, the firm has about 800,000 clients (Delta Air Lines, DHL) and some 5 million people wear its garb each day. Cintas, which sells, leases, and rents uniforms, operates 415 facilities across the US and Canada; it leases half of them. In addition to offering shirts, jackets, slacks, and footwear, the company provides cleanroom apparel and flame resistant clothing. Other products offered by Cintas include uniform cleaning, first aid and safety products, document handling/storage, and cleanroom supplies. Cintas chairman and founder Richard T. Farmer owns nearly 14% of the company. His son Scott runs the business.

	Annual Growth	5/03	5/04	5/05	5/06	5/07
Sales ($ mil.)	8.4%	2,686.6	2,814.1	3,067.3	3,403.6	3,706.9
Net income ($ mil.)	7.6%	249.3	272.2	300.5	327.2	334.5
Market value ($ mil.)	(0.9%)	6,315.6	7,768.6	6,889.5	6,912.4	6,086.8
Employees	6.3%	—	—	—	32,000	34,000

CIPRICO INC.

NASDAQ (GM): CPCI

7003 W. Lake St., Ste. 400
St. Louis Park, MN 55426
Phone: 952-540-2400
Fax: 952-540-2402
Web: www.ciprico.com

CEO: Steven D. Merrifield
CFO: Monte S. Johnson
HR: –
FYE: September 30
Type: Public

Ciprico offers a wide array of redundant arrays. The company makes disk array storage products for high-end computer systems. Disk arrays contain a series of standard, independent hard drives packaged into a subsystem that functions as one device and provides high-volume storage and retrieval capacity. The company's lines of disk arrays are designed for high-performance visual computing applications such as film and video special effects and combat simulation systems. Ciprico offers its military customers ruggedized versions of many of its products.

	Annual Growth	9/03	9/04	9/05	9/06	9/07
Sales ($ mil.)	(27.5%)	31.2	18.1	13.2	11.9	8.6
Net income ($ mil.)	—	(3.9)	(7.4)	(2.4)	(3.7)	(8.1)
Market value ($ mil.)	13.2%	23.4	17.2	21.5	22.6	38.3
Employees	22.1%	—	—	51	—	76

CIRCOR INTERNATIONAL, INC.

NYSE: CIR

25 Corporate Dr., Ste. 130
Burlington, MA 01803
Phone: 781-270-1200
Fax: 781-270-1299
Web: www.circor.com

CEO: A. William (Bill) Higgins
CFO: Frederic M. (Fred) Burditt
HR: Susan M. McCuaig
FYE: December 31
Type: Public

CIRCOR is overflowing with ways to control and direct industrial fluids. The company makes instrumentation and fluid regulation products, including precision valves, tube and pipe fittings, and regulators for hydraulic, pneumatic, cryogenic, and steam systems. CIRCOR's remaining sales come from making valves and other products for the oil and gas industry. The company sells its products (through approximately 1,500 distributors) to more than 10,000 aerospace, energy, chemical, pharmaceutical, and industrial customers in about 130 countries worldwide. CIRCOR spun off from Watts Industries (now Watts Water Technologies) in 1999.

	Annual Growth	12/03	12/04	12/05	12/06	12/07
Sales ($ mil.)	16.7%	359.5	381.8	450.5	591.7	665.7
Net income ($ mil.)	20.6%	17.9	11.8	20.4	29.3	37.9
Market value ($ mil.)	20.3%	368.8	362.1	406.0	595.3	771.9
Employees	21.7%	—	—	2,300	2,800	—

CIRCUIT CITY STORES, INC.

NYSE: CC

9950 Mayland Dr.
Richmond, VA 23233
Phone: 804-486-4000
Fax: 804-527-4164
Web: www.circuitcity.com

CEO: Philip J. Schoonover
CFO: Bruce H. Besanko
HR: Eric A. Jonas Jr.
FYE: Last day of February
Type: Public

A short circuit in this city might leave a lot of electronic gadgets on the shelves. Circuit City Stores is a top consumer electronics retailer in the US (along with Best Buy and Wal Mart), with some 680 superstores in about 45 states. The big-box outlets offer a wide array of TVs, DVD players, and audio systems, as well as CDs and DVDs. Circuit City also sells personal computers and peripherals, mobile computing devices, telephones, and video games. In addition to its retail stores, the company sells products online. Circuit City's international operations are conducted by Canadian subsidiary InterTAN, which operates about 780 locations in that country. Blockbuster has bid $1.3 billion to acquire Circuit City.

	Annual Growth	2/04	2/05	2/06	2/07	2/08
Sales ($ mil.)	4.8%	9,745.4	10,472.4	11,597.7	12,429.8	11,743.7
Net income ($ mil.)	—	(89.3)	61.7	139.8	(8.3)	(319.9)
Market value ($ mil.)	(24.4%)	2,279.6	2,940.8	4,200.2	3,243.1	746.4
Employees	(3.2%)	—	45,946	46,007	43,011	—

CIRCUIT RESEARCH LABS, INC.

OTC: CRLI

7970 S. Kyrene Rd.
Tempe, AZ 85284
Phone: 480-403-8300
Fax: 480-403-8301
Web: www.crlsystems.com

CEO: Charles Jayson Brentlinger
CFO: Rebecca A. (Becky) Nation
HR: Rebecca A. (Becky) Nation
FYE: December 31
Type: Public

The signal is clear at Circuit Research Labs (CRL). The company makes audio processing equipment used by radio and TV stations, Internet sites, and recording studios to control their broadcast frequencies and improve sound quality. CRL also markets noise reduction systems and a line of encoders used to send high-quality audio via the Internet. The company's level controllers and event timers are used to regulate the loudness and timing of audio signals in production studios. Broadcasters and their suppliers, including Harris Corporation and Broadcast Supply Worldwide, are CRL's main customers. Charles Brentlinger, chairman and CEO, controls about 45% of the company.

	Annual Growth	12/03	12/04	12/05	12/06	12/07
Sales ($ mil.)	1.0%	12.4	13.2	15.2	12.7	12.9
Net income ($ mil.)	—	(0.4)	(1.5)	2.6	(2.2)	0.1
Market value ($ mil.)	4.8%	2.1	2.4	7.3	2.3	2.5
Employees						

CIRRUS DESIGN CORPORATION

4515 Taylor Circle
Duluth, MN 55811
Phone: 218-727-2737
Fax: 218-727-2148
Web: www.cirrusdesign.com

CEO: Alan Klapmeier
CFO: Brent Wouters
HR: –
FYE: December 31
Type: Private

Cirrus Design enables its customers to reach the clouds, be they cirrus, cumulus, or stratus. The company manufactures the SRV, SR20-G2, SR22, SR22-Turbo, and SR22-Turbo GTS single-engine, four-seater, piston-powered aircraft. Prices range from about $214,000 for a base model SRV to $532,000 for a fully-loaded SR22-Turbo GTS. Cirrus aircraft are made primarily of composite materials rather than aluminum; the company believes composites allow for an aerodynamically superior design. All Cirrus models come with parachutes that will lower the aircraft to the ground in case of emergency. The company was founded in 1984 by CEO Alan Klapmeier and his brother, Dale.

	Annual Growth	12/03	12/04	12/05	12/06	12/07
Est. sales ($ mil.)	—	—	—	—	—	58.7
Employees	—	—	—	—	—	800

⊞ CIRRUS LOGIC, INC.

NASDAQ (GS): CRUS

2901 Via Fortuna
Austin, TX 78746
Phone: 512-851-4000
Fax: 512-851-4977
Web: www.cirrus.com

CEO: Jason P. Rhode
CFO: Thurman K. Case
HR: Jo-Dee M. Benson
FYE: Saturday nearest March 31
Type: Public

Cirrus Logic's approach to the chip business is hardly cloudy. The fabless semiconductor company, which has long been a leader in audio chips of all kinds, develops integrated circuits (ICs) for specialized applications in consumer entertainment devices. Its more than 600 products include digital audio converters, audio encoder/decoders (codecs), video encoders, and digital amplifiers. Cirrus Logic has also developed system-on-a-chip products, which unite processors, controllers, memory, and other components on a single chip. The company gets more than 60% of its sales outside the US, primarily from customers in the Asia/Pacific region.

	Annual Growth	3/04	3/05	3/06	3/07	3/08
Sales ($ mil.)	(1.9%)	196.3	194.9	193.7	182.3	181.9
Net income ($ mil.)	—	46.5	(13.4)	52.4	27.9	(5.8)
Market value ($ mil.)	(5.5%)	632.1	378.4	747.5	675.3	503.2
Employees	(11.4%)	767	603	424	456	473

CIRTRAN CORPORATION

OTC: CIRC

4125 S. 6000 West
West Valley City, UT 84128
Phone: 801-963-5112
Fax: 801-963-5180
Web: www.cirtran.com

CEO: Iehab J. Hawatmeh
CFO: David L. Harmon
HR: –
FYE: December 31
Type: Public

CirTran provides contract electronics manufacturing services, through which it makes printed circuit boards and cables for customers in consumer electronics, networking equipment, the automotive industry, and other markets. In 2004 the company established an Asian subsidiary in Shenzhen, China, which undertakes manufacturing services for a wider variety of products, including cooking appliances, fitness equipment, and hair products. CirTran's Racore Technology subsidiary makes Ethernet adapter cards for PCs. Racore's customers include the Fire Department of New York City (FDNY), Lear Siegler, Lockheed Martin, the US Air Force, and Walt Disney World. Nearly all of the company's sales are in the US.

	Annual Growth	12/03	12/04	12/05	12/06	12/07
Sales ($ mil.)	79.3%	1.2	8.9	13.0	8.7	12.4
Net income ($ mil.)	—	(2.9)	(0.7)	(0.5)	(2.8)	(7.2)
Market value ($ mil.)	35.6%	4.9	12.8	15.8	9.2	16.5
Employees	16.6%	65	77	110	108	120

⊞ CISCO SYSTEMS, INC.

NASDAQ (GS): CSCO

170 W. Tasman Dr., Bldg. 10
San Jose, CA 95134
Phone: 408-526-4000
Fax: 408-526-4100
Web: www.cisco.com

CEO: John T. Chambers
CFO: Frank Calderoni
HR: Leo Scrivner
FYE: Last Sunday in July
Type: Public

Cisco Systems routes packets and routs competitors with equal efficiency. Dominating the market for IP-based networking equipment, the company provides routers and switches used to direct data, voice, and video traffic. Other products include remote access servers, IP telephony equipment, optical networking components, Internet conferencing systems, set-top boxes, and network service and security systems. It sells its products primarily to large enterprises and telecommunications service providers, but it also markets products designed for small businesses and consumers through its Linksys division.

	Annual Growth	7/03	7/04	7/05	7/06	7/07
Sales ($ mil.)	16.6%	18,878.0	22,045.0	24,801.0	28,484.0	34,922.0
Net income ($ mil.)	19.6%	3,578.0	4,401.0	5,741.0	5,580.0	7,333.0
Market value ($ mil.)	7.3%	133,521.8	140,896.2	121,238.6	110,197.6	176,717.0
Employees	30.0%	—	—	38,413	49,926	—

⊞ CIT GROUP INC.

NYSE: CIT

505 5th Ave.
New York, NY 10017
Phone: 212-771-0505
Fax: –
Web: www.cit.com

CEO: Jeffrey M. (Jeff) Peek
CFO: Joseph M. Leone
HR: James J. (Jim) Duffy
FYE: December 31
Type: Public

If you haven't heard of CIT Group, then you're O-U-T of the proverbial loop. On the big business landscape for about a century, CIT Group is a commercial finance firm offering lending, leasing, and advisory services to middle-market companies and more than half of the *FORTUNE* 1000 in such industries as energy, health care, communications, and entertainment. Financial services include debt restructuring and equipment financing to the aerospace and transportation industries. Its real estate services include mortgage debt, mezzanine debt, and net lease financing. CIT Group has more than $80 billion in managed assets and serves 1 million clients in more than 50 countries around the world.

	Annual Growth	12/03	12/04	12/05	12/06	12/07
Assets ($ mil.)	18.1%	46,342.8	51,111.3	63,386.6	77,067.9	90,248.0
Net income ($ mil.)	—	566.9	753.6	949.1	1,046.0	(81.0)
Market value ($ mil.)	(12.0%)	7,614.4	9,661.2	10,309.9	11,058.9	4,563.9
Employees	2.8%	—	—	6,340	7,345	6,700

CITADEL BROADCASTING CORPORATION

NYSE: CDL

7201 W. Lake Mead Blvd., Ste. 400
Las Vegas, NV 89128
Phone: 702-804-5200
Fax: 702-804-5936
Web: www.citadelbroadcasting.com

CEO: Farid Suleman
CFO: Randy L. Taylor
HR: Susan Arville
FYE: December 31
Type: Public

You might say this company is interested in letters — radio call letters, that is. Citadel Broadcasting is the #3 radio broadcaster in the US in terms of number of stations (behind Clear Channel Communications and Cumulus Media), with more than 220 AM and FM stations serving more than 50 markets around the country. Most of the company's stations operate in market clusters, sharing administration and other back-office functions. The stations offer a variety of music formats, as well as news, talk, and sports. In addition, Citadel owns ABC Radio Network, one of the leading syndicators of radio news and entertainment programming. Theodore Forstmann owns almost 30% of the company through his Forstmann Little & Co.

	Annual Growth	12/03	12/04	12/05	12/06	12/07
Sales ($ mil.)	18.0%	371.5	411.5	419.9	432.9	719.8
Net income ($ mil.)	—	(89.6)	74.6	69.8	(48.0)	(1,285.2)
Market value ($ mil.)	(33.3%)	2,748.5	2,020.4	1,532.5	1,129.9	543.6
Employees	(1.1%)	—	—	3,428	3,392	—

CITATION CORPORATION

27275 Haggerty Rd., Ste. 420
Novi, MI 48377
Phone: 248-522-4500
Fax: −
Web: www.citation.net

CEO: Douglas J. (Doug) Grimm
CFO: Robert C. Sawyer
HR: William (Bill) Goodin
FYE: Sunday nearest September 30
Type: Private

That's the ticket! Citation is forging ahead with a fresh cast of characters. After being taken private by management and investment firm Kelso & Company, the company has altered its primary role as a metal castings supplier and recast itself as a producer of machined and assembled, as well as cast and forged, components. Citation makes a wide range of iron, steel, and aluminum products, primarily for automotive equipment manufacturers and other industrial customers. Products include chassis and suspension components, off-road equipment, and oil field components. Because of soaring steel prices, Citation filed Chapter 11 bankruptcy protection in 2004.

	Annual Growth	9/03	9/04	9/05	9/06	9/07
Est. sales ($ mil.)	—	—	—	—	—	714.5
Employees	—	—	—	—	—	4,600

CITGO PETROLEUM CORPORATION

1293 Eldridge Pkwy.
Houston, TX 77077
Phone: 832-486-4000
Fax: 832-486-1814
Web: www.citgo.com

CEO: Alejandro Granado
CFO: Phil Reedy
HR: −
FYE: December 31
Type: Subsidiary

From the get-go CITGO Petroleum has been refining and marketing petroleum products, including jet fuel, diesel fuel, heating oils, and lubricants. It markets CITGO branded gasoline through about 8,000 independent retail outlets in the US, mainly east of the Rockies. CITGO Petroleum owns oil refineries in Illinois, Louisiana, and Texas. The company has refining capacity of 749,000 barrels per day and access to a total of more than 1.1 million barrels per day of refining capacity. Petroleum is the operating subsidiary of PDV America, itself a subsidiary of Venezuela's PDVSA.

CITI TRENDS, INC.

NASDAQ (GS): CTRN

104 Coleman Blvd.
Savannah, GA 31408
Phone: 912-236-1561
Fax: 912-443-3663
Web: www.cititrends.com

CEO: R. Edward (Ed) Anderson
CFO: Bruce D. Smith
HR: Ivy D. Council
FYE: Saturday nearest January 31
Type: Public

Citi Trends hopes to transport its customers to Trend City as quickly as possible. The urban fashion apparel and accessory chain operates about 320 stores in 20 US states focusing primarily on the African-American market. Its brand-name and private-label offerings — which include hip-hop jeans and oversized T-shirts; men's, women's, and children's clothing; shoes; housewares; and accessories — are sold at 20%-60% less than department and specialty stores' regular prices. Founded in 1946 as Allied Department Stores, the company was acquired by Hampshire Equity Partners and was renamed Citi Trends in 1999. The fast-growing company went public in 2005.

	Annual Growth	1/04	1/05	1/06	1/07	1/08
Sales ($ mil.)	29.2%	157.2	203.4	289.8	381.9	437.5
Net income ($ mil.)	24.6%	5.9	7.3	14.2	21.4	14.2
Market value ($ mil.)	(40.8%)	—	—	607.9	544.1	213.0
Employees	11.8%	—	—	2,800	3,000	3,500

CITIGROUP GLOBAL MARKETS INC.

388 Greenwich St.
New York, NY 10013
Phone: 212-816-6000
Fax: −
Web: www.citigroupcib.com/capital

CEO: Vikram S. Pandit
CFO: Cliff Verron
HR: John L. Donnelly
FYE: December 31
Type: Subsidiary

Citigroup Global Markets (CGMI) is the brokerage and securities arm of banking behemoth Citigroup. It provides brokerage, investment banking, and asset management services to businesses, governments, and individuals. The investment bank expanded in Japan with its parent company's acquisition of a majority of Nikko Cordial in 2007; it has offices in major cities in the Americas, Europe/Middle East/Africa, and the Asia/Pacific. CGMI has venerable antecedents — it is the successor to Salomon Smith Barney and operates as Smith Barney Investments, among other brands.

	Annual Growth	12/03	12/04	12/05	12/06	12/07
Est. sales ($ mil.)	—	—	—	—	—	2,147.5
Employees	—	—	—	—	—	39,000

CITIGROUP INC.

NYSE: C

399 Park Ave.
New York, NY 10043
Phone: 212-559-1000
Fax: 212-793-3946
Web: www.citigroup.com

CEO: Vikram S. Pandit
CFO: Gary L. Crittenden
HR: Michael Schlein
FYE: December 31
Type: Public

This is the Citi. One of the largest financial services firms on the planet, Citigroup (aka Citi) has more than 3,000 bank branches and consumer finance offices in the US and Canada, plus more than 2,000 additional locations in about 100 other countries. The first US bank with more than $1 trillion in assets, Citigroup and its many subsidiaries offer deposits and loans (mainly through Citibank), credit cards, investment banking, brokerage, wealth management, alternative investments, and a panoply of other retail and corporate financial services. Former CEO Chuck Prince resigned in late 2007 as Citigroup was dealing with some $35 billion in writedowns of subprime mortgage-related securities and other investments.

	Annual Growth	12/03	12/04	12/05	12/06	12/07
Assets ($ mil.)	14.7%	1,264,032.0	1,484,101.0	1,494,037.0	1,884,318.0	2,187,631.0
Net income ($ mil.)	(32.9%)	17,853.0	17,046.0	24,589.0	21,538.0	3,617.0
Market value ($ mil.)	(12.5%)	250,318.3	250,277.9	241,690.3	273,598.1	147,040.5
Employees	12.3%	—	—	307,000	337,000	387,000

CITIZEN WATCH CO. OF AMERICA INC.

1000 W. 190th St.
Torrance, CA 90502
Phone: 800-321-1023
Fax: −
Web: www.citizenwatch.com/us/frame_noflash.html

CEO: Laurence R. Grunstein
CFO: −
HR: −
FYE: March 31
Type: Subsidiary

Where most people hear the ticking of the second hand, Citizen Watch Co. of America also hears the ringing of the till. The company is the North American sales and marketing arm of Japan-based Citizen Watch. Citizen Watch products include designs for sports, casual, and fashion wear for men and women. Focusing on technology, Citizen Watch boasts the slimmest LCD watch, one that uses voice recognition, and a professional dive watch with electronic depth sensor. Its Eco-Drive collection of environmentally friendly timepieces is fueled by light, rather than a battery. The company sells is products through retail jewelry and department stores. Its Japanese parent bought rival Bulova in 2008.

CITIZENS & NORTHERN CORPORATION

NASDAQ (CM): CZNC

90-92 Main St.
Wellsboro, PA 16901
Phone: 570-724-3411
Fax: 570-723-8097
Web: www.cnbankpa.com

CEO: Craig G. Litchfield
CFO: Mark A. Hughes
HR: –
FYE: December 31
Type: Public

Citizens & Northern is the holding company for Citizens & Northern Bank and First State Bank, commercial banks that serve north-central Pennsylvania and southern New York. The banks with some 24 offices provide checking and savings accounts, IRAs, and CDs. The company's lending activities mainly consist of residential mortgages (nearly 60% of its loan portfolio) and commercial mortgages (more than 25%). Subsidiary Citizens & Northern Investment provides investment services; Bucktail Life Insurance provides credit, life, and property/casualty reinsurance. In 2005, Citizens & Northern acquired Canisteo Valley (holding company of First State Bank), expanding its operations into New York.

	Annual Growth	12/03	12/04	12/05	12/06	12/07
Assets ($ mil.)	4.7%	1,066.9	1,123.0	1,162.9	1,127.4	1,283.8
Net income ($ mil.)	(10.6%)	16.3	14.9	13.0	12.0	10.4
Market value ($ mil.)	(6.8%)	208.0	214.7	206.5	178.8	156.7
Employees	4.8%	293	324	354	—	353

CITIZENS BANCSHARES CORPORATION

OTC: CZBS

75 Piedmont Ave. NE
Atlanta, GA 30302
Phone: 404-659-5959
Fax: 678-406-4039
Web: www.ctbconnect.com

CEO: James E. Young
CFO: Samuel J. Cox
HR: –
FYE: December 31
Type: Public

Citizens Bancshares was not founded by the proletariat, but it does share the wealth with its stockholders. One of the largest minority-owned financial institutions in the US, Citizens Bancshares is the holding company for Citizens Trust Bank, a regional commercial bank serving central Georgia and Alabama from about 10 branch offices. The bank provides traditional services such as checking and savings accounts, NOW and money market accounts, CDs, IRAs, credit cards, and investment services. Its lending portfolio includes mortgages secured by property in metropolitan Atlanta, small business loans, and consumer installment loans.

	Annual Growth	12/03	12/04	12/05	12/06	12/07
Assets ($ mil.)	(1.6%)	360.4	331.4	328.6	335.2	338.4
Net income ($ mil.)	17.9%	1.5	2.3	2.3	3.0	2.9
Employees	(7.8%)	174	164	147	133	126

CITIZENS COMMUNICATIONS COMPANY

NYSE: CZN

3 High Ridge Park
Stamford, CT 06905
Phone: 203-614-5600
Fax: 203-614-4602
Web: www.czn.net

CEO: Mary Agnes (Maggie) Wilderotter
CFO: Donald R. Shassian
HR: Cecilia K. McKenney
FYE: December 31
Type: Public

Serving city dwellers and country folk alike, Citizens Communications provides phone, television, and Internet services to about 3 million primarily residential access lines in parts of 24 states. The company is active largely in rural and suburban markets, where it is the incumbent local-exchange carrier (ILEC) operating under the Frontier Communications brand. Citizens provides satellite TV through a partnership with DISH Network. The company does also provide telephone services and equipment, as well as data and Internet pacakges to business clients.

	Annual Growth	12/03	12/04	12/05	12/06	12/07
Sales ($ mil.)	(1.6%)	2,444.9	2,193.0	2,162.5	2,025.4	2,288.0
Net income ($ mil.)	3.4%	187.9	72.2	202.4	344.6	214.6
Market value ($ mil.)	4.2%	3,536.1	4,683.5	4,013.5	4,630.9	4,172.2
Employees	(1.7%)	—	—	6,103	5,446	5,900

CITIZENS FINANCIAL CORP.

OTC: CIWV

213 3rd St.
Elkins, WV 26241
Phone: 304-636-4095
Fax: 304-636-6924
Web: www.cnbelkins.com

CEO: Robert J. (Bob) Schoonover
CFO: Nathaniel S. Bonnell
HR: Carla R. Fisher
FYE: December 31
Type: Public

The proletariat should not confuse Citizens Financial with Citizens Financial Corporation (in Kentucky), Citizens Financial Group (Rhode Island), or Citizens Financial Services (Pennsylvania). *This* Citizens Financial helps the citizens of north central and northeastern West Virginia manage their money and finances. The company is the parent company of Citizens National Bank, which offers savings and checking accounts, consumer and commercial loans, trust services, and a range of other programs. Real estate loans (construction and mortgages combined) account for some 75% of the bank's loan portfolio.

	Annual Growth	12/03	12/04	12/05	12/06	12/07
Assets ($ mil.)	4.2%	209.1	213.8	238.2	243.0	246.6
Net income ($ mil.)	(15.9%)	2.0	1.7	2.0	2.1	1.0
Market value ($ mil.)	23.2%	8.9	9.5	10.6	35.7	20.6
Employees	—	—	—	—	—	88

CITIZENS FINANCIAL GROUP, INC.

1 Citizens Plaza
Providence, RI 02903
Phone: 401-456-7000
Fax: 401-456-7819
Web: www.citizensbank.com

CEO: Ellen Alemany
CFO: James B. (Jim) Fitzgerald
HR: Katherine (Kathy) Ferguson McKenzie
FYE: December 31
Type: Subsidiary

One of the largest foreign-owned banks in the country, Citizens Financial Group is the US banking arm of Royal Bank of Scotland (RBS). The parent of Citizens Bank and Charter One Bank has more than 1,600 branches (many of them in supermarkets) in the Northeast (Connecticut, Delaware, Massachusetts, New Hampshire, New Jersey, New York, Pennsylvania, Rhode Island, and Vermont) and the Midwest (Illinois, Indiana, Michigan, Ohio), where the company expanded by buying superregional bank Charter One in 2004. The company operates in four business groups: commercial markets, commercial real estate, consumer and business banking, and payments and lending.

	Annual Growth	12/02	12/03	12/04	12/05	12/06
Sales ($ mil.)	30.8%	3,508.8	3,906.4	5,359.8	8,511.1	10,279.0
Employees	19.2%	15,339	15,500	25,000	26,000	—

CITIZENS FINANCIAL SERVICES, INC.

OTC: CZFS

15 S. Main St.
Mansfield, PA 16933
Phone: 570-662-2121
Fax: 570-662-3278
Web: www.firstcitizensbank.com

CEO: Randall E. (Randy) Black
CFO: Mickey L. Jones
HR: Cynthia T. (Cindy) Pazzaglia
FYE: December 31
Type: Public

Citizens Financial Services is an upstanding resident of the financial community. The holding company for First Citizens National Bank serves north-central Pennsylvania's Tioga, Potter, and Bradford counties and southern New York. Through some 15 branches, the bank offers checking, savings, time, and deposit accounts as well as real estate, commercial, industrial, residential, and consumer loans. Residential mortgage loans account for more than half of the bank's total loan portfolio. The Trust and Investment division offers investment advice and employee benefits coordination, as well as estate and retirement planning services. Insurance is offered through the First Citizen's Insurance Agency subsidiary.

	Annual Growth	12/03	12/04	12/05	12/06	12/07
Assets ($ mil.)	6.2%	463.9	499.4	529.2	572.2	591.0
Net income ($ mil.)	8.1%	4.9	5.3	5.3	5.8	6.7
Market value ($ mil.)	(3.2%)	63.8	65.0	57.7	62.2	56.0
Employees	—	—	—	—	—	184

An in-depth profile of this company is available to Hoover's Online members at hoovers.com.

381

CITIZENS FIRST BANCORP, INC.

NASDAQ (GS): CTZN

525 Water St.
Port Huron, MI 48060
Phone: 810-987-8300
Fax: 810-987-7537
Web: www.cfsbank.com

CEO: Marshall J. Campbell
CFO: Timothy D. Regan
HR: –
FYE: December 31
Type: Public

Citizens First Bancorp is the holding company for Citizens First Savings Bank, which serves the "thumb" of Michigan's Lower Peninsula through about two dozen locations. The bank attracts deposits from local individuals, businesses, and municipalities by offering such products as savings, checking, and money market accounts; certificates of deposit; and trust services. Real estate loans (including one- to four-family mortgages, commercial and multi-family mortgages, residential construction loans, and home equity loans and lines of credit) make up about three-quarters of Citizens First Bancorp's loan portfolio. Subsidiaries offer title insurance, mutual funds, and annuities.

	Annual Growth	12/03	12/04	12/05	12/06	12/07
Assets ($ mil.)	13.3%	1,094.3	1,393.4	1,654.2	1,775.1	1,804.4
Net income ($ mil.)	(37.3%)	12.3	8.2	9.0	9.1	1.9
Market value ($ mil.)	(15.3%)	189.7	205.2	192.4	250.6	97.4
Employees	5.5%	—	—	390	—	434

CITIZENS FIRST CORPORATION

NASDAQ (GM): CZFC

1805 Campbell Ln.
Bowling Green, KY 42104
Phone: 270-393-0700
Fax: 270-393-0716
Web: www.citizensfirstbank.com

CEO: Mary D. Cohron
CFO: M. Todd Kanipe
HR: Tonia Harris
FYE: December 31
Type: Public

Citizens First puts the folks of southwestern Kentucky before all else. Founded in 1975 as a small private-investment club, Citizens First is the holding company for Citizens First Bank, which serves consumers and small to midsized local businesses through around 10 locations in Kentucky's Warren, Hart, Barren, and Simpson counties. The company's loan portfolio includes commercial real estate loans (accounting for more than 40%), residential mortgages (representing almost 30%), and business loans (more than 25%). Citizens First bought Kentucky Banking Centers from Farmers Capital Bank Corporation in 2006, adding three branches to its banking network.

	Annual Growth	12/03	12/04	12/05	12/06	12/07
Assets ($ mil.)	20.6%	163.5	169.5	195.5	338.8	346.4
Net income ($ mil.)	—	(0.3)	1.0	2.2	2.2	1.3
Market value ($ mil.)	18.5%	10.1	11.7	14.9	31.5	19.9
Employees	—	—	—	—	—	—

CITIZENS HOLDING COMPANY

AMEX: CIZN

521 Main St.
Philadelphia, MS 39350
Phone: 601-656-4692
Fax: 601-656-4183
Web: www.citizensholdingcompany.com

CEO: Greg L. McKee
CFO: Robert T. Smith
HR: –
FYE: December 31
Type: Public

Citizens Holding Company has taken the proletariat approach to banking. The firm is the holding company for The Citizens Bank of Philadelphia, Mississippi, which operates some 20 locations in the eastern part of the state. Founded in 1908, the bank targets individuals and local businesses, offering such deposit products as checking and savings accounts, money market accounts, CDs, and IRAs, as well as trust services. Lending activities consist mostly of commercial, financial, and agricultural loans (about half of the company's loan portfolio) and real estate mortgages (more than 30%). Citizens Holding offers discount brokerage services through an agreement with First Tennessee Bank.

	Annual Growth	12/03	12/04	12/05	12/06	12/07
Assets ($ mil.)	5.4%	550.8	587.2	607.7	621.2	680.9
Net income ($ mil.)	(0.4%)	7.0	7.6	8.0	8.4	6.9
Market value ($ mil.)	(6.1%)	113.8	102.5	113.0	112.2	88.6
Employees	—	—	—	250	—	—

CITIZENS, INC.

NYSE: CIA

400 E. Anderson Ln.
Austin, TX 78752
Phone: 512-837-7100
Fax: 512-836-9785
Web: www.citizensinc.com

CEO: Harold E. Riley
CFO: Larry E. Carson
HR: –
FYE: December 31
Type: Public

Citizens aims to prepare its customers for "two of life's possibilities": living and dying. Didn't know you had a choice, eh? A large part of Citizens' strategy is providing ordinary life insurance in niche markets outside the US. Through its CICA Life Insurance Company, it issues life insurance in US dollars to wealthy individuals in Latin America and Taiwan. On the other end of the economic and life spectrum, its Home Service segment sells life insurance to lower-income individuals in Louisiana, primarily to cover final expenses and burial costs. In a macabre synergy, the company also owns a funeral home in the state. Chairman and CEO Harold Riley is the controlling shareholder of Citizens.

	Annual Growth	12/03	12/04	12/05	12/06	12/07
Assets ($ mil.)	19.2%	390.1	661.2	661.9	711.2	787.9
Net income ($ mil.)	52.1%	3.1	7.7	7.3	8.7	16.6
Market value ($ mil.)	(6.2%)	307.9	238.5	218.9	265.9	238.2
Employees	6.6%	120	600	550	490	155

CITIZENS REPUBLIC BANCORP, INC

NASDAQ (GS): CRBC

328 S. Saginaw St.
Flint, MI 48502
Phone: 810-766-7500
Fax: 810-342-7090
Web: www.citizensonline.com

CEO: William R. (Bill) Hartman
CFO: Charles D. Christy
HR: Susan P. Brockett
FYE: December 31
Type: Public

Attention, Citizens of the Republic! Citizens Republic Bancorp (formerly Citizens Banking Corporation) is the holding company for Citizens Bank, Republic Bank, and F&M Bank-Iowa, which together provide traditional banking services through more than 230 offices primarily in Michigan, but also in such markets as central Iowa, the Cleveland and Indianapolis metro areas, and several parts of Wisconsin. The company changed its name following its 2006 purchase of rival Republic Bancorp for more than $1 billion. Citizens Republic Bancorp is active in commercial banking, consumer banking, and wealth management. Subsidiaries provide brokerage services, lease financing, insurance, and annuities.

	Annual Growth	12/03	12/04	12/05	12/06	12/07
Assets ($ mil.)	15.0%	7,711.1	7,706.0	7,751.9	14,008.3	13,506.0
Net income ($ mil.)	11.2%	65.9	76.1	80.5	63.3	100.8
Market value ($ mil.)	(6.1%)	1,414.9	1,485.3	1,192.4	2,005.4	1,098.7
Employees	8.5%	—	—	2,123	2,940	2,501

CITIZENS SOUTH BANKING CORPORATION

NASDAQ (GM): CSBC

519 S. New Hope Rd.
Gastonia, NC 28054
Phone: 704-868-5200
Fax: 704-868-5226
Web: www.citizenssouth.com

CEO: Kim S. Price
CFO: Gary F. Hoskins
HR: Betty B. Gaddis
FYE: December 31
Type: Public

Never mind the region, Citizens South Banking Corporation is more concerned with whether interest rates will rise again. The holding company owns Citizens South Bank, which provides banking products and services from more than a dozen branch offices in the suburbs of Charlotte, North Carolina. Deposit products include checking, savings, and money market accounts; CDs; and IRAs. The bank also issues credit cards, performs trust services, and writes real estate loans (about 80% of its loan portfolio), consumer loans, and business loans. Its Citizens South Financial Services subsidiary (dba Citizens South Investment Services) sells uninsured financial products.

	Annual Growth	12/03	12/04	12/05	12/06	12/07
Assets ($ mil.)	12.0%	495.8	509.0	701.1	743.4	779.1
Net income ($ mil.)	13.8%	3.4	3.0	3.3	5.4	5.7
Market value ($ mil.)	(11.6%)	126.4	129.3	99.1	105.0	77.1
Employees	0.0%	—	—	160	151	160

⊞ CITRIX SYSTEMS, INC.

NASDAQ (GS): CTXS

851 W. Cypress Creek Rd.
Fort Lauderdale, FL 33309
Phone: 954-267-3000
Fax: 954-267-9319
Web: www.citrix.com

CEO: Mark B. Templeton
CFO: David J. Henshall
HR: David R. Friedman
FYE: December 31
Type: Public

Citrix Systems takes connectivity to the next level. The company provides access infrastructure products that enable PCs, IP phones, and other devices to remotely and securely access applications across wired and wireless networks. Its product line includes application virtualization software, VPN appliances, and password management tools, with most applications capable of being deployed in both Windows and UNIX-based computing environments. The company also offers consulting, support, and training services, as well as online managed services for meetings and presentations, technical support, and remote desktop access.

	Annual Growth	12/03	12/04	12/05	12/06	12/07
Sales ($ mil.)	24.0%	588.6	741.2	908.7	1,134.3	1,391.9
Net income ($ mil.)	14.0%	126.9	131.6	166.3	183.0	214.5
Market value ($ mil.)	19.6%	3,480.2	4,167.6	5,073.9	4,833.6	7,121.6
Employees	25.1%	1,885	2,656	3,171	3,742	4,620

CITY CAPITAL CORPORATION

Pink Sheets: CTCC

2000 Mallory Lane, Ste. 130-301
Franklin, TN 37067
Phone: 877-367-1493
Fax: 888-216-8858
Web: www.citycapitalcorp.net

CEO: Ephren W. Taylor II
CFO: –
HR: –
FYE: December 31
Type: Public

City Capital Corporation finds making capital a capital idea. The investment management firm seeks to acquire assets that can be improved and sold at a profit. Its Goshen Energy subsidiary has joined with Native American Biofuels International to develop renewable energy resources and biodiesel production infrastructure on tribal lands; it also distributes biodiesel for Verde Bio Fuels. City Capital Rehabilitation was formed to renovate distressed properties; it owns an Ohio apartment building. Shortly after selling or discontinuing a handful of property developments and artificial turf company Perfect Turf, the company in 2007 shed its Business Development Company (BDC) status.

	Annual Growth	12/03	12/04	12/05	12/06	12/07
Sales ($ mil.)	—	—	—	—	—	0.2
Net income ($ mil.)	—	—	—	—	—	(7.0)
Employees	—	—	—	—	—	—

CITY FURNITURE INC.

6701 N. Hiatus Rd.
Tamarac, FL 33321
Phone: 954-597-2200
Fax: 954-718-3360
Web: www.city-furniture.com

CEO: Keith Koenig
CFO: –
HR: Kurt Nichols
FYE: December 31
Type: Private

With its generic name, City Furniture could open up shop in just about any location and lay claim to the city. Founded in 1971 as a modest 800 sq. ft. home furnishings showroom, City Furniture (formerly Waterbed City) today sells home furnishings through more than 20 showrooms across the state of Florida (Broward, Martin, Miami-Dade, and Palm Beach counties). Alongside countless others in its industry, City Furniture obtains the majority of its imported furniture from China. As part of a licensing agreement, the company plans to open 14 additional stores under the Ashley Furniture HomeStores brand name.

	Annual Growth	12/03	12/04	12/05	12/06	12/07
Est. sales ($ mil.)	—	—	—	—	—	114.6
Employees	—	—	—	—	—	1,050

CITY HOLDING COMPANY

NASDAQ (GS): CHCO

25 Gatewater Rd.
Cross Lanes, WV 25313
Phone: 304-769-1100
Fax: 304-769-1111
Web: www.cityholding.com

CEO: Charles R. (Skip) Hageboeck
CFO: David L. Bumgarner
HR: –
FYE: December 31
Type: Public

"Take Me Home, Country Roads" may be the (unofficial) state song of West Virginia, but City Holding hopes all roads lead to its City National Bank of West Virginia subsidiary, which operates more than 55 branches in the Mountaineer State. It also has about 10 branches in neighboring areas of Ohio and Kentucky. Targeting individuals and regional businesses, the bank offers standard deposit products, loans, credit cards, Internet banking, and trust and investment services. It also runs an insurance agency subsidiary, City Insurance Professionals.

	Annual Growth	12/03	12/04	12/05	12/06	12/07
Assets ($ mil.)	2.9%	2,214.4	2,213.2	2,502.6	2,507.8	2,482.8
Net income ($ mil.)	3.9%	43.7	46.3	50.3	53.2	51.0
Market value ($ mil.)	(1.5%)	583.6	601.2	650.8	715.2	548.4
Employees	2.6%	—	—	770	—	811

⊞ CITY NATIONAL CORPORATION

NYSE: CYN

City National Center, 400 N. Roxbury Dr.
Beverly Hills, CA 90210
Phone: 310-888-6000
Fax: 310-888-6045
Web: www.cnb.com

CEO: Russell D. Goldsmith
CFO: Christopher J. (Chris) Carey
HR: Kate Dwyer
FYE: December 31
Type: Public

For celebrity sightings, forget the Hollywood Homes Tour and camp out at City National Bank. With more than 60 branches in Southern California, the San Francisco Bay area, Nevada, and New York City, the subsidiary of City National Corporation has been known as "Bank to the Stars" since opening in Beverly Hills, California in the 1950s. It offers a variety of services, including personal and business banking, investment management and advisory, and trust services. The bank focuses on providing customized service, tailoring its offerings to the needs of its high-powered clientele. Its niche market consists of small to midsized businesses, entrepreneurs, professionals, and affluent individuals.

	Annual Growth	12/03	12/04	12/05	12/06	12/07
Assets ($ mil.)	5.1%	13,018.2	14,231.5	14,581.9	14,884.4	15,889.3
Net income ($ mil.)	4.5%	186.7	206.3	234.7	233.5	222.7
Market value ($ mil.)	(1.5%)	3,056.6	3,500.5	3,586.4	3,409.3	2,872.4
Employees	7.1%	—	—	2,539	3,000	2,914

CITYBANK

NASDAQ (CM): CTBK

14807 Highway 99
Lynnwood, WA 98087
Phone: 425-745-5933
Fax: –
Web: www.citybankwa.com

CEO: Conrad Hanson
CFO: Chantha Bunphoath
HR: Belinda J. Faylona
FYE: December 31
Type: Public

CityBank urbanely operates about ten branches and loan production offices in Snohomish and King counties in northwestern Washington State. Personal and business banking products include such standard fare as checking and savings accounts, money market accounts, CDs, and individual retirement accounts. Additional investment services for individuals include stocks, bonds, mutual funds, and annuities. Construction loans make up more than half of the company's loan portfolio. In 2005 the company sold its merchant and debit card processing business to NOVA Information Systems (now Elavon) and online data retrieval subsidiary Diligenz to Corporation Service Company.

	Annual Growth	12/03	12/04	12/05	12/06	12/07
Est. sales ($ mil.)	—	—	—	—	—	62.4
Employees	—	—	—	—	—	143

⊞ An in-depth profile of this company is available to Hoover's Online members at hoovers.com.

CITYSEARCH

8833 Sunset Blvd.	CEO: Jay Herratti
West Hollywood, CA 90069	CFO: John Cherry
Phone: 310-360-4500	HR: Dena Grablowsky
Fax: –	FYE: December 31
Web: www.citysearch.com	Type: Business segment

This online enterprise tracks down things to do all around town. Citysearch is a leading provider of local entertainment and business listings on the Internet, operating city-specific Web sites covering metropolitan areas across the US. In addition to searchable listings, the sites offer a variety of reviews and guides to help people find the best restaurants, night clubs, and other attractions that their city has to offer. Citysearch also provides local information on more than a dozen areas in Australia, Canada, and Europe. It operates as a unit of Barry Diller's IAC/InterActiveCorp, which has announced plans to split into five companies.

⊞ CKE RESTAURANTS, INC.   NYSE: CKR

6307 Carpinteria Ave., Ste. A	CEO: Andrew F. Puzder
Carpinteria, CA 93013	CFO: Theodore (Ted) Abajian
Phone: 805-745-7500	HR: Victoria Straschil
Fax: 714-490-3630	FYE: Last Monday in January
Web: www.ckr.com	Type: Public

There's really nothing junior about this company, other than the name of its flagship hamburger chain. CKE Restaurants is a leading fast-food operator with more than 3,000 company-owned and franchised eateries across the country. Its Carl's Jr. chain includes more than 1,100 locations primarily in California and other Western States known for their signature Six Dollar Burger. CKE also owns Hardee's Food Systems which operates and franchises more than 1,900 Hardee's locations, mostly in the Midwest and Southeast. CKE owns and operates nearly a third of its restaurants and franchises the rest.

	Annual Growth	1/04	1/05	1/06	1/07	1/08
Sales ($ mil.)	2.1%	1,413.4	1,519.9	1,518.3	1,588.4	1,534.6
Net income ($ mil.)	—	(53.2)	18.0	194.6	50.2	31.1
Market value ($ mil.)	11.8%	436.3	855.6	935.9	1,329.1	682.2
Employees	(5.3%)	—	—	29,000	30,000	26,000

CKX, INC.   NASDAQ (GS): CKXE

650 Madison Ave.	CEO: Robert F. X. Sillerman
New York, NY 10022	CFO: Thomas P. Benson
Phone: 212-838-3100	HR: –
Fax: 212-872-1473	FYE: December 31
Web: ir.ckx.com	Type: Public

CKX is ready to sing *Viva Las Vegas*, but any performance will be critiqued by *American Idol's* Simon Cowell. The company controls 85% of Elvis Presley Enterprises, which manages the King's estate and licenses his likeness, songs, and name, as well as operating tours of Graceland. The company also owns 19 Entertainment, the firm responsible for the *American Idol* TV show, and has a "long-term agreement" with *Idol* creator Simon Fuller. Additionally, CKX has a stake in the name, image, likeness, and intellectual property of Muhammad Ali. Entertainment impresario Robert Sillerman, who owns more than 30% of the company, has offered to take the company private.

	Annual Growth	12/03	12/04	12/05	12/06	12/07
Sales ($ mil.)	48.7%	—	—	120.6	210.1	266.8
Net income ($ mil.)	—	—	—	(5.9)	9.2	12.1
Market value ($ mil.)	(0.3%)	—	—	1,135.3	1,066.4	1,128.0
Employees	15.8%	—	—	487	564	—

CKX LANDS, INC.   AMEX: CKX

751 Bayou Pines East	CEO: Joseph K. Cooper
Lake Charles, LA 70601	CFO: Brian R. Jones
Phone: 337-310-0547	HR: –
Fax: –	FYE: December 31
	Type: Public

Revenues come naturally to CKX Lands. Formerly named Calcasieu Real Estate & Oil, CKX Lands owns or has stakes in about 14,000 acres in Louisiana that host oil and gas wells, mines, timber, and agricultural operations. Formed in 1930, the company does not perform any of these operations itself. Instead, it generates revenues through royalties from the natural resources produced from its land. Originally set up to receive mineral royalties spun off by a bank to its shareholders, CKX Lands' growth strategy is built around acquiring landholdings in southwest Louisiana. Its largest customers, Cox & Perkins and Unit Petroleum, each account for about 20% of the company's sales.

	Annual Growth	12/03	12/04	12/05	12/06	12/07
Sales ($ mil.)	12.0%	2.1	2.7	2.7	2.7	3.3
Net income ($ mil.)	26.3%	1.1	1.6	1.6	1.5	2.8
Market value ($ mil.)	12.8%	14.1	19.7	20.5	25.8	22.8
Employees	11.8%	—	—	4	—	5

CLACENDIX, INC.   OTC: IONN

2001 Rte. 46	CEO: Norman E. (Norm) Corn
Parsippany, NJ 07054	CFO: Patrick E. Delaney
Phone: 973-402-4251	HR: –
Fax: 973-402-8912	FYE: December 31
Web: www.clacendix.com	Type: Public

Clacendix took its eye off of network infrastructure. Formerly called ION Networks, the company provided security software, tokens, and appliances that protected enterprise data and networks from external and internal security threats. The company's customers included telecommunications service providers, enterprises, and government entities. Faced with declining sales and mounting losses, the company decided to sell its assets in 2007. Network security specialist Cryptek completed its acquisition of the ION assets for $3.2 million in early 2008. Clacendix will use the proceeds of the sale to pay down debt. The company plans to merge with a private company seeking to go public.

	Annual Growth	12/03	12/04	12/05	12/06	12/07
Sales ($ mil.)	0.0%	3.3	3.6	4.6	3.4	3.3
Net income ($ mil.)	—	(0.6)	(0.3)	0.2	(0.8)	0.1
Market value ($ mil.)	17.4%	1.0	5.7	4.6	3.3	2.0
Employees	—	—	—	—	—	—

CLAIM JUMPER RESTAURANTS LLC

16721 Millikan Ave.	CEO: Robert Ott
Irvine, CA 92606	CFO: Gary Campanaro
Phone: 949-756-9001	HR: Tina Burke
Fax: 949-756-8733	FYE: December 31
Web: www.claimjumper.com	Type: Private

Claim Jumper Restaurants owns and operates more than 40 casual dining restaurants in California and about a half dozen other states. The chain offers a menu heavy on meat and potatoes that also includes sandwiches, seafood, and a variety of appetizers. A few of its restaurant locations also offer catering services. In addition, the company licenses the Claim Jumper name to frozen food maker American Pie which sells branded frozen diners and desserts through about 3,000 grocery stores in a dozen states. Craig Nickoloff opened the first Claim Jumper restaurant in 1977. The company is controlled by private equity firm Leonard Green & Partners.

	Annual Growth	12/03	12/04	12/05	12/06	12/07
Est. sales ($ mil.)	—	—	—	—	—	78.1
Employees	—	—	—	—	—	3,600

CLAIMSNET.COM, INC.

OTC: CLAI

14860 Montfort Dr., Ste. 250
Dallas, TX 75254
Phone: 972-458-1701
Fax: 972-458-1737
Web: www.claimsnet.com

CEO: Don Crosbie
CFO: Laura M. Bray
HR: –
FYE: December 31
Type: Public

Say good-bye to those cramped little boxes! Claimsnet.com has put the insurance claims process online. Founded in 1996, Claimsnet lets insurance companies and other health care payers log on to a Web site and file all claims information to doctors, provider organizations, and other medical and dental services providers. It collects transaction, implementation, development, license, and support fees for this service. In 2008 the company acquired Acceptius, a provider of data processing services catering to the health care industry; the deal allows Claimsnet to offer its customers conversion and claims repricing.

	Annual Growth	12/03	12/04	12/05	12/06	12/07
Sales ($ mil.)	27.8%	0.6	1.0	1.3	1.5	1.6
Net income ($ mil.)	—	(0.5)	(0.7)	(0.3)	(0.4)	(0.5)
Market value ($ mil.)	(20.5%)	10.4	6.8	4.9	4.9	4.2
Employees	—	—	—	—	—	11

CLAIRE'S STORES, INC.

3 SW 129th Ave.
Pembroke Pines, FL 33027
Phone: 954-433-3900
Fax: 954-433-3999
Web: www.clairestores.com

CEO: Eugene S. (Gene) Kahn
CFO: J. Per Brodin
HR: Joseph A. DeFalco
FYE: Saturday nearest January 31
Type: Private

If the difference between men and boys is the price of their toys, for young women and girls, it may be the price of their accessories. For thrifty, fashion-conscious females ages 7 to 27, Claire's Stores is the queen of costume jewelry, handbags, and hair bows. Claire's operates more than 3,000 boutiques, primarily in malls, that include Claire's and Icing by Claire's. The chain is present in all 50 US states, Puerto Rico, the US Virgin Islands, and Canada, and about 10 European countries. Founded by Rowland Schaefer and later run by his daughters, Bonnie and Marla Schaefer, Claire's Store was sold to the New York-based private equity firm Apollo Management for $3.1 billion in 2007.

	Annual Growth	1/03	1/04	1/05	1/06	1/07
Sales ($ mil.)	10.3%	1,001.5	1,132.8	1,279.4	1,369.8	1,481.0
Net income ($ mil.)	24.9%	77.7	115.0	143.1	172.3	188.8
Employees	3.2%	16,325	16,000	17,500	18,000	18,500

CLANCY SYSTEMS INTERNATIONAL, INC.

Pink Sheets: CLSI

2250 S. Oneida St., Ste. 308
Denver, CO 80224
Phone: 303-753-0197
Fax: 303-759-4681
Web: www.clancysystems.com

CEO: Stanley J. Wolfson
CFO: Lizabeth M. Wolfson
HR: –
FYE: September 30
Type: Public

Clancy Systems designs, develops, and manufactures automated parking enforcement and management systems, including a wireless ticket-writing and printing system. Municipalities, universities, and institutions are among its customers. Clancy Systems also offers online transaction services for processing payments for tickets and registrations. In addition, the company offers software for making double-sided identification badges, a virtual parking permit platform, and a rust-proof vehicle immobilization system (marketed as The Denver Boot). CEO Stanley Wolfson and his wife, Lizabeth Wolfson, the company's CFO, together own about 35% of Clancy Systems.

	Annual Growth	9/03	9/04	9/05	9/06	9/07
Sales ($ mil.)	5.2%	3.1	3.1	3.0	3.5	3.8
Net income ($ mil.)	(15.9%)	0.2	0.0	0.2	0.3	0.1
Market value ($ mil.)	(2.0%)	6.2	7.3	5.0	5.7	5.7
Employees	—	—	—	—	—	10

CLARCOR INC.

NYSE: CLC

840 Cresent Centre Dr., Ste. 600
Franklin, TN 37067
Phone: 615-771-3100
Fax: 615-771-5603
Web: www.clarcor.com

CEO: Norman E. (Norm) Johnson
CFO: Bruce A. Klein
HR: David J. Lindsay
FYE: Saturday nearest November 30
Type: Public

CLARCOR cleans up with filters. The company's industrial and environmental filtration unit makes air and antimicrobial filters for commercial, industrial, and residential buildings, along with filters used in industrial processes. Brands include Airguard, Facet, and Purolator. Companies in CLARCOR's engine and mobile filtration business make products under brands such as Baldwin and Clark that filter the air, oil, fuel, coolant, and hydraulic fluids used in car, truck, heavy equipment, and marine engines. CLARCOR's consumer packaging group makes custom-designed metal, plastic, and composite containers for food, drug, toiletry, and chemical products.

	Annual Growth	11/03	11/04	11/05	11/06	11/07
Sales ($ mil.)	5.6%	741.4	787.7	874.0	904.3	921.2
Net income ($ mil.)	13.6%	54.5	64.0	76.4	82.7	90.7
Market value ($ mil.)	33.4%	554.1	672.6	1,530.8	1,681.1	1,752.7
Employees	4.5%	—	—	5,034	5,048	5,500

CLARENDON INSURANCE GROUP

466 Lexington Avenue, 19th Fl.
New York, NY 10017
Phone: 212-790-9700
Fax: 212-790-9801
Web: www.clarendon.biz

CEO: Patrick Fee
CFO: Gary Ropiecki
HR: –
FYE: December 31
Type: Subsidiary

Clarendon Insurance Group is there to fill in missing pieces while other pieces are being picked up. Clarendon Insurance Group is the US-based property and casualty subsidiary of Hannover Re. Clarendon's particular forté is Specialty Insurance, which requires specific and customized detail management in terms of claims, loss control, and risk transfer mechanisms. Functions in this area include underwriting, legal compliance, IT, finance, and claims. Its clients include, among others, reinsurers as well as general insurance agents and brokers.

	Annual Growth	12/03	12/04	12/05	12/06	12/07
Est. sales ($ mil.)	—	—	—	—	—	32.2
Employees	—	—	—	—	—	85

CLARIA CORPORATION

555 Broadway St.
Redwood City, CA 94063
Phone: 650-980-1500
Fax: 650-980-1599
Web: www.claria.com

CEO: Scott VanDeVelde
CFO: Richard S. (Rich) Mora
HR: –
FYE: December 31
Type: Private

Once a king of adware and spyware, Claria has now set its sights on tracking personalized consumer behavior. In the not-so-distant past, Claria served targeted ads to more than 40 million computer users (the advertising messages were broadcast through software applications that tracked the user's online behavior and presented appropriate pop-up ads). However, after vociferous criticism from the antispyware community, Claria exited the adware business in 2006, ceasing its pop-up ads altogether in July. Claria's new products, PersonalWeb and Axon, offer the user a personalized Web page and provides them with advertising and related content based on their search habits and Web browsing behavior.

	Annual Growth	12/03	12/04	12/05	12/06	12/07
Est. sales ($ mil.)	—	—	—	—	—	18.6
Employees	—	—	—	—	—	190

An in-depth profile of this company is available to Hoover's Online members at hoovers.com.

385

CLARIAN HEALTH PARTNERS, INC.

1701 N. Senate Blvd.
Indianapolis, IN 46202
Phone: 317-962-2000
Fax: 317-962-4533
Web: www.clarian.org

CEO: Daniel F. (Dan) Evans Jr.
CFO: Marvin Pember
HR: –
FYE: December 31
Type: Not-for-profit

One of the largest health systems in Indiana, Clarian Health Partners includes three major hospitals — Methodist Hospital, Indiana University Hospital, and Riley Hospital for Children — that have nearly 1,400 beds in all. Methodist Hospital features a Level 1 trauma center and the Methodist Research Institute, which conducts clinical trials in a number of areas including cardiology and transplantation. Two other community hospitals — 170-bed Clarian North Medical Center and the smaller Clarian West Medical Center — are affiliates of the system. Formed in 1997, Clarian Health offers additional health services through a network of primary and specialty care clinics and a home health care business.

	Annual Growth	12/03	12/04	12/05	12/06	12/07
Est. sales ($ mil.)	—	—	—	—	—	2,147.5
Employees	—	—	—	—	—	14,820

CLARIANT CORPORATION

4000 Monroe Rd.
Charlotte, NC 28205
Phone: 704-331-7000
Fax: 704-331-7825
Web: www.clariant-northamerica.com

CEO: Kenneth (Ken) Golder
CFO: Eric Fromm
HR: Cary W. Campbell
FYE: December 31
Type: Subsidiary

Clariant Corporation is clearly into the chemicals business. The company is divided into four segments: Textile, Leather, and Paper Chemicals; Functional Chemicals; Pigments and Additives; and Masterbatches (which are color and additive concentrates). As the North American subsidiary of Swiss specialty chemicals maker Clariant Ltd, Clariant Corp. oversees operations in Canada and the US and has about 25 manufacturing facilities and service centers throughout the US and Canada. Its customers include the agriculture, automotive, plastics, pharmaceutical, printing, and textile industries.

	Annual Growth	12/03	12/04	12/05	12/06	12/07
Est. sales ($ mil.)	—	—	—	—	—	915.6
Employees	—	—	—	—	—	3,730

CLARIENT, INC.

NASDAQ (CM): CLRT

31 Columbia
Aliso Viejo, CA 92656
Phone: 949-425-5700
Fax: 949-425-5701
Web: www.clarientinc.com

CEO: Ronald A. (Ron) Andrews Jr.
CFO: Raymond J. (Ray) Land
HR: –
FYE: December 31
Type: Public

Nobody wants to get cancer, but at least Clarient can tell you what you're up against. The firm is a specialized diagnostic services provider, offering a collection of advanced tests that detect and monitor the progression of various types of cancer. Its services — including immunohistochemistry, flow cytometry, and genetic testing — aim to not only find malignancies, but to provide information doctors use to prescribe the most effective treatments. Until 2007 Clarient made cancer-detecting cellular imaging systems under the ACIS brand. That year, it sold its ACIS business to a subsidiary of Carl Zeiss and completed its transition to a diagnostic services provider.

	Annual Growth	12/03	12/04	12/05	12/06	12/07
Sales ($ mil.)	37.9%	11.9	9.8	20.1	33.6	43.0
Net income ($ mil.)	—	(7.9)	(19.6)	(14.8)	(15.9)	(8.8)
Market value ($ mil.)	4.8%	123.1	111.4	86.9	123.3	148.6
Employees	—	—	—	139	—	—

CLARION CORPORATION OF AMERICA

6200 Gateway Dr.
Cypress, CA 90630
Phone: 310-327-9100
Fax: 310-327-1999
Web: www.clarion.com

CEO: Matt Matsuda
CFO: –
HR: Steve Dean
FYE: March 31
Type: Subsidiary

Clarion Corporation of America wants your car stereo to be loud and Clarion. The company markets and distributes electronic entertainment, communications, security, and navigation products for automobiles and boats to retailers, distributors, and carmakers including Ford, Honda, and Nissan. The company's products include audio amplifiers, car stereos, mobile CB radios, navigation and computing systems, satellite radio systems, and subwoofers and other speakers. Established in 1967, Clarion Corporation of America is the US sales and marketing subsidiary of Japan-based electronics manufacturer Clarion Co.

	Annual Growth	3/03	3/04	3/05	3/06	3/07
Est. sales ($ mil.)	—	—	—	—	—	289.8
Employees	—	—	—	—	—	230

CLARION TECHNOLOGIES, INC.

Pink Sheets: CLAR

4595 Broadmoor SE, Ste. 300
Grand Rapids, MI 49512
Phone: 616-698-7277
Fax: 616-698-1296
Web: www.clariontechnologies.com

CEO: Steven W. Olmstead
CFO: Robert Bronsink
HR: –
FYE: Saturday nearest December 31
Type: Public

Clarion Technologies is constantly molding its business. The company is a custom manufacturer of injection-molded plastic products for companies in the automotive and consumer goods industries. Auto products include interior and exterior trim parts and components of door panels. Clarion's products for the consumer goods market include parts for refrigerators and other home appliances, as well as drawer components and trim. Clarion's major customers include Electrolux Home Products and Lear Corporation, which together account for more than three-quarters of the company's sales. William Blair Mezzanine Capital owns 46% of Clarion; chairman Craig Weirda and his family own nearly 40%.

	Annual Growth	12/01	12/02	12/03	12/04	*12/05
Sales ($ mil.)	8.3%	105.6	80.6	97.7	117.7	145.5
Net income ($ mil.)	—	(35.1)	(7.2)	0.8	(1.7)	(5.7)
Employees	—	—	—	—	—	—

*Most recent year available

CLARITAS INC.

5375 Mira Sorrento Pl., Ste. 400
San Diego, CA 92121
Phone: 858-622-0800
Fax: 858-550-5800
Web: www.claritas.com

CEO: Matthew (Matt) O'Grady
CFO: –
HR: –
FYE: December 31
Type: Subsidiary

Claritas helps companies get a clearer picture of their customers. The company provides data and customer relationship management (CRM) systems that are designed to increase the effectiveness of its clients' marketing efforts. Users can track and analyze customer behavior and design targeted marketing programs using that information. It also provides systems integration and consulting through its Integras unit. Claritas operates as part of the marketing information division of business information giant Nielsen (formerly VNU). It was founded in 1971 by Jonathan Robbin as General Analytics Corporation and acquired by VNU in 1982.

	Annual Growth	12/03	12/04	12/05	12/06	12/07
Est. sales ($ mil.)	—	—	—	—	—	96.0
Employees	—	—	—	—	—	455

CLARK CONSULTING

2100 Ross Ave., Ste. 2200
Dallas, TX 75201
Phone: 352-893-6767
Fax: 952-893-6797
Web: www.clarkconsulting.com

CEO: Kurt J. Laning
CFO: Nancy S. Johnson
HR: Shannon Jud
FYE: December 31
Type: Subsidiary

Clark Consulting tries to make sure businesses offer benefits that will help keep their best executives. The firm provides benefits and compensation consulting services to corporations, banks, and health care organizations. It helps develop and implement benefit plans to cover retirement and disability, and administers executive benefit and insurance plans for some 3,800 companies. Subsidiaries offer executive compensation consulting, financial planning, and lobbying services. The company operates from about 50 offices across the US. In early 2007, Clark was acquired by a unit of insurer AEGON and now operates within AEGON's Extraordinary Markets Division.

CLARK ENTERPRISES, INC.

7500 Old Georgetown Rd., 15th Fl.
Bethesda, MD 20814
Phone: 301-657-7100
Fax: 301-657-7263
Web: www.clarkenterprisesinc.com

CEO: A. James Clark
CFO: –
HR: –
FYE: December 31
Type: Private

Like Clark Kent, this firm holds some super powers. Clark Enterprises, one of the largest privately held companies in the Washington, DC area, holds interests in real estate, private equity, venture capital, and construction companies. The company's real estate holdings under Clark Realty include some 5 million sq. ft. of office space, 15,000 residential units, and 300,000 sq. ft. of warehouse space. The Clark Construction Group, its flagship subsidiary, is a top US contractor that performs construction management, general contracting, design, and consulting services. Other units include residential builder Seawright Homes and highway construction company Shirley Contracting.

	Annual Growth	12/02	12/03	12/04	12/05	12/06
Sales ($ mil.)	3.6%	2,800.0	2,750.0	2,800.0	2,844.0	3,220.0
Employees	(1.7%)	4,500	4,200	3,200	4,200	4,200

CLARK MATERIAL HANDLING COMPANY

700 Enterprise Dr.
Lexington, KY 40510
Phone: 859-422-6400
Fax: 859-422-7400
Web: www.clarkmhc.com

CEO: Dennis Lawrence
CFO: –
HR: Sherry Myers
FYE: December 31
Type: Private

Dealing with CLARK Material Handling can be an uplifting experience. Founded in 1917 to make material-handling trucks, CLARK has produced more than 1 million forklifts. Selling through its global network of 550 dealers, the company's line of forklifts includes internal combustion trucks, electric riders, narrow-aisle stackers, and powered hand trucks. CLARK also supplies aftermarket parts, as well as Totalift-brand parts to fit other manufacturers' forklifts. The company has more than 250,000 lift trucks operating in North America and more than 350,000 units globally. Young An, a South Korean industrial conglomerate, controls the company.

CLARKSTON FINANCIAL CORPORATION   OTC: CKFC

6600 Highland Rd., Ste. 24
Waterford, MI 48327
Phone: 248-922-0086
Fax: 248-886-1432
Web: www.clarkstonstatebank.com

CEO: J. Grant Smith
CFO: James W. Distelrath
HR: –
FYE: December 31
Type: Public

Clarkston Financial, the holding company for Clarkston State Bank, threw its hat into the ring of retail banking in 1998. The community bank serves consumers and small to midsized businesses from six branches in Oakland County, Michigan, north of Detroit. The bank offers a full range of consumer services, including checking, savings, and NOW accounts, as well as CDs. Clarkston Savings Bank uses funds from deposits primarily for commercial lending; on a more limited scale, it also originates consumer and construction loans and residential mortgages. Clarkston Financial opened a new financial institution, Huron Valley State Bank, in 2005; Clarkston owns 55% of it.

	Annual Growth	12/02	12/03	12/04	12/05	*12/06
Assets ($ mil.)	17.6%	115.3	142.6	163.4	195.6	220.4
Net income ($ mil.)	—	0.8	1.5	1.3	0.0	(0.7)
Employees	—	—	—	—	—	60

*Most recent year available

CLAYMONT STEEL HOLDINGS, INC.

4001 Philadelphia Pike
Claymont, DE 19703
Phone: 302-792-5400
Fax: 800-374-1561
Web: www.claymontsteel.com

CEO: Jeff Bradley
CFO: Allen Egner
HR: –
FYE: December 31
Type: Subsidiary

Claymont Steel prefers to keep its business discrete. Through subsidiary Claymont Steel, Inc., the company is a leading manufacturer of custom discrete steel plate in North America, commanding about 20% of that market east of the Rocky Mountains. Its mix of custom and commodity steel plates are used by bridge fabricators, tool and die manufacturers, railcar builders, and service centers. Claymont produces some 400,000 tons of steel plate annually via its facility in Claymont, Delaware. H.I.G. Capital acquired Claymont in 2005, took it public the next year. In 2008, Russian steel producer Evraz bought Claymont for $565 million. It soon began to refer to the company as Evraz Claymont Steel.

	Annual Growth	12/02	12/03	12/04	12/05	12/06
Sales ($ mil.)	45.4%	—	108.5	239.6	278.4	333.4
Net income ($ mil.)	—	—	(6.7)	42.0	40.9	32.0
Employees	—	—	—	—	—	415

CLAYTON, DUBILIER & RICE, INC.

375 Park Ave., 18th Fl.
New York, NY 10152
Phone: 212-407-5200
Fax: 212-407-5252
Web: www.cdr-inc.com

CEO: Donald J. Gogel
CFO: –
HR: –
FYE: December 31
Type: Private

Clayton, Dubilier & Rice (CD&R) specializes in turnaround situations. With a reputation as a hands-on manager of its portfolio companies, the private equity firm typically targets units of large corporations, structures a leveraged buyout (LBO), and works with existing management to improve operations. Since it was formed in 1978, CD&R has invested in more than 40 businesses in the US and Europe. In 2007 the company led an investor group that bought ServiceMaster, and joined with Bain Capital and The Carlyle Group to buy the wholesale construction supply business of The Home Depot for about $8.5 billion.

	Annual Growth	12/03	12/04	12/05	12/06	12/07
Est. sales ($ mil.)	—	—	—	—	—	1,100.3
Employees	—	—	—	—	—	15,500

CLAYTON HOLDINGS, INC.

NASDAQ (GM): CLAY

2 Corporate Dr.
Shelton, CT 06484
Phone: 203-926-5600
Fax: 203-926-5750
Web: www.clayton.com

CEO: Frank P. Filipps
CFO: Frederick C. (Rick) Herbst
HR: –
FYE: December 31
Type: Public

Clayton Holdings provides technology-based services to help lenders, investors, and other financial services firms manage their operations and risk. Clayton Holdings was formed in 2005 when TA Associates combined two of its portfolio companies, Clayton Fixed Income Services and Clayton Services, as subsidiaries operating under a single holding company. Clayton Services offers operations support, loan and portfolio analysis, and consulting for lenders and capital markets firms, and it provides transaction management, compliance, and other software. Clayton Fixed Income Services provides credit risk management services and risk-filtering technologies for the fixed-income securities market.

	Annual Growth	12/03	12/04	12/05	12/06	12/07
Sales ($ mil.)	15.7%	85.2	156.1	207.5	239.2	152.6
Net income ($ mil.)	—	15.4	16.7	5.1	7.9	(97.2)
Employees	(2.8%)	—	1,973	2,354	2,524	1,813

CLAYTON HOMES, INC.

500 Alcoa Trail
Maryville, TN 37804
Phone: 865-380-3000
Fax: 865-380-3750
Web: www.clayton.net

CEO: Kevin T. Clayton
CFO: John J. Kalec
HR: Sharon G. Kennedy
FYE: December 31
Type: Subsidiary

Clayton Homes leapfrogged Fleetwood Enterprises and Champion Enterprises with the acquisition of Oakwood Homes to become the #1 maker (by units) of manufactured homes in the US. A Berkshire Hathaway subsidiary, its one- and two-story homes range in price from $20,000 to more than $100,000 for luxury models and range in size from 500 sq. ft. to 2,400 sq. ft. Clayton Homes distributes its products in 49 states through a network of about 1,650 retailers (about 450 company-owned stores and 1,200 independent retailers). Clayton Homes also operates nearly 70 manufactured housing communities and owns financing, loan-servicing, and insurance subsidiaries.

CLAYTON WILLIAMS ENERGY, INC.

NASDAQ (GM): CWEI

6 Desta Dr., Ste. 3000
Midland, TX 79705
Phone: 432-682-6324
Fax: 432-688-3247
Web: www.claytonwilliams.com

CEO: Clayton W. Williams
CFO: Mel G. Riggs
HR: LuAnn Bolding
FYE: December 31
Type: Public

Former Texas gubernatorial candidate Clayton Williams once devoted his energy to politics. Now he's devoted to the independent oil and gas firm that he founded. Clayton Williams Energy explores for oil and gas deposits in Louisiana, New Mexico, and Texas and exploits those resources. In 2006 the company had proved reserves of 271.5 billion cu. ft. of natural gas equivalent. Most of those reserves are in the Permian Basin and East Texas. It also operates 94 miles of gas pipeline and processing plants in Texas and Mississippi. Williams is CEO and controls the firm. In 2004 and 2005 Clayton Williams Energy boosted its reserves with the acquisition of Southwest Royalties and a property in Ward County.

	Annual Growth	12/03	12/04	12/05	12/06	12/07
Sales ($ mil.)	23.0%	172.0	206.3	283.6	266.0	393.9
Net income ($ mil.)	(28.5%)	22.9	(14.0)	0.3	17.8	6.0
Market value ($ mil.)	6.9%	271.0	247.0	451.4	404.9	353.8
Employees	3.4%	—	—	174	—	186

CLEAN DIESEL TECHNOLOGIES, INC.

NASDAQ (CM): CDTI

300 Atlantic St., Ste. 702
Stamford, CT 06901
Phone: 203-327-7050
Fax: 203-323-0461
Web: www.cdti.com

CEO: Bernhard Steiner
CFO: Ann B. Ruple
HR: –
FYE: December 31
Type: Public

Clean Diesel Technologies has developed a few cool technologies to counteract global warming. The company is starting to commercialize its chemical fuel additives and other products for reducing diesel engine emissions and improving fuel economy. These include its platinum fuel catalysts, which are marketed in Europe and the US under the Platinum Plus brand. Clean Diesel Technologies also manufactures and licenses nitrogen oxide reduction systems (under the brand name ARIS) and chemical fuel additives to help control diesel engine emissions. The company has a licensing deal with Mitsui to use the ARIS technology.

	Annual Growth	12/03	12/04	12/05	12/06	12/07
Sales ($ mil.)	69.0%	0.6	0.7	0.8	1.1	4.9
Net income ($ mil.)	—	(3.2)	(4.1)	(5.4)	(5.4)	(4.5)
Market value ($ mil.)	43.0%	44.7	29.2	25.4	57.3	186.9
Employees	—	—	—	—	—	17

CLEAN ENERGY FUELS CORP.

NASDAQ (GM): CLNE

3020 Old Ranch Pkwy., Ste. 200
Seal Beach, CA 90740
Phone: 562-493-2804
Fax: 562-493-4532
Web: www.cleanenergyfuels.com

CEO: Andrew J. Littlefair
CFO: Richard R. Wheeler
HR: –
FYE: December 31
Type: Public

Forget cooking with gas, Clean Energy Fuels is driving with gas. Natural gas, that is. The company operates 170 gas stations in the US and Canada where its more than 275 fleet customers can tank up their more than 14,000 fleet vehicles with compressed natural gas (CNG) or liquefied natural gas (LNG). Clean Energy also helps customers buy and finance natural gas vehicles and obtain government incentives. The company buys CNG from local utilities and produces LNG at its 35-million-gallon-capacity plant in Texas. Clean Energy plans to build a LNG plant in the Western US and to buy fleet vehicles that it will later sell to customers. Founder and billionaire oilman T. Boone Pickens owns 55.6% of the company.

	Annual Growth	12/03	12/04	12/05	12/06	12/07
Sales ($ mil.)	30.7%	40.3	57.6	78.0	91.6	117.7
Net income ($ mil.)	—	0.0	2.1	17.3	(77.5)	(8.9)
Market value ($ mil.)	—	—	—	—	—	670.3
Employees	—	—	—	—	—	—

CLEAN HARBORS, INC.

NASDAQ (GS): CLHB

42 Longwater Dr.
Norwell, MA 02061
Phone: 781-792-5000
Fax: 781-792-5900
Web: www.cleanharbors.com

CEO: Alan S. McKim
CFO: James M. Rutledge
HR: Darren Scandone
FYE: December 31
Type: Public

One of North America's leading hazardous waste management companies, Clean Harbors does more than its name suggests. Clean Harbors' technical services, which account for most of the company's sales, encompass the collection, transportation, treatment, and disposal of hazardous waste, including chemical and laboratory waste but not nuclear waste. The company's 49 waste management facilities includes nine landfills, six incineration locations, and six wastewater treatment centers. Among Clean Harbors' 45,000-plus customers are commercial and industrial companies, educational and research organizations, and health care providers. Alan McKim, the company's chairman and CEO, controls 15% of Clean Harbors.

	Annual Growth	12/03	12/04	12/05	12/06	12/07
Sales ($ mil.)	11.6%	611.0	643.2	711.2	829.8	946.9
Net income ($ mil.)	—	(17.3)	2.6	25.6	46.7	44.2
Market value ($ mil.)	70.6%	123.9	216.2	557.6	953.0	1,050.9
Employees	10.6%	—	—	3,900	4,574	4,769

An in-depth profile of this company is available to Hoover's Online members at hoovers.com.

CLEAR CHANNEL COMMUNICATIONS, INC.

NYSE: CCU

200 E. Basse Rd.	CEO: Mark P. Mays
San Antonio, TX 78209	CFO: Randall T. Mays
Phone: 210-822-2828	HR: Bill Hamersly
Fax: 210-822-2299	FYE: December 31
Web: www.clearchannel.com	Type: Public

This company leaves few open channels on the radio dial. Clear Channel Communications is the #1 radio company in the US, with about 1,000 stations located throughout the country. Its Premier Radio Networks produces syndicated radio content for more than 5,000 stations. Clear Channel also sells spot advertising for more than 3,200 radio stations and nearly 400 TV stations through Katz Media. In addition to radio, the company owns a 90% stake in Clear Channel Outdoor Holdings, one of the world's largest outdoor advertising companies with nearly 900,000 display locations worldwide. The company has agreed to be taken private by an investment group led by Thomas H. Lee Partners and Bain Capital.

	Annual Growth	12/03	12/04	12/05	12/06	12/07
Sales ($ mil.)	(6.5%)	8,930.9	9,418.5	6,610.4	7,067.0	6,816.9
Net income ($ mil.)	(4.9%)	1,145.6	(4,038.2)	935.7	691.5	938.5
Market value ($ mil.)	(11.3%)	27,813.1	18,319.8	16,925.6	17,552.1	17,188.1
Employees	(14.2%)	—	—	31,800	30,900	23,400

CLEAR CHANNEL OUTDOOR HOLDINGS, INC.

NYSE: CCO

200 E. Basse Rd.	CEO: Mark P. Mays
San Antonio, TX 78209	CFO: Randall T. Mays
Phone: 210-832-3700	HR: –
Fax: –	FYE: December 31
Web: www.clearchanneloutdoor.com	Type: Public

In the great outdoors, billboards in clear view mean money for Clear Channel Outdoor Holdings. The company is a leading display advertising operator, with almost 900,000 properties in some 65 countries. Besides billboards, the company sells advertising on buses and trains and on "street furniture" such as bus stops and information kiosks in metropolitan markets. It has about 210,000 display spots in the Americas, where its operations include selling space in airports and malls and on the sides of high-profile buildings, as well as creating displays that feature video and moving parts. Clear Channel Communications, the #1 radio broadcaster, owns about 90% of the company.

	Annual Growth	12/03	12/04	12/05	12/06	12/07
Sales ($ mil.)	10.8%	2,174.6	2,447.0	2,666.1	2,897.7	3,281.8
Net income ($ mil.)	—	(35.0)	(155.4)	61.6	153.1	246.0
Market value ($ mil.)	25.9%	—	—	706.5	1,104.3	1,120.0
Employees	(43.8%)	—	—	7,600	7,700	2,400

CLEARCUBE TECHNOLOGY, INC.

8834 Capital of Texas Hwy. North	CEO: Randy Printz
Austin, TX 78759	CFO: Donald (Don) Neville
Phone: 512-652-3500	HR: –
Fax: 512-652-3501	FYE: December 31
Web: www.clearcube.com	Type: Private

ClearCube Technology aims to clear some cubicles. The company designs personal computing systems that eliminate the need for bulky desktop PCs. Its Blade units house an Intel processor, memory, and hard drive, and are contained in centralized, stackable racks. Computer users connect to Blades through ClearCube's Command Ports. Roughly the size of a videocassette, the units contain ports for peripheral devices such as monitors and keyboards and can be located as much as 200 meters from the Blades. ClearCube customers include Lillian Vernon, Morgan Stanley, and Starwood Hotels & Resorts. The company was founded in 1997.

	Annual Growth	12/03	12/04	12/05	12/06	12/07
Est. sales ($ mil.)	—	—	—	—	—	44.3
Employees	—	—	—	—	—	160

CLEARFIELD, INC.

NASDAQ (GM): CLFD

5480 Nathan Ln. North, Ste. 120	CEO: Cheri Beranek Podzimek
Plymouth, MN 55442	CFO: –
Phone: 763-476-6866	HR: –
Fax: 763-475-8457	FYE: September 30
Web: www.apacn.com	Type: Public

Clearfield provides fiber optic cable and related optical networking equipment. Products include fiber distribution panels and cable management systems, optical components (couplers, multiplexers, and splitters), and copper and fiber optic cable assemblies. It sells directly to telecom service providers and OEMs. Formerly called APA Enterprises, the company merged its operations with those of its primary subsidiary, APA Cables & Networks (APACN), and changed its name to Clearfield in 2008. Previously the company also operated an optronics unit, but it exited that business in 2007.

	Annual Growth	3/04	3/05	3/06	3/07	*9/07
Sales ($ mil.)	(3.5%)	11.9	13.9	15.7	18.6	10.3
Net income ($ mil.)	—	(6.5)	(3.4)	(3.3)	(2.2)	(1.3)
Market value ($ mil.)	(19.6%)	29.6	16.7	23.2	14.5	12.3
Employees	(3.3%)	147	127	128	133	—

*Fiscal year change

CLEARONE COMMUNICATIONS, INC.

OTC: CLRO

5225 Wiley Post Way, Ste. 500	CEO: Zeynep (Zee) Hakimoglu
Salt Lake City, UT 84116	CFO: Greg A. LeClaire
Phone: 801-975-7200	HR: –
Fax: 801-977-0087	FYE: June 30
Web: www.clearone.com	Type: Public

ClearOne Communications wants voices to carry, loud and clear. The company provides audio conferencing systems to small and large enterprises, educational institutions, churches, and government agencies. It also sells related products including microphones and equipment carts. ClearOne's conferencing systems connect large venues such as auditoriums and board rooms, as well as desktops and small conference rooms. The company markets its products worldwide, selling primarily through distributors who in turn sell to systems integrators and resellers.

	Annual Growth	6/03	6/04	6/05	6/06	6/07
Sales ($ mil.)	(8.8%)	57.6	33.9	31.6	37.6	39.9
Net income ($ mil.)	—	(36.0)	(9.9)	16.1	2.1	5.2
Market value ($ mil.)	21.0%	23.8	60.7	41.7	42.6	51.1
Employees	—	—	—	—	—	—

CLEARPOINT BUSINESS RESOURCES, INC.

NASDAQ (CM): CPBR

1600 Manor Dr., Ste. 110	CEO: Michael D. (Mike) Traina
Chalfont, PA 18914	CFO: John G. (Jack) Phillips
Phone: 215-997-7710	HR: –
Fax: 215-997-7711	FYE: December 31
Web: www.clear-point.com	Type: Public

ClearPoint Business Resources aims to score points with customers by helping them obtain temporary employees. Through its iLabor online platform, the company enables customers to find temporary staff members from ClearPoint-approved third-party staffing vendors. Customers use ClearPoint's StaffPillar technology to manage human resources, including permanent as well as contract employees. ClearPoint, through third-party vendors, also offers business process outsourcing (BPO) services and project-based staffing in industries such as distribution, logistics, and transportation.

	Annual Growth	12/03	12/04	12/05	12/06	12/07
Sales ($ mil.)	—	—	—	—	—	191.7
Net income ($ mil.)	—	—	—	—	—	(12.4)
Market value ($ mil.)	—	—	—	—	—	27.9
Employees	—	—	—	—	—	—

An in-depth profile of this company is available to Hoover's Online members at hoovers.com.

389

CLEARSTORY SYSTEMS, INC.

Pink Sheets: CSYS

1 Research Dr., Ste. 200 B
Westborough, MA 01581
Phone: 508-870-4000
Fax: 508-870-5585
Web: www.clearstorysystems.com

CEO: Henry F. Nelson
CFO: –
HR: –
FYE: March 31
Type: Public

ClearStory Systems (formerly INSCI Corp.) is a friend to trees everywhere. The enterprise content management software provider helps companies store, access, and present documents, reports, statements, e-mails, and digital files. ClearStory's software includes an electronic statement presentation system that stores and retrieves electronic files. The company's ActiveMedia product allows companies to manage media content such as graphics, images, and video. ClearStory sells directly and through alliances with Unisys and Xerox. SCP Private Equity Partners owns a majority stake in the company.

	Annual Growth	3/02	3/03	3/04	3/05	*3/06
Sales ($ mil.)	8.1%	8.5	9.2	8.8	11.6	11.6
Net income ($ mil.)	—	0.4	1.4	(2.3)	(1.2)	(1.2)
Employees	—	—	—	—	—	72

*Most recent year available

CLEARWIRE CORPORATION

NASDAQ (GM): CLWR

4400 Carillon Point
Kirkland, WA 98033
Phone: 425-216-7600
Fax: 425-216-7900
Web: www.clearwire.com

CEO: Craig O. McCaw
CFO: John A. Butler
HR: Christine M. Bertany
FYE: December 31
Type: Public

Clearwire obviously has tomorrow in mind. The company operates a wireless broadband network that provides services to nearly 400,000 subscribers primarily in the US and Europe. Services include high-speed Internet access and computer telephony. Its service areas cover about four dozen markets located mainly along the West Coast and in Texas, Florida, North Carolina, and the Midwest. Internationally, Clearwire serves broadband users in Brussels, Belgium; Dublin, Ireland; Seville, Spain; and Denmark, through Danske Telecom; as well as in Mexico, through partner MVSNet. The company was founded in 2003 and is controlled by wireless pioneer Craig McCaw (founder of the one-time leading cellular service McCaw Cellular).

	Annual Growth	12/03	12/04	12/05	12/06	12/07
Sales ($ mil.)	—	0.0	15.3	33.5	100.2	151.4
Net income ($ mil.)	—	(1.4)	(33.0)	(139.9)	(284.2)	(727.5)
Market value ($ mil.)	—	—	—	—	—	1,858.6
Employees	—	—	—	—	—	—

CLEARY GOTTLIEB STEEN & HAMILTON LLP

1 Liberty Plaza
New York, NY 10006
Phone: 212-225-2000
Fax: 212-225-3999
Web: www.cgsh.com

CEO: Mark A. Walker
CFO: Renée M. Lercher
HR: Norma F. Cirincione
FYE: December 31
Type: Partnership

Cleary Gottlieb Steen & Hamilton may be a big cheese in the Big Apple, but the law firm also has made a name for itself in the international arena. Cleary Gottlieb's attorneys work from 12 offices scattered across the globe and are known for their work in such practice areas as corporate finance, mergers and acquisitions, litigation, and intellectual property. The firm boasts almost 800 attorneys, with a third of those based outside the US. Representative clients have included British Airways, Deutsche Telekom, and other multinational and international corporations. The firm was founded in 1946 by former Root Clark Buckner partners George Cleary, Leo Gottlieb, Fowler Hamilton, and Mel Steen.

	Annual Growth	12/03	12/04	12/05	12/06	12/07
Est. sales ($ mil.)	—	—	—	—	—	758.8
Employees	—	—	—	—	—	2,200

CLEAVER-BROOKS, INC.

11950 W. Lake Park Dr.
Milwaukee, WI 53224
Phone: 414-359-0600
Fax: 414-438-4930
Web: www.cleaver-brooks.com

CEO: Welch P. Goggins
CFO: Jeffrey G. Beine
HR: Eric Master
FYE: March 31
Type: Private

When it comes to boilers and burners, leave it to Cleaver-Brooks. Formerly known as Aqua-Chem, the company sold the assets of its Water Technologies division (which developed water treatment products for commercial, government, military, and industrial customers) in 2006 to Altus Capital Partners, a buyout firm. The new company took on the Aqua-Chem corporate moniker, while the former Aqua-Chem renamed itself after its Cleaver-Brooks unit, which manufactures commercial and industrial boilers, burners, and accessories. Other units include Gonzales Manufacturing, Energy Recovery International, Lincoln Manufacturing, and Nebraska Boiler.

	Annual Growth	3/03	3/04	3/05	3/06	3/07
Est. sales ($ mil.)	—	—	—	—	—	209.7
Employees	—	—	—	—	—	1,000

CLECO CORPORATION

NYSE: CNL

2030 Donahue Ferry Rd.
Pineville, LA 71360
Phone: 318-484-7400
Fax: 318-484-7488
Web: www.cleco.com

CEO: Michael H. (Mike) Madison
CFO: R. Russell Davis
HR: Catherine C. Powell
FYE: December 31
Type: Public

Down in the Louisiana bayous, Cleco comes alive with the click of a light switch. The holding company's utility unit, Cleco Power, generates, transmits, and distributes electricity to approximately 273,000 residential and business customers in 106 communities in Louisiana. Cleco Power has a generating capacity of about 1,360 MW from its interests in fossil-fueled power plants. It also purchases power from other utilities and energy marketers, and it sells some excess power to wholesale customers. Subsidiary Cleco Midstream Resources develops merchant power plants and offers energy management services.

	Annual Growth	12/03	12/04	12/05	12/06	12/07
Sales ($ mil.)	4.0%	876.2	59.1	914.0	996.2	1,025.4
Net income ($ mil.)	—	(34.9)	12.5	59.1	64.8	84.7
Market value ($ mil.)	18.6%	844.0	997.9	1,045.4	1,511.7	1,668.2
Employees	0.3%	1,203	1,165	1,158	2,067	1,216

CLEMENS FAMILY CORPORATION

2700 Funks Rd.
Hatfield, PA 19440
Phone: 215-368-2500
Fax: 215-362-1750
Web: www.clemensfamilycorp.com

CEO: Philip A. (Phil) Clemens
CFO: David Budnick
HR: David J. Kolesky
FYE: April 30
Type: Private

The Clemens Family Corporation manufactures processed pork products from bacon to scrapple through its Hatfield Quality Meats business. Its Hatfield-branded products are sold through grocers in the northeastern and mid-Atlantic US. The family-owned company also owns Country View Family Farms, which raises and slaughters pigs (for Hatfield products), Wild Bill's Foods, which manufactures and sells beef jerky, and CFC Logistics, which provides blast freezing, cold storage, and distribution services. Clemens shut down CFC Logistics' irradiation operations, which had provided irradiation services to both food and non-food manufacturers, in 2005.

	Annual Growth	4/03	4/04	4/05	4/06	4/07
Est. sales ($ mil.)	—	—	—	—	—	93.5
Employees	—	—	—	—	—	1,667

An in-depth profile of this company is available to Hoover's Online members at hoovers.com.

CLEMENT PAPPAS & CO., INC.

10 N. Parsonage Rd.
Seabrook, NJ 08302
Phone: 856-455-1000
Fax: 856-455-8746
Web: www.clementpappas.com

CEO: Dean C. Pappas
CFO: Dmitri Pappas
HR: Barbara Ashley
FYE: March 31
Type: Private

The Clement Pappas company makes canned, bottled, and shelf-stable apple, cranberry, and other fruit juices, as well as canned cocktail mixers and cranberry sauce. It markets in Canada and the US under its Crofter's Organic and Ruby Kist brands. It also makes the organic Grown Right brand as well as private-label and food service brands. In 2007, The company acquired the HR Nicholson Company juice and beverage supplier to the foodservice industry under private labels and its own brand, Bombay. Clement Pappas & Co., Inc, was founded by Clement Dimitri Pappas, who emigrated to the US in 1914. It continues to be owned and operated by the Pappas family.

	Annual Growth	3/03	3/04	3/05	3/06	3/07
Est. sales ($ mil.)	—	—	—	—	—	165.4
Employees	—	—	—	—	—	793

CLEVELAND BIOLABS, INC.

NASDAQ (CM): CBLI

73 High St.
Buffalo, NY 14203
Phone: 716-849-6810
Fax: –
Web: www.cbiolabs.com

CEO: Michael Fonstein
CFO: John A. Marhofer Jr.
HR: –
FYE: December 31
Type: Public

Cleveland BioLabs' goals are simple: develop drugs that help healthy cells stay that way, as well as drugs that promote cell death in cancerous tumors. The company has based its research on the suppression and stimulation of the process known as apoptosis, a form of cell-death that occurs after exposure to radiation, toxic chemicals, or internal stresses. In development are two product lines: Protectans (suppressing apoptosis in healthy cells after radiation exposure) and Curaxins (stimulating apoptosis in some forms of cancer). Protectans have applications in cancer treatment and in providing some protection after a nuclear event (accidental or intentional).

	Annual Growth	12/03	12/04	12/05	12/06	12/07
Sales ($ mil.)	111.5%	0.1	0.6	1.1	1.7	2.0
Net income ($ mil.)	—	(0.1)	(2.5)	(2.4)	(7.2)	(27.0)
Market value ($ mil.)	90.4%	—	—	—	59.6	113.5
Employees	—	—	—	—	—	—

THE CLEVELAND CLINIC FOUNDATION

9500 Euclid Ave.
Cleveland, OH 44195
Phone: 216-444-2200
Fax: –
Web: www.clevelandclinic.org

CEO: Delos M. (Toby) Cosgrove
CFO: Steven C. Glass
HR: Robert W. Coulton Jr.
FYE: December 31
Type: Foundation

Cleveland may be home to the Rock and Roll Hall of Fame, but you don't have to have the rocking pneumonia or the boogie woogie flu to visit another Cleveland institution: The Clinic. The heart of the Cleveland Clinic Foundation, the hospital has more than 1,000 beds and offers specialized care, including organ transplantation, minimally invasive surgery, and cancer treatment, along with medical education and research opportunities. The foundation includes an international care center, children's hospital, and a rehabilitation facility. The Cleveland Clinic Foundation is part of the Cleveland Clinic Health System, which includes community health care centers in and around Cleveland.

	Annual Growth	12/03	12/04	12/05	12/06	12/07
Est. sales ($ mil.)	—	—	—	—	—	2,147.5
Employees	—	—	—	—	—	20,000

THE CLEVELAND ELECTRIC ILLUMINATING COMPANY

76 S. Main St.
Akron, OH 44308
Phone: 800-646-0400
Fax: 330-384-3866
Web: www.firstenergycorp.com

CEO: Anthony J. Alexander
CFO: Richard H. (Rich) Marsh
HR: –
FYE: December 31
Type: Subsidiary

The Cleveland Electric Illuminating Company (CEI) has a glowing reputation. The utility, commonly referred to as The Illuminating Company, distributes electricity to a base population of about 1.8 million inhabitants of northeastern Ohio. CEI has 25,240 miles of distribution lines and 2,135 miles of transmission lines. The utility also has more than 4,470 MW of generating capacity from interests in fossil-fueled and nuclear power plants (which are operated by fellow FirstEnergy subsidiaries), and it engages in wholesale energy transactions with other power companies.

CLEVELAND-CLIFFS INC

NYSE: CLF

1100 Superior Ave.
Cleveland, OH 44114
Phone: 216-694-5700
Fax: 216-694-4880
Web: www.cleveland-cliffs.com

CEO: Joseph A. Carrabba
CFO: Laurie Brlas
HR: Randy L. Kummer
FYE: December 31
Type: Public

Cleveland-Cliffs' favorite period in history: the Iron Age; the company produces iron ore pellets, a key component of steelmaking. It owns or holds stakes in six iron ore properties, including Northshore Mining and Empire Iron, that represent more than 45% of North American iron ore pellet production capacity. Cleveland-Cliffs' mines produce more than 35 million tons of iron ore pellets annually. The company's share is about 20 million tons, and the remainder represents the holdings of other mine owners. Cleveland-Cliffs sells its iron ore pellets primarily in the US and Canada but also in Europe and China. The company owns an 80% stake in Australian iron miner Portman, which supplies the Asia/Pacific region.

	Annual Growth	12/03	12/04	12/05	12/06	12/07
Sales ($ mil.)	27.6%	857.7	1,206.7	1,739.5	1,933.4	2,275.2
Net income ($ mil.)	—	(32.7)	323.6	277.6	280.1	270.0
Market value ($ mil.)	201.6%	26.5	280.4	485.3	990.7	2,196.6
Employees	2.5%	—	—	4,085	4,189	—

CLICK COMMERCE, INC.

233 N. Michigan Ave., 22nd Fl.
Chicago, IL 60601
Phone: 312-482-9006
Fax: 312-482-8557
Web: www.clickcommerce.com

CEO: Eric Meerschaert
CFO: Mike Drazin
HR: Katie Weems
FYE: December 31
Type: Subsidiary

Click Commerce helps companies change the channel. The company offers channel management, collaborative commerce, and compliance automation software that enterprises use to manage their sales channels and supply chains, collaborate with partners and customers, improve service processes, and track compliance. Other applications include tools for warehouse management, supply chain execution, secure communications, relationship and opportunity management, sales and service management, and product information and content management. Click Commerce was acquired by Illinois Tool Works for approximately $292 million in 2006.

An in-depth profile of this company is available to Hoover's Online members at hoovers.com.

391

CLIF BAR INC.

1610 5th St.
Berkeley, CA 94710
Phone: 510-558-7855
Fax: 510-558-7872
Web: www.clifbar.com

CEO: Gary J. Erickson
CFO: Richard (Rich) Boragno
HR: David Jericoff
FYE: December 31
Type: Private

Clif Bar found a toehold in a niche market and has climbed steadily up ever since. The company is a leading maker of natural energy, nutrition, and snack bars. Its high-carbohydrate CLIF and LUNA bars are aimed at sports enthusiasts and busy folk of all stripes and are distributed in bike shops, outdoor stores, and natural food markets, as well as grocery stores, convenience stores, and other retail outlets nationwide. In addition to its CLIF and LUNA bars, the company offers various iterations of its product, including MOJO, Nectar, and Builders bars, along with a children's version called ZBar. It also sells CLIF Shots — energy drinks and gels fortified with electrolytes.

	Annual Growth	12/03	12/04	12/05	12/06	12/07
Est. sales ($ mil.)	—	—	—	—	—	88.5
Employees	—	—	—	—	—	170

CLIFTON GUNDERSON LLP

301 SW Adams St., Ste. 600
Peoria, IL 61602
Phone: 309-671-4560
Fax: 309-671-4576
Web: www.cliftoncpa.com

CEO: Carl R. George
CFO: David E. Bailey
HR: Lauren J. Malensek
FYE: May 31
Type: Partnership

From its Midwest roots, Clifton Gunderson has branched out to spread its all-American brand of accounting. The firm offers accouting, auditing, business valuation, management consulting, and tax services to clients in industries including agribusiness, health care, and manufacturing. Subsidiaries provide financial planning, technology consulting, and investment services. The firm also provides international services through an affiliation with HLB International, a member organization that represents more than 100 nations. Clifton Gunderson has about 50 offices in some 20 states.

	Annual Growth	5/03	5/04	5/05	5/06	5/07
Est. sales ($ mil.)	—	—	—	—	—	89.2
Employees	—	—	—	—	—	1,460

CLIFTON SAVINGS BANCORP, INC.

NASDAQ (GS): CSBK

1433 Van Houten Ave.
Clifton, NJ 07015
Phone: 973-473-2200
Fax: 973-473-0451
Web: www.cliftonsavings.com

CEO: Walter Celuch
CFO: Christine R. Piano
HR: Josephine T. Scavone
FYE: March 31
Type: Public

You don't need CliffsNotes to figure out that Clifton Savings Bancorp is the holding company of Clifton Savings Bank, which operates 10 branches in northeastern New Jersey's Bergen and Passaic counties. The bank serves consumer and business clients, offering checking and savings accounts, IRAs, CDs, and mortgages and other loans. Its lending portfolio is dominated by real estate loans, primarily one- to four-family residential mortgages; the bank also issues multifamily real estate, commercial real estate, construction, land development, and consumer loans. Mutual holding company Clifton MHC owns a majority of Clifton Savings Bancorp's common stock.

	Annual Growth	3/04	3/05	3/06	3/07	3/08
Assets ($ mil.)	4.9%	742.3	841.9	834.9	805.0	899.1
Net income ($ mil.)	(10.3%)	3.7	5.3	3.7	2.5	2.4
Market value ($ mil.)	(9.5%)	410.6	341.9	323.7	343.8	275.3
Employees	(6.2%)	—	109	98	96	—

CLINICAL DATA, INC.

NASDAQ (GM): CLDA

1 Gateway Center, Ste. 702
Newton, MA 02458
Phone: 617-527-9933
Fax: 617-965-0445
Web: www.clda.com

CEO: Andrew J. (Drew) Fromkin
CFO: C. Evan Ballantyne
HR: Lynn Ferrucci
FYE: March 31
Type: Public

Clinical Data's products and services are central to health and life. The company provides molecular and pharmacogenomics services, as well as clinical diagnostics, in the field of patient care. Following a series of acquisitions, divestitures, and reorganizations, Clinical Data operates through two divisions: Cogenics, which offers services for both research and regulated environments in the health care and life sciences industries; and PGxHealth, which develops genetic tests, pharmocogenetic tests, and therapeutic products. Customers in North America represent about two-thirds of Clinical Data's sales.

	Annual Growth	3/03	3/04	3/05	3/06	3/07
Sales ($ mil.)	41.5%	15.9	52.5	56.4	68.8	63.7
Net income ($ mil.)	—	0.1	2.2	3.4	(50.9)	(37.5)
Market value ($ mil.)	109.9%	7.1	38.2	48.1	116.4	138.6
Employees	49.1%	93	218	247	472	459

CLINTON GROUP, INC.

9 W. 57 St., 26th Fl.
New York, NY 10019
Phone: 212-825-0400
Fax: 212-825-0079
Web: www.clinton.com

CEO: George E. Hall
CFO: John L. Hall
HR: –
FYE: December 31
Type: Private

This group doesn't feature space-suit wearing funkmeisters or former presidents. But hedge fund manager Clinton Group does administer more than $1 billion in assets for banks, insurance firms, pension funds, and wealthy individuals in the US and abroad. It also manages $6 billion in collateralized debt obligations. Through a holding company, Clinton Group is controlled by George Hall, who co-founded the company in 1991. The company's investment strategy involves taking simultaneous long and short positions on mortgage-backed securities, convertible bonds, sovereign debt, and equities.

	Annual Growth	12/03	12/04	12/05	12/06	12/07
Est. sales ($ mil.)	—	—	—	—	—	12.0
Employees	—	—	—	—	—	102

THE CLOROX COMPANY

NYSE: CLX

1221 Broadway
Oakland, CA 94612
Phone: 510-271-7000
Fax: 510-832-1463
Web: www.thecloroxcompany.com

CEO: Donald R. (Don) Knauss
CFO: Daniel J. (Dan) Heinrich
HR: Jacqueline P. (Jackie) Kane
FYE: June 30
Type: Public

Bleach is the cornerstone of Clorox. It offers its namesake household cleaning products, where it is a leader worldwide, and reaches beyond bleach. Clorox makes laundry and cleaning items (Formula 409, Pine-Sol, Tilex), dressing/sauce (Hidden Valley, KC Masterpiece), cat litter (Fresh Step, Scoop Away), car care products (Armor All, STP), the Brita water-filtration system (in North America), and charcoal briquettes (Kingsford, Match Light). Its First Brands buy gave Clorox Glad-brand plastic wraps, storage bags, and containers. Clorox entered the natural personal care niche with its acquisition of Burt's Bees in late 2007. Jerry Johnston, former chairman and CEO, retired in May 2006.

	Annual Growth	6/03	6/04	6/05	6/06	6/07
Sales ($ mil.)	4.0%	4,144.0	4,324.0	4,388.0	4,644.0	4,847.0
Net income ($ mil.)	0.4%	493.0	549.0	1,096.0	444.0	501.0
Market value ($ mil.)	0.8%	9,113.3	11,454.5	8,451.8	9,224.7	9,393.0
Employees	0.0%	—	—	7,600	7,600	—

CLST HOLDINGS, INC.

Pink Sheets: CLHI

17304 Preston Rd., Ste. 420	CEO: Robert A. Kaiser
Dallas, TX 75252	CFO: Robert A. Kaiser
Phone: 972-267-0500	HR: –
Fax: 972-267-0504	FYE: November 30
Web: www.clstholdings.com	Type: Public

If CLST Holdings sent a text message to your mobile phone, it might say, "c u later." The company, formerly called CellStar, was a leading wholesaler of cellular phones. It distributed phones and accessories made by manufacturers including Nokia, Kyocera Wireless, LG Electronics, and Motorola to retailers, carriers, exporters, and dealers in North America and Latin America. Its distribution services included inventory, logistics, testing and repair, wireless activation services, and e-commerce management plans. Faced with declining sales, the company announced plans to divest its operations in 2006.

	Annual Growth	11/02	11/03	11/04	11/05	*11/06
Sales ($ mil.)	(19.1%)	2,196.6	1,793.4	1,272.0	987.3	943.1
Net income ($ mil.)	—	(29.9)	(19.7)	(118.1)	(24.6)	4.8
Employees	(10.7%)	1,100	1,050	1,100	1,290	700

*Most recent year available

CLUBCORP USA, INC.

3030 LBJ Fwy., Ste. 600	CEO: Eric L. Affeldt
Dallas, TX 75234	CFO: –
Phone: 972-243-6191	HR: John H. Longstreet
Fax: 972-888-7558	FYE: December 31
Web: www.clubcorp.com	Type: Private

This company makes its green from the green — the golf green, that is. ClubCorp is the world's largest operator of golf courses and private clubs with about 170 facilities throughout the US and in Mexico and Australia. Its resorts and golf courses include such well-known venues as Firestone Country Club (Akron, Ohio), Homestead Resort (Hot Springs, Virginia), and Mission Hills Country Club (Rancho Mirage, California). ClubCorp also operates private business and sports clubs. Robert Dedman started the company in 1957. It is owned by private equity firm KSL Capital Partners.

	Annual Growth	12/02	12/03	12/04	12/05	12/06
Sales ($ mil.)	1.9%	947.0	911.5	944.1	1,028.1	1,020.0
Employees	(2.6%)	20,000	19,000	18,500	18,300	18,000

CLX INVESTMENT COMPANY, INC.

OTC: CLXN

29970 Technology Dr., Ste. 203	CEO: Vera Leonard
Murrieta, CA 92563	CFO: –
Phone: 951-677-6735	HR: –
Fax: 951-677-6573	FYE: September 30
Web: www.clxinvestments.com	Type: Public

CLX Investment Company, operating as CLX Medical, jumped out of the oil and gas business and into the world of health care. Founded as an oil and gas exploration and development company, the company now focuses on private equity investments. In 2007 the firm gained a majority stake in medical diagnostics firm Zonda; it now plans to invest in technologies that will complement and supplement Zonda's enzymatic detection technology. The company sold its stake in government training company eStrategy Solutions in 2007 and plans to sell its stake in electronic billboard firm ActionView.

	Annual Growth	9/02	9/03	9/04	9/05	*9/06
Sales ($ mil.)	0.0%	—	—	—	0.1	0.1
Net income ($ mil.)	—	—	—	—	(1.1)	(0.3)
Market value ($ mil.)	—	—	—	—	2.7	—
Employees	—	—	—	—	—	1

*Most recent year available

CME GROUP INC.

NYSE: CME

20 S. Wacker Dr.	CEO: Craig S. Donohue
Chicago, IL 60606	CFO: James E. (Jamie) Parisi
Phone: 312-930-1000	HR: Eileen (Beth) Keeve
Fax: 312-466-4410	FYE: December 31
Web: www.cmegroup.com	Type: Public

CME Group doesn't tell futures, but it does sell them. The company owns the Chicago Mercantile Exchange, launched in 1898 as The Chicago Butter and Egg Board, and the Chicago Board of Trade (CBOT), the futures exchange that it acquired for approximately $12 billion in 2007. CME and CBOT provide a marketplace for agricultural commodities, as well as for interest rate, equity, government paper, and foreign exchange futures. Products are traded on its CME GLOBEX electronic trading system, on its floors via an open outcry system using elaborate hand signals (the pits are scheduled to close in 2008), and through privately negotiated transactions. The company is buying New York rival NYMEX.

	Annual Growth	12/03	12/04	12/05	12/06	12/07
Sales ($ mil.)	34.0%	—	—	977.3	1,089.9	1,756.1
Net income ($ mil.)	46.5%	—	—	306.9	407.4	658.5
Market value ($ mil.)	69.7%	—	—	12,694.8	17,757.4	36,548.7
Employees	22.1%	—	—	1,321	1,430	1,970

CMGI, INC.

NASDAQ (GM): CMGI

1100 Winter St., Ste. 4600	CEO: Joseph C. (Joe) Lawler
Waltham, MA 02451	CFO: Steven G. Crane
Phone: 781-663-5001	HR: James J. (Jim) Herb
Fax: 781-663-5100	FYE: July 31
Web: www.cmgi.com	Type: Public

CMGI provides supply chain management services and invests in technology ventures. Its ModusLink subsidiary offers inventory management and distribution services for customers across a number of high-tech industries, including computer hardware and software, consumer electronics, and telecommunications equipment. It configures and distributes products from more than 30 facilities in 12 countries. The company's largest customer, Hewlett-Packard, accounted for about 30% of the company's revenues in fiscal 2007. CMGI also has a technology-focused venture capital business called Ventures.

	Annual Growth	7/03	7/04	7/05	7/06	7/07
Sales ($ mil.)	27.2%	437.0	397.4	1,069.8	1,148.9	1,143.0
Net income ($ mil.)	—	(216.3)	87.0	26.5	14.9	49.4
Market value ($ mil.)	2.0%	708.1	554.2	920.7	506.4	767.5
Employees	(7.4%)	—	—	3,728	3,729	3,200

CMP MEDIA LLC

600 Community Dr.	CEO: Steve Weitzner
Manhasset, NY 11030	CFO: Adam K. Marder
Phone: 516-562-5000	HR: Marvlieu Jolla Hall
Fax: 516-562-7830	FYE: December 31
Web: www.cmp.com	Type: Subsidiary

A subsidiary of UK-based United Business Media, CMP Media is one of the world's top technology publishers. Its stable of offerings includes magazines such as *CRN* and *InformationWeek*. The company is active online through Web versions of its print publications, and portals such as ChannelWeb (for computer resellers and VARs) and TechWeb (technology news). The company also organizes events such as the Game Developer Conference and Web 2.0 Expo. CMP additionally offers marketing services, product testing, and custom research and consulting.

	Annual Growth	12/03	12/04	12/05	12/06	12/07
Est. sales ($ mil.)	—	—	—	—	—	209.4
Employees	—	—	—	—	—	1,850

An in-depth profile of this company is available to Hoover's Online members at hoovers.com.

CMS ENERGY CORPORATION

NYSE: CMS

1 Energy Plaza
Jackson, MI 49201
Phone: 517-788-0550
Fax: 517-788-1859
Web: www.cmsenergy.com

CEO: David W. Joos
CFO: Thomas J. Webb
HR: John M. Butler
FYE: December 31
Type: Public

Michigan consumers rely on CMS Energy. The energy holding company's utility, Consumers Energy, has a generating capacity of 9,300 MW (primarily fossil-fueled) and distributes electricity and natural gas to about 3.5 million customers in Michigan. The company sells wholesale electricity, natural gas, and other commodities; its independent power projects have a gross capacity of 1,078 MW. CMS Energy's had international interests in plants, pipelines, and utilities in Africa, Asia, and Latin America but is divesting these in order to focus on domestic operations. In 2007 CMS Energy sold its trouble-plagued Palisades nuclear plant to Entergy.

	Annual Growth	12/03	12/04	12/05	12/06	12/07
Sales ($ mil.)	3.5%	5,677.0	5,587.0	6,413.0	6,899.0	6,504.0
Net income ($ mil.)	—	(44.0)	121.0	(84.0)	(79.0)	(215.0)
Market value ($ mil.)	29.9%	1,372.6	2,037.7	3,199.5	3,720.8	3,912.2
Employees	(4.8%)	—	—	8,713	8,640	7,898

CNA FINANCIAL CORPORATION

NYSE: CNA

333 S. Wabash
Chicago, IL 60604
Phone: 312-822-5000
Fax: 312-822-6419
Web: www.cna.com

CEO: Thomas F. Motamed
CFO: D. Craig Mense
HR: —
FYE: December 31
Type: Public

CNA Financial is the umbrella organization for a wide range of insurance providers, including Continental Casualty and Continental Assurance. The company primarily provides commercial coverage, with such standard offerings as workers' compensation, general and professional liability, and other products for businesses and institutions. CNA also sells specialty insurance including professional liabilty for doctors, lawyers, and architects, and vehicle warranty service contracts. The company also offers commercial surety bonds, risk and health care claims management, claims administration, and information services. Holding company Loews owns about 90% of CNA.

	Annual Growth	12/03	12/04	12/05	12/06	12/07
Assets ($ mil.)	(4.6%)	68,503.0	62,411.0	58,786.0	60,283.0	56,732.0
Net income ($ mil.)	—	(1,433.0)	446.0	264.0	1,108.0	851.0
Market value ($ mil.)	14.1%	5,389.2	6,846.8	8,378.9	10,931.1	9,128.6
Employees	(3.5%)	—	—	10,100	9,800	9,400

CNA SURETY CORPORATION

NYSE: SUR

333 S. Wabash Ave.
Chicago, IL 60604
Phone: 312-822-5000
Fax: 312-755-3737
Web: www.cnasurety.com

CEO: John F. Welch
CFO: John F. Corcoran
HR: Barbara A. Wood
FYE: December 31
Type: Public

If the job doesn't get done, CNA Surety pays the price. One of the largest surety companies in the US, CNA Surety offers contract and commercial surety bonds, which guarantee fulfillment of contracts. The company's Western Surety unit handles fidelity, commercial, and contract bonds and international surety and credit insurance; Surety Bonding, another subsidiary, specializes in commercial and contract bonds to small businesses. Contract surety (for construction contractors) accounts for nearly two-thirds of CNA Surety's premiums. CNA Surety sells its products in all 50 states through a network of independent agents and brokers. CNA Financial owns 62% of CNA Surety.

	Annual Growth	12/03	12/04	12/05	12/06	12/07
Assets ($ mil.)	6.6%	1,169.1	1,174.5	1,262.6	1,368.3	1,507.7
Net income ($ mil.)	—	(14.1)	39.7	38.4	82.8	92.5
Market value ($ mil.)	20.9%	408.7	574.3	631.4	943.2	873.2
Employees	(0.5%)	—	—	747	—	739

CNB CORPORATION

Pink Sheets: CNBW

1400 3rd Ave.
Conway, SC 29528
Phone: 843-248-5721
Fax: 843-488-8279
Web: www.conwaynationalbank.com

CEO: W. Jennings Duncan
CFO: L. Ford Sanders II
HR: —
FYE: December 31
Type: Public

CNB likes to C customers coming through the door. CNB is the holding company for The Conway National Bank, which primarily serves individuals and small to midsized businesses in eastern South Carolina. Tracing its roots back more than a century, the bank offers traditional deposit products including checking and savings accounts, IRAs, and NOW accounts. Mortgages and construction loans dominate the company's lending activities (together comprising about three-fourths of its loan book); the bank also offers commercial, industrial, consumer, and agricultural loans. CNB operates about a dozen branches in Horry and Georgetown counties.

	Annual Growth	12/03	12/04	12/05	12/06	12/07
Assets ($ mil.)	—	—	—	—	—	865.6
Net income ($ mil.)	—	—	—	—	—	9.7
Employees	—	—	—	—	—	264

CNB CORPORATION

OTC: CNBZ

303 N. Main St.
Cheboygan, MI 49721
Phone: 231-627-7111
Fax: 231-627-7283
Web: www.cnbismybank.com

CEO: Susan A. Eno
CFO: —
HR: —
FYE: December 31
Type: Public

See the national bank you were looking for? Look at CNB Corporation. The institution is a holding company for Citizens National Bank of Cheboygan, which targets individuals and local businesses through a handful of full-service branches in the Michigan counties of Cheboygan, Emmet, and Presque Isle. The bank offers standard fare such as checking, savings, money market, individual retirement accounts, and NOW accounts. It also offers brokerage services and life insurance through partnerships. Bank subsidiary CNB Mortgage Corporation handles all residential mortgages. Citizens National Bank was originally founded in 1931.

	Annual Growth	12/03	12/04	12/05	12/06	12/07
Assets ($ mil.)	0.1%	—	254.1	252.7	251.9	255.2
Net income ($ mil.)	1.1%	—	3.0	3.3	3.3	3.1
Market value ($ mil.)	(14.8%)	—	60.0	55.1	52.7	37.2
Employees	—	—	—	—	87	—

CNB FINANCIAL CORPORATION

NASDAQ (GS): CCNE

1 S. 2nd St.
Clearfield, PA 16830
Phone: 814-765-9621
Fax: 814-765-4511
Web: www.bankcnb.com

CEO: William F. Falger
CFO: Charles R. Guarino
HR: —
FYE: December 31
Type: Public

CNB Financial is the holding company for CNB Bank (formerly County National Bank), which provides traditional deposit and loan services through more than 20 branches and two loan production offices in northwestern and central Pennsylvania. In 2006 the company opened ERIEBANK, a division of County National Bank, in Erie, Pennsylvania. Commercial, financial, and agricultural loans make up almost 40% of CNB Financial's loan portfolio, which also includes residential mortgages (about 30%) and commercial mortgages (more than 25%). Other offerings include credit cards, investments, life and accidental death and disability insurance, and merchant card processing.

	Annual Growth	12/03	12/04	12/05	12/06	12/07
Assets ($ mil.)	5.1%	701.8	725.2	764.0	780.8	856.3
Net income ($ mil.)	0.0%	9.1	7.9	9.1	9.6	9.1
Market value ($ mil.)	17.1%	61.5	139.4	127.3	125.7	115.9
Employees	—	—	—	246	—	—

CNBC, INC.

900 Sylvan Ave.
Englewood Cliffs, NJ 07632
Phone: 201-735-2622
Fax: 201-735-3200
Web: www.cnbc.com

CEO: Mark Hoffman
CFO: Satpal Brainch
HR: Nikki Gonzalez
FYE: December 31
Type: Subsidiary

Getting to the bottom of business news is top priority for CNBC. The cable network, a unit of NBC Universal Cable, reaches more than 95 million homes in the US and Canada with 24-hour financial news and information, as well as interviews with business leaders, industry experts, and stock analysts. After the markets close and on the weekends, CNBC shifts to more in-depth programming such as *Meet the Press* and *The Chris Matthews Show*, as well as entertainment programming including golf tournaments. Its international divisions, including CNBC Asia, CNBC Europe, and CNBC World, reach more than 250 million additional homes around the world. In addition to TV, CNBC provides news and information online.

	Annual Growth	12/03	12/04	12/05	12/06	12/07
Est. sales ($ mil.)	—	—	—	—	—	43.8
Employees	—	—	—	—	—	400

⊞ CNET NETWORKS, INC.

NASDAQ (GS): CNET

235 Second St.
San Francisco, CA 94105
Phone: 415-344-2000
Fax: –
Web: www.cnetnetworks.com

CEO: Neil M. Ashe
CFO: Alexander J. (Zander) Lurie
HR: Jose Martin
FYE: December 31
Type: Public

Tune into this network and you can get the scoop on the latest and greatest technology, food, and entertainment. CNET Networks provides technology related information, product reviews, and price comparisons through its flagship Web site CNET.com. The company has been extending its customer base from the IT market into holdings that cover more general consumer categories. Those sites include GameSpot (video game-related content), CHOW (content for food and drink enthusiasts), BNET (information for business managers), and TV.com (content for television fans). A consortium of investment funds led by hedge fund Jana Partners has a 21% stake in CNET; CBS has announced plans to buy the firm for about $1.8 billion.

	Annual Growth	12/03	12/04	12/05	12/06	12/07
Sales ($ mil.)	13.3%	246.2	291.2	354.2	387.4	405.9
Net income ($ mil.)	—	(26.3)	11.7	19.6	6.8	176.5
Market value ($ mil.)	9.5%	969.1	1,622.2	2,184.2	1,361.7	1,392.4
Employees	7.4%	—	—	2,340	2,620	2,700

CNG FINANCIAL CORP.

5155 Financial Way
Mason, OH 45040
Phone: 513-336-7735
Fax: 513-573-4680
Web: www.checkngo.com

CEO: Jared A. Davis
CFO: Stephen Curtis
HR: –
FYE: December 31
Type: Private

If your finances are touch-and-go, you can go to Check 'n Go. The subsidiary of CNG Financial provides customers with payday loans, which are unsecured, short-term cash advances often used to cover unplanned expenses. Loan amounts range from $50 to $1,500. Other products include installment loans through CNG partner First Bank of Delaware, which range from $750 to more than $1,500. Borrowers can apply at any of Check 'n Go's more than 1,400 branch locations in some 35 states, or online via the company's Web site.

	Annual Growth	12/03	12/04	12/05	12/06	12/07
Est. sales ($ mil.)	—	—	—	—	—	358.8
Employees	—	—	—	—	—	3,000

CNH CAPITAL AMERICA LLC

233 Lake Ave.
Racine, WI 53403
Phone: 262-636-6011
Fax: 262-626-3602
Web: www.cnhcapital.com

CEO: Steven (Steve) Bierman
CFO: –
HR: –
FYE: December 31
Type: Subsidiary

CNH Capital America reaps the benefits of its relationship to parent CNH Global, a world leader in the manufacturing of agricultural and construction equipment. The company provides funding services to buyers and dealers of CNH Global's products. Throughout the US and Canada, CNH Capital America offers loans, leases, and revolving accounts to retail, commercial, and municipal customers who purchase Case, Case IH, Kobelco, and New Holland brand machinery. The company's eqpower service facilitates online purchases and sales of used agricultural equipment. The firm also offers related insurance and warranty products.

	Annual Growth	12/03	12/04	12/05	12/06	12/07
Est. sales ($ mil.)	—	—	—	—	—	35.7
Employees	—	—	—	—	—	400

CNL FINANCIAL GROUP, INC.

CNL Center at City Commons, 450 S. Orange Ave.
Orlando, FL 32801
Phone: 407-650-1000
Fax: 407-650-1011
Web: www.cnl.com

CEO: James M. Seneff Jr.
CFO: Tracy G. Schmidt
HR: Lisa A. Schultz
FYE: December 31
Type: Private

CNL Financial Group is a real estate mother hen. The company develops and incubates real estate businesses until they can be launched into the world. Founded in 1973 by CEO James Seneff Jr., the firm's current collection of companies includes CNL Lifestyle Co, the advisor to CNL Lifestyle Properties, a non-traded real estate investment trust (REIT); and CNL Securities, which provides funding for CNL Financial Group and its joint venture partners. CNL Financial also owns several firms that manage the investments of its affiliate companies. Other ventures include banking, commercial finance, and property development.

	Annual Growth	12/03	12/04	12/05	12/06	12/07
Est. sales ($ mil.)	—	—	—	—	—	77.4
Employees	—	—	—	—	—	600

CNX GAS CORPORATION

NYSE: CXG

5 Penn Center West, Ste. 401
Pittsburgh, PA 15276
Phone: 412-200-6700
Fax: 412-200-6761
Web: www.cnxgas.com

CEO: Nicholas J. Deluliis
CFO: William J. Lyons
HR: –
FYE: December 31
Type: Public

CNX Gas may sound like a product for riot control, but it is in fact a company that produces a more innocuous, but valuable, commodity. A part of CONSOL Energy, CNX Gas is one of the most productive coalbed methane gas (CBM) producers in the US. Through its properties in the Appalachian Basin (primarily in Pennsylvania, Tennessee, Virginia, and West Virginia) CNX Gas is responsible for producing about 58.3 billion cu. ft. of gas per year. In 2007 the company had 1.3 trillion cu. ft. of proved reserves. That year it acquired 1 million acres of coalbed methane properties from Peabody Energy for $66.5 million. CONSOL owns 82% of the company.

	Annual Growth	12/03	12/04	12/05	12/06	12/07
Sales ($ mil.)	(11.8%)	—	—	613.4	513.9	477.3
Net income ($ mil.)	15.2%	—	—	102.2	159.9	135.7
Market value ($ mil.)	25.3%	—	—	—	3,847.0	4,821.7
Employees	44.8%	—	—	134	—	281

⊞ An in-depth profile of this company is available to Hoover's Online members at hoovers.com.

395

COACH, INC.

NYSE: COH

516 W. 34th St.
New York, NY 10001
Phone: 212-594-1850
Fax: 212-594-1682
Web: www.coach.com

CEO: Lew Frankfort
CFO: Michael F. (Mike) Devine III
HR: Melanie Hughes
FYE: Saturday nearest June 30
Type: Public

Coach is riding in style, thanks to the company's leather items and some savvy licensing deals. The firm designs and manufactures (mostly through third parties) high-end leather goods and accessories, including purses, outerwear, luggage, and gloves. Coach, founded in 1941, also licenses its name for watches, eyewear, fragrances, and footwear. The company sells its wares through department and outlet stores (in the US and in 18 other countries), catalogs, and its Web site. It also runs about 260 retail stores in North America (with plans to add more by 2009), as well as in Japan. The firm got into selling scents in late 2006.

	Annual Growth	6/03	6/04	6/05	6/06	6/07
Sales ($ mil.)	28.7%	953.2	1,321.1	1,710.4	2,111.5	2,612.5
Net income ($ mil.)	45.9%	146.6	261.8	388.6	494.3	663.7
Market value ($ mil.)	98.3%	1,142.4	4,369.8	12,696.3	11,057.9	17,653.8
Employees	31.6%	—	—	5,700	7,500	—

COACH USA, LLC

160 S. Route 17 N.
Paramus, NJ 07652
Phone: 201-225-7500
Fax: 201-225-7590
Web: www.coachusa.com

CEO: Dale Moser
CFO: –
HR: –
FYE: April 30
Type: Subsidiary

Bus operator Coach USA gets a little coaching from across the Atlantic. One of the largest bus companies in the US, Coach USA is a unit of Stagecoach Group, a UK-based bus and train operator. Coach USA, through about 20 subsidiaries, operates scheduled routes (including airport transportation), charters, and sightseeing tours, primarily in the Northeast and the Midwest. The company's fleet includes buses, vans, minibuses (with a 24- to 30-passenger capacity), and school buses. Coach USA's megabus.com unit, modeled after a Stagecoach offering, provides low-fare scheduled intercity express service to more than a dozen midwestern markets.

	Annual Growth	4/03	4/04	4/05	4/06	4/07
Est. sales ($ mil.)	—	—	—	—	—	783.5
Employees	—	—	—	—	—	5,000

COACHMEN INDUSTRIES, INC.

NYSE: COA

423 North Main St.
Middlebury, IN 46540
Phone: 574-825-5821
Fax: 574-825-8141
Web: www.coachmen.com

CEO: Richard M. Lavers
CFO: Colleen Zuhl
HR: Leslie G. Thimlar
FYE: December 31
Type: Public

Coachmen Industries manufactures homes that travel and homes that stay put. The company makes motor homes, travel trailers, and camping trailers (including fifth-wheel models) under such brands as Coachmen, Sportscoach, Georgie Boy, and Viking. It also makes modular housing including single- and multi-family housing and apartments, as well as structures used in commercial or municipal applications. Coachmen sells its RVs through about 760 independent dealers located across the US; it sells modular buildings to residential developers and to businesses, mainly in the midwestern and southeastern US.

	Annual Growth	12/03	12/04	12/05	12/06	12/07
Sales ($ mil.)	(9.3%)	711.1	865.1	702.4	564.4	480.8
Net income ($ mil.)	—		7.4	15.3	(26.4)	(31.8)	(38.8)
Market value ($ mil.)	(24.0%)	281.7	273.0	186.1	173.0	93.9
Employees	(20.8%)	—	—	3,677	2,655	2,305

COACTIVE MARKETING GROUP, INC.

NASDAQ (CM): CMKG

75 Ninth Ave.
New York, NY 10011
Phone: 212-660-3800
Fax: 212-660-3878
Web: www.coactivemarketing.com

CEO: Charles F. (Charlie) Tarzian
CFO: Fred Kaseff
HR: Gloria Pervolaris
FYE: March 31
Type: Public

CoActive Marketing Group wants a little action and a lot of attention. Through various subsidiaries, the company provides integrated marketing services primarily for manufacturers of packaged goods and consumer product manufacturers such as Coca-Cola, Fisher Price, and Safeway. The group's services include strategic consulting, direct marketing, sales promotion (sampling and sweepstakes), event marketing, multicultural marketing, and interactive services. It designs and coordinates displays, artwork, and sales campaigns on a local, regional, and national level. One client, Diageo North America, accounted for more than 60% of the company's revenue in 2007. CoActive Marketing Group was established in 1992.

	Annual Growth	3/04	3/05	3/06	3/07	3/08
Sales ($ mil.)	5.2%	69.7	83.9	96.9	95.9	85.5
Net income ($ mil.)	—	(2.8)	1.1	(1.8)	1.0	1.5
Market value ($ mil.)	7.7%	16.3	22.9	14.6	14.8	22.0
Employees	—	—	—	—	4,545	—

COAST BANCORP

OTC: CTBP

500 Marsh St.
San Luis Obispo, CA 93401
Phone: 805-541-0400
Fax: 805-541-5758
Web: www.coastnationalbank.com

CEO: Jack C. Wauchope
CFO: Karan C. Pohl
HR: –
FYE: December 31
Type: Public

Dude, where's my car loan? Maybe with Coast Bancorp, holding company for Coast National Bank. Founded in 1997, the bank operates branches in the California communities of Arroyo Grande, Los Osos, Morro Bay, Paso Robles, and San Luis Obispo, as well as loan production offices in Fresno and Santa Maria. It offers traditional products and services including checking, savings, money market, and individual retirement accounts; certificates of deposit; debit and credit cards; and Internet banking. The bank's primary source of revenue is generated from loans to customers who are predominantly small to midsized businesses and individuals.

	Annual Growth	12/02	12/03	12/04	12/05	*12/06
Assets ($ mil.)	10.3%	122.0	142.1	159.9	185.7	180.7
Net income ($ mil.)	15.0%	0.8	1.0	1.1	1.1	1.4
Market value ($ mil.)	19.8%	11.1	15.0	18.3	20.2	22.9
Employees	—	—	—	—	—	—

*Most recent year available

THE COAST DISTRIBUTION SYSTEM, INC.

AMEX: CRV

350 Woodview Ave.
Morgan Hill, CA 95037
Phone: 408-782-6686
Fax: 408-782-7790
Web: www.coastdistribution.com

CEO: Jim Musbach
CFO: Sandra A. Knell
HR: David Smeltzer
FYE: December 31
Type: Public

This company's products are at home on the road or on the water. The Coast Distribution System is a leading provider of accessories, replacement parts, and supplies for recreational vehicles (RVs) and a leading distributor of boating and marine accessories and parts. The company distributes more than 15,000 products, such as appliances, awnings, boat covers, life jackets, and trailer hitches, to more than 14,000 customers, primarily RV and boat dealerships, supply stores, and service centers. The Coast Distribution System delivers its products from 17 warehouses in the US and Canada.

	Annual Growth	12/03	12/04	12/05	12/06	12/07
Sales ($ mil.)	1.2%	156.5	171.8	176.3	179.1	164.3
Net income ($ mil.)	(46.8%)	2.5	4.4	3.8	3.0	0.2
Market value ($ mil.)	1.0%	25.0	34.4	33.0	38.2	26.1
Employees	2.5%	—	—	400	410	—

COASTAL BANKING COMPANY, INC.

OTC: CBCO

36 Sea Island Pkwy.
Beaufort, SC 29901
Phone: 843-522-1228
Fax: 843-524-4510
Web: www.coastalbanking.com

CEO: Michael G. Sanchez
CFO: Paul R. Garrigues
HR: –
FYE: December 31
Type: Public

Hoping to provide traditional small-town banking amid rapid growth in the Southeast, a group of area banking veterans formed Coastal Banking Company in 2000. The holding company owns Lowcountry National Bank, which operates two branches in southern South Carolina and First National Bank of Nassau County which operates about five branches in northeastern Florida and in Georgia under The Georgia Bank name. The banks offer standard products and services, including loans, checking and savings accounts, NOW accounts, and CDs.

	Annual Growth	12/03	12/04	12/05	12/06	12/07
Assets ($ mil.)	41.4%	107.9	146.1	355.2	426.2	431.6
Net income ($ mil.)	30.4%	0.9	1.1	1.5	3.4	2.6
Market value ($ mil.)	22.8%	15.3	16.5	45.1	54.1	34.8
Employees	—	—	—	—	—	92

COASTAL PACIFIC FOOD DISTRIBUTORS, INC.

1015 Performance Dr.
Stockton, CA 95206
Phone: 209-983-2454
Fax: 209-983-8009
Web: www.cpfd.com

CEO: Jerry Jared
CFO: John Payne III
HR: Amber Parker
FYE: January 31
Type: Private

If an army really does move on its stomach, then this company keeps the military in high gear. Coastal Pacific Food Distributors (CPF) is a leading wholesale food distributor serving the US armed forces in the western US and in the Far East. The company delivers a full line of groceries to military bases, including US Army, Navy, Air Force, and Marine facilities, from three distribution centers in California and Washington. CPF also offers information system programming services for its customers to track sales and shipping. The company was founded in 1986.

	Annual Growth	1/03	1/04	1/05	1/06	1/07
Est. sales ($ mil.)	—	—	—	—	—	926.1
Employees	—	—	—	—	—	290

COBIZ FINANCIAL INCORPORATED

NASDAQ (GS): COBZ

821 17th St.
Denver, CO 80202
Phone: 303-293-2265
Fax: –
Web: www.cobizfinancial.com

CEO: Steven Bangert
CFO: Lyne B. Andrich
HR: –
FYE: December 31
Type: Public

CoBiz Financial is reaching new heights in the Rockies and in the Valley of the Sun. It's the holding company for CoBiz Bank, which operates as Colorado Business Bank and Arizona Business Bank. The former operates more than 10 branches in the Denver, Boulder, and Vail areas; the latter has about a half-dozen branches in and around Phoenix. CoBiz's locations operate as separate community banks, each with a local president that has decision-making authority; the downtown Denver office provides back-office support to all branches. In addition to banking, CoBiz offers insurance, investment banking, employee benefits consulting, investment advice, wealth management, and trust services through various subsidiaries.

	Annual Growth	12/03	12/04	12/05	12/06	12/07
Assets ($ mil.)	14.2%	1,403.9	1,699.6	1,933.1	2,112.4	2,391.0
Net income ($ mil.)	15.3%	13.0	17.6	20.0	22.8	23.0
Market value ($ mil.)	19.1%	169.8	445.6	406.7	500.3	341.9
Employees	—	—	—	467	—	—

COBRA ELECTRONICS CORPORATION

NASDAQ (GM): COBR

6500 W. Cortland St.
Chicago, IL 60707
Phone: 773-889-8870
Fax: 773-794-1930
Web: www.cobra.com

CEO: James R. Bazet
CFO: Michael Smith
HR: Lucy Vallicelli
FYE: December 31
Type: Public

Cobra Electronics' CB radios, radar detectors, and power inverters (capable of powering a laptop using a vehicle battery) are good buddies while your rig is on the road. Cobra manufactures hand-held GPS devices, marine radios, "Plug and Go" mobile navigation devices, and micro inverters with a USB port for use with an iPod, BlackBerry, and other devices. Products are made by suppliers in Asia and sold in the US, Canada, and Europe through consumer electronics stores, discount retailers, and truck stops. Cobra Electronics has boosted CB radio sales by launching limited-edition models cobranded with icons such as Harley-Davidson and Dale Earnhardt.

	Annual Growth	12/03	12/04	12/05	12/06	12/07
Sales ($ mil.)	8.0%	114.8	122.9	133.1	153.7	155.9
Net income ($ mil.)	—	1.8	2.4	12.0	(1.6)	(4.4)
Market value ($ mil.)	(10.3%)	48.5	52.3	86.8	61.5	31.4
Employees	—	—	—	151	—	—

⨃ COCA-COLA BOTTLING CO. CONSOLIDATED

NASDAQ (GM): COKE

4100 Coca-Cola Plaza
Charlotte, NC 28211
Phone: 704-557-4400
Fax: 704-551-4646
Web: www.cokebottling.com

CEO: J. Frank Harrison III
CFO: James E. (Jamie) Harris
HR: Kevin A. Henry
FYE: Sunday nearest December 31
Type: Public

Southerners like their drinks sweet, and for Coca-Cola Bottling Co. Consolidated (CCBCC), there's nothing sweeter than a Coke. CCBCC produces, bottles, and distributes beverages, principally the products of The Coca-Cola Company. Its distribution area is mainly in the southeastern US. The company is the #2 Coke bottler in the US (behind Coca-Cola Enterprises), serving areas in 11 US states — home to almost 19 million prospective and hopefully thirsty consumers. Coca-Cola Classic accounts for more than 50% of CCBCC's sales. The company does, however, own its own brands, including vitamin-enhanced Respect and Tum-E Yummies; energy drinks Frigid Dog, Scalded Dog, and Strait Dog; and Country Breeze tea.

	Annual Growth	12/03	12/04	12/05	12/06	12/07
Sales ($ mil.)	4.4%	1,210.8	1,256.5	1,380.2	1,431.0	1,436.0
Net income ($ mil.)	(10.3%)	30.7	21.9	23.0	23.2	19.9
Market value ($ mil.)	3.0%	350.2	379.0	285.7	454.6	394.4
Employees	(3.3%)	—	—	6,200	5,700	5,800

COCA-COLA BOTTLING CO. UNITED, INC.

4600 East Lake Blvd.
Birmingham, AL 35217
Phone: 205-841-2653
Fax: 205-841-9168

CEO: Claude B. Nielsen
CFO: Hafiz Chandiwala
HR: Debbie Myles
FYE: December 31
Type: Private

Coca-Cola Bottling Co. United brings icy-cold Cokes to the sunny South. Founded in 1902, Coke United serves up "the real thing" in The Coca-Cola Company's home turf, reaching consumers from Atlanta, Georgia, to Baton Rouge, Louisiana. It is the #3 Coca-Cola bottler (the world's #1 soft drink) in the US. Brands include Coca-Cola Classic, Diet Coke, Fresca, Sprite, and Vanilla Coke. Its 101-year-old subsidiary, Chattanooga Coca-Cola Bottling Co., is the world's oldest Coca-Cola franchise. In 2007 the company began building an $80 million production and distribution center in Baton Rouge.

	Annual Growth	12/03	12/04	12/05	12/06	12/07
Est. sales ($ mil.)	—	—	—	—	—	636.4
Employees	—	—	—	—	—	2,800

⨃ An in-depth profile of this company is available to Hoover's Online members at hoovers.com.

THE COCA-COLA COMPANY

NYSE: KO

1 Coca-Cola Plaza	CEO: E. Neville Isdell
Atlanta, GA 30313	CFO: Gary P. Fayard
Phone: 404-676-2121	HR: Cynthia P. McCague
Fax: –	FYE: December 31
Web: www.coca-cola.com	Type: Public

Coke is it — "it" being the world's #1 soft-drink company. The Coca-Cola Company owns four of the top five soft-drink brands (Coca-Cola, Diet Coke, Fanta, and Sprite). Its other brands include Barq's, Minute Maid, POWERade, and Dasani water. In North America, it sells Groupe Danone's Evian. Coca-Cola sells brands from Dr Pepper Snapple Group (Crush, Dr Pepper, and Schweppes) outside Australia, Europe, and North America. The firm makes or licenses more than 400 drink products in more than 200 nations. Although it does no bottling itself, Coke owns 35% of Coca-Cola Enterprises (the #1 Coke bottler in the world); 32% of Mexico's bottler Coca-Cola FEMSA; and 23% of European bottler Coca-Cola Hellenic Bottling.

	Annual Growth	12/03	12/04	12/05	12/06	12/07
Sales ($ mil.)	8.2%	21,044.0	21,962.0	23,104.0	24,088.0	28,857.0
Net income ($ mil.)	8.3%	4,347.0	4,847.0	4,872.0	5,080.0	5,981.0
Market value ($ mil.)	3.5%	123,907.7	100,324.9	95,494.4	111,843.5	142,255.7
Employees	28.3%	—	—	55,000	71,000	90,500

COCA-COLA ENTERPRISES INC.

NYSE: CCE

2500 Windy Ridge Pkwy.	CEO: John Franklin Brock
Atlanta, GA 30339	CFO: William W. (Bill) Douglas III
Phone: 770-989-3000	HR: Timothy W. Johnson
Fax: 770-989-3788	FYE: December 31
Web: www.cokecce.com	Type: Public

The scientists and the suits at The Coca-Cola Company (TCCC) concoct the secret recipes and market the brands, but Coca-Cola Enterprises (CCE) does much of the bottling and distribution of the soft drinks. The world's #1 Coke bottler, CCE accounts for 18% of worldwide sales of Coca-Cola's beverages. CCE also bottles and distributes other beverages, including Canada Dry and Dr Pepper (both brands owned by Dr Pepper Snapple Group), Nestea (Nestlé), bottled waters, and juices. It sells soft drinks in nearly every state, the US Virgin Islands, Canada, and six European countries. The company's territories consist of more than 414 million potential customers. The Coca-Cola Company owns approximately 35% of CCE.

	Annual Growth	12/03	12/04	12/05	12/06	12/07
Sales ($ mil.)	4.8%	17,330.0	18,158.0	18,706.0	19,804.0	20,936.0
Net income ($ mil.)	1.3%	676.0	596.0	514.0	(1,143.0)	711.0
Market value ($ mil.)	6.2%	9,967.3	9,792.2	9,082.7	9,795.3	12,675.4
Employees	0.0%	—	—	73,000	74,000	73,000

CODE HENNESSY & SIMMONS LLC

10 S. Wacker Dr., Ste. 3175	CEO: Andrew W. Code
Chicago, IL 60606	CFO: Michael L. Keesey
Phone: 312-876-1840	HR: –
Fax: 312-876-3854	FYE: December 31
Web: www.chsonline.com	Type: Partnership

Code Hennessy & Simmons makes no secret of its desire to invest. The company puts its money and expertise into spin-offs, IPOs, and add-on acquisitions. It also helps public companies go private. Code Hennessy & Simmons looks for opportunities in the manufacturing, service, and distribution industries — it avoids certain volatile industries, such as high-tech — and typically invests $40 million to $400 million, taking board seats at the companies in which it invests. Founded in 1988, Code Hennessy & Simmons manages more than $2.5 billion in five funds.

	Annual Growth	12/03	12/04	12/05	12/06	12/07
Est. sales ($ mil.)	—	—	—	—	—	44.9
Employees	—	—	—	—	—	800

CODORUS VALLEY BANCORP, INC.

NASDAQ (GM): CVLY

105 Leader Heights Rd.	CEO: Larry J. Miller
York, PA 17405	CFO: Jann Allen Weaver
Phone: 717-747-1519	HR: Matthew A. Clemens
Fax: 717-741-9582	FYE: December 31
Web: www.peoplesbanknet.com	Type: Public

Codorus Valley Bancorp is people oriented. The firm is the holding company for PeoplesBank, which operates more than a dozen branches in southeastern Pennsylvania's York County and Hunt Valley, Maryland. The bank offers a full range of commercial and consumer services, including checking and savings accounts and CDs. Some three-fourths of the bank's loan portfolio consists of business, industrial, and agricultural loans; residential mortgage, construction, land development, and consumer loans round out its lending activities. Subsidiary Codorus Valley Financial Advisors offers investment products, and its SYC Settlement Services provides real estate settlement services.

	Annual Growth	12/03	12/04	12/05	12/06	12/07
Assets ($ mil.)	12.4%	372.5	407.7	476.0	548.2	594.6
Net income ($ mil.)	17.1%	3.4	4.0	4.6	5.3	6.4
Market value ($ mil.)	6.9%	46.5	47.4	52.9	64.5	60.6
Employees	6.2%	—	—	181	—	204

COEUR D'ALENE MINES CORPORATION

NYSE: CDE

400 Coeur d'Alene Mines Bldg., 505 Front Ave.	CEO: Dennis E. Wheeler
Coeur d'Alene, ID 83816	CFO: Mitchell J. Krebs
Phone: 208-667-3511	HR: Larry A. Nelson
Fax: 208-667-2213	FYE: December 31
Web: www.coeur.com	Type: Public

Coeur d'Alene Mines gets to the heart of the matter when it comes to precious metals. A leading primary silver producer, the company holds interests in silver and gold properties in North America, South America, Africa, and Australia. It produces about 12 million ounces of silver and 100,000 ounces of gold annually. Coeur d'Alene has proved and probable reserves of about 215 million ounces of silver and 1.5 million ounces of gold. Coeur d'Alene produces most of its revenue from the Rochester mine in Nevada and the Cerro Bayo mine in Chile. In 2007 it bought Australian miner Bolnisi Gold and the Canadian Palmarejo in a deal valued at $1.1 billion.

	Annual Growth	12/03	12/04	12/05	12/06	12/07
Sales ($ mil.)	18.1%	110.5	133.4	172.3	216.6	215.3
Net income ($ mil.)	—	(66.2)	(16.9)	10.6	88.5	43.9
Market value ($ mil.)	21.9%	1,231.9	943.1	1,111.8	1,376.1	2,719.2
Employees	(22.8%)	—	—	1,206	931	—

COFFEE HOLDING CO., INC.

AMEX: JVA

4401 1st Ave., Ste. 1507	CEO: Andrew Gordon
Brooklyn, NY 11232	CFO: Andrew Gordon
Phone: 718-832-0800	HR: –
Fax: 718-832-0892	FYE: October 31
Web: www.coffeeholding.com	Type: Public

Coffee Holding Co. has brewed up the idea of selling a wide spectrum of raw and roasted Arabica coffee beans to wholesalers like Green Mountain Roasters as well as private-label coffees to foodservice suppliers such as Nash Finch. Coffee Holding imports its beans from Indonesia, Mexico, and South America through several dealers. In addition to producing private-label coffees for stores, the company also sells name brands including IL CLASSICO and S&W. Its Cafe Caribe espresso coffee targets the Hispanic market. The company has expanded its offerings through partnerships. CEO Andrew Gordon, son of company founder Sterling Gordon, and the Gordon family own about 60% of the company.

	Annual Growth	10/03	10/04	10/05	10/06	10/07
Sales ($ mil.)	29.8%	20.2	28.0	41.5	51.2	57.4
Net income ($ mil.)	10.7%	0.6	0.9	1.2	0.7	0.9
Market value ($ mil.)	(10.1%)	—	—	35.2	21.6	28.4
Employees	5.9%	—	—	74	79	83

COGDELL SPENCER INC.

NYSE: CSA

4401 Barclay Downs Dr., Ste. 300
Charlotte, NC 28209
Phone: 704-940-2900
Fax: 704-940-2957
Web: www.cogdellspencer.com

CEO: Frank C. Spencer
CFO: Charles M. (Chuck) Handy
HR: –
FYE: December 31
Type: Public

Cogdell Spencer puts its money where your health is. The self-administered real estate investment trust (REIT) acquires, develops, and manages health care properties, including surgery centers, medical office buildings, and rehabilitation facilities, most of which are located on hospital campuses. It owns or manages about 120 properties, totaling more than 5 million sq. ft. of space in a dozen states; the majority are located in South Carolina, North Carolina, and Georgia. Subsidiary Marshall Erdman & Associates designs and builds health care facilities. It has provided planning, engineering, construction, and related services for more than 5,000 properties throughout the US.

	Annual Growth	12/03	12/04	12/05	12/06	12/07
Sales ($ mil.)	12.8%	42.0	44.7	46.4	55.8	67.9
Net income ($ mil.)	—	3.7	8.0	(1.8)	(9.1)	(6.3)
Market value ($ mil.)	34.9%	—	—	135.1	172.0	245.8
Employees	18.6%	—	75	80	127	125

COGENT COMMUNICATIONS GROUP, INC.

NASDAQ (GM): CCOI

1015 31st St. NW
Washington, DC 20007
Phone: 202-295-4200
Fax: 202-295-9061
Web: www.cogentco.com

CEO: David (Dave) Schaeffer
CFO: Thaddeus (Tad) Weed
HR: –
FYE: December 31
Type: Public

Cogent Communications Group offers a forceful sales pitch: broadband data at the speed of light. The company operates a fiber-optic IP network that spans the Atlantic — from Canada and the US to Western Europe. It offers dedicated Internet access to businesses through Ethernet connections linking more than 1,100 office buildings to its network. Its more than 12,300 customers include financial services companies, universities, and law firms. Cogent Communications also sells access to its network and provides colocation and modem management services to Internet service providers (ISPs), hosting companies, and other big bandwidth users.

	Annual Growth	12/03	12/04	12/05	12/06	12/07
Sales ($ mil.)	33.0%	59.4	91.3	135.2	149.1	185.7
Net income ($ mil.)	—	140.7	(89.7)	(67.5)	(53.8)	(31.0)
Market value ($ mil.)	38.8%	305.9	17.9	242.1	793.6	1,136.4
Employees	12.6%	—	—	340	—	431

COGENT, INC.

NASDAQ (GS): COGT

209 Fair Oaks Ave.
South Pasadena, CA 91030
Phone: 626-799-8090
Fax: 626-799-8996
Web: www.cogentsystems.com

CEO: Ming Hsieh
CFO: Paul Kim
HR: –
FYE: December 31
Type: Public

Cogent knows the power of good security. The company provides Automated Fingerprint Identification Systems (AFIS) that governments, law enforcement agencies, and other organizations use to capture, analyze, and compare fingerprints. Cogent's offerings include proprietary fingerprint biometrics software, hardware, and professional services such as consulting, implementation, and systems integration. The company's customers include the US Department of Homeland Security, Los Angeles County, and various programs in Europe. Chairman, president, and CEO Ming Hsieh controls more than 55% of Cogent.

	Annual Growth	12/03	12/04	12/05	12/06	12/07
Sales ($ mil.)	34.6%	32.2	87.7	159.9	101.7	105.8
Net income ($ mil.)	32.8%	9.2	42.6	65.3	29.7	28.6
Market value ($ mil.)	(26.5%)	—	2,666.0	2,132.2	1,041.7	1,060.0
Employees	18.9%	—	—	164	195	—

COGENTRIX ENERGY, LLC

9405 Arrowpoint Blvd.
Charlotte, NC 28273
Phone: 704-525-3800
Fax: 704-529-5313
Web: www.cogentrix.com

CEO: Larry Kellerman
CFO: John O'Connor
HR: Linda Okowita
FYE: December 31
Type: Private

Tricks are for kids, but Cogentrix Energy serves up a power treat for customers though its electric generating facilities. The company develops, owns, and operates independent power plants, located primarily in the US. Cogentrix Energy has an operational generating capacity of 3,300 MW from its stakes in more than 20 coal- and gas-fired facilities. The company also sells electricity wholesale to utilities and power marketers, primarily through long-term purchase or conversion contracts. New York-based investment firm Goldman Sachs Group acquired Cogentrix Energy in 2003.

	Annual Growth	12/03	12/04	12/05	12/06	12/07
Est. sales ($ mil.)	—	—	—	—	—	26.0
Employees	—	—	—	—	—	578

COGNEX CORPORATION

NASDAQ (GS): CGNX

1 Vision Dr.
Natick, MA 01760
Phone: 508-650-3000
Fax: 508-650-3344
Web: www.cognex.com

CEO: Robert J. (Bob) Shillman
CFO: Richard A. Morin
HR: –
FYE: December 31
Type: Public

Cognex machines see what mere mortals cannot. The company is one of the world's largest producers of systems that, linked to a video camera, serve as eyes where human vision is insufficient. Semiconductor, consumer goods, health care, and automotive companies, among others, use the company's machine vision systems to position and identify products, gauge sizes, and locate defects. Customers include manufacturers such as Ford Motor, Palomar Technologies, and Inex Vision Systems. Cognex also offers consulting and educational services, as well as technical support for its products. Sales to customers located outside the US account for more than 60% of sales.

	Annual Growth	12/03	12/04	12/05	12/06	12/07
Sales ($ mil.)	10.7%	150.1	202.0	216.9	238.4	225.7
Net income ($ mil.)	14.0%	15.9	37.7	35.7	39.9	26.9
Market value ($ mil.)	(8.4%)	1,242.9	1,287.7	1,419.4	1,057.7	873.4
Employees	3.9%	—	—	740	760	799

COGNIGEN NETWORKS, INC.

OTC: CGNW

6405 218th St. SW, Ste. 305
Mountlake Terrace, WA 98043
Phone: 425-329-2300
Fax: 425-329-2301
Web: www.cognigen.com

CEO: Robert K. Bench
CFO: Gary L. Cook
HR: –
FYE: June 30
Type: Public

BayHill Capital (formerly Cognigen Networks) resells telecommunications services via the Web. The company primarily earns commissions from online sales of domestic and international long-distance calling cards — as well as Internet access, wireless phone, and other telecom services — using independent sales agents and affinity group marketing programs. Telecom services are provided in partnership with such carriers as Covista and PowerNet Global. Through subsidiary Commission River, BayHill Capital provides affiliate marketing services for the real estate industry.

	Annual Growth	6/03	6/04	6/05	6/06	6/07
Sales ($ mil.)	(15.3%)	10.9	10.7	11.8	10.1	5.6
Net income ($ mil.)	—	0.4	(2.9)	1.8	(1.3)	(0.7)
Employees	—	—	—	—	—	4

An in-depth profile of this company is available to Hoover's Online members at hoovers.com.

399

COGNIS CORPORATION

5051 Estecreek Dr.
Cincinnati, OH 45232
Phone: 513-482-3000
Fax: 513-482-5503
Web: www.na.cognis.com

CEO: Paul S. Allen
CFO: George Annen
HR: Linda Crawford
FYE: December 31
Type: Subsidiary

Cognis Corporation is the North American presence of the German chemical manufacturer Cognis Deutschland. The company focuses on three product lines — care chemicals, coating technology, and oleochemicals — and accounts for about a quarter of its parent's total sales. Cognis Corp. operates from nine locations spread throughout the US and Canada. An investment group led by Permira and Goldman Sachs bought Cognis from Henkel in 2001.

COGNIZANT TECHNOLOGY SOLUTIONS

NASDAQ (GS): CTSH

500 Glenpointe Centre West
Teaneck, NJ 07666
Phone: 201-801-0233
Fax: 201-801-0243
Web: www.cognizant.com

CEO: Francisco (Frank) D'Souza
CFO: Gordon J. Coburn
HR: Sriram Rajagopal
FYE: December 31
Type: Public

Cognizant Technology Solutions Corporation (CTS) remains mindful of the state of your software. CTS provides application maintenance services, data warehousing, software development and integration, and reengineering services for legacy systems, primarily to medium-sized and large businesses. The majority of its sales are to customers in North America, including IMS Health, First Data, and ACNielsen. Most of the company's software development centers and employees are located in India, with others in the US. CTS serves clients in industries including financial services, health care, retail, and manufacturing.

	Annual Growth	12/03	12/04	12/05	12/06	12/07
Sales ($ mil.)	55.2%	368.2	586.7	885.8	1,424.3	2,135.6
Net income ($ mil.)	57.2%	57.4	100.2	166.3	232.8	350.1
Market value ($ mil.)	91.0%	734.1	2,839.9	3,502.5	5,498.2	9,775.1
Employees	51.0%	—	—	24,300	38,800	55,400

COHEN & STEERS, INC.

NYSE: CNS

280 Park Ave.
New York, NY 10017
Phone: 212-832-3232
Fax: 212-832-3622
Web: www.cohenandsteers.com

CEO: Martin Cohen
CFO: Matthew S. (Matt) Stadler
HR: –
FYE: December 31
Type: Public

For Cohen & Steers, REITs have the right stuff — for investing, that is. The company focuses primarily on asset management and investment banking products and services relating to real estate investment trusts (REITs) and other real estate investments; it also invests in electric and gas utilities. Cohen & Steers has about $30 billion in assets under management held in some 30 real estate mutual funds, as well as in around 80 separate accounts managed for institutional investors. The company also provides investment banking services for clients in the real estate sector.

	Annual Growth	12/03	12/04	12/05	12/06	12/07
Assets ($ mil.)	76.2%	34.5	160.3	198.6	285.1	332.2
Net income ($ mil.)	58.0%	12.1	7.3	31.9	3.2	75.5
Market value ($ mil.)	28.9%	—	575.1	660.0	1,560.5	1,233.1
Employees	37.1%	—	—	117	—	220

COHERENT, INC.

NASDAQ (GS): COHR

5100 Patrick Henry Dr.
Santa Clara, CA 95054
Phone: 408-764-4000
Fax: 408-764-4800
Web: www.coherentinc.com

CEO: John R. Ambroseo
CFO: Helene (Leen) Simonet
HR: Ronald A. (Ron) Victor
FYE: Saturday nearest September 30
Type: Public

Coherent's message to light is simple and clear: "Stick together!" The company makes lasers, laser instrumentation systems, and precision optical and optomechanical devices for a wide range of commercial and scientific uses. Its products are used to manufacture semiconductors and CDs, and in scientific instruments. Coherent's electro-optical lasers and laser systems also have applications for micromachining, information storage, multimedia entertainment, imaging and reprographics, and telecommunications. More than two-thirds of Coherent's sales are to customers outside the US.

	Annual Growth	9/03	9/04	9/05	9/06	9/07
Sales ($ mil.)	10.3%	406.2	495.0	516.3	584.7	601.2
Net income ($ mil.)	—	(45.9)	17.4	39.9	45.4	15.9
Market value ($ mil.)	8.1%	740.6	788.4	912.7	1,088.7	1,012.0
Employees	2.3%	2,136	2,218	2,189	2,345	2,339

COHU, INC.

NASDAQ (GS): COHU

12367 Crosthwaite Cir.
Poway, CA 92064
Phone: 858-848-8100
Fax: 858-848-8185
Web: www.cohu.com

CEO: James A. Donahue
CFO: Jeffrey D. Jones
HR: –
FYE: December 31
Type: Public

Cohu tries to blend various technologies into one coherent business. Of the company's three segments, the largest is Delta Design, a top maker of the test handling equipment that protects semiconductors during testing procedures. The company's customers include chip giants Advanced Micro Devices (28% of sales), Intel (27%), and Texas Instruments. Other operations include Cohu Electronics (closed-circuit television systems for surveillance, medical, and industrial applications) and Broadcast Microwave Services (microwave radios, antenna systems, and support equipment). The company derives about two-thirds of sales from customers outside the US.

	Annual Growth	12/03	12/04	12/05	12/06	12/07
Sales ($ mil.)	14.9%	138.6	176.2	238.9	270.1	241.4
Net income ($ mil.)	—	(0.1)	16.7	34.0	17.7	8.0
Market value ($ mil.)	(3.6%)	410.2	401.1	511.8	457.6	354.7
Employees	—	—	—	—	—	1,000

COINMACH SERVICE CORP.

303 Sunnyside Blvd., Ste. 70
Plainview, NY 11803
Phone: 516-349-8555
Fax: 516-349-9125
Web: www.coinmachservicecorp.com

CEO: Stephen R. (Steve) Kerrigan
CFO: Robert M. (Bob) Doyle
HR: Cathy Chambers
FYE: March 31
Type: Private

You won't find much dirty laundry at Coinmach. The leading US supplier of coin- and card-operated laundry equipment and related services has helped customers do millions of loads of laundry. Leasing laundry rooms in apartments and dormitories, Coinmach owns and operates more than 870,000 washing machines and dryers at about 80,000 locations nationwide. The company also owns Appliance Warehouse, which rents machines to apartment residents, laundromats, and management companies. Subsidiary Super Laundry designs and builds or retrofits retail laundromats and distributes laundry equipment. In mid-2007, Coinmach was acquired by Babcock & Brown, an investment firm located in Australia, for $1.3 billion in 2007.

	Annual Growth	3/03	3/04	3/05	3/06	3/07
Sales ($ mil.)	0.9%	535.2	531.1	538.6	543.5	555.3
Net income ($ mil.)	—	(3.2)	(31.3)	(35.3)	(24.6)	0.2
Employees	(0.6%)	1,994	—	2,082	—	1,950

An in-depth profile of this company is available to Hoover's Online members at hoovers.com.

COINSTAR, INC.

NASDAQ (GS): CSTR

1800 114th Ave. SE	CEO: David W. (Dave) Cole
Bellevue, WA 98004	CFO: Brian V. Turner
Phone: 425-943-8000	HR: Denise Rubin
Fax: 425-637-0045	FYE: December 31
Web: www.coinstar.com	Type: Public

Coinstar takes the contents of your penny jar and turns it into real money. The company owns and operates more than 15,400 coin-counting machines in the US, Canada, and the UK and some 300,000 entertainment services (skill-crane, bulk vending, and kiddie ride) machines across the US and Mexico. Coinstar also operates more than 17,500 point-of-sale terminals in the US and the UK. The coin-counting units are located mainly in supermarkets (such as Kroger and SUPERVALU); the entertainment services machines can be found in more than 27,000 retail locations including Wal-Mart and Kmart stores. Coinstar also offers prepaid services cards, money transfers, and gift cards.

	Annual Growth	12/03	12/04	12/05	12/06	12/07
Sales ($ mil.)	32.7%	176.1	307.1	459.7	534.4	546.3
Net income ($ mil.)	—	19.6	20.4	22.3	18.6	(22.3)
Market value ($ mil.)	19.4%	384.4	676.9	634.1	850.3	780.9
Employees	(2.5%)	—	—	2,000	1,900	1,900

COLAS INC.

10 Madison Ave., 4th Fl.	CEO: Michel Roullet
Morristown, NJ 07960	CFO: Dominique J. Leveille
Phone: 973-290-9082	HR: –
Fax: 973-290-9088	FYE: December 31
	Type: Subsidiary

Paving over amber waves of grain is Colas Inc., the US arm of global road construction powerhouse Colas. With operations in about 10 states, the contractor serves both the public and private sectors, primarily in the industrial and retail markets, providing construction on roads, highways, airport runways, and commercial buildings. Sister company Barrett Paving Materials is also engaged in the paving of US roads. North of the border, Colas Canada represents the Canadian market. Colas Inc., together with the rest of the company's North American business units, accounts for about 18% of its parent's annual revenues.

	Annual Growth	12/03	12/04	12/05	12/06	12/07
Est. sales ($ mil.)	—	—	—	—	—	1,733.3
Employees	—	—	—	—	—	4,500

COLD STONE CREAMERY, INC.

9311 E. Via de Ventura	CEO: Daniel (Dan) Beem
Scottsdale, AZ 85258	CFO: Walt Schultz
Phone: 480-362-4800	HR: –
Fax: 480-362-4812	FYE: December 31
Web: www.coldstonecreamery.com	Type: Subsidiary

This chain of ice cream shops is known for using mineral assets. Cold Stone Creamery has about 1,400 premium ice cream franchises across the US, as well as in China, Japan, Korea, and Puerto Rico. True to its name, the company's ingredients are blended into the ice cream on a cold stone. Patrons can create their own flavors by choosing from a variety of mix-ins, such as candy, fruit, and cookie dough. The shops also offer yogurt, sorbet, and other frozen treats. A small number of locations are operated by the company. Founders Donald and Susan Sutherland opened their first Cold Stone Creamery in Tempe, Arizona, in 1988. The company is owned by multi-concept franchisor Kahala Corp.

COLDWATER CREEK, INC.

NASDAQ (GS): CWTR

1 Coldwater Creek Dr.	CEO: Daniel (Dan) Griesemer
Sandpoint, ID 83864	CFO: Timothy O. (Tim) Martin
Phone: 208-263-2266	HR: Brett K. Avner
Fax: 208-263-1582	FYE: Saturday nearest January 31
Web: www.coldwater-creek.com	Type: Public

Shoppers quench their thirst for classic, casual clothing from Coldwater Creek's stores and catalogs. The upscale multi-channel retailer sells mostly traditional apparel through several catalogs, a Web site, some 300 full-line stores, and about 30 retail outlets, targeting middle- and upper-income baby boomers. *Northcountry*, the company's main catalog, features women's apparel, jewelry, and art. *Spirit* offers more upscale women's apparel and jewelry, while its *Sport* catalog (introduced in 2004) features casual women's activewear; all apparel catalogs include plus-sizes. Coldwater Creek was founded as a single catalog in 1984 by Dennis and Ann Pence.

	Annual Growth	1/04	1/05	1/06	1/07	1/08
Sales ($ mil.)	22.1%	518.8	590.3	779.7	1,054.6	1,151.5
Net income ($ mil.)	—	12.5	29.1	41.6	55.4	(2.5)
Market value ($ mil.)	57.6%	103.5	737.0	1,910.4	1,781.4	638.3
Employees	27.0%	—	—	8,170	11,577	13,171

COLEMAN CABLE, INC.

NASDAQ (GM): CCIX

1530 Shields Dr.	CEO: G. Gary Yetman
Waukegan, IL 60085	CFO: Richard N. Burger
Phone: 847-672-2300	HR: Cliff Sanderson
Fax: 847-689-1192	FYE: December 31
Web: www.colemancable.com	Type: Public

Coleman Cable cuts the mustard when it comes to cable and wire products. The company, which has 8,300 active customers, is a manufacturer of electrical and electronic wire and cable products that range from automotive spark plug wires and battery cables to coaxial cables used to connect audio and video devices. Typical customers are members of the automotive, construction, electronic, HVAC, irrigation, and voice and data industries. Coleman's brands include Baron, Polar Solar, Royal, Seoprene, and Signal. The cable and wire manufacturer operates domestic manufacturing and warehouse facilities, and it sells its products through industrial and specialty distributors throughout North America.

	Annual Growth	12/03	12/04	12/05	12/06	12/07
Sales ($ mil.)	38.7%	233.6	285.8	346.2	423.4	864.1
Net income ($ mil.)	30.7%	5.1	(9.0)	11.1	29.4	14.9
Market value ($ mil.)	—	—	—	—	—	158.6
Employees	—	—	—	—	—	—

THE COLEMAN COMPANY, INC.

3600 N. Hydraulic	CEO: Sam A. Solomon
Wichita, KS 67219	CFO: Daniel J. (Dan) Hogan
Phone: 316-832-2700	HR: George Retter
Fax: 316-832-3060	FYE: December 31
Web: www.coleman.com	Type: Subsidiary

The Coleman Company makes what it takes to be a happy camper. As a leading maker of outdoor recreation gear, it also produces coolers, backpacks, footwear, camp stoves/grills, and other camping accessories, sold under the BackHome, Coleman, Campingaz, Exponent, and Peak 1 brands. Coleman has sales offices and distribution facilities worldwide and sells its products mainly through mass merchandisers, home centers, and other retail stores, as well as through its Web site and a network of Coleman Company Factory Outlet stores. Founded in 1900, Coleman was acquired in 2005 by Jarden Corporation, which bought Pure Fishing in early 2007.

An in-depth profile of this company is available to Hoover's Online members at hoovers.com.

401

COLEMAN NATURAL FOODS, LLC

1767 Denver West Marriott Rd., Ste. 200
Golden, CO 80401
Phone: 303-468-2920
Fax: 303-277-9263
Web: www.colemannatural.com

CEO: Mark McKay
CFO: –
HR: –
FYE: December 31
Type: Private

Coleman Natural Foods cooked up a new recipe for a natural meat roll-up. The company acquired and consolidated BC Natural Foods and KDSB Holdings into one multi-species meat company. Coleman Natural offers natural, organic, antibiotic-free, vegetarian-fed chicken, pork, lamb, and bison. It also provides processed meats such as sausage, hot dogs, and bacon, as well as ready-to-eat and frozen convenience meat products. The company's brand names include Coleman, Rocky, Rosie, and Hans. Coleman sells its meats to grocery retailers, and specialty and natural food store and foodservice operations throughout the US. Its products may also be ordered through the company's Web site.

	Annual Growth	12/03	12/04	12/05	12/06	12/07
Est. sales ($ mil.)	—	—	—	—	—	672.2
Employees	—	—	—	—	—	2,300

COLEY PHARMACEUTICAL GROUP, INC.

93 Worcester St., Ste. 101
Wellesley, MA 02481
Phone: 781-431-9000
Fax: 781-431-6403
Web: www.coleypharma.com

CEO: Robert L. Bratzler
CFO: Charles H. (Chuck) Abdalian Jr.
HR: –
FYE: December 31
Type: Subsidiary

Coley Pharmaceutical Group believes you have the power to fight cancer — you just might need a little stimulation. The company develops TLR (toll-like receptor) therapeutics which stimulate the immune system to fight disease. Its lead product candidate, CPG 7909, is in clinical trials for non-small cell lung cancer, breast cancer, melanoma, and T cell lymphoma. Coley also targets respiratory conditions such as asthma, as well as infectious diseases; it is developing a vaccine adjuvant to enhance the efficacy of vaccines for cancer and infectious diseases. Coley has been acquired by Pfizer, its development and commercialization partner for CPG 7909.

	Annual Growth	12/02	12/03	12/04	12/05	12/06
Sales ($ mil.)	9.2%	14.2	6.6	14.3	15.9	20.2
Net income ($ mil.)	—	(20.0)	(30.5)	(34.0)	(38.1)	(29.8)
Employees	2.3%	127	—	—	136	—

COLFAX CORPORATION

NYSE: CFX

8730 Stony Point Pkwy., Ste. 150
Richmond, VA 23235
Phone: 804-560-4070
Fax: 804-560-4076
Web: www.colfaxcorp.com

CEO: John A. Young
CFO: G. Scott Faison
HR: Steven W. (Steve) Weidenmuller
FYE: December 31
Type: Public

The cold, hard facts are that Colfax works hard to be a top maker and marketer of pumps and pump-related products. Examples include centrifugal pumps, two- and three-screw pumps, and progressing pumps. Colfax serves customers in the commercial marine, oil and gas, power generation, and engineering industries. The company operates through 10 business units differentiated by product type and geography. More than two thirds of its sales come from outside the US. Its network includes more than 500 distributors that serve about 80 countries. Colfax has grown its manufacturing capabilities primarily through acquisitions, but it has also established a manufacturing facility in China. The company went public in 2008.

	Annual Growth	12/03	12/04	12/05	12/06	12/07
Sales ($ mil.)	17.8%	—	309.7	345.5	393.6	506.3
Net income ($ mil.)	4.2%	—	57.3	12.2	0.1	64.9
Employees	2.8%	—	—	—	2,002	2,059

COLGATE-PALMOLIVE COMPANY

NYSE: CL

300 Park Ave.
New York, NY 10022
Phone: 212-310-2000
Fax: 212-310-2475
Web: www.colgate.com

CEO: Ian M. Cook
CFO: Stephen C. Patrick
HR: Irene Lin
FYE: December 31
Type: Public

Colgate-Palmolive takes a bite out of grime. The company is a top maker and marketer of toothpaste and a worldwide leader in oral care products (mouthwashes, toothpaste, toothbrushes). Its Tom's of Maine unit covers the natural toothpaste niche. Colgate-Palmolive's Hill's Pet Nutrition subsidiary makes Science Diet and Prescription Diet pet foods, as well. Colgate-Palmolive also makes and markets personal care items (deodorants, shampoos, soaps) and household cleaners (bleaches, laundry products, soaps). The company operates in some 70 countries and sells products in more than 200. Colgate-Palmolive is nearing the end of a multiyear restructuring plan.

	Annual Growth	12/03	12/04	12/05	12/06	12/07
Sales ($ mil.)	8.6%	9,903.4	10,584.2	11,396.9	12,237.7	13,789.7
Net income ($ mil.)	5.1%	1,421.3	1,327.1	1,351.4	1,353.4	1,737.4
Market value ($ mil.)	10.4%	26,711.5	26,942.1	28,312.0	33,445.8	39,684.4
Employees	0.3%	—	—	35,800	34,700	36,000

THE COLIBRI GROUP

100 Niantic Ave.
Providence, RI 02907
Phone: 401-943-2100
Fax: 401-943-4230
Web: www.colibri.com

CEO: Thomas L. (Tom) Bendheim
CFO: Steve Sylvia
HR: Jo-Ann Johnson
FYE: December 31
Type: Private

The Colibri Group is counting on jewelry always being in style and its brands becoming household names. The company sells men's and women's jewelry (necklaces, bracelets, lockets, earrings, pendants, cuff links), pens, money clips, timepieces (watches, clocks), cigarette lighters, and accessories worldwide. Its brands include Colibri of London, Princess Pride, Dolan-Bullock, Krementz, and Seth Thomas. In mid-2005 The Colibri Group was acquired by a trio of investment firms, including one in China, and Fred Levinger, who with his father bought the company in 1971, when it logged less than $2 million in sales. Thomas Bendheim joined the firm as its president and CEO in December 2005.

	Annual Growth	12/03	12/04	12/05	12/06	12/07
Est. sales ($ mil.)	—	—	—	—	—	31.9
Employees	—	—	—	—	—	433

COLLABERA

25 Airport Rd.
Morristown, NJ 07960
Phone: 973-889-5200
Fax: 973-292-1643
Web: www.g-c-i.com

CEO: Dominick Cavuoto
CFO: Paul K. Kothari
HR: Michael (Mike) Chirico
FYE: December 31
Type: Private

Founded in 1991, Collabera furnishes information technology (IT) management and services to companies around the world in such industries as banking and financial services, manufacturing, telecommunications, insurance, and utilities. The company's services include systems analysis and design, application development, staffing, e-commerce applications, enterprise resource planning software implementation, and data migration. Customers have included AT&T, Goldman Sachs, Johnson & Johnson, and Sun Microsystems. Collabera has operations in Europe, India, and the US, and has expansion plans slated for Brazil and China.

	Annual Growth	12/03	12/04	12/05	12/06	12/07
Est. sales ($ mil.)	—	—	—	—	—	300.0
Employees	—	—	—	—	—	4,000

COLLABNET, INC.

8000 Marina Blvd., Ste. 600
Brisbane, CA 94005
Phone: 650-228-2500
Fax: 650-228-2501
Web: www.collab.net

CEO: Bill Portelli
CFO: Tom Clark
HR: –
FYE: December 31
Type: Private

CollabNet is at the forefront of the outsourcing trend for software development — not as a service provider, but as a provider of technologies to make outsourcing work. The company's collaborative software development technology enables geographically dispersed teams of software developers to collaborate around the clock. Its applications include tools for virtual development workspaces, software development, knowledge management, communications, project management, and security. In 2007 the company acquired the Sourceforge operations of VA Software.

	Annual Growth	12/03	12/04	12/05	12/06	12/07
Est. sales ($ mil.)	—	—	—	—	—	20.0
Employees	—	—	—	—	—	180

COLLAGENEX PHARMACEUTICALS, INC.

41 University Dr., Ste. 200
Newtown, PA 18940
Phone: 215-579-7388
Fax: 215-579-8577
Web: www.collagenex.com

CEO: Humberto Antunes
CFO: –
HR: –
FYE: December 31
Type: Subsidiary

CollaGenex Pharmaceuticals has a tendency to let generic problems get under its skin. After the FDA approved a generic competitor to flagship dental drug Periostat in 2005, the company stopped promoting the product. Instead it turned its focus to its dermatology line, which includes in-licensed and internally developed therapies. Oracea, approved by the FDA in 2006, treats rosacea; MediGene has marketing rights to the drug in Europe and some other foreign markets. Its Pandel topical steroid treats skin irritations, and it is co-marketing topical antifungal Alcortin and topical steroid Novacort with Primus Pharmaceuticals. CollaGenex was acquired by fellow dermatology drugmaker Galderma Laboratories in 2008.

	Annual Growth	12/03	12/04	12/05	12/06	12/07
Sales ($ mil.)	4.7%	52.9	52.2	26.4	26.4	63.6
Net income ($ mil.)	—	6.4	6.5	(18.8)	(33.4)	(8.8)
Employees	—	—	—	80	—	—

COLLECTIVE BRANDS, INC.

NYSE: PSS

3231 SE 6th Ave.
Topeka, KS 66607
Phone: 785-233-5171
Fax: 785-368-7510
Web: www.paylessshoesource.com

CEO: Matthew E. (Matt) Rubel
CFO: Ullrich E. Porzig
HR: Jay A. Lentz
FYE: Saturday nearest January 31
Type: Public

Collective Brands is looking to bank on its collective efforts in shoe making and retailing. The holding company boasts a portfolio of premium and moderate footwear and accessories through its Stride Rite unit, a wide reach of about 4,900 Payless ShoeSource and Stride Rite retail outlets, and an established licensing and brand management unit in Collective Licensing. Collective Brands was formed in August 2007, when powerhouse Payless ShoeSource acquired Stride Rite, which is primarily a wholesaler to department stores and operates leased departments at Macy's stores. With brands such as Keds, Saucony, and Robeez, the company operates in the US, Canada, the Caribbean, Central and South America, and Puerto Rico.

	Annual Growth	1/04	1/05	1/06	1/07	1/08
Sales ($ mil.)	2.2%	2,783.3	2,656.5	2,667.3	2,796.7	3,035.4
Net income ($ mil.)	—	(0.1)	(2.0)	66.4	122.0	42.7
Market value ($ mil.)	5.3%	913.8	772.7	1,599.2	2,272.3	1,122.0
Employees	12.5%	—	—	27,550	31,000	—

COLLECTORS UNIVERSE, INC.

NASDAQ (GM): CLCT

1921 E. Alton Ave.
Santa Ana, CA 92705
Phone: 949-567-1234
Fax: 949-833-7955
Web: www.collectors.com

CEO: Michael R. Haynes
CFO: Joseph J. (Joe) Wallace
HR: –
FYE: June 30
Type: Public

Before you sell that rare silver dollar or those old baseball cards, you might want to find out exactly what it is you have. Collectors Universe provides authentication, grading, and information services for sellers and buyers of coins, sports cards, stamps, autographs, and diamonds and colored gemstones. The company charges a fee (usually between $4 and $200) to determine the authenticity, quality, and worth of an item. Coins and sports cards account for most of the company's business. Collectors Universe also publishes price guides, market reports, rarity reports, and other information in print form, as well as on its Web site.

	Annual Growth	6/03	6/04	6/05	6/06	6/07
Sales ($ mil.)	(6.2%)	52.3	26.4	33.6	36.9	40.5
Net income ($ mil.)	—	(10.4)	1.7	4.8	3.7	(0.5)
Market value ($ mil.)	57.4%	21.2	81.2	148.7	116.7	129.9
Employees	22.6%	—	—	186	228	—

COLLEGE ENTRANCE EXAMINATION BOARD

45 Columbus Ave.
New York, NY 10023
Phone: 212-713-8000
Fax: 212-713-8143
Web: www.collegeboard.com

CEO: W. Gaston Caperton III
CFO: Thomas (Tom) Higgins
HR: Juliet Weissman
FYE: June 30
Type: Not-for-profit

The College Entrance Examination Board is a nonprofit association that serves high school students, parents, educators, and educational institutions nationwide. Its members — schools, colleges, universities, and other educational institutions — number 5,400. The College Board offers guidance counseling, financial aid, student assessment, standardized testing, workshops, and professional development courses. Among the tests the College Board administers are the Scholastic Assessment Test (SAT), College-Level Examination Program (CLEP), and the Advanced Placement Program (AP). The organization also studies education policy and makes recommendations. It was founded in 1900.

	Annual Growth	6/03	6/04	6/05	6/06	6/07
Est. sales ($ mil.)	—	—	—	—	—	484.9
Employees	—	—	—	—	—	598

COLLIERS INTERNATIONAL PROPERTY CONSULTANTS, INC.

50 Milk St., 20th Fl.
Boston, MA 02109
Phone: 617-722-0221
Fax: 617-722-0224
Web: www.colliers.com

CEO: Margaret Wigglesworth
CFO: –
HR: –
FYE: December 31
Type: Private

No matter where your business lives, Colliers International can help you find the best commercial property, *propiedad, propriété,* or *eigentum.* An affiliation of independently-owned commercial real estate firms, Colliers International is one of the world's largest commercial real estate dealers, with more than 260 offices in about 60 countries. Colliers International agencies provide property brokerage, investment sales, development, and management and consulting services to tenants, owners, and investors. Altogether, the group's member firms manage more than 670 million sq. ft. of space on six continents.

	Annual Growth	12/03	12/04	12/05	12/06	12/07
Sales ($ mil.)	—	—	—	—	—	1,600.0
Employees	—	—	—	—	—	10,092

An in-depth profile of this company is available to Hoover's Online members at hoovers.com.

403

COLLINS INDUSTRIES, INC.

15 Compound Dr.
Hutchinson, KS 67501
Phone: 620-663-5551
Fax: 620-663-1630
Web: www.collinsind.com

CEO: Randall Swift
CFO: Hans H. Heinsen
HR: John L. Dreasher
FYE: October 31
Type: Private

The vehicles made by Collins Industries demand attention. Founded in 1971, the company is one of the largest US makers of ambulances and specialty vehicles such as small school buses, shuttle and midsized commercial buses, and terminal trucks (used to move trailers and containers in warehouses and other storage areas). Collins also makes commercial bus chassis, industrial sweepers, and road construction equipment. The company markets its products under brand names that include Capacity, Collins Bus, Waldon/Lay-Mor, Wheeled Coach, and World Trans. In late 2006 Collins was acquired by Steel Partners II (an investment partnership) and American Industrial Partners (a private equity firm) for about $110 million.

	Annual Growth	10/03	10/04	10/05	10/06	10/07
Est. sales ($ mil.)	—	—	—	—	—	127.4
Employees	—	—	—	—	—	920

COLLINS STEWART LLC

350 Madison Ave.
New York, NY 10017
Phone: 212-389-8000
Fax: 212-389-8810
Web: www.collinsstewart.com/USBusiness

CEO: Andrew (Andy) Arno
CFO: Bob Thompson
HR: Winnie Romanoff
FYE: December 31
Type: Subsidiary

One of Wall Street's Old Guard, boutique investment banking firm Collins Stewart LLC (formerly C.E. Unterberg, Towbin) offers direct investments and private placements, support for IPOs, mergers and acquisitions, and other financial advisory services. Founded more than 70 years ago, the company focuses on technology, health care, and global security firms. It serves affluent individual investors through its private banking division, which also manages corporate assets. Its research department covers small to medium-sized companies in a variety of tech sector segments. UK stock brokerage Collins Stewart in 2007 bought C.E. Unterberg, Towbin, which had been one of the last private partnerships on the Street.

	Annual Growth	12/03	12/04	12/05	12/06	12/07
Est. sales ($ mil.)	—	—	—	—	—	64.5
Employees	—	—	—	—	—	150

COLOMER USA

5344 Overmeyer Dr.
Jacksonville, FL 32254
Phone: 904-693-1200
Fax: 904-693-5365
Web: www.thecolomergroup.com

CEO: Gerard Schoor
CFO: —
HR: —
FYE: December 31
Type: Private

Colomer USA hopes to make *every* day a good hair day for its customers. Formerly Revlon Professional Products, the company makes and markets a variety of haircare products and specializes in ethnic haircare (primarily marketed to African-American and Hispanic consumers). Colomer USA operates under five divisions: consumer products, cosmetics, general US markets, multicultural, and professional products. Its brand names include American Crew, Intercosmo, Creme of Nature, African Pride, Revlon Realistic, Fabulaxer, Ginseng Miracle, 911, All Ways Natural, and HerbaRich. The haircare line was purchased from Revlon in 2000 by a group led by Colomer's chairman, Carlos Colomer, a former Revlon manager.

	Annual Growth	12/03	12/04	12/05	12/06	12/07
Est. sales ($ mil.)	—	—	—	—	—	286.5
Employees	—	—	—	—	—	950

THE COLONIAL BANCGROUP, INC.

NYSE: CNB

100 Colonial Bank Blvd.
Montgomery, AL 36117
Phone: 334-240-5000
Fax: 334-676-5345
Web: www.colonialbank.com

CEO: Robert E. (Bobby) Lowder
CFO: Sarah H. Moore
HR: —
FYE: December 31
Type: Public

The Colonial BancGroup is colonizing the South. The company owns Colonial Bank, which operates about 340 branches mostly in Florida, but also in Alabama, Georgia, Nevada, and Texas. It offers such standard banking fare as checking and savings accounts, CDs, and credit cards, in addition to insurance and investment products. Other nonbanking services include trust, discount brokerage, and asset management. The bank's lending activities primarily consist of real estate loans, with construction loans accounting for nearly 40% of the company's portfolio, commercial mortgages contributing about 30%, and residential real estate making up about 15%. The bank also makes agricultural, business, and consumer loans.

	Annual Growth	12/03	12/04	12/05	12/06	12/07
Assets ($ mil.)	12.4%	16,273.3	18,896.6	21,426.2	22,784.3	25,976.0
Net income ($ mil.)	4.8%	149.9	172.9	228.5	265.8	180.9
Employees	4.2%	3,939	4,303	4,607	4,700	4,646

COLONIAL BANKSHARES, INC.

NASDAQ (GM): COBK

2745 S. Delsea Dr.
Vineland, NJ 08360
Phone: 856-205-0058
Fax: 856-205-0509
Web: www.colonialbankfsb.com

CEO: Edward J. Geletka
CFO: L. Joseph Stella III
HR: —
FYE: December 31
Type: Public

Community banking is a revolutionary idea for Colonial Bankshares. The holding company owns Colonial Bank, a regional thrift serving southern New Jersey from six locations. The bank offers products and services including checking and savings accounts, bank cards, loans, and brokerage. It uses funds from deposits to originate primarily real estate loans, with one- to four-family mortgages accounting for nearly 50% of its loan portfolio. It also writes construction, business, home equity, and consumer loans, as well as loans for other types of real estate. Mutual holding company Colonial Bankshares MHC owns about 55% of Colonial Bankshares; it owned 100% before the company's 2005 public stock offering.

	Annual Growth	12/03	12/04	12/05	12/06	12/07
Assets ($ mil.)	17.1%	243.5	291.0	336.9	383.6	457.9
Net income ($ mil.)	(8.3%)	1.7	1.9	1.8	1.6	1.2
Market value ($ mil.)	(2.7%)	—	—	47.7	62.3	45.2
Employees	—	—	—	75		

COLONIAL COMMERCIAL CORP.

OTC: CCOM

275 Wagaraw Rd.
Hawthorne, NJ 07506
Phone: 973-427-8224
Fax: 973-427-6981
Web: www.colonialcomm.com

CEO: William Pagano
CFO: William Salek
HR: —
FYE: December 31
Type: Public

Colonial Commercial Corp., through subsidiaries Universal Supply Group, The RAL Supply Group, American/Universal Supply, and S&A Supply, provides HVAC products, climate-control systems, and plumbing fixtures to mostly builders and HVAC contractors in New York and New Jersey. It supplies control system design, custom fabrication, technical support, training, and consultation services (but not installation) for engineers and installers. RAL Supply Group offers plumbing fixtures, water systems and water-treatment products, and heating and cooling equipment. About 85% of Colonial's 2007 sales come from the replacement market. Chairman Michael Goldman owns about 27% of the company; CEO William Pagano, about 16%.

	Annual Growth	12/03	12/04	12/05	12/06	12/07
Sales ($ mil.)	16.5%	44.7	61.5	66.7	71.5	82.4
Net income ($ mil.)	—	1.3	1.7	2.1	0.8	(0.1)
Market value ($ mil.)	30.4%	2.2	6.4	9.5	8.7	6.3
Employees	—	—	—	—	—	—

COLONIAL GROUP INC.

101 N. Lathrop Ave.
Savannah, GA 31415
Phone: 912-236-1331
Fax: 912-235-3881
Web: www.colonialgroupinc.com

CEO: Robert H. Demere Jr.
CFO: Francis A. (Frank) Brown
HR: David (Dave) Deason
FYE: September 30
Type: Private

Colonial Group presides over an empire of oil and gas and shipping related companies in the Southeastern US. The group provides storage and distribution services for liquid and dry bulk products including bulk chemicals, motor fuels, industrial fuel oil, and retail gas. It also provides ship bunkering, commercial shipping, and tug and barge services. Colonial Group also operates more than 70 gas stations and convenience stores in Georgia, North Carolina, and South Carolina through its Enmark Stations unit. In addition, subsidiary Georgia Kaolin Terminals provides storage facilities for customers in the US kaolin industry.

	Annual Growth	12/02	12/03	*9/04	9/05	9/06
Est. sales ($ mil.)	35.1%	1,500.0	2,500.0	3,600.0	4,500.0	5,000.0
Employees	5.1%	900	1,100	1,000	1,100	1,100
						*Fiscal year change

COLONIAL PIPELINE COMPANY

1185 Sanctuary Pkwy., Ste. 100
Alpharetta, GA 30004
Phone: 678-762-2200
Fax: 678-762-2813
Web: www.colpipe.com

CEO: Norm J. Szydlowski
CFO: Rodney L. Gray
HR: –
FYE: December 31
Type: Private

With a reach that extends far beyond the original English colonies, Colonial Pipeline delivers about 100 million gallons of gasoline, diesel, home heating oil, aviation, and military fuels per day to cities and businesses across the Eastern and Southern US. The 5,519-mile Colonial system transports these fuels from Alabama, Louisiana, Mississippi, and Texas, to 267 marketing terminals near major population centers in the Southeast and along the Eastern Seaboard. The company has shipper terminals in 12 states and the District of Columbia. Colonial Pipeline is owned by a consortium of companies, including Koch (28%), HUTTS (23%), Shell Pipeline (16%), and Industry Funds Management (16%).

	Annual Growth	12/03	12/04	12/05	12/06	12/07
Est. sales ($ mil.)	—	—	—	—	—	798.7
Employees	—	—	—	—	—	634

COLONIAL PROPERTIES TRUST

NYSE: CLP

2101 6th Ave. North, Ste. 750
Birmingham, AL 35203
Phone: 205-250-8700
Fax: 205-250-8890
Web: www.colonialprop.com

CEO: C. Reynolds Thompson III
CFO: Weston M. Andress
HR: John P. Rigrish
FYE: December 31
Type: Public

Whether you call it the South or the Sunbelt, Colonial Properties keeps much of it covered with its residential properties. The self-administered real estate investment trust (REIT) owns and operates 120 multifamily apartment complexes with approximately 35,000 units, as well as some 50 office properties. The REIT also owns undeveloped land adjacent to some of its properties. Colonial Properties offers management, leasing, and brokerage services for commercial real estate clients. It is active in such markets as Charlotte and Raleigh, North Carolina; Atlanta; Orlando; Richmond, Virginia; Dallas and Austin, Texas; and Phoenix.

	Annual Growth	12/03	12/04	12/05	12/06	12/07
Sales ($ mil.)	4.7%	334.2	337.4	495.4	496.1	401.5
Net income ($ mil.)	61.5%	52.3	54.6	219.6	203.5	355.9
Market value ($ mil.)	0.6%	1,045.2	1,083.8	1,889.7	2,163.3	1,068.5
Employees	(14.3%)	—	—	1,700	—	1,250

COLONY BANKCORP, INC.

NASDAQ (GM): CBAN

115 S. Grant St.
Fitzgerald, GA 31750
Phone: 229-426-6000
Fax: 229-426-6039
Web: www.colonybank.com

CEO: Al D. Ross
CFO: Terry L. Hester
HR: –
FYE: December 31
Type: Public

Colony Bankcorp seems to be colonizing Georgia. The multibank holding company owns seven financial institutions doing business under variations of the Colony Bank name throughout central and southern portions of the state. The banks operate more than 25 branches in all. They offer traditional fare such as checking and savings accounts, NOW and IRA accounts, and CDs. Real estate loans, including residential and commercial mortgages and construction and farmland loans, make up the largest portion of the company's loan portfolio, at more than 80%. The banks also issue business and consumer loans.

	Annual Growth	12/03	12/04	12/05	12/06	12/07
Assets ($ mil.)	8.6%	868.6	997.6	1,108.3	1,213.5	1,208.8
Net income ($ mil.)	6.0%	6.8	8.1	9.0	10.1	8.6
Market value ($ mil.)	10.3%	74.1	124.9	179.4	127.3	109.7
Employees	—	—	—	348	—	—

COLONY CAPITAL, LLC

1999 Avenue of the Stars, Ste. 1200
Los Angeles, CA 90067
Phone: 310-282-8820
Fax: 310-282-8808
Web: www.colonyinc.com

CEO: Thomas J. Barrack Jr.
CFO: Mark M. Hedstrom
HR: –
FYE: December 31
Type: Private

Colony Capital is one of the world's top real estate investment firms, with some $30 billion invested, some of it on behalf of institutional clients. The company owns office, hospitality, gaming, residential, and retail properties around the world. Its holdings include stakes in France-based hotel operator Accor and luxury hotel chain Fairmont Raffles. In 2007 the company backed a nearly $5 billion offer for Station Casinos to be bought out by its founders and management. Colony Capital is controlled by chairman and CEO Tom Barrack, a renowned dealmaker who originally formed the firm in 1991 to invest in debt from the savings and loan crisis.

	Annual Growth	12/03	12/04	12/05	12/06	12/07
Est. sales ($ mil.)	—	—	—	—	—	475.1
Employees	—	—	—	—	—	6,685

COLOR KINETICS INCORPORATED

3 Burlington Woods Dr., 4th Fl.
Burlington, MA 01803
Phone: 617-423-9999
Fax: 617-423-9998
Web: www.colorkinetics.com

CEO: William J. (Bill) Sims
CFO: David K. Johnson
HR: Paula LaPalme
FYE: December 31
Type: Subsidiary

Color Kinetics (CK) can give a chameleon a run for its money. The company, founded in 1997, manufactures digital lighting products used in a variety of commercial and consumer applications. Its Chromacore products can generate virtually millions of colors and a variety of dynamic lighting effects by utilizing microprocessor-controlled light emitting diodes (LEDs). CK also manufactures the power supplies and controllers used in conjunction with its lighting products. Customers include members of the aerospace, architectural, entertainment, and vending and gaming industries. Color Kinetics is a part of Luminaires, which itself is a division of Royal Philips Electronics' lighting unit.

	Annual Growth	12/02	12/03	12/04	12/05	12/06
Sales ($ mil.)	34.1%	20.2	28.9	40.2	52.9	65.4
Net income ($ mil.)	—	(7.5)	(0.7)	2.4	4.3	3.2
Employees	26.7%	—	76	87	122	—

COLOR SPOT NURSERIES, INC.

2575 Olive Hill Rd.	CEO: Michael F. Vukelich
Fallbrook, CA 92028	CFO: Rodney Omps
Phone: 760-695-1430	HR: Trecia Pinchesfsky
Fax: 760-731-6762	FYE: December 31
Web: www.colorspot.com	Type: Private

Color Spot Nurseries is firmly rooted in Western soil. As one of the US's leading wholesale nurseries, Color Spot produces more than 1,000 types of plants, including bedding plants, shrubs, potted plants, ground cover, and Christmas trees. Color Spot supplies more than 2,000 retailers and commercial customers, including The Home Depot and Wal-Mart. Its customers are primarily located in the western and southwestern US. The company operates about 10 production facilities in California and Texas. Color Spot Nurseries was founded in 1983.

COLORADO SPRINGS UTILITIES

111 S. Cascade Ave.	CEO: Jerry Forte
Colorado Springs, CO 80903	CFO: Edward Easterlin
Phone: 719-448-4800	HR: –
Fax: 719-668-7288	FYE: December 31
Web: www.csu.org	Type: Government-owned

Even scenic areas need creature comforts, and that's where utilities come in. Community-owned Colorado Springs Utilities provides natural gas, electric, and water and wastewater services to 645,000 customers in the Pikes Peak region. The municipal utility has about 206,000 electricity customers, 182,000 natural gas customers, and 130,000 water and 127,000 wastewater customers. Colorado Springs Utilities' service territories include Colorado Springs, Manitou Springs, and several of the suburban residential areas surrounding the city. The military installations of Fort Carson, Peterson Air Force Base, and the US Air Force Academy are also serviced by the multi-utility.

	Annual Growth	12/03	12/04	12/05	12/06	12/07
Est. sales ($ mil.)	—	—	—	—	—	690.6
Employees	—	—	—	—	—	1,800

COLSON & COLSON GENERAL CONTRACTOR INC.

2260 McGilchrist St. SE	CEO: William E. (Bill) Colson
Salem, OR 97302	CFO: Gregory Tibbot
Phone: 503-586-7401	HR: –
Fax: 503-370-4205	FYE: December 31
Web: www.colson-colson.com	Type: Private

Colson & Colson knows that old age isn't for sissies. The company builds and manages retirement communities (more than 300) for senior citizens in the US, Canada, and England. It primarily develops affordable retirement properties nationwide for former affiliate Holiday Retirement Corp. (HRC), the #1 owner and manager of retirement homes in the US and Canada. Colson's activities include site selection, property rezoning, construction and construction financing, and obtaining equity funds. The company acts as general partner for each project. The Colson family owns the majority of Colson & Colson.

COLT'S MANUFACTURING COMPANY, LLC

545 New Park Ave.	CEO: William M. (Bill) Keys
West Hartford, CT 06110	CFO: –
Phone: 860-236-6311	HR: Mike Magouirk
Fax: 860-244-1442	FYE: December 31
Web: www.coltsmfg.com	Type: Private

The Colt .45 may have won the West, but it took a New York investment firm to save Colt's Manufacturing from a post-Cold War decline in weapons sales and tough foreign competition. Through its subsidiaries, Colt's Manufacturing makes handguns (Cowboy, Defender) and semiautomatic rifles (M-4). The company has distributors throughout Europe, Asia, and Australia. Founded in 1836 by Samuel Colt, the company is about 85%-owned by investment firm Zilkha & Co., who has been reviving the company since 1994 when it bought the firm out of bankruptcy.

	Annual Growth	12/03	12/04	12/05	12/06	12/07
Est. sales ($ mil.)	—	—	—	—	—	12.0
Employees	—	—	—	—	—	86

COLUMBIA BANCORP

NASDAQ (GS): CBBO

401 E. 3rd St., Ste. 200	CEO: Roger L. Christensen
The Dalles, OR 97058	CFO: Greg B. Spear
Phone: 541-298-6649	HR: Charla L. Fraley
Fax: 541-298-3157	FYE: December 31
Web: www.columbiariverbank.com	Type: Public

You won't find salmon running Columbia River Bank. Owned by holding company Columbia Bancorp, the bank provides community banking services to individuals, farmers, ranchers, and local businesses in Oregon and southern Washington through about two dozen branches. Deposit products include checking and savings accounts and CDs. The bank's lending activities consist of construction loans (more than 30% of the company's loan portfolio), commercial real estate loans (nearly 30%), and business loans (about 15%), and to a lesser extent, residential, agricultural, consumer, and credit card loans.

	Annual Growth	12/03	12/04	12/05	12/06	12/07
Assets ($ mil.)	15.6%	584.1	715.4	841.2	1,033.2	1,042.7
Net income ($ mil.)	10.3%	9.8	10.7	13.7	15.8	14.5
Market value ($ mil.)	4.9%	137.2	157.3	198.0	264.0	165.9
Employees	—	—	—	312		

COLUMBIA BANKING SYSTEM, INC.

NASDAQ (GS): COLB

1301 A St.	CEO: Melanie J. Dressel
Tacoma, WA 98402	CFO: Gary R. Schminkey
Phone: 253-305-1900	HR: Kent Roberts
Fax: 253-305-0317	FYE: December 31
Web: www.columbiabank.com	Type: Public

Columbia Banking System hopes money will flow through the Pacific Northwest through its three subsidiary banks. Columbia State Bank (also known as Columbia Bank) operates some 50 branches in Washington, from Puget Sound to the timber country in the southwestern part of the state, as well as in Oregon. Mt. Rainier Bank (acquired in 2007) has seven branches in Washington's King and Pierce counties. Although it will continue to operate as the Bank of Astoria, the financial institution will merge into Columbia Banking System. Targeting individuals and local businesses, the banks offer standard retail services such as checking and savings accounts, CDs, IRAs, loans, and mortgages.

	Annual Growth	12/03	12/04	12/05	12/06	12/07
Assets ($ mil.)	16.2%	1,744.3	2,177.6	2,377.3	2,553.1	3,178.7
Net income ($ mil.)	13.5%	19.5	22.5	29.6	32.1	32.4
Market value ($ mil.)	17.8%	277.1	389.7	452.0	564.0	533.7
Employees	—	—	—	651		

COLUMBIA FOREST PRODUCTS INC.

222 SW Columbia, Ste. 1575
Portland, OR 97201
Phone: 503-224-5300
Fax: 503-224-5294
Web: www.columbiaforestproducts.com

CEO: Harry L. Demorest
CFO: Clifford (Cliff) Barry
HR: –
FYE: December 31
Type: Private

Columbia Forest Products is one of North America's largest manufacturers of hardwood plywood, veneer, and laminated products as well as hardwood logs. The employee-owned company makes products used in cabinets, architectural millwork, commercial fixtures, and more. Columbia Forest Products specializes in Northern Appalachian hardwoods. Its rotary veneer is used by the cabinetry, door, furniture, and decorative plywood industries. The company sells its products to original equiment manufacturers, wholesale distributors, and mass merchandisers. Columbia Forest Products began in 1957 with a plywood plant in Oregon and has grown to operate around a dozen plants in the US and Canada.

	Annual Growth	12/02	12/03	12/04	12/05	12/06
Sales ($ mil.)	(4.8%)	—	—	—	1,050.0	1,000.0
Employees	12.5%	—	—	—	4,000	4,500

COLUMBIA HOUSE COMPANY

1 Penn Plaza, 250 W. 34th St., 5th Fl.
New York, NY 10119
Phone: 212-287-0081
Fax: –
Web: www.columbiahouse.com

CEO: Stuart Goldfarb
CFO: Fred Christensen
HR: –
FYE: December 31
Type: Subsidiary

DVDs are the name of the game for Columbia House. Initially a 50-50 joint venture between entertainment giants Sony and Time Warner, Columbia House is the top club-based direct marketer (with members in the US, Canada, and Mexico) of DVDs in North America. The company sells more than 9,500 DVD titles via mail order and online. Its TV on DVD club features a wide variety of television programming. German media giant Bertelsmann owns the company after buying out the various stakes from investment firm Blackstone Group, Sony, and Time Warner.

	Annual Growth	12/03	12/04	12/05	12/06	12/07
Est. sales ($ mil.)	—	—	—	—	—	401.9
Employees	—	—	—	—	—	2,300

COLUMBIA LABORATORIES, INC.

NASDAQ (GM): CBRX

354 Eisenhower Pkwy., 2nd Fl., Plaza I
Livingston, NJ 07039
Phone: 973-994-3999
Fax: 973-994-3001
Web: www.columbialabs.com

CEO: Robert S. (Bob) Mills
CFO: James A. Meer
HR: –
FYE: December 31
Type: Public

Not to be confused with *Colombia,* the drugs made by this Columbia are perfectly legal. Columbia Laboratories develops and markets women's health pharmaceutical products based upon its patented bioadhesive drug delivery technology. The company's progesterone gel products include Crinone 8% and Prochieve 8%, which are used to treat infertility and amenorrhea (loss of menstrual period). Columbia retains US marketing rights to sell these products to reproductive endocrinologists, obstetricians, and gynecologists. It also promotes an orally-administered product, Striant, a testosterone replacement therapy for men. Columbia Laboratories' products in development include vaginal lidocaine to treat menstrual cramps.

	Annual Growth	12/03	12/04	12/05	12/06	12/07
Sales ($ mil.)	7.2%	22.4	17.9	22.0	17.4	29.6
Net income ($ mil.)	—	(21.1)	(25.1)	(9.3)	(12.6)	(14.3)
Market value ($ mil.)	(17.2%)	250.0	110.6	194.2	255.7	117.4
Employees	—	—	—	54	—	—

COLUMBIA RECORDS GROUP

550 Madison Ave.
New York, NY 10022
Phone: 212-833-8000
Fax: 212-833-5401
Web: www.columbiarecords.com

CEO: Steve Barnett
CFO: Stephen Russo
HR: –
FYE: March 31
Type: Business segment

This company helped start America's love affair with records and it is still churning out the hits. Tracing its roots back to the 1880s, Columbia Records Group is one of the leading recording labels in the US. It boasts a roster of popular artists such as Aerosmith, Dixie Chicks, Beyonce, and Bruce Springsteen. It has also produced soundtrack albums for such films as *A Mighty Wind, Men in Black II,* and *Strictly Ballroom,* as well as compilation albums such as *We're a Happy Family — A Tribute to The Ramones.* In addition to recorded CDs, the label markets DVDs and distributes videos and streaming audio over the Internet. Columbia is a division of music giant Sony BMG Music Entertainment.

COLUMBIA SPORTSWEAR COMPANY

NASDAQ (GS): COLM

14375 NW Science Park Dr.
Portland, OR 97229
Phone: 503-985-4000
Fax: 503-985-5800
Web: www.columbia.com

CEO: Timothy P. (Tim) Boyle
CFO: Bryan L. Timm
HR: Susan G. Popp
FYE: December 31
Type: Public

Gertrude Boyle is proud to be called one tough mother. The octogenarian chairwoman and star of Columbia Sportswear's popular "tough mother" and "tested tough" ads transformed her father's floundering sportswear firm into a top US skiwear seller and one of the world's biggest outerwear makers. The company popularized the three-in-one Bugaboo jacket (its shell and lining can each be worn separately or zipped together). Columbia also makes leather outerwear, sportswear, Sorel brand boots, and other rugged footwear, as well as accessories such as gloves and caps. The Boyles (Gertrude; son Tim, president and CEO; and daughter Sarah Bany) own more than 60% of Columbia Sportswear.

	Annual Growth	12/03	12/04	12/05	12/06	12/07
Sales ($ mil.)	9.3%	951.8	1,095.3	1,155.8	1,287.7	1,356.0
Net income ($ mil.)	4.7%	120.1	138.6	130.7	123.0	144.4
Market value ($ mil.)	(7.9%)	2,193.8	2,391.9	1,759.5	2,005.1	1,579.5
Employees	6.2%	—	—	2,712	2,810	3,057

COLUMBIA SUSSEX CORPORATION

740 Centre View Blvd.
Crestview Hills, KY 41017
Phone: 859-578-1100
Fax: 859-578-1154
Web: www.columbiasussex.com

CEO: William J. (Bill) Yung III
CFO: Theodore R. (Ted) Mitchel
HR: –
FYE: December 31
Type: Private

Columbia Sussex develops and manages more than 60 hotels and casinos in about 30 states. Its hotels operate under banners such as Hilton, Marriott, and Starwood. Its casinos are located in Mississippi (Lighthouse Point), Louisiana (Amelia Belle), and Nevada (Lake Tahoe Horizon), among other states. Wimar Tahoe, the casino affiliate of Columbia Sussex that did business as Columbia Entertainment, turned heads in 2007 when it purchased Aztar Corporation, owner of the Las Vegas Tropicana, for about $2 billion. (After the deal, Wimar Tahoe took on the Tropicana identity and began operating as Tropicana Entertainment LLC.) CEO William Yung and his family own Columbia Sussex. Yung founded the company in 1972.

	Annual Growth	12/03	12/04	12/05	12/06	12/07
Est. sales ($ mil.)	—	—	—	—	—	970.4
Employees	—	—	—	—	—	15,000

An in-depth profile of this company is available to Hoover's Online members at hoovers.com.

407

COLUMBIA UNIVERSITY

2960 Broadway
New York, NY 10027
Phone: 212-854-1754
Fax: 212-749-0397
Web: www.columbia.edu

CEO: Lee C. Bollinger
CFO: Anne R. Sullivan
HR: Kate Sheeran
FYE: June 30
Type: School

Predating the American Revolution, Columbia University (founded as King's College in 1754) is the fifth-oldest institution of higher learning in the US. With a student population of more than 24,600 and a main campus spread across 36 acres in Manhattan, Columbia's 15 schools and colleges grant undergraduate and graduate degrees in about 100 disciplines, including its well-known programs in journalism, law, and medicine. The Ivy League university's more than 3,500-member faculty has included nearly 70 Nobel laureates, as well as former Vice President Al Gore. Columbia, which operates four sites in New York City and one in Paris, also has a strong reputation for research.

	Annual Growth	6/02	6/03	6/04	6/05	6/06
Sales ($ mil.)	7.8%	2,008.7	2,074.4	2,198.6	2,500.6	2,709.9
Employees	(2.4%)	15,300	—	12,400	12,631	13,904

COLUMBUS FAIR AUTO AUCTION

4700 Groveport Rd.
Columbus, OH 43207
Phone: 614-497-2000
Fax: 614-497-1132
Web: www.cfaa.com

CEO: Keith Whann
CFO: Bill Stackhouse
HR: –
FYE: December 31
Type: Private

Blink at Columbus Fair Auto Auction (CFAA) and you may miss a good deal. The company offers about 193,000 vehicles for sale annually. The sales are weekly auctions held at a specially designed 85-acre facility in Obetz, Ohio. The site has 11 lanes with the capacity to run 4,000 vehicles at each auction. The company's auctions are frequented by more than 1,000 auto dealers from 20 states. CFAA also provides high-volume factory sales for such manufacturers as General Motors, Daimler AG, Kia, and Suzuki. The auction is owned by president Alexis Jacobs. Her father, the late William Jacobs, founded the company in 1959.

	Annual Growth	12/03	12/04	12/05	12/06	12/07
Est. sales ($ mil.)	—	—	—	—	—	180.8
Employees	—	—	—	—	—	620

COLUMBUS MCKINNON CORPORATION

NASDAQ (GM): CMCO

140 John James Audubon Pkwy.
Amherst, NY 14228
Phone: 716-689-5400
Fax: 716-689-5598
Web: www.cmworks.com

CEO: Timothy T. (Tim) Tevens
CFO: Karen L. Howard
HR: Richard A. Steinberg
FYE: March 31
Type: Public

Columbus McKinnon gives new meaning to the question, "Need a lift?" Through its operating units the company makes equipment for handling, lifting, and positioning materials. It markets its products under names such as Coffing, Duff-Norton, Shaw-Box, and Yale (NACCO Industries makes Yale forklifts). Columbus McKinnon's top products are sold mainly to construction, general manufacturing, and transportation markets which include hoists, chains, cranes, forged products, and industrial components. Hoists are the firm's biggest selling product, bringing in about 50% of sales. In addition to OEMs, the company sells to hardware distributors and rental outlets. Some 70% of Columbus McKinnon's sales are in the US.

	Annual Growth	3/04	3/05	3/06	3/07	3/08
Sales ($ mil.)	8.8%	444.6	514.8	556.0	589.8	623.3
Net income ($ mil.)	136.1%	1.2	16.7	59.8	34.1	37.3
Market value ($ mil.)	50.7%	114.1	203.6	500.2	421.5	588.1
Employees	5.5%	—	—	3,081	3,250	—

COLUMBUS SOUTHERN POWER COMPANY

1 Riverside Plaza
Columbus, OH 43215
Phone: 614-716-1000
Fax: 614-716-1823

CEO: Michael G. (Mike) Morris
CFO: Holly K. Koeppel
HR: –
FYE: December 31
Type: Subsidiary

Columbus Southern Power may not have discovered that people in southern Ohio have a need for electricity, but it is obligated to provide it. The utility, founded in 1937, transmits and distributes electricity to 746,000 customers in central and southern Ohio, including the capital city of Columbus. The utility, a subsidiary of American Electric Power, operates 15,480 miles of electric lines and has power plant interests that give it 3,200 MW of coal- and natural gas-fired generating capacity. It also sells bulk power to wholesale customers, such as municipal utilities and energy marketers.

	Annual Growth	12/02	12/03	12/04	12/05	12/06
Sales ($ mil.)	6.6%	1,400.2	1,431.9	1,433.6	1,542.3	1,806.7
Employees	1.3%	1,171	1,125	1,150	1,178	1,233

COMARCO, INC.

NASDAQ (GM): CMRO

25541 Commercentre Dr.
Lake Forest, CA 92630
Phone: 949-599-7400
Fax: 949-599-1415
Web: www.comarco.com

CEO: Samuel M. Inman III
CFO: Winston E. Hickman
HR: –
FYE: January 31
Type: Public

Comarco helps keep the wireless world working. The company's Comarco Wireless Technologies subsidiary provides wireless network monitoring products to telecommunications carriers and equipment vendors. Its testing equipment and billing system software help operators of cellular and PCS networks optimize their systems and monitor quality. Comarco also installs and maintains emergency call boxes. The company markets a line of battery chargers, called ChargeSource, designed for mobile phones, notebook computers, and other portable devices.

	Annual Growth	1/04	1/05	1/06	1/07	1/08
Sales ($ mil.)	(9.3%)	34.3	29.2	46.9	47.8	23.2
Net income ($ mil.)	—	(1.3)	(10.1)	6.3	1.8	(10.0)
Market value ($ mil.)	(14.5%)	74.3	59.5	88.0	56.4	39.7
Employees	(15.5%)	—	—	142	120	—

COMBE INCORPORATED

1101 Westchester Ave.
White Plains, NY 10604
Phone: 914-694-5454
Fax: 914-461-4402
Web: www.combe.com

CEO: Christopher B. (Chris) Combe
CFO: Douglas M. McGraime
HR: –
FYE: June 30
Type: Private

Combe makes powders and creams you're itching to buy. The firm's products portfolio includes an array of items in the anti-itch niche, including Lanacane, Scalpicin, Gynecort, and Vagisil. Combe combats other human indignities, too, including loose dentures (Sea-Bond), stinky feet (Odor-Eaters), and gray hair (Grecian Formula, Just for Men). Combe's acquisition of J.B. Williams in 2002 added Aqua Velva, Brylcreem, and Cepacol to its brands, among others. The family-owned firm was founded in 1949 by Ivan Combe, who created Clearasil in 1950 and made it the #1 acne medication before selling it off in 1960. Combe's products are sold in more than 60 countries.

	Annual Growth	6/03	6/04	6/05	6/06	6/07
Est. sales ($ mil.)	—	—	—	—	—	71.0
Employees	—	—	—	—	—	600

COMBIMATRIX CORPORATION

NASDAQ (CM): CBMX

6500 Harbour Heights Pkwy., Ste. 303
Mukilteo, WA 98275
Phone: 425-493-2000
Fax: 425-493-2010
Web: www.combimatrix.com

CEO: Amit Kumar
CFO: Scott Burell
HR: –
FYE: December 31
Type: Public

Not only does CombiMatrix offer an array of products, it offers arrays as products. The company develops technology to make customizable microarrays for biotech and pharmaceutical firms and other researchers. The arrays are collections of short DNA strands arranged on either a semiconductor chip or glass slide, on which researchers perform experiments and monitor the reactions of genes. Such experiments are useful in the process of discovering and developing new drugs, as well as in the areas of molecular diagnostics, proteomic and genomic research, biosensors, and other fields. At one time a unit of Acacia Research, Combimatrix was spun off into a separate public company in 2007.

	Annual Growth	12/03	12/04	12/05	12/06	12/07
Sales ($ mil.)	(32.6%)	—	19.6	8.0	5.7	6.0
Net income ($ mil.)	—	—	0.7	(12.4)	(20.0)	(12.6)
Market value ($ mil.)	—	—	—	—	—	45.4
Employees	—	—	—	—	56	—

COMBINATORX, INCORPORATED

NASDAQ (GM): CRXX

245 1st St., 16th Fl.
Cambridge, MA 02142
Phone: 617-301-7000
Fax: 617-301-7010
Web: www.combinatorx.com

CEO: Alexis Borisy
CFO: Robert Forrester
HR: –
FYE: December 31
Type: Public

CombinatoRx is looking for the right one-two punch combo. The company develops combinations of previously approved drugs to target multiple disease pathways rather than the traditional way of singling out genes or proteins for modification. CombinatoRx has chosen to develop compounds that have already received regulatory approval in the US, Europe, or Japan, with the hope of moving them more quickly and inexpensively through the drug development process. It has eight candidates in early clinical trials. Its drug candidates could treat cancer, type 2 diabetes, rheumatoid arthritis, and other immuno-inflammatory diseases.

	Annual Growth	12/03	12/04	12/05	12/06	12/07
Sales ($ mil.)	320.8%	—	0.2	4.7	13.3	14.9
Net income ($ mil.)	—	—	(22.3)	(29.5)	(34.3)	(53.3)
Market value ($ mil.)	(9.9%)	—	—	190.5	249.7	154.6
Employees	31.9%	—	72	95	—	—

COMCAR INDUSTRIES, INC.

502 E. Bridgers Ave.
Auburndale, FL 33823
Phone: 863-967-1101
Fax: 863-965-1023
Web: www.comcar.com

CEO: Mark Bostick
CFO: Robert Fox
HR: –
FYE: December 31
Type: Private

Comcar Industries comprises a comprehensive collection of trucking companies. Comcar's transportation offerings, provided through subsidiaries such as Commercial Carrier Corporation (CCC), Midwest Coast Transport, and Willis Shaw Express, include flatbed, refrigerated, liquid and dry bulk, and standard dry van truckload services. Overall, Comcar companies operate about 3,600 tractors and 6,400 trailers from more than 50 terminals. Comcar also provides logistics, tractor and trailer leasing, and warehousing services, through units such as Comcar Logistics, Commercial Warehousing, and Super Cool Cold Storage. Guy Bostick, father of CEO Mark Bostick, founded Comcar in 1953. The Bostick family owns the company.

COMCAST CABLE COMMUNICATIONS, INC.

1500 Market St.
Philadelphia, PA 19102
Phone: 215-665-1700
Fax: 215-981-7790
Web: www.comcast.com

CEO: Stephen B. (Steve) Burke
CFO: David A. Scott
HR: Suzanne L. Keenan
FYE: December 31
Type: Subsidiary

Capturing couch potatoes from Connecticut to California, Comcast Cable Communications is the cable television component of parent Comcast Corporation. Comcast Cable Communications has more than 24 million basic cable customers, making it the largest US cable company (ahead of #2 Time Warner Cable). The company counts more than 15 million subscribers to its digital cable services and it has about 13 million broadband Internet access subscribers. Another 4 million subscribers use the Comcast Digital Phone service to make calls over the Internet. Comcast Cable also oversees the regional sports and news network operations of its parent company.

⊞ COMCAST CORPORATION

NASDAQ (GS): CMCSA

1 Comcast Center
Philadelphia, PA 19103
Phone: 215-286-1700
Fax: –
Web: www.comcast.com

CEO: Brian L. Roberts
CFO: Michael J. Angelakis
HR: Charisse R. Lillie
FYE: December 31
Type: Public

Commerce plus broadcasting equals Comcast. The company's core cable division has more than 24 million subscribers and is the largest provider in the US (well ahead of #2 Time Warner Cable). Comcast Cable derives the bulk of its revenue from television, Internet, and digital phone services. Its broadband Internet service reaches about 13 million subscribers while Comcast Digital Voice, a Voice over Internet Protocol (VoIP) telephone service, has about 4 million customers. Comcast also has programming interests, such as VERSUS and The Golf Channel, and it owns E! Entertainment Television. One-third of Comcast is controlled by CEO Brian Roberts, son of founder and former chairman Ralph Roberts.

	Annual Growth	12/03	12/04	12/05	12/06	12/07
Sales ($ mil.)	13.9%	18,348.0	20,307.0	22,255.0	24,966.0	30,895.0
Net income ($ mil.)	(5.5%)	3,240.0	970.0	928.0	2,533.0	2,587.0
Market value ($ mil.)	6.0%	29,675.4	30,167.2	23,559.0	58,143.3	37,498.1
Employees	11.8%	—	—	80,000	90,000	100,000

COMDATA CORPORATION

5301 Maryland Way
Brentwood, TN 37027
Phone: 615-370-7000
Fax: 615-370-7209
Web: www.comdata.com

CEO: Jim Burns
CFO: –
HR: Diane Cothran
FYE: December 31
Type: Subsidiary

Comdata is into financial services for the long haul, literally speaking. The wholly owned subsidiary of Ceridian simplifies funds transfer for trucking companies and drivers by providing fleet charge cards and real-time reporting and analysis of transaction information. The company also provides payroll services via its cards and logistical consulting services for trucking companies; it also facilitates quick fuel-ups via its point-of-sale and pay-at-the-pump technologies. The company goes beyond the transportation sector to offer retail, loyalty, and other card services to the aviation, retail, government, hospitality and entertainment, and construction industries.

	Annual Growth	12/03	12/04	12/05	12/06	12/07
Est. sales ($ mil.)	—	—	—	—	—	411.6
Employees	—	—	—	—	—	1,814

⊞ An in-depth profile of this company is available to Hoover's Online members at hoovers.com.

409

COMERICA INCORPORATED

NYSE: CMA

Comerica Bank Tower, 1717 Main St.
Dallas, TX 75201
Phone: 800-521-1190
Fax: –
Web: www.comerica.com

CEO: Ralph W. Babb Jr.
CFO: Elizabeth S. Acton
HR: Jacquelyn H. Wolf
FYE: December 31
Type: Public

If you have a cosigner, Comerica will be your copilot. Organized into three business lines, the bank holding company's Business Bank division focuses on business and asset-based lending to middle-market, large corporate, and government entities; it offers lines of credit and international trade finance, among other services. The Retail Bank provides small business and consumer banking services including deposits, mortgages, small-business loans, and merchant services. The Wealth and Institutional Management arm deals in private banking and asset management, trust products, insurance, and retirement services. Comerica has about 480 branches and other offices, mostly in Arizona, California, Michigan, and Texas.

	Annual Growth	12/03	12/04	12/05	12/06	12/07
Assets ($ mil.)	4.3%	52,592.0	51,766.0	53,013.0	58,001.0	62,331.0
Net income ($ mil.)	0.9%	661.0	757.0	861.0	893.0	686.0
Market value ($ mil.)	(9.7%)	9,810.5	10,402.4	9,246.2	9,246.4	6,529.0
Employees	(0.6%)	—	—	11,343	11,270	—

COMFORCE CORPORATION

AMEX: CFS

415 Crossways Park Dr.
Woodbury, NY 11797
Phone: 516-437-3300
Fax: 516-396-9528
Web: www.comforce.com

CEO: John C. Fanning
CFO: Harry V. Maccarrone
HR: –
FYE: Last Sunday in December
Type: Public

COMFORCE isn't the latest Chuck Norris movie. It's a staffing, consulting, and outsourcing company that provides clients with temporary employees for high-skills jobs in the information technology, telecommunications, and health care industries, and the tools to manage such contingent workforces. The company's PrO Unlimited subsidiary provides outsourced temporary workforce management services to *FORTUNE* 1000 companies. COMFORCE also provides payroll, funding, and outsourcing services to independent consulting and staffing firms through its financial outsourcing services division. The company has 30 offices (22 company-owned and eight licensed) throughout the US.

	Annual Growth	12/03	12/04	12/05	12/06	12/07
Sales ($ mil.)	11.3%	381.7	480.9	539.8	567.8	586.7
Net income ($ mil.)	—	(23.2)	1.8	6.3	4.1	6.0
Market value ($ mil.)	38.4%	9.0	45.2	34.2	41.0	33.0
Employees	(8.2%)	—	—	22,525	560	19,000

COMFORT SYSTEMS USA, INC.

NYSE: FIX

777 Post Oak Blvd., Ste. 500
Houston, TX 77056
Phone: 713-830-9600
Fax: 713-830-9696
Web: www.comfortsystemsusa.com

CEO: William F. (Bill) Murdy
CFO: William George III
HR: Andrew D. Estrada
FYE: December 31
Type: Public

Comfort Systems USA alters ambient air automatically. Comfort Systems sells and services commercial HVAC (heating, ventilation, and air conditioning) systems in apartments, health care facilities, office buildings, manufacturing plants, retail centers, and schools. The company maintains some 60 locations in nearly 50 cities throughout the US. In addition to HVAC services, Comfort Systems designs building automation control systems that integrate, monitor, and operate HVAC, lighting, and access control systems. Some company locations also offer fire protection, plumbing, and electrical services.

	Annual Growth	12/03	12/04	12/05	12/06	12/07
Sales ($ mil.)	9.0%	785.0	819.5	899.5	1,056.5	1,109.5
Net income ($ mil.)	—	(5.6)	10.7	(6.2)	28.7	32.5
Market value ($ mil.)	25.3%	209.4	301.3	367.8	514.6	515.6
Employees	11.6%	—	—	5,955	6,647	—

COMM BANCORP, INC.

NASDAQ (GM): CCBP

125 N. State St.
Clarks Summit, PA 18411
Phone: 570-586-0377
Fax: 570-587-4374
Web: www.combk.com

CEO: William F. Farber Sr.
CFO: Scott A. Seasock
HR: Mary Ann Musho
FYE: December 31
Type: Public

Comm Bancorp is the holding company for the Community Bank and Trust Company, which operates nearly 20 small-town and rural branches outside Scranton in northeastern Pennsylvania. Targeting individuals and small to midsized local business customers, the bank offers such standard retail services as checking and savings accounts, money market accounts, and CDs. Real estate mortgages make up more than half of the bank's portfolio, which is rounded out by business, real estate construction, and consumer loans. Subsidiary Comm Realty manages the bank's foreclosed properties. Comm Bancorp also provides commercial leasing, asset management, and insurance services. It was established in 1934.

	Annual Growth	12/03	12/04	12/05	12/06	12/07
Assets ($ mil.)	1.9%	509.5	528.3	543.6	540.4	549.0
Net income ($ mil.)	10.1%	4.7	4.7	5.2	6.3	6.9
Market value ($ mil.)	1.7%	72.0	77.9	77.3	79.1	77.0
Employees	0.8%	—	—	194	—	197

COMMAND CENTER, INC.

OTC: CCNI

3773 W. 5th Ave.
Post Falls, ID 83854
Phone: 208-773-7450
Fax: 208-773-7467
Web: www.commandlabor.com

CEO: Glenn Welstad
CFO: Brad E. Herr
HR: –
FYE: December 31
Type: Public

This company wants to be the George Patton of the temporary staffing market. Command Center operates about 80 temporary staffing stores across more than 20 US states that provide workers for event services, hospitality, light industrial, and office jobs. In addition, its Harborview unit designs software used in temporary staffing store operations. In early 2007, the company expanded its reach in the western US when it acquired Anytime Labor, an operator of three staffing offices residing in Portland, Oregon. CEO Glenn Welstad owns about 37% of the company; executives Kevin Semerad and Ronald Junck own 13% and 15%, respectively.

	Annual Growth	12/03	12/04	12/05	12/06	12/07
Sales ($ mil.)	296.3%	0.4	0.3	2.2	71.3	98.7
Net income ($ mil.)	—	0.0	0.1	0.3	(2.4)	(26.0)
Market value ($ mil.)	(15.5%)	—	—	80.0	118.6	57.2
Employees	—	—	—	—	—	290

COMMAND SECURITY CORPORATION

AMEX: MOC

Lexington Park
LaGrangeville, NY 12540
Phone: 845-454-3703
Fax: 845-454-0075
Web: www.commandsecurity.com

CEO: Barry I. Regenstein
CFO: Barry I. Regenstein
HR: Robert Sagginario
FYE: March 31
Type: Public

At its customers' command are the security guards employed by Command Security. Most of the company's business comes from its aviation services division. Although passenger screening services have been taken over by the US government, Command Security personnel are called upon for tasks such as baggage-related security duties, document verification, and skycap and wheelchair escort services, in addition to general security services. Delta Air Lines, the company's largest customer, accounts for about 16% of sales. Command Security's guard services division provides security guards for commercial, governmental, and institutional clients. Investment firm Trinad Capital owns 22% of the company.

	Annual Growth	3/03	3/04	3/05	3/06	3/07
Sales ($ mil.)	(0.1%)	94.3	75.9	79.7	85.2	93.8
Net income ($ mil.)	(2.0%)	1.3	(0.3)	(0.4)	(0.1)	1.2
Market value ($ mil.)	50.7%	6.3	7.2	15.7	28.9	32.4
Employees	—	—	—	—	3,400	—

COMMERCE BANCSHARES, INC.

NASDAQ (GS): CBSH

1000 Walnut	CEO: David W. Kemper
Kansas City, MO 64106	CFO: A. Bayard Clark III
Phone: 816-234-2000	HR: Sara E. Foster
Fax: 816-234-2019	FYE: December 31
Web: www.commercebank.com	Type: Public

C'mon to Commerce Bancshares if you're looking for the company that owns Commerce Bank, which operates some 350 locations in Missouri, Kansas, Illinois, Oklahoma, and Colorado through multiple bank charters. It also runs a credit card-issuing bank in Nebraska. In addition to its consumer banking segment (which includes mortgage, lending, and brokerage services), Commerce Bancshares has segments devoted to commercial banking and services (lending, leasing, cash management, and more) and to money management (trust, estate planning, and portfolio management). Business loans, including commercial mortgages and operating loans, make up more than half of Commerce Bancshares' loan portfolio.

	Annual Growth	12/03	12/04	12/05	12/06	12/07
Assets ($ mil.)	3.2%	14,287.2	14,250.4	13,885.5	15,230.3	16,204.8
Net income ($ mil.)	0.0%	206.5	220.3	223.3	219.8	206.7
Market value ($ mil.)	4.1%	2,741.1	2,963.5	3,200.1	3,229.4	3,224.8
Employees	(5.5%)	—	—	5,059	4,478	4,520

COMMERCE ENERGY GROUP, INC.

AMEX: EGR

600 Anton Blvd., Ste. 2000	CEO: Gregory L. Craig
Costa Mesa, CA 92626	CFO: C. Douglas Mitchell
Phone: 800-962-4655	HR: Helga Sherlock
Fax: 714-259-2501	FYE: July 31
Web: www.commerceenergygroup.com	Type: Public

Commerce Energy (formerly Commonwealth Energy) works for the common good of customer choice in terms of supplying electricity and natural gas. The company's primary subsidiary, Commerce Energy, Inc., is a nonregulated retail energy provider that operates under the trade name electricAmerica and serves approximately 196,000 customers in California, Florida, Maryland, Michigan, New Jersey, New York, Nevada, Ohio, Pennsylvania, and Texas. In 2005, the company purchased the retail electric power and natural gas sales business of American Communications Network. Commonwealth Energy also markets wholesale power; other subsidiaries offer energy consulting (Skipping Stone) and outsourcing (UtiliHost) services.

	Annual Growth	7/03	7/04	7/05	7/06	7/07
Sales ($ mil.)	22.4%	165.5	210.6	253.9	247.1	371.6
Net income ($ mil.)	0.5%	5.4	(21.7)	(6.1)	(2.2)	5.5
Market value ($ mil.)	8.2%	—	50.4	46.8	40.9	63.8
Employees	10.2%	173	—	160	—	255

THE COMMERCE GROUP, INC.

211 Main St.	CEO: Gerald Fels
Webster, MA 01570	CFO: Randall V. Becker
Phone: 508-943-9000	HR: Cathleen M. Moynihan
Fax: 508-949-4921	FYE: December 31
Web: www.commerceinsurance.com	Type: Subsidiary

Commerce Group, through its subsidiaries, provides personal and commercial property/casualty insurance, primarily auto and homeowners insurance. Its flagship Commerce Insurance is among the largest personal auto and homeowners insurers in the state of Massachusetts — in part because of its affinity marketing programs with AAA clubs, and in part because it is required by law to accept virtually all personal auto insurance business submitted by its agencies. Commerce Insurance also sells commercial auto, earthquake, flood, business, and personal umbrella insurance. Its Commerce West and American Commerce subsidiaries sell auto insurance in 15 western states. Spanish insurer MAPFRE owns Commerce Group.

	Annual Growth	12/03	12/04	12/05	12/06	12/07
Assets ($ mil.)	5.5%	3,164.2	3,610.4	3,927.0	4,110.9	3,914.7
Net income ($ mil.)	4.4%	160.9	214.4	243.9	241.5	190.9
Employees	1.0%	—	—	2,166	2,187	—

COMMERCEFIRST BANCORP, INC.

NASDAQ (CM): CMFB

1804 West St., Ste. 200	CEO: Richard J. (Rick) Morgan
Annapolis, MD 21401	CFO: Michael T. Storm
Phone: 410-280-6695	HR: –
Fax: 410-280-8565	FYE: December 31
Web: www.commerce1st.com	Type: Public

With a name like CommerceFirst, you know where this company's priorities lie. CommerceFirst Bancorp is the holding company for CommerceFirst Bank, which opened in 2000 and operates two branches in Annapolis and Lanham, Maryland. Targeting business customers, it offers deposit products including checking and savings accounts, NOW accounts, money markets, and CDs. The bank uses funds from deposits to write exclusively business loans (including SBA loans) and commercial mortgages. CommerceFirst Bank is opening additional offices in Glen Burnie and Columbia.

	Annual Growth	12/03	12/04	12/05	12/06	12/07
Assets ($ mil.)	30.5%	51.3	75.9	112.5	141.3	148.8
Net income ($ mil.)	82.1%	0.1	1.1	1.0	1.3	1.1
Market value ($ mil.)	27.7%	7.6	10.7	24.7	24.7	20.2
Employees	—	—	—	21	—	—

COMMERCIAL BANCSHARES, INC.

OTC: CMOH

118 S. Sandusky Ave.	CEO: Robert E. Beach
Upper Sandusky, OH 43351	CFO: Scott A. Oboy
Phone: 419-294-5781	HR: –
Fax: 419-294-2350	FYE: December 31
Web: www.csbanking.com	Type: Public

If Commercial Bancshares were planning to produce a commercial, it's quite probable the subject would be Commercial Savings Bank. The holding company owns the community bank, which serves northwestern Ohio from about 10 branches. The bank offers standard retail and business services, including checking and savings accounts, certificates of deposit, and loans. Commercial loans make up the largest portion of the bank's loan portfolio (more than two-thirds); other offerings include consumer finance loans, home equity loans, credit card loans, and residential mortgages.

	Annual Growth	12/03	12/04	12/05	12/06	12/07
Assets ($ mil.)	(0.6%)	272.8	296.6	303.5	273.7	266.2
Net income ($ mil.)	—	1.3	1.5	1.7	1.8	(0.3)
Market value ($ mil.)	(0.6%)	29.9	30.6	31.0	31.1	29.2
Employees	(2.8%)	—	143	139	—	—

COMMERCIAL FURNITURE GROUP

10650 Gateway Blvd.	CEO: Seamus Bateson
St. Louis, MO 63132	CFO: Neal R. Restivo
Phone: 314-991-9200	HR: –
Fax: 314-991-9262	FYE: Saturday nearest October 31
Web: www.commercialfurnituregroup.com	Type: Private

Thank Commercial Furniture Group (CFG) for a place to sit down in public. The company, formerly Falcon Products, produces commercial furniture, particularly tables (banquet, conference) and seating. The company makes furniture on contract for the office, health care, foodservice, hospitality, and education markets. CFG's stable of brands, mostly gained through acquisitions, include Epic, Falcon, Howe, Thonet, and Shelby Williams. The company has operations in the Americas, China, the Czech Republic, Denmark, and the UK. Seamus Bateson, formerly head of Furniture Brands International's Maitland-Smith unit, became chairman, president, and CEO in early 2006.

	Annual Growth	10/03	10/04	10/05	10/06	10/07
Est. sales ($ mil.)	—	—	—	—	—	65.2
Employees	—	—	—	—	—	800

An in-depth profile of this company is available to Hoover's Online members at hoovers.com.

411

COMMERCIAL METALS COMPANY

NYSE: CMC

6565 N. MacArthur Blvd., Ste. 800
Irving, TX 75039
Phone: 214-689-4300
Fax: 214-689-5886
Web: www.commercialmetals.com

CEO: Murray R. McClean
CFO: William B. Larson
HR: Elva Arista
FYE: August 31
Type: Public

Commercial Metals Company (CMC) wants to steel the limelight. CMC's marketing and distribution segment buys and sells primary and secondary metals, fabricated metals, and other industrial metals. Its domestic mills division includes mills (four minimills and a copper tubing minimill) and a fabrication mill (rebar and tubing minimills). The domestic fabrication unit runs a heat-treating plant and makes steel fence posts, steel beams, and steel joists. CMC's recycling unit operates more than 35 secondary metals-processing plants that shred, shear, and pulverize scrap metal, which is then sold to steel mills and nonferrous ingot producers. CMC's CMCZ division operates a minimill in Poland and makes wire rod.

	Annual Growth	8/03	8/04	8/05	8/06	8/07
Sales ($ mil.)	30.5%	2,875.9	4,768.3	6,592.7	7,555.9	8,329.0
Net income ($ mil.)	108.2%	18.9	132.0	285.8	356.4	355.4
Market value ($ mil.)	122.4%	140.0	256.0	869.9	2,545.1	3,425.4
Employees	7.4%	—	—	11,027	11,734	12,730

COMMERCIAL NATIONAL FINANCIAL

NASDAQ (GM): CNAF

900 Ligonier St.
Latrobe, PA 15650
Phone: 724-539-3501
Fax: 724-537-9966
Web: www.cnbthebank.com

CEO: Gregg E. Hunter
CFO: Thomas D. Watters
HR: –
FYE: December 31
Type: Public

Commercial National Financial Corporation is the holding company for Commercial Bank & Trust of PA, which operates about 10 branches in western Pennsylvania's Westmoreland County. Targeting individuals and local businesses, the bank offers standard deposit services, as well as mutual funds, investment counseling, and brokerage and trust services. Commercial Bank & Trust of PA's loan portfolio consists mostly of residential mortgages (more than 55%) and commercial mortgages (about 30%), in addition to business, construction, consumer, and municipal loans. The bank was formed in 1934.

	Annual Growth	12/03	12/04	12/05	12/06	12/07
Assets ($ mil.)	(1.1%)	385.0	320.4	322.4	338.2	367.6
Net income ($ mil.)	(3.7%)	3.6	0.6	3.4	3.0	3.1
Market value ($ mil.)	(10.8%)	89.9	75.1	64.3	60.7	57.0
Employees	(1.4%)	—	—	110	—	107

COMMERCIAL VEHICLE GROUP, INC.

NASDAQ (GS): CVGI

6530 W. Campus Way
New Albany, OH 43054
Phone: 614-289-5360
Fax: 614-289-5367
Web: www.cvgrp.com

CEO: Mervin Dunn
CFO: Chad M. Utrup
HR: James F. Williams
FYE: December 31
Type: Public

CB radio lingo might have gone the way of mood rings, but Commercial Vehicle Group (CVG) is still a trucker's good buddy. The company makes components for the cabs of heavy-duty trucks that help keep drivers comfortable and safe. Products include seats and suspension seat systems, interior trim (instrument panels, door panels, headliners), mirrors, wiper systems, and controls. Its customers include heavy-duty truck manufacturers such as PACCAR (14% of sales), Navistar's International Truck (11%), and Daimler Trucks' North America subsidiary (formerly Freightliner, 11%). Besides truck manufacturers, CVG sells its products to the fleet maintenance aftermarket and manufacturers of construction equipment and buses.

	Annual Growth	12/03	12/04	12/05	12/06	12/07
Sales ($ mil.)	24.8%	287.6	380.4	754.5	918.8	696.8
Net income ($ mil.)	—	4.0	17.5	49.4	58.0	(3.3)
Market value ($ mil.)	(7.4%)	—	392.7	397.1	465.8	312.3
Employees	8.4%	—	—	5,339	5,790	—

COMMODORE APPLIED TECHNOLOGIES, INC.

OTC: CXIA

507 Knight St., Ste. B
Richland, WA 99352
Phone: 509-943-2565
Fax: 509-913-2910
Web: www.commodore.com

CEO: Shelby T. Brewer
CFO: Ted R. Sharp
HR: Maryagnes Jones
FYE: December 31
Type: Public

Commodore Applied Technologies has SET its sights on cleaning up the environment. The company's SET (solvated electron technology) is a nonthermal process that removes PCBs, pesticides, dioxins, radioactivity, and other contaminants from water and soil. Commodore is working to commercialize SET; in the meantime, the company gets more than 90% of its sales from its Commodore Advanced Sciences unit, which provides waste containment, remediation, and removal management services, mainly for government agencies. Projects undertaken by Commodore Advanced Sciences have included US government radioactive waste sites in Oak Ridge, Tennessee, and Rocky Flats, Colorado.

	Annual Growth	12/03	12/04	12/05	12/06	12/07
Sales ($ mil.)	46.2%	0.7	0.7	10.3	7.3	3.2
Net income ($ mil.)	—	(3.0)	(2.4)	(2.7)	(1.9)	(2.0)
Market value ($ mil.)	(66.2%)	30.6	34.9	1.4	1.2	—
Employees	—	—	—	—	33	—

COMMONWEALTH BANKSHARES, INC.

NASDAQ (GM): CWBS

403 Boush St.
Norfolk, VA 23510
Phone: 757-446-6900
Fax: 757-446-6929
Web: www.bankofthecommonwealth.com

CEO: Edward J. Woodard Jr.
CFO: Cynthia A. Sabol
HR: –
FYE: December 31
Type: Public

Commonwealth Bankshares is the holding company for the Bank of the Commonwealth, which has about 10 branches in the Hampton Roads area of southeastern Virginia. The commercial bank attracts deposits from individuals and small to midsized businesses in the communities of Chesapeake, Norfolk, Portsmouth, and Virginia Beach by offering checking and savings accounts, IRAs, and CDs. In addition, it has subsidiaries that offer residential mortgages, brokerage and investment services, and insurance. Commercial mortgages represent nearly half of the company's loan portfolio; construction and development loans are more than a quarter. The bank also originates business and consumer loans.

	Annual Growth	12/03	12/04	12/05	12/06	12/07
Assets ($ mil.)	27.6%	318.3	374.1	549.5	715.2	843.1
Net income ($ mil.)	45.5%	2.5	3.1	6.6	10.1	11.2
Market value ($ mil.)	38.8%	29.6	46.5	92.2	171.1	110.0
Employees	29.6%	—	—	142	184	—

COMMONWEALTH BIOTECHNOLOGIES, INC.

NASDAQ (CM): CBTE

601 Biotech Dr.
Richmond, VA 23235
Phone: 804-648-3820
Fax: 804-648-2641
Web: www.cbi-biotech.com

CEO: Paul D'Sylva
CFO: James H. (Jim) Brennan
HR: –
FYE: December 31
Type: Public

Working for the good of all, Commonwealth Biotechnologies (also known as CBI) provides research services to life sciences companies, academic institutions, and government agencies. Through subsidiaries CBI Services, Exelgen, and Mimotopes (the last two acquired in 2007), the company provides a variety of drug discovery and biotech research services, including DNA sequencing; peptide and protein sequencing; and monoclonal antibody production. The company also performs DNA testing for the forensic and paternity testing markets through Fairfax Identity Labs (FIL). In 2008 CBI struck a deal with Chinese contract research organization Venturepham to set up a joint venture providing clinical development services.

	Annual Growth	12/03	12/04	12/05	12/06	12/07
Sales ($ mil.)	24.9%	5.1	5.8	7.8	6.5	12.4
Net income ($ mil.)	—	(0.1)	(0.4)	0.1	(1.1)	(2.8)
Market value ($ mil.)	14.7%	8.1	19.2	15.6	7.1	14.1
Employees	—	—	—	65	—	—

COMMONWEALTH EDISON COMPANY

440 S. LaSalle St.
Chicago, IL 60605
Phone: 312-394-4321
Fax: 312-394-2231
Web: www.exeloncorp.com/ourcompanies/comed

CEO: Frank M. Clark Jr.
CFO: Robert K. (Bob) McDonald
HR: –
FYE: December 31
Type: Subsidiary

Commonwealth Edison (ComEd) faces the not-so-common task of powering up Chicago. ComEd, a subsidiary of utility holding company Exelon, distributes electricity to 3.8 million homes and businesses in Chicago and surrounding areas of Northern Illinois. The utility owns approximately 84,390 circuit miles of transmission and distribution lines; it receives most of its power supply from sister company Exelon Generation. ComEd has joined regional organization PJM Interconnection, which manages wholesale activities on the utility's transmission grid. ComEd has warned that bankruptcy could be in its future if not allowed to purchase power in a more economical manner, such as an energy auction.

	Annual Growth	12/02	12/03	12/04	12/05	12/06
Sales ($ mil.)	(0.1%)	6,124.0	5,814.0	5,803.0	6,264.0	6,101.0
Net income ($ mil.)	—	790.0	707.0	—	—	(112.0)
Employees	(2.3%)	—	5,900	5,600	5,500	5,500

COMMSCOPE, INC.

NYSE: CTV

1100 CommScope Place SE
Hickory, NC 28603
Phone: 828-324-2200
Fax: 828-328-3400
Web: www.commscope.com

CEO: Frank M. Drendel
CFO: Jearld L. Leonhardt
HR: James L. Wright
FYE: December 31
Type: Public

CommScope doesn't need to be coaxed into making cable. The company manufactures coaxial, fiber-optic, and other high-performance cable products for data, voice, and video transmission. Its products include high-bandwidth cable that can provide cable television, telephone, and Internet access through a single line, primarily for business enterprise applications and broadband service providers. CommScope also is a top provider of coaxial cable for satellite television providers; other applications include cables for local area networks and video automation wiring (broadcast and security). The company's customers include Anixter and Comcast. CommScope has acquired rival Andrew for $2.65 billion in cash and stock.

	Annual Growth	12/03	12/04	12/05	12/06	12/07
Sales ($ mil.)	35.5%	573.3	1,152.7	1,337.2	1,623.9	1,930.8
Net income ($ mil.)	—	(70.6)	75.8	50.0	130.1	204.8
Market value ($ mil.)	35.8%	968.7	1,029.8	1,124.7	1,820.7	3,290.7
Employees	87.7%	—	—	4,400	4,550	15,500

COMMUNICATION INTELLIGENCE CORPORATION

OTC: CICI

275 Shoreline Dr., Ste. 500
Redwood Shores, CA 94065
Phone: 650-802-7888
Fax: 650-802-7777
Web: www.cic.com

CEO: Guido D. DiGregorio
CFO: Francis V. (Frank) Dane
HR: –
FYE: December 31
Type: Public

If your intelligent communication involves hunting and pecking, try Communication Intelligence Corp. (CIC). The company's handwriting recognition software, including its SignatureOne and iSign products, recognizes character strokes of words from English, Chinese, and Western European languages and converts them to digital text. Industries served by CIC include banking, insurance, and financial services. Customers have included Charles Schwab and Wells Fargo.

	Annual Growth	12/03	12/04	12/05	12/06	12/07
Sales ($ mil.)	(8.5%)	3.0	7.3	3.1	2.3	2.1
Net income ($ mil.)	—	(2.3)	1.6	(4.0)	(3.3)	(3.4)
Market value ($ mil.)	(5.9%)	37.0	60.3	45.8	22.0	29.0
Employees	(15.0%)	48	33	27	23	25

COMMUNICATIONS SUPPLY CORPORATION

200 E. Lies Rd.
Carol Stream, IL 60188
Phone: 630-221-6400
Fax: 630-221-6420
Web: www.gocsc.com

CEO: Steven J. (Steve) Riordan
CFO: Matt Zimmerman
HR: –
FYE: December 31
Type: Subsidiary

Communications Supply Corporation (CSC) carries a heavy download. CSC is a leading distributor of communication network equipment and supplies. The company distributes networking products and provides services through about 30 locations in the US. Its primary offerings include cable system (cabling, cabling components), network application (line cards, fiber-optic solutions), and low-voltage products (coaxial accessories, fire alarm cable). CSC also provides materials management and integration services. CSC was founded in 1972. Harvest Partners, a private equity investment firm, acquired the company in 2004. Harvest sold CSC to WESCO International in 2006.

COMMUNICATIONS SYSTEMS, INC.

AMEX: JCS

213 S. Main St.
Hector, MN 55342
Phone: 320-848-6231
Fax: 320-848-2702
Web: www.commsystems.com

CEO: Jeffrey K. Berg
CFO: David T. McGraw
HR: Karen J. Nesburg Bleick
FYE: December 31
Type: Public

Aptly named Communications Systems makes connectors and wiring systems for telecommunications networks. The company operates through subsidiaries. Its Suttle and Austin Taylor units make connectors, adapters, and other devices for voice, data, and video communications. Transition Networks makes converters that move data between copper wire and fiber-optic networks, LAN switches, and print servers. JDL Technologies provides schools with telecom network development services and software. Communications Systems sells directly and through distributors.

	Annual Growth	12/03	12/04	12/05	12/06	12/07
Sales ($ mil.)	4.3%	102.4	110.8	109.7	115.4	121.2
Net income ($ mil.)	29.1%	2.7	4.8	4.5	4.5	7.5
Market value ($ mil.)	11.5%	65.6	102.1	106.5	88.5	101.4
Employees	—	—	—	473	—	—

COMMUNICATIONS TEST DESIGN INC

1373 Enterprise Dr.
West Chester, PA 19380
Phone: 610-436-5203
Fax: 610-429-3861
Web: www.ctdi.com

CEO: Gerald J. (Jerry) Parsons
CFO: Larry Morgan
HR: –
FYE: December 31
Type: Private

Communications Test Design (CTDI) repairs, installs, tests, and manufactures telecommunications equipment. The company's main business is providing repair and maintenance services to wireless and wireline carriers and equipment manufacturers. But it also offers warehousing and distribution services, product quality testing, and equipment installation — from laying cable to installing customer premise equipment. Additionally, CTDI makes a line of broadband switching and access equipment and provides contract manufacturing services. It added to its access and transport product offering with the acquisition of Zhone's eLuminant line. Founded in 1975, the company operates worldwide.

	Annual Growth	12/03	12/04	12/05	12/06	12/07
Est. sales ($ mil.)	—	—	—	—	—	733.7
Employees	—	—	—	—	—	3,700

An in-depth profile of this company is available to Hoover's Online members at hoovers.com.

413

COMMUNITY BANCORP

NASDAQ (GM): CBON

400 S. 4th St., Ste. 215
Las Vegas, NV 89101
Phone: 702-878-0700
Fax: 702-947-3502
Web: www.communitybanknv.com

CEO: Edward M. (Ed) Jamison
CFO: Cathy Robinson
HR: –
FYE: December 31
Type: Public

Las Vegas = Lost Wages? Not if Community Bank of Nevada has something to say about it. The subsidiary of holding company Community Bancorp (not to be confused with the similarly named firm in Vermont) operates about 15 branches in and around Sin City. The company also owns Community Bank of Arizona (formerly Cactus Commerce Bank), which operates in the Phoenix metro area. The banks offer such deposit products as checking and savings accounts, NOW and money market accounts, CDs, and IRAs. Community Bancorp has played a part in Las Vegas' rapid growth by lending to area businesses; the loan portfolio is strongly dominated by construction loans and commercial mortgages.

	Annual Growth	12/03	12/04	12/05	12/06	12/07
Assets ($ mil.)	38.3%	463.4	574.0	892.7	1,570.4	1,693.5
Net income ($ mil.)	40.7%	5.2	5.4	10.1	15.6	20.4
Market value ($ mil.)	(4.8%)	—	206.5	233.1	313.6	178.4
Employees	31.9%	—	—	166	244	289

COMMUNITY BANCORP.

OTC: CMTV

4811 US Rte. 5
Derby, VT 05829
Phone: 802-334-7915
Fax: 802-334-8266
Web: www.communitynationalbank.com

CEO: Stephen P. Marsh
CFO: Louise Bonvechio
HR: –
FYE: December 31
Type: Public

Winters may be cold in Vermont, but Community Bancorp. hopes to warm the hearts of its customers with its hometown banking services. It is the holding company for Community National Bank, which has been serving Vermont since 1851. Through nearly 20 branches, the bank offers such products and services as checking and savings accounts, CDs, IRAs, residential and commercial mortgages, and business, consumer, and other loans. In conjunction with two other regional banks, the company is part of Community Financial Services Group, which offers trust and investment planning services. At the end of 2007 Community Bancorp. acquired LyndonBank, which added about a half-dozen branches to its network.

	Annual Growth	12/03	12/04	12/05	12/06	12/07
Assets ($ mil.)	11.0%	330.7	334.8	353.8	351.8	502.0
Net income ($ mil.)	(2.7%)	3.8	3.4	3.4	3.4	3.4
Market value ($ mil.)	1.3%	58.4	61.8	62.0	52.3	61.6
Employees	—	—	—	—	—	—

COMMUNITY BANK SHARES OF INDIANA, INC.

NASDAQ (CM): CBIN

101 W. Spring St.
New Albany, IN 47150
Phone: 812-944-2224
Fax: 812-949-6812
Web: www.cbinonline.com

CEO: James D. Rickard
CFO: Paul A. Chrisco
HR: Carl Page
FYE: December 31
Type: Public

Community Bank Shares of Indiana is the holding company for Your Community Bank (formerly Community Bank of Southern Indiana) and Scott County State Bank. The banks serve customers from around two dozen locations in southern Indiana and Louisville, Kentucky. It offers deposit products such as checking, money market, and savings accounts, as well as IRAs and CDs. Their lending activities center on commercial mortgages and residential real estate loans (each around 30% of the company's loan portfolio), but also include business, construction, and consumer (including home equity, home improvement, and auto) loans and credit cards.

	Annual Growth	12/03	12/04	12/05	12/06	12/07
Assets ($ mil.)	12.1%	521.3	590.1	665.0	816.6	823.6
Net income ($ mil.)	11.1%	2.3	2.6	3.8	4.1	3.5
Market value ($ mil.)	4.8%	48.1	56.3	59.4	77.4	58.0
Employees	13.1%	—	—	197	241	252

COMMUNITY BANK SYSTEM, INC.

NYSE: CBU

5790 Widewaters Pkwy.
DeWitt, NY 13214
Phone: 315-445-2282
Fax: 315-445-2997
Web: www.communitybankna.com

CEO: Mark E. Tryniski
CFO: Scott A. Kingsley
HR: Bernadette R. Barber
FYE: December 31
Type: Public

Community Bank System is right up front about what it is. The holding company owns Community Bank, which operates about 130 branches across nearly 25 counties in upstate New York and five counties in northeastern Pennsylvania, where it operates as First Liberty Bank and Trust. Focusing on small, underserved towns, the bank offers such services as checking and savings, money market, and NOW accounts. The bank's loan portfolio is divided nearly equally among business loans, residential mortgages, and consumer loans. Community Bank System also provides trust services, brokerage services, insurance products, and employee benefits plan administration.

	Annual Growth	12/03	12/04	12/05	12/06	12/07
Assets ($ mil.)	5.1%	3,855.4	4,393.8	4,152.7	4,497.8	4,697.5
Net income ($ mil.)	1.5%	40.4	50.2	50.8	38.4	42.9
Market value ($ mil.)	14.1%	347.0	865.6	675.5	690.5	588.8
Employees	—	—	—	1,299		

COMMUNITY BANKSHARES, INC.

AMEX: SCB

102 Founders Ct.
Orangeburg, SC 29118
Phone: 803-535-1060
Fax: 803-535-1065
Web: www.communitybanksharesinc.com

CEO: Samuel L. Erwin
CFO: William W. Traynham
HR: Jeffrey R. Scott
FYE: December 31
Type: Public

Community Bankshares has its own community of South Carolina residents. The bank has about 10 offices in central and northeastern South Carolina. Primarily serving area consumers and smaller businesses, the banks offer standard deposit products and services including checking and savings accounts, money market and NOW accounts, and IRAs. Real estate mortgages account for about 60% of the company's loan portfolio; it also writes commercial loans (more than 20%) and consumer and construction loans. The institution also originates and brokers loans through its mortgage division.

	Annual Growth	12/03	12/04	12/05	12/06	12/07
Assets ($ mil.)	5.4%	466.6	512.4	556.8	578.5	576.6
Net income ($ mil.)	(17.5%)	5.6	3.2	1.0	5.0	2.6
Market value ($ mil.)	(8.0%)	83.4	80.4	74.9	74.8	59.8
Employees	(2.6%)	—	—	194		184

COMMUNITY CAPITAL BANCSHARES, INC.

NASDAQ (CM): ALBY

2815 Meredyth Dr.
Albany, GA 31707
Phone: 229-446-2265
Fax: 229-446-7030
Web: www.albanybankandtrust.com

CEO: John H. Monk Jr.
CFO: David J. Baranko
HR: Misty Bruce
FYE: December 31
Type: Public

Community Capital Bancshares has taken hometown to heart. In 1999 the company opened Albany Bank & Trust, a community bank serving southwestern Georgia through three branches. It then made its first acquisition in 2003, buying First Bank of Dothan, which is now AB&T National Bank and operates two branches in Alabama. The banks offer standard deposit products and services including checking and savings accounts, money market accounts, CDs, and IRAs. The company mainly uses these deposits to fund residential and commercial construction loans and mortgages, as well as business and consumer loans. Real estate loans comprise about 80% of its loan book.

	Annual Growth	12/03	12/04	12/05	12/06	12/07
Assets ($ mil.)	8.9%	158.7	195.3	309.5	296.9	223.0
Net income ($ mil.)	—	0.6	0.9	0.1	0.4	(0.2)
Employees	(17.6%)	—	—	81	84	55

COMMUNITY CAPITAL CORPORATION

NASDAQ (GM): CPBK

1402-C Hwy. 72 West	CEO: William G. Stevens
Greenwood, SC 29649	CFO: R. Wesley Brewer
Phone: 864-941-8200	HR: –
Fax: 864-941-8283	FYE: December 31
Web: www.comcapcorp.com	Type: Public

A quintessential small town bank for quintessential small towns, Community Capital is the holding company for CapitalBank, which operates more than a dozen branches in western South Carolina. Targeting individuals and small to medium-sized businesses, the bank provides standard deposit services such as checking and savings accounts, money market accounts, IRAs, and certificates of deposit. Residential real estate mortgages, which the company also sells into the secondary market, account for about 40% of its loan portfolio; commercial mortgages are nearly 25%. Other lending activities include business, construction, agricultural, and consumer loans.

	Annual Growth	12/03	12/04	12/05	12/06	12/07
Assets ($ mil.)	18.0%	412.8	549.1	598.8	713.2	800.6
Net income ($ mil.)	8.4%	5.0	5.8	7.1	5.8	6.9
Market value ($ mil.)	0.4%	82.7	112.3	105.0	67.8	83.9
Employees	—	—	—	200	—	—

COMMUNITY CENTRAL BANK CORPORATION

NASDAQ (GM): CCBD

120 N. Main St.	CEO: David A. Widlak
Mt. Clemens, MI 48043	CFO: Ray T. Colonius
Phone: 586-783-4500	HR: Debbie Reinhardt
Fax: 586-783-9471	FYE: December 31
Web: www.communitycentralbank.com	Type: Public

The communities served by Community Central Bank Corporation are in the Detroit area — specifically Mt. Clemens and Rochester Hills. Founded in 1996, Community Central Bank operates branches that attract consumers, small to midsized businesses, and government entities. Standard banking services offered include checking, savings, NOW, and money market accounts, and CDs. Commercial real estate loans account for more than 60% of the company's loan portfolio, followed by residential mortgages (about 20%), business loans, home equity lines, and consumer loans. In 2005 Community Central acquired River Place Financial Corp., a private bank previously owned by the descendants of brewery founder Julius Stroh.

	Annual Growth	12/03	12/04	12/05	12/06	12/07
Assets ($ mil.)	9.8%	357.9	391.5	462.0	505.0	520.3
Net income ($ mil.)	(24.0%)	2.1	2.2	3.1	2.1	0.7
Market value ($ mil.)	(7.3%)	31.4	32.2	43.8	43.8	23.2
Employees	—	—	—	91	—	—

COMMUNITY COFFEE COMPANY L.L.C.

3332 Partridge Ln., Bldg. A	CEO: Matthew C. (Matt) Saurage
Baton Rouge, LA 70809	CFO: Annette L. Vaccaro
Phone: 225-368-3900	HR: Lia G. Thompson
Fax: 225-368-4507	FYE: June 30
Web: www.communitycoffee.com	Type: Private

Community Coffee is a cuppa Joe with a Cajun patois, don't you know. Boasting the largest family-owned retail coffee brand (Community Coffee) in the US, the company markets in 11 southern states. And there's more brewing: some 35 CC's Coffee Houses have sprung up since the original New Orleans coffee shop opened in 1995. In addition to New Orleans, CC's Coffee House has locations in Baton Rouge and Lafayette, Louisiana. In 2001 CC expanded to Texas but later closed those locations due to disappointing sales. CC's sells gourmet coffee, pastries, and whole beans. Community Coffee is owned by the descendants of Henry Norman Saurage, who founded it in 1919.

	Annual Growth	6/03	6/04	6/05	6/06	6/07
Est. sales ($ mil.)	—	—	—	—	—	148.3
Employees	—	—	—	—	—	1,000

COMMUNITY FINANCIAL CORPORATION

NASDAQ (CM): CFFC

38 N. Central Ave.	CEO: P. Douglas Richard
Staunton, VA 24401	CFO: R. Jerry Giles
Phone: 540-886-0796	HR: –
Fax: 540-885-0643	FYE: March 31
Web: www.cbnk.com	Type: Public

Community Financial is the holding company for Community Bank, originally organized as a Virginia building and loan association in 1928. The institution has a number of branches in the central portion of the state and two offices near the coast in Virginia Beach. Deposit options include checking, savings, NOW, and money market accounts; IRAs; and CDs. The bank also issues credit cards. Its loan portfolio is chiefly composed of residential mortgages, commercial and multifamily residential mortgages, and consumer loans (which together account for about 80% of its portfolio). Construction and business loans round out the loan portfolio.

	Annual Growth	3/04	3/05	3/06	3/07	3/08
Assets ($ mil.)	9.9%	337.0	399.6	422.6	463.1	491.3
Net income ($ mil.)	2.1%	3.5	3.8	4.3	4.1	3.8
Market value ($ mil.)	11.2%	22.6	23.4	23.5	50.5	34.7
Employees	—	—	—	143	—	—

COMMUNITY FIRST BANCORPORATION

OTC: CFOK

449 Hwy. 123 Bypass	CEO: Frederick D. Shepherd Jr.
Seneca, SC 29678	CFO: Frederick D. Shepherd Jr.
Phone: 864-886-0206	HR: –
Fax: 864-886-0912	FYE: December 31
Web: www.c1stbank.com	Type: Public

Community First Bancorporation, the holding company for Community First Bank, puts financial matters first in the northwestern corner of South Carolina. The commercial bank offers traditional retail products including checking and savings accounts, NOW accounts, money markets, CDs, and IRAs. Deposit funds are primarily used to originate real estate loans: single- to four-family mortgages account for about 50% of its loan book, while commercial and industrial mortgages account for some 10%. It also writes construction, consumer, and commercial loans.

	Annual Growth	12/03	12/04	12/05	12/06	12/07
Assets ($ mil.)	9.4%	280.5	305.4	320.7	353.9	402.1
Net income ($ mil.)	2.4%	3.0	3.4	3.7	3.0	3.3
Market value ($ mil.)	14.3%	33.1	44.0	49.6	63.6	56.5
Employees	23.3%	—	—	—	73	90

COMMUNITY HEALTH SYSTEMS, INC.

NYSE: CYH

4000 Meridian Blvd.	CEO: Wayne T. Smith
Franklin, TN 37067	CFO: W. Larry Cash
Phone: 615-465-7000	HR: Linda K. Parsons
Fax: –	FYE: December 31
Web: www.chs.net	Type: Public

Community Health Systems (CHS) isn't much of a city dweller. The hospital operator prefers small town America, owning or leasing some 115 hospitals mostly in rural areas or small cities in more than 25 states. Its hospitals (which contain a total of about 17,000 beds) typically act as the sole or primary acute health care provider in their service areas. They offer a variety of medical, surgical, and emergency services and generally have ancillary facilities that include doctors' offices, home health agencies, outpatient surgery centers, and diagnostic imaging facilities. In 2007 CHS acquired Triad Hospitals, adding hospitals in non-urban areas and a few urban markets.

	Annual Growth	12/03	12/04	12/05	12/06	12/07
Sales ($ mil.)	25.9%	2,834.6	3,332.6	3,738.3	4,365.6	7,127.5
Net income ($ mil.)	(30.7%)	131.5	151.4	167.5	168.3	30.3
Market value ($ mil.)	7.9%	2,623.0	2,442.7	3,587.3	3,434.7	3,561.4
Employees	20.7%	—	—	32,300	39,000	—

COMMUNITY HOSPITALS OF INDIANA, INC.

1500 N. Ritter Ave.
Indianapolis, IN 46219
Phone: 317-355-1411
Fax: 317-351-7723
Web: www.ecommunity.com

CEO: William E. (Bill) Corley
CFO: Thomas P. Fischer
HR: Jill Parris
FYE: December 31
Type: Not-for-profit

Community Hospitals of Indiana (dba Community Health Network) keeps the residents of central Indiana in good health. The health care system includes four acute care hospitals (all operating under the Community Hospital moniker and including Community Hospital Anderson) and The Indiana Heart Hospital, where Hoosiers can go to keep their tickers ticking. The Community Health Network, founded in 1956, has more than 866 beds total. The network also includes outpatient and specialty services facilities, including the Hook Rehabilitation Centers, which offer inpatient and outpatient physical, occupational, and other rehabilitative therapy care.

	Annual Growth	12/03	12/04	12/05	12/06	12/07
Est. sales ($ mil.)	—	—	—	—	—	1,089.3
Employees	—	—	—	—	—	5,000

COMMUNITY NEWSPAPER HOLDINGS, INC.

3500 Colonnade Pkwy., Ste. 600
Birmingham, AL 35243
Phone: 205-298-7100
Fax: 205-298-7108
Web: www.cnhi.com

CEO: Donna J. Barrett
CFO: Lynn Pearson
HR: –
FYE: December 31
Type: Private

It's possible that Community Newspaper Holdings (CNHI) might be holding your community's newspaper. CNHI owns more than 140 daily, weekly, and semi-weekly publications in about 25 states, with a large presence in Oklahoma and Texas. Its holdings also include Massachusetts-based Eagle Tribune Publishing Company, owner of the *Eagle-Tribune*. In addition to its publishing operations, the company runs companion Web sites for many of its papers. Ralph Martin, formerly with the newspaper operations of Thomson Reuters (then known as Thomson Corporation), founded CNHI in 1997. The company is backed by state pension manager Retirement Systems of Alabama.

	Annual Growth	12/03	12/04	12/05	12/06	12/07
Est. sales ($ mil.)	—	—	—	—	—	382.7
Employees	—	—	—	—	—	6,501

COMMUNITY SHORES BANK CORPORATION

NASDAQ (CM): CSHB

1030 W. Norton Ave.
Muskegon, MI 49441
Phone: 231-780-1800
Fax: 231-780-1860
Web: www.communityshores.com

CEO: Heather D. Brolick
CFO: Tracey A. Welsh
HR: –
FYE: December 31
Type: Public

Community Shores Bank Corporation believes the residents and businesses of western Michigan want a local bank with locals looking after their money, so the holding company operates Community Shores Bank, which has three branches that serve Muskegon and Ottawa counties. Commercial and real estate loans to local businesses make up more than three-quarters of the bank's loan portfolio. It also offers consumer, construction, and residential real estate loans, in addition to deposit products like checking and savings accounts and certificates of deposit.

	Annual Growth	12/03	12/04	12/05	12/06	12/07
Assets ($ mil.)	10.4%	184.1	193.5	222.2	247.0	273.5
Net income ($ mil.)	—	1.1	0.8	1.2	1.3	(0.8)
Market value ($ mil.)	(16.0%)	17.6	18.1	21.8	19.6	8.8
Employees	17.5%	—	—	71	—	98

COMMUNITY TRUST BANCORP, INC.

NASDAQ (GS): CTBI

346 N. Mayo Trail
Pikeville, KY 41501
Phone: 606-432-1414
Fax: 606-437-3366
Web: www.ctbi.com

CEO: Jean R. Hale
CFO: Kevin J. Stumbo
HR: –
FYE: December 31
Type: Public

Even Pike County's Hatfields and McCoys might agree that Community Trust Bancorp is a good place to store your loot. One of the largest bank holding companies in Kentucky, it's the parent of Community Trust Bank, which operates some 75 branches throughout the state and in southern West Virginia. The bank targets individuals and businesses, offering them such standard retail products as checking and savings accounts, money market and NOW accounts, and CDs. Its loan portfolio consists largely of commercial loans (about half of the total), real estate mortgages (more than a quarter), and consumer loans (nearly 20%). The remainder is made up of real estate construction and equipment lease financing loans.

	Annual Growth	12/03	12/04	12/05	12/06	12/07
Assets ($ mil.)	4.1%	2,474.0	2,709.1	2,849.2	2,969.8	2,902.7
Net income ($ mil.)	6.1%	28.9	31.0	34.4	39.1	36.6
Market value ($ mil.)	2.9%	369.6	480.4	461.2	629.5	414.2
Employees	0.4%	—	—	1,003	—	1,011

COMMUNITY VALLEY BANCORP

NASDAQ (CM): CVLL

2041 Forest Ave.
Chico, CA 95928
Phone: 530-899-2344
Fax: 530-891-3498
Web: www.communityvalleybancorp.com

CEO: Keith C. Robbins
CFO: John F. Coger
HR: Debbie Miley
FYE: December 31
Type: Public

Community Valley Bancorp is the holding company for Butte Community Bank, which serves individuals and businesses through more than a dozen branches in the northern California counties of Anderson, Chico, Colusa, Corning, Magalia, Marysville, Oroville, Paradise, Red Bluff, Redding, and Yuba City. It also operates loan production offices in Citrus Heights and Gridley. In addition to offering loans, the bank provides deposit products including CDs, and checking, savings, and retirement accounts. Sister subsidiary Butte Community Insurance writes car, health, farm, and other policies. Butte Community Bank is one of the largest US Department of Agriculture (USDA) lenders in the country.

	Annual Growth	12/03	12/04	12/05	12/06	12/07
Assets ($ mil.)	10.7%	386.7	449.7	494.8	550.0	580.6
Net income ($ mil.)	5.2%	5.3	5.6	7.2	7.2	6.5
Market value ($ mil.)	20.2%	36.7	50.5	105.6	112.9	76.7
Employees	—	—	—	—	—	—

COMMUNITY WEST BANCSHARES

NASDAQ (GM): CWBC

445 Pine Ave.
Goleta, CA 93117
Phone: 805-692-5821
Fax: 805-692-5835
Web: www.communitywest.com

CEO: Lynda J. Nahra
CFO: Charles G. Baltuskonis
HR: Marcy L. Shewmon
FYE: December 31
Type: Public

You don't need a compass to find your money at Community West Bancshares. The firm is the holding company for Community West Bank (formerly Goleta National Bank), which serves individuals and small to midsized businesses in Southern California through branches in the cities of Goleta, Santa Barbara, Santa Maria, Ventura, and Westlake Village. Services include checking and savings accounts and CDs, as well as health savings accounts. Nearly 40% of the bank's loan portfolio is secured by real estate loans. Community West also has a handful of offices that write small business administration loans in Alabama, Colorado, California, Florida, Georgia, North Carolina, Oregon, South Carolina, Tennessee, and Washington.

	Annual Growth	12/03	12/04	12/05	12/06	12/07
Assets ($ mil.)	19.0%	304.3	365.2	444.4	516.6	609.8
Net income ($ mil.)	14.6%	2.2	3.8	5.6	5.3	3.8
Market value ($ mil.)	1.5%	51.4	77.2	81.1	91.0	54.6
Employees	—	—	—	147	—	—

COMMVAULT SYSTEMS, INC.

NASDAQ (GM): CVLT

2 Crescent Place
Oceanport, NJ 07757
Phone: 732-870-4000
Fax: 732-870-4525
Web: www.commvault.com

CEO: N. Robert (Bob) Hammer
CFO: Louis F. (Lou) Miceli
HR: William (Bill) Beattie
FYE: March 31
Type: Public

CommVault Systems wants to have a lock on data management. The company provides software that customers use to store and manage enterprise data. Its products are used for tasks such as data migration, backup, archiving, data replication, and disaster recovery. Its customers come from industries such as manufacturing, financial services, health care, and transportation, as well as from the public sector. CommVault's strategic partners include systems integrators and professional services firms, distributors and resellers, and technology providers.

	Annual Growth	3/04	3/05	3/06	3/07	3/08
Sales ($ mil.)	34.2%	61.2	82.6	109.5	151.1	198.3
Net income ($ mil.)	—	(11.7)	0.5	10.8	64.3	20.8
Market value ($ mil.)	(22.0%)	—	—	—	679.9	530.1
Employees	—	—	—	—	727	—

COMPASS BANCSHARES, INC.

15 S. 20th St.
Birmingham, AL 35233
Phone: 205-297-3000
Fax: 205-297-7363
Web: www.compassweb.com

CEO: Garrett R. (Gary) Hegel
CFO: –
HR: E. Lee Harris Jr.
FYE: December 31
Type: Subsidiary

The needle of this Compass points south. Compass Bancshares is the holding company for Compass Bank, which operates some 400 branches in Alabama, Arizona, Colorado, Florida, New Mexico, and Texas. Compass offers such services as deposit accounts, credit cards, discount brokerage, lease financing, employee benefit plans, and insurance sales; it also offers wealth management and other services. It provides small business banking services such as commercial real estate loans, business credit cards, and 401(k) employee services. Compass Bancshares is a subsidiary of Banco Bilbao Vizcaya Argentaria (BBVA).

	Annual Growth	12/02	12/03	12/04	12/05	12/06
Assets ($ mil.)	9.4%	23,884.7	26,963.1	28,181.9	30,798.2	34,199.8
Net income ($ mil.)	10.0%	314.4	341.9	360.2	401.8	460.4
Employees	3.9%	7,200	7,700	7,832	8,000	8,400

COMPASS DIVERSIFIED HOLDINGS

NASDAQ (GS): CODI

61 Wilton Rd., 2nd Fl.
Westport, CT 06880
Phone: 203-221-1703
Fax: 203-221-8253
Web: www.compassdiversifiedtrust.com

CEO: Ihab Joseph (Joe) Massoud
CFO: James J. (Jim) Bottiglieri
HR: –
FYE: December 31
Type: Public

Compass Diversified Holdings (formerly Compass Diversified Trust) helps companies navigate their way towards profitability. The holding company invests in and manages mid-market businesses with promise. Its strategy is two-fold: help those companies in its portfolio grow and increase profits, and increase the size of its portfolio. The companies in its portfolio come from a variety of industries and include human resources outsourcing firm CBS Personnel, industrial equipment manufacturer Aeroglide Corporation, promotional products maker HALO Holding, and hard coatings company Silvue.

	Annual Growth	12/03	12/04	12/05	12/06	12/07
Sales ($ mil.)	123.4%	—	—	—	410.9	917.9
Net income ($ mil.)	—	—	—	—	(19.3)	40.4
Market value ($ mil.)	33.9%	—	—	—	350.7	469.7
Employees	—	—	—	—	—	—

COMPASS GROUP USA, INC.

2400 Yorkmont Rd.
Charlotte, NC 28217
Phone: 704-329-4000
Fax: 704-329-4010
Web: www.cgnad.com

CEO: Gary R. Green
CFO: Thomas (Tom) Ondrof
HR: Chris Ashcroft
FYE: September 30
Type: Subsidiary

This company points the way to managed foodservices. Compass Group USA provides catering and dining services to corporate clients, educational and health care facilities, and sports and entertainment venues through a number of subsidiaries. Its operating units include Bon Appétit Management Co., Chartwells Educational Dining Services, and Morrison Management Specialists. Its Levy Restaurants unit also operates fine dining locations, as well as concessions at sports and entertainment venues. In addition, the company offers vending services and on-site dining. A division of UK-based Compass Group, Compass Group USA was formed in 1994 through the acquisition of Canteen Vending Services.

	Annual Growth	9/03	9/04	9/05	9/06	9/07
Est. sales ($ mil.)	—	—	—	—	—	250.5
Employees	—	—	—	—	—	4,200

COMPASS MINERALS INTERNATIONAL, INC.

NYSE: CMP

9900 W. 109th St., Ste. 600
Overland Park, KS 66210
Phone: 913-344-9200
Fax: 913-338-7932
Web: www.compassminerals.com

CEO: Angelo C. Brisimitzakis
CFO: Rodney L. (Rod) Underdown
HR: –
FYE: December 31
Type: Public

Salt is Compass Minerals' true north. The company is one of the largest salt producers in North America. Its salt products include rock, evaporated, and solar salt and are used for applications such as water softening, road deicing, and food preparation. Compass Minerals operates through subsidiaries North American Salt, Great Salt Lake Minerals (a top producer of the crop nutrient sulfate of potash), Sifto Canada, and Salt Union (based in the UK). It has approximately 10 manufacturing facilities in Canada, the UK, and the US. The company went public in 2003; Apollo Management controlled Compass Minerals prior to the IPO.

	Annual Growth	12/03	12/04	12/05	12/06	12/07
Sales ($ mil.)	9.3%	600.6	695.1	742.3	660.7	857.3
Net income ($ mil.)	25.5%	32.3	49.8	30.9	55.0	80.0
Market value ($ mil.)	32.4%	430.9	748.6	781.2	1,013.0	1,326.0
Employees	2.7%	—	—	1,506	1,557	1,588

COMPELLENT TECHNOLOGIES, INC.

NYSE Arca: CML

7625 Smetana Lane
Eden Prairie, MN 55344
Phone: 952-294-3300
Fax: –
Web: compellent.com

CEO: Philip E. (Phil) Soran
CFO: John R. (Jack) Judd
HR: –
FYE: December 31
Type: Public

Compellent Technologies can take a byte out of your storage woes. Storage Center, the company's main product, is a storage area network (SAN) that enables users to deposit, recover, and manage large amounts of data. The product combines software with standards-based hardware and has been purchased by nearly 600 customers worldwide, in such industries as education, financial services, government, health care, insurance, retail, and transportation. Third-party hardware maintenance provider Anacomp offers storage equipment, network device, and peripherals repair services to Compellent Technologies' end users. The firm was founded in 2002 by chairman and CEO Philip Soran, COO John Guider, and CTO Lawrence Aszmann.

	Annual Growth	12/03	12/04	12/05	12/06	12/07
Sales ($ mil.)	135.9%	—	3.9	9.9	23.3	51.2
Net income ($ mil.)	—	—	(11.4)	(9.1)	(6.8)	(7.8)
Employees	—	—	—	—	153	—

COMPETITIVE TECHNOLOGIES, INC.

AMEX: CTT

777 Commerce Dr., Ste. 100
Fairfield, CT 06825
Phone: 203-368-6044
Fax: 203-368-5399
Web: www.competitivetech.net

CEO: John B. Nano
CFO: –
HR: –
FYE: July 31
Type: Public

It doesn't matter how great your invention is if you can't get it to market — that's where Competitive Technologies (CTT) comes in. The company helps individuals, corporations, government agencies, and universities commercialize their inventions. Clients such as Sony and the University of Illinois have used CTT's services, which include feasibility and marketability evaluations, as well as application for and enforcement of patents. CTT focuses on inventions in life and physical sciences as well as digital technologies. The company, established in 1971, also represents companies seeking to license technologies for commercial purposes.

	Annual Growth	7/03	7/04	7/05	7/06	7/07
Sales ($ mil.)	6.2%	3.3	8.0	14.2	5.2	4.2
Net income ($ mil.)	—	(1.9)	3.0	5.7	(2.4)	(8.9)
Market value ($ mil.)	20.4%	9.7	24.8	42.3	18.7	20.3
Employees	—	—	—	—	—	15

COMPLETE PRODUCTION SERVICES, INC.

NYSE: CPX

11700 Old Katy Rd., Ste. 300
Houston, TX 77079
Phone: 281-372-2300
Fax: 281-372-2301
Web: www.completeproduction.com

CEO: Joseph C. Winkler III
CFO: J. Michael Mayer
HR: Kenneth L. Nibling
FYE: December 31
Type: Public

In order to compete (with the big boys) Complete Production Services has merged three companies to set itself up as a major provider of specialized services and products that help oil and gas companies develop reserves, enhance production, and reduce costs. Focusing on hydrocarbon-rich basins in North America that have long-term growth potential, the company offers a range of oil field services, including drilling, completion and production services (intervention, downhole and wellsite services, and fluid handling), and product sales. Complete Production Services is banking on the growing demand for natural gas exploration to drive demand for its products and services. The company is 34.4%-owned by SCF-IV, L.P.

	Annual Growth	12/03	12/04	12/05	12/06	12/07
Sales ($ mil.)	100.1%	103.3	320.8	757.7	1,212.4	1,655.2
Net income ($ mil.)	217.0%	1.6	13.9	53.9	139.1	161.6
Market value ($ mil.)	(13.9%)	—	—	—	1,513.3	1,302.4
Employees	25.5%	—	—	4,485	6,397	7,062

COMPORIUM COMMUNICATIONS

332 E. Main St.
Rock Hill, SC 29730
Phone: 803-326-6011
Fax: 803-326-5709
Web: www.comporium.com

CEO: Bryant Barnes
CFO: Dan Robertson
HR: Patricia Woods
FYE: December 31
Type: Private

Comporium Communications is a member of the Comporium Group of companies, which provide telecommunications and related services in York County and Lancaster County, South Carolina. The group offers traditional telephone services, such as local-exchange access and long-distance, as well as data and Internet, cable TV, security, and directory publishing services. Comporium also resells wireless phone service from AT&T Mobility (formerly Cingular Wireless).

	Annual Growth	12/03	12/04	12/05	12/06	12/07
Est. sales ($ mil.)	—	—	—	—	—	68.2
Employees	—	—	—	—	—	536

COMPOSITES ONE LLC

85 W. Algonquin Rd.
Arlington Heights, IL 60005
Phone: 847-437-0200
Fax: 847-437-0664
Web: www.compositesone.com

CEO: Steven L. (Steve) Dehmlow
CFO: Jim Sieber
HR: –
FYE: December 31
Type: Private

Composites One (C1) helps composites fabricators compose their products. The company distributes a variety of fiberglass and composite materials, such as additives, adhesives, gel coats, pigments, putties, polyester, and vinyl ester resins. The composite materials that C1 focuses on are fibers impregnated with plastic resins to add strength and corrosion-resistance and at the same time keep the material lightweight. A joint venture formed in 1999 by GLS and Cook Composites and Polymers, it maintains more than 30 distribution centers and serves 10,000 customers throughout North America. Among the chemical manufacturers whose products C1 distributes are Hexcel, Owens Corning, Georgia Pacific, and DuPont.

	Annual Growth	12/03	12/04	12/05	12/06	12/07
Est. sales ($ mil.)	—	—	—	—	—	120.0
Employees	—	—	—	—	—	600

COMPREHENSIVE CARE CORPORATION

OTC: CHCR

3405 W. Dr. Martin Luther King Jr. Blvd., Ste. 101
Tampa, FL 33607
Phone: 813-288-4808
Fax: 813-288-4844
Web: www.compcare.com

CEO: John M. Hill
CFO: Robert J. Landis
HR: –
FYE: December 31
Type: Public

Comprehensive Care makes sure that health insurance covers the mind as well as the body. Through its Comprehensive Behavioral Care subsidiary (CompCare, for short), the company manages behavioral health care, including psychiatric and substance abuse services, for commercial and government-run health plans in about a dozen states. For the most part it operates under capitation agreements, in which the plans pay CompCare a fixed monthly fee for each member. The firm maintains a network of about 3,500 behavioral health providers, through which it manages the care of private health plan members, as well as Medicare and Medicaid participants. Hythiam acquired a controlling share of the firm in 2007.

	Annual Growth	5/04	5/05	5/06	*12/06	12/07
Sales ($ mil.)	7.9%	27.6	24.5	24.0	10.3	37.4
Net income ($ mil.)	—	(0.8)	(0.3)	(0.2)	(0.9)	(3.5)
Market value ($ mil.)	(12.5%)	7.5	10.7	12.7	15.7	4.4
Employees	—	—	—	70	—	—

*Fiscal year change

COMPSYCH CORPORATION

NBC Tower, 455 N. Cityfront Plaza Dr.
Chicago, IL 60611
Phone: 312-595-4000
Fax: 312-595-3125
Web: www.compsych.com

CEO: Richard A. Chaifetz
CFO: Robert K. Jacobson
HR: –
FYE: December 31
Type: Private

ComPsych Corporation provides employee assistance programs such as behavioral health, work-life, wellness, and crisis intervention services. The company's offerings are designed to help individuals improve their behavioral and physical health and address the personal, family, and life issues of employees at its client companies. ComPsych was founded in 1984; it serves more than 25 million individuals and 10,000 organizations throughout the US and in more than 90 other countries worldwide.

	Annual Growth	12/03	12/04	12/05	12/06	12/07
Est. sales ($ mil.)	—	—	—	—	—	109.4
Employees	—	—	—	—	—	2,000

COMPUCREDIT CORPORATION

NASDAQ (GS): CCRT

5 Concourse Pkwy., Ste. 400
Atlanta, GA 30328
Phone: 770-828-2000
Fax: 770-870-5183
Web: www.compucredit.com

CEO: David G. Hanna
CFO: J. Paul Whitehead III
HR: Cindy Robinson
FYE: December 31
Type: Public

Suffering from a fiscal near-death experience? Let CompuCredit resuscitate you. CompuCredit operates in four segments: credit card receivables, in which it targets customers with low credit scores and charges them more for the risk; retail micro-loans, or payday loans, as they are more commonly known; auto financing, in which it buys and services used car loans; and charged-off credit card receivables, in which subsidiary Jefferson Capital Systems collects on debt other companies have written off. The company's retail operations include more than 500 payday loan stores under names including First American Cash Advance and First Southern Cash Advance.

	Annual Growth	12/03	12/04	12/05	12/06	12/07
Assets ($ mil.)	25.3%	761.4	1,003.5	1,821.2	2,113.9	1,874.2
Net income ($ mil.)	—	121.7	100.7	171.4	107.5	(51.0)
Market value ($ mil.)	(14.7%)	1,000.4	1,401.0	2,101.0	2,193.3	529.5
Employees	7.4%	—	—	3,400	3,600	3,923

COMPUDYNE CORPORATION

2530 Riva Rd., Ste. 201
Annapolis, MD 21401
Phone: 410-224-4415
Fax: 410-266-8815
Web: www.compudyne.com

CEO: James O'Neill
CFO: Geoffrey F. (Geoff) Feidelberg
HR: –
FYE: December 31
Type: Private

The thin blue line lends to CompuDyne's bottom line. The security contractor does everything from designing prison security systems to making bulletproof doors for facilities such as state prisons, courthouses, and US embassies. Business segments include Institutional Security Systems (security systems for prisons and other facilities); Attack Protection (attack-resistant windows and doors); Integrated Electronic Systems (public security systems for the federal government); and Public Safety and Justice (dispatch systems for law enforcement and emergency service agencies). A group consisting of affiliates of investment firm The Gores Group and industry executive Stuart Mackiernan acquired CompuDyne in 2007.

	Annual Growth	12/02	12/03	12/04	12/05	12/06
Sales ($ mil.)	(1.3%)	155.6	193.3	142.8	141.6	147.5
Net income ($ mil.)	—	1.8	3.4	(8.2)	(8.7)	(15.0)
Employees	(6.4%)	923	—	—	766	707

COMPUMED, INC.

OTC: CMPD

5777 W. Century Blvd., Ste. 1285
Los Angeles, CA 90045
Phone: 310-258-5000
Fax: 310-645-5880
Web: www.compumed.net

CEO: Maurizio Vecchione
CFO: Phuong Dang
HR: –
FYE: September 30
Type: Public

CompuMed won't comp your meds, but it might interpret your ECG. Through its CardioGram software, the company provides online analyses of ECGs (electrocardiograms) for more than 500 hospitals, clinics, and other health care facilities throughout the US. The firm's ECG services are available 24 hours a day. CompuMed also rents and, to a lesser extent, sells ECG equipment. The company's additional product, OsteoGram, monitors osteoporosis by analyzing bone density; the test involves taking a hand X-ray and can be performed using standard X-ray equipment.

	Annual Growth	9/03	9/04	9/05	9/06	9/07
Sales ($ mil.)	5.1%	1.8	1.9	2.3	2.1	2.2
Net income ($ mil.)	—	(0.4)	(0.3)	(0.3)	(0.4)	(1.4)
Market value ($ mil.)	12.7%	7.7	4.3	9.2	8.5	12.5
Employees	—	—	—	—	—	—

COMPUSA INC.

7795 W. Flagler St., Ste. 35
Miami, FL 33144
Phone: 305-415-2199
Fax: –
Web: www.compusa.com

CEO: Richard Leeds
CFO: Lawrence P. (Larry) Reinhold
HR: –
FYE: December 31
Type: Subsidiary

A pioneer in big-box computer retail, CompUSA has been reduced to about 15 stores (down from more than 200 outlets in 2006), mostly in Florida, but also in Texas, and Puerto Rico, as well as an e-commerce site. Declining PC sales led to the 2007 decision to close or sell all of the retailer's stores. The CompUSA brand, Web site, and 16 retail outlets were acquired by Systemax in 2008 as a vehicle for the expansion of its TigerDirect subsidiary, a multichannel retailer of computers, consumer electronics, digital media technology, and peripherals. Prior to its purchase by Systemax, CompUSA was bought by liquidator Gordon Brothers Group, which acquired it from its previous owner, Mexico's Grupo Carso.

COMPUTER PROGRAMS AND SYSTEMS, INC.

NASDAQ (GS): CPSI

6600 Wall St.
Mobile, AL 36695
Phone: 251-639-8100
Fax: 251-639-8214
Web: www.cpsinet.com

CEO: J. Boyd Douglas
CFO: Darrell G. West
HR: –
FYE: December 31
Type: Public

Computer Programs and Systems, Inc. (CPSI) wants to make sure your neighborhood hospital isn't suffering from clogged information systems. CPSI develops, installs, and supports financial and clinical information management software and information technology systems for small and midsized hospitals in the US. The company, which targets community hospitals and small specialty hospitals, boasts a client base of more than 500 hospitals. Operating on UNIX and Windows platforms, CPSI's software enables health care providers to manage their patients, staff, finances, and facilities. The company also offers systems implementation, as well as billing, statement processing, and business office outsourcing services.

	Annual Growth	12/03	12/04	12/05	12/06	12/07
Sales ($ mil.)	7.9%	81.3	82.7	108.8	116.0	110.0
Net income ($ mil.)	13.0%	7.9	7.1	14.6	15.8	12.9
Market value ($ mil.)	3.9%	211.1	242.8	440.2	365.6	245.8
Employees	(9.1%)	—	—	858	—	709

COMPUTER SCIENCES CORPORATION

NYSE: CSC

3170 Fairview Park Dr.
Falls Church, VA 22042
Phone: 703-876-1000
Fax: –
Web: www.csc.com

CEO: Michael W. (Mike) Laphen
CFO: Donald G. DeBuck
HR: Nathan G. (Gus) Siekierka
FYE: Friday nearest March 31
Type: Public

Providing a wide array of consulting and outsourcing services isn't rocket science, it's computer science. Computer Sciences Corporation (CSC) is one of the world's leading providers of systems integration and other technology services, including application development, data hosting, networking, and management consulting. It provides business process outsourcing (BPO) services in such areas as billing and payment processing, customer relationship management (CRM), and human resources. A major government and defense contractor, CSC generates about a third of its revenues from federal agencies.

	Annual Growth	3/04	3/05	3/06	3/07	3/08
Sales ($ mil.)	2.8%	14,767.6	14,058.6	14,615.6	14,854.9	16,499.5
Net income ($ mil.)	1.2%	519.4	810.2	634.0	397.3	544.6
Market value ($ mil.)	(6.1%)	7,919.4	8,684.6	10,401.8	9,035.1	6,165.6
Employees	0.0%	—	79,000	79,000	79,000	—

An in-depth profile of this company is available to Hoover's Online members at hoovers.com.

419

COMPUTER TASK GROUP, INCORPORATED

NASDAQ (CM): CTGX

800 Delaware Ave.	CEO: James R. Boldt
Buffalo, NY 14209	CFO: Brendan M. Harrington
Phone: 716-882-8000	HR: Arthur W. (Bud) Crumlish
Fax: 716-887-7464	FYE: December 31
Web: www.ctg.com	Type: Public

Computer Task Group (CTG) uses its information technology (IT) expertise to take clients' computer systems to task. The company offers a wide range of professional technology services, including custom application development, facilities management, systems integration, and IT staffing. It also provides strategic consulting services to assess its clients' technology needs, as well as project management and application outsourcing management services. CTG serves clients through offices in the US, Canada, and Europe.

	Annual Growth	12/03	12/04	12/05	12/06	12/07
Sales ($ mil.)	6.6%	252.3	237.1	294.5	327.3	325.3
Net income ($ mil.)	12.3%	2.7	(1.4)	2.4	3.5	4.3
Market value ($ mil.)	6.8%	81.2	116.9	80.9	95.0	105.7
Employees	—	—	—	3,600	—	—

COMPUTERIZED THERMAL IMAGING, INC.

Pink Sheets: COIB

1719 W. 2800 South	CEO: Richard V. Secord
Ogden, UT 84401	CFO: Richard V. Secord
Phone: 801-776-4700	HR: –
Fax: 801-459-6063	FYE: June 30
Web: www.cti-net.com	Type: Public

Computerized Thermal Imaging (CTI) makes medical imaging and infrared treatment systems to diagnose and treat pain. Its Thermal Image Processor measures body heat to find areas of pain or soft-tissue injury, while its Photonic Stimulator uses infrared light emissions to relieve aches and pains. CTI has been seeking FDA approval for its breast imaging system (BCS 2100), a potential breast cancer diagnostic tool. Additionally, CTI makes the Turbine Blade Inspection System, which is used to test turbine blades in aircraft and power generation equipment. Difficulty getting FDA approval for the BCS 2100, years of losses, and an inability to raise capital have led the company to substantially reduce operations.

	Annual Growth	6/02	6/03	6/04	6/05	*6/06
Sales ($ mil.)	(42.3%)	0.9	1.5	0.4	0.2	0.1
Net income ($ mil.)	—	(21.7)	(11.7)	(2.5)	(0.7)	(0.3)
Employees	—	75	—	—	—	—

*Most recent year available

COMPUWARE CORPORATION

NASDAQ (GS): CPWR

1 Campus Martius	CEO: Peter (Pete) Karmanos Jr.
Detroit, MI 48266	CFO: Laura L. Fournier
Phone: 313-227-7300	HR: Laura L. Fournier
Fax: 313-227-7555	FYE: March 31
Web: www.compuware.com	Type: Public

Compuware is more than aware of the power of diversity. The company's products include testing, development, and management software for programs running on mainframe computer systems, distributed computer networks, and Web-based systems. Compuware also makes application development, implementation, and support software for programmers, as well as file, data, and systems management tools. Compuware's service offerings include consulting, systems integration, custom programming, maintenance, and support. The company sells directly and through distributors to corporate and government customers.

	Annual Growth	3/04	3/05	3/06	3/07	3/08
Sales ($ mil.)	(0.7%)	1,264.7	1,231.8	1,205.4	1,213.0	1,229.6
Net income ($ mil.)	28.2%	49.8	76.5	143.0	158.1	134.4
Market value ($ mil.)	(9.4%)	2,855.4	2,796.5	2,959.0	2,875.8	1,920.4
Employees	(2.4%)	—	7,908	7,510	7,539	—

COMPX INTERNATIONAL INC.

NYSE: CIX

5430 LBJ Fwy., Ste. 1700	CEO: David A. Bowers
Dallas, TX 75240	CFO: Darryl R. Halbert
Phone: 972-448-1400	HR: –
Fax: 972-448-1445	FYE: December 31
Web: www.compxnet.com	Type: Public

CompX International tries to keep the workday smooth, theft-free, and painless. The company makes ball bearing slides, cabinet locks, and ergonomic computer support systems. Its primary customers are office furniture makers, but its components are also used in recreational vehicles, vending equipment, mailboxes, appliances, and computers. CompX's ball bearing slides are sold under names such as Dynaslide and Waterloo; its locks are sold under such names as National Cabinet Lock, Fort Lock, and Chicago Lock. NL Industries owns about two-thirds of CompX International.

	Annual Growth	12/03	12/04	12/05	12/06	12/07
Sales ($ mil.)	(3.8%)	207.5	182.6	186.4	190.1	177.7
Net income ($ mil.)	62.2%	1.3	(3.0)	0.4	11.7	9.0
Market value ($ mil.)	2.5%	32.8	85.6	83.9	106.2	36.2
Employees	—	—	—	1,230	—	—

COMSCORE, INC.

NASDAQ (GM): SCOR

11465 Sunset Hills Rd., Ste. 200	CEO: Magid M. Abraham
Reston, VA 20190	CFO: –
Phone: 703-438-2000	HR: Glenn Krauser
Fax: 703-438-2051	FYE: December 31
Web: www.comscore.com	Type: Public

comScore knows the score when it comes to measuring online audience behavior. The company provides data, analysis, and consultancy to clients looking to fortify their marketing, sales, and trading initiatives. Its global panel of more than 2 million Internet users measures and tracks consumer behaviors, demographics, and advertising responsiveness for clients in such industries as travel, pharmaceuticals, finance, and telecommunications. Branded products include its comScore Media Metrix suite of Web site and online advertising network measurement tools and its comScore Marketing Solutions products, which provide custom research as well as analysis from its panel.

	Annual Growth	12/03	12/04	12/05	12/06	12/07
Est. sales ($ mil.)	—	—	—	—	—	87.2
Net income ($ mil.)	—	—	—	—	—	19.3
Market value ($ mil.)	—	—	—	—	—	931.6
Employees	—	—	—	—	—	452

COMSTOCK HOMEBUILDING COMPANIES, INC.

NASDAQ (GM): CHCI

11465 Sunset Hills Rd., Ste. 510	CEO: Christopher (Chris) Clemente
Reston, VA 20190	CFO: Bruce J. Labovitz
Phone: 703-883-1700	HR: –
Fax: 703-760-1520	FYE: December 31
Web: www.comstockhomebuilding.com	Type: Public

While people take stock of their lives, Comstock takes stock of its portfolio. The homebuilder develops land and builds single-family homes, townhouses, and mid- and high-rise condominiums in Washington, DC; Raleigh, North Carolina; and Atlanta. The company annually delivers some 200 homes with an average price of approximately $240,000. Its customer base includes first-time homebuyers, buyers looking to move up, empty nesters, and active retirees. Comstock's single-family homes range from roughly 1,400 sq. ft. to more than 6,000 sq. ft. and in price from the $100,000s to the $600,000s; its townhomes range in size from 1,200 sq. ft. to 4,500 sq. ft. and in price from the $100,000s to the $500,000s.

	Annual Growth	12/03	12/04	12/05	12/06	12/07
Sales ($ mil.)	48.0%	55.5	96.0	224.3	245.9	266.2
Net income ($ mil.)	—	5.9	14.3	27.6	(39.8)	(87.5)
Market value ($ mil.)	(64.6%)	—	201.3	158.9	81.2	8.9
Employees	3.7%	121	—	130	—	—

An in-depth profile of this company is available to Hoover's Online members at hoovers.com.

COMSTOCK RESOURCES, INC.
NYSE: CRK

5300 Town and Country Blvd., Ste. 500	CEO: M. Jay Allison
Frisco, TX 75034	CFO: Roland O. Burns
Phone: 972-668-8800	HR: Roland O. Burns
Fax: 972-668-8812	FYE: December 31
Web: www.comstockresources.com	Type: Public

Comstock Resources' stock in trade is producing natural gas and oil. The mid-sized independent oil and gas company has proved reserves of more than 1 trillion cu. ft. of natural gas equivalent (80% in the form of natural gas) on its properties in five major areas — East Texas /North Louisiana, Mississippi, South Texas, Southeast Texas, and the Gulf of Mexico. Comstock Resources operates 504 of the 881 producing wells in which it holds an interest. The company has grown by exploiting its existing reserves and through acquisitions. Comstock Resources owns a controlling interest in Bois d'Arc Energy, a publicly held company which conducts exploration and production operations in the Gulf of Mexico.

	Annual Growth	12/03	12/04	12/05	12/06	12/07
Sales ($ mil.)	30.8%	235.1	261.6	303.3	511.9	687.1
Net income ($ mil.)	6.3%	53.9	46.9	60.5	70.7	68.9
Market value ($ mil.)	23.6%	662.2	786.1	1,311.0	1,378.9	1,544.6
Employees	46.1%	—	—	89	130	—

COMSYS IT PARTNERS, INC.
NASDAQ (GM): CITP

4400 Post Oak Pkwy., Ste. 1800	CEO: Larry L. Enterline
Houston, TX 77027	CFO: –
Phone: 713-386-1400	HR: Terry V. Bell
Fax: 713-961-0719	FYE: Sunday nearest December 31
Web: www.comsys.com	Type: Public

In need of a technical whiz? COMSYS IT Partners supplies temporary information technology (IT) personnel from more than 50 offices in the US, as well as from facilities in Canada and the UK. The company also helps companies recruit and hire permanent IT professionals and provides ad hoc project teams that develop and implement applications either on- or offsite. COMSYS IT Partners employs about 5,000 IT professionals and serves customers in the finance, health care, pharmaceutical, telecom, manufacturing, and transportation industries, as well as government entities. The company was formed when COMSYS Holding merged with publicly traded Venturi Partners in 2004.

	Annual Growth	12/03	12/04	12/05	12/06	12/07
Sales ($ mil.)	19.4%	—	437.0	661.7	736.6	743.3
Net income ($ mil.)	—	—	(55.2)	2.2	21.0	33.3
Market value ($ mil.)	27.1%	—	155.2	207.2	389.6	318.4
Employees	(6.2%)	—	—	5,661	4,297	4,986

COMTECH TELECOMMUNICATIONS CORP.
NASDAQ (GS): CMTL

68 S. Service Rd., Ste. 230	CEO: Fred V. Kornberg
Melville, NY 11747	CFO: Michael D. Porcelain
Phone: 631-962-7000	HR: –
Fax: 631-962-7001	FYE: July 31
Web: www.comtechtel.com	Type: Public

Comtech means contact. Through its subsidiaries, Comtech Telecommunications operates in three divisions: telecommunications transmission, mobile data communications, and RF microwave amplifiers. The company makes equipment used largely by the US government and related defense contractors. Other customers include satellite systems integrators, communications service providers, and oil companies. Its transmission equipment includes modems, frequency converters, high-power amplifiers, very-small-aperture terminal (VSAT) satellite transceivers and antennas, and microwave radios.

	Annual Growth	7/03	7/04	7/05	7/06	7/07
Sales ($ mil.)	26.5%	174.0	223.4	307.9	391.5	445.7
Net income ($ mil.)	61.0%	9.7	21.8	36.7	45.3	65.2
Market value ($ mil.)	57.7%	167.2	188.8	797.9	634.1	1,034.8
Employees	6.2%	—	—	1,090	1,228	1,230

COMTEL TELCOM ASSETS LP

433 Las Colinas Blvd. East, Ste. 1300	CEO: James Cashiola
Irving, TX 75039	CFO: –
Phone: 972-910-1900	HR: –
Fax: –	FYE: December 31
Web: www.excel.com	Type: Private

If it wasn't apparent from the name, Comtel Telcom Assets is in the communications game. The company, which does business as Excel Telecommunications, provides wholesale telecommunications services to residential customers, small businesses, and communications service resellers. Clients include call centers, among others. Services offered include domestic and international long-distance, broadcast fax, wireless voice, and toll-free numbers; Excel also provides teleconferencing and Web conferencing services. The company's MyExcel Internet service provides dial-up access to the Web.

	Annual Growth	12/03	12/04	12/05	12/06	12/07
Est. sales ($ mil.)	—	—	—	—	—	450.0
Employees	—	—	—	—	—	—

⊞ COMTEX NEWS NETWORK, INC.
OTC: CMTX

625 N. Washington St., Ste. 301	CEO: Chip Brian
Alexandria, VA 22314	CFO: –
Phone: 703-820-2000	HR: –
Fax: 703-820-2005	FYE: June 30
Web: www.comtexnews.net	Type: Public

Start spreading the news. Comtex News Network is a distributor of news on the Internet, specializing in the business and financial market. The company gathers news and content from more than 10,000 national and international news bureaus, agencies, and publications (including PR Newswire, United Press International, and The Associated Press). Clients include MarketWatch, Factiva, and other information distributors. Comtex's distribution system offers stories sorted by topic, keyword, or geographic location. Products include news from categories such as health care and sports, in addition to top headlines and customized financial and industry news. Chairman C. W. Gilluly owns 18% of the company.

	Annual Growth	6/03	6/04	6/05	6/06	6/07
Sales ($ mil.)	(6.5%)	9.3	8.2	8.0	7.7	7.1
Net income ($ mil.)	—	(1.3)	(1.2)	0.7	(0.5)	(0.1)
Market value ($ mil.)	(2.0%)	3.3	2.7	1.9	11.6	3.1
Employees	—	—	—	—	25	—

COMVERGE, INC.
NASDAQ (GM): COMV

120 Eagle Rock Rd., Ste. 190	CEO: Robert M. (Bob) Chiste
East Hanover, NJ 07936	CFO: Arthur (Bud) Vos IV
Phone: 973-884-5970	HR: –
Fax: 973-884-3504	FYE: December 31
Web: www.comverge.com	Type: Public

Comverge seeks a convergence of communications enabling the lights to stay on. The company provides "energy intelligence" software to electric utilities and other energy suppliers and sells automated meters and related equipment with communications links. The company's products are used by more than 500 utilities and energy providers in Asia, Latin America, the Middle East, and North America. US customers have included Gulf Power, Buckeye Power, Duke Energy, Detroit Edison, and PEPCO. Its products include software and hardware that help control energy load, read meters remotely, manage billing, and detect theft and outages.

	Annual Growth	12/03	12/04	12/05	12/06	12/07
Sales ($ mil.)	37.6%	15.4	17.3	23.4	33.9	55.2
Net income ($ mil.)	—	(9.3)	(9.3)	(8.0)	(6.2)	(6.6)
Market value ($ mil.)	—	—	—	—	—	657.9
Employees	9.5%	89	—	—	117	—

⊞ An in-depth profile of this company is available to Hoover's Online members at hoovers.com.

421

COMVERSE TECHNOLOGY, INC.

Pink Sheets: CMVT

810 Seventh Ave.
New York, NY 10019
Phone: 212-739-1000
Fax: –
Web: www.cmvt.com

CEO: Andre Dahan
CFO: Joseph R. (Joe) Chinnici
HR: Lance Miyamoto
FYE: January 31
Type: Public

Comverse Technology helps others converse. Through multiple subsidiaries, the company makes communications systems and software that phone companies use to offer call answering, voice and fax mail, communications surveillance and recording, and other services. Comverse also makes digital monitoring systems for call centers and telecom software for information processing. Subsidiary Ulticom provides software used to enable call switching, database, and messaging systems and manage number, routing, and billing data. The company's customers include more than 500 communication and content service providers in more than 130 countries, including BellSouth, Sprint Nextel, and Brazilian telecomm provider Sercomte.

	Annual Growth	1/01	1/02	1/03	1/04	*1/05
Sales ($ mil.)	(5.9%)	1,225.1	1,270.2	735.9	765.9	959.4
Net income ($ mil.)	(30.7%)	249.1	54.6	(129.5)	(5.4)	57.3
Employees	(13.3%)	6,370	5,650	4,789	—	—

*Most recent year available

CONAGRA FOODS FOOD INGREDIENTS COMPANY, INC.

1 ConAgra Dr.
Omaha, NE 68102
Phone: 402-595-4000
Fax: –
Web: www.conagrafoodingredients.com

CEO: Gregory A. (Greg) Heckman
CFO: –
HR: –
FYE: Last Sunday in May
Type: Subsidiary

You probably don't realize it, but ConAgra Food Ingredients (CFI) adds a little spice to your meals, no matter if you're eating in or eating out. A subsidiary of US agriculture giant ConAgra Foods, the company manufactures food ingredients such as spices and flavorings (Spicetec); dehydrated and pureed vegetables, garlic, chilies, and onions (Gilroy Foods); and grain products for use in the baking industry (ConAgra Mills). It also offers such sevices as distribution, risk management, and global ingredient sourcing. ConAgra Food Ingredients operates as part of its parent company's Food and Ingredients division, along with Lamb Weston and ConAgra Foodservice.

	Annual Growth	5/02	5/03	5/04	5/05	5/06
Sales ($ mil.)	—	—	—	—	—	4,375.0
Employees	—	—	—	—	—	—

CONAGRA FOODS, INC.

NYSE: CAG

1 ConAgra Dr.
Omaha, NE 68102
Phone: 402-595-4000
Fax: 402-595-4707
Web: www.conagra.com

CEO: Gary M. Rodkin
CFO: André J. Hawaux
HR: Peter M. (Pete) Perez
FYE: Last Sunday in May
Type: Public

ConAgra Foods fills Americans' refrigerators, freezers, and pantries and, ultimately, their tummies. The company is a US top food producer, offering packaged and frozen foods. ConAgra's brands are a cornucopia of America's well-known foods, including Banquet, Chef Boyardee, Egg Beaters, Healthy Choice, Hunt's, Jiffy, Orville Redenbacher's, PAM, Slim Jim, and Van Camp's. It is also one of the country's largest foodservice suppliers, offering convenience foods and ingredients. The company has sold off its agricultural segments and a number of non-core brands in order to produce only branded and value-added packaged foods.

	Annual Growth	5/03	5/04	5/05	5/06	5/07
Sales ($ mil.)	(11.8%)	19,839.2	14,522.1	14,566.9	11,579.4	12,028.2
Net income ($ mil.)	(0.3%)	774.8	811.3	641.5	533.8	764.6
Market value ($ mil.)	0.4%	12,351.0	14,656.0	13,788.0	11,606.8	12,567.7
Employees	(19.7%)	—	—	38,000	33,000	24,500

CONAIR CORPORATION

1 Cummings Point Rd.
Stamford, CT 06902
Phone: 203-351-9000
Fax: –
Web: www.conair.com

CEO: Ronald T. Diamond
CFO: Dennis Ling
HR: John Mayorek
FYE: December 31
Type: Private

Counterintelligence has shown that Conair has a place in many bathrooms and kitchens. Personal products by Conair, Rusk, and Jheri Redding, include curling irons, hair dryers, mirrors, shavers, and salon products designed for both home and professional salon use. Its garment care products include fabric steamers, irons, and presses. Conair also sells Interplak electric toothbrushes and Scünci hair accessories. Products are sold at discount chains, department stores, and mass merchants (Bed Bath & Beyond, Target, Wal-Mart) throughout the US. Lee Rizzuto, who founded Conair in 1959 with his parents, pleaded guilty to tax evasion in 2002.

	Annual Growth	12/02	12/03	12/04	12/05	12/06
Sales ($ mil.)	9.7%	1,176.0	1,277.2	1,340.0	1,488.0	1,700.0
Employees	(6.3%)	4,373	4,000	3,331	3,459	3,367

CONCENTRA INC.

5080 Spectrum Dr., Ste. 1200 West
Addison, TX 75001
Phone: 972-364-8000
Fax: 972-387-0019
Web: www.concentra.com

CEO: James M. (Jim) Greenwood
CFO: Thomas E. (Tom) Kiraly
HR: Tammy S. Steele
FYE: December 31
Type: Private

Concentra concentrates on keeping employees healthy. The company's main business is providing occupational health care services through its network of more than 300 medical centers in 40 states, as well as at numerous workplace clinics across the country. Services provided at the centers include pre-employment screening, injury care, vaccinations, and physical therapy. The company also provides a suite of services (which it calls Auto Injury Solutions) to property/casualty insurers, offering bill review, claims processing, and other services related to auto injury cases. Concentra is owned by private equity firm Welsh, Carson, Anderson & Stowe.

	Annual Growth	12/02	12/03	12/04	12/05	12/06
Sales ($ mil.)	6.8%	999.0	1,050.7	1,102.3	1,155.1	1,298.8
Net income ($ mil.)	—	(3.6)	43.3	(10.0)	53.8	32.7
Employees	3.1%	10,254	10,000	10,370	11,285	11,585

CONCEPTUS, INC.

NASDAQ (GM): CPTS

331 E. Evelyn
Mountain View, CA 94041
Phone: 650-628-4700
Fax: 650-610-8368
Web: www.conceptus.com

CEO: Mark M. Sieczkarek
CFO: Gregory E. Lichtwardt
HR: –
FYE: December 31
Type: Public

Though you might not think so from the name, Conceptus makes products to hinder conception, not help it along. The company makes and sells Essure, a birth control system that permanently blocks conception with a micro-coil device implanted in the fallopian tube. Essure can be inserted during an outpatient procedure that lasts less than one hour and does not require general anesthesia. Conceptus markets the product primarily to gynecologists in the US through a direct sales force and internationally through distributors in Australia, Canada, and Spain; the company acquired its French distributor in 2008.

	Annual Growth	12/03	12/04	12/05	12/06	12/07
Sales ($ mil.)	70.1%	7.7	11.6	21.2	41.9	64.4
Net income ($ mil.)	—	(39.5)	(26.1)	(21.8)	(18.5)	(11.6)
Market value ($ mil.)	21.3%	264.8	208.3	366.6	623.2	574.1
Employees	—	—	—	139	—	—

CONCHO RESOURCES INC.

NYSE: CXO

550 W. Texas Ave., Ste. 1300
Midland, TX 79701
Phone: 432-683-7443
Fax: 432-683-7441
Web: www.conchoresources.com

CEO: Timothy A. Leach
CFO: Curt F. Kamradt
HR: –
FYE: December 31
Type: Public

Concho Resources explores and develops properties, located primarily in the Permian Basin region of eastern New Mexico and the western area of Texas, for the production of oil and gas. It also owns properties in North Dakota and Arkansas. More than half of the company's 467 billion cu. ft. in proven reserves is made up of crude oil while the rest consists of natural gas. Concho Resources gets two-thirds of its sales from crude oil. Customers include such energy marketers as Navajo Refining Company (53% of sales) and DCP Midstream (18%). The company has over 80 producing wells in operation. Chase Oil owns 48% of the company.

	Annual Growth	12/03	12/04	12/05	12/06	12/07
Sales ($ mil.)	334.0%	—	3.6	54.9	198.3	294.3
Net income ($ mil.)	—	—	(2.7)	2.0	19.7	25.4
Market value ($ mil.)	—	—	—	—	—	1,562.9
Employees	41.3%	—	—	—	80	113

CONCORD CAMERA CORP.

NASDAQ (GM): LENS

4000 Hollywood Blvd., 6th Fl., North Tower
Hollywood, FL 33021
Phone: 954-331-4200
Fax: 954-981-3055
Web: www.concord-camera.com

CEO: Ira B. Lampert
CFO: Blaine A. Robinson
HR: –
FYE: Saturday nearest June 30
Type: Public

Want the big picture on disposable cameras? It would definitely include Concord, one of the world's largest producers of the devices. Concord Camera makes single-use and conventional 35mm and Advanced Photo System (APS) cameras, as well as digital cameras. Its products, made mostly in China, are sold under private labels, as well as under names Concord, EasyShot, Go Wireless, Jenoptik, Fun Shooter, Goldline, Keystone, Le Clic, and Polaroid (through license). The company also sells to retailers, with Wal-Mart accounting for more than 40% of sales and Walgreens another 21%. Investment firm MT Trading LLC owns some 19% of the company and Concord Camera chairman, president, and CEO Ira Lampert owns about 9%.

	Annual Growth	6/03	6/04	6/05	6/06	6/07
Sales ($ mil.)	(17.8%)	189.8	203.1	174.4	137.5	86.7
Net income ($ mil.)	—	6.4	(31.2)	(44.9)	(19.6)	(11.7)
Market value ($ mil.)	(59.1%)	966.1	479.5	35.3	18.7	26.9
Employees	(22.8%)	—	—	181	—	108

CONCUR TECHNOLOGIES, INC.

NASDAQ (GM): CNQR

18400 NE Union Hill Rd.
Redmond, WA 98052
Phone: 425-702-8808
Fax: 425-702-8828
Web: www.concur.com

CEO: S. Steven (Steve) Singh
CFO: John F. Adair
HR: –
FYE: September 30
Type: Public

Having trouble keeping track of "entertainment" expenses from that "business" trip to Las Vegas? Concur Technologies offers corporate expense management software that enables businesses to automate and streamline the process for submitting and approving employee expense reports. Concur's software features Web-based modules for tracking, submitting, and processing reports for travel and entertainment costs, as well as applications to track employee requests for vendor payments. Concur licenses its software directly to companies and offers its applications by subscription through application service providers.

	Annual Growth	9/03	9/04	9/05	9/06	9/07
Sales ($ mil.)	22.8%	56.7	56.5	71.8	97.1	129.1
Net income ($ mil.)	69.2%	1.0	2.0	5.4	34.2	8.2
Market value ($ mil.)	38.2%	377.3	346.0	441.4	525.9	1,377.4
Employees	20.7%	—	—	395	500	575

CONCURRENT COMPUTER CORPORATION

NASDAQ (GM): CCUR

4375 River Green Pkwy., Ste. 100
Duluth, GA 30096
Phone: 678-258-4000
Fax: 678-258-4300
Web: www.ccur.com

CEO: Dan Mondor
CFO: Emory O. Berry
HR: Suzanne Smith
FYE: June 30
Type: Public

Concurrent Computer hawks its wares worldwide. The company provides high-performance computing systems that can simulate a jet fighter or deliver a blockbuster. Digital cable and DSL service providers use its MediaHawk servers and software to offer their customers video-on-demand services. Concurrent also produces RedHawk real-time Linux systems that process large amounts of data instantaneously for such applications as military simulation and training, weather satellite data acquisition, and product design. The company's Everstream data collection suite allows customers to store and analyze data from disparate interactive TV systems. Concurrent also provides integration services.

	Annual Growth	6/03	6/04	6/05	6/06	6/07
Sales ($ mil.)	(2.1%)	75.4	79.2	78.7	71.6	69.2
Net income ($ mil.)	—	(24.5)	(5.7)	(7.7)	(9.3)	(12.2)
Market value ($ mil.)	(5.0%)	1,821.1	1,243.4	1,355.6	1,867.0	1,484.6
Employees	—	—	—	—	—	—

CONE DENIM LLC

804 Green Valley Rd., Ste. 300
Greensboro, NC 27408
Phone: 336-379-6220
Fax: 336-379-6287
Web: www.cone.com

CEO: John L. Bakane
CFO: Gary L. Smith
HR: Robert (Bob) Garren
FYE: Sunday nearest December 31
Type: Subsidiary

When it comes to denim, Cone Denim (formerly Cone Mills) wears the pants. The world's #1 maker of denim is also the largest commission printer of home-furnishings fabrics in North America. Levi Strauss & Co., its largest customer, makes its 501 jeans solely from Cone Denim's proprietary fabric. The company makes jacquard fabrics and offers commission finishing, including custom printing and dyeing services, to the home decorative, specialty apparel, and craft fabrics markets. Cone Denim has a joint venture in Mexico to produce denims. After filing for Chapter 11 bankruptcy protection, Cone Mills was bought by International Textile Group for $90 million ($46 million in cash and $44 million in debt) in 2004.

	Annual Growth	12/03	12/04	12/05	12/06	12/07
Est. sales ($ mil.)	—	—	—	—	—	207.6
Employees	—	—	—	—	—	3,200

CONEXANT SYSTEMS, INC.

NASDAQ (GS): CNXT

4000 MacArthur Blvd.
Newport Beach, CA 92660
Phone: 949-483-4600
Fax: –
Web: www.conexant.com

CEO: D. Scott Mercer
CFO: Karen Roscher
HR: Michael H. (Mike) Vishny
FYE: September 30
Type: Public

Conexant Systems' chips help electronic devices connect. The company, whose communications chips are found in most of the world's fax machines, has spun off several business units to focus on providing integrated circuits and subsystems for a variety of communications devices, including computer and cable modems, TV set-top boxes, and cordless and cellular telephones. Conexant has sold its chips to a broad range of top high-tech manufacturers, including Apple, Dell, Hewlett-Packard, Microsoft, Motorola, and Samsung Electronics. Conexant gets more than 80% of its sales from the Asia/Pacific region, predominantly in China.

	Annual Growth	9/03	9/04	9/05	9/06	9/07
Sales ($ mil.)	7.8%	600.0	901.8	722.7	970.8	808.9
Net income ($ mil.)	—	(705.3)	(544.7)	(176.0)	(122.6)	(402.5)
Market value ($ mil.)	(21.6%)	15,629.2	7,492.1	8,475.6	9,704.0	5,908.3
Employees	18.8%	1,450	2,400	2,400	3,120	2,890

An in-depth profile of this company is available to Hoover's Online members at hoovers.com.

423

CONFIGURESOFT, INC.

4390 Arrowswest Dr.
Colorado Springs, CO 80907
Phone: 719-447-4600
Fax: 719-447-4601
Web: www.configuresoft.com

CEO: Mark K. Ruport
CFO: Steven M. Johnson
HR: –
FYE: December 31
Type: Private

Configuresoft provides software that automates, centralizes, and lowers the cost of configuration management across Windows, UNIX, and Linux platforms. Applications in the company's Enterprise Configuration Manager (ECM) suite include change management, data migration, enterprise security, patch management, and system configuration. Configuresoft was founded in 1999 as Fundamental Software. Among its investors are JMI and Bradcohill. Configuresoft has international distributors in Australia, Canada, and Europe.

	Annual Growth	12/03	12/04	12/05	12/06	12/07
Est. sales ($ mil.)	—	—	—	—	—	30.0
Employees	—	—	—	—	—	180

CONGOLEUM CORPORATION

3500 Quakerbridge Rd.
Mercerville, NJ 08619
Phone: 609-584-3000
Fax: 609-584-3522
Web: www.congoleum.com

CEO: Roger S. Marcus
CFO: Howard N. Feist III
HR: Robert Ingram
FYE: December 31
Type: Public

Congoleum has got your floors covered. The company specializes in making flooring products for residential and commercial use, including resilient sheet flooring (linoleum or vinyl flooring), do-it-yourself vinyl tile, and commercial flooring. The company markets its products through a network of about a dozen distributors in more than 50 North American locations, as well as directly to large market retailers. Customers use its products for new construction, as well as commercial, remodeling, and manufactured housing applications. Congoleum also buys sundries and accessories for resale.

	Annual Growth	12/03	12/04	12/05	12/06	12/07
Sales ($ mil.)	(1.9%)	220.7	229.5	237.6	219.5	204.3
Net income ($ mil.)	—	(6.8)	3.0	(21.6)	0.7	(0.7)
Employees	—	—	—	833	—	—

CONMED CORPORATION

NASDAQ (GS): CNMD

525 French Rd.
Utica, NY 13502
Phone: 315-797-8375
Fax: 315-797-0321
Web: www.conmed.com

CEO: Joseph J. (Joe) Corasanti
CFO: Robert D. Shallish Jr.
HR: Beth Bowers
FYE: December 31
Type: Public

Doctors and their patients get a charge out of CONMED's surgical equipment. The medical technology company develops and manufactures a wide range of surgical and medical procedure instruments. CONMED's products include electrosurgical systems, powered surgical instruments, suction equipment, arthroscopic devices, and related accessory equipment. Endoscopy products include trocars, clip appliers, scissors, and surgical staplers. CONMED also manufactures ECG electrodes for heart monitoring and other patient care products such as wound dressings. The company sells its products in more than 100 countries through its sales divisions and local distributors.

	Annual Growth	12/03	12/04	12/05	12/06	12/07
Sales ($ mil.)	8.7%	497.1	558.4	617.3	646.8	694.3
Net income ($ mil.)	6.6%	32.1	33.5	32.0	(12.5)	41.5
Market value ($ mil.)	(1.2%)	692.7	823.6	667.0	647.0	661.3
Employees	1.6%	—	—	3,100	3,200	3,200

CONNECTICARE, INC.

175 Scott Swamp Rd.
Farmington, CT 06032
Phone: 860-674-5700
Fax: 860-674-2030
Web: www.connecticare.com

CEO: Mickey Herbert
CFO: Michael Wise
HR: Dick Rogers
FYE: December 31
Type: Subsidiary

ConnectiCare is one of the largest HMOs in Connecticut. In 1979 a group of doctors at Hartford Hospital planted the seeds for what would become ConnectiCare; today, the company's nearly 245,000 members in Connecticut, western Massachusetts, and upstate New York choose from HMO or point-of-service options. The company has a network of all Connecticut hospitals, 60 acute care hospitals, and more than 17,000 care providers. ConnectiCare also established a charitable foundation as part of its reorganization to for-profit status. The company is a subsidiary of Health Insurance Plan of Greater New York.

	Annual Growth	12/03	12/04	12/05	12/06	12/07
Est. sales ($ mil.)	—	—	—	—	—	191.8
Employees	—	—	—	—	—	500

CONNECTICUT WATER SERVICE, INC.

NASDAQ (GS): CTWS

93 W. Main St.
Clinton, CT 06413
Phone: 860-669-8636
Fax: 860-669-5579
Web: www.ctwater.com

CEO: Eric W. Thornburg
CFO: David C. Benoit
HR: Kristen A. Johnson
FYE: December 31
Type: Public

A splash from Connecticut Water Service (CWS) might have helped Mark Twain's Yankee wake up from King Arthur's court. CWS's six water companies serve about 83,250 residential, commercial, and industrial customers in 41 Connecticut towns and one Massachusetts town. The non-operating holding company's subsidiaries gather water from wells and reservoirs and produce 49 million gallons daily. They also offer fire protection and other water-related services. CWS's growth strategy is based on acquisitions: It expanded into Massachusetts with its 2001 purchase of Barnstable Holding, and in 2002 it purchased Connecticut utility Unionville Water.

	Annual Growth	12/03	12/04	12/05	12/06	12/07
Sales ($ mil.)	5.8%	47.1	48.5	47.5	46.9	59.0
Net income ($ mil.)	(1.1%)	9.2	9.4	10.3	6.9	8.8
Market value ($ mil.)	(2.7%)	220.3	212.9	200.2	188.2	197.4
Employees	—	—	—	191	—	—

THE CONNECTION

11351 Rupp Dr.
Burnsville, MN 55337
Phone: 952-948-5488
Fax: 952-948-5498
Web: www.the-connection.com

CEO: Fredrick L. (Fred) Weiner
CFO: John Meier
HR: –
FYE: December 31
Type: Private

Since 1981, The Connection has been providing inbound call center services to companies. With five locations in the US (four contact centers in Nebraska, New Mexico, and New York), the company works with several industries including financial services, telecommunications, and public utilities. It specializes in providing sales order processing, reservations scheduling, lead generation, customer service, and Web-based call center services. In late 2007, The Connection shut down a call center in Las Vegas, New Mexico due to increased competition.

	Annual Growth	12/03	12/04	12/05	12/06	12/07
Est. sales ($ mil.)	—	—	—	—	—	47.2
Employees	—	—	—	—	—	1,500

THE CONNELL COMPANY

200 Connell Dr.	CEO: Grover Connell
Berkeley Heights, NJ 07922	CFO: Terry Connell
Phone: 908-673-3700	HR: Maureen Waldron
Fax: 908-673-3800	FYE: December 31
Web: www.connellco.com/TCC.htm	Type: Private

The Connell Company can sell you a boatload of rice or it can help you lease a building to store it in. Connell's core business is rice distribution, conducted through its Connell Rice & Sugar division. Its rice products, both domestically and foreign grown, include milled rice, brown rice, and paddy rice; its brand names include East Winds and Snow White. However, the company's other operations have grown into full-fledged divisions that deal in such varied goods and services as used semiconductor-wafer fabricating equipment; export sales of food manufacturing equipment; commercial real estate development and leasing; heavy equipment leasing and exporting; purchasing and supply management; and financial services.

	Annual Growth	12/03	12/04	12/05	12/06	12/07
Est. sales ($ mil.)	—	—	—	—	—	99.2
Employees	—	—	—	—	—	200

CONNELL LIMITED PARTNERSHIP

1 International Place	CEO: Francis A. (Frank) Doyle III
Boston, MA 02110	CFO: Kurt J. Keady
Phone: 617-737-2700	HR: Catherine R. Gallagher
Fax: 617-737-1617	FYE: December 31
Web: www.connell-lp.com	Type: Partnership

Limited partnership, unlimited appetite for growth. Connell Limited Partnership acquires and operates manufacturing companies with growth opportunities in the aluminum alloy and industrial equipment sectors. Connell's primary businesses, Anchor Danly (die sets and die makers' supplies) and Yuba Heat Transfer (heat transfer equipment), serve customers in the aerospace, appliance, automotive, electronics, and power and process industries. Connell started operating in 1987. The company has sold its Wabash Alloys subsidiary (aluminum recycling) to Aleris International.

CONNEXUS CORPORATION

2101 Rosecrans Ave., Ste. 2000	CEO: Arthur (Art) Shaw
El Segundo, CA 90245	CFO: Mark Lambert
Phone: 310-647-6000	HR: Lynn Johnson
Fax: 310-647-6001	FYE: December 31
Web: www.connexuscorp.com	Type: Private

Connexus Corporation, formerly VendareNetblue, is an online media and marketing firm that uses the Web to connect advertisers with their target customers. The company provides services such as performance-driven search marketing, lead generation, display advertising, e-mail marketing, and promotions to Web publishers and advertisers. Holdings also include proprietary consumer sites such as Jackpot.com and Uproar.com (online gaming sites) and JustEyes (vision correction information). The firm has offices in California and New York. Connexus is an Idealab company.

	Annual Growth	12/03	12/04	12/05	12/06	12/07
Est. sales ($ mil.)	—	—	—	—	—	7.2
Employees	—	—	—	—	—	185

CONN'S, INC.

NASDAQ (GS): CONN

3295 College St.	CEO: Thomas J. Frank Sr.
Beaumont, TX 77701	CFO: Michael J. Poppe
Phone: 409-832-1696	HR: –
Fax: 409-832-4344	FYE: January 31
Web: www.conns.com	Type: Public

Conn's has managed to outlive human life expectancy. With more than 115 years under its belt, the retailer sells appliances (refrigerators, freezers, washers, dryers) and consumer electronics (VCRs, DVD players, camcorders, LCD and plasma-screen TVs) through about 70 stores in Texas, Okalahoma, and Louisiana, and via its Web site. Conn's also offers home office equipment, lawn and garden products, and other home products such as bedding. The retailer began as a small plumbing and heating business in 1890. Conn's is about 50% owned by SF Holding Corp. (an investment arm of Stephens Group), which is considering various alternatives for the retailer, including taking the company private.

	Annual Growth	1/04	1/05	1/06	1/07	1/08
Sales ($ mil.)	13.3%	499.3	567.1	701.2	760.7	824.1
Net income ($ mil.)	13.1%	24.3	30.1	41.1	40.3	39.7
Market value ($ mil.)	4.0%	369.6	385.1	1,024.9	558.8	431.8
Employees	5.4%	—	—	2,800	2,950	—

CONOCOPHILLIPS

NYSE: COP

600 N. Dairy Ashford Rd.	CEO: James J. (Jim) Mulva
Houston, TX 77079	CFO: John A. Carrig
Phone: 281-293-1000	HR: Carin S. Knickel
Fax: –	FYE: December 31
Web: www.conocophillips.com	Type: Public

Formed by the merger of Conoco and Phillips Petroleum, ConocoPhillips is the #3 integrated oil and gas company in the US, behind Exxon Mobil and Chevron, and consolidated that position by buying Burlington Resources (for a reported $35 billion). The company explores for oil and gas in more than 30 countries and has estimated proved reserves of 11.2 billion barrels of oil equivalent, excluding its Syncrude (Canadian oil sands) assets. It has a refining capacity of more than 2.7 million barrels per day and sells petroleum at 8,750 retail outlets in the US under the 76, Conoco, and Phillips 66 brands. Other operations include chemicals, gas gathering, fuels technology, and power generation.

	Annual Growth	12/03	12/04	12/05	12/06	12/07
Sales ($ mil.)	16.6%	105,097.0	136,916.0	183,364.0	188,523.0	194,495.0
Net income ($ mil.)	25.9%	4,735.0	8,129.0	13,529.0	15,550.0	11,891.0
Market value ($ mil.)	57.4%	23,214.6	31,209.5	82,835.6	121,627.2	142,502.2
Employees	(4.3%)	—	—	35,600	38,400	32,600

CONOLOG CORPORATION

NASDAQ (CM): CNLGD

5 Columbia Rd.	CEO: Robert S. Benou
Somerville, NJ 08876	CFO: Robert S. Benou
Phone: 908-722-8081	HR: –
Fax: 908-722-5461	FYE: July 31
Web: www.conolog.com	Type: Public

Conolog is no longer sending mixed signals. The company makes small electronic and electromagnetic components that military, industrial, and utilities customers use for microwave, radio, and telephone transmission. Its products include transducers, receivers, electromagnetic-wave filters, and signal-processing equipment. Its products for commercial customers, electrical and industrial utilities in particular, are carried under the INIVEN brand name, taken from a company Conolog acquired in 1981. Leading customers include the US military and power utilities Bonneville Power, NSTAR, and Tucson Power.

	Annual Growth	7/03	7/04	7/05	7/06	7/07
Sales ($ mil.)	(22.7%)	1.4	1.0	0.6	0.6	0.5
Net income ($ mil.)	—	(1.4)	(6.5)	(3.0)	(3.3)	(8.1)
Market value ($ mil.)	(7.5%)	38.5	25.0	47.2	11.3	28.2
Employees	(8.1%)	21	15	13	14	15

An in-depth profile of this company is available to Hoover's Online members at hoovers.com.

425

CONRAD INDUSTRIES, INC.

Pink Sheets: CNRD

1100 Brashear Ave., Ste. 200
Morgan City, LA 70381
Phone: 985-702-0195
Fax: 985-702-1126
Web: www.conradindustries.com

CEO: John P. (Johnny) Conrad Jr.
CFO: Cecil A. Hernandez
HR: Shane Alfred
FYE: December 31
Type: Public

Conrad Industries builds, converts, and repairs small and medium-size vessels for commercial and government customers. The company works on such vessels as barges, lift boats, towboats, and tugboats. Its boat-conversion projects mainly involve lengthening vessel mid-bodies or modifying vessels to perform different functions. Conrad Industries operates shipyards along the Gulf Coast in Louisiana and Texas. Conrad also offers the fabrication of modular components used on offshore drilling rigs, as well as storage and offloading marine vessels. The company was founded in 1948.

	Annual Growth	12/03	12/04	12/05	12/06	12/07
Sales ($ mil.)	49.9%	33.4	37.1	64.6	121.8	168.5
Net income ($ mil.)	—	(6.8)	(7.1)	0.1	5.9	19.2
Employees	17.4%	262	275	384	520	498

CONRAIL INC.

2001 Market St., 8th Fl.
Philadelphia, PA 19103
Phone: 215-209-2000
Fax: 215-209-4819
Web: www.conrail.com

CEO: Ronald L. Batory
CFO: Joseph Rogers
HR: Anthony Carlini
FYE: December 31
Type: Private

Conrail is the holding company for Consolidated Rail, a freight railroad system that operates in heavily industrialized portions of the northeastern US. Most of the railroad lines and switching and terminal facilities formerly operated by Conrail have been taken over by the company's owners, railroads CSX (42%) and Norfolk Southern (58%). Conrail, however, continues to operate some lines and facilities in the Philadelphia and Detroit metropolitan areas and in much of New Jersey. To serve customers along those lines, CSX and Norfolk Southern pay Conrail for line access, and Conrail acts as the local switching and terminal management agent.

CONSECO, INC.

NYSE: CNO

11825 N. Pennsylvania St.
Carmel, IN 46032
Phone: 317-817-6100
Fax: 317-817-2847
Web: www.conseco.com

CEO: C. James Prieur
CFO: Edward J. (Ed) Bonach
HR: Susan L. (Sue) Menzel
FYE: December 31
Type: Public

With a name drawn from its roots — the company began as Security National and soon acquired Consolidated National, becoming Conseco — this company has pruned and transplanted itself into a protector of working families and senior citizens. Conseco offers insurance and related products, targeted to seniors and middle-income prospects. Its three units include Bankers Life, which markets and distributes Medicare supplement, life, and long-term care insurance and annuities; Conseco Insurance Group, which offers specified disease insurance, as well as Medicare supplement and certain life insurance and annuities; and Colonial Penn, which offers life insurance to consumers through direct selling.

	Annual Growth	12/03	12/04	12/05	12/06	12/07
Assets ($ mil.)	2.9%	29,920.1	30,755.5	31,557.3	32,717.3	33,514.8
Net income ($ mil.)	—	2,298.0	294.8	324.9	96.5	(179.9)
Market value ($ mil.)	1.5%	2,182.5	3,013.6	3,510.6	3,040.3	2,319.2
Employees	(0.6%)	—	—	4,000	4,000	3,950

CONSOL ENERGY INC.

NYSE: CNX

Consol Plaza, 1800 Washington Rd.
Pittsburgh, PA 15241
Phone: 412-831-4000
Fax: 412-831-4103
Web: www.consolenergy.com

CEO: J. Brett Harvey
CFO: William J. Lyons
HR: Albert A. Aloia
FYE: December 31
Type: Public

Consolation prizes don't interest CONSOL Energy. CONSOL is one of the US's largest coal mining companies, along with Peabody Energy and Arch Coal. The company has some 4.5 billion tons of proved reserves, mainly in northern and central Appalachia and the Illinois Basin, and produces about 65 million tons of coal annually. CONSOL primarily mines high BTU coal, which burns cleaner than lower grades. Customers include electric utilities and steel mills; Allegheny Energy is its largest customer by far. CONSOL delivers coal using its own railroad cars, export terminals, and fleet of towboats and barges. The company also engages in natural gas exploration and production; its proved reserves total 1.3 trillion cu. ft.

	Annual Growth	12/03	12/04	12/05	12/06	12/07
Sales ($ mil.)	14.1%	2,222.5	2,776.8	3,810.4	3,715.2	3,762.2
Net income ($ mil.)	—	(7.8)	198.6	580.9	408.9	267.8
Market value ($ mil.)	83.0%	1,163.7	1,860.4	3,015.4	5,868.7	13,037.5
Employees	3.2%	—	—	7,257	7,253	7,728

CONSOLIDATED COMMUNICATIONS

NASDAQ (CM): CNSL

121 S. 17th St.
Mattoon, IL 61938
Phone: 217-235-3311
Fax: 217-258-7883
Web: www.consolidated.com

CEO: Robert J. (Bob) Currey
CFO: Steven L. Childers
HR: –
FYE: December 31
Type: Public

Combining operations in Illinois and Texas, Consolidated Communications Holdings, Inc., provides voice and data telecommunications to business and residential customers. The company operates rural local-exchange carriers that offer local access and long-distance, Internet access, business phone systems, and related services through more than 230,000 local access lines and nearly 53,000 digital subscriber lines (DSLs) in service. The company also offers directory publishing and carrier services. Operating subsidiaries include Illinois Consolidated Telephone Company (ICTC), Consolidated Communications of Fort Bend Company, and Consolidated Communications of Texas Company.

	Annual Growth	12/03	12/04	12/05	12/06	12/07
Sales ($ mil.)	25.6%	132.3	269.6	321.4	320.8	329.3
Net income ($ mil.)	20.0%	5.5	(1.1)	(4.5)	13.3	11.4
Market value ($ mil.)	23.1%	—	—	386.8	543.4	585.9
Employees	—	—	—	1,229	—	—

CONSOLIDATED CONTAINER COMPANY LLC

3101 Towercreek Pkwy., Ste. 300
Atlanta, GA 30339
Phone: 678-742-4600
Fax: 678-742-4750
Web: www.cccllc.com

CEO: Jeffrey M. Greene
CFO: Richard P. Sehring
HR: –
FYE: December 31
Type: Private

Being flexible allowed Consolidated Container to can its former name (Continental Can). Consolidated Container is one of the largest manufacturers of rigid plastic containers in the US. The company markets its products to the dairy, water, agricultural, food, and industrial chemical industries and manufactures containers for a variety of products, including water, milk, ketchup, salsa, soap, motor oil, antifreeze, insect repellent, fertilizers, and medical supplies. Dean Foods and Procter & Gamble are major customers. Consolidated Container was formed when Suiza Foods merged its plastics business with Reid Plastics.

	Annual Growth	12/02	12/03	12/04	12/05	12/06
Sales ($ mil.)	3.5%	746.5	739.8	761.3	846.4	857.6
Employees	(0.8%)	4,130	4,000	3,500	3,300	4,000

An in-depth profile of this company is available to Hoover's Online members at hoovers.com.

CONSOLIDATED EDISON COMPANY OF NEW YORK, INC.

4 Irving Place	CEO: Kevin Burke
New York, NY 10003	CFO: Robert N. Hoglund
Phone: 212-460-4600	HR: Claude Trahan
Fax: 212-477-2536	FYE: December 31
Web: www.coned.com	Type: Subsidiary

Consolidated Edison Company of New York (Con Edison of New York) keeps the nightlife pulsing in The Big Apple. The utility, a subsidiary of Consolidated Edison, distributes electricity throughout most of New York City and Westchester County. The company distributes electricity to more than 3.2 million residential and business customers in New York City; it also delivers natural gas to about 1.1 million customers. The utility also provides natural gas and steam services in portions of the New York metropolitan area. Con Edison of New York owns and operates more than 130,500 miles of overhead and underground power distribution lines.

	Annual Growth	12/03	12/04	12/05	12/06	12/07
Sales ($ mil.)	4.9%	8,166.0	8,006.0	9,272.0	9,288.0	9,885.0
Net income ($ mil.)	9.2%	602.0	529.0	705.0	697.0	855.0
Employees	2.8%	—	—	—	13,500	13,877

CONSOLIDATED EDISON, INC.

NYSE: ED

4 Irving Place	CEO: Kevin Burke
New York, NY 10003	CFO: Robert N. Hoglund
Phone: 212-460-4600	HR: –
Fax: 212-982-7816	FYE: December 31
Web: www.conedison.com	Type: Public

Utility holding company Consolidated Edison (Con Edison) is the night light for the city that never sleeps. Con Edison's main subsidiary, Consolidated Edison Company of New York, distributes electricity to more than 3.2 million residential and business customers in New York City; it also delivers natural gas to about 1.1 million customers. Subsidiary Orange and Rockland Utilities serves more than 424,350 electric and gas customers in three states. Con Edison's nonutility operations include retail and wholesale energy marketing, independent power production, and infrastructure project development.

	Annual Growth	12/03	12/04	12/05	12/06	12/07
Sales ($ mil.)	7.5%	9,827.0	9,758.0	11,690.0	12,137.0	13,120.0
Net income ($ mil.)	15.2%	528.0	537.0	719.0	737.0	929.0
Market value ($ mil.)	11.1%	8,715.1	10,610.0	10,288.8	11,260.2	13,288.4
Employees	2.3%	—	—	14,537	14,795	15,214

CONSOLIDATED ELECTRICAL DISTRIBUTORS, INC.

31356 Via Colinas, Ste. 107	CEO: H. Dean Bursch
Westlake Village, CA 91362	CFO: Jeff Wofford
Phone: 818-991-9000	HR: –
Fax: 818-991-6842	FYE: December 31
Web: www.cedcareers.com	Type: Private

Electrical equipment wholesaler Consolidated Electrical Distributors (CED) has US distribution wired. With more than 500 locations nationwide, the family-owned business is one of the largest distributors of electrical products in the country. CED supplies load centers, panelboards, transformers, switches, motor controls, drives, and similar products to residential and commercial contractors and industrial customers. Founded in 1957 as The Electric Corporation of San Francisco, the company has grown by acquiring electrical distributors; since it usually keeps the acquired firm's name and management team, CED now does business under about 80 names. The Colburn family owns CED.

	Annual Growth	12/02	12/03	12/04	12/05	12/06
Est. sales ($ mil.)	9.3%	2,300.0	2,300.0	2,600.0	2,800.0	3,280.0
Employees	1.0%	5,000	5,000	5,200	5,200	5,200

CONSOLIDATED GRAPHICS, INC.

NYSE: CGX

5858 Westheimer, Ste. 200	CEO: Joe R. Davis
Houston, TX 77057	CFO: Jon C. Biro
Phone: 713-787-0977	HR: Rachel S. Koenig
Fax: 713-787-5013	FYE: March 31
Web: www.consolidatedgraphics.com	Type: Public

One of the leading commercial printers in North America, Consolidated Graphics unites many companies under one banner. The firm operates as a holding company; its printing subsidiaries exist as separate businesses run by their own management teams. Operations include 70 sheetfed, web, and digital printing facilities in more than 25 states and Ontario, Canada. Consolidated Graphics prints products such as annual reports, brochures, catalogs, corporate communications, direct mail pieces, manuals, and point-of-purchase displays, among other items. The company also provides fulfillment and mailing services for printed materials, as well as digital asset management and online print procurement.

	Annual Growth	3/04	3/05	3/06	3/07	3/08
Sales ($ mil.)	11.5%	708.1	779.0	879.0	1,006.2	1,095.4
Net income ($ mil.)	31.2%	20.0	32.7	38.5	50.7	59.3
Market value ($ mil.)	4.4%	521.9	723.8	714.8	1,014.0	621.0
Employees	5.0%	4,800	5,324	5,005	5,550	—

CONSOLIDATED RESTAURANT OPERATIONS, INC.

12200 Stemmons Fwy., Ste. 100	CEO: John D. Harkey Jr.
Dallas, TX 75234	CFO: Paul Hargett
Phone: 972-241-5500	HR: –
Fax: 972-888-8198	FYE: December 31
Web: www.croinc.com	Type: Private

Consolidated Restaurant Operations (CRO) offers several dining concepts on its menu. The company operates and franchises about 135 casual and upscale dining restaurants, including its flagship concept El Chico. The chain offers traditional and contemporary Mexican cuisine through about 100 locations. CRO's other concepts include Cantina Laredo, Cool River Cafe, Silver Fox Steakhouse, and III Forks. Most of its restaurants operate in Texas and about a dozen other mostly southern states. Partners Gene Street, John Harkey, John Cracken, and Steve Harnett formed CRO in 1998.

CONSOLIDATED-TOMOKA LAND CO.

AMEX: CTO

1530 Cornerstone Blvd., Ste. 100	CEO: William H. (Bill) McMunn
Daytona Beach, FL 32117	CFO: Bruce W. Teeters
Phone: 386-274-2202	HR: Linda Crisp
Fax: 386-274-1223	FYE: December 31
Web: www.consolidatedtomoka.com	Type: Public

From golf courses and retail centers to timber and hay farms, Florida land developer Consolidated-Tomoka owns a chunk of the Sunshine State. The company's holdings include about 25 retail properties (tenants include CVS, Walgreen, and Best Buy), a couple of golf courses (including the national headquarters of the LPGA), and some 11,000 acres of agricultural land that the company is converting into other income properties. The company also holds subsurface oil, gas, and mineral interests on some 500,000 acres throughout Florida and properties in North Carolina and Georgia. Institutional investors own more than 45% of the company.

	Annual Growth	12/03	12/04	12/05	12/06	12/07
Sales ($ mil.)	6.3%	33.2	42.0	43.5	43.6	42.4
Net income ($ mil.)	0.6%	13.2	14.6	14.8	14.0	13.5
Market value ($ mil.)	18.2%	183.9	242.6	401.8	412.2	358.9
Employees	(7.8%)	—	—	20	—	17

An in-depth profile of this company is available to Hoover's Online members at hoovers.com.

427

CONSONA CORPORATION

450 E. 96th St., Ste. 300
Indianapolis, IN 46240
Phone: 317-249-1200
Fax: 317-249-1999
Web: www.consona.com

CEO: Jeff Tognoni
CFO: Kathy Kinder
HR: –
FYE: December 31
Type: Private

Consona (formerly Made2Manage Systems) provides enterprise information systems for small and midsized manufacturers. Its products help companies administer and manage a number of business processes — including customer relationship management (CRM), enterprise resource planning (ERP), and supply chain management (SCM). Consona also offers a wide range of professional services, including implementation, support, and training. The company was taken private by Battery Ventures' affiliate BV Holding Company in a $30 million transaction in August 2003.

	Annual Growth	12/03	12/04	12/05	12/06	12/07
Est. sales ($ mil.)	—	—	—	—	—	32.6
Employees	—	—	—	—	—	417

CONSONA CRM INC.

12131 113th Ave. NE, Ste. 101
Kirkland, WA 98034
Phone: 425-250-5800
Fax: 425-823-3075
Web: www.onyx.com

CEO: Pete Strom
CFO: –
HR: –
FYE: December 31
Type: Subsidiary

Consona CRM provides customer relationship management (CRM) software that links marketing, sales, service, technical support, and other customer-facing functions, providing a central repository for all customer information. With its software, employees can market and sell products and service customers; customers can access information, order products, and obtain service; and businesses can collaborate with partners. The company also offers services such as training, consulting, maintenance, and technical support. Fomerly called Onyx Software, the company was acquired by Consona for about $92 million in 2006.

	Annual Growth	12/03	12/04	12/05	12/06	12/07
Est. sales ($ mil.)	—	—	—	—	—	24.5
Employees	—	—	—	—	—	245

CONSPIRACY ENTERTAINMENT HOLDINGS, INC.

OTC: CPYE

612 Santa Monica Blvd.
Santa Monica, CA 90401
Phone: 310-260-6150
Fax: 310-260-1450
Web: www.conspiracygames.com

CEO: Sirus Ahmadi
CFO: Keith Tanaka
HR: Keith Tanaka
FYE: December 31
Type: Public

Conspiracy Entertainment has all sorts of theories about capitalizing on the video game market. The company is a Los Angeles-based producer of kid-friendly, value-priced video games for play on the PC and on gaming consoles from Sony, Microsoft, and Nintendo. Conspiracy has co-published games featuring the Warner Bros. licensed characters of *Tiny Toons* and *Tom & Jerry*; other titles include *Amazing Live Sea Monkeys*, *Enclave*, and *Road Trip*. President and CEO Sirus Ahmadi owns about 40% of the company.

	Annual Growth	12/03	12/04	12/05	12/06	12/07
Sales ($ mil.)	38.4%	2.4	1.4	1.4	0.8	8.8
Net income ($ mil.)	—	(2.3)	(2.5)	1.0	(1.5)	(0.9)
Market value ($ mil.)	(56.4%)	56.7	3.4	—	1.5	2.0
Employees	—	—	—	—	—	—

CONSTANT CONTACT, INC.

NASDAQ (GM): CTCT

Reservoir Place, 1601 Trapelo Rd., Ste. 329
Waltham, MA 02451
Phone: 781-472-8100
Fax: 781-472-8101
Web: www.constantcontact.com

CEO: Gail F. Goodman
CFO: Steven R. (Steve) Wasserman
HR: –
FYE: December 31
Type: Public

Constant Contact makes sure businesses never lose touch with their customers. The company provides Web-based marketing software and services for managing e-mail campaigns. Its offerings include tools for creating, implementing, tracking, managing, and analyzing marketing materials. It also provides tools for managing newsletters and surveys. The company's customers include retailers, restaurants, and other businesses, as well as non-profit organizations and churches. Formerly called Roving Software, the company changed its name to Constant Contact in 2006.

	Annual Growth	12/03	12/04	12/05	12/06	12/07
Sales ($ mil.)	84.0%	—	8.1	14.7	27.5	50.5
Net income ($ mil.)	—	—	(0.6)	(1.3)	(7.8)	(8.3)
Market value ($ mil.)	—	—	—	—	—	593.8
Employees	15.6%	—	—	—	275	318

CONSTAR INTERNATIONAL INC.

NASDAQ (GM): CNST

1 Crown Way
Philadelphia, PA 19154
Phone: 215-552-3700
Fax: 215-552-3707
Web: www.constar.net

CEO: Michael J. Hoffman
CFO: Walter S. Sobon
HR: –
FYE: December 31
Type: Public

Constar International's PET won't fetch your paper, but it will hold your water, soda, or peanut butter. Constar, which was spun off by Crown Cork & Seal (now Crown Holdings) in 2002, is one of North America's largest makers of polyethylene terephthalate (PET) plastic food and beverage containers. Its customers include soda kingpins PepsiCo and Coca-Cola, as well as food producers such as ConAgra (Wesson Oil). Soft drink and water bottles remain the most common use of PET packaging, but other applications, such as teas, juices, condiments, and beer, have also become popular. In addition, the company makes plastic closures and non-PET containers.

	Annual Growth	12/03	12/04	12/05	12/06	12/07
Sales ($ mil.)	4.4%	742.3	844.2	975.0	927.0	881.6
Net income ($ mil.)	—	(220.6)	(6.8)	(60.0)	(12.0)	(26.4)
Market value ($ mil.)	(6.1%)	66.7	97.0	43.8	88.0	51.9
Employees	(8.8%)	—	—	2,017	1,839	—

CONSTELLATION BRANDS, INC.

NYSE: STZ

370 Woodcliff Dr., Ste. 300
Fairport, NY 14450
Phone: 585-218-3600
Fax: 585-218-3601
Web: www.cbrands.com

CEO: Robert S. (Rob) Sands
CFO: Robert (Bob) Ryder
HR: W. Keith Wilson
FYE: Last day in February
Type: Public

Thinking about alcohol makes this company starry-eyed. Constellation Brands is a leading beer, wine, and spirits maker with more than 250 brands, which it sells in some 150 countries. Its wine division accounts for nearly 55% of sales, and is anchored by its domestic winemaking subsidiary Constellation Wines U.S., a global leader in wine production, offering brands such as Robert Mondavi, Vendange, and Arbor Mist, as well as such premium labels as Ravenswood and Simi. The company also imports beers such as Corona and Tsingtao, markets distilled spirits such as Fleishmann's and Barton, and produces and distributes cider, wine, and bottled water in the UK.

	Annual Growth	2/04	2/05	2/06	2/07	2/08
Sales ($ mil.)	1.5%	3,552.4	4,087.6	4,603.5	5,216.4	3,773.0
Net income ($ mil.)	—	220.4	276.5	325.3	331.9	(613.3)
Market value ($ mil.)	25.3%	1,498.9	5,220.8	5,246.3	4,951.1	3,693.6
Employees	1.9%	—	—	7,900	9,200	8,200

CONSTELLATION ENERGY GROUP, INC.

NYSE: CEG

750 E. Pratt St.
Baltimore, MD 21202
Phone: 410-783-2800
Fax: 410-783-3629
Web: www.constellation.com

CEO: Mayo A. Shattuck III
CFO: John R. Collins
HR: –
FYE: December 31
Type: Public

Constellation Energy Group's leading light is still utility Baltimore Gas and Electric (BGE), which distributes electricity and natural gas in central Maryland. The company trades and markets wholesale energy through subsidiary Constellation Energy Commodities Group, which is one of the top power marketers in North America. Constellation Energy also operates independent power plants with more than 8,700 MW of generating capacity through its Constellation Generation unit, and it competes in retail energy supply through Constellation NewEnergy. In 2007 this unit acquired Cornerstone Energy, creating one of the largest natural gas marketing companies in the US.

	Annual Growth	12/03	12/04	12/05	12/06	12/07
Sales ($ mil.)	21.6%	9,703.0	12,549.7	17,132.0	19,284.9	21,193.2
Net income ($ mil.)	31.2%	277.3	539.7	623.1	936.4	821.5
Market value ($ mil.)	29.1%	6,571.8	7,707.5	10,298.5	12,432.4	18,242.5
Employees	2.1%	—	9,570	9,850	9,645	10,200

CONSTELLATION ENERGY PARTNERS LLC

NYSE Arca: CEP

111 Market Pl.
Baltimore, MD 21202
Phone: 410-468-3500
Fax: 410-783-3629
Web: www.constellationenergypartners.com

CEO: Stephen R. Brunner
CFO: Charles C. (Chuck) Ward
HR: –
FYE: December 31
Type: Public

Constellation Energy Partners' domain is decidedly more terrestrial than stellar. A subsidiary of Constellation Energy's Commodities Group, it is a coalbed methane exploration and production company that operates exclusively in Alabama's Black Warrior Basin. In 2007 Constellation Energy Partners reported proved reserves of 302.8 billion cu. ft. of natural gas equivalent. The company's properties are located in the Robinson Bend Field and were first developed by Torch Energy and then by Everlast Energy. Constellation Energy Partners acquired the properties from Everlast; it still is required to make royalty payments to Torch Energy Royalty Trust.

	Annual Growth	12/03	12/04	12/05	12/06	12/07
Sales ($ mil.)	—	—	—	—	—	82.7
Net income ($ mil.)	—	—	—	—	—	14.2
Employees	—	—	—	—	—	—

CONSULATE HEALTH CARE, INC.

800 Concourse Pkwy. South, Ste. 200
Maitland, FL 32751
Phone: 407-571-1550
Fax: 407-571-1599
Web: www.consulatemgt.com

CEO: Joseph D. Conte
CFO: Eugene R. (Gene) Curcio
HR: Jo Anne Annichiarico
FYE: December 31
Type: Private

Consulate Health Care (formerly Tandem Health Care) is a consummate elder care provider. The company offers long-term care, including assisted living, skilled nursing, and independent living services, to residents of its facilities in six states. Consulate owns, manages, and leases some 80 nursing homes and other long-term health care centers, with about 8,000 beds total. It also provides rehabilitation, diagnostic imaging, hospice, and pharmacy services. In addition, Consulate offers Alzheimer's care and short-term transitional care programs for patients needing complex medical treatment. In 2007 Behrman Capital sold the company to JER Partners and retirement community investor Formation Capital.

CONSULIER ENGINEERING, INC.

NASDAQ (CM): CSLR

2391 Old Dixie Hwy.
Riviera Beach, FL 33404
Phone: 561-842-2492
Fax: 561-845-3237
Web: www.consulier.com

CEO: Warren B. Mosler
CFO: Alan R. Simon
HR: –
FYE: December 31
Type: Public

Consulier Engineering has designs on all sorts of markets. Consulier's subsidiary, Patient Care Technology Systems (PCTS), provides medical software for hospital emergency departments, including passive tracking technologies for emergency departments and operating rooms. Consulier also has an interest in environmentally safe products maker BioSafe Systems, which develops alternatives to traditionally toxic pesticides. Warren Mosler owns nearly 80% of Consulier Engineering, which he formed in 1985.

	Annual Growth	12/03	12/04	12/05	12/06	12/07
Sales ($ mil.)	82.1%	0.2	0.1	1.0	1.6	2.2
Net income ($ mil.)	—	(0.8)	(2.6)	(1.2)	(1.5)	(0.2)
Market value ($ mil.)	8.8%	14.3	18.1	23.4	26.6	20.0
Employees	—	—	—	—	—	—

CONSUMER PORTFOLIO SERVICES, INC.

NASDAQ (GM): CPSS

16355 Laguna Canyon Rd.
Irvine, CA 92618
Phone: 949-753-6800
Fax: 949-753-6805
Web: www.consumerportfolio.com

CEO: Charles E. Bradley Jr.
CFO: Jeffrey P. (Jeff) Fritz
HR: Missy Hennessey
FYE: December 31
Type: Public

Consumer Portfolio Services (CPS) buys, sells, and services auto loans made to consumers who probably don't have portfolios. In other words, the company lends to subprime borrowers who can't get traditional financing due to poor or limited credit. CPS purchases contracts from more than 10,255 dealers in 46 states, some 85% of which are franchised new car dealers. The remaining are independent used car dealers, and the bulk of the contracts CPS acquires finance used vehicles. CPS generally securitizes (bundles and sells) the loans that it acquires. The company has operations in California, Florida, Illinois, and Virginia.

	Annual Growth	12/03	12/04	12/05	12/06	12/07
Assets ($ mil.)	46.7%	492.5	766.6	1,155.1	1,728.3	2,282.8
Net income ($ mil.)	142.8%	0.4	(15.9)	3.4	39.6	13.9
Market value ($ mil.)	(3.9%)	76.6	105.1	125.7	140.5	65.4
Employees	15.4%	—	—	749	789	997

CONSUMER PRODUCT DISTRIBUTORS, INC.

705 Meadow St.
Chicopee, MA 01013
Phone: 413-592-4141
Fax: 413-592-5870
Web: www.jpolep.com

CEO: Jeffrey M. (Jeff) Polep
CFO: Bill Fitzsimmons
HR: Stephen (Steve) Martin
FYE: September 30
Type: Private

Consumer Product Distributors helps convenience stores provide convenient services to their customers. The company, which operates as J. Polep Distribution Services, is a leading wholesale supplier serving more than 4,000 convenience retailers throughout New England and in New York. The bulk of its business is focused on cigarettes and other tobacco products, but it also distributes alcohol, candy and food products, and general merchandise. In addition, J. Polep provides merchandising, sales and marketing, and technology services. The family-owned company was founded as Polep Tobacco in 1898 by Charles Polep.

	Annual Growth	9/03	9/04	9/05	9/06	9/07
Est. sales ($ mil.)	—	—	—	—	—	524.1
Employees	—	—	—	—	—	400

An in-depth profile of this company is available to Hoover's Online members at hoovers.com.

429

CONSUMERS BANCORP, INC.

OTC: CBKM

614 E. Lincoln Way
Minerva, OH 44657
Phone: 330-868-7701
Fax: 330-868-3460
Web: www.consumersbancorp.com

CEO: Steven L. Muckley
CFO: Renee K. Wood
HR: Stella Tsirellis
FYE: June 30
Type: Public

You don't have to be a consumer to do business with Consumers — it's happy to serve businesses, as well. Consumers Bancorp is the holding company for Consumers National Bank, which serves eastern Ohio's Minerva and surrounding communities from about 10 branch offices. It offers standard retail products and services, including savings and checking accounts, CDs, IRAs, and money market accounts. Business loans make up about half of the bank's loan portfolio; real estate mortgages, consumer loans, and construction loans round out the company's lending activities.

	Annual Growth	6/03	6/04	6/05	6/06	6/07
Assets ($ mil.)	2.6%	182.1	186.2	191.2	203.6	202.0
Net income ($ mil.)	(12.3%)	2.2	2.1	2.0	1.2	1.3
Market value ($ mil.)	(18.5%)	48.7	49.4	36.4	28.3	21.5
Employees	—	—	—	—	—	—

CONSUMERS ENERGY COMPANY

1 Energy Plaza
Jackson, MI 49201
Phone: 517-788-0550
Fax: 800-363-4806
Web: www.consumersenergy.com

CEO: David W. Joos
CFO: Thomas J. Webb
HR: –
FYE: December 31
Type: Subsidiary

Consumers Energy Company makes sure that the energy consumers in Michigan have the power to crank up their heaters and the gas to fire up their stoves. The company's operating area includes all 68 counties of Michigan's lower peninsula. All told, Consumers Energy has a generating capacity of 9,300 MW (primarily fossil-fueled), and distributes electricity to 1.8 million customers and natural gas to 1.7 million customers. Included in the utility's arsenal of power production is electricity generated from fossil-fueled, nuclear, and hydroelectric power plants. Consumers Energy is a subsidiary and primary operating unit of CMS Energy.

	Annual Growth	12/02	12/03	12/04	12/05	12/06
Sales ($ mil.)	8.2%	4,169.0	4,435.0	4,711.0	5,232.0	5,721.0
Net income ($ mil.)	(15.4%)	363.0	196.0	279.0	(96.0)	186.0
Employees	(0.9%)	8,311	7,947	8,050	8,114	8,026

CONSUMERS UNION OF UNITED STATES, INC.

101 Truman Ave.
Yonkers, NY 10703
Phone: 914-378-2000
Fax: 914-378-2900
Web: www.consumersunion.org

CEO: James A. (Jim) Guest
CFO: Richard B. (Rich) Gannon
HR: Richard (Rick) Lustig
FYE: May 31
Type: Not-for-profit

Consumers Union of United States (CU) inspires both trust and fear. Best known for publishing *Consumer Reports* magazine, the independent not-for-profit organization also serves as a consumer watchdog through other print publications (newsletters and guides), TV and radio reports, and the Web (ConsumerReports.org). Its subscriber site rates products ranging from candy bars to cars. CU tests and rates thousands of products annually through its National Testing and Research Center, which conducts laboratory testing and survey research. CU accepts no advertising and derives income from the sale of *Consumer Reports* and other services, and from non-commercial contributions, grants, and fees.

	Annual Growth	5/03	5/04	5/05	5/06	5/07
Sales ($ mil.)	13.9%	—	—	196.6	215.7	255.2
Net income ($ mil.)	151.6%	—	—	—	12.4	31.2
Employees	11.6%	—	—	450	519	560

THE CONTAINER STORE INC.

500 Freeport Pkwy.
Coppell, TX 75019
Phone: 972-538-6000
Fax: 972-538-7623
Web: www.containerstore.com

CEO: Kip Tindell
CFO: Jodi L. Taylor
HR: –
FYE: March 31
Type: Private

With its packets, pockets, and boxes, The Container Store has the storage products niche well-contained. Its merchandise ranges from backpacks to recipe holders. The home organization pioneer operates about 45 stores in more than 15 states, mostly in major cities in California, Colorado, Georgia, Illinois, Maryland, New York, and Texas. The stores carry more than 9,000 items; the firm's Elfa brand wire shelving (manufactured in Sweden) accounts for about one-fifth of sales. The company touts a low employee-turnover rate, thanks in part to high wages. The Container Store was founded in 1978; Leonard Green & Partners acquired a majority stake in mid-2007.

	Annual Growth	3/02	3/03	3/04	3/05	3/06
Est. sales ($ mil.)	16.0%	—	—	375.0	425.0	505.0
Employees	(5.2%)	—	—	3,926	—	3,529

CONTANGO OIL & GAS COMPANY

AMEX: MCF

3700 Buffalo Speedway, Ste. 960
Houston, TX 77098
Phone: 713-960-1901
Fax: 713-960-1065
Web: contango.com

CEO: Kenneth R. Peak
CFO: Kenneth R. Peak
HR: –
FYE: June 30
Type: Public

It takes two to tango but several more to make Contango, a successful independent oil and natural gas company. Contango Oil & Gas (named after a term used by oil and gas traders to describe anticipated rising prices in the futures market) explores for and acquires oil and gas properties in the Gulf of Mexico and in the Arkansas Fayetteville Shale. Contango, which holds proved reserves of about 8.9 billion cu. ft. of natural gas equivalent, has strategic exploration alliances with Juneau Exploration, Alta Resources, and others. In 2004 the company sold its south Texas natural gas and oil assets to Edge Petroleum for $50 million. CEO Kenneth Peak owns 15% of Contango.

	Annual Growth	6/03	6/04	6/05	6/06	6/07
Sales ($ mil.)	(13.8%)	33.9	27.7	4.3	0.9	18.7
Net income ($ mil.)	—	(4.3)	7.7	12.4	(0.2)	(2.7)
Market value ($ mil.)	97.6%	38.0	81.9	135.4	212.1	579.4
Employees	—	—	—	6	—	—

CONTECH CONSTRUCTION PRODUCTS INC.

9025 Centre Pointe Dr., Ste. 400
West Chester, OH 45069
Phone: 513-645-7000
Fax: 513-645-7993
Web: www.contech-cpi.com

CEO: Patrick M. Harlow
CFO: Richard J. Caserta
HR: Brenda Harmon
FYE: June 30
Type: Private

CONTECH Construction Products keeps the gutters going. The company makes, distributes, and installs civil engineering products related to environmental storm water, drainage, bridges, and earth stabilization, serving clients working on commercial, industrial, public, and large-scale residential projects. Products range from retaining walls and water-detention vaults to storm water pipes and bridges in a variety of types for vehicular or pedestrian use. CONTECH Construction Products has a national sales organization of more than 350 people, as well. Apax Partners acquired the company in 2006.

	Annual Growth	6/02	6/03	6/04	6/05	6/06
Sales ($ mil.)	25.6%	—	—	—	750.0	942.0
Employees	18.2%	—	—	—	1,819	2,150

CONTIGROUP COMPANIES, INC.

277 Park Ave.
New York, NY 10172
Phone: 212-207-5100
Fax: 212-207-5499
Web: www.contigroup.com

CEO: Paul J. Fribourg
CFO: Michael J. Zimmerman
HR: Teresa E. McCaslin
FYE: March 31
Type: Private

Knowing its place on the food chain, ContiGroup Companies (CGC) focuses on meat production. CGC operates through subsidiary Wayne Farms, a major poultry processor, and Five Rivers Ranch Cattle Feeding, a 50-50 joint venture with Smithfield Foods that is one of the world's largest feedlot enterprises. Overseas, it has interests in flour milling, animal feed production, and pork and poultry processing. CGC's investment arm, ContiInvestments, manages diverse holdings. Chairman and CEO Paul Fribourg (a descendant of founder Simon Fribourg) and his family own CGC.

	Annual Growth	3/02	3/03	3/04	3/05	3/06
Sales ($ mil.)	(18.2%)	3,300.0	2,000.0	2,200.0	1,900.0	1,480.0
Employees	(1.6%)	14,500	13,500	15,500	14,500	13,600

CONTINENTAL AIRLINES, INC.   NYSE: CAL

1600 Smith St., Dept. HQSEO
Houston, TX 77002
Phone: 713-324-2950
Fax: 713-324-2687
Web: www.continental.com

CEO: Lawrence W. (Larry) Kellner
CFO: Jeffrey J. (Jeff) Misner
HR: Michael P. (Mike) Bonds
FYE: December 31
Type: Public

If it's a continent, chances are it's accessible via Continental Airlines. The carrier serves about 145 markets in the US and 140 in other countries from hubs in Cleveland; Houston; Newark, New Jersey; and Guam. Its network includes destinations served by regional carriers operating as Continental Express and Continental Connection. Overall, Continental has about 370 mainline jets and 270 aircraft in its regional operations. The carrier supplements its offerings through code-sharing with fellow members of the SkyTeam alliance, which includes Air France, Alitalia, Delta, KLM, and Northwest Airlines, as well as with other airlines. (Code-sharing allows airlines to sell tickets on one another's flights.)

	Annual Growth	12/03	12/04	12/05	12/06	12/07
Sales ($ mil.)	12.5%	8,870.0	9,899.0	11,208.0	13,128.0	14,232.0
Net income ($ mil.)	86.4%	38.0	(409.0)	(68.0)	343.0	459.0
Market value ($ mil.)	19.4%	1,074.4	899.9	1,849.9	3,787.4	2,185.1
Employees	6.0%	—	38,255	42,200	43,770	45,610

CONTINENTAL MATERIALS CORPORATION   AMEX: CUO

200 S. Wacker Dr., Ste. 4000
Chicago, IL 60606
Phone: 312-541-7200
Fax: 312-541-8089

CEO: James G. Gidwitz
CFO: Joseph J. Sum
HR: –
FYE: Saturday nearest December 31
Type: Public

Continental Materials divides its product plate between construction and heating, ventilation, and air conditioning (HVAC). Its construction products segment, which accounts for half of sales, produces ready-mix concrete, aggregates, metal doors, and related products. They are sold primarily to contractors, government entities, and consumers in Colorado. Continental Materials' HVAC segment makes wall furnaces, console heaters, fan coils, and evaporative air coolers that it markets to wholesale distributors and retail home centers throughout the Southwest.

	Annual Growth	12/03	12/04	12/05	12/06	12/07
Sales ($ mil.)	8.8%	120.2	126.9	139.0	158.8	168.4
Net income ($ mil.)	—	2.3	2.4	2.8	2.0	(0.6)
Market value ($ mil.)	(2.9%)	46.4	44.9	46.7	42.5	41.3
Employees	—	—	—	—	—	—

CONTINENTAL PROMOTION GROUP, INC.

4904 Eisenhower Blvd., Ste. 250
Tampa, FL 33634
Phone: 813-249-3100
Fax: 813-249-3138
Web: www.cpginc.com

CEO: Daniel D. (Dan) Granger
CFO: Ray Ipjian
HR: Joseph P. (Joe) Port
FYE: December 31
Type: Private

Continental Promotion Group (CPG) builds and manages promotional marketing programs that pay off. The company's services include premium, literature, and gift card fulfillment, rebate fulfillment, sweepstakes and contest administration, and Internet promotion management. Not bound by its name, Continental Promotion Group handles clients in 50 countries and six languages, promoting brands, products, and services for such companies as Amazon.com, Costco, and Sharp Electronics. It operates out of offices in Tampa, Florida and Tempe, Arizona and internationally in Toronto, Canada and Tipperary, Ireland.

	Annual Growth	12/03	12/04	12/05	12/06	12/07
Est. sales ($ mil.)	—	—	—	—	—	60.8
Employees	—	—	—	—	—	1,050

CONTINENTAL RESOURCES, INC.

175 Middlesex Tpke., Ste. 1
Bedford, MA 01730
Phone: 781-275-0850
Fax: 781-533-0395
Web: www.continentalresources.com

CEO: James F. McCann Sr.
CFO: James M. Bunt
HR: Cathy Shattuck
FYE: December 31
Type: Private

Continental Resources' rivers of revenue cover a vast terrain of technology. The company's Test and Measurement division sells, rents, and leases new and used instruments, such as spectrum analyzers, signal generators, and various probes. The Custom Computing Solutions division integrates computer systems and networks, and is one of the largest resellers of Sun Microsystems equipment in the US. The Enterico division focuses on selling IBM systems and servers. Continental Resources also makes power supplies and converters through its Wall Industries subsidiary. The family of CEO James McCann Sr. owns Continental Resources, which was formed in 1962.

	Annual Growth	12/03	12/04	12/05	12/06	12/07
Est. sales ($ mil.)	—	—	—	—	—	355.5
Employees	—	—	—	—	—	372

CONTINENTAL RESOURCES, INC.   NYSE: CLR

302 N. Independence
Enid, OK 73702
Phone: 580-233-8955
Fax: 580-548-5253
Web: www.contres.com

CEO: Harold G. Hamm
CFO: John D. Hart
HR: –
FYE: December 31
Type: Public

The continental resources that Continental Resources searches for are oil and natural gas assets beneath the North American continent, in the Rocky Mountain, Mid-Continent, and Gulf Coast regions. The independent oil and gas exploration and production company has added reserves of 89 million barrels of oil equivalent through internal growth (aka "growing through the drill bit") between early 2003 and the end of 2007. Continental Resources has estimated proved reserves of 134.6 million barrels of oil equivalent. It holds more than 1 million net acres of leasehold properties.

	Annual Growth	12/03	12/04	12/05	12/06	12/07
Sales ($ mil.)	16.4%	317.6	418.9	375.8	483.6	582.2
Net income ($ mil.)	87.8%	2.3	27.9	194.3	253.1	28.6
Market value ($ mil.)	—	—	—	—	—	4,412.4
Employees	—	302	—	—	—	—

CONTINENTAL TIRE NORTH AMERICA, INC.

1800 Continental Blvd.
Charlotte, NC 28273
Phone: 704-588-5895
Fax: –
Web: www.continentaltire.com

CEO: Matthias Schonberg
CFO: Tim Rogers
HR: –
FYE: December 31
Type: Subsidiary

Continental Tire North America rounds out tire production across the Atlantic for its German parent. The North American subsidiary of Germany-based tire and automotive component manufacturer Continental AG makes tires for cars, light- and heavy duty-trucks, motorhomes, SUVs, and agricultural and industrial vehicles (such as dozers and loaders). Brand names include ContiExtreme, ContiTrac, ContiSport, ContiTouring, and ContiPremier. In addition to Continental-branded tires, the company also produces General, Euzkadi, and other private-brand tires that can be found in North America.

	Annual Growth	12/03	12/04	12/05	12/06	12/07
Est. sales ($ mil.)	—	—	—	—	—	849.5
Employees	—	—	—	—	—	8,200

CONTINUCARE CORPORATION

AMEX: CNU

7200 Corporate Center Dr., Ste. 600
Miami, FL 33126
Phone: 305-500-2000
Fax: 305-500-2080
Web: www.continucare.com

CEO: Richard C. Pfenniger Jr.
CFO: Fernando L. Fernandez
HR: –
FYE: June 30
Type: Public

Continucare keeps on caring for South and Central Florida's Medicare recipients. The company provides primary care medical services through a network of 20 centers in Broward, Miami-Dade, and Hillsborough counties. It also provides practice management services to about 15 independent doctors' practices affiliated with Humana. A majority of the patients who seek care at Continucare clinics and practices are members of Medicare Advantage health plans; virtually all of the company's revenue comes from managed care contracts with HMOs operated by Humana, Vista Healthplan of South Florida, and Wellcare.

	Annual Growth	6/03	6/04	6/05	6/06	6/07
Sales ($ mil.)	21.0%	101.4	101.8	112.2	133.0	217.1
Net income ($ mil.)	181.7%	0.1	4.7	15.9	5.3	6.3
Market value ($ mil.)	85.2%	17.8	96.6	121.5	207.2	209.3
Employees	48.6%	—	—	255	—	563

CONVERA CORPORATION

NASDAQ (GM): CNVR

1921 Gallows Rd., Ste. 200
Vienna, VA 22182
Phone: 703-761-3700
Fax: 703-761-1990
Web: www.convera.com

CEO: Patrick C. (Pat) Condo
CFO: Matthew G. Jones
HR: –
FYE: January 31
Type: Public

Convera can help you uncover all sorts of information. The company's software and services enable customers to create search engines customized to meet the specialized information needs of their audience by combining proprietary content with Web content. In 2007 the company sold the assets of its RetrievalWare business and provided a royalty-free license for certain intellectual property for $23 million in cash to Fast Search & Transfer. Through Allen & Company, director Herbert Allen and his family owns 42% of Convera.

	Annual Growth	1/04	1/05	1/06	1/07	1/08
Sales ($ mil.)	(56.0%)	29.3	25.7	21.0	16.7	1.1
Net income ($ mil.)	—	(18.1)	(19.8)	(14.3)	(44.8)	(9.1)
Market value ($ mil.)	(11.0%)	179.7	180.6	370.0	189.6	113.0
Employees	0.6%	—	—	179	180	—

CONVERGENT RESOURCES, INC.

6 Concourse Pkwy., Ste. 2920
Atlanta, GA 30328
Phone: 770-730-0015
Fax: 770-730-0144
Web: www.cri-usa.com

CEO: Peter Picciocca
CFO: Kurt Miller
HR: –
FYE: December 31
Type: Private

Convergent Resources strives to avoid a divergence when it comes to collections. The company and its subsidiaries provide accounts receivable management services and collection services to a variety of industries throughout the US. AHC offers complex health care industry collection services to hospitals, helping them recover payments from insurers and other creditors. Comprehensive Healthcare Solutions (CHS) offers medical practice management services. ER Solutions provides consumer accounts receivable services. Credit Clearing House is a collections agency.

	Annual Growth	12/03	12/04	12/05	12/06	12/07
Est. sales ($ mil.)	—	—	—	—	—	71.7
Employees	—	—	—	—	—	1,657

CONVERGYS CORPORATION

NYSE: CVG

201 E. 4th St.
Cincinnati, OH 45202
Phone: 513-723-7000
Fax: 513-421-8624
Web: www.convergys.com

CEO: David F. (Dave) Dougherty
CFO: Earl C. Shanks
HR: Clark D. Handy
FYE: December 31
Type: Public

Convergys is conversant in the language of outsourcing. The company is one of the world's leading providers of business process outsourcing (BPO) services, such as billing, human resources administration, and customer care. Its Human Resources unit offers outsourcing of benefits and payroll operations, staffing, and training. Its Customer Management division, the largest teleservices business in the US, provides both inbound and outbound call handling for sales, marketing, and support through 80 call centers. Convergys also offers bill processing services and provisioning software to telecommunications companies through its Information Management Group.

	Annual Growth	12/03	12/04	12/05	12/06	12/07
Sales ($ mil.)	5.6%	2,288.8	2,487.7	2,582.1	2,789.8	2,844.3
Net income ($ mil.)	(0.3%)	171.6	111.5	122.6	166.2	169.5
Market value ($ mil.)	(0.5%)	3,048.5	2,627.7	2,802.3	4,270.9	2,982.6
Employees	14.2%	—	—	65,700	75,000	—

CONVERSE INC.

One High St.
North Andover, MA 01845
Phone: 978-983-3300
Fax: 978-983-3502
Web: www.converse.com

CEO: Jack A. Boys
CFO: –
HR: –
FYE: May 31
Type: Subsidiary

Once a popular basketball shoe maker, Converse was close to throwing in the towel, but eventually rebounded under NIKE. Converse has sold some 750 million pairs of its classic Chuck Taylor All Star canvas basketball shoes, appealing to everyone from school kids to clothing designers. It also licenses its name to sports apparel. Products also are made under names One Star and Jack Purcell and are sold through retailers and licensees in some 100 countries. Following years of declining sales, CVEO Corporation (which owned Converse) filed for Chapter 11 bankruptcy protection in 2001. Chairman Marsden Cason backed a firm that bought Converse. In 2003 the company was sold to NIKE.

	Annual Growth	5/03	5/04	5/05	5/06	5/07
Est. sales ($ mil.)	—	—	—	—	—	55.6
Employees	—	—	—	—	—	261

CONVERSION SERVICES INTERNATIONAL, INC.
AMEX: CVN

100 Eagle Rock Ave.	CEO: Scott Newman
East Hanover, NJ 07936	CFO: William Hendry
Phone: 973-560-9400	HR: –
Fax: 973-560-9500	FYE: December 31
Web: www.csiwhq.com	Type: Public

Conversion Services International (CSI) helps clients investigate data warehousing and business intelligence technologies. The company provides strategic and technology consulting, integrating products from such vendors as Business Objects, Cognos, MicroStrategy, and SAS Institute. Its customers, primarily located in the northeastern US, come mostly from the financial services, health care, pharmaceutical, and telecommunications industries. The company's client roster includes Amedisys, Bank of America, France Telecom, Goldman Sachs, Jaguar Cars, Pfizer, and Tiffany & Co.

	Annual Growth	2/03	*12/04	12/05	12/06	12/07
Sales ($ mil.)	—	0.0	25.2	27.6	25.7	21.5
Net income ($ mil.)	—	(1.3)	(33.3)	(5.1)	(9.6)	(10.2)
Market value ($ mil.)	(80.2%)	—	2,837.4	28.7	19.6	22.0
Employees	(5.2%)	—	210	199	—	—

*Fiscal year change

CONVIO, INC.

11400 Burnet Rd., Bldg. 5, Ste. 200	CEO: Gene Austin
Austin, TX 78759	CFO: James R. (Jim) Offerdahl
Phone: 512-652-2600	HR: Angela G. (Angie) McDermott
Fax: 512-652-2699	FYE: December 31
Web: www.convio.com	Type: Private

Convio takes an approach *con brio* to helping not-for-profit organizations, institutions of higher education, and associations raise money, organize volunteer efforts, manage online content, and get their message out. The company's online constituent relationship management (eCRM) software and services connect potential donors and volunteers to groups they may support, and vice versa. It continues to expand the functionality to its software, adding modules for specialized efforts such as tribute-based fundraising. Convio's clients include the AFL-CIO, The American Red Cross, the ASPCA, NPR, Susan G. Komen For the Cure, and the Texas Exes. Granite Ventures holds a 21% stake in the company.

	Annual Growth	12/03	12/04	12/05	12/06	12/07
Sales ($ mil.)	66.6%	5.6	9.0	13.3	21.5	43.1
Net income ($ mil.)	—	—	(6.3)	(5.8)	(5.0)	(10.5)
Employees	48.4%	66	—	135	301	320

⊞ CON-WAY INC.
NYSE: CNW

2855 Campus Dr., Ste. 300	CEO: Douglas W. Stotlar
San Mateo, CA 94403	CFO: Kevin C. Schick
Phone: 650-378-5200	HR: Scott J. Engers
Fax: 650-357-9160	FYE: December 31
Web: www.con-way.com	Type: Public

Con-way is a leading provider of trucking and logistics services. The company's less-than-truckload (LTL) unit, Con-way Freight, provides regional and interregional service throughout North America. (LTL carriers consolidate loads from multiple shippers into a single truckload.) Con-way Freight operates a fleet of about 8,300 tractors and 24,000 trailers from a network of some 340 terminals. Con-way offers truckload transportation services through its Con-way Truckload subsidiary (formerly known as CFI), which maintains a fleet of about 2,600 tractors and 8,100 trailers. Con-way's Menlo Worldwide unit provides contract logistics, freight brokerage, and supply chain management services.

	Annual Growth	12/03	12/04	12/05	12/06	12/07
Sales ($ mil.)	(3.7%)	5,104.3	3,712.4	4,169.6	4,221.5	4,387.4
Net income ($ mil.)	13.5%	92.0	(115.9)	223.0	266.1	152.9
Market value ($ mil.)	(8.2%)	—	—	—	2,045.6	1,878.3
Employees	0.0%	—	—	21,800	21,800	—

CONWOOD SALES CO., LLC

813 Ridge Lake Blvd., #100	CEO: William M. (Bill) Rosson
Memphis, TN 38120	CFO: Michael D. Flaherty
Phone: 901-761-2050	HR: Carol Novosad
Fax: 901-767-1302	FYE: January 31
Web: www.cwdlp.com	Type: Subsidiary

Conwood loves a bear market when it comes to moist snuff and other smokeless tobacco products. The company makes the Grizzly and Kodiak brands of moist tobacco and is the second-largest manufacturer of smokeless tobacco products in the US. Conwood also makes loose-leaf tobacco (including Morgan's, Levi Garrett, and Taylor's Pride brands), snuff (Garrett, Dental, and Tube Rose brands), and an assortment of other smokeless tobacco products (including twist, moist, and plug). Conwood was acquired by Reynolds American in mid-2006 for $3.5 billion in cash. It now generates nearly 4% of Reynolds American's annual revenue.

	Annual Growth	1/03	1/04	1/05	1/06	1/07
Est. sales ($ mil.)	—	—	—	—	—	38.0
Employees	—	—	—	—	—	80

COOK GROUP INCORPORATED

750 Daniels Way	CEO: Kem Hawkins
Bloomington, IN 47404	CFO: David Breedlove
Phone: 812-339-2235	HR: –
Fax: 800-554-8335	FYE: December 31
Web: www.cookgroup.com	Type: Private

Cook Group makes sure your goose isn't cooked if you've got heart disease. Flagship subsidiary Cook Incorporated makes catheters, wire guides, stents, and other devices used in minimally invasive cardiac procedures. Cook Group operates a host of other medical manufacturing subsidiaries that make urological and gynecological devices, endoscopic accessories, and vascular products. Additionally, industrial parts manufacturers Sabin and K-Tube make plastic parts used for medical and other industrial applications, and Cook Pharmica offers contract manufacturing services to the biotech industry. The company, one of the world's largest privately held medical device firms, was founded by chairman William Cook in 1963.

	Annual Growth	12/02	12/03	12/04	12/05	12/06
Est. sales ($ mil.)	—	—	—	—	—	1,500.0
Employees	—	—	—	—	—	6,300

COOL CUTS 4 KIDS, INC.

1701 W. Euless Blvd., Ste. 200	CEO: Ron Mayle
Euless, TX 76040	CFO: Lance Loshelder
Phone: 817-571-6089	HR: –
Fax: 817-858-0040	FYE: –
Web: www.coolcuts4kids.com	Type: Private

Cool Cuts 4 Kids is a salon chain focused on keeping kids' hands busy while another set of hands creates a totally cool 'do. The company operates some 60 salons primarily in Texas, and also in about 10 other states. Children sit on seats fashioned as cars or motorcycles and watch videos or play the latest Nintendo games while getting haircuts. There's even an enclosed play area for smaller kids waiting for cuts. Special services include cornrow braiding with beads or other accessories and shampoo with a chlorine removal treatment. Salon giant Regis owns 20% of Cool Cuts and may exercise its option to purchase the company in 2008.

An in-depth profile of this company is available to Hoover's Online members at hoovers.com.

433

THE COOPER COMPANIES, INC.

NYSE: COO

6140 Stoneridge Mall Rd., Ste. 590
Pleasanton, CA 94588
Phone: 925-460-3600
Fax: –
Web: www.coopercos.com

CEO: Robert S. Weiss
CFO: Eugene J. (Gene) Midlock
HR: Ruby Varner
FYE: October 31
Type: Public

The Cooper Companies makes specialty medical devices in two niche markets: vision care and gynecology. Its CooperVision subsidiary makes specialty contact lenses, including toric lenses for astigmatism and cosmetic lenses; through its acquisition of Ocular Sciences, the company also offers lenses for more common vision problems such as nearsightedness and farsightedness. Subsidiary CooperSurgical specializes in women's health care; its wide range of products include bone densitometers (for diagnosing osteoporosis), hysteroscopes, and fetal monitors. The company markets its products through its own sales representatives in North America and through a mix of direct sales and distributors elsewhere.

	Annual Growth	10/03	10/04	10/05	10/06	10/07
Sales ($ mil.)	23.3%	411.8	490.2	806.6	859.0	950.6
Net income ($ mil.)	—	68.8	92.8	91.7	66.2	(11.2)
Market value ($ mil.)	7.8%	1,394.0	2,304.0	3,058.6	2,567.3	1,884.5
Employees	3.9%	—	—	7,034	7,500	7,600

COOPER INDUSTRIES, LTD.

NYSE: CBE

600 Travis St., Ste. 5800
Houston, TX 77002
Phone: 713-209-8400
Fax: 713-209-8996
Web: www.cooperindustries.com

CEO: Kirk S. Hachigian
CFO: Terry A. Klebe
HR: James P. Williams
FYE: December 31
Type: Public

Cooper Industries likes to keep customers from blowing a fuse. Cooper makes electrical products, tools, hardware, and metal support products. The company's electrical products include electrical and circuit protection devices, residential and industrial lighting, and electrical power and distribution products for use by utility companies. Cooper's tool offerings include such venerable brands as Crescent wrenches and pliers, Apex impact sockets, Plumb hammers, and Weller soldering and welding supplies. Subsidiary Cooper B-Line makes metal support products that include conduits, cable trays, and fasteners. Customers in the US provide more than 70% of Cooper Industries' sales.

	Annual Growth	12/03	12/04	12/05	12/06	12/07
Sales ($ mil.)	9.8%	4,061.4	4,462.9	4,730.4	5,184.6	5,903.1
Net income ($ mil.)	47.0%	148.3	339.8	163.9	464.0	692.3
Market value ($ mil.)	36.4%	2,696.2	3,141.4	3,344.3	4,120.9	9,320.5
Employees	3.8%	27,188	26,863	28,903	30,561	31,504

COOPER TIRE & RUBBER COMPANY

NYSE: CTB

701 Lima Ave.
Findlay, OH 45840
Phone: 419-423-1321
Fax: 419-424-4212
Web: www.coopertire.com

CEO: Roy V. Armes
CFO: Philip G. (Phil) Weaver
HR: Mark W. Krivoruchka
FYE: December 31
Type: Public

Cooper Tire & Rubber is a real wheeler-dealer. As its name indicates, the company makes and distributes tires and rubber products for the transportation industry. Through its North American Tire and International Tire divisions, Cooper makes tires for passenger cars, light trucks, and medium-duty trucks. It also makes tread rubber and related equipment for the retread industry. Cooper's primary customers are independent tire dealers, wholesalers, and retailers. The company sold its Cooper-Standard Automotive (2004) and its Oliver Rubber Company (2007) subsidiaries, and has used the proceeds to fund assorted pension plans, reduce debt, and buy back a large amount of the company's stock.

	Annual Growth	12/03	12/04	12/05	12/06	12/07
Sales ($ mil.)	(4.4%)	3,514.4	2,081.6	2,155.2	2,676.2	2,932.6
Net income ($ mil.)	12.8%	73.8	201.4	(9.4)	(78.5)	119.6
Market value ($ mil.)	(11.1%)	1,581.4	1,512.2	939.4	877.7	989.2
Employees	23.5%	—	—	8,762	13,361	13,355

COOPERATIVE BANKSHARES, INC.

NASDAQ (GM): COOP

201 Market St.
Wilmington, NC 28401
Phone: 910-343-0181
Fax: 910-251-1652
Web: www.coop-bank.com

CEO: Frederick Willetts III
CFO: Todd L. Sammons
HR: Dare C. Rhodes
FYE: December 31
Type: Public

The word of the day is always "cooperation" at Cooperative Bankshares. It's the holding company for Cooperative Bank, which operates two dozen branches primarily throughout the coastal and inland communities of eastern North Carolina. Targeting individuals and small to midsized businesses, the bank provides checking and savings accounts, CDs, and IRAs. Investment products and services such as discount securities brokerage, annuities, and mutual funds are available through a third-party provider. Residential mortgages account for more than half of Cooperative Bankshares' loan portfolio, which also includes commercial real estate, construction, business, and consumer loans.

	Annual Growth	12/03	12/04	12/05	12/06	12/07
Assets ($ mil.)	16.5%	502.3	550.1	746.3	860.1	926.8
Net income ($ mil.)	10.7%	5.4	4.7	5.5	7.6	8.1
Market value ($ mil.)	24.3%	32.4	34.6	58.4	116.5	77.3
Employees	5.8%	—	—	208	220	—

COOPERATIVE REGIONS OF ORGANIC PRODUCERS POOL

1 Organic Way
LaFarge, WI 54639
Phone: 608-625-2602
Fax: 608-625-2600
Web: www.organicvalley.coop

CEO: George Siemon
CFO: Mike Bedessem
HR: –
FYE: December 31
Type: Cooperative

Cooperative Regions of Organic Producers Pool (CROPP) is one of the largest organic farmer cooperatives in the US. Its some 1,200 farmer-members produce the Organic Valley Family of Farms brand of fluid and shelf-stable milk, along with cheese, butter, and soy milk. Beyond the dairy barn, the cooperative also offers organic citrus juices, produce, eggs, meats, and poultry. Organic Valley retail products are sold at food retailers, and its ingredients are marketed to other organic food processors. Wisconsin-headquartered CROPP's member/farmers are located in California, Florida, and the northeast, northwest, and midwest regions of the US.

	Annual Growth	12/02	12/03	12/04	12/05	12/06
Sales ($ mil.)	—	—	—	—	—	335.0
Employees	—	—	—	—	—	—

COOPER-STANDARD AUTOMOTIVE INC.

39550 Orchard Hill Place
Novi, MI 48375
Phone: 248-596-5900
Fax: 248-596-6535
Web: www.cooperstandard.com

CEO: James S. (Jim) McElya
CFO: Allen J. Campbell
HR: Edward A. (Ed) Hasler
FYE: December 31
Type: Private

When it comes to cars, Cooper-Standard Automotive upholds its standards. The company was created when Cooper Tire & Rubber acquired The Standard Products Company (1999) and Siebe Automotive (2000). The company's body and chassis division makes noise, vibration, and heat control systems, as well as interior sealing systems. Cooper-Standard's fluid systems division manufactures various tubes and hoses used in braking, fuel, and emissions systems. Its customers have included automakers Chrysler, Ford Motor, and General Motors. Cooper-Standard Automotive operates about 75 manufacturing facilities worldwide.

	Annual Growth	12/02	12/03	12/04	12/05	12/06
Sales ($ mil.)	8.5%	1,586.0	1,662.2	1,858.9	1,827.4	2,200.0
Employees	9.3%	—	—	13,605	13,429	16,266

COORSTEK, INC.

16000 Table Mountain Pkwy.
Golden, CO 80403
Phone: 303-271-7000
Fax: 303-271-7009
Web: www.coorstek.com

CEO: John K. Coors
CFO: Steve Rask
HR: Janet D. Comerford
FYE: December 31
Type: Private

CoorsTek isn't a high-tech beer company. Rather, it produces precision-machined metals, technical ceramics, and engineered plastics used in the aerospace, automotive, computer, military contracting, power generation and distribution, and telecommunications industries, among others. The company — which was once a part of the Adolph Coors Company (now Molson Coors Brewing) and later part of Coors spinoff ACX Technologies (now Graphic Packaging) — has used acquisitions and product development to shift its emphasis from engineered ceramics to components and assemblies for the semiconductor production equipment market. The company was taken private by CEO John Coors and his family in 2003.

	Annual Growth	12/03	12/04	12/05	12/06	12/07
Est. sales ($ mil.)	—	—	—	—	—	145.0
Employees	—	—	—	—	—	2,900

COPANO ENERGY, L.L.C.

NASDAQ (GS): CPNO

2727 Allen Pkwy., Ste. 1200
Houston, TX 77019
Phone: 713-621-9547
Fax: 713-621-9545
Web: www.copanoenergy.com

CEO: John R. Eckel Jr.
CFO: Matthew J. (Matt) Assiff
HR: Jeff Casey
FYE: December 31
Type: Public

Copano Energy hopes its business goes down the tubes. The natural gas pipeline and processing company operates and maintains a network of natural gas gathering and intrastate pipelines (totaling more than 6,000 miles) in Texas' Gulf Coast region and in Oklahoma and Wyoming. This includes 144 miles of pipelines owned by Webb/Duval Gatherers, an unconsolidated general partnership 62.5%-owned by Copano Energy. The company also provides natural gas processing operations through its Houston Central Processing plant and Sheridan NGL pipeline. Copano Energy chairman and CEO John Eckel holds an 8% stake in the company.

	Annual Growth	12/03	12/04	12/05	12/06	12/07
Sales ($ mil.)	31.3%	384.6	437.7	747.7	860.3	1,141.7
Net income ($ mil.)	—	(4.7)	(0.9)	30.4	65.1	63.2
Market value ($ mil.)	157.7%	—	100.6	275.3	524.3	1,721.8
Employees	41.2%	80	—	206	225	—

COPART, INC.

NASDAQ (GS): CPRT

4665 Business Center Dr.
Fairfield, CA 94534
Phone: 707-639-5000
Fax: 707-639-5196
Web: www.copart.com

CEO: Willis J. Johnson
CFO: William E. Franklin
HR: Thomas E. Wylie
FYE: July 31
Type: Public

What happens after cars are totaled in wrecks or natural disasters? How about stolen cars recovered *after* the insurance settlement? Perhaps Copart happens — it takes junked cars and auctions them for insurers, auto dealers, and car rental agencies. The buyers are mostly rebuilders, licensed dismantlers, and used-car dealers and exporters. They can bid in person or on Copart's online auction site (known as Virtual Bidding Second Generation, or VB2 for short). Copart also provides services such as towing and storage to buyers and other salvage companies, as well as an online database and search engine for used parts. The company has about 130 storage facilities throughout North America and the UK.

	Annual Growth	7/03	7/04	7/05	7/06	7/07
Sales ($ mil.)	12.7%	347.4	400.8	457.1	528.6	560.7
Net income ($ mil.)	24.2%	57.2	79.2	102.1	96.9	136.3
Market value ($ mil.)	31.0%	843.1	2,004.2	2,209.7	2,409.5	2,485.7
Employees	2.3%	—	—	2,421	—	2,536

THE COPLEY PRESS, INC.

7776 Ivanhoe Ave.
La Jolla, CA 92037
Phone: 858-454-0411
Fax: 858-729-7629
Web: www.copleynewspapers.com

CEO: David C. Copley
CFO: Dean P. Dwyer
HR: James F. Vargas
FYE: December 31
Type: Private

You might say this company is big news in San Diego. The Copley Press owns and operates *The San Diego Union-Tribune*, one of the country's leading newspapers with a circulation of more than 300,000. Copley press also publishes *Today's Local News*, a free community paper serving areas surrounding San Diego, and it operates SignOnSanDiego.com, the online companion to the *Union-Tribune*. In addition, the company runs Copley News Service, a news syndicate that distributes daily and weekly news, as well as photos, comics, and feature stories. Copley Press was founded in 1928 by publisher Colonel Ira Clifton Copley. His family, led by David Copley, continues to run the company.

COPYTELE, INC.

OTC: COPY

900 Walt Whitman Rd.
Melville, NY 11747
Phone: 631-549-5900
Fax: 631-549-5974
Web: www.copytele.com

CEO: Denis A. Krusos
CFO: Henry P. Herms
HR: –
FYE: October 31
Type: Public

CopyTele doesn't want anyone to know what travels over your telephone line, let alone copy it. The company provides secure communications products. Its stand-alone devices provide encryption for secure voice, fax, and data communication. The ULP-1 is an add-on PCMCIA card for laptops, which secures e-mail and other software from viruses. Boeing uses CopyTele's encryption products on the Thuraya satellite communications network, which is employed by the US military in Iraq. Boeing has become the exclusive distributor for many of the company's security products.

	Annual Growth	10/03	10/04	10/05	10/06	10/07
Sales ($ mil.)	25.7%	0.2	0.5	0.4	0.5	0.5
Net income ($ mil.)	—	(3.1)	(3.4)	(4.4)	(7.6)	(5.5)
Market value ($ mil.)	23.9%	40.9	91.5	47.8	59.8	96.2
Employees	(7.5%)	45	45	33	31	33

CORAM, INC.

1675 Broadway, Ste. 900
Denver, CO 80202
Phone: 303-292-4973
Fax: 303-298-0043
Web: www.coram-healthcare.com

CEO: John J. Arlotta
CFO: –
HR: Faye Major
FYE: December 31
Type: Subsidiary

Coram infuses healing for its patients. The company provides a variety of home infusion (intravenous) services such as tube feeding and antibiotic treatments for transplant and congestive heart failure patients. Coram also offers pain management and nutrition support, as well as specialty drug distribution services. In addition, the company provides medical and respiratory therapy equipment and — through subsidiary CTI Network — offers support services for clinical research studies. Its health care providers treat more than 17,000 patients each month. The company, founded in 1979, operates more than 70 branches in about 40 states and Canada. It was acquired by Apria Healthcare in 2007.

	Annual Growth	12/03	12/04	12/05	12/06	12/07
Est. sales ($ mil.)	—	—	—	—	—	4.1
Employees	—	—	—	—	—	200

An in-depth profile of this company is available to Hoover's Online members at hoovers.com.

435

CORBIS CORPORATION

710 2nd Ave., Ste. 200
Seattle, WA 98104
Phone: 206-373-6000
Fax: 206-373-6100
Web: www.corbis.com

CEO: Gary Shenk
CFO: Sue McDonald
HR: Steve Lodis
FYE: December 31
Type: Private

If a picture is worth a thousand words, then Corbis has lots to say. The company's archive of more than 100 million images is one of the largest in the world, along with that of rival Getty Images. Corbis licenses its images — contemporary and archival photography, art, illustrations, and footage — for commercial and editorial use in print and electronic media. Customers can find and license images via the company's Web site. Corbis also offers artist representation (matching photographers with assignments), rights services (securing rights to images controlled by third parties), and media management (hosting of others' digital content). Microsoft co-founder Bill Gates owns Corbis, which he founded in 1989.

	Annual Growth	12/02	12/03	12/04	12/05	12/06
Sales ($ mil.)	10.1%	—	—	—	228.0	251.0
Employees	—	—	—	—	—	1,100

CORCEPT THERAPEUTICS INCORPORATED

NASDAQ (GM): CORT

149 Commonwealth Dr.
Menlo Park, CA 94025
Phone: 650-327-3270
Fax: 650-327-3218
Web: www.corcept.com

CEO: Joseph K. Belanoff
CFO: Anne M. LeDoux
HR: Mark Strem
FYE: December 31
Type: Public

Corcept Therapeutics wants to help people who are beyond blue. The biotechnology firm's lead drug candidate is CORLUX, which it still hopes will be useful in the treatment of psychotic major depression (PMD). However, Phase III trials on CORLUX have missed their goals, and the company is tinkering with dosages for future Phase III trials. The drug blocks the release of cortisol, elevated levels of which may contribute to PMD. CORLUX's primary ingredient is mifepristone, commonly known as RU-486 or the "abortion pill." Corcept is also evaluting CORLUX's ability to prevent weight gain in patients taking other antipsychotic medicines.

	Annual Growth	12/03	12/04	12/05	12/06	12/07
Sales ($ mil.)	66.7%	—	—	—	0.3	0.5
Net income ($ mil.)	—	—	—	—	(24.9)	(11.6)
Market value ($ mil.)	286.1%	—	—	—	31.7	122.2
Employees	—	—	—	—	14	—

CORE MOLDING TECHNOLOGIES, INC.

AMEX: CMT

800 Manor Park Dr.
Columbus, OH 43228
Phone: 614-870-5000
Fax: 614-870-5051
Web: www.coremt.com

CEO: Kevin L. Barnett
CFO: Herman F. Dick Jr.
HR: Scott Jones
FYE: December 31
Type: Public

The core business of Core Molding Technologies is reinforced plastic parts. Through compression molding, sprayup, hand layup, and vacuum-assisted resin infusion molding, the company makes truck components (air deflectors, fenders, hoods) and personal watercraft parts (decks, hulls, and engine hatches, made primarily for Yamaha). Navistar owns about 10% of Core Molding Technologies and accounts for more than half of its sales. Other major customers include heavy-duty truck manufacturers Daimler Trucks North America (formerly Freightliner) and PACCAR.

	Annual Growth	12/03	12/04	12/05	12/06	12/07
Sales ($ mil.)	7.2%	92.8	111.8	130.5	162.3	122.7
Net income ($ mil.)	21.5%	1.7	5.1	6.3	10.4	3.7
Market value ($ mil.)	13.6%	28.6	27.1	76.8	98.5	47.5
Employees	—	—	—	—	1,377	—

CORE-MARK HOLDING COMPANY, INC.

NASDAQ (GS): CORE

395 Oyster Point Blvd., Ste. 415
South San Francisco, CA 94080
Phone: 650-589-9445
Fax: 650-952-4284
Web: www.coremark.com

CEO: J. Michael (Mike) Walsh
CFO: Stacy Loretz-Congdon
HR: Henry J. Hautau
FYE: December 31
Type: Public

Core-Mark Holding Company is the phoenix of smokes and snacks distributors. It's the sole entity that emerged from the ashes of the Fleming Companies' 2003 bankruptcy. From its two dozen distribution facilities, Core-Mark distributes packaged consumables (including cigarettes, tobacco, candy, snacks, grocery items, nonalcoholic beverages, and health and beauty aids) to 21,000 convenience retailers, mass merchandisers, and drug, liquor, and specialty stores. Cigarettes account for more than two-thirds of sales. Core-Mark's largest customers include Couche-Tard and Valero; each has a dedicated distribution facility. The firm serves customers in 45 western and central US states and five Canadian provinces.

	Annual Growth	12/03	12/04	12/05	12/06	12/07
Sales ($ mil.)	6.6%	—	—	4,891.1	5,314.4	5,560.9
Net income ($ mil.)	29.8%	—	—	14.3	20.6	24.1
Market value ($ mil.)	(2.1%)	—	—	312.9	341.5	300.0
Employees	8.5%	—	—	3,430	3,745	4,035

COREMETRICS, INC.

1840 Gateway Dr., Ste. 320
San Mateo, CA 94404
Phone: 650-762-1400
Fax: 650-762-1499
Web: www.coremetrics.com

CEO: Joe Davis
CFO: Mark Resnick
HR: –
FYE: December 31
Type: Private

Want to know who's clicking on your Web site, and where, and how? Coremetrics provides Web-based analytics and precision marketing software that companies use to analyze the behavior of their online customers and Web site visitors. The company's software captures and stores site visitor activity data, then converts the data into individual visitor profiles that give online marketers, information technology managers, and e-commerce company executives insight into how their Web sites are being used. Customers have included Bank of America, Columbia House, Motorola, and Williams-Sonoma.

	Annual Growth	12/03	12/04	12/05	12/06	12/07
Est. sales ($ mil.)	—	—	—	—	—	16.9
Employees	—	—	—	—	—	215

CORGENIX MEDICAL CORPORATION

OTC: CONX

11575 Main St.
Broomfield, CO 80020
Phone: 303-457-4345
Fax: 303-457-4519
Web: www.corgenix.com

CEO: Douglass T. (Doug) Simpson
CFO: William H. Critchfield
HR: –
FYE: June 30
Type: Public

Corgenix Medical wants to take a peek inside you. The company makes *in vitro* diagnostics to detect autoimmune, liver, and vascular diseases. Its line of more than 50 diagnostics are used by reference labs, hospitals and clinics, researchers, and other medical facilities around the world. It sells directly to customers in the US and the UK and through independent distributors elsewhere. To expand its product line and its customer base, Corgenix Medical is developing new tests to diagnose aspirin resistance, fibromyalgia, and atherosclerosis; it is also developing tests that detect potential bioterrorism agents using grant funding from the National Institutes of Health.

	Annual Growth	6/03	6/04	6/05	6/06	6/07
Sales ($ mil.)	10.3%	5.0	5.3	5.6	6.6	7.4
Net income ($ mil.)	—	(0.3)	(0.1)	(0.6)	(1.6)	(2.4)
Market value ($ mil.)	22.8%	1.8	5.5	2.6	4.5	4.2
Employees	—	—	—	—	—	—

CORILLIAN CORPORATION

3400 NW John Olsen Place
Hillsboro, OR 97124
Phone: 503-629-3300
Fax: 503-617-1450
Web: www.corillian.com

CEO: Alex P. Hart
CFO: Paul K. Wilde
HR: Marianna Miller
FYE: December 31
Type: Subsidiary

Corillian can help you manage your millions. Banks, credit unions, brokers, financial portals, and other financial services providers use Corillian's software to develop and deploy online financial services for their customers. The company's Corillian Voyager software enables consumers to view personal account and other market information, receive and pay bills, and manage personal finances via the Internet. The company, whose software supports corporate, small business, and credit card banking operations, also offers consulting, application hosting, and related services. In 2007 the company was acquired by CheckFree for about $245 million; CheckFree was acquired by Fiserv later in 2007.

	Annual Growth	12/02	12/03	12/04	12/05	12/06
Sales ($ mil.)	11.8%	39.1	46.1	50.8	49.2	61.0
Net income ($ mil.)	—	(17.3)	5.1	10.5	2.7	(1.1)
Employees	7.4%	246	227	224	305	—

CORINTHIAN COLLEGES, INC.

NASDAQ (GS): COCO

6 Hutton Centre Dr., Ste. 400
Santa Ana, CA 92707
Phone: 714-427-3000
Fax: 714-724-5111
Web: www.cci.edu

CEO: Jack D. Massimino
CFO: Kenneth S. Ord
HR: Jim Wade
FYE: June 30
Type: Public

Corinthian Colleges believes more in marketable skills than in ivory towers. One of the largest for-profit, post-secondary education companies in the US, Corinthian Colleges focuses on career-oriented students, operating nearly 100 colleges in 25 states, as well as more than 15 in Ontario, Canada. Its institutions include Florida Metropolitan University (FMU), Bryman College, and the National School of Technology. The majority of Corinthian's students are enrolled in associate's degree or diploma programs, but the FMU campus also offers bachelor's and master's degrees. Additionally, Corinthian Colleges offers online degrees through FMU Online and Everest College.

	Annual Growth	6/03	6/04	6/05	6/06	6/07
Sales ($ mil.)	15.9%	517.3	804.3	963.6	966.7	933.2
Net income ($ mil.)	(42.5%)	65.9	81.6	58.4	41.5	7.2
Market value ($ mil.)	6.8%	1,058.5	2,234.1	1,164.6	1,238.4	1,376.8
Employees	4.6%	—	—	8,185	9,500	8,950

CORN PRODUCTS INTERNATIONAL, INC.

NYSE: CPO

5 Westbrook Corporate Center
Westchester, IL 60154
Phone: 708-551-2600
Fax: 708-551-2700
Web: www.cornproducts.com

CEO: Samuel C. (Sam) Scott III
CFO: Cheryl K. Beebe
HR: James J. (Jim) Hirchak
FYE: December 31
Type: Public

Sweet sodas and diet dishes alike get their base from Corn Products International. The company makes food ingredients and industrial products from corn and other starch-based raw materials. It has customers that make food and beverages, pharmaceuticals, and paper. Almost two-thirds of its sales come from sweeteners, including high-fructose corn syrup used to sweeten soft drinks. The company also produces corn starch (a thickener for processed foods), corn oil, and corn gluten (for animal feed). Spun off by Bestfoods in 1997, Corn Products International operates manufacturing plants throughout Africa, Asia, and North and South America.

	Annual Growth	12/03	12/04	12/05	12/06	12/07
Sales ($ mil.)	12.7%	2,102.0	2,283.0	2,360.0	2,621.0	3,391.0
Net income ($ mil.)	27.0%	76.0	94.0	90.0	124.0	198.0
Market value ($ mil.)	46.2%	590.0	1,963.0	1,733.6	2,524.0	2,692.0
Employees	0.7%	—	—	7,000	7,600	7,100

CORNELL COMPANIES, INC.

NYSE: CRN

1700 West Loop South, Ste. 1500
Houston, TX 77027
Phone: 713-623-0790
Fax: 713-623-2853
Web: www.cornellcompanies.com

CEO: James E. Hyman
CFO: John R. Nieser
HR: –
FYE: December 31
Type: Public

Graduating from this Cornell might not impress people as much as earning a degree from the Ivy League university with the same name. Cornell Companies designs, builds, and operates secure and community-based correctional centers. It runs more than 70 adult and juvenile facilities with about 18,500 beds in 15 states and Washington, DC. The company's adult and juvenile community-based facilities (including halfway houses) provide services such as General Equivalency Diploma (GED) programs, job training and placement, recreation and leisure activities, health care (including mental health and drug counseling), and life skills training.

	Annual Growth	12/03	12/04	12/05	12/06	12/07
Sales ($ mil.)	7.3%	271.6	291.0	310.8	360.9	360.6
Net income ($ mil.)	31.3%	4.0	(7.4)	0.3	11.9	11.9
Market value ($ mil.)	14.3%	199.0	204.8	190.6	257.8	339.4
Employees	—	—	—	4,513	—	—

CORNERSTONE BANCSHARES, INC.

OTC: CSBQ

835 Georgia Ave.
Chattanooga, TN 37402
Phone: 423-385-3000
Fax: 423-385-3100
Web: www.cscbank.com

CEO: Gregory B. Jones
CFO: –
HR: –
FYE: December 31
Type: Public

Pardon me boys, is Cornerstone Bancshares the holding company for Cornerstone Community Bank? Yes, and you'll find it has a handful of branches in and around Chattanooga, Tennessee. Consumer and business customers alike take advantage of the regional bank's services, including deposit accounts, loans, and lines of credit. Among its loan offerings are mortgage, home equity, commercial real estate, rental property, and construction. Commercial real estate accounts for about one-third of the bank's loan portfolio.

	Annual Growth	12/03	12/04	12/05	12/06	12/07
Assets ($ mil.)	21.9%	201.0	248.6	323.6	374.9	444.4
Net income ($ mil.)	(17.0%)	1.9	2.6	4.3	5.8	0.9
Market value ($ mil.)	78.7%	6.8	22.7	37.2	107.4	69.4
Employees	—	—	—	—	—	116

CORNING INCORPORATED

NYSE: GLW

1 Riverfront Plaza
Corning, NY 14831
Phone: 607-974-9000
Fax: 607-974-8091
Web: www.corning.com

CEO: Wendell P. Weeks
CFO: James B. Flaws
HR: Pamela C. Schneider
FYE: December 31
Type: Public

Most of Corning's cooking is done lightly these days, and its growth is on display. The materials pioneer is the world's top maker of fiber-optic cable, which it invented nearly four decades ago. Once known mainly for its kitchenware and lab products, the company is now a leading provider of optical fiber and cable products and communications network equipment. Its display technologies unit produces glass substrates for flat-panel displays. Other major business segments include environmental technologies (ceramics for catalytic converters), and life sciences (laboratory equipment). Corning gets more than half of its sales in the Asia/Pacific region, principally from Taiwan and Japan.

	Annual Growth	12/03	12/04	12/05	12/06	12/07
Sales ($ mil.)	17.4%	3,090.0	3,854.0	4,579.0	5,174.0	5,860.0
Net income ($ mil.)	—	(223.0)	(2,165.0)	585.0	1,855.0	2,150.0
Market value ($ mil.)	28.0%	14,007.5	16,572.2	30,197.8	29,281.1	37,616.3
Employees	4.7%	20,600	24,700	26,000	24,500	24,800

An in-depth profile of this company is available to Hoover's Online members at hoovers.com.

437

CORNING NATURAL GAS CORPORATION

OTC: CNIG

330 W. William St.
Corning, NY 14830
Phone: 607-936-3755
Fax: 607-962-2844
Web: www.corninggas.com

CEO: Michael I. (Mike) German
CFO: Firouzeh Sarhangi
HR: Stanley G. (Jerry) Sleve
FYE: September 30
Type: Public

Corning Natural Gas has cornered the market for natural gas supply in Corning, New York. The company is a regulated transmission and distribution utility serving 14,500 residential and business customers in Corning and surrounding areas; the company also sells gas wholesale to two nearby communities. It has about 400 miles of gas distribution and transmission pipelines in its service areas with a population of approximately 50,000. Corning Natural Gas has sold its non-regulated businesses, including its gas appliances unit, and its mortgage and retail property leasing concerns, and it has discontinued the operations of its accounting and tax preparation unit, Tax Center International.

	Annual Growth	9/03	9/04	9/05	9/06	9/07
Sales ($ mil.)	(1.2%)	25.5	22.0	22.9	26.9	24.3
Net income ($ mil.)	—	(0.1)	0.6	0.6	(3.6)	0.3
Market value ($ mil.)	18.2%	6.8	5.2	7.8	8.1	13.2
Employees	—	—	—	—	—	—

THE CORPORATE EXECUTIVE BOARD COMPANY

NASDAQ (GS): EXBD

1919 N. Lynn St.
Arlington, VA 22209
Phone: 571-303-3000
Fax: 571-303-5014
Web: www.executiveboard.com

CEO: Thomas L. Monahan III
CFO: Timothy R. (Tim) Yost
HR: Melody L. Jones
FYE: December 31
Type: Public

Don't fear the competition; learn from them. So says The Corporate Executive Board Company (CEB), a provider of business research and analysis services to more than 4,700 companies worldwide. Its 40-plus program areas cover "best practices" in such areas as finance, human resources, information technology, operations, and sales and marketing. Unlike consulting firms, which engage with one client at a time, CEB operates on a membership-based business model. Members subscribe to one or more of the company's programs and participate in the research and analysis, thus sharing expertise with others. Besides reports on best practices, CEB offers seminars, customized research briefs, and decision-support tools.

	Annual Growth	12/03	12/04	12/05	12/06	12/07
Sales ($ mil.)	26.2%	210.2	280.7	362.2	460.6	532.7
Net income ($ mil.)	22.6%	35.7	53.7	75.1	79.2	80.6
Market value ($ mil.)	4.7%	1,740.0	2,606.0	3,541.6	3,415.7	2,088.7
Employees	22.2%	—	—	1,865	2,279	—

CORPORATE EXPRESS US, INC.

1 Environmental Way
Broomfield, CO 80021
Phone: 303-664-2000
Fax: 303-664-3474
Web: www.corporateexpress.com

CEO: Jay Mutschler
CFO: Robert VanHees
HR: –
FYE: December 31
Type: Subsidiary

This firm knows that office supplies can go fast when business is booming. Corporate Express is a top North American wholesale distributor of office products and equipment, including furniture, stationery, and storage systems. It provides computer equipment and software, copiers, data storage systems, printers, and supplies. Corporate Express offers business forms, labels, and document management services, as well as promotional products and apparel. A unit of Corporate Express NV, it operates through about 200 North American facilities, including approximately 50 distribution centers. The firm's Dutch parent has agreed to be acquired by US office products giant Staples for about $2.7 billion.

	Annual Growth	12/03	12/04	12/05	12/06	12/07
Sales ($ mil.)	2.6%	3,939.0	3,628.0	4,369.0	4,900.0	4,367.1
Employees	(1.8%)	10,775	10,544	10,000	10,000	10,000

CORPORATE OFFICE PROPERTIES TRUST

NYSE: OFC

6711 Columbia Gateway Dr., Ste. 300
Columbia, MD 21046
Phone: 443-285-5400
Fax: 443-285-7650
Web: www.copt.com

CEO: Randall M. (Rand) Griffin
CFO: Stephen E. Riffee
HR: Peg Ohrt
FYE: December 31
Type: Public

The name says "corporate" but it's really about government. A self-managed real estate investment trust (REIT), Corporate Office Properties Trust develops and operates suburban office buildings, most leased to the federal government and defense contractors. It owns about 220 properties totaling more than 17 million sq. ft. in Colorado, Maryland, New Jersey, Pennsylvania, Texas, and Virginia. It also has some 20 office properties under development, about 1,500 undeveloped acres, and interests in various other properties. Its biggest tenant is the US government, which accounts for 16% of the rent. Other top tenants include Booz Allen Hamilton, Computer Sciences Corporation, and Northrop Grumman.

	Annual Growth	12/03	12/04	12/05	12/06	12/07
Sales ($ mil.)	18.8%	206.2	243.5	329.1	361.4	410.2
Net income ($ mil.)	3.0%	30.9	37.0	39.0	49.2	34.8
Market value ($ mil.)	24.7%	617.3	1,081.3	1,419.0	2,165.0	1,492.0
Employees	—	—	—	257	—	—

CORRECTIONS CORPORATION OF AMERICA

NYSE: CXW

10 Burton Hills Blvd.
Nashville, TN 37215
Phone: 615-263-3000
Fax: 615-263-3140
Web: www.correctionscorp.com

CEO: John D. Ferguson
CFO: Todd J. Mullenger
HR: William K. (Bill) Rusak
FYE: December 31
Type: Public

Corrections Corporation of America (CCA) has locked up a big share of the private prison market. The company operates more than 60 correctional, detention, and juvenile facilities with a capacity of some 78,000 beds in about 20 states and Washington, DC. CCA contracts with federal, state, and local authorities to manage the facilities, about 40 of which are company-owned. CCA also owns three facilities that are managed by other companies. Federal correctional and detention authorities account for 40% of CCA's sales. The company provides rehabilitation and education programs for inmates of its facilities.

	Annual Growth	12/03	12/04	12/05	12/06	12/07
Sales ($ mil.)	9.3%	1,036.7	1,148.3	1,192.6	1,331.1	1,478.8
Net income ($ mil.)	(1.5%)	141.8	62.5	50.1	105.2	133.4
Market value ($ mil.)	81.8%	336.5	477.5	595.0	1,380.5	3,673.2
Employees	3.2%	—	—	15,500	16,000	—

CORRPRO COMPANIES, INC.

Pink Sheets: CRRP

1090 Enterprise Dr.
Medina, OH 44256
Phone: 330-723-5082
Fax: 330-723-0694
Web: www.corrpro.com

CEO: William V. Larkin Jr.
CFO: Robert M. Mayer
HR: –
FYE: March 31
Type: Public

Rust never sleeps, and neither does Corrpro. Founded in 1984, Corrpro provides corrosion control services to the energy, environmental, and infrastructure industries through offices worldwide. Specializing in cathodic protection systems (an electrochemical process that prevents and retards rust), Corrpro treats bridges, offshore oil platforms, pipelines, ships, storage tanks, and water-treatment equipment for its customers. It also treats and repairs other steel-reinforced structures that are prone to corrosion. Corrpro maintains research and testing labs, offers engineering and remote monitoring services, and sells related materials and equipment, including protective coatings.

	Annual Growth	3/03	3/04	3/05	3/06	3/07
Sales ($ mil.)	10.8%	104.2	130.1	134.6	139.7	156.8
Net income ($ mil.)	—	(28.8)	(5.5)	8.5	(4.7)	2.8
Employees	—	—	—	716	—	—

CORTELCO SYSTEMS PUERTO RICO, INC.

OTC: CPROF

Parque Industrial Caguas Oeste, Rd. 156, Km 58.2, Valle Tomlina
Caguas, PR 00727
Phone: 787-785-0000
Fax: 787-281-1752

CEO: Juan Carlos Ramos
CFO: Francisco Sanchez
HR: –
FYE: July 31
Type: Public

Cortelco Systems Puerto Rico (CSPR) sells, installs, and services voice and data telecommunications equipment, including PBX, call center, and Voice over Internet Protocol (VoIP) systems. The company does most of its business in Puerto Rico, but has operations elsewhere in the Caribbean and Latin America. CSPR was spun off from eOn Communications in 2002. eOn chairman and CEO David Lee owns a 51% stake in the company.

	Annual Growth	7/03	7/04	7/05	7/06	7/07
Sales ($ mil.)	0.3%	7.7	7.3	7.4	7.4	7.8
Net income ($ mil.)	—	(1.8)	(1.5)	0.0	0.2	0.1
Market value ($ mil.)	—	—	—	—	—	1.3
Employees	—	—	—	—	—	64

CORTEX PHARMACEUTICALS, INC.

AMEX: COR

15241 Barranca Pkwy.
Irvine, CA 92618
Phone: 949-727-3157
Fax: 949-727-3657
Web: www.cortexpharm.com

CEO: Roger G. Stoll
CFO: Maria S. Messinger
HR: –
FYE: December 31
Type: Public

Cortex Pharmaceuticals develops drugs to treat neurodegenerative and psychiatric disorders. Its research focuses on the AMPA receptor, which facilitates communication between nerve cells; the firm's Ampakine compounds may enhance this receptor's activity. Its lead drug candidate is CX717, which it is developing for a number of indications including respiratory depression (a potentially fatal side effect of some anesthetics and post-surgical painkillers), Alzheimer's disease, attention deficit hyperactivity disorder (ADHD), and daytime sleepiness. The firm believes Ampakine drugs may also be helpful in treating a variety of other brain-related disorders, including depression, autism, and Huntington's disease.

	Annual Growth	6/03	6/04	*12/04	12/05	†12/06
Sales ($ mil.)	(30.7%)	5.2	7.0	1.9	2.6	1.2
Net income ($ mil.)	—	(1.2)	(6.0)	(4.1)	(11.6)	(16.0)
Market value ($ mil.)	4.1%	37.2	74.0	—	74.8	43.7
Employees	0.0%	25	24	23	26	25

*Fiscal year change   †Most recent year available

CORTLAND BANCORP

OTC: CLDB

194 W. Main St.
Cortland, OH 44410
Phone: 330-637-8040
Fax: 330-638-3018
Web: www.cortland-banks.com

CEO: Lawrence A. Fantauzzi
CFO: James M. Gasior
HR: Stephen A. Telego Sr.
FYE: December 31
Type: Public

Cortland Bancorp is the place to keep your bucks in the Buckeye State. Cortland Bancorp is the holding company for Cortland Savings and Banking Company (aka Cortland Banks), a community-oriented institution serving northeastern Ohio from a baker's dozen banking locations. Cortland Banks offers standard banking services including checking and savings accounts, debit cards, and commercial and consumer loans and mortgages. Other offerings include discount brokerage and trust services. The company originates commercial (more than 50% of its loan portfolio), consumer, and home equity loans.

	Annual Growth	12/03	12/04	12/05	12/06	12/07
Assets ($ mil.)	3.0%	438.4	446.4	459.7	471.8	492.7
Net income ($ mil.)	(6.0%)	5.5	4.8	4.3	4.6	4.3
Market value ($ mil.)	(16.2%)	107.0	90.4	77.0	81.3	52.9
Employees	—	—	—	—	—	177

CORUS BANKSHARES, INC.

NASDAQ (GS): CORS

3959 N. Lincoln Ave.
Chicago, IL 60613
Phone: 800-555-5710
Fax: 773-832-3460
Web: www.corusbank.com

CEO: Robert J. Glickman
CFO: Timothy H. (Tim) Taylor
HR: Jennifer Haughey
FYE: December 31
Type: Public

Money is at the heart of the matter for Corus Bankshares, the holding company for Corus Bank, which operates about a dozen branches in the Chicago metropolitan area. The bank offers consumers and businesses traditional retail banking products, such as checking, savings, money market, and time deposit accounts. Its primary emphasis is on commercial real estate loans (especially condominium construction) which make up around 98% of its loan portfolio. In Chicago and Milwaukee, Corus Bankshares provides clearing, depository, and credit services to nearly 500 check-cashing businesses.

	Annual Growth	12/03	12/04	12/05	12/06	12/07
Assets ($ mil.)	25.1%	3,643.8	5,017.8	8,458.7	10,057.8	8,926.6
Net income ($ mil.)	16.1%	58.4	97.9	137.2	189.4	106.2
Market value ($ mil.)	7.8%	434.9	667.2	785.7	1,297.6	587.0
Employees	0.1%	—	—	519	534	520

⊞ CORVEL CORPORATION

NASDAQ (GS): CRVL

2010 Main St., Ste. 600
Irvine, CA 92614
Phone: 949-851-1473
Fax: 949-851-1469
Web: www.corvel.com

CEO: Daniel J. Starck
CFO: Scott R. McCloud
HR: Sharon O'Connor
FYE: March 31
Type: Public

CorVel has carved out a niche providing medical cost containment for workers' compensation programs, group health plans, and auto insurers. CorVel helps insurers, third-party administrators, and self-insured employers keep down medical costs associated with workers' compensation claims and get employees back on the job as soon as is practicable. Among other things, CorVel reviews medical bills to make sure they are in line with state fee schedules, using its automated online MedCheck software. It also maintains a preferred provider organization (PPO) and provides case management and vocational rehabilitation services. Clients access CorVel's range of services through its CareMC Web portal.

	Annual Growth	3/04	3/05	3/06	3/07	3/08
Assets ($ mil.)	7.2%	106.3	105.3	100.1	113.8	140.6
Net income ($ mil.)	10.0%	16.0	10.2	9.8	18.6	23.4
Market value ($ mil.)	13.4%	255.6	143.2	138.2	422.5	421.9
Employees	(6.0%)	—	2,980	2,323	2,631	—

CORVU CORPORATION

Pink Sheets: CRVU

3400 W. 66th St., Ste. 445
Edina, MN 55435
Phone: 952-944-7777
Fax: 952-944-7447
Web: www.corvu.com

CEO: Justin M. MacIntosh
CFO: –
HR: –
FYE: June 30
Type: Public

CorVu helps its customers see inside their businesses. The company offers balanced scorecard and performance management software that enables clients to identify business trends and measure performance based on corporate data. Products include CorBusiness (graphical data analysis, reporting, and performance alerts) and CorStrategy (risk management, budgeting, performance management, forecasting, and strategic modeling). CorVu also offers its RapidROI services program, which includes consulting, design, implementation, performance tuning, and training.

	Annual Growth	6/02	6/03	6/04	6/05	*6/06
Sales ($ mil.)	5.8%	12.3	15.7	16.2	13.2	15.4
Net income ($ mil.)	31.6%	0.4	3.7	(2.1)	(6.6)	1.2
Employees	—	—	—	—	—	—

*Most recent year available

⊞ An in-depth profile of this company is available to Hoover's Online members at hoovers.com.

439

COSI, INC.

NASDAQ (GM): COSI

1751 Lake Cook Rd., Ste. 600
Deerfield, IL 60015
Phone: 847-597-8800
Fax: 847-597-8884
Web: www.getcosi.com

CEO: James F. (Jim) Hyatt
CFO: William E. (Bill) Koziel
HR: Becky Iliff
FYE: Monday nearest December 31
Type: Public

Cosi's recipe calls for one part coffee house, one part sandwich shop, and one part cocktail bar. The company operates and franchises more than 140 eclectic Così cafés in about 20 states offering premium and specialty coffees and made-to-order sandwiches. Its menu also features breakfast items (including its bagel-inspired Squagels), salads, soups, and desserts. Most of the company's restaurants also offer dinner and drinks after 5 p.m., while its Così Downtown units (primarily located in non-residential business districts) close in the evening. Così also offers delivery and catering services. More than 100 locations are company owned while the rest are franchised.

	Annual Growth	12/03	12/04	12/05	12/06	12/07
Sales ($ mil.)	5.8%	107.3	110.6	117.2	126.9	134.6
Net income ($ mil.)	—	(26.6)	(18.4)	(13.1)	(12.3)	(20.8)
Market value ($ mil.)	11.4%	59.3	187.7	319.4	201.9	91.4
Employees	—	—	—	2,727	—	—

COSINE COMMUNICATIONS, INC.

Pink Sheets: COSN

61 E. Main
Los Gatos, CA 95030
Phone: 408-399-6494
Fax: 408-399-6491
Web: www.cosinecom.com

CEO: Terry R. Gibson
CFO: Terry R. Gibson
HR: —
FYE: December 31
Type: Public

CoSine Communications is trying to switch businesses. The company was a manufacturer of switches and software that telecom service providers used to manage their Internet protocol networks, but the company shuttered its operations and ceased its support services in 2004. CoSine had agreed to be acquired by telecom equipment maker Tut Systems, but the deal fell through in 2005. CoSine is seeking to acquire an operating business. Steel Partners controls about 45% of the company.

	Annual Growth	12/02	12/03	12/04	12/05	*12/06
Sales ($ mil.)	(50.6%)	23.6	14.6	9.7	3.3	1.4
Net income ($ mil.)	—	(94.0)	(34.9)	(37.3)	(1.2)	0.4
Employees	(72.0%)	163	5	0	1	1

*Most recent year available

COSMETIC ESSENCE, INC.

2182 Rte. 35 South
Holmdel, NJ 07733
Phone: 732-888-7788
Fax: 732-888-6086
Web: www.cosmeticessence.com

CEO: John Croddick Sr.
CFO: Joe Atencio
HR: —
FYE: December 31
Type: Subsidiary

Time isn't the only thing that is of the essence in the world of cosmetics. A contract manufacturer catering to the personal care products industry, Cosmetic Essence specializes in product formulation and manufacturing, contract filling of alcohol-based products, packaging, and distribution. Its products, which include color cosmetics, cremes, fragrances, and lotions, are distributed to leading branded manufacturers and major retailers nationwide. Cosmetic Essence is owned by Onex Corporation.

	Annual Growth	12/03	12/04	12/05	12/06	12/07
Est. sales ($ mil.)	—	—	—	—	—	167.0
Employees	—	—	—	—	—	1,400

COST PLUS, INC.

NASDAQ (GS): CPWM

200 4th St.
Oakland, CA 94607
Phone: 510-893-7300
Fax: 510-893-3681
Web: www.costplusworldmarket.com

CEO: Barry J. Feld
CFO: Jane L. Baughman
HR: Joan S. Fujii
FYE: Saturday nearest January 31
Type: Public

Cost Plus adorns dining rooms and picnics with wicker, wine, and cheese. The retailer's some 300 Cost Plus World Market and World Market stores sell furniture, rugs, baskets, and ceramics, as well as exotic food and beverages. Designed to resemble upscale world markets, Cost Plus' stores are located near major malls in about 35 states. The company targets women between the ages of 22 and 55. Much of what it sells is imported from more than 50 countries; many of its 10,000-plus items are proprietary and are sold under its World Market private label. Some of the first Cost Plus franchises renamed themselves to launch Pier 1 Imports, and a rivalry was born. Indeed, in mid-2008 Pier 1 bid to acquire Cost Plus.

	Annual Growth	1/04	1/05	1/06	1/07	1/08
Sales ($ mil.)	6.3%	801.6	908.6	970.4	1,040.3	1,023.9
Net income ($ mil.)	—	33.0	30.2	20.2	(22.5)	(55.5)
Market value ($ mil.)	(44.0%)	947.3	575.3	442.1	233.2	93.2
Employees	4.2%	—	—	6,170	6,741	6,705

COSTAR GROUP, INC.

NASDAQ (GS): CSGP

2 Bethesda Metro Center, 10th Fl.
Bethesda, MD 20814
Phone: 301-215-8300
Fax: 301-718-2444
Web: www.costar.com

CEO: Andrew C. Florance
CFO: Brian J. Radecki
HR: Lauren Fitzgerald
FYE: December 31
Type: Public

CoStar has all the dirt on the commercial real estate industry. A provider of commercial real estate information, CoStar has a proprietary database of some 2.7 million properties in the US, the UK, and France. The database contains information on nearly 67 billion sq. ft. of available space, including 7 billion sq. ft. of sale and lease listings. It also has more than 5 million digital images of buildings, floor plans, and maps. CoStar also offers property research, tenant profiling, and its *CoStar Advisor* newsletter. Clients include government agencies, real estate brokerages, real estate investment trusts (REITs), and property owners and managers.

	Annual Growth	12/03	12/04	12/05	12/06	12/07
Sales ($ mil.)	19.3%	95.1	112.1	134.3	158.9	192.8
Net income ($ mil.)	255.1%	0.1	25.0	6.5	12.4	15.9
Market value ($ mil.)	5.4%	745.5	845.2	806.2	1,022.0	920.1
Employees	21.6%	—	—	1,076	1,308	—

COSTCO WHOLESALE CORPORATION

NASDAQ (GS): COST

999 Lake Dr.
Issaquah, WA 98027
Phone: 425-313-8100
Fax: —
Web: www.costco.com

CEO: James D. (Jim) Sinegal
CFO: Richard A. Galanti
HR: John Matthews
FYE: Sunday nearest August 31
Type: Public

Wal-Mart isn't the biggest in *every* business. Costco Wholesale is the largest wholesale club operator in the US (ahead of Wal-Mart's SAM'S CLUB). The company operates about 530 membership warehouse stores serving more than 50 million cardholders in 40 US states and Puerto Rico, Canada, Japan, Mexico, South Korea, Taiwan, and the UK, primarily under the Costco Wholesale name. Stores offer discount prices on an average of about 4,000 products (many in bulk packaging), ranging from alcoholic beverages and appliances to fresh food, pharmaceuticals, and tires. Certain club memberships also offer products and services such as car and home insurance, mortgage and real estate services, and travel packages.

	Annual Growth	8/03	8/04	8/05	8/06	8/07
Sales ($ mil.)	10.9%	42,545.6	48,107.0	52,935.2	60,151.2	64,400.2
Net income ($ mil.)	10.7%	721.0	882.4	1,063.1	1,103.2	1,082.8
Market value ($ mil.)	16.3%	14,753.7	19,453.9	20,373.3	21,888.9	26,985.6
Employees	3.7%	—	—	118,000	127,000	127,000

COST-U-LESS, INC.

3633 136th Place SE, Ste. 110
Bellevue, WA 98006
Phone: 425-945-0213
Fax: 425-945-0214
Web: www.costuless.com

CEO: J. Jeffrey (Jeff) Meder
CFO: Martin P. Moore
HR: –
FYE: Last Sunday in December
Type: Private

Cost-U-Less hopes it lives up to its name. The company runs nearly a dozen warehouse club stores on remote island locations to avoid heavy competition. The stores (averaging 32,000 sq. ft.) are found on islands such as American Samoa, Fiji, Guam, Hawaii, Netherlands Antilles, and the US Virgin Islands, as well as one mainland store in Sonora, California. With no membership fees, locals can buy US brand-name and ethnic beverages, candy, snacks, meat, produce, frozen foods, tobacco, health and beauty aids, office products, electronics, housewares, and sporting goods. Cost-U-Less opened its first outlet in 1989 in Maui, Hawaii.

	Annual Growth	12/02	12/03	12/04	12/05	12/06
Sales ($ mil.)	5.9%	176.2	177.1	209.4	219.4	222.0
Net income ($ mil.)	73.2%	0.3	1.4	2.7	3.0	2.7
Employees	6.3%	500	—	—	600	—

🔲 COTT CORPORATION

NYSE: COT

5519 W. Idlewild Ave.
Tampa, FL 33634
Phone: 813-313-1800
Fax: –
Web: www.cott.com

CEO: David T. (Dave) Gibbons
CFO: Juan Figuereo
HR: Abilio Gonzales
FYE: Saturday nearest December 31
Type: Public

Cott is sweet on its customers. The company is a leading producer of store-brand carbonated beverages in Canada, the UK, and the US. In addition to soda, Cott Corporation makes bottled water, juices, ready-to-drink teas, and energy and sports drinks. The company produces, packages, and distributes more than 75 retailer-, licensed-, and Cott Corporation-owned brand soft-drink beverages for grocery, mass-merchandise, drugstore, and convenience store chain customers, as well as wholesalers. Cott operates 15 beverage production facilities in North America and six overseas. Its products are sold in some 60 countries worldwide.

	Annual Growth	12/03	12/04	12/05	12/06	12/07
Sales ($ mil.)	5.8%	1,417.8	1,646.3	1,755.3	1,771.8	1,776.4
Net income ($ mil.)	—	77.4	78.3	24.6	(17.5)	(71.4)
Market value ($ mil.)	(29.8%)	1,989.7	1,766.7	1,054.2	1,026.7	483.0
Employees	(9.2%)	—	—	3,484	3,163	—

COTTON INCORPORATED

6399 Weston Pkwy.
Cary, NC 27513
Phone: 919-678-2220
Fax: 919-678-2230
Web: www.cottoninc.com

CEO: J. Berrye Worsham III
CFO: David N. Byrd
HR: Angie Moe
FYE: December 31
Type: Association

Battling both boll weevils and synthetic fibers, Cotton Incorporated bolsters the US cotton industry through its research and marketing efforts. To the public, Cotton Inc. is known for its white-on-brown "Seal of Cotton" logo — recognized by about 75% of Americans — and its (now retired) advertising slogan, "The fabric of our lives." Founded in 1970, Cotton Inc. is funded by growers of upland cotton, cotton importers, and cotton-product makers. Its board consists of 55 members and 55 alternates, all of whom are cotton producers. They represent more than 30,000 producers in 18 states. The company has international offices throughout the world. Cotton Inc. is overseen by the US Department of Agriculture.

	Annual Growth	12/03	12/04	12/05	12/06	12/07
Est. sales ($ mil.)	—	—	—	—	—	72.6
Employees	—	—	—	—	—	157

COTY INC.

2 Park Ave.
New York, NY 10016
Phone: 212-479-4300
Fax: 212-479-4399
Web: www.coty.com

CEO: Bernd Beetz
CFO: Michael Fishoff
HR: Géraud-Marie Lacassagne
FYE: June 30
Type: Subsidiary

Sarah Jessica Parker, J.Lo, and Celine Dion all go to Coty to smell good. It is the world's leading maker of mass-market fragrances for men and women. Coty scents have turned heads since François Coty created his first perfume, La Rose Jacqueminot, in 1904. Its boudoir includes moderately priced fragrances and colognes sold by mass retailers and prestige brands found in department stores. Coty's brands include Jennifer Lopez, JOOP!, Jovan, Rimmel, Stetson, and Vivienne Westwood. The company also offers aromatherapy, foot care, nail care, oral care, and sun care items. German consumer goods giant Joh. A. Benckiser GmbH acquired Coty in 1996 to operate its fragrance and cosmetics businesses.

	Annual Growth	6/02	6/03	6/04	6/05	6/06
Sales ($ mil.)	—	—	—	—	—	2,900.0
Employees	—	—	—	—	—	—

COUNTRY COACH INC.

135 E 1st Ave.
Junction City, OR 97448
Phone: 541-998-3720
Fax: –
Web: www.countrycoach.com

CEO: Jay Howard
CFO: Mark D. Andersen
HR: Janet Kehoe
FYE: December 31
Type: Private

Country Coach is no horse-and-buggy operation. Country Coach manufactures diesel-powered motor home models such as Affinity, Allure, Inspire, Intrigue, and Magna, as well as bus conversions under the Country Coach Prevost brand. The company's models range 34 to 45 feet in length and offer a variety of floorplans, including multiple slide-out options. With the exception of the Prevost Conversion, all Country Coach RVs are built on the company's proprietary DynoMax chassis. Riley Investment Management acquired Country Coach from National R.V. Holdings for $52 million in early 2007.

	Annual Growth	12/03	12/04	12/05	12/06	12/07
Est. sales ($ mil.)	—	—	—	—	—	187.5
Employees	—	—	—	—	—	1,500

COUNTRY FINANCIAL

1711 GE Rd.
Bloomington, IL 61702
Phone: 309-821-3000
Fax: 309-821-5160
Web: www.countryfinancial.com

CEO: John D. Blackburn
CFO: David A. Magers
HR: Deanna L. Frautschi
FYE: December 31
Type: Private

Shout it out loud: COUNTRY Financial (formerly COUNTRY Insurance & Financial Services) provides exactly that ALL OVER THE COUNTRY. The company provides life, property/casualty, farm and ranch, disability, and other traditional insurance products. Its COUNTRY Trust Bank also offers services and products such as retirement planning, investment advice, asset management, and mutual funds. The company focuses on farm-related products, including crop insurance and farm vehicle policies. COUNTRY traces its roots back to 1925, when a group of agricultural workers created a fire and lightning insurance company.

🔲 An in-depth profile of this company is available to Hoover's Online members at hoovers.com.

441

COUNTRYWIDE FINANCIAL CORPORATION

NYSE: CFC

4500 Park Granada
Calabasas, CA 91302
Phone: 818-225-3000
Fax: 818-225-4051
Web: www.countrywide.com

CEO: Angelo R. Mozilo
CFO: Eric P. Sieracki
HR: Leora I. Goren
FYE: December 31
Type: Public

Countrywide Financial gives credit where credit is due. One of the top independent residential mortgage lending firms in the US (it is the #3 lender by loan volume), the company writes, sells, and services single-family home mortgages through its Countrywide Bank (about 90% of its mortgage activity) and Countrywide Home Loans subsidiaries. It also offers home equity loans, commercial mortgages, and subprime mortgages. Its capital markets segment buys and sells mortgages and offers asset management and brokerage services. It provides life, property/casualty, and reinsurance products through Balboa Insurance Group. The company has some 660 branches in the US. Bank of America is buying Countrywide.

	Annual Growth	12/03	12/04	12/05	12/06	12/07
Assets ($ mil.)	21.3%	97,949.8	128,495.7	175,085.4	199,946.2	211,730.1
Net income ($ mil.)	—	2,372.9	2,197.6	2,528.1	2,674.9	(703.5)
Market value ($ mil.)	2.8%	4,664.5	21,526.8	20,515.0	24,841.0	5,215.1
Employees	10.2%	34,298	42,141	54,456	54,655	50,600

COURIER CORPORATION

NASDAQ (GS): CRRC

15 Wellman Ave.
N. Chelmsford, MA 01863
Phone: 978-251-6000
Fax: 978-251-8228
Web: www.courier.com

CEO: James F. Conway III
CFO: Peter M. Folger
HR: —
FYE: Last Saturday in September
Type: Public

Courier dispatches books for playing, praying, and puzzling over. One of the largest book printers in the US, Courier manufactures a variety of books for educational, religious, and specialty trade publishers and organizations. The company's book printing operations, which account for more than 75% of Courier's sales, produce more than 175 million books per year and serve more than 500 customers; its largest clients include Bible distributor The Gideons International (about 20% of sales) and publishing giant Pearson (about 16% of sales). A book publisher itself, Courier offers books for niche markets through subsidiaries Creative Homeowner, Dover Publications, and Research & Education Association.

	Annual Growth	9/03	9/04	9/05	9/06	9/07
Sales ($ mil.)	9.9%	202.0	211.2	227.0	269.0	294.6
Net income ($ mil.)	6.3%	20.1	20.5	22.1	28.4	25.7
Market value ($ mil.)	25.1%	181.5	220.7	428.5	462.2	444.1
Employees	11.2%	—	—	1,479	—	1,830

COURION CORPORATION

1881 Worcester Rd.
Framingham, MA 01701
Phone: 508-879-8400
Fax: 508-879-8500
Web: www.courion.com

CEO: Christopher Zannetos
CFO: Robert P. (Bob) Cirrone
HR: —
FYE: December 31
Type: Private

Courion definitely identifies with the need for good security. The company provides identity management software for administering security features such as passwords, user profiles, and digital certificates. Courion's software helps companies such as Hewitt Associates, Boeing, and Target set security policies, maintain authentication information in corporate directories, and manage user authentication and account provisioning. Courion's software includes self-service features and encompasses interactions with employees, customers, and trading partners.

	Annual Growth	12/03	12/04	12/05	12/06	12/07
Est. sales ($ mil.)	—	—	—	—	—	16.1
Employees	—	—	—	—	—	88

COURT SQUARE CAPITAL PARTNERS

Park Avenue Plaza, 55 E. 52nd St., 34th Fl.
New York, NY 10055
Phone: 212-752-6110
Fax: 212-752-6184
Web: www.courtsquare.com

CEO: Dave Thomas
CFO: —
HR: —
FYE: December 31
Type: Private

Court Square Capital Partners (formerly Citicorp Venture Capital) is courting technology and manufacturing companies. Spun off from Citigroup in 2006, the private equity and venture capital firm specializes in leveraged buyouts of middle-market companies. It manages approximately $6 billion of capital commitments. (In order to avoid potential conflicts of interest with its customers or its other investment funds, Citigroup no longer has any equity invested in the company.) Court Street Capital owns stakes in enterprises such as specialty chemicals firm MacDermid, telecommunications services provider NTELOS, and information technology management company CompuCom Systems (acquired in 2007).

	Annual Growth	12/03	12/04	12/05	12/06	12/07
Est. sales ($ mil.)	—	—	—	—	—	415.0
Employees	—	—	—	—	—	2,900

COUSINS PROPERTIES INCORPORATED

NYSE: CUZ

191 Peachtree St. NE, Ste. 3600
Atlanta, GA 90909
Phone: 404-407-1000
Fax: 404-407-1002
Web: www.cousinsproperties.com

CEO: Thomas D. (Tom) Bell Jr.
CFO: James A. (Jim) Fleming
HR: —
FYE: December 31
Type: Public

Cousins Properties manages a *primo* brood of office, multi-family, retail, and industrial holdings. The real estate investment trust (REIT) invests in, develops, and manages commercial properties, primarily in the Southeast US. Its portfolio (some of which is owned through joint ventures) includes some 20 office/medical buildings with 5 million sq. ft. of leasable space, about a dozen shopping centers, and a handful of industrial properties. Most properties are located in Atlanta; other core markets include California, Florida, and Texas. Bank of America, Coca-Cola, and IBM are among its major tenants. Retired chairman and founder Thomas Cousins is the company's largest shareholder with a 15% stake.

	Annual Growth	12/03	12/04	12/05	12/06	12/07
Sales ($ mil.)	4.9%	136.6	136.8	155.7	169.9	165.4
Net income ($ mil.)	(39.3%)	242.2	407.8	49.7	232.7	32.9
Market value ($ mil.)	(6.7%)	1,494.4	1,516.3	1,433.8	1,825.1	1,133.3
Employees	2.4%	—	—	448	488	470

COVAD COMMUNICATIONS GROUP, INC.

110 Rio Robles
San Jose, CA 95134
Phone: 408-952-6400
Fax: 408-952-7687
Web: www.covad.com

CEO: Patrick J. (Pat) Bennett
CFO: Justin Spencer
HR: —
FYE: December 31
Type: Private

Covad Communications converts conventional copper wires for quick connectivity. The company uses digital subscriber line (DSL) and T-1 technologies to provide broadband Internet access largely on a wholesale basis to customers in 235 metropolitan markets spanning 44 US states. Covad's main customers are Internet service providers (ISPs) — such as EarthLink, AT&T, and AOL — and other resellers. In addition to its wholesale business, the company offers wired and wireless broadband access and Voice over Internet Protocol (VoIP) service directly to small and midsized businesses. Covad is owned by private buyout specialist Platinum Equity.

	Annual Growth	12/03	12/04	12/05	12/06	12/07
Sales ($ mil.)	5.6%	388.9	429.2	443.2	474.3	484.2
Net income ($ mil.)	—	(112.3)	(60.8)	(15.7)	(13.9)	(43.0)
Employees	(7.5%)	—	—	1,045	967	

COVANCE INC.

NYSE: CVD

210 Carnegie Center
Princeton, NJ 08540
Phone: 609-452-4440
Fax: 609-452-9375
Web: www.covance.com

CEO: Joseph L. (Joe) Herring
CFO: William E. Klitgaard
HR: Donald Kraft
FYE: December 31
Type: Public

Behind every great drug company stands a great contract research organization (CRO), and Covance is one of the biggest. Covance helps pharmaceutical and biotech companies develop new drugs, providing preclinical testing services, as well as designing and carrying out human clinical trials to determine if the drugs are safe and effective. Services include toxicology studies, biostatistical analysis, clinical laboratory testing, and post-marketing studies. Among the company's customers are pharmaceutical, biotech, and medical device companies; Covance also offers laboratory testing services to companies in the chemical, agrochemical, and food industries.

	Annual Growth	12/03	12/04	12/05	12/06	12/07
Sales ($ mil.)	13.8%	974.2	1,056.4	1,250.4	1,406.1	1,631.5
Net income ($ mil.)	23.3%	76.1	97.9	119.6	145.0	175.9
Market value ($ mil.)	34.9%	1,675.7	2,412.6	3,049.4	4,325.6	5,547.3
Employees	9.2%	—	—	7,300	8,100	8,700

COVANSYS CORPORATION

32605 W. Twelve Mile Rd.
Farmington Hills, MI 48334
Phone: 248-488-2088
Fax: 248-488-2089
Web: www.covansys.com

CEO: Rajendra B. (Raj) Vattikuti
CFO: James S. Trouba
HR: Ganapathy (Ravi) Ravindran
FYE: December 31
Type: Subsidiary

Covansys wants its customers to get the best out of their computer systems. The company provides a variety of information technology (IT) services — including software development, systems integration, and packaged software implementation — primarily to midsized clients in the financial services, health care, manufacturing, retail, and utility industries. Covansys primarily operates from software development and training centers in India; the company also has administrative operations in the US. The company is a subsidiary of Computer Sciences Corp.

	Annual Growth	12/02	12/03	12/04	12/05	12/06
Sales ($ mil.)	4.4%	383.0	378.6	374.4	434.1	455.5
Net income ($ mil.)	74.2%	3.9	9.9	17.5	37.5	35.9
Employees	17.5%	4,404	4,701	5,804	6,800	8,400

COVANTA ENERGY CORPORATION

40 Lane Rd.
Fairfield, NJ 07004
Phone: 973-882-9000
Fax: 973-882-7234
Web: www.covantaholding.com/site/about/company.html

CEO: Anthony J. (Tony) Orlando
CFO: Mark A. Pytosh
HR: Robert T. Monteleone
FYE: December 31
Type: Subsidiary

The power ball is back in Covanta Energy's court. The major operating arm of Covanta Holding, the power producer has interests in 57 power plants located in the Americas, Asia, and Europe. Its plants use a variety of fuels, including municipal solid waste, wood waste (biomass), landfill gas, water (hydroelectric), natural gas, coal, and heavy fuel. Covanta Energy has 34 waste-to-energy plants in the US. These specialized plants can convert 15 million tons of waste into more than 8 million MW hours of electricity annually and create 10 billion pounds of steam that are sold to a variety of industries.

COVANTA HOLDING CORPORATION

NYSE: CVA

40 Lane Rd.
Fairfield, NJ 07004
Phone: 973-882-9000
Fax: 973-882-7076
Web: www.covantaholding.com

CEO: Anthony J. (Tony) Orlando
CFO: Mark A. Pytosh
HR: –
FYE: December 31
Type: Public

Covanta Holding has seen the light: Through several strategic acquisitions (including Covanta Energy), the former insurance-focused company has made itself a leader in the waste and energy services markets. The company owns or operates 57 energy generation facilities (47 in the US). It also collects municipal waste and uses said waste in more than 30 waste-to-energy facilities in the US. Covanta Holding writes policies for automobile drivers through its National American Insurance Company of California subsidiary. Chairman Samuel Zell holds 21% of the company through his SZ Investments unit.

	Annual Growth	12/03	12/04	12/05	12/06	12/07
Sales ($ mil.)	140.8%	42.6	578.6	978.8	1,268.5	1,433.1
Net income ($ mil.)	—	(69.2)	34.1	59.3	105.8	130.5
Market value ($ mil.)	41.5%	—	—	2,126.0	3,250.9	4,257.5
Employees	(1.4%)	—	—	3,600	3,300	3,500

COVENANT HEALTH

100 Fort Sanders West Blvd.
Knoxville, TN 37922
Phone: 865-374-1000
Fax: 865-531-5272
Web: www.covenanthealth.com

CEO: Tony Spezia
CFO: John Geppi
HR: Sam Buschetta
FYE: December 31
Type: Not-for-profit

Covenant Health is an integrated not-for-profit health care system that serves eastern Tennessee. Covenant Health has five acute care hospitals, a psychiatric hospital, two rehabilitation centers, three home health care agencies, a childcare facility, a nursing home, and a physician practice management company. Covenant Health also provides health insurance to more than 150,000 members in east Tennessee, northern Georgia, and southwestern Virginia through its PHP Companies subsidiary. The company offers additional health coverage through subsidiary Cariten Healthcare, a managed care organization with a network of more than 7,500 physicians.

	Annual Growth	12/03	12/04	12/05	12/06	12/07
Est. sales ($ mil.)	—	—	—	—	—	1,056.9
Employees	—	—	—	—	—	2,469

COVENANT TRANSPORTATION GROUP, INC.

NASDAQ (GS): CVTI

400 Birmingham Hwy.
Chattanooga, TN 37419
Phone: 423-821-1212
Fax: 423-821-5442
Web: www.covenanttransport.com

CEO: David R. Parker
CFO: Joey B. Hogan
HR: David Manning
FYE: December 31
Type: Public

Truckload freight carrier Covenant Transportation Group promises its customers speedy service on long-haul and regional routes. The company operates a fleet of 3,600 tractors and 8,700 trailers, including both dry vans and temperature-controlled units. In addition to for-hire transportation, Covenant offers dedicated contract carriage, in which drivers and equipment are assigned long-term to a customer or route, and freight brokerage services. The company gets business from manufacturers, retailers, and other transportation companies; among its top customers are Georgia-Pacific, Wal-Mart, and UPS.

	Annual Growth	12/03	12/04	12/05	12/06	12/07
Sales ($ mil.)	5.2%	582.5	603.6	643.0	683.8	712.5
Net income ($ mil.)	—	12.2	3.4	5.2	(1.4)	(16.7)
Market value ($ mil.)	(23.9%)	234.3	256.6	162.6	132.8	78.5
Employees	(15.7%)	—	—	5,712	4,817	

An in-depth profile of this company is available to Hoover's Online members at hoovers.com.

443

COVENTRY HEALTH CARE, INC.

NYSE: CVH

6705 Rockledge Dr., Ste. 900
Bethesda, MD 20817
Phone: 301-581-0600
Fax: 301-493-0731
Web: www.cvty.com

CEO: Dale B. Wolf
CFO: Shawn M. Guertin
HR: Patrisha L. Davis
FYE: December 31
Type: Public

Size matters in the tough world of managed care, and Coventry Health Care wants to measure up. Expanding through numerous acquisitions of local health plans, the firm provides health care coverage to more than 4 million members, primarily in the Midwest, Mid-Atlantic, and Southeast. It offers HMO, PPO, and point-of-service plans to employer groups, as well as Medicare Advantage, Medicare prescription drug coverage, Medicaid managed care plans, and other coverage directly to individuals. Its Specialty unit administers (but doesn't underwrite) workers' compensation programs, providing services such as bill review and case management to insurers and self-insured employers.

	Annual Growth	12/03	12/04	12/05	12/06	12/07
Sales ($ mil.)	21.5%	4,535.1	5,312.0	6,611.3	7,733.8	9,879.5
Net income ($ mil.)	25.8%	250.1	337.1	501.6	560.0	626.1
Market value ($ mil.)	37.1%	2,596.0	3,192.3	9,268.4	7,980.0	9,162.2
Employees	23.5%	—	—	9,830	10,250	15,000

COVER-ALL TECHNOLOGIES INC.

OTC: COVR

55 Lane Rd., Ste. 300
Fairfield, NJ 07004
Phone: 973-461-5200
Fax: 973-461-5257
Web: www.cover-all.com

CEO: John W. Roblin
CFO: Ann F. Massey
HR: –
FYE: December 31
Type: Public

Cover-All Technologies keeps insurers covered. The company offers software and services for carriers, agents, and brokers in the property/casualty insurance industry. Cover-All's software, which the company licenses and offers as a hosted application, automates insurance rating and policy issuance. Its My Insurance Center site, an Internet-based portal for insurance professionals, helps agents with policy quoting, rating, issuance, and billing; provides an insurance policy database for quick access to policy information; and offers applications for managing insurance agencies.

	Annual Growth	12/03	12/04	12/05	12/06	12/07
Sales ($ mil.)	6.9%	7.5	9.3	7.3	7.3	9.8
Net income ($ mil.)	31.6%	0.4	0.8	(1.4)	(1.0)	1.2
Market value ($ mil.)	40.8%	8.1	10.1	9.1	13.4	32.0
Employees	—	—	—	—	45	—

⊞ COVISTA COMMUNICATIONS, INC.

Pink Sheets: CVST

4803 Hwy. 58 North, Ste. 200
Chattanooga, TN 37416
Phone: 423-648-9700
Fax: 423-648-9705
Web: www.covista.com

CEO: Henry G. Luken III
CFO: –
HR: –
FYE: January 31
Type: Public

Covista Communications offers alternative telecommunications services to business and residential customers, mostly in Georgia, New Jersey, New York, Pennsylvania, and Tennessee. Once primarily a long-distance provider, the company has added local service in some markets; it also provides Internet and data networking services. In addition to commercial and residential service, Covista sells wholesale termination services and colocation facilities to telecom carriers. The company operates its own switching facilities in Chattanooga, Tennessee; Dallas; and Minneapolis.

	Annual Growth	1/01	1/02	1/03	1/04	*1/05
Sales ($ mil.)	(18.1%)	133.2	95.3	101.0	84.1	59.8
Net income ($ mil.)	—	(8.6)	(12.0)	(9.4)	(0.9)	(5.3)
Employees	11.4%	212	243	263	—	—

*Most recent year available

COWEN GROUP, INC.

NASDAQ (GM): COWN

1221 Avenue of the Americas
New York, NY 10020
Phone: 646-562-1000
Fax: 646-562-1861
Web: www.cowen.com

CEO: David M. (Greg) Malcolm
CFO: Thomas K. Conner
HR: Christopher A. (Chris) White
FYE: December 31
Type: Public

Ever herd of Cowen Group? Primary subsidiary Cowen and Company (formerly SG Cowen) specializes in investment banking for small to midsized companies in the alternative energy, consumer health care, media, technology, and telecommunications industries. It also performs equities research in those sectors. The company offers mergers and acquisitions advice, securities underwriting, equity offerings, private equity placements, and market-making, as well as securities sales and trading for institutional investors. Subsidiary Cowen Asset Management, LLC focuses its investment activities on US-based small and midsized companies; its UK counterpart provides traditional asset management.

	Annual Growth	12/03	12/04	12/05	12/06	12/07
Sales ($ mil.)	(3.0%)	295.9	293.1	294.3	345.0	261.6
Net income ($ mil.)	—	(74.3)	55.1	12.1	37.9	(11.3)
Market value ($ mil.)	(56.2%)	—	—	—	317.0	138.8
Employees	(5.1%)	650	—	—	537	527

COWLITZ BANCORPORATION

NASDAQ (GM): CWLZ

927 Commerce Ave.
Longview, WA 98632
Phone: 360-423-9800
Fax: 360-423-3562
Web: www.cowlitzbancorp.com

CEO: Richard J. Fitzpatrick
CFO: Gerald L. Brickey
HR: –
FYE: December 31
Type: Public

Cowlitz Bancorporation is the holding company for Cowlitz Bank and its Bay Bank division, which serve southwestern Washington and the Seattle and Portland, Oregon, areas through about 10 branches and loan production offices. Targeting small and midsized businesses and retail customers, the banks mainly use deposits to originate commercial mortgages (around 30% of the company's loan portfolio), business loans (34%), and construction, residential mortgage, and consumer loans. The company also originates long-term residential real estate loans through its Bay Mortgage division.

	Annual Growth	12/03	12/04	12/05	12/06	12/07
Assets ($ mil.)	17.6%	268.8	273.3	370.1	468.4	514.2
Net income ($ mil.)	0.0%	0.1	1.9	3.0	4.8	0.1
Market value ($ mil.)	7.8%	43.9	46.5	68.7	82.0	59.1
Employees	13.4%	—	—	119	135	—

⊞ COX COMMUNICATIONS, INC.

1400 Lake Hearn Dr.
Atlanta, GA 30319
Phone: 404-843-5000
Fax: –
Web: www.cox.com

CEO: Patrick J. (Pat) Esser
CFO: Mark F. Bowser
HR: Mae A. Douglas
FYE: December 31
Type: Subsidiary

Cox Communications carries the complete collection of cable capacity. Cox provides basic cable service to more than 6 million customers, including 2.7 million digital cable subscribers and 3 million Internet access subscribers, making it the third-largest US cable company, behind Comcast and Time Warner Cable. Cox provides telecommunications services as a competitive local-exchange carrier (CLEC). In addition, the company offers voice and data communications to businesses, and has investments in TV programming and broadband technology firms. Media conglomerate Cox Enterprises controlled 63% of Cox Communications until it bought out the rest of the company for $8.5 billion and took it private.

An in-depth profile of this company is available to Hoover's Online members at hoovers.com.

COX ENTERPRISES, INC.

6205 Peachtree Dunwoody Rd.
Atlanta, GA 30328
Phone: 678-645-0000
Fax: 678-645-1079
Web: www.coxenterprises.com

CEO: James C. Kennedy
CFO: Robert C. (Bob) O'Leary
HR: Marybeth H. Leamer
FYE: December 31
Type: Private

The Cox family has been working at this enterprise for more than 100 years. One of the largest media conglomerates in the US, family-owned Cox Enterprises publishes 17 daily newspapers (including *The Atlanta Journal-Constitution*) and about 25 non-dailies (weeklies and shoppers) and owns 15 TV stations through Cox Television. It also owns Cox Communications (which was a public company until a Cox Enterprises buyout in late 2004), one of the US's largest cable systems with more than 6 million subscribers. Other operations include 95% of Cox Radio, owner of about 80 radio stations in nearly 20 markets; Manheim, which sells 10 million vehicles through auctions worldwide; and a majority stake in AutoTrader.com.

	Annual Growth	12/03	12/04	12/05	12/06	12/07
Sales ($ mil.)	8.8%	10,700.0	11,552.0	12,000.0	13,200.0	15,000.0
Employees	1.6%	77,000	77,000	77,000	80,000	82,000

COX RADIO, INC.

NYSE: CXR

6205 Peachtree Dunwoody Rd.
Atlanta, GA 30328
Phone: 678-645-0000
Fax: 678-645-5294
Web: www.coxradio.com

CEO: Robert F. (Bob) Neil
CFO: Neil O. Johnston
HR: –
FYE: December 31
Type: Public

Whether you're looking for urban adult music in Miami or talk radio in Atlanta, Cox Radio has the frequency. The company is one of the nation's largest radio broadcasters, with more than 80 stations in about 20 markets, including Atlanta, Houston, and Miami. Through Cox Radio Syndication the company produces such programs as Neal Boortz (talk radio) and distributes its shows to more than 200 affiliate stations through a partnership with the Jones Radio Network (owned by Jones International). Its Cox Radio Interactive also creates Web sites for its stations and sells advertising on those sites. Media conglomerate Cox Enterprises controls 95% of the company through its 65% equity holding.

	Annual Growth	12/03	12/04	12/05	12/06	12/07
Sales ($ mil.)	1.1%	425.9	438.2	437.9	440.5	444.9
Net income ($ mil.)	(58.9%)	66.6	68.0	61.3	(24.5)	1.9
Market value ($ mil.)	(22.1%)	1,049.3	691.8	554.5	600.1	385.6
Employees	—	—	—	2,136	—	—

CP KELCO

1000 Parkwood Circle, Ste. 1000
Atlanta, GA 30339
Phone: 678-247-7300
Fax: 678-247-2797
Web: www.cpkelco.com

CEO: Donald (Don) Rubright
CFO: Anthony (Tony) Lettich
HR: Thomas K. (Tom) Johnson
FYE: December 31
Type: Subsidiary

Don't worry, teachers. CP Kelco has brought enough gum for the entire class. The company's products include carrageenan, gellan gum, xanthan gum, and microparticulated whey protein. CP Kelco, a subsidiary of J. M. Huber, makes additives used to give food, industrial, personal care, and pharmaceutical products (everything from jam and ketchup to paint and cosmetics) the desired texture, viscosity, and stability. To boost its xanthan gum business, CP Kelco acquired Chinese producer Shandong Gold Millet Biological Products early in 2006. The company operates from 10 manufacturing facilities worldwide.

CPAC, INC.

2364 Leicester Rd.
Leicester, NY 14481
Phone: 585-382-3223
Fax: 585-382-3031
Web: www.cpac-fuller.com

CEO: Thomas N. Hendrickson
CFO: Thomas J. Weldgen
HR: Elizabeth (Liz) Ross
FYE: March 31
Type: Private

CPAC can make your face and floor shine. The company's Fuller Brands segment (more than half of sales) boasts some 2,700 consumer and industrial products, including brushes, cleaning chemicals, brooms, and personal care products. The segment also licenses the Stanley Home Products brand and makes Stanley cleaning and personal care products for sale at home parties. CPAC's imaging segment manufactures and markets branded and private-label chemicals and equipment for photographic, graphic arts, and health care applications. Products include photographic chemical silver-recovery equipment; the shift to digital imaging has hurt this segment. The company is owned by private equity group Buckingham Capital Partners.

	Annual Growth	3/02	3/03	3/04	3/05	3/06
Sales ($ mil.)	(2.9%)	97.8	95.3	90.0	87.2	87.0
Net income ($ mil.)	(35.6%)	2.9	(4.1)	(3.3)	(3.8)	0.5
Employees	(5.3%)	588	576	531	528	473

CPI AEROSTRUCTURES, INC.

AMEX: CVU

60 Heartland Blvd.
Edgewood, NY 11717
Phone: 631-586-5200
Fax: 631-586-5814
Web: www.cpiaero.com

CEO: Edward J. Fred
CFO: Vincent (Vince) Palazzolo
HR: Katie Clare
FYE: December 31
Type: Public

To build an aircraft, some assembly is required, and that's where CPI Aerostructures comes in. CPI Aero makes structural aircraft subassemblies for the US Air Force and other US military customers. Primary military products include skin panels, flight control surfaces, leading edges, wing tips, engine components, cowl doors, and nacelle and inlet assemblies for military aircraft such as the A-10 Warthog, C-5 Galaxy, C-130 Hercules, E-3 Sentry AWACs jet, and T-38 Talon. CPI Aero also makes aprons and engine mounts for commercial aircraft such as business jets.

	Annual Growth	12/03	12/04	12/05	12/06	12/07
Sales ($ mil.)	0.6%	27.3	30.3	25.5	17.9	28.0
Net income ($ mil.)	(31.0%)	8.4	5.1	1.5	(1.3)	1.9
Market value ($ mil.)	(5.6%)	63.1	62.0	54.8	39.4	50.1
Employees	(15.3%)	—	—	72	61	—

CPI CORP.

NYSE: CPY

1706 Washington Ave.
St. Louis, MO 63103
Phone: 314-231-1575
Fax: 314-231-8150
Web: www.cpicorp.com

CEO: Renato Cataldo Jr.
CFO: Dale Heins
HR: Dan Duggan
FYE: First Saturday in February
Type: Public

CPI gets the picture. One of the largest preschool portrait photographers in North America, the company operates about 3,100 photographic studios in the US, Canada, and Puerto Rico, mainly in Sears and Wal-Mart stores. The firm operates about 1,000 Sears Portrait Studios (SPS) in Sears and Sears Grand outlets. CPI's 2007 purchase of rival PCA added 2,000-plus photo studios under the PictureMe Portrait Studio (PMPS) name inside Wal-Mart stores throughout North America and Mexico. All of the company's SPS and about a third of its PMPS locations in the US offer digital imaging technology and a choice of poses and print sizes, as well as photo accessories.

	Annual Growth	1/04	1/05	1/06	1/07	1/08
Sales ($ mil.)	8.9%	301.7	281.9	292.0	293.8	424.0
Net income ($ mil.)	31.6%	1.2	(18.5)	6.4	16.3	3.6
Market value ($ mil.)	(7.3%)	178.3	119.7	146.6	345.6	131.8
Employees	15.2%	7,300	8,800	7,100	7,700	12,854

An in-depth profile of this company is available to Hoover's Online members at hoovers.com.

445

CPI INTERNATIONAL, INC.

NASDAQ (GS): CPII

607 Hansen Way
Palo Alto, CA 94303
Phone: 650-846-2900
Fax: 650-846-3276
Web: www.cpii.com

CEO: O. Joe Caldarelli
CFO: Joel A. Littman
HR: –
FYE: Friday nearest September 30
Type: Public

CPI International makes broadcast and wireless components, such as satellite communications transmitters, amplifiers, sensors, X-ray equipment, power supplies, transmitters, and microwave components. Its radio-frequency (RF) and microwave components go into a great deal of military hardware (governments account for about half of sales), including Aegis-class cruisers and destroyers, electronic warfare decoys, Patriot missile systems, and fighter aircraft. The company's products also go into civilian communications equipment, industrial gear, medical systems, and scientific instruments. CPI International sells in more than 90 countries, with the US providing more than half of sales.

	Annual Growth	9/03	9/04	9/05	9/06	9/07
Sales ($ mil.)	7.2%	265.4	202.3	320.7	339.7	351.1
Net income ($ mil.)	8.1%	16.5	2.7	13.7	17.2	22.5
Market value ($ mil.)	47.2%	—	—	—	211.4	311.2
Employees	3.4%	1,490	1,510	1,700	1,610	1,700

CPS ENERGY

145 Navarro St.
San Antonio, TX 78205
Phone: 210-353-2000
Fax: 210-353-3021
Web: www.citypublicservice.com

CEO: Milton B. Lee
CFO: Richard E. (Rick) Williamson
HR: Paula Gold-Williams
FYE: January 31
Type: Government-owned

And the award for being the energy distributor for the ninth largest city in the US goes to . . . City Public Service Board of San Antonio, Texas (CPS). Serving about 677,000 electricity customers and almost 318,000 natural gas customers, the utility operates in a nearly 1,600-sq.-mi. service territory. CPS also has a generating capacity of 5,100 MW from its 16 fossil-fueled power plants and its ownership interests in the South Texas Nuclear Project and the Desert Sky Wind Farm in West Texas. As a municipally owned utility, CPS is exempt from retail competition in Texas, which took effect for investor-owned utilities in 2002.

	Annual Growth	1/03	1/04	1/05	1/06	1/07
Est. sales ($ mil.)	—	—	—	—	—	1,770.1
Employees	—	—	—	—	—	4,100

CPS TECHNOLOGIES CORPORATION

OTC: CPSH

111 S. Worcester St.
Chartley, MA 02712
Phone: 508-222-0614
Fax: 508-222-0220
Web: www.alsic.com

CEO: Grant C. Bennett
CFO: Grant C. Bennett
HR: –
FYE: December 31
Type: Public

CPS Technologies (formerly Ceramics Process Systems) makes thermal management components for electronics using aluminum silicon carbide (ALSiC) metal matrix composites. Products include substrates, baseplates, and heat spreaders which are used by customers in motor controller and wireless communications component applications. The company also licenses its technology to other manufacturers; revenue from royalties, however, has dwindled away to virtually nothing. CPS Technologies makes around two-thirds of its sales outside the US, although most of its customers are actually based in the US.

	Annual Growth	12/03	12/04	12/05	12/06	12/07
Sales ($ mil.)	32.7%	4.0	6.8	7.2	11.9	12.4
Net income ($ mil.)	—	0.0	1.0	0.3	1.8	0.9
Market value ($ mil.)	70.0%	4.1	14.8	12.9	18.8	33.9
Employees	21.5%	62	82	94	133	135

C. R. BARD, INC.

NYSE: BCR

730 Central Ave.
Murray Hill, NJ 07974
Phone: 908-277-8000
Fax: 908-277-8240
Web: www.crbard.com

CEO: Timothy M. Ring
CFO: Todd C. Schermerhorn
HR: Bronwen K. Kelly
FYE: December 31
Type: Public

C. R. Bard is no upstart in the world of health care. The medical technology company has been in the business for more than a century and introduced the Foley urological catheter (still one of its top sellers) in 1934. Its products fall into four general therapeutic categories: vascular, urology, oncology, and surgical specialties. Among other things, the company makes stents, catheters, and guidewires used in angioplasties and other vascular procedures; urology catheters and products used to treat urinary incontinence; and catheters for delivering chemotherapy treatments. Its line of surgical tools, made by subsidiary Davol, includes devices used in laparoscopic and orthopedic procedures and for hernia repair.

	Annual Growth	12/03	12/04	12/05	12/06	12/07
Sales ($ mil.)	11.3%	1,433.1	1,656.1	1,771.3	1,985.5	2,202.0
Net income ($ mil.)	24.6%	168.5	302.8	337.1	272.1	406.4
Market value ($ mil.)	45.8%	2,102.5	6,696.9	6,856.5	8,558.8	9,498.1
Employees	7.1%	—	—	8,900	9,400	10,200

C.R. ENGLAND, INC.

4701 W. 2100 South
Salt Lake City, UT 84120
Phone: 801-972-2712
Fax: 801-977-6703
Web: www.crengland.com

CEO: Dean D. England
CFO: Keith Wallace
HR: Chad England
FYE: December 31
Type: Private

London might have its cool, foggy days, but the England of C.R. England is always chilly. Truckload freight carrier C.R. England hauls refrigerated and dry cargo throughout the US. The company also serves parts of Canada and, through alliances, parts of Mexico. C.R. England's fleet includes some 3,500 tractors and about 5,600 trailers. Besides for-hire freight hauling, C.R. England offers dedicated contract carriage, in which drivers and equipment are assigned to a customer long-term; and logistics services, including freight brokerage. C.R. England was founded in 1920 by Chester Rodney England and is run by his descendants.

	Annual Growth	12/03	12/04	12/05	12/06	12/07
Est. sales ($ mil.)	—	—	—	—	—	708.2
Employees	—	—	—	—	—	4,500

CRA INTERNATIONAL, INC.

NASDAQ (GS): CRAI

200 Clarendon St., Ste. T-33
Boston, MA 02116
Phone: 617-425-3000
Fax: 617-425-3132
Web: www.crai.com

CEO: James C. Burrows
CFO: Wayne D. Mackie
HR: –
FYE: Last Saturday in November
Type: Public

Whether you need an expert to help you run your business, testify for you in court, or evaluate the finances of an acquisition candidate, CRA International wants to help. The company's consultants offer economic and business counsel from more than 25 offices, mainly in North America but also in Europe, the Middle East, and the Asia/Pacific region. CRA has organized its practices into three main areas: finance (valuation and accounting, insurance, and risk management); litigation and applied economics (competition, intellectual property, trade, and transfer pricing); and business consulting. Clients include companies from a variety of industries, government agencies, and law firms.

	Annual Growth	11/03	11/04	11/05	11/06	11/07
Sales ($ mil.)	24.6%	163.5	216.7	295.5	349.9	394.6
Net income ($ mil.)	30.0%	11.4	16.3	24.6	27.4	32.6
Market value ($ mil.)	11.0%	333.3	428.5	514.6	598.4	506.0
Employees	7.6%	—	—	906	733	1,049

An in-depth profile of this company is available to Hoover's Online members at hoovers.com.

CRAFTMADE INTERNATIONAL, INC.

NASDAQ (GM): CRFT

650 S. Royal Ln., Ste. 100
Coppell, TX 75019
Phone: 972-393-3800
Fax: 972-304-3753
Web: www.craftmade.com

CEO: James R. (Jimmy) Ridings
CFO: J. Marcus Scrudder
HR: Ric DeCastro
FYE: June 30
Type: Public

Craftmade International is no celebrity, but it is accustomed to fans and bright lights. The company designs and distributes ceiling fans and lights, mainly for home use. Operating through the Craftmade and Trade Source International (TSI) units, the company markets more than 50 fan models, nearly 80 types of accompanying light kits, and other accessories. It also offers Accolade-brand bathstrip and outdoor lighting, and it sells lamps and distributes communication cable components. Asian contractors make most of Craftmade's goods, which are sold by US retailers and wholesalers. The company has 50% stakes in Prime/Home Impressions and Design Trends. CEO James Ridings owns about 11% of the company.

	Annual Growth	6/03	6/04	6/05	6/06	6/07
Sales ($ mil.)	9.5%	71.8	121.2	116.8	118.1	103.3
Net income ($ mil.)	(3.5%)	6.8	7.7	6.4	7.1	5.9
Market value ($ mil.)	(2.3%)	97.6	101.6	84.2	87.2	89.0
Employees	—	—	—	130	—	—

CRAIGSLIST, INC.

1381 9th Ave.
San Francisco, CA 94122
Phone: 415-566-6394
Fax: 415-504-6394
Web: www.craigslist.org

CEO: Jim Buckmaster
CFO: –
HR: –
FYE: –
Type: Private

Just who is this Craig fellow, and why is his list so popular? Online community bulletin board craigslist was founded by computer programmer Craig Newmark, who in 1995 began informing people about events around San Francisco through a list server. The service later evolved into a Web site (craigslist.org) that has become a forum for locals in metropolitan areas such as San Francisco, New York, and Boston to post listings for jobs, housing, companionship and dating, furniture and other used items, events, and additional community information. The firm charges businesses a fee to post job openings on about a dozen city sites, including San Francisco, New York, and Los Angeles. eBay owns about 25% of craigslist.

CRAIN COMMUNICATIONS INC

1155 Gratiot Ave.
Detroit, MI 48207
Phone: 313-446-6000
Fax: 313-446-1616
Web: www.crain.com

CEO: Rance E. Crain
CFO: Thomas M. (Tom) Marantette Jr.
HR: Laura Anger
FYE: December 31
Type: Private

These Crains have been whooping it up in the publishing business for almost 100 years. Crain Communications publishes some 30 business, consumer, and trade journals worldwide, mostly in North America and Europe. Its portfolio includes *AutoWeek*, *TelevisionWeek*, and *RCR Wireless News*, as well as its flagship publication *Advertising Age*. Crain also publishes business journals in four major US cities (Chicago, Cleveland, Detroit, and New York City), operates trade shows, and publishes trade content online. Its Crain News Service provides business news and information to other media outlets. The founding Crain family continues to own and operate the company.

CRANE & CO., INC.

30 South St.
Dalton, MA 01226
Phone: 413-684-2600
Fax: 413-684-4278
Web: www.crane.com

CEO: Lansing E. Crane
CFO: –
HR: Richard C. Kendall
FYE: December 31
Type: Private

If the bill isn't worth the paper it's printed on, then Crane & Co. didn't make it, and you can take that to the bank! Crane has been making currency paper for the US Mint since 1879. The company also makes fine cotton papers for business and social correspondence. Crane uses millions of pounds of denim fabric to make US currency paper. Crane's nonwoven wares are used in a variety of industrial, commercial, and consumer applications including filtration products, surfboards, and circuit boards. Members of the sixth generation of the founding Crane family own and manage the company.

	Annual Growth	12/03	12/04	12/05	12/06	12/07
Est. sales ($ mil.)	—	—	—	—	—	206.3
Employees	—	—	—	—	—	1,400

CRANE CO.

NYSE: CR

100 First Stamford Place
Stamford, CT 06902
Phone: 203-363-7300
Fax: 203-363-7295
Web: www.craneco.com

CEO: Eric C. Fast
CFO: Eric C. Fast
HR: Elise M. Kopczick
FYE: December 31
Type: Public

In many cultures the crane is a symbol of longevity and this Crane might be as well. Founded in 1855, the company makes a variety of industrial products, including fluid handling equipment (valves and pumps), aerospace and electronic components (sensing and control systems), engineered materials (plastic composites and substrates), merchandising systems (vending machines), and controls (diagnostic, measurement, and control devices). Crane serves the power generation, transportation, defense, commercial construction, food and beverage, and chemical industries, among others. Richard Crane formed the company to supply railroad parts to a burgeoning industry in Chicago.

	Annual Growth	12/03	12/04	12/05	12/06	12/07
Sales ($ mil.)	12.5%	1,636.0	1,890.3	2,061.3	2,256.9	2,619.2
Net income ($ mil.)	—	104.3	(105.4)	136.0	165.9	(62.3)
Market value ($ mil.)	8.9%	1,834.4	1,707.4	2,152.4	2,215.7	2,580.9
Employees	7.4%	—	—	10,400	11,870	12,000

CRANE PLUMBING, L.L.C.

41 Cairns Rd.
Mansfield, OH 44903
Phone: 419-521-3219
Fax: 419-524-0501
Web: www.craneplumbing.com

CEO: Kevin Oak
CFO: John Sluzynski
HR: Betty Fritz
FYE: December 31
Type: Private

One of North America's largest manufacturers of plumbing fixtures and accessories, Crane Plumbing makes toilets, lavatories, sinks, bath tubs, whirlpools, showers, vanities, urinals, and water fountains. Its brands include Crane Plumbing, Universal-Rundle, Fiat Products, Sanymetal, and Showerite. The company makes its products from such materials as steel, fiberglass, vitreous china, stone, and marble for use in commercial buildings, homes, hospitals, hotels, and schools. Its products are sold at some 4,000 retail and 3,000 wholesale locations. Crane Plumbing operates about 20 manufacturing facilities in the US and Canada. Investment firm Sun Capital Partners acquired Crane Plumbing in 2005.

	Annual Growth	12/03	12/04	12/05	12/06	12/07
Est. sales ($ mil.)	—	—	—	—	—	154.3
Employees	—	—	—	—	—	2,700

An in-depth profile of this company is available to Hoover's Online members at hoovers.com.

447

CRANEL, INC.

8999 Gemini Pkwy.
Columbus, OH 43240
Phone: 614-431-8000
Fax: 614-431-8388
Web: www.cranel.com

CEO: James H. (Jim) Wallace
CFO: Michael A. Tracy
HR: Michael A. Tracy
FYE: December 31
Type: Private

Cranel hopes to hook you up with technology services, document imaging software, and data storage products. The company operates through three business units: Adexis (data access, management, and protection products), Cranel Imaging (document imaging and storage products), and Versitec (document imaging IT services). In addition to its proprietary technology offerings, its divisions also implement and integrate third-party hardware and software, as well as providing a variety of information technology services such as consulting, support, and training. The company was founded in 1985.

	Annual Growth	12/03	12/04	12/05	12/06	12/07
Est. sales ($ mil.)	—	—	—	—	—	37.2
Employees	—	—	—	—	—	175

CRAVATH, SWAINE & MOORE LLP

Worldwide Plaza, 825 8th Ave.
New York, NY 10019
Phone: 212-474-1000
Fax: 212-474-3700
Web: www.cravath.com

CEO: Evan R. Chesler
CFO: J. Christopher Craig
HR: Lina Maglara
FYE: December 31
Type: Partnership

With more than 450 attorneys working from offices in New York and London, Cravath, Swaine & Moore is a leading corporate law firm. Cravath is well-known for its work in such areas as banking and finance, capital markets, and mergers and acquisitions; other practice areas include executive compensation and benefits, litigation, tax, and trusts and estates. Over the years Cravath has counted major enterprises such as IBM and Time Warner among its clients. The firm, which traces its origins back to 1819, owes its present structure to Paul Cravath, who took the reins early in the 20th century and is credited by many with developing the configuration of the modern-day law firm.

	Annual Growth	12/03	12/04	12/05	12/06	12/07
Est. sales ($ mil.)	—	—	—	—	—	121.2
Employees	—	—	—	—	—	1,400

CRAWFORD & COMPANY

NYSE: CRD

1001 Summit Blvd.
Atlanta, GA 30319
Phone: 404-256-0830
Fax: 404-300-1905
Web: www.crawfordandcompany.com

CEO: Jeffrey T. (Jeff) Bowman
CFO: W. Bruce Swain Jr.
HR: –
FYE: December 31
Type: Public

Crawford & Company is an international insurance services firm providing claims adjustment and risk management services to insurers and self-insured companies. Services include workers' compensation and property/casualty claims investigation, evaluation, and resolution; statistical and financial reporting; and medical case management. Subsidiaries provide class-action settlement services, property damage repairs, and computer-based information systems and analytical forecasting. Crawford & Company has more than 700 offices in more than 60 countries. Members of the Crawford family own a majority of the firm.

	Annual Growth	12/03	12/04	12/05	12/06	12/07
Sales ($ mil.)	8.2%	768.0	811.7	854.8	900.4	1,051.3
Net income ($ mil.)	20.2%	7.7	25.2	12.9	15.0	16.1
Market value ($ mil.)	(14.6%)	170.4	169.1	140.9	154.2	90.8
Employees	23.3%	—	—	7,525	9,280	—

CRAY INC.

NASDAQ (GM): CRAY

411 1st Ave. South, Ste. 600
Seattle, WA 98104
Phone: 206-701-2000
Fax: 206-701-2500
Web: www.cray.com

CEO: Peter J. Ungaro
CFO: Brian C. Henry
HR: Linda Howitson
FYE: December 31
Type: Public

Cray makes computers that aren't just good — they're super. Its massively parallel and vector supercomputers provide the firepower behind research ranging from weather forecasting and scientific research to design engineering and classified government projects. The company also provides maintenance and support services (about a quarter of revenues in 2007), and it sells data storage products from partners including BlueArc, LSI, and Quantum. Many of Cray's sales are to US government agencies and commercial customers that serve those agencies; it also targets schools and industrial companies. The company primarily utilizes a direct sales force.

	Annual Growth	12/03	12/04	12/05	12/06	12/07
Sales ($ mil.)	(5.9%)	237.0	149.2	201.1	221.0	186.1
Net income ($ mil.)	—	63.3	(204.0)	(64.3)	(12.1)	(5.7)
Market value ($ mil.)	(49.0%)	2,883.7	1,633.6	484.0	383.0	195.5
Employees	0.8%	—	—	787	—	800

CREATIVE ARTISTS AGENCY, INC.

2000 Avenue of the Stars
Los Angeles, CA 90067
Phone: 424-288-2000
Fax: 424-288-2900
Web: www.caa.com

CEO: Richard Lovett
CFO: –
HR: –
FYE: –
Type: Private

Arguably the most powerful talent agency in the business, Creative Artists Agency (CAA) represents clients working in film, TV, theater, music, and literature. The firm represents a gaggle of the day's top female stars such as Cameron Diaz, Nicole Kidman, Angelina Jolie, Julia Roberts, and Meryl Streep. Other heavy-hitting clients include actors Tom Cruise, Tom Hanks, and musicians Alanis Morissette and Beyoncé Knowles, as well as corporate clients such as Coca-Cola and toymaker Mattel. Supplemental services include strategic counsel, financing, and consulting. Its Intelligence Group/Youth Intelligence unit tracks and conducts behavior research for consumers from ages 8 to 39. CAA was founded in 1975.

CREDENCE SYSTEMS CORPORATION

NASDAQ (GS): CMOS

1421 California Cir.
Milpitas, CA 95035
Phone: 408-635-4300
Fax: 408-635-4985
Web: www.credence.com

CEO: Lavi A. Lev
CFO: Kevin C. (Casey) Eichler
HR: Brett Hooper
FYE: October 31
Type: Public

Credence Systems supplies semiconductor makers with the proof they need to believe in their chips. The company makes automatic test equipment and related software used during the design, validation, and manufacturing stages of semiconductor production. Credence's products test analog, digital, mixed-signal, and radio-frequency wireless integrated circuits used in PCs, phones, cars, cameras, televisions, and other products. Credence offers sales and support through its own domestic and overseas branches and through a worldwide network of suppliers. The company derives about 70% of its sales from customers outside North America.

	Annual Growth	10/03	10/04	10/05	10/06	10/07
Sales ($ mil.)	26.1%	182.4	439.8	429.3	474.4	461.1
Net income ($ mil.)	—	(113.1)	(64.5)	(119.9)	(481.6)	12.4
Market value ($ mil.)	(26.4%)	1,040.7	643.9	765.7	324.0	306.0
Employees	9.3%	1,075	2,101	1,810	1,513	1,532

CREDIT ACCEPTANCE CORPORATION
NASDAQ (GM): CACC

25505 W. Twelve Mile Rd., Ste. 3000
Southfield, MI 48034
Phone: 248-353-2700
Fax: 248-827-8553
Web: www.creditacceptance.com

CEO: Brett A. Roberts
CFO: Kenneth S. Booth
HR: Steve M. Dion
FYE: December 31
Type: Public

In the world of Credit Acceptance Corporation (CAC), to purchase a car is not an impossible dream for problem borrowers — just an expensive reality. Working with independent and franchised automobile dealers in the US, CAC provides capital for auto loans to people with substandard credit. The company also provides other services to dealers, including payment servicing, receivables management, marketing, and sales staff training. Texas is the company's largest market. Founder and chairman Donald Foss owns more than 60% of the company.

	Annual Growth	12/03	12/04	12/05	12/06	12/07
Assets ($ mil.)	(0.0%)	943.8	591.3	619.4	725.2	942.2
Net income ($ mil.)	18.1%	28.2	57.3	72.6	58.6	54.9
Market value ($ mil.)	(0.8%)	644.6	939.0	596.1	1,005.9	625.1
Employees	—	—	—	—	788	—

CREDIT SUISSE (USA), INC.

11 Madison Ave.
New York, NY 10010
Phone: 212-325-2000
Fax: 212-325-6665
Web: www.credit-suisse.com/us/en

CEO: Robert S. (Rob) Shafir
CFO: Paul O'Keefe
HR: –
FYE: December 31
Type: Subsidiary

Out with the old, in with the new. Once known as Credit Suisse First Boston (USA), Credit Suisse (USA) is a subsidiary of Swiss banking powerhouse Credit Suisse Group. The company is one of the top US investment banks, offering securities underwriting and trading, mergers and acquisitions advice, research, private equity investment, and risk management products. Credit Suisse (USA) also provides asset management and financial advisory services to high-net-worth individuals and corporate investors. The company's lineage includes investment banks Donaldson, Lufkin & Jenrette (DLJ) and First Boston, among its predecessors.

CREDITRISKMONITOR.COM, INC.
OTC: CRMZ

704 Executive Blvd., Ste. A
Valley Cottage, NY 10989
Phone: 845-230-3000
Fax: 845-267-4110
Web: www.creditriskmonitor.com

CEO: Jerome S. (Jerry) Flum
CFO: Lawrence (Larry) Fensterstock
HR: Lawrence (Larry) Fensterstock
FYE: December 31
Type: Public

Need to monitor credit risk? CreditRiskMonitor.com provides online financial information and news about some 40,000 public companies, marketing the service to corporate credit managers, who use the data to make credit decisions. Subscribers get access to such information as summary financial statements, quarterly results, comparative analysis, and stock quotes. The firm also provides foreign coverage, with access to more than 20 million credit reports through affiliations with third-party providers. CreditRiskMonitor.com was formed in 1998 after its management bought Market Guide's credit information database. CEO Jerry Flum controls nearly 70% of the firm.

	Annual Growth	12/03	12/04	12/05	12/06	12/07
Sales ($ mil.)	13.6%	3.0	3.3	3.8	4.3	5.0
Net income ($ mil.)	—	(0.8)	(0.1)	1.0	0.0	0.4
Market value ($ mil.)	58.2%	3.0	3.1	12.7	23.1	18.5
Employees	—	—	—	—	—	—

CREDO PETROLEUM CORPORATION
NASDAQ (GS): CRED

1801 Broadway, Ste. 900
Denver, CO 80202
Phone: 303-297-2200
Fax: 303-297-2204
Web: www.credopetroleum.com

CEO: James T. Huffman
CFO: David E. Dennis
HR: –
FYE: October 31
Type: Public

CREDO Petroleum believes strongly in fossil fuels: It explores for, produces, and markets natural gas and crude oil in the US Gulf Coast, Midcontinent, and Rocky Mountain regions. The company has traditionally concentrated on shallow and medium-depth properties (7,000-9,000 feet), but in 2005 it launched new projects in Kansas and South Texas (where it is drilling to well depths ranging from 10,000 to 15,500 feet). The company has estimated proved reserves of 16.6 billion cu. ft. of gas and 422,000 barrels of oil. Subsidiary United Oil operates the company's properties in Oklahoma, and CREDO Petroleum's other subsidiary, SECO Energy, owns royalty interests in the Rocky Mountains.

	Annual Growth	10/03	10/04	10/05	10/06	10/07
Sales ($ mil.)	18.9%	8.5	10.3	14.0	16.5	17.0
Net income ($ mil.)	18.4%	3.1	3.7	5.2	5.9	6.1
Market value ($ mil.)	31.4%	30.3	55.4	166.1	123.8	90.4
Employees	0.0%	—	—	12	12	12

CREE, INC.
NASDAQ (GS): CREE

4600 Silicon Dr.
Durham, NC 27703
Phone: 919-313-5300
Fax: 919-313-5558
Web: www.cree.com

CEO: Charles M. (Chuck) Swoboda
CFO: John T. Kurtzweil
HR: Margaret Chadwick
FYE: Last Sunday in June
Type: Public

Cree has created a name for itself in lights. Its blue, green, and near-ultraviolet light-emitting diodes (LEDs) — made from silicon carbide (SiC) and gallium nitride (GaN) — are used by companies in products such as dashboard lights, market tickers, and video screens, including the giant screen in New York's Times Square. Cree also sells SiC wafers, which yield semiconductors that work at higher temperatures and voltages than standard silicon devices, and SiC and GaN materials. Leading customers include Sumitomo (24% of sales), OSRAM, and Seoul Semiconductor (14%). Asia accounts for about three-fourths of sales.

	Annual Growth	6/03	6/04	6/05	6/06	6/07
Sales ($ mil.)	14.4%	229.8	306.9	389.1	423.0	394.1
Net income ($ mil.)	13.2%	34.9	58.0	91.1	76.7	57.3
Market value ($ mil.)	17.8%	1,204.6	1,612.9	2,007.8	1,814.1	2,320.9
Employees	—	—	—	1,322	—	—

CRESCENT BANKING COMPANY
NASDAQ (CM): CSNT

7 Caring Way
Jasper, GA 30143
Phone: 678-454-2266
Fax: 678-454-2282
Web: www.crescentbank.com

CEO: J. Donald Boggus Jr.
CFO: Leland W. Brantley Jr.
HR: –
FYE: December 31
Type: Public

This crescent gives a whole new meaning to the term "dough boy." Crescent Banking Company is the holding company of Crescent Bank & Trust, which serves north-central Georgia from about a dozen branches and loan offices. The bank offers standard services such as checking and savings accounts, money market accounts, CDs, and IRAs. It mainly uses funds from deposits to originate loans in its market area. Real estate construction and land development loans account for more than half of its total portfolio, which also consists of real estate mortgages (about 40%), as well as agricultural, business, and consumer installment loans.

	Annual Growth	12/03	12/04	12/05	12/06	12/07
Assets ($ mil.)	25.9%	366.4	513.4	704.1	779.7	920.3
Net income ($ mil.)	(22.0%)	17.3	(0.8)	4.1	7.3	6.4
Market value ($ mil.)	14.5%	39.1	32.8	45.9	60.8	67.2
Employees	(24.4%)	—	—	196	199	112

CRESCENT FINANCIAL CORPORATION

NASDAQ (CM): CRFN

1005 High House Rd.
Cary, NC 27513
Phone: 919-460-7770
Fax: 919-460-2512
Web: www.crescentstatebank.com

CEO: Michael G. Carlton
CFO: Bruce W. Elder
HR: –
FYE: December 31
Type: Public

This Crescent can help you wrench the most bang from your buck. Crescent Financial is the holding company for Crescent State Bank, which operates about a dozen branches in central North Carolina. The community bank offers standard products and services, including checking and savings accounts, certificates of deposit, and credit cards. Commercial mortgages make up about half of its loan portfolio; construction loans make up more than a quarter. The company also writes business loans, home equity loans, and residential mortgages. Its Crescent Investment Services division offers financial planning products and services, including retirement plans, mutual funds, insurance, and other investments.

	Annual Growth	12/03	12/04	12/05	12/06	12/07
Assets ($ mil.)	32.2%	273.7	331.2	410.8	697.9	835.5
Net income ($ mil.)	40.9%	1.6	2.3	3.1	4.9	6.3
Market value ($ mil.)	41.1%	22.8	37.7	60.4	96.1	90.2
Employees	16.3%	—	—	99	129	134

CRESCENT REAL ESTATE EQUITIES LIMITED PARTNERSHIP

777 Main St., Ste. 2100
Fort Worth, TX 76102
Phone: 817-321-2100
Fax: 817-321-2000
Web: www.crescent.com

CEO: John C. Goff
CFO: Jane E. Mody
HR: Thomas (Tom) Shaw Jr.
FYE: December 31
Type: Subsidiary

Crescent Real Estate Equities, a real estate investment trust (REIT), owns or has interests in more than 50 office properties totalling some 23 million sq. ft. Most of its properties are in the Dallas, Houston, Miami, Denver, and Las Vegas markets. In addition to its office holdings, the company owns three upscale resorts in Massachusetts, Arizona, and California. It also has interests in upscale residential developments in Arizona, California, Colorado, North Carolina, and Texas. Crescent was acquired by Morgan Stanley's real estate division in 2007.

	Annual Growth	12/02	12/03	12/04	12/05	12/06
Sales ($ mil.)	(2.2%)	1,016.4	949.2	978.8	1,023.5	928.7
Net income ($ mil.)	(21.4%)	87.7	26.0	172.9	95.3	33.4
Employees	2.8%	671	728	747	749	748

CRESTRON ELECTRONICS, INC.

15 Volvo Dr.
Rockleigh, NJ 07647
Phone: 201-767-3400
Fax: 201-767-1905
Web: www.crestron.com

CEO: George Feldstein
CFO: –
HR: –
FYE: June 30
Type: Private

Crestron Electronics doesn't mind if its customers have control issues. Crestron provides hardware and software used to control audio and video systems, as well as computer networks, security systems, and environmental systems such as temperature and lighting. Its products include amplifiers, controllers, management software, remotes, touch panels, tuners, cabling, and cabinet enclosures. It markets to businesses, consumers, government agencies, and schools worldwide; the company's commercial customers include retailers, hotels and casinos, restaurants, airports, and museums. Crestron was established in 1971.

	Annual Growth	6/03	6/04	6/05	6/06	6/07
Est. sales ($ mil.)	—	—	—	—	—	250.0
Employees	—	—	—	—	—	1,000

CRETE CARRIER CORPORATION

400 NW 56th St.
Lincoln, NE 68528
Phone: 402-475-9521
Fax: 402-479-2075
Web: www.cretecarrier.com

CEO: Tonn M. Ostergard
CFO: Dean Troester
HR: –
FYE: September 30
Type: Private

Holding company Crete Carrier Corporation's flagship business, Crete Carrier, provides dry van truckload freight transportation services in the 48 contiguous states. It operates from some two dozen terminals, mainly in the midwestern and southeastern US. The company's Shaffer Trucking unit transports temperature-controlled cargo, and Hunt Transportation (no relation to J.B. Hunt Transport Services) hauls heavy equipment and other cargo on flatbed trailers. Overall, the companies operate more than 5,300 tractors and more than 13,000 trailers. Family-owned Crete Carrier was founded in 1966 by chairman Duane Acklie; president and CEO Tonn Ostergard is his son-in-law.

	Annual Growth	9/02	9/03	9/04	9/05	9/06
Sales ($ mil.)	—	—	—	—	—	1,003.7
Employees	—	—	—	—	—	6,100

CRIMSON EXPLORATION, INC.

OTC: CXPO

717 Texas Ave., Ste. 2900
Houston, TX 77002
Phone: 713-236-7400
Fax: 713-236-4424
Web: www.crimsonexploration.com

CEO: Allan D. Keel
CFO: E. Joseph Grady
HR: –
FYE: December 31
Type: Public

Independent oil and gas company Crimson Exploration has operations that extend from the Gulf (of Mexico) to the West (Texas and points beyond). The company owns and operates more than 140 wells located primarily in the Permian Basin of West Texas and in East Texas. It also operates in Colorado, Louisiana, and Mississippi. In 2006 Crimson Exploration had estimated proved reserves of 31.4 billion cu. ft. of natural gas and 2.5 million barrels of oil. The company is targeting expansion through acquisition in its existing areas of operation and in the shallow waters of the Gulf of Mexico.

	Annual Growth	12/03	12/04	12/05	12/06	12/07
Sales ($ mil.)	77.6%	11.0	11.2	17.7	21.7	109.5
Net income ($ mil.)	—	(3.0)	8.1	(3.5)	1.9	(0.4)
Employees	18.5%	34	26	30	33	67

CRISPIN PORTER + BOGUSKY

3390 Mary St., Ste. 300
Miami, FL 33133
Phone: 305-859-2070
Fax: 305-854-3419
Web: www.cpbgroup.com

CEO: Jeff Hicks
CFO: –
HR: –
FYE: December 31
Type: Private

Full-service ad agency Crispin Porter + Bogusky provides media planning and buying, research, public relations, and creative ad services in addition to production services for print and broadcast. The agency's work (known for its consistent doses of eccentricity) includes the Truth campaign (youth smoking prevention) for the American Legacy Foundation, Coca-Cola's Coke Zero product, and Burger King's Internet sensation, the Subservient Chicken (in which users can get an online chicken to do just about anything). The agency was also named to handle Miller Brewing's Miller Lite brand in 2006. Crispin Porter is a subsidiary of marketing and advertising conglomerate MDC Partners.

	Annual Growth	12/03	12/04	12/05	12/06	12/07
Est. sales ($ mil.)	—	—	—	—	—	56.5
Employees	—	—	—	—	—	155

CRITICAL CARE SYSTEMS INTERNATIONAL, INC.

Executive Tower, 61 Spit Brook Rd.
Nashua, NH 03060
Phone: 603-888-1500
Fax: 603-888-0990
Web: www.criticalcaresystems.com

CEO: Paul F. McConnell
CFO: John C. Prior
HR: Michelle D. LeDell
FYE: December 31
Type: Subsidiary

Critical Care Systems International (formerly Curative Health Services) is a specialty health care services company offering infusion therapy from specialty pharmacy locations across the country. The company operates via two main business units. Its Specialty Infusion unit provides pharmaceutical products and related services for patients with chronic or severe conditions. Its Bleeding Disorders Services unit treats patients with such disorders as hemophilia. The company provides services to pediatric and adult patients, either at home or at its ambulatory infusion sites. Critical Care Systems was acquired by Medco Health late in 2007.

	Annual Growth	12/03	12/04	12/05	12/06	12/07
Est. sales ($ mil.)	—	—	—	—	—	261.1
Employees	—	—	—	—	—	948

CRITICAL PATH, INC.

OTC: CPTH

2 Harrison St., 2nd Fl.
San Francisco, CA 94105
Phone: 415-541-2500
Fax: 415-541-2300
Web: www.criticalpath.net

CEO: Mark E. Palomba
CFO: James A. Clark
HR: −
FYE: December 31
Type: Public

Critical Path provides messaging applications that enable wireless companies and ISPs to offer mobile e-mail, anti-spam protection, and text messaging. Critical Path's identity management applications provide assistance to call centers in the form of password management and directory integration. In addition to telecom carriers and ISPs, the company sells to corporate and government clients. In late 2007 Critical Path announced plans to take the company private. The company has divested itself of certain assets and operations in recent years, including selling its hosted messaging operations to Tucows in 2006 and its Supernews usenet hosting business to GigaNews in 2008.

	Annual Growth	12/03	12/04	12/05	12/06	12/07
Sales ($ mil.)	(11.7%)	72.3	71.1	66.8	46.4	44.0
Net income ($ mil.)	—	(62.1)	(52.0)	(13.6)	(11.0)	(10.4)
Employees	(16.5%)	418	355	331	246	203

CRITICAL THERAPEUTICS, INC.

NASDAQ (GM): CRTX

60 Westview St.
Lexington, MA 02421
Phone: 781-402-5700
Fax: 781-402-5729
Web: www.criticaltherapeutics.com

CEO: Trevor Phillips
CFO: Jeffrey E. Young
HR: −
FYE: December 31
Type: Public

Critical Therapeutics wants to help asthma sufferers breathe a little easier. The drug discovery firm is focused on developing and commercializing therapeutic products to prevent and treat the acute inflammation associated with asthma and critical care diseases. It has acquired worldwide rights from Abbott Laboratories for Zyflo, an immediate-release zileuton that has FDA approval to treat chronic asthma. The company has also launched a controlled-release version, Zyflo CR, which is marketed through the firm's direct sales force and marketing partner Dey. Critical Therapeutics has announced plans to merge with privately held respiratory therapy firm Cornerstone BioPharma.

	Annual Growth	12/03	12/04	12/05	12/06	12/07
Sales ($ mil.)	89.5%	1.0	4.4	6.2	13.1	12.9
Net income ($ mil.)	—	(20.1)	(31.1)	(47.1)	(48.8)	(37.0)
Market value ($ mil.)	(34.1%)	—	192.7	245.0	87.5	55.3
Employees	(32.4%)	—	—	175	—	80

CROCS, INC.

NASDAQ (GS): CROX

6328 Monarch Park Place
Niwot, CO 80503
Phone: 303-848-7000
Fax: 303-468-4266
Web: www.crocs.com

CEO: Ronald R. (Ron) Snyder
CFO: Russ Hammer
HR: −
FYE: December 31
Type: Public

Crocs is taking a bite out of the footwear industry. Its colorful slip-on shoes have gained popularity in the watersports arena and in mainstream fashion. Its shoes, branded as Crocs, are made of proprietary closed-cell resin and designed for men, women, and children; Jibbitz are their popular decorative add-on charms. The firm operates manufacturing facilities in Canada, Mexico, Brazil, and Italy, while suppliers in Asia, Europe, and the US make the rest. Crocs sells through retailers such as Dillard's, Nordstrom, and The Sports Authority, as well as through its own stores and kiosks worldwide. Crocs is expanding on both domestic and international fronts and through acquisitions, such as Ocean Minded in 2007.

	Annual Growth	12/03	12/04	12/05	12/06	12/07
Sales ($ mil.)	415.5%	1.2	13.5	108.6	354.7	847.3
Net income ($ mil.)	—	(1.2)	(1.5)	17.0	64.4	168.2
Market value ($ mil.)	250.9%	—	—	—	862.2	3,025.7
Employees	173.2%	—	260	1,130	2,900	5,300

CROGHAN BANCSHARES, INC.

OTC: CHBH

323 Croghan St.
Fremont, OH 43420
Phone: 419-332-7301
Fax: 419-355-2266
Web: www.croghan.com

CEO: Steven C. Futrell
CFO: Kendall W. Rieman
HR: −
FYE: December 31
Type: Public

Croghan Bancshares is helping to share the wealth in the Buckeye state. The firm is the holding company for Croghan Colonial Bank, a community financial institution serving Fremont, Ohio and the surrounding area. With some 10 branch locations, the bank provides standard banking products and services, including checking and savings accounts, money markets, and loans. The bank's services include business loan originations, consumer loans, construction loans, and bank credit cards. It acquired Custar State Bank in 2005; its single office now operates as a Croghan Colonial branch.

	Annual Growth	12/03	12/04	12/05	12/06	12/07
Assets ($ mil.)	3.1%	402.8	417.2	461.9	458.9	455.1
Net income ($ mil.)	0.5%	5.4	5.1	5.7	5.5	5.5
Market value ($ mil.)	(0.6%)	62.7	69.6	69.0	63.8	61.1
Employees	—	—	—	—	—	164

CROSCILL, INC.

261 5th Ave.
New York, NY 10016
Phone: 212-689-7222
Fax: 212-481-8656
Web: www.croscill.com

CEO: Douglas J. (Doug) Kahn
CFO: Anthony (Tony) Cassella
HR: Richard Wold
FYE: December 31
Type: Private

Croscill has made its bed in the textile industry. The firm makes coordinated home furnishings, including linens for bedrooms, bathrooms, and windows. It also makes pillows, pet beds, table lamps, and accent furniture. Croscill's products, made at its handful of North Carolina plants, are sold through about 10 Croscill outlets, mostly in the South, at major retailers such as Dillard's, Linens 'n Things, and Bed Bath & Beyond, and by mail order in Australia, Canada, Japan, the UK, and the US. Croscill claims credit for producing the first decorative comforter and originating the concept of coordinated merchandise. Founded in 1945 by George Kahn, the firm is still owned and operated by the Kahn family.

	Annual Growth	12/03	12/04	12/05	12/06	12/07
Est. sales ($ mil.)	—	—	—	—	—	45.3
Employees	—	—	—	—	—	800

CROSMAN CORPORATION

7629 Routes 5 and 20
East Bloomfield, NY 14443
Phone: 585-657-6161
Fax: 585-657-5405
Web: www.crosman.com

CEO: Ken D'Arcy
CFO: Robert A. Beckwith
HR: Kathy Chapman
FYE: December 31
Type: Private

There's more than air in the cross hairs at Crosman. A leading air gun maker, the company has more than 50 models of rifles and pistols, as well as paintball guns, ammo, and accessories (scopes, sights, targets, loaders, and clips). Other air guns are offered under the Benjamin Sheridan, Walther, and Smith & Wesson names. Founded in 1923, Crosman focuses on selling to select retailers and sporting goods chains such as Wal-Mart and Dick's Sporting Goods. Its joint paintball venture with Procaps (called Game Face) offers paintball markers, ammo, and related gear. The Compass Group, which acquired Crosman in 2004, sold the company to an affiliate of Wachovia Capital Partners for about $143 million in early 2007.

	Annual Growth	12/03	12/04	12/05	12/06	12/07
Est. sales ($ mil.)	—	—	—	—	—	12.3
Employees	—	—	—	—	—	250

CROSS COUNTRY HEALTHCARE, INC.

NASDAQ (GS): CCRN

6551 Park of Commerce Blvd. NW
Boca Raton, FL 33487
Phone: 561-998-2232
Fax: 800-768-8128
Web: www.crosscountry.com

CEO: Joseph A. Boshart
CFO: Emil Hensel
HR: –
FYE: December 31
Type: Public

Cross Country Healthcare is one of the largest health care staffing firms in the US. Under the Cross Country Staffing brand, the company places traveling nurses and other health care professionals with more than 4,000 acute care hospitals, pharmaceutical companies, nursing homes, schools, and other related facilities across the nation. The firm coordinates travel and housing arrangements for its nurses, whose assignments usually last about three months at a time. Cross Country Healthcare also provides health care education and training, as well as recruiting services for doctors and health care executives. Subsidiaries of the company include Med-Staff and Cejka Search.

	Annual Growth	12/03	12/04	12/05	12/06	12/07
Sales ($ mil.)	1.1%	686.9	654.1	645.4	655.2	718.3
Net income ($ mil.)	(1.2%)	25.8	20.7	14.8	16.6	24.6
Market value ($ mil.)	(1.4%)	476.4	582.6	572.9	700.4	449.7
Employees	(2.4%)	—	—	6,598	6,616	6,285

CROSS TIMBERS ROYALTY TRUST

NYSE: CRT

901 Main St., 17th Fl.
Dallas, TX 75283
Phone: 214-209-2400
Fax: 214-209-2431
Web: www.crosstimberstrust.com

CEO: Nancy G. Willis
CFO: Louis G. Baldwin
HR: –
FYE: December 31
Type: Public

Cross Timbers Royalty Trust distributes royalties from oil and natural gas properties in Texas, Oklahoma, and New Mexico. The trust, which was formed in 1991, does not operate or control any of its properties. Instead, it owns stakes in wells located primarily in gas properties in the San Juan Basin of northwestern New Mexico. The trust's estimated proved gas reserves are 1.7 million barrels of oil and 27.7 billion cu. ft. of gas. XTO Energy (formerly Cross Timbers Oil), which markets the trust's oil and gas, distributed all of its trust units as a dividend to its stockholders in 2003.

	Annual Growth	12/03	12/04	12/05	12/06	12/07
Sales ($ mil.)	11.9%	12.9	15.2	20.6	25.8	20.2
Net income ($ mil.)	11.7%	12.7	14.9	20.3	25.5	19.8
Market value ($ mil.)	9.6%	171.6	239.3	293.4	303.7	247.5
Employees	—	—	—	0		

CROSSTEX ENERGY, INC.

NASDAQ (GS): XTXI

2501 Cedar Springs Rd., Ste. 600
Dallas, TX 75201
Phone: 214-953-9500
Fax: 214-953-9501
Web: www.crosstexenergy.com

CEO: Barry E. Davis
CFO: William W. Davis
HR: Jennifer K. Johnson
FYE: December 31
Type: Public

Crosstex Energy Inc. owns and controls the general partner of natural gas company Crosstex Energy L.P. Crosstex Energy's energy sources and markets are found along the Gulf Coast, from Texas to Florida. Its midstream unit is engaged in natural gas gathering, processing, transmission, and marketing, and its treating division focuses on cleaning natural gas of carbon dioxide and hydrogen sulfide to enable the gas to meet pipeline quality requirements. The company buys natural gas from more than 40 independent producers. Crosstex Energy's assets include 5,000 miles of natural pipeline, 12 processing plants, four fractionators, and 225 gas treating plants. Chieftain Capital Management owns about 18% of the company.

	Annual Growth	12/03	12/04	12/05	12/06	12/07
Sales ($ mil.)	39.7%	1,013.7	1,978.8	3,033.1	3,141.8	3,860.4
Net income ($ mil.)	(2.3%)	13.4	8.7	49.1	16.5	12.2
Market value ($ mil.)	115.5%	—	171.2	268.3	1,455.9	1,713.8
Employees	23.0%	—	—	496	610	—

CROSSTEX ENERGY, L.P.

NASDAQ (GS): XTEX

2501 Cedar Springs, Ste. 100
Dallas, TX 75201
Phone: 214-953-9500
Fax: 214-953-9501
Web: www.crosstexenergy.com

CEO: Barry E. Davis
CFO: William W. Davis
HR: Jennifer K. Johnson
FYE: December 31
Type: Public

Across the Gulf of Mexico region of the US, Crosstex Energy is hard at work pushing natural gas. The company gathers, transports, treats, and processes natural gas through more than 5,000 miles of pipeline, 12 processing plants, four fractionators, and 225 gas treating plants. Its revenues are generated through the purchase and resale of natural gas from more than 40 independent producers located along the US Gulf Coast from Texas to Florida. Through its treating division, Crosstex cleans carbon dioxide and hydrogen sulfide from natural gas, enabling it to meet pipeline quality requirements. Crosstex Energy, Inc., owns and controls the general partner of Crosstex Energy, L.P.

	Annual Growth	12/03	12/04	12/05	12/06	12/07
Sales ($ mil.)	39.7%	1,013.7	1,978.8	3,033.1	3,141.8	3,860.4
Net income ($ mil.)	(2.2%)	15.2	23.7	19.2	(4.2)	13.9
Market value ($ mil.)	69.4%	90.0	288.7	527.1	781.7	740.4
Employees	23.0%	—	—	496	610	—

CROSSTOWN TRADERS, INC.

3740 E. 34th St.
Tucson, AZ 85713
Phone: 520-745-4500
Fax: 520-747-1068
Web: www.oldpueblotraders.com

CEO: Lori Twomey
CFO: Edwin A. Neumann
HR: Robert M. (Bob) Chessen
FYE: January 31
Type: Subsidiary

Crosstown Traders swaps clothing, footwear, and gourmet foods — not just across town, but with shoppers across the country via its catalogs and related e-commerce sites. The company's catalog of catalogs includes Figi's, a purveyor of specialty food and gift products, as well as Old Pueblo Traders, Bedford Fair Lifestyles, Regalia, Intimate Appeal, Brownstone Studio, and Coward Shoe, to name a few, all of which peddle women's shoes and apparel. The direct retailer also operates three outlet stores. Crosstown Traders was acquired by Charming Shoppes, a retail chain specializing in women's plus-size clothing, in mid-2005.

	Annual Growth	1/03	1/04	1/05	1/06	1/07
Est. sales ($ mil.)	—	—	—	—	—	700.6
Employees	—	—	—	—	—	4,000

CROWE CHIZEK AND COMPANY LLC

330 E. Jefferson Blvd.
South Bend, IN 46624
Phone: 574-232-3992
Fax: 574-236-8692
Web: www.crowechizek.com

CEO: Chuck Allen
CFO: Jim Fulton
HR: Julie Wood
FYE: March 31
Type: Partnership

If your company has something to crow about, Crowe Chizek is sure to find out. Crowe Chizek and Company, one of the top 10 accounting firms in the US, has about 20 offices in eight states, primarily in the Midwest and South. The firm offers auditing and assurance, benefit plan services, financial advice, forensic services, tax consulting, and more to state and local governments, auto dealerships, and clients in such industries as agriculture, construction, education, financial services, health care, manufacturing, wholesaling, and distribution.

CROWLEY MARITIME CORPORATION

9487 Regency Sq. Blvd.
Jacksonville, FL 32225
Phone: 904-727-2200
Fax: 904-727-2501
Web: www.crowley.com

CEO: Thomas B. (Tom) Crowley Jr.
CFO: John C. Calvin
HR: William A. (Bill) Pennella
FYE: December 31
Type: Private

Crowley Maritime has pushed and pulled its way into prominence as a leading tug and barge operator. The company's Liner Services unit provides scheduled transportation of containers, trailers, and other cargo, mainly between ports in the US, the Caribbean, and Central America. Other Crowley Maritime units transport oil and chemical products and oil field equipment and provide ship escort, marine salvage, logistics, and fuel distribution services. Overall, the company's fleet includes more than 210 vessels. Crowley Maritime is owned by members of the founding Crowley family, including chairman and CEO Thomas Crowley, and company employees. The company was founded in 1892.

	Annual Growth	12/02	12/03	12/04	12/05	12/06
Sales ($ mil.)	10.7%	977.9	978.0	999.7	1,190.8	1,467.7
Net income ($ mil.)	22.1%	17.3	12.8	24.9	38.9	38.4
Employees	1.0%	3,913	4,000	—	4,300	4,074

CROWN CASTLE INTERNATIONAL CORP.

NYSE: CCI

1220 Augusta Dr., Ste. 500
Houston, TX 77057
Phone: 713-570-3000
Fax: 713-570-3100
Web: www.crowncomm.net

CEO: John P. Kelly
CFO: W. Benjamin (Ben) Moreland
HR: Lisa Davidson
FYE: December 31
Type: Public

Crown Castle International rules over a kingdom of radio towers. Its subsidiaries and joint ventures provide broadcast, data, and wireless communications infrastructure services in Australia, Puerto Rico, and the US. The company's clients include AT&T Mobility (formerly Cingular), Optus, Sprint Nextel, Verizon Wireless, and Vodafone Australia. They lease antenna space on Crown Castle's about 24,000 owned or managed towers. The company has sites primarily in the US and Puerto Rico, and has about 1,400 towers in Australia. It also designs networks, selects and develops sites, and installs antennas.

	Annual Growth	12/03	12/04	12/05	12/06	12/07
Sales ($ mil.)	10.5%	930.3	603.9	676.8	788.2	1,385.5
Net income ($ mil.)	—	(398.4)	235.1	(401.5)	(41.9)	(222.8)
Market value ($ mil.)	48.2%	2,435.0	3,728.4	5,763.8	6,527.2	11,752.3
Employees	23.6%	—	—	785	1,160	1,200

CROWN CENTRAL LLC

1 N. Charles St., Ste. 2100
Baltimore, MD 21201
Phone: 410-539-7400
Fax: 410-659-4747
Web: www.crowncentral.com

CEO: Robert A. Fritz
CFO: –
HR: –
FYE: December 31
Type: Private

Independent oil marketer Crown Central's crown doesn't shine as bright as it used to, but it still shines. The company offers fleet fueling services and maintains branding ownership of some 75 "Crown" retail stations and stores operated by independent distributors and dealers in the Mid-Atlantic and Southeast. Its two refineries in Texas, with a total capacity of 152,000 barrels per day, were sold in 2005; most of its 300 gas stations were sold in 2004 and 2005. Rosemore, the holding company of Henry Rosenberg and his family, took control of Crown Central in 2001 after beating out a competing bid for control from rival Apex Oil.

	Annual Growth	12/03	12/04	12/05	12/06	12/07
Est. sales ($ mil.)	—	—	—	—	—	1,566.4
Employees	—	—	—	—	—	2,600

CROWN CRAFTS, INC.

NASDAQ (CM): CRWS

916 S. Burnside Ave.
Gonzales, LA 70737
Phone: 225-647-9100
Fax: 225-647-8331
Web: www.crowncrafts.com

CEO: E. Randall Chestnut
CFO: Amy Vidrine Samson
HR: Alicia Hill
FYE: Sunday nearest March 31
Type: Public

Prospects for new opportunities keep Crown Crafts drooling. Operating through its subsidiaries, Hamco and Crown Crafts Infant Products, it designs and sells textile products for infants and juveniles including baby bibs, burp cloths, bathing accessories, and bedding. Crown Crafts, founded in 1957, has sought to regain profitability by selling or shuttering its US manufacturing operations and relying on foreign contractors, mainly in China, to make its goods. Its products are sold in department and specialty stores, mass retailers, catalog houses, and outlet stores. In 2007 Crown Crafts sold its Churchill Weavers business (citing competition from imports) and bought Springs Global US's infant and toddler line.

	Annual Growth	3/04	3/05	3/06	3/07	3/08
Sales ($ mil.)	(3.5%)	86.2	83.9	72.6	72.0	74.9
Net income ($ mil.)	8.5%	3.1	2.4	8.0	7.6	4.3
Market value ($ mil.)	60.6%	5.2	4.7	6.1	48.0	34.8
Employees	—	—	—	—	145	—

CROWN EQUIPMENT CORPORATION

44 S. Washington St.
New Bremen, OH 45869
Phone: 419-629-2311
Fax: 419-629-2900
Web: www.crown.com

CEO: James F. Dicke II
CFO: Kent W. Spille
HR: Randall W. (Randy) Niekamp
FYE: March 31
Type: Private

The jewels in the crown of Crown Equipment Corporation are electric heavy-duty lift trucks used for maneuvering goods in warehouses and distribution centers. A market leader, the company's products include narrow-aisle stacking equipment, powered pallet trucks, and forklift trucks. Its equipment can move 4-ton loads and stack pallets nearly 45 feet high. Crown Equipment sells its products globally through retailers. The company, founded in 1945 by brothers Carl and Allen Dicke, originally made temperature controls for coal furnaces. It began making material-handling equipment in the 1950s. The Dicke family still controls Crown Equipment.

	Annual Growth	3/02	3/03	3/04	3/05	3/06
Sales ($ mil.)	14.7%	966.0	1,000.0	1,090.0	1,466.0	1,670.0
Employees	6.3%	6,500	6,800	6,900	7,636	8,300

An in-depth profile of this company is available to Hoover's Online members at hoovers.com.

CROWN HOLDINGS, INC.

NYSE: CCK

1 Crown Way
Philadelphia, PA 19154
Phone: 215-698-5100
Fax: 215-676-7245
Web: www.crowncork.com

CEO: John W. Conway
CFO: Alan W. Rutherford
HR: Gary L. Burgess
FYE: December 31
Type: Public

Crown Holdings knows how to keep a lid on it. The company is a top world-wide producer of consumer packaging; metal food and beverage cans and related packaging are the company's primary source of income. Its product portfolio also includes aerosol cans and a wide variety of metal caps, crowns, and closures, as well as specialty packaging such as decorative novelty containers and industrial paint cans. Crown Holdings also makes canmaking equipment and replacement parts. The company has divested most of its plastic closure and container operations.

	Annual Growth	12/03	12/04	12/05	12/06	12/07
Sales ($ mil.)	3.9%	6,630.0	7,199.0	6,908.0	6,982.0	7,727.0
Net income ($ mil.)	—	(32.0)	51.0	(362.0)	309.0	528.0
Market value ($ mil.)	28.7%	1,495.1	2,274.8	3,255.9	3,403.9	4,098.3
Employees	(9.6%)	—	—	24,000	21,700	—

CROWN MEDIA HOLDINGS, INC.

NASDAQ (GM): CRWN

12700 Ventura Blvd., Ste. 200
Studio City, CA 91604
Phone: 818-755-2400
Fax: 818-755-2564
Web: www.hallmarkchannel.com

CEO: Henry S. Schleiff
CFO: Brian C. Stewart
HR: –
FYE: December 31
Type: Public

Family-friendly TV is the jewel in this Crown. Crown Media Holdings owns and operates the Hallmark Channel, a cable network that specializes in family-oriented TV fare. It features mostly third-party programming, including such TV series as *7th Heaven, Little House on the Prairie,* and *Matlock,* as well as made for TV movies, feature films, and miniseries. The channel reaches more than 89 million US homes. Crown Media also operates the Hallmark Movie Channel, a 24-hour channel that primarily offers feature films and miniseries; it reaches about 5.5 million homes. Hallmark Cards has about 95% voting control of the company.

	Annual Growth	12/03	12/04	12/05	12/06	12/07
Sales ($ mil.)	3.1%	207.5	241.3	197.4	201.2	234.4
Net income ($ mil.)	—	(205.1)	(316.8)	(232.8)	(389.0)	(159.0)
Market value ($ mil.)	(7.2%)	610.8	635.2	679.7	269.0	453.4
Employees	(32.9%)	—	351	186	158	—

CRUM & FORSTER HOLDINGS CORP.

305 Madison Ave.
Morristown, NJ 07962
Phone: 973-490-6600
Fax: 973-490-6940
Web: www.cfins.com

CEO: Douglas M. (Doug) Libby
CFO: Mary Jane Robertson
HR: –
FYE: December 31
Type: Subsidiary

Crum & Forster looks out for the best interests of employers. Through eight subsidiaries, the company offers an array of property/casualty insurance products to businesses, including management liability, automobile, and workers' compensation coverage. Crum & Forster also offers THE DEFENDER, a broad commercial umbrella policy. In addition, the company's ECom products secure businesses against the growing risks, from hackers to power failures, associated with the Internet and e-commerce. The company's products are sold through some 1,300 independent brokers across the US. Acquired by Fairfax Financial Holdings in 1998, Crum & Forster has been a wholly owned subsidiary ever since.

	Annual Growth	12/02	12/03	12/04	12/05	12/06
Assets ($ mil.)	—	—	—	—	—	6,443.6
Net income ($ mil.)	—	—	—	—	—	312.3
Employees	—	—	—	—	—	400

CRUNCH FITNESS INTERNATIONAL, INC.

22 W. 19th St., Fl. 4
New York, NY 10011
Phone: 212-993-0300
Fax: 212-367-0960
Web: www.crunch.com

CEO: Tim Miller
CFO: Keith A. McGowan
HR: Daniel Espino
FYE: December 31
Type: Private

Crunch Fitness helps city folk stay in shape. The company operates about 30 physical fitness facilities in urban locations across the US. Crunch offers trendy workouts such as Crunch Striptease, African Dance, Cardio A Go Go, and Hip-Hop Groove. It also offers personal training sessions to its members. The company sells a variety of related fitness products including apparel, exercise videos, books, and music compilation CDs. Crunch Fitness was founded in 1989 as a small basement aerobics studio with no air-conditioning in Manhattan's East Village. Bally Fitness acquired the company in 2002 and sold it off in 2006.

	Annual Growth	12/03	12/04	12/05	12/06	12/07
Est. sales ($ mil.)	—	—	—	—	—	118.7
Employees	—	—	—	—	—	2,200

CRUTCHFIELD CORPORATION

1 Crutchfield Park
Charlottesville, VA 22911
Phone: 434-817-1000
Fax: 434-817-1010
Web: www.crutchfield.com

CEO: William G. (Bill) Crutchfield Jr.
CFO: Richard Stavitski
HR: Mark Maynard
FYE: December 31
Type: Private

Crutchfield Corporation wants you to lean on it when choosing consumer electronics. The company sells its wares via catalog, call center, online, and through two retail stores in Virginia. Its products include televisions, home theater systems, DVD players, VCRs, camcorders, digital cameras, and speakers. Crutchfield also sells automotive audio and video products, such as speakers, amplifiers, and navigation systems. It carries major brands, including Sony, Pioneer, and Kenwood. The firm was founded by Bill Crutchfield in 1974, and was one of the first electronics retailers to launch an e-commerce site (1995). Its catalog is mailed to about 6 million households. Crutchfield entered the Canadian market in 2007.

CRUZAN INTERNATIONAL, INC.

222 Lakeview Ave., Ste. 1500
West Palm Beach, FL 33401
Phone: 561-655-8977
Fax: 561-655-9718
Web: www.todhunter.com

CEO: Ola Salmén
CFO: Ezra Shashoua
HR: –
FYE: October 30
Type: Subsidiary

Cruzan International's spirits give brandy its buzz. The company, which changed its name from Todhunter International in 2005 to emphasize its leading rum brand, distills citrus juice by-products and molasses to make brandies, rums, wines, and other spirits for sale to liquor makers as bulk alcohol. Cruzan also bottles beverages under contract; produces and imports spirits; and makes cooking wine, industrial alcohol, vinegar, and an alcohol byproduct for animal feed. Trinidadian distiller Angostura Holdings Limited owned more than 60% of the company until 2005, but sold its stake to the V&S Group for more than $120 million. A V&S subsidiary acquired all of Cruzan in 2006.

	Annual Growth	10/03	10/04	10/05	10/06	10/07
Est. sales ($ mil.)	—	—	—	—	—	133.5
Employees	—	—	—	—	—	415

CRYOCOR, INC.

9717 Pacific Heights Blvd.
San Diego, CA 92121
Phone: 858-909-2200
Fax: 858-909-2300
Web: www.cryocor.com

CEO: Joseph M. (Joe) Fitzgerald
CFO: Sam R. Leno
HR: –
FYE: December 31
Type: Subsidiary

CryoCor has found that being cold-hearted can be helpful sometimes. The company makes a minimally invasive disposable catheter and cooling console to treat common cardiac arrhythmias (heart rhythm disorders) known as atrial fibrillation and atrial flutter. Unlike commonly used heat-based cardiac ablation, its cryoablation system inserts a catheter into a blood vessel connected with the heart and uses extreme cold to destroy targeted cells and help the heart function normally. The cryoablation system has been approved in Europe and has received preliminary approval in the US.

	Annual Growth	12/03	12/04	12/05	12/06	12/07
Sales ($ mil.)	18.9%	0.3	0.5	0.8	0.5	0.6
Net income ($ mil.)	—	(11.2)	(15.8)	(17.1)	(15.1)	(15.8)
Employees	—	—	—	46	—	—

CRYOLIFE, INC.

NYSE: CRY

1655 Roberts Blvd. NW
Kennesaw, GA 30144
Phone: 770-419-3355
Fax: 770-426-0031
Web: www.cryolife.com

CEO: Steven G. Anderson
CFO: D. Ashley Lee
HR: –
FYE: December 31
Type: Public

CryoLife preserves lives, as well as the cardiovascular tissues that keep life going. The company takes human heart valves and blood vessels from deceased volunteer donors, processes them, and stores them in liquid nitrogen freezers (a process called cryopreservation). It then ships them to surgeons, who implant them during cardiac and vascular repair procedures. For some preserved tissue, the company uses its proprietary SynerGraft technology, which reduces the presence of donor cells and makes the tissue more compatible with the recipient. In addition to its tissue preservation operations, CryoLife develops implantable biomaterials, including BioGlue, an adhesive used to seal internal surgical wounds.

	Annual Growth	12/03	12/04	12/05	12/06	12/07
Sales ($ mil.)	12.3%	59.5	62.4	69.3	81.3	94.8
Net income ($ mil.)	—	(32.3)	(18.8)	(19.5)	0.4	7.2
Market value ($ mil.)	17.7%	114.2	165.5	82.5	190.5	219.2
Employees	5.6%	—	—	363	—	405

CRYSTAL RIVER CAPITAL, INC.

NYSE: CRZ

3 World Financial Ctr., 200 Vesey St., 10th Fl.
New York, NY 10281
Phone: 212-549-8400
Fax: 212-549-8304
Web: www.crystalriverreit.com

CEO: William Powell
CFO: Craig J. Laurie
HR: –
FYE: December 31
Type: Public

Crystal River Capital has no crystal ball, but it hopes its investment decisions prove to be far-sighted. The real estate investment trust (REIT) manages a portfolio worth some $4 billion consisting primarily of residential mortgage-backed securities; it also invests in commercial mortgage-backed securities, whole mortgage loans, and entities that own real estate, as well as diversified asset-backed securities and alternative assets. Formed in 2005, the company is managed by Hyperion Brookfield Asset Management, a subsidiary of Toronto-based Brookfield Asset Management.

	Annual Growth	12/03	12/04	12/05	12/06	12/07
Sales ($ mil.)	17.3%	—	—	—	201.2	236.1
Net income ($ mil.)	—	—	—	—	46.9	(345.9)
Market value ($ mil.)	(44.2%)	—	—	—	638.8	356.7
Employees	—	—	—	—	—	—

CSB BANCORP, INC.

OTC: CSBB

91 N. Clay St.
Millersburg, OH 44654
Phone: 330-674-9015
Fax: –
Web: www.csb1.com

CEO: Eddie L. Steiner
CFO: Paula J. Meiler
HR: Julie A. Jones
FYE: December 31
Type: Public

CSB Bancorp has a financial hold on the center of the Buckeye State. The firm is the holding company for The Commercial and Savings Bank, which serves Holmes County and surrounding areas of east-central Ohio from about 10 branches. It offers traditional retail banking products and services including checking and savings accounts, IRAs, and loans. Its loan portfolio is composed mostly of business loans and residential mortgages; in addition, the company originates commercial mortgages, construction loans, and installment loans. The Commercial and Savings Bank also offers brokerage and trust services. CSB Bancorp is buying another area community bank, the three-branch Indian Village Community Bank.

	Annual Growth	12/03	12/04	12/05	12/06	12/07
Assets ($ mil.)	3.4%	306.2	317.3	321.0	327.2	350.3
Net income ($ mil.)	13.6%	2.1	2.5	2.9	3.1	3.5
Market value ($ mil.)	(0.8%)	45.0	52.9	54.1	46.8	43.4
Employees	—	—	—	—	—	133

CSG SYSTEMS INTERNATIONAL, INC.

NASDAQ (GS): CSGS

9555 Maroon Cir.
Englewood, CO 80112
Phone: 303-200-2000
Fax: 303-804-4965
Web: www.csgsystems.com

CEO: Peter E. Kalan
CFO: Randy R. Wiese
HR: Rae-Ellen Hamilton
FYE: December 31
Type: Public

CSRs love CSG. CSG Systems International makes life a little easier for customer service representatives (CSRs) with its customer care and billing services, which provide outsourced transaction processing and customer service automation services for cable TV, direct broadcast satellite, online services, and telecom companies. CSG's offerings are used to set up customer accounts, process orders, manage invoices, and perform marketing analysis. The company primarily serves the North American cable and direct broadcast satellite communications markets.

	Annual Growth	12/03	12/04	12/05	12/06	12/07
Sales ($ mil.)	(6.4%)	545.3	529.8	377.3	383.1	419.3
Net income ($ mil.)	—	(26.3)	47.2	53.2	59.8	60.8
Market value ($ mil.)	(6.9%)	671.8	954.0	1,068.8	1,251.8	504.5
Employees	10.4%	—	—	1,540	1,685	1,877

CSK AUTO CORPORATION

NYSE: CAO

645 E. Missouri Ave., Ste. 400
Phoenix, AZ 85012
Phone: 602-265-9200
Fax: 602-631-7321
Web: www.cskauto.com

CEO: Lawrence N. (Larry) Mondry
CFO: James D. (Jim) Constantine
HR: John Saar
FYE: Sunday nearest January 31
Type: Public

CSK Auto likes people who look under their own hoods. The retailer of automotive parts and accessories sells mainly to do-it-yourselfers but also to auto professionals and commercial installers. CSK Auto owns some 1,350 stores in about 22 states under the names Checker Auto Parts, Schuck's Auto Supply, Kragen Auto Parts, and Murray's Discount Auto Stores. Kragen Auto Parts runs more than 500 stores, mostly in California; Checker Auto Parts operates about 490 stores throughout the West and Hawaii; and Schucks' some 220 stores are in Washington, Oregon, Idaho, Alaska, and California. CSK Auto has agreed to be acquired by rival O'Reilly Automotive for about $500 million, plus debt.

	Annual Growth	1/04	1/05	1/06	1/07	1/08
Sales ($ mil.)	4.1%	1,578.1	1,577.5	1,651.3	1,907.8	1,851.7
Net income ($ mil.)	—	10.8	36.9	57.8	6.3	(11.1)
Market value ($ mil.)	(18.7%)	907.2	693.9	696.9	723.4	395.4
Employees	—	—	—	14,762	—	—

An in-depth profile of this company is available to Hoover's Online members at hoovers.com.

455

CSL BEHRING

1020 1st Ave.
King of Prussia, PA 19406
Phone: 610-878-4000
Fax: 610-878-4009
Web: www.cslbehring.com

CEO: Peter Turner
CFO: –
HR: Kathy Quay
FYE: December 31
Type: Subsidiary

Take away the red and white blood cells from blood and you get plasma, a protein-rich fluid. CSL Behring is among the world's largest fully integrated plasma collection companies. Through subsidiary ZLB Plasma, the company collects plasma through dozens of facilities in the US and Germany. CSL Behring also develops plasma protein biotherapeutics to treat a range of other disorders, including hemophilia, immune disorders, and emphysema. The company takes the second part of its name from Emil von Behring, a German doctor who worked to find treatments for infectious diseases. Formerly known as ZLB Behring, the company was formed by parent CSL Limited from the ashes of Aventis Behring and ZLB Bioplasma.

	Annual Growth	12/03	12/04	12/05	12/06	12/07
Est. sales ($ mil.)	—	—	—	—	—	351.1
Employees	—	—	—	—	—	5,800

CSP INC.

NASDAQ (GM): CSPI

43 Manning Rd.
Billerica, MA 01821
Phone: 978-663-7598
Fax: 978-663-0150
Web: www.cspi.com

CEO: Alexander R. Lupinetti
CFO: Gary W. Levine
HR: Gary Levine
FYE: September 30
Type: Public

CSP primarily provides information technology services, including the resale and integration of computer hardware and software, through its MODCOMP subsidiary. Other services include maintenance and custom software development. MODCOMP serves clients in Germany, the UK, and the US; industries served include financial services, manufacturing, and telecommunications. CSP's systems segment develops and builds computer signal processing systems for aerospace and defense markets. Its MultiComputer product line includes systems used for radar, sonar, surveillance, and other applications; sales are made directly in the US and through distributors and resellers to customers in Asia, India, and Europe.

	Annual Growth	9/03	9/04	9/05	9/06	9/07
Sales ($ mil.)	30.4%	32.5	52.8	57.5	68.9	94.0
Net income ($ mil.)	—	(1.4)	1.2	0.8	2.0	4.1
Market value ($ mil.)	16.3%	16.1	26.8	26.2	32.3	29.5
Employees	(4.2%)	—	—	147	—	135

CSS INDUSTRIES, INC.

NYSE: CSS

1845 Walnut St., Ste. 800
Philadelphia, PA 19103
Phone: 215-569-9900
Fax: 215-569-9979
Web: www.cssindustries.com

CEO: Christopher J. Munyan
CFO: Clifford E. Pietrafitta
HR: William G. Kiesling
FYE: March 31
Type: Public

Every day is Christmas at CSS Industries, maker of seasonal and everyday decorative products such as gift wrap, gift bags, ribbons, bows, stationery, and cards, as well as floral, craft, and packaging items. The company also makes dye for Easter eggs (Dudley's), valentines for classroom exchange, and Halloween makeup and costumes. Customers include mass-merchandise retailers, warehouse clubs, and drug and food chains, primarily in the US and Canada. (Wal-Mart and Target account for a combined 39% of sales.) Originally founded as a furniture and department store retailer in 1923, the company shifted gears in the mid-1980s through acquisitions, such as The Paper Magic Group, Berwick Offray, and C.R. Gibson.

	Annual Growth	3/04	3/05	3/06	3/07	3/08
Sales ($ mil.)	(2.0%)	539.3	536.4	525.5	530.7	498.3
Net income ($ mil.)	(4.0%)	29.9	30.7	21.8	23.9	25.4
Market value ($ mil.)	(2.3%)	393.4	379.5	343.3	406.5	358.9
Employees	(20.6%)	—	—	3,400	2,700	—

CSX CORPORATION

NYSE: CSX

500 Water St., 15th Fl.
Jacksonville, FL 32202
Phone: 904-359-3200
Fax: 904-633-3450
Web: www.csx.com

CEO: Michael J. Ward
CFO: Oscar Munoz
HR: Robert J. Haulter
FYE: Last Friday in December
Type: Public

CSX banks on the railway as the right way to make money. Its main subsidiary, CSX Transportation (CSXT), operates a major rail system (some 21,000 route miles) in the eastern US. The freight carrier links 23 states, the District of Columbia, and two Canadian provinces. Freight hauled by the company includes a wide variety of merchandise, coal, automotive products, and intermodal containers. CSX's rail segment, which accounts for more than 80% of the company's sales, also includes units that operate motor vehicle distribution centers and bulk cargo terminals. Subsidiary CSX Intermodal arranges the transportation of freight by combinations of road and rail carriers.

	Annual Growth	12/03	12/04	12/05	12/06	12/07
Sales ($ mil.)	6.5%	7,793.0	352.0	8,618.0	9,566.0	10,030.0
Net income ($ mil.)	52.7%	246.0	140.0	1,145.0	1,310.0	1,336.0
Market value ($ mil.)	47.3%	3,834.7	4,321.0	5,539.1	15,072.2	18,056.1
Employees	(0.8%)	—	35,847	35,000	36,000	35,000

CSX TRANSPORTATION INC.

500 Water St., 15th Fl.
Jacksonville, FL 32202
Phone: 904-359-3200
Fax: 904-359-2459
Web: www.csxt.com

CEO: Michael J. Ward
CFO: Oscar Munoz
HR: –
FYE: Last Friday in December
Type: Subsidiary

CSX Transportation, the primary subsidiary of CSX, provides rail freight transportation over a network of about 21,000 route miles of track in 23 states in the eastern half of the US, the District of Columbia, and two Canadian provinces. Freight carried by the railroad includes merchandise (agricultural products, chemicals, food and consumer products, forest products, metals, and phosphates and fertilizer), coal, motor vehicles and related products, and intermodal containers. Merchandise accounts for the largest share of CSX Transportation's revenue. Sister company CSX Intermodal arranges transportation of containerized freight by road and rail.

CT CORPORATION

11 8th Ave.
New York, NY 10011
Phone: 212-894-8940
Fax: 212-894-8581
Web: www.ctadvantage.com

CEO: Gene A. Landoe
CFO: Joseph (Joe) D'Avanzo
HR: –
FYE: December 31
Type: Subsidiary

CT helps Inc.'s and Corp.'s dot their i's and cross their t's. The company assists large and small businesses and their lawyers in their efforts to comply with the various rules that govern the existence of corporate entities. CT's services include acting as a registered agent and handling corporate, Uniform Commercial Code, and SEC filings. The company operates from offices throughout the US, as well as through a network of correspondents. Subsidiary CT Tymetrix makes software used to manage law practices. CT, which was founded in 1892, is a unit of Netherlands-based publisher Wolters Kluwer.

	Annual Growth	12/03	12/04	12/05	12/06	12/07
Est. sales ($ mil.)	—	—	—	—	—	135.3
Employees	—	—	—	—	—	1,563

CTI GROUP (HOLDINGS) INC.

OTC: CTIG

333 N. Alabama St., Ste. 240
Indianapolis, IN 46204
Phone: 317-262-4666
Fax: 317-262-4849
Web: www.ctigroup.com

CEO: John Birbeck
CFO: Manfred (Fred) Hanuschek
HR: –
FYE: December 31
Type: Public

CTI Group (Holdings) helps companies act on their transactions. The company provides software and services for billing, customer care, and telemanagement. Targeting service providers in the telecom, information technology, financial, cable, and health care industries, CTI offers software that analyzes billing data (SmartBill), automates telecommunications spending (SmartSpend), and handles call accounting (Proteus). The company also offers professional services and outsourced call center management, output processing, training, support, and marketing services. CTI has acquired billing services provider Ryder Systems (not to be confused with Ryder System) for about $11 million.

	Annual Growth	12/03	12/04	12/05	12/06	12/07
Sales ($ mil.)	12.9%	13.1	16.2	15.3	12.8	21.3
Net income ($ mil.)	—	(2.5)	0.9	0.5	(1.1)	(1.5)
Market value ($ mil.)	(5.3%)	10.2	10.8	9.3	8.8	8.2
Employees	—	—	—	—	—	—

CTI INDUSTRIES CORPORATION

NASDAQ (CM): CTIB

22160 N. Pepper Rd.
Barrington, IL 60010
Phone: 847-382-1000
Fax: 847-382-1219
Web: www.ctiindustries.com

CEO: Howard W. Schwan
CFO: Stephen M. Merrick
HR: Bertha Vertiz
FYE: December 31
Type: Public

Ballooning profits would be most welcome at CTI Industries Corporation. The company's metalized and latex balloons are decorated with messages and cartoon characters, such as Garfield and Miss Spider. It sells balloons and novelty inflatable items to distributors, retailers, grocers, and florists. CTI Industries also makes wrapping and custom film for commercial and industrial uses such as food packaging (candy wrappers) and dunnage bags (inflatable pouches used as cushioning during shipping). Its top three customers account for about 50% of sales. Chairman John Schwan and EVP Stephen Merrick each own approximately 27% of CTI.

	Annual Growth	12/03	12/04	12/05	12/06	12/07
Sales ($ mil.)	0.1%	36.3	37.2	29.2	35.4	36.5
Net income ($ mil.)	—	(0.6)	(2.5)	(0.3)	1.9	0.1
Market value ($ mil.)	22.6%	4.3	2.8	5.9	10.4	9.8
Employees	(68.2%)	—	—	280	89	—

CTPARTNERS

28601 Chagrin Blvd., Ste. 600
Cleveland, OH 44122
Phone: 216-682-3200
Fax: 216-464-6172
Web: www.ctnet.com

CEO: Brian M. Sullivan
CFO: David Nocifora
HR: –
FYE: December 31
Type: Private

CTPartners (formerly Christian & Timbers) finds the hidden treasures of senior management. Founded in 1980, the company performs CEO, board member, and senior-level executive management searches for both large and emerging companies around the globe. It has special expertise in filling top-level technology positions, but also operates a number of other industry practices, including financial services, human resources, media and entertainment, and telecommunications. Placing executives with such companies as Sony, American Express, and Reed Elsevier Group, the company promises to deliver talent within 100 days.

	Annual Growth	12/02	12/03	12/04	12/05	12/06
Sales ($ mil.)	—	—	—	—	—	115.0
Employees	—	—	—	—	—	330

CTS CORPORATION

NYSE: CTS

905 West Blvd. North
Elkhart, IN 46514
Phone: 574-293-7511
Fax: 574-293-6146
Web: www.ctscorp.com

CEO: Vinod M. Khilnani
CFO: Donna L. Belusar
HR: James L. Cummins
FYE: December 31
Type: Public

CTS could stand for components and sensors. The company makes electronic components for OEMs in the communications, computer, and automotive industries. Products include automotive sensors, oscillators, quartz crystals, resistors, and switches. CTS also makes radio-frequency modules for wireless phones, pointing sticks for notebook computer keyboards, and cofired ceramics for use in Global Positioning System (GPS) devices. In addition the company provides contract design and manufacturing of backplanes and interconnect systems. Customers include Hewlett-Packard (17% of sales) and Motorola. About 60% of the company's sales comes from outside the US.

	Annual Growth	12/03	12/04	12/05	12/06	12/07
Sales ($ mil.)	10.3%	463.0	531.3	617.5	655.6	685.9
Net income ($ mil.)	19.2%	12.6	20.0	22.2	24.2	25.4
Market value ($ mil.)	(4.8%)	414.8	477.2	396.6	562.4	340.7
Employees	(1.5%)	5,041	4,487	4,902	4,977	4,746

⊞ CUBIC CORPORATION

AMEX: CUB

9333 Balboa Ave.
San Diego, CA 92123
Phone: 858-277-6780
Fax: 858-277-1878
Web: www.cubic.com

CEO: Walter J. Zable
CFO: William W. Boyle
HR: Bernard A. (Bernie) Kulchin
FYE: September 30
Type: Public

Cubic equips people to fight their way through both enemy and subway lines. For the former, it makes combat-simulation training products; for the latter, it makes automatic fare-collection (AFC) systems. Besides training systems, Cubic's defense segment provides training and support services to military forces and makes electronic communications and surveillance equipment. On the transit side, Cubic has installed its AFC systems worldwide in cities such as New York, San Francisco, London, Sydney, and Washington, DC. Founder and CEO Walter Zable controls 40% of the company.

	Annual Growth	9/03	9/04	9/05	9/06	9/07
Sales ($ mil.)	8.8%	634.1	722.0	804.4	821.4	889.9
Net income ($ mil.)	3.3%	36.5	36.9	11.6	24.1	41.6
Market value ($ mil.)	13.8%	671.2	611.9	457.4	523.2	1,126.8
Employees	0.0%	—	—	6,000	6,000	6,000

CUBIST PHARMACEUTICALS, INC.

NASDAQ (GS): CBST

65 Hayden Ave.
Lexington, MA 02421
Phone: 781-860-8660
Fax: 781-861-0566
Web: www.cubist.com

CEO: Michael W. (Mike) Bonney
CFO: David W. J. McGirr
HR: Maureen Powers
FYE: December 31
Type: Public

Fighting infection is a modern art form at Cubist Pharmaceuticals. The company is developing antimicrobial agents that aim to treat drug-resistant infections typically found in hospitals and other health care institutions. Its flagship product Cubicin is an intravenous antibiotic that is FDA-approved to fight staph infections of the skin and blood; it has also received regulatory approval in Europe and a handful of non-European countries to treat certain kinds of infections. Cubist markets the drug in the US using its own sales force. It has agreements with numerous other firms to develop and market the drug internationally; its partners include Novartis for Europe, Merck for Japan, and AstraZeneca for China.

	Annual Growth	12/03	12/04	12/05	12/06	12/07
Sales ($ mil.)	198.7%	3.7	68.1	120.6	194.8	294.6
Net income ($ mil.)	—	(115.0)	(76.5)	(31.9)	(0.4)	48.2
Market value ($ mil.)	23.9%	488.4	605.1	1,144.5	996.1	1,151.5
Employees	11.1%	—	—	369	410	—

CUISINE SOLUTIONS, INC.

AMEX: FZN

85 S. Bragg St., Ste. 600
Alexandria, VA 22312
Phone: 703-270-2900
Fax: 703-750-1158
Web: www.cuisinesolutions.com

CEO: Stanislas Vilgrain
CFO: Ronald R. Zilkowski
HR: –
FYE: Last Saturday in June
Type: Public

Whether you're traveling for pleasure or to serve your country, this company tries to make sure you get a good meal. Cuisine Solutions is a leading supplier of prepared meals for a variety of customers, including travel and transportation providers, the military, retail stores, and foodservice operators. Through its production facilities in the US and France, the company makes fully cooked and frozen meals, including chicken, seafood, and beef items, along with pasta and sauces, and distributes those meals throughout the US and in Europe. The family of chairman Jean-Louis Vilgrain owns about 60% of the company.

	Annual Growth	6/03	6/04	6/05	6/06	6/07
Sales ($ mil.)	30.4%	27.8	36.7	46.3	64.1	80.3
Net income ($ mil.)	—	(4.1)	(1.0)	1.7	3.7	10.5
Market value ($ mil.)	83.5%	8.9	28.5	103.7	83.0	100.6
Employees	18.4%	180	230	263	302	354

CULLEN/FROST BANKERS, INC.

NYSE: CFR

100 W. Houston St.
San Antonio, TX 78205
Phone: 210-220-4011
Fax: 210-220-4325
Web: www.frostbank.com

CEO: Richard W. (Dick) Evans Jr.
CFO: Phillip D. Green
HR: Emily A. Skillman
FYE: December 31
Type: Public

One of the largest independent bank holding companies in Texas, Cullen/Frost Bankers owns Frost National Bank through a second-tier holding company, the New Galveston Company. The bank serves individuals and local businesses through more than 100 branches in Texas; the company also serves clients in Mexico. Frost National Bank offers commercial and consumer deposit products and loans, international banking, insurance, trust and brokerage services, and correspondent banking. Subsidiaries include Frost Insurance Agency, Frost Brokerage Services, and investment banking firm Frost Securities. Commercial and industrial loans make up more than 45% of Frost Bank's loan portfolio; commercial mortgages are around 25%.

	Annual Growth	12/03	12/04	12/05	12/06	12/07
Assets ($ mil.)	8.7%	9,672.1	9,952.8	11,741.4	13,224.2	13,485.0
Net income ($ mil.)	12.9%	130.5	141.3	165.4	193.6	212.1
Market value ($ mil.)	9.1%	2,100.6	2,523.5	2,924.6	3,340.2	2,971.8
Employees	5.7%	—	—	3,386	3,652	3,781

CULLIGAN INTERNATIONAL COMPANY

9399 West Higgins Rd.
Rosemont, IL 60018
Phone: 847-430-2800
Fax: 847-430-1524
Web: www.culligan.com

CEO: Mark Seals
CFO: Maria Henry
HR: Janet Snow-Godfrey
FYE: June 30
Type: Private

"Hey Culligan Man!" To be sure, the phrase made famous by an ad campaign still rings in the ears of Culligan International workers. Formerly a subsidiary of Veolia Environnement, Culligan produces filters for tap water, household water softeners, microfiltration products, desalination systems, and portable deionization services for commercial and industrial users. The franchised "Culligan Man" noted in the advertising phrase delivers bottled water and water systems to consumers and businesses throughout the US and in more than 90 other countries. Besides Culligan, the company's brand names include Everpure, Elga, and Bruner. Buyout firm Clayton, Dubilier & Rice acquired the company for $610 million in 2004.

CULP, INC.

NYSE: CFI

1823 Eastchester Dr.
High Point, NC 27265
Phone: 336-889-5161
Fax: 336-889-7246
Web: www.culpinc.com

CEO: Franklin N. Saxon
CFO: Kenneth R. Bowling
HR: Teresa Huffman
FYE: Sunday nearest April 30
Type: Public

Culp just wants to keep on ticking. The company is one of the world's largest makers of furniture upholstery fabrics and mattress fabrics (known as ticking). Its upholstery fabrics include wovens (jacquards and dobbies), prints (heat-transfer), and velvets (woven and tufted). Culp's fabrics are used in upholstering residential and commercial furniture such as recliners, sofas, and love seats. Its ticking is used for covering mattresses and box springs. Major customers include furniture makers Bassett, Furniture Brands International, and La-Z-Boy (11% of sales), and mattress makers Sealy and Serta. Chairman Robert G. Culp III (son of the founder) owns nearly 18% of the company.

	Annual Growth	4/03	4/04	4/05	4/06	4/07
Sales ($ mil.)	(7.3%)	339.6	318.1	286.5	261.1	250.5
Net income ($ mil.)	—	(24.9)	7.2	(17.9)	(11.8)	(1.3)
Market value ($ mil.)	16.7%	57.6	99.4	54.3	54.1	106.8
Employees	(31.6%)	—	—	1,900	1,300	—

CULVER FRANCHISING SYSTEM, INC.

540 Water St.
Prairie du Sac, WI 53578
Phone: 608-643-7980
Fax: 608-643-7982
Web: www.culvers.com

CEO: Craig C. Culver
CFO: Joseph (Joe) Koss
HR: Lisa Ganser
FYE: December 31
Type: Private

If you think ButterBurgers are better burgers, then you must be a fan of Culver's. Culver Franchising System operates a chain of more than 350 Culver's quick-service restaurants, popular for their signature ButterBurgers (hamburgers served on a grilled buttered bun) and frozen custard. The menu also includes chicken, fish, and pork sandwiches, salads, and dinner items such as shrimp and Norwegian cod. The chain has locations in Wisconsin and about 15 other states. Nearly all of the restaurants are operated by franchisees. President Craig Culver and his family started the business in 1984.

	Annual Growth	12/03	12/04	12/05	12/06	12/07
Est. sales ($ mil.)	—	—	—	—	—	45.8
Employees	—	—	—	—	—	290

CUMBERLAND FARMS, INC.

777 Dedham St.
Canton, MA 02021
Phone: 781-828-4900
Fax: 781-828-9624
Web: www.cumberlandfarms.com

CEO: Lily Haseotes Bentas
CFO: –
HR: Foster G. Macrides
FYE: September 30
Type: Private

Once a one-cow dairy, Cumberland Farms now operates a network of more than 1,100 convenience stores and gas stations in about a dozen eastern seaboard states from Maine to Florida. The company has its own grocery distribution and bakery operations to supply its stores. Cumberland owns a two-thirds limited partnership in petroleum wholesaler Gulf Oil, giving it the right to use and license Gulf trademarks in Delaware, New Jersey, New York, most of Ohio, Pennsylvania, and the New England states. The first convenience-store operator in New England, Cumberland was founded in 1939 by Vasilios and Aphrodite Haseotes. The Haseotes' children, including CEO Lily Haseotes Bentas, own the company.

	Annual Growth	9/02	9/03	9/04	9/05	9/06
Sales ($ mil.)	42.4%	1,700.0	2,000.0	2,100.0	3,300.0	7,000.0
Employees	(1.8%)	6,976	6,976	7,000	7,000	6,500

An in-depth profile of this company is available to Hoover's Online members at hoovers.com.

CUMBERLAND GENERAL STORE, LLC

P.O. Box 4468   CEO: Tim Seanor
Alpharetta, GA 30023   CFO: –
Phone: 678-240-0407   HR: –
Fax: 678-240-0410   FYE: –
Web: www.cumberlandgeneral.com   Type: Private

When you say retro at Cumberland General Store, you're really talking the 80s — the 1880s, to be more precise. Cumberland General Store markets items that would be appropriate for a rural home or farm in the 19th century. The company sells appliances, hardware, toys, kitchen supplies, and other products (that typically require little or no electricity) from a single store in Alpharetta, Georgia, as well as through its well known catalog and online. Customers include back-to-nature enthusiasts, residents of areas without electricity, and producers of period movies and television shows. In 2005 the store and company moved from Crossville, Tennessee to its current location in Georgia.

CUMBERLAND PACKING CORP.

2 Cumberland St.   CEO: Jeffrey (Jeff) Eisenstadt
Brooklyn, NY 11205   CFO: Peter Marshall
Phone: 718-858-4200   HR: Stephen Isaacs
Fax: 718-260-9017   FYE: December 31
Web: www.cpack.com   Type: Private

There's no shame in being artificial at Cumberland Packing. The company makes Sweet 'N Low, the pink-packaged, saccharin-based sugar substitute. It also makes Natra Taste (an aspartame sugar substitute), Nu-Salt (a sodium-free salt substitute), and Sweet One (an acesulfame potassium sweetener). Its other brands include Butter Buds (butter-flavored granules), and Sugar In The Raw (turbinado sugar). In addition to the ubiquitous pink presence of Sweet 'N Low on restaurant tables, Cumberland's products are sold by food retailers and food manufacturers worldwide. The company is owned by CEO and president Jeff Eisenstadt and his family.

	Annual Growth	12/03	12/04	12/05	12/06	12/07
Est. sales ($ mil.)	—	—	—	—	—	103.5
Employees	—	—	—	—	—	436

CUMMINS, INC.

NYSE: CMI

500 Jackson St.   CEO: Theodore M. (Tim) Solso
Columbus, IN 47201   CFO: Pat Ward
Phone: 812-377-5000   HR: Jill Cook
Fax: 812-377-3334   FYE: December 31
Web: www.cummins.com   Type: Public

Cummins is in it for the long haul. The company is the world's leader in the manufacture of large diesel engines. The company's engines also power school buses, medium-duty trucks, pickup trucks (primarily the Dodge Ram), and equipment for mining and construction. Cummins claims just under one-third of the North American market for heavy-duty truck engines. The company also makes power generation products such as its Onan generator sets and Stamford alternators. Other products and brands include Fleetguard (filtration), Kuss (fuel filters), and Holset (turbochargers).

	Annual Growth	12/03	12/04	12/05	12/06	12/07
Sales ($ mil.)	20.0%	6,296.0	8,438.0	9,918.0	11,362.0	13,048.0
Net income ($ mil.)	96.1%	50.0	350.0	550.0	715.0	739.0
Market value ($ mil.)	122.6%	524.9	970.4	1,042.1	1,539.3	12,877.1
Employees	6.2%	—	—	33,500	34,600	37,800

CUMMINS-AMERICAN CORPORATION

852 Feehanville Dr.   CEO: John E. Jones
Mount Prospect, IL 60056   CFO: John Diedrich
Phone: 847-299-9550   HR: Joan Cantrell
Fax: 847-299-4940   FYE: December 31
Web: cummins-allison.com   Type: Private

Cummins-American knows how to bring the money in and sort it out. The company owns Glenview State Bank, which offers personal and business banking services through around 10 branches in Chicago's northern suburbs. Cummins-American's other subsidiary, Cummins-Allison, makes a variety of coin and currency sorters, counters, wrappers, scanners, and dispensers; check signers, imprinters, and endorsers; and paper shredders and perforators. It also produces cash management software. These products are sold around the world to banks, government agencies, and the retail, gaming, and vending industries. The family of chairman and CEO John Jones owns a majority of the company.

	Annual Growth	12/03	12/04	12/05	12/06	12/07
Est. sales ($ mil.)	—	—	—	—	—	50.8
Employees	—	—	—	—	—	550

CUMULUS MEDIA INC.

NASDAQ (GS): CMLS

14 Piedmont Ctr., Ste. 1400   CEO: Lewis W. (Lew) Dickey Jr.
Atlanta, GA 30305   CFO: Martin R. (Marty) Gausvik
Phone: 404-949-0700   HR: –
Fax: 404-949-0740   FYE: December 31
Web: www.cumulus.com   Type: Public

Cumulus Media reigns over an empire of radio stations. The company is the #2 radio station ownership group in the US (behind Clear Channel) with more than 300 owned or operated stations in more than 55 mid-sized markets throughout the country. In each of its markets, Cumulus has built clusters of stations that realize cost savings through shared administrative and sales operations. In addition to its core mid-market stations, Cumulus, through a partnership with a group of private equity firms, owns about 30 stations in such large markets as Atlanta, Dallas, and San Francisco. Chairman and CEO Lewis Dickey, along with his family, controls about 40% of Cumulus Media.

	Annual Growth	12/03	12/04	12/05	12/06	12/07
Sales ($ mil.)	1.5%	309.5	320.1	327.8	334.3	328.3
Net income ($ mil.)	—	5.0	30.4	(213.4)	(44.6)	(223.8)
Market value ($ mil.)	(29.1%)	1,184.0	854.6	614.7	367.0	299.1
Employees	0.2%	—	—	3,392	3,400	—

CUNA MUTUAL GROUP

5910 Mineral Point Rd.   CEO: Jeff Post
Madison, WI 53705   CFO: Jeffrey D. (Jeff) Holley
Phone: 608-238-5851   HR: –
Fax: –   FYE: December 31
Web: www.cunamutual.com   Type: Mutual company

CUNA would soonah eat tuna than make its products available to banks. CUNA Mutual offers the more than 9,500 credit unions in the US (as well as those in 20 other countries) a range of products and services, including life insurance, investment advisory, and information technology. Group member CUNA Mutual Insurance Society offers accident, health, and life insurance. Additionally, the group offers customers such technology services as Web site enhancement and automated lending software. CUNA Mutual was founded in 1935 by pioneers of the credit union movement and is owned by its credit union policyholders.

	Annual Growth	12/03	12/04	12/05	12/06	12/07
Assets ($ mil.)	4.2%	12,885.0	14,004.0	14,574.0	15,046.2	15,201.9
Net income ($ mil.)	8.2%	134.0	136.0	124.0	186.6	183.6
Employees	(6.9%)	6,000	6,000	5,500	5,500	4,500

CUNO INCORPORATED

400 Research Pkwy.
Meriden, CT 06450
Phone: 203-237-5541
Fax: 203-238-8977
Web: www.cuno.com

CEO: Timothy B. (Tim) Carney
CFO: Frederick C. (Fred) Flynn Jr.
HR: David A. Edgar
FYE: October 31
Type: Subsidiary

CUNO looks at liquids and gases through rose-colored filters. The company, a unit of 3M, makes a full line of filtration products for the health care, fluid-processing, and potable-water markets. Its filters remove contaminants as small as molecules and as large as sand particles from liquids and gases. They are used to purify drugs, paints and resins, oil and gas, and home drinking water. Under its Scientific Application Support banner, CUNO assigns its own scientists to work with customers when creating new products. The company operates offices worldwide and eight manufacturing plants in Australia, Brazil, Europe, Japan, and the US and has sales offices worldwide. CUNO was acquired by 3M in 2005.

	Annual Growth	10/03	10/04	10/05	10/06	10/07
Est. sales ($ mil.)	—	—	—	—	—	274.5
Employees	—	—	—	—	—	2,200

CUPERTINO ELECTRIC, INC.

1132 N. 7th St.
San Jose, CA 95112
Phone: 408-808-8000
Fax: 408-275-8575
Web: www.cei.com

CEO: James S. (Jim) Ryley
CFO: Earl C. Charles
HR: Rose Baldwin
FYE: December 31
Type: Private

Cupertino Electric likes to get its customers wired. The electrical contractor builds and maintains electrical power and data infrastructure systems for commercial, industrial, and institutional facilities, including semiconductor plants, biotech installations, data centers, network systems, and schools. It provides generation facilities for companies that are not on a grid or need additional power. Subsidiary Ceitronics installs audio, video, fire, security, and other systems for companies and schools in the western US. Cupertino Electric's clients include Hewlett-Packard, Microsoft, and Oracle.

	Annual Growth	12/03	12/04	12/05	12/06	12/07
Est. sales ($ mil.)	—	—	—	—	—	335.0
Employees	—	—	—	—	—	1,608

CURAGEN CORPORATION

NASDAQ (GM): CRGN

322 E. Main St.
Branford, CT 06405
Phone: 203-481-1104
Fax: 203-483-2552
Web: www.curagen.com

CEO: Timothy M. (Tim) Shannon
CFO: Sean Cassidy
HR: Nathalie Richard
FYE: December 31
Type: Public

In the war against cancer, CuraGen is looking for the ultimate weapon. The drug company's main focus is on developing an antibody therapy to treat metastatic melanoma and breast cancer. The anticancer compound (called CR011-vcMMAE) is a monoclonal antibody that is combined with a cell-killing drug using technology from Seattle Genetics. CuraGen had been developing its other lead candidate, belinostat, with TopoTarget, but in 2008 it sold the anticancer drug to its partner. The previous year CuraGen sold its majority-owned subsidiary 454 Life Sciences, which provides DNA sequencing equipment and services, to Roche.

	Annual Growth	12/03	12/04	12/05	12/06	12/07
Sales ($ mil.)	(65.3%)	6.9	6.3	23.5	39.6	0.1
Net income ($ mil.)	—	(74.5)	(90.4)	(73.2)	(59.8)	25.4
Market value ($ mil.)	(38.2%)	366.1	362.6	171.4	259.4	53.4
Employees	—	—	—	666	—	—

CURASCRIPT, INC.

6272 Lee Vista Blvd.
Orlando, FL 32822
Phone: 407-852-4903
Fax: 888-773-7386
Web: www.curascript.com

CEO: David A. Lowenberg
CFO: Steve Jenson
HR: –
FYE: Saturday nearest December 31
Type: Subsidiary

CuraScript is one of the top specialty pharmacy distribution companies in the US. A subsidiary of pharmacy benefit manager Express Scripts, the company provides specialty medications to people with chronic diseases that require high-cost injectable or infusible biotech drugs. Through a network of specialty pharmacies in eight states, CuraScript SP offers home delivery of drugs, while its CuraScript SD distributes drugs to doctors' offices and clinics. It also provides support services to patients in the form of on-call pharmacists, insurance counseling, and online communities. Its FreedomFP unit dispenses fertility drugs to doctors and patients.

	Annual Growth	12/03	12/04	12/05	12/06	12/07
Est. sales ($ mil.)	—	—	—	—	—	2,147.5
Employees	—	—	—	—	—	2,025

CURIS, INC.

NASDAQ (GM): CRIS

61 Moulton St.
Cambridge, MA 02138
Phone: 617-503-6500
Fax: 617-503-6501
Web: www.curis.com

CEO: Daniel R. (Dan) Passeri
CFO: Michael P. (Mike) Gray
HR: –
FYE: December 31
Type: Public

Curis's cancer patients and Sega's gamers might one day have an unlikely hero in common: Sonic the Hedgehog. Drug development firm Curis is studying hedgehog signaling pathways (including the sonic hedgehog pathway, named after the Sega mascot) to find treatments for cancer, neurological disease, and cardiovascular conditions. Such signaling pathways regulate tissue growth and repair, and the company is looking for ways to either stimulate them or slow them down as a means of treating disease. Curis is collaborating with Genentech to develop cancer drugs using hedgehog pathways. The company also has internal development programs for cancer treatments using other signaling pathways.

	Annual Growth	12/03	12/04	12/05	12/06	12/07
Sales ($ mil.)	10.3%	11.1	4.9	6.0	16.7	16.4
Net income ($ mil.)	—	(11.6)	(13.9)	(14.9)	(8.8)	(7.0)
Market value ($ mil.)	(23.7%)	182.5	248.0	172.0	62.2	62.0
Employees	—	—	—	68	—	—

CURTISS-WRIGHT CORPORATION

NYSE: CW

4 Becker Farm Rd., 3rd Fl.
Roseland, NJ 07068
Phone: 973-597-4700
Fax: 973-597-4799
Web: www.curtisswright.com

CEO: Martin R. Benante
CFO: Glenn E. Tynan
HR: Kenneth Lewis
FYE: December 31
Type: Public

Once an aeronautical pioneer — its engines powered the B-17 bomber and *The Spirit of St. Louis* — Curtiss-Wright makes lower-visibility products these days. The company's fast-growing flow control business makes special valves for military and commercial applications, including nuclear submarines, nuclear power plants, and refineries. Products of the company's motion control business include actuation systems that control wing flaps, open bomb-bay doors, and stabilize aiming systems. The motion control segment also makes electronic control products for military ground vehicles, along with ruggedized computer systems. Curtiss-Wright also offers metal treatment services.

	Annual Growth	12/03	12/04	12/05	12/06	12/07
Sales ($ mil.)	20.9%	746.1	955.0	1,130.9	1,282.2	1,592.1
Net income ($ mil.)	18.8%	52.3	65.1	75.3	80.6	104.3
Market value ($ mil.)	69.6%	270.5	363.8	593.7	1,632.4	2,238.6
Employees	12.8%	—	—	5,892	6,233	7,500

CURVES INTERNATIONAL, INC.

100 Ritchie Rd.
Waco, TX 76712
Phone: 254-399-9285
Fax: 254-399-9731
Web: www.curvesinternational.com

CEO: H. Gary Heavin
CFO: Ronnie Glaesmann
HR: –
FYE: December 31
Type: Private

Curves International is turning heads with its successful women's gym franchise. With more than 4 million members, the company operates one of the nation's fastest-growing franchise systems by targeting busy women with limited time for exercise. It franchises some 10,000 Curves for Women fitness centers worldwide (in the US and more than 50 additional countries). The centers offer 30-minute fitness workout sessions featuring strength and cardio training. The company was founded in 1992 when Gary and Diane Heavin opened a center in Harlingen, Texas. The company began franchise operations in 1995.

	Annual Growth	12/03	12/04	12/05	12/06	12/07
Est. sales ($ mil.)	—	—	—	—	—	3.6
Employees	—	—	—	—	—	138

CUSHMAN & WAKEFIELD, INC.

51 W. 52nd St.
New York, NY 10019
Phone: 212-841-7500
Fax: –
Web: www.cushmanwakefield.com

CEO: Bruce E. Mosler
CFO: –
HR: Ron Whitley
FYE: December 31
Type: Subsidiary

Cushman & Wakefield heeds the maxim, "Buy land — they aren't making any more." With some 200 offices in about 50 countries, it serves the real estate needs of corporations and financial institutions around the globe. In addition to property management and brokerage services, Cushman & Wakefield also provides research and analysis on markets worldwide, portfolio optimization, supply chain management, and owner and investor services. Its Sonnenbeck-Goldman subsidiary offers real estate investment banking and is part of its Global Capital Markets platform. In 2007 Italy-based investment firm IFIL bought the 72% stake of Cushman & Wakefield owned by the Rockefeller Group.

CUSTOM BUILDING PRODUCTS INC.

13001 Seal Beach Blvd.
Seal Beach, CA 90740
Phone: 562-598-8808
Fax: 562-598-4008
Web: www.custombuildingproducts.com

CEO: Thomas R. (Tom) Peck II
CFO: –
HR: Jenny Klein
FYE: December 31
Type: Private

Custom Building Products manufactures tile setting grout and adhesives. Products include epoxies, cement, household and industrial glues, sealants, acrylic resins, clay mortars, putties, and latex, as well as installation tools, cleaning and maintenance equipment, gypsum products, and concrete repair products. The company manufactures and distributes its wares from approximately 10 locations in North America. Its customers include architects, contractors, dealers, distributors, and do-it-yourselfers. Custom Building Products was founded in 1945 by Thomas Peck Sr.

	Annual Growth	12/03	12/04	12/05	12/06	12/07
Est. sales ($ mil.)	—	—	—	—	—	186.2
Employees	—	—	—	—	—	1,200

CUSTOM SENSORS & TECHNOLOGIES, INC.

14501 Princeton Ave.
Moorpark, CA 93021
Phone: 805-552-3599
Fax: 805-552-3577
Web: cst.schneider-electric.com

CEO: Charles L. (Chuck) Treadway
CFO: John LaBoskey
HR: David H. Pike
FYE: December 31
Type: Subsidiary

Custom Sensors & Technologies (CST) is taking a custom approach to the sensor business. The company (formerly BEI Technologies) makes electronic sensors and engineered subsystems used in factory and process automation, aerospace and military equipment, telecommunications gear, and a wide range of transportation applications. CST's products, which include DC motors, optical encoders, servo systems, and trackballs, help determine exact positions and link the actions of precision mechanisms, such as automotive stability-enhancement systems. Major customers include German automotive systems maker Continental Teves and the US government.

	Annual Growth	12/03	12/04	12/05	12/06	12/07
Est. sales ($ mil.)	—	—	—	—	—	305.8
Employees	—	—	—	—	—	5,268

CUTERA, INC.

NASDAQ (GS): CUTR

3240 Bayshore Blvd.
Brisbane, CA 94005
Phone: 415-657-5500
Fax: 415-330-2444
Web: www.cutera.com

CEO: Kevin P. Connors
CFO: Ronald J. Santilli
HR: Stacie Rodgers
FYE: December 31
Type: Public

Cutera has a handle on hairy situations and a firm plan for flabby faces. The firm makes lasers for medical and aesthetic use in doctors' offices and spas. Its FDA-approved devices are marketed under the names CoolGlide, Solera, and Xeo and are used for hair removal and treatments to reduce pigmented lesions (age and sun spots), wrinkles, and veins. Its Titan line of products uses deep tissue heating to firm up saggy skin. The company markets its products through a direct sales force and a distributor in the US and relies on a small sales group and distributors in more than 30 other countries.

	Annual Growth	12/03	12/04	12/05	12/06	12/07
Sales ($ mil.)	27.0%	39.1	52.6	75.6	100.7	101.7
Net income ($ mil.)	35.7%	3.1	3.8	13.8	2.1	10.5
Market value ($ mil.)	13.4%	—	137.0	321.9	349.4	200.0
Employees	13.3%	—	—	195	221	—

⊞ CUTTER & BUCK INC.

701 N. 34th St., Ste. 400
Seattle, WA 98103
Phone: 206-830-6812
Fax: 206-448-0589
Web: www.cutterbuck.com

CEO: Ernest R. (Ernie) Johnson
CFO: Michael Gats
HR: –
FYE: April 30
Type: Private

Relatively unknown less than a decade ago, Cutter & Buck has climbed onto the leader board of the nation's top makers of golf apparel. Cutter & Buck sells men's and women's golf apparel and other sportswear through golf pro shops, resorts, and specialty stores throughout North America, as well as to corporate accounts. It sells its products in other countries through distributors. Most of its sales come from men's apparel. Cutter & Buck divides its apparel into two lines: the ephemeral fashion line, with brighter colors, and the seasonless and less-expensive classics line. Its corporate marketing division puts company logos on products for corporate golf events and recognition programs. New Wave Group AB owns the company.

	Annual Growth	4/02	4/03	4/04	4/05	4/06
Sales ($ mil.)	(6.8%)	173.9	131.7	128.4	126.6	131.3
Net income ($ mil.)	—	(10.4)	(12.0)	7.9	8.6	6.3
Employees	(14.1%)	699	443	379	374	380

CV THERAPEUTICS, INC.

NASDAQ (GM): CVTX

3172 Porter Dr.
Palo Alto, CA 94304
Phone: 650-384-8500
Fax: 650-858-0390
Web: www.cvt.com

CEO: Louis G. Lange
CFO: Daniel K. (Dan) Spiegelman
HR: Diane L. Liguori
FYE: December 31
Type: Public

CV Therapeutics is more interested in *Cardio Vascular* drug research than fixing up resumés. The drug development company specializes in small-molecule drugs to treat chronic cardiovascular diseases. The firm's FDA-approved Ranexa, licensed from a Roche subsidiary, treats chronic angina for patients who have not responded to other treatments. CV Therapeutics won approval for its cardiac imaging agent, Lexiscan, in 2008; the drug is marketed by Astellas Pharma. The company is developing Ranexa as a first-line angina treatment and is seeking approval in Europe; it is also working on Tecadenoson, which potentially treats heart arrhythmias.

	Annual Growth	12/03	12/04	12/05	12/06	12/07
Sales ($ mil.)	64.5%	11.3	20.4	19.0	36.8	82.8
Net income ($ mil.)	—	(110.9)	(155.1)	(228.0)	(274.3)	(181.0)
Market value ($ mil.)	6.2%	428.2	796.6	1,109.3	820.0	544.5
Employees	136.6%	—	265	627	—	—

CVB FINANCIAL CORP.

NASDAQ (GS): CVBF

701 N. Haven Ave., Ste. 350
Ontario, CA 91764
Phone: 909-980-4030
Fax: 909-481-2131
Web: www.cbbank.com

CEO: Christopher D. (Chris) Myers
CFO: Edward J. Biebrich Jr.
HR: David M. Krebs
FYE: December 31
Type: Public

CVB Financial is into the California Vibe, Baby. The holding company's Citizens Business Bank offers community banking services to primarily small and midsized businesses, but also consumers through more than 40 offices in eight central and southern California counties. Its deposit products include checking, money market, and savings accounts, as well as CDs. Commercial real estate loans account for about half of the bank's loan portfolio, which is rounded out by agribusiness, consumer, and commercial loans. It provides auto and equipment leases and brokers mortgage loans through its Citizens Financial Services Division; trust services are offered through its CitizensTrust Division.

	Annual Growth	12/03	12/04	12/05	12/06	12/07
Assets ($ mil.)	13.0%	3,854.4	4,511.0	5,423.0	6,094.3	6,294.0
Net income ($ mil.)	3.5%	52.8	61.5	70.6	71.9	60.6
Market value ($ mil.)	12.2%	542.0	937.5	1,129.0	1,107.9	859.9
Employees	—	—	—	—	719	—

CVD EQUIPMENT CORPORATION

OTC: CVV

1860 Smithtown Ave.
Ronkonkoma, NY 11779
Phone: 631-981-7081
Fax: 631-981-7095
Web: www.cvdequipment.com

CEO: Leonard A. Rosenbaum
CFO: Glen R. Charles
HR: –
FYE: December 31
Type: Public

CVD Equipment has expanded well beyond the chemical vapor deposition (CVD) equipment that gave it its name. Its Chemical Vapor Deposition unit makes gear that performs its namesake function, depositing precise layers of chemicals onto semiconductor wafers during chip manufacturing. The Stainless Design Concepts unit makes gas and chemical delivery control systems for handling the ultrapure materials used in chip fabrication. The Equipment Consulting Services group advises semiconductor manufacturers on equipment purchases, and refurbishes used equipment. CVD's Conceptronic unit makes equipment used in chip packaging and board fabrication. Exports account for about 20% of sales.

	Annual Growth	12/03	12/04	12/05	12/06	12/07
Sales ($ mil.)	8.5%	9.8	9.9	11.2	13.4	13.6
Net income ($ mil.)	—	(0.3)	0.1	0.4	0.6	0.8
Market value ($ mil.)	47.4%	4.0	4.2	9.1	18.5	18.6
Employees	7.5%	86	96	119	108	115

CVF TECHNOLOGIES CORPORATION

OTC: CNVT

8604 Main St., Ste. 1
Williamsville, NY 14221
Phone: 716-565-4711
Fax: 716-565-4717
Web: www.cvfcorp.com

CEO: Jeffrey I. Dreben
CFO: Robert L. Miller
HR: Robert L. Miller
FYE: December 31
Type: Public

It's a dirty job, but someone has to do it. CVF Technologies owns stakes in firms that produce natural fertilizer, petroleum-eating bacteria, and filters used at water treatment plants. The company owns 85% of Ecoval, which produces environmentally friendly fertilizers, herbicides, and other garden products under the Nature's Glory brand. Petrozyme Technologies, of which CVF owns half, manufactures petroleum-eating bacteria that are used in environmental clean-up projects. Another holding, Biorem, makes biofilters to combat air pollution and to control odors at water treatment facilities. CVF provides initial funding and consulting to small firms like these, hoping to see them through an acquisition or IPO.

	Annual Growth	12/03	12/04	12/05	12/06	12/07
Sales ($ mil.)	(30.8%)	8.7	8.0	0.5	1.5	2.0
Net income ($ mil.)	—	(2.3)	(1.9)	5.3	(1.9)	(2.1)
Market value ($ mil.)	(28.2%)	4.5	6.6	4.4	2.4	1.2
Employees	—	—	—	—	—	43

CVR ENERGY, INC.

NYSE: CVI

2277 Plaza Dr., Ste. 500
Sugar Land, TX 77479
Phone: 281-207-3200
Fax: –
Web: www.coffeyvillegroup.com/aboutCVRMain.aspx

CEO: John J. (Jack) Lipinski
CFO: James T. Rens
HR: –
FYE: December 31
Type: Public

The CV of CVR Energy (formerly Coffeyville Resources) highlights its two primary refinery products — petroleum and nitrogen fertilizer. The company operates a 113,500 barrels-per-day-throughput-capacity oil refinery in Coffeyville, Kansas, and a crude oil gathering system in Kansas and Oklahoma. It also has asphalt and refined fuels storage and terminalling plants in Phillipsburg, Kansas. CVR Energy is controlled by Coffeyville Acquisitions, LLC, a partnership of GS Capital Partners, the private equity arm of Goldman Sachs, and the private equity investment firm Kelso & Company.

	Annual Growth	12/03	12/04	12/05	12/06	12/07
Sales ($ mil.)	23.8%	1,262.2	1,741.0	2,435.0	3,037.6	2,966.9
Net income ($ mil.)	—	27.9	60.9	(66.8)	191.6	(67.6)
Market value ($ mil.)	—	—	—	—	—	2,148.4
Employees	(0.8%)	442	—	570	577	428

CVS CAREMARK CORPORATION

NYSE: CVS

1 CVS Dr.
Woonsocket, RI 02895
Phone: 401-765-1500
Fax: 401-762-9227
Web: www.cvs.com

CEO: Thomas M. (Tom) Ryan
CFO: David B. (Dave) Rickard
HR: V. Michael Ferdinandi
FYE: December 31
Type: Public

CVS Caremark (formerly CVS) interprets the scrawl of more US doctors than anyone. The CVS pharmacy chain fills more prescriptions at more drugstores than any other drugstore operator, although it trails rival Walgreen in total sales. Following its acquisitions of the Eckerd chain and stores from Albertsons, CVS operates about 6,250 stores in some 40 states. In 2007 CVS purchased prescription benefits management (PBM) firm Caremark Rx for about $26.5 billion. Caremark was combined with CVS's PBM and specialty pharmacy subsidiary PharmaCare Management Services, which offered managed-care drug programs to insurers, employers, and other health care plan providers, to form Caremark Pharmacy Services.

	Annual Growth	12/03	12/04	12/05	12/06	12/07
Sales ($ mil.)	30.2%	26,588.0	30,594.3	37,006.2	43,813.8	76,329.5
Net income ($ mil.)	32.8%	847.3	918.8	1,224.7	1,368.9	2,637.0
Market value ($ mil.)	68.8%	7,071.4	9,035.6	21,514.0	25,523.5	57,458.3
Employees	16.2%	—	—	148,000	176,000	200,000

CYANOTECH CORPORATION

NASDAQ (CM): CYAN

73-4460 Queen Kaahumanu Hwy., Ste. 102
Kailua-Kona, HI 96740
Phone: 808-326-1353
Fax: 808-329-4533
Web: www.cyanotech.com

CEO: Andrew H. Jacobson
CFO: William R. Maris
HR: –
FYE: March 31
Type: Public

Cyanotech transforms the scum of the earth into health products. The majority of the company's sales come from Spirulina Pacifica, a nutritional supplement made from tiny blue-green vegetable algae and sold as powder, flakes, and tablets. The firm also produces BioAstin, an astaxanthin-based dietary supplement full of antioxidants. Cyanotech produces the microalgae used in its product lines at a 90-acre production facility on the Kona Coast of Hawaii. It sells them primarily to health food and dietary supplement makers. In order to focus on its nutritional supplement business, the company has discontinued some other product lines, including NatuRose, an algae-based pigmentation used to color farm-raised fish.

	Annual Growth	3/04	3/05	3/06	3/07	3/08
Sales ($ mil.)	(0.4%)	11.6	11.4	11.1	9.7	11.4
Net income ($ mil.)	—	0.4	0.5	(0.4)	(7.4)	(1.1)
Market value ($ mil.)	(25.1%)	26.1	25.5	15.1	8.6	8.2
Employees	(3.1%)	—	64	62	—	—

CYBERKINETICS NEUROTECHNOLOGY SYSTEMS, INC.

OTC: CYKN

100 Foxborough Blvd., Ste. 240
Foxborough, MA 02035
Phone: 508-549-9981
Fax: 508-549-9985
Web: www.cyberkineticsinc.com

CEO: Timothy R. (Tim) Surgenor
CFO: Kimi Iguchi
HR: –
FYE: December 31
Type: Public

Ever wish you could control your computer with the power of your thoughts? Cyberkinetics Neurotechnology Systems (CNS) is developing technology that could make that possible. Its lead product, the Andara Oscillating Field Stimulator (OFS), uses low-level electrical fields to stimulate nerve fiber growth, and restore or improve sensation and movement to patients with recent spinal cord injuries. The company's BrainGate platform helps create bi-directional links between the brain and a computer and is being developed to help paralysis victims and patients with certain neurodegenerative diseases communicate. Oxford Bioscience Partners has a 31% stake in the company.

	Annual Growth	12/03	12/04	12/05	12/06	12/07
Sales ($ mil.)	13.6%	—	1.5	1.1	1.7	2.2
Net income ($ mil.)	—	—	(7.1)	(9.3)	(12.3)	(10.1)
Employees	2.9%	—	33	35	38	36

CYBERONICS, INC.

NASDAQ (GM): CYBX

Cyberonics Bldg., 100 Cyberonics Blvd.
Houston, TX 77058
Phone: 281-228-7200
Fax: 281-218-9332
Web: www.cyberonics.com

CEO: Daniel J. (Dan) Moore
CFO: Gregory H. (Greg) Browne
HR: George E. Parker III
FYE: Last Friday in April
Type: Public

Cyberonics makes the first medical device to be cleared by the FDA for treating epilepsy. The Cyberonics system is a pacemaker-like device implanted under the collarbone with a lead attached to the vagus nerve in the neck. The device delivers intermittent signals to the brain, dubbed vagus nerve stimulation (VNS), to control epileptic seizures. The signals can be programmed by the physician with a personal computer; patients can activate additional signals with a hand-held magnet if they feel a seizure coming on. The system is also approved for use in Australia, Canada, and the European Union.

	Annual Growth	4/04	4/05	4/06	4/07	4/08
Sales ($ mil.)	2.3%	110.7	103.4	123.4	131.0	121.2
Net income ($ mil.)	—	6.8	(12.2)	(59.1)	(51.2)	(10.3)
Market value ($ mil.)	(6.2%)	555.7	934.0	590.9	585.8	429.5
Employees	(9.0%)	—	660	645	547	—

CYBEROPTICS CORPORATION

NASDAQ (GM): CYBE

5900 Golden Hills Dr.
Minneapolis, MN 55416
Phone: 763-542-5000
Fax: 763-542-5100
Web: www.cyberoptics.com

CEO: Kathleen P. (Kitty) Iverson
CFO: Jeffrey A. Bertelsen
HR: –
FYE: December 31
Type: Public

CyberOptics keeps a close eye on the printed circuit board market. The company makes non-contact sensors and integrated systems that use proprietary laser and optics technology to measure the characteristics and placement of electronic components during and after the assembly of printed circuit boards. Product lines include LaserAlign sensors, which ensure accurate component placement, and Process Insight, real-time statistical process control software. CyberOptics also makes the SE 300 quality control system, which measures solder paste deposition; the machine generates almost one-quarter of sales. Sales to customers outside of the US account for nearly 90% of sales.

	Annual Growth	12/03	12/04	12/05	12/06	12/07
Sales ($ mil.)	13.4%	35.6	58.0	42.2	57.1	58.8
Net income ($ mil.)	—	(2.6)	10.6	7.2	6.4	5.0
Market value ($ mil.)	4.3%	89.1	131.6	120.0	112.5	105.3
Employees	7.2%	141	165	170	179	186

CYBERSOURCE CORPORATION

NASDAQ (GM): CYBS

1295 Charleston Rd.
Mountain View, CA 94043
Phone: 650-965-6000
Fax: 650-625-9145
Web: www.cybersource.com

CEO: William S. (Bill) McKiernan
CFO: Steven D. Pellizzer
HR: –
FYE: December 31
Type: Public

Cyber security has to start somewhere. CyberSource provides software and services that help ensure that e-commerce and other Internet-based transactions are processed securely. Companies use its software to process credit card payments and electronic checks, as well as to screen for payment fraud. Other applications manage gift certificate programs and verify personal information. The company's software can be integrated with other enterprise applications from vendors such as Microsoft, Oracle, and SAP. In addition to its software, CyberSource offers outsourced payment processing and fraud detection services.

	Annual Growth	12/03	12/04	12/05	12/06	12/07
Sales ($ mil.)	43.6%	27.5	36.7	50.5	70.3	117.0
Net income ($ mil.)	—	(5.4)	4.5	9.3	14.4	2.4
Market value ($ mil.)	63.4%	171.2	239.0	224.0	384.7	1,220.5
Employees	63.7%	—	185	247	496	

CYBERTEL CAPITAL CORPORATION

OTC: CBEL

4603 NE St. Johns Rd., Ste. B
Vancouver, WA 98661
Phone: 858-646-7410
Fax: 858-646-7414

CEO: James A. Wheeler
CFO: Richard F. Schmidt
HR: –
FYE: December 31
Type: Public

Cybertel Capital (formerly Cybertel Communications) wants to help the folks who can help other folks in times of emergency. Through its subsidiary The Swiftsure Group (acquired in 2006), the company resells and integrates WAVE (Wide Area Voice Environment); the voice, video, and data communications tool is used by emergency first responders, homeland security, and other public safety organizations. Cybertel Capital in 2006 also acquired HBLN Services (now AireWire), which offers consulting and technical services to telecommunications firms and service providers. President and CEO James Wheeler owns 73% of the company.

	Annual Growth	12/03	12/04	12/05	12/06	12/07
Sales ($ mil.)	—	0.8	0.2	0.1	0.2	0.0
Net income ($ mil.)	—	(3.1)	(5.0)	(1.0)	(0.9)	(1.5)
Employees	(42.3%)	9	4	1	3	1

An in-depth profile of this company is available to Hoover's Online members at hoovers.com.

463

CYBEX INTERNATIONAL, INC.

NASDAQ (GM): CYBI

10 Trotter Dr.
Medway, MA 02053
Phone: 508-533-4300
Fax: 508-533-5500
Web: www.ecybex.com

CEO: John Aglialoro
CFO: –
HR: –
FYE: December 31
Type: Public

Cybex International won't get you to cyberspace but it can help you get a second glance at the grocery store. The firm makes premium-priced strength training and cardiovascular equipment sold to commercial markets, including health clubs, hotels, and schools, and to consumers via independent retailers. Cybex's selection of products includes stationary bikes, treadmills, free weights, and single- and multi-station strength training equipment. It sells its products through about 75 distributors worldwide. Its Cybex UK subsidiary provides sales and distribution throughout Europe. Chairman John Aglialoro and his wife, director Joan Carter, own 34% of Cybex through investment company UM Holdings.

	Annual Growth	12/03	12/04	12/05	12/06	12/07
Sales ($ mil.)	12.9%	90.2	103.0	114.7	126.9	146.5
Net income ($ mil.)	—	(1.8)	3.2	0.1	20.0	9.8
Market value ($ mil.)	64.4%	10.8	61.7	56.0	103.2	79.1
Employees	3.6%	—	—	528	547	—

CYCLE COUNTRY ACCESSORIES CORP.

AMEX: ATC

1701 38th Ave. West
Spencer, IA 51301
Phone: 712-262-4191
Fax: 712-262-0248
Web: www.cyclecountry.com

CEO: Jeff Tetzlaff
CFO: David (Dave) Davis
HR: –
FYE: September 30
Type: Public

Cycle Country Accessories turns ATVs into beasts of burden. The company makes all-terrain vehicle (ATV) accessories such as snowplow blades, lawnmowers, spreaders, sprayers, tillage equipment, winch mounts, utility boxes, and wheel covers for Honda, Yamaha, Kawasaki, Suzuki, Polaris, and Arctic Cat, and other ATV models. Cycle Country also makes hubcaps for golf carts, riding lawnmowers, and light-duty trailers. Its products are sold through nearly 10 distributors in the US and 30 foreign countries. The company also makes pull-behind implements and other accessories for riding mowers under the Weekend Warrior brand, and offers contract manufacturing services. Sales outside the US account for about 15% of sales.

	Annual Growth	9/03	9/04	9/05	9/06	9/07
Sales ($ mil.)	0.5%	13.9	20.7	17.2	16.5	14.2
Net income ($ mil.)	18.9%	0.2	1.6	0.8	0.6	0.4
Market value ($ mil.)	(11.4%)	19.0	27.0	18.2	14.6	11.7
Employees	(6.9%)	—	—	120	—	104

CYGNE DESIGNS, INC.

NASDAQ (CM): CYDS

11 W. 42nd St.
New York, NY 10036
Phone: 212-997-7767
Fax: –

CEO: Samuel J. (Jay) Furrow Jr.
CFO: Nomaan Yousef
HR: –
FYE: Saturday nearest January 31
Type: Public

Cygne (pronounced "see-nya") Designs has had its wings clipped in recent years. The firm, whose name is French for "swan," designs and makes private-label women's casual and professional apparel. While it formerly feathered its nest with customers Ann Taylor and Limited Brands, today it almost exclusively caters to Limited Brands' former subsidiary, New York & Company, which sells its apparel under its own label, as well as JCPenney, Kohl's, Target, and AEO. It also makes Hippie, Hint Jeans, and Voyou brands. Hubert Guez, personally and through his partnership with Diversified Apparel Resources and the Guez Living Trust, owns some 77% of the its stock. Cygne's chairman Bernard Manuel owns nearly 19%.

	Annual Growth	1/04	1/05	1/06	1/07	1/08
Sales ($ mil.)	37.1%	27.1	29.0	58.5	118.8	95.8
Net income ($ mil.)	—	0.4	0.3	(6.2)	(0.2)	(63.9)
Market value ($ mil.)	44.3%	4.7	4.2	118.6	58.0	20.5
Employees	(7.2%)	—	812	719	700	—

CYIOS CORPORATION

OTC: CYIO

1300 Pennsylvania Ave., Ste. 700
Washington, DC 20004
Phone: 202-204-3006
Fax: 202-315-3458
Web: www.cyios.com

CEO: Timothy (Tim) Carnahan
CFO: Timothy (Tim) Carnahan
HR: Barbara Cornwell
FYE: December 31
Type: Public

CYIOS is a holding company for two operating subsidiaries. The first, which has the same name as the parent company and is referred to as CYIOS DC, is a provider of information technology (IT) systems integration services for agencies within the Department of Defense. The second subsidiary, CKO, offers an online office management software product called XO Office software. The company had previously provided telecommunications services as WorldTeq, but has ceased those operations. As China Print, it acquired CYIOS in a reverse merger in 2005. CEO Tim Carnahan owns 67% of the company.

	Annual Growth	12/03	12/04	12/05	12/06	12/07
Sales ($ mil.)	28.8%	0.8	0.3	2.3	1.7	2.2
Net income ($ mil.)	—	(0.3)	(1.8)	(0.3)	(0.9)	0.3
Market value ($ mil.)	(53.5%)	95.8	3.9	6.0	2.8	4.5
Employees	—	—	—	—	—	—

CYMER, INC.

NASDAQ (GS): CYMI

17075 Thornmint Ct.
San Diego, CA 92127
Phone: 858-385-7300
Fax: 858-385-7100
Web: www.cymer.com

CEO: Robert P. (Bob) Akins
CFO: Nancy J. Baker
HR: –
FYE: December 31
Type: Public

Simon says, "Cymer makes lasers." The company is the leading manufacturer of excimer lasers used in semiconductor manufacturing. (The term excimer comes from excited dimer — an excited molecule with two atoms.) Cymer's deep-ultraviolet (DUV) lasers achieve finer resolution than older mercury arc lamp models, enabling semiconductor makers to put more circuits on a chip and to produce more chips per wafer. The company's customers include photolithography systems makers ASML (33% of sales), Nikon (19%), and Canon. Cymer manufactures its own products in California. It has installed more than 3,000 light sources around the world, in plants run by AMD, Fujitsu, IBM, Intel, NEC, Samsung, and TI, among others.

	Annual Growth	12/03	12/04	12/05	12/06	12/07
Sales ($ mil.)	18.2%	267.5	418.1	383.6	543.9	521.7
Net income ($ mil.)	—	(15.4)	43.2	46.5	95.7	88.4
Market value ($ mil.)	(0.5%)	1,678.8	1,092.8	1,350.7	1,836.0	1,648.3
Employees	7.5%	766	770	879	975	1,022

CYNOSURE, INC.

NASDAQ (GM): CYNO

5 Carlisle Rd.
Westford, MA 01886
Phone: 978-256-4200
Fax: 978-256-6556
Web: www.cynosurelaser.com

CEO: Michael R. Davin
CFO: Timothy W. Baker
HR: –
FYE: December 31
Type: Public

Beauty may be skin deep, but that's just deep enough for Cynosure to help. The company makes laser and pulsed-light devices used to perform non-invasive aesthetic procedures to remove hair, treat varicose veins, remove tattoos, and reduce the appearance of birthmarks, freckles, and cellulite. Folks who want to go deeper can opt for its minimally invasive procedures to remove unwanted fat using lasers. Cynosure's systems are marketed under such names as Apogee, Cynergy, and Smartlipo. Its customers include doctors and health spas served by distributors in more than 50 countries. Italian laser maker El. En. controls more than 20% of the company's voting shares and manufactures many of the company's products.

	Annual Growth	12/03	12/04	12/05	12/06	12/07
Sales ($ mil.)	46.3%	27.1	41.6	56.3	78.4	124.3
Net income ($ mil.)	—	(0.5)	5.3	4.2	(0.6)	14.5
Market value ($ mil.)	42.9%	—	—	122.8	112.4	250.7
Employees	—	—	—	184	—	—

An in-depth profile of this company is available to Hoover's Online members at hoovers.com.

CYPRESS BIOSCIENCE, INC.

NASDAQ (GM): CYPB

4350 Executive Dr., Ste. 325	CEO: Jay D. Kranzler
San Diego, CA 92121	CFO: Sabrina Martucci Johnson
Phone: 858-452-2323	HR: –
Fax: 858-452-1222	FYE: December 31
Web: www.cypressbio.com	Type: Public

Cypress Bioscience explores the swampy waters of functional somatic syndromes, a group of chronic symptom-based disorders that are, on the whole, poorly understood. The biotech company's primary target is fibromyalgia, a condition marked by pain, stiffness, and fatigue that tends to affect adult women. Cypress Bioscience licensed a drug called milnacipran from French drugmaker Pierre Fabre as a potential therapy for fibromyalgia. With its development partner Forest Laboratories, the firm is guiding the drug through late-stage clinical trials. Cypress Bioscience has also partnered with Collegium Pharmaceutical to develop reformulations and analogs of milnacipran.

	Annual Growth	12/03	12/04	12/05	12/06	12/07
Sales ($ mil.)	(1.2%)	—	14.4	8.4	4.3	13.9
Net income ($ mil.)	—	—	(11.2)	(8.6)	(8.3)	3.5
Market value ($ mil.)	24.6%	—	213.5	184.5	249.3	412.8
Employees	—	—	—	15	—	—

THE CYPRESS GROUP

65 E. 55th St., Fl. 28	CEO: James A. (Jim) Stern
New York, NY 10022	CFO: –
Phone: 212-705-0150	HR: –
Fax: 212-705-0199	FYE: December 31
Web: www.cypressgp.com	Type: Private

If you want your company to branch out, perhaps The Cypress Group can help. The private equity firm owns stakes in companies in the automotive, financial services, manufacturing, and media and entertainment industries. Its portfolio includes holdings in about ten firms, including Cooper-Standard Automotive, CPI International, Danka Business Systems, and Scottish Re Group Limited. Cypress Group is an active investor that often becomes involved in the day-to-day management of its portfolio companies. The firm has made more than $4 billion in investments since it was founded in 1989.

CYPRESS SEMICONDUCTOR CORPORATION

NYSE: CY

198 Champion Ct.	CEO: T. J. Rodgers
San Jose, CA 95134	CFO: Brad W. Buss
Phone: 408-943-2600	HR: –
Fax: 408-943-4730	FYE: Monday nearest December 31
Web: www.cypress.com	Type: Public

In Silicon Valley, it's perfectly logical for a giant Cypress to put its roots down in pure silicon. Cypress Semiconductor makes more than 400 types of integrated circuits; its non-memory products include programmable logic devices, clock and timing chips, Universal Serial Bus (USB) microcontrollers, and specialty products for the computer and data communications markets. It also makes memory chips, especially static random-access memories (SRAMs), and silicon solar cells. Customers include computer, networking, and telecom equipment makers such as Cisco Systems, EMC, Logitech, Motorola, and Sony. Customers outside of North America account for more than 60% of sales.

	Annual Growth	12/03	12/04	12/05	12/06	12/07
Sales ($ mil.)	17.5%	836.8	948.4	886.4	1,091.6	1,596.4
Net income ($ mil.)	—	(5.3)	24.7	(92.2)	39.5	394.3
Market value ($ mil.)	23.9%	2,524.1	1,507.2	1,952.8	2,443.5	5,948.6
Employees	18.3%	4,033	4,500	5,100	5,800	7,900

CRYO-CELL INTERNATIONAL, INC.

OTC: CCEL

700 Brooker Creek Blvd., Ste. 1800	CEO: Mercedes Walton
Oldsmar, FL 34677	CFO: Jill M. Taymans
Phone: 813-749-2100	HR: –
Fax: 813-855-4745	FYE: November 30
Web: www.cryo-cell.com	Type: Public

Cryo-Cell International freezes the ties that bind. The company collects and cryogenically stores umbilical cord blood stem cells, giving expectant parents the opportunity to place a bet that evolving research will make the preservation cost a growing bargain for treating disease. Specimens collected in the US are processed and stored at its facility in Oldsmar, Florida. The company also offers services in some Latin American countries and in India. Cryo-Cell markets its services primarily by providing information to obstetricians, pediatricians, childbirth educators, and other health care providers.

	Annual Growth	11/03	11/04	11/05	11/06	11/07
Sales ($ mil.)	23.2%	7.6	12.2	14.4	17.2	17.5
Net income ($ mil.)	—	(7.5)	2.8	1.0	(2.8)	(5.0)
Market value ($ mil.)	8.5%	10.7	31.3	41.5	29.6	14.8
Employees	—	—	—	—	—	—

CYTEC INDUSTRIES INC.

NYSE: CYT

5 Garret Mountain Plaza	CEO: David Lilley
West Paterson, NJ 07424	CFO: David M. Drillock
Phone: 973-357-3100	HR: Joseph E. Marosits
Fax: 973-357-3065	FYE: December 31
Web: www.cytec.com	Type: Public

Cytec Industries covers its business bases. The company produces the building-block chemicals from which it makes engineered materials (composites and adhesives for the aerospace industry), specialty chemicals (resins and coatings for metal, plastic, and wood), and additives used in treating water and in industrial processes. Cytec also sells its building-block chemicals (acrylonitrile, melamine, and sulfuric acid) to third parties. In 2006 the company sold its water treatment chemicals and acrylamide manufacturing operations to Kemira for about $240 million. The divestiture was designed to allow Cytec to pare down its operations and place its focus on core business lines.

	Annual Growth	12/03	12/04	12/05	12/06	12/07
Sales ($ mil.)	24.2%	1,471.8	1,721.3	2,925.7	3,329.5	3,503.8
Net income ($ mil.)	27.8%	77.4	126.1	59.1	194.9	206.5
Market value ($ mil.)	18.3%	1,496.9	2,048.3	2,205.2	2,691.2	2,927.3
Employees	(8.2%)	—	—	7,300	6,700	—

CYTOGENIX, INC.

OTC: CYGX

3100 Wilcrest Dr., Ste. 140	CEO: Malcolm H. Skolnick
Houston, TX 77042	CFO: Pamela Schertz
Phone: 713-789-0070	HR: –
Fax: 713-789-0702	FYE: December 31
Web: www.cytogenix.com	Type: Public

CytoGenix wants disease to get lost in translation. The company's gene therapy technology might stop diseases at the translation stage of protein production, when messenger RNA assembles disease-causing proteins. CytoGenix is initially targeting skin diseases. Lead product candidates include SIMPLEVIR, a topical cream for herpes, and INFLAMOX, a cream for a variety of skin ailments, including psoriasis, acne, contact dermatitis, and rosacea. Other drug candidates target human papillomavirus, which causes cervical cancer, and the human rhinovirus, the culprit of many colds.

	Annual Growth	12/03	12/04	12/05	12/06	12/07
Sales ($ mil.)	0.0%	—	—	—	0.1	0.1
Net income ($ mil.)	—	—	—	—	(8.4)	(6.3)
Market value ($ mil.)	(79.1%)	—	—	—	84.4	17.6
Employees	—	—	—	—	—	—

An in-depth profile of this company is available to Hoover's Online members at hoovers.com.

465

CYTOKINETICS, INCORPORATED

NASDAQ (GM): CYTK

280 E. Grand Ave.
South San Francisco, CA 94080
Phone: 650-624-3000
Fax: 650-624-3010
Web: www.cytokinetics.com

CEO: Robert I. Blum
CFO: Sharon A. Surrey-Barbari
HR: David Cragg
FYE: December 31
Type: Public

Cytokinetics studies the cytoskeleton to get to the heart of the problem. The biopharmaceutical firm's development pipeline includes a lead drug candidate — in oral and intravenous formulations — designed for the treatment of heart failure based on a cytoskeletal protein in the heart muscle. It is being developed in collaboration with Amgen. Several other candidates are targeting multiple types of cancer; early clinical trials of these anti-cancer candidates were supported by GlaxoSmithKline and the National Cancer Institute. Cytokinetics is responsible for additional clinical development but may seek future strategic alliances to help advance this set of drugs into later-stage trials.

	Annual Growth	12/03	12/04	12/05	12/06	12/07
Sales ($ mil.)	6.4%	10.6	13.4	8.9	3.1	13.6
Net income ($ mil.)	—	(32.7)	(37.2)	(42.3)	(57.1)	(48.9)
Market value ($ mil.)	(7.2%)	—	291.6	194.3	323.8	233.2
Employees	—	—	—	150	—	—

CYTOMEDIX, INC.

AMEX: GTF

416 Hungerford Dr., Ste. 330
Rockville, MD 20850
Phone: 240-499-2680
Fax: 240-499-2690
Web: www.cytomedix.com

CEO: Kshitij Mohan
CFO: Andrew Maslan
HR: –
FYE: December 31
Type: Public

Here's a concept — using the body's own faculties to heal wounds. Cytomedix is developing autologous platelet therapies, which use a patient's own blood plasma to promote healing. Its AutoloGel System includes a centrifuge and blood draw kit. The centrifuge is used to separate key blood components, including platelets, growth factors, and the fibrin matrix scaffold, which are then combined with reagents to make a topical gel. When applied to a wound, the gel spurs the body's own healing process. AutoloGel has received FDA approval to treat chronic exuding wounds such as diabetic ulcers.

	Annual Growth	12/03	12/04	12/05	12/06	12/07
Sales ($ mil.)	14.6%	1.1	1.1	1.5	2.0	1.9
Net income ($ mil.)	—	(4.1)	(8.1)	(6.5)	(2.0)	(5.0)
Market value ($ mil.)	39.1%	15.2	51.3	61.5	29.9	56.8
Employees	—	—	—	11	—	—

CYTORI THERAPEUTICS, INC.

NASDAQ (GM): CYTX

3020 Callan Rd.
San Diego, CA 92121
Phone: 858-458-0900
Fax: 858-458-0994
Web: www.cytoritx.com

CEO: Christopher J. Calhoun
CFO: Mark E. Saad
HR: –
FYE: December 31
Type: Public

Attention lovers of liposuction: Cytori Therapeutics needs your fat. The firm (formerly known as MacroPore Biosurgery) is developing therapies using regenerative adult stem cells derived from adipose, otherwise known as fat tissue. Cytori's Celution is an adipose tissue extraction system that is marketed in Europe and Asia for reconstructive surgery purposes. The company is developing therapies based on the Celution system intended to treat cardiovascular disease, spine and orthopedic injuries, pelvic health conditions, and gastrointestinal disorders. Cytori has a joint venture with Olympus Corporation to develop future products based on its Celution system.

	Annual Growth	12/03	12/04	12/05	12/06	12/07
Sales ($ mil.)	(19.2%)	14.1	6.8	5.6	7.9	6.0
Net income ($ mil.)	—	(9.3)	(2.1)	(26.5)	(25.5)	(28.7)
Employees	2.2%	—	—	137	133	143

CYTRX CORPORATION

NASDAQ (CM): CYTR

11726 San Vicente Blvd., Ste. 650
Los Angeles, CA 90049
Phone: 310-826-5648
Fax: 310-826-6139
Web: www.cytrx.com

CEO: Steven A. Kriegsman
CFO: Mitchell K. Fogelman
HR: –
FYE: December 31
Type: Public

With its molecular chaperones, CytRx keeps an eye on the suspicious activities of proteins. The drug developer is working on small molecule therapies using its chaperone amplification technology, a method of boosting a certain corrective response in cells to protein misfires that cause disease. Its lead drug candidate is arimoclomol, a potential treatment for the neurodegenerative disorder Lou Gehrig's disease; it is also developing the compound as a treatment for stroke. Another candidate, iroxanadine, is undergoing clinical trials for the treatment of diabetic ulcers. In 2008 CytRx spun off its research programs related to RNA interference (RNAi) into publicly traded biotech firm RXi Pharmaceuticals.

	Annual Growth	12/03	12/04	12/05	12/06	12/07
Sales ($ mil.)	194.3%	0.1	0.4	0.2	2.1	7.5
Net income ($ mil.)	—	(17.8)	(16.4)	(15.1)	(16.8)	(21.9)
Market value ($ mil.)	41.6%	62.8	54.5	60.1	144.2	252.5
Employees	(10.7%)	—	—	28	25	—

DAC TECHNOLOGIES GROUP INTERNATIONAL, INC.

OTC: DAAT

12120 Colonial Glenn Rd., Ste. 6200
Little Rock, AR 72210
Phone: 501-661-9100
Fax: 501-661-9108
Web: www.dactec.com

CEO: David A. Collins
CFO: Robert C. Goodwin
HR: –
FYE: December 31
Type: Public

This company's aim is to give it its best shot. DAC Technologies Group International primarily manufactures about 40 GunMaster gun cleaning kits, gun locks, trigger locks, Sportsman's Lighter, security safes, specialty safes, personal protection devices, and items for the health care industry. About 66% of DAC's sales were generated from mass merchant Wal-Mart. The company also sells its wares through gun shops, sporting goods stores (Dick's Sporting Goods, Cabela's), and safe retailers. As the gun care market matures, DAC in 2008 expanded its products portfolio to make and market household cleaning items and fireplace equipment, mostly for existing customer Wal-Mart.

	Annual Growth	12/02	12/03	12/04	12/05	*12/06
Sales ($ mil.)	53.4%	2.8	4.8	9.4	13.4	15.5
Net income ($ mil.)	—	0.0	0.3	1.0	1.2	0.8
Market value ($ mil.)	38.7%	3.8	6.7	17.5	14.6	14.0
Employees	—	—	—	—	—	11

*Most recent year available

DAG MEDIA, INC.

NASDAQ (CM): DAGM

192 Lexington Ave.
New York, NY 10016
Phone: 212-489-6800
Fax: 212-779-2947
Web: www.newyellow.com

CEO: Assaf Ran
CFO: Inbar Evron-Yogev
HR: –
FYE: December 31
Type: Public

DAG Media prefers to let businesses, not fingers, do the walking. The company offers a patent-pending technology in the form of an online service, Nextyellow.com, that lets consumers search for a product or service; the consumer's request is matched with appropriate businesses, and the matched businesses then call or e-mail the customer. Vendor partners pay DAG Media monthly fees to be featured in the matching process. The company formed its DAG Interactive subsidiary to develop its Next Yellow matching software. In 2007 the company formed subsidiary DAG Funding, which offers short-term, secured, commercial loans to small businesses.

	Annual Growth	12/03	12/04	12/05	12/06	12/07
Assets ($ mil.)	(16.2%)	14.4	13.7	10.2	8.3	7.1
Net income ($ mil.)	—	1.6	1.0	(0.5)	(0.2)	0.0
Market value ($ mil.)	(15.4%)	—	—	—	5.1	4.3
Employees	—	—	19	—	—	—

D'AGOSTINO SUPERMARKETS, INC.

1385 Boston Post Rd.
Larchmont, NY 10538
Phone: 914-833-4000
Fax: 914-833-4060
Web: www.dagnyc.com

CEO: Nicholas (Nick) D'Agostino Jr.
CFO: –
HR: Frank Tucciarone
FYE: July 31
Type: Private

D'Agostino Supermarkets sells food for the body and soul to New York City residents. The company operates nearly 20 grocery stores, mostly in Manhattan but also in Westchester County, New York that feature deli and floral departments, seafood and meat counters, and an ample supply of fresh and organic produce. In addition to name-brand items, the grocer sells everything from ice cream to chips and chickens under its D'Agostino label; it also has developed the Earth Goods product line for environment- and health-conscious shoppers. Founded in 1932 by Nicola and Pasquale D'Agostino, the regional supermarket chain in still owned and operated by the D'Agostino family.

	Annual Growth	7/03	7/04	7/05	7/06	7/07
Est. sales ($ mil.)	—	—	—	—	—	119.1
Employees	—	—	—	—	—	1,100

DAHL'S FOODS, INC.

4343 Merle Hay Rd.
Des Moines, IA 50310
Phone: 515-278-1657
Fax: 515-278-0012
Web: www.dahlsfoods.com

CEO: David Sinnwell
CFO: –
HR: –
FYE: December 31
Type: Private

Dahl's Foods is a dominant force in the Iowa grocery market with about a dozen Dahl's Food Mart supermarkets in the Des Moines metropolitan area. Dahl's prides itself on offering low prices and good service, with extras like drive-up service at some stores. All Dahl's stores have in-store pharmacies. To compete with the likes of Wal-Mart and Costco Wholesale, and local rival Hy-Vee, the regional grocery chain has begun selling gas and more recently added in-store Quick Care Clinics to several of its stores in partnership with Mercy Medical Center. Founded by W. T. Dahl in 1931, the grocery company was sold to its employees (organized under the name Foods Inc.) in 1970.

	Annual Growth	12/03	12/04	12/05	12/06	12/07
Est. sales ($ mil.)	—	—	—	—	—	173.3
Employees	—	—	—	—	—	1,600

DAILY JOURNAL CORPORATION

NASDAQ (GM): DJCO

915 E. 1st St.
Los Angeles, CA 90012
Phone: 213-229-5300
Fax: 213-680-3682
Web: www.dailyjournal.com

CEO: Gerald L. Salzman
CFO: Gerald L. Salzman
HR: –
FYE: September 30
Type: Public

Legal matters dominate the news in these papers. Daily Journal Corporation is a leading newspaper publisher with more than a dozen papers serving markets primarily in California. Its flagship papers include the *Los Angeles Daily Journal* and the *San Francisco Daily Journal*, which offer in-depth coverage of legal cases and court matters in addition to general interest news. The company also publishes legal affairs magazine *California Lawyer*, operates subscription-based access to court case and real estate information, and publishes a legal directory for California. Chairman Charles Munger (who also serves as vice chairman of Berkshire Hathaway) and Ira Marshall control 40% of Daily Journal Corporation.

	Annual Growth	9/03	9/04	9/05	9/06	9/07
Sales ($ mil.)	0.7%	34.2	34.8	34.3	32.4	35.1
Net income ($ mil.)	21.9%	2.4	3.7	4.3	2.4	5.3
Market value ($ mil.)	10.5%	40.4	51.1	66.0	58.0	60.2
Employees	(3.7%)	—	—	275	275	255

DAILY NEWS, L.P.

450 W. 33rd St.
New York, NY 10001
Phone: 212-210-2100
Fax: 212-643-7831
Web: www.nydailynews.com

CEO: Marc Z. Kramer
CFO: Tom Peck
HR: Jeff Zomper
FYE: Last Sunday in December
Type: Private

This daily news might not always be fit to print, but it at least keeps New Yorkers entertained. Daily News, L.P. publishes the *Daily News*, the big city tabloid that goes toe-to-toe with the *New York Post* (owned by Rupert Murdoch's News Corp.) by penning over-the-top headlines and sensational stories. The paper, founded in 1919, is distributed primarily in the New York City area and boasts a circulation of about 700,000. It also publishes stories and features, as well as classified ads, online through its Web site. Real estate magnate Mortimer Zuckerman, who also owns news magazine *U.S. News & World Report*, and Fred Drasner bought the paper in 1993.

	Annual Growth	12/03	12/04	12/05	12/06	12/07
Est. sales ($ mil.)	—	—	—	—	—	93.7
Employees	—	—	—	—	—	1,600

DAILY RACING FORM, LLC

100 Broadway, 7th Fl.
New York, NY 10005
Phone: 212-366-7600
Fax: 212-366-7773
Web: www.drf.com

CEO: Brent Diamond
CFO: Joe Lyons
HR: –
FYE: December 31
Type: Private

Daily Racing Form wrote about Seabiscuit long before Laura Hillenbrand. Published by Daily Racing Form, LLC, the newspaper has been providing horse racing aficionados with odds, race results, and other in-depth information about the Sport of Kings since 1894. The paper is sold primarily at race tracks, off-track betting parlors, and newsstands; it also offers content to online subscribers. In addition to its newspaper, Daily Racing Form publishes books and provides news and gambling odds on other sports. The company and its paper are owned by Arlington Capital Partners.

	Annual Growth	12/03	12/04	12/05	12/06	12/07
Est. sales ($ mil.)	—	—	—	—	—	9.5
Employees	—	—	—	—	—	135

DAIMLER FINANCIAL SERVICES NORTH AMERICA LLC

36455 Corporate Dr.
Farmington Hills, MI 48331
Phone: 248-991-6700
Fax: 248-957-2997
Web: www.daimlerchryslerservices.com/dcservices_na

CEO: Klaus Entenmann
CFO: Paul E. Knauss
HR: Janet Marzett
FYE: December 31
Type: Subsidiary

Daimler Financial Services is darn-near one of the leading financial services companies in the world. Also known as Daimler Financial, the company operates more than 100 locations in about 40 countries. Daimler Financial Services North America (also known as Daimler Financial Services Americas) serves as headquarters for the company's operations in Canada, Mexico, and the US. Doing business under several related names, the company finances Daimler-brand auto and truck dealers' inventories and about a third of all vehicle purchases. Subsidiary Daimler Insurance provides dealers with floor plan and property/casualty insurance.

	Annual Growth	12/03	12/04	12/05	12/06	12/07
Est. sales ($ mil.)	—	—	—	—	—	202.5
Employees	—	—	—	—	—	4,700

An in-depth profile of this company is available to Hoover's Online members at hoovers.com.

467

DAIMLER TRUCKS NORTH AMERICA LLC

4747 N. Channel Ave.
Portland, OR 97217
Phone: 503-745-8000
Fax: 503-745-8921
Web: www.daimler-trucksnorthamerica.com

CEO: Chris Patterson
CFO: Juergen Kritschgau
HR: Phil Bezaire
FYE: December 31
Type: Subsidiary

Daimler Trucks North America (formerly Freightliner) is all over the road. The company, a subsidiary of automaker Daimler AG, is the #1 heavy truck maker in the US (Daimler is the world's top maker of commercial vehicles). In addition to the familiar Freightliner brand, Daimler Trucks also makes heavy-duty trucks under the Western Star and Sterling nameplates, and manufactures school buses under the Thomas Built brand. Freightliner Custom Chassis makes chassis for motor homes, walk-in vans, and buses. Affiliate Detroit Diesel makes medium- and heavy-duty diesel engines. Daimler Trucks' products are distributed through more than 800 independent and company-owned dealers throughout North America.

	Annual Growth	12/03	12/04	12/05	12/06	12/07
Est. sales ($ mil.)	—	—	—	—	—	2,147.5
Employees	—	—	—	—	—	20,000

DAIRY FARMERS OF AMERICA, INC.

10220 N. Ambassador Dr.
Kansas City, MO 64153
Phone: 816-801-6455
Fax: 816-801-6456
Web: www.dfamilk.com

CEO: Richard P. (Rick) Smith
CFO: David Meyer
HR: Annette Regan
FYE: December 31
Type: Cooperative

The members of the Dairy Farmers of America (DFA) are partners in cream. DFA is one of the world's largest dairy cooperatives, with more than 18,000 members in 48 US states. The co-op produces some 34% of the US milk supply with an annual pool of more than 61 billion pounds of milk. Along with fresh and shelf-stable fluid milk, the co-op also produces cheese, butter, whey, dried milk powder, and other dairy products for industrial, wholesale, and retail customers worldwide. DFA seeks strength by adding value-added products and looks for joint ventures to distribute its milk and milk-based food ingredients to wider regions.

	Annual Growth	12/03	12/04	12/05	12/06	12/07
Sales ($ mil.)	12.5%	6,932.9	8,953.5	8,908.6	7,898.8	11,100.0
Employees	0.0%	4,000	—	—	4,000	4,000

DAISY MANUFACTURING COMPANY

400 W. Stribing
Rogers, AR 72756
Phone: 479-636-1200
Fax: 479-636-1601
Web: www.daisy.com

CEO: Ray Hobbs
CFO: Luke Moffitt
HR: Marianne McBeth
FYE: December 31
Type: Private

Daisy Manufacturing, the world's oldest and largest maker of pellet and air-powered guns, ammunition, and accessories, aims to please. The company's BB guns come in a number of models for every level of shooter. Daisy makes the Red Ryder BB gun (more than 9 million sold since its debut in 1938), plus air rifles, pistols, CO2 pistols, slingshots, and branded apparel. Daisy began in 1882 as the Plymouth (Michigan) Iron Windmill Company, and its first airgun was introduced in 1886 as a premium for farmers who purchased windmills. The Daisy Airgun Museum in Rogers, Arkansas, displays more than 150 historical items and includes an indoor shooting range. Charter Oak Partners owns a majority interest in the company.

	Annual Growth	12/03	12/04	12/05	12/06	12/07
Est. sales ($ mil.)	—	—	—	—	—	8.6
Employees	—	—	—	—	—	180

DAK AMERICAS LLC

5925 Carnegie Blvd., Ste. 500
Charlotte, NC 28209
Phone: 704-940-7500
Fax: 704-940-7501
Web: www.dakfibers.com

CEO: Hector Camberos
CFO: Jorge P. Young
HR: –
FYE: December 31
Type: Subsidiary

DAK Americas manufactures products that are high in fiber and contain resins, but it has nothing to do with your breakfast cereal. The company's three units are DAK Resins, DAK Fibers, and DAK Monomers. A former joint venture between DuPont and Mexico's Alfa, S.A. de C.V., DAK Americas is now controlled solely by Alfa's Alpek subsidiary. Its primary products are terephthalic acid (TPA), PET resins, and polyester staple fibers, all used in the production of various textiles to make apparel, home furnishings, and items such as tea bags and diapers.

	Annual Growth	12/03	12/04	12/05	12/06	12/07
Est. sales ($ mil.)	—	—	—	—	—	875.0
Employees	—	—	—	—	—	770

DAKOTA GROWERS PASTA COMPANY, INC.

One Pasta Ave.
Carrington, ND 58421
Phone: 701-652-2855
Fax: 701-652-3552
Web: www.dakotagrowers.com

CEO: Timothy J. Dodd
CFO: Edward O. Irion
HR: –
FYE: July 31
Type: Private

Dakota Growers Pasta Company is trying to put an *al dente* in the noodle market. The company is a supplier of branded and private-label pasta products and flours to retail, foodservice, and ingredient companies in North America. Its brand names include Dreamfields, Pasta Growers, Pasta Sanita, Primo Piatto, and Zia Briosa. It also sells organic pasta under the Dakota Growers Pasta label and provides customers with private-label services. The company started out in 1991 as a wheat-growers cooperative; it became a private corporation in 2002. In 2004 the company took over New World Pasta's foodservice unit and now distributes the Ronzoni, Prince, San Giorgio, and Mrs. Weiss pasta brands to the foodservice sector.

	Annual Growth	7/03	7/04	7/05	7/06	7/07
Sales ($ mil.)	8.7%	136.8	144.7	155.6	171.5	191.1
Net income ($ mil.)	—	(0.4)	0.3	2.5	4.4	6.5
Employees	2.9%	388	367	409	416	435

DAKTRONICS, INC.

NASDAQ (GS): DAKT

331 32nd Ave.
Brookings, SD 57006
Phone: 605-697-4000
Fax: 605-697-4700
Web: www.daktronics.com

CEO: James B. (Jim) Morgan
CFO: William R. (Bill) Retterath
HR: Carla S. Gatzke
FYE: Saturday nearest April 30
Type: Public

Daktronics always knows the score. The company designs and manufactures electronic display systems. Its products include scoreboards, game timers, shot clocks, and animation displays for sports facilities; advertising and information displays for businesses; and electronic messaging displays used by transportation departments for motorist alerts. Other applications include airport information, securities trading, and outdoor advertising signs. Daktronics has converted many of its products to LED technology. The company's high-profile installations include two of the biggest scoreboards in the world, for the football stadiums of the Miami Dolphins and the University of Texas Longhorns.

	Annual Growth	4/04	4/05	4/06	4/07	4/08
Sales ($ mil.)	24.2%	209.9	230.4	309.4	433.2	499.7
Net income ($ mil.)	10.3%	17.7	15.7	21.0	24.4	26.2
Market value ($ mil.)	31.3%	200.3	194.9	763.1	945.5	596.0
Employees	23.9%	1,442	1,630	2,100	3,200	3,400

DALE CARNEGIE & ASSOCIATES, INC.

290 Motor Pkwy.
Hauppauge, NY 11788
Phone: 631-415-9300
Fax: 631-415-9390
Web: www.dale-carnegie.com

CEO: Peter V. Handal
CFO: Chris Noonan
HR: Nellie Perreira
FYE: August 31
Type: Private

Be a good listener, remember names, and network, and you might find success the Dale Carnegie way. Dale Carnegie & Associates, started by the author of the 1937 bestseller *How to Win Friends and Influence People*, teaches sales, teamwork, and public-speaking skills. The company runs courses in more than 75 countries and in more than 25 languages, and boasts some 7 million graduates and more than 2,700 professional instructors. Dale Carnegie & Associates offers courses for individuals and custom-made programs for corporations. The company was founded in 1912 by Dale Carnegie.

	Annual Growth	8/03	8/04	8/05	8/06	8/07
Est. sales ($ mil.)	—	—	—	—	—	3.6
Employees	—	—	—	—	—	100

DALE JARRETT RACING ADVENTURE, INC.

OTC: DJRT

120A N. Main Ave.
Newton, NC 28658
Phone: 828-466-8837
Fax: 828-465-5088
Web: www.racingadventure.com

CEO: Timothy B. (Tim) Shannon
CFO: Timothy B. (Tim) Shannon
HR: –
FYE: December 31
Type: Public

Gentlemen, start your engines! Dale Jarrett Racing Adventure brings the thrills (but hopefully not the spills) of NASCAR racing to doctors, lawyers, Indian chiefs — and even average joes, assuming they have enough "fuel" to foot the bill. Packages range from riding three laps in the passenger seat with a professional driver to 60 laps of actual driving at speeds of up to 165 mph (after instruction). Events are held at racetracks around the country (including Talladega Superspeedway and Atlanta Motor Speedway).

	Annual Growth	6/04	*12/04	12/05	12/06	12/07
Sales ($ mil.)	9.2%	1.9	1.2	1.8	2.1	2.7
Net income ($ mil.)	—	(0.3)	(0.3)	(0.3)	0.1	(0.9)
Market value ($ mil.)	17.6%	5.4	4.9	5.7	3.8	10.4
Employees	—	—	—	—		

*Fiscal year change

DALLAS COUNTY HOSPITAL DISTRICT

5201 Harry Hines Blvd.
Dallas, TX 75235
Phone: 214-590-8000
Fax: 214-590-8096
Web: www.parklandhospital.com

CEO: Ron J. Anderson
CFO: John Dragovits
HR: –
FYE: December 31
Type: Not-for-profit

Dallas County Hospital District may do business as Parkland Health and Hospital System (PHSS), but many people know it simply as Parkland, the hospital where JFK died. At the heart of the health system is Parkland Memorial Hospital, Dallas' only public hospital. PHHS also includes a network of community primary clinics; Parkland Community Health Plan, a regional HMO for Medicaid and Children's Health Insurance Program (CHIP) members; and HEALTHplus, a medical assistance program for uninsured Dallas County residents. Parkland Memorial Hospital has nearly 1,000 beds and is the primary teaching institution of The University of Texas Southwestern Medical Center, located next to the hospital.

	Annual Growth	12/03	12/04	12/05	12/06	12/07
Est. sales ($ mil.)	—	—	—	—	—	291.9
Employees	—	—	—	—	—	6,200

DALLAS COWBOYS FOOTBALL CLUB, LTD.

1 Cowboys Pkwy.
Irving, TX 75063
Phone: 972-556-9900
Fax: 972-556-9304
Web: www.dallascowboys.com

CEO: Jerral W. (Jerry) Jones
CFO: George Mitchell
HR: Vincent Thomson
FYE: February 28
Type: Private

Legend has it that there's a hole in the roof of Texas Stadium so God can watch his favorite team. Dallas Cowboys Football Club operates the famed Dallas Cowboys professional football franchise, one of the most popular teams in the National Football League and the winner of a record five Super Bowl titles (a mark it shares with the San Francisco 49ers and Pittsburgh Steelers). The franchise, often called "America's Team," was founded in 1960 by Clint Murchison Jr. and Bedford Wynne and competed for the NFL championship twice in that decade (losing both times to the Green Bay Packers). Jerry Jones has owned the team since 1989.

DALLAS MARKET CENTER CO. LTD.

2100 Stemmons Fwy.
Dallas, TX 75207
Phone: 214-655-6100
Fax: 800-637-6833
Web: www.dallasmarketcenter.com

CEO: William M. (Bill) Winsor
CFO: Nancy Winton
HR: –
FYE: December 31
Type: Private

Dallas Market Center (DMC) is where shop owners go to shop. The largest wholesale merchandise market in the world, DMC hosts some 50 tradeshow events each year, with leading manufacturers showing more than 50,000 product lines of apparel, garden accessories, gifts, gourmet food, home furnishings, and lighting to hundreds of thousands of retail buyers from all across the globe. DMC operates four buildings that house 2,000 permanent showrooms, as well as temporary exhibit show space. There, it hosts fashion shows, product displays, educational programs and seminars, and industry award galas. DMC was founded in 1957 by Trammell Crow and is majority owned by CNL Financial affiliate CNL Income Properties.

	Annual Growth	12/03	12/04	12/05	12/06	12/07
Est. sales ($ mil.)	—	—	—	—	—	17.9
Employees	—	—	—	—	—	350

🔲 DAL-TILE CORPORATION

7834 C.F. Hawn Fwy.
Dallas, TX 75217
Phone: 214-398-1411
Fax: 214-309-4835
Web: www.daltile.com

CEO: Harold G. Turk
CFO: Michael F. McGlothlin
HR: Gerald V. DeFalco
FYE: December 31
Type: Subsidiary

Dal-Tile International never fails to floor its customers: A subsidiary of Mohawk Industries, the company is the US's largest and best-known maker of ceramic tile. Dal-Tile — which sells its floor, wall, quarry, and mosaic tiles under the Daltile, Ahnzu, and American Olean brand names — manufactures ceramic, porcelain, and natural stone tiles at around 10 plants in the US and Mexico and sells them through more than 450 company-operated sales service centers in the US and Canada, and through independent distributors and retailers such as The Home Depot and Lowe's. Not surprisingly, Dal-Tile also markets its own line of related tile products. Customers include architects, builders, developers, and homeowners.

🔲 An in-depth profile of this company is available to Hoover's Online members at hoovers.com.

469

DAMON'S INTERNATIONAL, INC.

4645 Executive Dr.	CEO: Bill Burk
Columbus, OH 43220	CFO: Bruce A. Jackson
Phone: 614-442-7900	HR: Jen Gulling
Fax: 614-442-7787	FYE: June 30
Web: www.damons.com	Type: Private

This company is grilling up business with a mix of food, sports, and games. Damon's International operates and franchises about 85 Damon's Grill casual-dining restaurants in 20 states, mostly in and around the Great Lakes area. Its eateries feature grilled steaks, ribs, chicken, and seafood, as well as such appetizers as the onion loaf. Each location offers a traditional dining room setting for patrons looking for a meal, as well as a sports-themed bar and entertainment area called Damon's Clubhouse that features televised sports and interactive trivia games. Founded in 1979, the restaurant chain was acquired by Alliance Development Group in 2006.

DAN RIVER INC.

2291 Memorial Dr.	CEO: Sanjay Purohit
Danville, VA 24541	CFO: Scott D. Batson
Phone: 434-799-7000	HR: Calvin Barnhardt
Fax: 434-799-7216	FYE: Saturday nearest December 31
Web: www.danriver.com	Type: Private

What do the NFL and the Wiggles have in common? Both are licensed to Dan River. The company makes apparel fabrics, including material for men's shirts, and home fashion items, such as comforters, draperies, pillowcases, and sheets. Home fashion items are sold through high-volume retailers such as Kmart and Wal-Mart. Its children's bedding features characters from Star Wars, Thomas and Friends, and more. The company also supplies sheets and pillowcases to the hospitality and health care industries. Dan River emerged from Chapter 11 in early 2005, but filed for Chapter 11 bankruptcy protection again in April 2008. Indian manufacturer Gujarat Heavy Chemicals Ltd. acquired the company in December 2005.

	Annual Growth	12/03	12/04	12/05	12/06	12/07
Est. sales ($ mil.)	—	—	—	—	—	227.1
Employees	—	—	—	—	—	3,500

DANA CLASSIC FRAGRANCES, INC.

720 S. Powerline Rd., Ste. D	CEO: Isaac F. Cohen
Deerfield Beach, FL 33442	CFO: –
Phone: 954-725-6810	HR: –
Fax: 954-725-6811	FYE: March 31
Web: www.danaclassics.com	Type: Private

Resurrecting established fragrances makes sense to Dana Classic Fragrances. The firm remarkets classic fragrances, primarily through mass marketers. It sells some 50 brands worldwide, including British Sterling, Canoe, Incognito, and English Leather for men and White Chantilly, Heaven Sent, NaVy, Love's Baby Soft, Toujours Moi, Ambush, and Tabu for women. Dana Classic Fragrances was formed in 1999 when it purchased the fragrance brands portfolio from bankrupt Renaissance Cosmetics by Fragrance Express. The firm also makes and markets artificial nails (Cosmar, Press & Go), cosmetics, and other personal care products (Frills). Dana Classic Fragrances is owned by investment group Dimeling, Schreiber and Park.

	Annual Growth	3/03	3/04	3/05	3/06	3/07
Est. sales ($ mil.)	—	—	—	—	—	34.1
Employees	—	—	—	—	—	80

DANA-FARBER CANCER INSTITUTE

44 Binney St.	CEO: Edward J. Benz Jr.
Boston, MA 02115	CFO: Dorothy E. Puhy
Phone: 617-632-3240	HR: –
Fax: 617-632-4421	FYE: September 30
Web: www.dana-farber.org	Type: Not-for-profit

The Dana-Farber Cancer Institute fights cancer on two fronts. It provides treatment to cancer patients young and old, and also researches new cancer diagnostics, treatments, and preventions. The organization's researchers are also researching AIDS and a host of other deadly diseases. Patients receive treatment from Dana-Farber through its cancer centers operated with Brigham and Women's Hospital, Children's Hospital Boston, Massachusetts General Hospital, and Beth Israel Deaconess Medical Center. The institute is affiliated with Harvard Medical School. Dana-Farber Cancer Institute is funded by the National Cancer Institute, the National Institute of Allergy and Infectious Diseases, and private contributions.

	Annual Growth	9/03	9/04	9/05	9/06	9/07
Est. sales ($ mil.)	—	—	—	—	—	616.0
Employees	—	—	—	—	—	3,000

DANA HOLDING CORPORATION   NYSE: DAN

4500 Dorr St.	CEO: Gary L. Convis
Toledo, OH 43615	CFO: James A. (Jim) Yost
Phone: 419-535-4500	HR: Richard W. (Rich) Spriggle
Fax: 419-535-4643	FYE: December 31
Web: www.dana.com	Type: Public

When it comes to building cars, it starts with the parts. Dana Holding Corporation manufactures many of the parts carmakers use to piece together new vehicles. Its core products include axles and driveshafts, as well as sealing, thermal, and structural products. Among its customers are OEMs such as Ford, Chrysler, General Motors, and Toyota. The company also supplies companies that make commercial and off-highway vehicles such as PACCAR and Navistar. Dana filed for Chapter 11 bankruptcy early in 2006 and emerged in early 2008, changing its name from Dana Corporation to Dana Holding Corporation.

	Annual Growth	12/03	12/04	12/05	12/06	12/07
Sales ($ mil.)	2.0%	8,067.0	8,972.0	8,699.0	8,504.0	8,721.0
Net income ($ mil.)	—	222.0	62.0	(1,605.0)	(739.0)	(551.0)
Employees	(22.2%)	—	—	—	45,000	35,000

DANAHER CORPORATION   NYSE: DHR

2099 Pennsylvania Ave. NW, 12th Fl.	CEO: H. Lawrence (Larry) Culp Jr.
Washington, DC 20006	CFO: Daniel L. Comas
Phone: 202-828-0850	HR: Henk van Duijnhoven
Fax: 202-828-0860	FYE: December 31
Web: www.danaher.com	Type: Public

If you've ever used Craftsman hand tools or bought something with a bar code on it, then odds are you've been in touch with Danaher's business. Its Professional Instrumentation group produces environmental and electronic testing technology. The Industrial Technologies unit makes motion control equipment and devices that read bar codes, and the Medical Technologies division makes dental products and medical instrumentation devices. Danaher's Tools and Components segment includes hand tools, automotive specialty tools, and accessories under brand names like Sears' Craftsman. Brothers Steven Rales (chairman) and Mitchell Rales (a director) together own approximately 20% of the company.

	Annual Growth	12/03	12/04	12/05	12/06	12/07
Sales ($ mil.)	20.1%	5,293.9	6,889.3	7,984.7	9,596.4	11,025.9
Net income ($ mil.)	26.4%	536.8	746.0	897.8	1,122.0	1,369.9
Market value ($ mil.)	41.0%	7,050.1	17,735.1	17,044.8	22,329.1	27,899.9
Employees	11.8%	—	—	40,000	45,000	50,000

An in-depth profile of this company is available to Hoover's Online members at hoovers.com.

D&E COMMUNICATIONS, INC.

NASDAQ (GM): DECC

124 E. Main St.
Ephrata, PA 17522
Phone: 717-733-4101
Fax: 717-859-4803
Web: www.decommunications.com

CEO: James W. Morozzi
CFO: Thomas E. Morell
HR: –
FYE: December 31
Type: Public

D&E Communications keeps rural Pennsylvania connected. The company is a rural local-exchange carrier (RLEC) in eight eastern Pennsylvania counties, providing local and long-distance voice service. D&E also operates as a competitive local-exchange carrier (CLEC) in markets adjacent to its RLEC operations. Its communications services include dial-up and high-speed Internet access, Web hosting, and voice-over-IP (VoIP). It also provides wholesale network access to other carriers. D&E generates a small portion of its revenues from systems integration services related to the design, installation, and support of local and wide-area networks.

	Annual Growth	12/03	12/04	12/05	12/06	12/07
Sales ($ mil.)	(3.1%)	173.1	176.3	176.3	162.1	152.6
Net income ($ mil.)	26.8%	4.1	(2.7)	13.7	6.7	10.6
Market value ($ mil.)	(2.0%)	225.6	171.9	119.5	182.1	208.4
Employees	—	—	—	640	—	—

D&H DISTRIBUTING CO.

2525 N. 7th St.
Harrisburg, PA 17110
Phone: 717-236-8001
Fax: 717-255-7838
Web: www.dandh.com

CEO: Israel (Izzy) Schwab
CFO: Robert J. Miller Jr.
HR: –
FYE: April 30
Type: Private

D&H Distributing sells computer and electronics products in the US and Canada. Its product portfolio includes computers and peripherals, electronic components, data storage devices, printing and imaging equipment, software, mobile devices, gaming systems, home appliances, surveillance systems, and digital music players. Clients include small and large resellers and retailers, system builders, and college bookstores. D&H also targets schools and government agencies. Suppliers include Hewlett-Packard, Intel, and Microsoft. D&H has been employee-owned since 1999.

	Annual Growth	4/02	4/03	4/04	4/05	4/06
Sales ($ mil.)	23.5%	760.0	857.0	1,070.0	1,465.0	1,770.0
Employees	15.6%	—	550	618	850	850

THE DANNON COMPANY, INC.

100 Hillside Ave.
White Plains, NY 10603
Phone: 914-872-8400
Fax: 914-872-1565
Web: www.dannon.com

CEO: Juan C. Dalto
CFO: Tony Cicio
HR: Charlene Binder
FYE: December 31
Type: Subsidiary

Yes, it's curdled milk with bacteria with a bit of jam added, but Dannon has lifted yogurt from health-food obscurity into a supermarket staple. The Dannon Company vies with General Mills, maker of Yoplait, for the #1 spot as the US's top yogurt producer (the two have traded off the honor in recent years). Dannon's approximately 100 flavors, styles, and sizes of yogurts come in regular, low-fat, and nonfat varieties, as well as in liquid ("drinkable") and smoothie forms. To better attract children, Dannon makes Danimals yogurt in kid-friendly packaging; to better attract moms, it continues to launch ever more indulgent and even fluffier yogurts.

	Annual Growth	12/03	12/04	12/05	12/06	12/07
Est. sales ($ mil.)	—	—	—	—	—	203.1
Employees	—	—	—	—	—	900

DARA BIOSCIENCES, INC.

NASDAQ (CM): DARA

8601 Six Forks Rd., Ste. 160
Raleigh, NC 27615
Phone: 919-872-5578
Fax: –
Web: www.darabiosciences.com

CEO: John Didsbury
CFO: John C. Thomas Jr.
HR: –
FYE: December 31
Type: Public

Metabolism out of whack? DARA BioSciences is working on it. The drug development company is testing drugs for metabolic diseases such as diabetes. However, it was not always thus for the company. Formerly called Point Therapeutics, the firm failed in its previous efforts to advance lead cancer drug talabostat and was forced to regroup and consider its options. The company turned to its preclinical pipeline, which included a potential diabetes drug, and then in 2008 executed a reverse merger with privately held DARA BioSciences, which brought along a complementary set of metabolic compounds, as well as programs focused on neuropathic pain and psoriasis.

	Annual Growth	12/02	12/03	12/04	12/05	*12/06
Sales ($ mil.)	100.0%	—	—	—	0.2	0.4
Net income ($ mil.)	—	—	—	—	(22.7)	(29.4)
Market value ($ mil.)	(64.2%)	—	—	—	113.0	40.5
Employees	(16.7%)	—	—	—	48	40

*Most recent year available

DARBY DENTAL SUPPLY

300 Jericho Quadrangle
Jericho, NY 11753
Phone: 516-683-1800
Fax: 516-688-2880
Web: www.darbydentalsupply.com

CEO: Carl Ashkin
CFO: James Conklin
HR: Jill Halpin
FYE: December 31
Type: Private

Hope you've been flossing, because The Darby Group is homing in on those pearly whites. The company, which had distributed medical supplies, as well as dental laboratory equipment and veterinary products, has been paring down those operations to focus on the telesales and distribution business of its Darby Dental Supply subsidiary. Through call centers located in four states, Darby Dental Supply sells more than 40,000 products (from instrument trays to X-ray equipment) to dentists across the US. In 2006 it sold several of its subsidiaries, including Darby Medical Supply and Darby Dental Laboratory Supply, to Henry Schein.

	Annual Growth	12/03	12/04	12/05	12/06	12/07
Est. sales ($ mil.)	—	—	—	—	—	350.0
Employees	—	—	—	—	—	650

DARDEN RESTAURANTS, INC.

NYSE: DRI

5900 Lake Ellenor Dr.
Orlando, FL 32809
Phone: 407-245-4000
Fax: 407-245-5389
Web: www.dardenrestaurants.com

CEO: Clarence Otis Jr.
CFO: C. Bradford (Brad) Richmond
HR: Ronald Bojalad
FYE: Last Sunday in May
Type: Public

This company has cornered not one but two dining markets: seafood and "Hospitaliano." Darden Restaurants is the #1 casual-dining operator (in terms of revenue) with more than 1,600 restaurants in the US and Canada. Its flagship chains include seafood segment leader Red Lobster and top Italian-themed concept Olive Garden. Both chains cater to families with mid-priced menu items, themed interiors, and primarily suburban locations. Darden also operates the LongHorn Steakhouse chain with about 300 outlets. In addition, the company operates a small chain of tropical-themed Bahama Breeze restaurants that offer Caribbean-inspired food, along with a casual grill and wine bar concept called Seasons 52.

	Annual Growth	5/03	5/04	5/05	5/06	5/07
Sales ($ mil.)	4.6%	4,655.0	5,003.4	5,278.1	5,720.6	5,567.1
Net income ($ mil.)	(3.5%)	232.3	227.2	290.6	338.2	201.4
Market value ($ mil.)	20.6%	3,026.8	3,564.7	5,064.0	5,366.9	6,408.2
Employees	2.3%	—	—	150,100	157,300	157,000

An in-depth profile of this company is available to Hoover's Online members at hoovers.com.

471

DARIGOLD, INC.

4058 Rainier Ave. South
Seattle, WA 98119
Phone: 206-284-7220
Fax: 206-722-2569
Web: www.darigold.com

CEO: John Underwood
CFO: Stephen (Steve) Boyd
HR: Jay Burton
FYE: March 31
Type: Subsidiary

Churning out dairy foods since 1918, Darigold is the processing and marketing subsidiary of an approximately 600-member cooperative, Northwest Dairy Association. With 11 processing plants, Darigold makes and distributes fluid milk, butter, cheese, and other cultured dairy products under private labels and the Darigold brand name. The company retired its dba name WestFarm Foods in 2006. Darigold offers its products to wholesale and retail food companies as well as foodservice operators. It numbers Albertsons, Cost Cutter, Food 4 Less, and Safeway among its customers.

	Annual Growth	3/03	3/04	3/05	3/06	3/07
Sales ($ mil.)	—	—	—	—	—	1,450.2
Employees	—	—	—	—	—	1,240

DARLING INTERNATIONAL INC.

NYSE: DAR

251 O'Connor Ridge Blvd., Ste. 300
Irving, TX 75038
Phone: 972-717-0300
Fax: 972-717-1588
Web: www.darlingii.com

CEO: Randall C. Stuewe
CFO: John O. Muse
HR: –
FYE: Saturday nearest December 31
Type: Public

It's not the most darling of businesses — in fact it's messy and it's stinky — but Darling International, the largest independent rendering operation in the US, is willing to do it. The company collects and processes animal by-products and used cooking grease from approximately 115,000 restaurants, butcher shops, grocery stores, and independent meat and poultry processors throughout the US. Its rendering operations produce yellow grease, tallow, and meat, bone, and blood meal, which Darling sells in the US as well as internationally to makers of soap, rubber, pet and livestock feed, and chemicals.

	Annual Growth	12/03	12/04	12/05	12/06	12/07
Sales ($ mil.)	18.8%	324.4	320.2	308.9	407.0	645.3
Net income ($ mil.)	25.7%	18.2	13.9	7.7	5.1	45.5
Market value ($ mil.)	51.7%	179.5	278.7	255.8	445.5	951.1
Employees	28.4%	—	—	1,110	1,830	1,830

⊞ DART CONTAINER CORPORATION

500 Hogsback Rd.
Mason, MI 48854
Phone: 517-676-3800
Fax: 517-676-3883
Web: www.dartcontainer.com

CEO: Robert C. Dart
CFO: Kevin Fox
HR: Mark Franks
FYE: December 31
Type: Private

Dart Container is a world cup winner — not in soccer, but in foam cups and containers. (It commands about half of the global market in foam cups.) The company uses a secret method of molding expandable polystyrene to make its products, which include cups, lids, dinnerware, and cutlery for customers such as hospitals, schools, and restaurants. To cut costs, Dart Container builds its own molding machinery and operates its own distribution trucks. The firm sells its recycled polystyrene to companies that make such items as insulation material and egg cartons. The Dart family controls the company.

	Annual Growth	12/02	12/03	12/04	12/05	12/06
Est. sales ($ mil.)	8.2%	1,100.0	1,200.0	1,250.0	1,388.0	1,510.0
Employees	3.3%	4,950	5,000	5,000	5,200	5,640

DART TRANSIT COMPANY

800 Lone Oak Rd.
Eagan, MN 55121
Phone: 651-688-2000
Fax: 651-683-1650
Web: www.dartadvantage.com

CEO: David Oren
CFO: Scott Buchanan
HR: John Basill
FYE: December 31
Type: Private

Dart Transit aims to land its customers' freight on the bull's-eye. The company provides truckload freight transportation, intermodal service (arrangement of freight transportation by multiple methods, such as truck and train), and logistics services, including freight brokerage and warehousing. It also offers dedicated transportation, in which drivers and equipment are assigned to a customer long-term. Overall, the company operates a fleet of some 2,750 tractors and 7,600 trailers. Earl Oren, father of company chairman Donald Oren, founded Dart Transit in 1938. The company is owned by the Oren family.

	Annual Growth	12/03	12/04	12/05	12/06	12/07
Sales ($ mil.)	—	—	—	—	—	504.5
Employees	—	—	—	—	—	340

DARWIN PROFESSIONAL UNDERWRITERS, INC.

NYSE: DR

9 Farm Springs Rd.
Farmington, CT 06032
Phone: 860-284-1300
Fax: 860-284-1301
Web: www.darwinpro.com

CEO: Stephen J. Sills
CFO: John L. (Jack) Sennott Jr.
HR: –
FYE: December 31
Type: Public

Having liability insurance is an evolutionary imperative at Darwin Professional Underwriters, a specialty insurer providing professional liability coverage to a number of customer groups, including health care facilities, doctors, insurance agents, and technology providers. Its three main product lines are errors and omissions (E&O) liability insurance, medical malpractice insurance, and directors and officers (D&O) liability insurance. It sells policies both on an admitted basis (through Darwin National Assurance) and a surplus lines basis (through Darwin Select) in most parts of the US. The company was founded in 2003 by CEO Stephen Stills and Alleghany, which owns more than half of the firm.

	Annual Growth	12/03	12/04	12/05	12/06	12/07
Assets ($ mil.)	78.2%	—	146.1	447.0	635.3	827.1
Net income ($ mil.)	—	(2.3)	0.1	3.7	16.0	32.2
Market value ($ mil.)	2.9%	—	—	—	399.8	411.5
Employees	50.9%	—	—	—	116	175

DASSAULT FALCON JET CORP.

Teterboro Airport, 200 Riser Rd.
Little Ferry, NJ 07643
Phone: 201-440-6700
Fax: 201-541-4515
Web: www.falconjet.com

CEO: John Rosanvallon
CFO: J. Morgan Young
HR: Robert Basso
FYE: December 31
Type: Subsidiary

Helping the rich, famous, or merely busy soar to new heights, Dassault Falcon Jet sells and supports Falcon 50EX, 900DX, 900EX, 7X, 2000DX, and 2000EX business jets. A subsidiary of Dassault Aviation, the company provides such offerings as engine maintenance, spare parts and tools distribution, parts exchange, special equipment testing, operational assistance, and pilot, maintenance, and cabin crew training. More than 1,600 Falcon jets have been produced since Dassault began production in 1963. The company builds its aircraft in France, then flies them to its facilities in the US for painting and installation of interiors and amenities.

DASSAULT SYSTÈMES SIMULIA CORP.

Rising Sun Mills, 166 Valley St.
Providence, RI 02909
Phone: 401-276-4400
Fax: 401-276-4408
Web: www.simulia.com

CEO: Scott A. Berkey
CFO: Jim Lambert
HR: Anthony J. (Tony) Bellantuoni
FYE: December 31
Type: Subsidiary

Dassault Systèmes Simulia Corp. (formerly ABAQUS) makes engineering analysis software that simulates the physical response of structures and solid bodies to load, temperature, contact, impact, and other stresses. Its finite element analysis tools are widely used in the aerospace, automotive, consumer goods, electronics, and manufacturing industries, among other fields. The company also provides related engineering, legal, technical consulting, and training services. The company was founded in 1978 as Hibbitt, Karlsson & Sorensen. In 2005 Dassault Systèmes acquired the company for approximately $413 million in cash.

	Annual Growth	12/03	12/04	12/05	12/06	12/07
Est. sales ($ mil.)	—	—	—	—	—	18.5
Employees	—	—	—	—	—	235

DATA DOMAIN, INC.

NASDAQ (GM): DDUP

2421 Mission College Blvd.
Santa Clara, CA 95054
Phone: 408-980-4800
Fax: 408-980-8620
Web: www.datadomain.com

CEO: Frank Slootman
CFO: Michael P. (Mike) Scarpelli
HR: Annie Chow
FYE: December 31
Type: Public

Data Domain has eminent knowledge of data protection technologies. The company develops disk-based storage appliances for data backup and disaster recovery. Based on proprietary compression technology, its systems are compatible with backup software from such providers as CommVault Systems, EMC Corporation, IBM, and Symantec. Data Domain also generates revenue from maintenance and support services. The company sells directly and through resellers worldwide. Its customers include enterprises in the defense, entertainment, finance, health care, legal, media, retail, and technology sectors, as well as government agencies and schools. Data Domain outsources its manufacturing to Flextronics.

	Annual Growth	12/03	12/04	12/05	12/06	12/07
Sales ($ mil.)	436.6%	—	0.8	8.1	46.4	123.6
Net income ($ mil.)	—	—	(9.8)	(13.8)	(4.0)	(3.7)
Market value ($ mil.)	—	—	—	—	—	1,493.8
Employees	121.0%	—	—	81	179	—

DATA I/O CORPORATION

NASDAQ (CM): DAIO

6464 185th Ave. NE
Redmond, WA 98052
Phone: 425-881-6444
Fax: 425-869-7423
Web: www.dataio.com

CEO: Frederick R. (Fred) Hume
CFO: Joel S. Hatlen
HR: –
FYE: Last Thursday in December
Type: Public

Data I/O knows the chip-programming business inside and out. The company makes programming systems used by electronics makers to tailor their integrated circuits (ICs) to suit a broad range of products. Data I/O makes both automated and non-automated programming systems. The automated models are used for high-volume applications; the non-automated programming systems include both single-site systems that program one device at a time and multisite systems for increased output. Industrial giant Siemens is a leading client, among 1,200-plus customers around the world. More than three-quarters of sales are outside the US.

	Annual Growth	12/03	12/04	12/05	12/06	12/07
Sales ($ mil.)	2.1%	24.7	27.3	28.3	28.8	26.8
Net income ($ mil.)	(11.4%)	1.3	(0.1)	0.6	0.1	0.8
Market value ($ mil.)	19.4%	28.2	24.4	35.1	30.5	57.4
Employees	(6.5%)	127	122	130	129	97

DATABANK IMX

12000 Baltimore Ave.
Beltsville, MD 20705
Phone: 301-210-5052
Fax: 301-210-5348
Web: www.databankimx.com

CEO: Dick Aschman
CFO: Steve Seminack
HR: –
FYE: December 31
Type: Private

DataBank IMX turns piles and files into organized information. Specializing in document management, the company offers such services as digital imaging, microfilm conversion, and document storage and retrieval through nearly 10 production facilities located in major US cities (including Boston, Chicago, and New York). DataBank IMX's services are targeted to clients in financial services, health care, engineering, education, and government services sectors. The company offers proprietary scanning and conversion software, and online storage and retrieval services, and provides related IT services. The company was formed in 2005 when DataBank, Inc. acquired all the assets of ImageMax.

	Annual Growth	12/03	12/04	12/05	12/06	12/07
Est. sales ($ mil.)	—	—	—	—	—	29.9
Employees	—	—	—	—	—	475

DATACARD CORPORATION

11111 Bren Rd. West
Minnetonka, MN 55343
Phone: 952-933-1223
Fax: 952-931-0418
Web: www.datacard.com

CEO: Jeffrey J. Hattara
CFO: Todd G. Wilkinson
HR: –
FYE: March 31
Type: Private

Datacard has a full deck of financial and identification products. The company, which does business as Datacard Group, offers card printers, laminators, digital cameras, engravers, mail handlers, and software that organizations use to manage, customize, and issue personalized credit and ID cards. Datacard products are used by financial institutions (credit cards, smart cards), corporations (badges), and government agencies (passports, national ID cards) in more than 100 countries. The company also offers consulting, graphic design, and systems integration services.

	Annual Growth	3/03	3/04	3/05	3/06	3/07
Sales ($ mil.)	—	—	—	—	—	400.0
Employees	—	—	—	—	—	1,400

⊞ DATALINK CORPORATION

NASDAQ (GM): DTLK

8170 Upland Cir.
Chanhassen, MN 55317
Phone: 952-944-3462
Fax: 952-944-7869
Web: www.datalink.com

CEO: Charles B. (Charlie) Westling
CFO: Gregory T. Barnum
HR: Mary E. West
FYE: December 31
Type: Public

Datalink serves up storage system smorgasbords. The company builds and implements high-end, custom-designed data storage systems for large corporations. Datalink's storage systems include data management software and storage devices based on optical, magnetic disk, and tape technologies. The company employs an open-system standard, building its offerings from products made by leading manufacturers such as Brocade Communications Systems, EMC, and Hitachi Data Systems. Datalink also provides support and maintenance services. Chairman and former CEO Greg Meland owns about a quarter of Datalink.

	Annual Growth	12/03	12/04	12/05	12/06	12/07
Sales ($ mil.)	18.2%	91.1	93.3	117.1	146.0	177.8
Net income ($ mil.)	—	(5.2)	(3.1)	(2.9)	8.5	1.2
Market value ($ mil.)	3.6%	39.9	30.2	40.4	84.4	46.0
Employees	—	—	—	147	—	—

DATALOGIC SCANNING, INC.

959 Terry St.
Eugene, OR 97402
Phone: 541-683-5700
Fax: 541-345-7140
Web: www.scanning.datalogic.com

CEO: William L. (Bill) Parnell Jr.
CFO: Chet Galka
HR: Rhone E. Lee
FYE: December 31
Type: Subsidiary

Datalogic Scanning (formerly PSC) is helping to replace the "cha-ching" of cash registers with the beeping of bar code scanners. The company's retail, commercial, and industrial bar code scanners speed up retail checkout, inventory management, shipping, parcel sorting, and other functions. Datalogic's software provides detailed analysis of its scanner products, allowing for easier maintenance and increased performance. Long an expert in bar code data collection, the company has also developed products for the burgeoning radio-frequency identification (RFID) market. Datalogic acquired PSC from Littlejohn & Co. for about $195 million in 2005. It changed the company's name to Datalogic Scanning in 2007.

	Annual Growth	12/03	12/04	12/05	12/06	12/07
Est. sales ($ mil.)	—	—	—	—	—	255.0
Employees	—	—	—	—	—	809

DATAMETRICS CORPORATION

OTC: DMCP

1717 Diplomacy Row
Orlando, FL 32809
Phone: 407-251-4577
Fax: 407-251-4588
Web: www.datametrics.com

CEO: John Marceca
CFO: Tami Tharp
HR: –
FYE: Last Sunday in October
Type: Public

DataMetrics serves customers that need their printers to be built like tanks. The company designs and manufactures rugged ink jet and laser printers and plotters for military and industrial applications. DataMetrics also offers ruggedized portable computers and peripherals such as monitors, storage drives, power sources, and keyboards. Its service offerings include design engineering, custom manufacturing, logistics, systems integration, and support. DataMetrics counts the US government, American Airlines, Lockheed Martin, and General Dynamics among its customers.

	Annual Growth	10/03	10/04	10/05	10/06	10/07
Sales ($ mil.)	(2.2%)	3.5	4.4	3.0	3.2	3.2
Net income ($ mil.)	—	(2.0)	(0.6)	(0.6)	(2.9)	(1.5)
Market value ($ mil.)	(53.2%)	72.3	57.8	6.8	1.4	3.5
Employees	(3.0%)	—	—	34	28	32

DATARAM CORPORATION

NASDAQ (GM): DRAM

186 Princeton Rd.
West Windsor, NJ 08550
Phone: 609-799-0071
Fax: 609-799-6734
Web: www.dataram.com

CEO: John H. Freeman
CFO: Mark E. Maddocks
HR: –
FYE: April 30
Type: Public

Dataram wants you to remember your DRAMs. The company makes add-in memory boards and memory modules that expand the capacity of computer servers and workstations running under the UNIX and Windows operating systems. Its products, which use DRAM memory devices, are compatible with systems from companies such as Sun Microsystems, Hewlett-Packard, IBM, Dell, and Silicon Graphics, and with microprocessors made by AMD and Intel. Sun Micro has licensed Dataram to sell memory components for its hardware products. About 70% of Dataram's sales are to customers in the US.

	Annual Growth	4/03	4/04	4/05	4/06	4/07
Sales ($ mil.)	(8.0%)	53.5	62.0	65.7	41.8	38.4
Net income ($ mil.)	—	(15.6)	2.3	6.7	2.8	0.8
Market value ($ mil.)	14.6%	21.2	58.8	35.1	49.1	36.7
Employees	2.0%	—	—	100	102	—

DATASCENSION, INC.

OTC: DSEN

407 W. Imperial Hwy., H 314
Brea, CA 92821
Phone: 832-615-4777
Fax: 714-276-9080
Web: www.datascension.com

CEO: D. Scott Kincer
CFO: David Lieberman
HR: –
FYE: December 31
Type: Public

Datascension (formerly Nutek) provides market research, data storage, data mining, document processing, and database design services through its Datascension International subsidiary. The company primarily provides telephone interviewing services for market research firms; in 2007 Ipsos-Reid, Orbis, and Synovate collectively accounted for 40% of its revenue. Datascension, which is also known as DSEN, owns operations in California, Costa Rica, and the Dominican Republic; as a result, it is attempting to zero in on the Spanish-speaking interviewing market.

	Annual Growth	12/03	12/04	12/05	12/06	12/07
Sales ($ mil.)	30.0%	7.1	8.5	9.8	14.8	20.3
Net income ($ mil.)	—	(0.2)	(6.1)	1.8	(1.1)	(0.9)
Market value ($ mil.)	(30.2%)	94.8	9.9	4.2	8.5	22.5
Employees	—	—	—	—	—	1,500

DATASCOPE CORP.

NASDAQ (GS): DSCP

14 Philips Pkwy.
Montvale, NJ 07645
Phone: 201-391-8100
Fax: 201-307-5400
Web: www.datascope.com

CEO: Lawrence Saper
CFO: Henry M. (Hank) Scaramelli
HR: James L. Cooper
FYE: June 30
Type: Public

Datascope helps doctors pump it up or patch it up. The company puts its heart into making medical instruments and products — including intra-aortic balloon pumps and catheters — for use in heart surgery, coronary angioplasty, and other cardiovascular procedures. Datascope also makes vascular grafts and patches for reconstructive blood vessel surgeries. One Datascope product, the VasoSeal, is a collagen seal that plugs arterial punctures after catheterization. Datascope markets its products worldwide. In 2008 it sold its patient monitoring business to Mindray, and it is exiting the vascular closure market. It has announced plans to consider strategic alternatives, including a possible sale of the company.

	Annual Growth	6/03	6/04	6/05	6/06	6/07
Sales ($ mil.)	3.6%	328.3	343.3	352.7	373.0	378.8
Net income ($ mil.)	(6.9%)	23.3	23.9	14.6	25.8	17.5
Market value ($ mil.)	8.2%	428.9	587.0	493.4	470.5	587.4
Employees	—	—	—	1,320	—	—

DATATEL, INC.

4375 Fair Lakes Ct.
Fairfax, VA 22033
Phone: 703-968-9000
Fax: 703-968-4573
Web: www.datatel.com

CEO: John F. Speer III
CFO: Kevin M. Boyce
HR: –
FYE: December 31
Type: Private

Datatel doesn't care if you're a Bruin, a Hurricane, or a Longhorn as long as you've got data that needs managing. The company, which serves higher education institutions across the country, makes software that manages information about students, finances, financial aid, human resources, and advancement. The company's software products streamline such processes as enterprise resource planning, e-recruitment, and alumni communications, serving more than 700 institutions throughout North America. Datatel was founded in 1968 by Ken Kendrick and Tom Davidson: they sold the company in 2005 to members of their executive team (backed by Thoma Cressey Equity Partners and Trident Capital).

	Annual Growth	12/03	12/04	12/05	12/06	12/07
Sales ($ mil.)	13.6%	—	—	—	108.0	122.7
Employees	0.5%	—	—	—	547	550

DATATRAK INTERNATIONAL, INC.

NASDAQ (CM): DATA

6150 Parkland Blvd., Ste. 100
Mayfield Heights, OH 44124
Phone: 440-443-0082
Fax: 440-442-3482
Web: www.datatraknet.com

CEO: Jeffrey A. (Jeff) Green
CFO: Raymond J. Merk
HR: –
FYE: December 31
Type: Public

Researchers rely on DATATRAK to keep track of their clinical data. The company develops online, hosted electronic data capture (EDC) software for the biotechnology, medical device, contract research, and pharmaceutical industries. The company' software speeds up the process of gathering data during clinical trials by collecting and electronically transmitting trial data from remote research sites to sponsors. DATATRAK also offers project management, site assessment, training, and hosting services.

	Annual Growth	12/03	12/04	12/05	12/06	12/07
Sales ($ mil.)	10.5%	7.1	11.3	15.7	17.7	10.6
Net income ($ mil.)	—	(1.0)	0.8	2.5	(4.5)	(10.9)
Market value ($ mil.)	(2.4%)	24.2	48.3	103.0	58.0	21.9
Employees	—	—	—	110	—	—

DATAWATCH CORPORATION

NASDAQ (GM): DWCH

Quorum Office Park, 271 Mill Rd.
Chelmsford, MA 01824
Phone: 978-441-2200
Fax: 978-441-1114
Web: www.datawatch.com

CEO: Kenneth P. (Ken) Bero
CFO: Murray P. Fish
HR: –
FYE: September 30
Type: Public

Datawatch keeps close tabs on data. The company makes data mining, business intelligence, and help desk software. Its products include Monarch, for extracting and manipulating data from ASCII or HTML files; Monarch Data Pump, a data replication and migration tool used to populate and refresh data marts and data warehouses; and MonarchRMS, Web-based report mining and analysis. Subsidiary Auxilor provides VisuallHelp Desk software, an IT support and help desk application for IBM's Lotus Domino platform. Customers have included Aetna, Ford, McDonald's, and the US Postal Service.

	Annual Growth	9/03	9/04	9/05	9/06	9/07
Sales ($ mil.)	9.3%	17.7	19.3	21.5	20.8	25.3
Net income ($ mil.)	17.2%	0.9	1.1	0.8	(0.6)	1.7
Market value ($ mil.)	25.9%	10.0	20.9	18.8	14.1	25.1
Employees	(2.4%)	—	—	127	—	121

DAVE & BUSTER'S, INC.

2481 Manana Dr.
Dallas, TX 75220
Phone: 214-357-9588
Fax: 214-350-0941
Web: www.daveandbusters.com

CEO: Stephen M. (Steve) King
CFO: –
HR: Nancy J. Duricic
FYE: Sunday after Saturday nearest January 31
Type: Private

Fun and games collide with food and drink at Dave & Buster's. The company owns and operates about 50 entertainment complexes in 20 states and Canada that offer casual dining, full bar service, and a cavernous game room. The adult fun spots feature the latest in video games and motion simulators, as well as games of skill in which players can win prizes. For dining, Dave & Buster's offers a menu that features traditional American fare such as burgers, seafood, and steak. Partners David Corriveau and James "Buster" Corley opened the first Dave & Buster's in 1982. Private equity firm Wellspring Capital Management owns more than 80% of the company; hedge fund manager HBK Investments owns the rest.

	Annual Growth	1/04	1/05	1/06	1/07	1/08
Sales ($ mil.)	10.3%	362.8	390.3	463.5	510.2	536.3
Net income ($ mil.)	—	10.9	12.9	4.3	(11.6)	(8.8)
Employees	9.2%	5,810	7,400	7,500	7,500	8,248

DAVE'S SUPERMARKETS INC.

5300 Richmond Rd.
Bedford Heights, OH 44146
Phone: 216-763-3200
Fax: 216-763-3206

CEO: Daniel (Dan) Saltzman
CFO: –
HR: –
FYE: December 31
Type: Private

Dave's Supermarkets operates more than a dozen grocery stores, primarily serving the various neighborhoods of Cleveland. Different locations cater to the different needs of the locals; the university location, for instance, sells fresh doughnuts every morning. The regional supermarket operator acquired four stores in Ohio from Tops Markets in late 2006 and converted them to the Dave's Supermarkets banner in 2007. The newly acquired stores all house Giant Eagle pharmacies. Founded by Dave Saltzman in the 1928, the family-owned company is run by his grandsons Dan and Steve. Their father, company chairman Burton Saltzman, retired in 2005 but is still active in the business.

	Annual Growth	12/03	12/04	12/05	12/06	12/07
Est. sales ($ mil.)	—	—	—	—	—	131.9
Employees	—	—	—	—	—	900

THE DAVEY TREE EXPERT COMPANY

1500 N. Mantua St.
Kent, OH 44240
Phone: 330-673-9511
Fax: 330-673-9843
Web: www.davey.com

CEO: Karl J. Warnke
CFO: David E. Adante
HR: Gordon L. Ober
FYE: December 31
Type: Private

Business at The Davey Tree Expert Company is as green as grass. The company's roots extend back to 1880 when John Davey founded the horticultural services company, which branched into residential, commercial, utility, and other natural resource management services. Among the services Davey offers are the treatment, planting, and removal of trees, shrubs, and other plant life; landscaping; tree surgery; and the application of fertilizers, herbicides, and insecticides. Other services include line clearing for public utilities, urban and utility forestry research and development, and environmental planning. Pacific Gas and Electric accounts for almost 10% of sales. Davey has been employee-owned since 1979.

	Annual Growth	12/02	12/03	12/04	12/05	12/06
Sales ($ mil.)	10.0%	319.3	346.3	398.6	431.6	467.5
Net income ($ mil.)	18.1%	7.2	8.7	12.3	13.3	14.0
Employees	(2.2%)	6,000	5,100	5,000	5,200	5,500

DAVID WEEKLEY HOMES

1111 N. Post Oak Rd.
Houston, TX 77055
Phone: 713-963-0500
Fax: 713-963-0322
Web: www.davidweekleyhomes.com

CEO: John Johnson
CFO: Stuart Bitting
HR: Michael (Mike) Brezina
FYE: December 31
Type: Private

A development home developed to *your* taste? David Weekley Homes can do it. Founded in 1976, it is one of the largest privately owned homebuilders in the US, annually building around 4,600 single-family detached homes that range from about 1,500 sq. ft. to 5,000 sq. ft. Weekley builds homes from hundreds of floor plans and offers custom upgrades. Prices range from the $100,000s to more than $800,000. The company's average home price is $275,000. The company builds in its own planned communities in Texas, Colorado, the Southeast, and the Mid-Atlantic. Founder and chairman David Weekley owns the firm.

	Annual Growth	12/02	12/03	12/04	12/05	12/06
Sales ($ mil.)	17.9%	—	—	—	1,272.0	1,500.0
Employees	(1.4%)	—	—	—	1,466	1,446

An in-depth profile of this company is available to Hoover's Online members at hoovers.com.

475

DAVID WILSON'S AUTOMOTIVE GROUP

1400 N. Tustin	CEO: David Wilson
Orange, CA 92867	CFO: Glenn Quintos
Phone: 714-639-6750	HR: Vicki Murphy
Fax: 714-771-0363	FYE: December 31
Web: www.preownedautosuperstore.com	Type: Private

First Orange County, then the world — or at least as far as Arizona and Mexico. Megadealer David Wilson's Automotive Group has its roots in Orange County, California, with about 15 branches that stretch to east to Scottsdale and now south to Puerto Vallarta, Mexico. David Wilson's Automotive locations sell new and used Acura, Ford, Honda, and Mazda cars as well as Toyota- and Lexus-brand vehicles. The group's dealerships also operate parts and service departments; some offer fleet services. Dealership Web sites allow customers to search inventory, schedule service appointments, and request quotes. In 1985 owner David Wilson bought Toyota of Orange and planted the seeds of his empire.

	Annual Growth	12/02	12/03	12/04	12/05	12/06
Sales ($ mil.)	—	—	—	—	—	1,700.0
Employees	—	—	—	—	—	—

DAVID'S BRIDAL, INC.

1001 Washington St.	CEO: Robert D. (Bob) Huth
Conshohocken, PA 19428	CFO: Gene S. Morphis
Phone: 610-943-5000	HR: Fred A. Postelle
Fax: 610-943-5048	FYE: Saturday nearest January 31
Web: www.davidsbridal.com	Type: Private

From prom night to the big day itself, David's Bridal wants to be there. With more than 275 stores nationwide and in Puerto Rico, it is the largest retail chain specializing in bridal gowns. All gowns are available off the rack and sell for less than $1,050. David's Bridal also sells veils and bridal accessories, as well as apparel for formal occasions. Formerly a division of Federated Department Stores (now Macy's, Inc.), which acquired the bridal chain in 2005 when it bought rival May Department Stores, David's Bridal was sold in early 2007 to an affiliate of Leonard Green & Partners for about $750 million. The sale included 10 Priscilla of Boston locations.

DAVIDSON COMPANIES

8 3rd St. North	CEO: William A. (Bill) Johnstone
Great Falls, MT 59401	CFO: Tom Nelson
Phone: 406-727-4200	HR: Dan McLaughlin
Fax: 406-791-7238	FYE: September 30
Web: www.dadco.com	Type: Private

Employee-owned Davidson Companies offers investment banking, asset management, and travel services in more than a dozen (mostly northwestern) states through its five subsidiaries. The company's flagship firm, D.A. Davidson & Co., was founded in 1935 and offers financial advice and a range of investment products. Davidson Trust Co. was acquired by the Davidson companies in 1986 and provides estate planning and wealth management to individuals and organizations. Davidson Investment Advisors offers portfolio management, while Davidson Travel is a full-service travel agency.

	Annual Growth	9/02	9/03	9/04	9/05	9/06
Sales ($ mil.)	(6.4%)	117.5	109.3	120.9	108.9	90.2
Employees	5.9%	730	700	800	866	—

DAVIS POLK & WARDWELL

450 Lexington Ave.	CEO: John R. Ettinger
New York, NY 10017	CFO: –
Phone: 212-450-4000	HR: Jacqueline Nunez
Fax: 212-450-3800	FYE: December 31
Web: www.dpw.com	Type: Partnership

Founded in 1849, Davis Polk & Wardwell is one of the oldest law firms in the US. Having built a notable corporate practice early on, it helped J. P. Morgan (now JPMorgan Chase) form General Electric. With more than 650 lawyers, the firm is known for its skill in litigation, securities, and mergers and acquisitions; other practice areas include real estate, tax, and technology. Davis Polk has served such high-profile clients as AT&T, Comcast, General Motors, RJR Nabisco, and Philip Morris. In addition, more than one-third of the firm's clients are non-US companies or governments. Davis Polk has 10 offices across seven countries.

	Annual Growth	12/03	12/04	12/05	12/06	12/07
Est. sales ($ mil.)	—	—	—	—	—	95.1
Employees	—	—	—	—	—	1,100

DAVIS SELECTED ADVISERS, L.P.

2949 E. Elvira Rd, Ste. 101	CEO: Christopher C. (Chris) Davis
Tucson, AZ 85706	CFO: Gary Tyc
Phone: 520-806-7600	HR: –
Fax: 520-434-3719	FYE: December 31
Web: www.davisfunds.com	Type: Private

Davis Selected Advisers (sometimes known as Davis Advisors) manages a family of some half-dozen mutual funds and holds significant equity stakes in several public firms. Other offerings for individual and institutional investors include annuities and managed accounts. The company oversees some $56 billion in assets, including more than $2 billion from the founding Davis family and Davis Advisors employees and directors. Though not as well-known as Warren Buffett, the Davises built their fortune by following the same "buy and hold for a long, long time" investment ethos of the Oracle of Omaha.

	Annual Growth	12/03	12/04	12/05	12/06	12/07
Est. sales ($ mil.)	—	—	—	—	—	625.0
Employees	—	—	—	—	—	240

DAVIS-STANDARD LLC

1 Extrusion Dr.	CEO: Charles E. Buckley
Pawcatuck, CT 06379	CFO: Robert (Bob) Armstrong
Phone: 860-599-1010	HR: Joe Genovese
Fax: 860-599-6258	FYE: December 31
Web: www.davis-standard.com	Type: Private

Davis-Standard designs and manufactures extrusion systems and process controls for the wire, cable, plastic, and rubber industries. Davis-Standard was a joint venture of Chemtura and private equity firm Hamilton Robinson; in late 2006, Chemtura sold its majority interest to Hamilton Robinson for $72 million in cash. In 2005 the former Davis-Standard's operations merged with those of fellow polymer processing equipment maker Black Clawson Converting Machinery, owned by Hamilton Robinson, to form the joint venture. Davis-Standard was founded in 1848 as a manufacturer of cotton gin machinery. A century later, the company began manufacturing extruders.

DAVITA INC.

NYSE: DVA

601 Hawaii St.
El Segundo, CA 90245
Phone: 310-536-2400
Fax: 310-536-2675
Web: www.davita.com

CEO: Kent J. Thiry
CFO: Richard K. (Rich) Whitney
HR: –
FYE: December 31
Type: Public

DaVita — an Italian phrase which means "gives life" — provides life-sustaining dialysis treatments to patients suffering from end-stage renal disease (also known as chronic kidney failure). The company operates one of the largest chains of dialysis centers in the US. DaVita has more than 1,350 centers in more than 40 states and Washington, DC, and provides dialysis and related services to more than 100,000 patients. The firm also offers home-based dialysis services, as well as inpatient dialysis in more than 700 hospitals, and it operates two clinical laboratories that specialize in routine testing of dialysis patients.

	Annual Growth	12/03	12/04	12/05	12/06	12/07
Sales ($ mil.)	27.1%	2,016.4	2,298.6	2,973.9	4,880.7	5,264.1
Net income ($ mil.)	21.4%	175.8	222.3	228.6	289.7	381.8
Market value ($ mil.)	37.7%	1,677.1	3,894.6	5,162.0	5,951.7	6,036.8
Employees	5.2%	—	—	28,000	28,900	31,000

DAWN FOOD PRODUCTS, INC.

3333 Sargent Rd.
Jackson, MI 49201
Phone: 517-789-4400
Fax: 517-789-4465
Web: www.dawnfoods.com

CEO: Carrie L. Jones-Barber
CFO: Jerry Baglien
HR: Tom Harmon
FYE: December 31
Type: Private

A muffin at Starbucks, a cookie from Mrs. Fields, a Weight Watchers low-cal blueberry muffin, or a warm donut from Krispy Kreme — it's all just another day in the kitchens at Dawn Food Products. The company provides more than 4,000 prebaked and fully baked grain products, such as cakes, muffins, cookies, donuts, and artisan breads, as well as all the fixings for bakery products, including bases, fillings, frozen dough, icings, ingredients, and mixes for the food industry. Its customers include food manufacturers, food service companies, institutional bakeries, restaurants, retail outlets, and supermarkets.

	Annual Growth	12/02	12/03	12/04	12/05	12/06
Sales ($ mil.)	12.6%	—	—	—	1,110.0	1,250.0
Employees	3.9%	—	—	—	3,850	4,000

DAWSON GEOPHYSICAL COMPANY

NASDAQ (GM): DWSN

508 W. Wall, Ste. 800
Midland, TX 79701
Phone: 432-684-3000
Fax: 432-684-3030
Web: www.dawson3d.com

CEO: Stephen C. Jumper
CFO: Christina W. Hagan
HR: Olga Smoot
FYE: September 30
Type: Public

The oil industry can be shaky at times, but Dawson Geophysical always looks for good vibrations. The company, founded in 1952, provides data acquisition and data processing services, including the analysis of 2-D, 3-D, and 4-D seismic data to assess potential underground oil and gas deposits. Dawson Geophysical's customers, both major and independent oil and gas operators, use the data in exploration and development activities. The company's 15 3-D seismic data acquisition crews work in the lower 48 states of the US; data processing is performed by geophysicists at the firm's computer center in Midland, Texas.

	Annual Growth	9/03	9/04	9/05	9/06	9/07
Sales ($ mil.)	49.5%	51.6	69.3	116.7	168.6	257.8
Net income ($ mil.)	—	(0.9)	8.6	10.0	15.9	27.2
Market value ($ mil.)	99.1%	37.8	117.9	226.4	224.2	593.6
Employees	31.5%	—	—	—	1,023	1,345

DAXOR CORPORATION

AMEX: DXR

350 5th Ave., Ste. 7120
New York, NY 10118
Phone: 212-330-8500
Fax: 212-244-0806
Web: www.daxor.com

CEO: Joseph Feldschuh
CFO: David Frankel
HR: Joseph Feldschuh
FYE: December 31
Type: Public

They might not give you a toaster with that new account, but Daxor's blood and sperm banks are open to attract new, uh, deposits. The company offers blood banking through subsidiary Scientific Medical Systems and operates sperm banks through its Idant division. Its main business, however, has been the development and commercialization of a blood volume analyzer, the BVA-100, which hospitals and other health care providers use to diagnose and treat heart and kidney failure, anemia, and other conditions, as well as to manage blood transfusions. CEO Joseph Feldschuh owns 67% of the company.

	Annual Growth	12/03	12/04	12/05	12/06	12/07
Sales ($ mil.)	17.4%	1.0	1.2	1.3	1.5	1.9
Net income ($ mil.)	—	(1.1)	(0.6)	(1.3)	(0.8)	10.6
Market value ($ mil.)	(1.1%)	68.4	106.0	79.9	68.5	65.4
Employees	(10.9%)	—	—	46	41	—

THE DAY & ZIMMERMANN GROUP

1500 Spring Garden St.
Philadelphia, PA 19130
Phone: 215-299-8000
Fax: 215-299-8030
Web: www.dayzim.com

CEO: Harold L. (Hal) Yoh III
CFO: Joseph W. (Joe) Ritzel
HR: Diana M. Newmier
FYE: December 31
Type: Private

Day & Zimmermann offers services as distinct as day and night. The company provides engineering and construction, design, plant maintenance, security, staffing, munitions decommissioning, validation, and asset management services worldwide. A top global contractor, Day & Zimmermann provides operations, contract support, and maintenance services to US and foreign governments, as well as commercial customers. Technical staffing subsidiary Yoh Services specializes in filling IT, engineering, and health care positions. Founded in 1901, Day & Zimmermann is owned and managed by the Yoh family, which has headed the firm for three generations.

	Annual Growth	12/03	12/04	12/05	12/06	12/07
Sales ($ mil.)	17.3%	—	—	1,600.0	1,900.0	2,200.0
Employees	9.5%	—	—	20,000	23,000	24,000

DAY INTERNATIONAL GROUP, INC.

130 W. 2nd St.
Dayton, OH 45401
Phone: 937-224-4000
Fax: 937-226-1855
Web: www.dayintl.com

CEO: Dennis R. Wolters
CFO: Thomas J. Koenig
HR: Dwaine R. Brooks
FYE: December 31
Type: Subsidiary

Day International Group helps printing companies tackle their image problems. The company makes image transfer products for the printing industry, including offset-printing blankets and sleeves (which transfer ink from printing plates to paper) and pressroom chemicals. Customers include advertising, magazine, newspaper, and packaging printers. In 2007, Day International was acquired by Flint Group, a maker of printing supplies, plates, and inks, and now operates as Flint's specialty product unit. Its current business operations began in 1938 with the production of synthetic roll covers. The company was originally founded in 1905 as the Dayton Rubber Company, a maker of garden hoses and fruit jar sealing rings.

	Annual Growth	12/02	12/03	12/04	12/05	12/06
Sales ($ mil.)	7.6%	259.9	289.0	362.7	363.3	348.1
Net income ($ mil.)	24.6%	9.8	(6.4)	(10.0)	(6.2)	23.6
Employees	0.4%	1,350	1,470	1,470	1,465	1,372

An in-depth profile of this company is available to Hoover's Online members at hoovers.com.

477

DAYSTAR TECHNOLOGIES, INC.

NASDAQ (CM): DSTI

2972 Stender Way
Santa Clara, CA 95054
Phone: 408-907-4600
Fax: 408-907-4637
Web: www.daystartech.com

CEO: Stephan J. DeLuca
CFO: Chris Lail
HR: –
FYE: December 31
Type: Public

Old Sol, otherwise known as the sun, is the "day star" providing energy through the solar cells of this company. DayStar Technologies makes energy-generating and -storing devices out of copper, indium, gallium, and selenium, dubbed CIGS solar cells. The company is developing manufacturing processes for its thin-film Photovoltaic Foil CIGS solar cells that will be cheaper to produce than conventional polycrystalline silicon solar cells, which currently dominate the market. DayStar has gotten out of the business of installing and maintaining solar panels for residences.

	Annual Growth	12/03	12/04	12/05	12/06	12/07
Sales ($ mil.)	0.0%	0.1	0.2	0.6	0.2	0.1
Net income ($ mil.)	—	(1.5)	(4.7)	(6.8)	(20.4)	(36.1)
Market value ($ mil.)	173.6%	—	10.0	59.6	29.3	203.9
Employees	83.3%	7	19	55	85	79

DAYTON SUPERIOR CORPORATION

NASDAQ (GM): DSUP

7777 Washington Village Dr., Ste. 130
Dayton, OH 45459
Phone: 937-428-6360
Fax: 937-428-9560
Web: www.daytonsuperior.com

CEO: Eric R. Zimmerman
CFO: Edward J. Puisis
HR: Kenneth Tynes
FYE: December 31
Type: Public

Superior products are all in a day's work for Dayton Superior. The company makes metal accessories and forms for keeping concrete and masonry structures in place while they are under construction. The bulk of Dayton Superior's sales come from its products, which include concrete accessories, such as anchoring and bracing for walls and bridge support framework. It also makes masonry products, welded dowel assemblies, paving products, and corrosive-preventing epoxy coatings and other chemicals. The company's rental equipment includes concrete forming systems and shoring systems. Odyssey Investment Partners controls about 54% of the company.

	Annual Growth	12/03	12/04	12/05	12/06	12/07
Sales ($ mil.)	6.3%	377.9	418.6	419.0	479.3	483.0
Net income ($ mil.)	—	(17.1)	(48.8)	(114.7)	(18.0)	(6.7)
Market value ($ mil.)	(66.3%)	—	—	—	220.4	74.4
Employees	(5.6%)	1,900	—	—	1,600	—

DCAP GROUP, INC.

NASDAQ (CM): DCAP

1158 Broadway
Hewlett, NY 11557
Phone: 516-374-7600
Fax: 516-295-7216
Web: www.dcapgroup.com

CEO: Barry B. Goldstein
CFO: Victor Brodsky
HR: –
FYE: December 31
Type: Public

DCAP Group keeps things D-covered. The company brokers insurance products, including boat, life, business, and primarily nonstandard consumer automobile coverage. Other offerings include motorcycle, homeowners, excess coverage, life, and business insurance. DCAP Group has more than 70 retail locations in New York and eastern Pennsylvania that it owns or franchises. While the stores currently operate under the brand names DCAP, Barry Scott, and Atlantic Insurance, by 2010 they should all be renamed DCAP. Additionally, some of the group's locations offer income tax preparation services.

	Annual Growth	12/03	12/04	12/05	12/06	12/07
Sales ($ mil.)	(9.6%)	8.7	15.1	13.9	11.1	5.8
Net income ($ mil.)	—	1.3	1.4	0.5	0.5	(0.1)
Market value ($ mil.)	(46.1%)	58.7	20.7	7.1	8.9	5.0
Employees	—	—	—	101	—	—

DCB FINANCIAL CORP

OTC: DCBF

110 Riverbend Ave.
Lewis Center, OH 43035
Phone: 740-657-7000
Fax: 740-657-7901
Web: www.dcbfinancialcorp.com

CEO: Jeffrey T. Benton
CFO: John A. Ustaszewski
HR: Brian E. Stanfill
FYE: December 31
Type: Public

DCB Financial is the holding company for The Delaware County Bank and Trust, which serves individual and commercial customers through some 20 branches in central Ohio. The bank offers traditional deposit products and services, including checking and savings accounts, safe deposit facilities, and IRAs. Its loan portfolio includes commercial mortgages, residential mortgages, and other commercial and consumer loans; the company has increasingly focused on construction loans. The Delaware County Bank and Trust also provides financial services such as brokerage and wealth management.

	Annual Growth	12/03	12/04	12/05	12/06	12/07
Assets ($ mil.)	5.3%	553.3	611.7	690.9	681.9	680.8
Net income ($ mil.)	(62.4%)	5.0	7.0	7.6	7.3	0.1
Market value ($ mil.)	(6.8%)	78.7	113.1	109.0	112.5	59.5
Employees	—	—	—	—	—	228

DCK WORLDWIDE LLC

1900 State Rt. 51
Large, PA 15025
Phone: 412-384-1000
Fax: 412-384-1150
Web: www.dckworldwide.com

CEO: Douglas P. Dick
CFO: Norman G. Fornella
HR: –
FYE: December 31
Type: Private

Without any help from Tom or Harry, dck worldwide, formerly Dick Corporation, is a general contractor and construction management firm that builds commercial, institutional, and industrial structures. Landmark projects include PNC Park, home of the Pittsburgh Pirates, and the preservation of Fallingwater, a home designed by Frank Lloyd Wright. It has also built more than 30,000 beds/cells in correctional facilities and helped construct a military complex at the Navy base at Guantanamo Bay, Cuba. dck worldwide is active mainly in the US, operating about a dozen offices, including one in Guam. The firm was founded by Noble Dick in 1922 and is still run by his descendants, including co-chairmen Douglas and David Dick.

	Annual Growth	12/03	12/04	12/05	12/06	12/07
Est. sales ($ mil.)	—	—	—	—	—	126.1
Employees	—	—	—	—	—	1,000

DCP MIDSTREAM PARTNERS, LP

NYSE: DPM

370 17th St., Ste. 2775
Denver, CO 80202
Phone: 303-633-2900
Fax: 303-605-2225
Web: www.dcppartners.com

CEO: Mark A. Borer
CFO: –
HR: –
FYE: December 31
Type: Public

DCP Midstream Partners is one of the largest natural gas gatherers in North America. It is also the largest producer and one of the largest marketers of natural gas liquids (NGLs). Following the spinoff of Spectra Energy from Duke Energy, Spectra Energy assumed Duke Energy's 50% holding in DCP (ConocoPhillips holds the other 50%). The company is also engaged in natural gas compressing, treating, processing, transporting, and selling. DCP Midstream Partners also transports and sells NGLs and distributes propane wholesale. It operates six natural gas gathering systems (primarily in Arkansas, Louisiana, Oklahoma, and Texas), three NGL pipelines, and eight propane storage terminals.

	Annual Growth	12/03	12/04	12/05	12/06	12/07
Sales ($ mil.)	19.3%	475.1	509.5	784.5	795.8	960.9
Net income ($ mil.)	—	10.0	20.4	38.0	33.0	(15.8)
Market value ($ mil.)	74.6%	—	—	253.7	357.8	773.8
Employees	33.6%	—	65	64	118	155

DCT INDUSTRIAL TRUST INC.

NYSE: DCT

518 17th St., Ste. 1700
Denver, CO 80202
Phone: 303-597-2400
Fax: 303-228-2201
Web: www.dctindustrial.com

CEO: Philip L. Hawkins
CFO: Stuart B. Brown
HR: –
FYE: December 31
Type: Public

DCT Industrial Trust is in da house! The warehouse, that is. The real estate investment trust (REIT) develops, owns, and manages bulk distribution and light industrial properties located in about two dozen high-volume distribution markets in the US and Mexico. About 85% of its portfolio consists of bulk distribution warehouses; light industrial properties make up most of the remainder. The more than 400 buildings that DCT Industrial Trust owns, has an interest in, or provides asset management for total some 74 million sq. ft. The REIT has also launched industrial funds to expand its institutional capital management platform. Tenants include the US Postal Service and B&G Foods.

	Annual Growth	12/03	12/04	12/05	12/06	12/07
Sales ($ mil.)	213.3%	2.7	34.1	123.2	219.1	260.2
Net income ($ mil.)	240.0%	0.3	(0.3)	(12.0)	(158.0)	40.1
Market value ($ mil.)	(21.1%)	—	—	—	1,986.6	1,567.6
Employees	—	—	—	—	64	—

DDB WORLDWIDE COMMUNICATIONS GROUP INC.

437 Madison Ave.
New York, NY 10022
Phone: 212-415-2000
Fax: 212-415-3414
Web: www.ddb.com

CEO: Charles E. (Chuck) Brymer
CFO: Keith Bremer
HR: –
FYE: December 31
Type: Subsidiary

Advertising is wassup at DDB Worldwide Communications Group. One of the world's top creative ad agencies, DDB has produced memorable spots for such brands as Avis ("We Try Harder"), Budweiser ("Wassup"), and Life Cereal ("Hey, Mikey"). It offers such services as brand building and consulting, campaign planning and management, and effectiveness measurement services, in addition to creative ad development. The firm operates through more than 200 offices in about 100 countries. Founded in 1949 by Ned Doyle, Maxwell Dane, and William Bernbach, DDB is one of the flagship agencies of holding company Omnicom Group.

DDI CORP.

NASDAQ (GM): DDIC

1220 Simon Circle
Anaheim, CA 92806
Phone: 714-688-7200
Fax: 714-688-7500
Web: www.ddiglobal.com

CEO: Mikel H. Williams
CFO: Sally Goff
HR: –
FYE: December 31
Type: Public

DDi takes a dynamic approach to manufacturing. DDi provides time-critical electronics design, fabrication, and assembly services for makers of communications and networking gear, computers, medical instruments, and military equipment. The company produces complete electronics systems, as well as subsystems, such as printed circuit boards (PCBs), backpanels, and wire harnesses. Its more than 1,000 customers include electronics manufacturers, such as Intel and Tyco Electronics. Nearly half of all orders are filled within 10 days, and some are turned around in 24 hours. DDi derives nearly all of its business from customers in North America.

	Annual Growth	12/03	12/04	12/05	12/06	12/07
Sales ($ mil.)	(7.1%)	243.1	189.0	184.6	198.1	181.1
Net income ($ mil.)	(73.9%)	150.4	(45.9)	(64.0)	(7.2)	0.7
Market value ($ mil.)	(52.3%)	2,443.8	81.1	17.3	162.5	126.3
Employees	(7.8%)	1,800	1,200	1,400	1,300	1,300

D.E. HARVEY BUILDERS, INC.

3630 Westchase
Houston, TX 77042
Phone: 713-783-8710
Fax: 713-783-5313
Web: www.harveybuilders.com

CEO: David E. Harvey Jr.
CFO: Andre Skains
HR: Audrey Mosley
FYE: December 31
Type: Private

D.E. Harvey Builders hammers out commercial construction services. The company provides general contracting and construction management services for mid- and high-rise commercial buildings; it also works on some light-industrial facilities and provides interior remodeling services. Projects include office buildings, condominiums, hotels and convention centers, retail stores, parking garages, and research facilities. D.E. Harvey's customers include Exxon Mobil, Faust Distributing, Hewlett-Packard, and Marriott. The firm, which does business as Harvey-Cleary in some markets, has offices in Houston and Austin, Texas, and in Gaithersburg, Maryland.

	Annual Growth	12/03	12/04	12/05	12/06	12/07
Est. sales ($ mil.)	—	—	—	—	—	411.8
Employees	—	—	—	—	—	300

D. E. SHAW & CO., L.P.

120 W. 45th St., 39th Fl., Tower 45
New York, NY 10036
Phone: 212-478-0000
Fax: 212-478-0100
Web: www.deshaw.com

CEO: David E. Shaw
CFO: –
HR: –
FYE: December 31
Type: Private

D. E. Shaw & Co. is always on the lookout for a good investment opportunity. Through various affiliates, the firm specializes in applying quantitative and qualitative trading strategies to hedge fund management and other investments. It makes private equity investments in early-stage and established firms involved in technology, health care, and financial services. It also acquires assets of distressed companies. The company's D.E. Shaw Research unit focuses on long-term scientific and technological projects. The company, which has some $33 billion in capital under management, was founded in 1988 by chairman and CEO David E. Shaw.

	Annual Growth	12/03	12/04	12/05	12/06	12/07
Est. sales ($ mil.)	—	—	—	—	—	24.7
Employees	—	—	—	—	—	260

DEALERADVANCE, INC.

OTC: DLAV

16801 Addison Rd., Ste. 310
Addison, TX 75001
Phone: 214-866-0606
Fax: 214-866-0460
Web: www.dealeradvance.com

CEO: Steven E. Humphries
CFO: David L. Wange
HR: –
FYE: December 31
Type: Public

Formerly Stronghold Technologies, DealerAdvance provides wireless and Internet products — enterprise software and handheld devices — to the automotive industry. It helps sales teams track customer purchasing information, search inventory, locate stock, and print forms. The company also offers software for sales training. In addition, DealerAdvance offers professional services such as training, support, installation, and maintenance. Former CEO Christopher Carey and Stanford Venture Capital Holdings own 26% and 37% of the company, respectively.

	Annual Growth	12/03	12/04	12/05	12/06	12/07
Sales ($ mil.)	(49.2%)	3.0	2.5	0.9	0.5	0.2
Net income ($ mil.)	—	(4.3)	(3.1)	(3.6)	(4.4)	(4.7)
Market value ($ mil.)	—	—	—	—	—	—
Employees	—	—	—	—	—	—

DEALER TIRE LLC

3711 Chester Ave.
Cleveland, OH 44114
Phone: 216-432-0088
Fax: 216-881-7923
Web: www.dealertire.com

CEO: Scott Mueller
CFO: Pete Waters
HR: Cindy Frick
FYE: December 31
Type: Private

Dealer Tire tirelessly makes deals to meet the tire needs of America's car dealerships. The company is the only US tire dealer focused exclusively on delivering tires and accessories to car and truck dealers nationwide. Dealer Tire is the factory-authorized supplier of tires for more than 6,000 dealerships, primarily those of leading German and Japanese automakers. Tire brands distributed by the company include BF-Goodrich, Continental, Dunlop, General Tire, Goodyear, Michelin, Pirelli, and Yokohama. Dealer Tire also supplies wheels and tire-related accessories.

	Annual Growth	12/03	12/04	12/05	12/06	12/07
Est. sales ($ mil.)	—	—	—	—	—	20.2
Employees	—	—	—	—	—	100

DEALERTRACK HOLDINGS, INC.

NASDAQ (GM): TRAK

1111 Marcus Ave., Ste. M04
Lake Success, NY 11042
Phone: 516-734-3600
Fax: 516-734-3809
Web: www.dealertrack.com

CEO: Mark F. O'Neil
CFO: Robert J. Cox III
HR: Ana M. Herrera
FYE: December 31
Type: Public

DealerTrack Holdings helps car dealers play their cards right in the financing game. The company provides Web-based software that links automotive dealerships with banks, finance companies, credit unions, credit reporting agencies, and other players in the car sales and financing process. Through its software, DealerTrack connects clients to its network of auto dealers, financing sources, and other service and information providers. The company, which generates revenues through subscriptions and transaction-based fees, also offers tools that automate credit application processing, ensure document legal compliance, and execute electronic financing contracts.

	Annual Growth	12/03	12/04	12/05	12/06	12/07
Sales ($ mil.)	56.8%	38.7	70.0	120.2	173.3	233.8
Net income ($ mil.)	—	(3.3)	11.3	4.5	19.3	19.8
Market value ($ mil.)	38.5%	—	—	742.3	1,164.1	1,424.2
Employees	26.1%	—	499	539	670	1,000

DEAN & DELUCA, INC.

560 Broadway
New York, NY 10012
Phone: 212-226-6800
Fax: 800-781-4050
Web: www.deandeluca.com

CEO: Beth M. Pritchard
CFO: Greg Coffey
HR: –
FYE: January 31
Type: Private

You could go to Manhattan's tony SoHo neighborhood for a taste of Dean & DeLuca, but increasingly, you don't have to. The purveyor of pricey gourmet foods, wines, and high-end kitchenware operates more than a dozen specialty markets and cafes throughout the US and is growing rapidly in Japan. Dean & DeLuca also offers its goods through consumer and corporate gift catalogs, as well as online. The company is expanding in Asia. It opened its first store in Tokyo in June 2003 through a distribution agreement with ITOCHU there. Joel Dean and Giorgio DeLuca opened their first market in SoHo in 1977.

	Annual Growth	1/03	1/04	1/05	1/06	1/07
Est. sales ($ mil.)	—	—	—	—	—	83.5
Employees	—	—	—	—	—	765

DEAN FOODS COMPANY

NYSE: DF

2515 McKinney Ave., Ste. 1200
Dallas, TX 75201
Phone: 214-303-3400
Fax: 214-303-3499
Web: www.deanfoods.com

CEO: Gregg L. Engles
CFO: Jack F. Callahan Jr.
HR: Tangela Arnwine
FYE: December 31
Type: Public

Dean Foods has become the king of milk by taking over other dairies' thrones. The leading US producer of fluid milk and dairy products, Dean has grown and continues to grow through acquisitions. Its retail and food service dairy products are sold under more than 50 regional, private-label, and national brand names, including Borden, Pet, Country Fresh, and Meadow Gold. In addition, the company manufactures coffee creamers, dips and yogurt, ice cream, and specialty dairy products (lactose-free milk, soy milk, flavored milks). Dean Foods also operates Horizon Organic, Rachel's Organic, and WhiteWave Foods.

	Annual Growth	12/03	12/04	12/05	12/06	12/07
Sales ($ mil.)	6.5%	9,184.6	10,822.3	10,505.6	10,098.6	11,821.9
Net income ($ mil.)	(22.0%)	355.7	285.4	327.5	225.4	131.4
Market value ($ mil.)	(5.8%)	4,346.9	3,784.1	5,054.3	5,427.5	3,419.6
Employees	(2.7%)	—	—	27,030	26,348	25,585

DEARBORN BANCORP, INC.

NASDAQ (GM): DEAR

1360 Porter St.
Dearborn, MI 48124
Phone: 313-565-5700
Fax: 313-561-2291
Web: www.fidbank.com

CEO: Michael J. Ross
CFO: –
HR: Elizabeth A. Pizzo
FYE: December 31
Type: Public

Frankly, my Dearborn, they do give a damn. Dearborn Bancorp is the holding company for Fidelity Bank (formerly Community Bank of Dearborn). The bank has about 30 branches and lending centers in suburban Detroit and points west, offering checking and savings accounts, money market accounts, and CDs. Lending activities include commercial mortgages (more than 70% of the company's loan portfolio), as well as residential, business, consumer, and construction loans. Dearborn Bancorp also has a subsidiary that provides auditing and consulting services to other community banks. Community Bank of Dearborn changed its name after its parent company acquired Fidelity Bank in 2007.

	Annual Growth	12/03	12/04	12/05	12/06	12/07
Assets ($ mil.)	23.8%	446.1	652.7	706.5	855.9	1,047.0
Net income ($ mil.)	(2.2%)	3.5	5.5	7.5	7.8	3.2
Market value ($ mil.)	8.6%	45.9	115.0	121.8	170.5	63.7
Employees	22.1%	—	—	151	161	225

DEARBORN WHOLESALE GROCERS L.P.

2801 S. Western Ave.
Chicago, IL 60608
Phone: 773-254-4300
Fax: 773-847-3838
Web: www.dearbornwholesale.com

CEO: Sherwin Friedman
CFO: Peter Westerberg
HR: –
FYE: June 30
Type: Private

Dearborn Wholesale Grocers is a full-service food distributor for retail food outlets, primarily in the Chicago area. The family-owned company delivers more than 23,000 items, including frozen and refrigerated foods, tobacco, health and beauty products, and general merchandise to supermarkets, convenience stores, and delis. It operates a fleet of 60 trucks that distribute goods in the Chicago area and portions of neighboring states. Dearborn Wholesale also operates about a half a dozen cash-and-carry stores, and it distributes private-label products under the Parade brand. The business traces its roots back to 1919, when the Friedman family acquired wholesale grocery business C. Moon and Sons.

	Annual Growth	6/03	6/04	6/05	6/06	6/07
Est. sales ($ mil.)	—	—	—	—	—	178.4
Employees	—	—	—	—	—	500

DEB SHOPS, INC.

9401 Blue Grass Rd.
Philadelphia, PA 19114
Phone: 215-676-6000
Fax: 215-698-7151
Web: www.debshops.com

CEO: Diane M. Paccione
CFO: Barry J. Susson
HR: –
FYE: January 31
Type: Private

Deb Shops just, like, knows fashion, totally, you know? Targeting fashion-conscious juniors, teens, and plus-sized misses, Deb Shops sells moderately priced accessories, coats, dresses, lingerie, shoes, and sportswear through about 345 stores across the US, most of them in malls in the Midwest and Northeast. The DEB chain makes up almost all of the company's stores. About half of all DEB stores contain plus-size departments. Other chains include CSO (outlet stores), and Tops 'N Bottoms (apparel for young men and juniors). Founded in 1932 as Joy Hosiery, Deb Shops was acquired by Lee Equity Partners for about $395 million in 2007.

	Annual Growth	1/03	1/04	1/05	1/06	1/07
Sales ($ mil.)	0.5%	317.7	298.6	303.8	325.0	324.7
Net income ($ mil.)	(4.3%)	25.5	12.8	17.9	25.3	21.4
Employees	(0.7%)	3,600	—	—	3,500	3,500

DEBEVOISE & PLIMPTON LLP

919 3rd Ave.
New York, NY 10022
Phone: 212-909-6000
Fax: 212-909-6836
Web: www.debevoise.com

CEO: Martin F. (Rick) Evans
CFO: Jeffrey Miller
HR: Rachel B. Dressler
FYE: December 31
Type: Partnership

A leading advocate for the interests of domestic and international businesses, Debevoise & Plimpton has more than 650 lawyers in more than half a dozen offices in the US, Europe, and the Asia/Pacific region. Corporate law represents the firm's largest practice area, but its expertise also spans litigation, tax, and trusts and estates. High-profile clients have included American Airlines, AXA Financial, MetLife, the NFL, and PriceWaterhouseCoopers. Eli Debevoise (a descendant of Eli Whitney) helped found the firm in 1931; after Francis Plimpton (father of author George Plimpton) joined in 1933, the firm's name was changed to Debevoise & Plimpton.

	Annual Growth	12/03	12/04	12/05	12/06	12/07
Est. sales ($ mil.)	—	—	—	—	—	184.7
Employees	—	—	—	—	—	2,130

DEBRUCE GRAIN, INC.

4100 N. Mulberry Dr.
Kansas City, MO 64116
Phone: 816-421-8182
Fax: 816-584-2350
Web: www.debruce.com

CEO: Paul DeBruce
CFO: Curt Heinz
HR: –
FYE: March 31
Type: Private

Got a few bushels of wheat and no place to keep it? DeBruce Grain stores, handles, and sells grain and fertilizer for the agribusiness industry. The company owns and operates 26 grain elevators in six states, boasting a total storage capacity of 101 million bushels, four fertilizer-distribution terminals, and seven retail fertilizer operations in Iowa and Texas. DeBruce also markets wholesale fertilizer. The company also has a facility in Guadalajara, Mexico, which serves DeBruce's international customers. Owner and CEO Paul DeBruce founded the company in 1978.

	Annual Growth	3/02	3/03	3/04	3/05	3/06
Sales ($ mil.)	19.7%	1,378.0	1,729.0	2,018.0	2,437.0	2,830.0
Employees	7.3%	400	420	420	500	530

DEBT RESOLVE, INC.

AMEX: DRV

707 Westchester Ave., Ste. L7
White Plains, NY 10604
Phone: 914-949-5500
Fax: 914-428-3044
Web: www.debtresolve.com

CEO: Kenneth Montgomery
CFO: David Rainey
HR: Nancy Hutter
FYE: December 31
Type: Public

Debt Resolve isn't intimidated by mountains of debt. The company provides a hosted software service that allows credit card companies and collection agencies to collect money from consumers who are past due on their credit card bills. The online service, branded as DebtResolve, uses an Internet-based bidding system that allows debtors and creditors to agree on acceptable repayment schedules. Customers include banks and other credit originators, credit card issuers, and third-party collection agencies, as well as assignees and buyers of consumer debt.

	Annual Growth	12/03	12/04	12/05	12/06	12/07
Sales ($ mil.)	—	0.0	0.0	0.0	0.1	2.8
Net income ($ mil.)	—	(2.6)	(2.7)	(5.4)	(21.7)	(12.6)
Market value ($ mil.)	(65.9%)	—	—	—	25.8	8.8
Employees	—	—	—	—	—	—

DECHERT LLP

Cira Centre, 2929 Arch St.
Philadelphia, PA 19104
Phone: 215-994-4000
Fax: 215-994-2222
Web: www.dechert.com

CEO: Barton J. Winokur
CFO: –
HR: Mary Ann Christ
FYE: December 31
Type: Partnership

The Dechert law firm might have a single name on its shingle, but it's no solo practice. The firm's 1,000-plus lawyers practice from a dozen offices in the US (mainly in eastern states) and five more in Europe. Dechert focuses on work related to business transactions, government relations (involving both the US and the European Union), litigation, and tax. Within those broad areas, the firm's specialties include asset management, corporate and securities, intellectual property, product liability, and real estate finance. Dechert draws clients from industries such as energy, financial services, media, retail, and technology. The firm was founded in 1875.

	Annual Growth	12/03	12/04	12/05	12/06	12/07
Est. sales ($ mil.)	—	—	—	—	—	154.4
Employees	—	—	—	—	—	1,782

DECISIONONE CORPORATION

426 W. Lancaster Ave.
Devon, PA 19333
Phone: 610-296-6000
Fax: 610-296-2910
Web: www.decisionone.com

CEO: Neal Bibeau
CFO: Richard S. (Rick) Martin
HR: Keith Black
FYE: June 30
Type: Private

Haven't figured out which computer technology support services to use? Try DecisionOne. The company offers computer maintenance, equipment installation and repair, and other technology support services for electronics manufacturers, technology resellers, and IT outsourcers in the US and Canada. Its services include consulting, technical call center support, network support, and logistics management. Top clients have included FUJIFILM, Sony, Sun Microsystems, and maintenance management services provider SU Group. The company also serves such public sector customers as the Department of Energy. DecisionOne was founded in 1969 as Decision Data, a provider of keypunch machines.

An in-depth profile of this company is available to Hoover's Online members at hoovers.com.

481

DECKERS OUTDOOR CORPORATION

NASDAQ (GS): DECK

495-A S. Fairview Ave.
Goleta, CA 93117
Phone: 805-967-7611
Fax: 805-967-7862
Web: www.deckers.com

CEO: Angel R. Martinez
CFO: Thomas R. (Tom) Hillebrandt
HR: Jennifer Foth
FYE: December 31
Type: Public

There's no business like shoe business for Deckers Outdoor. It makes and markets Teva sports sandals — a cross between a hiking boot and a flip-flop. Tevas are used for walking, hiking, and rafting, among other pursuits. While imitations flood the market, the company distinguishes Teva from its numerous competitors by avoiding distribution in off-price outlets. Other product lines include Simple (casual footwear) and UGG (sheepskin boots and shoes). Deckers Outdoor's products are made by independent contractors in Asia, Australia, and New Zealand. It sells them through independent distributors, catalogs, the Internet, and five company-owned outlets.

	Annual Growth	12/03	12/04	12/05	12/06	12/07
Sales ($ mil.)	38.8%	121.1	214.8	264.8	304.4	448.9
Net income ($ mil.)	64.4%	9.1	25.5	31.8	30.6	66.4
Market value ($ mil.)	78.3%	199.5	572.5	343.4	754.7	2,016.4
Employees	28.2%	—	—	225	276	370

DECORATOR INDUSTRIES, INC.

AMEX: DII

10011 Pines Blvd., Ste. 201
Pembroke Pines, FL 33024
Phone: 954-436-8909
Fax: 954-436-1778
Web: www.decoratorindustries.com

CEO: William A. Johnson
CFO: Michael K. Solomon
HR: Diana Hinton
FYE: Saturday nearest December 31
Type: Public

Travelers can sleep easier, thanks to Decorator Industries. The company makes and sells window coverings that keep the light out, and bedspreads and comforters that keep the warmth in. Products include draperies, curtains, blinds, valance boards, pillows, cushions, and more. Decorator Industries sells its merchandise to manufactured home builders, makers of recreational vehicles (RVs), and to hotels, motels, and other customers nationwide. Fleetwood Enterprises, a maker of RVs and manufactured housing, is one of the company's largest customers. Decorator Industries was established in 1953. William Bassett, chairman, owns about 14% of the company.

	Annual Growth	12/03	12/04	12/05	12/06	12/07
Sales ($ mil.)	2.5%	41.8	50.5	50.5	52.2	46.1
Net income ($ mil.)	—	1.6	1.4	1.4	0.4	(0.8)
Market value ($ mil.)	(7.7%)	17.6	22.8	23.6	22.2	12.8
Employees	—	—	—	731	—	—

DECORIZE, INC.

OTC: DCZI

1938 E. Phelps
Springfield, MO 65802
Phone: 417-879-3326
Fax: 417-879-3330
Web: www.decorize.com

CEO: Stephen R. (Steve) Crowder
CFO: Dan Graham
HR: Gaylen Ball
FYE: June 30
Type: Public

Rather than standardize, Decorize wants to spice things up in your living space. The company, founded in 2000, makes and wholesales imported home furnishings. In addition to furniture, Decorize imports accent pieces including lamps, frames, vases, mirrors, and baskets. It sources its wares directly to retailers from factories in China, Indonesia, the Philippines, and India. Decorize consolidated its brands in recent years. Products marketed to specialty retailers (66% of 2007 revenue) maintain the GuildMaster brand, while products targeting large retailers (34% of 2007 revenue) are marketed under the Decorize brand name.

	Annual Growth	6/03	6/04	6/05	6/06	6/07
Sales ($ mil.)	0.8%	15.4	12.1	10.8	9.2	15.9
Net income ($ mil.)	—	(1.1)	(4.4)	(2.6)	(2.2)	(0.7)
Market value ($ mil.)	95.4%	—	—	—	6.8	13.3
Employees	81.6%	—	—	131	—	432

DECRANE AEROSPACE

8425 Pulsar Place, Ste. 340
Columbus, OH 43240
Phone: 614-848-7700
Fax: 614-848-9610
Web: www.decraneaircraft.com

CEO: Richard J. (Dick) Kaplan
CFO: Matthew W. Hughes
HR: –
FYE: December 31
Type: Private

DeCrane Aerospace (formerly DeCrane Aircraft Holdings) makes bigwigs comfy jetting from coast to coast. Its Cabin Management division offers products for corporate aircraft interiors, including furnishings, in-flight entertainment systems, composite components, and seating products. DeCrane's other operating group, Systems Integration, provides auxiliary fuel and power systems and aircraft modification services. Aircraft manufacturers Boeing, Bombardier, and Textron, which owns Cessna, have been among some of DeCrane's better-known customers. Investment firm DLJ Merchant Banking Partners owns a controlling stake in the company.

DEEP DOWN, INC.

OTC: DPDW

15473 East Fwy.
Channelview, TX 77530
Phone: 281-862-2201
Fax: 281-862-2522
Web: www.deepdowninc.com

CEO: Ronald E. (Ron) Smith
CFO: Eugene L. Butler
HR: –
FYE: December 31
Type: Public

Deep Down has given up on medical equipment and decided to dig deep for a living. The company (formerly Mediquip Holdings) acquired Deep Down in 2006 in a reverse merger, taking on that company's subsea service business as well as its name. An umbilical and flexible pipe installation engineering and installation management company, Deep Down also fabricates component parts for subsea distribution systems and assemblies that specialize in the development of offshore subsea fields. The company's product include umbilicals, flow lines, distribution systems, pipeline terminations, controls, winches, and launch and retrieval systems. It serves clients in the Gulf of Mexico and internationally.

	Annual Growth	1/04	1/05	1/06	*12/06	12/07
Sales ($ mil.)	48.4%	4.0	5.6	2.3	1.0	19.4
Net income ($ mil.)	—	(1.1)	(1.2)	(3.3)	(3.3)	0.9
Market value ($ mil.)	(59.0%)	2,981.3	2.8	5.2	16.6	84.3
Employees	—	—	—	—	—	—

*Fiscal year change

DEERE & COMPANY

NYSE: DE

1 John Deere Place
Moline, IL 61265
Phone: 309-765-8000
Fax: 309-765-5671
Web: www.deere.com

CEO: Robert W. (Bob) Lane
CFO: Michael J. Mack Jr.
HR: David C. Everitt
FYE: October 31
Type: Public

You might say that Deere & Company enjoys its customers going to seed. The company, one of the world's two largest makers of farm equipment (CNH Global is the other), is also a leading producer of industrial, forestry, and lawn-care equipment. Its farm equipment includes tractors, tillers, harvesting machinery, and soil-preparation machinery. Construction equipment includes backhoes, skid steers, dump trucks, waste equipment, and excavators. For the forestry industry Deere makes harvesters, feller bunchers, and knuckleboom loaders. Deere's other products include residential and commercial lawn-care products and equipment, and golf- and turf-care products.

	Annual Growth	10/03	10/04	10/05	10/06	10/07
Sales ($ mil.)	11.6%	15,534.6	19,986.1	21,930.5	22,147.8	24,082.2
Net income ($ mil.)	29.7%	643.1	1,406.1	1,446.8	1,693.8	1,821.7
Market value ($ mil.)	46.6%	7,381.1	7,378.6	7,186.7	9,672.2	34,049.8
Employees	4.7%	—	—	47,400	46,500	52,000

An in-depth profile of this company is available to Hoover's Online members at hoovers.com.

DEERFIELD CAPITAL CORP.

NYSE: DFR

1 O'Hare Center, 9th Fl., 6250 N. River Rd.
Rosemont, IL 60018
Phone: 773-380-1600
Fax: 773-380-1601
Web: www.deerfieldcapital.com

CEO: Jonathan W. Trutter
CFO: Richard G. Smith
HR: –
FYE: December 31
Type: Public

Deerfield Capital (formerly Deerfield Triarc) invests in real estate-related securities and other assets. Founded in 2004, the real estate investment trust (REIT) invests in high-quality residential mortgage-backed securities, commercial mortgage-backed securities, alternative investments, and leveraged finance instruments, such as corporate mezzanine loans and bonds. It has some $8 billion of assets under management. In late 2007 the REIT acquired its former parent Deerfield & Company from Triarc and changed its name to Deerfield Capital. The deal streamlined its operations and brought in Deerfield Capital Management, which oversees more than $14 billion in fixed-income investments for institutional clients.

	Annual Growth	12/03	12/04	12/05	12/06	12/07
Sales ($ mil.)	169.2%	—	—	68.2	469.9	494.4
Net income ($ mil.)	—	—	—	45.9	71.6	(96.2)
Market value ($ mil.)	(13.1%)	—	—	707.7	875.7	534.1
Employees	—	—	—	—	—	—

DEL GLOBAL TECHNOLOGIES CORP.

OTC: DGTC

11550 W. King St.
Franklin Park, IL 60131
Phone: 847-288-7000
Fax: 847-288-7011
Web: www.delglobal.com

CEO: James A. Risher
CFO: Mark Zorko
HR: –
FYE: Saturday nearest July 31
Type: Public

Del Global Technologies has a high-tech cure for what ails you. The firm makes medical and dental X-ray systems used by hospitals and doctors, dentists, and veterinarians. It sells its products through distributors worldwide under the Villa, Del, Universal, and DynaRad brand names and provides some of its dental products under private-label agreements. Through its RFI subsidiary, Del Global Technologies also makes precision electronic components and subassemblies for makers of everything from weapons systems to satellites to MRI machines; RFI's brands include Filtron, Sprague, and Stanley.

	Annual Growth	7/03	7/04	7/05	7/06	7/07
Sales ($ mil.)	1.4%	98.6	83.8	84.9	83.0	104.2
Net income ($ mil.)	—	(15.0)	(15.8)	0.4	0.1	3.8
Market value ($ mil.)	40.6%	—	—	28.7	19.8	56.7
Employees	(8.0%)	462	332	—	—	331

🏠 DEL MONTE FOODS COMPANY

NYSE: DLM

1 Market @ The Landmark
San Francisco, CA 94105
Phone: 415-247-3000
Fax: 415-247-3565
Web: www.delmonte.com

CEO: Richard G. Wolford
CFO: David L. Meyers
HR: –
FYE: Sunday nearest April 30
Type: Public

How does Del Monte Foods' garden grow? Very well indeed. One of the US's largest manufacturers of branded canned fruit, vegetables, tuna, and broths, Del Monte has been harvesting acquisitions and new products. Its flagship products (canned corn, green beans, peas, peaches, pears, and pineapples) are purchased mostly from US growers. The company makes tomato-based foods such as ketchup and tomato sauce. Its retail brands include College Inn, Del Monte, Contadina, and StarKist. Del Monte makes pets grow too, with a stable of pet-food and -treat brands, including 9Lives, Gravy Train, Milk-Bone, and Meow Mix. In addition, the company makes commercial food ingredients and products for the food-service industry.

	Annual Growth	4/04	4/05	4/06	4/07	4/08
Sales ($ mil.)	4.5%	3,129.9	3,180.9	2,998.6	3,414.9	3,736.8
Net income ($ mil.)	(5.2%)	164.6	117.9	169.9	112.6	133.1
Market value ($ mil.)	(7.0%)	2,319.2	2,202.9	2,333.4	2,374.0	1,734.1
Employees	2.0%	—	17,500	16,700	18,200	—

DEL TACO LLC

25521 Commercentre Dr.
Lake Forest, CA 92630
Phone: 949-462-9300
Fax: 949-462-7444
Web: www.deltaco.com

CEO: Shirlene Lopez
CFO: –
HR: Arlene Petokas
FYE: December 31
Type: Private

This taco stand caters to the burger and fries crowd, as well as the burrito fans. Del Taco is the #2 quick-service Mexican chain in the US (behind YUM! Brand's Taco Bell division), with about 500 locations in about a dozen mostly western states. Its restaurants offer tacos, burritos, and quesadillas, along with such traditional fast-food fare as hamburgers, French fries, and shakes. Del Taco's menu also includes a variety of salads and breakfast burritos. Most of Del Taco's locations are company-owned. Founded in 1964, the company was acquired in 2006 by Sagittarius Brands (parent of the Captain D's seafood chain).

	Annual Growth	12/03	12/04	12/05	12/06	12/07
Est. sales ($ mil.)	—	—	—	—	—	334.4
Employees	—	—	—	—	—	5,599

DELAWARE NORTH COMPANIES, INC.

40 Fountain Plaza
Buffalo, NY 14202
Phone: 716-858-5000
Fax: 716-858-5479
Web: www.delawarenorth.com

CEO: Jeremy M. Jacobs Sr.
CFO: Karen L. Kemp
HR: Eileen Morgan
FYE: December 31
Type: Private

This company makes few concessions when it comes to selling hot dogs and sodas at the ball game. Delaware North is a leading provider of food services and hospitality services at airports, sports stadiums, and tourist destinations throughout the US and in a handful of other countries. Its Sportservice division operates concessions at more than 50 major and minor league sporting arenas, while its Travel Hospitality Services division runs concessions and retail operations at more than 40 airports. In addition, the company operates Boston's TD Banknorth Garden. Delaware North was founded in 1915 by brothers Charles, Louis, and Marvin Jacobs and is still controlled by the Jacobs family.

	Annual Growth	12/02	12/03	12/04	12/05	12/06
Sales ($ mil.)	6.3%	1,600.0	1,700.0	1,700.0	2,000.0	2,040.0
Employees	15.6%	28,000	30,000	30,000	40,000	50,000

🏠 DELEK US HOLDINGS, INC.

NYSE: DK

7102 Commerce Way
Brentwood, TN 37027
Phone: 615-771-6701
Fax: 615-224-1185
Web: www.delekus.com

CEO: Ezra Uzi Yemin
CFO: Edward (Ed) Morgan
HR: Kathy Roadarmel
FYE: December 31
Type: Public

Delek US Holdings takes a holistic approach to the petroleum business with refining, marketing and supply, and retail operations. Its MAPCO Express business operates about 500 convenience store/gas stations under the MAPCO Express, East Coast, and Discount Food Mart banners in the southeastern US. Israeli conglomerate Delek Group took the company public in mid-2006 and owns about three-quarters of its stock. Proceeds from the IPO are being used to repay other parts of the Delek Group and to fund future acquisitions. To that end, in 2007 its MAPCO Express subsidiary acquired more than 100 combination gas and convenience stores in eastern Tennessee and northern Georgia from Calfree Co. for about $65 million.

	Annual Growth	12/03	12/04	12/05	12/06	12/07
Sales ($ mil.)	68.4%	—	857.9	2,031.9	3,207.7	4,097.1
Net income ($ mil.)	136.4%	—	7.3	64.1	93.0	96.4
Market value ($ mil.)	29.5%	—	—	—	838.2	1,085.7
Employees	—	—	—	—	3,064	—

🏠 An in-depth profile of this company is available to Hoover's Online members at hoovers.com.

483

DELHAIZE AMERICA, INC.

2110 Executive Dr.
Salisbury, NC 28145
Phone: 704-633-8250
Fax: 704-636-5024
Web: www.delhaizegroup.com

CEO: Pierre-Olivier Beckers
CFO: Carol M. Herndon
HR: –
FYE: Saturday nearest December 31
Type: Subsidiary

Belgian food retailer Delhaize "Le Lion" has a big cub — Delhaize America. A holding company for its growing number of US supermarket subsidiaries, Delhaize America runs one of the Southeast's biggest supermarket chains, Food Lion (about 1,300 stores located mainly in the Carolinas and Virginia, but also in eight other eastern seaboard states). It also operates the Hannaford Bros. supermarket chain (about 165 stores in New England and New York), and 70 Harveys supermarkets. In Florida, the firm has converted all of its grocery stores to the Sweetbay format. Parent Delhaize Group formed Delhaize America in 1999. The international food retailer bought the rest of Delhaize America in April 2001.

	Annual Growth	12/02	12/03	12/04	12/05	12/06
Sales ($ mil.)	3.5%	15,043.5	15,553.2	15,839.9	16,564.9	17,289.2
Net income ($ mil.)	—	(32.4)	182.8	254.1	332.3	376.0
Employees	(0.2%)	109,822	107,746	105,395	104,066	108,883

DELI MANAGEMENT, INC.

2400 Broadway St.
Beaumont, TX 77702
Phone: 409-838-1976
Fax: 409-838-1906
Web: www.jasonsdeli.com

CEO: Joseph V. (Joe) Tortorice Jr.
CFO: Patrick (Pat) Broussard
HR: Alex Cone
FYE: December 31
Type: Private

This company knows a good sandwich when it sees one. Deli Management operates the Jason's Deli chain of sandwich shops, with more than 160 locations in Texas and more than 20 other states. The restaurants serve more than 90 varieties of sandwiches as well as soups, salads, baked potatoes, and desserts. Many locations feature a salad bar and ice cream sundae bar; the chain also offers organic and trans-fat free items. Most Jason's outposts provide delivery and catering services, as well as online ordering. About half of the restaurants are company-owned, while the rest are franchised. President Joe Tortorice and partner Rusty Coco founded the company in 1976.

	Annual Growth	12/03	12/04	12/05	12/06	12/07
Est. sales ($ mil.)	—	—	—	—	—	247.0
Employees	—	—	—	—	—	4,000

DELiA*S, INC.

NASDAQ (GM): DLIA

50 W. 23rd St.
New York, NY 10010
Phone: 212-590-6200
Fax: 212-590-6300
Web: www.delias.com

CEO: Robert E. (Rob) Bernard
CFO: Stephen A. (Steve) Feldman
HR: Andy Romeo
FYE: January 31
Type: Public

If you think getting your teenager out of the mall will keep money in your pocket, think again: dELiA*s has her covered — or almost covered — with bare-midriff peasant tops, short shorts, and barely-there sandals, not to mention Feng Shui necklaces and iridescent lip gloss. The multichannel retailer sells trendy clothing, accessories, and home furnishings to girls ages 12 to 19 (known as the Millennials) through about 85 dELiA*s stores, a catalog, and its Web site. The stores, located in about 25 states along the East Coast and in the Midwest, offer apparel and accessories under the dELiA*s, Alloy, and CCS brands. Youth marketer Alloy spun off dELiA*s in late 2005.

	Annual Growth	1/04	1/05	1/06	1/07	1/08
Sales ($ mil.)	11.2%	—	199.4	226.7	257.6	274.3
Net income ($ mil.)	—	—	(9.4)	(10.3)	5.8	(2.3)
Market value ($ mil.)	(40.3%)	—	—	208.2	328.4	74.2
Employees	11.2%	—	1,352	1,605	1,673	—

DELL INC.

NASDAQ (GS): DELL

1 Dell Way
Round Rock, TX 78682
Phone: 512-338-4400
Fax: 512-283-6161
Web: www.dell.com

CEO: Michael S. Dell
CFO: Brian T. Gladden
HR: Andrew C. (Andy) Esparza
FYE: Sunday nearest January 31
Type: Public

The name Dell may be synonymous with "direct," but the computer giant has a more diverse approach to the market these days. The world's #1 direct-sale computer vendor provides a broad range of computer products for the consumer and enterprise markets. In addition to a full line of desktop and notebook PCs, Dell offers network servers, workstations, storage systems, printers, projectors, and Ethernet switches. The company also markets third-party software and peripherals. Dell's growing services unit provides systems integration, support, and training. The company announced plans to begin selling through retail stores in 2007.

	Annual Growth	1/04	1/05	1/06	1/07	1/08
Sales ($ mil.)	10.2%	41,444.0	49,205.0	55,908.0	57,420.0	61,133.0
Net income ($ mil.)	2.7%	2,645.0	3,043.0	3,572.0	2,583.0	2,947.0
Market value ($ mil.)	(16.3%)	85,472.6	102,034.1	68,175.8	52,355.5	41,921.0
Employees	17.7%	46,000	56,000	66,100	90,500	88,200

DELMARVA POWER & LIGHT COMPANY

800 King St.
Wilmington, DE 19899
Phone: 800-375-7117
Fax: 302-283-6090
Web: www.conectiv.com

CEO: Gary R. Stockbridge
CFO: –
HR: –
FYE: December 31
Type: Subsidiary

Delmarva Power & Light (formerly Conectiv) has a delmarvelous proposition — connecting people to its energy supply network. The company is engaged in the transmission and distribution of electricity in Delaware and portions of Maryland; it delivers electricity to 496,000 customers. Delmarva Power & Light also provides natural gas (in Delaware) to about 122,000 customers. The company has refocused on its core utility operations after several years of engagement in nonregulated energy activities. Delmarva Power & Light is a subsidiary of Pepco Holdings.

DELOITTE TOUCHE TOHMATSU

1633 Broadway
New York, NY 10019
Phone: 212-489-1600
Fax: 212-489-1687
Web: www.deloitte.com/dtt

CEO: James H. (Jim) Quigley
CFO: Jeffrey P. (Jeff) Rohr
HR: Vassi Naidoo
FYE: May 31
Type: Partnership

This company is "deloitted" to make your acquaintance, particularly if you're a big business in need of accounting services. Deloitte Touche Tohmatsu (doing business as Deloitte) is one of accounting's Big Four, along with Ernst & Young, KPMG, and PricewaterhouseCoopers. Deloitte offers traditional audit and fiscal-oversight services from some 70 member firms in more than 140 countries. It also provides human resources, tax, and technology services, as well as services to governments and lending agencies working in emerging markets, including China and India. Units include Deloitte & Touche (the US accounting arm) and Deloitte Consulting. Consulting accounts for more than 20% of Deloitte's revenues.

	Annual Growth	5/03	5/04	5/05	5/06	5/07
Sales ($ mil.)	11.2%	15,100.0	16,400.0	18,200.0	20,000.0	23,100.0
Employees	5.3%	119,237	115,000	121,283	135,000	146,600

DELPHAX TECHNOLOGIES INC.

Pink Sheets: DLPX

6100 W. 110th St.
Bloomington, MN 55438
Phone: 952-939-9000
Fax: 952-939-1151
Web: www.delphax.com

CEO: Dieter P. Schilling
CFO: Gregory S. Furness
HR: Les B. Weibye
FYE: September 30
Type: Public

You don't have to be an oracle to know that Delphax Technologies doesn't like blank checks. The company makes digital print production systems based on its patented electron-beam imaging technology for roll-fed and cut-sheet printing applications. Its machines not only print addresses and numbers on checks, but also print payroll and accounts payable checks with audit trail capabilities. Delphax's CR Series roll-feed printing systems produce up to 2,000 pages per minute. Its Foliotronic finishing systems bind financial forms into books. Customers include check printers Deluxe Corporation and Harland Clarke. While Delphax sells its products globally, about 80% of sales are in the US.

	Annual Growth	9/03	9/04	9/05	9/06	9/07
Sales ($ mil.)	(6.4%)	58.0	53.6	51.6	48.7	44.6
Net income ($ mil.)	—	(1.8)	(0.4)	0.3	(9.6)	(0.8)
Market value ($ mil.)	(28.4%)	22.4	20.9	18.8	9.6	5.9
Employees	(7.6%)	393	389	340	288	286

DELPHI CORPORATION

Pink Sheets: DPHI

5725 Delphi Dr.
Troy, MI 48098
Phone: 248-813-2000
Fax: 248-813-2670
Web: www.delphi.com

CEO: Rodney O'Neal
CFO: Robert J. (Bob) Dellinger
HR: Kevin M. Butler
FYE: December 31
Type: Public

Delphi has taken to the road alone after being spun off from General Motors in 1999. One of the world's largest makers of auto parts, Delphi makes nearly everything mechanical and electrical/electronic that goes into cars. Its primary business divisions include Electrical/Electronic Architecture (vehicle electrical systems), Powertrain Systems (engine management, fuel, and emissions systems), Electronics and Safety (sensors, security systems, seat belts, airbags, navigation and entertainment systems), and Thermal Systems (climate control, radiators, heat exchangers). About 37% of Delphi's business comes from former parent GM. Delphi filed Chapter 11 in 2005.

	Annual Growth	12/03	12/04	12/05	12/06	12/07
Sales ($ mil.)	(5.6%)	28,096.0	28,622.0	26,947.0	26,392.0	22,283.0
Net income ($ mil.)	—	(56.0)	(4,753.0)	(2,357.0)	(5,464.0)	(3,065.0)
Employees	(1.1%)	—	—	—	171,400	169,500

DELPHI FINANCIAL GROUP, INC.

NYSE: DFG

1105 N. Market St., Ste. 1230
Wilmington, DE 19899
Phone: 302-478-5142
Fax: 302-427-7663
Web: www.delphifin.com

CEO: Robert Rosenkranz
CFO: Thomas W. Burghart
HR: –
FYE: December 31
Type: Public

Delphi Financial knows that an employee with a good dental plan is happier than one without. The company specializes in the employee benefits market, primarily for small to midsized businesses. Through Reliance Standard Life and Safety National Casualty, Delphi Financial sells such insurance products as life, disability, excess workers' compensation, and personal accident insurance. Its Matrix Absence Management subsidiary provides disability and absence management services to larger employers. The company also offers asset accumulation products, mainly annuities, to individuals and groups. Delphi Financial products are sold through independent brokers and agents.

	Annual Growth	12/03	12/04	12/05	12/06	12/07
Assets ($ mil.)	9.9%	4,177.5	4,829.5	5,276.2	5,670.5	6,094.8
Net income ($ mil.)	13.6%	98.9	123.5	113.3	142.1	164.5
Market value ($ mil.)	24.9%	707.0	935.9	959.3	1,942.5	1,718.8
Employees	15.1%	—	—	1,170	1,410	1,551

DELTA AIR LINES, INC.

NYSE: DAL

1030 Delta Blvd.
Atlanta, GA 30320
Phone: 404-715-2600
Fax: 404-715-5042
Web: www.delta.com

CEO: Richard H. Anderson
CFO: Edward H. (Ed) Bastian
HR: Michael H. (Mike) Campbell
FYE: December 31
Type: Public

Just as a delta is a symbol for change in math, Delta Air Lines symbolizes the changing mathematics of the airline industry. A leading US carrier, behind American and United, Delta will become the world's largest airline if it can complete a proposed combination with Northwest Airlines. On its own and through its Delta Connection regional carriers (including subsidiary Comair), Delta serves about 315 destinations in about 60 countries. It operates from hubs in Atlanta, Cincinnati, New York, and Salt Lake City. Delta extends its offerings as part of the SkyTeam code-sharing and marketing alliance, which includes carriers such as Air France, KLM, and Korean Air Lines, as well as Continental and Northwest.

	Annual Growth	12/03	12/04	12/05	12/06	12/07
Sales ($ mil.)	9.5%	13,303.0	15,002.0	16,191.0	17,171.0	19,154.0
Net income ($ mil.)	—	(773.0)	(5,198.0)	(3,818.0)	(6,203.0)	1,612.0
Market value ($ mil.)	—	—	—	—	—	4,351.2
Employees	(0.6%)	—	—	55,700	51,300	55,044

DELTA APPAREL, INC.

AMEX: DLA

2750 Premiere Pkwy., Ste. 100
Duluth, GA 30097
Phone: 678-775-6900
Fax: 678-775-6992
Web: www.deltaapparel.com

CEO: Robert W. (Bob) Humphreys
CFO: Deborah H. (Deb) Merrill
HR: –
FYE: Saturday nearest June 30
Type: Public

Delta Apparel has been there, done that, and made the T-shirt. The manufacturer produces knitted cotton and polyester/cotton T-shirts, tank tops, and sweatshirts primarily for the screen-printing industry. The company sells its products to department stores, distributors, screen printers, and mass merchants nationwide. Garments are finished at facilities in the US (Alabama and North Carolina), Mexico, El Salvador, and Honduras. Delta Apparel acquired activewear maker M. J. Soffe in 2003, Junkfood Clothing in 2005, and Fun-Tees in 2006. The Mickel family and chairman Erwin Maddrey II own about half of the company.

	Annual Growth	6/03	6/04	6/05	6/06	6/07
Sales ($ mil.)	24.6%	129.5	208.1	228.1	270.1	312.4
Net income ($ mil.)	0.8%	6.1	9.7	11.2	14.8	6.3
Market value ($ mil.)	47.6%	32.1	48.7	111.6	146.4	152.4
Employees	—	—	—	4,100	—	—

DELTA DENTAL OF CALIFORNIA

100 1st St.
San Francisco, CA 94105
Phone: 415-972-8300
Fax: 415-972-8466
Web: www.deltadentalca.org

CEO: Gary D. Radine
CFO: Michael J. Castro
HR: Michelle Wagner
FYE: December 31
Type: Not-for-profit

Delta Dental of California (formerly Delta Dental Plan of California) doesn't just help keep the mouths of movie stars clean. A not-for-profit organization, the company is a member of the Delta Dental Plans Association and has affiliates nationwide. Delta Dental of California provides dental coverage through HMOs, preferred provider plans (PPOs), and such government programs as California's Denti-Cal. The company serves about 18 million enrollees in California; its programs cover more than one-third of California residents. Together with Delta Dental of Pennsylvania, Delta Dental of California formed a holding company that serves about 20 million members throughout the US.

An in-depth profile of this company is available to Hoover's Online members at hoovers.com.

485

DELTA DENTAL PLANS ASSOCIATION

1515 W. 22nd St., Ste. 1200	CEO: Kim Volk
Oak Brook, IL 60523	CFO: –
Phone: 630-574-6001	HR: –
Fax: 630-574-6999	FYE: December 31
Web: www.deltadental.com	Type: Association

Delta Dental is responsible for miles of smiles. Established in 1966, Delta Dental Plans Association is the largest dental benefits provider in the nation. The not-for-profit company provides dental benefits and related administrative services to approximately 50 million people through its nationwide network of independent affiliates. The association has some 40 affiliates that contract with more than 80,000 large and small employer groups to provide dental benefits through HMO, PPO, and POS (Point of Service) plans. The Delta Dental Premier plan offers access to more than 120,000 contracted dentists.

DELTA FAUCET COMPANY

55 E. 111th St.	CEO: Keith Allman
Indianapolis, IN 46280	CFO: Rick Burkman
Phone: 317-848-1812	HR: Renee Backmeyer
Fax: 317-574-5567	FYE: December 31
Web: www.deltafaucet.com	Type: Business segment

Delta Faucet — so named because its revolutionary circa-1954 single-handled faucet's cam resembled the Greek letter "delta" — is in the upper pantheon of the world's largest faucet makers. The company's plethora of kitchen and bathroom faucets (including its signature single-handled models), shower systems, and accessories, including soap dishes, towel racks, and shelves, are sold under the Delta, Peerless, and Brizo brands. A division of Masco Corporation, Delta distributes its products in the US through retail stores, wholesale showrooms, and builders and contractors. The company sells in more than 50 countries.

	Annual Growth	12/03	12/04	12/05	12/06	12/07
Est. sales ($ mil.)	—	—	—	—	—	439.0
Employees	—	—	—	—	—	5,000

DELTA MUTUAL, INC.

OTC: DLTM

111 N. Branch St.	CEO: Peter F. Russo
Sellersville, PA 18960	CFO: Martin G. Chilek
Phone: 215-258-2800	HR: –
Fax: 215-258-2870	FYE: December 31
Web: www.deltamutual.com	Type: Public

Delta Mutual tried to clean up during the Internet boom by providing online mortgage services. Today, it really does clean up. Literally. This development-stage company has shifted its direction to being an environmental services provider. Through subsidiaries, Delta Mutual offers waste processing and reclamation technology and equipment, as well as energy efficient construction technologies to low-cost housing development projects. Its operations are concentrated in the US, Asia/Pacific, the Middle East, and Puerto Rico. Investor Neal Berman owns about 10% of the company.

	Annual Growth	12/02	12/03	12/04	12/05	*12/06
Sales ($ mil.)	—	—	—	—	0.0	0.3
Net income ($ mil.)	—	—	—	—	(2.6)	(2.5)
Employees	—	—	—	—	—	—

*Most recent year available

DELTA NATURAL GAS COMPANY, INC.

NASDAQ (GM): DGAS

3617 Lexington Rd.	CEO: Glenn R. Jennings
Winchester, KY 40391	CFO: John B. Brown
Phone: 859-744-6171	HR: James B. Potter
Fax: 859-744-6552	FYE: June 30
Web: www.deltagas.com	Type: Public

Delta digs blue grass and natural gas. Delta Natural Gas provides gas to some 39,000 retail customers in central and southeastern Kentucky and has 2,500 miles of gathering, transmission, and distribution lines. It also provides transportation services to wholesale customers and operates an underground gas storage field. The regulated utility buys most of its gas supply from interstate gas marketers. Delta Natural Gas's production subsidiary, Enpro, has interests in 35 producing gas wells and it has proved developed reserves of 3.1 billion cu. ft. of natural gas. Other subsidiaries include Delta Resources and Delgasco, which purchase gas from marketers and resell it to utilities and large customers.

	Annual Growth	6/03	6/04	6/05	6/06	6/07
Sales ($ mil.)	9.5%	68.4	79.2	84.2	117.3	98.2
Net income ($ mil.)	8.7%	3.8	3.8	5.0	5.0	5.3
Market value ($ mil.)	3.4%	74.4	79.2	83.6	79.8	85.1
Employees	—	—	—	152	—	—

DELTA PETROLEUM CORPORATION

NASDAQ (GM): DPTR

370 17th St., Ste. 4300	CEO: Roger A. Parker
Denver, CO 80202	CFO: Kevin K. Nanke
Phone: 303-293-9133	HR: –
Fax: 303-298-8251	FYE: December 31
Web: www.deltapetro.com	Type: Public

An independent oil and gas exploration and production company, Delta Petroleum has been dealt a good hand in estimated proved reserves. In 2007 it reported reserves of 375.6 billion cu. ft. of natural gas equivalent, 77% of which is in the Rocky Mountains. The company also has major assets in the Gulf Coast region. It has oil and gas leasehold properties covering approximately 871,000 net undeveloped acres. Delta Petroleum operates three major subsidiaries: Castle Texas Exploration Limited Partnership; Delta Exploration Company, Inc.; and Piper Petroleum Company. It controls Amber Resources.

	Annual Growth	6/04	6/05	*12/05	12/06	12/07
Sales ($ mil.)	45.7%	36.4	94.7	61.8	181.4	164.2
Net income ($ mil.)	—	—	5.1	15.1	(0.6)	0.4	(149.4)
Market value ($ mil.)	24.7%	517.1	162.1	1,041.2	1,260.8	1,252.2
Employees	13.3%	—	95	96	122	—

*Fiscal year change

DELTATHREE, INC.

NASDAQ (CM): DDDC

75 Broad St., 31st Fl.	CEO: Shimmy Zimels
New York, NY 10004	CFO: Richard B. Grant
Phone: 212-500-4850	HR: Shely Sussman
Fax: 212-500-4888	FYE: December 31
Web: corp.deltathree.com	Type: Public

Deltathree supplies the pipes that make phone calls via the Internet possible. The company manages an international Voice over Internet Protocol (VoIP) network. The integrated network offers distribution through both service provider and reseller channels. It also offers phone service through its direct-to-consumer Web site under the iConnectHere (or ICH) brand. Using downloadable software, customers can place calls from their computers to traditional telephones as well as through a variety of IP-based services. It also provides operational management services such as account provisioning, billing, and payment processing.

	Annual Growth	12/03	12/04	12/05	12/06	12/07
Sales ($ mil.)	22.3%	13.2	21.1	29.7	38.0	29.5
Net income ($ mil.)	—	(8.3)	(3.3)	(0.9)	0.5	(9.3)
Employees	9.5%	103	136	147	144	148

DELTEK, INC.

NASDAQ (GS): PROJ

13880 Dulles Corner Ln.
Herndon, VA 20171
Phone: 703-734-8606
Fax: 703-734-1146
Web: www.deltek.com

CEO: Kevin T. Parker
CFO: Mark L. Wabschall
HR: Holly C. Kortright
FYE: December 31
Type: Public

Deltek isn't afraid to tackle tough projects. The company provides project management software designed to meet the needs of professional services firms and project-based businesses. Its applications handle expense reporting, human resources administration, materials management, customer management, and sales force automation. Deltek integrates tools from partners such as Cognos and Microsoft with its own software, and it provides consulting and implementation services. Donald and Kenneth deLaski (father and son) co-founded Deltek in 1983. Deltek went public in 1996, was taken private again in 2002, and had a second IPO in 2007. Private equity firm New Mountain Capital controls 74% of the company.

	Annual Growth	12/03	12/04	12/05	12/06	12/07
Sales ($ mil.)	31.9%	—	121.2	153.0	228.3	278.3
Net income ($ mil.)	(6.9%)	—	27.9	8.7	15.3	22.5
Market value ($ mil.)	—	—	—	—	—	655.6
Employees	20.6%	—	—	—	1,041	1,255

DELTIC TIMBER CORPORATION

NYSE: DEL

210 E. Elm St.
El Dorado, AR 71731
Phone: 870-881-9400
Fax: 870-881-6454
Web: www.deltic.com

CEO: Ray C. Dillon
CFO: Kenneth D. Mann
HR: –
FYE: Saturday nearest December 31
Type: Public

Deltic Timber might beg to differ with the phrase "Money doesn't grow on trees." The company annually harvests some 550,000 tons of timber from the nearly 440,000 acres of timberlands that it owns, primarily in Arkansas and northern Louisiana; its two sawmills then convert the timber, mainly southern pine, into softwood lumber products, which it sells to wholesale distributors, lumber treaters, and truss manufacturers for use in residential construction to make roof trusses, laminated beams, and decking. In addition to its timber and lumber businesses, Deltic Timber develops real estate in central Arkansas and through its subsidiary, Del-Tin Fiber, and manufactures medium density fiberboard (MDF).

	Annual Growth	12/03	12/04	12/05	12/06	12/07
Sales ($ mil.)	(1.2%)	134.9	142.0	168.4	153.1	128.3
Net income ($ mil.)	6.3%	8.7	11.1	14.5	11.3	11.1
Market value ($ mil.)	14.9%	365.4	518.3	640.1	694.5	636.5
Employees	(1.7%)	—	—	481	—	465

DELUXE CORPORATION

NYSE: DLX

3680 Victoria St. North
Shoreview, MN 55126
Phone: 651-483-7111
Fax: 651-481-4163
Web: www.deluxe.com

CEO: Lee J. Schram
CFO: Richard S. Greene
HR: Jeff Stoner
FYE: December 31
Type: Public

When money can move at the speed of a mouse click, Deluxe wants to do more than keep its revenues in check. The company is a leading printer of checks in the US, serving the nation's banks, credit unions, and financial services companies. Checks and business forms account for the majority of Deluxe's sales; it also sells checkbook covers and address labels, as well as stationery, greeting cards, labels, and packaging supplies online. Deluxe also sells stored-value gift cards. The company's Direct Checks division is the nation's #1 direct-to-consumer seller of personal and business checks under the brands Checks Unlimited and Designer Checks. The company operates about two dozen printing and fulfillment facilities.

	Annual Growth	12/03	12/04	12/05	12/06	12/07
Sales ($ mil.)	6.6%	1,242.1	1,567.0	1,716.3	1,639.7	1,606.4
Net income ($ mil.)	(7.1%)	192.5	198.0	157.5	100.9	143.5
Market value ($ mil.)	(5.0%)	2,073.7	1,876.4	1,529.2	1,298.3	1,690.4
Employees	(1.9%)	—	—	8,310	8,396	7,991

DELUXE ENTERTAINMENT SERVICES GROUP, INC.

1377 N. Serrano Ave.
Hollywood, CA 90027
Phone: 323-462-6171
Fax: 323-960-7016
Web: www.bydeluxe.com

CEO: Cyril Drabinsky
CFO: –
HR: –
FYE: December 31
Type: Subsidiary

Deluxe Entertainment Services Group provides movie production services such as film processing; printing and distribution; post-production and subtitling services; titles design and digital video effects; DVD compression, encoding, and authoring; digital cinema services, digital asset management and digital distribution; and marketing fulfillment services. Clients include all major Hollywood studios. Since 1943 the company has received 10 Academy Awards for technical achievement. Deluxe Entertainment Services Group is a subsidiary of MacAndrews & Forbes Holdings Inc. Deluxe can trace its history back to 1919, when Fox Film Corporation built Deluxe Laboratory on its lot for film processing and printing.

	Annual Growth	12/03	12/04	12/05	12/06	12/07
Est. sales ($ mil.)	—	—	—	—	—	100.0
Employees	—	—	—	—	—	1,200

DELUXEPINPOINT

500 Main St.
Groton, MA 01471
Phone: 978-448-6111
Fax: 978-449-3419
Web: www.nebs.com

CEO: Richard L. (Rich) Schulte
CFO: Barbara Baklund
HR: Martie Woods
FYE: December 31
Type: Subsidiary

DELUXEPINPOINT provides office supplies and business services to customers throughout the country. The company was formed when parent company Deluxe Corporation combined New England Business Service (NEBS) with its other small business segment. The company is a leading supplier of forms, checks, labels, envelopes, and other printed business stationery, as well as office supplies, equipment, and furniture; shipping and packaging materials; and software. It offers its 50,000 products primarily through direct sales efforts and online through its Web site. In addition, the company provides business services such as payroll outsourcing, payment processing, and custom printing, primarily to small businesses in the US and Canada.

	Annual Growth	12/03	12/04	12/05	12/06	12/07
Est. sales ($ mil.)	—	—	—	—	—	271.0
Employees	—	—	—	—	—	3,611

DEMANDTEC, INC.

NASDAQ (GM): DMAN

1 Circle Star Way, Ste. 200
San Carlos, CA 94070
Phone: 650-226-4600
Fax: 650-556-1190
Web: www.demandtec.com

CEO: Daniel R. (Dan) Fishback
CFO: Mark A. Culhane
HR: –
FYE: February 28
Type: Public

The laws of supply and demand become a little more high-tech in DemandTec's hands. The company makes software that helps manufacturers and suppliers predict consumer demand and develop strategies for pricing and promotions. Designed to help clients improve their planning and profitability, the company's consumer demand management (CDM) software is available in versions tailored to the needs of retailers (with tools for pricing, promotions, and markdowns) and consumer products manufacturers. Customers have included Best Buy, General Mills, and Office Depot.

	Annual Growth	2/04	2/05	2/06	2/07	2/08
Sales ($ mil.)	46.5%	—	19.5	32.5	43.5	61.3
Net income ($ mil.)	—	—	(9.3)	(2.7)	(1.5)	(4.5)
Market value ($ mil.)	—	—	—	—	—	274.1
Employees	—	—	—	—	—	251

An in-depth profile of this company is available to Hoover's Online members at hoovers.com.

487

DEMATIC CORP.

507 Plymouth Ave. NE
Grand Rapids, MI 49505
Phone: 616-913-7700
Fax: 616-913-7701
Web: www.dematic.us

CEO: John Baysore
CFO: Thomas Doeke
HR: Herbert Fitzon
FYE: September 30
Type: Subsidiary

Dematic Corp. (formerly Rapistan, and Siemens Logistics and Assembly Inc.) knows how to get a handle on things. The company, the North American division of Dematic GmbH & Co., designs and manufactures automated material handling systems, including sorting systems, conveyor systems, warehouse control software, and order fulfillment and picking systems; it also provides logistics services to manufacturing companies. Dematic's specialty is offering warehouse automation and order fulfillment systems for retail, wholesale, and other businesses. The company changed its name to Dematic in 2006.

DEMOULAS SUPER MARKETS INC.

875 East St.
Tewksbury, MA 01876
Phone: 978-851-8000
Fax: 978-640-8390

CEO: Arthur Demoulas
CFO: Donald Mulligan
HR: Lucille Lopez
FYE: December 31
Type: Private

The Demoulas super market chain is ripe with family history all rolled up into numerous Market Baskets. Demoulas Super Markets runs some 60 grocery stores under the Market Basket banner in Massachusetts and New Hampshire. One store still operates under the "DeMoulas" banner. The grocery retailer also manages real estate interests. Market Basket supermarkets are typically located in shopping centers with other retail outlets, including properties owned by the company through its real estate arm, Retail Management and Development (RMD), Inc. Begun as a mom-and-pop grocery store, the Demoulas sons transformed the chain into a traditional, yet modern, concept.

	Annual Growth	12/02	12/03	12/04	12/05	12/06
Est. sales ($ mil.)	3.7%	1,900.0	1,950.0	1,950.0	2,000.0	2,200.0
Employees	0.6%	12,700	12,900	—	12,000	13,000

DENBURY RESOURCES INC.

NYSE: DNR

5100 Tennyson Pkwy., Ste. 1200
Plano, TX 75024
Phone: 972-673-2000
Fax: 972-673-2150
Web: www.denbury.com

CEO: Gareth Roberts
CFO: Phil Rykhoek
HR: Sandy Sandusky
FYE: December 31
Type: Public

Denbury Resources has long since capped its oil and gas operations in its native Canada to try its luck in the Deep South. The independent exploration and production company has estimated proved reserves of 194.8 million barrels of oil equivalent and working interests in wells and significant operating acreage in Mississippi; onshore Alabama; in the Barnett Shale formation near Fort Worth, Texas; and in properties in Southeast Texas. In Mississippi it owns the largest reserves of CO_2 used for tertiary oil recovery east of the Mississippi River. CO_2 is used to force oil out of the ground from abandoned wells.

	Annual Growth	12/03	12/04	12/05	12/06	12/07
Sales ($ mil.)	30.7%	333.0	383.0	560.4	731.5	972.0
Net income ($ mil.)	45.5%	56.5	82.4	166.5	202.5	253.1
Market value ($ mil.)	149.3%	188.5	387.9	1,306.4	1,669.3	7,281.3
Employees	22.1%	—	—	460	596	686

DENDREON CORPORATION

NASDAQ (GM): DNDN

3005 1st Ave.
Seattle, WA 98121
Phone: 206-256-4545
Fax: 206-256-0571
Web: www.dendreon.com

CEO: Mitchell H. Gold
CFO: Gregory T. (Greg) Schiffman
HR: –
FYE: December 31
Type: Public

Dendreon wants to boost your immunity from the start. It is developing therapeutic vaccines that goose the body's immune system to help it fight cancer by targeting dendritic cells, which initiate an immune response to disease-causing antigens. Its lead candidate is Provenge, a therapeutic vaccine that targets prostate cancer. Dendreon is also working on a therapeutic vaccine called Neuvenge as a treatment for breast, colon, ovarian, and kidney cancers, and it has research programs investigating cancer-fighting monoclonal antibodies and small molecule drugs. Its partners for its antibody programs include Amgen and Genentech.

	Annual Growth	12/03	12/04	12/05	12/06	12/07
Sales ($ mil.)	(59.9%)	27.0	5.0	0.2	0.3	0.7
Net income ($ mil.)	—	(28.5)	(75.2)	(81.6)	(91.6)	(99.3)
Market value ($ mil.)	9.4%	362.1	636.6	385.4	346.9	517.9
Employees	—	—	—	208	—	—

[H] DENNY'S CORPORATION

NASDAQ (CM): DENN

203 E. Main St.
Spartanburg, SC 29319
Phone: 864-597-8000
Fax: 864-597-8780
Web: www.dennys.com

CEO: Nelson J. Marchioli
CFO: F. Mark Wolfinger
HR: Janis S. Emplit
FYE: December 31
Type: Public

Feel like getting slammed for breakfast? The home of the Grand Slam Breakfast, Denny's is one of the leading full-service, family-style restaurant chains in the US, with about 1,550 of its signature eateries located across the country. Its family-style restaurants are typically open 24 hours a day, seven days a week, and serve breakfast, lunch, and dinner. The menu features a variety of breakfast items (which account for the majority of company sales) along with such standard fare as hamburgers, steaks, salads, and desserts. The company owns and operates about 400 of its restaurants, while the rest are franchised or operate under licensing agreements.

	Annual Growth	12/03	12/04	12/05	12/06	12/07
Sales ($ mil.)	(0.0%)	940.9	960.0	978.7	994.0	939.4
Net income ($ mil.)	—	(31.5)	(37.7)	(7.3)	30.3	34.7
Market value ($ mil.)	120.8%	16.8	395.9	358.7	445.4	399.3
Employees	(11.8%)	—	—	27,000	27,000	21,000

DENSO INTERNATIONAL AMERICA, INC.

24777 Denso Dr.
Southfield, MI 48033
Phone: 248-350-7500
Fax: 248-213-2337
Web: www.densocorp-na.com

CEO: Haruya Maruyama
CFO: Bill Steffan
HR: –
FYE: March 31
Type: Subsidiary

DENSO International America is the holding company for DENSO's North American operations. The company oversees more than 30 joint venture and affiliate companies — mostly in the US, but also in Mexico and Canada. In addition to manufacturing everything from heater cores and oil coolers to alternators and air conditioners, DENSO International also has significant research and development operations. The company's customers include General Motors, Honda of America, Toyota Motor Sales, Mercedes-Benz U.S. International, Deere & Company, and Harley-Davidson.

	Annual Growth	3/03	3/04	3/05	3/06	3/07
Est. sales ($ mil.)	—	—	—	—	—	6,500.0
Employees	—	—	—	—	—	17,000

DENTAL PATIENT CARE AMERICA, INC.   OTC: DPAT

2825 E. Cottonwood Pkwy., Ste. 500
Salt Lake City, UT 84121
Phone: 801-990-3311
Fax: 801-990-3313

CEO: Michael Silva
CFO: Brad Berrett
HR: –
FYE: December 31
Type: Public

Dental Patient Care America (formerly Mountain Oil) wants to help dentists as well as their patients. Formerly dedicated to developing oil and gas properties, the company completely switched gears in 2004 with a reverse buyout. DCPA's Dental Cooperative subsidiary provides a dental practice network co-op that allows dentists in the co-op to obtain insurance, profit sharing, and purchasing benefits. Subsidiary DentistDirect offers employers dental benefit plans for their employees. In 2005 nearly all of DCPA's revenue (98%) came from Dental Cooperative; most of its business is conducted within the state of Utah. CEO Michael Silva and president Marlon Berret together own nearly 25% of the company.

	Annual Growth	12/03	12/04	12/05	12/06	12/07
Sales ($ mil.)	96.8%	0.1	0.5	0.4	0.3	1.5
Net income ($ mil.)	—	0.0	(0.2)	(0.3)	(0.5)	(0.3)
Market value ($ mil.)	(34.4%)	—	15.9	4.4	7.0	4.5
Employees	—	—	—	—	—	—

⊞ DENTSPLY INTERNATIONAL INC.   NASDAQ (GS): XRAY

221 W. Philadelphia St.
York, PA 17405
Phone: 717-845-7511
Fax: 717-849-4760
Web: www.dentsply.com

CEO: Bret W. Wise
CFO: William R. Jellison
HR: Rachel P. McKinney
FYE: December 31
Type: Public

Open wider, please, so that DENTSPLY International can fit more of its products in your mouth. The dental equipment maker's products include dental prosthetics, crown and bridge materials, precious-metal alloys, and dental implants. DENTSPLY also makes dental X-ray systems, handpieces, ultrasonic scalers, and polishers, as well as other dental equipment. The company also makes all of the consumable sundries used by dentists, including tooth whiteners, fluoride pastes, and sealants. The company manufactures its various products under more than 100 brand names. DENTSPLY markets its goods through distributors as well as directly to dentists, dental labs, and dental schools in more than 120 countries.

	Annual Growth	12/03	12/04	12/05	12/06	12/07
Sales ($ mil.)	6.4%	1,570.9	1,694.2	1,715.1	1,810.5	2,009.8
Net income ($ mil.)	10.5%	174.2	253.2	45.4	223.7	259.6
Market value ($ mil.)	39.5%	1,791.0	2,264.9	2,118.1	4,531.2	6,789.0
Employees	5.5%	—	—	8,000	8,500	8,900

DEPOMED, INC.   NASDAQ (GM): DEPO

1360 O'Brien Dr.
Menlo Park, CA 94025
Phone: 650-462-5900
Fax: 650-462-9993
Web: www.depomedinc.com

CEO: Carl A. Pelzel
CFO: Tammy L. Cameron
HR: –
FYE: December 31
Type: Public

For joke tellers and Depomed, it's all about the delivery. The drug company makes proprietary drug therapies using its patented delivery technology AcuForm, an extended-release technology that stretches out the time a pill stays in the stomach, thus reducing the number of necessary doses and possibly lessening side effects. Depomed's internal development efforts have yielded two FDA-approved products: Glumetza, an extended-release formulation of common diabetes drug metformin, and ProQuin XR, a treatment for urinary tract infections. King Pharmaceuticals, which had marketed Glumetza in the US, terminated its promotion efforts in 2007.

	Annual Growth	12/03	12/04	12/05	12/06	12/07
Sales ($ mil.)	184.6%	1.0	0.2	4.4	9.6	65.6
Net income ($ mil.)	—	(30.0)	(26.9)	(24.5)	(39.7)	49.2
Market value ($ mil.)	(10.7%)	245.1	187.3	244.1	145.0	156.0
Employees	—	—	—	90	—	—

THE DEPOSITORY TRUST & CLEARING CORPORATION

55 Water St., 22nd Fl.
New York, NY 10041
Phone: 212-855-1000
Fax: 212-855-8440
Web: www.dtcc.com

CEO: Donald F. Donahue
CFO: Ellen Fine Levine
HR: Anthony J. Portannese
FYE: December 31
Type: Private

It's clear that securities trading just wouldn't be the same without The Depository Trust & Clearing Corporation (DTCC), whose subsidiaries provide the infrastructure for clearing, settlement, and custody of most US securities transactions. DTCC was established in 1999 when operating companies The Depository Trust Company (DTC) and the National Securities Clearing Company (NSCC) — both of which were founded in the 1970s — were combined under a single holding structure. DTC is the world's largest securities depository and a clearinghouse for trading settlement; NSCC processes most broker-to-broker equity, corporate, and municipal bond trades in the US.

	Annual Growth	12/03	12/04	12/05	12/06	12/07
Est. sales ($ mil.)	—	—	—	—	—	751.2
Employees	—	—	—	—	—	3,000

DERMA SCIENCES, INC.   OTC: DSCI

214 Carnegie Center, Ste. 300
Princeton, NJ 08540
Phone: 609-514-4744
Fax: 609-514-0502
Web: www.dermasciences.com

CEO: Edward J. Quilty
CFO: John E. Yetter
HR: –
FYE: December 31
Type: Public

Time may eventually heal all wounds, but in the meantime there's Derma Sciences. The company has three product lines: sprays, ointments, and dressings for basic and chronic skin wounds (burns, abrasions, bedsores, and venous ulcers); wound closure strips and fasteners; and skin care products such as lotions, soaps, and bath sponges. The company's direct sales force sells its products, which are designed for use in nursing homes, hospitals, and other health care facilities, to distributors and large institutions in the US; it also sells internationally through distribution agreements, primarily in Canada, Europe, and Latin America.

	Annual Growth	12/03	12/04	12/05	12/06	12/07
Sales ($ mil.)	17.5%	17.9	19.9	23.5	27.9	34.1
Net income ($ mil.)	—	0.0	(2.3)	(0.9)	0.7	(2.3)
Market value ($ mil.)	49.2%	8.9	7.4	6.8	21.2	44.0
Employees	—	—	—	—	—	—

DEROYAL INDUSTRIES, INC.

200 DeBusk Ln.
Powell, TN 37849
Phone: 865-938-7828
Fax: 865-362-1230
Web: www.deroyal.com

CEO: Autry O. V. (Pete) DeBusk
CFO: –
HR: Rebecca Harmon
FYE: December 31
Type: Private

DeRoyal Industries helps doctors give their patients DeRoyal treatment. The company makes medical equipment and surgical supplies. Products include suction canisters, custom procedural trays, surgical safety and critical care products, anesthesia and temperature monitoring supplies, birthing and neonatal care items, angiography and endoscopy products, rehabilitation and therapy products, and wound care dressings. The company also has a unit devoted to the disposal of medical products and waste. Beyond its catalog of products, DeRoyal Industries has the ability to handle contract manufacturing for those inside and outside the medical industry.

	Annual Growth	12/03	12/04	12/05	12/06	12/07
Est. sales ($ mil.)	—	—	—	—	—	168.3
Employees	—	—	—	—	—	2,000

⊞ An in-depth profile of this company is available to Hoover's Online members at hoovers.com.

DESERET MANAGEMENT CORPORATION

60 E. South Temple, Ste. 575
Salt Lake City, UT 84111
Phone: 801-538-0651
Fax: 801-538-0655
Web: www.deseretmanagement.com

CEO: Rodney H. Brady
CFO: Dale G. Bailey
HR: –
FYE: December 31
Type: Holding company

While the Church of Jesus Christ of Latter-day Saints handles the spiritual, Deseret Management takes care of the worldly. The holding company oversees a portfolio of for-profit ventures for the Mormon Church, including Bonneville International Corporation (radio and TV stations), Deseret Book Company (inspirational publishing), and Salt Lake City's *Deseret Morning News* newspaper. Its holdings also include life insurance and financial services provider Beneficial Life Insurance and corporate hospitality and catering provider Temple Square Hospitality. Deseret Management also has real estate holdings through two other subsidiaries. The Mormon Church formed the holding company in 1966.

	Annual Growth	12/02	12/03	12/04	12/05	12/06
Est. sales ($ mil.)	—	—	—	—	—	266.4
Employees	—	—	—	—	—	3,494

DESERT SCHOOLS FEDERAL CREDIT UNION

148 N. 48th St.
Phoenix, AZ 85034
Phone: 602-433-7000
Fax: –
Web: www.desertschools.org

CEO: Susan C. Frank
CFO: –
HR: –
FYE: December 31
Type: Not-for-profit

One of the largest credit unions in Arizona, Desert Schools Federal Credit Union operates about 60 branch locations in the Phoenix area, serving more than 325,000 members. Established in 1939 by a group of 15 teachers, the credit union offers banking products and services, including checking and savings accounts, IRAs, and CDs; it also provides online banking services. Subsidiary Desert Schools Financial Services sells insurance products and investment services. Membership is available to any individual living, working, or attending church or school in Gila, Maricopa, or Pinal counties.

	Annual Growth	12/02	12/03	12/04	12/05	12/06
Assets ($ mil.)	13.2%	1,754.8	1,978.5	2,212.1	2,570.0	2,885.0
Net income ($ mil.)	10.1%	27.0	27.4	28.0	35.7	39.7
Employees	27.3%	—	700	1,000	1,134	—

DESIGN WITHIN REACH, INC.

NASDAQ (GM): DWRI

225 Bush St., 20th Fl.
San Francisco, CA 94104
Phone: 415-676-6500
Fax: 415-676-6871
Web: www.dwr.com

CEO: Ray Brunner
CFO: John D. Hellmann
HR: Suzanne Ewing
FYE: Saturday nearest December 31
Type: Public

Design Within Reach (commonly referred to as DWR) may be just *out of reach* for the average Joe's pocketbook. Founded by professional designer Rob Forbes in 1998, the company sells modern-design, European-style home furnishings (sofas, lounge chairs, coffee and end tables, shelving units, dining tables, office chairs, rugs, lighting, Sonno mattresses, and related accessories) and has been featured on decorating television series such as *Queer Eye for the Straight Guy* and *Trading Spaces*. Its contemporary goods are sold through more than 65 retail studios in some 22 states and the District of Columbia, a catalog (more than a half million copies distributed per month), and online through its Web site.

	Annual Growth	12/03	12/04	12/05	12/06	12/07
Sales ($ mil.)	24.3%	81.1	120.6	158.2	178.1	193.9
Net income ($ mil.)	(43.8%)	3.0	3.7	(2.1)	(8.3)	0.3
Market value ($ mil.)	(33.7%)	—	187.2	75.9	71.1	54.6
Employees	14.3%	—	—	356	407	—

DETREX CORPORATION

Pink Sheets: DTRX

24901 Northwestern Hwy., Ste. 410
Southfield, MI 48075
Phone: 248-358-5800
Fax: 248-799-7192
Web: www.detrex.com

CEO: Thomas E. (Tom) Mark
CFO: Steven J. (Steve) Quinlan
HR: Robert M. (Bob) Currie
FYE: December 31
Type: Public

Detrex Corporation has one word for you: *plastics*. OK, three words: *plastics* and *specialty chemicals*. Detrex subsidiary Harvel Plastics, which accounts for more than two-thirds of Detrex's sales, makes PVC and CPVC pipe and custom extrusions. Detrex's other division, The Elco Corporation, makes lubricant additives (such as hydraulic fluid additives), fine chemicals, and semiconductor-grade hydrochloric acid. The company has operations throughout the US and customers in 50 countries, though a clear majority of Detrex's sales are to the US. Those customers include manufacturers of appliances, automobiles, and farm implements. Summit Capital Partners owns 37% of Detrex.

	Annual Growth	12/03	12/04	12/05	12/06	12/07
Est. sales ($ mil.)	—	—	—	—	—	74.4
Employees	—	—	—	—	—	200

DETROIT DIESEL CORPORATION

13400 Outer Dr. West
Detroit, MI 48239
Phone: 313-592-5000
Fax: 313-592-7323
Web: www.detroitdiesel.com

CEO: Friedrich Baumann
CFO: –
HR: Phil Bezaire
FYE: December 31
Type: Subsidiary

Detroit Diesel Corporation (DDC) says keep on truckin' so it can continue making diesel engines. DDC sells its diesel engines to the truck, auto, and marine markets. The Series 60, a heavy-duty diesel engine with electronic controls, is its best seller. DDC also remanufactures two- and four-cycle engines. It markets its engines directly and through a worldwide network of some 800 authorized distributor and dealer locations. Most sales are made directly to truck makers in the US. Italian subsidiary VM Motori supplies 4-cylinder, turbocharged engines to the international automotive market. Detroit Diesel is a brand affiliate of Daimler AG's Daimler Trucks North America LLC division (formerly Freightliner).

	Annual Growth	12/03	12/04	12/05	12/06	12/07
Est. sales ($ mil.)	—	—	—	—	—	555.0
Employees	—	—	—	—	—	6,660

THE DETROIT EDISON COMPANY

2000 2nd Ave.
Detroit, MI 48226
Phone: 313-235-4000
Fax: 313-235-8055
Web: my.dteenergy.com

CEO: Anthony F. Earley Jr.
CFO: David E. Meador
HR: –
FYE: December 31
Type: Subsidiary

Ford is not the only power plant in Detroit. Detroit Edison generates and distributes electricity to 2.2 million customers in Michigan. The utility, a unit of power player DTE Energy, has more than 11,000 MW of generating capacity from its interests in fossil-fueled, nuclear, and hydroelectric power plants. It operates more than 45,700 circuit miles of distribution lines and owns and operates 678 distribution substations. Detroit Edison also sells excess power to wholesale customers and provides coal transportation services. Customers choosing to purchase power from alternative electric suppliers accounted for 4% of retail sales in 2007.

	Annual Growth	12/02	12/03	12/04	12/05	12/06
Sales ($ mil.)	4.0%	4,054.0	3,695.0	3,568.0	4,462.0	4,737.0
Net income ($ mil.)	(2.6%)	356.0	246.0	150.0	274.0	321.0
Employees	21.1%	—	4,062	7,838	7,980	7,217

DETROIT MEDICAL CENTER

3990 John R. St.
Detroit, MI 48201
Phone: 313-578-2000
Fax: 313-578-3225
Web: www.dmc.org

CEO: Michael E. Duggan
CFO: Jay B. Rising
HR: Ruthann Liagre
FYE: December 31
Type: Not-for-profit

The Detroit Medical Center serves patients throughout southeastern Michigan with more than 2,000 beds and some 3,000 physicians. The center is made up of eight hospitals and numerous outpatient facilities, as well as DMC University Laboratories, which provides clinical laboratory services to the medical system. The Detroit Medical Center is a teaching and clinical research site for Wayne State University; it is also allied with the Barbara Ann Karmanos Cancer Institute and the Kresge Eye Institute. The medical center's specialized services include cardiology, orthopedics, rehabilitation, and organ transplants.

	Annual Growth	12/03	12/04	12/05	12/06	12/07
Est. sales ($ mil.)	—	—	—	—	—	762.0
Employees	—	—	—	—	—	16,144

DEUTSCH, INC.

111 8th Ave.
New York, NY 10011
Phone: 212-981-7600
Fax: 212-981-7525
Web: www.deutschinc.com

CEO: Linda Sawyer
CFO: Nina Werner
HR: —
FYE: December 31
Type: Subsidiary

Advertising is the big idea at Deutsch. The firm, led by advertising-guru-turned-television-personality Donny Deutsch, is one of the leading agencies in the US, offering creative development and brand marketing services through offices in New York City, Los Angeles, and Toronto. Clients have included Expedia, Johnson & Johnson, and Old Navy. Deutsch also does interactive and direct marketing work, as well as event marketing. In addition, the agency creates branded entertainment through its Media Bridge Entertainment unit. Founded in 1969, Deutsch is a subsidiary of global advertising company Interpublic Group.

DEUTSCHE BANK ALEX. BROWN

1 South St., 28th Fl.
Baltimore, MD 21202
Phone: 410-727-1700
Fax: 410-895-3450
Web: www.alexbrown.db.com

CEO: Michael A. Burke
CFO: —
HR: —
FYE: December 31
Type: Business segment

Deutsche Bank Alex. Brown is the private client-services division of Deutsche Bank Securities, which is part of the Corporate and Investment Bank unit of German colossus Deutsche Bank. The company provides a range of advisory, brokerage, and investment services to high-net-worth individual investors in the US. For corporate clients, Deutsche Bank Alex. Brown provides advice on mergers and acquisitions, acquisition finance, and project finance. The company also administers employee stock purchase plans, retirement plans, and directed stock programs. It has more than 15 US offices and more than $60 billion of assets under control.

DEUTSCHE BANK BERKSHIRE MORTGAGE, INC.

Irvine Center Drive, Ste. 150
Irvine, CA 92618
Phone: 949-754-6300
Fax: —
Web: www.dbberkshiremortgage.com

CEO: Steve Wendel
CFO: Alan Reese
HR: —
FYE: December 31
Type: Subsidiary

Deutsche Bank Berkshire Mortgage (DBBM; formerly Berkshire Mortgage Finance) doesn't fund homes in the hoity-toity western Massachusetts region. Instead, it's one of the nation's largest commercial mortgage lenders. Deutsche Bank Berkshire Mortgage handles origination and underwriting, and DB Mortgage Services provides servicing and asset management. The company helps corporate clients acquire and refinance primarily multifamily residential and commercial properties, including student housing and senior housing. It has a portfolio of $20 billion comprising more than 2,000 loans in 48 states and Washington, DC. DBBM is a part of Deutsche Bank's Commercial Real Estate Group.

	Annual Growth	12/03	12/04	12/05	12/06	12/07
Est. sales ($ mil.)	—	—	—	—	—	20.3
Employees	—	—	—	—	—	260

DEUTSCHE BANK SECURITIES INC.

60 Wall St.
New York, NY 10005
Phone: 212-250-2500
Fax: 212-454-1706

CEO: Richard Bryne
CFO: —
HR: —
FYE: December 31
Type: Subsidiary

Deutsche Bank Securities, the US investment banking and securities arm of German banking colossus Deutsche Bank, is not shy about flexing its financial muscle. The firm offers underwriting, financial advisory services, and mergers and acquisitions assistance. Deutsche Bank Securities also provides investment products, brokerage, and financial advice to wealthy individual investors through its Deutsche Bank Alex. Brown division. The company has underwritten IPOs, including MAP Pharmaceuticals and NYSE.

	Annual Growth	12/03	12/04	12/05	12/06	12/07
Est. sales ($ mil.)	—	—	—	—	—	23.0
Employees	—	—	—	—	—	200

DEVCON INTERNATIONAL CORP.

NASDAQ (GM): DEVC

595 S. Federal Hwy., Ste. 500
Boca Raton, FL 33432
Phone: 561-208-7200
Fax: 561-208-0166
Web: www.devc.com

CEO: Richard C. Rochon
CFO: Mark M. McIntosh
HR: Sherry Eldridge
FYE: December 31
Type: Public

Devcon International wants to pave its way to a secure future. The company is focused on its security services business, which provides electronic security services. Devcon operates primarily in Florida and the New York City metropolitan area. Products include burglary, fire, medical, environmental, video and CCTV (closed-circuit television), and security access systems. The company markets to residential and commercial clients. In 2007 Devcon completed its three-year transformation from a construction and materials company to a security firm through a series of divestitures and acquisitions.

	Annual Growth	12/03	12/04	12/05	12/06	12/07
Sales ($ mil.)	0.2%	55.3	69.2	84.9	105.6	55.8
Net income ($ mil.)	—	(8.6)	10.6	(14.3)	(29.4)	(23.7)
Market value ($ mil.)	(10.0%)	24.2	91.9	62.1	34.4	15.9
Employees	1.2%	—	—	695	703	—

An in-depth profile of this company is available to Hoover's Online members at hoovers.com.

491

DEVELOPERS DIVERSIFIED REALTY CORPORATION

NYSE: DDR

3300 Enterprise Pkwy.	CEO: Scott A. Wolstein
Beachwood, OH 44122	CFO: William H. Schafer
Phone: 216-755-5500	HR: Nan R. Zieleniec
Fax: 216-755-1500	FYE: December 31
Web: www.ddrc.com	Type: Public

Developers Diversified Realty (DDR) is a self-administered real estate investment trust (REIT) that acquires, develops, renovates, leases, and manages retail and office properties. Its portfolio includes more than 675 community shopping centers, about 30 enclosed malls and other retail properties, about a half dozen office and industrial centers, and around 1,600 acres of undeveloped land. More than 40% of its shopping centers are owned through joint ventures. Altogether, the firm owns or manages more than 160 million sq. ft. of leasable space in about 45 states, as well as Brazil and Puerto Rico.

	Annual Growth	12/03	12/04	12/05	12/06	12/07
Sales ($ mil.)	18.7%	476.1	598.9	727.2	818.1	944.8
Net income ($ mil.)	3.5%	240.3	269.8	282.6	253.3	276.0
Market value ($ mil.)	12.0%	2,901.6	4,795.6	5,123.6	6,860.7	4,573.7
Employees	17.0%	—	—	548	641	—

DEVELOPMENT DIMENSIONS INTERNATIONAL, INC.

1225 Washington Pike	CEO: William C. (Bill) Byham
Bridgeville, PA 15017	CFO: William D. (Bill) Koch
Phone: 412-257-0600	HR: –
Fax: 412-257-2942	FYE: August 31
Web: www.ddiworld.com	Type: Private

Development Dimensions International (DDI) helps businesses hire, develop, and retain executive talent. The company provides a variety of services in areas such as selection system design and implementation, training and hiring outsourcing, and leader and executive assessment and development. In addition, DDI offers services in performance and succession management, work analysis, and workforce development. The company serves customers in industries such as manufacturing, health care, technology, finance, and telecommunications. Working with such clients as Microsoft, Coca-Cola, and General Motors, the company has 75 offices in more than 25 countries. William Byham and Douglas Bray founded DDI in 1970.

	Annual Growth	8/03	8/04	8/05	8/06	8/07
Est. sales ($ mil.)	—	—	—	—	—	46.8
Employees	—	—	—	—	—	850

DEVEREUX FOUNDATION

444 Devereux Dr.	CEO: Robert Q. (Bob) Kreider
Villanova, PA 19085	CFO: Margaret (Maggie) McGill
Phone: 610-520-3000	HR: Merdic J. McLeod Jr.
Fax: 610-542-3136	FYE: December 31
Web: www.devereux.org	Type: Foundation

Devereux Foundation endeavors to make a difference in the lives of people with behavioral, psychological, intellectual, or neurological problems. A not-for-profit organization, Devereux serves children, adolescents, adults and their families through some 15 centers in about a dozen states. Its offerings include hospitalization, respite care, family counseling, and vocational training. Devereux also conducts behavioral health research and provides consulting services for other organizations with similar concerns. The group's work began in 1912 when a Philadelphia educator, Helena Devereux, started working with three special education students in her parents' house.

	Annual Growth	12/03	12/04	12/05	12/06	12/07
Est. sales ($ mil.)	—	—	—	—	—	388.0
Employees	—	—	—	—	—	6,000

DEVON ENERGY CORPORATION

NYSE: DVN

20 N. Broadway	CEO: J. Larry Nichols
Oklahoma City, OK 73102	CFO: Danny J. Heatly
Phone: 405-235-3611	HR: Paul R. Poley
Fax: 405-552-4550	FYE: December 31
Web: www.devonenergy.com	Type: Public

Independent oil and gas producer Devon Energy is buying its way into the big leagues. With acquisitions of PennzEnergy, Northstar Energy, and Santa Fe Snyder, it has become an oil and gas heavyweight. It got stouter by buying Anderson Exploration and Mitchell Energy & Development. It also acquired Ocean Energy for $3.5 billion and merged it with its Devon Newco unit. Devon has proved reserves of 677 million barrels of oil, 9 trillion cu. ft. of natural gas, and 321 million barrels of natural gas liquids. It has exploration and production assets in the Gulf of Mexico, western Canada, and in other major oil patches worldwide such as Azerbaijan, Brazil, and China.

	Annual Growth	12/03	12/04	12/05	12/06	12/07
Sales ($ mil.)	11.5%	7,352.0	9,189.0	10,741.0	10,578.0	11,362.0
Net income ($ mil.)	19.9%	1,747.0	2,186.0	2,930.0	2,846.0	3,606.0
Market value ($ mil.)	55.5%	6,759.3	18,833.7	27,731.1	29,785.5	39,494.1
Employees	10.8%	—	—	4,075	4,600	5,000

DEVRY INC.

NYSE: DV

1 Tower Ln., Ste. 1000	CEO: Daniel M. Hamburger
Oakbrook Terrace, IL 60181	CFO: Richard M. (Rick) Gunst
Phone: 630-571-7700	HR: Donna N. Jennings
Fax: 630-571-0317	FYE: June 30
Web: www.devry.com	Type: Public

DeVry isn't exactly Ivy League, but the company is definitely in the big leagues when it comes to technical and business education. The for-profit company operates about 25 large DeVry University campuses (as well as some 60 smaller teaching centers), offering undergraduate and master's programs in technology- and business-related fields. Additionally, DeVry owns Ross University, which runs a medical school and a veterinary school in the Caribbean, and Chamberlain College of Nursing (fomerly Deaconess College of Nursing). DeVry also prepares potential accountants and financial analysts for their professional exams through its Becker Professional Review programs.

	Annual Growth	6/03	6/04	6/05	6/06	6/07
Sales ($ mil.)	8.3%	679.6	784.9	781.3	843.3	933.5
Net income ($ mil.)	5.6%	61.2	58.1	28.5	43.0	76.2
Market value ($ mil.)	10.4%	1,630.8	1,928.5	1,402.5	1,554.5	2,419.9
Employees	(2.7%)	—	—	5,700	4,800	5,400

DEWEY & LEBOEUF LLP

1301 Avenue of the Americas	CEO: Gordon E. Warnke
New York, NY 10019	CFO: Peter Casey
Phone: 212-259-8000	HR: Alanna Liu
Fax: 212-259-6333	FYE: September 30
Web: www.deweyleboeuf.com	Type: Partnership

International law firm Dewey & LeBoeuf has 1,300 lawyers in about 25 offices worldwide. One of the leading law firms headquartered in New York, Dewey & LeBoeuf has areas of expertise in antitrust, bankruptcy, government investigations, real estate, tax, and trade law, as well as mergers and acquisitions. The firm is the result of the October 2007 merger between law firms Dewey Ballantine and LeBoeuf, Lamb, Greene & MacRae. Dewey Ballantine was initially founded in 1909; the Dewey in the name refers to former partner Thomas Dewey, a three-term New York governor and two-time Republican presidential nominee in the 1940s. LeBoeuf Lamb was established in 1929.

	Annual Growth	9/02	9/03	9/04	9/05	9/06
Sales ($ mil.)	3.9%	350.0	374.0	380.5	350.0	408.5
Employees	—	—	—	—	—	—

THE DEWEY ELECTRONICS CORPORATION

OTC: DEWY

27 Muller Rd.
Oakland, NJ 07436
Phone: 201-337-4700
Fax: 201-337-3976
Web: www.deweyelectronics.com

CEO: John H. D. Dewey
CFO: –
HR: –
FYE: June 30
Type: Public

The Dewey Electronics Corporation powers the military and powders the slopes. The company's electronics segment, which accounts for nearly all of Dewey's sales, provides the US Army with diesel-operated tactical generator sets and produces underwater speed and distance measuring instrumentation for the US Navy. Dewey's HEDCO subsidiary designs, manufactures, and services the Snow Cub brand of snowmaking equipment, which it has sold to more than 300 ski resorts around the world. The family of late CEO Gordon Dewey owns about 40% of the company.

	Annual Growth	6/03	6/04	6/05	6/06	6/07
Sales ($ mil.)	(4.2%)	6.4	6.0	6.2	7.3	5.4
Net income ($ mil.)	—	0.3	0.8	0.0	(0.6)	(1.7)
Market value ($ mil.)	(16.4%)	7.8	4.8	10.0	6.5	3.8
Employees	5.9%	—	—	34	36	—

DEXCOM, INC.

NASDAQ (GM): DXCM

5555 Oberlin Dr.
San Diego, CA 92121
Phone: 858-200-0200
Fax: 858-200-0201
Web: www.dexcom.com

CEO: Terrance H. (Terry) Gregg
CFO: Jess Roper
HR: Steven R. (Steve) Pacelli
FYE: December 31
Type: Public

DexCom offers alternatives to diabetic fingertip tests. The company develops and markets glucose monitoring systems that measure and wirelessly transmit blood sugar levels from a sensor on the patient to a small receiver. Patients can access blood glucose trends and real-time information by pressing a button and are alerted when levels are too high or low. Diabetics can insert sensors themselves for the short-term system, which can be used for three to seven days. Products are direct marketed to physicians, endocrinologists, and diabetes educators.

	Annual Growth	12/03	12/04	12/05	12/06	12/07
Sales ($ mil.)	109.1%	—	—	—	2.2	4.6
Net income ($ mil.)	—	—	—	—	(46.6)	(45.9)
Market value ($ mil.)	(9.0%)	—	—	—	277.7	252.7
Employees	—	—	—	—	—	—

DEXTERRA, INC.

21540 30th Dr. Southeast, Ste. 230
Bothell, WA 98021
Phone: 425-939-3100
Fax: 425-415-1225
Web: www.dexterra.com

CEO: Rob Loughan
CFO: Kenneth A. (Ken) Goldman
HR: –
FYE: December 31
Type: Private

Dexterra provides mobile business software used to automate field workforces, integrate enterprise applications, and manage mobile workforces. Customers in the manufacturing, warehousing, facilities, transportation, utilities, consumer goods, and other industries use the company's Dexterra Mobile Platform to give managers a window onto their mobile workforces and manage field workforce change. Dexterra's mobile applications, which integrate with third-party customer relationship management and enterprise resource planning systems, include tools for case management, field services and sales, merchandising, and facilities management. The company was founded in 2002.

	Annual Growth	12/03	12/04	12/05	12/06	12/07
Est. sales ($ mil.)	—	—	—	—	—	15.9
Employees	—	—	—	—	—	140

DEY, INC.

2751 Napa Valley Corporate Dr.
Napa, CA 94558
Phone: 707-224-3200
Fax: 707-224-9264
Web: www.deyinc.com

CEO: Carolyn Myers
CFO: Pamela R. Marrs
HR: Sandy Cooper
FYE: December 31
Type: Subsidiary

Dey helps people breathe easier. The company, a subsidiary of generic drug-maker Mylan, makes prescription drugs for the treatment of allergies and respiratory diseases. Its premeasured unit-dose inhalation products include treatments for asthma and chronic obstructive pulmonary disease (COPD). Its DuoNeb medication, used in air-driven breathing devices called nebulizers, treats emphysema, chronic bronchitis, and COPD. Dey also markets EpiPen auto-injectors, used by patients to self-administer epinephrine for allergic reactions. It also offers several nonbranded generic nebulizer treatments.

	Annual Growth	12/03	12/04	12/05	12/06	12/07
Est. sales ($ mil.)	—	—	—	—	—	127.4
Employees	—	—	—	—	—	1,000

DG FASTCHANNEL

NASDAQ (GM): DGIT

750 W. John Carpenter Fwy., Ste. 700
Irving, TX 75039
Phone: 972-581-2000
Fax: 972-581-2001
Web: www.dgfastchannel.com

CEO: Scott K. Ginsburg
CFO: Omar A. Choucair
HR: –
FYE: December 31
Type: Public

Commercials don't signify bathroom breaks for DG FastChannel (formerly Digital Generation Systems, which did business as DG Systems). The company provides digital distribution services for advertisers, agencies, newspaper publishers, and TV and radio broadcasters. Ad agencies and other content providers route their clients' audio and video spots to radio and TV stations and other traditional media outlets through DG FastChannel's two nationwide digital distribution networks. Electronic transmissions are made across the Internet and via satellite. Chairman and CEO Scott Ginsburg owns about 20% of the company, which became DG FastChannel in 2006 after purchasing competitor FastChannel Network for $37.5 million.

	Annual Growth	12/03	12/04	12/05	12/06	12/07
Sales ($ mil.)	14.1%	57.7	62.4	58.3	68.7	97.7
Net income ($ mil.)	25.4%	4.2	3.2	(1.1)	(0.6)	10.4
Market value ($ mil.)	115.0%	—	—	—	213.6	459.1
Employees	18.6%	—	—	317	376	—

DGSE COMPANIES, INC.

AMEX: DGC

11311 Reeder Rd.
Dallas, TX 75229
Phone: 972-484-3662
Fax: 972-241-0646
Web: www.dgse.com

CEO: L. S. Smith
CFO: John Benson
HR: –
FYE: December 31
Type: Public

Attracted to things gold and shiny? If so, DGSE Companies is for you. The firm buys and sells jewelry, bullion, rare coins, fine watches, and more to retail and wholesale customers across the US through its various Web sites and retail stores in California, Texas, and South Carolina. Its Web sites allow customers to buy and sell jewelry interactively, shop online, and obtain current precious-metal prices. DGSE also owns Fairchild Watches, a leading vintage watch wholesaler and the rare coin dealer Superior Galleries. The company's National Pawn subsidiary operates a pair of pawn shops in Dallas, Texas, that focus on jewelry. Chairman and CEO L. S. Smith owns more than 60% of the company's voting shares.

	Annual Growth	12/03	12/04	12/05	12/06	12/07
Sales ($ mil.)	24.5%	26.2	28.6	35.6	44.1	63.0
Net income ($ mil.)	—	(0.5)	0.3	0.5	0.6	0.8
Market value ($ mil.)	44.1%	11.5	13.9	9.8	12.5	49.8
Employees	(7.4%)	—	—	54	50	—

An in-depth profile of this company is available to Hoover's Online members at hoovers.com.

493

DHL EXPRESS (USA), INC.

1200 S. Pine Island Rd., Ste. 600
Plantation, FL 33324
Phone: 954-888-7000
Fax: 954-888-7310
Web: www.dhl-usa.com

CEO: Ken Allen
CFO: Ian D. Clough
HR: Scott M. Northcutt
FYE: December 31
Type: Subsidiary

When the colors are flown in the US express delivery market, DHL wants its signature yellow to someday be as prominent as the brown of UPS or the purple of FedEx. DHL Express (USA) is the US arm of express delivery giant DHL, which itself is a subsidiary of Germany's Deutsche Post. The operations of DHL Express (USA) are coordinated with those of other DHL express delivery units; overall, DHL serves some 120,000 locations in more than 220 countries and territories worldwide. Besides its express delivery operations, DHL offers supply chain management and freight forwarding services.

	Annual Growth	12/03	12/04	12/05	12/06	12/07
Est. sales ($ mil.)	—	—	—	—	—	1,530.6
Employees	—	—	—	—	—	30,000

DHL GLOBAL FORWARDING

1200 S. Pine Island Rd., Ste. 140
Plantation, FL 33324
Phone: 954-888-7000
Fax: 954-888-7301
Web: www.us.danzas.com

CEO: Hans Toggweiler
CFO: Tasso Flath
HR: –
FYE: December 31
Type: Business segment

DHL Global Forwarding can arrange to keep cargo rolling through the land, sailing over the sea, or flying in the air. The company provides freight forwarding services, including customs brokerage, and logistics services, including warehousing and distribution. (As a freight forwarder, DHL Global Forwarding buys transportation capacity from carriers and resells it to customers.) The company is part of the DHL empire, which also includes units that focus on express delivery, supply chain management, and overland transport within Europe. DHL, in turn, is a unit of Deutsche Post.

DHL GLOBAL MAIL

2700 S. Commerce Pkwy., Ste. 400
Weston, FL 33331
Phone: 954-903-6300
Fax: 954-349-6379
Web: globalmail.com

CEO: Joe Phelan
CFO: Terry Hilsman
HR: –
FYE: December 31
Type: Subsidiary

DHL Global Mail doesn't actually deliver the mail, but the company does work to speed its arrival. A provider of mail processing and distribution services for business customers, DHL Global Mail operates from more than 15 terminals throughout the US. The company takes mail from its customers that is bound for many places, sorts it, and gets it to the United States Postal Service distribution facility closest to its destination. It provides international distribution services through affiliates; overall, the DHL Global Mail network consists of about 50 processing facilities and serves some 200 countries. The company is part of the mail business segment of its parent, German postal service Deutsche Post.

	Annual Growth	12/03	12/04	12/05	12/06	12/07
Est. sales ($ mil.)	—	—	—	—	—	17.9
Employees	—	—	—	—	—	350

DI GIORGIO CORPORATION

380 Middlesex Ave.
Carteret, NJ 07008
Phone: 732-541-5555
Fax: 732-541-3730
Web: www.whiterose.com

CEO: Stephen R. Bokser
CFO: Sharon Konzelman
HR: Jackie Simmons
FYE: Saturday nearest December 31
Type: Subsidiary

This company delivers little apples (and other foods) to the Big Apple. Operating primarily through its White Rose division, Di Giorgio Corporation is a leading food wholesaler and distributor serving the New York City market. It offers more than 21,000 products to food retailers ranging from independents and members of co-ops to regional chains. Di Giorgio distributes national brands, as well as frozen and refrigerated products sold under its White Rose brand, a name known in New York for well over a century. In addition to New York City, it serves customers on Long Island, in New Jersey, and in the greater Philadelphia area. Di Giorgio was acquired by distribution co-op Associated Wholesalers (AWI) in 2006.

THE DIAGEO CHATEAU & ESTATE WINES COMPANY

240 Gateway Rd. West
Napa, CA 94558
Phone: 707-299-2600
Fax: –
Web: www.diageowines.com

CEO: Raymond S. (Ray) Chadwick
CFO: –
HR: –
FYE: June 30
Type: Subsidiary

You might find aromas of orange and jasmine complemented by spicy pepper and herb notes lingering at Diageo Chateau & Estate Wines. A subsidiary of powerhouse alcoholic beverage maker Diageo, the company produces and markets the wines of Beaulieu Vineyard, Sterling Vineyards, Chalone Vineyard, Sterling Vintners Collection, Solaris, and Jade Mountain, as well as the French wines of Barton & Guestier and other European producers. The company is a large importer of Bordeaux wines into the US. Its portfolio of wines comes from its vineyards in California and the Bordeaux, Burgundy, and other regions of France.

DIAGEO NORTH AMERICA, INC.

801 Main Ave.
Norwalk, CT 06901
Phone: 203-229-2100
Fax: 203-229-8901
Web: www.diageo.com

CEO: Ivan M. Menezes
CFO: Catherine K. (Cathy) Jessup
HR: Eliana Zem
FYE: June 30
Type: Subsidiary

A subsidiary of Diageo plc, one of the world's largest producers of alcoholic drinks, Diageo North America makes up the largest portion (almost 40%) of its parent company's total sales. North America is also Diageo's largest market by volume. In the US, Diageo asks distributors to dedicate people exclusively to the sale of Diageo brands. Included among the company's brands are many well-known libations, including Baileys Irish Cream, Captain Morgan rum, Crown Royal Canadian whiskey, Cuervo tequila, Gilbey's Gin, Guinness Draught, Harp beer, J&B scotch, Johnnie Walker, Seagram's VO, Smirnoff vodka, Sterling Vineyards wines, and Tanqueray.

THE DIAL CORPORATION

15501 N. Dial Blvd.
Scottsdale, AZ 85260
Phone: 480-754-3425
Fax: –
Web: www.dialcorp.com

CEO: Bradley A. (Brad) Casper
CFO: –
HR: –
FYE: Saturday nearest December 31
Type: Subsidiary

Don't look for dirt on The Dial Corporation — it works hard to keep squeaky clean and as fresh as a daisy. Dial makes one of the top-selling soaps in the US and has leading brands in each of its core product segments — personal care products (Dial, Coast, Soft & Dri, Right Guard, Tone), laundry items (20 Mule Team, Borateem, Fels-Naptha, Purex, Sta-Flo, Trend, Zout), and home care (Combat, Renuzit, SoftScrub). Dial became a subsidiary of Henkel KGaA in 2004. Soon thereafter Brad Casper replaced president and CEO Herb Baum, who retired in April 2005. Dial bought Gillette's Right Guard, Soft & Dri, and Dry Idea brands from Procter & Gamble in 2006.

	Annual Growth	12/03	12/04	12/05	12/06	12/07
Est. sales ($ mil.)	—	—	—	—	—	373.2
Employees	—	—	—	—	—	2,900

THE DIALOG CORPORATION

11000 Regency Pkwy., Ste. 10
Cary, NC 27518
Phone: 919-462-8600
Fax: 919-468-9890
Web: www.dialog.com

CEO: David Brown
CFO: Mike Eastwood
HR: Alton (Al) Zink
FYE: December 31
Type: Subsidiary

The Dialog Corporation believes in open communication. The firm provides digital research services and information through more than 1.4 billion unique records to clients in science, engineering, finance, and law. Dialog's sources include 900 databases of intellectual property, such as scientific and technical research reports, journal articles, and business, news, and industry publications. The company has operations in nearly 30 countries. Dialog is part of Thomson Scientific, itself a unit of financial information giant Thomson Reuters. Thomson Reuters has announced plans to sell Dialog to ProQuest Information and Learning.

	Annual Growth	12/03	12/04	12/05	12/06	12/07
Est. sales ($ mil.)	—	—	—	—	—	42.6
Employees	—	—	—	—	—	600

DIALYSIS CORPORATION OF AMERICA

NASDAQ (GM): DCAI

1302 Concourse Dr., Ste. 204
Linthicum, MD 21090
Phone: 410-694-0500
Fax: 410-694-0596
Web: www.dialysiscorporation.com

CEO: Stephen W. Everett
CFO: Andrew J. Jeanneret
HR: –
FYE: December 31
Type: Public

Dialysis Corporation of America (DCA) operates about 35 outpatient dialysis clinics in more than half a dozen US states, providing life-sustaining services to patients with chronic kidney failure (also known as end-stage renal disease). The company also provides inpatient dialysis through contracts with about a dozen hospitals, all of them in markets where it has has outpatient facilities; and, through its dialysis clinics, DCA provides training and support to patients who use peritoneal dialysis at home. Many of the company's clinics are owned jointly with local nephrologists; others are wholly owned by DCA.

	Annual Growth	12/03	12/04	12/05	12/06	12/07
Sales ($ mil.)	25.2%	30.3	41.0	45.4	62.5	74.5
Net income ($ mil.)	29.6%	1.1	2.2	1.9	3.0	3.1
Market value ($ mil.)	32.3%	26.6	207.3	92.9	121.6	81.4
Employees	(5.1%)	—	—	493	468	—

DIAMOND ENTERTAINMENT CORPORATION

OTC: DMONE

800 Tucker Ln.
Walnut, CA 91789
Phone: 909-839-1989
Fax: 909-869-1990

CEO: Mulugetta Bezzabeh
CFO: Fred U. Odaka
HR: –
FYE: March 31
Type: Public

Diamond Entertainment is eschewing its entertainment business for a career in health care. The company acquired Rx Africa PLC, a company that makes drugs that treat AIDS/HIV, malaria, and other diseases in Ethiopia, in 2007. The company decided to focus its business on pharmaceuticals and has sold off its DVD inventory. Previously, Diamond Entertainment had distributed budget videos and DVDs, including collections starring Abbott and Costello, Ozzie and Harriet, and Martin and Lewis. Its some 1,000 video titles — most in the public domain — included motion pictures, television episodes, sports, Bible stories, cartoons, and educational programs. DMEC also sold children's toys through subsidiary Jewel Products International.

	Annual Growth	3/03	3/04	3/05	3/06	3/07
Sales ($ mil.)	(8.6%)	3.3	5.0	6.9	3.5	2.3
Net income ($ mil.)	—	(0.5)	0.1	0.4	(1.6)	(8.9)
Employees	0.0%	22	36	—	22	—

DIAMOND FOODS, INC.

NASDAQ (GS): DMND

1050 S. Diamond St.
Stockton, CA 95205
Phone: 209-467-6000
Fax: 209-461-7309
Web: www.diamondnuts.com

CEO: Michael J. Mendes
CFO: Steven M. (Steve) Neil
HR: Samuel J. (Sam) Keiper
FYE: July 31
Type: Public

Shy, you ask? Not a bit. Diamond Foods is always coming out of its shell. The company sells a wide array of tree nuts and value-added nut products. Walnuts account for some 60% of its sales but Diamond also offers almonds, Brazil nuts, hazelnuts, pecans, pine nuts, and Spanish peanuts for use in home cooking, snacks, in-shell eating, and as ingredients for other food manufacturers. The company also sells nuts to restaurants and other foodservice outlets. In addition to US markets, Diamond Foods also does business internationally, mainly in Germany, Spain, Italy, and Japan.

	Annual Growth	7/03	7/04	7/05	7/06	7/07
Sales ($ mil.)	14.3%	306.6	366.4	428.3	477.2	522.6
Net income ($ mil.)	(51.7%)	154.7	177.6	182.8	7.3	8.4
Market value ($ mil.)	(13.3%)	—	—	344.6	241.7	259.0
Employees	6.1%	—	—	670	—	754

DIAMOND GLASS COMPANIES

220 Division St.
Kingston, PA 18704
Phone: 570-287-9915
Fax: 570-287-3490
Web: www.diamondtriumphglass.com

CEO: Kenneth (Ken) Levine
CFO: Rich Bunchalk
HR: Alicia Deeds
FYE: December 31
Type: Private

Diamond Glass Companies has scratched its way to the top. The company provides automotive glass replacement in more than 40 states through some 215 company-owned service centers and about 900 mobile installation vehicles. In addition to automotive work, the company handles commercial and residential glass replacement. The services firm changed its name from Diamond Triumph Auto Glass to Diamond Glass to mirror its diversification beyond the automotive glass replacement industry. Diamond Glass Companies now operates under four main brands: Diamond Glass Companies; Triumph Glass; Settles Glass; and Agents Glass. The company, founded in 1923, filed for Chapter 11 bankruptcy protection in April 2008.

	Annual Growth	12/03	12/04	12/05	12/06	12/07
Est. sales ($ mil.)	—	—	—	—	—	208.4
Employees	—	—	—	—	—	1,600

An in-depth profile of this company is available to Hoover's Online members at hoovers.com.

DIAMOND HILL INVESTMENT GROUP, INC.

NASDAQ (GM): DHIL

325 John H. McConnell Blvd., Ste. 200
Columbus, OH 43215
Phone: 614-255-3333
Fax: 614-255-3363
Web: www.diamond-hill.com

CEO: Roderick H. (Ric) Dillon Jr.
CFO: James F. (Jim) Laird Jr.
HR: –
FYE: December 31
Type: Public

Diamond Hill Investment Group takes a shine to investing. Operating through flagship subsidiary Diamond Hill Capital Management, the firm oversees approximately $5 billion in assets, most of it invested in mutual funds. Serving institutional and individual clients, the company administers several mutual funds and sells them mainly through independent investment advisors, broker-dealers, financial planners, investment consultants, and third-party marketing firms. It also manages separate accounts and hedge funds.

	Annual Growth	12/03	12/04	12/05	12/06	12/07
Assets ($ mil.)	100.5%	3.3	4.0	12.8	37.2	53.3
Net income ($ mil.)	—	(1.0)	(0.2)	3.7	8.1	9.9
Market value ($ mil.)	98.4%	10.6	27.0	55.0	153.9	164.0
Employees	41.4%	—	—	21	32	42

DIAMOND MANAGEMENT & TECHNOLOGY

NASDAQ (GM): DTPI

875 N. Michigan Ave., Ste. 3000
Chicago, IL 60611
Phone: 312-255-5000
Fax: 312-255-6000
Web: www.diamondconsultants.com

CEO: Adam J. Gutstein
CFO: Karl E. Bupp
HR: Edmund (Ed) Brady III
FYE: March 31
Type: Public

At Diamond Management & Technology Consultants, Inc., gems come in the form of advice. The firm specializes in providing clients with strategic and operational assistance regarding the use of technology in their businesses. Diamond focuses on helping companies in industries such as financial services, health care, insurance, and telecommunications. The firm also works with clients in the public sector, and its enterprise practice seeks out business from companies in a variety of industries, including manufacturers and retailers of consumer products. Employing more than 500 consultants, Diamond operates from offices in the US, the UK, and India.

	Annual Growth	3/04	3/05	3/06	3/07	3/08
Sales ($ mil.)	3.7%	177.1	219.8	163.7	190.3	205.1
Net income ($ mil.)	—	(5.4)	33.0	(10.6)	31.4	21.1
Market value ($ mil.)	(15.0%)	334.2	554.4	352.9	370.5	174.7
Employees	(9.7%)	—	751	554	613	—

DIAMOND OFFSHORE DRILLING, INC.

NYSE: DO

15415 Katy Fwy., Ste. 100
Houston, TX 77094
Phone: 281-492-5300
Fax: 281-492-5316
Web: www.diamondoffshore.com

CEO: Lawrence R. Dickerson
CFO: Gary T. Krenek
HR: R. Lynn Charles
FYE: December 31
Type: Public

This Diamond is an oiler's best friend. Diamond Offshore Drilling is a contract offshore oil and gas driller capable of descending the deep blue to depths of 7,500 feet. A leading US drilling contractor, Diamond Offshore has 30 semi-submersibles, 13 jack-up rigs (mobile drilling platforms), and one drillship. Operating in waters off six of the world's continents, Diamond Offshore contracts with major oil and gas companies, including Anadarko Petroleum and PETROBRAS. Subsidiary Diamond Offshore Team Solutions provides project management and other drilling-related services. Loews Corp. owns about 51% of the company.

	Annual Growth	12/03	12/04	12/05	12/06	12/07
Sales ($ mil.)	39.4%	680.9	814.7	1,221.0	2,052.6	2,567.7
Net income ($ mil.)	—	(48.4)	(7.2)	260.3	706.8	846.5
Market value ($ mil.)	65.1%	2,652.4	5,149.1	8,968.1	10,329.6	19,719.6
Employees	9.5%	—	—	4,500	4,800	5,400

DIAMOND RESORTS HOLDINGS, LLC

3865 W. Cheyenne Ave.
North Las Vegas, NV 89032
Phone: 702-804-8600
Fax: 702-304-7066
Web: www.diamondresorts.com

CEO: James A. Weissenborn
CFO: Robert Krawczyk
HR: –
FYE: September 30
Type: Private

Diamond Resorts Corporation, formerly Sunterra Corporation, can take you to some of the sunniest places on Earth. The time-share vacation company, which does business as Diamond Resorts International, owns or manages more than 100 resorts in the Caribbean, Europe, and North America. Some 350,000 families vacation at the company's resorts through the purchase of either vacation intervals (generally a one-week stay) or vacation points (redeemable for varying lengths of stay). In 2007 Las Vegas-based Diamond Resorts acquired Sunterra for some $700 million, including $375 million of Sunterra debt, and Sunterra was renamed Diamond Resorts.

DIAMONDROCK HOSPITALITY COMPANY

NYSE: DRH

6903 Rockledge Dr., Ste. 800
Bethesda, MD 20817
Phone: 240-744-1150
Fax: –
Web: www.drhc.com

CEO: William W. McCarten
CFO: Mark W. Brugger
HR: –
FYE: December 31
Type: Public

If diamonds are a girl's best friend, then DiamondRock Hospitality must be an investor's best friend. Operating as an umbrella partnership real estate investment trust (UPREIT), DiamondRock primarily functions through its taxable REIT subsidiary Bloodstone TRS. It owns (but does not operate) about 20 upper upscale full-service hotels with more than 9,500 rooms in North America, with an emphasis on such markets as New York, Los Angeles, Chicago, Boston, and Atlanta. Its hotels are all operated under brands owned by Marriott International, Starwood Hotels & Resorts Worldwide, and Hilton Hotels Corporation.

	Annual Growth	12/03	12/04	12/05	12/06	12/07
Sales ($ mil.)	76.0%	—	—	229.4	491.9	710.9
Net income ($ mil.)	—	—	—	(7.3)	35.2	68.3
Market value ($ mil.)	52.8%	—	—	607.8	1,372.2	1,419.1
Employees	13.4%	—	—	14	—	18

DIAPULSE CORPORATION OF AMERICA

Pink Sheets: DIAC

321 E. Shore Rd.
Great Neck, NY 11023
Phone: 516-466-3030
Fax: 516-829-8069
Web: www.diapulse.com

CEO: David M. Ross
CFO: –
HR: –
FYE: December 31
Type: Public

Energize! Diapulse Corporation of America makes and sells the Diapulse Wound Treatment System, a machine that generates nonthermal electromagnetic energy for the treatment of postoperative pain and edema for soft-tissue wounds such as bed sores, diabetic ulcers, and venous ulcers. Buyers of the Diapulse system include hospitals, assisted-living and long-term care facilities, clinics, physicians, and individual patients who use the equipment at home. Diapulse Corp. both rents and sells its technology, and the equipment is covered by Medicare and many insurance plans. Chairman and president Jesse Ross owns 55% of the company.

	Annual Growth	12/03	12/04	12/05	12/06	12/07
Sales ($ mil.)	(9.6%)	1.2	1.1	1.0	0.9	0.8
Net income ($ mil.)	—	(0.3)	(0.1)	(0.4)	(0.4)	(0.1)
Employees	—	—	—	—	—	—

DIASYS CORPORATION

Pink Sheets: DYXC

81 W. Main St.
Waterbury, CT 06702
Phone: 203-755-5083
Fax: 203-755-5105
Web: www.diasys.com

CEO: Frederic H. Neikrug
CFO: Morris Silverman
HR: –
FYE: June 30
Type: Public

For those who would rather not handle the test results, DiaSys makes workstations to facilitate urine and fecal analysis for detection of parasites, cysts, and other items. The company's R/S series workstations can be loaded with multiple urine samples, which are transferred to microscopes for examination and then purged. The FE series workstations operate similarly for fecal examination. DiaSys also sells diagnostic products and kits that are used in conjunction with the workstations. The company markets its products worldwide both directly and through distribution agreements with Cardinal HealthCare and Thermo Fisher Scientific. Chairman and CFO Morris Silverman owns 31% of the company.

	Annual Growth	6/03	6/04	6/05	6/06	6/07
Sales ($ mil.)	(10.9%)	2.7	1.9	1.9	1.7	1.7
Net income ($ mil.)	—	(1.6)	(3.0)	(2.0)	(1.0)	(0.8)
Employees	—	—	—	15	—	—

DICE HOLDINGS, INC.

NYSE: DHX

3 Park Ave.
New York, NY 10016
Phone: 212-725-6550
Fax: 212-725-6559
Web: www.diceholdingsinc.com

CEO: Scot W. Melland
CFO: Michael P. Durney
HR: –
FYE: December 31
Type: Public

Dice Holdings rolls along with Web sites devoted to employee recruiting and career development. Through its flagship, Dice.com, the company provides job postings and career-related resources for technology professionals in the US. The company also operates ClearanceJobs.com, for people with US government security clearances; eFinancialCareers.com, aimed at the worldwide financial services industry; and JobsintheMoney.com, for accounting and finance professionals in the US. It also puts on job fairs. Most of the company's revenue comes from employers, who pay to post job listings and view resumes. Investment firms General Atlantic and Quadrangle Group together own a controlling stake in Dice Holdings.

	Annual Growth	12/03	12/04	12/05	12/06	12/07
Sales ($ mil.)	182.8%	—	—	17.8	83.7	142.4
Net income ($ mil.)	—	—	—	(1.7)	6.8	15.5
Market value ($ mil.)	—	—	—	—	—	496.8
Employees	—	—	—	202	—	—

DICK'S SPORTING GOODS, INC.

NYSE: DKS

300 Industry Dr., RIDC Park West
Pittsburgh, PA 15275
Phone: 724-273-3400
Fax: 724-227-1904
Web: www.dickssportinggoods.com

CEO: Edward W. (Ed) Stack
CFO: Timothy E. (Tim) Kullman
HR: Kathy Sutter
FYE: Saturday nearest January 31
Type: Public

See Dick's shoppers run, putt, dunk, dribble — and buy. Fast-growing Dick's Sporting Goods operates about 340 stores in more than 35 states. The stores contain on average five smaller shops ("Store-Within-A-Store") featuring sporting goods, apparel, and footwear for leisure pursuits ranging from football, golf, and cycling to hunting and camping. Dick's also sells online. Besides brands such as NIKE and adidas, Dick's carries Ativa, Walter Hagen, and others exclusive to the firm. Dick Stack opened his first store in 1948. The chain is now headed by son Ed, who owns about 25% of the company and controls the voting shares. Dick's bought rival Galyan's in 2004, and Golf Galaxy and Chick's in 2007.

	Annual Growth	1/04	1/05	1/06	1/07	1/08
Sales ($ mil.)	27.5%	1,470.8	2,109.4	2,625.0	3,114.2	3,888.4
Net income ($ mil.)	31.1%	52.4	68.9	73.0	112.6	155.0
Market value ($ mil.)	61.5%	411.1	589.7	671.5	1,048.4	2,793.7
Employees	20.8%	—	—	18,100	19,920	26,400

DIEBOLD, INCORPORATED

NYSE: DBD

5995 Mayfair Rd.
North Canton, OH 44720
Phone: 330-490-4000
Fax: 330-490-3794
Web: www.diebold.com

CEO: Thomas W. Swidarski
CFO: Kevin J. Krakora
HR: Sheila M. Rutt
FYE: December 31
Type: Public

Cash is king at Diebold. The company is one of the leading producers of automated teller machines (ATMs). In addition, Diebold offers automated or staffed banking facilities, such as its MicroBranch prefabricated branch offices, which can be installed in grocery stores and malls. Originally a manufacturer of safes, the company is still active in its original market, offering products including vaults and security systems for financial institutions. Diebold also provides electronic voting machines and services ranging from product maintenance to installation consulting and plan design. United Technologies made an unsolicited offer to acquire Diebold for $2.6 billion in cash in 2008.

	Annual Growth	12/02	12/03	12/04	12/05	*12/06
Sales ($ mil.)	10.6%	1,940.2	2,109.7	2,380.9	2,587.1	2,906.2
Net income ($ mil.)	(3.3%)	99.2	174.8	183.8	96.8	86.6
Market value ($ mil.)	0.7%	2,972.4	3,913.6	3,996.0	2,611.4	3,056.8
Employees	4.3%	13,072	—	—	14,603	15,451

*Most recent year available

DIEDRICH COFFEE, INC.

NASDAQ (GM): DDRX

28 Executive Pk., Ste. 200
Irvine, CA 92614
Phone: 949-260-1600
Fax: 949-260-1610
Web: www.diedrich.com

CEO: J. Russell (Russ) Phillips
CFO: Sean M. McCarthy
HR: –
FYE: Wednesday nearest June 30
Type: Public

Diedrich Coffee has coffee lovers buzzing with satisfaction. The company operates a chain of coffeehouses with about 150 locations in more than 30 states operating under the Gloria Jean's, Coffee People, and Diedrich Coffee banners. The outlets offer fresh-brewed coffee, baked goods, and other beverage items, as well as fresh roasted coffee and other coffee-related products. The company also supplies wholesale coffee to restaurants (such as Ruth's Hospitality Group's Ruth's Chris steakhouse chain), office coffee suppliers, and other hospitality and specialty retail customers. Chairman Paul Heeschen controls nearly 50% of Diedrich Coffee.

	Annual Growth	6/03	6/04	6/05	6/06	6/07
Sales ($ mil.)	(9.6%)	54.8	54.6	52.5	59.5	36.6
Net income ($ mil.)	—	(1.2)	0.3	14.6	(7.8)	(1.8)
Market value ($ mil.)	9.9%	16.5	28.4	24.8	16.5	24.0
Employees	(47.7%)	—	—	815	—	223

DIERBERGS MARKETS INC.

16690 Swingley Ridge Rd.
Chesterfield, MO 63017
Phone: 636-532-8884
Fax: 636-812-1603
Web: www.dierbergs.com

CEO: Gregory (Greg) Dierberg
CFO: Connie Hawley
HR: Linda Ryan
FYE: December 31
Type: Private

Dierbergs Markets has a taste of what folks in St. Louis like to eat. Dierbergs operates about two dozen upscale supermarkets in the St. Louis area, where rival Schnuck Markets is the market leader. Dierbergs' stores offer food, drugs, photo processing, and video centers, as well as cooking schools, banks, self-service checkout, Krispy Kreme donuts, and made-to-order Chinese food at some locations. Dierbergs Florist and Gifts, affiliated with FTD, offers gift baskets and floral services at its stores and over the Internet for local and international delivery. Founded as a trading outpost in 1854, Dierbergs has been owned and operated by the Dierberg family since 1914.

	Annual Growth	12/03	12/04	12/05	12/06	12/07
Est. sales ($ mil.)	—	—	—	—	—	447.4
Employees	—	—	—	—	—	4,126

An in-depth profile of this company is available to Hoover's Online members at hoovers.com.

497

DIETRICH INDUSTRIES, INC.

500 Grant St., Ste. 2226
Pittsburgh, PA 15219
Phone: 412-281-2805
Fax: 412-281-2965
Web: www.dietrichmetalframing.com

CEO: George P. Stoe
CFO: Sam Depasquale
HR: Nancy Albert
FYE: May 31
Type: Subsidiary

If the Three Pigs knew what they were doing, they'd have evaded the Big Bad Wolf in a building built by Dietrich Industries (dba Dietrich Metal Framing). The subsidiary of Worthington Industries makes metal framing products, systems, and services from its 38 US locations. Its steel products are used in all phases of building construction, from exterior framing to interior, floor, and truss framing. Dietrich Metal Framing also makes connectors, clips, and framing hardware as well as finishing products such as beads and trims. The company was founded in 1959 and made a part of the Worthington family in 1996.

DIGI INTERNATIONAL INC.

NASDAQ (GS): DGII

11001 Bren Rd. East
Minnetonka, MN 55343
Phone: 952-912-3444
Fax: 952-912-4952
Web: www.digi.com

CEO: Joseph T. (Joe) Dunsmore
CFO: Subramanian (Kris) Krishnan
HR: Tracy Roberts
FYE: September 30
Type: Public

Digi serves up peripherals on a serial platter. Digi International makes serial cards and ports for connecting peripherals to networks. It also sells networking devices that utilize the popular USB (Universal Serial Bus) interface. The company's products are used in point-of-sales (POS) systems, as well as industrial automation, medical, hospitality, and building automation applications. Digi manufactures microprocessors and software used to connect electronic devices to networks. The company sells directly and through resellers and distributors such as Tech Data.

	Annual Growth	9/03	9/04	9/05	9/06	9/07
Sales ($ mil.)	13.9%	102.9	111.2	125.2	144.7	173.3
Net income ($ mil.)	—	(37.3)	8.7	17.7	11.1	19.8
Market value ($ mil.)	28.4%	134.0	249.3	245.1	374.6	363.8
Employees	8.3%	—	—	481	549	564

DIGI-KEY CORPORATION

701 Brooks Ave. South
Thief River Falls, MN 56701
Phone: 218-681-6674
Fax: 218-681-3380
Web: www.digikey.com

CEO: Ronald Stordahl
CFO: Marie Finney
HR: Rick Trontvet
FYE: December 31
Type: Private

Digi-Key holds more than one key to electronics distribution. The company distributes electronic components to businesses and consumers mainly in the US, Canada, Europe, and Japan. Digi-Key uses an entirely in-house sales force and does business by means of telemarketing and a catalog featuring more than 1 million products from 350-plus manufacturers, such as 3M, Freescale, and Texas Instruments. Its products, ranging from AC line cords to zinc-oxide non-linear resistors, also are available through a downloadable catalog featured on the company's Web site. Founded in 1971 by CEO and owner Ronald Stordahl, Digi-Key takes its name from the ham radio digital electronic keyer kit Stordahl developed and sold in college.

	Annual Growth	12/03	12/04	12/05	12/06	12/07
Est. sales ($ mil.)	—	—	—	—	—	229.8
Employees	—	—	—	—	—	1,150

DIGIMARC CORPORATION

NASDAQ (GM): DMRC

9405 SW Gemini Dr.
Beaverton, OR 97008
Phone: 503-469-4800
Fax: 503-469-4777
Web: www.digimarc.com

CEO: Bruce Davis
CFO: Michael E. McConnell
HR: –
FYE: December 31
Type: Public

Digimarc is making its mark. The company provides digital watermarking software that embeds code in printed and digital content, including photographs, music, movies, financial instruments, and identification documents. Customers use Digimarc's software to control copyrights, license online content, and manage digital assets. Digimarc's products are used to create identification cards such as driver's licenses and office security badges. The bulk of the company's sales come from government contracts for the supply of secure identification systems.

	Annual Growth	12/03	12/04	12/05	12/06	12/07
Sales ($ mil.)	6.4%	85.6	92.9	101.1	104.3	109.8
Net income ($ mil.)	—	1.5	(9.0)	(23.1)	(11.7)	(0.4)
Market value ($ mil.)	(7.9%)	267.7	193.1	122.8	186.3	192.6
Employees	—	—	—	449	—	—

DIGIRAD CORPORATION

NASDAQ (GM): DRAD

13950 Stowe Dr.
Poway, CA 92064
Phone: 858-726-1600
Fax: 858-726-1700
Web: www.digirad.com

CEO: Mark L. Casner
CFO: Todd P. Clyde
HR: Marc E. Shapiro
FYE: December 31
Type: Public

Digirad gives cardiologists the nuclear option. The firm makes and sells nuclear imaging equipment, including the Cardius XPO series of gamma cameras, used to detect heart disease. It also makes a general imaging machine, the 2020tc imager, which measures such physiological activity as blood flow, metabolism, and heart function. The company sells its products to doctors' offices, as well as hospitals and imaging centers, through a direct sales force and distributors. However, its primary source of revenue is its Digirad Imaging Solutions (DIS) unit, which runs a mobile imaging service that provides access to the company's imaging equipment through lease agreements.

	Annual Growth	12/03	12/04	12/05	12/06	12/07
Sales ($ mil.)	7.1%	56.2	68.1	68.2	71.9	73.9
Net income ($ mil.)	—	(1.7)	0.2	(9.6)	(6.3)	(1.4)
Market value ($ mil.)	(24.5%)	—	160.0	75.2	77.4	68.9
Employees	—	—	—	601	—	—

DIGITAL FEDERAL CREDIT UNION

220 Donald Lynch Blvd.
Marlborough, MA 01752
Phone: 508-263-6700
Fax: 508-263-6430
Web: www.dcu.org

CEO: Carlo Cestra
CFO: James Regan
HR: Donna Russo
FYE: December 31
Type: Not-for-profit

Walk-ins *and* log-ons accepted. Digital Federal Credit Union (DCU) has about 15 branch locations in Massachusetts and New Hampshire plus single branches in Colorado and Georgia. Not confined to just brick-and-mortar branches, the credit union also serves its customers via telephone and the Internet. The member-owned cooperative offers a range of commercial and retail deposit and lending products, including savings, checking, money market, and IRA accounts; CDs; auto, mortgage, and home equity loans; and insurance and investment products. DCU was founded in 1979 and serves about 300,000 members nationwide.

	Annual Growth	12/03	12/04	12/05	12/06	12/07
Est. sales ($ mil.)	—	—	—	—	—	182.7
Employees	—	—	—	—	—	650

DIGITAL INSIGHT CORPORATION

26025 Mureau Rd.
Calabasas, CA 91302
Phone: 818-871-0000
Fax: 818-878-7555
Web: www.digitalinsight.com

CEO: Sasan Goodarzi
CFO: –
HR: –
FYE: December 31
Type: Subsidiary

Digital Insight helps small to midsized banks avoid holdups of all sorts — online as well as offline. The company's software enables bank and credit union customers to make balance inquiries, view transaction histories, transfer funds, and pay bills over the Internet. Other software offerings include AnyTimeLender, which enables Internet-based loan services, and e-commerce software which enables banks to create Internet portals. Digital Insight also offers Web site creation, hosting, and maintenance services. In 2007 the company was acquired by Intuit for $1.35 billion.

DIGITAL LIGHTWAVE, INC.

OTC: DIGL

5775 Rio Vista Dr.
Clearwater, FL 33760
Phone: 727-442-6677
Fax: 727-442-5660
Web: www.lightwave.com

CEO: Kenneth T. (Ted) Myers
CFO: Kenneth T. (Ted) Myers
HR: –
FYE: December 31
Type: Public

Digital Lightwave puts optical test drivers on the right track. The company makes equipment for monitoring, maintaining, and managing fiber-optic networks. Digital Lightwave's Network Information Computers are portable touch-screen devices used to test networks and transmission equipment during installation and use. Its Network Access Agents are unattended software-controlled devices installed in optical networks to monitor and test network performance remotely from a central location. Founder and chairman Bryan Zwan owns about 91% of Digital Lightwave. The company owes nearly $36 million to Optel Capital, which is controlled by Zwan. About two-thirds of Digital Lightwave's sales are in the US.

	Annual Growth	12/03	12/04	12/05	12/06	12/07
Sales ($ mil.)	12.7%	7.5	13.7	12.9	10.5	12.1
Net income ($ mil.)	—	(32.4)	(12.9)	(21.1)	(14.5)	(2.5)
Market value ($ mil.)	1.2%	25.6	45.1	7.4	5.4	26.8
Employees	(13.9%)	69	96	79	35	38

DIGITAL POWER CORPORATION

AMEX: DPW

41324 Christy St.
Fremont, CA 94538
Phone: 510-657-2635
Fax: 510-353-4023
Web: www.digipwr.com

CEO: Ben-Zion (Benzi) Diamant
CFO: Uri Friedlander
HR: –
FYE: December 31
Type: Public

Digital Power is a real switch hitter. The company makes power supplies, such as AC/DC switchers and DC/DC converters, for computer and electronics OEMs. Its products protect electronic components and circuits from power surges while converting a single input voltage into different output voltages. Most of Digital Power's products, which can be easily modified to meet the specific needs of its 400 customers, are made by subcontractors in China and Mexico. UK-based subsidiary Digital Power Limited, doing business as Gresham Power Electronics, makes AC/DC power supplies, uninterruptible power supplies, and power inverters; it accounts for more than half of sales.

	Annual Growth	12/03	12/04	12/05	12/06	12/07
Sales ($ mil.)	13.3%	7.4	8.7	10.9	12.6	12.2
Net income ($ mil.)	—	(1.0)	(1.2)	0.0	0.1	0.1
Market value ($ mil.)	18.8%	4.5	7.7	5.4	8.4	9.1
Employees	(5.3%)	41	37	32	33	33

DIGITAL REALTY TRUST, INC.

NYSE: DLR

560 Mission St., Ste. 2900
San Francisco, CA 94105
Phone: 415-738-6500
Fax: 415-738-6501
Web: www.digitalrealtytrust.com

CEO: Michael F. Foust
CFO: A. William Stein
HR: –
FYE: December 31
Type: Public

Digital Realty Trust puts its chips in the technology real estate sector. The real estate investment trust (REIT) owns data centers, Internet and data communications hubs, and technology office and manufacturing properties. Its portfolio consists of more than 50 properties in the US and about a dozen more in Europe; combined, the properties contain more than 12 million sq. ft. of rentable space. Chairman Robert Magnuson owns more than 40% of Digital Realty Trust through Global Innovation Partners, of which he is CEO. Digital Realty Trust acquired its first 20 properties from Global Innovation Partners in conjunction with its 2004 IPO.

	Annual Growth	12/03	12/04	12/05	12/06	12/07
Sales ($ mil.)	58.2%	63.1	107.1	208.8	281.9	395.3
Net income ($ mil.)	25.1%	16.6	4.6	16.1	31.4	40.6
Market value ($ mil.)	105.7%	—	288.5	619.2	1,857.2	2,509.6
Employees	66.3%	20	—	53	—	153

DIGITAL RIVER, INC.

NASDAQ (GS): DRIV

9625 W. 76th St., Ste. 150
Eden Prairie, MN 55344
Phone: 952-253-1234
Fax: 952-253-8497
Web: www.digitalriver.com

CEO: Joel A. Ronning
CFO: Thomas M. (Tom) Donnelly
HR: –
FYE: December 31
Type: Public

Digital River helps keep the e-commerce flowing. The company provides technology and services that enable its clients to sell their products on the Web without building an e-commerce platform from the ground up. Using its own proprietary server technology, Digital River offers Web development and hosting, transaction processing, fulfillment, and fraud screening services to more than 40,000 customers operating online retail and distribution businesses. It also provides its customers with Web traffic data that allows them to better market their online presence. Security software client Symantec accounted for 26% of total sales in 2007. Digital River has been growing through a steady stream of acquisitions.

	Annual Growth	12/03	12/04	12/05	12/06	12/07
Sales ($ mil.)	36.3%	101.2	154.1	220.4	307.6	349.3
Net income ($ mil.)	42.6%	17.1	35.3	54.3	60.8	70.8
Market value ($ mil.)	17.8%	696.1	1,400.3	1,041.9	2,257.2	1,341.0
Employees	15.5%	—	—	948	1,086	1,265

DIGITAS INC.

33 Arch St.
Boston, MA 02110
Phone: 617-369-8000
Fax: 617-369-8111
Web: www.digitasinc.com

CEO: David W. Kenny
CFO: Joe Tomasulo
HR: Joel Idelson
FYE: December 31
Type: Subsidiary

This company knows the important bits (and bytes) about interactive marketing. Digitas provides digital communications and direct marketing services through several operating agencies: Digitas Health, iBase, Prodigious Worldwide, Webformance, and Publicis Modem (formerly Modem Media). The agency offers Web site design, e-mail management, and demand generation services that enable clients to build marketing campaigns across a plethora of media channels. It has worked for such big clients as American Express, Bristol-Myers Squibb, General Motors, Procter & Gamble, and Whirlpool. In early 2007, Digitas was acquired by French advertising conglomerate Publicis for $1.3 billion.

An in-depth profile of this company is available to Hoover's Online members at hoovers.com.

499

DILLARD'S, INC.

NYSE: DDS

1600 Cantrell Rd.
Little Rock, AR 72201
Phone: 501-376-5200
Fax: 501-399-7831
Web: www.dillards.com

CEO: William (Bill) Dillard II
CFO: James I. Freeman
HR: Molly Myers
FYE: Saturday nearest January 31
Type: Public

Tradition is trying to catch up with the times at Dillard's. Sandwiched between retail giant Macy's and discount chains, such as Kohl's, Dillard's is being forced to rethink its strategy. The department store chain operates about 325 locations in some 30 states, covering the Sunbelt and the central US. Its stores cater to middle- and upper-middle-income women, selling name-brand and private-label merchandise with a focus on apparel and home furnishings. Women's apparel and accessories account for more than a third of sales. Founded in 1938 by William Dillard, today family members, through the W. D. Company, control nearly all of the company's voting shares.

	Annual Growth	1/04	1/05	1/06	1/07	1/08
Sales ($ mil.)	(1.6%)	7,863.7	7,816.3	7,708.0	7,810.1	7,370.8
Net income ($ mil.)	55.1%	9.3	117.7	121.5	245.6	53.8
Market value ($ mil.)	2.1%	1,348.0	2,051.9	1,939.3	2,663.0	1,463.0
Employees	(2.1%)	—	—	52,056	51,385	49,938

DIME COMMUNITY BANCSHARES, INC.

NASDAQ (GS): DCOM

209 Havemeyer St.
Brooklyn, NY 11211
Phone: 718-782-6200
Fax: 718-486-7535
Web: www.dsbwdirect.com

CEO: Vincent F. Palagiano
CFO: Kenneth J. Mahon
HR: Nancy Bacione
FYE: December 31
Type: Public

Hey brother, Dime Community Bancshares could spare some change, if you qualify. It is the holding company for The Dime Savings Bank of Williamsburgh, which operates about two dozen branches in Brooklyn, Queens, the Bronx, and in Nassau County, New York. Founded in 1864 as a state-chartered mutual savings bank, it offers standard deposit products and services, including checking, savings, and money market accounts. Multifamily residential mortgages account for some two-thirds of the company's loan portfolio, which also includes single- to four-family residential loans and commercial mortgages. Bank subsidiaries include brokerage Havemeyer Investments and two real estate investment trusts (REITs).

	Annual Growth	12/03	12/04	12/05	12/06	12/07
Assets ($ mil.)	4.2%	2,971.7	3,377.3	3,126.2	3,173.4	3,501.2
Net income ($ mil.)	(18.7%)	51.3	46.2	36.2	30.6	22.4
Market value ($ mil.)	(4.5%)	521.1	665.6	539.9	510.8	433.0
Employees	—	—	—	—	397	—

DIMENSIONAL FUND ADVISORS, INC.

1299 Ocean Ave.
Santa Monica, CA 90401
Phone: 310-395-8005
Fax: 310-395-6140
Web: www.dfaus.com

CEO: David G. Booth
CFO: David Martin
HR: –
FYE: December 31
Type: Private

The added dimension that Dimensional Fund Advisors applies to asset management is that of academia. The fund manager bases its investing strategies on economic theory and research generated within the hallowed halls of such institutions as the University of Chicago, Dartmouth College, Harvard University, Yale University, and the University of Pennsylvania's Wharton School. Founded by chairman David Booth in 1981, Dimensional (also known as DFA) offers securities trading and investment management to institutional investors and financial advisors from offices around the world. Booth and co-founder Rex Sinquefield own about half of DFA, which has some $150 billion under management.

	Annual Growth	12/03	12/04	12/05	12/06	12/07
Est. sales ($ mil.)	—	—	—	—	—	263.0
Employees	—	—	—	—	—	255

DINEEQUITY, INC.

NYSE: DIN

450 N. Brand Blvd.
Glendale, CA 91203
Phone: 818-240-6055
Fax: 818-637-3131
Web: dineequity.com

CEO: Julia A. Stewart
CFO: Thomas G. (Tom) Conforti
HR: John Jakubek
FYE: December 31
Type: Public

This company shows an equal bias for breakfast, lunch, and dinner. Formerly IHOP Corp., DineEquity is one of the leading chain restaurant companies in the US, with its two flagship concepts, the International House of Pancakes (IHOP) and Applebee's Neighborhood Grill & Bar. The #3 family-style diner chain behind Denny's and Waffle House, IHOP has more than 1,300 mostly franchised restaurants that are open 24 hours a day. The chain is best known for its breakfast menu, but it also offers standard family fare (sandwiches, burgers, salads) for lunch and dinner. Applebee's is the #1 casual dining chain with more than 1,970 locations in about 20 countries offering a wide variety of appetizers and entrees.

	Annual Growth	12/03	12/04	12/05	12/06	12/07
Sales ($ mil.)	4.6%	404.8	359.0	348.0	349.6	484.6
Net income ($ mil.)	—	36.8	33.4	43.9	44.5	(0.5)
Employees	500.1%	—	—	897	—	32,300

DINEWISE, INC.

OTC: DWIS

500 Bi-County Blvd., Ste. 400
Farmingdale, NY 11735
Phone: 631-694-1111
Fax: 631-694-4064
Web: www.dinewise.com

CEO: Paul Roman
CFO: Thomas McNeill
HR: –
FYE: December 31
Type: Public

For Americans who would rather dial than dice, DineWise delivers meals directly to the door in 48 states. The direct marketer serves up flash-frozen, chef-prepared meals for time-pressed chefs to microwave at home. DineWise also offers diet meals, as well as meals tailored to fit special diets, including diabetic and low-sodium regimens. Complete meals include entrees, sides, and vegetables. Customers can order by phone, catalog, or by using the company's Web site. Founded in 1959 as Colorado Prime Foods, in 2006 the company changed its name to DineWise and went public. Colorado Prime, best know for its beef, remains a core part of the business.

	Annual Growth	12/03	12/04	12/05	12/06	12/07
Sales ($ mil.)	(2.8%)	—	—	—	10.9	10.6
Net income ($ mil.)	—	—	—	—	(3.5)	(1.1)
Market value ($ mil.)	(91.7%)	—	—	—	22.5	1.9
Employees	—	—	—	—	26	—

DIODES INCORPORATED

NASDAQ (GS): DIOD

15660 Dallas Pkwy., Ste. 850
Dallas, TX 75248
Phone: 972-385-2810
Fax: –
Web: www.diodes.com

CEO: Keh-Shew Lu
CFO: Carl C. Wertz
HR: Edmund (Ed) Tang
FYE: December 31
Type: Public

Diodes Incorporated knows how important it is to be discrete in business. The company manufactures discrete semiconductors — fixed-function devices that are much less complex than integrated circuits. Diodes' products are used by makers of automotive, computing, consumer electronics, and telecommunications gear. The company makes hundreds of products (including diodes, transistors, and rectifiers) that vary in voltage, current, and switching speeds. Customers include Delphi, Intel, Nortel Networks, and Samsung Electronics. Lite-On Semiconductor, a company that is part of Taiwan's Lite-On Technology, owns about 22% of Diodes. Lite-On Semiconductor is also Diodes' biggest customer and its biggest supplier.

	Annual Growth	12/03	12/04	12/05	12/06	12/07
Sales ($ mil.)	30.8%	136.9	185.7	214.8	343.3	401.2
Net income ($ mil.)	55.9%	10.1	25.5	33.3	48.1	59.7
Market value ($ mil.)	83.3%	109.9	143.4	522.8	614.1	1,240.1
Employees	24.5%	1,087	1,370	1,621	2,268	2,612

DIONEX CORPORATION

NASDAQ (GS): DNEX

1228 Titan Way
Sunnyvale, CA 94085
Phone: 408-737-0700
Fax: 408-730-9403
Web: www.dionex.com

CEO: Lukas Braunschweiler
CFO: Craig A. McCollam
HR: –
FYE: June 30
Type: Public

Dionex's instruments keep the contaminants away while scientists play. The company makes instruments and related accessories that are used for substance analysis, including identifying contaminants in everything from drinking water to industrial chemicals. Dionex leads the market for ion chromatography instruments, devices used by chemists to isolate and quantify charged molecules in complex chemical mixtures. It also specializes in high-performance liquid chromatography (used to separate and identify biological molecules such as amino acids, carbohydrates, and proteins), sample extraction, and sample handling automation equipment. About three-quarters of the company's sales come from outside of the US.

	Annual Growth	6/03	6/04	6/05	6/06	6/07
Sales ($ mil.)	11.1%	214.9	258.8	279.3	291.3	327.3
Net income ($ mil.)	9.6%	31.4	41.4	45.5	35.7	45.3
Market value ($ mil.)	12.6%	831.9	1,149.8	879.0	1,072.7	1,337.9
Employees	—	—	—	1,064	—	—

DIPPIN' DOTS, INCORPORATED

5101 Charter Oak Dr.
Paducah, KY 42001
Phone: 270-443-8994
Fax: 270-443-8997
Web: www.dippindots.com

CEO: Tom Leonard
CFO: Connie Ulrich
HR: Janice Johnson
FYE: December 31
Type: Private

Dippin' Dots is the product of a scientist with a sweet tooth. Experimenting with cryogenics in 1988, microbiologist Curt Jones used liquid nitrogen to flash-freeze ice cream into tiny beads and named his creations Dippin' Dots. Today nearly 300 US franchised vendors sell Dippin' Dots ice cream, frozen yogurt, and ice throughout the US. Recognizing that its product is partly entertainment, the company doesn't sell Dippin' Dots (which come in about 20 flavors) in grocery stores, but does sell them in amusement parks, malls, movie theaters, restaurants, and sports arenas across the US and overseas.

	Annual Growth	12/03	12/04	12/05	12/06	12/07
Est. sales ($ mil.)	—	—	—	—	—	46.4
Employees	—	—	—	—	—	200

DIRECT GENERAL CORPORATION

1281 Murfreesboro Rd.
Nashville, TN 37217
Phone: 615-399-0600
Fax: 800-541-0856
Web: www.direct-general.com

CEO: Daniel Tarantin
CFO: J. Todd Hagely
HR: –
FYE: December 31
Type: Subsidiary

It's an Adair family affair. Founded in 1991, Direct General offers nonstandard personal automobile coverage, life insurance, and hospital indemnity insurance. The company also operates a premium financing subsidiary (where the insurer makes a loan that is backed by the unearned portion of the insurance premiums being financed). Direct General sells its products through more than 500 neighborhood sales offices, primarily in the southeastern part of the US. The company was acquired by private investment partnerships Calera Capital and TPG Capital in 2007.

	Annual Growth	12/02	12/03	12/04	12/05	12/06
Assets ($ mil.)	10.6%	569.1	751.2	787.5	841.0	851.0
Net income ($ mil.)	(2.5%)	31.0	43.1	54.0	39.0	28.0
Employees	17.0%	1,530	2,000	2,265	2,453	—

DIRECT INSITE CORP.

OTC: DIRI

80 Orville Dr.
Bohemia, NY 11716
Phone: 631-873-2900
Fax: 631-563-8085
Web: www.directinsite.com

CEO: James A. Cannavino
CFO: Michael J. Beecher
HR: Dawn Valenti
FYE: December 31
Type: Public

Direct Insite helps give its customers insight into their customers. The company's hosted software and services provide data mining and analysis, reporting, electronic invoice management, and electronic bill presentment and payment functions. Its products are used to manage such functions as customer service workflows, order processing, dispute resolution, and accounts payable and receivable. Direct Insite serves clients in more than 60 countries. IBM is responsible for about 70% of the company's sales.

	Annual Growth	12/03	12/04	12/05	12/06	12/07
Sales ($ mil.)	8.1%	7.4	7.6	8.9	8.9	10.1
Net income ($ mil.)	—	(5.2)	(1.3)	(1.0)	0.3	2.1
Market value ($ mil.)	38.5%	4.0	7.7	3.1	4.3	14.9
Employees	—	—	—	—	—	—

DIRECTED ELECTRONICS, INC.

NASDAQ (GM): DEIX

1 Viper Way
Vista, CA 92081
Phone: 760-598-6200
Fax: 760-598-6400
Web: www.directed.com

CEO: James E. (Jim) Minarik
CFO: Kevin P. Duffy
HR: Alan P. Heim
FYE: December 31
Type: Public

Please step away from the vehicle. Directed Electronics, one of the world's top manufacturers of auto security systems, delivers products with a bite — or sting — intended to keep would-be car thieves at arm's length. Brand names include Viper, Python, and Hornet. Directed Electronics also makes keyless entry and remote start systems for automobiles and offers GPS tracking systems. In addition, the company manufactures car audio equipment, including speakers and amplifiers. Directed Electronics sells its products in more than 70 countries. Miami-based investment firm Trivest Partners (and affiliates of Trivest) control a nearly 40% stake in Directed Electronics.

	Annual Growth	12/03	12/04	12/05	12/06	12/07
Sales ($ mil.)	32.1%	131.8	189.9	304.6	437.8	401.1
Net income ($ mil.)	—	12.5	14.0	(5.1)	21.0	(140.0)
Market value ($ mil.)	(65.6%)	—	—	356.4	288.1	42.2
Employees	47.7%	—	235	236	513	—

THE DIRECTV GROUP, INC.

NASDAQ (GS): DTV

2230 E. Imperial Hwy.
El Segundo, CA 90245
Phone: 310-964-5000
Fax: 310-535-5225
Web: www.directv.com

CEO: Chase Carey
CFO: Patrick T. Doyle
HR: –
FYE: December 31
Type: Public

DIRECTV takes television straight to the masses. The DIRECTV Group operates DIRECTV, the largest US direct broadcast satellite (DBS) provider, ahead of #2 EchoStar Communications' DISH Network. The DIRECTV Group provides service to nearly 17 million customers in the US and about 4.8 million customers through its DIRECTV Latin America segment. Additionally, regional US local phone companies Verizon and BellSouth bundle DIRECTV video services along with their voice and Internet communications packages. The company offers high-definition channels in its largest US markets and is rolling out video-on-demand (VOD) services for customers. Liberty Media owns 41% of DIRECTV.

	Annual Growth	12/03	12/04	12/05	12/06	12/07
Sales ($ mil.)	14.3%	10,121.2	11,360.0	13,164.5	14,755.5	17,246.0
Net income ($ mil.)	—	(361.8)	(1,949.2)	335.9	1,420.1	1,451.0
Market value ($ mil.)	3.8%	22,899.4	23,198.5	19,641.4	30,588.7	26,548.0
Employees	15.6%	—	—	9,200	11,200	12,300

An in-depth profile of this company is available to Hoover's Online members at hoovers.com.

501

DISCOUNT DRUG MART INC.

211 Commerce Dr.
Medina, OH 44256
Phone: 330-725-2340
Fax: 330-722-2990
Web: www.discount-drugmart.com

CEO: Parviz Boodjeh
CFO: Thomas J. (John) McConnell
HR: Michael Eby
FYE: March 31
Type: Private

Drugs are merely part of the story at Discount Drug. One of the largest drugstore chains in northeastern Ohio, the company offers pharmacy services, nonprescription medications, and medical supplies, as well as food, housewares, beauty products, video rentals, photo developing, stamps, pet supplies, hardware, and more. Its more than 65 stores are 25,000 sq. ft. on average, about twice the size of rival drugstores. Discount Drug also runs mail-order and online prescription services through subsidiary Immediate Pharmaceutical Services. The company is expanding into central Ohio. Chairman and CEO Parviz Boodjeh owns Discount Drug, which was founded in 1969.

	Annual Growth	3/03	3/04	3/05	3/06	3/07
Est. sales ($ mil.)	—	—	—	—	—	292.7
Employees	—	—	—	—	—	2,700

DISCOUNT TIRE CO. INC.

20225 N. Scottsdale Rd.
Scottsdale, AZ 85255
Phone: 480-606-6000
Fax: 480-951-8619
Web: www.discounttire.com

CEO: Tom Englert
CFO: Christian Roe
HR: –
FYE: December 31
Type: Private

Concerned about that upcoming "re-tire-ment"? Discount Tire Co., one of the largest independent tire dealers in the US, can provide several options. With about 680 stores in nearly 20 states, the company sells such leading brands as Michelin, Goodyear, and Uniroyal, as well as wheels (Enkei, Konig, Weld Racing). Discount Tire operates mostly in the West, Midwest, and Southwest. Some of the company's West Coast stores operate as America's Tire Co. because of a name conflict. Customers can search for tires by make and model on the company's Web site. Chairman and owner Bruce Halle founded the company in 1960 with six tires — four of them recaps.

	Annual Growth	12/02	12/03	12/04	12/05	12/06
Sales ($ mil.)	9.8%	1,417.0	1,541.0	1,670.0	1,856.0	2,060.0
Employees	5.3%	8,944	9,500	9,500	10,100	10,980

DISCOVER FINANCIAL SERVICES

NYSE: DFS

2500 Lake Cook Rd.
Riverwoods, IL 60015
Phone: 224-405-0900
Fax: 224-405-4993
Web: www.discoverfinancial.com

CEO: David W. Nelms
CFO: Roy A. Guthrie
HR: –
FYE: November 30
Type: Public

Seems cardholders aren't the only ones getting paid to discover. Discover Financial Services, formerly a business segment of Morgan Stanley, is best known for issuing Discover-brand credit cards, which are used by more than 50 million members at some 4 million merchant locations in 30 countries and territories. The company's cards, which include several levels of business and consumer cards, repay cardholders a percentage of the purchase price each time they use their cards. But there's more to this business than just plastic. Discover Financial Services also has a payment-processing network and owns the PULSE Network ATM system.

	Annual Growth	11/03	11/04	11/05	11/06	11/07
Assets ($ mil.)	—	—	—	—	—	37,376.1
Net income ($ mil.)	—	—	—	—	—	588.6
Market value ($ mil.)	—	—	—	—	—	8,297.4
Employees	—	—	—	—	—	12,800

DISCOVERY COMMUNICATIONS, LLC

1 Discovery Place
Silver Spring, MD 20910
Phone: 240-662-2000
Fax: 240-662-1868
Web: corporate.discovery.com

CEO: David M. Zaslav
CFO: Roger F. Millay
HR: Tony Amato
FYE: December 31
Type: Joint venture

This company helps people discover nature and science programming right from their living rooms. Discovery Communications (DCI) is a leading operator of cable channels focused primarily on such topics as history, natural and physical science, and technology. Its portfolio is anchored by the Discovery Channel, which reaches about 95 million US homes and is broadcast in more than 170 other countries. DCI also runs Animal Planet, The Military Channel, The Science Channel, and TLC (The Learning Channel). In addition, the company offers video-on-demand, and it publishes content online. Discovery Holding owns about 66% of DCI; Advance/Newhouse Communications, an affiliate of Advance Publications, owns about 33%.

DISCOVERY HOLDING COMPANY

NASDAQ (GS): DISCA

12300 Liberty Blvd.
Englewood, CO 80112
Phone: 720-875-4000
Fax: 720-875-7469
Web: www.discoveryholding.com

CEO: John C. Malone
CFO: David J. A. Flowers
HR: –
FYE: December 31
Type: Public

You might be surprised by what you discover about this business' media holdings. While Discovery Holding Company owns a 66% stake in cable broadcaster Discovery Communications (Discovery Channel, TLC, Animal Planet), the company's revenue actually comes from its operating subsidiary Ascent Media Group. Ascent is a leading provider of audio and video post-production services to the film and television industry. With facilities located in Los Angeles, San Francisco, and New York, among other places, Ascent has earned some 15 Academy Awards for sound and video editing. Liberty Media chieftain John Malone owns 30% voting control of the company.

	Annual Growth	12/03	12/04	12/05	12/06	12/07
Sales ($ mil.)	8.7%	506.1	631.2	694.5	688.1	707.2
Net income ($ mil.)	—	—	—	33.3	(46.0)	(68.4)
Market value ($ mil.)	29.1%	—	—	4,061.7	4,315.3	6,767.2
Employees	(32.1%)	—	—	7,800	4,000	3,600

DISCOVERY LABORATORIES, INC.

NASDAQ (GM): DSCO

2600 Kelly Rd., Ste. 100
Warrington, PA 18976
Phone: 215-488-9300
Fax: 215-488-9301
Web: www.discoverylabs.com

CEO: Robert J. Capetola
CFO: John G. Cooper
HR: Kathryn A. Cole
FYE: December 31
Type: Public

If you're waiting to exhale, Discovery Laboratories may be able to help. The biotechnology company focuses on treatments for respiratory disorders, particularly for babies in intensive care. Its lead candidate, Surfaxin, is under FDA review for the prevention of respiratory distress syndrome in premature infants. Discovery Labs bases its therapies on surfactants, which are naturally produced by the lungs and essential for breathing. Its Aerosurf product is a surfactant therapy in aerosol form, developed as an alternative to endotracheal intubation and conventional mechanical ventilation. Other potential disease targets include acute lung injury, asthma, chronic obstructive pulmonary disease, and cystic fibrosis.

	Annual Growth	12/03	12/04	12/05	12/06	12/07
Sales ($ mil.)	—	1.0	1.2	0.1	0.0	0.0
Net income ($ mil.)	—	(24.3)	(46.2)	(58.9)	(46.3)	(40.0)
Market value ($ mil.)	(17.4%)	445.7	384.1	407.6	164.2	207.8
Employees	17.0%	65	90	160	100	122

DISCOVERY TOYS, INC.

6400 Brisa St.
Livermore, CA 94550
Phone: 925-606-2600
Fax: –
Web: www.discoverytoysinc.com

CEO: Jane Leitch
CFO: Bill Moss
HR: –
FYE: September 30
Type: Subsidiary

Business is all fun and games at Discovery Toys. The company sells toys, games, books, and software through more than 26,000 educational consultants who go to customers' homes in the US and Canada. Products are divided into the following categories: toys, books, games, family lifestyle, and music. The products are sorted by appropriate age groups: infant to toddler, toddler to preschool, school years. Founded in 1978 by Lane Nemeth, Discovery Toys was acquired in 2001 by Eos International (formerly dreamlife, begun by self-improvement guru Tony Robbins as an online personal and professional network).

DISNEY ABC CABLE NETWORKS GROUP

3800 W. Alameda Ave.
Burbank, CA 91505
Phone: 818-569-7500
Fax: –

CEO: Anne M. Sweeney
CFO: Jewell Engstrom
HR: Robert Mendez
FYE: September 30
Type: Subsidiary

Disney ABC Cable Networks Group wants to work a little magic on the television dial. The unit of Disney-ABC Television Group owns and operates a portfolio of cable television channels including ABC Family, the Disney Channel, and SOAPnet. It also owns Jetix, one of the leading children's television distributors in Europe, and Toon Disney. In addition, Disney ABC Cable Networks holds a 37% stake in A&E Television and a 50% stake in Lifetime Entertainment. Disney-ABC Television Group oversees the television broadcasting, production, and distribution operations of parent Walt Disney.

DISCUS DENTAL, INC.

8550 Higuera St.
Culver City, CA 90232
Phone: 310-845-8200
Fax: 310-845-1537
Web: www.discusdental.com

CEO: Robert Hayman
CFO: –
HR: David Earling Anderson
FYE: December 31
Type: Private

Discus Dental wants to talk about white teeth. The dental supply company offers a number of teeth-whitening products under brand names that include Zoom!, Nite White, and Day White. It ships its products directly to customers in an effort to avoid dealer markups, and it provides volume discounts. The company also sells oral hygiene products, restoratives, impression materials, and practice management software, and it provides training and marketing services. In 2006 Discus Dental bought the Associated Centers business of BSML, which provides teeth-whitening services through about 5,000 independent dental offices in some 50 countries.

	Annual Growth	12/03	12/04	12/05	12/06	12/07
Est. sales ($ mil.)	—	—	—	—	—	130.0
Employees	—	—	—	—	—	400

DISTINCTIVE APPLIANCES, INC.

1440 Bridge Gate Dr.
Diamond Bar, CA 91765
Phone: 626-799-1000
Fax: 626-441-9632
Web: www.dacor.com

CEO: S. Michael (Mike) Joseph
CFO: Ralph L. Heiman
HR: –
FYE: December 31
Type: Private

This company would love to make Dacor a part of your everyday décor. Distinctive Appliances (dba Dacor) makes and distributes high-end stoves, grills, ventilation equipment, and other cooking appliances and accessories. The manufacturer has showrooms in Atlanta, San Francisco, Chicago, and Baltimore and also sells its products through specialty appliance retailers nationwide. Stan Joseph, who later founded Dacor with his wife Florence in 1965, created the first complete kitchen ventilation system, which became an essential feature of modern homes by the late 1950s. Their sons, Mike (chairman and CEO) and Tony (director), run the company today.

	Annual Growth	12/03	12/04	12/05	12/06	12/07
Est. sales ($ mil.)	—	—	—	—	—	168.3
Employees	—	—	—	—	—	550

📶 DISH NETWORK CORPORATION

NASDAQ (GS): DISH

9601 S. Meridian Blvd.
Englewood, CO 80112
Phone: 303-723-1000
Fax: 303-723-1999
Web: www.dishnetwork.com

CEO: Charles W. (Charlie) Ergen
CFO: Bernard L. (Bernie) Han
HR: Stephen W. Wood
FYE: December 31
Type: Public

DISH Network (formerly EchoStar Communications) serves up fare intended to whet almost everyone's appetite for televised entertainment. The company is the #2 provider of direct broadcast satellite TV service (behind DIRECTV) in the US. The DISH Network provides programming to more than 13 million subscribers; customers include home viewers as well as business customers in such industries as hospitality, restaurants, and retail. DISH also has partnerships with ISPs and voice communications providers, including EarthLink, Qwest, and Sprint Nextel to offer bundled services. Co-founder and CEO Charlie Ergen holds about 50% of the company's total equity and about 80% of the vote.

	Annual Growth	12/03	12/04	12/05	12/06	12/07
Sales ($ mil.)	17.9%	5,739.3	7,151.2	8,425.5	9,818.5	11,090.4
Net income ($ mil.)	35.5%	224.5	214.8	1,514.5	608.3	756.0
Market value ($ mil.)	(0.8%)	7,178.2	6,343.8	4,906.6	6,932.0	6,963.6
Employees	4.7%	—	—	21,000	21,000	23,000

DISTRIBUTED ENERGY SYSTEMS CORP.

NASDAQ (GM): DESC

10 Technology Dr.
Wallingford, CT 06492
Phone: 203-678-2000
Fax: 203-949-8016
Web: www.distributed-energy.com

CEO: Bernard H. (Bud) Cherry
CFO: Peter J. Tallian
HR: Richard (Dick) Park
FYE: December 31
Type: Public

Distributed Energy Systems doesn't think alternative energy is fuelish. Through Proton Energy Systems, the company makes proton exchange membrane (PEM) electrochemical devices, such as hydrogen generators and regenerative fuel cells. Proton Energy's HOGEN hydrogen generators produce high-purity hydrogen from electricity and water for use with fuel cells and for a wide variety of manufacturing and laboratory applications, while its UNIGEN regenerative fuel cells convert electricity to hydrogen so it can be stored and converted back to electricity as needed. Customers in the US account for most of Distributed Energy's sales. In June 2008 the company filed for Chapter 11 protection from creditors.

	Annual Growth	12/03	12/04	12/05	12/06	12/07
Sales ($ mil.)	62.7%	4.2	22.5	45.0	45.1	29.4
Net income ($ mil.)	—	(16.8)	(22.4)	(16.2)	(53.4)	(49.9)
Market value ($ mil.)	(36.9%)	101.1	89.6	281.8	143.1	16.0
Employees	(3.1%)	227	241	266	317	200

📶 An in-depth profile of this company is available to Hoover's Online members at hoovers.com.

503

DISTRIBUTION PLUS INC.

825 Green Bay Rd., Ste. 200
Wilmette, IL 60091
Phone: 847-256-8289
Fax: 847-256-8299
Web: www.distribution-plus.com

CEO: Jim DeKeyser
CFO: Kevin Carmody
HR: Bart McGuinn
FYE: December 31
Type: Subsidiary

Distribution Plus is a leading wholesale food distributor that specializes in gourmet, organic, and ethnic food products. It offers more than 55,000 items through six distribution centers covering more than 20 states. Distribution Plus serves food service operators, retail grocers, and customers in other retail trades. Founded in 1989, the company is controlled by the Irish Dairy Board.

DITECH NETWORKS, INC.

NASDAQ (GM): DITC

825 E. Middlefield Rd.
Mountain View, CA 94043
Phone: 650-623-1300
Fax: 650-564-9599
Web: www.ditechcom.com

CEO: Todd Simpson
CFO: William J. Tamblyn
HR: Glenda Dubsky
FYE: April 30
Type: Public

Echoes can be fun when bouncing your name off a canyon wall, but not during an urgent phone call. Ditech Networks' echo-cancellation equipment regulates the distracting echoes that can occur in long-distance, satellite, and cell phone calls. It has also developed voice processing products for Voice over Internet Protocol (VoIP) networks. The company primarily markets through a direct sales force in the US; it utilizes resellers and distributors overseas. Ditech's customers include Verizon Wireless and Orascom Telecom. Verizon accounted for more than 60% of the company's revenues in fiscal 2007.

	Annual Growth	4/03	4/04	4/05	4/06	4/07
Sales ($ mil.)	15.4%	47.4	69.6	94.1	54.9	84.0
Net income ($ mil.)	—	(75.1)	8.2	71.1	(0.9)	5.3
Market value ($ mil.)	23.7%	123.4	473.3	361.9	305.0	288.8
Employees	17.4%	—	—	184	216	—

DIVERSIFIED MACHINE INC.

28059 Center Oaks Ct.
Wixom, MI 48393
Phone: 248-277-4400
Fax: 248-277-4399
Web: www.divmi.com

CEO: Bruce R. Swift
CFO: Shankar Kiru
HR: –
FYE: December 31
Type: Private

Diversified Machine knows you can't move your wheels without a powertrain. The company (formerly Uni Boring) machines and assembles powertrain components — including intake manifolds, cylinder heads, and exhaust manifolds — primarily for Ford, Chrysler, and General Motors. Diversified Machine operates about a half dozen manufacturing plants in Michigan and one in Indiana. An investor group led by auto industry veteran Bruce Swift bought the former Uni Boring out of bankruptcy in November 2005 and changed its name to Diversified Machine. Besides Swift, who serves as the company's chairman and CEO, shareholders in Diversified Machine include investment firms Carlyle Group and Relativity Fund/JME.

	Annual Growth	12/03	12/04	12/05	12/06	12/07
Est. sales ($ mil.)	—	—	—	—	—	131.4
Employees	—	—	—	—	—	400

DIVERSIFIED THERMAL SOLUTIONS, INC.

OTC: DVTS

4126 Delp St., Ste. 200
Memphis, TN 38118
Phone: 901-365-7650
Fax: 901-365-9617
Web: www.dthermal.com

CEO: B. Grant Hunter
CFO: J. Terry Medovitch
HR: –
FYE: December 31
Type: Public

When the heat is on, companies look to Diversified Thermal Solutions to protect their heat-generating equipment. The company manufactures refractory products, such as clay and brick, for the linings of high-temperature furnaces and reactors. Diversified Thermal Solutions is expanding in the Southeast and Northeast of the US, primarily targeting non-ferrous industries such as aluminum, incineration, paper, and petrochemical operations. Prior to the refractory business, the company was involved in providing international long distance communications service. President and CEO B. Grant Hunter controls more than a third of Diversified Thermal Solutions.

	Annual Growth	12/03	12/04	12/05	12/06	12/07
Sales ($ mil.)	118.5%	0.5	0.1	8.7	10.3	11.4
Net income ($ mil.)	—	(0.1)	(0.6)	(0.2)	1.3	(0.1)
Market value ($ mil.)	—	—	—	—	—	1.5
Employees	—	—	—	—	—	—

DIVX, INC.

NASDAQ (GM): DIVX

4780 Eastgate Mall
San Diego, CA 92121
Phone: 858-882-0600
Fax: 858-882-0601
Web: www.divx.com

CEO: Kevin Hell
CFO: Dan L. Halvorson
HR: –
FYE: December 31
Type: Public

FX from DVDs benefit from DivX, a digital media format for content playback, creation, and distribution. DivX the company first introduced a video compression-decompression (or codec) software library that has been downloaded more than 250 million times. It has built on the success of this technology by distributing the DivX software through its own Web site and through licenses with consumer video hardware original equipment manufacturers (OEMs) including LG Electronics, Samsung, and Philips. CEO Kevin Hell and executives Darrius Thompson, Joe Bezdek, Tay Nguyen, and Gej Vashisht-Rota founded DivX in 2000.

	Annual Growth	12/03	12/04	12/05	12/06	12/07
Sales ($ mil.)	82.2%	7.7	16.4	33.0	59.3	84.9
Net income ($ mil.)	—	(3.9)	(4.3)	2.3	16.4	9.2
Market value ($ mil.)	(36.2%)	—	—	—	762.1	486.1
Employees	—	—	—	—	108	—

THE DIXIE GROUP, INC.

NASDAQ (GM): DXYN

104 Nowlin Ln., Ste. 101
Chattanooga, TN 37421
Phone: 423-510-7000
Fax: 706-876-5896
Web: www.thedixiegroup.com

CEO: Daniel K. Frierson
CFO: Gary A. Harmon
HR: W. Derek Davis
FYE: Last Saturday in December
Type: Public

The Dixie Group takes its business to the carpet. Once a traditional textile manufacturer, the company now makes high-end carpet and rugs, as well as yarns (used to manufacture carpets). Dixie sells residential and commercial broadloom carpets to retail outlets, home builders, and other customers primarily through its Dixie Home, Masland Carpets, and Fabrica International brands. The Dixie Home unit sells tufted broadloom carpets to home centers, selected retailers, and distributors. Dixie Group started as the Dixie Mercerizing Company in 1920.

	Annual Growth	12/03	12/04	12/05	12/06	12/07
Sales ($ mil.)	8.2%	234.1	292.0	318.5	331.1	320.8
Net income ($ mil.)	—	(17.0)	12.3	10.1	7.7	6.3
Market value ($ mil.)	2.2%	88.5	191.5	161.1	153.0	96.6
Employees	—	—	—	1,500	—	—

DIXON TICONDEROGA COMPANY

195 International Pkwy.
Heathrow, FL 32746
Phone: 407-829-9000
Fax: 800-232-9396
Web: www.dixonticonderoga.com

CEO: Donald S. (Don) Currie
CFO: Jose Martinez
HR: –
FYE: September 30
Type: Private

Dixon Ticonderoga hits the mark with pencil users everywhere. A top US maker of wood-cased graphite pencils (it developed the #2 pencil in 1913), the company also makes Dixon markers, Prang art materials, a line of school supplies featuring Looney Tunes and Scooby Doo characters, and general office supplies. In addition, Dixon Ticonderoga offers advertising specialty pencils, crayons, markers, and pens. Customers include major discounters like Wal-Mart and office products superstores such as Office Depot. In 2005 Dixon Ticonderoga was acquired by Italian-based Fila-Fabbrica, maker of writing implements, for about $22.5 million.

	Annual Growth	9/03	9/04	9/05	9/06	9/07
Est. sales ($ mil.)	—	—	—	—	—	88.0
Employees	—	—	—	—	—	1,403

DJO INCORPORATED

1430 Decision St.
Vista, CA 92081
Phone: 760-727-1280
Fax: 800-936-6569
Web: www.djortho.com

CEO: Leslie H. (Les) Cross
CFO: Vickie L. Capps
HR: Tom Capizzi
FYE: December 31
Type: Subsidiary

This deejay doesn't spin any records, but its products may help heal your knees. Orthopedic sports medicine firm DJO Incorporated (formerly dj Orthopedics) makes devices that regenerate and repair soft tissue and bone. Its more than 700 products — marketed under brand names such as DonJoy, Aircast, and ProCare — include rigid knee braces, soft goods that support necks and joints, and a pain management system that delivers local anesthetic. The company markets to surgeons, hospitals, physical therapists, athletic trainers, and other health care professionals. DJO merged with ReAble Therapeutics in 2007.

	Annual Growth	12/02	12/03	12/04	12/05	12/06
Sales ($ mil.)	22.6%	182.6	197.9	256.0	286.2	413.1
Net income ($ mil.)	—	(15.2)	12.1	14.0	29.2	12.6
Employees	25.7%	1,200	—	—	1,700	3,000

DLA PIPER

6225 Smith Ave.
Baltimore, MD 21209
Phone: 410-580-3000
Fax: 410-580-3001
Web: www.dlapiper.com

CEO: Francis B. Burch Jr.
CFO: Raymond Dearchs
HR: Clarissa Peterson
FYE: December 31
Type: Partnership

DLA Piper, one of the world's largest law firms, has some 3,400 lawyers operating out of about 65 offices in the US, Europe, the Middle East, Africa, and the Asia/Pacific region. It serves corporate clients through a broad range of practices divided into a dozen key groups; specialties include intellectual property, regulatory and government affairs, and technology and media. The firm, which shortened its name from DLA Piper Rudnick Gray Cary in 2006, was formed in 2005 when Maryland-based Piper Rudnick merged with California-based Gray Cary Ware & Freidenrich and UK firm DLA.

	Annual Growth	12/03	12/04	12/05	12/06	12/07
Est. sales ($ mil.)	—	—	—	—	—	580.7
Employees	—	—	—	—	—	3,323

DLI HOLDING CORP.

726 RexCorp Plaza
Uniondale, NY 11553
Phone: 516-844-2020
Fax: –
Web: www.dellabs.com

CEO: Charles J. Hinkaty
CFO: Joseph (Joe) Sinicropi
HR: –
FYE: June 30*
Type: Subsidiary

Beauty is a science at DLI Holding Corp. Through its main operating company Del Laboratories, the company primarily makes and markets a variety of cosmetics, including nail care and nail color products, color cosmetics, beauty implements (tweezers, eyelash curlers, clippers), and bath and body care items. Beauty products are marketed under brand names such as Sally Hansen, LaCross, and N.Y.C. New York Color. Its over-the-counter pharmaceuticals segment features oral analgesics Orajel, Gentle Naturals baby care, the Dermarest skincare line, and Pronto lice treatment products. DLI Holding was acquired by fragrance-and-beauty giant Coty Inc. in late 2007.

	Annual Growth	12/02	12/03	12/04	12/05	12/06
Sales ($ mil.)	3.8%	—	—	395.2	397.6	425.9
Net income ($ mil.)	—	—	—	14.7	(13.9)	(19.7)
Employees	—	—	—	—	—	1,700

*Fiscal year change

DMX, INC.

600 Congress Ave., Fl. 14
Austin, TX 78701
Phone: 512-380-8500
Fax: –
Web: www.dmxmusic.com

CEO: John D. Cullen
CFO: Kimberly K. Shipman
HR: Sheri Michalec
FYE: December 31
Type: Private

DMX (formerly DMX MUSIC) gives the sights, sounds, and scents of your business a twist. The company provides what it calls "sensory branding" through the distribution of commercial-free music, video, on-air and on-hold messages, and environmental fragrances to companies around the globe. Clients include retailers, hotels, health clubs, resorts, and casinos such as Gold's Gym, The Cheesecake Factory, Abercrombie & Fitch, and Disney World. DMX has license agreements with more than 1,700 record labels. The company also provides music for cable television networks. Founded in 1971, DMX is owned by private investment firm THP Capstar; the company is merging with chief rival Muzak.

DNAPRINT GENOMICS, INC.

OTC: DNAG

1621 W. University Pkwy.
Sarasota, FL 34243
Phone: 941-366-3400
Fax: 941-952-9770
Web: www.dnaprint.com

CEO: Richard Gabriel
CFO: –
HR: –
FYE: December 31
Type: Public

Is race just a social construct? DNAPrint Genomics doesn't think so. The firm offers ANCESTRYbyDNA, a kit that identifies in a DNA sample the single nucleotide polymorphisms (SNPs) associated with geographic ancestral heritage (or biogeographical ancestry). A customer can learn what percentage he is African, Native American, Indo-European, and East Asian. Since certain population groups are more susceptible to certain diseases or drug responses, knowing one's biogeographical ancestry could help predict future health issues or guide medical choices. DNAPrint also conducts research and development of compounds and tools for medical use through collaborative and license agreements.

	Annual Growth	12/02	12/03	12/04	12/05	*12/06
Sales ($ mil.)	86.1%	0.2	0.7	0.8	1.3	2.4
Net income ($ mil.)	—	(3.1)	(7.8)	(3.7)	(8.7)	(12.4)
Employees	—	—	—	—	—	—

*Most recent year available

An in-depth profile of this company is available to Hoover's Online members at hoovers.com.

505

DNB FINANCIAL CORPORATION

OTC: DNBF

4 Brandywine Ave.	CEO: William S. Latoff
Downingtown, PA 19335	CFO: Gerald F. Sopp
Phone: 610-269-1040	HR: Ronald K. Dankanich
Fax: 610-873-5298	FYE: December 31
Web: www.dnb4you.com	Type: Public

DNB Financial Corporation is interested in Pennsylvania. The institution is the holding company for DNB First, National Association (formerly Downingtown National Bank), which operates branches in Chester County in southeastern Pennsylvania. Founded in 1860, the bank serves consumers, but mainly lends to area businesses, with mortgages secured by commercial property and commercial operating loans. Deposit products include checking and savings accounts, money market and retirement accounts, and CDs. Subsidiary DNB Advisors provides financial planning, trust and custody, and estate settlement services.

	Annual Growth	12/03	12/04	12/05	12/06	12/07
Assets ($ mil.)	7.5%	409.0	441.1	473.0	525.2	545.8
Net income ($ mil.)	6.5%	1.4	0.3	2.2	1.8	1.8
Market value ($ mil.)	(3.3%)	47.7	45.5	42.5	47.7	41.6
Employees	(0.7%)	—	—	—	139	138

DNC MULTIMEDIA CORPORATION

Pink Sheets: DCNM

11050 Regal Forest Dr.	CEO: Robert Lott
Suwanee, GA 30024	CFO: M. Dewey Bain
Phone: 770-476-7903	HR: —
Fax: —	FYE: December 31
	Type: Public

DnC Multimedia (formerly PlanetLink Communications) hangs with the stars as the developer of a GPS-based vehicle tracking system that it sells to commercial customers in the US and Mexico. The system, developed by its PlanetTRAKS subsidiary and marketed under the TransTRAK system brand name, consists of a vehicle-mounted GPS (global positioning system) device, proprietary software, and a mapping component from MapQuest; it allows users to monitor speed, positioning, and other information using any Internet-enabled device. DnC Multimedia's customers include Two Men and a Truck franchisees and Mexico City-based bus company Estrella Blanca.

	Annual Growth	12/02	12/03	12/04	12/05	*12/06
Sales ($ mil.)	(26.0%)	1.0	0.4	0.0	0.2	0.3
Net income ($ mil.)	—	(6.0)	(0.9)	(2.4)	(3.2)	(2.4)
Employees	—	—	—	—	—	1

*Most recent year available

DND TECHNOLOGIES, INC.

Pink Sheets: DNDT

375 E. Elliot Rd., Bldg. 6	CEO: Douglas N. Dixon
Chandler, AZ 85225	CFO: G. Dennis Key
Phone: 480-892-7020	HR: —
Fax: 480-892-8044	FYE: December 31
Web: www.aspectsys.com	Type: Public

DND Technologies would like to etch its name into the annals of the semiconductor equipment industry. Through its Aspect Systems, Inc. (ASI) subsidiary, DND offers semiconductor wafer etching machinery, as well as a product called a hot gas box used to clean wafer fabrication equipment. The company also refurbishes and distributes equipment made by others. Customers include Intel, National Semiconductor, RF Micro Devices, Taiwan Semiconductor Manufacturing, and Texas Instruments. Chairman, president, and CEO Douglas Dixon owns nearly 55% of DND, which takes its name from his initials.

	Annual Growth	12/02	12/03	12/04	12/05	*12/06
Sales ($ mil.)	7.1%	5.4	8.7	15.8	13.8	7.1
Net income ($ mil.)	—	(1.5)	(2.7)	1.2	(4.6)	(1.9)
Employees	(15.9%)	52	42	55	62	26

*Most recent year available

DO IT BEST CORP.

6502 Nelson Rd.	CEO: Robert N. (Bob) Taylor
Fort Wayne, IN 46803	CFO: David (Dave) Dietz
Phone: 260-748-5300	HR: Daniel B. (Dan) Starr
Fax: 260-748-5620	FYE: June 30
Web: www.doitbestcorp.com	Type: Cooperative

If you're building a house or fixing one up, you might as well Do it Best — at least, that's the hope of the hardware industry's second-largest cooperative after Ace Hardware. Do it Best has more than 4,100 member-owned stores in the US and more than 45 other countries. Besides the usual tools and building materials, merchandise includes automotive items, bicycles, camping gear, housewares, office supplies, and small appliances. The co-op, whose buying power enables members to get retail products at competitive prices, also offers unifying branding programs using the Do it Best and Do it center names. Do it Best (formerly Hardware Wholesalers) began in 1945; it bought the Our Own Hardware co-op in 1998.

	Annual Growth	6/03	6/04	6/05	6/06	6/07
Est. sales ($ mil.)	—	—	—	—	—	2,147.5
Employees	—	—	—	—	—	1,549

DOALL COMPANY

1480 S. Wolf Rd.	CEO: Michael L. Wilkie
Wheeling, IL 60090	CFO: Steve Lund
Phone: 847-824-8191	HR: —
Fax: 847-484-2045	FYE: May 31
Web: www.doall.com	Type: Private

DoALL wants to be the end-all and the be-all of metal-cutting saws. For eight decades, it has engineered and manufactured saw machinery and accessories for the metalworking industry. Its DoALL Sawing Products division makes band saw tools, blades, and cutting fluids. To meet its customers' needs for a single supplier of industrial equipment, DoALL also distributes more than 300,000 items from abrasives and cutting products to coolants and safety products made by 50,000 brand-name OEMs. The DoALL Global Industrial Supply (DGI Supply) division operates a global network of supply centers. Founded in 1927, the company is owned by the founding Wilkie family and is headed by Michael Wilkie.

DOANE PET CARE COMPANY

210 Westwood Place South, Ste. 400	CEO: Douglas J. (Doug) Cahill
Brentwood, TN 37027	CFO: Philip K. Woodlief
Phone: 615-373-7774	HR: —
Fax: 615-309-1187	FYE: December 31
Web: www.doanepetcare.com	Type: Subsidiary

Doane Pet Care has no quibble with kibble. A leading manufacturer of dry pet foods in the US, the company also makes soft-dry food, soft treats, and dog biscuits. Doane also makes products for other pet food companies. Its customers include mass merchandisers, such as Wal-Mart, grocery and pet store chains, and farm and feed stores. The company is part of candy and pet food behemoth Mars's petcare division.

DOCTOR'S ASSOCIATES INC.

325 Bic Dr.
Milford, CT 06461
Phone: 203-877-4281
Fax: 203-876-6674
Web: www.subway.com

CEO: Frederick A. (Fred) DeLuca
CFO: David Worroll
HR: –
FYE: December 31
Type: Private

You don't have to go underground to catch this Subway. Doctor's Associates operates the Subway chain of sandwich shops, the second-largest quick service chain behind McDonald's. It boasts more than 29,000 locations in 85 countries, with more US locations than the Golden Arches. Virtually all Subway restaurants are franchised and offer such fare as hot and cold sub sandwiches, turkey wraps, and salads. Subways are located in freestanding buildings, as well as in airports, convenience stores, sports facilities, and other locations. Doctor's Associates is owned by co-founders Fred DeLuca (CEO) and Peter Buck, who opened the first Subway in 1965.

DOCUMENT CAPTURE TECHNOLOGIES, INC.

OTC: DCMT

1772 Technology Dr.
San Jose, CA 95110
Phone: 408-436-9888
Fax: 408-436-6151
Web: www.docucap.com

CEO: David P. Clark
CFO: Carolyn (Martha) Ellis
HR: –
FYE: December 31
Type: Public

Document Capture Technologies (formerly known as Sysview Technology and Syscan Imaging) is a developer of contact image sensor (CIS) modules used in such office equipment as fax machines and PC scanners. The company's portable image scanners are sold under the TravelScan and DocketPORT brand names. Syscan Imaging Ltd., a Hong Kong firm, owns nearly half of Document Capture Technologies. Document Capture Technologies has engaged the investment firm of Oppenheimer & Co. to advise the company on ways to enhance shareholder value, including potential sales, mergers, combinations, and partnerships.

	Annual Growth	12/03	12/04	12/05	12/06	12/07
Sales ($ mil.)	35.0%	—	6.1	7.8	12.5	15.0
Net income ($ mil.)	—	—	(0.2)	(1.5)	(5.2)	(1.1)
Market value ($ mil.)	(11.6%)	—	—	—	13.8	12.2
Employees	(8.0%)	—	18	26	36	14

DOCUMENT SCIENCES CORPORATION

NASDAQ (CM): DOCX

5958 Priestly Dr.
Carlsbad, CA 92008
Phone: 760-602-1400
Fax: 760-602-1450
Web: www.docscience.com

CEO: John L. (Jack) McGannon
CFO: Todd W. Schmidt
HR: –
FYE: December 31
Type: Public

Document Sciences can help you create the document or sign it on the dotted line. The company develops content publishing software designed to facilitate businesses' communications with their customers. Its software produces, publishes, and manages personalized and regulated documents that can be printed in high volumes, e-mailed, or distributed online. Document Sciences, which targets clients in the financial services, health care, government, and commercial outsourcing markets, also offers outsourced software development services. Xerox spun off Document Sciences in 1996. In late 2007 the company agreed to be acquired by EMC for about $85 million.

	Annual Growth	12/02	12/03	12/04	12/05	*12/06
Sales ($ mil.)	9.7%	23.1	20.5	23.4	29.6	33.4
Net income ($ mil.)	—	1.6	(1.8)	0.7	0.0	(1.5)
Employees	41.5%	127	—	—	360	

*Most recent year available

DOCUMENT SECURITY SYSTEMS, INC.

AMEX: DMC

28 E. Main St., Ste. 1525
Rochester, NY 14614
Phone: 585-325-3610
Fax: 585-325-2977
Web: www.documentsecurity.com

CEO: Patrick White
CFO: Patrick White
HR: –
FYE: December 31
Type: Public

Document Security Systems caters to those who are insecure about their security, particularly on paper. The company develops anticounterfeiting products. Document Security Systems' offerings include technology that prevents documents from being accurately scanned or copied and authentication coding that can be used in conjunction with a handheld reader to verify that a document is genuine. Document Security Systems also sells paper that displays words such as "void" or "unauthorized copy" if it goes through a copier, fax machine, or scanner. The company considers document security to be its core business, so it sold its retail copying and quick-printing unit in 2007.

	Annual Growth	12/03	12/04	12/05	12/06	12/07
Sales ($ mil.)	46.6%	1.3	1.6	1.8	4.8	6.0
Net income ($ mil.)	—	(1.5)	(1.7)	(2.8)	(4.8)	(7.0)
Market value ($ mil.)	16.7%	47.8	78.0	160.6	150.3	88.6
Employees	0.0%	—	22	22	—	—

DODGE & COX

555 California St., 40th Fl.
San Francisco, CA 94104
Phone: 415-981-1710
Fax: 415-986-2924
Web: www.dodgeandcox.com

CEO: John A. Gunn
CFO: –
HR: –
FYE: December 31
Type: Private

Helping clients steer clear of financial potholes is all in a day's work for Dodge & Cox. The asset management firm, founded in 1930, provides mutual funds and separately managed accounts, specializing in low costs and long-term investments. Its four fund offerings are a stock fund, an international stock fund, a balanced fund, and an income fund. (Dodge & Cox's stock fund and balanced fund reopened to new investors in 2008.) Employee-owned Dodge & Cox, which has around $150 billion in accounts under management, shuns publicity (even advertising) and managed to avoid the tech-stock bust with its focus on value-oriented stocks.

	Annual Growth	12/03	12/04	12/05	12/06	12/07
Est. sales ($ mil.)	—	—	—	—	—	20.9
Employees	—	—	—	—	—	160

THE DOE RUN COMPANY

1801 Park 270 Dr., Ste. 300
St. Louis, MO 63146
Phone: 314-453-7100
Fax: 314-453-7177
Web: www.doerun.com

CEO: A. Bruce Neil
CFO: Theodore P. (Terry) Fox III
HR: Barb Shephard
FYE: October 31
Type: Private

The Doe Run Company assures us that no female deer are harmed in the production of its metal products. The company is primarily involved in mining, milling, smelting, and refining lead. It is also engaged in the recycling and fabrication of lead and lead products. Doe Run has operations in Arizona, Missouri, and Washington. The venerable US company expanded outside of the US for the first time in 1997 when it acquired smelters and refineries in Peru. Ten years later it reorganized and made those operations an affiliated company rather than a subsidiary. It's a part of the Renco Group.

	Annual Growth	10/03	10/04	10/05	10/06	10/07
Est. sales ($ mil.)	—	—	—	—	—	1,029.4
Employees	—	—	—	—	—	4,271

An in-depth profile of this company is available to Hoover's Online members at hoovers.com.

507

DOLAN MEDIA COMPANY

NYSE: DM

1200 Baker Bldg., 706 2nd Ave. South, Ste. 1200	CEO: James P. (Jim) Dolan
Minneapolis, MN 55402	CFO: Scott J. Pollei
Phone: 612-317-9420	HR: –
Fax: 612-317-9434	FYE: December 31
Web: www.dolanmedia.com	Type: Public

Local business news makes the world go around for Dolan Media. The company is a leading business news publisher with more than 40 daily and weekly newspapers serving mostly markets on the East Coast and in the Midwest. Its portfolio includes *The Daily Record* (Baltimore), *Massachusetts Lawyer Weekly*, and *New Orleans CityBusiness*. Dolan also publishes more than 15 free non-dailies and operates a number of Web sites in conjunction with its newspapers. In addition to publishing, the company has subsidiaries that provide printing and a variety of other business services for law firms.

	Annual Growth	12/03	12/04	12/05	12/06	12/07
Sales ($ mil.)	43.3%	—	51.7	77.9	111.6	152.0
Net income ($ mil.)	—	—	(1.3)	(7.5)	(20.3)	(54.0)
Market value ($ mil.)	—	—	—	—	—	731.8
Employees	—	—	—	—	—	

DOLBY LABORATORIES, INC.

NYSE: DLB

100 Potrero Ave.	CEO: N. William Jasper Jr.
San Francisco, CA 94103	CFO: Kevin J. Yeaman
Phone: 415-558-0200	HR: Bruce Nottage
Fax: 415-863-1373	FYE: Last Friday in September
Web: www.dolby.com	Type: Public

Talk about having a sound business model. Dolby Laboratories is the market leader in developing sound processing and noise reduction systems for use in professional and consumer audio and video equipment. Though it does make some of its own products, Dolby mostly licenses its technology to other manufacturers. The firm has about 1,000 patents and 870 trademarks worldwide. In film, the Dolby Digital format has become the de facto audio standard; its systems equip movie screens around the globe. The company has expanded into digital audio compression. American engineer and physicist Ray Dolby founded the firm in London in 1965 and moved it to San Francisco in 1977. He controls 91% of the company's voting power.

	Annual Growth	9/03	9/04	9/05	9/06	9/07
Sales ($ mil.)	22.0%	217.5	289.0	328.0	391.5	482.0
Net income ($ mil.)	46.5%	31.0	39.8	52.3	89.6	142.8
Market value ($ mil.)	80.1%	—	—	529.9	745.9	1,718.5
Employees	8.8%	—	—	825	864	976

⊞ DOLE FOOD COMPANY, INC.

1 Dole Dr.	CEO: David A. DeLorenzo
Westlake Village, CA 91362	CFO: Joseph S. Tesoriero
Phone: 818-879-6600	HR: Sue Hagen
Fax: 818-879-6615	FYE: Saturday nearest December 31
Web: www.dole.com	Type: Private

Bananas might be Dole Food's favorite fruit because they have "a-peel," but as the world's largest producer of fresh fruits and vegetables, it grows and markets much more than the slipper-peeled fruit. The company is the world's top producer of bananas (158 million boxes a year) and the #2 producer of pineapples (behind Fresh Del Monte Produce). It also markets citrus, table grapes, dried fruits, nuts, and fresh-cut flowers. Dole offers value-added products (packaged salads, novelty canned pineapple shapes) to insulate itself from fluctuating commodity markets. Sourcing from some 75 countries, Dole sells more than 200 products in more than 90 countries.

	Annual Growth	12/03	12/04	12/05	12/06	12/07
Sales ($ mil.)	9.8%	4,773.1	5,316.2	5,870.6	6,171.5	6,931.0
Net income ($ mil.)	—	83.9	134.4	—	(89.0)	(57.5)
Employees	(6.5%)	59,000	64,000	72,000	47,000	45,000

DOLLAR BANK, FSB

3 Gateway Center	CEO: Robert P. Oeler
Pittsburgh, PA 15222	CFO: –
Phone: 412-261-4900	HR: –
Fax: 412-261-7567	FYE: December 31
Web: www.dollarbank.com	Type: Private

Dollar Bank wants to help you save your pennies. Founded in 1855, Dollar Bank serves business and retail customers from more than 50 branches and loan offices in the Pittsburgh and Cleveland metropolitan areas. It offers standard deposit, mortgage, and lending services to consumers and business clients. One- to four-family residential mortgages represent approximately 80% of the bank's loan portfolio. One of the largest mutual banks in the country, Dollar Bank is also a pioneer in online banking (and prior to that, telephone banking), providing interactive calculators for CDs, IRAs, mortgages, and loans on its Web site.

	Annual Growth	12/03	12/04	12/05	12/06	12/07
Est. sales ($ mil.)	—	—	—	—	—	69.9
Employees	—	—	—	—	—	1,200

DOLLAR FINANCIAL CORP.

NASDAQ (GS): DLLR

1436 Lancaster Ave., Ste. 300	CEO: Jeffrey A. (Jeff) Weiss
Berwyn, PA 19312	CFO: Randall (Randy) Underwood
Phone: 610-296-3400	HR: –
Fax: 610-296-7844	FYE: June 30
Web: www.dfg.com	Type: Public

Dollar Financial is checking you out! Or maybe cashing your check? Through its subsidiary Dollar Financial Group, the company operates more than 1,400 check-cashing stores (about a quarter are franchised) in the US, Canada, and the UK. The stores do business under such names as Money Mart, Loan Mart, Insta-Cheques, and Money Shop. In addition to check cashing, the stores offer payday lending, money wires, transfers, electronic tax filing, and reloadable Visa debit cards. Its We The People franchise system provides legal document processing services. Dollar Financial's customers are typically low- to moderate-income earners who don't use or have access to banks.

	Annual Growth	6/03	6/04	6/05	6/06	6/07
Sales ($ mil.)	16.9%	244.4	270.9	291.6	328.5	455.7
Net income ($ mil.)	—	(8.6)	(28.0)	(0.4)	7.0	(32.2)
Market value ($ mil.)	89.5%	—	—	191.8	421.2	688.7
Employees	—	—	—	3,909	—	—

⊞ DOLLAR GENERAL CORPORATION

100 Mission Ridge	CEO: Richard W. (Rick) Dreiling
Goodlettsville, TN 37072	CFO: David M. Tehle
Phone: 615-855-4000	HR: Challis M. Lowe
Fax: 615-855-5252	FYE: Friday nearest January 31
Web: www.dollargeneral.com	Type: Private

Dollar General's at ease with living off the crumbs of Wal-Mart. The retailer commands a chain of more than 8,200 discount stores in about 35 states, primarily in the southern and eastern US, the Midwest, and the Southwest. Offering basic household items such as cleaning supplies and health and beauty aids, as well as some apparel and food, the firm targets low-, middle-, and fixed-income customers. Its stores are generally located in small towns off the radar of giant discounters. Its big-city stores (about 30% of its total) are situated in lower-income neighborhoods. About a third of its stores' goods are priced at $1 or less. Dollar General was taken private by affiliates of KKR and Goldman Sachs in 2007.

	Annual Growth	1/04	1/05	1/06	1/07	1/08
Sales ($ mil.)	8.4%	6,872.0	7,660.9	8,582.2	9,169.8	9,495.3
Net income ($ mil.)	—	301.0	344.2	350.2	137.9	(12.8)
Employees	5.5%	57,800	63,200	64,500	71,500	71,500

DOLLAR THRIFTY AUTOMOTIVE GROUP, INC.

NYSE: DTG

5330 E. 31st St.
Tulsa, OK 74135
Phone: 918-660-7700
Fax: 918-669-2934
Web: www.dtag.com

CEO: Gary L. Paxton
CFO: Scott L. Thompson
HR: –
FYE: December 31
Type: Public

Drivers hoping to save a buck might look to Dollar Thrifty Automotive Group (DTG), which rents cars under the Dollar Rent A Car and Thrifty Car Rental brands. Overall, Dollar and Thrifty rent cars from about 830 locations in the US and Canada, more than half of which are company-owned locations. Both brands target the airport rental market; Thrifty also maintains off-airport locations. The combined DTG fleet of more than 140,000 vehicles is made up mainly of Chrysler models. Although the brands retain distinct identities, key operations and administrative functions have been consolidated under the DTG umbrella.

	Annual Growth	12/03	12/04	12/05	12/06	12/07
Sales ($ mil.)	9.4%	1,227.9	1,424.0	1,507.6	1,660.7	1,760.8
Net income ($ mil.)	(50.4%)	19.8	50.8	76.4	51.7	1.2
Market value ($ mil.)	(5.8%)	647.5	756.2	915.1	1,071.1	508.8
Employees	0.8%	—	8,300	8,400	8,500	8,500

DOLLAR TREE, INC.

NASDAQ (GS): DLTR

500 Volvo Pkwy.
Chesapeake, VA 23320
Phone: 757-321-5000
Fax: 757-321-5111
Web: www.dollartree.com

CEO: Robert (Bob) Sasser
CFO: Kathleen E. Mallas
HR: James E. Fothergill
FYE: Saturday nearest January 31
Type: Public

Dollars may not grow on trees, but outlets of Dollar Tree's stores seem to. The company operates more than 3,400 Dollar Tree, Deal$, and Dollar Bills discount stores in 48 states, that sell a changing mix of housewares, toys, seasonal items, food, health and beauty aids, gifts, and books — most priced at $1 or less. About 40% of its merchandise is imported, primarily from China. The stores are located in high-traffic strip centers anchored by mass merchandisers and supermarkets, malls, and in small towns. Dollar Tree bought the Deal$ chain in 2006 and the Greenbacks chain in 2003. Founded in 1986 as Dollar Tree Stores, the company reorganized and changed its name to Dollar Tree, Inc., in 2008.

	Annual Growth	1/04	1/05	1/06	1/07	1/08
Sales ($ mil.)	10.9%	2,799.9	3,126.0	3,393.9	3,969.4	4,242.6
Net income ($ mil.)	3.2%	177.6	180.3	173.9	192.0	201.3
Market value ($ mil.)	(8.9%)	3,624.8	3,022.2	2,667.0	3,163.3	2,495.1
Employees	6.7%	—	—	37,400	42,200	42,600

⊞ DOMINICK'S FINER FOODS, LLC

711 Jorie Blvd.
Oak Brook, IL 60523
Phone: 630-891-5000
Fax: 630-891-5210
Web: www.dominicks.com

CEO: Don Keprta
CFO: Tom Frey
HR: Dwayne Howard
FYE: Saturday nearest December 31
Type: Subsidiary

Dominick's Finer Foods is still an unhappy member of the large Safeway family. The company is the second-largest supermarket operator in the metropolitan Chicago area (after the SUPERVALU-owned Jewel-Osco supermarket chain). Dominick's has about 80 stores, including about 30 "Lifestyle" stores with upscale deli and bakery departments and expanded produce areas, floral departments, and in-store cafes. The rest are mostly conventional supermarkets. Dominick's also operates a commissary that produces its prepared foods. Supermarket giant Safeway, which bought Dominick's in 1998, has decided to keep the chain, which was on the block in the early 2000s, but failed to attract a buyer.

	Annual Growth	12/03	12/04	12/05	12/06	12/07
Est. sales ($ mil.)	—	—	—	—	—	1,952.8
Employees	—	—	—	—	—	18,000

DOMINION ENTERPRISES

150 Granby St.
Norfolk, VA 23510
Phone: 757-351-7000
Fax: 757-314-2500
Web: www.dominionenterprises.com

CEO: Conrad M. Hall
CFO: Cathy Cheny
HR: Sunny Sonner
FYE: December 31
Type: Subsidiary

Dominion Enterprises can help you sell what you've got, no matter what it is. The company publishes information and provides resources in the real estate, apartment, specialty vehicle, employment, and travel industries. Its more than 500 magazine titles include *Boat Trader*, *The Employment Guide*, and *For Rent*. Dominion Enterprises also operates more than 40 Web sites, such as Homes.com, ForRent.com, and TraderOnline.com. In addition, the company owns businesses that offer Internet marketing, Web site design and hosting, lead generation, customer relationship management software, and data capture and distribution services. Dominion Enterprises is a unit of Landmark Communications.

	Annual Growth	12/03	12/04	12/05	12/06	12/07
Est. sales ($ mil.)	—	—	—	—	—	427.5
Employees	—	—	—	—	—	5,700

DOMINION HOMES, INC.

Pink Sheets: DHOM

5000 Tuttle Crossing Blvd.
Dublin, OH 43016
Phone: 614-356-5000
Fax: 614-356-6010
Web: www.dominionhomes.com

CEO: Douglas G. (Doug) Borror
CFO: William G. Cornely
HR: –
FYE: December 31
Type: Public

Dominion Homes is the master of its domain: some 60 communities in central Ohio, with around 16% of the market, and in and around Louisville and Lexington, Kentucky. Dominion Homes annually builds around 1,300 single-family entry-level, move-up, and executive homes that range from about 1,000 sq. ft. to 3,500 sq. ft. and from about $100,000 to more than $400,000. A joint venture with Wells Fargo offers mortgage services, and affiliate Alliance Title Agency sells title insurance. In 2008 Dominion Homes was taken private by a group of investors including founder and CEO Donald Borror, Silver Point Capital, and Angelo, Gordon.

	Annual Growth	12/03	12/04	12/05	12/06	12/07
Sales ($ mil.)	(28.4%)	563.5	542.0	415.7	256.8	148.0
Net income ($ mil.)	—	31.8	20.2	5.3	(34.0)	(82.2)
Employees	—	—	—	434	—	—

DOMINION RESOURCES BLACK WARRIOR TRUST

NYSE: DOM

901 Main St., Ste. 1700
Dallas, TX 75202
Phone: 214-209-2400
Fax: 214-209-2431
Web: www.dom-dominionblackwarriortrust.com

CEO: Ron E. Hooper
CFO: –
HR: –
FYE: December 31
Type: Public

Dominion Resources Black Warrior Trust knows that when the wells get old, financial warriors (aka shareholders) don't give up on the economic possibilities. The trust holds royalty interests in 532 natural gas producing wells and is set to terminate when these wells no longer produce enough gas to be profitable. The trust receives, then distributes to shareholders, 65% of the gross proceeds that Dominion Resources (via its subsidiary Dominion Black Warrior Basin) earns by selling the natural gas from its wells in the Black Warrior Basin of Alabama. In 2007 the trust had proved reserves of 26.9 billion cu. ft. of natural gas equivalent.

	Annual Growth	12/03	12/04	12/05	12/06	12/07
Sales ($ mil.)	1.4%	20.8	24.4	32.0	31.5	22.0
Net income ($ mil.)	1.4%	19.8	23.5	31.0	30.5	20.9
Market value ($ mil.)	(10.7%)	223.7	283.4	380.7	207.5	142.5
Employees						

⊞ An in-depth profile of this company is available to Hoover's Online members at hoovers.com.

509

DOMINION RESOURCES, INC.

NYSE: D

120 Tredegar St.
Richmond, VA 23219
Phone: 804-819-2000
Fax: 804-819-2233
Web: www.dom.com

CEO: Thomas F. Farrell II
CFO: Thomas N. Chewning
HR: –
FYE: December 31
Type: Public

And darkness shall have no dominion, as far as Dominion Resources is concerned. Through its Dominion Virginia Power the company transmits and distributes electricity to 2.4 million customers and natural gas to 1.7 million customers in five states. Its Dominion Generation unit manages the company's regulated and nonregulated power plants (26,500 MW of owned or controlled capacity); subsidiary Dominion Energy trades and markets energy, oversees 6,000 miles of natural gas pipelines, and operates underground gas storage facilities (975 billion cu. ft. of capacity). In 2007 Dominion sold most of its oil and gas exploration and production assets for a total of nearly $14 billion.

	Annual Growth	12/03	12/04	12/05	12/06	12/07
Sales ($ mil.)	6.7%	12,078.0	13,972.0	18,041.0	16,482.0	15,674.0
Net income ($ mil.)	68.1%	318.0	1,249.0	1,033.0	1,380.0	2,539.0
Market value ($ mil.)	27.5%	10,372.4	11,515.8	13,394.2	14,630.1	27,378.7
Employees	(1.2%)	—	—	17,400	17,500	17,000

DOMINO'S PIZZA, INC.

NYSE: DPZ

30 Frank Lloyd Wright Dr.
Ann Arbor, MI 48106
Phone: 734-930-3030
Fax: 734-747-6210
Web: www.dominos.com

CEO: David A. Brandon
CFO: Wendy A. Beck
HR: Patricia A. (Patti) Wilmot
FYE: Sunday nearest December 31
Type: Public

Domino's knows the rules of the pizza delivery game. The company is the world's #2 pizza chain (behind YUM! Brands' Pizza Hut division), with more than 8,600 delivery locations in more than 50 countries. (The chain includes more than 5,100 stores in the US.) Domino's menu features several different styles of pizza with a wide array of topping options, as well as bread sticks, cheese bread, and chicken wings. Its stores are principally delivery locations and generally do not have any dine-in seating. The company owns and operates about 570 locations in the US, while the rest are franchised. Bain Capital owns nearly 30% of the company.

	Annual Growth	12/03	12/04	12/05	12/06	12/07
Sales ($ mil.)	2.3%	1,333.3	1,446.5	1,511.6	1,437.3	1,462.9
Net income ($ mil.)	(0.7%)	39.0	62.3	108.3	106.2	37.9
Market value ($ mil.)	(30.5%)	—	—	1,625.9	1,748.6	785.2
Employees	(2.5%)	—	13,500	13,500	13,300	12,500

DON DAVIS AUTO GROUP, INC.

1901 N Collins St.
Arlington, TX 76011
Phone: 817-461-1000
Fax: 817-679-0610
Web: www.dondavisautogroup.com

CEO: Robert Howard
CFO: Jim Brown
HR: Rosellen Dugan
FYE: December 31
Type: Private

The Don Davis Auto Group rounds up wheels for Rangers and Cowboys fans. The company sells new cars and trucks from Chrysler, Dodge, Ford, Jeep, Lincoln-Mercury, Nissan, Scion, and Toyota at about half a dozen dealerships in Arlington and Grapevine, Texas. The Don Davis Auto Group also sells used cars and provides collision repair and service. It moves about 8,000 vehicles each year. The group was founded in 1979 by Don Davis, who owns 80% of the capital stock. CEO Robert Howard owns the other 20%.

	Annual Growth	12/03	12/04	12/05	12/06	12/07
Est. sales ($ mil.)	—	—	—	—	—	287.2
Employees	—	—	—	—	—	865

DON MIGUEL MEXICAN FOODS, INC.

2125 E. Orangewood Ave.
Anaheim, CA 92806
Phone: 714-634-8441
Fax: 714-937-0493
Web: www.donmiguel.com

CEO: Robert Schult Jr.
CFO: Michael Chaignot
HR: –
FYE: November 30
Type: Private

Don Miguel Mexican Foods makes tastebuds say "Olé!" The company manufactures and sells refrigerated and frozen Mexican meals and snacks for the retail market. Its brands include Don Miguel, El Charrito, Piñata, Lean Olé, and XLNT, and its products include frozen burritos, tacos, taquitos, tamales, and family-style dinner entrees, as well as fresh tortillas and chili mixes. The company's manufacturing facility is in Dallas (it closed its Anaheim, California, plant in 2006). Don Miguel is owned by private investment firm TSG Consumer Partners (formerly The Shansby Group).

	Annual Growth	11/03	11/04	11/05	11/06	11/07
Est. sales ($ mil.)	—	—	—	—	—	55.2
Employees	—	—	—	—	—	600

DONALDSON COMPANY, INC.

NYSE: DCI

1400 W. 94th St.
Minneapolis, MN 55431
Phone: 952-887-3131
Fax: 952-887-3155
Web: www.donaldson.com

CEO: William M. (Bill) Cook
CFO: Thomas R. (Tom) VerHage
HR: Sandra N. Joppa
FYE: July 31
Type: Public

Think of Donaldson as a Felix Unger of the industrial world. The company makes filtration systems designed to remove contaminants from air and liquids. Donaldson's engine products business makes air intake and exhaust systems, liquid-filtration systems, and replacement parts; products are sold to manufacturers of construction, mining, and transportation equipment, as well as parts distributors and fleet operators. Caterpillar accounts for 10% of Donaldson's overall sales. The company's industrial products include dust, fume, and mist collectors and air filtration systems used in industrial gas turbines, computer disk drives, and manufacturers' clean rooms.

	Annual Growth	7/03	7/04	7/05	7/06	7/07
Sales ($ mil.)	12.0%	1,218.3	1,415.0	1,595.7	1,694.3	1,918.8
Net income ($ mil.)	12.1%	95.3	106.3	110.6	132.3	150.7
Market value ($ mil.)	28.4%	1,058.3	2,297.7	2,706.1	2,649.0	2,880.0
Employees	3.6%	—	—	11,180	11,500	12,000

DONEGAL GROUP INC.

NASDAQ (GS): DGICA

1195 River Rd.
Marietta, PA 17547
Phone: 717-426-1931
Fax: 717-426-7009
Web: www.donegalgroup.com

CEO: Donald H. Nikolaus
CFO: Jeffrey D. Miller
HR: Kevin G. Burke
FYE: December 31
Type: Public

"Risk" is Donegal Group's middle name. Through about five subsidiaries, including Atlantic States Insurance and Southern Insurance Company of Virginia, Donegal Group provides clients in 18 mid-Atlantic, midwestern, and southeastern states with personal, farm, and commercial property/casualty insurance products. The group's personal insurance offerings range from auto and boat policies to homeowners and fire coverage; its commercial insurance products include business owners, multi-peril, and workers' compensation. Donegal Group has a joint banking venture with Donegal Mutual Insurance, which owns about 65% of the company; the venture, federal savings bank Province Bank, has three branches in Pennsylvania.

	Annual Growth	12/03	12/04	12/05	12/06	12/07
Assets ($ mil.)	8.5%	602.0	735.4	781.4	831.7	834.1
Net income ($ mil.)	20.3%	18.3	31.6	37.0	40.2	38.3
Market value ($ mil.)	29.3%	121.4	133.1	248.6	385.7	339.2
Employees	—	—	—	—	—	—

DONNA KARAN INTERNATIONAL INC.

550 7th Ave.
New York, NY 10018
Phone: 212-789-1500
Fax: –
Web: www.donnakaran.com

CEO: Mark Weber
CFO: Tisha Kalberer
HR: Christina Nichols
FYE: Sunday nearest December 31
Type: Subsidiary

Known for clothes both classic and comfortable, Donna Karan International (DKI) defines the metropolitan flair that bridges the difference between stylishly casual and conventional. The firm designs and sells men's and women's clothes, including suits, sportswear, accessories, and shoes, under the Donna Karan New York, DKNY, DKNY Jeans, and DKNY Active labels. DKI sells to upscale department and specialty stores and through its own retail stores. It also licenses third parties to run most of its international stores. Fashion leviathan LVMH holds a majority stake in DKI. Designer Donna Karan still remains in creative control of her company's fashion lines, but has struggled to rejuvenate the Donna Karan brand.

	Annual Growth	12/03	12/04	12/05	12/06	12/07
Est. sales ($ mil.)	—	—	—	—	—	95.8
Employees	—	—	—	—	—	2,060

DOPACO, INC.

100 Arrandale Blvd.
Exton, PA 19341
Phone: 610-269-1776
Fax: 610-524-9188
Web: www.dopaco.com

CEO: Robert Cauffman
CFO: Rick Scanlan
HR: Don Heisey
FYE: December 31
Type: Subsidiary

A "does packaging company," Dopaco manufactures folding cartons, beverage cups and lids (both hot and cold), carriers, nested cartons and dispensers, clamshells, food trays, and paper plates for the food service industry. It also provides customized packaging design services. Major customers include Jack in the Box, Burger King, McDonald's, and Wendy's. With its headquarters located in Pennsylvania, Dopaco owns and operates eight plants in North America, but in 2008 it announced the closure of its Bakersfield, California, plant. Dopaco is a subsidiary of manufacturing giant Cascades Inc.

DOR BIOPHARMA INC.

OTC: DORB

850 Bear Tavern Rd.
Ewing, NJ 08628
Phone: 786-425-3848
Fax: 786-425-3853
Web: www.dorbiopharma.com

CEO: Christopher J. Schaber
CFO: Evan Myrianthopoulos
HR: –
FYE: December 31
Type: Public

DOR BioPharma is opening the door to more effective biodefense. The company's BioDefense unit is focusing on the development of nasally administered vaccines for such bioterror threats as ricin and botulinum toxins. Ricin vaccine candidate RiVax is in early-stage clinical trials. Through its BioTherapeutics division, DOR BioPharma is developing lead candidate orBec, an orally administered drug using the same active ingredient as GlaxoSmithKline's allergy and asthma drug Beconase; orBec is a potential therapy for intestinal graft-versus-host disease, a life-threatening complication of bone marrow transplantation.

	Annual Growth	12/03	12/04	12/05	12/06	12/07
Sales ($ mil.)	89.9%	0.1	1.0	3.1	2.3	1.3
Net income ($ mil.)	—	(5.3)	(5.9)	(4.7)	(8.2)	(6.2)
Market value ($ mil.)	(12.1%)	27.1	27.1	13.7	16.5	16.1
Employees	—	—	—	8	—	—

DORAL FINANCIAL CORPORATION

NYSE: DRL

1451 Franklin D. Roosevelt Ave.
San Juan, PR 00920
Phone: 787-474-6700
Fax: –
Web: www.doralfinancial.com

CEO: Glen R. Wakeman
CFO: Marangal I. Domingo
HR: Lesbia Blanco
FYE: December 31
Type: Public

The Caribbean is home to more than just sun and fun. Doral Financial offers mortgage, retail, and business banking in Puerto Rico. Traditionally known as a mortgage-banking concern, the company has refocused its efforts to become a broader based community banking institution. The company's Doral Bank has about 40 branches in the Commonwealth. In addition to mortgages, Doral Financial offers construction, business, consumer, and other loans. Besides providing mortgage banking services through Doral Bank, the company sells insurance products through Doral Insurance Agency. Doral Financial is shuttering its investment activities; it gave up its broker license and its membership in FINRA in 2007.

	Annual Growth	12/03	12/04	12/05	12/06	12/07
Assets ($ mil.)	(2.7%)	10,394.0	17,835.7	17,298.8	11,856.4	9,304.4
Net income ($ mil.)	—	321.3	214.8	13.2	(223.9)	(170.9)
Market value ($ mil.)	(65.6%)	69,662.8	106,290.2	22,881.2	6,196.2	970.7
Employees	—	—	—	—	1,278	—

DORCHESTER MINERALS, L.P.

NASDAQ (GM): DMLP

3838 Oak Lawn Ave., Ste. 300
Dallas, TX 75219
Phone: 214-559-0300
Fax: 214-559-0301

CEO: William Casey McManemin
CFO: H. C. Allen Jr.
HR: –
FYE: December 31
Type: Public

The stakeholders of Dorchester Minerals are enjoying the benefits of three natural resource exploitation enterprises that came together as one. The oil and gas exploration company was formed by the 2003 merger of oil trust Dorchester Hugoton with Republic Royalty and Spinnaker Royalty. Dorchester Mineral's holdings include 74,714 net acres in Oklahoma and 7,055 net acres in Kansas. The company holds assets (producing and nonproducing mineral, royalty, overriding royalty, net profits, and leasehold interests) in properties in 573 counties in 25 states. In 2006 it had proved reserves of 668 billion cu. ft. of natural gas and 3.8 million barrels of oil.

	Annual Growth	12/03	12/04	12/05	12/06	12/07
Sales ($ mil.)	7.4%	49.2	56.8	79.8	74.9	65.4
Net income ($ mil.)	—	(26.8)	30.1	52.8	50.2	43.0
Market value ($ mil.)	2.0%	524.9	675.5	719.3	622.1	568.5
Employees	1.9%	—	—	26	—	27

DOREL JUVENILE GROUP, INC.

2525 State St.
Columbus, IN 47201
Phone: 812-372-0141
Fax: 812-372-0893
Web: www.djgusa.com

CEO: Dave Taylor
CFO: Steve Willeke
HR: Tim Ferguson
FYE: December 31
Type: Subsidiary

Getting little ones around town safely is Dorel Juvenile Group's primary push. The company makes infant car seats, strollers, high chairs, changing tables, monitors, and toddler beds and cribs. Dorel Juvenile's own brands include Cosco, Maxi-Cosi, and Safety 1st and in Europe Bébé Confort, Maxi-Cosi, Quinny, Monbébé, Babidéal, Baby Relax, and Safety 1st. It licenses other big-name brands, such as Eddie Bauer, Playskool, and Disney Baby. Dorel Juvenile is a division of Canadian company Dorel Industries. The unit was formed in 2000 when Safety 1st was acquired and its operations were folded into Dorel's existing juvenile operation, Cosco. Dave Taylor succeeded Camillo Lisio as CEO in 2006.

	Annual Growth	12/03	12/04	12/05	12/06	12/07
Est. sales ($ mil.)	—	—	—	—	—	579.1
Employees	—	—	—	—	—	320

An in-depth profile of this company is available to Hoover's Online members at hoovers.com.

511

DORMAN PRODUCTS, INC.

NASDAQ (GM): DORM

3400 E. Walnut St.
Colmar, PA 18915
Phone: 215-997-1800
Fax: 215-997-8577
Web: www.rbinc.com

CEO: Richard N. Berman
CFO: Mathias J. Barton
HR: Penny Boyer
FYE: Last Saturday in December
Type: Public

Dorman Products is singing the blues under a new name. Formerly R&B, Inc., Dorman distributes car parts, fasteners, and service products to the automotive aftermarket from its stock of more than 90,000 auto parts and fasteners. Products include intake manifolds, window handles, oil-drain plugs, and lug nuts. About 90% of Dorman's revenue comes from parts sold under the company's brand names. Dorman sells to retailers such as AutoZone and Advance Auto Parts and to distributors and parts manufacturers for resale under private labels. Brothers Richard and Steven Berman (CEO and EVP, respectively) and their families own about 30% of Dorman.

	Annual Growth	12/03	12/04	12/05	12/06	12/07
Sales ($ mil.)	10.2%	222.1	249.5	278.1	295.8	327.7
Net income ($ mil.)	9.6%	13.3	17.1	17.1	13.8	19.2
Market value ($ mil.)	40.4%	66.0	110.1	168.3	191.8	256.7
Employees	6.9%	—	—	879	961	1,005

DOSKOCIL MANUFACTURING COMPANY, INC.

4209 Barnett Blvd.
Arlington, TX 76017
Phone: 817-467-5116
Fax: 817-472-9810
Web: www.doskocil.com

CEO: Larry E. Rembold
CFO: Susan Richman
HR: Chris Yu
FYE: June 30
Type: Private

Doskocil Manufacturing likes a little of this and a little of that. Through its subsidiaries, the company makes pet carriers, kennels, bedding, exercise pens, feeders, litter pans, and other products for dogs and cats, under the brand Petmate. Doskocil, part of the portfolio of private investment firm Westar, was founded by Ben Doskocil in his garage in 1961. It has grown through acquisitions in recent years, such as its 2006 purchase of Aspen Pet Products, which specializes in pet accessories and manufactures and markets chew toys, treats, leashes, and collars.

DOT FOODS, INC.

1 Dot Way
Mount Sterling, IL 62353
Phone: 217-773-4411
Fax: 217-773-3321
Web: www.dotfoods.com

CEO: John M. Tracy
CFO: William H. (Bill) Metzinger
HR: Mike Hulsen
FYE: December 31
Type: Private

Dot Foods, the largest food service redistributor in the US, started out in business as one station wagon that hauled dairy goods around and went by the name of Associated Dairy Products. The company now owns more than 700 trucks (under the name Dot Transportation) that distribute some 70,000 products including food, flatware, serve ware, and janitorial supplies from some 700 manufacturers to its customers — more than 3,300 food service distributors. Dot has about 10 distribution facilities located across the country. Its edotfoods unit offers ordering and fulfillment services online. The company also sells food ingredients to dairies, bakeries, confectioners, meat processors, and other food manufacturers.

	Annual Growth	12/02	12/03	12/04	12/05	12/06
Sales ($ mil.)	15.3%	1,410.0	1,573.0	1,930.0	2,164.0	2,490.0
Employees	9.9%	2,000	2,200	2,500	2,746	2,916

DOT HILL SYSTEMS CORP.

NASDAQ (GM): HILL

2200 Faraday Ave., Ste. 100
Carlsbad, CA 92008
Phone: 760-931-5500
Fax: 760-931-5527
Web: www.dothill.com

CEO: Dana W. Kammersgard
CFO: Hanif I. Jamal
HR: –
FYE: December 31
Type: Public

Dot Hill Systems attacks data storage problems. The company makes RAID (redundant array of independent disks) storage products. Dot Hill targets enterprises in data-intensive industries such as financial services and telecommunications with its SANnet storage area networks (SANs) offerings. It outsources its manufacturing to companies such as Flextronics, MiTAC, and SYNNEX. Dot Hill has shifted away from direct sales to selling through channel partners; key partner Sun Microsystems resells the company's SANnet products. The company has agreements with Network Appliance and Fujitsu Siemens Computers to jointly design and develop data storage products.

	Annual Growth	12/03	12/04	12/05	12/06	12/07
Sales ($ mil.)	2.5%	187.4	239.4	233.8	239.2	207.1
Net income ($ mil.)	—	12.1	11.6	26.6	(80.8)	(60.2)
Market value ($ mil.)	(35.8%)	656.1	342.3	308.8	176.9	111.3
Employees	(2.6%)	—	—	275	269	261

DOTS, INC.

30801 Carter St.
Solon, OH 44139
Phone: 440-349-7000
Fax: 440-349-7001
Web: www.dots.com

CEO: Robert A. (Bob) Glick
CFO: J.E. (Rick) Bunka
HR: –
FYE: December 31
Type: Private

DOTS operates about 400 women's clothing and accessory stores in two dozen states, mostly along the East Coast and in the Midwest. The stores, which target female shoppers between the ages of 18 and 45, sell low-priced fashion apparel and accessories for the junior, misses, and plus-size markets. The fast-growing company has been opening new stores in some big markets, including Texas and Georgia. Overall, the apparel and accessories chain is aiming to open 150 new stores by 2010. William Blair Capital Partners owns a nearly 48% equity interest in DOTS, which has plans for continued national expansion, including California eventually.

	Annual Growth	12/03	12/04	12/05	12/06	12/07
Est. sales ($ mil.)	—	—	—	—	—	136.7
Employees	—	—	—	—	—	2,500

DOUBLE EAGLE PETROLEUM CO.

NASDAQ (GS): DBLE

777 Overland Trail, Ste. 206
Casper, WY 82601
Phone: 307-237-9330
Fax: 307-266-1823
Web: www.dble.us

CEO: Richard D. (Dick) Dole
CFO: Kurtis Hooley
HR: Carol A. Osborne
FYE: December 31
Type: Public

It's double or nothing for Double Eagle Petroleum (formerly Double Eagle Petroleum and Mining) which gambles on hitting pay dirt as it explores for and produces oil and gas in the Rocky Mountains of Utah and Wyoming. Double Eagle Petroleum owns interests in 664 producing wells, and natural gas accounts for 96% of the oil and gas independent's production. The company has proved reserves of more than 360,000 barrels of oil and 48.5 billion cu. ft. of natural gas, and leases acreage in seven states. Double Eagle Petroleum sells its oil and gas on the spot market. Former CEO Stephen Hollis owns 8.5% of the company.

	Annual Growth	12/03	12/04	12/05	12/06	12/07
Sales ($ mil.)	29.6%	6.1	13.3	20.5	19.0	17.2
Net income ($ mil.)	—	1.0	4.0	4.0	2.1	(11.6)
Market value ($ mil.)	3.2%	127.1	165.1	175.2	212.1	144.2
Employees	—	—	14	—	—	—

⊞ DOUBLECLICK INC.

111 8th Ave., 10th Fl.
New York, NY 10011
Phone: 212-271-2542
Fax: 212-287-1203
Web: www.doubleclick.com

CEO: David S. Rosenblatt
CFO: Charles T. (Charlie) Dickson
HR: Debbie Josephs
FYE: December 31
Type: Subsidiary

Help with online advertising is only a DoubleClick away. The company provides targeted online display advertising placement and scheduling services for both advertisers and Web site publishers through its DART suite of products and services. DoubleClick also offers consulting services and research reports related to online advertising. The company's Performics unit provides search engine results placement and affiliate marketing services. Overall, DoubleClick has more than 30 offices and data centers across the US, Europe, and the Asia/Pacific region. DoubleClick is a unit of Internet search giant Google, which acquired the company in March 2008.

	Annual Growth	12/03	12/04	12/05	12/06	12/07
Est. sales ($ mil.)	—	—	—	—	—	346.7
Employees	—	—	—	—	—	850

DOUBLE-TAKE SOFTWARE, INC.

NASDAQ (GM): DBTK

257 Turnpike Rd., Ste. 210
Southborough, MA 01772
Phone: 877-335-5674
Fax: 508-229-0866
Web: www.nsisoftware.com

CEO: Dean F. Goodermote
CFO: S. Craig Huke
HR: –
FYE: December 31
Type: Public

Double-Take Software helps companies take a second look at their data protection. Formerly called NSI Software, the company provides data replication and storage software designed to help businesses protect and manage data assets. It also offers professional services such as consulting, implementation, support, and training. The company's customers come from fields such as education, financial and legal services, government, health care, manufacturing, retail, and telecommunications. Double-Take sells to server makers such as Dell and Hewlett-Packard, distributors including Bell Microproducts and Tech Data, and through resellers.

	Annual Growth	12/03	12/04	12/05	12/06	12/07
Sales ($ mil.)	36.4%	23.9	29.8	40.7	60.8	82.8
Net income ($ mil.)	—	(8.0)	(8.0)	(3.8)	6.8	20.1
Market value ($ mil.)	78.4%	—	—	—	267.0	476.3
Employees	15.3%	200	—	—	301	354

DOUGLAS EMMETT, INC.

NYSE: DEI

808 Wilshire Blvd., Ste. 200
Santa Monica, CA 90401
Phone: 310-255-7700
Fax: 310-255-7888
Web: www.douglasemmett.com

CEO: Jordan L. Kaplan
CFO: William Kamer
HR: –
FYE: December 31
Type: Public

Office Space is more than a movie to Douglas Emmett. The self-administered and self-managed real estate investment trust (REIT) invests in and manages commercial and multifamily properties. It owns about 50 office properties (totaling 11.8 million sq. ft.) in the heart of Hollywood and surrounding areas and in Hawaii. The REIT owns the famed Sherman Oaks Galleria, an open-air mall and office-space development in Southern California. The company also has nearly 3,000 apartment units in tony West Los Angeles neighborhoods and Honolulu. Douglas Emmett's holdings include some of the most notable addresses on the West Coast, such as Burbank's Studio Plaza and office tower 100 Wilshire. The REIT went public in 2006.

	Annual Growth	12/03	12/04	12/05	12/06	12/07
Sales ($ mil.)	97.6%	34.0	33.4	35.2	433.7	518.2
Net income ($ mil.)	—	9.7	9.3	9.6	(37.0)	(13.0)
Market value ($ mil.)	(18.8%)	—	—	—	3,058.0	2,483.3
Employees	9.5%	—	—	400	400	480

DOV PHARMACEUTICAL, INC.

Pink Sheets: DOVP

150 Pierce St.
Somerset, NJ 08873
Phone: 732-907-3600
Fax: 732-907-3799
Web: www.dovpharm.com

CEO: Barbara G. Duncan
CFO: Barbara G. Duncan
HR: Delia Cottrell
FYE: December 31
Type: Public

DOV Pharmaceutical is all lovey-dovey with neurotransmitter receptors. The biopharmaceutical company primarily focuses on products that treat central nervous system disorders. One of its lead candidates is a triple reuptake inhibitor called DOV 21,947, which is designed to treat depression and obesity. Its bicifadine and diltiazem candidates are undergoing clinical trials for postsurgical pain and hypertension, respectively. Indiplon, which is supposed to treat insomnia, is under discussions with the FDA and may be subject to additional requirements before it can be commercialized. DOV Pharmaceutical has development alliances with XTL Biopharmaceuticals, Blue Note Pharmaceuticals, and Neurocrine Biosciences.

	Annual Growth	12/03	12/04	12/05	12/06	12/07
Sales ($ mil.)	35.8%	3.0	2.5	8.6	26.0	10.2
Net income ($ mil.)	—	(26.7)	(32.9)	(53.0)	(38.4)	(7.6)
Market value ($ mil.)	(55.1%)	220.5	409.2	339.0	7.2	9.0
Employees	—	—	—	111	—	—

⊞ DOVER CORPORATION

NYSE: DOV

280 Park Ave., Fl. 34W
New York, NY 10017
Phone: 212-922-1640
Fax: 212-922-1656
Web: www.dovercorporation.com

CEO: Ronald L. (Ron) Hoffman
CFO: Robert G. Kuhbach
HR: –
FYE: December 31
Type: Public

The "D" in Dover could stand for diversity. Dover manages more than 40 companies that make equipment ranging from garbage trucks to ink-jet printers. Undoing a 2004 reorganization, Dover has realigned its operating companies from six segments into four: Electronic Technologies, Engineered Systems, Fluid Management, and Industrial Products. Dover sees a number of benefits from the corporate reorganization, including more defined market segments and greater clarity for shareholders and Wall Street. The US accounts for more than half of Dover's sales.

	Annual Growth	12/03	12/04	12/05	12/06	12/07
Sales ($ mil.)	13.1%	4,413.3	5,488.1	6,078.4	6,511.6	7,226.1
Net income ($ mil.)	22.6%	292.9	412.8	510.1	561.8	661.1
Market value ($ mil.)	2.6%	8,065.8	8,534.6	8,213.4	10,015.6	8,943.3
Employees	6.8%	25,700	28,100	31,650	33,000	33,400

DOVER DOWNS GAMING & ENTERTAINMENT, INC.

NYSE: DDE

1131 N. DuPont Hwy.
Dover, DE 19901
Phone: 302-674-4600
Fax: 302-857-3253
Web: www.doverdowns.com

CEO: Denis McGlynn
CFO: Timothy R. Horne
HR: –
FYE: December 31
Type: Public

Dover Downs Gaming & Entertainment is betting on being the first stop for gamblers in the First State. Spun off from Dover Motorsports, the company operates three facilities, all in Dover, Delaware, adjacent to Dover Motorsports' Dover Downs International Speedway. Dover Downs Casino is home to more than 2,500 video slot machines; Dover Downs Hotel and Conference Center is a 500-room hotel featuring ballroom, concert hall, and meeting room facilities; and Dover Downs Raceway features harness racing and simulcast horse race betting.

	Annual Growth	12/03	12/04	12/05	12/06	12/07
Sales ($ mil.)	6.4%	188.8	227.7	216.9	236.4	242.4
Net income ($ mil.)	11.0%	17.2	16.4	26.0	25.3	26.1
Market value ($ mil.)	26.3%	65.2	81.8	100.4	206.1	165.8
Employees	(0.9%)	—	—	922	—	906

⊞ An in-depth profile of this company is available to Hoover's Online members at hoovers.com.

513

DOVER MOTORSPORTS, INC.

NYSE: DVD

1131 N. DuPont Hwy.
Dover, DE 19901
Phone: 302-674-4600
Fax: –
Web: www.dovermotorsportsinc.com

CEO: Denis McGlynn
CFO: Timothy R. Horne
HR: Jamie Libby
FYE: December 31
Type: Public

This company makes its money when rubber meets the pavement at one of its tracks. Dover Motorsports is a leading operator of racetracks that host more than a dozen top auto racing events each year. Its tracks include Gateway International Raceway near St. Louis, Memphis Motorsports Park, Nashville Superspeedway, and its flagship Dover International Speedway in Delaware. The tracks hold events sponsored by all the major US racing leagues, including NASCAR, the Indy Racing League, and the National Hot Rod Association. Chairman Henry Tippie has more than 50% voting control of the company as executor of the estate of the late chairman John Rollins.

	Annual Growth	12/03	12/04	12/05	12/06	12/07
Sales ($ mil.)	(2.1%)	93.6	93.6	91.0	91.3	86.1
Net income ($ mil.)	—	(22.1)	2.4	4.6	(35.3)	3.7
Market value ($ mil.)	17.2%	58.0	97.1	100.8	86.8	109.5
Employees	—	—	—	139	—	—

DOVER SADDLERY, INC.

NASDAQ (GM): DOVR

525 Great Rd.
Littleton, MA 01460
Phone: 978-952-8062
Fax: 978-952-8065
Web: www.doversaddlery.com

CEO: Stephen L. Day
CFO: Michael W. Bruns
HR: –
FYE: December 31
Type: Public

Dover Saddlery is an upscale specialty retailer and direct marketer of equestrian products. The company's specialty is English-style riding gear, and its selection features riding apparel, tack, and stable supplies, as well as horse health care products. Its brand-name products include names such as Ariat, Grand Prix, Hermes, Mountain Horse, Passier, Prestige, and Smith Brothers. Dover sells through catalogs, a Web site, and about 10 retail stores in the northeastern US and Texas operating under the Dover Saddlery and Smith Brothers banners. The company was founded in 1975 by US Equestrian Team members, including company directors Jim and Dave Powers.

	Annual Growth	12/03	12/04	12/05	12/06	12/07
Sales ($ mil.)	11.6%	52.5	58.7	62.7	73.1	81.4
Net income ($ mil.)	(11.4%)	1.3	1.4	0.8	1.4	0.8
Market value ($ mil.)	(33.5%)	—	—	40.6	36.7	18.0
Employees	43.0%	—	—	330	472	—

DOW AGROSCIENCES LLC

9330 Zionsville Rd.
Indianapolis, IN 46268
Phone: 317-337-3000
Fax: –
Web: www.dowagro.com

CEO: Jerome A. Peribere
CFO: Gordon Slack
HR: Nick Gray
FYE: December 31
Type: Subsidiary

Dow AgroSciences, a subsidiary of Dow Chemical, doesn't want its customers to be bugged. The subsidiary makes insecticides, herbicides, and fungicides for agricultural applications, as well as for residential pest control. It also develops genetically modified (GM) seeds under the Mycogen and Phytogen names. Dow AgroSciences splits its operations into five product lines: plant genetics and biotechnology (in addition to seeds, the unit has developed food products like the heart-healthy Natreon canola oil), weed management, disease management, pest management, and urban pest management. It has operations in more than 50 countries.

THE DOW CHEMICAL COMPANY

NYSE: DOW

2030 Dow Center
Midland, MI 48674
Phone: 989-636-1000
Fax: 989-832-1556
Web: www.dow.com

CEO: Andrew N. Liveris
CFO: Geoffery E. (Geoff) Merszei
HR: Julie Fasone Holder
FYE: December 31
Type: Public

Dow Chemical is a leader in the production of plastics, chemicals, hydrocarbons, and agrochemicals. The largest chemical company in the US and #2 worldwide (ahead of ExxonMobil and behind BASF), Dow also is a leader in performance plastics (engineering plastics, polyurethanes, and materials for Dow Automotive). Other products include polyethylene resins for packaging (such as Styrofoam-brand insulation), fibers, and films, as well as performance chemicals such as acrylic acid. The company also manufactures commodity chemicals (chlor-alkalies and glycols) and agricultural chemicals. Its Hydrocarbons and Energy unit makes petrochemicals. Dow makes more than 3,000 products.

	Annual Growth	12/03	12/04	12/05	12/06	12/07
Sales ($ mil.)	13.2%	32,632.0	40,161.0	46,307.0	49,124.0	53,513.0
Net income ($ mil.)	13.7%	1,730.0	2,797.0	4,515.0	3,724.0	2,887.0
Market value ($ mil.)	(1.0%)	38,554.0	47,179.4	42,380.8	38,226.2	37,069.2
Employees	4.0%	—	—	42,413	42,578	45,856

DOW CORNING CORPORATION

2200 W. Salzburg Rd.
Midland, MI 48640
Phone: 989-496-4000
Fax: 989-496-4393
Web: www.dowcorning.com

CEO: Stephanie A. Burns
CFO: Joseph D. (Don) Sheets
HR: Derek A. O'Malley-Keyes
FYE: December 31
Type: Joint venture

Dow Corning knows about cooperation. The company began as a joint venture of chemical titan Dow and glass giant Corning in 1943 and ranks among the longest lasting partnerships of its kind in the US. Dow Corning produces more than 7,000 silicone-based products such as adhesives, insulating materials, and lubricants for aerospace, automotive, and electrical uses. Because silicone does not conduct electricity, it is also used in its hard polycrystalline form (silicon) as the material on which semiconductors are built. With plants worldwide, the company sells more than half of its products outside the US. Through its Xiameter brand and Web site, Dow Corning sells products online to more than 80 countries.

	Annual Growth	12/02	12/03	12/04	12/05	12/06
Sales ($ mil.)	13.9%	2,610.1	2,872.5	3,372.6	3,878.7	4,391.6
Net income ($ mil.)	83.7%	58.7	176.6	238.3	506.5	668.4
Employees	2.4%	8,200	8,200	—	—	9,000

DOW JONES & COMPANY, INC.

1 World Financial Center, 200 Liberty St.
New York, NY 10281
Phone: 212-416-2000
Fax: 413-592-4783
Web: www.dj.com

CEO: Leslie F. (Les) Hinton
CFO: Stephen Daintith
HR: Susie Frazelle
FYE: December 31
Type: Subsidiary

Dow Jones & Company has its finger on the pulse of the global economy. A leading provider of news and business information, the company publishes *The Wall Street Journal,* the leading financial daily and one of the most widely read US newspapers, with a circulation of about 2 million. Dow Jones also publishes international editions of the *Journal,* as well as a portfolio of community newspapers through its Ottaway Newspapers subsidiary. The company also owns online business news site MarketWatch, operates research service Factiva, and publishes *Barron's.* In addition, Dow Jones offers syndicated news, financial information, and stock market data. Rupert Murdoch's News Corporation acquired Dow Jones in 2007.

	Annual Growth	12/02	12/03	12/04	12/05	12/06
Sales ($ mil.)	3.4%	1,559.2	1,548.5	1,671.5	1,769.7	1,783.9
Net income ($ mil.)	17.7%	201.5	170.6	99.6	60.4	386.6
Employees	2.1%	6,816	—	6,500	6,900	7,400

DOWNEY FINANCIAL CORP.

NYSE: DSL

3501 Jamboree Rd.
Newport Beach, CA 92660
Phone: 949-854-3100
Fax: 949-854-4979
Web: www.downeysavings.com

CEO: Daniel D. Rosenthal
CFO: Brian E. Côté
HR: Kendice K. Briggs
FYE: December 31
Type: Public

Looking for Downy softness? Try your grocer. Looking for Downey Financial? Well, try your grocer. Downey Financial is the holding company for Downey Savings and Loan Association, which operates more than 170 branches, mostly in California, but also in Arizona (about half of which are located in supermarkets). The thrift offers transaction products such as savings, checking, and money market accounts and CDs. Its lending activities focus on originating first mortgages secured by residential properties. It also makes commercial, construction, and other consumer loans. The bank opened its first branch in 1957 in Downey, California.

	Annual Growth	12/03	12/04	12/05	12/06	12/07
Assets ($ mil.)	3.6%	11,646.0	15,648.8	17,094.3	16,209.4	13,409.1
Net income ($ mil.)	—	101.7	107.7	217.4	205.2	(56.6)
Market value ($ mil.)	(11.2%)	1,392.0	1,587.7	1,904.9	2,021.6	866.5
Employees	(16.2%)	—	—	2,633	2,625	1,850

DPAC TECHNOLOGIES CORP.

OTC: DPAC

5675 Hudson Industrial Park
Hudson, OH 44236
Phone: 330-655-9000
Fax: 330-655-9070
Web: www.dpactech.com

CEO: Steven D. (Steve) Runkel
CFO: Stephen J. (Steve) Vukadinovich
HR: –
FYE: December 31
Type: Public

DPAC Technologies takes networking to the air. Through its QuaTech subsidiary, the company provides device connectivity and wireless networking products. Its offerings include the Airborne line of wireless LAN modules, which are made to be easily embedded into existing designs for electronic gear. The company also has a line of plug-and-play wireless device servers and Ethernet bridges. Its device connectivity operations design multi-port serial adapters and boards. DPAC Technologies sells through distributors, systems integrators, resellers, and manufacturers.

	Annual Growth	2/03	2/04	2/05	*12/06	12/07
Sales ($ mil.)	(23.0%)	34.5	19.6	1.4	13.7	12.1
Net income ($ mil.)	—	2.5	(13.9)	(10.5)	(1.0)	(0.8)
Employees	(22.4%)	105	65	22	45	38

*Fiscal year change

DPL INC.

NYSE: DPL

1065 Woodman Dr.
Dayton, OH 45432
Phone: 937-224-6000
Fax: 937-259-7147
Web: www.dplinc.com

CEO: Paul M. Barbas
CFO: John J. Gillen
HR: Daniel J. (Dan) McCabe
FYE: December 31
Type: Public

When it's dark in Dayton, DPL turns on the lights. The holding company's main subsidiary, regulated utility Dayton Power and Light (DP&L), which was established in 1911, brightens the night for more than 515,000 electricity customers in west central Ohio. Nonregulated subsidiary DPL Energy markets wholesale power generated at DPL's power plants, which produce more than 3,760 MW of primarily coal-fired generating capacity. DPL has sold its gas distribution business. Other activities include retail power marketing, street lighting, and financial support services.

	Annual Growth	12/03	12/04	12/05	12/06	12/07
Sales ($ mil.)	8.1%	—	1,199.9	1,284.9	1,393.5	1,515.7
Net income ($ mil.)	0.7%	—	217.3	174.4	139.6	221.8
Market value ($ mil.)	2.0%	—	3,176.5	3,317.0	3,139.7	3,367.0
Employees	6.4%	—	—	1,381	1,452	1,562

DPR CONSTRUCTION, INC.

1450 Veterans Blvd.
Redwood City, CA 94063
Phone: 650-474-1450
Fax: 650-474-1451
Web: www.dprinc.com

CEO: Peter C. Nosler
CFO: Gary Wohl
HR: Jorinne Liberatore
FYE: December 31
Type: Private

From bio labs to wafer fabs, the projects of DPR Construction reflect the focus of its commercial building operations. The general contractor and construction manager builds projects for the biotechnology, pharmaceutical, health care, education, and semiconductor markets. DPR also specializes in corporate offices, entertainment facilities (theme parks and studios), energy efficiency projects, and warehouse and distribution centers. Clients have included Apple, Banner Health, Pixar Animation, and Pfizer. President Doug Woods, CEO Peter Nosler, and secretary and treasurer Ron Davidowski (the D, P, and R) founded the company in 1990. The employee-owned company has 10 offices in the US.

	Annual Growth	12/02	12/03	12/04	12/05	12/06
Sales ($ mil.)	—	—	—	—	—	1,580.0
Employees	—	—	—	—	—	2,200

⊞ D.R. HORTON, INC.

NYSE: DHI

301 Commerce St., Ste. 500
Fort Worth, TX 76102
Phone: 817-390-8200
Fax: 817-390-1704
Web: www.drhorton.com

CEO: Donald J. (Don) Tomnitz
CFO: Bill W. Wheat
HR: Paula Hunter-Perkins
FYE: September 30
Type: Public

When D.R. Horton heard a Who, it built the little guy a house. The top homebuilder in the US, ahead of Lennar, D.R. Horton sold more than 53,000 homes in fiscal 2006. D.R. Horton mainly builds single-family homes designed for the entry-level and move-up markets. Homes range from 1,000 sq. ft. to 5,000 sq. ft., with an average selling price of about $273,000; its luxury homes can cost up to $900,000. D.R. Horton operates more than 40 divisions, building in 84 metropolitan markets in 27 states. It also provides mortgage financing and title services to homebuyers.

	Annual Growth	9/03	9/04	9/05	9/06	9/07
Sales ($ mil.)	6.7%	8,728.1	10,840.8	13,863.7	15,051.3	11,296.5
Net income ($ mil.)	—	626.0	975.1	1,470.5	1,233.3	(712.5)
Market value ($ mil.)	12.4%	2,530.4	5,795.4	11,334.6	7,502.3	4,034.1
Employees	(16.3%)	—	—	8,900	8,772	6,231

DR PEPPER SNAPPLE GROUP, INC.

NYSE: DPS

5301 Legacy Dr.
Plano, TX 75024
Phone: 972-673-7000
Fax: 972-673-7980
Web: www.drpeppersnapplegroup.com

CEO: Larry D. Young
CFO: John O. Stewart
HR: Lawrence N. Solomon
FYE: December 31
Type: Public

It's a snap decision about what doctor to choose. Dr Pepper Snapple Group (DPS) is the bottler and distributor of Dr Pepper soda and Snapple drinks for North America. Serving Canada, Mexico, and the US, the company (formerly Cadbury Schweppes Americas Beverages) offers a portfolio of non-alcoholic beverages including flavored, carbonated soft drinks, and non-carbonated soft drinks, along with ready-to-drink teas, juices, juice drinks, and mixers. Among its brands are A&W Root Beer, Country Time, Hawaiian Punch, Mott's, Schweppes, and Squirt, as well as old favorites such as Hires and RC Cola. DPS is the #3 soda business in North America, after #1 Coke and #2 Pepsi.

	Annual Growth	12/03	12/04	12/05	12/06	12/07
Sales ($ mil.)	—	—	—	—	—	5,700.0
Employees	—	—	—	—	—	20,000

⊞ An in-depth profile of this company is available to Hoover's Online members at hoovers.com.

DRAKE BEAM MORIN, INC.

750 3rd Ave., 28th Fl.
New York, NY 10017
Phone: 212-692-7700
Fax: 212-297-0426
Web: www.dbm.com

CEO: Robert L. Gasparini
CFO: –
HR: –
FYE: December 31
Type: Private

Drake Beam Morin (DBM) is always in transition. The company provides strategic human resources services, focusing on employee selection, development, retention, and transition. DBM is best known for outplacement and transition services, which help corporate clients plan for workforce reductions and assist former employees in finding new positions. It also aids clients in improving hiring practices through workshops, research studies, and online hiring site JobScout. DBM also offers executive coaching and training to optimize workforce effectiveness and offers research, analysis, and consulting to increase employee retention. Operating through 200 worldwide locations, the company was founded in 1967.

DREAMS, INC.

AMEX: DRJ

2 S. University Dr., Ste. 325
Plantation, FL 33324
Phone: 954-377-0002
Fax: 954-475-8785
Web: www.fieldofdreams.com

CEO: Ross Tannenbaum
CFO: Dorothy Doucet-Sillano
HR: –
FYE: December 31
Type: Public

Talk about a dream team: Troy Aikman, Emmitt Smith, Randy Moss, and Jerry Rice. These sports heroes mean money to Dreams, a maker of sports memorabilia. Doing business as Field of Dreams, the company owns and operates more than 15 mall stores across the US — in addition to 10 franchise stores — that sell autographed balls, jerseys, photographs, plaques, and other collectibles, which it licenses from the NFL, MLB, NHL, NBA, NCAA, and NASCAR. Its Dream Products unit (doing business as Mounted Memories and Schwartz Sports) oversees the manufacturing and distribution duties, while the Dreams Franchise Corporation unit is in the business of selling retail store franchises to individual business owners.

	Annual Growth	3/04	3/05	3/06	3/07	*12/07
Sales ($ mil.)	28.6%	21.8	33.0	42.7	56.0	59.7
Net income ($ mil.)	—	(0.5)	(0.5)	2.5	1.0	0.8
Market value ($ mil.)	(13.0%)	118.4	16.9	181.7	125.3	67.9
Employees	41.7%	—	—	180	255	

*Fiscal year change

DREAMWORKS ANIMATION SKG INC.

NYSE: DWA

1000 Flower St.
Glendale, CA 91201
Phone: 818-695-5000
Fax: 818-695-9944
Web: www.dreamworksanimation.com

CEO: Jeffrey Katzenberg
CFO: Lewis W. (Lew) Coleman
HR: –
FYE: December 31
Type: Public

While live action isn't a nightmare for DreamWorks Animation SKG, the company definitely prefers CGI. The company is producer of computer animated features — including the box office hits *Madagascar, Bee Movie, Shrek*, and the record-breaking *Shrek 2* (the highest-grossing animated film ever). DreamWorks Animation develops content that is distributed and marketed by Paramount Pictures. DreamWorks Animation previously released films in collaboration with Aardman Animations (*Wallace & Gromit: Curse of the Were-Rabbit* and *Flushed Away*); however, the partnership ended in 2007. The 2007 release of *Shrek the Third* again broke records. In 2004 former parent DreamWorks spun off the company.

	Annual Growth	12/03	12/04	12/05	12/06	12/07
Sales ($ mil.)	26.4%	301.0	1,078.2	462.3	394.8	767.2
Net income ($ mil.)	—	(187.2)	333.0	104.6	15.1	218.4
Market value ($ mil.)	2.8%	—	1,954.6	1,284.5	2,589.6	2,122.4
Employees	6.4%	—	—	1,280	1,300	1,450

⊞ DREAMWORKS SKG

1000 Flower St.
Glendale, CA 91201
Phone: 818-733-7000
Fax: 818-695-7574
Web: www.dreamworks.com

CEO: Stacey Snider
CFO: –
HR: –
FYE: December 31
Type: Subsidiary

DreamWorks woke up to media consolidation. Created in 1994 by Steven Spielberg (film director and producer), Jeffrey Katzenberg (former Disney film executive and animation guru), and David Geffen (recording industry maven), DreamWorks produces live-action movies (*Transformers*) and TV shows (*Las Vegas*). Initially an experiment in creating a diversified media company, DreamWorks struggled with any business beyond filmed entertainment and shed its other operations, including arcade business GameWorks (a venture with SEGA and Universal Pictures) and a music label (sold to Universal Music). Big money maker DreamWorks Animation was spun off to shareholders. The three founders sold DreamWorks to rival Paramount in 2006.

THE DREES COMPANY

211 Grandview Dr., Ste. 300
Fort Mitchell, KY 41017
Phone: 859-578-4200
Fax: 859-341-5854
Web: www.dreeshomes.com

CEO: David Drees
CFO: Mark Williams
HR: Effie McKeehan
FYE: March 31
Type: Private

Drees Co. is a leading home builder in Cincinnati and one of the top private builders in the US. Customers may choose from homes that range from about $100,000 to more than $900,000. It also builds condominiums, apartments, and commercial buildings through its nine divisions. The company is expanding through acquisitions such as the addition of the home building assets of Zaring National in Cincinnati (Zaring Premier Homes), Indianapolis, and Nashville, Tennessee, and Ausherman Homes (renamed Drees) in Frederick, Maryland (near Washington, DC). The Drees Co. offers financing through its First Equity Mortgage subsidiary.

	Annual Growth	3/02	3/03	3/04	3/05	3/06
Sales ($ mil.)	7.2%	848.4	822.3	978.0	1,183.0	1,120.0
Employees	2.7%	1,100	1,232	1,200	1,339	1,226

⊞ THE DRESS BARN, INC.

NASDAQ (GS): DBRN

30 Dunnigan Dr.
Suffern, NY 10901
Phone: 845-369-4500
Fax: 845-369-4829
Web: www.dressbarn.com

CEO: David R. Jaffe
CFO: Armand Correia
HR: David Montieth
FYE: Last Saturday in July
Type: Public

Although its name is evocative of *Green Acres*, The Dress Barn caters to women who have more to do and less to spend than Mrs. Douglas. The retailer operates about 1,425 stores including about 600 combination Dress Barn/Dress Barn Woman stores and 600-plus Maurices locations in strip malls and outlet centers in 48 states and Washington, DC, to suit the budget-conscious career woman. The retailer's Dress Barn, Dress Barn Woman (larger sizes), and combination stores sell in-season, moderate- to better-quality women's apparel and accessories at discount prices and cater to professional women in their mid-30s to mid-50s. Founders chairman Elliot Jaffe and his wife Roslyn opened the first Dress Barn store in 1962.

	Annual Growth	7/03	7/04	7/05	7/06	7/07
Sales ($ mil.)	19.2%	707.1	754.9	1,000.3	1,300.3	1,426.6
Net income ($ mil.)	88.6%	8.0	30.9	52.6	78.9	101.2
Market value ($ mil.)	56.5%	188.7	248.1	368.2	1,296.2	1,132.7
Employees	6.7%	—	—	12,000	12,800	—

DRESSER, INC.

15455 Dallas Pkwy., Ste. 1100
Addison, TX 75001
Phone: 972-361-9800
Fax: 972-361-9903
Web: www.dresser.com

CEO: John P. Ryan
CFO: Robert D. (Bob) Woltil
HR: Mark J. Scott
FYE: December 31
Type: Private

Is your energy business all dressed up with no place to flow? Not if Dresser can help it. The company, formerly Dresser Industries (and once a part of Halliburton), makes flow control products (valves, actuators, meters, fittings, and the like for oil and gas exploration), measurement systems (gas pumps and point-of-sale terminals made by business unit Dresser Wayne for gas stations and convenience stores), and power systems (Waukesha engines and Roots blowers and compressors). Dresser serves companies in the oil and gas, power generation, transportation, chemical, and process industries. The company maintains a presence in more than 100 countries, with manufacturing or support facilities in more than 20.

	Annual Growth	12/02	12/03	12/04	12/05	12/06
Sales ($ mil.)	3.6%	1,589.4	1,657.0	1,991.7	1,700.0	1,830.0
Employees	(6.3%)	7,900	8,300	8,800	6,500	6,100

DRESSER-RAND GROUP INC.

NYSE: DRC

1200 W. Sam Houston Pkwy N.
Houston, TX 77043
Phone: 713-467-2221
Fax: 716-375-3178
Web: www.dresser-rand.com

CEO: Vincent R. (Vince) Volpe Jr.
CFO: Mark E. Baldwin
HR: Elizabeth C. (Beth) Powers
FYE: December 31
Type: Public

All dressed up with no place to go? Not so for the Dresser-Rand Group. The company makes centrifugal and reciprocating compressors, steam and gas turbines, expanders, multiphase turbine separators, and related control systems. It also offers aftermarket services, such as repairs, technical support, and upgrades for both its own products and equipment made by others. Dresser-Rand has customers in the oil and gas production, chemical, paper, steel, and industrial power and energy recovery markets. Once a subsidiary of Ingersoll-Rand, Dresser-Rand was bought by private equity firm First Reserve, which specializes in energy industry investments. More than half of its sales comes from outside North America.

	Annual Growth	12/03	12/04	12/05	12/06	12/07
Sales ($ mil.)	17.4%	—	—	1,208.2	1,501.5	1,665.0
Net income ($ mil.)	69.6%	—	—	37.1	78.8	106.7
Market value ($ mil.)	27.3%	—	—	2,066.8	2,091.6	3,351.5
Employees	6.6%	—	—	5,277	5,612	6,000

DREW INDUSTRIES INCORPORATED

NYSE: DW

200 Mamaroneck Ave.
White Plains, NY 10601
Phone: 914-428-9098
Fax: 914-428-4581
Web: www.drewindustries.com

CEO: Leigh J. Abrams
CFO: Joseph S. Giordano III
HR: –
FYE: December 31
Type: Public

Drew Industries knows that when one door closes, another one opens — and that goes for windows too. The company supplies aluminum and vinyl windows and doors for recreational vehicles (about 75% of sales) and manufactured homes (25%) through more than 30 facilities in 14 states. The company's Kinro subsidiary produces windows, doors, and screens. Its Lippert Components subsidiary makes axles, ramps, and chassis parts, as well as specialty trailers for hauling boats and snowmobiles. Customers include manufactured home builders Clayton Homes and Champion Enterprises and RV makers Fleetwood Enterprises and Thor Industries.

	Annual Growth	12/03	12/04	12/05	12/06	12/07
Sales ($ mil.)	17.3%	353.1	530.9	669.2	729.2	668.6
Net income ($ mil.)	19.7%	19.4	25.1	33.6	31.0	39.8
Market value ($ mil.)	43.5%	141.8	186.5	605.4	564.0	601.0
Employees	(18.7%)	—	—	4,541	3,690	—

DREYER'S GRAND ICE CREAM HOLDINGS, INC.

5929 College Ave.
Oakland, CA 94618
Phone: 510-652-8187
Fax: 510-450-4621
Web: www.dreyersinc.com

CEO: Timothy F. (Tim) Kahn
CFO: Steve Barbour
HR: Andy Euser
FYE: Last Saturday in December
Type: Subsidiary

This company takes a licking and keeps on selling. Dreyer's Grand Ice Cream is the leading US ice cream producer. The company manufactures premium ice creams and frozen dairy desserts under its namesake Dreyer's and its Edy's brands for distribution throughout the US and overseas. The company also makes and distributes Healthy Choice ice creams for ConAgra. In addition, Dreyer's distributes Nestlé's Häagen-Dazs and ice cream novelties and operates the Häagen-Dazs Shoppe Company, which franchises ice cream parlors. Dreyer's is a subsidiary of Swiss food giant Nestlé.

	Annual Growth	12/03	12/04	12/05	12/06	12/07
Est. sales ($ mil.)	—	—	—	—	—	1,588.4
Employees	—	—	—	—	—	5,979

DRI CORPORATION

NASDAQ (CM): TBUS

5949 Sherry Ln., Ste. 1050
Dallas, TX 75225
Phone: 214-378-8992
Fax: 214-378-8437
Web: www.digrec.com

CEO: David L. Turney
CFO: Stephen P. Slay
HR: Agne I. Axelsson
FYE: December 31
Type: Public

DRI drives transportation technology. The company designs automatic voice announcement systems and electronic destination signs for mass transit operators, as well as vehicle location systems. Its Talking Bus announcement systems broadcast stops and transfer information for buses, subways, trains and other private and commercial vehicles. The company also makes electronic destination signs that display transit information for buses. DRI counts vehicle makers, transit operators, and state and local governments among its customers. The company operates through subsidiaries in the US (Digital Recorders, TwinVision) and abroad (Mobitec).

	Annual Growth	12/03	12/04	12/05	12/06	12/07
Sales ($ mil.)	7.1%	44.0	47.8	45.3	51.3	57.9
Net income ($ mil.)	—	(1.3)	(3.2)	(5.9)	(3.9)	0.7
Market value ($ mil.)	25.9%	10.8	37.4	14.9	12.0	27.2
Employees	0.3%	—	—	185	—	186

DRIL-QUIP, INC.

NYSE: DRQ

13550 Hempstead Hwy.
Houston, TX 77040
Phone: 713-939-7711
Fax: 713-939-8063
Web: www.dril-quip.com

CEO: Larry E. Reimert
CFO: Jerry M. Brooks
HR: –
FYE: December 31
Type: Public

Dril-Quip equips the folks with the drills — the oil and gas industry. Its products include drilling and production riser systems, subsea and surface wellheads and production trees, wellhead connectors and diverters, mud-line hanger systems, and specialty connectors and pipe. The company, which specializes in deepwater or severe-condition equipment, also provides installation, reconditioning, and tool-rental services. Dril-Quip has major manufacturing plants in Singapore, the UK, and the US. Cochairmen and co-founders Larry Reimert, Gary Smith, and Mike Walker own 10%, 10%, and 14% of the company, respectively.

	Annual Growth	12/03	12/04	12/05	12/06	12/07
Sales ($ mil.)	22.6%	219.5	221.6	340.8	442.7	495.6
Net income ($ mil.)	86.6%	8.9	12.5	32.6	86.9	107.9
Market value ($ mil.)	100.3%	140.9	209.9	454.8	1,580.4	2,270.6
Employees	11.7%	—	—	1,514	—	1,890

An in-depth profile of this company is available to Hoover's Online members at hoovers.com.

517

DRIVETIME AUTOMOTIVE GROUP, INC.

4020 E. Indian School Rd.
Phoenix, AZ 85018
Phone: 602-852-6600
Fax: 602-852-6686
Web: www.drivetime.com

CEO: Ray Fidel
CFO: Mark G. Sauder
HR: –
FYE: December 31
Type: Private

In this story the ugly duckling changes into DriveTime. DriveTime Automotive, formerly known as Ugly Duckling, is a leading used-car dealership chain, primarily targeting low-income customers and those with credit problems. To cater to these subprime customers, the company is a "buy here-pay here" dealer, meaning it finances and services car loans rather than using outside lenders (interest rates range from 13% to 30%). DriveTime operates about 100 dealerships in metropolitan areas in 10 mostly southern and western states. The cars undergo a 53-point inspection and are run through Experian AutoCheck, an auto history database. The company was taken private in 2002 by a group led by chairman Ernest Garcia.

DRS TECHNOLOGIES, INC.

NYSE: DRS

5 Sylvan Way
Parsippany, NJ 07054
Phone: 973-898-1500
Fax: 973-898-4730
Web: www.drs.com

CEO: Mark S. Newman
CFO: Richard A. Schneider
HR: Andrea J. Mandel
FYE: March 31
Type: Public

Methods used to track military activity are complex, but DRS Technologies makes the tasks manageable with electronic systems that process, display, and store complex military and aerospace data. Its offerings include surveillance and radar systems, ruggedized computers, weapons-targeting systems, flight recorders, communications systems, thermal-imaging systems, air combat training systems, and video recorders for defense and aerospace applications. DRS, which has acquired and integrated Integrated Defense Technologies — and has acquired Engineered Support Systems — relies on US government agencies (primarily the DoD) for 90% of sales. Italy's Finmeccanica has agreed to buy DRS for a reported $4 billion.

	Annual Growth	3/04	3/05	3/06	3/07	3/08
Sales ($ mil.)	34.7%	1,001.3	1,308.6	1,735.5	2,821.1	3,295.4
Net income ($ mil.)	38.8%	44.7	60.7	81.5	127.1	165.8
Market value ($ mil.)	33.6%	757.2	1,167.6	2,190.0	2,122.0	2,411.2
Employees	(1.0%)	—	—	9,800	9,700	

DRUG FAIR GROUP, INC.

800 Cottontail Ln.
Somerset, NJ 08873
Phone: 732-748-8900
Fax: 732-748-7200
Web: www.drugfair.com

CEO: Timothy R. (Tim) LaBeau
CFO: Don DeSantis
HR: Barrie Levine
FYE: September 30
Type: Private

Drug Fair Group (dba Drug Fair) operates about 50 pharmacy and general merchandise stores under the Drug Fair and Cost Cutters banners in northern and central New Jersey. Its stores offer prescription services, as well as over-the-counter medicines and supplements, and a variety of grocery items. Founded in 1954 and owned by Community Distributors Inc., the ailing regional drugstore chain was bought by an affiliate of the Florida-based private investment firm Sun Capital Partners in late 2005. Following the acquisition, Sun Capital recruited Duane Reade executive Timothy R. LaBeau as CEO to reposition the Drug Fair and Cost Cutter brands.

	Annual Growth	9/03	9/04	9/05	9/06	9/07
Est. sales ($ mil.)	—	—	—	—	—	150.5
Employees	—	—	—	—	—	1,700

DRUGSTORE.COM, INC.

NASDAQ (GM): DSCM

411 108th Ave. NE, Ste. 1400
Bellevue, WA 98004
Phone: 425-372-3200
Fax: 425-372-3800
Web: www.drugstore.com

CEO: Dawn G. Lepore
CFO: Tracy Wright
HR: Robert Hargadon
FYE: December 31
Type: Public

drugstore.com hopes it has the right Rx for e-commerce success. The e-tailer sells name-brand and private-label health and beauty items and prescription and OTC drugs from its Web sites and by telephone. It also sends refill reminders by e-mail and offers information about drug and health issues. The company's Vision Direct subsidiary sells contact lenses online. A partnership with bricks-and-mortar drugstore chain Rite Aid, one of the nation's leading chains, allows drugstore.com customers to pick up prescriptions at Rite Aid pharmacies and enables drugstore.com to sell private-label Rite Aid products, as well as vitamins from retailer GNC Corporation. Founded in 1998, the company has yet to turn a profit.

	Annual Growth	12/03	12/04	12/05	12/06	12/07
Sales ($ mil.)	16.1%	245.7	360.1	399.4	415.8	445.7
Net income ($ mil.)	—	(18.6)	(47.7)	(20.9)	(13.0)	(11.5)
Market value ($ mil.)	(5.2%)	391.4	276.9	264.8	345.3	315.9
Employees	4.4%	—	—	780	732	850

DRUMMOND COMPANY, INC.

1000 Urban Center Dr., Ste. 300
Birmingham, AL 35242
Phone: 205-945-6300
Fax: 205-945-6440
Web: www.drummondco.com

CEO: Garry N. Drummond Sr.
CFO: Jack Stilwell
HR: B. Blackburn
FYE: December 31
Type: Private

Drummond does business from the ground down. The company operates the Shoal Creek underground coal mine in Alabama and the Pribbenow surface coal mine in Colombia. Drummond's ABC Coke unit produces foundry coke, which is used mainly in the automotive, construction, and sugar industries, at a plant in Alabama. In addition, Drummond develops housing communities and office parks in Alabama, California, and Florida. H. E. Drummond began his company in 1935 on land homesteaded by his mother; eventually his five sons entered the business. The Drummond family still owns and manages the company.

	Annual Growth	12/02	12/03	12/04	12/05	12/06
Sales ($ mil.)	(1.6%)	—	—	—	1,798.0	1,770.0
Employees	0.0%	—	—	—	5,100	5,100

DRURY INNS, INC.

721 Emerson Rd., Ste. 400
St. Louis, MO 63141
Phone: 314-429-2255
Fax: 314-429-5166
Web: www.druryhotels.com

CEO: Charles L. (Chuck) Drury Jr.
CFO: Carr Trovillion
HR: –
FYE: December 31
Type: Private

Drury isn't dreary but it is for the weary. The company offers more than 90 places for travelers to rest their heads in more than 15 states, mostly Missouri (about 35 locations) and Texas (about 20). Its hotel brands include Drury Inn, Drury Suites, Drury Inn & Suites, and Pear Tree Inn. The company also has three Drury Plaza Hotel locations that offer enhanced meeting space and on-site dining. The chain, established in 1973 by the Drury family, was one of the first hotels in the limited-service segment. The family runs the company and owns all the Drury hotels.

	Annual Growth	12/03	12/04	12/05	12/06	12/07
Est. sales ($ mil.)	—	—	—	—	—	160.0
Employees	—	—	—	—	—	120

DRYCLEAN USA, INC.

AMEX: DCU

290 NE 68th St.
Miami, FL 33138
Phone: 305-754-4551
Fax: 305-754-8010
Web: www.dryclean-usa.com

CEO: Michael S. Steiner
CFO: Venerando J. Indelicato
HR: –
FYE: June 30
Type: Public

Dryclean USA is anything but hard pressed. The firm franchises and licenses more than 400 retail dry cleaners in four US states, the Caribbean, and Latin America. However, most of its sales are generated by unit Steiner-Atlantic, which sells coin-operated laundry machines, steam boilers, and other laundry equipment; most are sold under the Aero-Tech, Green-Jet, and Multi-Jet names to some 750 customers that include Dryclean USA, independent dry cleaners, hotels, and hospitals. Other divisions offer business brokerage and turn-key development of new dry cleaning businesses. Chairman William Steiner; his son, CEO Michael Steiner; and COO Alan Greenstein together own almost 65% of the firm and vote as a block.

	Annual Growth	6/03	6/04	6/05	6/06	6/07
Sales ($ mil.)	12.4%	14.3	14.7	18.4	20.4	22.8
Net income ($ mil.)	10.7%	0.6	0.5	0.7	0.8	0.9
Market value ($ mil.)	32.6%	4.5	11.2	17.9	12.9	14.1
Employees	(1.4%)	—	—	35	—	34

DSC LOGISTICS

1750 S. Wolf Rd.
Des Plaines, IL 60018
Phone: 800-372-1960
Fax: 847-390-7276
Web: www.dsclogistics.com

CEO: Ann M. Drake
CFO: –
HR: Janice Miller
FYE: December 31
Type: Private

DSC Logistics knows the ABCs of supply chain management. The third-party logistics company manages services such as warehousing, transportation, and packaging for its customers; it also offers logistics consulting services. DSC maintains a network of about 20 logistics centers spread throughout the US; overall, the company's facilities offer about 15 million sq. ft. of storage space. Customers have included Georgia-Pacific, J.R. Simplot, and Kimberly-Clark. DSC founder Jim McIlrath, the father of CEO Ann Drake, started the company as Dry Storage Corporation in 1960 after a former boss refused to offer dry storage along with refrigerated storage services.

DSL.NET, INC.

50 Barnes Park North, Ste. 104
Wallingford, CT 06492
Phone: 203-284-6100
Fax: 203-284-6102
Web: www.dsl.net

CEO: David F. (Dave) Struwas
CFO: Walter R. Keisch
HR: –
FYE: December 31
Type: Subsidiary

DSL.net lets others fight it out for the big fish in the pond. The company provides high-speed Internet access and data communications to small and midsized businesses using digital subscriber line (DSL) and T-1 technology. Other services include integrated voice and data systems using Voice over Internet Protocol (VoIP), Web hosting, virtual private networks (VPNs), and remote access to corporate networks. The company saw the network double in size with its acquisition of Network Access Solutions in 2003. That year it also acquired voice and data services provider TalkingNets. DSL.net was acquired by Costa Mesa, California-based managed IP services firm MegaPath Networks in 2007.

	Annual Growth	12/03	12/04	12/05	12/06	12/07
Est. sales ($ mil.)	—	—	—	—	—	15.9
Employees	—	—	—	—	—	98

DSP GROUP, INC.

NASDAQ (GS): DSPG

2580 North First St., Ste. 460
San Jose, CA 95131
Phone: 408-986-4300
Fax: 408-986-4323
Web: www.dspg.com

CEO: Eliyahu Ayalon
CFO: Dror Levy
HR: Orit Menkes
FYE: December 31
Type: Public

DSP Group loves the sound of its own voice . . . chips. The company's name derives from the digital signal processors (DSPs) and related speech compression software it develops; these products convert speech and other audio data into digital values for telephone answering devices, PCs, wireless products, and consumer electronics. DSP's top customers include the Tomen Electronics distribution unit of Japan's Toyota Tsusho (37% of sales), Philips, and Sony. Panasonic Mobile Communications accounts for most of the sales made through Tomen Electronics, and 23% of DSP Group's revenues. The company gets most of its sales in the Asia/Pacific region.

	Annual Growth	12/03	12/04	12/05	12/06	12/07
Sales ($ mil.)	12.9%	152.9	157.5	187.2	216.9	248.8
Net income ($ mil.)	—	25.4	51.1	29.5	22.4	(4.8)
Market value ($ mil.)	(14.5%)	714.0	628.9	716.6	615.8	381.0
Employees	24.3%	210	284	291	319	502

DST OUTPUT, LLC

5220 Robert J. Mathews Pkwy.
El Dorado Hills, CA 95762
Phone: 916-939-4960
Fax: 916-941-4173
Web: www.dstoutput.com

CEO: Steven J. (Steve) Towle
CFO: Rick Maner
HR: Mary Ann Sutherland
FYE: December 31
Type: Subsidiary

DST Output prints 'em out and spits 'em out. From medical bills to marketing materials, DST Output prints and sends more than 2 billion bills, statements, invoices, and informational documents per year to consumers via mail and electronic delivery. It has operations in the US, Canada, and the UK and counts companies in the communications, financial services, health care, insurance, and utilities industries as clients. The company's TransPromo service allows clients to incorporate direct marketing messages onto standard billing statements. In addition, DST Output provides electronic bill presentment and payment services. It is a subsidiary of information processing software maker DST Systems.

⊞ DST SYSTEMS, INC.

NYSE: DST

333 W. 11th St.
Kansas City, MO 64105
Phone: 816-435-1000
Fax: 816-435-8618
Web: www.dstsystems.com

CEO: Thomas A. (Tom) McDonnell
CFO: Kenneth V. Hager
HR: –
FYE: December 31
Type: Public

The feeling is mutual at DST Systems. A leading provider of information processing software and services for the mutual fund industry, DST's Financial Services segment processes millions of mutual fund accounts and offers software, systems, and processing services for banks, investment firms, and insurance companies. The company's Output Solutions unit manages statement and bill mailings and customer communications. Its applications and services are used to address a wide range of tasks including business process management, investment management, customer care, and health care claims processing and administration.

	Annual Growth	12/03	12/04	12/05	12/06	12/07
Sales ($ mil.)	(1.2%)	2,416.3	2,428.6	2,515.1	2,235.8	2,302.5
Net income ($ mil.)	28.5%	320.8	222.8	424.6	272.9	874.7
Market value ($ mil.)	9.2%	3,523.7	4,180.0	4,295.5	5,968.6	5,019.0
Employees	2.4%	—	—	10,500	10,500	11,000

⊞ An in-depth profile of this company is available to Hoover's Online members at hoovers.com.

519

DSW INC.

NYSE: DSW

810 DSW Dr.
Columbus, OH 43219
Phone: 614-237-7100
Fax: –
Web: www.dswshoe.com

CEO: Jay L. Schottenstein
CFO: Douglas J. (Doug) Probst
HR: Kathleen C. Maurer
FYE: Saturday nearest January 31
Type: Public

While you don't have to watch out for trees in this jungle, you may want to watch your back. DSW sells discounted brand-name footwear for men and women through about 260 stores in 35 states, as well as online. In addition to more than 2,000 styles of dress, casual, and athletic shoes, stores offer handbags, hosiery, and accessories. DSW's *Thrill of the Hunt* TV ads features fashionable women eyeing the same pair of shoes, then transitions to them closing in "for the kill." The company is opening new stores at a pace of about 30 per year through 2010. It also operates more than 375 leased departments inside stores operated by other retailers. DSW went public in mid-2005.

	Annual Growth	1/04	1/05	1/06	1/07	1/08
Sales ($ mil.)	15.4%	791.3	961.1	1,144.1	1,279.1	1,405.6
Net income ($ mil.)	38.1%	14.8	35.0	37.2	65.5	53.8
Market value ($ mil.)	(13.8%)	—	—	437.1	666.1	325.1
Employees	17.2%	—	—	4,950	5,800	—

DTE ENERGY COMPANY

NYSE: DTE

2000 2nd Ave.
Detroit, MI 48226
Phone: 313-235-4000
Fax: 313-235-8055
Web: www.dteenergy.com

CEO: Anthony F. Earley Jr.
CFO: David E. Meador
HR: Larry E. Steward
FYE: December 31
Type: Public

Detroit gets a charge from its Lions, Tigers, and DTE Energy, oh my. The holding company's main subsidiary, Detroit Edison, distributes electricity to some 2.2 million customers in southeastern Michigan. The utility's power plants (mainly fossil-fueled) have a generating capacity of more than 11,100 MW. The company's Michigan Consolidated Gas (MichCon) unit distributes natural gas to 1.3 million customers. DTE Energy's nonregulated operations include energy marketing and trading; coal transportation and procurement; energy management services for commercial and industrial customers; independent and on-site power generation; and gas exploration, production, and processing.

	Annual Growth	12/03	12/04	12/05	12/06	12/07
Sales ($ mil.)	4.8%	7,041.0	7,114.0	9,022.0	9,022.0	8,506.0
Net income ($ mil.)	16.8%	521.0	431.0	537.0	433.0	971.0
Market value ($ mil.)	1.9%	6,643.1	7,512.2	7,679.8	8,575.3	7,175.7
Employees	(5.2%)	—	—	11,410	10,527	10,262

DTS, INC.

NASDAQ (GS): DTSI

5171 Clareton Dr.
Agoura Hills, CA 91301
Phone: 818-706-3525
Fax: 818-706-1868
Web: www.dtsonline.com

CEO: Jon E. Kirchner
CFO: Melvin L. (Mel) Flanigan
HR: Sharon K. Faltemier
FYE: December 31
Type: Public

DTS (formerly Digital Theater Systems) surrounds movie lovers with sound. The company's multichannel audio systems are used throughout the world in movie theaters, as well as consumer electronics such as audio/video receivers; DVD and Blu-ray HD players; personal computers; car audio products; video game consoles; and home theater systems. In 2008 the company sold its image enhancement and restoration services business, DTS Digital Images, in order to focus on licensing its technology in consumer audio products. DTS has licensing agreements with all the world's major consumer electronics manufacturers (Sony, Matsushita, and Philips).

	Annual Growth	12/03	12/04	12/05	12/06	12/07
Sales ($ mil.)	0.7%	51.7	61.4	75.3	78.3	53.1
Net income ($ mil.)	—	9.9	10.0	7.9	3.0	(20.4)
Market value ($ mil.)	2.6%	407.7	343.6	258.6	436.0	451.8
Employees	80.5%	—	174	314	—	—

DUANE READE INC.

440 9th Ave.
New York, NY 10001
Phone: 212-273-5700
Fax: 212-244-6527
Web: www.duanereade.com

CEO: John A. Lederer
CFO: John K. Henry
HR: Vincent A. Scarfone
FYE: Saturday nearest December 31
Type: Private

Duane Reade is the Big Apple of drugstores. Named after the two streets where its first store was located, the company is the market leader in densely-populated Manhattan. In all, the company operates about 230 stores in New York and about a dozen in New Jersey. Many of the company's stores are in high-traffic Manhattan (giving the firm more sales per square foot than any other US drugstore chain). Duane Reade's stores vary greatly in size (1,600-14,700 sq. ft.). The company sells prescription drugs, but about half of sales come from items such as over-the-counter medications, food and beverages, and health and beauty aids. Duane Reade was taken private in mid-2004 by equity group Oak Hill Capital Partners.

	Annual Growth	12/02	12/03	12/04	12/05	12/06
Sales ($ mil.)	(0.6%)	—	—	1,600.0	1,589.0	1,580.0
Employees	(1.6%)	—	—	6,300	6,100	6,100

DUCHOSSOIS INDUSTRIES, INC.

845 N. Larch Ave.
Elmhurst, IL 60126
Phone: 630-279-3600
Fax: 630-530-6091
Web: www.duch.com

CEO: Craig J. Duchossois
CFO: Michael E. Flannery
HR: Melanie Ditore
FYE: December 31
Type: Private

Business is no longer a horse race for holding company Duchossois Industries. The former owner of Chicago's Arlington International Racecourse, Duchossois Industries (pronounced Deshy-swa) has sold its interests in the track to Churchill Downs. The company now focuses on its interests in the industrial, consumer products, and technology sectors. Subsidiary The Chamberlain Group is the world's top maker of residential and commercial door openers, and it is a leading maker of access control products. In 2005 the company acquired systems integration provider AMX Corporation. The Duchossois family controls Duchossois Industries; it also holds a minority stake in Churchill Downs.

DUCKWALL-ALCO STORES, INC.

NASDAQ (GM): DUCK

401 Cottage St.
Abilene, KS 67410
Phone: 785-263-3350
Fax: 785-263-7531
Web: www.duckwall.com

CEO: Donny Johnson
CFO: Jon Ramsey
HR: Daniel J. Curoe
FYE: Sunday nearest January 31
Type: Public

Some retailers prize locations where they can battle competitors toe-to-toe; Duckwall-ALCO prizes locations that the big national discount chains, such as Wal-Mart and Target, wouldn't even consider. The retailer runs about 200 ALCO and ALCO Market Place discount stores and some 60 Duckwall variety stores in small towns in more than 20 states in the central US. ALCO stores, situated in towns with populations of 5,000 or fewer, account for about 95% of the company's sales. Product lines include crafts, electronics, fabrics, furniture, hardware, toys, and apparel. The smaller Duckwall stores carry about a third of ALCO's merchandise and are located in about 10 states in towns with populations below 2,500.

	Annual Growth	1/04	1/05	1/06	1/07	1/08
Sales ($ mil.)	3.6%	433.3	433.9	435.0	475.3	499.0
Net income ($ mil.)	—	6.5	3.9	2.0	5.7	(0.2)
Market value ($ mil.)	6.6%	64.4	83.7	96.9	137.3	83.3
Employees	0.0%	—	—	4,800	4,800	—

⊞ DUCOMMUN INCORPORATED

NYSE: DCO

23301 Wilmington Ave.
Carson, CA 90745
Phone: 310-513-7280
Fax: 310-513-7279
Web: www.ducommun.com

CEO: Joseph C. Berenato
CFO: Joseph C. Berenato
HR: Gary Parkinson
FYE: December 31
Type: Public

Plans are always up in the air at Ducommun (rhymes with "uncommon"). The company makes aerostructures and electromechanical components for commercial and military aircraft. Ducommun AeroStructures manufactures structural components and subassemblies using shaped aluminum, composites, and titanium. Ducommun Technologies makes electromechanical components such as switch assemblies, actuators, gyroscopes, keyboard panels, and avionics racks. Sales of products destined for military applications account for more than half of the company's sales. Aircraft giant Boeing accounts for about 37% of Ducommun's sales.

	Annual Growth	12/03	12/04	12/05	12/06	12/07
Sales ($ mil.)	12.9%	225.9	224.9	249.7	319.0	367.3
Net income ($ mil.)	4.9%	16.2	11.2	16.0	14.3	19.6
Market value ($ mil.)	16.0%	221.3	209.4	215.9	235.2	400.9
Employees	17.4%	—	—	1,353	—	1,865

DUFF & PHELPS CORPORATION

NYSE: DUF

55 East 52nd. St., Fl. 31
New York, NY 10055
Phone: 212-871-2000
Fax: –
Web: www.duffandphelps.com

CEO: Noah Gottdiener
CFO: Jacob L. Silverman
HR: –
FYE: December 31
Type: Public

Duff & Phelps provides financial advisory and investment banking services to public and private corporations, investment firms, law firms, and public accounting firms. The company specializes in offering fairness opinions regarding financial reporting, tax valuations, real estate and other asset valuations, and dispute resolution. Its investment banking services include mergers and acquisitions advice, financial restructurings, private placements of shares, or other transactions. Its Chanin Capital Partners unit provides similar services to smaller firms. Duff & Phelps has about 15 US offices, five in Europe, and one in Tokyo. The company went public in 2007.

	Annual Growth	12/03	12/04	12/05	12/06	12/07
Sales ($ mil.)	126.4%	—	30.5	78.2	259.3	353.9
Net income ($ mil.)	(30.7%)	—	1.8	(12.5)	10.5	0.6
Market value ($ mil.)	—	—	—	—	—	257.1
Employees	—	—	—	—	870	—

⊞ DUKE ENERGY CORPORATION

NYSE: DUK

526 S. Church St.
Charlotte, NC 28202
Phone: 704-594-6200
Fax: 704-382-3814
Web: www.duke-energy.com

CEO: James E. (Jim) Rogers
CFO: David L. Hauser
HR: Karen R. Feld
FYE: December 31
Type: Public

Duke Energy is a John Wayne-sized power business. The company has 3.9 million electric customers and about 500,000 gas customers in the South and Midwest. Its US Franchised Electric and Gas unit operates primarily through its Duke Energy Carolinas, Duke Energy Ohio, Duke Energy Indiana and Duke Energy Kentucky regional businesses. The company's Commercial Power unit has 8,020 MW of unregulated generation. Duke Energy International has almost 4,000 MW of generation (mostly in Latin America). Crescent Resources (a joint venture with Morgan Stanley Real Estate Fund) manages land holdings and develops real estate projects.

	Annual Growth	12/03	12/04	12/05	12/06	12/07
Sales ($ mil.)	(13.0%)	22,154.0	22,503.0	16,746.0	15,184.0	12,720.0
Net income ($ mil.)	—	(1,323.0)	1,490.0	1,824.0	1,863.0	1,500.0
Market value ($ mil.)	22.7%	11,216.2	14,594.3	15,339.2	25,134.8	25,454.5
Employees	(6.6%)	—	—	20,400	—	17,800

DUKE ENERGY INDIANA, INC.

1000 E. Main St.
Plainfield, IN 46168
Phone: 704-594-6200
Fax: –
Web: www.duke-energy.com

CEO: James E. (Jim) Rogers
CFO: David L. Hauser
HR: Christopher C. (Chris) Rolfe
FYE: December 31
Type: Subsidiary

Duke Energy Indiana (formerly PSI Energy) brings a spark to the Hoosier state. One of Indiana's largest utilities, Duke Energy subsidiary Duke Energy Indiana transmits and distributes electricity to 69 of the state's 92 counties (approximately 774,000 customers). The utility also owns power plants (7,305 MW of primarily fossil-fueled capacity), which are operated by its parent's merchant energy division. Duke Energy Indiana's service area covers about 22,000 sq. mi. with an estimated population of 2.3 million in north central, central, and southern Indiana.

	Annual Growth	12/02	12/03	12/04	12/05	12/06
Sales ($ mil.)	6.9%	1,610.6	1,603.0	1,753.7	1,975.0	2,107.0
Net income ($ mil.)	(13.3%)	214.2	133.4	165.0	197.8	121.0
Employees	0.8%	—	1,583	1,572	1,607	—

DUKE ENERGY OHIO, INC.

526 S. Church St.
Charlotte, NC 28202
Phone: 704-594-6200
Fax: 704-382-3814
Web: www.duke-energy.com

CEO: James E. (Jim) Rogers
CFO: David L. Hauser
HR: –
FYE: December 31
Type: Subsidiary

Duke Energy Ohio (formerly Cincinnati Gas & Electric) distributes electricity and natural gas in Cincinnati and surrounding areas (including portions of Indiana and Kentucky). The subsidiary of energy holding company Duke Energy has 800,000 power and 500,000 gas customers. Duke Energy Ohio serves residential, commercial, and industrial customers over approximately 19,500 miles of distribution lines and an approximate 2,500-mile transmission system in Ohio and Kentucky. The company's Commercial Power's assets comprise approximately 7,600 MW of power generation primarily located in the Midwest.

	Annual Growth	12/03	12/04	12/05	12/06	12/07
Est. sales ($ mil.)	—	—	—	—	—	2,147.5
Employees	—	—	—	—	—	2,122

DUKE MANUFACTURING COMPANY

2305 N. Broadway St.
St. Louis, MO 63102
Phone: 314-231-1130
Fax: 314-231-5074
Web: www.dukemfg.com

CEO: John J. (Jack) Hake
CFO: –
HR: Robin Hake
FYE: December 31
Type: Private

Duke Manufacturing makes food preparation and serving equipment for use in educational, health care, industrial, and restaurant applications. The company's offerings include baking stations, buffet equipment, chef's units, convection ovens, dish tables, food warmers, sinks, salad bars, and ventilation systems. Duke Manufacturing's Next Generation product line offers serving systems that include concave front decor panels, stainless steel countertops, shelving, signage, graphics, and other presentation aids. Its major national customers include Burger King, Campbell's, Subway, and TCBY. CEO Jack Hake controls the company.

	Annual Growth	12/03	12/04	12/05	12/06	12/07
Est. sales ($ mil.)	—	—	—	—	—	58.8
Employees	—	—	—	—	—	475

⊞ An in-depth profile of this company is available to Hoover's Online members at hoovers.com.

521

DUKE REALTY CORPORATION

NYSE: DRE

600 E. 96th St., Ste. 100
Indianapolis, IN 46240
Phone: 317-808-6000
Fax: 317-808-6770
Web: www.dukerealty.com

CEO: Dennis D. (Denny) Oklak
CFO: Mike Pitts
HR: Denise K. Dank
FYE: December 31
Type: Public

Duke Realty's got something of a suburban empire on its hands. The self-managed and self-administered real estate investment trust (REIT) owns and develops suburban office and industrial properties primarily in the Midwest and Southeast, where it focuses on metropolitan markets. Warehouses and light industrial centers account for nearly 60% of its property holdings; offices comprise about 40%. In addition to more than 700 properties totaling some 120 million sq. ft., the company owns 7,700 acres of undeveloped land. Duke Realty's service operations include construction and development, asset and property management, and leasing.

	Annual Growth	12/03	12/04	12/05	12/06	12/07
Sales ($ mil.)	2.7%	1,049.8	1,166.0	1,136.4	1,193.4	1,170.1
Net income ($ mil.)	8.8%	199.2	188.7	355.7	204.1	279.5
Market value ($ mil.)	(2.6%)	4,234.4	4,878.4	4,498.9	5,477.4	3,812.2
Employees	12.8%	—	—	1,100	1,250	1,400

DUKE UNIVERSITY

207 Allen Bldg.
Durham, NC 27708
Phone: 919-684-8111
Fax: 919-684-3200
Web: www.duke.edu

CEO: Richard H. (Dick) Brodhead
CFO: Tallman Trask III
HR: H. Clint Davidson Jr.
FYE: June 30
Type: School

Duke University is home to some 13,000 students who attend classes in nine schools and colleges. Trinity College of Art and Sciences, the Fuqua School of Business, and the Pratt School of Engineering are among the most well known; its law and medical schools are also highly regarded nationally. The private institution has an endowment of about $5.9 billion. Notable alumni include Richard Nixon, Melinda French Gates, and talk show host Charlie Rose. Founded in 1838 as Trinity College, Duke adopted its present name in 1924 after American Tobacco Co. magnate James Duke established the Duke Endowment.

	Annual Growth	6/03	6/04	6/05	6/06	6/07
Est. sales ($ mil.)	—	—	—	—	—	1,832.9
Employees	—	—	—	—	—	26,000

DUKE UNIVERSITY HEALTH SYSTEM

3701 Duke Medical Center
Durham, NC 27706
Phone: 919-684-8111
Fax: —
Web: dukehealth.org

CEO: Victor J. Dzau
CFO: Kenneth C. Morris
HR: —
FYE: June 30
Type: Private

Antibodies inside ya dukin' it out? Better get to the Duke University Health Center — no, no, not the campus infirmary, the Medical Center. At the core of the Duke University Health System is the Duke University Hospital. The system also includes two community hospitals in Durham (Durham Regional Hospital) and Raleigh (Duke Raleigh Hospital), North Carolina. Its network of medical facilities provides such services as primary and specialty care, home and hospice care, clinical research, and public education programs. The total bed capacity of all three hospitals combined is 1,544. Duke University Health Center is part of Duke University Medical School.

	Annual Growth	6/02	6/03	6/04	6/05	6/06
Est. sales ($ mil.)	6.8%	—	1,300.0	1,400.0	1,500.0	1,584.0
Employees	194.0%	—	—	—	10,391	30,551

THE DUN & BRADSTREET CORPORATION

NYSE: DNB

103 JFK Pkwy.
Short Hills, NJ 07078
Phone: 973-921-5500
Fax: 973-921-6056
Web: www.dnb.com

CEO: Steven W. (Steve) Alesio
CFO: Anastasios G. (Tasos) Konidaris
HR: Patricia A. Clifford
FYE: December 31
Type: Public

For The Dun & Bradstreet Corporation, there's no business like "know" business. The company, known as D&B, is one of the world's leading suppliers of business information, services, and research. Its database contains statistics on more than 125 million companies in more than 200 countries, including the largest volume of business-credit information in the world. D&B sells that information and integrates it into software products and Web-based applications. D&B also offers marketing information and purchasing-support services. The company made a major commitment to provide information via the Internet in 2003 when it acquired Hoover's, the publisher of this profile.

	Annual Growth	12/03	12/04	12/05	12/06	12/07
Sales ($ mil.)	3.6%	1,386.4	1,414.0	1,443.6	1,531.3	1,599.2
Net income ($ mil.)	14.3%	174.5	211.8	221.2	240.7	298.1
Market value ($ mil.)	8.3%	3,664.0	4,092.8	4,490.1	4,975.7	5,034.2
Employees	6.1%	—	—	4,350	4,400	4,900

DUNAVANT ENTERPRISES, INC.

3797 New Getwell Rd.
Memphis, TN 38118
Phone: 901-369-1500
Fax: 901-369-1608
Web: www.dunavant.com

CEO: William B. Dunavant III
CFO: —
HR: Mike Andereck
FYE: June 30
Type: Private

King Cotton is alive and well in Memphis. Homegrown Dunavant Enterprises is one of the largest cotton traders in the world. Dunavant was founded in 1960 by William Dunavant, his son Billy (who is allergic to cotton), and Samuel T. Reeves. (The elder Dunavant died shortly after the founding, and Reeves left in 1995 to form Pinnacle Trading.) The company, which grew by selling aggressively to China and the Soviet Union, maintains offices in Africa, Asia, Australia, Europe, Latin America, and the southern US. Other operations include cotton ginning, trucking, warehousing, real estate development, and commodities trading. Dunavant Enterprises is owned by the Dunavant family and company employees.

	Annual Growth	6/02	6/03	6/04	6/05	6/06
Sales ($ mil.)	7.8%	1,000.0	1,099.0	1,664.0	1,704.0	1,350.0
Employees	10.7%	2,000	2,000	2,115	2,250	3,004

DUNBAR ARMORED, INC.

50 Schilling Rd.
Hunt Valley, MD 21031
Phone: 410-584-9800
Fax: 410-527-7103
Web: www.dunbararmored.com

CEO: James L. (Jim) Dunbar
CFO: Juergen Laue
HR: Dominick Valencia
FYE: December 31
Type: Private

Dunbar Armored gets paid to take the money and run — to the bank. The company provides armored transportation to major banks and retailers through more than 50 branch locations throughout the US. It also offers alarm installation and monitoring, armored air transport, ATM, bank vault, cash handling, and security guard patrol services through six subsidiaries (Dunbar Alarm Systems, Dunbar Armored, Dunbar BankPak, Dunbar Cash Vault Services, Dunbar Global Logistics, and Dunbar Guard Services).

	Annual Growth	12/03	12/04	12/05	12/06	12/07
Est. sales ($ mil.)	—	—	—	—	—	45.2
Employees	—	—	—	—	—	4,000

DUNCAN ENERGY PARTNERS L.P.

NYSE: DEP

1100 Louisiana St., 10th Fl.
Houston, TX 77002
Phone: 713-381-6500
Fax: 713-381-6668
Web: www.deplp.com

CEO: Richard H. (Hank) Bachmann
CFO: W. Randall Fowler
HR: –
FYE: December 31
Type: Public

Duncan Energy Partners (DEP) goes deep to make its money. The company, a spinoff from Enterprise Products Partners, finds, stores, and transports natural gas and other petrochemicals. Its operations include Mont Belvieu Caverns (33 salt dome storage "tanks" with a 100 million barrels capacity), the Acadian Gas pipeline in Louisiana, propylene pipelines between Texas and Louisiana, and a 286-mile-long intrastate natural gas liquids (NGLs) pipeline. Acadian Gas' 1,000 miles of pipelines connect on- and off-shore gas fields with statewide distributors, power plants, and industrial customers. Enterprise Products Partners, also chaired by oilman Dan Duncan, controls 26.4% of DEP.

	Annual Growth	12/03	12/04	12/05	12/06	12/07
Sales ($ mil.)	—	—	—	—	—	863.7
Net income ($ mil.)	—	—	—	—	—	24.3
Market value ($ mil.)	—	—	—	—	—	443.2
Employees	—	—	—	—	—	0

DUNE ENERGY, INC.

AMEX: DNE

Two Shell Plaza, 777 Walker St., Ste. 2450
Houston, TX 77002
Phone: 713-229-6300
Fax: 713-229-6388
Web: www.duneenergy.com

CEO: James A. Watt
CFO: Frank T. Smith Jr.
HR: –
FYE: December 31
Type: Public

Like sand piling up in a sand dune, Dune Energy is looking to pile up profits from its three Texas oil and gas properties. The oil and gas exploration and production independent has leases on 7,798 acres on the Welder Ranch in Victoria County and 1,567 acres in the Pearsall Field, located in Frio County. It also has a minor working interest in the Los Mogotes Field, in Zapata County. Dune Energy has proved reserves of 441,000 barrels of oil and 27.1 billion cu. ft. of natural gas. Russian gas group ITERA's Itera Holdings unit controls 58.3% of the company.

	Annual Growth	12/03	12/04	12/05	12/06	12/07
Sales ($ mil.)	338.5%	—	1.0	3.7	7.6	84.3
Net income ($ mil.)	—	—	(1.1)	(1.6)	(53.6)	(28.4)
Market value ($ mil.)	64.3%	—	36.5	142.7	138.5	161.7
Employees	—	—	—	11	—	—

DUNHAM'S ATHLEISURE CORPORATION

5000 Dixie Hwy.
Waterford, MI 48329
Phone: 248-674-4991
Fax: 248-674-4980
Web: www.dunhamssports.com

CEO: Jeffrey G. (Jeff) Lynn
CFO: –
HR: Dan Cislak
FYE: December 31
Type: Private

It's all about athletic leisure at Dunham's Athleisure. The company's Dunham's Sports stores sell sporting goods through about 125 locations in more than 10 midwestern and northeastern states. The stores average 30,000 square feet and offer gear for team sports, individual endeavors, and outdoor pursuits as well as apparel, fan merchandise, electronics, and fitness machines (treadmills, stationary bikes, steppers, rowers, ellipticals). Dunham's also carries a full line of casual apparel, footwear, and eyewear for men, women, and children. The company began as Dunham's Bait and Tackle in 1937.

	Annual Growth	12/03	12/04	12/05	12/06	12/07
Est. sales ($ mil.)	—	—	—	—	—	145.9
Employees	—	—	—	—	—	2,000

DUNKIN' BRANDS, INC.

130 Royall St.
Canton, MA 02021
Phone: 781-737-3000
Fax: 781-737-4000
Web: www.dunkinbrands.com

CEO: Jon L. Luther
CFO: Kate S. Lavelle
HR: Paul Leech
FYE: August 31
Type: Private

Doughnuts and ice cream make sweet bedfellows at Dunkin' Brands. The company is a multi-concept food service franchisor, with more than 13,000 locations in 50 countries, including its popular Dunkin' Donuts and Baskin-Robbins chains. With more than 7,000 shops in 30 countries (4,400 of which are in North America), Dunkin' Donuts is the world's leading chain of donut shops. Baskin-Robbins is a leading seller of ice cream and frozen snacks with its nearly 6,000 outlets (about half are located in the US). About 1,100 locations offer a combination of the company's brands. Dunkin' Brands is owned by a group of private investment firms.

DUNKIN' DONUTS NORTHEAST DISTRIBUTION CENTER, INC.

150 Depot St.
Bellingham, MA 02019
Phone: 508-553-2600
Fax: 508-422-3866

CEO: Bryan Hartnett
CFO: Kevin Cardullo
HR: Kate Nortonedge
FYE: December 31
Type: Cooperative

When it's time to make the donuts, this is where you'll find the supplies. Dunkin' Donuts Northeast Distribution Center is one of several cooperative distribution hubs owned by and serving Dunkin' Donuts and Baskin-Robbins franchisees around the country. (Both chains are owned by Dunkin' Brands.) The company supplies about 2,000 stores in New England and upstate New York with ingredients and other food products, as well as restaurant equipment and supplies. It was founded by owners of 250 Dunkin' Donuts franchises in 1982.

	Annual Growth	12/03	12/04	12/05	12/06	12/07
Est. sales ($ mil.)	—	—	—	—	—	498.5
Employees	—	—	—	—	—	425

DUNN-EDWARDS CORPORATION

4885 E. 52nd Place
Los Angeles, CA 90040
Phone: 323-771-3330
Fax: 323-826-2650
Web: www.dunnedwards.com

CEO: Ken Edwards
CFO: Dennis R. (Denny) Kromer
HR: Gary Jones
FYE: December 31
Type: Private

If you want to paint the town red, it's a "Dunn" deal. Dunn-Edwards manufactures paints, varnishes, lacquers, and enamels, as well as paint-related products ranging from ladders to spray equipment. Through more than 90 retail outlets, the company caters to architects, designers, home builders, and property managers in the Southwest; it also serves do-it-yourselfers, though professionals account for 90% of sales. Founded in 1925 by Frank Dunn, Dunn-Edwards is owned lock, stock, and bucket by the employees and the Edwards family. Among the places coated with Dunn-Edwards paint are the Shrine Auditorium and Mann's Chinese Theater in Los Angeles and Caesars Palace in Las Vegas.

	Annual Growth	12/03	12/04	12/05	12/06	12/07
Est. sales ($ mil.)	—	—	—	—	—	300.0
Employees	—	—	—	—	—	1,700

An in-depth profile of this company is available to Hoover's Online members at hoovers.com.

DUPONT AUTOMOTIVE

950 Stephenson Hwy.
Troy, MI 48083
Phone: 248-583-8000
Fax: 248-583-8157
Web: automotive.dupont.com

CEO: Marty M. McQuade
CFO: –
HR: –
FYE: December 31
Type: Association

DuPont Automotive has a hand in your car from beginning to end. It has been working with the auto industry for nearly a century, providing everything from the glass in a sunroof down to the rubber in the tires, from thermoplastic front end systems to the R&D involved in producing tail lights. The $6 billion unit of DuPont operates from more than 100 plants and labs in more than 70 countries and is the largest provider of coatings to the automotive industry. The company's plants make coatings and plastics and provides compounding services to the auto industry in North America, Asia, and Europe.

DUPONT FABROS TECHNOLOGY, INC.

NYSE: DFT

1212 New York Ave., NW, Ste. 900
Washington, DC 20005
Phone: 202-728-0044
Fax: –
Web: www.dftechnology.com

CEO: Hossein Fateh
CFO: Steven G. Osgood
HR: –
FYE: December 31
Type: Public

Forget Greyskull, national and international technology companies call on the power of DuPont Fabros Technology. The company owns, develops, operates, and manages wholesale data centers — the facilities that house, power, and cool computer servers for such technology companies as Microsoft, Yahoo!, and Google. Playing landlord and nanny for computer servers, DuPont Fabros Technology establishes its rental rates based on the amount of power reserved for tenant use and the square footage they occupy. DuPont Fabros Technology has four data centers located in Northern Virginia, two data centers under development, and plans to build six more data centers in Virginia, New Jersey, and California.

	Annual Growth	12/03	12/04	12/05	12/06	12/07
Sales ($ mil.)	—	—	—	—	—	61.3
Net income ($ mil.)	—	—	—	—	—	(100.9)
Market value ($ mil.)	—	—	—	—	—	694.9
Employees	—	—	—	—	—	—

DUQUESNE LIGHT COMPANY

411 7th Ave.
Pittsburgh, PA 15219
Phone: 412-393-6000
Fax: 412-393-5517
Web: www.duquesnelight.com

CEO: Morgan K. O'Brien
CFO: Mark E. Kaplan
HR: –
FYE: December 31
Type: Subsidiary

Duquesne Light is the first and last resort for light for many in the Keystone State. The company provides electricity to about 580,000 customers in southwestern Pennsylvania over its 17,000-mile transmission and distribution system. The utility, a subsidiary of Duquesne Light Holdings (formerly DQE), sold its generation assets in 2000 (prior to deregulation in the state), but still acts as a generation Provider of Last Resort (POLR) for customers who do not choose an alternative supplier. In 2006 Duquesne Light Holdings acquired Atlantic City Electric's 108 MW ownership interests in the Keystone and Conemaugh coal-fired power plants.

	Annual Growth	12/02	12/03	12/04	12/05	12/06
Sales ($ mil.)	(6.5%)	944.6	806.1	789.3	792.4	723.2
Net income ($ mil.)	(51.1%)	75.4	69.6	67.8	73.0	4.3
Employees	0.0%	—	—	—	1,400	1,400

DUQUESNE LIGHT HOLDINGS, INC.

411 7th Ave.
Pittsburgh, PA 15219
Phone: 412-393-6000
Fax: 412-393-5517
Web: www.duquesnelight.com

CEO: Morgan K. O'Brien
CFO: Mark E. Kaplan
HR: –
FYE: December 31
Type: Private

As energy markets deregulate, Duquesne Light Holdings (formerly DQE) is restructuring PDQ. Its principal subsidiary, regulated utility Duquesne Light, distributes electricity to 580,000 customers in southwestern Pennsylvania. The company has been divesting noncore assets to concentrate on its power utility and energy services businesses; it changed its name in 2003 to mark the shift. In 2006 Duquesne Light Holdings acquired Atlantic City Electric's 108 MW ownership interests in the Keystone and Conemaugh coal-fired power plants. The next year a consortium led by Macquarie Infrastructure Partners and Diversified Utilities and Energy Trust acquired Duquesne Light for about $3 billion in cash and debt.

DURA AUTOMOTIVE SYSTEMS, INC.

Pink Sheets: DRRA

2791 Research Dr.
Rochester Hills, MI 48309
Phone: 248-299-7500
Fax: 248-299-7501
Web: www.duraauto.com

CEO: Lawrence A. Denton
CFO: C. Timothy (Tim) Trenary
HR: Theresa Skotak
FYE: December 31
Type: Public

You wouldn't be able to keep the pedal to the metal without Dura Automotive Systems' driver control systems. The company is a leading supplier of pedal systems, parking brake mechanisms, manual and automatic transmission gear shifter systems, and automotive cables. Dura Automotive also makes door and window systems and trim, as well as engineered assemblies such as tailgate latches and seating adjustment controls. The company's major customers include Ford (22% of sales), Volkswagen (10%), GM (9%), and Lear (6%). Dura has filed for Chapter 11 protection from creditors.

	Annual Growth	12/02	12/03	12/04	12/05	*12/06
Sales ($ mil.)	(3.0%)	2,360.3	2,380.8	2,492.5	2,344.1	2,090.8
Net income ($ mil.)	—	(288.7)	22.3	11.7	1.8	(910.7)
Employees	(21.5%)	18,800	17,800	17,000	15,800	7,150

*Most recent year available

DURECT CORPORATION

NASDAQ (GM): DRRX

2 Results Way
Cupertino, CA 95014
Phone: 408-777-1417
Fax: 408-777-3577
Web: www.durect.com

CEO: James E. Brown
CFO: Matthew J. Hogan
HR: –
FYE: December 31
Type: Public

DURECT wants your medicine to go DURECTly where it's needed. It is developing drug-delivery systems to provide long-term therapy for such conditions as chronic pain, heart disease, cancer, and Alzheimer's. Drug delivery technologies provided by DURECT include SABER, a controlled-release injectable; TRANSDUR, a transdermal patch; ORADUR, a sustained release oral gel-cap; DUROS, an osmotic implant; and DURIN, a biodegradable implant. Its R&D efforts are conducted independently and collaboratively. DURECT sells biodegradable polymers (Lactel) and osmotic pumps (ALZET) to pharmaceutical and medical research firms through direct sales representatives and distributors.

	Annual Growth	12/03	12/04	12/05	12/06	12/07
Sales ($ mil.)	27.0%	11.8	13.9	28.6	21.9	30.7
Net income ($ mil.)	—	(22.7)	(27.6)	(18.1)	(33.3)	(24.3)
Market value ($ mil.)	38.9%	127.9	170.1	312.4	307.3	476.5
Employees	—	—	—	138	—	—

DUSA PHARMACEUTICALS, INC.

NASDAQ (GM): DUSA

25 Upton Dr.
Wilmington, MA 01887
Phone: 978-657-7500
Fax: 978-657-9193
Web: www.dusapharma.com

CEO: Robert F. (Bob) Doman
CFO: Richard C. Christopher
HR: —
FYE: December 31
Type: Public

DUSA Pharmaceuticals has seen the light. The company develops photodynamic and photodetection therapies for treating and diagnosing a variety of dermatological conditions using a combination of drugs and light. In the US, DUSA markets its Levulan Kerastick brand topical solution, a product that is used in combination with the BLU-U light to treat actinic keratoses, or precancerous skin lesions caused by sun exposure. On its own, BLU-U is also FDA approved to treat moderate acne. DUSA's 2006 acquisition of Sirius Laboratories expanded the company's product line for acne to include Nicomide, an oral prescription, and ClindaReach, a topical prescription.

	Annual Growth	12/03	12/04	12/05	12/06	12/07
Sales ($ mil.)	129.4%	1.0	8.0	11.3	25.6	27.7
Net income ($ mil.)	—	(14.8)	(15.6)	(15.0)	(31.4)	(14.7)
Market value ($ mil.)	(8.3%)	70.5	241.3	183.5	83.8	49.8
Employees	—	—	—	66	—	—

DVL, INC.

OTC: DVLN

70 E. 55th St., 7th Fl.
New York, NY 10022
Phone: 212-350-9900
Fax: 212-350-9911

CEO: Alan E. Casnoff
CFO: Henry Swain
HR: —
FYE: December 31
Type: Public

As far as DVL is concerned, making money is all in the family. The commercial finance company owns and services commercial mortgages held by more than 40 affiliated limited partnerships (in which it is general partner). DVL's partnerships hold some 1.9 million sq. ft. of commercial, industrial, and office space; a percentage of its income comes from tenant rental payments. Retail giant Wal-Mart is its largest tenant. The company also owns residual interests in securitized portfolios and offers real estate asset management and administrative services for its partnerships.

	Annual Growth	12/03	12/04	12/05	12/06	12/07
Sales ($ mil.)	4.9%	9.1	8.9	9.3	9.4	11.0
Net income ($ mil.)	39.9%	0.6	1.5	1.7	1.8	2.3
Employees	(5.9%)	—	12	10	10	10

DWS SCUDDER DISTRIBUTORS, INC.

222 S. Riverside Plaza
Chicago, IL 60606
Phone: 312-537-7000
Fax: —
Web: www.dws-scudder.com

CEO: Axel Schwarzer
CFO: —
HR: —
FYE: December 31
Type: Business segment

Mutual funds are DWS Scudder's bread and butter. Formerly Scudder Investments, DWS Scudder is the US mutual fund management division of Deutsche Asset Management (DeAM), which in turn is part of German banking giant Deutsche Bank. The company's products include defined-contribution retirement plans, individual retirement accounts (IRAs), variable annuities, closed-end funds, and money market funds, in addition to its family of more than 70 mutual funds. DWS Scudder serves large corporations, financial institutions, governments, and foundations, as well as individual investors.

	Annual Growth	12/03	12/04	12/05	12/06	12/07
Est. sales ($ mil.)	—	—	—	—	—	4.9
Employees	—	—	—	—	—	60

THE DWYER GROUP, INC.

1020 N. University Parks Dr.
Waco, TX 76707
Phone: 254-745-2400
Fax: 254-745-2590
Web: www.dwyergroup.com

CEO: Dina Dwyer-Owens
CFO: Thomas J. (Tom) Buckley
HR: Gayla Wortham
FYE: December 31
Type: Private

Odd jobs are an everyday business for The Dwyer Group. The company is made up of a handful of trade service franchising businesses whose operations include plumbing, electrical repairs, and carpet cleaning. Among the businesses under the Dwyer umbrella are Mr. Rooter (plumbing services), Rainbow International (carpet and upholstery cleaning and repair), and Glass Doctor (auto, home, and commercial glass replacement). The Dwyer Group has some 750 franchises in the US and Canada, and about 240 franchises in 14 other countries. Established in 1980 by Don Dwyer with the formation of its first company, Rainbow International, The Dwyer Group is owned by private equity firm The Riverside Company.

	Annual Growth	12/03	12/04	12/05	12/06	12/07
Est. sales ($ mil.)	—	—	—	—	—	12.4
Employees	—	—	—	—	—	217

DXP ENTERPRISES, INC.

NASDAQ (GS): DXPE

7272 Pinemont
Houston, TX 77040
Phone: 713-996-4700
Fax: 713-996-4701
Web: www.dxpe.com

CEO: David R. Little
CFO: Mac McConnell
HR: Rob Kobler
FYE: December 31
Type: Public

DXP Enterprises is well-equipped to meet its customers' needs. The company distributes maintenance, repair, and operating (MRO) equipment and products, primarily to the oil and gas, petrochemical, and wood products industries. It also distributes centrifugal pumps, rotary gear pumps, plunger pumps, and other fluid-handling equipment as well as bearings and power transmission equipment, general mill (cutting tools) and safety supplies, and electrical products (wire conduit). DXP's MRO unit also provides system design, fabrication, and repair services. DXP's electrical contractor division sells a range of electrical products including wire conduit, wiring devices, electrical fittings and boxes, and tools.

	Annual Growth	12/03	12/04	12/05	12/06	12/07
Sales ($ mil.)	31.1%	150.7	160.6	185.4	279.8	444.5
Net income ($ mil.)	69.7%	2.1	2.8	5.5	11.9	17.4
Market value ($ mil.)	105.2%	16.6	19.8	86.9	186.2	295.3
Employees	37.2%	453	448	519	763	1,603

DYAX CORP.

NASDAQ (GM): DYAX

300 Technology Sq.
Cambridge, MA 02139
Phone: 617-225-2500
Fax: 617-225-2501
Web: www.dyax.com

CEO: Henry E. Blair
CFO: Stephen S. (Steve) Galliker
HR: Erin Boyer
FYE: December 31
Type: Public

Dyax is arming the war against disease. The biopharmaceutical company develops drugs from its proprietary phage display binding technology that rapidly identifies proteins, peptides, and antibodies it can use to treat disease. Its lead drug candidate, DX-88, may be used to treat hereditary angioedema and to reduce blood loss during cardiopulmonary bypass surgeries — it is currently undergoing clinical trials. Dyax has numerous other products in its discovery and development pipeline, including key candidate DX-2240 which is designed to inhibit cancerous tumor growth.

	Annual Growth	12/03	12/04	12/05	12/06	12/07
Sales ($ mil.)	11.5%	16.9	16.6	19.9	12.8	26.1
Net income ($ mil.)	—	(7.4)	(33.1)	(30.9)	(50.3)	(56.3)
Market value ($ mil.)	2.2%	202.8	228.0	200.4	132.4	221.2
Employees	—	—	—	144	—	—

An in-depth profile of this company is available to Hoover's Online members at hoovers.com.

525

DYCOM INDUSTRIES, INC.

NYSE: DY

11770 US Hwy. 1, Ste. 101
Palm Beach Gardens, FL 33408
Phone: 561-627-7171
Fax: 561-627-7709
Web: www.dycomind.com

CEO: Steven E. Nielsen
CFO: H. Andrew (Drew) DeFerrari
HR: –
FYE: July 31
Type: Public

The telecommunications industry dials Dycom Industries for construction and engineering assistance. Operating through about three dozen subsidiaries, the company primarily designs, builds, and maintains coaxial, copper, and fiber-optic cable systems for local and long-distance phone companies and cable TV operators. Dycom also provides wiring services for businesses and government agencies, installs and maintains electrical lines for utilities, and locates underground wires and pipelines for excavators. But its main mission is to provide infrastructure support to the telecom industry. AT&T, Comcast, and Verizon Communications together account for nearly half of sales.

	Annual Growth	7/03	7/04	7/05	7/06	7/07
Sales ($ mil.)	16.5%	618.2	872.7	986.6	1,023.7	1,137.8
Net income ($ mil.)	25.1%	17.1	58.6	24.3	18.2	41.9
Market value ($ mil.)	9.2%	800.9	1,309.2	1,192.4	746.9	1,139.1
Employees	13.7%	—	—	8,228	9,352	—

DYNACQ HEALTHCARE, INC.

NASDAQ (CM): DYII

10304 Interstate 10 East, Ste. 369
Houston, TX 77029
Phone: 713-378-2000
Fax: 713-673-6416
Web: www.dynacq.com

CEO: Chiu Moon Chan
CFO: Philip S. Chan
HR: Myrna Lee
FYE: August 31
Type: Public

Dynacq Healthcare is a holding company that owns and operates acute care specialty hospitals providing electively scheduled surgeries, such as bariatric (weight loss) and orthopedic surgeries and pain management procedures. Dynacq operates Vista Hospital in Garland, Texas and Surgery Specialty Hospitals of America in Pasadena, Texas, (suburbs of Dallas and Houston, respectively). Most of Dynacq's revenues come from workers' compensation insurance and commercial insurers on an out-of-network basis. Chairman and CEO Chiu Moon Chan owns more than half of Dynacq.

	Annual Growth	8/03	8/04	8/05	8/06	8/07
Sales ($ mil.)	(17.0%)	90.0	62.8	55.3	36.0	42.8
Net income ($ mil.)	(33.0%)	20.9	(1.6)	(5.1)	(5.9)	4.2
Market value ($ mil.)	4.7%	—	86.9	73.7	31.5	99.8
Employees	(9.4%)	402	—	412	—	271

DYNAMEX INC.

NASDAQ (GS): DDMX

5429 LBJ Fwy., Ste. 1000
Dallas, TX 75240
Phone: 214-560-9000
Fax: 214-560-9349
Web: www.dynamex.com

CEO: Richard K. (Rick) McClelland
CFO: Ray E. Schmitz
HR: –
FYE: July 31
Type: Public

Dynamex knows the dynamics of same-day delivery. The company provides both scheduled and on-demand delivery of time-sensitive items such as medical supplies, financial documents, electronics, office products, and auto parts. It concentrates on intracity deliveries. Dynamex operates from about 50 facilities in the US and Canada; it uses third-party air and ground carriers to provide same-day intercity services. Most of the company's drivers are independent contractors. Dynamex also enables customers to outsource certain logistics functions, including the management of dedicated vehicle fleets and facilities such as mailrooms and inventory-tracking call centers.

	Annual Growth	7/03	7/04	7/05	7/06	7/07
Sales ($ mil.)	13.3%	250.8	287.9	321.1	358.4	413.8
Net income ($ mil.)	18.5%	7.6	12.8	11.2	12.4	15.0
Market value ($ mil.)	28.0%	90.8	177.8	205.4	222.8	243.7
Employees	(43.6%)	—	—	6,290	6,300	2,000

DYNAMIC MATERIALS CORPORATION

NASDAQ (GS): BOOM

5405 Spine Rd.
Boulder, CO 80301
Phone: 303-665-5700
Fax: 303-604-1897
Web: www.dynamicmaterials.com

CEO: Yvon Pierre Cariou
CFO: Richard A. (Rick) Santa
HR: Philippe Roquette
FYE: December 31
Type: Public

Dynamic Materials Corporation (DMC) has an explosive personality when it comes to working with metal. The company (formerly Explosive Fabricators) uses explosives to metallurgically bond, or "clad," metal plates (usually joining a corrosion-resistant alloy and carbon steel). Clad metal is used to make heavy-duty industrial pressure vessels and heat exchangers. The company also produces components using more traditional metalworking techniques such as machining, rolling, and hydraulic expansion. DMC's AMK Welding subsidiary machines and welds parts primarily for the commercial aircraft and aerospace industries.

	Annual Growth	12/03	12/04	12/05	12/06	12/07
Sales ($ mil.)	42.3%	40.3	54.2	79.3	113.5	165.2
Net income ($ mil.)	—	(0.7)	2.8	10.4	20.8	24.6
Market value ($ mil.)	213.2%	7.6	32.3	353.0	336.7	732.3
Employees	16.0%	—	—	181	210	—

DYNAMICS RESEARCH CORPORATION

NASDAQ (GM): DRCO

60 Frontage Rd.
Andover, MA 01810
Phone: 978-289-1500
Fax: 978-470-0201
Web: www.drc.com

CEO: James P. Regan
CFO: David Keleher
HR: Steven P. (Steve) Wentzell
FYE: December 31
Type: Public

Research is this company's middle name. No really. Dynamics Research Corporation (DRC) provides computer-based systems development, engineering, management, and logistics support services to the US government and its contractors, state and local agencies, and corporate customers. A majority of its business (about 80% of sales) comes from various agencies within the Department of Defense, including the US Air Force, Army, and Navy. Its Metrigraphics division produces precision components — including optical discs and fine line circuits — for commercial manufacturing customers in the computing, telecom, and medical markets.

	Annual Growth	12/03	12/04	12/05	12/06	12/07
Sales ($ mil.)	(1.6%)	244.8	275.7	300.4	259.0	229.6
Net income ($ mil.)	1.5%	6.7	9.4	11.4	4.1	7.1
Market value ($ mil.)	(6.8%)	136.2	155.8	140.5	90.8	102.9
Employees	(12.3%)	—	—	1,822	—	1,400

DYNASIL CORPORATION OF AMERICA

OTC: DYSL

385 Cooper Rd.
West Berlin, NJ 08091
Phone: 856-767-4600
Fax: 856-767-6813
Web: www.dynasil.com

CEO: Craig T. Dunham
CFO: Laura Lunardo
HR: –
FYE: September 30
Type: Public

Dynasil Corporation of America likes playing with the dynamics of silica. The company manufactures custom synthetic-fused silica and quartz products primarily used in industrial optical materials. Its products include filters, lenses, prisms, reflectors, windows, and mirrors. Customers use the company's fabricated optical products in lasers, aircraft, optical equipment, analytical instruments, semiconductors, and electronics. Manufacturers Corning, Schott Glass Technologies, and General Electric supply the company with some fused silica, fused quartz, and optical materials. Dynasil sells its products in the US and overseas.

	Annual Growth	9/03	9/04	9/05	9/06	9/07
Sales ($ mil.)	47.2%	2.3	2.3	5.1	6.9	10.8
Net income ($ mil.)	—	(0.4)	(0.2)	0.2	0.5	0.5
Market value ($ mil.)	91.5%	—	—	2.7	3.1	9.8
Employees	49.5%	16	17	47	75	80

An in-depth profile of this company is available to Hoover's Online members at hoovers.com.

DYNATEM, INC.

Pink Sheets: DYTM

23263 Madero St., Ste. C
Mission Viejo, CA 92691
Phone: 949-855-3235
Fax: 949-770-3481
Web: www.dynatem.com

CEO: Michael Horan
CFO: Belen Ramos
HR: –
FYE: May 31
Type: Public

Dynatem designs embedded computing systems based on Intel and Freescale microprocessor architectures. It also offers computer input/output boards. The company focuses on VMEbus-based products, VMEbus being a standard architecture for embedded electronics. Dynatem also supports the PCI and CompactPCI architectures. Among computer and real-time operating systems, Dynatem products support Linux, QNX, Solaris, VxWorks, and Windows. Dynatem executive Eileen Schmalbach owns about 46% of the company; her brother, Dynatem CEO Michael Horan, owns another 10%.

	Annual Growth	5/02	5/03	5/04	5/05	*5/06
Sales ($ mil.)	6.3%	2.9	3.8	4.5	2.5	3.7
Net income ($ mil.)	(15.9%)	0.2	0.4	0.4	(0.8)	0.1
Employees	—	—	—	—	—	19

*Most recent year available

DYNATRONICS CORPORATION

NASDAQ (CM): DYNT

7030 Park Centre Dr.
Salt Lake City, UT 84121
Phone: 801-568-7000
Fax: 801-568-7711
Web: www.dynatronics.com

CEO: Kelvyn H. Cullimore, Jr.
CFO: Terry M. Atkinson
HR: –
FYE: June 30
Type: Public

Dynatronics makes medical equipment to keep active people on the go. Its products include electrotherapy, ultrasound, and infrared light therapy equipment; medical supplies such as wraps, braces, bandages, walking aids, and training equipment; rehabilitation therapy tables; and aesthetic products sold under the Synergie brand. Its Synergie Aesthetic Massage System (AMS) uses vacuum massage for cosmetic weight loss, and its Synergie Peel is a microdermabrasion device that reduces wrinkles. The company's products are sold through several distribution channels, including directly through its own distributors, through independent dealers, and via catalog.

	Annual Growth	6/03	6/04	6/05	6/06	6/07
Sales ($ mil.)	1.3%	16.9	20.6	20.4	19.5	17.8
Net income ($ mil.)	—	0.0	0.9	0.7	0.2	(0.1)
Market value ($ mil.)	21.3%	6.8	20.3	17.6	10.8	14.8
Employees	—	—	—	—	—	—

DYNAVAX TECHNOLOGIES CORPORATION

NASDAQ (GM): DVAX

2929 7th St., Ste. 100
Berkeley, CA 94710
Phone: 510-848-5100
Fax: 510-848-1327
Web: www.dynavax.com

CEO: Dino Dina
CFO: Deborah A. Smeltzer
HR: Cecilia Vitug
FYE: December 31
Type: Public

Dynavax Technologies is trying to reprogram the way the body reacts to disease. The firm focuses on immunostimulatory sequences (ISS), short strands of DNA found to strengthen the immune system. The company's lead candidate in clinical trials is HEPLISAV, a hepatitis B vaccine. Dynavax is working on other candidates which might lead to treatments for asthma, colorectal cancer, and hepatitis C. HEPLISAV is being developed in a partnership with Merck & Co. Dynavax has also partnered with AstraZeneca to research preclinical work on a treatment for asthma and chronic obstructive pulmonary disease.

	Annual Growth	12/03	12/04	12/05	12/06	12/07
Sales ($ mil.)	104.9%	0.8	14.8	14.7	4.8	14.1
Net income ($ mil.)	—	(17.4)	(16.0)	(20.6)	(52.0)	(60.0)
Market value ($ mil.)	1.0%	—	197.0	128.3	364.6	203.2
Employees	49.9%	—	—	77	—	173

DYNCORP INTERNATIONAL INC.

NYSE: DCP

3190 Fairview Park Dr., Ste. 700
Falls Church, VA 22042
Phone: 571-722-0210
Fax: 571-722-0252
Web: www.dyn-intl.com

CEO: William L. (Bill) Ballhaus
CFO: Michael J. Thorne
HR: Dianne Walker
FYE: Friday nearest March 31
Type: Public

DynCorp International works behind the scenes to support US military and diplomatic efforts on the front lines. Its Government Services division was divided in 2008 into two separate divisions: Logistics and Construction Management (LCM) and International Security Services (ISS). Combined the divisions account for about 66% of the company's sales. Contracts with the US Department of State to train police officers overseas constitute the largest single business unit. DynCorp International's Maintenance and Technical Support Services division offers engineering and maintenance services for aircraft, support equipment, and weapons systems. Investment firm Veritas Capital controls 57% of DynCorp International.

	Annual Growth	3/04	3/05	3/06	3/07	3/08
Sales ($ mil.)	15.2%	1,214.3	1,920.9	1,967.0	2,082.3	2,139.8
Net income ($ mil.)	—	0.0	0.1	7.2	27.0	48.0
Market value ($ mil.)	9.7%	—	—	—	860.1	943.9
Employees	6.0%	—	14,100	14,400	14,600	16,800

⊞ DYNEGY INC.

NYSE: DYN

1000 Louisiana St., Ste. 5800
Houston, TX 77002
Phone: 713-507-6400
Fax: 713-507-6808
Web: www.dynegy.com

CEO: Bruce A. Williamson
CFO: Holli C. Nichols
HR: Julius Cox
FYE: December 31
Type: Public

Power dynamo Dynegy (short for "dynamic energy") has made dynamic changes, restructuring operations around its electricity production unit. Following its 2007 combination with private equity fund LS Power, the company's power generation portfolio consists of a nearly 20,000 MW fleet of about 30 power plants fueled by coal, fuel oil, and natural gas. Dynegy also acquired a 50% interest (alongside LS Power) in a development joint venture, whose focus is on high-return greenfield and brownfield development projects including natural gas, coal, and renewable options. Former majority shareholder — that baton now resides with LS Power — Chevron Corporation sold its shares in Dynegy the same year.

	Annual Growth	12/03	12/04	12/05	12/06	12/07
Sales ($ mil.)	(14.4%)	5,787.0	6,153.0	2,313.0	2,017.0	3,103.0
Employees	(18.6%)	4,103	2,223	1,371	1,339	1,800

DYNEX CAPITAL, INC.

NYSE: DX

4551 Cox Rd., Ste. 300
Glen Allen, VA 23060
Phone: 804-217-5800
Fax: 804-217-5860
Web: www.dynexcapital.com

CEO: Thomas B. Akin
CFO: Jeffrey L. Childress
HR: Alison G. Griffin
FYE: December 31
Type: Public

Dynex Capital is a real estate investment trust (REIT) that invests in loans and fixed-income securities backed by single-family residential and commercial mortgage loans. The company isn't too picky, investing in both investment-grade and subprime loans and adjustable-rate and fixed-rate loans. However, citing competition and a "lack of compelling opportunities" in a volatile marketplace, the company makes few new investments and has been slimming down its balance sheet by selling off assets, including all of its manufactured home lending and delinquent property-tax receivable portfolios.

	Annual Growth	12/03	12/04	12/05	12/06	12/07
Sales ($ mil.)	(32.9%)	152.2	136.7	74.4	50.5	30.8
Net income ($ mil.)	—	(21.1)	(3.4)	9.6	4.9	8.9
Market value ($ mil.)	12.9%	66.3	95.1	83.9	86.0	107.6
Employees	(25.8%)	—	—	20	17	11

DYNTEK, INC.

OTC: DYNK

19700 Fairchild Rd., Ste. 230
Irvine, CA 92612
Phone: 949-271-6700
Fax: 949-271-6799
Web: www.dyntek.com

CEO: Ron Ben-Yishay
CFO: Karen Rosenberger
HR: June Hazzard
FYE: June 30
Type: Public

DynTek sees a bright future in technology services. The company, previously a provider of medication and services to diabetes patients, now provides a variety of information technology services to local and state governments, schools, and commercial enterprises. Its services include technology procurement, systems integration, business process outsourcing, network engineering, and technical support. While its marketing emphasis focuses on its IT services business, nearly three-quarters of sales are derived from the resale of hardware and software from partners such as Cisco, IBM, Microsoft, and Novell.

	Annual Growth	6/03	6/04	6/05	6/06	6/07
Sales ($ mil.)	15.8%	52.7	50.0	76.6	80.8	94.8
Net income ($ mil.)	—	(13.8)	(19.0)	(22.6)	(28.3)	(11.1)
Employees	—	—	—	—	—	237

E COM VENTURES, INC.

NASDAQ (CM): ECMV

251 International Pkwy.
Sunrise, FL 33325
Phone: 954-335-9100
Fax: 954-335-9026
Web: www.perfumania.com

CEO: Michael W. Katz
CFO: Donovan Chin
HR: Susie Stubbs
FYE: Saturday nearest January 31
Type: Public

E Com Ventures makes dollars with scents. The holding company owns scent-seller Perfumania, which runs about 300 stores in some 35 states (about a third are located in California, Florida, and Texas) and Puerto Rico, offering about 300 fragrances (including its own Nature's Elements) at deeply discounted prices. In addition to scents for men and women, Perfumania sells cosmetics, skincare, and bath and body products. E Com Ventures also operates perfumania.com and is a wholesale supplier of fragrances to other retailers. In 2000 E Com bought back the perfumania.com Web site, which it had partially spun off in 1999 as e-business firm Envision Development (which ceased operations in November 2000).

	Annual Growth	1/04	1/05	1/06	1/07	1/08
Sales ($ mil.)	9.2%	212.6	225.0	233.7	243.6	301.8
Net income ($ mil.)	—	(12.9)	3.2	14.3	4.5	0.0
Market value ($ mil.)	18.3%	38.4	42.6	50.1	71.7	75.0
Employees	7.1%	1,363	1,420	1,420	1,599	1,794

E! ENTERTAINMENT TELEVISION, INC.

5750 Wilshire Blvd.
Los Angeles, CA 90036
Phone: 323-954-2400
Fax: 323-954-2661
Web: www.eentertainment.com

CEO: Ted Harbert
CFO: Steve Dolcemaschio
HR: David Walkley
FYE: December 31
Type: Private

Telling the true stories of Hollywood fuels this network. E! Entertainment Television is a cable television network that provides 80 million subscribers with a non-stop dose of celebrity gossip and entertainment news. The company also owns sister channel Style Network (40 million subscribers) and the E! Online Web site. The E! network cut one of its highest profile deals ever in late 2005 when it picked up the Paris Hilton and Nicole Richie reality show *The Simple Life* (cancelled in 2007) from FOX. The company is owned by cable TV provider Comcast.

E. GLUCK CORPORATION

29-10 Thomson Ave.
Long Island City, NY 11101
Phone: 718-784-0700
Fax: 718-482-2702
Web: www.armitron.com

CEO: Eugen Gluck
CFO: Renee Jacobs
HR: Kim Fuch
FYE: December 31
Type: Private

E. Gluck wonders, "Do you have the time?" The company makes and markets quartz watches that bear monikers such as Anne Klein, Nine West, and its own Armitron. It also makes watches featuring Warner Bros. and Cartoon Network characters. E. Gluck uses edgy styling, microfiber bands, and digital colors to attract younger customers, and interchangeable bracelets and bezels (and even diamonds) for the more sophisticated set; functional watches are made for the US Army. Its moderately priced watches, which carry a lifetime guarantee on working parts, are sold in US department and jewelry stores. Owner and CEO Eugen Gluck founded the company in 1955.

	Annual Growth	12/03	12/04	12/05	12/06	12/07
Est. sales ($ mil.)	—	—	—	—	—	20.0
Employees	—	—	—	—	—	400

EACO CORPORATION

OTC: EACO

1500 N. Lakeview Ave.
Anaheim, CA 92807
Phone: 714-876-2490
Fax: 714-876-2410
Web: www.eacocorp.com

CEO: Glen F. Ceiley
CFO: Glen F. Ceiley
HR: –
FYE: Wednesday nearest December 31
Type: Public

EACO Corporation lost its appetite for the buffet business. The company formerly operated as the sole franchisee of Ryan's Restaurant Group restaurants in Florida until 2004. The following year it sold its chain of 16 Whistle Junction and Florida Buffet locations to Banner Buffets. The company generates a small amount of revenue from a handful of rental properties, including four restaurants in Florida and two properties leased to industrial tenants in California, while it looks to invest in other real estate opportunities. Tenant NES Rentals accounts for nearly half of EACO's rental revenues. CEO Glen Ceiley owns more than 60% of the company through electronics distributor Bisco Industries.

	Annual Growth	12/03	12/04	12/05	12/06	12/07
Sales ($ mil.)	(57.7%)	37.6	37.8	0.2	0.8	1.2
Net income ($ mil.)	—	(2.4)	(2.0)	9.4	(6.8)	(5.0)
Market value ($ mil.)	—	—	—	—	—	1.6
Employees	—	—	—	—	0	—

EADS NORTH AMERICA, INC.

1616 N. Fort Myers Dr., Ste. 1600
Arlington, VA 22209
Phone: 703-236-3300
Fax: 703-236-3301
Web: www.eadsnorthamerica.com

CEO: Ralph D. Crosby Jr.
CFO: Christopher Emerson
HR: David M. Fink
FYE: December 31
Type: Subsidiary

EADS North America is the holding company for parent EADS' operations in North America. Operations are broken down into six primary divisions: Fixed-wing aircraft and helicopters (American Eurocopter, Airbus North America, EADS CASA North America, EADS Socata Aircraft), Defense systems and homeland security (EADS North America Defense Security and Systems Solutions, EADS North America Defense), Avionics and controls (Fairchild Controls), Communications (EADS Secure Networks North America), Space (Astrium North America), and Test equipment and services (EADS North America Defense Test and Services, TYX Corporation).

	Annual Growth	12/03	12/04	12/05	12/06	12/07
Est. sales ($ mil.)	—	—	—	—	—	113.6
Employees	—	—	—	—	—	1,550

EAGLE BANCORP
OTC: EBMT

1400 Prospect Ave.
Helena, MT 59601
Phone: 406-442-3080
Fax: 406-457-4035
Web: www.americanfederalsavingsbank.com

CEO: Peter J. Johnson
CFO: Clinton J. Morrison
HR: –
FYE: June 30
Type: Public

Eagle Bancorp hopes to soar majestically over the competition. The holding company (unrelated to the Maryland company of the same name) owns American Federal Savings Bank, a thrift that serves businesses and residents of southwestern Montana through five branches. American Federal primarily writes mortgages on one- to four-family residences (these comprise more than half of its loan book); the rest of its portfolio consists of home equity loans, commercial mortgages, and consumer, business, and construction loans. The bank's deposit products include checking, money market, and savings accounts; CDs; and IRAs. Mutual holding company Eagle Financial MHC owns a majority of Eagle Bancorp.

	Annual Growth	6/03	6/04	6/05	6/06	6/07
Assets ($ mil.)	4.8%	203.1	203.0	206.4	226.2	244.7
Net income ($ mil.)	(1.3%)	1.9	2.1	1.7	1.8	1.8
Market value ($ mil.)	1.1%	33.9	39.2	33.1	34.5	35.5
Employees	—	—	—	—	—	—

EAGLE BANCORP, INC.
NASDAQ (CM): EGBN

7815 Woodmont Ave.
Bethesda, MD 20814
Phone: 301-986-1800
Fax: 301-986-8529
Web: www.eaglebankmd.com

CEO: Ronald D. (Ron) Paul
CFO: James H. Langmead
HR: Joanie Heavey
FYE: December 31
Type: Public

For those nest eggs that need a little help hatching, holding company Eagle Bancorp would recommend its community-oriented EagleBank subsidiary. The bank serves businesses and individuals through about 10 branches in Washington, DC, and its Maryland suburbs. Deposit products include checking, savings, and money market accounts; certificates of deposit; and IRAs. Commercial, residential, and construction real estate loans combined represent 70% of its loan portfolio, which also includes business (it has significant expertise as a Small Business Administration lender), consumer, and home equity loans.

	Annual Growth	12/03	12/04	12/05	12/06	12/07
Assets ($ mil.)	17.6%	443.0	553.5	672.3	773.5	846.4
Net income ($ mil.)	24.5%	3.2	5.1	7.5	8.0	7.7
Market value ($ mil.)	20.1%	56.5	65.8	127.9	164.9	117.6
Employees	9.2%	—	—	145	171	173

EAGLE BROADBAND, INC.
Pink Sheets: EAGB

227 W. Main St.
League City, TX 77573
Phone: 281-316-7500
Fax: 281-332-5401
Web: www.eaglebroadband.com

CEO: C. James (Jim) Reinhartsen
CFO: Mark Mann
HR: –
FYE: August 31
Type: Public

Eagle Broadband keeps people talking (and entertained) with a number of broadband, Internet Protocol (IP), and satellite communications services. Its bundled broadband service lets service providers, cities, real estate developers, and others offer IP-based digital services such as high-speed Internet, voice, and video; the IP video solution is offered in conjunction with satellite operator GlobeCast. Eagle Broadband also makes IP set-top boxes (MediaPro) that hotels and others use to offer in-room entertainment. The company filed for Chapter 11 bankruptcy protection in 2007.

	Annual Growth	8/02	8/03	8/04	8/05	*8/06
Sales ($ mil.)	(39.9%)	29.8	11.6	12.5	8.6	3.9
Net income ($ mil.)	—	(36.8)	(36.5)	(39.0)	(57.0)	(26.9)
Employees	(33.3%)	222	—	—	95	44

*Most recent year available

EAGLE BULK SHIPPING INC.
NASDAQ (GS): EGLE

477 Madison Ave., Ste. 1405
New York, NY 10022
Phone: 212-785-2500
Fax: 212-785-3311
Web: www.eagleships.com

CEO: Sophocles N. Zoullas
CFO: Alan S. Ginsberg
HR: –
FYE: December 31
Type: Public

Some eagles soar through the skies, but Eagle Bulk Shipping rides the waves. The company owns a fleet of about 20 Handymax dry bulk carriers that it charters to customers, typically on one- to three-year contracts. Most of its vessels are classified as Supramaxes — large Handymaxes, essentially. The Supramaxes range in capacity from 50,000 to 60,000 deadweight tons (DWT) and feature on-board cranes for cargo loading and unloading. Overall, the company's fleet has a carrying capacity of more than 915,000 DWT. Cargo carried by charterers of Eagle Bulk Shipping's vessels includes cement, coal, fertilizer, grain, and iron ore.

	Annual Growth	3/04	3/05	*12/05	12/06	12/07
Sales ($ mil.)	—	—	0.0	56.1	104.7	124.8
Net income ($ mil.)	—	—	(0.8)	6.7	33.8	52.2
Market value ($ mil.)	53.3%	—	—	527.7	622.5	1,240.6
Employees	820.6%	—	4	295	339	—

*Fiscal year change

EAGLE EXPLORATION COMPANY
OTC: EGXP

1801 Broadway, Ste. 1010
Denver, CO 80202
Phone: 303-296-3677
Fax: –

CEO: Raymond N. Joeckel
CFO: Paul M. Joeckel
HR: –
FYE: March 31
Type: Public

Eagle Exploration is digging its talons into some big nests. The company was originally hatched as an oil and gas exploration firm but turned its eagle eye towards real estate in the early 1990s. It invests in and develops residential and commercial real estate; the company is a member of a consortium that is buying land north of Denver for residential development. Eagle Exploration also owns stakes in some oil and gas properties and related assets (and still its sole source of revenue). CEO Raymond Joeckel and his family have a controlling stake in the company.

	Annual Growth	3/04	3/05	3/06	3/07	3/08
Sales ($ mil.)	0.0%	0.1	0.0	0.1	0.1	0.1
Net income ($ mil.)	—	(0.2)	(0.2)	(0.2)	0.2	(0.1)
Market value ($ mil.)	—	—	—	—	—	—
Employees	—	—	—	—	—	—

EAGLE FAMILY FOODS, INC.

735 Taylor Rd., Ste. 200
Gahanna, OH 43230
Phone: 614-501-4200
Fax: 614-501-4299
Web: www.eaglebrand.com

CEO: Richard Smucker
CFO: –
HR: –
FYE: Saturday nearest June 30
Type: Subsidiary

The holidays wouldn't be the same if you didn't invite Eagle Family Foods. The company makes some familiar Borden branded products, including egg nog and sweetened condensed milk (Eagle Brand, Magnolia, and Meadow Gold are Eagle's other brands) and mincemeat pie filling (None Such) — all products used at Thanksgiving and Christmas time. (About 40% the company's sales occur in November and December.) In addition, with fewer people whipping up desserts from scratch, Eagle Family Foods launched a line of dessert kits based on its Eagle Brand sweetened condensed milk.

	Annual Growth	6/02	6/03	6/04	6/05	6/06
Sales ($ mil.)	9.4%	143.8	128.7	115.8	149.7	206.0
Net income ($ mil.)	—	(31.7)	(54.6)	(2.4)	(8.6)	(11.4)
Employees	(2.5%)	247	165	163	158	223

An in-depth profile of this company is available to Hoover's Online members at hoovers.com.

529

EAGLE HOSPITALITY PROPERTIES TRUST, INC.

100 E. RiverCenter Blvd., Ste. 480
Covington, KY 41011
Phone: 859-581-5900
Fax: 859-581-4650
Web: www.eaglehospitality.com

CEO: J. William (Bill) Blackham
CFO: –
HR: –
FYE: December 31
Type: Private

This company's nest egg is in hotel properties. Eagle Hospitality Properties, a real estate investment trust (REIT), owns more than a dozen hotels located in about 10 states and Puerto Rico. The properties include full-service or all-suites hotels that operate under the Hilton, Marriott, Hyatt, and Embassy Suites brands. In 2007 AP AIMCAP, a joint venture of Apollo Real Estate, Aimbridge Hospitality, and JF Capital Advisors, acquired Eagle Hospitality Properties; after the transaction was complete, AP AIMCAP took on the Eagle Hospitality Properties Trust, Inc. moniker.

	Annual Growth	12/02	12/03	12/04	12/05	12/06
Sales ($ mil.)	21.3%	69.8	74.7	82.3	116.4	151.0
Net income ($ mil.)	—	(1.1)	(0.7)	2.6	7.5	11.3
Employees	42.9%	—	—	7	10	—

EAGLE MATERIALS INC.

NYSE: EXP

3811 Turtle Creek Blvd., Ste. 1100
Dallas, TX 75219
Phone: 214-432-2000
Fax: 214-432-2100
Web: www.eaglematerials.com

CEO: Steven R. (Steve) Rowley
CFO: Mark V. Dendle
HR: –
FYE: March 31
Type: Public

Eagle Materials is perched near the top of the building materials business. The company produces and distributes gypsum wallboard and cement (each accounting for about 40% of revenues), ready-mix concrete and aggregates, and recycled paperboard. It sells its products to residential, commercial, and industrial construction customers throughout the US. The company has about 250 railcars for shipping its wallboard products to customers across the country. Eagle Materials is a spinoff of mega-homebuilder Centex Corporation, which founded the company in 1963.

	Annual Growth	3/04	3/05	3/06	3/07	3/08
Sales ($ mil.)	10.5%	502.6	616.5	859.7	922.4	749.5
Net income ($ mil.)	10.0%	66.9	106.7	161.0	202.7	97.8
Market value ($ mil.)	69.2%	188.5	262.4	3,208.3	2,138.2	1,543.9
Employees	1.4%	—	1,557	1,600	1,600	—

EAGLE ROCK ENERGY PARTNERS, L.P.

NASDAQ (GM): EROC

16701 Greenspoint Park Dr., Ste. 200
Houston, TX 77060
Phone: 281-408-1200
Fax: 281-408-1399
Web: www.eaglerockenergy.com

CEO: Joseph A. Mills
CFO: Darin G. Holderness
HR: –
FYE: December 31
Type: Public

The Eagles are into soft rock whereas Eagle Rock Energy Partners digs the gathering, compressing, treating, processing, transporting, and selling of natural gas. The company also fractionates and transports natural gas liquids (NGLs). Eagle Rock Energy Partners has primary assets in Alabama, Louisiana, Mississippi, and Texas, and proved reserves of 117.3 billion cu. ft. of natural gas of equivalent. The Panhandle operations include more than 3,808 miles of natural gas gathering pipelines and six natural gas processing plants. Southeast Texas and Louisiana assets include more than 990 miles of gas gathering pipelines. Directors own 32% of the company through Eagle Rock Holdings, L.P.

	Annual Growth	12/03	12/04	12/05	12/06	12/07
Sales ($ mil.)	—	0.0	10.6	73.7	478.4	910.6
Net income ($ mil.)	—	0.4	21.0	2.8	(23.3)	(145.6)
Market value ($ mil.)	119.7%	—	—	—	421.9	926.8
Employees	34.2%	—	—	150	163	270

EAGLE TEST SYSTEMS, INC.

NASDAQ (GM): EGLT

2200 Millbrook Dr.
Buffalo Grove, IL 60089
Phone: 847-367-8282
Fax: 847-367-8640
Web: www.eagletest.com

CEO: Leonard A. (Len) Foxman
CFO: Stephen J. (Steve) Hawrysz
HR: Marge F. Rodino
FYE: September 30
Type: Public

This eagle hunts for flaws, not paws. Eagle Test Systems makes automated test equipment (ATE) systems used to test analog, mixed-signal (analog with digital), and radio-frequency (RF) semiconductor devices as they are being manufactured. The company's SmartPin technology enables the test instruments to run sequential subtests without software intervention, while its SimulTest technology allows for simultaneous testing of multiple devices. Customers include Infineon Technologies, International Rectifier, Intersil, National Semiconductor, and Texas Instruments (around 31% of sales). Eagle Test Systems gets about two-thirds of sales outside of the US, primarily in Malaysia.

	Annual Growth	9/03	9/04	9/05	9/06	9/07
Sales ($ mil.)	11.4%	55.8	111.2	63.5	124.7	86.0
Net income ($ mil.)	2.7%	9.6	22.0	7.4	22.6	10.7
Market value ($ mil.)	(21.3%)	—	—	—	374.3	294.5
Employees	10.3%	237	240	245	302	351

EAGLEPICHER CORPORATION

2424 John Daly Rd.
Inkster, MI 48141
Phone: 313-278-5956
Fax: 313-278-5982
Web: www.epcorp.com

CEO: David L. Treadwell
CFO: Patrick S. (Pat) Aubry
HR: Benjamin DePompei
FYE: December 30
Type: Private

EaglePicher Corporation's customers range from General Motors to general industry. EaglePicher's automotive units include Hillsdale (engine, transmission, and driveline components), and Wolverine (gaskets). EaglePicher Medical Power provides batteries to the medical device industry; EaglePicher technologies makes batteries for use in the aerospace and defense industries, among others. EP Minerals offers filtration products. EaglePicher filed Chapter 11 in 2005 and emerged from restructuring in 2006. EaglePicher sold its pharmaceutical unit to Aptuit Inc. in early 2007. Later that year the company sold its EP Boron division to Ceradyne for nearly $70 million in cash.

	Annual Growth	12/03	12/04	12/05	12/06	12/07
Est. sales ($ mil.)	—	—	—	—	—	119.0
Employees	—	—	—	—	—	1,400

E. & J. GALLO WINERY

600 Yosemite Blvd.
Modesto, CA 95354
Phone: 209-341-3111
Fax: –
Web: www.gallo.com

CEO: Joseph E. (Joe) Gallo
CFO: –
HR: –
FYE: December 31
Type: Private

E. & J. Gallo Winery brings merlot to the masses. The company is one of the world's largest wine makers thanks in part to its inexpensive jug and box brands, including Carlo Rossi, Peter Vella, and Boone's Farm brands. The vintner owns seven wineries and about 20,000 acres of California vineyards. It is the leading US exporter of California wine, selling its some 60 brands in more than 90 countries across the globe. Among its premium wines and imports are those of Gallo Family Vineyards Sonoma Reserve and the Italian wine, Ecco Domani. For those who prefer a little more kick to their imbibing, Gallo distills several lines of brandy and one gin label.

	Annual Growth	12/02	12/03	12/04	12/05	12/06
Est. sales ($ mil.)	10.7%	1,800.0	2,000.0	3,000.0	2,700.0	2,700.0
Employees	0.0%	4,600	4,600	—	4,400	4,600

E & S INTERNATIONAL ENTERPRISES, INC

5900 Canoga Ave.
Woodland Hills, CA 91367
Phone: 818-887-0700
Fax: 818-702-6344
Web: www.esintl.com

CEO: Philip Asherian
CFO: –
HR: –
FYE: December 31
Type: Private

E & S International Enterprises (also known as ESI) has its fingers in a lot of pies. The company manufactures and sells a variety of consumer products through its subsidiaries. Once a consumer electronics distributor, the company has expanded its product line to include such items as sporting goods, mobile phone batteries, and appliances. It also acts as a broker between manufacturers and retailers, sometimes handling warranty and support functions for the makers. ESI is also in the business of acquiring commercial and residential real estate. The company was founded in 1945 as an electronics distributor.

	Annual Growth	12/03	12/04	12/05	12/06	12/07
Est. sales ($ mil.)	—	—	—	—	—	69.7
Employees	—	—	—	—	—	177

EARL G. GRAVES LTD.

130 5th Ave., 10th Fl.
New York, NY 10011
Phone: 212-242-8000
Fax: 212-886-9633
Web: www.blackenterprise.com

CEO: Earl G. (Butch) Graves Jr.
CFO: Jacques Jiha
HR: Natalie M. Hibbert
FYE: December 31
Type: Private

The eponymous Earl G. Graves Ltd. (founded in 1968 by chairman and publisher Earl G. Graves) publishes *BLACK ENTERPRISE*, a business magazine aimed at African-American executives that reaches some 4 million readers. The company also operates a related Web site (blackenterprise.com) and publishes books through a partnership with John Wiley & Sons. The firm's Black Enterprise Unlimited division stages events (such as the Black Enterprise/General Motors Entrepreneurs Conference), produces radio reports, and provides ancillary products and services. Its Black Enterprise/Greenwich Street Corporate Growth Fund is a private equity investment fund that finances minority-owned or -managed businesses.

	Annual Growth	12/03	12/04	12/05	12/06	12/07
Est. sales ($ mil.)	—	—	—	—	—	35.0
Employees	—	—	—	—	—	96

EARL SCHEIB, INC.

Pink Sheets: ESHB

15206 Ventura Blvd., Ste. 200
Sherman Oaks, CA 91403
Phone: 818-981-9992
Fax: 818-981-8803
Web: www.earlscheib.com

CEO: Christian K. (Chris) Bement
CFO: John K. Minnihan
HR: John J. Greer
FYE: April 30
Type: Public

The founding gravel-voiced pitchman has passed on, but Earl Scheib still paints cars. Automobile paint-and-body repair chain Earl Scheib owns and operates about 100 stores in more than 20 states. About half of the company's facilities are in California. Known for low-priced paint jobs, Earl Scheib stores also offer cosmetic body work, as well as glass replacement and pin-striping. In addition, the company operates a painting and collision repair facility for large commercial vehicles, known as Quality Fleet & Truck Center, in California. Earl Scheib manufactures its own paint at a plant in Missouri.

	Annual Growth	4/03	4/04	4/05	4/06	4/07
Sales ($ mil.)	(0.5%)	47.2	47.8	48.5	48.8	46.2
Net income ($ mil.)	—	(1.9)	(1.3)	—	3.0	(2.0)
Employees	—	—	—	800	—	—

EARLE M. JORGENSEN COMPANY

10650 Alameda St.
Lynwood, CA 90262
Phone: 323-567-1122
Fax: 323-563-5500
Web: www.emjmetals.com

CEO: R. Neil McCaffery
CFO: –
HR: Inger Dickinson
FYE: March 31
Type: Subsidiary

One of the largest steel distributors in North America, Earle M. Jorgensen primarily sells bars, tubing, and plate products made from carbon, alloy, and stainless steels; aluminum; and brass. Customers include companies in the construction and farm equipment, general machining, industrial equipment, oil and gas, and transportation industries; machining companies account for more than a quarter of sales. The company operates a network of about 40 service centers and processing facilities in the US and Canada. It has been a subsidiary of former rival Reliance Steel & Aluminum since 2006.

	Annual Growth	3/02	3/03	3/04	3/05	3/06
Est. sales ($ mil.)	—	—	—	—	—	1,789.8
Net income ($ mil.)	—	—	—	—	—	76.3
Employees	—	—	—	—	—	1,774

EARTH FARE, INC.

145 Cane Creek Industrial Park Dr., Ste. 150
Fletcher, NC 28732
Phone: 828-281-4800
Fax: 828-254-7556
Web: www.earthfare.com

CEO: Jack Murphy
CFO: Gary Jones
HR: Lucinda Austin
FYE: December 31
Type: Private

The destination for shoppers looking for organic milk, soy, and antibiotic-free poultry is Earth Fare, naturally. The regional organic and natural foods supermarket chain operates about a dozen stores in the Carolinas, Georgia, and Tennessee. Its stores are smaller (the largest is 28,000 sq. ft.) than those of its conventional supermarket competitors and national natural foods chains like Whole Foods Market. Even so, Earth Fare stores offer about 26,000 natural and organic products, house cafes and juice bars, sell vitamins and herbs, and offer deli service and cooking classes. Earth Fare was founded in 1975 by Roger Derrough as a single Dinner for the Earth store. Derrough owns Earth Fare with other investors.

	Annual Growth	12/03	12/04	12/05	12/06	12/07
Est. sales ($ mil.)	—	—	—	—	—	22.9
Employees	—	—	—	—	—	350

EARTH SEARCH SCIENCES, INC.

OTC: ESSE

306 Stoner Loop Rd., Ste. 6
Lakeside, MT 59922
Phone: 406-751-5200
Fax: 406-752-7433
Web: www.earthsearch.com

CEO: Larry F. Vance
CFO: Tami J. Story
HR: –
FYE: March 31
Type: Public

The technology used by Earth Search Sciences (ESSI) is rooted in the stars, not the ground. The company has developed remote sensing instruments (using what is called hyperspectral remote sensing technology) based on NASA's Airborne Visible and Infra-Red Imaging Spectrometer (AVIRIS). The instruments designed by ESSI collect and analyze data for use in oil and gas exploration, mining, hazardous material remediation, and ecosystem monitoring, among other things. The company has served customers in the private, military, and government sectors. Chairman and CEO Larry Vance owns 74% of the company.

	Annual Growth	3/03	3/04	3/05	3/06	3/07
Sales ($ mil.)	(40.5%)	0.8	0.5	0.4	0.4	0.1
Net income ($ mil.)	—	(5.4)	(3.9)	(5.2)	(2.2)	3.7
Market value ($ mil.)	(77.1%)	—	2,331.7	29.1	15.5	27.9
Employees	0.0%	4	—	—	4	—

An in-depth profile of this company is available to Hoover's Online members at hoovers.com.

531

EARTHFIRST TECHNOLOGIES, INCORPORATED

Pink Sheets: EFTI

2515 E. Hanna Ave.
Tampa, FL 33610
Phone: 813-238-5010
Fax: 813-238-8490
Web: www.earthfirsttech.com

CEO: John D. Stanton
CFO: Frank W. Barker Jr.
HR: –
FYE: December 31
Type: Public

Electrical contracting gives EarthFirst Technologies the power to pursue its interests in turning waste into energy. Subsidiary Electric Machinery Enterprises (EME) is an electrical contractor and accounts for nearly all of EarthFirst Technologies' sales, but the company is also developing technologies to dispose of and recycle waste products. EarthFirst Technologies' vacuum distillation reactor treats such solid waste products as discarded rubber tires. The company's plasma reactor breaks down waste liquids (used oil, grease, and antifreeze) to produce a synthetic gas. Another unit produces alternative fuels. Entities affiliated with chairman John Stanton own about 65% of EarthFirst Technologies.

	Annual Growth	12/02	12/03	12/04	12/05	*12/06
Sales ($ mil.)	72.3%	—	—	15.3	41.7	45.4
Net income ($ mil.)	—	—	—	(2.3)	(17.7)	(19.9)
Employees	(4.1%)	—	—	275	273	253

*Most recent year available

EARTHLINK, INC.

NASDAQ (GS): ELNK

1375 Peachtree St.
Atlanta, GA 30309
Phone: 404-815-0770
Fax: 404-892-7616
Web: www.earthlink.net

CEO: Rolla P. Huff
CFO: Kevin M. Dotts
HR: Stacie Hagan
FYE: December 31
Type: Public

As one of the largest ISPs in the US, EarthLink is trying to bridge the gap between dial-up users and high-speed Internet access. The company provides Internet connections to nearly 4 million consumer and small-business subscribers. EarthLink provides premium broadband access to about one quarter of those customers. It offers other services such as Web hosting and advertising. The company provides cable access through agreements with companies such as Time Warner Cable and Comcast Cable, and DSL access through BellSouth, Covad, AT&T, and others. Investment firms Coghill Capital, Steel Partners, and Sterling Capital each own about 10% of the company.

	Annual Growth	12/03	12/04	12/05	12/06	12/07
Sales ($ mil.)	(3.5%)	1,401.9	1,382.2	1,290.1	1,301.3	1,216.0
Net income ($ mil.)	—	(62.2)	111.0	142.8	5.0	(135.1)
Market value ($ mil.)	(16.3%)	1,590.4	1,713.3	1,459.7	870.7	781.6
Employees	(24.1%)	—	—	1,732	2,210	998

EAST WEST BANCORP, INC.

NASDAQ (GS): EWBC

135 N. Los Robles Ave.
Pasadena, CA 91101
Phone: 626-768-6000
Fax: 626-799-3167
Web: www.eastwestbank.com

CEO: Dominic Ng
CFO: Thomas J. Tolda
HR: –
FYE: December 31
Type: Public

Getting directions to this bank may be tricky. East West Bancorp is the holding company for East West Bank, which operates more than 70 branches in and around Los Angeles and the San Francisco Bay area, plus one each in Houston, Beijing, Shanghai, and Hong Kong. The bank offers personal and business loans; checking, savings, and money market accounts; CDs; insurance; and merchant credit card processing services. It caters to the Chinese-American community and provides international banking and trade financing to importers/exporters doing business in the Asia/Pacific region. East West Bank offers multilingual service in English, Cantonese, Mandarin, Spanish, and Vietnamese.

	Annual Growth	12/03	12/04	12/05	12/06	12/07
Assets ($ mil.)	30.7%	4,055.4	6,028.9	8,278.3	10,823.7	11,852.2
Net income ($ mil.)	28.6%	59.0	78.0	108.4	143.4	161.2
Market value ($ mil.)	23.6%	655.7	2,202.9	2,068.0	2,175.9	1,529.8
Employees	12.4%	—	—	1,078	1,312	1,361

EASTER SEALS, INC.

230 W. Monroe St., Ste. 1800
Chicago, IL 60606
Phone: 312-726-6200
Fax: 312-726-1494
Web: www.easter-seals.org

CEO: Lou Lowenkron
CFO: –
HR: –
FYE: August 31
Type: Not-for-profit

A year round effort that has nothing to do with Easter, seals, or flowers, the National Easter Seal Society annually helps more than 1 million children and adults with disabilities through more than 550 service centers in the US. The organization offers services such as medical rehabilitation, job training, child care, and adult day services. It started in 1907 as the National Society for Crippled Children and launched its first "seal" campaign around Easter in 1934. Supporters placed stickers or seals depicting the lily, a symbol of renewal, on letters and envelopes. The campaign was so successful and the symbol so associated with the organization that it changed its name in 1967.

	Annual Growth	8/03	8/04	8/05	8/06	8/07
Est. sales ($ mil.)	—	—	—	—	—	86.2
Employees	—	—	—	—	—	200

EASTERN AMERICAN NATURAL GAS TRUST

NYSE: NGT

919 Congress Ave., Ste. 500
Austin, TX 78701
Phone: 800-852-1422
Fax: 512-479-2553

CEO: Michael J. (Mike) Ulrich
CFO: –
HR: –
FYE: December 31
Type: Public

Shareholders of Eastern American Natural Gas Trust know all about the clean-burning, royalty-producing attributes of natural gas. The trust receives royalty interests from 670 producing natural gas wells in West Virginia and Pennsylvania and operated by Eastern American Energy. The trust distributes the royalties to its shareholders quarterly. As a grantor trust, Eastern American Natural Gas Trust does not pay federal income taxes, and the production on some of its wells qualifies for tax credits because the wells are located on hard-to-drill formations. The trust, which has proved reserves of 13.8 billion cu. ft. of natural gas on its properties, will be liquidated no later than 2013.

	Annual Growth	12/03	12/04	12/05	12/06	12/07
Sales ($ mil.)	2.7%	13.2	14.4	18.2	17.7	14.7
Net income ($ mil.)	2.4%	10.9	12.0	14.6	14.2	12.0
Market value ($ mil.)	0.6%	153.6	149.0	168.2	165.7	157.1
Employees	—	—	—	—	—	—

EASTERN BANK CORPORATION

265 Franklin St.
Boston, MA 02110
Phone: 617-897-1008
Fax: 617-897-1105
Web: www.easternbank.com

CEO: Richard E. Holbrook
CFO: Charles M. Johnston
HR: Nancy Huntington Stager
FYE: December 31
Type: Mutual company

Mutually owned Eastern Bank has more than 70 branches throughout Massachusetts. Founded in 1818, the bank offers retail and commercial banking products, including checking and savings accounts, investments, and credit cards. Its lending activities focus on one- to four-family residential mortgages, commercial real estate loans, and consumer loans. The bank's Eastern Investment Advisors division provides wealth management services. Insurance agency subsidiary Eastern Insurance offers personal and commercial coverage, as well as group benefit plans, through more than 20 locations.

	Annual Growth	12/03	12/04	12/05	12/06	12/07
Assets ($ mil.)	11.0%	4,475.2	5,125.5	6,259.4	6,580.0	6,794.8
Net income ($ mil.)	7.1%	47.6	43.1	49.2	72.4	62.6
Employees	3.2%	1,295	1,462	1,519	1,459	1,469

THE EASTERN COMPANY

AMEX: EML

112 Bridge St.
Naugatuck, CT 06770
Phone: 203-729-2255
Fax: 203-723-8653
Web: www.easterncompany.com

CEO: Leonard F. Leganza
CFO: John L. Sullivan III
HR: −
FYE: Saturday nearest December 31
Type: Public

The Eastern Company has latched on to the security industry. The company makes locks and industrial hardware, including latches, handles, hinges, combination locks, tubular key locks, and electronic switch locks. It makes security products for use in truck trailers and other vehicles, gaming and coin-operated machines, smart card systems, lab equipment, and soft-sided luggage. Eastern also owns a foundry that makes metal anchoring devices to support mine roofs, clamps for construction, and brake-system components. The company sells mainly to manufacturers, distributors, and locksmiths through its operations in Canada, China, Hong Kong, Mexico, Taiwan, and the US.

	Annual Growth	12/03	12/04	12/05	12/06	12/07
Sales ($ mil.)	15.3%	88.3	100.1	109.1	138.5	156.3
Net income ($ mil.)	31.3%	3.4	4.8	4.4	9.7	10.1
Market value ($ mil.)	29.8%	37.5	48.5	47.4	106.5	106.3
Employees	—	—	—	642	—	—

EASTERN INSURANCE HOLDINGS, INC.

NASDAQ (GM): EIHI

25 Race Ave.
Lancaster, PA 17603
Phone: 717-396-7095
Fax: 717-399-3781
Web: www.easterninsuranceholdings.com

CEO: Bruce M. Eckert
CFO: Kevin M. Shook
HR: −
FYE: December 31
Type: Public

Through its operating subsidiaries, Eastern Insurance Holdings sells workers' compensation and some group benefits coverage to companies with fewer than 300 employees. It sells its workers' compensation products mostly in suburban Delaware, Maryland, and Pennsylvania through subsidiaries Eastern Alliance and Allied Eastern; its Eastern Re unit, based in the Cayman Islands, provides workers compensation products through "rent-a-captive" arrangements to self-insured groups. Eastern Life and Heath Insurance Company (formerly known as Educators Mutual) underwrites group benefits, including dental, term life, and disability coverage, for businesses in the mid-Atlantic, southeastern, and midwestern states.

	Annual Growth	12/03	12/04	12/05	12/06	12/07
Assets ($ mil.)	51.1%	—	111.7	111.2	368.2	385.5
Net income ($ mil.)	91.2%	1.4	1.8	1.1	8.3	18.7
Market value ($ mil.)	5.6%	—	—	—	165.3	174.5
Employees	(8.1%)	—	—	148	136	—

EASTERN MOUNTAIN SPORTS, INC.

1 Vose Farm Rd.
Peterborough, NH 03458
Phone: 603-924-9571
Fax: 603-924-9138
Web: www.emsonline.com

CEO: William O. (Will) Manzer
CFO: Robert (Bob) Mayorsen
HR: −
FYE: January 31
Type: Private

Eastern Mountain Sports (EMS) can prepare you for a life of climb. A former subsidiary of American Retail Group, EMS sells a wide range of outdoor gear and apparel from about 70 stores in the Northeast and its Web site. Outdoor enthusiasts can purchase or rent tents, sleeping bags, and other equipment — choosing from brands such as Patagonia, Columbia, The North Face, and Teva. EMS offers outdoor skills clinics, provides guides for hire, and arranges day and overnight trips; it also operates climbing and kayaking schools in Connecticut, Massachusetts, New Hampshire, and New York. President and CEO Will Manzer led a management buyout of the company from American Retail Group in September 2004.

EASTERN VIRGINIA BANKSHARES, INC.

NASDAQ (GM): EVBS

330 Hospital Rd.
Tappahannock, VA 22560
Phone: 804-443-8400
Fax: 804-445-1047
Web: www.evb.org

CEO: Joe A. Shearin
CFO: Ronald L. (Ron) Blevins
HR: M. Robin Jett
FYE: December 31
Type: Public

Founded in 1997, Eastern Virginia Bankshares is the holding company for EVB, a community bank that operates more than 20 branches in — believe it or not — eastern Virginia. Targeting individuals and local business customers, the bank offers such standard retail services as checking and savings accounts, money market accounts, CDs, IRAs, and online banking. Residential mortgages make up more than 40% of the the company's loan portfolio, which also includes commercial real estate, construction, business, and consumer loans. Subsidiary EVB Financial Services owns interests in companies that offer investment and insurance products.

	Annual Growth	12/03	12/04	12/05	12/06	12/07
Assets ($ mil.)	8.2%	677.2	696.3	763.9	851.4	926.7
Net income ($ mil.)	5.5%	7.1	7.2	6.7	7.2	8.8
Market value ($ mil.)	(8.1%)	141.4	127.0	104.5	137.2	100.8
Employees	1.5%	—	—	296	—	305

EASTGROUP PROPERTIES, INC.

NYSE: EGP

300 One Jackson Place, 188 E. Capitol St.
Jackson, MS 39201
Phone: 601-354-3555
Fax: 601-352-1441
Web: www.eastgroup.net

CEO: David H. Hoster II
CFO: N. Keith McKey
HR: Carolyn Black
FYE: December 31
Type: Public

EastGroup Properties has its compass pointing all across the Sunbelt. The equity real estate investment trust (REIT) acquires, develops, and manages industrial properties primarily in Florida, Texas, Arizona, and California. It typically focuses on operating multi-tenant distribution and bulk distribution facilities, from 5,000 to 50,000 sq. ft. in size, located near major transportation hubs. Its portfolio includes more than 200 industrial properties and one office building, totaling roughly 23 million sq. ft. EastGroup Properties is 11% owned by T. Rowe Price Associates. Chairman Leland Speed and CEO David Hoster each hold about a 1% interest in the company.

	Annual Growth	12/03	12/04	12/05	12/06	12/07
Sales ($ mil.)	8.6%	108.4	114.7	126.5	133.6	150.7
Net income ($ mil.)	9.8%	20.4	23.3	22.2	29.2	29.7
Market value ($ mil.)	10.2%	675.2	807.0	994.9	1,269.4	996.4
Employees	1.6%	—	—	61	—	63

[H] EASTMAN CHEMICAL COMPANY

NYSE: EMN

200 S. Wilcox Dr.
Kingsport, TN 37660
Phone: 423-229-2000
Fax: 423-229-2145
Web: www.eastman.com

CEO: J. Brian Ferguson
CFO: Richard A. (Rich) Lorraine
HR: Norris P. Sneed
FYE: December 31
Type: Public

Eastman Chemical can recall its past through photos — it was once part of film giant Eastman Kodak. The company has developed into a major producer of chemicals, fibers, and plastics. Among Eastman's operating segments are its CASPI (coatings, adhesives, specialty polymers, and inks), Specialty Plastics (engineering polymers), and Fibers (acetate tow and textile fibers) units. Its Performance Polymers segment is the #1 maker of polyethylene terephthalate (PET), a plastic used to make packaging for soft drinks, food, and water. The last segment manufactures Performance Chemicals and Intermediates. Eastman's products go into such items as food and medical packaging, films, and toothbrushes.

	Annual Growth	12/03	12/04	12/05	12/06	12/07
Sales ($ mil.)	4.2%	5,800.0	6,580.0	7,059.0	7,450.0	6,830.0
Net income ($ mil.)	—	(270.0)	170.0	557.0	409.0	300.0
Market value ($ mil.)	12.4%	3,053.4	4,573.0	4,206.2	4,954.2	4,867.1
Employees	(8.3%)	—	—	12,000	11,000	—

[H] An in-depth profile of this company is available to Hoover's Online members at hoovers.com.

533

EASTMAN KODAK COMPANY

NYSE: EK

343 State St.
Rochester, NY 14650
Phone: 585-724-4000
Fax: 585-724-1089
Web: www.kodak.com

CEO: Antonio M. Perez
CFO: Frank S. Sklarsky
HR: Robert L. (Bob) Berman
FYE: December 31
Type: Public

When Kodak made Brownies, folks began to say cheese. The inventor of the Brownie camera (1900), Kodak has retouched its image from a top maker of photographic film to a provider of imaging technology products and services to the photographic and graphic communications markets. The firm has restructured itself to focus less on sales of film and more on sales of digital cameras and imaging systems. It operates through three business segments: Consumer Digital Group (CDG), Film Products Group (FPG), and Graphic Communications Group (GCG). Kodak's shift to become a digital technology business has involved purging some 30,000 employees. The firm has long-term plans to sell ink jet printers and flat-panel displays.

	Annual Growth	12/03	12/04	12/05	12/06	12/07
Sales ($ mil.)	(6.2%)	13,317.0	13,517.0	14,268.0	13,274.0	10,301.0
Net income ($ mil.)	26.4%	265.0	556.0	(1,362.0)	(601.0)	676.0
Market value ($ mil.)	(3.8%)	7,356.5	9,246.0	6,721.0	7,417.9	6,298.6
Employees	(27.4%)	—	—	51,100	40,900	26,900

EASTON-BELL SPORTS, INC.

7855 Haskell Ave., Ste. 200
Van Nuys, CA 91406
Phone: 818-902-5800
Fax: –
Web: www.eastonbellsports.com

CEO: Paul E. Harrington
CFO: Mark A. Tripp
HR: Jackelyn E. Werblo
FYE: Last Saturday in December
Type: Private

Afraid your favorite athlete might take a knockin' on the noggin? Easton-Bell Sports (EBS) products can help soften the blow. A leading helmet maker, EBS caters to baseball, softball, football, hockey, cycling, and auto racing markets, as well as snow and motorcycle sports. Its items are sold under Blackburn, VistaLite, Easton, Giro, Bell, and Riddell names. Through its Easton Sports, it is a top maker and distributor of hockey sticks and baseball bats. EBS sells its products through retailers the likes of Wal-Mart to local sports shops and has licensing agreements for brands Fisher-Price and Mongoose for its accessories. The firm was created through a merger between Riddell Bell and Easton Sports in 2006.

	Annual Growth	6/03	*12/04	12/05	12/06	12/07
Sales ($ mil.)	35.5%	215.0	165.9	379.9	639.0	724.6
Net income ($ mil.)	—	—	(13.1)	3.1	(5.9)	14.5
Employees	42.2%	550	—	1,421	2,823	2,248

*Fiscal year change

EASYLINK SERVICES INTERNATIONAL

NASDAQ (CM): ESIC

33 Knightsbridge Rd., Ste. 100
Piscataway, NJ 08854
Phone: 800-828-7115
Fax: 732-652-3810
Web: www.easylink.com

CEO: Thomas J. Stallings
CFO: Glen E. Shipley
HR: –
FYE: July 31
Type: Public

EasyLink Services International Corporation makes sure clients get the message. The company provides electronic data interchange (EDI) software and services. Its data translation systems allow trading partners with incompatible information systems to exchange invoices, purchase orders, shipping notices, and other documents. The company offers services ranging from consulting and training to outsourced document processing. Clients include GlaxoSmithKline and Revlon. Formerly called Internet Commerce Corporation (ICC), the company purchased EasyLink Services, a provider of document conversion and messaging services, in 2007; after the acquisition ICC changed its name to EasyLink Services International.

	Annual Growth	7/03	7/04	7/05	7/06	7/07
Sales ($ mil.)	16.0%	12.1	11.7	16.7	19.8	21.9
Net income ($ mil.)	—	(6.0)	(4.1)	0.2	3.0	2.7
Market value ($ mil.)	—	—	—	—	—	66.3
Employees	—	—	—	—	134	—

EAT AT JOE'S LTD.

OTC: JOES

670 White Plains Rd., Ste. 120
Scarsdale, NY 10583
Phone: 914-725-2700
Fax: 914-725-8663

CEO: Joseph (Joe) Fiore
CFO: Joseph (Joe) Fiore
HR: –
FYE: December 31
Type: Public

Eat At Joe's operates a casual-dining theme restaurant at the Philadelphia airport that offers breakfast, lunch, and dinner menus with such fare as hot dogs, burgers, and meatloaf. The concept features such interior appointments as 1950s-era Harley-Davidsons, booths resembling 1957 Chevy interiors, and tabletop jukeboxes. CEO Joseph Fiore owns more than 60% of Eat at Joe's.

	Annual Growth	12/03	12/04	12/05	12/06	12/07
Sales ($ mil.)	3.9%	1.2	1.3	1.3	1.4	1.4
Net income ($ mil.)	—	(0.3)	(0.5)	(0.4)	(0.5)	(0.6)
Market value ($ mil.)	(1.2%)	—	1.1	—	—	1.1
Employees	—	—	—	—	—	—

EAT'N PARK HOSPITALITY GROUP

285 E. Waterfront Dr.
Pittsburgh, PA 15230
Phone: 412-461-2000
Fax: 412-461-6000
Web: www.eatnpark.com

CEO: Jeff Broadhurst
CFO: Daniel S. (Dan) Wilson
HR: Bonnie Scott
FYE: December 31
Type: Private

Despite its name, this company does not run a wildlife preserve designed by Willy Wonka. Eat'n Park Hospitality Group operates about 80 Eat'n Park family-style restaurants located primarily in Pennsylvania. The eateries offer a full breakfast menu along with standard lunch and dinner fare. The company also runs a handful of 1950s themed Park Classic Diners and the upscale Six Penn Kitchen. In addition, Eat'n Park Hospitality offers foodservices and catering through subsidiaries Parkhurst Dining Services and CURA Hospitality. Eat'n Park was founded by Pittsburgh restaurateur Larry Hatch and a group of investors in 1949. The company is controlled by the family of chairman James Broadhurst.

EATON CORPORATION

NYSE: ETN

Eaton Center, 1111 Superior Ave.
Cleveland, OH 44114
Phone: 216-523-5000
Fax: 216-523-4787
Web: www.eaton.com

CEO: Alexander M. (Sandy) Cutler
CFO: Richard H. Fearon
HR: Susan J. Cook
FYE: December 31
Type: Public

When it comes to diversification, Eaton favors an all-you-can-eat approach. The manufacturer has made dozens of acquisitions (as well as divestitures) over the past decade. Eaton's game plan calls for nurturing businesses in which it holds a strong market share. The company's product lines include electrical power distribution and control equipment, engine components, and hydraulic and fluid power products for aerospace, automotive, and other industrial uses. Eaton is also one of the world's largest manufacturers of grips for golf clubs. The company operates manufacturing facilities in dozens of countries throughout the world. Eaton gets more than half of its sales outside the US.

	Annual Growth	12/03	12/04	12/05	12/06	12/07
Sales ($ mil.)	12.8%	8,061.0	9,817.0	11,115.0	12,370.0	13,033.0
Net income ($ mil.)	26.7%	386.0	648.0	805.0	950.0	994.0
Market value ($ mil.)	14.4%	8,260.5	11,092.8	9,962.9	10,985.5	14,154.7
Employees	5.8%	51,000	55,000	59,000	60,000	64,000

EATON VANCE CORP.

NYSE: EV

4582 S. Ulster St. Pkwy., Ste. 1100
Denver, CO 80237
Phone: 303-757-8101
Fax: –
Web: www.eatonvance.com

CEO: Thomas E. (Tom) Faust Jr.
CFO: Robert J. (Bob) Whelan
HR: –
FYE: October 31
Type: Public

A veritable supermarket of investing, Eaton Vance offers more than 70 mutual funds and manages investments for institutional and wealthy individual clients. Its signature investment products include tax-managed funds, municipal bond funds, floating-rate bank-loan funds, closed-end funds, and domestic and international equity funds. Its Eaton Vance Distributors unit markets and sells its funds, separate accounts, and retail managed accounts via sales associates in the US, Europe, and Latin America, as well as a network of independent brokers, banks, and insurance firms. Chairman Jim Hawkes owns almost 25% of the firm; he and 15 other shareholders control Eaton Vance through a voting trust.

	Annual Growth	10/03	10/04	10/05	10/06	10/07
Assets ($ mil.)	10.1%	658.7	743.6	702.5	668.2	966.8
Net income ($ mil.)	7.7%	106.1	138.9	159.9	159.4	142.8
Market value ($ mil.)	49.2%	1,190.3	1,453.3	3,216.9	3,824.8	5,893.5
Employees	179.2%	—	—	757	869	5,900

EATZI'S CORPORATION

3403 Oak Lawn Ave.
Dallas, TX 75219
Phone: 214-599-8602
Fax: –
Web: www.eatzis.com

CEO: Phil Romano
CFO: Gary Evans
HR: –
FYE: December 31
Type: Private

Eatzi's operates a gourmet food outlet in Dallas under the eatZi's Market & Bakery banner. The take-out restaurant offers chef-prepared foods along with pastries, and baked goods. The store also carries a wide selection of wines, cheeses, and other products. In addition, Eatzi's offers party planning and catering services. Restaurant impresario Phil Romano, founder of Romano's Macaroni Grill, Fuddruckers, and Cozymel's, started the concept as a joint venture with Brinker International in 1996. Private investment firm Castanea Partners bought the business in 2002, with Romano retaining a small stake.

	Annual Growth	12/03	12/04	12/05	12/06	12/07
Est. sales ($ mil.)	—	—	—	—	—	20.5
Employees	—	—	—	—	—	750

EAU TECHNOLOGIES, INC.

OTC: EAUI

1464 W. 40 South, Ste. 200
Lindon, UT 84042
Phone: 801-443-1031
Fax: 801-443-1027
Web: www.eau-x.com

CEO: Wade R. Bradley
CFO: Brian D. Heinhold
HR: –
FYE: December 31
Type: Public

Of all the vowels, O is EAU's bread and butter (as in H2O). Using water electrolysis technology, EAU Technologies (formerly Electric Aquagenics Unlimited) makes equipment and process systems that clean and disinfect surfaces and foods. Its Empowered Water generators are sold and leased to companies in search of improved cleaning and sanitizing. The firm's water-based, non-toxic products reduce bacteria, viruses, spores, and molds in food processing, living surfaces, and other environments. Director Peter Ullrich, individually and through his Water Science firm, owns 26% of EAU (63% if he exercises his warrants). Water Science is also EAU's biggest customer and it licenses EAU technology in Latin America.

	Annual Growth	12/03	12/04	12/05	12/06	12/07
Sales ($ mil.)	44.2%	—	0.3	0.7	2.0	0.9
Net income ($ mil.)	—	—	(4.0)	(13.3)	(8.5)	(10.9)
Market value ($ mil.)	(13.5%)	—	26.9	24.1	11.1	17.4
Employees	—	—	—	—	29	—

EAUTOCLAIMS, INC.

OTC: EACC

110 E. Douglas Rd.
Oldsmar, FL 34677
Phone: 813-749-1020
Fax: 813-749-1040
Web: www.eautoclaims.com

CEO: Jeffery D. (Jeff) Dickson
CFO: Larry C. Colton
HR: –
FYE: July 31
Type: Public

eAutoclaims provides online vehicle collisions claims technology for insurance providers, agents, administrators, and self-insured fleet management companies. The firm arranges vehicle repairs for collisions claims; it maintains on online network of some 2,500 service shops. (Repair shops in its network give eAutoclaims a discount of 10% to 15% in exchange for the business they receive through the arrangement.) In addition to managing repairs, eAutoclaims handles repair estimate audits and coordinates independent adjustor contracting, car rentals, towing service, and accident reporting.

	Annual Growth	7/03	7/04	7/05	7/06	7/07
Sales ($ mil.)	(23.3%)	34.1	27.2	14.6	14.9	11.8
Net income ($ mil.)	—	(1.2)	(2.2)	(2.4)	(2.3)	(0.4)
Market value ($ mil.)	9.9%	10.3	13.0	12.2	12.9	15.0
Employees	—	—	—	—	—	—

EBAGS, INC.

6060 Greenwood Plaza Blvd., Ste. 110
Greenwood Village, CO 80111
Phone: 303-694-1933
Fax: 303-694-9491
Web: www.ebags.com

CEO: Jon Nordmark
CFO: Mark DeOrio
HR: –
FYE: June 30
Type: Private

For the sake of its own success, eBags certainly hopes it's *in the bag*. The company is an online retailer of backpacks, briefcases and laptop bags, handbags, luggage, sports and duffel bags, and travel accessories (toiletry kits, camera bags). Its lineup of some 30,000 products feature more than 500 brand names including Samsonite, JanSport, and Nike. Other eBag divisions include eBags UK and 6pm.com (formerly Shoedini.com), an online retailer of men's and women's footwear. In September 2005, eBags expanded its global reach when it launched a new German website. It sold 6pm.com to Zappos.com in 2007.

	Annual Growth	6/03	6/04	6/05	6/06	6/07
Est. sales ($ mil.)	—	—	—	—	—	4.0
Employees	—	—	—	—	—	72

EBAY INC.

NASDAQ (GS): EBAY

2145 Hamilton Ave.
San Jose, CA 95125
Phone: 408-376-7400
Fax: 408-376-7401
Web: www.ebay.com

CEO: John J. Donahoe
CFO: Robert H. (Bob) Swan
HR: Elizabeth L. (Beth) Axelrod
FYE: December 31
Type: Public

"I got it on eBay" is barreling its way into the lexicon of the new millennium and placing a cyber-grin on the corporate face of online auctioneer extraordinaire eBay. The company is a cyber-forum for selling more than 50,000 categories of merchandise — from Beanie Babies to fine antiques — hosting about 500,000 online stores worldwide. eBay, which generates revenue through listing and selling fees and through advertising, boasts more than 275 million registered users. In 2007, eBay acquired one of the fastest growing online ticket sellers, StubHub, for $307 million.

	Annual Growth	12/03	12/04	12/05	12/06	12/07
Sales ($ mil.)	37.2%	2,165.1	3,271.3	4,552.4	5,969.7	7,672.3
Net income ($ mil.)	(5.8%)	441.8	778.2	1,082.0	1,125.6	348.3
Market value ($ mil.)	21.3%	20,975.4	77,866.8	60,688.8	41,151.2	45,420.9
Employees	9.1%	—	—	12,600	13,200	15,000

An in-depth profile of this company is available to Hoover's Online members at hoovers.com.

535

EBIX, INC.

NASDAQ (GM): EBIX

5 Concourse Pkwy., Ste. 3200
Atlanta, GA 30328
Phone: 678-281-2020
Fax: 678-281-2019
Web: www.ebix.com

CEO: Robin Raina
CFO: Robert (Bob) Kerris
HR: –
FYE: December 31
Type: Public

Ebix (formerly Delphi Information Systems) sells insurance industry software products and professional services to property/casualty insurers, brokerages, and individuals in Asia, Australia, Europe, and North America. The company's Ebix.com Web site acts as an online auction house where buyers and carriers can exchange bids for auto, home, health, life, and other types of insurance, while paying Ebix a fee on each transaction. Its Ebix.one and e.global agency management software build upon its legacy products with added workflow and customer relationship management capabilities. UK insurer BRiT Insurance Holdings owns 25% of the firm.

	Annual Growth	12/03	12/04	12/05	12/06	12/07
Sales ($ mil.)	31.3%	14.4	20.0	24.1	29.3	42.8
Net income ($ mil.)	65.3%	1.7	2.2	4.3	6.0	12.7
Market value ($ mil.)	72.0%	28.4	43.7	54.2	79.6	248.7
Employees	207.4%	—	—	95	292	—

EBSCO INDUSTRIES INC.

5724 Hwy. 280 East
Birmingham, AL 35242
Phone: 205-991-6600
Fax: 205-995-1636
Web: www.ebscoind.com

CEO: F. Dixon Brooke Jr.
CFO: Richard L. (Rick) Bozzelli
HR: John Thompson
FYE: June 30
Type: Private

Few portfolios are more diverse than that of EBSCO Industries (short for Elton B. Stephens Company). Among the conglomerate's more than 40 information services, manufacturing, and sales subsidiaries are magazine subscription and fulfillment firms, a fishing lure manufacturer, a rifle manufacturer, a specialty office and computer furniture retailer, and a real estate company. Its main businesses revolve around the publishing industry: EBSCO operates a subscription management agency and is one of the largest publishers of digital information. It has a database of more than 300,000 title listings from more than 78,000 publishers worldwide. The family of founder Elton B. Stephens Sr. owns the company.

	Annual Growth	6/02	6/03	6/04	6/05	6/06
Sales ($ mil.)	13.2%	1,400.0	1,400.0	1,800.0	2,000.0	2,300.0
Employees	0.0%	5,000	4,500	5,000	5,000	5,000

EBY-BROWN COMPANY, LLC

280 W. Shuman Blvd., Ste. 280
Naperville, IL 60566
Phone: 630-778-2800
Fax: 630-778-2830
Web: www.eby-brown.com

CEO: Richard W. (Dick) Wake
CFO: Mark Smetana
HR: Steve Bundy
FYE: September 30
Type: Private

Eby-Brown makes its money on such vices as munchies and nicotine. The company is a leading convenience-store supplier that distributes more than 16,000 products to about 12,000 customers in 28 states mostly east of the Mississippi. It operates eight distribution centers that supply such items as beverages, candy and snack foods, frozen and refrigerated foods, tobacco products, and general merchandise. In addition, the company offers advertising and promotion services for its customers. Eby-Brown was founded in 1887 by the Wake family, which continues to own the company.

	Annual Growth	9/02	9/03	9/04	9/05	9/06
Sales ($ mil.)	3.6%	3,600.0	3,670.0	3,100.0	4,100.0	4,150.0
Employees	2.9%	2,100	2,100	2,100	2,150	2,350

ECB BANCORP, INC.

NASDAQ (GM): ECBE

35050 US Hwy. 264
Engelhard, NC 27824
Phone: 252-925-9411
Fax: 252-925-8491
Web: www.ecbbancorp.com

CEO: Arthur H. Keeney III
CFO: Gary M. Adams
HR: –
FYE: December 31
Type: Public

ECB Bancorp Enjoys Community Banking. The holding company owns The East Carolina Bank, which serves individuals, small to midsized businesses, and local governments through about 20 branches in eastern North Carolina and the Outer Banks. The bank, which opened in a barbershop in 1920, provides checking, savings, money market, NOW, and individual retirement accounts, plus certificates of deposit. It mainly originates real estate loans (approximately 75% of its loan portfolio), including residential and commercial mortgages and construction and land development loans. The East Carolina Bank also writes commercial, consumer, and credit card loans.

	Annual Growth	12/03	12/04	12/05	12/06	12/07
Assets ($ mil.)	10.3%	435.0	501.9	547.7	624.1	643.9
Net income ($ mil.)	5.3%	3.9	3.3	4.8	5.6	4.8
Market value ($ mil.)	6.5%	58.1	59.6	54.9	94.6	74.7
Employees	3.6%	—	—	203	—	218

ECC CAPITAL CORPORATION

Pink Sheets: ECRO

1733 Alton Pkwy.
Irvine, CA 92606
Phone: 949-955-8700
Fax: 866-405-6836
Web: www.ecccapital.com

CEO: Steven G. Holder
CFO: Roque A. Santi
HR: –
FYE: December 31
Type: Public

ECC Capital refused to conform — to credit scoring criteria. The real estate investment trust (REIT) originates and purchases non-conforming residential real estate loans. Subsidiary Performance Credit, which used to act as a wholesale originator of nonconforming loans, now provides financing to ECC Capital's clients. The company is licensed in California, Georgia, Illinois, Massachusetts, Minnesota, Mississippi, and New Hampshire. In 2007 ECC Capital sold its wholesale mortgage banking subsidiary Encore Credit to Bear Stearns. Concurrent with that transaction, the REIT also sold its portfolio of direct-to-consumer loans to ResCap. It is now seeking a buyer for the remainder of its securitized assets.

	Annual Growth	12/03	12/04	12/05	12/06	12/07
Sales ($ mil.)	(12.9%)	—	191.4	343.5	259.7	126.6
Net income ($ mil.)	—	—	28.3	(64.1)	(134.6)	(104.5)
Employees	(57.1%)	—	—	1,667	715	—

ECHELON CORPORATION

NASDAQ (GM): ELON

550 Meridian Ave.
San Jose, CA 95126
Phone: 408-938-5200
Fax: 408-790-3800
Web: www.echelon.com

CEO: M. Kenneth (Ken) Oshman
CFO: Oliver R. (Chris) Stanfield
HR: Jill Hollister
FYE: December 31
Type: Public

Echelon wants to take control systems to the next level. The company designs hardware and software that link and automate industrial equipment, building environments, and devices ranging from light switches to conveyor belts. Its open-source operating system, LonWorks Network Services, lets equipment interact through local networks and the Internet. Echelon's hardware — transceivers, routers, network interfaces — can sense, monitor, and control such equipment as automatic doors, security systems, and railcars. Echelon also provides an automated electricity metering system called Networked Energy Services (NES).

	Annual Growth	12/03	12/04	12/05	12/06	12/07
Sales ($ mil.)	3.9%	118.2	109.9	74.4	57.3	137.6
Net income ($ mil.)	—	1.9	5.3	(19.7)	(24.4)	(15.7)
Market value ($ mil.)	16.9%	450.2	347.6	311.6	312.9	840.8
Employees	8.9%	—	—	269	283	319

ECHO THERAPEUTICS, INC.

OTC: ECTE

10 Forge Pkwy.	CEO: Patrick T. (Pat) Mooney
Franklin, MA 02038	CFO: Harry G. Mitchell
Phone: 508-553-8850	HR: –
Fax: 508-553-8760	FYE: December 31
Web: www.echotx.com	Type: Public

Echo Therapeutics (formerly Sontra Medical) tries not to scratch the surface. The company develops SonoPrep, an instrument for transdermal (through the skin) drug delivery and diagnostics. The device uses ultrasound technology to painlessly introduce drugs without breaking the skin. The SonoPrep technology is being developed for use in glucose monitoring. After circling the drain in late 2006 the firm's board voted to cease operations, but just as the company was selling off its assets it received a cash injection from investors including Sherbrooke Partners, allowing the company to keep running. The following year Sontra acquired private transdermal therapeutics firm Echo Therapeutics and changed its name.

	Annual Growth	12/03	12/04	12/05	12/06	12/07
Sales ($ mil.)	(49.2%)	1.5	0.0	0.2	0.1	0.1
Net income ($ mil.)	—	(2.5)	(5.4)	(5.7)	(5.3)	(13.2)
Market value ($ mil.)	14.6%	17.1	46.9	10.5	—	29.5
Employees	—	—	—	21	—	—

ECHOSTAR CORPORATION

NASDAQ (GS): SATS

90 Inverness Circle East	CEO: Charles W. (Charlie) Ergen
Englewood, CO 80112	CFO: Bernard L. (Bernie) Han
Phone: 303-706-4444	HR: –
Fax: –	FYE: December 31
Web: www.echostar.com	Type: Public

EchoStar is thinking outside the set-top box. Spun off from DISH Network at the beginning of 2008, the company provides set-top boxes to direct-to-home satellite service providers. Its set-top portfolio includes standard and high-definition devices, some of which incorporate digital video recorders. Other products include satellite dishes, remote controls, and analog-to-digital converters. In addition to its traditional business, the company plans to launch a fixed satellite service business using its fleet of eight owned or leased in-orbit satellites. EchoStar also owns Sling Media, which provides equipment that allows consumers to remotely manage and watch TV programming on their PCs or handheld devices.

	Annual Growth	12/03	12/04	12/05	12/06	12/07
Sales ($ mil.)	1.0%	—	—	1,513.7	1,525.3	1,544.1
Net income ($ mil.)	—	—	—	(44.9)	(34.2)	(85.3)
Employees	—	—	—	—	—	1,500

ECLIPSE AVIATION CORPORATION

2503 Clark Carr Loop SE	CEO: Vern Raburn
Albuquerque, NM 87106	CFO: J. Mark Borseth
Phone: 505-245-7555	HR: Tina Rulo
Fax: 505-241-8800	FYE: December 31
Web: www.eclipseaviation.com	Type: Private

Eclipse Aviation hopes to obscure the competition with its Eclipse 500 jet. The company makes a six-passenger plane which is powered by two Pratt & Whitney turbofan engines. Eclipse Aviation hopes its economical jets will become the backbone of a national air limousine service designed to offer private jet travel to passengers at fares that are competitive with conventional full-fare airline ticket prices. Florida-based DayJet, a company that intends to offer such a service, has ordered 239 Eclipse 500s. Investors from the aerospace, automotive, and information technology industries control Eclipse Aviation.

	Annual Growth	12/03	12/04	12/05	12/06	12/07
Est. sales ($ mil.)	—	—	—	—	—	36.7
Employees	—	—	—	—	—	500

ECLIPSYS CORPORATION

NASDAQ (GS): ECLP

Three Ravinia Dr.	CEO: R. Andrew (Andy) Eckert
Atlanta, GA 30346	CFO: Robert J. (Bob) Colletti
Phone: 404-847-5000	HR: Jan Smith
Fax: 404-847-5700	FYE: December 31
Web: www.eclipsys.com	Type: Public

Eclipsys is casting a shadow on disorganized health care. The company's software helps health care organizations manage and automate clinical, administrative, and financial functions, including patient information access, medical records and clinical documentation, prescription ordering, billing, reimbursement, and performance analysis. Its products also include tools for application integration and decision support. In addition to its software offerings, Eclipsys sells third-party hardware (including desktop and network products) and offers implementation, integration, hosting, product support, maintenance, and training services.

	Annual Growth	12/03	12/04	12/05	12/06	12/07
Sales ($ mil.)	17.0%	254.7	309.1	383.3	427.5	477.5
Net income ($ mil.)	—	(56.0)	(32.6)	0.5	4.1	41.1
Market value ($ mil.)	26.3%	535.2	968.4	944.7	1,080.2	1,361.8
Employees	9.9%	—	—	2,020	2,220	—

⊞ ECOLAB INC.

NYSE: ECL

370 Wabasha St. North	CEO: Douglas M. (Doug) Baker Jr.
St. Paul, MN 55102	CFO: Steven L. Fritze
Phone: 651-293-2233	HR: Michael L. Meyer
Fax: 651-293-2092	FYE: December 31
Web: www.ecolab.com	Type: Public

Ecolab cleans up by cleaning up. The company offers cleaning, sanitation, pest-elimination, and maintenance products and services to hospitality, institutional, and industrial customers. Its institutional division serves hotels and restaurants, food service and health care facilities, schools, and commercial and institutional laundries. Other divisions focus on products for textile care, water care, fast food, and pest control. Ecolab makes most of its products, although the company sells some products made by other manufacturers. Henkel owns more than 25% of the company.

	Annual Growth	12/03	12/04	12/05	12/06	12/07
Sales ($ mil.)	9.8%	3,761.8	4,184.9	4,534.8	4,895.8	5,469.6
Net income ($ mil.)	11.4%	277.4	310.5	319.5	368.6	427.2
Market value ($ mil.)	15.7%	7,045.5	9,047.5	9,217.8	11,360.4	12,638.6
Employees	7.8%	—	—	22,400	23,130	26,050

ECOLLEGE.COM

NASDAQ (GM): ECLG

1 N. LaSalle St., Ste. 1800	CEO: Oakleigh Thorne
Chicago, IL 60602	CFO: Reid E. Simpson
Phone: 312-706-1710	HR: David Smith
Fax: 312-706-1703	FYE: December 31
Web: www.ecollege.com	Type: Public

You don't have to eat dorm food if you go to college online. eCollege.com is propelling higher education into cyberspace by creating online campuses for universities and high schools. The company sets up online academic communities replete with computer-based courses, testing, online registration, and other student services. Customers include career colleges, community colleges, school districts, and universities. eCollege.com also has corporate clients who use its services to build online training courses for employees.

	Annual Growth	12/02	12/03	12/04	12/05	*12/06
Sales ($ mil.)	21.8%	23.7	36.9	89.3	102.9	52.1
Net income ($ mil.)	—	(4.9)	0.6	19.4	5.9	(2.3)
Employees	6.5%	210	412	443	519	270

*Most recent year available

⊞ An in-depth profile of this company is available to Hoover's Online members at hoovers.com.

537

ECOLOGY AND ENVIRONMENT, INC.

AMEX: EEI

Buffalo Corporate Center, 368 Pleasant View Dr.
Lancaster, NY 14086
Phone: 716-684-8060
Fax: 716-684-0844
Web: www.ene.com

CEO: Gerhard J. Neumaier
CFO: John Mye
HR: Janet Steinbruckner
FYE: July 31
Type: Public

Every day is Earth Day at environmental consulting and testing company Ecology and Environment. The company, which operates in more than 30 countries, provides environmental impact assessments, air pollution control, wastewater analyses, and other site-planning and laboratory services. The company also offers hazardous waste site evaluations and field assessments across the US and conducts counter-terrorism preparedness exercises. It provides cleanups of Superfund sites and emergency response to hazardous waste spills for the EPA. The four founders of Ecology and Environment control about 64% of the company.

	Annual Growth	7/03	7/04	7/05	7/06	7/07
Sales ($ mil.)	3.4%	90.5	89.5	74.5	81.8	103.5
Net income ($ mil.)	—	(1.2)	2.4	(1.6)	2.6	3.1
Market value ($ mil.)	8.7%	22.0	21.1	15.8	23.3	30.8
Employees	11.5%	—	—	700	—	870

EDAC TECHNOLOGIES CORPORATION

NASDAQ (CM): EDAC

1806 New Britain Ave.
Farmington, CT 06032
Phone: 860-677-2603
Fax: 860-674-2718
Web: www.edactechnologies.com

CEO: Dominick A. Pagano
CFO: Glenn L. Purple
HR: Carol Foley
FYE: Saturday nearest December 31
Type: Public

Operating through its Gros-Ite and Apex Machine Tool divisions, Edac Technologies designs and produces tools, gauges, and other equipment and parts used by the aerospace industry in the manufacture and inspection of jet engines. Edac's specialties include jet turbine cases made from difficult-to-machine alloys such as aluminum, titanium, and high-nickel alloys. Edac also makes and repairs a variety of spindles, which are integral parts of machine tools used in a wide range of manufacturing industries. Edac's manufacturing facilities include computerized, numerically controlled (CNC) machining centers. The company also can provide grinding, welding, painting, and assembly services.

	Annual Growth	12/03	12/04	12/05	12/06	12/07
Sales ($ mil.)	18.1%	25.7	33.3	35.0	38.3	50.0
Net income ($ mil.)	(14.7%)	6.6	2.9	3.3	1.5	3.5
Market value ($ mil.)	80.4%	4.7	7.4	16.7	13.8	49.4
Employees	—	—	—	—	—	—

EDD HELMS GROUP, INC.

Pink Sheets: EDDH

17850 NE 5th Ave.
Miami, FL 33162
Phone: 305-653-2520
Fax: 305-651-5527
Web: www.eddhelms.com

CEO: W. Edd Helms Jr.
CFO: Dean A. Goodson
HR: –
FYE: May 31
Type: Public

Like a friend's sentiment in your junior high yearbook, the Edd Helms Group wants you to "stay cool." The contractor provides electrical, mechanical, and data communication services, as well as air conditioning and marine air conditioning and refrigeration services in South Florida through its DataTelcom, Edd Helms Electric, Edd Helms Air Conditioning, and Edd Helms Marine Air Conditioning and Refrigeration subsidiaries. It offers tradeshow services under the name Edd Helms Trade Show Power & Lighting and exposition services through Edd Helms Special Event Power & Lighting. Founded in 1985 by chairman W. Edd Helms, Jr., the group serves commercial, residential, and marine customers from three locations.

	Annual Growth	5/03	5/04	5/05	5/06	5/07
Sales ($ mil.)	7.9%	16.8	16.2	17.1	21.2	22.8
Net income ($ mil.)	—	(0.1)	(0.3)	0.2	0.8	0.9
Employees	—	129	—	—	—	—

EDDIE BAUER HOLDINGS, INC.

NASDAQ (GM): EBHI

10401 NE 8th St., Ste. 500
Bellevue, WA 98004
Phone: 425-755-6544
Fax: 425-755-7696
Web: www.eddiebauer.com

CEO: Neil S. Fiske
CFO: Marv Toland
HR: R. Thomas (Tom) Helton
FYE: Saturday nearest December 31
Type: Public

Eddie Bauer Holdings is a descendant of former top US direct retailer Spiegel. The holding company is the parent of the Eddie Bauer retail business, which sells outdoorsy apparel and accessories through catalogs, online, and at some 390 stores throughout North America. Eddie Bauer also licenses its name for eyewear, furniture, bicycles, and Ford SUVs. About a quarter of Eddie Bauer's sales come from catalogs and its Web site. Spiegel filed for bankruptcy in 2003 and later sold its Spiegel and Newport News catalogs to Golden Gate Capital for about $82 million. The company, which reorganized and emerged from Chapter 11 as Eddie Bauer Holdings in June 2005, rejected a $286 million takeover deal in 2007.

	Annual Growth	12/03	12/04	12/05	12/06	12/07
Sales ($ mil.)	(5.6%)	1,317.2	1,157.9	1,059.4	1,013.5	1,044.3
Net income ($ mil.)	—	(0.3)	43.7	38.1	(212.0)	(101.7)
Market value ($ mil.)	(28.7%)	—	—	—	275.9	196.6
Employees	(9.8%)	—	—	11,826	9,613	9,629

EDELBROCK CORPORATION

2700 California St.
Torrance, CA 90503
Phone: 310-781-2222
Fax: 310-320-1187
Web: www.edelbrock.com

CEO: O. Victor Edelbrock
CFO: Aristedes T. Feles
HR: Jackie Langlais
FYE: June 30
Type: Private

Speed demon Edelbrock makes performance-enhancing parts for cars, light trucks, recreational vehicles, race cars, and motorcycles. Its products include carburetors, intake manifolds, cylinder heads, air cleaners, camshafts, exhaust systems, and a wide array of other aftermarket parts. The company markets its products mainly through automotive chain stores, mail-order houses, and warehouse distributors. Edelbrock also makes a line of aftermarket engine parts specifically for Harley-Davidson motorcycles. The Edelbrock family — led by company chairman, president, and CEO Victor Edelbrock — controls the company.

	Annual Growth	6/03	6/04	6/05	6/06	6/07
Est. sales ($ mil.)	—	—	—	—	—	66.9
Employees	—	—	—	—	—	722

EDELMAN

200 E. Randolph Dr., 63rd Fl.
Chicago, IL 60601
Phone: 312-240-3000
Fax: 312-240-2900
Web: www.edelman.com

CEO: Richard W. Edelman
CFO: Victor (Vic) Malanga
HR: Laura Pietraszek
FYE: June 30
Type: Private

If image truly is everything, then Edelman may be one of the most indispensable companies around. The PR firm is the largest independent agency in the industry, conducting work for heavy hitters such as General Motors and Microsoft. With more than 45 offices worldwide, the company provides its services through 15 practices (including financial communications and investor relations, corporate affairs, diversity marketing, litigation, and public affairs) covering five industries. Edelman has fiercely guarded its independent status despite the still-growing trend toward consolidation. Chairman Daniel Edelman owns the company. It bought Silicon Valley PR firm A&R Partners (now called A&R Edelman) in 2006.

	Annual Growth	6/02	6/03	6/04	6/05	6/06
Sales ($ mil.)	17.9%	—	—	255.2	291.0	354.5
Employees	25.6%	—	—	—	2,069	2,599

EDEN BIOSCIENCE CORPORATION

NASDAQ (CM): EDEN

11816 North Creek Pkwy. North
Bothell, WA 98011
Phone: 425-806-7300
Fax: 425-806-7400
Web: www.edenbio.com

CEO: Bradley S. (Brad) Powell
CFO: Bradley S. (Brad) Powell
HR: –
FYE: December 31
Type: Public

Pests, diseases, or chemicals in the Garden of Eden? Perish the thought. Eden Bioscience's plant protection products help plants protect themselves. The company's Harp-N-Tek Messenger products utilize naturally occurring proteins called harpins that trigger a plant's natural defense system against pests and disease while activating growth processes such as photosynthesis and nutrient intake. Its primary products are seed treatment and plant food, both of which use the Harp-N-Tek technology. Messenger had been marketed to farmers, but Eden branched out into the home and garden market in 2003. By early 2007 the company sold its operations geared toward the agricultural/professional market to Plant Health Care.

	Annual Growth	12/03	12/04	12/05	12/06	12/07
Sales ($ mil.)	(36.1%)	1.8	1.0	3.8	3.8	0.3
Net income ($ mil.)	—	(11.2)	(8.9)	(10.9)	(9.4)	(1.0)
Market value ($ mil.)	(53.7%)	104.5	71.7	42.5	13.9	4.8
Employees	—	—	—	25	—	—

EDENTIFY, INC.

OTC: EDFY

74 W. Broad St., Ste. 350
Bethlehem, PA 18018
Phone: 610-814-6830
Fax: 610-814-6836
Web: www.edentify.us

CEO: Terrence M. DeFranco
CFO: –
HR: –
FYE: December 31
Type: Public

Edentify aims to end identity crimes. The development-stage company owns intellectual property related to the prevention of identity theft. Its technology includes both data analysis and monitoring and biometrics-based systems. It is targeting such customers as government entities, health care providers, and financial services companies. Edentify's biometric technology includes facial and voice recognition systems, combined with inner-lip analysis. Edentify acquired Budgethotels Network in 2005 through a reverse stock split. Budgethotels' InfoCenter business (travel-related display advertising and lodging reservations) was spun off to shareholders as part of the transaction.

	Annual Growth	11/02	11/03	11/04	*12/05	†12/06
Sales ($ mil.)	(38.5%)	0.7	0.6	0.3	0.0	0.1
Net income ($ mil.)	—	(0.3)	(0.3)	(0.2)	(2.1)	(8.6)
Employees	33.3%	—	—	—	12	16

*Fiscal year change †Most recent year available

EDGAR ONLINE, INC.

NASDAQ (GM): EDGR

50 Washington St.
Norwalk, CT 06854
Phone: 203-852-5666
Fax: 203-852-5667
Web: www.edgar-online.com

CEO: Philip D. Moyer
CFO: John C. Ferrara
HR: –
FYE: December 31
Type: Public

Need the inside scoop on companies that file documents with the SEC? Just ask EDGAR. EDGAR Online (whose name is an acronym for Electronic Data Gathering Analysis and Retrieval) provides electronic SEC filings. Its EDGAR Pro service is a subscription-based offering with unlimited access to filings and advanced searching, filtering, and downloading tools, and its less expensive EDGAR Access has limited access. Its I-Metrix Professional product offers complex data analysis. EDGAR Online also provides digital data feeds to corporations for use in intranet, extranet, and other applications. The company receives additional revenue from advertising and e-commerce.

	Annual Growth	12/03	12/04	12/05	12/06	12/07
Sales ($ mil.)	5.8%	14.3	12.9	14.2	16.3	17.9
Net income ($ mil.)	—	(2.2)	(2.2)	(5.6)	(5.9)	(7.4)
Market value ($ mil.)	33.2%	28.4	32.8	45.5	90.2	89.3
Employees	—	—	—	90	—	—

EDGE PETROLEUM CORPORATION

NASDAQ (GS): EPEX

1301 Travis, Ste. 2000
Houston, TX 77002
Phone: 713-654-8960
Fax: 713-654-7722
Web: www.edgepet.com

CEO: John W. Elias
CFO: Kirsten A. Hink
HR: –
FYE: December 31
Type: Public

Edge Petroleum goes high-tech to gain an edge over its rivals in the oil and gas exploration and production business. The company relies on visualization software and a 3-D seismic database to find natural gas and oil prospects onshore along the Gulf of Mexico region. Edge Petroleum has proved reserves of 102.1 billion cu. ft. of natural gas equivalent, of which 86% is natural gas and natural gas liquids. Although its primary operations are in Texas, where most of its net developed acreage is located, the company also has major developed holdings in Alabama, Louisiana, Mississippi, and New Mexico. In 2004 the company acquired Contango Oil & Gas' south Texas natural gas and oil interests for about $50 million.

	Annual Growth	12/03	12/04	12/05	12/06	12/07
Sales ($ mil.)	47.6%	33.9	67.0	121.2	129.7	160.9
Net income ($ mil.)	11.3%	4.3	15.1	33.4	(41.3)	6.6
Market value ($ mil.)	7.5%	127.3	249.3	428.9	318.1	169.9
Employees	—	—	—	67	—	—

EDGEN MURRAY CORPORATION

18444 Highland Rd.
Baton Rouge, LA 70809
Phone: 225-756-9868
Fax: 225-756-7953
Web: www.edgenmurray.com

CEO: Daniel J. (Dan) O'Leary
CFO: David L. Laxton III
HR: Marcy Bienvenu
FYE: December 31
Type: Private

Steel products distributor Edgen Murray supplies carbon steel and alloy pipe, fittings, and plates, primarily to the oil and gas, process, and power generation industries. The company divides its operations into two product groups (carbon products and alloy products) and four geographic regions (the Americas, Asia/Pacific, Europe/West Africa, and the Mid-East). Nearly two-thirds of its business is with oil and gas producers or companies that service that industry. New York investment firm Jefferies Capital Partners owns a controlling interest in Edgen Murray. In 2005 Harvest Partners sold the former Edgen Corporation to Jefferies and members of the Edgen management team.

	Annual Growth	12/02	12/03	12/04	12/05	12/06
Sales ($ mil.)	39.3%	—	147.0	207.8	301.9	397.7
Net income ($ mil.)	—	—	(4.7)	16.2	(2.2)	11.9
Employees	(31.0%)	—	—	—	377	260

🏢 EDGEWATER TECHNOLOGY, INC.

NASDAQ (GM): EDGW

20 Harvard Mill Sq.
Wakefield, MA 01880
Phone: 781-246-3343
Fax: 781-246-5903
Web: www.edgewater.com

CEO: Shirley Singleton
CFO: Kevin R. Rhodes
HR: Kristin Zaepfel
FYE: December 31
Type: Public

Edgewater Technology is on the cutting edge of technology management consulting. Among other things, Edgewater helps businesses improve call center operations, design customized software applications, and build integrated systems. Its managed services division allows clients to outsource management and maintenance of information technology (IT) facilities. The company has expertise in such industries as financial services, health care, insurance, and higher education. It targets middle-market clients and offers specialized services to divisions of large (Global 2000) firms. Its clients have included American Express, Merrill, and MIT.

	Annual Growth	12/03	12/04	12/05	12/06	12/07
Sales ($ mil.)	28.7%	25.0	25.3	43.1	60.1	68.5
Net income ($ mil.)	72.2%	1.0	(0.6)	1.6	3.2	8.8
Market value ($ mil.)	14.8%	55.9	51.7	63.0	70.4	97.1
Employees	21.4%	—	205	282	303	367

🏢 An in-depth profile of this company is available to Hoover's Online members at hoovers.com.

539

EDIBLE ARRANGEMENTS, LLC

95 Barnes Road	CEO: Tariq Farid
Wallingford, CT 06492	CFO: –
Phone: 203-774-8000	HR: –
Fax: 203-774-0531	FYE: –
Web: www.ediblearrangements.com	Type: Private

"Please don't eat the daisies" simply doesn't apply here. Edible Arrangements creates "flower" bouquets out of fruit by cutting shapes out of pineapples, adding melon balls, and surrounding the whole thing with strawberries, grapes, and apple wedges on skewers. The company also offers smoothies and fruit salads at some shops. Edible Arrangements has more than 800 franchised locations (including pending locations) in the US, Canada, the UK, and the Middle East. CEO Tariq Farid started Edible Arrangements in 1999 after doing software consulting for a similar business.

EDIETS.COM, INC.

NASDAQ (CM): DIET

1000 Corporate Dr., Ste. 600	CEO: Stephen J. Rattner
Fort Lauderdale, FL 33334	CFO: Thomas J. Hoyer
Phone: 954-360-9022	HR: –
Fax: 954-360-9095	FYE: December 31
Web: www.ediets.com	Type: Public

eDiets.com is banking on your losing proposition. The firm's Web site allows some 66,000 fat-fighting clients to enter personal information and receive a customized, software-generated program to help them lose weight. eDiets.com also offers support message boards, an electronic newsletter, nutrition advice from a panel of experts, vitamins and supplements, and a nationwide meal delivery service. Two-thirds of the company's sales come from subscription revenue. Partnerships with Bristol-Myers Squibb, Microsoft, and AOL help generate Internet traffic to the company's site. eDiets Europe represents the company's operations overseas. Investment firm Prides Capital Partners owns about 54% of eDiets.com.

	Annual Growth	12/03	12/04	12/05	12/06	12/07
Sales ($ mil.)	(6.2%)	38.3	45.4	53.7	48.8	29.7
Net income ($ mil.)	—	(1.7)	(9.9)	1.3	(4.1)	(9.4)
Market value ($ mil.)	7.2%	111.8	94.4	133.3	95.7	147.4
Employees	(28.0%)	—	—	150	108	—

E.DIGITAL CORPORATION

OTC: EDIG

16770 W. Bernardo Dr.	CEO: William (Will) Blakeley
San Diego, CA 92127	CFO: Robert Putnam
Phone: 866-502-8234	HR: Beth Lovison
Fax: 858-304-3023	FYE: March 31
Web: www.edigital.com	Type: Public

e.Digital believes that the future is digital. The company provides engineering services, product reference designs, and technology platforms to customers focusing on the digital video and audio markets. e.Digital, however, plans to focus future growth on selling its eVU mobile entertainment device which features a 7-inch LCD screen, dual stereo headphone jacks, embedded credit card reader, and touch screen capabilities. The eVu is geared towards customers in the airline, health care, military, and travel and leisure industries.

	Annual Growth	3/04	3/05	3/06	3/07	3/08
Sales ($ mil.)	13.3%	3.4	4.3	3.3	1.8	5.6
Net income ($ mil.)	—	(2.5)	(2.4)	(3.1)	(3.1)	(1.7)
Market value ($ mil.)	(2.0%)	47.2	32.4	30.1	58.9	43.6
Employees	6.3%	—	—	16	17	—

EDISON INTERNATIONAL

NYSE: EIX

2244 Walnut Grove Ave.	CEO: John E. Bryson
Rosemead, CA 91770	CFO: Thomas R. (Tom) McDaniel
Phone: 626-302-2222	HR: Diane L. Featherstone
Fax: 626-302-2517	FYE: December 31
Web: www.edison.com	Type: Public

Although Edison International has been around the world, the company's largest subsidiary is still Southern California Edison (SCE), which distributes electricity to a population of more than 13 million people in central, coastal, and southern California and is the leading purchaser of renewable energy in the US. Edison had created an international portfolio through Edison Mission Energy (EME), but it has pulled back on most of its international operations. After having sold off plants in Asia and Europe, it now markets energy in only North America and Turkey. The company also provides consulting, management, and maintenance services for energy projects.

	Annual Growth	12/03	12/04	12/05	12/06	12/07
Sales ($ mil.)	2.0%	12,135.0	10,199.0	11,852.0	12,622.0	13,113.0
Net income ($ mil.)	7.5%	821.0	916.0	1,137.0	1,181.0	1,098.0
Market value ($ mil.)	24.9%	7,145.0	10,435.7	14,208.6	14,817.9	17,388.5
Employees	4.4%	—	—	15,838	16,139	17,275

EDISON MISSION ENERGY

18101 Von Karman Ave., Ste. 1700	CEO: Theodore F. (Ted) Craver Jr.
Irvine, CA 92612	CFO: W. James (Jim) Scilacci Jr.
Phone: 949-752-5588	HR: Jenene Wilson
Fax: 949-263-9162	FYE: December 31
Web: www.edison.com	Type: Subsidiary

Edison Mission Energy (EME) once wanted to conquer the nonregulated energy sector, but now it'll settle for a piece of the US market. The company, a subsidiary of Edison International, has interests in 28 power plants in the US and one in Turkey (Doga project) that give it a net physical generating capacity of more than 10,620 MW. EME sells power through contracts with large utilities, regional distributors, and other energy companies; it also trades energy on the open markets. A decline in wholesale energy prices in the early 2000s forced EME to retreat to its home soil and sell off nearly all of its foreign holdings.

	Annual Growth	12/02	12/03	12/04	12/05	12/06
Sales ($ mil.)	(5.0%)	2,749.7	3,180.6	1,639.0	2,248.0	2,239.0
Net income ($ mil.)	100.7%	25.5	19.6	122.0	432.0	414.0
Employees	(9.9%)	2,662	2,610	1,768	1,745	1,751

EDISON SCHOOLS INC.

521 5th Ave., 11th Fl.	CEO: Terry Stecz
New York, NY 10175	CFO: Christopher P. (Chris) Corrini
Phone: 212-419-1700	HR: Tom Modero
Fax: 212-419-1604	FYE: June 30
Web: www.edisonschools.com	Type: Private

For-profit schools? What an idea! Edison Schools, the nation's largest private operator of public schools, teaches some 285,000 students in around 100 public schools in the US and the UK through district partnerships and charter schools. Edison also offers summer school, after-school, and supplemental educational services (SES) programs (through Newton Learning). It has been the center of the national debate on the privatization of public schools, having faced questions about whether for-profit companies should run American public schools. Results have been mixed for Edison, which has seen rave reviews from some parents but contracts cancelled in several school districts.

	Annual Growth	6/03	6/04	6/05	6/06	6/07
Est. sales ($ mil.)	—	—	—	—	—	8.7
Employees	—	—	—	—	—	14,000

An in-depth profile of this company is available to Hoover's Online members at hoovers.com.

EDMUNDS.COM, INC.

1620 26th St., Ste. 400 South
Santa Monica, CA 90404
Phone: 310-309-6300
Fax: 310-309-6466
Web: www.edmunds.com

CEO: Jeremy Anwyl
CFO: –
HR: –
FYE: March 31
Type: Private

Edmund knows a thing or two about cars. Edmunds.com operates the Web sites Edmunds.com (automotive information), Inside Line (online magazine for automotive enthusiasts), and CarSpace (automotive lifestyle social networking site). Its True Market Value automotive pricing service provides valuations for new and used vehicles. The company's content, tools, and services are licensed to third parties, and it has supplied content for auto sections of Internet properties such as the NYTimes.com, AOL, and CNN.com. Edmunds.com was founded in 1966, and expanded to the Web in 1995. Investors include the Peter Steinlauf family, CNET Networks, Cox Enterprises, GE Pension Trust, and AutoLogic Holdings.

	Annual Growth	3/03	3/04	3/05	3/06	3/07
Est. sales ($ mil.)	—	—	—	—	—	98.0
Employees	—	—	—	—	—	320

EDO CORPORATION

60 E. 42nd St., 42nd Fl.
New York, NY 10165
Phone: 212-716-2000
Fax: 212-716-2049
Web: www.edocorp.com

CEO: James M. Smith
CFO: Frederic B. Bassett
HR: Patricia Comiskey
FYE: December 31
Type: Subsidiary

EDO products can be found in the air, on land, at sea, and in space. Its operations are split into two divisions. The Electronic Systems and Communications unit's offerings include airborne electronic warfare systems; reconnaissance and surveillance systems; command, control, communications, and computers; and antenna products. EDO's Engineered Systems and Services division includes aircraft armament, mine countermeasure systems, sonar systems and components, professional and engineering services, and integrated composite structures. The US government accounts for more than 80% of the company's sales. EDO became part of ITT Defense Electronics & Services after ITT Corporation acquired it late in 2007.

	Annual Growth	12/02	12/03	12/04	12/05	12/06
Sales ($ mil.)	21.4%	328.9	460.7	536.2	648.5	715.2
Net income ($ mil.)	2.3%	10.6	14.8	29.1	26.3	11.6
Employees	20.0%	1,931	—	—	3,000	4,000

EDUCATE, INC.

1001 Fleet St.
Baltimore, MD 21202
Phone: 410-843-8000
Fax: 410-843-8441
Web: www.educate-inc.com

CEO: R. Christopher (Chris) Hoehn-Saric
CFO: Kevin E. (Ken) Shaffer
HR: Troy Albright
FYE: December 31
Type: Private

For Educate, Inc., the name says it all. Its portfolio of companies includes Sylvan Learning Center which offers tutoring to students in pre-K through 12th grade. Certified teachers provide personalized instruction in reading, writing, math, study skills, and test prep for college entrance and state exams via more than 1,000 franchised and company-owned centers throughout North America. Educate also owns HOP, LLC, the maker of Hooked on Phonics reading materials, and Catapult Learning which offers supplemental reading and math education services in schools. Educate also offers online tutoring services for Sylvan and Catapult students.

	Annual Growth	12/02	12/03	12/04	12/05	12/06
Sales ($ mil.)	8.7%	—	—	300.3	330.4	354.7
Net income ($ mil.)	—	—	—	6.4	15.4	(11.9)
Employees	(11.0%)	—	—	12,827	9,486	10,161

EDUCATION MANAGEMENT CORPORATION

210 6th Ave., 33rd Fl.
Pittsburgh, PA 15222
Phone: 412-562-0900
Fax: 412-562-0598
Web: www.edumgt.com

CEO: Todd S. Nelson
CFO: Edward H. West
HR: Roberta L. Troike
FYE: June 30
Type: Private

Worried that traditional higher education could leave you enlightened but unemployed? Education Management Corporation (EDMC) has the solution. The company operates The Art Institutes, which have nearly 40 locations in cities in the US and Canada, in addition to Argosy University, South University, and Brown Mackie College. The schools offer associate's degrees, certificate programs, undergraduate and graduate-level programs, and doctoral degrees. EDMC's educational institutions boast a total student enrollment of around 96,000 at some 80 locations. The company filed to go public in 2007.

	Annual Growth	6/03	6/04	6/05	6/06	6/07
Sales ($ mil.)	15.7%	—	—	1,019.3	1,170.2	1,363.7
Net income ($ mil.)	(43.5%)	—	—	101.6	80.7	32.4
Employees	(8.8%)	—	—	12,150	7,880	10,100

EDUCATION REALTY TRUST, INC.

NYSE: EDR

530 Oak Court Dr., Ste. 300
Memphis, TN 38117
Phone: 901-259-2500
Fax: 901-259-2594
Web: www.educationrealty.com

CEO: Paul O. Bower
CFO: Randall H. (Randy) Brown
HR: Susan B. Arrison
FYE: December 31
Type: Public

This company can give your college student a home away from home. Education Realty Trust, a self-administered real estate investment trust (REIT), develops, buys, owns, and operates residential communities for university students. It owns about 40 communities with approximately 25,000 beds in some 20 states. Through its Allen & O'Hara Education Services subsidiary, the REIT manages another 30 properties owned by others, including colleges and charitable organizations. Education Realty Trust communities offer private rooms as well as amenities such as fitness centers, tanning beds, game rooms, hot tubs, swimming pools — and even study rooms.

	Annual Growth	12/03	12/04	12/05	12/06	12/07
Sales ($ mil.)	17.3%	—	—	87.2	119.3	119.9
Net income ($ mil.)	—	—	—	(15.6)	(12.2)	(5.4)
Market value ($ mil.)	(2.8%)	—	—	338.5	404.5	319.6
Employees	—	—	—	1,038	—	—

EDUCATIONAL DEVELOPMENT CORPORATION

NASDAQ (GM): EDUC

10302 E. 55th Place
Tulsa, OK 74146
Phone: 918-622-4522
Fax: 918-665-7919
Web: www.edcpub.com

CEO: Randall W. White
CFO: Marilyn R. Welborn
HR: Marilyn R. Welborn
FYE: Last day of February
Type: Public

Educational Development Corporation (EDC) likes being in a bind, as long as the cover appeals to youngsters. The company is the exclusive US distributor of a line of about 1,400 children's books published by the UK's Usborne Publishing Limited. EDC's Home Business Division markets the books to individuals using independent sales reps who sell through personal Web sites, home parties, direct sales, and book fairs; this division also distributes books to public and school libraries. EDC's Publishing Division distributes the Usborne line to a network of book, toy, and other retail stores. The company also offers more than 60 Usborne Kid Kits, which combine books with related materials such as toys.

	Annual Growth	2/04	2/05	2/06	2/07	2/08
Sales ($ mil.)	0.1%	30.4	31.6	31.8	31.4	30.5
Net income ($ mil.)	(1.1%)	2.4	2.4	2.4	2.4	2.3
Market value ($ mil.)	(16.2%)	42.9	38.8	30.2	28.8	21.1
Employees	1.2%	—	—	81	82	—

An in-depth profile of this company is available to Hoover's Online members at hoovers.com.

EDUCATIONAL TESTING SERVICE

Rosedale Road
Princeton, NJ 08541
Phone: 609-921-9000
Fax: 609-734-5410
Web: www.ets.org

CEO: Kurt M. Landgraf
CFO: Frank R. Gatti
HR: Yvette Donado
FYE: June 30
Type: Not-for-profit

For college-bound high school students, taking the SAT is as much a rite of adulthood as getting a driver's license. Educational Testing Service (ETS), the creator of the Scholastic Assessment Test (SAT), develops and administers more than 12 million achievement, occupational, and admissions tests a year. In addition to the SAT, ETS develops other tests, including the Advanced Placement (AP) Program tests, CLEP, GSAT, GRE, and TOEFL. Founded in 1947, the not-for-profit group is the world's largest private testing and research organization. The ETS Research unit conducts research projects focusing on education. Test-development subsidiary Prometric is a for-profit unit of the group.

	Annual Growth	6/03	6/04	6/05	6/06	6/07
Est. sales ($ mil.)	—	—	—	—	—	803.5
Employees	—	—	—	—	—	2,433

EDWARD DON & COMPANY

2500 S. Harlem Ave.
North Riverside, IL 60546
Phone: 708-442-9400
Fax: 708-442-0436
Web: www.don.com

CEO: Steven R. (Steve) Don
CFO: James P. (Jim) Jones
HR: Marla Schneider
FYE: December 31
Type: Private

Edward Don & Company sells just about anything to institutional kitchen managers, including the kitchen sink. The company provides foodservice equipment and supplies to restaurants, government institutions, hospitals, hotels, and schools. It stocks bar and fountain supplies, catering and cooking equipment, flatware, tableware, tables and chairs, paper goods, cleaning products, sanitation supplies, and about 12,000 other products. It operates six distribution centers and a fleet of more than 100 trucks. Edward Don also designs and builds full-service kitchens for the foodservice industry. The company, owned by the Don family, has some 12,000 customers throughout the world. It was founded in Chicago in 1921.

EDWARDS LIFESCIENCES CORPORATION

NYSE: EW

1 Edwards Way
Irvine, CA 92614
Phone: 949-250-2500
Fax: 949-250-2525
Web: www.edwards.com

CEO: Michael A. Mussallem
CFO: Thomas M. Abate
HR: Robert C. Reindl
FYE: December 31
Type: Public

Edwards Lifesciences has its heart in the right place. Named for the co-inventor of the first artificial heart valve, Miles "Lowell" Edwards, the company is a spin-off of Baxter International. Its main products are still heart valve devices, including valves made from animal tissue and annuloplasty rings that repair damaged valves. The company also makes monitoring systems that measure heart function during surgery; various types of cannulae (surgical tubes used for drainage, delivery, or filtration); and embolectomy catheters that remove blood clots from peripheral arteries. Edwards Lifesciences markets its products worldwide through a direct salesforce and distributors.

	Annual Growth	12/03	12/04	12/05	12/06	12/07
Sales ($ mil.)	6.1%	860.5	931.5	997.9	1,037.0	1,091.1
Net income ($ mil.)	9.4%	79.0	1.7	79.3	130.5	113.0
Market value ($ mil.)	9.8%	1,789.2	2,452.4	2,476.8	2,714.2	2,603.0
Employees	1.8%	—	—	5,400	5,550	5,600

⊞ EFJ, INC.

NASDAQ (GM): EFJI

1440 Corporate Dr.
Irving, TX 75038
Phone: 972-819-0700
Fax: 972-819-0639
Web: www.efji.com

CEO: Michael E. Jalbert
CFO: Jana A. Bell
HR: Michael B. Gamble
FYE: December 31
Type: Public

EFJ makes sure certain communications remain on the QT. Through its E.F. Johnson division, the company makes radio and radio-security systems for police departments, government agencies, the military, and cellular service providers. Its primary products are handheld and mobile radios, base stations, and signal repeaters. EFJ's Transcrypt International subsidiary makes security modules that encrypt and decode radio and wireless phone signals to prevent eavesdropping. Its 3e Technologies International (3eTI) unit provides federal government and military agencies with secure communications products.

	Annual Growth	12/03	12/04	12/05	12/06	12/07
Sales ($ mil.)	28.8%	56.2	80.9	94.6	96.7	154.6
Net income ($ mil.)	—	4.0	10.0	22.5	(6.8)	(37.7)
Market value ($ mil.)	(8.4%)	102.4	178.0	263.5	176.7	72.1
Employees	—	—	—	272	—	—

EFOODSAFETY.COM, INC.

OTC: EFSF

7702 E. Doubletree Ranch Rd., Ste. 300
Scottsdale, AZ 85258
Phone: 480-607-2606
Fax: 480-348-3999
Web: www.efoodsafety.com

CEO: Patricia Ross-Gruden
CFO: Patricia Ross-Gruden
HR: –
FYE: April 30
Type: Public

eFoodSafety.com is a development-stage company with a handful of products and potential products intended to make the world a better place. Subsidiary Knock-Out Technologies has developed an environmentally-safe germicidal topical spray that kills some of the most frequent bacterial pathogens. The company is also developing a sporicidal to kill anthrax, and has formulated Citroxin, a product designed to knock out avian flu viruses. The company's MedElite subsidiary distributes medical products such as the scar cream Talsyn. Other subsidiaries hold such products as Cinnergen, a cinnamon-based non-prescription diabetes product, the Immune Boost Bar nutritional supplement, and the PurEffect acne care treatment.

	Annual Growth	4/03	4/04	4/05	4/06	4/07
Sales ($ mil.)	—	0.0	0.0	0.1	0.5	1.2
Net income ($ mil.)	—	0.0	(1.7)	(4.3)	(9.4)	(3.6)
Market value ($ mil.)	3.8%	—	52.1	38.5	56.8	58.3
Employees	—	4	—	—	—	—

EGAIN COMMUNICATIONS CORPORATION

OTC: EGAN

345 E. Middlefield Rd.
Mountain View, CA 94043
Phone: 650-230-7500
Fax: 650-230-7600
Web: www.egain.com

CEO: Ashutosh (Ashu) Roy
CFO: Eric N. Smit
HR: –
FYE: June 30
Type: Public

eGain helps eBusinesses offer eService to their eCustomers. eGain Communications offers call center software that integrates online and telephone communications with other data sources. The company's software suite includes applications for routing e-mails, giving customers self-service options, enabling live Web chat, and providing call center agents with customer information. In addition, eGain provides such services as consulting, hosting, maintenance, implementation, and support. Its customers have included AT&T, Cox Newspapers, and Hewlett-Packard.

	Annual Growth	6/03	6/04	6/05	6/06	6/07
Sales ($ mil.)	0.4%	22.1	19.6	20.4	22.6	22.5
Net income ($ mil.)	—	(11.5)	(4.9)	(0.8)	(1.1)	(7.7)
Market value ($ mil.)	(3.0%)	17.3	3.9	9.9	19.9	15.3
Employees	33.3%	—	—	—	57	76

EGAMES, INC.

Pink Sheets: EGAM

2000 Cabot Blvd. West, Ste. 110
Langhorne, PA 19047
Phone: 215-750-6606
Fax: –
Web: www.egames.com

CEO: Gerald W. (Jerry) Klein
CFO: Thomas W. (Tom) Murphy
HR: –
FYE: June 30
Type: Public

eGames is taking a G-rated (or should that be E-rated?) approach to PC entertainment. The company markets video games that are usually rated E (for everyone) that are easy to use and nonviolent. Its titles, which include *Bowling Mania* and *MahJongg Master*, typically sell for $20 or less and are marketed in North America under such brand names as eGames, Home Office Help, and RealAge. eGames sells its products at national retail chains (Wal-Mart, Target, Best Buy, K-Mart) and office supply stores and warehouse clubs (Office Max, Sam's Club); it also sells through wholesale distributor Atari, Take-Two Interactive, and various inventory liquidators. eGames also offers online games through its eGames.com Web site.

	Annual Growth	6/02	6/03	6/04	6/05	*6/06
Sales ($ mil.)	(18.5%)	10.9	7.2	8.0	5.3	4.8
Net income ($ mil.)	—	2.2	1.6	1.7	(0.2)	(1.0)
Employees	—	—	—	—	—	20

*Most recent year available

EG&G

200 Orchard Ridge Dr., Ste. 100
Gaithersburg, MD 20878
Phone: 301-258-6554
Fax: 301-721-2202
Web: www.urscorp.com/EGG_Division

CEO: Randall A. (Randy) Wotring
CFO: William F. Neeb Jr.
HR: Robert (Bob) Rudisin
FYE: December 31
Type: Business segment

EG&G has been deployed to the front line of a number of government contracts. The company, a division of engineering giant URS, provides outsourced management and technical support services to the US departments of Defense and Homeland Security and other federal agencies. EG&G operates through two main units, Aerospace Technical Services (installations management, logistics, field services, flight training) and Engineering and Technology Services Division (support for defense and homeland security systems). EG&G was founded in 1947 by scientists Harold Edgerton, Kenneth Germeshausen, and Herbert Grier.

EGON ZEHNDER INTERNATIONAL

350 Park Ave., 8th Fl.
New York, NY 10022
Phone: 212-519-6000
Fax: 212-519-6060
Web: www.egonzehnder.com

CEO: John J. Grumbar
CFO: Stefan Reckhenrich
HR: –
FYE: October 31
Type: Private

Egon Zehnder gives corporate engines a tune-up (and supplies replacement parts). Operating through more than 60 offices in almost 40 countries, Egon Zehnder is one of the world's largest senior-level executive recruitment firms, along with Heidrick & Struggles and Korn/Ferry. It also specializes in management appraisals and corporate governance. The firm operates through such practice groups as technology, life sciences, consumer, and financial services. Egon Zehnder's clients include both start-up companies and large corporations, as well as government, educational, and cultural organizations. Founded by Egon Zehnder in 1964, the company is owned by its partners.

EGPI FIRECREEK, INC.

OTC: EFCR

6564 Smoke Tree Ln.
Scottsdale, AZ 85253
Phone: 480-948-6581
Fax: 480-443-1403
Web: www.egpifirecreek.net

CEO: Dennis R. Alexander
CFO: Dennis R. Alexander
HR: –
FYE: December 31
Type: Public

The fire in EGPI Firecreek's belly is for oil and gas exploration and production. Once dependent on the sale of private leisure and commercial vessels, EGPI Firecreek has refocused on oil and gas activities. In 2004 the company (then known as Energy Producers) acquired Firecreek Petroleum, and became EGPI Firecreek. It has a strategic alliance with Sahara Group, an oil and gas concern with expertise in Eastern Europe, North Africa, Russia, and Turkey. In 2006 EGPI Firecreek began the production and sale of natural gas from wells in Sweetwater County, Wyoming. It also gained rights to explore in the Ukraine. The company has proved reserves of 2.6 billion cu. ft. of natural gas equivalent.

	Annual Growth	12/03	12/04	12/05	12/06	12/07
Sales ($ mil.)	100.0%	—	—	—	0.2	0.4
Net income ($ mil.)	—	—	—	—	(4.3)	(1.5)
Market value ($ mil.)	(33.4%)	—	—	—	3.6	2.4
Employees	—	—	—	—	—	—

EHARMONY.COM, INC.

888 E. Walnut Ave.
Pasadena, CA 91101
Phone: 626-795-4814
Fax: 626-585-4040
Web: www.eharmony.com

CEO: Gregory L. (Greg) Waldorf
CFO: John Powers
HR: Jim Lambert
FYE: December 31
Type: Private

Looking to settle down harmoniously? eharmony.com (which does business as eHarmony) is an online service that attempts to match compatible singles who are looking for long-term relationships. The company focuses on helping clients find their "soul mate" by giving them a detailed questionnaire emphasizing compatibility matching and communication. (It has patented its "Compatibility Matching System.") The site counts more than 20 million registered users. In 2006 the company launched eHarmony Marriage, an Internet service aimed at strengthening marriages. The company was founded in 2000 by author and clinical psychologist Dr. Neil Clark Warren.

	Annual Growth	12/03	12/04	12/05	12/06	12/07
Est. sales ($ mil.)	—	—	—	—	—	4.1
Employees	—	—	—	—	—	119

EHEALTH, INC.

NASDAQ (GM): EHTH

440 E. Middlefield Rd.
Mountain View, CA 94043
Phone: 650-584-2700
Fax: 650-961-2153
Web: www.ehealthinsurance.com

CEO: Gary L. Lauer
CFO: Stuart M. Huizinga
HR: –
FYE: December 31
Type: Public

eHealth brought e-commerce to the insurance business. Through its subsidiary eHealthInsurance Services, the company sells health insurance online to some 500,000 individual, family, and small business members. The company is licensed to sell in all 50 states and Washington, DC, and it has partnerships with some 160 health insurance carriers. It offers more than 7,000 products online — including health, dental, and vision insurance products from the likes of Aetna, Humana, Kaiser Permanente, and Unicare, as well as more than 40 Blue Cross and Blue Shield licensees. The company was founded in 1997.

	Annual Growth	12/03	12/04	12/05	12/06	12/07
Sales ($ mil.)	41.0%	22.2	30.2	41.8	61.3	87.8
Net income ($ mil.)	—	(3.2)	(3.3)	(0.4)	16.5	31.6
Market value ($ mil.)	81.2%	—	—	—	437.4	792.7
Employees	—	—	—	—	357	—

E. I. DU PONT DE NEMOURS AND COMPANY

NYSE: DD

1007 Market St.
Wilmington, DE 19898
Phone: 302-774-1000
Fax: 302-999-4399
Web: www.dupont.com

CEO: Charles O. (Chad) Holliday Jr.
CFO: Jeffrey L. Keefer
HR: Ann K. M. Gualtieri
FYE: December 31
Type: Public

E. I. du Pont de Nemours wants to cover your house, feed your crops, and coat your car. The #3 US chemical maker (behind Dow and ExxonMobil Chemicals) operates through five business units. These segments produce coatings (automotive finishes and coatings), crop protection chemicals and genetically modified seeds, electronic materials (LCDs, sensors, and fluorochemicals), polymers and resins for packaging and other uses, and safety and security materials (under brand names like Tyvek, Kevlar, and Corian). In this decade, the company has slimmed down, exiting the pharmaceutical business and spinning off its fibers operations, and DuPont is now focusing on biotechnology and safety and protection.

	Annual Growth	12/03	12/04	12/05	12/06	12/07
Sales ($ mil.)	2.5%	27,730.0	27,995.0	28,491.0	28,982.0	30,653.0
Net income ($ mil.)	32.4%	973.0	1,780.0	2,053.0	3,148.0	2,988.0
Market value ($ mil.)	(3.5%)	45,765.4	48,772.4	39,083.4	44,913.9	39,652.2
Employees	0.0%	—	—	60,000	59,000	60,000

EILEEN FISHER, INC.

2 Bridge St.
Irvington, NY 10533
Phone: 914-591-5700
Fax: 914-591-8824
Web: www.eileenfisher.com

CEO: Eileen Fisher
CFO: Kenneth Pollak
HR: –
FYE: December 31
Type: Private

Eileen Fisher — the woman and the company — cares about customers' comfort as well as their sense of fashion. The company makes and markets upscale women's business and casual clothing, including eco-friendly items. Eileen Fisher's apparel is sold through about 35 of its namesake boutiques and outlets in about a dozen states, as well as through department and specialty stores (including Nordstrom, Saks Fifth Avenue, and Neiman Marcus) nationwide and in Canada. The company also offers personal shopping services for US customers. After working in the fields of graphic arts and interior design, Eileen Fisher founded the company in 1984 in New York.

	Annual Growth	12/03	12/04	12/05	12/06	12/07
Est. sales ($ mil.)	—	—	—	—	—	15.9
Employees	—	—	—	—	—	650

EINSTEIN NOAH RESTAURANT GROUP, INC.

NASDAQ (GM): BAGL

555 Zang St., Ste. 300
Lakewood, CO 80228
Phone: 303-568-8000
Fax: 303-568-8039
Web: www.einsteinnoah.com

CEO: Paul J. B. Murphy III
CFO: Richard P. (Rick) Dutkiewicz
HR: Michael (Mike) Serchia
FYE: Tuesday nearest December 31
Type: Public

Bagels and coffee are key ingredients for this company. Einstein Noah Restaurant Group (formerly New World Restaurant Group) is the largest bagel shop operator in the US, with more than 600 company-owned and franchised locations in 36 states. Its flagship chain, Einstein Bros. Bagel, offers more than a dozen varieties of fresh-made bagels and spreads, along with coffee, pastries, and a menu of sandwiches and salads at its more than 450 outlets. In addition to Einstein, New World operates the Noah's New York Bagels, Manhattan Bagel, Chesapeake Bagel Bakery, and New World Coffee chains. More than 400 locations are company-owned.

	Annual Growth	12/03	12/04	12/05	12/06	12/07
Sales ($ mil.)	1.3%	383.3	373.9	389.1	390.0	402.9
Net income ($ mil.)	—	(67.7)	(17.4)	(14.0)	(6.9)	12.6
Market value ($ mil.)	131.8%	—	23.1	45.3	79.5	288.2
Employees	—	7,464	—	—	—	—

EISAI INC.

100 Tice Blvd.
Woodcliff Lake, NJ 07677
Phone: 201-692-1100
Fax: 201-692-1804
Web: www.eisai.com

CEO: Hajime Shimizu
CFO: Kenneth R (Ken) Klauser
HR: Robert Fogleman
FYE: March 31
Type: Subsidiary

Eisai Inc. develops and markets pharmaceuticals to treat a variety of ills. As the US arm of Eisai Co., its current product roster includes Alzheimer's treatment Aricept, Aciphex for acid reflux, and anti-convulsants Cerebyx and Zonegran. In addition to its drug manufacturing and marketing operations, the company has research operations, including Eisai Research Institute of Boston and Eisai Medical Research. The company co-develops and markets its drugs in "co-promotional" agreements with other large pharmaceutical companies including Pfizer, Janssen, and Elan. Eisai Inc. has an extensive pipeline of potential drugs to address cancer, epilepsy, and migraines.

	Annual Growth	3/03	3/04	3/05	3/06	3/07
Est. sales ($ mil.)	—	—	—	—	—	2,000.0
Employees	—	—	—	—	—	550

EISNER LLP

750 3rd Ave.
New York, NY 10017
Phone: 212-949-8700
Fax: 212-891-4100
Web: www.eisnerllp.com

CEO: Richard Eisner
CFO: Brett James
HR: Rick Fisher
FYE: January 31
Type: Partnership

Welcome to the wonderful world of numbers! Eisner provides accounting and consulting services for clients (typically middle market businesses) in the northeastern US, specializing in such industries as health sciences, sports and entertainment, not-for-profits, financial services, and technology. Offerings include auditing and accounting, tax planning, legal support, bankruptcy consulting, corporate finance, employee benefits plan services, and information technology consulting. Services outside the US are provided through Eisner's Cayman Islands office, as well as through its affiliation with Baker Tilly International. Eisner was founded in 1963.

	Annual Growth	1/03	1/04	1/05	1/06	1/07
Est. sales ($ mil.)	—	—	—	—	—	99.4
Employees	—	—	—	—	—	450

EL DORADO FURNITURE CORPORATION

4200 NW 167th St.
Miami, FL 33054
Phone: 305-624-9700
Fax: 305-624-8772
Web: www.eldoradofurniture.com

CEO: Luis Capó
CFO: Ivan Trabal
HR: Henry E. Hererro
FYE: December 31
Type: Private

The road to El Dorado Furniture Corporation is covered in sand. The company sells home furnishings in South Florida, with a dozen or so retail outlets in Miami. It sells indoor furniture for the whole house, as well as home office items and decorative pieces. The stores are designed to look like a small town with building facades off a main street and even feature cafes. El Dorado, one of the largest Hispanic-owned retail enterprises in the US, was founded in 1967 and is still operated by the Capó family.

	Annual Growth	12/03	12/04	12/05	12/06	12/07
Est. sales ($ mil.)	—	—	—	—	—	174.5
Employees	—	—	—	—	—	875

EL PASO CORPORATION

NYSE: EP

El Paso Bldg., 1001 Louisiana St.
Houston, TX 77002
Phone: 713-420-2600
Fax: 713-420-4417
Web: www.elpaso.com

CEO: Douglas L. (Doug) Foshee
CFO: David M. (Mark) Leland
HR: Susan B. (Sue) Ortenstone
FYE: December 31
Type: Public

Out in the West Texas town of El Paso this company fell in love with the natural gas industry. Founded in 1928 in its namesake Texas city, El Paso Corp. is primarily engaged in gas transportation and storage, oil and gas exploration and production, and gas gathering and processing. Operator of the largest gas transportation system in the US, El Paso has interests in 42,000 miles of interstate pipeline. Subsidiary El Paso Exploration and Production has estimated proved reserves of 2.9 trillion cu. ft. of natural gas equivalent in Brazil, Egypt, and the US. The company also has interests in global energy projects, including power plants, and it markets wholesale energy commodities.

	Annual Growth	12/03	12/04	12/05	12/06	12/07
Sales ($ mil.)	(8.8%)	6,711.0	6,543.0	4,017.0	4,281.0	4,648.0
Net income ($ mil.)	—	(1,928.0)	(947.0)	(606.0)	475.0	1,110.0
Market value ($ mil.)	23.6%	5,177.7	6,690.3	8,019.1	10,652.0	12,077.2
Employees	(6.4%)	—	—	5,700	5,050	4,992

EL PASO ELECTRIC COMPANY

NYSE: EE

Stanton Tower, 100 N. Stanton
El Paso, TX 79901
Phone: 915-543-5711
Fax: 915-521-4787
Web: www.epelectric.com

CEO: J. Frank Bates
CFO: Scott D. Wilson
HR: –
FYE: December 31
Type: Public

El Paso Electric creates currents along the Rio Grande River. The utility transmits and distributes electricity to some 360,000 customers in West Texas and southern New Mexico. More than half of the company's sales come from its namesake city and nearby Las Cruces, New Mexico. The firm has 1,500 MW of nuclear and fossil-fueled generating capacity. El Paso Electric also purchases power from other utilities and marketers, and sells wholesale power in Texas and New Mexico, as well as in Mexico. Its largest customers include military installations, such as Fort Bliss in Texas and White Sands Missile Range and Holloman Air Force Base in New Mexico.

	Annual Growth	12/03	12/04	12/05	12/06	12/07
Sales ($ mil.)	7.2%	664.4	708.6	803.9	816.5	877.4
Net income ($ mil.)	5.7%	60.0	35.2	35.5	67.4	74.8
Market value ($ mil.)	16.2%	633.0	895.9	1,010.3	1,118.2	1,154.5
Employees	0.0%	—	—	1,000	1,000	1,000

EL PASO PIPELINE PARTNERS, L.P.

NYSE: EPB

1001 Louisiana St.
Houston, TX 77002
Phone: 713-420-2600
Fax: –

CEO: James C. (Jim) Yardley
CFO: John R. (J. R.) Sult
HR: –
FYE: December 31
Type: Public

While El Paso Pipeline Partners might seem like the way El Paso gets great Mexican food across the border, it's actually a natural gas pipeline and storage company. The firm, which consists primarily of Wyoming Interstate Company (WIC) and partial interests in Colorado Interstate Gas Company (CIG) and Southern Natural Gas Company (SNG), has 12,300 miles of pipeline, and storage facilities totaling 89 billion cu. ft. Parent El Paso Corporation owns the remainder of CIG and SNG. El Paso Pipeline Partners' customers include local distribution companies, industrial users, electricity generators, and natural gas marketing and trading companies. El Paso Corporation will retain about 70% of the company post-IPO.

	Annual Growth	12/03	12/04	12/05	12/06	12/07
Sales ($ mil.)	—	—	—	—	—	110.0
Net income ($ mil.)	—	—	—	—	—	66.0
Market value ($ mil.)	—	—	—	—	—	1,432.6
Employees	—	—	—	—	—	—

EL POLLO LOCO HOLDINGS, INC.

3333 Michelson Dr., Ste. 550
Irvine, CA 92612
Phone: 949-399-2000
Fax: 949-251-1703
Web: www.elpolloloco.com

CEO: Stephen E. (Steve) Carley
CFO: Joseph N. (Joe) Stein
HR: Jeanne A. Scott
FYE: December 31
Type: Private

This chicken restaurant chain is crazy from the Mexican heat. El Pollo Loco Holdings operates and franchises more than 360 fast-casual restaurants operating under the El Pollo Loco banner that specialize in Mexican-style chicken dishes. The chain's menu includes chicken burritos and tacos, as well as salads and a complete chicken dinner. Most El Pollo Loco outlets are in California, while a small number can be found in Arizona, Illinois, Nevada, and Texas. More than 200 El Pollo Loco locations are operated by franchisees. Juan Francisco Ochoa started the chain in Mexico in 1975. El Pollo Loco is owned by private equity firm Trimaran Capital Partners.

ELAMEX, S.A. DE C.V.

Pink Sheets: ELAMF

1800 Northwestern Dr.
El Paso, TX 79912
Phone: 915-298-3061
Fax: 915-298-3065
Web: www.elamex.com

CEO: Richard R. Harshman
CFO: Alma D. Diaz
HR: –
FYE: December 31
Type: Public

It may sound nutty, but Elamex has a sweet tooth for candy. The company, located in El Paso, Texas, manufactures candy and also packages nuts through its subsidiary Franklin Connections. It sold its bankrupt Precision Industries metal stamping unit (which serves the appliance and automotive industries). The company also sold Qualcore, its Mexico-based stamped metal and plastic parts joint venture with GE. Accel SA, a Mexico-based diversified manufacturer, owns a majority of Elamex; Elamex's chairman, Eloy Vallina, is also Accel's chairman.

	Annual Growth	12/00	12/01	12/02	12/03	*12/04
Sales ($ mil.)	(13.5%)	174.7	132.0	134.3	157.3	97.6
Net income ($ mil.)	—	17.4	(11.0)	(6.0)	(34.6)	(5.2)
Employees	(23.3%)	3,464	1,860	2,039	—	—

*Most recent year available

ELAN PHARMACEUTICALS

800 Gateway Blvd.
San Francisco, CA 94080
Phone: 650-877-0900
Fax: 650-877-7669
Web: www.elan.com

CEO: Lars G. Ekman
CFO: –
HR: –
FYE: December 31
Type: Subsidiary

Elan Pharmaceuticals is part of the brains behind the brawn of drugmaker Elan Corporation. The US-based subsidiary provides research and discovery services, such as the identification and development of new drug candidates, to its Irish parent, which specializes in treatments for neurological and autoimmune diseases, as well as severe pain medication. Drugs under investigation include possible treatments for Alzheimer's disease, Parkinson's disease, multiple sclerosis, and Crohn's disease. The subsidiary also handles marketing of Elan's products in the US.

	Annual Growth	12/03	12/04	12/05	12/06	12/07
Est. sales ($ mil.)	—	—	—	—	—	92.2
Employees	—	—	—	—	—	727

An in-depth profile of this company is available to Hoover's Online members at hoovers.com.

545

ELCOM INTERNATIONAL, INC.

Pink Sheets: ELCO

10 Oceana Way
Norwood, MA 02062
Phone: 781-501-4000
Fax: –
Web: www.elcom.com

CEO: Gregory D. King
CFO: David Elliott
HR: –
FYE: December 31
Type: Public

If only sales were as easy for Elcom to procure as the products bought and sold with its software. Elcom International's PECOS (Professional Electronic Commerce Online System) software enables clients to automate procurement functions such as pricing, invoicing, and payment. Its application suite, which Elcom offers as either a licensed or hosted application, includes tools for managing the order cycle, creating rapid requisitions, and building electronic marketplaces to conduct online transactions with suppliers and distributors. Elcom also provides integration services for suppliers and buyers to help them manage catalog information and other content.

	Annual Growth	12/02	12/03	12/04	12/05	*12/06
Sales ($ mil.)	(9.6%)	4.8	3.0	3.8	2.7	3.2
Net income ($ mil.)	—	(9.9)	(5.4)	(3.3)	(5.8)	(6.8)
Employees	2.7%	—	—	37	36	39

*Most recent year available

ELDERHOSTEL, INC.

11 Ave. de Lafayette
Boston, MA 02111
Phone: 617-426-7788
Fax: –
Web: www.elderhostel.org

CEO: James A. (Jim) Moses
CFO: David Stahl
HR: –
FYE: September 30
Type: Not-for-profit

Welcome! Benvenuto! Het welkom! Elderhostel offers a wide variety of educational travel programs to adults ages 55 and over. The not-for-profit organization offers about 8,000 non-credit, personal-enrichment programs in more than 90 countries, from Africa to Antarctica. Programs are taught by experts such as professors, local scholars, and museum professionals and include lectures, field trips, and hands-on activities. Participants experience and learn about art, literature, music, nature, and traditional cultures. Elderhostel was founded in 1975 by world traveler and social activist Marty Knowlton and University of New Hampshire administrator David Bianco.

	Annual Growth	9/03	9/04	9/05	9/06	9/07
Est. sales ($ mil.)	—	—	—	—	—	190.3
Employees	—	—	—	—	—	180

ELDORADO ARTESIAN SPRINGS, INC.

OTC: ELDO

1783 Dogwood St.
Louisville, CO 80027
Phone: 303-499-1316
Fax: 303-499-1339
Web: www.eldoradosprings.com

CEO: Douglas A. Larson
CFO: Cathleen M. Shoenfeld
HR: –
FYE: March 31
Type: Public

If Cortez had sought a wealth of water instead of streets of gold, he might have headed for Eldorado Artesian Springs. Eldorado bottles and sells water from springs it owns in the foothills of the Rocky Mountains. About 70% of the company's sales come from home and office delivery of large bottles of its natural spring water (and water cooler rentals); smaller bottles are sold in stores. The water is distributed primarily in Colorado but also in regions of bordering states. For decades, the company's primary business was a resort. The company continues to operate the resort's spring-fed pool.

	Annual Growth	3/04	3/05	3/06	3/07	3/08
Sales ($ mil.)	2.5%	7.7	7.6	7.9	8.3	8.5
Net income ($ mil.)	—	(0.1)	(0.6)	0.0	0.1	(0.3)
Market value ($ mil.)	40.6%	3.3	6.7	4.9	5.3	12.9
Employees	—	—	—	—	—	—

ELECSYS CORPORATION

AMEX: ASY

15301 W. 109th St.
Lenexa, KS 66219
Phone: 913-647-0158
Fax: 913-647-0132
Web: www.elecsyscorp.com

CEO: Karl B. Gemperli
CFO: Todd A. Daniels
HR: –
FYE: April 30
Type: Public

Many companies elect Elecsys to make their electronics. Elecsys is a contract manufacturer of electronic assemblies and displays. Through subsidiary DCI, Inc., the company makes custom electronic assemblies — including printed circuit boards, electronic modules, LCDs, and light-emitting diodes (LEDs) — for OEMs in the aerospace, communications, medical, and other industries. Five customers account for about half of the company's sales. In 2007 Elecsys acquired the assets of Radix International, a supplier of ultra-rugged handheld computers and portable printers. DCI previously manufactured most of Radix's product line on a contract basis.

	Annual Growth	4/03	4/04	4/05	4/06	4/07
Sales ($ mil.)	15.1%	11.3	10.6	12.3	14.7	19.8
Net income ($ mil.)	—	(1.4)	0.0	0.7	1.7	1.0
Market value ($ mil.)	43.5%	4.4	3.3	10.5	12.6	18.7
Employees	3.1%	114	80	97	106	129

ELECTRIC & GAS TECHNOLOGY, INC.

Pink Sheets: ELGT

3233 W. Kingsley Rd.
Garland, TX 75041
Phone: 972-840-3223
Fax: 972-271-8925
Web: www.elgt.com

CEO: Daniel A. Zimmerman
CFO: Daniel A. Zimmerman
HR: Daniel A. Zimmerman
FYE: July 31
Type: Public

Oil and water may not mix, but electric and gas does — in the business plan of Electric & Gas Technology (EGTI). Logic Metals Technology, EGTI's subsidiary, fabricates electronic enclosures and equipment panels for telecommunications and electronics industries. Another EGTI subsidiary, Reynolds Equipment, makes equipment that measures natural gas usage. Customers include electric and gas utilities and pipeline and production companies. The father and son team of S. Mort (chairman) and Daniel (president, CEO, and director) Zimmerman, together, own nearly 42% of EGTI.

	Annual Growth	7/02	7/03	7/04	7/05	*7/06
Sales ($ mil.)	7.0%	9.7	13.6	6.4	8.5	12.7
Net income ($ mil.)	—	(2.5)	(1.2)	(3.0)	0.2	(1.5)
Employees	—	—	—	—	—	122

*Most recent year available

ELECTRIC BOAT CORPORATION

75 Eastern Point Rd.
Groton, CT 06340
Phone: 860-433-3000
Fax: 860-433-1400
Web: www.gdeb.com

CEO: John P. Casey
CFO: John V. Leonard Jr.
HR: Robert H. Nardone
FYE: December 31
Type: Subsidiary

The name's a mite understated: Electric Boat designs, builds, and maintains nuclear attack and ballistic-missile submarines for the US Navy. A subsidiary of defense giant General Dynamics, Electric Boat was established in 1899 and won its first US Navy contract the next year. The company has delivered its third and final Seawolf-class submarine (Jimmy Carter-SSN23) to the US Navy and is working on several Virginia-class submarines that it is building with Northrop Grumman after having delivered the first one in 2004. Electric Boat continues to provide support and maintenance for Seawolf-, Ohio-, and Los Angeles-class submarines. Electric Boat operates in Connecticut, Virginia, and Rhode Island.

	Annual Growth	12/03	12/04	12/05	12/06	12/07
Est. sales ($ mil.)	—	—	—	—	—	827.1
Employees	—	—	—	—	—	10,800

ELECTRIC ENERGY, INC.

2100 Portland Rd.
Joppa, IL 62953
Phone: 618-543-7531
Fax: 618-543-7420

CEO: Robert L. (Bob) Powers
CFO: –
HR: –
FYE: December 31
Type: Private

It does not take a genius to figure out what business Electric Energy (EEI) is involved in. The company generates 1,000 MW of electric capacity at its coal-fired power plant in Joppa, Illinois, and 55 MW at it natural gas fired facility at the same location. The independent producer sells its power output to its shareholders. The Missouri-based utility holding company Ameren holds an 80% stake in EEI; Ameren purchased Dynegy's 20% stake in 2004 as part of its acquisition of Illinois Power Company (which now operates as AmerenIP). Kentucky Utilities (a subsidiary of LG&E Energy) owns the remaining 20% of the company.

	Annual Growth	12/03	12/04	12/05	12/06	12/07
Est. sales ($ mil.)	—	—	—	—	—	174.4
Employees	—	—	—	—	—	257

ELECTRIC INSURANCE COMPANY

75 Sam Fonzo Dr.
Beverly, MA 01915
Phone: 978-921-2080
Fax: 978-236-5700
Web: www.electricinsurance.com

CEO: Marc A. Meiches
CFO: Laurence J. (Larry) Cohen
HR: Nicholas L. (Nick) Schulson
FYE: December 31
Type: Private

The future looks bright for Electric Insurance. The company was established in 1966 to provide insurance benefits exclusively to General Electric employees but in 2003 expanded coverage to the general public. Electric Insurance underwrites auto, homeowner, renter, and umbrella insurance to more than 125,000 policyholders; independent agencies sell the company's products. The firm also writes commercial insurance policies for General Electric. The company's online customer service includes quotes, glass claims, and 24/7 policy management. Electric Insurance is licensed in all 50 US states; Washington, DC; and Puerto Rico.

	Annual Growth	12/03	12/04	12/05	12/06	12/07
Est. sales ($ mil.)	—	—	—	—	—	401.2
Employees	—	—	—	—	—	550

ELECTRIC POWER BOARD OF THE METROPOLITAN GOVERNMENT OF NASHVILLE AND DAVIDSON COUNTY

1214 Church St.
Nashville, TN 37246
Phone: 615-736-6900
Fax: 615-747-3596
Web: www.nespower.com

CEO: Decosta E. Jenkins
CFO: Teresa Broyles-Aplin
HR: Herb Deberry
FYE: June 30
Type: Government-owned

The Electric Power Board of the Metropolitan Government of Nashville and Davidson County is a mouthful. Its operating name, Nashville Electric Service (NES), sounds much better. And talking of sound, the legendary "Nashville Sound" would be hard to hear without the resources of this power distributor, which serves almost 351,500 customers in central Tennessee. NES is one of the largest government-owned utilities in the US. The company is required to purchase power from another government-owned operator, the Tennessee Valley Authority (TVA). Anticipating deregulation, both NES and TVA are expecting changes in their relationship.

	Annual Growth	6/03	6/04	6/05	6/06	6/07
Est. sales ($ mil.)	—	—	—	—	—	903.3
Employees	—	—	—	—	—	990

ELECTRO ENERGY INC.

NASDAQ (CM): EEEI

30 Shelter Rock Rd.
Danbury, CT 06810
Phone: 203-797-2699
Fax: 203-797-2697
Web: www.electroenergyinc.com

CEO: Michael E. Reed
CFO: Timothy E. Coyne
HR: –
FYE: December 31
Type: Public

With a name like "Electro Energy," you know this isn't a company that makes cheesecake or toys for dogs. Batteries are the name of the game for this company. Electro Energy Inc. (EEI) makes specialty nickel-cadmium batteries for the American military and government contractors, and it is developing bipolar nickel-metal hydride batteries for use by the military, NASA, and other government agencies. EEI's products are found in F-16 and F/A-18 fighter aircraft, B-1 and B-52 bombers, and Cobra helicopters. The US government (about 38% of sales), Sandia National Laboratories (18%), EaglePicher (14%), and Lockheed Martin (12%) are Electro Energy's biggest customers.

	Annual Growth	12/03	12/04	12/05	12/06	12/07
Sales ($ mil.)	—	0.0	6.8	3.9	4.7	3.6
Net income ($ mil.)	—	0.0	(1.6)	(3.3)	(6.0)	(18.1)
Market value ($ mil.)	(43.5%)	—	790.4	376.8	161.5	142.6
Employees	(7.5%)	—	67	58	52	53

⊞ ELECTRO RENT CORPORATION

NASDAQ (GM): ELRC

6060 Sepulveda Blvd.
Van Nuys, CA 91411
Phone: 818-787-2100
Fax: 818-786-4354
Web: www.electrorent.com

CEO: Daniel Greenberg
CFO: Craig R. Jones
HR: Peter M. Shapiro
FYE: May 31
Type: Public

Electro Rent isn't the electronica version of the popular musical — the company rents, leases, and resells electronic test and measurement equipment and computers. The company's suppliers include Agilent Technologies, Olympus, and Tektronix, while its computer products come from such manufacturers as Dell, Hewlett-Packard, IBM, and Toshiba. Electro Rent provides new and used equipment to government agencies and companies in the aerospace, defense, and electronics industries. Chairman Daniel Greenberg and his brother, Phillip, own about one-quarter of the company.

	Annual Growth	5/03	5/04	5/05	5/06	5/07
Sales ($ mil.)	3.6%	108.8	94.1	107.6	114.8	125.3
Net income ($ mil.)	—	(15.0)	12.0	24.3	22.2	21.0
Market value ($ mil.)	10.1%	253.2	271.6	294.9	421.5	372.0
Employees	6.0%	—	—	—	284	301

⊞ ELECTRO SCIENTIFIC INDUSTRIES, INC.

NASDAQ (GM): ESIO

13900 NW Science Park Dr.
Portland, OR 97229
Phone: 503-641-4141
Fax: 503-671-5571
Web: www.esi.com

CEO: Nicholas (Nick) Konidaris
CFO: Paul Oldham
HR: Ellen Raim
FYE: Saturday nearest March 31*
Type: Public

Electro Scientific Industries (ESI) uses science — and a lot of engineering — to help its customers produce electronics on an industrial scale. The company's manufacturing and test equipment is used to make and inspect electronic components found in automotive electronics, PCs, and wireless communications gear. Its offerings include yield improvement systems, circuit fine-tuning equipment, and miniature capacitor test products. ESI also makes electronic packaging equipment, as well as machine vision systems that inspect and verify chip and circuit board quality. The company's customers include Canon, Hynix Semiconductor, Kulicke and Soffa, Kyocera, Samsung Electronics, and STMicroelectronics.

	Annual Growth	5/04	5/05	5/06	5/07	*3/08
Sales ($ mil.)	4.5%	207.2	233.4	207.0	250.8	247.2
Net income ($ mil.)	8.7%	11.9	19.8	20.8	23.5	16.6
Market value ($ mil.)	(9.1%)	642.1	518.5	573.8	596.0	438.7
Employees	—	—	563	—	—	—

*Fiscal year change

⊞ An in-depth profile of this company is available to Hoover's Online members at hoovers.com.

547

ELECTROGLAS, INC.

NASDAQ (CM): EGLS

5729 Fontanoso Way
San Jose, CA 95138
Phone: 408-528-3000
Fax: 408-528-3562
Web: www.electroglas.com

CEO: Thomas M. (Tom) Rohrs
CFO: Thomas E. Brunton
HR: —
FYE: May 31
Type: Public

Electroglas pulls out its high-tech magnifying glass to help chip makers keep an eye on production quality. The company makes automated wafer probers that check 200mm or 300mm semiconductor wafers for defects before the wafers are separated and packaged as individual chips. Its test handling systems, which are designed to operate with various types of chip packaging, help test chips in the final stages of production. The company also develops software that analyzes and improves chip production yields; all of its products are intended to help customers improve the efficiency and output of their wafer fabrication facilities. Electroglas gets more than half of its sales from international customers.

	Annual Growth	12/02	12/03	12/04	*5/06	5/07
Sales ($ mil.)	(6.0%)	57.1	45.0	63.0	44.3	44.6
Net income ($ mil.)	—	(73.6)	(59.0)	(6.4)	(34.0)	(18.8)
Market value ($ mil.)	14.7%	32.9	78.8	103.0	91.9	57.1
Employees	(17.3%)	469	254	279	278	219

*Fiscal year change

ELECTROGRAPH SYSTEMS, INC.

50 Marcus Blvd.
Hauppauge, NY 11788
Phone: 631-436-5050
Fax: 888-632-9479
Web: www.electrograph.com

CEO: Alan M. Smith
CFO: Frank Lincks
HR: Rose Ann Gordon
FYE: July 31
Type: Private

In the realm of big screens, Electrograph Systems knows that plasma is king. Formerly Manchester Technologies, the company distributes plasma displays from well-known manufacturers, such as LG, Panasonic, and Philips. Through its nationwide reseller network, it also offer LCD flat panels, desktop monitors, display mounts, projectors, audio-visual equipment, and other peripherals. In addition to being a distributor, Electrograph offers factory-authorized service and repair, as well as technical and installation support. It serves customers in education, government, hospitality, retail, and transportation throughout North America via a dozen US sales offices and multiple distribution centers.

	Annual Growth	7/03	7/04	7/05	7/06	7/07
Est. sales ($ mil.)	—	—	—	—	—	38.5
Employees	—	—	—	—	—	146

ELECTROLUX HOME CARE PRODUCTS NORTH AMERICA

807 N. Main St.
Bloomington, IL 61701
Phone: 309-828-2367
Fax: 309-823-5203
Web: www.eureka.com

CEO: John J. Case
CFO: Jan Wolansky
HR: —
FYE: December 31
Type: Business segment

No one knows if Fred Wardell exclaimed "Eureka!" when he came up with the idea for a vacuum company, but that's what he named it in 1909. The vacuum cleaner company stuck with its birth name right up until 2004, when it was rechristened Electrolux Home Care Products North America by its parent company, Sweden-based AB Electrolux. The company name change coincided with its reacquisition of the Electrolux name in North America. Today, the consumer products firm sells more than 130 vacuum models under the Electrolux, Sanitaire, Beam, and, yes, Eureka brands.

ELECTROLUX HOME PRODUCTS - NORTH AMERICA

250 Bobby Jones Expwy.
Augusta, GA 30907
Phone: 706-651-1751
Fax: —
Web: www.electroluxusa.com

CEO: Keith R. McLoughlin
CFO: Marty O'Gorman
HR: —
FYE: December 31
Type: Business segment

Electrolux Home Products is the North American marketing and distribution arm of Sweden-based — and #1 appliance maker — AB Electrolux. Electrolux is also a top brand in US markets. The division sells home appliances (air conditioners, refrigerators, microwave ovens, stoves, electric and gas cooktops, dishwashers, washers, dryers, vacuum cleaners) and outdoor products (lawn mowers, garden tractors, barbecue gas grills) through home improvement retailers such as Lowe's. AB Electrolux generates most of its revenue from home appliances and 35% of its 2006 sales were from North America. Brands include Electrolux, Frigidaire, Eureka, Husqvarna, Poulan, and Weed Eater.

	Annual Growth	12/03	12/04	12/05	12/06	12/07
Est. sales ($ mil.)	—	—	—	—	—	2,147.5
Employees	—	—	—	—	—	22,000

ELECTRONIC ARTS INC.

NASDAQ (GS): ERTS

209 Redwood Shores Pkwy.
Redwood City, CA 94065
Phone: 650-628-1500
Fax: 650-628-1422
Web: www.ea.com

CEO: John S. Riccitiello
CFO: Eric F. Brown
HR: Gabrielle Toledano
FYE: March 31
Type: Public

Electronic Arts (EA) has a knack for the craft of creating video games. EA is a leading video game publisher, with popular titles such as *Madden NFL*, *The Sims*, *Need for Speed*, and *Medal of Honor*. It also distributes titles for third-party labels (including *Rock Band*) and publishes games based on Hollywood franchises such as *The Lord of the Rings*, *The Godfather*, *Harry Potter*, and *Batman*. EA develops its games for PCs and console systems from Sony, Nintendo, and Microsoft. In early 2008 the company offered $2 billion to purchase Take-Two Interactive, publisher of the *Grand Theft Auto* franchise; Take-Two rejected the offer.

	Annual Growth	3/04	3/05	3/06	3/07	3/08
Sales ($ mil.)	5.5%	2,957.1	3,129.0	2,951.0	3,091.0	3,665.0
Net income ($ mil.)	—	577.3	504.0	236.0	76.0	(454.0)
Market value ($ mil.)	(0.5%)	16,193.6	16,074.6	16,689.6	15,662.0	15,874.6
Employees	13.8%	—	6,100	7,200	7,900	9,000

ELECTRONIC CLEARING HOUSE, INC.

NASDAQ (CM): ECHO

730 Paseo Camarillo
Camarillo, CA 93010
Phone: 805-419-8700
Fax: 805-419-8694
Web: www.echo-inc.com

CEO: Charles J. (Chuck) Harris
CFO: Alice L. Cheung
HR: Scott Gardner
FYE: September 30
Type: Public

This company has no sweepstakes and Ed McMahon does *not* work for it. Electronic Clearing House (ECHO) provides transaction and processing services related to credit cards, debit cards, and checks. The company's XpressCheX and National Check Network (NCN) units provide a wide range of check-related services, including authorization, guarantee, conversion, collection, and verification; the NCN database comprises positive and negative consumer checking account data from more than 250 collection agencies. Through MerchantAmerica, ECHO provides credit card, debit card, and check payment processing services to retailers and banks. In late 2007 Intuit announced plans to buy the company.

	Annual Growth	9/03	9/04	9/05	9/06	9/07
Sales ($ mil.)	17.3%	40.6	47.6	55.5	75.3	76.9
Net income ($ mil.)	—	(3.4)	2.8	1.0	2.3	(2.4)
Market value ($ mil.)	16.3%	41.4	56.4	60.9	122.8	75.9
Employees	—	—	—	—	—	239

ELECTRONIC CONTROL SECURITY INC.　　OTC: EKCS

790 Bloomfield Ave.	CEO: Arthur Barchenko
Clifton, NJ 07012	CFO: Natalie Barchenko
Phone: 973-574-8555	HR: Natalie Barchenko
Fax: 973-574-8562	FYE: June 30
Web: www.anti-terrorism.com	Type: Public

This company keeps the perimeter secure. Electronic Control Security (known as ECSI) designs, manufactures, and installs electronic integrated security systems for government and commercial facilities worldwide, including airports, military bases, nuclear power plants, pipelines, and ports. The company also provides risk assessment consulting services. ECSI operates throughout the US and in the Middle East; however, the US accounted for all of the company's 2007 sales. Major customers of ECSI include the US Department of Defense, the US Department of Energy, and the US Department of Transportation.

	Annual Growth	6/03	6/04	6/05	6/06	6/07
Sales ($ mil.)	6.8%	4.3	2.1	6.0	8.8	5.6
Net income ($ mil.)	—	(0.6)	(1.1)	(0.1)	(1.7)	(1.1)
Market value ($ mil.)	39.1%	2.7	7.3	12.2	4.8	10.0
Employees	(22.2%)	—	—	—	27	21

ELECTRONIC DATA SYSTEMS CORPORATION　　NYSE: EDS

5400 Legacy Dr.	CEO: Ronald A. (Ron) Rittenmeyer
Plano, TX 75024	CFO: Ronald P. (Ron) Vargo
Phone: 972-604-6000	HR: Tina M. Sivinski
Fax: 972-605-6033	FYE: December 31
Web: www.eds.com	Type: Public

They started it! Electronic Data Systems (EDS) pioneered the computer outsourcing business, and now it is the largest independent systems management and services provider in the US (rival IBM is #1 worldwide). EDS delivers such services as systems integration, network and systems operations, data center management, application development, and outsourcing. The company is one of the largest federal government contractors, but it also serves commercial customers in a wide range of industries, including health care, manufacturing, and transportation. Top clients include the US Navy and former parent General Motors. EDS agreed to be acquired by Hewlett-Packard for about $13.9 billion in cash in 2008.

	Annual Growth	12/03	12/04	12/05	12/06	12/07
Sales ($ mil.)	0.8%	21,476.0	20,669.0	19,757.0	21,268.0	22,134.0
Net income ($ mil.)	—	(1,698.0)	158.0	150.0	470.0	716.0
Market value ($ mil.)	(2.7%)	11,794.0	11,903.5	12,579.8	14,169.4	10,569.5
Employees	9.2%	—	—	117,000	131,000	139,500

ELECTRONIC SYSTEMS TECHNOLOGY, INC.　　OTC: ELST

415 N. Quay St., Bldg. B1	CEO: T. L. Kirchner
Kennewick, WA 99336	CFO: Jon Correio
Phone: 509-735-9092	HR: –
Fax: 509-783-5475	FYE: December 31
Web: www.esteem.com	Type: Public

Electronic Systems Technology (EST) makes wireless modems that it markets under the ESTeem brand. EST targets the modems for applications in industrial automation, the military, and public safety. The ESTeem line includes Ethernet radios that can be used for handling video and voice over Internet protocol (VoIP) transmissions. EST buys parts from Hitachi, Intersil, Integrated Microelectronics, Motorola, Mitsubishi, Murata Manufacturing, Rakon, and Toko America for its products. Assembly of EST's products is farmed out to Manufacturing Services.

	Annual Growth	12/03	12/04	12/05	12/06	12/07
Sales ($ mil.)	9.3%	2.1	2.3	2.4	2.6	3.0
Net income ($ mil.)	31.6%	0.1	0.2	0.1	0.2	0.3
Market value ($ mil.)	9.9%	3.0	4.0	3.1	3.3	4.4
Employees	—	—	—	—	—	16

ELECTRONICS FOR IMAGING INC.　　NASDAQ (GS): EFII

303 Velocity Way	CEO: Guy Gecht
Foster City, CA 94404	CFO: John Ritchie
Phone: 650-357-3500	HR: Jackie Cimino
Fax: 650-357-3907	FYE: December 31
Web: www.efi.com	Type: Public

Electronics For Imaging (EFI) wants to take control of your color. The company makes hardware and software systems for commercial and enterprise digital printing and print management. EFI's Fiery line includes stand-alone print servers, as well as print controllers that copier and printer vendors such as Canon, Konica Minolta, Ricoh, and Xerox integrate into their equipment. The company also has pacts with printing service providers such as AlphaGraphics. EFI's Print MIS software provides supply chain and customer relationship management from print job submission to fulfillment. Its inkjet products include superwide format printers (VUTEk) and industrial printers (Jetrion).

	Annual Growth	12/03	12/04	12/05	12/06	12/07
Sales ($ mil.)	13.1%	379.6	394.6	468.5	564.6	620.6
Net income ($ mil.)	0.3%	26.5	38.0	(4.1)	(0.2)	26.8
Market value ($ mil.)	(3.3%)	1,415.4	937.1	1,496.8	1,531.4	1,236.5
Employees	—	—	—	—	1,723	—

ELECTRO-SENSORS, INC.　　NASDAQ (CM): ELSE

6111 Blue Circle Dr.	CEO: Bradley D. Slye
Minnetonka, MN 55343	CFO: Bradley D. Slye
Phone: 952-930-0100	HR: Jennifer Gilyard
Fax: 952-930-0130	FYE: December 31
Web: www.electro-sensors.com	Type: Public

Electro-Sensors supports the manufacturing process with sensitive loving care. The company's Controls Division, which accounts for the bulk of sales, makes computerized systems that monitor and regulate the production speed of industrial machinery. Electro-Sensors also has an AutoData Systems unit, which makes software that reads hand-printed characters, check marks, and bar code information from scanned or faxed forms. AutoData Systems has an exclusive license to use a neural network algorithm developed by PPT Vision. Company director and secretary Peter Peterson and his family own 38% of the company.

	Annual Growth	12/03	12/04	12/05	12/06	12/07
Sales ($ mil.)	12.7%	4.4	4.8	4.9	5.8	7.1
Net income ($ mil.)	—	(0.1)	0.2	0.8	1.7	1.2
Market value ($ mil.)	10.8%	13.2	13.1	13.6	17.4	19.8
Employees	—	—	—	29	—	—

ELEGANT ILLUSIONS, INC.　　Pink Sheets: EILL

542 Lighthouse Ave., Ste. 5	CEO: James Cardinal
Pacific Grove, CA 93950	CFO: Gavin Gear
Phone: 831-649-1814	HR: James Cardinal
Fax: 831-649-1001	FYE: December 31
Web: www.elegantillusions.com	Type: Public

You can't believe all you see at Elegant Illusions, but you can believe some of it. The company operates about 15 stores in nine US states and on St. Croix, US Virgin Islands. Most sell copies of fine jewelry, although a couple sell the real thing. Elegant Illusions also has two fine jewelry stores and an art gallery in New Orleans. The fake jewelry includes different styles of rings, earrings, and pendants featuring lab-created emeralds, rubies, sapphires, and opals in 14 carat gold and white gold settings. Executives James Cardinal and the married duo of Gavin and Tamara Gear own the majority of the company. The Gears started Elegant Illusions at a former hot dog stand on Cannery Row in San Francisco.

	Annual Growth	12/03	12/04	12/05	12/06	12/07
Est. sales ($ mil.)	—	—	—	—	—	13.6
Employees	—	—	—	—	—	124

ELEMENT K CORPORATION

500 Canal View Blvd.	CEO: Paul Krause
Rochester, NY 14623	CFO: William Jacques
Phone: 585-240-7500	HR: Donna Maxwell
Fax: 585-240-7760	FYE: December 31
Web: www.elementk.com	Type: Subsidiary

Element K . . . That would be potassium, right? Element K doesn't teach chemistry, but it does offer a range of services, products, and technology geared toward learning and education for corporations, government agencies, universities, and individuals. The firm helps clients build, implement, and manage training programs that utilize print and online tools. Its more than 2,000 online courses include instructor-led classes, self-paced tutorials, and reference materials covering information technology (IT), general business, and professional courses. The company was founded in 1982 and counts Wasserstein & Co. as a major investor. In 2006 Element K was acquired by global learning solutions provider NIIT.

ELGIN NATIONAL INDUSTRIES, INC.

2001 Butterfield Rd., Ste. 1020	CEO: Fred C. Schulte
Downers Grove, IL 60515	CFO: Wayne J. Conner
Phone: 630-434-7200	HR: Lynn C. Batory
Fax: 630-434-7272	FYE: December 31
Web: www.eni.com	Type: Private

Managing more than a dozen businesses is all in a day's work for Elgin National Industries, which operates a diverse group of manufacturing and engineering services companies. Through its Manufactured Products division, the company makes highly engineered products such as centrifuges, fasteners, and electrical switch gear equipment. Its Engineering Services division provides bulk materials handling systems, as well as design, engineering, procurement, and construction management services for mineral processors. The electric utility, industrial equipment, mining, and mineral processing industries use the company's products and services. Chairman and CEO Fred Schulte owns 58% of the company.

ELI LILLY AND COMPANY

NYSE: LLY

Lilly Corporate Center, 893 S. Delaware	CEO: John C. Lechleiter
Indianapolis, IN 46285	CFO: Derica W. Rice
Phone: 317-276-2000	HR: Anthony (Tony) Murphy
Fax: –	FYE: December 31
Web: www.lilly.com	Type: Public

Eli Lilly hopes everything will come up roses for you, healthwise. Although best known for its widely popular antidepressant Prozac, the company develops medicines for a wide variety of ailments. Its top drugs include schizophrenia therapy Zyprexa, pancreatic cancer treatment Gemzar, antidepressant Cymbalta, osteoporosis medication Evista, Humalog insulin, and erectile dysfunction treatment Cialis. In addition to neurological, oncological, and diabetes drugs, the company also makes growth hormones, anti-ulcer agents, and cardiovascular therapies, as well as animal health products.

	Annual Growth	12/03	12/04	12/05	12/06	12/07
Sales ($ mil.)	10.3%	12,582.5	13,857.9	14,645.3	15,691.0	18,633.5
Net income ($ mil.)	3.6%	2,560.8	1,810.1	1,979.6	2,662.7	2,953.0
Market value ($ mil.)	(6.4%)	79,031.6	64,237.7	63,954.5	58,959.9	60,561.0
Employees	(2.4%)	—	—	42,600	41,500	40,600

ELITE MODEL MANAGEMENT CORPORATION

404 Park Ave. South, 9th Fl.	CEO: Jane Stewart
New York, NY 10016	CFO: Maureen Curtin
Phone: 212-529-9700	HR: –
Fax: 212-475-0572	FYE: December 31
Web: www.elitemodel.com	Type: Private

Who says modeling agents are a bunch of elitists? Elite Model Management does. The agency created the term "supermodel" in the 1980s and helped launch the careers of some of the world's most well-known models including Cindy Crawford, Claudia Schiffer, Naomi Campbell, and Linda Evangelista. It has more than 750 models working at some 30 agencies in such cities as Los Angeles, Milan, New York, and Paris. In 1972 John Casablancas (who has since retired) and Alain Kittler founded Elite in Paris. In 2004 its New York office filed Chapter 11 after lawsuits filed by former employees and models drained the agency of cash. Elite was subsequently purchased by investor Creative World Management for nearly $8 million.

ELITE PHARMACEUTICALS, INC.

AMEX: ELI

165 Ludlow Ave.	CEO: Bernard Berk
Northvale, NJ 07647	CFO: Marc I. Gittelman
Phone: 201-750-2646	HR: –
Fax: 201-750-2755	FYE: March 31
Web: www.elitepharma.com	Type: Public

Elite Pharmaceuticals isn't above peddling generics. Subsidiary Elite Laboratories develops generic versions of existing controlled-release drugs whose patents are about to expire. Its sole commercial product is an allergy therapeutic (Lodrane 24) marketed by ECR Pharmaceuticals. Products in various stages of testing include oxycodone pain medications, anti-infectives, and treatments for gastrointestinal disorders and cardiovascular indications. Elite Laboratories also provides contract research and development services for other drugmakers. The company has teamed with PLIVA, Inc., the US subsidiary of Croatian drugmaker PLIVA, to develop a generic anti-infective.

	Annual Growth	3/03	3/04	3/05	3/06	3/07
Sales ($ mil.)	16.4%	0.6	0.3	0.3	0.6	1.1
Net income ($ mil.)	—	(4.1)	(6.5)	(5.9)	(6.9)	(11.8)
Market value ($ mil.)	31.9%	16.1	36.2	79.3	47.8	48.9
Employees	—	—	—	—	26	—

ELIZABETH ARDEN, INC.

NASDAQ (GS): RDEN

2400 SW 145th Ave., 2nd Fl.	CEO: E. Scott Beattie
Miramar, FL 33027	CFO: Stephen J. Smith
Phone: 954-364-6900	HR: Sandy Garcia
Fax: 954-364-6910	FYE: June 30
Web: www.elizabetharden.com	Type: Public

Sweet scents are behind Elizabeth Arden's red door. The firm owns, manufactures, and licenses some 100 perfumes and distributes more than 300 fragrances to mass retailers. Scents are marketed under several brand names, including Elizabeth Arden, Red Door, 5th avenue, and White Shoulders, as well as Elizabeth Taylor's White Diamonds. It also makes and sells colognes (Halston, Wings, Grey Flannel) and skin care products (Ceramide, Millennium, Visible Difference). The firm purchased Unilever's Elizabeth Arden and Elizabeth Taylor fragrances and skin care unit in 2001 and adopted the Elizabeth Arden name. Third-party manufacturer Cosmetic Essence makes Elizabeth Arden products and a separate firm runs its salons.

	Annual Growth	1/03	1/04	*6/05	6/06	6/07
Sales ($ mil.)	10.7%	752.0	814.4	920.5	954.5	1,127.5
Net income ($ mil.)	19.8%	18.1	2.0	37.6	32.8	37.3
Market value ($ mil.)	32.5%	225.2	506.2	684.3	67.6	694.1
Employees	13.8%	1,800	—	2,350	2,650	—

*Fiscal year change

ELKAY MANUFACTURING COMPANY

2222 Camden Ct.
Oak Brook, IL 60523
Phone: 630-574-8484
Fax: 630-574-5012
Web: www.elkay.com

CEO: Ronald C. (Ron) Katz
CFO: Timothy J. (Tim) Bondy
HR: Walter E. Reilly
FYE: December 31
Type: Private

Someone's in the kitchen with Dinah, and it's Elkay Manufacturing. Elkay makes sinks, cabinets, drinking fountains, faucets, water coolers, and water filtration products. The family-owned company sells residential and commercial stainless steel sinks under such names as Celebrity, Lustertone, and Gourmet. It also offers kitchen accessories (colanders, cutting boards, soap dispensers). Elkay began making cabinets in 1993. Brands include Yorktowne, Medallion, and MasterCraft. Elkay is the parent of a dozen privately held companies and one joint venture, Elkay Pacific Rim (water dispensing). Elkay Manufacturing was founded in 1920 by the Katz family to make sinks for butlers' pantries and sculleries.

ELLEN TRACY LLC

575 7th Ave.
New York, NY 10018
Phone: 212-944-6999
Fax: 212-398-1678
Web: www.ellentracy.com

CEO: Mark Mendelson
CFO: Yoram Arieven
HR: –
FYE: December 31
Type: Private

Selling fashion for success, not excess, Ellen Tracy dresses professional women in clothing known for its comfort and conservative stylishness. The Ellen Tracy label adorns business attire, dresses, and evening wear in regular and large sizes sold at better department stores, on the Internet, and at one flagship store. The firm also offers sportswear and footwear under the Company label and company B®and Matter licenses the Ellen Tracy name. Its markets included Canada, Germany, Japan, Spain, and the US before it was purchased from Liz Claiborne in April 2008 by investors Windsong Brands and Hilco Consumer Capital, along with Radius Partners and Barry Sternlicht, former Starwood Hotels chief executive.

	Annual Growth	12/03	12/04	12/05	12/06	12/07
Est. sales ($ mil.)	—	—	—	—	—	4.1
Employees	—	—	—	—	—	130

THE ELMIRA SAVINGS BANK, FSB

NASDAQ (CM): ESBK

333 E. Water St.
Elmira, NY 14901
Phone: 607-734-3374
Fax: 607-732-4007
Web: www.elmirasavingsbank.com

CEO: Michael P. Hosey
CFO: Thomas M. Carr
HR: Bradley V. Serva
FYE: December 31
Type: Public

The Elmira Savings Bank is a community bank that serves individuals and small to midsized businesses through about a dozen offices in upstate New York's Chemung, Cayuga, Steuben, and Tompkins counties and in northern Pennsylvania's Tioga County. The bank offers traditional retail services such as savings, checking, NOW, and money market accounts; certificates of deposit; and IRAs. For businesses, Elmira offers commercial and construction mortgages; development and SBA loans; and lines of credit. For individuals, it originates auto and RV, home equity, and personal loans. Elmira Savings Bank bought four bank branches in central New York from First Niagara Financial Group in 2007.

	Annual Growth	12/03	12/04	12/05	12/06	12/07
Est. sales ($ mil.)	—	—	—	—	—	5.1
Employees	—	—	—	—	—	105

E-LOAN, INC.

6230 Stoneridge Mall Rd.
Pleasanton, CA 94588
Phone: 925-847-6200
Fax: 925-847-0831
Web: www.eloan.com

CEO: Mark E. Lefanowicz
CFO: Darren Nelson
HR: Ro Carbone
FYE: December 31
Type: Subsidiary

E-LOAN wants to E-LIMINATE the hassles associated with borrowing money. A direct-to-consumer lender, E-LOAN offers visitors the opportunity to search and apply for thousands of loans on its Web site. E-LOAN offers home mortgage loans, as well as home equity and refinance, auto, debt consolidation, student, and unsecured personal loans. It also offers access to credit cards, savings accounts, and CDs. Since the company was launched in 1997, it has originated and sold more than $30 billion in consumer loans. Puerto Rico-based Popular acquired E-LOAN in 2005.

	Annual Growth	12/03	12/04	12/05	12/06	12/07
Est. sales ($ mil.)	—	—	—	—	—	147.0
Employees	—	—	—	—	—	1,000

ELOYALTY CORPORATION

NASDAQ (GM): ELOY

150 Field Dr., Ste. 250
Lake Forest, IL 60045
Phone: 847-582-7000
Fax: 847-582-7001
Web: www.eloyaltyco.com

CEO: Kelly D. Conway
CFO: Christopher B. (Chris) Min
HR: –
FYE: December 31
Type: Public

eLoyalty hopes its services and tools make customers feel like eRoyalty. The company is a customer relationship management (CRM) services provider. It offers management consulting, systems integration, and managed services aimed at developing and implementing strategies. eLoyalty's services are designed to integrate customer contacts generated from a variety of sources, including information gathered from e-mails, call centers, field sales, and Internet channels. It also offers systems designed to measure financial and operating metrics associated with CRM programs.

	Annual Growth	12/03	12/04	12/05	12/06	12/07
Sales ($ mil.)	13.0%	62.6	72.6	79.0	89.8	102.1
Net income ($ mil.)	—	(18.3)	(5.9)	(7.6)	(11.1)	(18.7)
Market value ($ mil.)	47.4%	25.9	43.6	78.3	170.2	122.5
Employees	9.2%	—	—	373	406	445

ELXSI CORPORATION

Pink Sheets: ELXS

3600 Rio Vista Ave., Ste. A
Orlando, FL 32805
Phone: 407-849-1090
Fax: 407-849-0625
Web: www.bickfords.com

CEO: Alexander M. (Sandy) Milley
CFO: David M. Doolittle
HR: Kenneth Allen
FYE: December 31
Type: Public

This restaurant operator comes with a side of technology. ELXSI Corporation's hospitality division operates about 30 family-style restaurants in New England, while its CUES division manufactures sewer inspection equipment. The eateries operate under the Bickford's Grille brand and offer casual dining with an emphasis on breakfast items served throughout the day. Its equipment manufacturing operation makes remote-control video cameras and robotic cutting devices used by municipalities and contractors. ELXSI is controlled by chairman and CEO Alexander Milley.

	Annual Growth	12/00	12/01	12/02	12/03	*12/04
Sales ($ mil.)	(1.8%)	103.7	105.4	98.8	98.7	96.3
Net income ($ mil.)	—	13.1	(6.5)	(3.6)	(0.3)	(14.5)
Employees	(8.6%)	3,040	2,848	2,719	—	2,119

*Most recent year available

An in-depth profile of this company is available to Hoover's Online members at hoovers.com.

551

EMACHINES, INC.

7565 Irvine Center Dr.
Irvine, CA 92618
Phone: 949-471-7000
Fax: 949-471-7041
Web: www.emachines.com

CEO: J. Edward (Ed) Coleman
CFO: John P. Goldsberry
HR: Lazane Smith
FYE: December 31
Type: Subsidiary

eMachines sees value in the PC market. Acquired by Gateway in 2004, eMachines now represents Gateway's value brand. eMachine products include personal computers and peripheral displays. Marketed toward budget-conscious consumers, its desktop and notebook PCs are sold by retailers such as Best Buy, Circuit City, and Office Depot. Former rival Gateway purchased eMachines for approximately $235 million in cash and stock. After the acquisition Gateway closed its retail stores and installed a number of eMachines executives in top management posts. eMachine products are sold exclusively through retailers.

	Annual Growth	12/03	12/04	12/05	12/06	12/07
Est. sales ($ mil.)	—	—	—	—	—	2,147.5
Employees	—	—	—	—	—	134

EMAGEON INC.

NASDAQ (GM): EMAG

1200 Corporate Dr., Ste. 200
Birmingham, AL 35242
Phone: 205-980-9222
Fax: 205-980-9815
Web: www.emageon.com

CEO: Charles A. (Chuck) Jett Jr.
CFO: John W. Wilhoite
HR: –
FYE: December 31
Type: Public

When you go to the hospital to get a picture taken of your gall bladder, Emageon wants to make sure that picture leaves nothing to your doctor's imagination. The company develops clinical analysis and medical image management software that helps doctors view, manipulate, and store medical images for diagnosis, disease screening, and therapy planning. In case two dimensions of your gall bladder aren't enough, Emageon's Web-enabled software lets physicians view it in 3-D and compare the picture with other images. Counting more than 250 hospitals as customers, the company targets health care organizations ranging from stand-alone imaging centers to large hospital systems.

	Annual Growth	12/03	12/04	12/05	12/06	12/07
Sales ($ mil.)	45.6%	23.3	45.8	73.8	123.5	104.6
Net income ($ mil.)	—	(11.4)	(10.5)	(5.0)	(6.0)	(7.1)
Market value ($ mil.)	(48.4%)	—	—	325.2	326.5	86.5
Employees	(59.2%)	—	—	469	—	78

EMAGIN CORPORATION

OTC: EMAN

10500 NE 8th St., Ste. 1400
Bellevue, WA 98004
Phone: 425-749-3600
Fax: 425-749-3601
Web: www.emagin.com

CEO: Thomas Paulsen
CFO: Paul Campbell
HR: –
FYE: December 31
Type: Public

eMagin is imagining eye-opening technology. The company develops virtual imaging and organic light-emitting diodes (OLEDs) that can be used in applications ranging from wearable PCs and virtual imaging devices to more mundane products such as DVD headset systems, video games, and high-definition televisions. The technology also extends to military use. eMagin's products use microcircuits and displays to magnify images of text or video. Subsidiary Virtual Vision develops near-eye and virtual image display products, including headset viewer systems. eMagin markets to OEMs and directly to customers in the government, industrial, and medical sectors.

	Annual Growth	12/03	12/04	12/05	12/06	12/07
Sales ($ mil.)	61.1%	2.6	3.6	3.7	8.2	17.5
Net income ($ mil.)	—	(4.7)	(12.7)	(16.5)	(15.3)	(18.5)
Market value ($ mil.)	(59.3%)	589.2	947.7	569.8	11.5	16.2
Employees	(31.6%)	—	—	98	67	—

EMAK WORLDWIDE, INC.

NASDAQ (CM): EMAK

6330 San Vicente Blvd.
Los Angeles, CA 90048
Phone: 323-932-4300
Fax: 323-932-4400
Web: emak.com

CEO: James L. (Jim) Holbrook Jr.
CFO: Michael W. (Mike) Sanders
HR: Duane V. Johnson
FYE: December 31
Type: Public

Marketer EMAK Worldwide has a few notions about promotions. The company plans and implements promotional programs using licensed popular characters from studios such as Warner Bros. and Universal. It then designs and arranges for the manufacturing of a variety of items, such as figurines and plush toys, for its clients' campaigns. Promotional items account for more than 75% of the company's sales; one customer, Burger King, accounts for about half of sales. To supplement its promotions offerings, EMAK has expanded its marketing services to include event and collaborative marketing, as well as retail and environmental design services.

	Annual Growth	12/03	12/04	12/05	12/06	12/07
Sales ($ mil.)	(7.0%)	219.1	236.7	223.4	181.4	164.2
Net income ($ mil.)	—	7.9	(9.7)	(39.9)	(2.3)	(7.6)
Market value ($ mil.)	(48.5%)	80.2	57.6	39.3	34.5	5.6
Employees	(10.7%)	—	—	383	342	—

EMBARCADERO TECHNOLOGIES, INC.

100 California St., Ste. 1200
San Francisco, CA 94111
Phone: 415-834-3131
Fax: 415-434-1721
Web: www.embarcadero.com

CEO: Raj P. Sabhlok
CFO: Michael Shahbazian
HR: Lorraine C. Gnecco
FYE: December 31
Type: Private

Thinking of embarking on a database development adventure? Embarcadero Technologies wants to be along for the ride. The company makes data lifecycle management software used to build, test, and manage application infrastructure and databases for large corporations. Embarcadero's software is used by customers in a variety of industries, including telecommunications, technology, financial services, and government agencies. Former chairman, president, and CEO Stephen Wong, who retired in January 2007, owns about 20% of the company. After several false starts, private equity group Thoma Cressey Bravo acquired Embarcadero in mid-2007 for about $200 million and took it private.

	Annual Growth	12/02	12/03	12/04	12/05	12/06
Sales ($ mil.)	5.0%	49.3	51.9	56.3	57.5	60.0
Net income ($ mil.)	24.7%	2.4	5.7	2.0	4.3	5.8
Employees	(6.5%)	290	274	283	288	222

EMBARQ CORPORATION

NYSE: EQ

5454 W. 110th St.
Overland Park, KS 66211
Phone: 913-323-4637
Fax: –
Web: www.embarq.com

CEO: Thomas A. (Tom) Gerke
CFO: Gene M. Betts
HR: E. J. Holland Jr.
FYE: December 31
Type: Public

Embarq splits its operations in two primary segments: telecommunications (voice, data, high-speed Internet, and wireless) and logistics (product sales to third parties). The company has about 4 million residential and 2 million business lines dedicated to local service. It also offers long-distance and high-speed Internet access (1.3 million customers) to consumers and businesses. Embarq offers wireless phone services through a partnership with former parent Sprint Nextel and it makes sales to wholesale customers. Subsidiary EMBARQ Logistics distributes plant equipment, telephones, and network access equipment and provides configuration services to other carriers. The company's service areas span 18 US states.

	Annual Growth	12/03	12/04	12/05	12/06	12/07
Sales ($ mil.)	1.2%	—	6,139.0	6,254.0	6,363.0	6,365.0
Net income ($ mil.)	(9.4%)	—	917.0	878.0	784.0	683.0
Market value ($ mil.)	(3.6%)	—	—	—	7,868.2	7,583.0
Employees	(10.0%)	—	—	—	20,000	18,000

EMC CORPORATION

NYSE: EMC

176 South St.
Hopkinton, MA 01748
Phone: 508-435-1000
Fax: 508-555-1212
Web: www.emc.com

CEO: Joseph M. (Joe) Tucci
CFO: David I. Goulden
HR: John T. (Jack) Mollen
FYE: December 31
Type: Public

EMC has braced itself for an all-out raid. Long a leading provider of RAID (redundant array of independent disks) storage systems, the company has its hands full trying to stay a step ahead in a crowded market. Banks, manufacturers, Internet service providers, retailers, and government agencies use EMC's systems to store and retrieve massive amounts of data. The company also sells a line of network attached storage (NAS) file servers, and a wide array of software designed to manage, protect, and share data. EMC sells its products directly and through distributors and manufacturers. Its biggest resale partner, Dell, sells co-branded EMC systems.

	Annual Growth	12/03	12/04	12/05	12/06	12/07
Sales ($ mil.)	20.7%	6,236.8	8,229.5	9,664.0	11,155.1	13,230.2
Net income ($ mil.)	35.4%	496.1	871.2	1,133.2	1,224.0	1,665.7
Market value ($ mil.)	5.7%	31,198.4	34,838.7	32,472.1	28,014.9	38,953.5
Employees	19.3%	—	—	26,500	31,100	37,700

EMC INSURANCE GROUP INC.

NASDAQ (GS): EMCI

717 Mulberry St.
Des Moines, IA 50309
Phone: 515-345-2902
Fax: 515-345-2895
Web: www.emcins.com

CEO: Bruce G. Kelley
CFO: Mark E. Reese
HR: –
FYE: December 31
Type: Public

EMC Insurance Group may be publicly traded, but in its heart it's a mutual insurance company. Subsidiaries EMCASCO Insurance, Illinois EMCASCO, and Dakota Fire Insurance sell property/casualty lines including automobile, property, liability, and workers' compensation insurance, primarily to small and medium-sized businesses. EMC Underwriters offers excess and surplus lines of insurance. EMC Reinsurance sells property/casualty treaty reinsurance. The group operates throughout the US, primarily in the Midwest; Iowa accounts for nearly 15% of premiums. Employers Mutual Casualty, a multiple-line property/casualty insurance company, owns 57% of EMC Insurance Group.

	Annual Growth	12/03	12/04	12/05	12/06	12/07
Assets ($ mil.)	7.5%	899.7	934.8	1,113.7	1,206.2	1,202.7
Net income ($ mil.)	20.1%	20.4	13.2	43.0	53.5	42.5
Market value ($ mil.)	7.6%	243.1	293.6	272.0	468.9	326.1
Employees	—	—	—	—	0	—

EMCLAIRE FINANCIAL CORP.

OTC: EMCF

612 Main St.
Emlenton, PA 16373
Phone: 724-867-2311
Fax: 724-867-1614
Web: www.emclairefinancial.com

CEO: David L. Cox
CFO: William C. Marsh
HR: –
FYE: December 31
Type: Public

Money may not grow on trees, but Emclaire Financial is the holding company for the Farmers National Bank of Emlenton. The institution operates about a dozen bank branches in west-central Pennsylvania and offers standard retail products and services, including checking and savings accounts, money market accounts, and CDs. The bank's loan portfolio consists largely of real estate loans; to a lesser extent, it makes business and consumer loans. Emclaire Financial offers investment advisory services through Farmers Financial Services, a partnership with Blue Vase Securities. It is acquiring the Elk County Savings and Loan Association.

	Annual Growth	12/03	12/04	12/05	12/06	12/07
Assets ($ mil.)	4.4%	262.5	273.4	275.5	300.6	311.7
Net income ($ mil.)	1.9%	2.5	2.6	2.6	2.0	2.7
Market value ($ mil.)	0.0%	32.6	33.3	33.7	37.1	32.6
Employees	—	—	—	—	—	—

EMCOR GROUP, INC.

NYSE: EME

301 Merritt Seven Corporate Park, 6th Fl.
Norwalk, CT 06851
Phone: 203-849-7800
Fax: 203-849-7900
Web: www.emcorgroup.com

CEO: Frank T. MacInnis
CFO: Mark A. Pompa
HR: –
FYE: December 31
Type: Public

The core of EMCOR Group is electrical and mechanical construction. One of the world's largest specialty construction firms, EMCOR designs, installs, operates, and maintains complex mechanical and electrical systems. These include systems for power generation and distribution, lighting, voice and data communications, plumbing, and heating, ventilation, and air-conditioning (HVAC). It also provides facilities services, including management and maintenance support. Through about 70 subsidiaries and joint ventures, the company serves various commercial, industrial, institutional, and utility customers. EMCOR operates primarily in the US (more than three-fourths of sales), Canada, and the UK.

	Annual Growth	12/03	12/04	12/05	12/06	12/07
Sales ($ mil.)	6.9%	4,534.6	4,747.9	4,714.5	5,021.0	5,927.1
Net income ($ mil.)	57.5%	20.6	33.2	60.0	86.6	126.8
Market value ($ mil.)	74.8%	165.0	172.1	525.1	904.7	1,540.6
Employees	5.6%	—	—	26,000	27,000	29,000

EMCORE CORPORATION

NASDAQ (GM): EMKR

10420 Research Rd. SE
Albuquerque, NM 87123
Phone: 505-332-5000
Fax: 505-332-5038
Web: www.emcore.com

CEO: Hong Q. Hou
CFO: Adam Gushard
HR: Monica Van Berkel
FYE: September 30
Type: Public

EMCORE is both compound and complex. The company's offerings include compound semiconductors — chips made from compound materials, such as gallium arsenide (GaAs) and gallium nitride (GaN), rather than silicon. Compound semiconductors are used in high-tech devices, including photovoltaic solar cells and optical components for high-speed telecommunications networks. EMCORE's customers include Alcatel-Lucent, Boeing, Cisco Systems, General Dynamics, Hewlett-Packard, Intel, Lockheed Martin, Motorola, Sycamore Networks, Tellabs, and the US government (13% of sales). The company draws about three-quarters of its sales from customers in North America.

	Annual Growth	9/03	9/04	9/05	9/06	9/07
Sales ($ mil.)	10.7%	113.1	93.1	127.6	143.5	169.6
Net income ($ mil.)	—	(38.5)	(13.4)	(13.1)	54.9	(58.7)
Market value ($ mil.)	46.2%	109.7	92.5	293.8	300.8	501.6
Employees	(0.4%)	749	588	650	750	738

EMD CHEMICALS INC.

480 S. Democrat Rd.
Gibbstown, NJ 08027
Phone: 856-423-6300
Fax: 856-423-4389
Web: www.emdchemicals.com

CEO: Meiken Krebs
CFO: Kathie Lamb
HR: Cliff Pettinelli
FYE: December 31
Type: Subsidiary

EMD Chemicals Inc. is the North American unit of German pharmaceutical giant Merck KGaA (not to be confused with American pharmaceutical giant Merck & Co. — they're separate and unrelated and have been so since 1917). EMD Chemicals specializes in producing pigments for automotive, packaging, plastics, and printing applications. The company is the result of the 2003 combination of four Merck divisions. It now operates through five units: Industrial Pigments, Rona (raw ingredients for cosmetics), Analytics and Reagents, Life Science Solutions (ingredients and services for pharmaceutical makers), and Optics (chemicals and raw materials for monocrystals and fiber optics).

	Annual Growth	12/03	12/04	12/05	12/06	12/07
Est. sales ($ mil.)	—	—	—	—	—	346.9
Employees	—	—	—	—	—	700

An in-depth profile of this company is available to Hoover's Online members at hoovers.com.

553

EMD SERONO, INC

1 Technology Place
Rockland, MA 02370
Phone: 781-982-9000
Fax: –
Web: www.emdserono.com

CEO: Fereydoun Firouz
CFO: –
HR: Andrew Suchoff
FYE: December 31
Type: Subsidiary

EMD Serono (formerly Serono) is serious when it comes to fighting disease. The company develops a variety of recombinant prescription medicines used in the treatment of neurological, fertility, and metabolic disorders and diseases such as multiple sclerosis, Lupus, and HIV. EMD Serono markets products such as Gonal-f, Luveris, Ovridel, Rebif, and Zorbtive in the US. The company is a subsidiary of Merck Serono, which has research facilities in France, Italy, Switzerland, and the US. EMD Serono has also begun to develop an oncology arm of its research.

	Annual Growth	12/03	12/04	12/05	12/06	12/07
Est. sales ($ mil.)	—	—	—	—	—	78.8
Employees	—	—	—	—	—	623

EMERGENCY FILTRATION PRODUCTS, INC.

Pink Sheets: EMFP

175 Cassia Way, Ste. A115
Henderson, NV 89014
Phone: 702-558-5164
Fax: 702-567-1893
Web: www.emergencyfiltration.com

CEO: Philip Dascher
CFO: Steve M. Hanni
HR: –
FYE: December 31
Type: Public

Emergency Filtration Products masks out germs. The company develops and manufactures CPR and environmental masks, replacement filters, and other related products designed to remove infectious bacteria and viruses from the air flow. The company's product line includes the NanoMask personal environmental mask, the RespAide CPR Isolation mask, and BVM (bag valve mask) filters. Its Superstat product provides clotting of the blood for surgery and wound care. Products under development include breathing circuit filters for ventilation and respiratory equipment and a BMV emergency life support device.

	Annual Growth	12/02	12/03	12/04	12/05	*12/06
Sales ($ mil.)	27.8%	0.3	0.8	0.4	0.6	0.8
Net income ($ mil.)	—	(1.1)	(0.7)	(1.6)	(1.6)	(5.5)
Employees	(25.3%)	—	12	4	25	5

*Most recent year available

EMERGENCY MEDICAL SERVICES CORPORATION

NYSE: EMS

6200 S. Syracuse Way, Ste. 200
Greenwood Village, CO 80111
Phone: 303-495-1200
Fax: 303-495-1466
Web: www.emsc.net

CEO: William A. (Bill) Sanger
CFO: Randel G. (Randy) Owen
HR: Kimberly Norman
FYE: December 31
Type: Public

Municipalities and hospitals can't call 911 when they have an emergency — but they can call Emergency Medical Services Corporation. The holding company is the parent of AMR Inc., the largest private ambulance service in the US, and EmCare Holdings, a leading medical staffing firm that specializes in filling the emergency room with doctors and nurses. AMR has approximately 3,100 contracts with clients (cities, government agencies, health care providers, and insurance companies) in more than 35 states for emergency and non-emergency transport services, and operates dispatch centers in some communities. EmCare provides staffing services to about 400 hospitals and physician groups in 40 states.

	Annual Growth	12/03	12/04	12/05	12/06	12/07
Sales ($ mil.)	12.8%	—	—	1,655.5	1,934.2	2,107.0
Net income ($ mil.)	72.5%	—	—	20.1	39.1	59.8
Market value ($ mil.)	48.4%	—	—	123.9	194.3	272.9
Employees	(1.7%)	—	—	18,644	18,038	18,015

EMERGENT BIOSOLUTIONS INC.

NYSE: EBS

2273 Research Blvd., Ste. 400
Rockville, MD 20850
Phone: 301-795-1800
Fax: 301-795-1899
Web: www.emergentbiosolutions.com

CEO: Fuad El-Hibri
CFO: R. Don Elsey
HR: –
FYE: December 31
Type: Public

Emergent BioSolutions protects your thorax against anthrax. Emergent BioSolutions develops and produces, for government and commercial markets, drugs that treat or protect against infectious diseases and bio-agents. The company supplies BioThrax (the US's only FDA-approved anthrax vaccine) primarily to the departments of Defense and Health and Human Services (HHS). Its biodefense unit is also developing a post-exposure treatment for anthrax and a preventive vaccine for botulinum toxin. For commercial markets, Emergent is working on therapies and vaccines for typhoid, Group B strep, and hepatitis B, among other things. Chairman and CEO Fuad El-Hibri controls more than half of the company.

	Annual Growth	12/03	12/04	12/05	12/06	12/07
Sales ($ mil.)	34.6%	55.8	83.5	130.7	152.7	182.9
Net income ($ mil.)	50.2%	4.5	11.5	15.8	22.8	22.9
Market value ($ mil.)	(51.1%)	—	—	—	308.0	150.5
Employees	7.3%	400	—	—	494	—

EMERGING VISION, INC.

OTC: ISEE

100 Quentin Roosevelt Blvd.
Garden City, NY 11530
Phone: 516-390-2100
Fax: –
Web: www.emergingvision.com

CEO: Christopher G. Payan
CFO: Brian P. Alessi
HR: Laura Hoffman
FYE: December 31
Type: Public

It's all coming back into focus at Emerging Vision. The firm owns and franchises some 160 optical outlets under the Sterling Optical, Site For Sore Eyes, Kindy Optical, and Singer Specs names in about 15 states, the District of Columbia, the US Virgin Islands, and Canada. All but 11 of the locations are franchised. The company also runs a specialized HMO (VisionCare of California). Refocusing on its optical operations to boost brand awareness, Emerging Vision has scrapped plans to sell its chain of retail stores and establish itself as an online supply chain serving optical businesses. Former director Benito Fernandez, who launched a 2004 proxy battle for the company, owns about 54% of the firm.

	Annual Growth	12/03	12/04	12/05	12/06	12/07
Sales ($ mil.)	37.2%	14.0	14.5	14.0	21.7	49.6
Net income ($ mil.)	—	(3.0)	0.9	0.3	1.9	0.4
Employees	0.4%	132	124	128	146	134

EMERITUS CORPORATION

AMEX: ESC

3131 Elliott Ave., Ste. 500
Seattle, WA 98121
Phone: 206-298-2909
Fax: 206-301-4500
Web: www.emeritus.com

CEO: Daniel R. Baty
CFO: Raymond R. Brandstrom
HR: –
FYE: December 31
Type: Public

The Emeritus Corporation honors the retirement set. The company operates assisted-living communities for senior citizens who don't need the more intensive care provided by nursing homes, but may need some help with daily activities such as feeding, bathing, housekeeping, and managing their medications. Emeritus' communities also organize social and recreational activities for residents, and most of them provide special services (called Join Their Journey programs) to support residents with Alzheimer's disease or other forms of dementia. Emeritus Corporation owns, leases, or manages more than 250 communities in about 35 states across the US.

	Annual Growth	12/03	12/04	12/05	12/06	12/07
Sales ($ mil.)	27.5%	206.7	317.9	387.7	421.9	545.6
Net income ($ mil.)	—	(8.1)	(40.5)	12.3	(14.6)	(48.7)
Market value ($ mil.)	84.6%	84.5	139.5	345.4	471.3	981.6
Employees	37.7%	—	—	8,548	—	16,205

EMERSON ELECTRIC CO.

NYSE: EMR

PO Box 4100, 8000 W. Florissant Ave.
St. Louis, MO 63136
Phone: 314-553-2000
Fax: 314-553-3527
Web: www.gotoemerson.com

CEO: David N. Farr
CFO: Walter J. Galvin
HR: Philip A. Hutchison
FYE: September 30
Type: Public

Ralph Waldo Emerson wrote, "Work and acquire, and thou hast chained the wheel of Chance." Emerson Electric would agree. The company, generally known as just Emerson, makes a host of electrical, electromechanical, and electronic products, many of which are used to control gases, liquids, and electricity. Emerson has pursued an active, aggressive acquisition strategy (with select divestitures along the way) in building up its global business with dozens of subsidiaries. The company has gathered its 60-plus business units and divisions under eight Emerson Brands. The US accounts for about half of sales. As old Ralph Waldo once said, "Make yourself necessary to somebody," and Emerson Electric follows that adage.

	Annual Growth	9/03	9/04	9/05	9/06	9/07
Sales ($ mil.)	12.8%	13,958.0	15,615.0	17,305.0	20,133.0	22,572.0
Net income ($ mil.)	18.3%	1,089.0	1,257.0	1,422.0	1,845.0	2,136.0
Market value ($ mil.)	39.5%	11,086.9	12,979.2	14,742.4	16,870.4	41,960.5
Employees	6.6%	106,700	107,800	114,200	127,800	137,700

EMERSON HOSPITAL

133 Old Rd. to Nine Acre Corner
Concord, MA 01742
Phone: 978-369-1400
Fax: 978-287-3674
Web: www.emersonhospital.org

CEO: Christine C. Schuster
CFO: –
HR: Eric Stastny
FYE: September 30
Type: Not-for-profit

Emerson Hospital fills a big hole for a small facility. With about 180 beds, the community hospital is staffed by some 270 doctors and specialists and provides medical services to about 300,000 individuals in the 25 towns in the Concord, Massachusetts region. The facility runs the Emerson Hospital-Massachusetts General Hospital (MGH) Radiation Oncology Program, which is housed within its Bethke Cancer Center. The hospital, founded in 1911, also operates outpatient clinics serving residents in nearby communities such as Groton, Sudbury, and Westford.

	Annual Growth	9/03	9/04	9/05	9/06	9/07
Est. sales ($ mil.)	—	—	—	—	—	67.4
Employees	—	—	—	—	—	1,450

EMERSON RADIO CORP.

AMEX: MSN

9 Entin Rd.
Parsippany, NJ 07054
Phone: 973-884-2098
Fax: 973-428-2010
Web: www.emersonradio.com

CEO: Adrian C. C. Ma
CFO: Greenfield Pitts
HR: –
FYE: Friday nearest March 31
Type: Public

Emerson Radio caters to the crowd that thinks a new stereo shouldn't cost an arm and a leg. The company designs and distributes a wide range of consumer electronics that are sold primarily at mass merchants, such as Wal-Mart and Target, and toy retailers under the Emerson and H.H. Scott brand names. Emerson's products include portable and shelf stereo systems, DVD players, VCRs, home theater systems, microwave ovens, and clocks. In 2006 the company launched a line of iPod compatible devices. Former CEO Geoffrey Jurick sold much of his stock to Hong Kong-based Grande Holdings Limited, which now owns about half of Emerson Radio's common stock.

	Annual Growth	3/03	3/04	3/05	3/06	3/07
Sales ($ mil.)	(4.9%)	347.8	263.8	320.7	233.8	284.4
Net income ($ mil.)	(36.5%)	21.5	(1.1)	5.9	16.6	3.5
Market value ($ mil.)	(17.6%)	188.6	101.7	95.8	101.2	86.8
Employees	(69.7%)	—	—	379	115	—

EMI MUSIC PUBLISHING

1290 Avenue of the Americas, 42nd Fl.
New York, NY 10104
Phone: 212-492-1200
Fax: 212-492-1865
Web: www.emimusicpub.com

CEO: Roger Faxon
CFO: Leo Corbett
HR: Anne Roche
FYE: March 31
Type: Business segment

EMI Music Publishing is looking after the business part of the music business. The division of UK-based recording giant EMI Group is the world's largest music publisher, administering the rights to more than a million songs. Its collection includes classics and standards such as "Blue Moon," "I Left My Heart in San Francisco," and "Santa Claus Is Comin' to Town," as well as more recent hits including "Crazy in Love," "Genie in a Bottle," and "Smells Like Teen Spirit." The company collects royalties for including its songs on CDs, as well as live performance fees. EMI Music Publishing also licenses its music for use in movies, television shows, and advertising.

	Annual Growth	3/02	3/03	3/04	3/05	3/06
Sales ($ mil.)	5.3%	593.6	631.4	726.5	752.8	729.9
Employees	0.2%	626	649	623	629	—

EMIGRANT BANK

5 E. 42nd St.
New York, NY 10017
Phone: 212-850-4521
Fax: 212-850-4372
Web: www.emigrant.com

CEO: Howard P. Milstein
CFO: –
HR: –
FYE: December 31
Type: Private

Emigrant Bank has built its business around the huddled masses longing to save. The bank, which also has four regional Emigrant Savings Bank affiliates in the Bronx, Brooklyn, Queens, and Long Island, serves customers in the New York metropolitan area from 35 branches. It also offers online banking to customers nationwide through its EmigrantDirect service. The bank provides standard products such as checking, savings, and money market accounts, CDs, IRAs, credit and debit cards, investments, and life insurance. New York Private Bank & Trust is Emigrant Bank's wealth management division. Emigrant Mortgage originates home loans in some 20 states.

	Annual Growth	12/02	12/03	12/04	12/05	12/06
Sales ($ mil.)	19.8%	—	—	—	533.7	639.5
Employees	(8.8%)	—	—	—	848	773

EMISPHERE TECHNOLOGIES, INC.

NASDAQ (GM): EMIS

240 Cedar Knolls Rd.
Cedar Knolls, NJ 07927
Phone: 973-532-8000
Fax: 914-347-2498
Web: www.emisphere.com

CEO: Michael V. Novinski
CFO: Michael R. (Mike) Garone
HR: –
FYE: December 31
Type: Public

Needle prick, be gone. Development-stage Emisphere Technologies is offering an alternative to traditional injection of certain drugs with an oral drug delivery technology called eligen, which is designed to improve the way certain therapeutic molecules (such as proteins, carbohydrates, and peptides) are administered to and absorbed by the body. With collaborative partners, including Novartis, Roche, and Genta, Emisphere is developing oral formulations that incorporate eligen to deliver drugs that treat such health problems as osteoporosis, diabetes, growth disorders, and cardiovascular disease. Emisphere was formed in 1986.

	Annual Growth	12/03	12/04	12/05	12/06	12/07
Sales ($ mil.)	78.9%	0.4	2.0	3.5	7.3	4.1
Net income ($ mil.)	—	(44.9)	(37.5)	(18.0)	(41.8)	(16.9)
Market value ($ mil.)	(4.3%)	98.7	77.2	101.5	149.4	82.8
Employees	—	—	—	118	—	—

An in-depth profile of this company is available to Hoover's Online members at hoovers.com.

EMMIS COMMUNICATIONS CORPORATION

NASDAQ (GS): EMMS

1 Emmis Plaza, 40 Monument Circle, Ste. 700	CEO: Jeffrey H. (Jeff) Smulyan
Indianapolis, IN 46204	CFO: Patrick M. Walsh
Phone: 317-266-0100	HR: Michael (Mickey) Levitan
Fax: 317-631-3750	FYE: Last day in February
Web: www.emmis.com	Type: Public

Emmis Communications is a leading diversified media company with operations in publishing and radio. It owns and operates more than 20 radio stations serving more than a half dozen markets in the US, including clusters of stations in Chicago, Los Angeles, and New York City. Emmis also owns Network Indiana, which syndicates programming to more than 70 affiliate stations, and it has radio stations in Belgium and other parts of Europe. In addition to broadcasting, the company owns a portfolio of regional magazines and specialty publications, including *Atlanta, Los Angeles,* and *Texas Monthly.* CEO Jeffrey Smulyan has about 70% voting control of the company.

	Annual Growth	2/04	2/05	2/06	2/07	2/08
Sales ($ mil.)	(14.6%)	679.9	618.5	387.4	359.5	361.2
Net income ($ mil.)	—	2.3	(304.4)	357.8	113.6	(1.4)
Market value ($ mil.)	(48.4%)	1,275.9	965.3	528.0	267.1	90.6
Employees	(2.1%)	—	—	1,940	1,900	—

EMPI, INC.

599 Cardigan Rd.	CEO: Donald D. Dumoulin
St. Paul, MN 55126	CFO: Tina Eskrow
Phone: 651-415-9000	HR: Anna Skar
Fax: 651-414-7414	FYE: December 31
Web: www.empi.com	Type: Subsidiary

Empi would probably feel empty if it wasn't able to ease the pain of patients. The company markets a wide range of medical products, including non-pharmaceutical pain management and rehabilitative electrotherapy devices. Its devices use low level electrical stimulation to acheive their results. Empi's product brands include Pronex, which provides traction to the cervical spine, Sportex for swelling reduction, and Minnova, a device that stimulates the pelvic floor to treat urinary incontinence. Empi sells to rehabilitation clinics and medical device distributors nationwide, as well as abroad. The company is a subsidiary of ReAble Therapeutics (formerly Encore Medical).

	Annual Growth	12/03	12/04	12/05	12/06	12/07
Est. sales ($ mil.)	—	—	—	—	—	185.0
Employees	—	—	—	—	—	780

THE EMPIRE DISTRICT ELECTRIC COMPANY

NYSE: EDE

602 Joplin St.	CEO: William L. (Bill) Gipson
Joplin, MO 64801	CFO: Gregory A. Knapp
Phone: 417-625-5100	HR: –
Fax: 417-625-5146	FYE: December 31
Web: www.empiredistrict.com	Type: Public

Empire District Electric (EDE) has the sovereign authority to light up its territory. The utility transmits and distributes electricity to a population base of more than 450,000 customers in southwestern Missouri and adjacent areas of Arkansas, Kansas, and Oklahoma. It also supplies water to three Missouri towns and natural gas through most of Missouri. EDE's interests in fossil-fueled and hydroelectric power plants give it a generating capacity of 1,255 MW, with an expected increase to 1,410 MW by 2010; it also buys and sells power on the wholesale market. In addition, the company is pursuing nonregulated opportunities such as leasing capacity on its fiber-optic network.

	Annual Growth	12/03	12/04	12/05	12/06	12/07
Sales ($ mil.)	10.8%	325.5	325.5	386.2	413.5	490.2
Net income ($ mil.)	3.0%	29.5	21.9	23.8	39.3	33.2
Market value ($ mil.)	8.7%	547.7	582.8	530.3	746.9	765.5
Employees	—	—	—	851	—	—

EMPIRE MERCHANTS

19-50 40th St.	CEO: E. Lloyd Sobel
Astoria, NY 11105	CFO: Terence Arlotta
Phone: 718-726-2500	HR: Annette Perry
Fax: 718-726-4428	FYE: March 31
Web: www.empiremerchants.com	Type: Subsidiary

Not easily shaken by competition, Empire Merchants (formerly Charmer Industries) has not stirred from its spot as a leading wine and liquor wholesaler in New York state. The company distributes a wide array of wines, spirits, and champagnes to licensed liquor stores throughout the region. In 2007 it combined its metro New York operations with those of Peerless Importers to form Empire Merchants. Founded in 1933, the company is a subsidiary of Maryland-based Charmer-Sunbelt Group, one of the largest wine and spirits wholesalers in the US. The Merinoff family controls Charmer-Sunbelt.

	Annual Growth	3/03	3/04	3/05	3/06	3/07
Est. sales ($ mil.)	—	—	—	—	—	329.6
Employees	—	—	—	—	—	1,000

EMPIRE RESORTS, INC.

NASDAQ (GM): NYNY

701 N. Green Valley Pkwy., Ste. 200	CEO: David P. Hanlon
Henderson, NV 89074	CFO: Ronald J. (Ron) Radcliffe
Phone: 702-990-3355	HR: –
Fax: 845-791-1402	FYE: December 31
Web: www.empireresorts.com	Type: Public

Empire Resorts has taken up permanent residence in New York's playground. The company operates Catskills-area harness horseracing track Monticello Gaming and Raceway, which features pari-mutuel wagering and more than 1,500 video gaming machines. The property also includes a clubhouse, entertainment lounge, bar, and food court. Empire Resorts is developing about 30 acres of land adjacent to its Monticello property for a casino that will feature some 160,000 square feet of gaming space with 3,500 slot machines and 125 table games.

	Annual Growth	12/03	12/04	12/05	12/06	12/07
Sales ($ mil.)	19.0%	—	44.9	86.8	98.1	75.7
Net income ($ mil.)	—	—	(12.7)	(18.5)	(7.1)	(24.6)
Market value ($ mil.)	(29.6%)	—	290.8	194.7	255.1	101.3
Employees	0.0%	—	380	380	—	—

EMPIRE RESOURCES, INC.

AMEX: ERS

1 Parker Plaza	CEO: Nathan Kahn
Fort Lee, NJ 07024	CFO: Sandra R. Kahn
Phone: 201-944-2200	HR: Deborah Waltuch
Fax: 201-944-2226	FYE: December 31
Web: www.empireresources.com	Type: Public

When it comes to aluminum, Empire Resources is especially resourceful. The company distributes semifinished aluminum products, including sheet, foil, wire, plate, and coil. Products are sold primarily to manufacturers of appliances, automobiles, packaging, and housing materials. Empire Resources provides a variety of related services, including sourcing of aluminum products, storage and delivery, and handling foreign exchange transactions. Company president and CEO Nathan Kahn and CFO Sandra Kahn, who are husband and wife, own 38% of Empire Resources.

	Annual Growth	12/03	12/04	12/05	12/06	12/07
Sales ($ mil.)	26.7%	184.4	212.6	358.5	426.0	475.5
Net income ($ mil.)	6.5%	3.5	4.8	9.5	8.7	4.5
Market value ($ mil.)	4.5%	37.6	39.5	106.6	107.1	44.9
Employees	30.0%	—	—	50	65	—

EMPIRE SOUTHWEST, LLC

1725 S. Country Club Dr.
Mesa, AZ 85210
Phone: 480-633-4000
Fax: 480-633-4489
Web: www.empire-cat.com

CEO: Jeffrey S. (Jeff) Whiteman
CFO: –
HR: –
FYE: October 31
Type: Private

With CAT-like tread, Empire Southwest has created a heavy equipment sales, rental, and leasing empire in the US Southwest (Arizona and California). One of the largest Caterpillar dealerships in the US, Empire Southwest operates through five divisions: hydraulic service, machinery, power systems, precision machining, and transport. The company's equipment includes backhoes, compactors, dozers, front shovels, loaders, pipelayers, telehandlers, and tractors. It also handles equipment used for mining and forestry projects. Empire Southwest also carries batteries, power generators, engines, tools, and has a service department.

	Annual Growth	10/03	10/04	10/05	10/06	10/07
Est. sales ($ mil.)	—	—	—	—	—	630.8
Employees	—	—	—	—	—	1,211

EMPIRIX INC.

20 Crosby Dr.
Bedford, MA 01730
Phone: 781-266-3200
Fax: 781-266-3201
Web: www.empirix.com

CEO: Gregor N. (Greg) Ferguson
CFO: Jim Eliason
HR: –
FYE: December 31
Type: Private

Empirix provides testing and monitoring applications that manage and enhance the performance of Web and voice applications, contact centers, and communications networks. Customers have included BBC Online, General Motors, Midland Loan, Nintendo, and Waddell & Reed Financial. The company was spun off from Teradyne, the electronic test equipment vendor, in 2000, with funding from Matrix Partners. Empirix has offices in Germany, Japan, South Korea, the UK, and the US.

	Annual Growth	12/03	12/04	12/05	12/06	12/07
Est. sales ($ mil.)	—	—	—	—	—	73.0
Employees	—	—	—	—	—	380

EMPLOYERS HOLDINGS, INC.

NYSE: EIG

9790 Gateway Dr., Ste. 100
Reno, NV 89521
Phone: 775-327-2700
Fax: 888-527-3422
Web: www.eig.com

CEO: Douglas D. Dirks
CFO: William E. Yocke
HR: –
FYE: December 31
Type: Public

Because worker's compensation is nothing to gamble with, employers in western states turn to Employers Holdings (formerly EIG Mutual Holding). The Reno-based holding company provides workers' compensation services including claims management, loss prevention consulting, and care management to individuals and businesses. The company provides workers' compensation services through Employer Insurance Company of Nevada (EICN) and Employers Compensation Insurance Company. Employers Holdings also operates Employers Occupational Health, which provides care management and claim dispute resolution services, and Elite Insurance Services, a managing general agency which provides administrative services.

	Annual Growth	12/03	12/04	12/05	12/06	12/07
Assets ($ mil.)	0.8%	3,094.2	3,195.7	—	—	3,191.2
Net income ($ mil.)	—	—	—	—	—	120.3
Market value ($ mil.)	—	—	—	—	—	829.1
Employees	—	—	—	—	—	—

EMPTORIS, INC.

200 Wheeler Rd.
Burlington, MA 01803
Phone: 781-993-9212
Fax: 781-993-9213
Web: www.emptoris.com

CEO: Avner Schneur
CFO: Pat Burke
HR: Jane Johnson
FYE: December 31
Type: Private

Emptoris makes Web-based supply chain management software that manages supplier information and analyzes company spending. Emptoris' software can be used to create questionnaires for qualifying vendors, evaluate vendor performance, and manage request for quotes and contracts, including multiple contracts with a single vendor. The company also offers modules that manage online auctions, analyze spending trends, and facilitate negotiations. Emptoris' software is used in the automotive, computer, consumer goods, and telecommunications industries. The company markets its software worldwide. Customers include American Express, Motorola, and Vodafone.

	Annual Growth	12/03	12/04	12/05	12/06	12/07
Est. sales ($ mil.)	—	—	—	—	—	14.9
Employees	—	—	—	—	—	423

EMRISE CORPORATION

NYSE Arca: ERI

9485 Haven Ave., Ste. 100
Rancho Cucamonga, CA 91730
Phone: 909-987-9220
Fax: 909-987-9228
Web: www.emrise.com

CEO: Carmine T. Oliva
CFO: John Donovan
HR: Gale Belger
FYE: December 31
Type: Public

The sun doesn't set on EMRISE. Through its worldwide subsidiaries, the company makes electronic components and communications equipment for customers in the aerospace, defense, and telecom industries. Its CXR Larus units produce network transmission and access equipment and a range of testing gear. EMRISE's EEC Corporation subsidiary manufactures power converters, digital and rotary switches, and subsystem assemblies. The company counts BAE SYSTEMS, EMS Technologies, Harris, Motorola, Raytheon, Rockwell Collins, Selex Airborne Systems, and Thales Air Defence among its top clients. EMRISE gets about half of its sales from the UK.

	Annual Growth	12/03	12/04	12/05	12/06	12/07
Sales ($ mil.)	19.1%	25.5	29.9	41.3	46.4	51.3
Net income ($ mil.)	—	1.2	1.5	1.4	(3.6)	(1.9)
Employees	13.5%	181	335	329	305	300

EMS TECHNOLOGIES, INC.

NASDAQ (GS): ELMG

660 Engineering Dr.
Norcross, GA 30092
Phone: 770-263-9200
Fax: 770-263-9207
Web: www.ems-t.com

CEO: Paul B. Domorski
CFO: Gary B. Shell
HR: Michael R. Robertson
FYE: December 31
Type: Public

EMS Technologies' wireless systems can help you communicate, whether you're walking the warehouse floor or floating in space. The company's LXE unit makes handheld and vehicle-mounted computers used for logistics management. EMS also makes microwave-based communications hardware for defense contractors through its Defense & Space Systems unit. Its SATCOM division makes aeronautical satellite antennas and Earth station antennas and control terminals used for emergency management. The company has significantly streamlined its operations in recent years.

	Annual Growth	12/03	12/04	12/05	12/06	12/07
Sales ($ mil.)	3.0%	256.2	260.4	310.0	261.1	287.9
Net income ($ mil.)	—	(37.4)	0.2	(11.4)	33.0	18.7
Market value ($ mil.)	20.4%	224.4	185.6	200.8	307.0	471.2
Employees	(8.0%)	—	—	1,300	900	1,100

An in-depth profile of this company is available to Hoover's Online members at hoovers.com.

557

EMTEC, INC.

OTC: ETEC

525 Lincoln Dr., 5 Greentree Center, Ste. 117
Marlton, NJ 08619
Phone: 856-552-4204
Fax: 856-552-4298
Web: www.emtecinc.com

CEO: Dinesh R. Desai
CFO: Stephen C. Donnelly
HR: –
FYE: August 31
Type: Public

Emtec provides information technology services, including data management, security consulting, and infrastructure design and implementation. The company resells computer hardware and software from leading providers such as Cisco Systems, Dell, Hewlett-Packard, Lenovo, Microsoft, Sun Microsystems, and VERITAS Software. It serves federal government agencies including the US Department of Defense, Department of Justice, and Department of Homeland Security; other customers include state government agencies, as well as corporate and educational organizations.

	Annual Growth	3/04	3/05	*8/05	8/06	8/07
Sales ($ mil.)	21.2%	100.4	112.7	162.6	224.5	217.0
Net income ($ mil.)	—	0.6	2.9	0.8	0.2	(2.3)
Market value ($ mil.)	1.3%	10.0	3.4	41.4	14.4	10.5
Employees	(3.8%)	—	—	230	—	213

*Fiscal year change

EMULEX CORPORATION

NYSE: ELX

3333 Susan St.
Costa Mesa, CA 92626
Phone: 714-662-5600
Fax: 714-241-0792
Web: www.emulex.com

CEO: James M. (Jim) McCluney
CFO: Michael J. Rockenbach
HR: Sadie A. Herrera
FYE: Sunday nearest June 30
Type: Public

Emulex provides the ties that bind in storage networks. The company is a leading provider of Fibre Channel host bus adapters (HBAs). Its LightPulse cards are used to connect storage devices in traditional direct-attached storage configurations, as well as storage area network (SAN) and network-attached storage (NAS) systems. Emulex has also developed HBAs based on the emerging iSCSI protocol. Emulex sells its products directly to OEMs and through resellers and distributors. Its customers include equipment manufacturers such as IBM (a quarter of sales in fiscal 2007), EMC (18%), and Hewlett-Packard (13%).

	Annual Growth	6/03	6/04	6/05	6/06	6/07
Sales ($ mil.)	11.1%	308.2	364.4	375.6	402.8	470.2
Net income ($ mil.)	(18.2%)	65.7	(532.3)	71.6	40.5	29.4
Market value ($ mil.)	(1.1%)	1,903.3	1,228.0	1,543.4	1,374.1	1,819.6
Employees	—	—	—	—	—	—

EMUSIC.COM, INC.

100 Park Ave., 17th Fl.
New York, NY 10017
Phone: 212-201-9240
Fax: 212-201-9204
Web: www.emusic.com

CEO: David Pakman
CFO: Thomas J. (Tom) Etergino
HR: –
FYE: December 31
Type: Private

EMusic.com was singing the blues. Now it's moved on to independent tunes. Formerly GoodNoise, EMusic is one of the oldest digital music subscription services in operation, allowing consumers to download music legally. However, business suffered as customers turned to newer services from Apple and RealNetworks. As a result, EMusic repositioned itself as a provider of music from independent labels, offering more than 2 million tracks from about 13,000 independent labels. Former chairman Bob Kohn and ex-CEO Gene Hoffman founded EMusic in 1998. VUNet USA bought the company in 2001 for $24 million but sold it to investment firm Dimensional Associates, the private equity arm of JDS Capital Management, in 2003.

	Annual Growth	12/03	12/04	12/05	12/06	12/07
Est. sales ($ mil.)	—	—	—	—	—	26.0
Employees	—	—	—	—	—	75

EMVELCO CORP.

NASDAQ (CM): EMVL

468 N. Camden Dr., Ste. 315
Beverly Hills, CA 90210
Phone: 310-285-5350
Fax: –
Web: www.emvelco.com

CEO: Yossi Attia
CFO: Yossi Attia
HR: –
FYE: December 31
Type: Public

EMVELCO (formerly Euroweb International) is continually evolving (from a brick-and-mortar operation — literally — to an Internet company, then from IT services to real estate). Founded in 1992 to build apartment complexes and telecommunications facilities in Hungary, the company switched gears in 1997 to become a provider of Internet access and telecommunications services. In 2005 the company changed directions again through the acquisition of Navigator Informatika, a Hungarian provider of applications development and information technology (IT) outsourcing and consulting. Most recently, it is honing in on major real estate projects, including its signature project, a condo building in Las Vegas.

	Annual Growth	12/03	12/04	12/05	12/06	12/07
Sales ($ mil.)	(17.4%)	14.8	36.6	2.0	0.0	6.9
Net income ($ mil.)	—	(1.6)	(0.7)	1.7	6.9	(10.9)
Market value ($ mil.)	(39.5%)	17.6	21.2	20.5	10.0	2.4
Employees	(94.1%)	—	—	85	5	—

EN POINTE TECHNOLOGIES, INC.

NASDAQ (CM): ENPT

18701 S. Figueroa St.
Gardena, CA 90248
Phone: 310-337-5955
Fax: 310-258-2301
Web: www.enpointe.com

CEO: Attiazaz (Bob) Din
CFO: Javed Latif
HR: –
FYE: September 30
Type: Public

En Pointe Technologies makes sure product procurement stays on point. The company provides hardware and software fulfillment and support services. It steers clear of physical inventories, relying instead on allied distributors such as Tech Data and Ingram Micro to fill orders. En Pointe also buys directly from manufacturers. Its online AccessPointe catalog features products from hundreds of providers, including Cisco Systems, Dell, Hewlett-Packard, and IBM. En Pointe also sells and maintains software licensing contracts and agreements from a variety of vendors, including Microsoft, Adobe, Novell, and Symantec. CEO Attiazaz (Bob) Din and his wife, Naureen Din, together control about 30% of En Pointe.

	Annual Growth	9/03	9/04	9/05	9/06	9/07
Sales ($ mil.)	4.6%	289.8	279.2	328.3	323.7	347.1
Net income ($ mil.)	—	(2.4)	1.4	0.1	0.5	1.6
Market value ($ mil.)	36.5%	6.0	13.2	18.7	18.1	20.8
Employees	1.9%	—	—	534	—	555

EN BRIDGE ENERGY MANAGEMENT, L.L.C.

NYSE: EEQ

1100 Louisiana St., Ste. 3300
Houston, TX 77002
Phone: 713-821-2000
Fax: 713-821-2230
Web: www.enbridgemanagement.com

CEO: Stephen J. J. (S. J. J.) Letwin
CFO: M. A. Maki
HR: –
FYE: December 31
Type: Public

Enbridge Energy Management, bridging the gap over a complex structure of pipeline partnerships, manages and controls the business of Enbridge Energy Partners (formerly Lakehead Pipe Line Partners). The company's only asset is an 18% limited partner interest in Enbridge Energy Partners, which owns the US part of North America's longest liquid petroleum pipeline (Lakehead System) and also has interests in natural gas gathering, treating, processing, and transmission operations in East Texas. Enbridge Energy Company, a wholly owned subsidiary of Enbridge Inc., holds a 17% stake in the company, and serves as the general partner of Enbridge Energy Partners.

	Annual Growth	12/00	12/01	12/02	12/03	*12/04
Sales ($ mil.)	—	—	—	—	—	28.8
Net income ($ mil.)	—	—	—	—	—	18.7
Market value ($ mil.)	—	—	—	—	—	546.9
Employees	—	—	—	—	—	—

*Most recent year available

ENBRIDGE ENERGY PARTNERS, L.P.

NYSE: EEP

1100 Louisiana St., Ste. 3300
Houston, TX 77002
Phone: 713-821-2000
Fax: 713-821-2232
Web: www.enbridgepartners.com

CEO: Stephen J. J. (S. J. J.) Letwin
CFO: M. A. Maki
HR: –
FYE: December 31
Type: Public

Heading up petroleum transportation around the Great Lakes is Enbridge Energy Partners (formerly Lakehead Pipe Line Partners), which owns the 1,900-mile US portion of the world's longest liquid petroleum pipeline. When combined with the Canadian segment (owned and operated by Enbridge Inc.), the pipeline system spans some 3,500 miles across North America. Other midstream assets include 5,000 miles of crude oil gathering and transportation lines and 28.9 million barrels of crude oil storage and terminaling capacity, and 11,500 miles of natural gas gathering and transportation pipelines. Enbridge Energy Management owns a 15% stake in the company.

	Annual Growth	12/03	12/04	12/05	12/06	12/07
Sales ($ mil.)	23.1%	3,172.3	4,291.7	6,476.9	6,509.0	7,282.6
Net income ($ mil.)	22.3%	111.7	138.2	89.2	284.9	249.5
Market value ($ mil.)	8.6%	2,004.3	2,413.6	2,192.3	2,466.5	2,791.8
Employees	—	—	—	0	0	0

ENBRIDGE (U.S.) INC.

1100 Louisiana St., Ste. 3300
Houston, TX 77002
Phone: 713-821-2000
Fax: 713-821-2230
Web: www.enbridge-us.com

CEO: Terrance L. (Terry) McGill
CFO: –
HR: –
FYE: December 31
Type: Subsidiary

Enbridge (U.S.), a subsidiary of Canada's Enbridge, provides oil and gas pipeline transportation services. The company holds interests in a range of US pipeline assets, including Alliance Pipeline, Enbridge Pipelines (Toledo), Mustang Pipe Line Partners, and Vector Pipeline. Enbridge (U.S.) is also an affiliate of Enbridge Energy Company. Enbridge (U.S.) expanded its operations through the 2005 acquisition of Shell Gas Transmission from Shell US Gas & Power. The acquisition added 11 transmission pipelines, which operate within five major pipeline corridors, to Enbridge (U.S.)'s asset holdings.

	Annual Growth	12/03	12/04	12/05	12/06	12/07
Est. sales ($ mil.)	—	—	—	—	—	215.2
Employees	—	—	—	—	—	1,000

ENCANA OIL & GAS (USA) INC.

370 17th St., Ste. 1700
Denver, CO 80202
Phone: 303-623-2300
Fax: 303-623-2400
Web: www.encana.com

CEO: Jeff E. Wojahn
CFO: Brian C. Ferguson
HR: –
FYE: December 31
Type: Subsidiary

EnCana Oil & Gas (USA) is a chip off the block of a Canadian energy giant. The company is an exploration and production subsidiary of integrated oil firm EnCana Corporation. EnCana Oil & Gas (USA) explores for and produces oil in its four key natural gas resource plays (87% of its total 2007 US natural gas production) located at Jonah and Piceance in the US Rockies and in the Fort Worth and East Texas basins in the state of Texas. EnCana's US operation. In 2007 EnCana Oil & Gas (USA)'s natural gas production averaged about 1,345 million cu. ft. per day.

	Annual Growth	12/03	12/04	12/05	12/06	12/07
Est. sales ($ mil.)	—	—	—	—	—	2,147.5
Employees	—	—	—	—	—	751

ENCISION INC.

AMEX: ECI

6797 Winchester Cir.
Boulder, CO 80301
Phone: 303-444-2600
Fax: 303-444-2693
Web: www.encision.com

CEO: John R. (Jack) Serino
CFO: Marcia K. McHaffie
HR: –
FYE: March 31
Type: Public

Encision enables doctors to make the cut during surgery. The company makes instruments for use in laparoscopic surgical procedures, including electrodes, graspers, monitors, and scissor inserts. Encision's instruments are similar to conventional electrosurgical instruments in size, shape, and functionality, but the company's products utilize "active electrode monitoring" to monitor the flow of the electrosurgical current during surgery. Doctors use Encision's products to reduce the risk of unintended electrosurgical burns or tissue injuries to patients, thereby decreasing the liability exposure of the surgeons and hospitals. CMED Partners LLLP owns about 28% of the company.

	Annual Growth	3/03	3/04	3/05	3/06	3/07
Sales ($ mil.)	12.8%	6.8	7.3	8.1	9.1	11.0
Net income ($ mil.)	—	0.2	0.0	(0.6)	(0.3)	(0.1)
Market value ($ mil.)	15.8%	14.4	23.3	17.4	21.9	25.9
Employees	6.1%	—	—	33	35	—

ENCOMPASS HOLDINGS, INC.

Pink Sheets: ECMH

1005 Terminal Way, Ste. 110
Reno, NV 89502
Phone: 775-324-8531
Fax: –
Web: www.encompassholdings.com

CEO: J. Scott Webber
CFO: –
HR: –
FYE: June 30
Type: Public

Surf's up at Encompass Holdings (formerly Nova Communications and before that, First Colonial Ventures). The company, which is always looking for companies that share a potential for growth and a need for capital, owns Aqua Xtremes. Aqua Xtremes makes XBoard, a jet-powered surfboard. In May 2005 it acquired Nacio Systems, a provider of outsourced information technology services (such as e-commerce, customer relationship management, and software auditing) for corporate customers. Its Xtreme Engines and Rotary Engine Technologies subsidiaries are working together to develop an engine for XBoard.

	Annual Growth	12/01	12/02	12/03	*6/05	†6/06
Sales ($ mil.)	(13.3%)	7.8	7.9	0.0	1.3	4.4
Net income ($ mil.)	—	(7.6)	3.8	(4.6)	(5.4)	(4.7)
Employees	—	—	—	—	—	—

*Fiscal year change †Most recent year available

ENCORE ACQUISITION COMPANY

NYSE: EAC

777 Main St., Ste. 1400
Fort Worth, TX 76102
Phone: 817-877-9955
Fax: 817-877-1655
Web: www.encoreacq.com

CEO: Jon S. (Jonny) Brumley
CFO: Robert C. Reeves
HR: Don Lott
FYE: December 31
Type: Public

"Drill it again, and buy some more oil and gas properties" appear to be operating guidelines for Encore Acquisition, an independent oil and natural gas company engaged in the acquisition, development, and exploitation of reserves in several basins. Operations include drilling in the Williston Basin of Montana and North Dakota, the Permian Basin of Texas and New Mexico, and the Anadarko Basin of Oklahoma. Its proved reserves of 206 million barrels of oil equivalent are primarily from its Cedar Creek Anticline asset (in Montana and North Dakota). Encore Acquisition was formed in 1998 by J.P. Morgan Partners, Warburg Pincus & Co., and Natural Gas Partners.

	Annual Growth	12/03	12/04	12/05	12/06	12/07
Sales ($ mil.)	36.1%	220.1	298.5	457.3	640.9	754.9
Net income ($ mil.)	(27.9%)	63.6	82.2	103.4	92.4	17.2
Market value ($ mil.)	37.4%	498.5	760.0	1,581.8	1,301.2	1,778.7
Employees	15.1%	—	—	205	236	—

An in-depth profile of this company is available to Hoover's Online members at hoovers.com.

559

ENCORE BANCSHARES, INC.

NASDAQ (GM): EBTX

9 Greenway Plaza, Ste. 1000
Houston, TX 77046
Phone: 713-787-3100
Fax: –
Web: www.encorebank.com

CEO: James S. D'Agostino Jr.
CFO: L. Anderson Creel
HR: Nancy L. Smith
FYE: December 31
Type: Public

Encore! Encore! Encore Bancshares is taking its bows as the holding company for Encore Bank. Encore operates around a dozen branches in Houston and a handful more in southwestern Florida, offering traditional retail banking products to businesses and individuals. It also provides mortgages and other loans and wealth management, and insurance to its customers through subsidiaries Town & Country Insurance Agency, Encore Trust Company, and Linscomb & Williams. The bank caters to wealthy clients (hence its focus on the Houston area and southwest Florida, two of the wealthiest regions in the US) with private bankers and relationship managers.

	Annual Growth	12/03	12/04	12/05	12/06	12/07
Assets ($ mil.)	3.2%	—	—	1,316.6	1,336.8	1,401.2
Net income ($ mil.)	(1.0%)	7.7	6.9	4.8	7.5	7.4
Market value ($ mil.)	—	—	—	—	—	202.4
Employees	—	183	—	—	—	—

ENCORE CAPITAL GROUP, INC.

NASDAQ (GS): ECPG

8875 Aero Dr., Ste. 200
San Diego, CA 92123
Phone: 858-560-2600
Fax: –
Web: www.mcmcg.com

CEO: J. Brandon Black
CFO: Paul J. Grinberg
HR: Alison James
FYE: December 31
Type: Public

Credit junkies, beware: Encore Capital Group has your number. The firm buys at a discount charged-off receivables that credit card issuers and other lenders have given up on, then does its best to collect the money. Encore Capital Group applies a "friendly, but firm approach" and concentrates on getting the balance owed over time via phone, direct mail, and legal action. The company's account managers evaluate customers' ability to pay, then develop tailored payment programs; the company also uses skip-tracers to track down stubborn debtors. Subsidiary Ascension Capital Group provides bankruptcy services to the finance industry.

	Annual Growth	12/03	12/04	12/05	12/06	12/07
Sales ($ mil.)	21.3%	117.5	178.5	221.8	255.1	254.0
Net income ($ mil.)	(5.0%)	18.4	23.2	31.1	24.0	15.0
Market value ($ mil.)	(9.5%)	332.2	527.1	393.0	287.3	222.6
Employees	5.1%	—	—	905	893	1,000

ENCORE ENERGY PARTNERS LP

NYSE: ENP

777 Main St., Ste. 1400
Fort Worth, TX 76102
Phone: 817-877-9955
Fax: –
Web: www.encoreenp.com

CEO: Jon S. (Jonny) Brumley
CFO: Robert C. Reeves
HR: –
FYE: December 31
Type: Public

Encore Energy Partners is banking on a second trip to the well. The partnership, formed by Encore Acquisition Company, acquires, exploits, and develops existing oil and natural gas properties. Encore's primary assets consist of oil and natural gas properties in the Elk Basin of Wyoming and Montana, and in West Texas' Permian Basin. In 2007 the company reported estimated proved reserves of 14.1 million barrels of oil and 39.1 billion cu. ft. of natural gas. Encore Energy plans to utilize its close ties to Encore Acquisition Company for future acquisitions.

	Annual Growth	12/03	12/04	12/05	12/06	12/07
Sales ($ mil.)	—	—	—	—	—	79.7
Net income ($ mil.)	—	—	—	—	—	(25.3)
Market value ($ mil.)	—	—	—	—	—	435.4
Employees	—	—	—	—	—	0

ENCORE WIRE CORPORATION

NASDAQ (GS): WIRE

1410 Millwood Rd.
McKinney, TX 75069
Phone: 972-562-9473
Fax: 972-542-4744
Web: www.encorewire.com

CEO: Daniel L. Jones
CFO: Frank J. Bilban
HR: Brad Rattan
FYE: December 31
Type: Public

Encore Wire likes to leave its customers applauding and calling for more — more wire, that is. A manufacturer of copper electrical building wire and cable, Encore produces Armored and THWN-2 cable (insulated feeder, circuit, and branch wiring for commercial and industrial buildings) and NM-B cable (sheathed cable used to wire homes, apartments, and manufactured housing). It also produces UF-B cable, an underground feeder cable for outside lighting and other remote uses in residential buildings. The company sells primarily to wholesale electrical distributors across the US and to some retail home-improvement centers.

	Annual Growth	12/03	12/04	12/05	12/06	12/07
Sales ($ mil.)	32.5%	384.8	603.2	758.1	1,249.3	1,184.8
Net income ($ mil.)	20.9%	14.4	33.4	50.1	115.1	30.8
Market value ($ mil.)	19.7%	180.0	344.8	590.4	512.3	370.0
Employees	10.1%	—	—	686	755	—

ENCORIUM GROUP, INC.

NASDAQ (CM): ENCO

1 Glenhardie Corporate Center, 1275 Drummers Ln., Ste. 100
Wayne, PA 19087
Phone: 610-975-9533
Fax: 610-975-9556
Web: www.encorium.com

CEO: Kai E. Lindevall
CFO: Philip L. (Phil) Calamia
HR: Nicole Haraczka
FYE: December 31
Type: Public

Encorium Group (formerly Covalent) has some strong bonds with its clients. The contract research organization (CRO) manages all stages of clinical trials for pharmaceutical, biotech, and medical device firms worldwide. Encorium uses both full-time and contract personnel to provide program design, clinical trial and data management, biostatistical analysis, medical and regulatory services, and quality assurance. The company also provides technology solutions, including systems that uses interactive speech recognition and Internet technology to coordinate trial participants and manage clinical data. It changed its name to Encorium in 2006 as it completed the acquisition of Finnish CRO Remedium Oy.

	Annual Growth	12/03	12/04	12/05	12/06	12/07
Sales ($ mil.)	8.5%	26.6	19.0	12.7	17.7	36.8
Net income ($ mil.)	—	(0.6)	(4.2)	(1.5)	(0.5)	(2.8)
Market value ($ mil.)	1.4%	33.8	34.4	29.4	92.9	35.6
Employees	214.3%	—	—	84	264	—

ENCYCLOPÆDIA BRITANNICA, INC.

331 N. La Salle St.
Chicago, IL 60610
Phone: 312-347-7159
Fax: 312-294-2104
Web: corporate.britannica.com

CEO: Jorge Cauz
CFO: Richard Anderson
HR: William J. Bowe
FYE: December 31
Type: Private

Encyclopædia Britannica thinks it knows everything, and it probably does. The company publishes reference works including its flagship 32-volume *Encyclopædia Britannica* (first published in 1768) and *Great Books of the Western World*. It also publishes a variety of dictionaries (*Merriam Webster's Collegiate Dictionary, Merriam Webster's Biographical Dictionary*) through its Merriam-Webster subsidiary. Most of the company's products are available online (Britannica.com), as well as on CD-ROM and DVD. The company also publishes Britannica Online School Edition, a reference site for students and teachers. Swiss financier Jacob Safra (a nephew of the late banking king Edmond Safra) owns the company.

ENCYSIVE PHARMACEUTICALS INC.

4848 Loop Central Dr., Ste. 700
Houston, TX 77081
Phone: 713-796-8822
Fax: 713-796-8232
Web: www.encysive.com

CEO: George W. Cole
CFO: Richard A. Goeggel
HR: Pamela (Pam) Mabry
FYE: December 31
Type: Subsidiary

Encysive Pharmaceuticals brings insight to cardiovascular drug discovery. Flagship drug Argatroban is an anticoagulant used to treat heparin-induced thrombocytopenia, or low blood platelet count. Partner GlaxoSmithKline markets the drug in the US and Canada. Another drug, Thelin, is approved in some non-US markets for the treatment of pulmonary arterial hypertension, and the company is working on gaining US approval for the drug. Additionally, Encysive has licensed several potential therapies for inflammatory diseases to its former subsidiary Revotar Biopharmaceuticals and to Schering-Plough. Encysive Pharmaceuticals was acquired by Pfizer in 2008.

	Annual Growth	12/03	12/04	12/05	12/06	12/07
Sales ($ mil.)	32.6%	11.6	13.8	14.0	19.0	35.9
Net income ($ mil.)	—	(35.3)	(54.7)	(74.9)	(109.3)	(100.7)
Employees	—	—	—	220	—	—

THE ENDEAVOR AGENCY, LLC.

9601 Wilshire Blvd., 3rd Fl.
Beverly Hills, CA 90210
Phone: 310-248-2000
Fax: 310-248-2020

CEO: Tom Strickler
CFO: -
HR: -
FYE: December 31
Type: Private

Finding good gigs for Hollywood talent is a huge endeavor. The Endeavor Agency helps by representing celebrities, many are famous for their TV work, including David E. Kelly (creator of *Ally McBeal* and *The Practice*), Aaron Sorkin (creator of *The West Wing*), Jennifer Garner (star of *Alias*), Tina Fey (former writer of *Saturday Night Live*), and documentary filmmaker Michael Moore (*Sicko*, *Fahrenheit 9/11*). Other clients include Reese Witherspoon, Jude Law, Martin Scorsese, Matt Damon, and Adam Sandler. The firm also packages the reality hit *Queer Eye for the Straight Guy* for Scout Productions. Endeavor formed when a group of agents left ICM in 1995. Interpublic owns a minority stake in the firm's marketing arm.

	Annual Growth	12/03	12/04	12/05	12/06	12/07
Est. sales ($ mil.)	—	—	—	—	—	7.4
Employees	—	—	—	—	—	190

ENDEAVOUR INTERNATIONAL CORPORATION

AMEX: END

1001 Fannin, Ste. 1600
Houston, TX 77002
Phone: 713-307-8700
Fax: -
Web: www.endeavourcorp.com

CEO: William L. (Bill) Transier
CFO: J. Michael (Mike) Kirksey
HR: -
FYE: December 31
Type: Public

Like famous British explorer Captain James Cook's vessel, the *Endeavour*, Endeavour International has been on quite a journey. The company started life as a graphics company (Expression Graphics) in 2000, before changing its name and business direction in 2002, when (as Continental Southern Resources) it began to focus on oil and gas exploration in the US. In 2004 it acquired NSNV, which held a North Sea seismic database, and became Endeavour International. It then sold its US assets. The company is buying up stakes in mature North Sea fields that the majors are moving away from. In 2006 Endeavour International had proved reserves of 9.9 million barrels of oil equivalent.

	Annual Growth	12/03	12/04	12/05	12/06	12/07
Sales ($ mil.)	—	0.0	3.7	38.7	54.1	176.1
Net income ($ mil.)	—	(32.8)	(23.4)	(31.4)	(6.8)	(49.1)
Market value ($ mil.)	20.4%	81.0	310.4	249.1	271.5	170.2
Employees	—	—	—	52	—	—

ENDECA TECHNOLOGIES INC.

101 Main St.
Cambridge, MA 02142
Phone: 617-674-6000
Fax: 617-674-6001
Web: www.endeca.com

CEO: Steve Papa
CFO: Daniel (Dan) Demmer
HR: -
FYE: December 31
Type: Private

Endeca Technologies doesn't want Internet surfers to drown in a sea of information. The company's enterprise search software categorizes and organizes search results, enabling users to narrow their choices when browsing online catalogs, information portals, and intranets. Endeca also offers tools for e-commerce searches and business intelligence analytics. Endeca targets clients in the media and publishing, financial services, manufacturing and distribution, government, and retail industries; customers have included Bank of America, Barnes & Noble, IBM, and Wal-Mart. Endeca has received investments from Ampersand Ventures, Bessemer Venture Partners, Silicon Valley Bancshares, and Venrock Associates.

	Annual Growth	12/03	12/04	12/05	12/06	12/07
Est. sales ($ mil.)	—	—	—	—	—	14.8
Employees	—	—	—	—	—	140

ENDICOTT INTERCONNECT TECHNOLOGIES INC.

1701 North St.
Endicott, NY 13760
Phone: 607-755-0123
Fax: 607-755-7000
Web: www.endicottinterconnect.com

CEO: James J. (Jay) McNamara Jr.
CFO: -
HR: James Sullivan
FYE: December 31
Type: Private

The plant's sign now says "EI" instead of "IBM," and a lot fewer people work there compared with decades ago, but other than that, it's business as usual — making printed circuit boards and semiconductor packages for a variety of electronic products. Endicott Interconnect Technologies (EI) was established by a local investor group in 2002 to purchase surplus facilities from IBM, which was looking to trim headcount and overhead at the time. The investors include the Maines family, owners of MAINES Paper & Food Service in nearby Conklin. In addition to packaging chips and building boards, Endicott Interconnect provides a number of manufacturing and technical services for complex electronic assemblies.

	Annual Growth	12/03	12/04	12/05	12/06	12/07
Est. sales ($ mil.)	—	—	—	—	—	138.5
Employees	—	—	—	—	—	1,700

ENDO PHARMACEUTICALS HOLDINGS INC.

NASDAQ (GS): ENDP

100 Endo Blvd.
Chadds Ford, PA 19317
Phone: 610-558-9800
Fax: 610-558-8979
Web: www.endo.com

CEO: David P. Holveck
CFO: Charles A. Rowland Jr.
HR: -
FYE: December 31
Type: Public

Endo Pharmaceuticals wants to curb the hurt. The drugmaker specializes in products for pain management. Its best-selling drug is Lidoderm, a lidocaine patch that treats the nerve pain caused by shingles. Endo also sells well-known pain meds Percodan and Percocet, as well as migraine therapy Frova. In addition to its portfolio of name-brand drugs, it sells some generic pain medications. The company markets its drugs in the US through its own domestic sales force; however, it outsources almost everything else, from manufacturing to distribution to clinical development acitivities.

	Annual Growth	12/03	12/04	12/05	12/06	12/07
Sales ($ mil.)	16.2%	595.6	615.1	820.2	909.7	1,085.6
Net income ($ mil.)	34.3%	69.8	143.3	202.3	137.8	227.4
Market value ($ mil.)	8.8%	2,551.6	2,770.3	4,018.6	3,684.7	3,577.6
Employees	30.4%	—	—	710	1,024	1,208

An in-depth profile of this company is available to Hoover's Online members at hoovers.com.

561

ENDOCARE, INC.

NASDAQ (CM): ENDO

201 Technology Dr.
Irvine, CA 92618
Phone: 949-450-5400
Fax: 949-450-5300
Web: www.endocare.com

CEO: Craig T. Davenport
CFO: Michael R. Rodriguez
HR: –
FYE: December 31
Type: Public

Endocare won't freeze your butt off, but it does the next best thing to treat prostate cancer. The company makes minimally invasive medical devices that use "cryoablation" to freeze enlarged or cancerous tissue, which gets broken up and reabsorbed by the body. Approved for tumor removal, the Cryocare Surgical System freezes targeted cells and is intended to reduce recovery time and complications. Endocare sells its products mainly to urologists, radiologists, hospitals, and other health care providers in the US, but it also does business internationally, mostly in Canada and China. The company's products are primarily applied in prostate cancer treatment but are also used in renal (kidney) tumor treatments.

	Annual Growth	12/03	12/04	12/05	12/06	12/07
Sales ($ mil.)	(0.7%)	30.5	32.7	28.3	28.0	29.7
Net income ($ mil.)	—	(25.5)	(37.6)	(13.7)	(10.8)	(8.9)
Market value ($ mil.)	(2.0%)	97.0	60.9	82.4	54.3	89.5
Employees	—	—	—	—	—	—

ENDOLOGIX, INC.

NASDAQ (GM): ELGX

11 Studebaker
Irvine, CA 92618
Phone: 949-595-7200
Fax: 949-457-9561
Web: www.endologix.com

CEO: John McDermott
CFO: Robert J. (Bob) Krist
HR: –
FYE: December 31
Type: Public

Medical device company Endologix strengthens weak arteries with its PowerLink Systems, which use a catheter and stent cage to treat abdominal aortic aneurysm (or weakening of the aortic wall). The device, which reduces blood pressure on the weakened portion of the aorta, offers a less invasive alternative to conventional surgery. Endologix sells the products in the US through its own team of sales representatives and in Europe through distributors (including LeMaitre Vascular). The company has also licensed some legacy technologies to Guidant.

	Annual Growth	12/03	12/04	12/05	12/06	12/07
Sales ($ mil.)	62.4%	4.0	4.2	7.1	14.7	27.8
Net income ($ mil.)	—	(5.9)	(9.7)	(15.5)	(17.5)	(15.1)
Market value ($ mil.)	1.6%	112.9	221.7	253.1	149.3	120.3
Employees	—	—	—	134	—	—

ENDWAVE CORPORATION

NASDAQ (GM): ENWV

130 Baytech Dr.
San Jose, CA 95134
Phone: 408-522-3100
Fax: 408-522-3102
Web: www.endwave.com

CEO: Edward A. Keible Jr.
CFO: Brett W. Wallace
HR: –
FYE: December 31
Type: Public

Endwave is riding the wireless tide. The company designs components and subsystems for broadband wireless systems. Its products are built using gallium arsenide (GaAs) integrated circuits. Telecom equipment makers such as Nokia Siemens Networks (60% of sales), Nortel, and Nera Networks (14%) use Endwave's radio-frequency (RF) modules and transceivers in cellular, point-to-point, and point-to-multipoint network access gear. The company also manufactures RF amplifiers, converters, and oscillators. Northrop Grumman Mission Systems supplies Endwave with GaAs chips. The company gets the majority of its sales from European customers.

	Annual Growth	12/03	12/04	12/05	12/06	12/07
Sales ($ mil.)	13.7%	33.8	33.2	48.7	62.2	56.5
Net income ($ mil.)	—	(7.9)	(4.4)	(0.9)	(1.3)	(5.4)
Market value ($ mil.)	(1.4%)	70.5	183.2	133.8	125.2	66.7
Employees	18.6%	108	141	141	151	214

ENER1, INC.

AMEX: HEV

500 W. Cypress Creek Rd., Ste. 100
Fort Lauderdale, FL 33309
Phone: 954-556-4020
Fax: 954-556-4031
Web: www.ener1.com

CEO: Peter Novak
CFO: –
HR: –
FYE: December 31
Type: Public

Ener1 is an energy-related technology holding company. The company develops products related to fuel cells and solar cells for the consumer, industrial, and military markets. Its NanoEner subsidiary develops nanotechnology-based products. Its EnerFuel unit develops fuel cell components and provides related testing services. Ener1 also owns more than 80% of EnerDel, a joint venture with Delphi, which develops lithium power technologies and products for stored energy and battery power — primary cells (non-rechargeable), rechargeable cells, battery packs, and electronics. Ener1 Group controls the company.

	Annual Growth	12/03	12/04	12/05	12/06	12/07
Sales ($ mil.)	—	0.0	0.0	0.1	0.1	0.3
Net income ($ mil.)	—	(8.9)	(35.8)	28.6	(41.3)	(51.7)
Market value ($ mil.)	(2.7%)	4,082.3	2,481.9	948.6	671.9	3,652.4
Employees	4.9%	—	90	62	73	104

ENERGAS RESOURCES, INC.

OTC: EGSR

800 NE 63rd St., 3rd Fl.
Oklahoma City, OK 73105
Phone: 405-879-1752
Fax: 405-879-0175
Web: www.energasresources.com

CEO: George G. Shaw
CFO: George G. Shaw
HR: Andy Biddy
FYE: January 31
Type: Public

Turning subterranean natural gas into a useful energy is the goal of exploration and development independent Energas Resources. Operating through its A.T. Gas Gathering Systems and TGC subsidiaries, the company is primarily focused on exploring and producing in the Arkoma Basin in Oklahoma, and the Powder River Basin in Wyoming. Energas Resources has proved reserves of 22,143 barrels of oil and 1.9 billion cu. ft. of natural gas. In 2007 the company sold most of its assets in the shallow Devonian Shale natural gas strata in the Appalachian Basin of Kentucky. President George Shaw owns about 24% of the company.

	Annual Growth	1/04	1/05	1/06	1/07	1/08
Sales ($ mil.)	7.5%	0.3	0.7	1.2	0.6	0.4
Net income ($ mil.)	—	(1.5)	(1.2)	(1.6)	(1.5)	(1.5)
Market value ($ mil.)	(25.6%)	7.8	21.9	32.6	2.5	2.4
Employees	—	—	—	—	10	—

ENERGEN CORPORATION

NYSE: EGN

605 Richard Arrington Jr. Blvd. North
Birmingham, AL 35203
Phone: 205-326-2700
Fax: 205-326-2704
Web: www.energen.com

CEO: James T. McManus II
CFO: Charles W. (Chuck) Porter Jr.
HR: William K. (Bill) Bibb
FYE: December 31
Type: Public

Energen's natural gas distribution business puts the energy out in Dixie, but the company also takes it in through gas and oil exploration operations that extend into the Southwest. The diversified energy company generates more than half of its sales from its regulated utility, Alabama Gas Corporation (Alagasco), which distributes natural gas to approximately 417,000 residential and 34,200 commercial and industrial customers. Energen has oil and gas exploration and production operations in the Southwest through subsidiary Energen Resources; the unit has estimated proved reserves of 1.7 trillion cu. ft. of natural gas equivalent.

	Annual Growth	12/03	12/04	12/05	12/06	12/07
Sales ($ mil.)	14.3%	842.2	937.4	1,128.4	1,394.0	1,435.1
Net income ($ mil.)	29.3%	110.7	127.5	173.0	273.6	309.2
Market value ($ mil.)	57.3%	743.1	1,078.3	2,669.3	3,365.0	4,548.5
Employees	1.4%	—	—	1,500	1,530	1,542

ENERGIZER HOLDINGS, INC.

NYSE: ENR

533 Maryville University Dr.
St. Louis, MO 63141
Phone: 314-985-2000
Fax: 314-985-2205
Web: www.energizer.com

CEO: Ward M. Klein
CFO: Daniel J. Sescleifer
HR: Peter J. Conrad
FYE: September 30
Type: Public

Energizer Holdings keeps going, and going . . . and leading the battery market in the process. Known for its pink bunny marketing icon, the company was spun off in 2000 by pet food maker Ralston Purina (now Nestlé Purina PetCare). Its products — which include alkaline, carbon zinc, lithium, miniature, and specialty batteries — are sold in more than 150 countries. The company's popular Energizer and Eveready brands account for about 38% of the US retail battery market. Energizer's e2 Lithium and e2 Titanium batteries provide more power for portable electronics, such as MP3 music players. Wal-Mart accounts for nearly 19% of sales. The company gets more than half of sales outside the US.

	Annual Growth	9/03	9/04	9/05	9/06	9/07
Sales ($ mil.)	10.8%	2,232.5	2,812.7	2,989.8	3,076.9	3,365.1
Net income ($ mil.)	17.3%	169.9	267.4	286.4	260.9	321.4
Market value ($ mil.)	19.4%	3,128.3	3,360.8	3,703.3	4,079.9	6,353.0
Employees	0.3%	14,602	12,955	14,848	14,800	14,800

ENERGY BRANDS INC.

17-20 Whitestone Expwy.
Whitestone, NY 11357
Phone: 718-746-0087
Fax: 718-747-1748
Web: www.energybrands.com

CEO: J. Darius Bikoff
CFO: Michael (Mike) Venuti
HR: –
FYE: December 31
Type: Subsidiary

Energy Brands is proud of its liquid assets. Also known as glacèau, the company makes waves with its line of enhanced waters. Its main brands are vitaminwater, which comes in more than a dozen flavors fortified with such nutrients as folic acid, magnesium, vitamin B-12, and zinc; electrolyte-enriched smartwater; and fruitwater, a flavored version of the former. Glacèau products are available trhoughout the US. J. Darius Bikoff founded the company in 1996. Bikoff is credited with creating enhanced water, sales of which have contined to climb as consumers look for healthier drink alternatives. Energy Brands is a subsidiary of Coca-Cola.

ENERGY CONVERSION DEVICES, INC.

NASDAQ (GS): ENER

2956 Waterview Dr.
Rochester Hills, MI 48309
Phone: 248-293-0440
Fax: 248-844-1214
Web: www.ovonic.com

CEO: Mark D. Morelli
CFO: Sanjeev Kumar
HR: Tom Schultz
FYE: June 30
Type: Public

Energy Conversion Devices (ECD) gets a charge out of its technology. ECD makes products that generate and store power and store information electronically. Through its Cobasys joint venture with Chevron, it makes rechargeable batteries to power items ranging from consumer electronics to electric vehicles. Subsidiary United Solar Ovonic makes flexible solar panels for telecom, lighting, and other uses. The company licenses its optical memory storage technology to Sony, Toshiba, and others. The firm's thin-film materials (optical and vapor barrier films) are used in beverage packaging and solar-controlled windows. Customers in the US account for nearly half of sales.

	Annual Growth	6/03	6/04	6/05	6/06	6/07
Sales ($ mil.)	14.9%	65.2	66.3	156.6	102.4	113.6
Net income ($ mil.)	—	(36.2)	(51.4)	50.3	(18.6)	(25.2)
Market value ($ mil.)	57.4%	199.8	276.1	635.3	1,422.9	1,226.5
Employees	—	—	—	—	—	—

ENERGY EAST CORPORATION

NYSE: EAS

52 Farm View Dr.
New Gloucester, ME 04260
Phone: 207-688-6300
Fax: 207-688-4354
Web: www.energyeast.com

CEO: Wesley W. von Schack
CFO: Robert D. Kump
HR: Richard R. Benson
FYE: December 31
Type: Public

Energy East has evolved into a major regional player. The utility holding company distributes electricity and natural gas in four northeastern states through subsidiaries Berkshire Gas, Central Maine Power, Connecticut Natural Gas, Maine Natural Gas, New York State Electric & Gas, Rochester Gas and Electric, and Southern Connecticut Gas. Overall, Energy East serves about 2 million electricity customers as well as 1 million natural gas customers. Other operations include power generation, energy marketing, gas transportation and processing, propane distribution, telecommunications, and energy infrastructure and management services. In 2007 Energy East agreed to be acquired by IBERDROLA for $4.5 billion.

	Annual Growth	12/03	12/04	12/05	12/06	12/07
Sales ($ mil.)	3.0%	4,593.8	4,756.7	5,298.5	5,230.7	5,178.1
Net income ($ mil.)	4.5%	210.4	229.3	256.8	259.8	251.3
Market value ($ mil.)	7.1%	3,276.3	3,925.1	3,367.6	3,668.1	4,307.4
Employees	(1.7%)	—	6,092	6,114	5,884	—

ENERGY FOCUS, INC.

NASDAQ (GM): EFOI

32000 Aurora Rd.
Solon, OH 44139
Phone: 440-715-1300
Fax: 440-715-1329
Web: www.energyfocusinc.com

CEO: Joseph (Joe) Kaveski
CFO: Nicholas G. Berchtold
HR: Donna Prunetti
FYE: December 31
Type: Public

The Illuminator may be coming to a theater near you, but it isn't a movie. It's Energy Focus (formerly Fiberstars), a manufacturer of fiber-optic lighting systems that can be used as alternatives to standard electrical lights. Energy Focus' systems are used to illuminate cinemas, shopping malls, performing arts centers, restaurants, and homes. The company's lighting products include acrylic accent fixtures, downlight fixtures, spotlights, display-case lighting, pool and spa lighting, and floor pavers. Energy Focus sells its products in the US, Asia, and Europe through independent sales reps, distributors, and swimming pool manufacturers.

	Annual Growth	12/03	12/04	12/05	12/06	12/07
Sales ($ mil.)	(4.2%)	27.2	29.7	28.3	27.0	22.9
Net income ($ mil.)	—	(0.6)	(0.7)	(7.4)	(9.6)	(11.3)
Market value ($ mil.)	25.8%	43.0	73.8	96.4	74.2	107.5
Employees	—	—	—	127	—	—

⊞ ENERGY FUTURE HOLDINGS CORP.

1601 Bryan St.
Dallas, TX 75201
Phone: 214-812-4600
Fax: –
Web: www.energyfutureholdings.com

CEO: John F. Young
CFO: David A. Campbell
HR: Molly Thompson
FYE: December 31
Type: Private

Energy Future Holdings' (formerly TXU) has seen the future and it works — powered by electricity. The company is the largest nonregulated retail electric provider in Texas (TXU Energy), with more than 2 million customers, and through its Luminant unit it has a generating capacity of more than 18,300 MW from its interests in nuclear and fossil-fueled power plants in the state. Energy Future Holdings has regulated power transmission and distribution operations through Oncor Electric Delivery. In 2007 the company was acquired in a $45 billion leveraged buyout by an investor group led by Goldman Sachs, Kohlberg Kravis Roberts, and Texas Pacific Group.

	Annual Growth	12/02	12/03	12/04	12/05	12/06
Sales ($ mil.)	2.0%	10,034.0	11,008.0	9,308.0	10,437.0	10,856.0
Net income ($ mil.)	—	(4,210.0)	582.0	485.0	1,722.0	2,552.0
Employees	(16.0%)	14,600	—	—	7,615	7,262

An in-depth profile of this company is available to Hoover's Online members at hoovers.com.

563

ENERGY KING, INC.

OTC: BEYV

4455 Lamont St., Ste. 3
San Diego, CA 92109
Phone: 858-272-6600
Fax: 858-272-9714
Web: www.beyv.com

CEO: Jeffrey R (Jeff) Hultman
CFO: Henry S. Leonard
HR: –
FYE: December 31
Type: Public

Energy King (formerly Buckeye Ventures) is warming up to the heating, ventilation, air conditioning (HVAC), and plumbing home services industries. The company maintains and installs residential HVAC units and performs window replacement. Formerly World Wide Motion Pictures (WWMPC), the company once produced and distributed movies and TV shows. The company held the distribution rights to nearly 300 film and TV titles and had a library of classics such as *As You Like It* with Laurence Olivier and *Santa Fe Trail* starring Ronald Reagan. The firm was founded in 1977 with the help of producer/director Otto Preminger. WWMPC became a subsidiary of Buckeye Ventures in 2006, but the film company has seen little activity.

	Annual Growth	12/03	12/04	12/05	12/06	12/07
Sales ($ mil.)	—	0.0	0.0	0.0	6.3	13.6
Net income ($ mil.)	—	(6.4)	(0.1)	(0.1)	(1.0)	(1.0)
Market value ($ mil.)	(70.6%)	—	—	—	19.7	5.8
Employees	—	—	—	—	—	—

ENERGY PARTNERS, LTD.

NYSE: EPL

201 St. Charles Ave., Ste. 3400
New Orleans, LA 70170
Phone: 504-569-1875
Fax: 504-569-1874
Web: www.eplweb.com

CEO: Richard A. Bachmann
CFO: Joseph T. Leary
HR: –
FYE: December 31
Type: Public

It pays for Energy Partners to have friends in the oil and gas business. The independent explorer and producer focuses on the deep and shallow waters of the Gulf of Mexico and the Gulf Coast. It partners with big oil companies to explore for reserves on properties the majors have left behind; Energy Partners earns an interest in the new reserves and production. The company has interests in more than 430 productive wells, and has proved reserves of 45.3 million barrels of oil equivalent. Energy Partners has grown through a combination of exploration, exploitation, and development drilling as well as strategic acquisitions of oil and natural gas fields.

	Annual Growth	12/03	12/04	12/05	12/06	12/07
Sales ($ mil.)	18.5%	230.2	295.2	403.0	449.5	454.6
Net income ($ mil.)	—	33.3	46.4	73.1	(50.4)	(80.0)
Market value ($ mil.)	(4.4%)	448.2	742.2	903.6	982.1	374.9
Employees	—	—	—	170	—	—

ENERGY TRANSFER EQUITY, L.P.

NYSE: ETE

3738 Oak Lawn Ave.
Dallas, TX 75219
Phone: 214-981-0700
Fax: 214-981-0703
Web: www.energytransfer.com

CEO: Kelcy L. Warren
CFO: John W. McReynolds
HR: –
FYE: August 31
Type: Public

Energy Transfer Equity is transferring some equity to get more out of its midstream energy assets. The company acts as the general partner of Energy Transfer Partners, which sells 604 million gallons of propane a year to more than 1 million customers in 40 states. It also operates about 14,000 miles of natural gas pipelines. Through its Energy Transfer Partners GP unit, Energy Transfer Equity owns a 2% general partnership stake in Energy Transfer Partners and about 31% of common stock. Energy Transfer Equity is managed by general partner LE GP, LLC.

	Annual Growth	8/03	8/04	8/05	8/06	8/07
Sales ($ mil.)	64.3%	931.0	2,347.0	6,168.8	7,859.1	6,792.0
Net income ($ mil.)	62.2%	46.2	450.2	146.8	107.1	319.4
Market value ($ mil.)	142.9%	—	—	—	3,371.4	8,189.0
Employees	41.8%	—	—	2,642	3,900	5,316

ENERGY TRANSFER PARTNERS, L.P.

NYSE: ETP

2838 Woodside St.
Dallas, TX 75204
Phone: 214-981-0700
Fax: 214-981-0703
Web: www.energytransfer.com

CEO: Kelcy L. Warren
CFO: Brian J. Jennings
HR: –
FYE: August 31
Type: Public

Energy Transfer Partners distributes natural gas and propane across the US. The company operates about 14,000 miles of interstate natural gas gathering and transmission pipelines, and 2,400 miles of intrastate pipelines, and related storage assets. It sells more than 604 million gallons of propane a year to more than 1 million customers in 40 states. Energy Transfer Partners was formerly controlled by AGL Resources, Atmos Energy, Piedmont Natural Gas, and TECO Energy; the utilities sold their interests to Energy Transfer Equity in 2004. In 2006 the company acquired Transwestern Pipeline from Southern Union and GE for about $1.5 billion. Energy Transfer Equity controls about 33% of Energy Transfer Partners.

	Annual Growth	8/03	8/04	8/05	8/06	8/07
Sales ($ mil.)	85.7%	571.5	2,482.3	6,168.8	7,859.1	6,792.0
Net income ($ mil.)	115.9%	31.1	99.2	349.4	515.8	676.1
Market value ($ mil.)	124.2%	281.9	966.5	3,953.9	5,278.4	7,128.5
Employees	29.0%	—	—	3,193	3,898	5,316

ENERGY WEST, INCORPORATED

NASDAQ (GM): EWST

1 1st Ave. South
Great Falls, MT 59401
Phone: 406-791-7500
Fax: 406-791-7560
Web: www.ewst.com

CEO: Richard M. Osborne
CFO: Thomas J. Smith
HR: –
FYE: June 30
Type: Public

Energy West keeps the Wild West warm. The company's energy marketing subsidiary, Energy West Resources, primarily sells natural gas to industrial and commercial customers in Montana and Wyoming. Energy West's regulated natural gas utility businesses serve 34,000 customers in the two states. The company's subsidiary Energy West Propane sells bulk fuel to wholesale and retail customers. Energy West also has gas gathering and production operations; it owns the Shoshone interstate and the Glacier gathering natural gas pipelines located in Montana and Wyoming, and has stakes in 165 natural gas producing wells.

	Annual Growth	6/03	6/04	6/05	6/06	6/07
Sales ($ mil.)	(6.9%)	79.2	73.3	76.7	84.3	59.4
Net income ($ mil.)	—	(0.1)	(0.6)	1.4	2.3	6.2
Employees	—	—	—	—	—	—

ENERGYSOLUTIONS, INC.

NYSE: ES

423 W. 300 South, Ste. 200
Salt Lake City, UT 84101
Phone: 801-649-2000
Fax: 801-321-0453
Web: www.energysolutions.com

CEO: R. Steve Creamer
CFO: Philip O. Strawbridge
HR: Terry Aubie
FYE: September 30
Type: Public

Environmental services company EnergySolutions wants to solve the problem posed by what's left over after electricity has been generated from nuclear fuel. The company provides nuclear waste management services, primarily to the US Department of Energy, including nuclear facility decommissioning and decontamination, spent fuel handling, and waste disposal. Three nuclear waste services companies — Envirocare of Utah, Scientech D&D, and BNG America — combined to form EnergySolutions. In 2007 the company, which has operations in the UK and the US, went public. ENV Holdings holds 62% of EnergySolutions.

	Annual Growth	12/03	12/04	12/05	12/06	12/07
Sales ($ mil.)	68.9%	—	226.7	370.1	427.1	1,092.6
Net income ($ mil.)	—	—	111.6	131.6	34.4	(8.9)
Market value ($ mil.)	—	—	—	—	—	2,383.3
Employees	—	—	—	—	1,500	—

ENERGYSOUTH, INC.

NASDAQ (GS): ENSI

2828 Dauphin St.	CEO: Constantine S. (Dean) Liollio
Mobile, AL 36606	CFO: Charles P. Huffman
Phone: 251-450-4774	HR: –
Fax: 251-478-5817	FYE: October 30*
Web: www.energysouth.com	Type: Public

EnergySouth distributes natural gas to help its customers stay upwardly mobile. The holding company's Mobile Gas Service utility distributes natural gas to 95,000 customers in and around Mobile, Alabama. Other subsidiaries include EnergySouth Services (contract and consulting work for utilities and industries) and MGS Storage Services, which owns a 91% general partnership interest in Bay Gas Storage (gas storage caverns and pipelines). Bay Gas is expanding its storage and transportation facilities to help serve natural gas-fired electric generating plants planned by neighboring utilities. EnergySouth is exiting the gas marketing business.

	Annual Growth	9/03	9/04	9/05	9/06	9/07
Sales ($ mil.)	7.9%	99.6	116.0	124.6	135.9	135.0
Net income ($ mil.)	9.6%	11.1	12.6	13.8	14.0	16.0
Market value ($ mil.)	39.2%	107.2	213.3	217.9	268.2	402.7
Employees	—	—	—	261		

*Fiscal year change

ENERJEX RESOURCES, INC.

OTC: EJXR

7300 W. 110th St., 7th Fl.	CEO: C. Stephen (Steve) Cochennet
Overland Park, KS 66210	CFO: –
Phone: 913-693-4600	HR: –
Fax: 913-693-4601	FYE: March 31
Web: www.enerjexresources.com	Type: Public

When other oil companies have given up, EnerJex Resources steps in and injects some capital. The oil and gas exploration and production company works primarily in Eastern Kansas, buying producing properties that it feels are undervalued or that were abandoned by other oil companies when oil prices were below $10 a barrel. The company, which has proved reserves of 1.2 million barrels of oil equivalent, holds full or partial interest in half a dozen oil, gas, and oil and gas projects across Kansas. It uses enhanced drilling techniques to recover additional oil and gas from already explored fields. EnerJex was formed in 2006 by the merger of Millennium Plastics Corporation and Midwest Energy.

	Annual Growth	3/04	3/05	3/06	3/07	3/08
Sales ($ mil.)	—	—	—	—	0.0	0.1	3.6
Net income ($ mil.)	—	—	—	(0.6)	(2.0)	(4.8)
Market value ($ mil.)	—	—	—	—	—	24.4
Employees	—	—	—	—	8	—

ENERLUME ENERGY MANAGEMENT CORP.

OTC: ENLU

2 Broadway	CEO: David J. Murphy
Hamden, CT 06518	CFO: Michael C. Malota
Phone: 203-248-4100	HR: –
Fax: 203-230-8667	FYE: June 30
Web: www.enerlumeenergymanagementcorp.com	Type: Public

This former host wants to save you money on your energy costs. Formerly Host America, EnerLume Energy Management is a manufacturer of electronic devices designed to save energy and reduce electricity costs. Its EnerLume-EM energy management system regulates the power consumption of fluorescent lighting fixtures, allowing businesses to cut energy costs without sacrificing lighting levels. The programmable devices can also be used to switch office lighting on and off. EnerLume sells its products through a network of distribution partners. The company's RS Services subsidiary provides electrical construction contracting services.

	Annual Growth	6/03	6/04	6/05	6/06	6/07
Sales ($ mil.)	(26.9%)	25.2	26.8	30.8	37.0	7.2
Net income ($ mil.)	—	(0.6)	(4.9)	(9.7)	(12.9)	(6.1)
Market value ($ mil.)	202.9%	—	—	—	7.9	23.8
Employees	(7.7%)	—	—	—	413	381

ENERNOC, INC.

NASDAQ (GM): ENOC

75 Federal St., Ste. 300	CEO: Timothy G. Healy
Boston, MA 02110	CFO: Neal Isaacson
Phone: 617-224-9900	HR: –
Fax: 617-224-9910	FYE: December 31
Web: www.enernoc.com	Type: Public

EnerNOC knocks on the door of large energy customers and kindly asks them to dim the lights. Not literally of course, but the company, founded in 2001, has added its technology to utility companies' traditional demand response model. Rather than manually calling up their largest end-users, EnerNOC's Network Operations Center (NOC) remotely monitors their customers' energy assets and has the capability to adjust their electrical use (whether its dimming lights, adjusting the ac, or turning on emergency generators). EnerNOC manages more than 1,110 MW of demand response capacity. It caters to commercial, industrial, and institutional organizations, as well as electric power grid operators and utilities.

	Annual Growth	12/03	12/04	12/05	12/06	12/07
Sales ($ mil.)	—	0.0	0.8	9.8	26.1	60.8
Net income ($ mil.)	—	(0.6)	(1.9)	(1.7)	(5.8)	(23.6)
Market value ($ mil.)	—	—	—	—	—	941.8
Employees	—	—	—	—	—	—

ENERSYS INC.

NYSE: ENS

2366 Bernville Rd.	CEO: John D. Craig
Reading, PA 19605	CFO: Michael T. (Mike) Philion
Phone: 610-208-1991	HR: –
Fax: 610-372-8457	FYE: March 31
Web: www.enersysinc.com	Type: Public

EnerSys' battery operations are charging off in different directions. The company makes stationary industrial batteries that provide uninterruptible power and backup power for electronic systems and motive power batteries for big equipment such as forklifts. Other products include battery chargers and accessories. Its Hawker subsidiary makes batteries with industrial and military applications. Company management and Morgan Stanley acquired Yuasa's Motive Power and Stationary Power operations in 2000 and renamed the company EnerSys. The battery manufacturer has more than 10,000 customers around the world, reached through direct sales or distributors. European customers account for more than half of sales.

	Annual Growth	3/04	3/05	3/06	3/07	3/08
Sales ($ mil.)	20.3%	969.1	1,083.9	1,283.3	1,504.5	2,026.6
Net income ($ mil.)	87.8%	4.8	32.4	30.7	45.2	59.7
Market value ($ mil.)	24.7%	—	604.7	642.5	808.2	1,173.5
Employees	7.2%	6,500	6,600	7,500	7,800	8,600

ENESCO, LLC

225 Windsor Dr.	CEO: Basil Elliott
Itasca, IL 60143	CFO: Marie Meisenbach Graul
Phone: 630-875-5300	HR: –
Fax: 630-875-5350	FYE: December 31
Web: www.enesco.com	Type: Private

Enesco collects from collectibles. The company is a global marketer of porcelain and cold-cast collectibles (figurines, cottages), giftware (ornaments, music boxes, plush animals), garden accessories, and home décor (tableware, sculpture). It offers about 25,000 products, including the Cherished Teddies line of figurines, for sale in the US, Canada, and Europe. Enesco's products also include licensed brands, such as Beatrix Potter, Bratz, Disney, Mary Engelbreit, and Pooh & Friends. Most of its products are manufactured in China. Enesco sells through some 44,000 retailers and catalogs; international markets provide more than a third of sales. Enesco filed for Chapter 11 bankruptcy protection in January 2007.

An in-depth profile of this company is available to Hoover's Online members at hoovers.com.

565

ENGINEERED MATERIALS SOLUTIONS INC.

39 Perry Ave.
Attleboro, MA 02703
Phone: 508-342-2235
Fax: 508-342-2538
Web: www.emsclad.com

CEO: Eric J. Olson
CFO: –
HR: –
FYE: December 31
Type: Private

Engineered Materials Solutions (EMS) is glad to produce clad metals and electrical contacts (in button, inlay, toplay, rivet forms). With clad metals, EMS bonds two or more metals (such as aluminum and steel) using a high pressure process to form a single strip of metal. The company manufactures products for the appliance, automotive, electrical, HVAC, and telecommunications industries. EMS opened a manufacturing facility in China in mid-2007. Although its roots date back to 1916, EMS was formed when it bought the metal materials division of Texas Instruments. Wickeder Westfalenstahl, a Germany-based metal fabrication company, acquired EMS in 2007.

	Annual Growth	12/03	12/04	12/05	12/06	12/07
Est. sales ($ mil.)	—	—	—	—	—	54.4
Employees	—	—	—	—	—	390

ENGLOBAL CORPORATION

AMEX: ENG

654 N. Sam Houston Pkwy. East, Ste. 400
Houston, TX 77060
Phone: 281-878-1000
Fax: 281-878-1010
Web: www.englobal.com

CEO: William A. (Bill) Coskey
CFO: Robert W. (Bob) Raiford
HR: Robert J. Church
FYE: December 31
Type: Public

ENGlobal hopes to engineer its way into the hearts of energy companies throughout the world. The company provides engineering and systems services, procurement, construction management, inspection, and control system automation services to the pipeline and process divisions of major oil and gas companies. It also designs and installs control and instrumentation systems for energy companies. Subsidiary ENGlobal Land (formerly WRC Corporation) provides land management, environmental compliance, and other services. Other subsidiaries include ENGlobal Automation Group, Inc. (EAG), which offers control system automation products, and Analyzer Technology, which provides online process analyzer systems.

	Annual Growth	12/03	12/04	12/05	12/06	12/07
Sales ($ mil.)	30.9%	123.7	148.9	233.6	303.1	363.2
Net income ($ mil.)	54.4%	2.2	2.4	4.8	(3.5)	12.5
Market value ($ mil.)	59.6%	47.3	72.7	220.8	172.4	307.3
Employees	19.0%	—	—	1,724	—	2,443

ENGMAN-TAYLOR COMPANY, INC.

W142 N9351 Fountain Blvd.
Menomonee Falls, WI 53051
Phone: 262-255-9300
Fax: 262-255-6512
Web: www.engman-taylor.com

CEO: Rick Star
CFO: –
HR: –
FYE: December 31
Type: Private

Engman-Taylor Company (ETCO), a family-owned enterprise, distributes tools (metal cutting tools, grinders, and saws) and other products such as adhesives and sealants, fasteners, material handling devices, and pneumatic and hydraulic equipment to manufacturing companies. The company also provides a comprehensive line of machine tools. ETCO's origin dates back to 1945, when brothers Carl and Joe Engman founded Engman Brothers in Milwaukee. It adapted its current name in 1956 after Bob Taylor acquired the company. Chairman Dick Star and Ed Melicher bought the company in 1974, but kept its name.

	Annual Growth	12/03	12/04	12/05	12/06	12/07
Est. sales ($ mil.)	—	—	—	—	—	70.0
Employees	—	—	—	—	—	130

ENHERENT CORP.

OTC: ENHT

101 Eisenhower Pkwy., Ste. 300
Roseland, NJ 07068
Phone: 973-795-1290
Fax: 973-795-1311
Web: www.enherent.com

CEO: Pamela A. Fredette
CFO: Arunava De
HR: Lori Stanley
FYE: December 31
Type: Public

Little "e," big on "IT." Information technology (IT) consultancy enherent provides software development and technical staffing. Its software integrates Web-enabled communication and transaction applications with legacy systems, as well as other enterprise information systems. Through its staffing business, enherent provides technical personnel and project management services. Targeting *FORTUNE* 1000 companies, enherent's customers come from industries such as financial services, health care, and manufacturing, and include AIG, Bank of America, New England Motor Freight, GlaxoSmithKline, and Wachovia Securities.

	Annual Growth	12/03	12/04	12/05	12/06	12/07
Sales ($ mil.)	26.2%	12.1	13.0	27.3	30.1	30.7
Net income ($ mil.)	—	(1.3)	(0.9)	(0.7)	(0.3)	0.4
Market value ($ mil.)	34.8%	1.7	7.0	6.3	3.1	5.6
Employees	—	—	—	—	—	—

ENLIVEN MARKETING TECHNOLOGIES

NASDAQ (CM): ENLV

498 7th Ave., Ste. 1810
New York, NY 10018
Phone: 212-201-0800
Fax: 212-201-0801
Web: www.viewpoint.com

CEO: Patrick Vogt
CFO: Christopher C. (Chris) Duignan
HR: –
FYE: December 31
Type: Public

Enliven Marketing Technologies Corporation provides the Viewpoint Toolbar, a Web search tool that attaches to the Internet Explorer browser. Its Viewpoint Platform enables users to create 3-D images of retail goods and allows online shoppers to interact with them. The company's Viewpoint Media Player broadcasts online content. Enliven also offers professional services including 3-D models and digital effects creation for the entertainment and gaming industries. Clients have included IBM, General Motors, Samsung, Kimberly-Clark, and Toyota. Formerly called Viewpoint, the company changed its name to Enliven Marketing Technologies at the beginning of 2008.

	Annual Growth	12/03	12/04	12/05	12/06	12/07
Sales ($ mil.)	8.5%	13.5	14.5	25.3	17.2	18.7
Net income ($ mil.)	—	(21.5)	(9.7)	(10.6)	(19.7)	(13.5)
Market value ($ mil.)	30.2%	39.3	175.3	71.2	45.8	113.0
Employees	—	—	—	126	—	—

ENNIS, INC.

NYSE: EBF

2441 Presidential Pkwy.
Midlothian, TX 76065
Phone: 972-775-9801
Fax: 972-775-9820
Web: www.ennis.com

CEO: Keith S. Walters
CFO: Richard L. Travis Jr.
HR: Richard Maresh
FYE: Last day of February
Type: Public

Ennis is in the forms and fashion business. It makes a variety of custom business forms and promotional products (Post-it Notes, presentation products, advertising specialty items). It also sells printed bank forms, secure and negotiable documents, and apparel. Most of its sales, however, come from custom items. The firm sells its products throughout the US — to end users and forms distributors and resellers. It operates about 40 manufacturing plants in 16 states, as well as in Mexico and Canada. Ennis runs about 30 subsidiaries, including Adams McClure (retail promotions), Northstar Computer Forms (bank forms), and Alstyle Apparel. Royce & Associates owns about 10% of the firm.

	Annual Growth	2/04	2/05	2/06	2/07	2/08
Sales ($ mil.)	23.9%	259.4	365.4	559.4	584.7	610.6
Net income ($ mil.)	25.5%	18.0	23.0	40.5	41.6	44.6
Market value ($ mil.)	10.4%	275.9	434.1	502.4	659.9	409.6
Employees	29.9%	2,200	6,200	5,950	6,383	6,256

ENODIS CORPORATION

2227 Welbilt Blvd.
New Port Richey, FL 34655
Phone: 727-375-7010
Fax: 727-375-0472
Web: www.enodisusa.com

CEO: Jim Weaks
CFO: Michael (Mike) Hicks
HR: –
FYE: Saturday nearest September 30
Type: Subsidiary

Before it gets to your plate, restaurant quality food passes through many of Enodis Corporation's products. The company runs the North American food-service equipment operations for its UK-based parent, Enodis plc, which include brand names and subsidiaries Scotsman, Garland, Frymaster, Cleveland, Delfield, Kysor/Warren, Lincoln, Convotherm, and Merrychef. The company also has an extensive line of heating products such as its Mealstream Oven, Xpress Grill, and Moisture +. The products are designed for rapid cooking or to maintain hot foods for restaurants, convenience stores, and other food service providers.

ENOVA SYSTEMS, INC.

AMEX: ENA

1560 W. 190th St.
Torrance, CA 90501
Phone: 310-527-2800
Fax: 310-527-7888
Web: www.enovasystems.com

CEO: Mike Staran
CFO: Jarett Fenton
HR: –
FYE: December 31
Type: Public

Enova Systems makes commercial digital power management systems for controlling and monitoring electric power in automobiles and stationary power generators. Products include hybrid-electric drive systems, electric drive motors, electric motor controllers, hybrid drive systems, battery care units, safety disconnect units, generator units, fuel cell management units, and fuel cell power conditioning units. The company counts EDO, First Auto Works of China, Ford Motor, Hyundai Motor, Navistar International, and Volvo/Mack among its customers. Enova gets about two-thirds of its sales outside the US, primarily in the UK.

	Annual Growth	12/03	12/04	12/05	12/06	12/07
Sales ($ mil.)	20.9%	4.3	2.5	6.1	1.7	9.2
Net income ($ mil.)	—	(3.2)	(3.4)	(2.1)	(4.8)	(9.4)
Market value ($ mil.)	(56.5%)	2,298.8	2,205.5	52.5	45.8	82.3
Employees	24.3%	31	31	33	43	74

ENPRO INDUSTRIES, INC.

NYSE: NPO

5605 Carnegie Blvd., Ste. 500
Charlotte, NC 28209
Phone: 704-731-1500
Fax: 704-731-1511
Web: www.enproindustries.com

CEO: Stephen E. (Steve) Macadam
CFO: William (Bill) Dries
HR: –
FYE: December 31
Type: Public

EnPro is a real pro when it comes to making engines, engineered products, and sealing systems. The company's Sealing Products segment offers sheet and metallic gaskets, metal seals, compression packing, rotary lip seals, elastomeric seals, hydraulic components, expansion joints, and PTFE products. EnPro's Engineered Products segment makes bearing products, air compressors, vacuum pumps, diesel and natural gas engines, and industrial tooling systems under the GGB, Quincy Compressor, and France Compressor Products brands. The company also makes heavy-duty, medium-speed diesel and natural gas engines under the Fairbanks Morse Engine brand name. EnPro Industries gets more than half of its sales in the US.

	Annual Growth	12/03	12/04	12/05	12/06	12/07
Sales ($ mil.)	9.0%	730.1	826.3	838.6	928.4	1,030.0
Net income ($ mil.)	4.9%	33.2	33.8	58.6	(158.9)	40.2
Market value ($ mil.)	23.4%	282.7	608.3	560.2	696.8	656.2
Employees	2.2%	4,300	4,200	4,200	4,400	4,700

ENRON CREDITORS RECOVERY CORP.

4 Houston Center, 1331 Lamar, Ste. 1600
Houston, TX 77010
Phone: 713-853-6161
Fax: 713-853-3129
Web: www.enron.com

CEO: John J. Ray III
CFO: Richard Lydeker
HR: –
FYE: December 31
Type: Private

Enron Creditors Recovery Corp. (formerly Enron Corp.) which transformed itself from a gas pipeline operator into the world's #1 energy trader, is now bankrupt and selling off its remaining assets. Once the largest buyer and seller of natural gas and electricity in the US, Enron also traded numerous other commodities. Enron has sold its North American power utility and gas pipeline assets, and its global interests in utilities and power plants. In 2006 former executives Ken Lay and Jeff Skilling were found guilty of the charges in the corporate scandal that led to Enron's demise. Lay died suddenly and the conviction against him was vacated. Skilling was sentenced to more than 24 years in prison.

	Annual Growth	12/03	12/04	12/05	12/06	12/07
Est. sales ($ mil.)	—	—	—	—	—	2,147.5
Employees	—	—	—	—	—	10,000

ENSCO INTERNATIONAL INCORPORATED

NYSE: ESV

500 N. Akard St., Ste. 4300
Dallas, TX 75201
Phone: 214-397-3000
Fax: 214-397-3370
Web: www.enscous.com

CEO: Daniel W. Rabun
CFO: James W. (Jay) Swent III
HR: Charles A. Mills
FYE: December 31
Type: Public

ENSCO International is well-ensconced as a leading offshore drilling contractor. The company owns a fleet of 46 offshore rigs, including 44 jack-ups, one barge rig, and one semisubmersible (capable of drilling in up to 8,500 ft. of water). ENSCO conducts most of its domestic drilling business in the Asia/Pacific region (which includes Asia, the Middle East, Australia, and New Zealand), Europe/Africa, and North and South America. In 2008, some 19 of its rigs were operating in the Asia/Pacific region. The company took delivery of its 44th jack-up rig in 2007.

	Annual Growth	12/03	12/04	12/05	12/06	12/07
Sales ($ mil.)	28.3%	790.8	768.0	1,046.9	1,813.5	2,143.8
Net income ($ mil.)	74.0%	108.3	102.8	294.2	769.7	992.0
Market value ($ mil.)	20.4%	4,089.1	4,795.9	6,803.3	7,599.1	8,579.3
Employees	5.3%	—	—	3,700	3,900	4,100

THE ENSIGN GROUP, INC.

NASDAQ (GM): ENSG

27101 Puerta Real, Ste. 450
Mission Viejo, CA 92691
Phone: 949-487-9500
Fax: –
Web: www.ensigngroup.net

CEO: Christopher R. Christensen
CFO: Alan J. Norman
HR: –
FYE: December 31
Type: Public

The Ensign Group hangs its insignia at about 60 senior living facilities in the western US. Most of its facilities (which Ensign either owns or operates under lease agreements) are nursing homes, but it also operates a few assisted-living facilities and has assisted-living wings at some of its nursing centers. The company has a decentralized operating structure, with its portfolio of homes organized into five regional operating companies, each with its own management team. In turn, each home operates under local, and largely independent, management. The Ensign Group went public in 2007.

	Annual Growth	12/03	12/04	12/05	12/06	12/07
Sales ($ mil.)	18.9%	—	244.5	300.9	358.6	411.3
Net income ($ mil.)	22.7%	—	11.1	18.4	22.5	20.5
Market value ($ mil.)	—	—	—	—	—	294.9
Employees	3.1%	—	—	—	5,435	5,603

An in-depth profile of this company is available to Hoover's Online members at hoovers.com.

567

ENSIGN-BICKFORD INDUSTRIES, INC.

100 Grist Mill Rd.
Simsbury, CT 06070
Phone: 860-843-2000
Fax: 860-843-2600
Web: www.e-bind.com

CEO: John A. H. Shober
CFO: Denise M. Grant
HR: Kevin W. Schultz
FYE: December 31
Type: Private

Finicky dog? Short fuse? Ensign-Bickford Industries has a solution. The company, which manufactures cable filler and synthetic tapes, has five subsidiaries. The Ensign-Bickford Company makes non-electric explosive initiation systems, Ensign-Bickford Aerospace and Defense makes high-tech products such as reactive armor and demolition products, and SCB Technologies makes semiconductor bridge devices used in electric igniters. Its more prosaic subsidiaries include AFB International, which makes taste enhancers for pet foods, and Ensign-Bickford Realty, a real estate company in Connecticut.

	Annual Growth	12/03	12/04	12/05	12/06	12/07
Est. sales ($ mil.)	—	—	—	—	—	185.2
Employees	—	—	—	—	—	1,600

ENTEGRIS, INC.

NASDAQ (GS): ENTG

3500 Lyman Blvd.
Chaska, MN 55318
Phone: 952-556-3131
Fax: 952-556-1880
Web: www.entegris.com

CEO: Gideon Argov
CFO: Gregory B. (Greg) Graves
HR: John J. (Joe) Murphy
FYE: December 31
Type: Public

Entegris products are integral to making semiconductors and computer disk drives. The company makes more than 10,000 products used to transport and protect semiconductor and disk drive materials during processing. Its semiconductor products include wafer carriers, storage boxes, and chip trays, as well as chemical delivery products, such as pipes, fittings, and valves. Its disk drive offerings include shippers, stamper cases, and transport trays. Top customers for Entegris include AMD, Dainippon Screen Manufacturing, Freescale Semiconductor, IBM, Seagate Technology, Siltronic, and Taiwan Semiconductor Manufacturing. The Asia/Pacific region generates more than half of sales.

	Annual Growth	8/03	8/04	8/05	*12/06	12/07
Sales ($ mil.)	26.0%	248.8	346.8	367.1	678.7	626.2
Net income ($ mil.)	141.7%	1.3	24.8	9.4	63.5	44.4
Market value ($ mil.)	(1.7%)	1,067.4	601.7	1,399.0	1,436.6	995.5
Employees	13.4%	1,830	2,248	2,750	3,000	3,022
						*Fiscal year change

ENTERASYS NETWORKS, INC.

50 Minuteman Rd.
Andover, MA 01810
Phone: 978-684-1000
Fax: 978-684-1658
Web: www.enterasys.com

CEO: Michael (Mike) Fabiaschi
CFO: Terry Schmid
HR: –
FYE: Saturday nearest December 31
Type: Private

Enterasys Networks provides companies with a sense of security. The company designs routers and switches for use in corporate networks. It also provides network management and security software and access points used to build wireless networks. The company's service offerings include network installation, maintenance, support, and outsourcing. It markets to the commercial, government, education, and health care markets. Enterasys was acquired by an investor group led by two private equity firms, The Gores Group and Tennenbaum Capital Partners, for about $386 million in cash in 2006.

	Annual Growth	12/03	12/04	12/05	12/06	12/07
Est. sales ($ mil.)	—	—	—	—	—	80.8
Employees	—	—	—	—	—	750

ENTERCOM COMMUNICATIONS CORP.

NYSE: ETM

401 City Ave., Ste. 809
Bala Cynwyd, PA 19004
Phone: 610-660-5610
Fax: 610-660-5620
Web: www.entercom.com

CEO: David J. Field
CFO: Stephen F. Fisher
HR: Stephen F. Fisher
FYE: December 31
Type: Public

The signals from Entercom Communications come through loud and clear. The company is among the largest radio broadcasters in the US, with more than 100 stations clustered in more than 20 markets, including Boston, Denver, Kansas City, and Seattle. Operating a number of stations in one market allows the company to combine such back office functions as finance and accounting, as well as advertising sales and marketing. Its stations program a variety of formats, including oldies, country, and adult contemporary, as well as talk, sports, and news. The Field family, including founder and chairman Joseph Field, controls more than 60% of Entercom.

	Annual Growth	12/03	12/04	12/05	12/06	12/07
Sales ($ mil.)	4.0%	401.1	423.5	432.5	440.5	468.4
Net income ($ mil.)	—	71.8	75.6	78.4	48.0	(8.4)
Market value ($ mil.)	(34.2%)	2,278.3	1,448.7	1,026.9	912.4	426.2
Employees	(0.8%)	—	—	2,380	—	2,343

⊞ ENTERGY CORPORATION

NYSE: ETR

639 Loyola Ave.
New Orleans, LA 70113
Phone: 504-576-4000
Fax: 504-576-4428
Web: www.entergy.com

CEO: J. Wayne Leonard
CFO: Leo P. Denault
HR: Terry R. Seamons
FYE: December 31
Type: Public

If Entergy had an Entergizer bunny for a mascot, it would stay fully charged. The integrated utility holding company's subsidiaries distribute electricity to 2.7 million customers in four southern states (Arkansas, Louisiana, Mississippi, and Texas) and provide natural gas to 179,000 customers in Louisiana. Entergy has interests in regulated and nonregulated power plants in North America that have a combined generating capacity of about 30,000 MW; however, the company has announced plans to spin off its non-utility nuclear operations (six power plants). The company markets wholesale energy commodities; however, it has divested its primary marketing and trading operations.

	Annual Growth	12/03	12/04	12/05	12/06	12/07
Sales ($ mil.)	5.7%	9,194.9	10,123.7	10,106.3	10,932.2	11,484.4
Net income ($ mil.)	4.5%	950.5	933.0	923.8	1,132.6	1,134.8
Market value ($ mil.)	15.3%	13,076.9	14,655.5	14,246.9	18,710.3	23,081.7
Employees	0.8%	—	—	14,100	13,800	14,322

ENTERGY GULF STATES LOUISIANA, L.L.C.

350 Pine St.
Beaumont, TX 77701
Phone: 409-838-6631
Fax: 504-576-4879
Web: www.entergy-louisiana.com

CEO: E. Renae Conley
CFO: –
HR: –
FYE: December 31
Type: Subsidiary

Entergy Gulf States Louisiana keeps energy flowing in the Bayou State. The utility, a subsidiary of Entergy Corporation and an affiliate of Entergy Louisiana, provides electrical service to more than 370,700 customers in the state of Louisiana; its customer base is composed of residential, commercial, industrial, and governmental entities. The company also owns the River Bend Steam Electric Generation Station, a Louisiana-based 931 MW nuclear facility. Together, Entergy Louisiana and Entergy Gulf States Louisiana serve about 1 million electric customers in 58 parishes.

	Annual Growth	12/03	12/04	12/05	12/06	12/07
Est. sales ($ mil.)	—	—	—	—	—	2,147.5
Employees	—	—	—	—	—	1,616

ENTERGY MISSISSIPPI, INC.

308 E. Pearl St.
Jackson, MS 39201
Phone: 601-368-5000
Fax: 601-969-2583
Web: www.entergy-mississippi.com

CEO: Carolyn C. Shanks
CFO: Jay A. Lewis
HR: Terry R. Seamons
FYE: December 31
Type: Subsidiary

Much like old man river that "just keeps rolling along" Entergy Mississippi keeps electricity flowing in the Magnolia state. A presence in 45 of the state's 82 counties, the utility provides electricity to 427,000 residential, business, and institutional customers (roughly 16% of electric customers in Mississippi) throughout the western half of its namesake state. Its client base includes approximately 357,560 residential, 62,600 commercial, and 3,000 industrial customers, as well as more than 4,060 governmental agencies. Entergy Mississippi is a subsidiary of the Louisiana-based utility holding company Entergy.

	Annual Growth	12/03	12/04	12/05	12/06	12/07
Est. sales ($ mil.)	—	—	—	—	—	1,372.8
Net income ($ mil.)	—	—	—	—	—	72.1
Employees	—	—	—	—	—	—

ENTEROMEDICS INC.

NASDAQ (GM): ETRM

2800 Patton Rd.
St. Paul, MN 55113
Phone: 651-634-3003
Fax: –
Web: www.enteromedics.com

CEO: Mark B. Knudson
CFO: Gregory S. (Greg) Lea
HR: –
FYE: December 31
Type: Public

EnteroMedics is trying to quiet those grumbling hunger pangs. The development-stage medical device company uses neuroblocking technology called VBLOC therapy to combat obesity. Its initial product in development, the Maestro System, is a device laparoscopically implanted near the diaphragm that uses electrical impulses to limit the expansion of the stomach, thereby producing a feeling of prolonged fullness. The Maestro System is in US and international clinical trials, with FDA approval and commercial sales anticipated by 2010. EnteroMedics plans to build a direct sales force to market the product to bariatric surgeons and weight management specialists.

	Annual Growth	12/00	12/01	12/02	12/03	*12/04
Sales ($ mil.)	—	—	—	—	—	0.0
Net income ($ mil.)	—	—	—	—	—	(3.4)
Employees	—	—	—	—	—	—

*Most recent year available

ENTERPRISE BANCORP, INC.

NASDAQ (GM): EBTC

222 Merrimack St.
Lowell, MA 01852
Phone: 978-459-9000
Fax: 978-656-5813
Web: www.enterprisebankandtrust.com

CEO: John P. (Jack) Clancy Jr.
CFO: James A. Marcotte
HR: –
FYE: December 31
Type: Public

Enterprising entrepreneurs might consider seeking financial assistance from Enterprise Bancorp. The holding company is parent to Enterprise Bank and Trust, a full-service commercial bank that specializes in lending to growing businesses, corporations, partnerships, and not-for-profits. Business loans (some 85% of the bank's loan portfolio) include commercial mortgage, construction, and working capital loans; revolving lines of credit; and equipment financing and asset-based lending products. Through about 15 branches (primarily located in northeastern Massachusetts' Middlesex County), the bank also offers consumer loans, deposit products, investment management, trust, and other services.

	Annual Growth	12/03	12/04	12/05	12/06	12/07
Assets ($ mil.)	7.6%	—	848.2	918.5	979.3	1,057.7
Net income ($ mil.)	9.7%	—	7.5	8.4	9.2	9.9
Market value ($ mil.)	30.2%	—	—	59.0	124.3	100.1
Employees	3.1%	—	—	269	—	286

ENTERPRISE FINANCIAL SERVICES CORP

NASDAQ (GM): EFSC

150 N. Meramec Ave.
Clayton, MO 63105
Phone: 314-725-5500
Fax: 314-812-4025
Web: www.enterprisebank.com

CEO: Peter F. Benoist
CFO: Frank H. Sanfilippo
HR: Mark Murtha
FYE: December 31
Type: Public

Enterprise Financial Services wants you to boldly bank where many have banked before. It's the holding company for Enterprise Bank & Trust, which primarily targets closely held businesses and their owners, but also serves individuals in the St. Louis and Kansas City metropolitan areas. Through about a dozen branches, Enterprise Bank & Trust offers standard products such as checking, savings, and money market accounts and CDs. Loans to businesses, including commercial mortgages and operating loans, make up most of the company's lending activities. The bank also originates consumer, construction, and residential mortgage loans.

	Annual Growth	12/03	12/04	12/05	12/06	12/07
Assets ($ mil.)	21.8%	907.7	1,059.9	1,287.0	1,535.6	1,999.1
Net income ($ mil.)	26.4%	6.9	8.2	11.3	15.5	17.6
Market value ($ mil.)	21.7%	134.7	180.9	237.2	376.0	295.4
Employees	18.1%	—	—	261	329	364

ENTERPRISE GP HOLDINGS L.P.

NYSE: EPE

1100 Louisiana, 10th Fl.
Houston, TX 77002
Phone: 713-381-6500
Fax: 713-381-8200
Web: www.enterprisegp.com

CEO: Ralph S. Cunningham
CFO: W. Randall Fowler
HR: Thomas M. (Tom) Zulin
FYE: December 31
Type: Public

It has taken a lot of enterprise to put Enterprise GP Holdings on top. It owns Enterprise Products GP, LLC, the general partner and 2% owner of Enterprise Products Partners L.P. Enterprise Products Partners is a leading player in the North American natural gas, natural gas liquids (NGLs), and crude oil industries, with a range of processing, transportation, and storage services. Enterprise GP Holdings also holds the general partner and limited partner interests in TEPPCO Partners (whose operations include natural gas processing, NGL fractionation, and crude oil transportation) and Energy Transfer Equity, L.P. Chairman Dan Duncan controls about 77% of Enterprise GP Holdings.

	Annual Growth	12/03	12/04	12/05	12/06	12/07
Sales ($ mil.)	49.5%	5,346.0	8,321.2	12,257.0	13,991.0	26,713.8
Net income ($ mil.)	52.4%	20.2	30.7	55.3	99.5	109.0
Market value ($ mil.)	16.6%	—	—	3,352.7	3,286.0	4,560.6
Employees	—	—	2,345	2,600	2,920	0

ENTERPRISE INFORMATICS INC.

OTC: SPCO

10052 Mesa Ridge Ct., Ste. 100
San Diego, CA 92121
Phone: 858-625-3000
Fax: 858-625-3010
Web: www.enterpriseinformatics.com

CEO: Alan Kiraly
CFO: John W. Low
HR: –
FYE: September 30
Type: Public

Forget bulky filing cabinets and snail mail. Enterprise Informatics' (formerly Spescom Software) document, configuration, and records management software enables companies to scan and capture documents, then store the information or distribute it electronically. The company offers its eB software suite for documents ranging from letters and invoices to large-scale engineering drawings and multimedia files. eB also includes lifecycle management for physical assets and organizational requirements.

	Annual Growth	9/03	9/04	9/05	9/06	9/07
Sales ($ mil.)	5.0%	7.4	9.0	5.8	7.0	9.0
Net income ($ mil.)	—	(3.0)	0.1	(3.5)	(1.0)	1.3
Employees	—	—	—	—	—	—

An in-depth profile of this company is available to Hoover's Online members at hoovers.com.

569

ENTERPRISE PRODUCTS PARTNERS L.P.

NYSE: EPD

1100 Louisiana St., 10th Fl.	CEO: Michael A. Creel
Houston, TX 77002	CFO: W. Randall Fowler
Phone: 713-381-6500	HR: –
Fax: 713-381-8200	FYE: December 31
Web: www.epplp.com	Type: Public

Both enterprising and productive, Enterprise Products Partners is a leading player in the North American natural gas, natural gas liquids (NGL), and crude oil industries, with a range of processing, transportation, and storage services. Operations include natural gas processing, NGL fractionation, and crude oil transportation. The hub of the company's business is Houston's Mont Belvieu refinery complex. Enterprise owns interests in 17,760 miles of gas pipeline, 13,760 miles of NGL pipeline, and more than 900 miles of crude oil pipeline. It also owns salt domes, drilling platforms, and fractionation and natural gas processing plants. Chairman Dan Duncan holds a 34% stake in Enterprise.

	Annual Growth	12/03	12/04	12/05	12/06	12/07
Sales ($ mil.)	33.4%	5,346.4	8,321.2	12,257.0	13,991.0	16,950.1
Net income ($ mil.)	50.3%	104.6	268.3	419.5	601.2	533.7
Market value ($ mil.)	27.5%	5,238.2	9,420.7	9,342.5	12,499.2	13,823.4
Employees	(26.9%)	—	—	2,600	1,900	—

ENTERPRISE RENT-A-CAR COMPANY

600 Corporate Park Dr.	CEO: Andrew C. (Andy) Taylor
St. Louis, MO 63105	CFO: William W. (Bill) Snyder
Phone: 314-512-5000	HR: Edward (Ed) Adams
Fax: 314-512-4706	FYE: July 31
Web: www.enterprise.com	Type: Private

This Enterprise helps customers to boldly go where they might not have gone before they rented a fresh set of wheels. A leading US car rental company, Enterprise Rent-A-Car maintains a fleet of some 711,000 vehicles from nearly 7,000 locations — more than 6,000 in the US and another 900 in Canada, Germany, Ireland, and the UK. Unlike rivals such as Hertz and Avis, which operate primarily from airports, Enterprise focuses on customers whose own cars are in the shop or who need a rental for vacations or other special occasions. Enterprise, which acquired rival Vanguard Car Rental, is controlled by chairman and CEO Andrew Taylor, whose father, Jack Taylor, founded the company in 1957.

	Annual Growth	7/03	7/04	7/05	7/06	7/07
Sales ($ mil.)	8.3%	6,900.0	7,400.0	8,230.0	9,000.0	9,500.0
Employees	5.7%	53,500	57,300	61,000	75,700	66,700

ENTERTAINMENT DISTRIBUTION

NASDAQ (GM): EDCI

825 8th Ave., 23rd Fl.	CEO: Jordan M. Copland
New York, NY 10019	CFO: Jordan M. Copland
Phone: 212-333-8400	HR: –
Fax: –	FYE: December 31
Web: www.edcllc.com	Type: Public

Entertainment Distribution Company, Inc., (EDC) decided to get into a more entertaining line of work. Once a provider of messaging systems, EDC now manufactures and distributes pre-recorded CDs and DVDs for music and movie firms. Formerly named Glenayre, the company acquired some CD and DVD manufacturing operations of Universal Music Group (UMG) in 2005. The acquired business, called Entertainment Distribution Company, became a unit of Glenayre and was its only continuing business segment. Glenayre subsequently changed its name to Entertainment Distribution Company. It has an agreement to make and distribute UMG's CDs and DVDs in North America and Europe.

	Annual Growth	12/03	12/04	12/05	12/06	12/07
Sales ($ mil.)	60.3%	58.2	50.6	267.8	348.5	384.6
Net income ($ mil.)	—	1.6	4.5	8.0	4.0	(15.1)
Market value ($ mil.)	(28.4%)	178.6	145.9	221.2	177.5	47.0
Employees	0.3%	—	—	2,193	2,200	—

ENTERTAINMENT PROPERTIES TRUST

NYSE: EPR

30 Pershing Rd., Ste. 201	CEO: David M. Brain
Kansas City, MO 64108	CFO: Mark A. Peterson
Phone: 816-472-1700	HR: –
Fax: 816-472-5794	FYE: December 31
Web: www.eprkc.com	Type: Public

Entertainment Properties Trust invests in today's Roman circus. Including properties under development, the self-administered real estate investment trust (REIT) owns nearly 80 movie megaplex theaters and eight entertainment retail centers, totaling about 9 million sq. ft., in more than two dozen states and Canada. The company buys properties from theater operators and leases them back to the original owners. More than half of Entertainment Properties' theaters are leased to AMC Entertainment. The company's retail holdings, located in California, Colorado, New York, and Ontario, are multi-tenant properties anchored by multiplexes that offer specialty restaurants and retail stores.

	Annual Growth	12/03	12/04	12/05	12/06	12/07
Sales ($ mil.)	26.8%	91.2	125.0	164.8	195.5	235.7
Net income ($ mil.)	29.2%	37.6	53.7	69.1	82.3	104.7
Market value ($ mil.)	17.9%	682.5	1,116.5	1,028.2	1,547.4	1,320.0
Employees	10.9%	—	—	13	—	16

ENTORIAN TECHNOLOGIES INC.

NASDAQ (GM): ENTN

8900 Shoal Creek Blvd., Ste. 125	CEO: Wayne R. Lieberman
Austin, TX 78757	CFO: W. Kirk Patterson
Phone: 512-454-9531	HR: Stephanie A. Lucie
Fax: 512-454-9409	FYE: December 31
Web: www.entorian.com	Type: Public

Entorian Technologies (formerly known as Staktek) piles the memory high for better performance. Entorian makes high-density memory modules that use its proprietary 3-D stacking technology, which it touts as allowing more memory to fit in less board space. The company's standard and custom products are used in network servers, routers, workstations, communications systems, data recorders, and handheld devices. Entorian's customers include Cisco, Dell, Hewlett-Packard, IBM, and Sun Microsystems. Micron Technology, while a competitor, is also a leading customer, representing 34% of sales. Most of Entorian's sales are in the US.

	Annual Growth	12/03	12/04	12/05	12/06	12/07
Sales ($ mil.)	(17.8%)	—	73.6	52.5	55.6	40.9
Net income ($ mil.)	—	—	7.8	(7.5)	(0.4)	(40.0)
Market value ($ mil.)	(27.0%)	—	234.9	359.6	245.6	91.5
Employees	4.0%	—	370	457	504	416

ENTRADE INC.

Pink Sheets: ETAD

500 Central Ave.	CEO: Peter R. Harvey
Northfield, IL 60093	CFO: –
Phone: 847-441-6650	HR: –
Fax: 847-441-6959	FYE: December 31
	Type: Public

Entrade was entranced by the online B2B portal craze, but it's now bidding on the auction business. Formerly ARTRA GROUP, it's focused on developing its Nationwide Auction Systems, once the leading asset liquidation businesses in the US. Nationwide specializes in the disposal of surplus property, such as vehicles, equipment, excess inventory, and repossessions. Nationwide has facilities in California, Delaware, Georgia, and Missouri. Entrade is looking to enhance the unit's business through Internet technology. The firm continues to have equity positions in several online B2B portals, like AssetTRADE, utiliparts.com, and pricecontainer.com. In March 2007 Entrade, through Nationwide, bought Cogent Financial Group.

	Annual Growth	12/02	12/03	12/04	12/05	*12/06
Sales ($ mil.)	—	—	—	—	—	57.3
Net income ($ mil.)	—	—	—	—	—	(27.5)
Employees	—	—	—	—	—	300

*Most recent year available

An in-depth profile of this company is available to Hoover's Online members at hoovers.com.

ENTRAVISION COMMUNICATIONS CORPORATION

NYSE: EVC

2425 Olympic Blvd., Ste. 6000 West
Santa Monica, CA 90404
Phone: 310-447-3870
Fax: 310-447-3899
Web: www.entravision.com

CEO: Walter F. Ulloa
CFO: Christopher T. Young
HR: Alexander K. LaBrie
FYE: December 31
Type: Public

This company wants to be the whole enchilada for advertisers trying to reach the US Hispanic market. Entravision Communications is the #2 Spanish-language media company in the country (behind Univision Communications) with about 50 television stations and 50 radio stations located mostly in the Southwest. It is the largest affiliate of Univision's two Spanish-language television networks, Univision and TeleFutura; Entravision's TV portfolio also includes a small number of stations affiliated with The CW Network, FOX, and MyNetworkTV. On the radio, the company offers a variety of programming formats, including music, news, sports, and talk radio.

	Annual Growth	12/03	12/04	12/05	12/06	12/07
Sales ($ mil.)	1.2%	238.0	259.0	281.0	291.8	250.1
Net income ($ mil.)	—	2.3	6.2	(9.7)	(134.6)	(43.1)
Market value ($ mil.)	(9.0%)	659.7	497.4	425.6	495.6	452.1
Employees	—	—	—	1,148	—	—

ENTREMED, INC.

NASDAQ (GM): ENMD

9640 Medical Center Dr.
Rockville, MD 20850
Phone: 240-864-2600
Fax: 240-864-2601
Web: www.entremed.com

CEO: James S. (Jim) Burns
CFO: Dane R. Saglio
HR: —
FYE: December 31
Type: Public

EntreMed is cancer's new enemy. The company develops drugs that inhibit angiogenesis, or the growth of new blood vessels. One of its lead product candidates is Panzem, an antiangiogenesis drug that may starve cancer tumors of the blood they need to grow, thus killing the cancer cells. Panzem is undergoing clinical testing as a treatment for multiple forms of solid tumors, including glioblastoma multiforme (brain cancer), as well as breast, prostate, and kidney cancer. Another candidate, MKC-1, is in clinical trials as a treatment for both solid tumors and hematological cancers. EntreMed receives royalties from sales of Thalomid, Celgene's multiple myeloma therapy. Celgene owns 27% of EntreMed.

	Annual Growth	12/03	12/04	12/05	12/06	12/07
Sales ($ mil.)	46.6%	1.6	0.5	5.9	6.9	7.4
Net income ($ mil.)	—	(19.5)	(12.6)	(16.3)	(49.9)	(22.4)
Market value ($ mil.)	(4.9%)	125.7	161.4	99.1	134.0	102.9
Employees	—	—	—	41	—	—

ENTROPIC COMMUNICATIONS, INC.

NASDAQ (GM): ENTR

6290 Sequence Dr.
San Diego, CA 92121
Phone: 858-768-3600
Fax: 858-768-3601
Web: www.entropic.com

CEO: Patrick C. Henry
CFO: David Lyle
HR: Suzanne (Suzy) Zoumaras
FYE: December 31
Type: Public

Entropic Communications is far from sluggish when it comes to broadband. The fabless semiconductor company designs specialized chipsets for video and broadband multimedia applications. Entropic is targeting digital home entertainment networks linked by coaxial cable connections, a market being promoted by cable TV services providers and others. The company's c.LINK technology enables networking among high-definition TVs, digital video recorders, and set-top boxes. Entropic is a charter member of the Multimedia over Coax Alliance (MoCA), an industry group standardizing technologies for networking consumer electronics. Actiontec Electronics (26% of sales), Jabil (15%), and Motorola (39%) are leading customers.

	Annual Growth	12/03	12/04	12/05	12/06	12/07
Sales ($ mil.)	574.0%	—	0.4	3.7	41.5	122.5
Net income ($ mil.)	—	—	(11.7)	(12.2)	(7.1)	(32.0)
Market value ($ mil.)	—	—	—	—	—	496.2
Employees	118.2%	—	—	59	220	281

ENTRUST, INC.

NASDAQ (GM): ENTU

1 Hanover Park, 16633 Dallas Pkwy.
Addison, TX 75001
Phone: 972-713-5800
Fax: 972-713-5805
Web: www.entrust.com

CEO: F. William (Bill) Conner
CFO: David Wagner
HR: —
FYE: December 31
Type: Public

Entrust has a multi-layered approach to network security. The company's software and services ensure the privacy of electronic communications and transactions across corporate networks and the Internet. Entrust's software is used to authenticate users via smart cards, passwords, and biometric devices, controlling access to information in e-mail, databases, Web pages, and business applications. The company also offers services such as consulting, deployment, and managed security services. The company targets vertical markets such as health care, financial services, and government agencies. Its customers include insurance brokerage Aon, online travel agency Expedia, and NASA.

	Annual Growth	12/03	12/04	12/05	12/06	12/07
Sales ($ mil.)	3.2%	87.9	91.0	98.1	95.2	99.7
Net income ($ mil.)	—	(35.9)	1.1	6.4	(15.4)	(6.2)
Market value ($ mil.)	(17.9%)	259.5	236.3	290.2	256.9	117.9
Employees	(2.1%)	—	—	475	503	455

ENTRX CORPORATION

Pink Sheets: ENTX

800 Nicollet Mall, Ste. 2690
Minneapolis, MN 55402
Phone: 612-333-0614
Fax: 612-338-7332
Web: metalclad.com

CEO: Peter L. Hauser
CFO: Brian D. Niebur
HR: —
FYE: December 31
Type: Public

The main focus of Entrx as of late has been to insulate and abate. The company provides insulation and asbestos abatement services through subsidiary Metalclad Insulation. Operating primarily in California, it installs insulation on pipes, ducts, furnaces, boilers, and other industrial equipment. It also maintains and removes insulation and sells specialty insulation products to public utilities, oil, petrochemical, and heavy construction companies. Customers that have contracted Metalclad include JE Merit Constructors Inc. and Southern California Edison Company. Chairman and CEO Peter Hauser owns about 13% of Entrx.

	Annual Growth	12/03	12/04	12/05	12/06	12/07
Sales ($ mil.)	15.2%	12.7	13.0	14.7	19.5	22.4
Net income ($ mil.)	—	(3.0)	0.6	(1.7)	2.0	0.6
Employees	—	—	—	—	—	17

ENVIRO VORAXIAL TECHNOLOGY, INC.

OTC: EVTN

821 NW 57th Place
Fort Lauderdale, FL 33309
Phone: 954-958-9968
Fax: 954-958-8057
Web: www.evtn.com

CEO: Alberto DiBella
CFO: Alberto DiBella
HR: —
FYE: December 31
Type: Public

Enviro Voraxial Technology has a voracious appetite for developing equipment to separate solids and liquids with different specific gravities. The company's Voraxial Separator can be used for wastewater treatment, grit and sand separation, oil and water separation, marine-oil-spill cleanup, bilge and ballast treatment, stormwater treatment, and food-processing-waste treatment. The separator is capable of processing volumes as low as 3 gallons per minute, as well as volumes or more than 10,000 gallons per minute with only one moving part. Chairman and CEO Alberto DiBella, officers, and directors control almost 35% of the company.

	Annual Growth	12/03	12/04	12/05	12/06	12/07
Sales ($ mil.)	—	0.0	0.0	0.1	0.3	0.3
Net income ($ mil.)	—	(1.3)	(1.7)	(1.1)	(0.8)	(1.9)
Market value ($ mil.)	1.8%	12.9	10.6	11.1	12.1	13.9
Employees	—	—	—	—	—	—

An in-depth profile of this company is available to Hoover's Online members at hoovers.com.

571

ENVIROKARE TECH, INC.

OTC: ENVK

641 Lexington Ave., 14th Fl.
New York, NY 10022
Phone: 212-634-6333
Fax: 212-634-6339
Web: www.envirokare.com

CEO: George E. Kazantzis
CFO: George E. Kazantzis
HR: –
FYE: December 31
Type: Public

Envirokare Tech isn't generating a lot of cash just yet, but it does have plenty of plastic. Founded in 1998, Envirokare has exclusive marketing and production rights to a technology developed by Thermoplastic Composite Design; this technology holds promise for a cheaper, more efficient method of manufacturing advanced composite materials. Speculative markets include construction (decking, steps), materials handling (pallets), and marine (boat hulls). In 2005 the development-stage company acquired Thermoplastic Composite Design and joined NOVA Chemicals in creating a joint venture (LRM Industries) for commercializing the long-fiber technology.

	Annual Growth	12/03	12/04	12/05	12/06	12/07
Sales ($ mil.)	(14.7%)	—	—	1.1	0.5	0.8
Net income ($ mil.)	—	—	—	(8.5)	(5.3)	(4.1)
Market value ($ mil.)	17.2%	—	—	17.7	32.8	24.3
Employees	—	—	—	4	—	—

ENVIRONMENTAL POWER CORPORATION

AMEX: EPG

1 Cate St., 4th Fl.
Portsmouth, NH 03801
Phone: 603-431-1780
Fax: 603-431-2650
Web: www.environmentalpower.com

CEO: Richard E. Kessel
CFO: Michael E. Thomas
HR: –
FYE: December 31
Type: Public

First water, then waste coal . . . what next? Throughout its history Environmental Power has taken over independent power projects. The company acquires or develops and then sells hydroelectric and waste-coal generation facilities. Its Buzzard Power subsidiary has ownership of the company's Scrubgrass coal-fired plant (83 MW). Subsidiary Microgy Cogeneration Systems holds an exclusive license to market an animal waste-to-energy conversion technology in North America; the unit has several projects in development stages. Chairman Joseph Cresci owns 11% of Environmental Power.

	Annual Growth	12/03	12/04	12/05	12/06	12/07
Sales ($ mil.)	(61.3%)	53.4	59.8	55.8	53.9	1.2
Net income ($ mil.)	—	(1.0)	(4.0)	(11.4)	(14.1)	(17.4)
Market value ($ mil.)	(19.4%)	168.5	52.5	66.8	85.4	71.2
Employees	16.9%	—	—	30	—	41

ENVIRONMENTAL SYSTEMS RESEARCH INSTITUTE, INC.

380 New York St.
Redlands, CA 92373
Phone: 909-793-2853
Fax: 909-307-3025
Web: www.esri.com

CEO: Jack Dangermond
CFO: Thomas G. (Tom) Pickett
HR: Cathy Mueller
FYE: December 31
Type: Private

For Environmental Systems Research Institute, success stems from thinking globally and mapping locally. The company, known as ESRI, is a leading developer of geographic information systems (GIS) software used to create and label digital maps, publish maps on the Internet, and build related databases. ESRI has customers in fields such as government, forestry, oil and gas, and transportation. The company's ArcGIS products dominate the field, with applications in containing oil spills, planning land use, monitoring rainforest depletion, and routing emergency vehicles, among other uses. ESRI was founded in 1969 with $1,100 by consultants Jack and Laura Dangermond.

ENVIRONMENTAL TECTONICS CORPORATION

AMEX: ETC

125 James Way
Southampton, PA 18966
Phone: 215-355-9100
Fax: 215-357-4000
Web: www.etcusa.com

CEO: William F. Mitchell
CFO: Duane D. Deaner
HR: Germaine Culbreth
FYE: Last Friday in February
Type: Public

Environmental Tectonics Corporation (ETC) believes virtual environments can teach us a lot about real life. Through its aircrew training systems segment, the company makes software-driven flight simulators, disaster simulators, and motion-based simulation rides for the amusement industry. Its NASTAR center provides space training and research services. ETC's industrial business segment makes steam and gas sterilizers, hyperbaric chambers (used for high-altitude training, decompression, and wound care), and environmental sampling and analysis chambers. The company's major customers have included L-3 Communications, the Royal Malaysian Air Force, the UK Ministry of Defence, and the US Army Corps of Engineers.

	Annual Growth	2/04	2/05	2/06	2/07	2/08
Sales ($ mil.)	(3.3%)	26.0	27.8	25.1	17.4	22.7
Net income ($ mil.)	—	(0.8)	(8.1)	(6.7)	(8.9)	(13.9)
Market value ($ mil.)	(28.4%)	63.4	51.4	45.5	30.2	16.7
Employees	—	—	—	—	257	—

ENXNET, INC.

OTC: EXNT

11333 E. Pine St., Ste. 75
Tulsa, OK 74116
Phone: 918-592-0015
Fax: 918-592-0016
Web: www.enxnet.com

CEO: Ryan Corley
CFO: Stephen (Steve) Hoelscher
HR: –
FYE: March 31
Type: Public

EnXnet licenses and markets emerging multimedia technologies, including video compression and content storage. It has acquired the licensing rights to a video compression technology called ClearVideo, used for distribution, downloading, and streaming of video and audio content over the Internet. Other licensed technologies include DVDPlus, a media storage product that combines a CD and DVD on the same disc, and CD/DVD anti-theft technologies. CEO Ryan Corley owns more than 50% of the company.

	Annual Growth	3/04	3/05	3/06	3/07	3/08
Sales ($ mil.)	—	—	—	—	0.0	0.0
Net income ($ mil.)	—	—	—	—	(1.0)	(0.8)
Market value ($ mil.)	(40.1%)	—	—	—	26.1	15.6
Employees	—	—	—	—	—	—

ENZO BIOCHEM, INC.

NYSE: ENZ

527 Madison Ave.
New York, NY 10022
Phone: 212-583-0100
Fax: –
Web: www.enzo.com

CEO: Elazar Rabbani
CFO: Barry W. Weiner
HR: –
FYE: July 31
Type: Public

For Enzo Biochem, antisense is perfectly sensible. The biotech company's Enzo Therapeutics subsidiary is developing antisense technology, a kind of gene therapy that switches off disease-causing genes, to fight such diseases as HIV, hepatitis, and Crohn's disease. This work is funded by two other subsidiaries. Enzo Clinical Labs provides diagnostic testing services in the New York City area. And Enzo Life Sciences makes reagents used by pharmaceutical and biotech companies, as well as academic institutions, in biomedical research. Enzo Biochem has collaborative partnerships with academic and research centers such as the University of Connecticut and the Hadassah University Hospital in Jerusalem.

	Annual Growth	7/03	7/04	7/05	7/06	7/07
Sales ($ mil.)	0.0%	52.8	41.6	43.4	39.8	52.9
Net income ($ mil.)	—	3.8	(6.2)	3.0	(15.7)	(13.3)
Market value ($ mil.)	(5.7%)	591.8	400.9	539.3	416.0	468.8
Employees	15.2%	—	—	342	—	454

ENZON PHARMACEUTICALS, INC.

NASDAQ (GM): ENZN

685 Rte. 202/206
Bridgewater, NJ 08807
Phone: 908-541-8600
Fax: 908-575-9457
Web: www.enzon.com

CEO: Jeffrey H. (Jeff) Buchalter
CFO: Craig A. Tooman
HR: Paul S. Davit
FYE: December 31
Type: Public

Enzon Pharmaceuticals has deadly diseases PEGged. The firm's proprietary PEGylation process enhances existing therapies by attaching a non-reactive polymer that allows them to avoid the immune system's radar and live in the blood longer. Its FDA-approved leukemia drug Oncaspar employs PEGylation technology, as does Adagen, an enzyme-replacement therapy for a rare immunodeficiency commonly called "Bubble Boy Disease." Enzon also receives royalties on several PEGylated drugs marketed by others, including Schering-Plough's PEG-Intron for hepatitis C and OSI Pharmaceuticals' Macugen.

	Annual Growth	6/04	6/05	*12/05	12/06	12/07
Sales ($ mil.)	2.3%	169.6	166.3	73.7	185.6	185.6
Net income ($ mil.)	110.9%	4.2	(89.6)	(291.3)	21.3	83.1
Market value ($ mil.)	(6.8%)	558.3	739.6	324.0	374.4	421.2
Employees	6.6%	—	306	306	—	371

*Fiscal year change

EOG RESOURCES, INC.

NYSE: EOG

1111 Bagby, Sky Lobby 2
Houston, TX 77002
Phone: 713-651-7000
Fax: 713-651-6995
Web: www.eogresources.com

CEO: Mark G. Papa
CFO: Timothy K. Driggers
HR: Patricia L. Edwards
FYE: December 31
Type: Public

EOG Resources hogs a resource — natural gas. The independent oil and gas company is engaged in exploring for natural gas and crude oil and developing, producing, and marketing those resources. EOG, an independent offspring of the once powerful Enron, has total estimated reserves of 6.8 trillion cu. ft. equivalent, including 6.1 trillion cu. ft. of natural gas reserves and 118 million barrels of crude oil, condensate, and natural gas liquid (NGL) reserves. The company operates in major production basins in Canada, offshore Trinidad, the US, and the UK sector of the North Sea. EOG is boosting its North American exploration activities and expanding its reserves.

	Annual Growth	12/03	12/04	12/05	12/06	12/07
Sales ($ mil.)	23.1%	1,825.1	2,271.2	3,620.2	3,904.4	4,190.8
Net income ($ mil.)	26.2%	430.1	624.9	1,259.6	1,299.9	1,089.9
Market value ($ mil.)	69.3%	2,675.8	4,243.3	17,761.0	15,221.3	22,002.3
Employees	12.1%	—	—	1,400	1,570	—

EON COMMUNICATIONS CORPORATION

NASDAQ (CM): EONC

185 Martinvale Ln.
San Jose, CA 95119
Phone: 408-694-9500
Fax: 408-694-9600
Web: www.eoncc.com

CEO: David S. Lee
CFO: Stephen R. (Steve) Bowling
HR: –
FYE: July 31
Type: Public

eOn Communications knows it's been ages since you've had a good customer service experience. The company's products integrate voice and Internet communications for large call centers and e-commerce customer contact centers. eOn's communications servers feature automatic call distribution, e-mail queuing, and customer identification. It also sells the Millennium voice switching hardware platform, a private branch exchange (PBX) system with computer telephony integration. Customers include Lillian Vernon, Circuit City, and Rockhurst University. Chairman and president David Lee owns about 30% of eOn.

	Annual Growth	7/03	7/04	7/05	7/06	7/07
Sales ($ mil.)	(11.6%)	17.5	18.0	21.4	12.0	10.7
Net income ($ mil.)	—	(1.5)	(0.9)	(2.0)	1.6	(1.3)
Market value ($ mil.)	(19.2%)	26.8	15.6	16.5	16.4	11.4
Employees	(27.1%)	—	—	173	—	92

E.ON U.S. LLC

220 W. Main St.
Louisville, KY 40232
Phone: 502-627-2000
Fax: 502-627-3609
Web: www.eon-us.com/about_eonus.asp

CEO: Victor A. (Vic) Staffieri
CFO: S. Bradford (Brad) Rives
HR: Paula H. Pottinger
FYE: December 31
Type: Subsidiary

E.ON U.S. (formerly LG&E Energy) may not be a Kentucky colonel, but it's a major power source in the state. Its regulated utilities, Louisville Gas and Electric and Kentucky Utilities, distribute electricity to 908,000 customers and natural gas to more than 318,000 customers in Kentucky and Virginia. The utilities have a combined generating capacity of 7,600 MW, primarily from coal-fired facilities. E.ON U.S.'s nonregulated businesses include international gas distribution and independent power production. E.ON U.S. is a subsidiary of German energy conglomerate E.ON.

	Annual Growth	12/03	12/04	12/05	12/06	12/07
Est. sales ($ mil.)	—	—	—	—	—	983.9
Employees	—	—	—	—	—	3,500

EOS INTERNATIONAL, INC.

5100 Park Rd.
Venetia, CA 94510
Phone: 707-747-2132
Fax: 707-747-2193

CEO: William (Bill) Moss
CFO: –
HR: –
FYE: September 30
Type: Private

Eos International likes direct sellers — direct-selling companies, that is. Eos buys firms that sell consumer products primarily through parties, catalogs, and the Internet. To that end, it owns direct sellers Discovery Toys (educational toys, books, and software) and IFS (product-based fundraising programs for schools). Its Regal Greetings & Gifts unit (greeting cards, gift wrap, and household and giftware items) folded in 2005 after bankruptcy. Self-improvement guru Anthony "Tony" Robbins founded the company as dreamlife in 1999, operating a Web site filled with content, coaching tools, and communities. Eos changed its business strategy in 2001 after the acquisition of Discovery Toys.

	Annual Growth	9/03	9/04	9/05	9/06	9/07
Est. sales ($ mil.)	—	—	—	—	—	12.6
Employees	—	—	—	—	—	649

EP MEDSYSTEMS, INC.

NASDAQ (CM): EPMD

575 Rte. 73 North, Bldg. D, Cooper Run Executive Park
West Berlin, NJ 08091
Phone: 856-753-8533
Fax: 856-753-8544
Web: www.epmedsystems.com

CEO: David I. Bruce
CFO: James J. Caruso
HR: Richard (Dick) Gibbons
FYE: December 31
Type: Public

EP MedSystems skips no beats designing products that diagnose, monitor, and treat cardiac arrhythmias (abnormal heartbeats). Its EP-4 Stimulator is a computerized electrophysiology clinical stimulator, while the EP WorkMate monitors heart activity and stores arrhythmia data. The ViewMate ultrasound imaging console and Viewflex catheters help physicians diagnose heart conditions. EP MedSystems sells to medical institutions and doctors through a direct sales force in the US; it sells through distributors abroad. In 2008 the company agreed to be acquired by St. Jude Medical.

	Annual Growth	12/03	12/04	12/05	12/06	12/07
Sales ($ mil.)	17.3%	10.0	16.4	16.7	15.6	18.9
Net income ($ mil.)	—	(6.9)	(4.4)	(5.8)	(6.5)	(5.5)
Net income ($ mil.)	—	(6.9)	(4.4)	(5.8)	(6.5)	(5.5)
Employees	1.2%	—	—	86	87	—

EPAM SYSTEMS, INC.

989 Lenox Dr., Ste. 305
Lawrenceville, NJ 08648
Phone: 609-844-0400
Fax: 609-844-0415
Web: www.epam.com

CEO: Arkadiy Dobkin
CFO: Ilya Cantor
HR: –
FYE: December 31
Type: Private

How do you say "offshoring" in Russian? Just ask EPAM Systems. The IT outsourcing company provides software development and other IT services to US and European customers from development centers in Belarus, Germany, Hungary, Russia, and Ukraine. In addition to software product development, the company offers assistance in such areas as e-commerce, data warehousing, customer relationship management, and application integration. EPAM also offers its own hosted and stand-alone enterprise software for sales force automation, content management, order management, and other business processes. Its clients include Reuters, Schlumberger, Halliburton, and Microsoft.

	Annual Growth	12/02	12/03	12/04	12/05	12/06
Sales ($ mil.)	71.7%	9.2	15.5	30.1	39.9	80.0
Employees	68.5%	310	625	1,010	1,400	2,500

EPIC RECORDS GROUP

550 Madison Ave.
New York, NY 10022
Phone: 212-833-8000
Fax: 212-833-4818
Web: www.epicrecords.com

CEO: Charlie Walk
CFO: –
HR: –
FYE: March 31
Type: Business segment

Rather than Homeric-length odes, these epic stories tend to play out across three-minute pop songs. Epic Records Group is one of the leading recording labels in the US, with a stable of artists that includes Audioslave, Good Charlotte, Jennifer Lopez, Oasis, and Shakira. It has also released the soundtracks to such films as *Chicago*, *Garden State*, and *Forest Gump*. In addition to recorded CDs, the label markets DVDs and videos, and it offers streaming audio and downloadable songs on the Internet. Originally formed as a jazz imprint of CBS Records in 1953, Epic is now a part of Sony BMG Music Entertainment.

EPIC SYSTEMS CORPORATION

1979 Milky Way
Verona, WI 53593
Phone: 608-271-9000
Fax: 608-271-7237
Web: www.epicsystems.com

CEO: Judith R. Faulkner
CFO: –
HR: –
FYE: December 31
Type: Private

Epic Systems tells a grand tale of health care technology. Founded in 1979, the company provides health care management software that integrates financial and clinical information across inpatient, ambulatory, and payer technology systems. Epic's software offerings include scheduling and registration tools, billing and managed care administration applications, inpatient and outpatient core clinical systems, electronic medical records applications, and applications for managing hospital pharmacy, emergency, surgery, radiology, laboratory, and intensive care departments.

	Annual Growth	12/03	12/04	12/05	12/06	12/07
Est. sales ($ mil.)	—	—	—	—	—	86.3
Employees	—	—	—	—	—	850

EPICEPT CORPORATION

777 Old Saw Mill River Rd.
Tarrytown, NY 10591
Phone: 914-606-3500
Fax: 914-606-3501
Web: www.epicept.com

CEO: John V. Talley
CFO: Robert W. Cook
HR: –
FYE: December 31
Type: Public

EpiCept is looking to rub relief — not salt — in your wounds. The company develops topical treatments for pain that target nerve receptors beneath the skin, as well as drug products to treat cancer. Its lead cancer drug candidate, Ceplene, is a remission maintenance therapy for leukemia patients. Other cancer candidates in clinical trial stages target brain cancer and solid tumors. EpiCept uses creams and patches to deliver the goods for pain relief; candidates under development could treat conditions such as lower back and neuropathic pain.

	Annual Growth	12/03	12/04	12/05	12/06	12/07
Sales ($ mil.)	(38.8%)	—	—	0.8	2.1	0.3
Net income ($ mil.)	—	—	—	(7.2)	(65.4)	(28.7)
Market value ($ mil.)	25.8%	—	—	—	46.3	58.3
Employees	(2.9%)	—	—	35	34	—

EPICOR SOFTWARE CORPORATION

NASDAQ (GS): EPIC

18200 Von Karman Ave., Ste. 1000
Irvine, CA 92612
Phone: 949-585-4000
Fax: 949-585-4091
Web: www.epicor.com

CEO: Thomas F. (Tom) Kelly
CFO: Russell Clark
HR: –
FYE: December 31
Type: Public

Epicor Software hopes the middle of the road proves paved with gold. The company provides enterprise resource planning software for midsized businesses. Epicor's software integrates back-office applications for manufacturing, distribution, and accounting with customer relationship management functions, including sales, marketing, and customer support. The company's software also includes collaborative applications that link employees, distributors, and suppliers, encompassing operations such as supply chain management, sourcing, and procurement.

	Annual Growth	12/03	12/04	12/05	12/06	12/07
Sales ($ mil.)	29.0%	155.4	226.2	289.4	384.1	429.8
Net income ($ mil.)	45.2%	9.3	25.3	52.0	23.8	41.3
Market value ($ mil.)	4.5%	589.9	749.0	787.5	794.5	703.3
Employees	24.1%	—	—	1,887	2,178	2,907

EPICUS COMMUNICATIONS GROUP, INC.

OTC: EPCG

1750 Osceola Dr.
West Palm Beach, FL 33409
Phone: 561-688-0440
Fax: –
Web: www.ecg-us.com

CEO: Mark Schaftlein
CFO: Ginny Bohrer
HR: –
FYE: May 31
Type: Public

Epicus Communications Group is a competitive local-exchange carrier (CLEC) offering local phone service and Internet access to 19,000 business and residential customers located mostly in eight southeastern US states. The company provides local exchange access and long-distance phone services, as well as data and Internet services. It markets its services using "Freedom Rings" and "AccessNOW" brands. Its local service uses lines leased from regional incumbent carrier BellSouth. CEO Mark Schaftlein owns 47% of the company; Gerard Haryman, its former president, owns 23%.

	Annual Growth	5/03	5/04	5/05	5/06	5/07
Sales ($ mil.)	(6.3%)	10.4	25.2	18.8	5.8	8.0
Net income ($ mil.)	—	(1.6)	(3.3)	(8.4)	(2.7)	(3.1)
Employees	—	—	—	—	—	—

EPIQ SYSTEMS, INC.

NASDAQ (GS): EPIQ

501 Kansas Ave.
Kansas City, KS 66105
Phone: 913-621-9500
Fax: 913-321-1243
Web: www.epiqsystems.com

CEO: Tom W. Olofson
CFO: Elizabeth M. (Betsy) Braham
HR: –
FYE: December 31
Type: Public

EPIQ Systems wants to make bankruptcy quick and painless. The company provides case and document management software for bankruptcy, class action, mass tort, and other legal proceedings. Its software automates tasks including legal notice and claims management, funds distribution, and government reporting. EPIQ's software line includes products for Chapter 7 liquidations, Chapter 13 individual debt reorganizations, and Chapter 11 reorganizations. The company, which caters primarily to bankruptcy trustees as opposed to debtors and creditors, also offers Chapter 11 case management services, as well as applications for class action, mass tort, and bankruptcy case administration.

	Annual Growth	12/03	12/04	12/05	12/06	12/07
Sales ($ mil.)	26.6%	67.9	125.4	106.3	224.2	174.4
Net income ($ mil.)	(5.6%)	8.7	9.7	(3.8)	35.1	6.9
Market value ($ mil.)	31.9%	202.9	174.5	238.0	220.4	614.2
Employees	0.0%	—	—	500	500	500

EPIX PHARMACEUTICALS, INC.

NASDAQ (GM): EPIX

4 Maguire Rd.
Lexington, MA 02421
Phone: 781-761-7600
Fax: 781-761-7641
Web: www.epixpharma.com

CEO: Michael G. Kauffman
CFO: Kimberlee C. (Kim) Drapkin
HR: Brenda Sousa
FYE: December 31
Type: Public

EPIX Pharmaceuticals wants to give you that special glow. The biopharmaceutical company has developed Vasovist, an injectable contrast agent used in magnetic resonance imaging (MRI) procedures to diagnose vascular diseases; it is approved for use and marketed in Europe by strategic partner Bayer Schering Pharma but has not received the regulatory green light in the US. EPIX also has several drug therapies in clinical development to treat diseases of the central nervous system as well as lung conditions. It is collaborating with GlaxoSmithKline on several programs.

	Annual Growth	12/03	12/04	12/05	12/06	12/07
Sales ($ mil.)	2.7%	13.5	12.3	7.2	6.0	15.0
Net income ($ mil.)	—	(20.8)	(20.4)	(24.3)	(157.4)	(62.8)
Market value ($ mil.)	(27.6%)	—	—	—	224.9	162.9
Employees	1.1%	86	90	96	89	—

EPLUS INC.

Pink Sheets: PLUS

13595 Dulles Technology Dr.
Herndon, VA 20171
Phone: 703-984-8400
Fax: 703-984-8600
Web: www.eplus.com

CEO: Phillip G. (Phil) Norton
CFO: Steven J. (Steve) Mencarini
HR: –
FYE: March 31
Type: Public

ePlus wants to rate an A-plus from its customers by meeting their hardware and software needs. The company resells and leases products from top IT infrastructure providers. Its offerings include security, storage, and networking products, as well as consulting and systems integration services. The company also offers supply chain management software and services; its proprietary applications include procurement, asset management, spend analytics, and document management tools. ePlus markets its products and services to medium-sized and large businesses, government agencies, and schools. Chairman, president, and CEO Phillip Norton owns more than a quarter of ePlus.

	Annual Growth	3/04	3/05	3/06	3/07	3/08
Sales ($ mil.)	26.6%	330.6	575.8	647.3	791.6	849.3
Net income ($ mil.)	12.9%	10.1	25.3	(0.5)	17.4	16.4
Employees	—	—	—	—	649	—

EPOCH HOLDING CORPORATION

NASDAQ (CM): EPHC

640 5th Ave., 18th Fl.
New York, NY 10019
Phone: 212-303-7200
Fax: 212-202-4948
Web: www.eipny.com

CEO: William W. Priest
CFO: Adam Borak
HR: Andrea Tasker Glogoff
FYE: June 30
Type: Public

Epoch Holding owns Epoch Investments Partners (EIP), which manages investments for retirement plans, mutual fund clients, endowments, foundations, and other high-net-worth clients. EIP has approximately $3.5 billion of assets under management, including some $1 billion added since the beginning of 2006. Formerly known as J Net Enterprises, the company was once one of Nevada's largest gaming-machine operators and even tried its hand at Internet-based e-commerce before acquiring EIP in 2004.

	Annual Growth	6/03	6/04	6/05	6/06	6/07
Assets ($ mil.)	17.3%	20.8	17.1	13.0	13.6	39.4
Net income ($ mil.)	—	(3.8)	(1.0)	(6.5)	(5.7)	7.9
Market value ($ mil.)	132.0%	9.2	53.5	78.5	99.9	266.9
Employees	16.9%	23	28	28	—	43

EPOLIN, INC.

OTC: EPLN

358-364 Adams St.
Newark, NJ 07105
Phone: 973-465-9495
Fax: 973-465-5353
Web: www.epolin.com

CEO: Greg Amato
CFO: James Ivchenko
HR: –
FYE: Last day of February
Type: Public

Welders and army tank drivers alike owe their continued ability to see to Epolin. The company develops near-infrared dyes used in the manufacture of eyewear for protection against lasers (used in range finders in tanks) and face shields used by welders. Epolin also makes intermediates for the specialty chemical industry. Additionally, Epolin sells its dyes as security inks for credit cards, drug and food labels, and official documents. Founder Murray Cohen stepped down as CEO in early 2006; he remains as chairman and chief scientist. Former sales exec Greg Amato replaced Cohen.

	Annual Growth	2/04	2/05	2/06	2/07	2/08
Sales ($ mil.)	7.5%	2.7	2.9	3.7	3.6	3.6
Net income ($ mil.)	3.9%	0.6	0.5	0.6	0.6	0.7
Market value ($ mil.)	7.7%	5.6	6.3	8.5	8.4	7.5
Employees	0.0%	—	—	10	10	—

EPSON AMERICA, INC.

3840 Kilroy Airport Way
Long Beach, CA 90806
Phone: 562-981-3840
Fax: 562-290-5220
Web: www.epson.com/cgi-bin/Store

CEO: John Lang
CFO: Alan Pound Sr.
HR: –
FYE: March 31
Type: Subsidiary

When it comes to digital images, Epson America snaps, scans, prints, and projects. A subsidiary of Japanese giant Seiko Epson, the company manufactures digital cameras, personal and professional flatbed scanners, document cameras, printers, and projectors. Its printer line includes personal ink jet and high-volume impact printers, as well as wide format and point-of-sale devices. It also offers printing and photography software, and supplies such as print cartridges and paper. Epson America, which represents Seiko Epson in North and South America, was founded in 1975.

An in-depth profile of this company is available to Hoover's Online members at hoovers.com.

575

EQUIFAX INC.

NYSE: EFX

1550 Peachtree St. NW
Atlanta, GA 30309
Phone: 404-885-8000
Fax: 404-885-8988
Web: www.equifax.com

CEO: Richard F. (Rick) Smith
CFO: Lee Adrean
HR: Coretha M. Rushing
FYE: December 31
Type: Public

Equifax knows you. Yes, you. One of the US's largest credit reporting agencies (alongside Experian and TransUnion), the company has information on more than 400 million worldwide credit holders. In addition to credit reports, Equifax provides credit card marketing and fraud detection services and offers database marketing, credit risk consulting, and such products as credit scoring software through a host of subsidiaries. Through subsidiary TALX, the company provides human resources and payroll outsourcing. Equifax's customers include financial institutions, retailers, automotive dealers, and mortgage companies. Equifax has operations in North America, South America, and Europe.

	Annual Growth	12/03	12/04	12/05	12/06	12/07
Sales ($ mil.)	10.7%	1,225.4	1,272.8	1,443.4	1,546.3	1,843.0
Net income ($ mil.)	13.4%	164.9	234.7	246.5	274.5	272.7
Market value ($ mil.)	9.7%	3,251.2	3,636.1	4,912.2	5,062.8	4,715.9
Employees	23.4%	—	—	4,600	4,960	7,000

EQUINIX, INC.

NASDAQ (GS): EQIX

301 Velocity Way, 5th Fl.
Foster City, CA 94404
Phone: 650-513-7000
Fax: 650-513-7900
Web: www.equinix.com

CEO: Stephen M. (Steve) Smith
CFO: Keith D. Taylor
HR: Keri Crask
FYE: December 31
Type: Public

In the Internet game, Equinix is the neutral playing field. The company provides data and network hosting and colocation facilities (it calls them Internet Business Exchanges, or IBXs) where ISPs, telecommunications carriers, and content providers can locate equipment and interconnect networks and operations. The company operates IBXs in Chicago; Dallas; Hong Kong; Los Angeles; New York; Silicon Valley, California; Singapore; Sydney; Tokyo; and Washington, DC. Equinix was founded in 1998.

	Annual Growth	12/03	12/04	12/05	12/06	12/07
Sales ($ mil.)	37.3%	117.9	163.7	221.1	286.9	419.4
Net income ($ mil.)	—	(84.2)	(68.6)	(42.6)	(6.4)	(5.2)
Market value ($ mil.)	71.7%	425.5	812.0	1,118.6	2,232.1	3,695.2
Employees	30.2%	—	—	537	616	911

EQUISTAR CHEMICALS, LP

1221 McKinney St., Ste. 700
Houston, TX 77010
Phone: 713-652-7200
Fax: 713-652-4151
Web: www.equistarchem.com

CEO: Morris Gelb
CFO: T. Kevin DeNicola
HR: John A. Hollinshead
FYE: December 31
Type: Subsidiary

Someone's got to build the building blocks too, you know? Equistar Chemicals, a subsidiary of LyondellBasell, does just that. Its primary product is ethylene, which is the world's most-used petrochemical and the basis for any number of other chemicals, plastics, and synthetics. Among the company's other products are propylene, butadiene, polyethylene, polypropylene, ethylene oxide, ethylene glycol, benzene, and toluene. Polyethylene is used in plastic bags and bottles; polypropylene is used in plastic caps, rigid packaging, automotive components, and carpet. The company was jointly owned by Lyondell and Millennium Chemicals until the former bought the latter in 2004; three years later Basell bought Lyondell.

	Annual Growth	12/02	12/03	12/04	12/05	12/06
Sales ($ mil.)	—	—	—	—	—	12,765.0
Net income ($ mil.)	—	—	—	—	—	614.0
Employees	—	—	—	—	—	3,260

EQUITABLE RESOURCES, INC.

NYSE: EQT

225 North Shore Dr.
Pittsburgh, PA 15212
Phone: 412-553-5700
Fax: 412-553-7781
Web: www.eqt.com

CEO: Murry S. Gerber
CFO: Philip P. (Phil) Conti
HR: Charlene Petrelli
FYE: December 31
Type: Public

Integrated natural gas company Equitable Resources hopes to get its fair share of the natural gas market. The company's Equitable Utilities unit distributes gas to 275,000 customers in Pennsylvania, West Virginia, and Kentucky; the division also has gas transportation, storage, marketing, and trading operations. Subsidiary Equitable Supply operates 7,500 miles of natural gas gathering pipeline and exploits proved reserves of 2.7 trillion cu. ft. of natural gas equivalent in the Appalachian region. In 2007 the unit drilled 634 gross wells (456 net), consisting of 88 horizontal shale wells, 266 coal bed methane wells, and 280 other vertical wells.

	Annual Growth	12/03	12/04	12/05	12/06	12/07
Sales ($ mil.)	6.8%	1,047.3	1,191.6	1,253.7	1,267.9	1,361.4
Net income ($ mil.)	10.9%	170.0	279.9	260.1	220.3	257.5
Market value ($ mil.)	48.5%	1,338.4	1,851.1	4,399.4	5,076.9	6,508.4
Employees	5.8%	—	—	1,250	1,340	1,400

EQUITY GROUP INVESTMENTS, L.L.C.

2 N. Riverside Plaza, Ste. 700
Chicago, IL 60606
Phone: 312-466-4001
Fax: 312-454-0157
Web: www.equityinternational.com

CEO: Donald J. (Don) Liebentritt
CFO: Philip G. Tinkler
HR: —
FYE: December 31
Type: Private

Equity Group Investments is the apex of financier Sam Zell's pyramid of business holdings. The Chicago-based private investment group controls a multibillion dollar mix of private and public, domestic and foreign businesses, and more. Zell's real estate portfolio makes him one of the US's largest owners of apartments (Equity Residential) and of property leased by manufactured homeowners (Equity LifeStyle Properties). Zell has acquired the Tribune Company, but plans to unload that firm's holdings in the Chicago Cubs. Zell co-founded Equity Group Investments in 1968 and has a controlling interest in it.

	Annual Growth	12/03	12/04	12/05	12/06	12/07
Est. sales ($ mil.)	—	—	—	—	—	13.1
Employees	—	—	—	—	—	54

EQUITY LIFESTYLE PROPERTIES, INC.

NYSE: ELS

2 N. Riverside Plaza, Ste. 800
Chicago, IL 60606
Phone: 312-279-1400
Fax: 312-279-1710
Web: www.mhchomes.com

CEO: Thomas P. Heneghan
CFO: Michael B. Berman
HR: —
FYE: December 31
Type: Public

Trailer park jokes aside, Equity LifeStyle Properties is a real estate investment trust (REIT) that owns and operates lifestyle-oriented residential properties aimed at retirees, empty nesters, vacationers, and second home owners. It leases developed areas for factory-built homes, cottages, cabins, and recreational vehicles. The REIT's portfolio includes more than 300 properties containing 113,000 lots in nearly 30 states and Canada. Its properties are similar to site-built residential subdivisions, with centralized entrances, utilities, gutters, curbs, and paved streets.

	Annual Growth	12/03	12/04	12/05	12/06	12/07
Sales ($ mil.)	11.5%	267.4	343.1	386.5	412.8	413.5
Net income ($ mil.)	4.4%	27.0	4.0	(2.3)	16.6	32.1
Market value ($ mil.)	7.0%	849.5	820.0	1,036.7	1,302.4	1,112.0
Employees	3.3%	—	—	1,500	1,400	1,600

EQUITY OFFICE PROPERTIES TRUST

2 N. Riverside Plaza, Ste. 2100
Chicago, IL 60606
Phone: 312-466-3300
Fax: 312-454-0332
Web: www.equityoffice.com

CEO: Richard D. Kincaid
CFO: Howard Weissman
HR: −
FYE: December 31
Type: Subsidiary

Equity Office adds headstones to the Grave Dancer's fold. Headed by Sam "Grave Dancer" Zell, Equity Office Properties (EOP) owns more than 125 office buildings in about 15 metropolitan areas that it has identified as target markets. It also develops properties. True to the "office" in its name, the firm unloaded most of its industrial holdings in 2004. Billionaire Zell's moniker springs from his success in transforming distressed properties into profitable investments. After a fierce bidding war against Vornado Realty, The Blackstone Group acquired EOP in 2007 for some $39 billion in one of the largest private equity transactions ever.

EQUITY ONE, INC.

NYSE: EQY

1600 NE Miami Gardens Dr.
North Miami Beach, FL 33179
Phone: 305-947-1664
Fax: 305-947-1734
Web: www.equityone.net

CEO: Jeffrey S. Olson
CFO: Gregory R. Andrews
HR: Barbara Miller
FYE: December 31
Type: Public

Equity One wants to be #1. The number one shopping center owner, that is. A real estate investment trust (REIT), Equity One acquires, develops, and manages shopping centers, with many properties located in Florida and in the Boston area. Its portfolio consists primarily of shopping centers anchored by supermarkets and drug stores totalling around 17.5 million sq. ft.; including land and other holdings, Equity One's portfolio comprises nearly 170 properties. Florida is Equity One's largest market. Publix (which leases nearly 15% of the company's space), Kroger, and Winn-Dixie are its biggest tenants. Chairman Chaim Katzman controls the REIT through his Israeli real estate firm Gazit-Globe.

	Annual Growth	12/03	12/04	12/05	12/06	12/07
Sales ($ mil.)	6.7%	190.0	229.9	253.0	233.4	246.6
Net income ($ mil.)	2.2%	63.7	97.8	92.7	177.0	69.4
Market value ($ mil.)	9.6%	1,170.7	1,746.5	1,743.5	1,965.1	1,688.1
Employees	(22.6%)	—	—	259	—	155

⊞ EQUITY RESIDENTIAL

NYSE: EQR

2 N. Riverside Plaza
Chicago, IL 60606
Phone: 312-474-1300
Fax: 312-454-8703
Web: www.equityapartments.com

CEO: David J. Neithercut
CFO: Mark J. Parrell
HR: John Powers
FYE: December 31
Type: Public

The "Grave Dancer" is also the lord of the rents. Sam Zell (whose moniker springs from his buying and turning around moribund properties) is at the head of the conga line at Equity Residential (now minus the "Properties Trust"), the nation's #1 apartment owner in sales. Rival AIMCO owns more units, but its affordable-housing focus keeps its revenue more modest. Equity Residential wholly or partially owns around 575 apartment communities with more than 150,000 units, comprising garden units, high rises, ranch-style properties, and military housing. The company focuses on growth areas, with California leading the way with the most Equity Residential complexes.

	Annual Growth	12/03	12/04	12/05	12/06	12/07
Sales ($ mil.)	2.8%	1,823.3	1,889.5	1,954.9	1,990.4	2,038.1
Net income ($ mil.)	16.1%	543.8	472.3	861.8	1,072.8	989.6
Market value ($ mil.)	4.7%	8,193.3	10,314.1	11,326.7	14,897.7	9,830.7
Employees	(10.6%)	—	—	6,000	5,200	4,800

ERESEARCHTECHNOLOGY, INC.

NASDAQ (GS): ERES

30 S. 17th St.
Philadelphia, PA 19103
Phone: 215-972-0420
Fax: 215-972-0414
Web: www.ert.com

CEO: Michael J. McKelvey
CFO: Steven M. Eisenstein
HR: −
FYE: December 31
Type: Public

eResearchTechnology (eRT) e-cares about your e-clinical e-trial. The firm offers support services and software to help streamline the clinical trials process that drugs and medical devices must pass to earn regulatory approval. eRT's products automate all aspects of the process, from setup and data gathering to analysis and FDA application preparation. Customers include drugmakers, medical device firms, and contract research organizations (CROs). Flagship product EXPeRT ensures cardiac safety by collecting, processing, and interpreting electrocardiogram (ECG) data. eRT also provides site support including ECG equipment rentals and sales. The firm markets its products through a global sales force.

	Annual Growth	12/03	12/04	12/05	12/06	12/07
Sales ($ mil.)	6.8%	66.8	109.4	86.8	86.4	86.8
Net income ($ mil.)	1.5%	14.5	29.7	15.4	8.3	15.4
Market value ($ mil.)	(1.1%)	618.4	797.7	740.3	338.0	592.3
Employees	—	—	—	355	—	—

ERGON, INC.

2829 Lakeland Dr., Ste. 2000
Jackson, MS 39232
Phone: 601-933-3000
Fax: 601-933-3350
Web: www.ergon.com

CEO: Leslie B. Lampton Sr.
CFO: A. Patrick (Pat) Busby
HR: Lance Mazerov
FYE: December 31
Type: Private

When it comes to work, Ergon (named after the Greek word for work) has it covered. Ergo, Ergon operates in six major business segments: asphalt and emulsions; information technology (embedded computing); oil and gas; real estate; refining and marketing; and transportation and terminaling. In addition to providing a range of petroleum products and services, the company manufactures and markets computer technology services and sells road maintenance systems, including emulsions and special coatings. Ergon also provides truck, rail, and marine transport services and sells residential and commercial real estate properties.

	Annual Growth	12/02	12/03	12/04	12/05	12/06
Est. sales ($ mil.)	31.4%	1,380.0	2,000.0	2,680.0	3,000.0	4,110.0
Employees	5.7%	2,000	2,300	2,300	2,500	2,500

ERHC ENERGY INC.

OTC: ERHE

5444 Westheimer Rd., Ste. 1570
Houston, TX 77056
Phone: 713-626-4700
Fax: 713-626-4704
Web: www.erhc.com

CEO: Peter C. Ntephe
CFO: Sylvan Odobulu
HR: −
FYE: September 30
Type: Public

Oil, out of Africa, is the hope of ERHC Energy (formerly Environmental Remediation Holding Corporation), an independent oil and gas company whose sole assets are oil and gas exploration concessions in Sao Tome in West Africa. ERHC is teaming up with larger oil and gas companies (such as Noble Energy and Pioneer Natural Resources) to help it develop its Sao Tome holdings. The company is also hoping to acquire interests in high-potential nonproducing international prospects in known oil producing areas. Former chairman and CEO Emeka Offor, the owner of Chrome Oil Services and Chrome Energy, owns 43% of ERHC.

⊞ An in-depth profile of this company is available to Hoover's Online members at hoovers.com.

ERICKSON AIR-CRANE, INC.

3100 Willow Springs Rd.
Central Point, OR 97502
Phone: 541-664-7615
Fax: 541-664-7613
Web: www.ericksonaircrane.com

CEO: Ralph Torney
CFO: Paul Gricus
HR: Mary Walden
FYE: December 31
Type: Private

Q: If a gallon of water weighs eight pounds, how do you get enough gallons into the sky to make a difference in fighting a forest fire? A: Ask Erickson Air-Crane. The company owns, operates, and maintains a fleet of heavy-duty S-64 Aircrane helicopters. The craft, which are capable of lifting up to 25,000 pounds, are used in firefighting (Helitanker), heavy construction, logging, and oil and gas support applications. Customers have included fire departments and forest managers in the US and in Greece, Italy, and South Korea. Erickson Air-Crane also manufactures S-64 helicopters under a certificate purchased from Sikorsky.

	Annual Growth	12/03	12/04	12/05	12/06	12/07
Est. sales ($ mil.)	—	—	—	—	—	44.2
Employees	—	—	—	—	—	620

ERICSSON INC.

6300 Legacy Dr.
Plano, TX 75024
Phone: 972-583-0000
Fax: –
Web: www.ericsson.com/US

CEO: Angel Ruiz
CFO: Jan Ögren
HR: Jill Little
FYE: December 31
Type: Subsidiary

Ericsson is Swede on North America. The subsidiary of Sweden-based global wireless infrastructure equipment leader and cell phone maker Telefonaktiebolaget LM Ericsson oversees the North American business of its parent. It makes antennas, transmitters, switching systems, and other gear used to build wireless networks. The company develops and markets its mobile handsets through a joint venture, Sony Ericsson. Ericsson also makes corporate networking gear, cable, satellite products, optical equipment, and software for mobile messaging. Services include network design and construction.

	Annual Growth	12/03	12/04	12/05	12/06	12/07
Est. sales ($ mil.)	—	—	—	—	—	683.6
Employees	—	—	—	—	—	8,000

ERIE INDEMNITY COMPANY

NASDAQ (GS): ERIE

100 Erie Insurance Place
Erie, PA 16530
Phone: 814-870-2785
Fax: 814-870-3126
Web: www.erie-insurance.com

CEO: John J. Brinling Jr.
CFO: Philip A. Garcia
HR: Patricia A. Rech
FYE: December 31
Type: Public

Erie Indemnity may be near a lake, but it prefers a pooling arrangement. Founded in 1925 as an auto insurer, it is now attorney-in-fact and manager of Erie Insurance Exchange, a reciprocal insurance exchange that pools the underwriting of several property/casualty insurance firms. Most of its revenues come from the management fees it charges Erie Insurance Exchange, but it also writes a bit of property/casualty insurance of its own through subsidiaries. Its reach includes coverage in about a dozen eastern states and it markets its products through some 8,400 independent agents. The company is the only publicly traded part of the Erie Insurance Group which also includes Erie Family Life Insurance.

	Annual Growth	12/03	12/04	12/05	12/06	12/07
Sales ($ mil.)	1.9%	1,048.8	1,123.1	1,124.9	1,134.0	1,132.3
Net income ($ mil.)	1.6%	199.7	226.4	231.1	204.0	212.9
Market value ($ mil.)	0.5%	2,716.1	3,311.5	3,253.9	3,349.9	2,767.8
Employees	(5.6%)	—	—	4,600	4,300	4,100

ERNST & YOUNG GLOBAL LIMITED

5 Times Sq., 14th Fl.
New York, NY 10036
Phone: 212-773-3000
Fax: 212-773-6350
Web: www.ey.com

CEO: James S. (Jim) Turley
CFO: Jeffrey H. (Jeff) Dworken
HR: Pierre Hurstel
FYE: June 30
Type: Partnership

Accounting may actually be the *second*-oldest profession, and Ernst & Young is one of the oldest practitioners. Ernst & Young is also one of the world's Big Four accounting firms (third in revenue behind PricewaterhouseCoopers and Deloitte Touche Tohmatsu, ahead of KPMG). It has some 700 offices providing auditing and accounting services in 140 countries. The firm also provides legal services and services relating to emerging growth companies, human resources issues, and corporate transactions (mergers and acquisitions, IPOs, and the like). Ernst & Young has one of the world's largest tax practices, serving multinational clients that have to comply with multiple local tax laws.

	Annual Growth	6/03	6/04	6/05	6/06	6/07
Sales ($ mil.)	12.7%	13,136.0	14,547.0	16,902.0	18,400.0	21,160.0
Employees	4.1%	103,000	100,601	106,650	114,000	121,000

ERNST & YOUNG L.L.P.

5 Times Sq., 14th Fl.
New York, NY 10036
Phone: 212-773-3000
Fax: 212-773-6350
Web: www.ey.com/global/content.nsf/US/Home

CEO: James S. (Jim) Turley
CFO: Jeffrey H. (Jeff) Dworken
HR: Pierre Hurstel
FYE: June 30
Type: Partnership

Ernst & Young L.L.P. is earnest about its chosen profession. The firm is the US arm of Ernst & Young Global, one of the Big Four accounting firms, which includes rivals KPMG, PricewaterhouseCoopers, and Deloitte Touche Tohmatsu. Ernst & Young provides audit, tax, and transaction advisory services to public and private companies in a wide variety of industries from offices all across the US, the District of Columbia, and Puerto Rico. The company is named for Arthur Young and Alwin C. Ernst who founded the two accounting firms that were later combined to form Ernst & Young.

	Annual Growth	6/03	6/04	6/05	6/06	6/07
Est. sales ($ mil.)	—	—	—	—	—	1,653.2
Employees	—	—	—	—	—	27,000

EROOMSYSTEM TECHNOLOGIES, INC.

OTC: ERMS

1072 Madison Ave.
Lakewood, NJ 08701
Phone: 732-730-0116
Fax: 732-810-0380
Web: www.eroomsystem.com

CEO: David A. Gestetner
CFO: David A. Gestetner
HR: –
FYE: December 31
Type: Public

eRoomSystem Technologies is keeping tabs for hotels. The company provides computer-based refreshment centers for the hospitality industry. Its eRoomSystem products track beverage and other refreshment purchases and automatically charge lodgers' accounts. The eRoomSystem generates reports on sales statistics, inventory control, and restocking requirements. The company's other products include room safes that feature reprogrammable electronic combinations. Through revenue-sharing agreements (roughly 70% of sales) the company installs its systems and takes a cut of the sales they generate. Chairman and CEO David Gestetner owns about 22% of the company.

	Annual Growth	12/03	12/04	12/05	12/06	12/07
Sales ($ mil.)	(5.4%)	1.5	1.6	1.6	1.3	1.2
Net income ($ mil.)	—	(1.7)	0.9	0.2	0.2	0.4
Market value ($ mil.)	18.8%	2.3	3.3	4.4	2.9	4.6
Employees	—	—	—	—	—	—

ESB FINANCIAL CORPORATION

NASDAQ (GS): ESBF

600 Lawrence Ave.
Ellwood City, PA 16117
Phone: 724-758-5584
Fax: 724-758-0576
Web: www.esbbank.com

CEO: Charlotte A. Zuschlag
CFO: Charles P. Evanoski
HR: John T. Stunda
FYE: December 31
Type: Public

ESB Financial is the holding company for ESB Bank, which provides banking services to individuals and businesses in western Pennsylvania. The bank has some two dozen branch locations in Allegheny, Beaver, Butler, and Lawrence counties; its offerings include standard retail services such as checking and savings accounts, CDs, and credit cards. The company's lending activities consist of residential mortgages (about half of its loan portfolio), as well as construction, commercial real estate, business, and consumer loans. Bank subsidiary ESB Financial Services provides financial planning services and investment products through a partnership with Raymond James Financial.

	Annual Growth	12/03	12/04	12/05	12/06	12/07
Assets ($ mil.)	8.3%	1,365.8	1,394.5	1,852.8	1,922.7	1,880.2
Net income ($ mil.)	(2.4%)	8.5	10.0	9.2	10.6	7.7
Market value ($ mil.)	(8.1%)	173.6	154.4	148.6	141.4	124.1
Employees	0.7%	—	—	282	—	286

ESCALA GROUP, INC.

Pink Sheets: ESCL

5 Frances J. Clarke Blvd.
Bethel, CT 06801
Phone: 203-702-8480
Fax: –
Web: www.escalagroup.com

CEO: Gregory N. (Greg) Roberts
CFO: Leon Losapio
HR: –
FYE: June 30
Type: Public

Escala Group has grown from its roots as a specialty auction house (named Greg Manning) dealing in stamps, coins, sports collectibles, art, and memorabilia into a holding company serving the global collectibles market. The company's name change in 2005 was meant to reflect the reorganization of its business into two main areas: collectibles (handled via both auctions and direct sales) and trading. Escala's trading operations consist of A-Mark Precious Metals, which sells bullion coins and other precious metals on a wholesale basis. Escala came under investigation in 2006 in connection with an alleged stamp fraud scheme. Its top management shifted in early 2008.

	Annual Growth	6/01	6/02	6/03	6/04	*6/05
Sales ($ mil.)	37.4%	67.4	80.8	101.2	212.9	240.3
Net income ($ mil.)	—	(16.3)	(13.2)	2.8	29.4	38.3
Employees	27.3%	64	54	—	—	168

*Most recent year available

ESCALADE, INCORPORATED

NASDAQ (GM): ESCA

817 Maxwell Ave.
Evansville, IN 47711
Phone: 812-467-4449
Fax: 812-467-1303
Web: www.escaladeinc.com

CEO: Robert J. Keller
CFO: Terry D. Frandsen
HR: Gary Allan
FYE: Saturday nearest December 31
Type: Public

Escalade isn't in the business of making high-end SUVs, but rather helping its customers get some high hoops from its vast line of sporting goods and basketball backboards. The company's sporting goods also include pool tables, table tennis, hockey and soccer tables, play systems, archery, darts, and fitness equipment. Escalade's products are sold under the Ping-Pong, STIGA, Murrey, Goalrilla, Silverback, USWeight, and Woodplay names, as well as private labels. Escalade's Martin Yale office products include data shredders, paper trimmers, and folding machines and are sold worldwide under brand names (Intimus, Master, Mead Hatcher) and private labels. Chairman Robert Griffin owns about 25% of Escalade.

	Annual Growth	12/03	12/04	12/05	12/06	12/07
Sales ($ mil.)	(4.3%)	221.7	220.7	185.6	191.5	185.6
Net income ($ mil.)	(11.1%)	14.9	8.2	12.9	8.5	9.3
Market value ($ mil.)	5.3%	95.3	172.3	152.4	139.9	117.2
Employees	—	—	—	805	—	—

ESCALATE RETAIL

9890 Towne Centre Dr., Ste. 100
San Diego, CA 92121
Phone: 858-457-3888
Fax: 858-457-2145
Web: www.escalateretail.com

CEO: Stewart M. (Stew) Bloom
CFO: Michael (Mike) Larkin
HR: –
FYE: December 31
Type: Private

Escalate Retail keeps stores well stocked with technology. The company provides retail management software, including planning, merchandising, analytics, supplier collaboration, and direct marketing applications. Serving traditional and online retailers across North America and Europe, it counts Bluefly, Home Depot, Nordstrom, Sony, and Williams-Sonoma among its clients. The company was formed in 2006 when Ecometry and GERS merged to create Escalate Retail. The deal was funded by Golden Gate Capital.

	Annual Growth	12/03	12/04	12/05	12/06	12/07
Est. sales ($ mil.)	—	—	—	—	—	28.9
Employees	—	—	—	—	—	370

ESCALON MEDICAL CORP.

NASDAQ (CM): ESMC

565 E. Swedesford Rd., Ste. 200
Wayne, PA 19087
Phone: 610-688-6830
Fax: 610-688-3641
Web: www.escalonmed.com

CEO: Richard J. DePiano
CFO: Robert M. O'Connor
HR: –
FYE: June 30
Type: Public

Escalon Medical keeps blood and eyes healthy. The company develops and markets blood testing products and ophthalmic medical devices. Its Drew Scientific division makes instruments and consumables for blood cell counting and analysis, including diabetes testing and hematology equipment. In the area of ophthalmology, the company makes ultrasound systems (through subsidiary Sonomed), intraocular gases, and other products used in eye exams and surgeries. Additionally, Escalon sells vascular access products (such as catheters, monitors, and needles) that help locate hard-to-reach blood vessels for injections. In 2006 the company acquired retinal imaging equipment maker MRP Group.

	Annual Growth	6/03	6/04	6/05	6/06	6/07
Sales ($ mil.)	30.4%	13.4	14.7	26.9	29.8	38.8
Net income ($ mil.)	36.5%	1.7	2.7	2.5	(2.0)	5.9
Market value ($ mil.)	24.1%	10.6	48.6	40.0	32.0	25.2
Employees	(0.3%)	—	—	180	—	179

ESCO CORPORATION

2141 NW 25th Ave.
Portland, OR 97210
Phone: 503-228-2141
Fax: 503-226-8071
Web: www.escocorp.com

CEO: Steven D. (Steve) Pratt
CFO: Gene K. Huey
HR: Nick Blauwiekel
FYE: Last Friday in December
Type: Private

ESCO is well ensconced as a global manufacturer of engineered metal parts, castings, and components for industrial machinery. The company's two operating groups are ESCO Engineered Products and ESCO Turbine Technologies. ESCO operates some 20 manufacturing facilities and provides such services as contract manufacturing, engineering, and supply chain management, as well as specialized services. The company serves the mining, construction, and industrial markets. ESCO was founded in Portland, Oregon, by C. F. Swigert in 1913 as Electric Steel Foundry; its products at that time included trolley car replacement parts.

An in-depth profile of this company is available to Hoover's Online members at hoovers.com.

ESCO TECHNOLOGIES INC.

NYSE: ESE

9900A Clayton Rd., Ste. 200
St. Louis, MO 63124
Phone: 314-213-7200
Fax: 314-213-7250
Web: www.escotechnologies.com

CEO: Victor L. (Vic) Richey Jr.
CFO: Gary E. Muenster
HR: Deborah J. Hanlon
FYE: September 30
Type: Public

Diversified manufacturing company ESCO Technologies focuses on three business segments: Filtration/Fluid Flow, Communications, and RF Shielding and Test. The company's filters are used in industrial applications, fuel systems, medical applications, and appliances. ESCO's communications equipment includes meter-reading technology and video surveillance systems used to monitor industrial applications. Test products include electromagnetic compatibility (EMC) equipment such as antennas, probes, turntables, and calibration equipment, as well as radio-frequency (RF) shielding products.

	Annual Growth	9/03	9/04	9/05	9/06	9/07
Sales ($ mil.)	7.4%	396.7	422.1	429.1	458.9	527.5
Net income ($ mil.)	—	(41.1)	35.7	43.5	31.3	33.7
Market value ($ mil.)	31.0%	290.4	436.8	1,280.0	1,190.8	855.7
Employees	6.8%	—	—	2,365	—	2,700

ESMARK INCORPORATED

NASDAQ (GS): ESMK

2500 Euclid Ave
Chicago Heights, IL 60411
Phone: 708-756-0400
Fax: 708-756-0099
Web: www.esmark.com

CEO: James P. (Jim) Bouchard
CFO: John Krupinski
HR: –
FYE: December 31
Type: Public

Esmark is using steel to build its fortune. Formed in 2003, it has acquired steel companies located throughout the Eastern half of the US since then. Esmark's subsidiaries are mostly steel service centers like Electric Coating Technologies, Sun Steel, Century Steel, and Miami Valley Steel Service. The company also works closely with European steel-making giant Ferrostaal on a trading joint venture called United Steel Group. Esmark is controlled by the Bouchard Group, which is led by brothers James and Craig Bouchard, CEO and president of Esmark, respectively. In 2008, though, Esmark chose to go with Russian steelmaker Severstal's $1.3 billion bid to buy the company. (Indian conglomerate Essar also had bid for Esmark.)

	Annual Growth	12/03	12/04	12/05	12/06	12/07
Sales ($ mil.)	—	—	—	—	—	412.8
Employees	—	—	—	—	—	765

ESPEY MFG. & ELECTRONICS CORP.

AMEX: ESP

233 Ballston Ave.
Saratoga Springs, NY 12866
Phone: 518-245-4400
Fax: 518-245-4421
Web: www.espey.com

CEO: Howard M. Pinsley
CFO: David A. O'Neil
HR: Peggy A. Murphy
FYE: June 30
Type: Public

Espey is on a power trip. Espey Mfg. & Electronics makes electronic equipment for high-voltage applications, including specialized electronic power supplies, transformers, and electronic system components. Its transformers and electronic systems include high-power radar transmitters, antennas, and iron-core products such as magnetic amplifiers and audio filters. Espey's products are used by industrial and military customers in radar, missile guidance and control, communications, aircraft navigation, and nuclear submarine control. Customers include Lockheed Martin, Raytheon, General Electric, and the US government. Espey's corporate retirement plan owns about 30% of the company.

	Annual Growth	6/03	6/04	6/05	6/06	6/07
Sales ($ mil.)	8.8%	19.8	22.5	18.8	20.9	27.7
Net income ($ mil.)	25.7%	1.0	1.0	1.0	1.6	2.5
Market value ($ mil.)	56.3%	9.4	11.6	15.5	38.5	55.8
Employees						

ESPN, INC.

ESPN Plaza, 935 Middle St.
Bristol, CT 06010
Phone: 860-766-2000
Fax: 860-766-2213
Web: espn.go.com

CEO: George W. Bodenheimer
CFO: Christine Driessen
HR: Daryl Smith
FYE: September 30
Type: Joint venture

ESPN is a superstar of the sports broadcasting world. The company is the leading cable sports broadcaster, reaching more than 97 million US homes with its stable of channels, including ESPN, ESPN2 (sporting events, news, and original programming), and ESPN Classic (historical sports footage). It also creates original programming for TV and radio and lends content for ESPN.com (operated by Walt Disney Internet Group), one of the most popular sports sites on the Internet. Its international operations extend the ESPN brand to another 190 countries. ESPN is 80% owned by Walt Disney (through ABC); Hearst has a 20% stake.

ESS TECHNOLOGY, INC.

NASDAQ (GM): ESST

48401 Fremont Blvd.
Fremont, CA 94538
Phone: 510-492-1088
Fax: 510-492-1098
Web: www.esstech.com

CEO: Robert L. Blair
CFO: John A. Marsh
HR: –
FYE: December 31
Type: Public

ESS loves to mix the sights and sounds of technology. ESS Technology designs multimedia chips for electronics devices such as DVD players, DivX movie players, and digital audio systems. Its decoder chips support a wide range of video and audio formats, while its encoder chips transform DVD players into recordable devices. Its image processors are used in digital still cameras and camera-enabled cell phones; ESS is de-emphasizing that business and discontinuing sales, however. Top customers of the fabless semiconductor company include LG Electronics (16% of sales), Philips, Samsung (31%), Sharp, and Sony. Imperium Partners Group has offered to buy ESS Technology for about $58 million in cash.

	Annual Growth	12/03	12/04	12/05	12/06	12/07
Sales ($ mil.)	(23.1%)	195.3	257.3	181.9	100.5	68.3
Net income ($ mil.)	(40.8%)	25.3	(35.5)	(99.6)	(44.1)	3.1
Market value ($ mil.)	(48.5%)	670.4	282.4	134.1	36.6	47.3
Employees	(26.8%)	498	536	517	260	143

ESSELTE CORPORATION

5 High Ridge Park, Ste. 205
Stamford, CT 06905
Phone: 203-658-1730
Fax: 203-658-1731
Web: www.esselte.com

CEO: Gary J. Brooks
CFO: Richard A. (Rich) Douville
HR: James (Jim) O'Leary
FYE: December 31
Type: Private

Write it, print it, staple it, drop it in a folder, and store it in a filing cabinet — Esselte is there for each step. Manufacturer of more than 30,000 products, the company is a leading manufacturer of office supplies worldwide. Esselte makes paper-based filing and document management items (files, binders, folders, covers), workspace products (staplers, letter trays), and computer accessories under the Esselte, Leitz, Oxford, Pendaflex, and Xyron brands. Customers range from wholesalers and direct marketers to office superstores and mass retailers. J. W. Childs Associates bought Esselte in 2002.

ESSEX PROPERTY TRUST, INC.

NYSE: ESS

925 E. Meadow Dr.
Palo Alto, CA 94303
Phone: 650-494-3700
Fax: 650-494-8743
Web: www.essexproperties.com

CEO: Keith R. Guericke
CFO: Michael T. Dance
HR: Suzanne M. Golden
FYE: December 31
Type: Public

Essex is collecting its own kingdom of hamlets on the West Coast. Essex Property Trust acquires, develops, and manages apartment communities, focusing on the metropolitan areas of Los Angeles, San Francisco, and Seattle. The self-managed and self-administered real estate investment trust (REIT) owns more than 130 residential communities with approximately 27,500 apartment units; about half are located in Southern California. Other portfolio assets include a handful of recreational vehicle parks, office buildings, and a manufactured home community. The REIT adds to its portfolio through acquisition and through the development and renovation of new properties.

	Annual Growth	12/03	12/04	12/05	12/06	12/07
Sales ($ mil.)	13.5%	234.4	283.5	327.3	348.1	388.5
Net income ($ mil.)	32.1%	38.0	79.7	79.7	62.8	115.6
Market value ($ mil.)	13.4%	1,465.9	1,930.2	2,123.7	3,026.6	2,425.2
Employees	—	—	—	—	820	—	—

ESSROC CEMENT CORP.

3251 Bath Pike
Nazareth, PA 18064
Phone: 610-837-6725
Fax: 610-837-9614
Web: www.essroc.com

CEO: Rodolfo Danielli
CFO: Glenn R. Dalrymple
HR: –
FYE: December 31
Type: Subsidiary

Essroc 'n' roll around the clock for Essroc Cement, a leading North American cement maker. The company operates a number of cement plants and other facilities in the US and Canada, and has an annual capacity of more than 6.5 million metric tons. Essroc makes bulk and packaged cement products, including portland cement, masonry cement, and, through its AXIM Concrete Technologies subsidiary, concrete admixtures used to improve the performance quality of cement. Essroc's brands include Brixment, Saylor's PLUS, and VELVET masonry. Founded in 1866 by David Saylor as Coplay Cement, the company is now a part of the Italy-based Italcementi.

	Annual Growth	12/03	12/04	12/05	12/06	12/07
Est. sales ($ mil.)	—	—	—	—	—	399.8
Employees	—	—	—	—	—	2,000

[L] THE ESTÉE LAUDER COMPANIES INC.

NYSE: EL

767 5th Ave.
New York, NY 10153
Phone: 212-572-4200
Fax: 212-572-3941
Web: www.elcompanies.com

CEO: William P. Lauder
CFO: Richard W. Kunes
HR: Amy DiGeso
FYE: June 30
Type: Public

The firm's Estée and Bobbi are counted among some of the closest friends to women worldwide. Estée Lauder sells cosmetics, fragrances, and skin care products, with brands including upscale Estée Lauder and Clinique and professional Bobbi Brown *essentials*. Its lines are sold in department stores, company stores, and by specialty retailers, as well as online. The firm has expanded its chain of freestanding retail stores (primarily for its M.A.C, Origins, and Aveda brands). The founding Lauder family controls about 88% of its voting shares. Estée Lauder bowed its Tom Ford collection in 2005 and in 2007 sold its Rodan + Fields line. Veteran Procter & Gamble executive Fabrizio Freda joined the firm in March 2008.

	Annual Growth	6/03	6/04	6/05	6/06	6/07
Sales ($ mil.)	8.3%	5,117.6	5,790.4	6,336.3	6,463.8	7,037.5
Net income ($ mil.)	8.9%	319.8	342.1	406.1	244.2	449.2
Market value ($ mil.)	6.2%	4,023.4	6,561.6	5,191.1	4,890.0	5,120.9
Employees	9.7%	—	—	23,700	26,200	28,500

[L] ESTERLINE TECHNOLOGIES CORPORATION

NYSE: ESL

City Center Bellevue, 500 108th Ave. NE, Ste. 1500
Bellevue, WA 98004
Phone: 425-453-9400
Fax: 425-453-2916
Web: www.esterline.com

CEO: Robert W. Cremin
CFO: Robert D. George
HR: Marcia J. M. Greenberg
FYE: October 31
Type: Public

Esterline Technologies has a trio of aerospace and defense business segments: Avionics & Controls, Sensors & Systems, and Advanced Materials. The Avionics & Controls unit makes interface systems — such as switches, indicators, keyboards, and displays — for aircraft and military vehicles, communications systems, and medical equipment. Sensors & Systems operations include temperature and pressure sensors, as well as fluid and motion control products. The Advanced Materials segment makes elastomer products and ordnance and military countermeasures (Esterline Defense Group).

	Annual Growth	10/03	10/04	10/05	10/06	10/07
Sales ($ mil.)	22.5%	562.5	628.2	835.4	972.3	1,266.6
Net income ($ mil.)	40.2%	23.9	39.6	58.0	55.6	92.3
Market value ($ mil.)	35.9%	466.5	673.7	936.4	955.9	1,590.1
Employees	21.6%	—	—	6,700	8,150	—

ESTES EXPRESS LINES, INC.

3901 W. Broad St.
Richmond, VA 23230
Phone: 804-353-1900
Fax: 804-353-8001
Web: www.estes-express.com

CEO: Robey W. (Rob) Estes Jr.
CFO: Gary D. Okes
HR: Thomas Donahue
FYE: December 31
Type: Private

Estes Express Lines is a multiregional less-than-truckload (LTL) freight hauler. (LTL carriers consolidate freight from multiple shippers into a single trailer.) The company operates a fleet of about 6,600 tractors and 22,800 trailers from a network of about 200 terminals throughout the US. Estes Express offers service in Canada through ExpressLINK alliance partner TST Overland Express; it works with other companies to offer service in the Caribbean and in Mexico. Founded by W. W. Estes in 1931, the company is owned and operated by the Estes family.

	Annual Growth	12/02	12/03	12/04	12/05	12/06
Est. sales ($ mil.)	26.0%	—	—	—	1,149.0	1,447.2
Employees	5.9%	—	—	—	13,051	13,824

ESURANCE INC.

650 Davis St.
San Francisco, CA 94111
Phone: 415-875-4500
Fax: 415-875-4501
Web: www.esurance.com

CEO: Gary C. Tolman
CFO: Jonathan Adkisson
HR: –
FYE: December 31
Type: Subsidiary

Esurance sells car insurance to the Internet-savvy customer. The company, which specializes in personal automobile insurance, offers quote comparisons and sells policies online, from its Web site and through select online agents. It also provides online access to accounts and makes telephone agents available for offline questions. Esurance sells auto insurance to customers in about 25 states, with California and Florida its leading markets. Subsidiaries Esurance Insurance Company and Esurance Property and Casualty Insurance underwrite the company's auto policies. Esurance has been a subsidiary of White Mountains Insurance Group since 2000.

	Annual Growth	12/03	12/04	12/05	12/06	12/07
Est. sales ($ mil.)	—	—	—	—	—	13.9
Employees	—	—	—	—	—	140

[L] An in-depth profile of this company is available to Hoover's Online members at hoovers.com.

581

ETELOS, INC.

OTC: ETLO

1900 O'Farrell St., Ste. 320
San Mateo, CA 94403
Phone: 425-458-4510
Fax: 425-458-4511
Web: www.etelos.com

CEO: Jeffrey L. (Jeff) Garon
CFO: David MacKenzie
HR: Randall G. Clark
FYE: December 31
Type: Public

Etelos is developing into a provider of Web applications tools with a higher profile. The company completed a reverse merger in 2008 with Tripath Technology, a bankrupt chip design firm, and became a publicly held venture in the process. Pursuing the software-as-a-service market, where companies offer applications as a resource on the Internet rather than as packages that need to be installed and maintained at a customer's facilities, Etelos offers what it calls a "platform as a service" for developing Web apps, a Web-based service that developers can access. Its Etelos Marketplace service allows developers to distribute, license, and support Web applications.

	Annual Growth	12/03	12/04	12/05	12/06	12/07
Sales ($ mil.)	0.0%	—	—	—	0.3	0.3
Net income ($ mil.)	—	—	—	—	(1.5)	(4.0)
Employees	112.5%	—	—	—	16	34

ETHAN ALLEN INTERIORS INC.

NYSE: ETH

Ethan Allen Drive
Danbury, CT 06811
Phone: 203-743-8000
Fax: 203-743-8298
Web: www.ethanallen.com

CEO: M. Farooq Kathwari
CFO: David R. Callen
HR: –
FYE: June 30
Type: Public

Furniture maker Ethan Allen Interiors (the holding company for Ethan Allen Inc.) has some revolutionary ideas for your living room. Named after the American patriot, the vertically integrated firm has about 10 furniture factories, including two saw mills. These make the Ethan Allen furnishings that are sold at more than 300 Ethan Allen stores located primarily in the US. About half of the stores are operated by independent dealers who are required to deal exclusively in Ethan Allen products and follow company guidelines. Products include case goods (wood furniture such as beds, dressers, and tables), upholstery items (sofas, recliners), and accessories (wall decor, lighting).

	Annual Growth	6/03	6/04	6/05	6/06	6/07
Sales ($ mil.)	2.6%	907.3	955.1	949.0	1,066.4	1,005.3
Net income ($ mil.)	(2.1%)	75.4	79.5	79.3	85.7	69.2
Market value ($ mil.)	(5.2%)	1,307.9	1,312.7	1,156.6	1,174.0	1,055.2
Employees	0.0%	—	—	6,400	6,400	—

ETOYS DIRECT, INC.

1099 18th St., Ste. 1800
Denver, CO 80202
Phone: 303-228-9000
Fax: 303-226-8600
Web: www.etoys.com

CEO: Michael J. Wagner
CFO: Barry Hollingsworth
HR: Gigi Healy
FYE: March 31
Type: Private

Virtual toystore eToys Direct makes online shopping a reality for harried parents. A former division of KB Toys (and previously named KBtoys.com), the company's catalog of 10,000 products includes toys, dolls, games, baby products, software, and collectibles. It also offers baby gifts and specialty toys including educational toys and games. PC software, DVDs and videos, kid's room décor, party supplies, and video games (not just educational ones) also grace the virtual shelves at eToys Direct. The company, which also operates the KBtoys.com Web site, was formed in 1999 and is owned by an affiliate of investment firm D. E. Shaw. eToys Direct merged with online retailer BabyUniverse in 2007.

	Annual Growth	3/03	3/04	3/05	3/06	3/07
Est. sales ($ mil.)	—	—	—	—	—	6.8
Employees	—	—	—	—	—	90

E*TRADE BANK

671 N. Glebe Rd. North, 10th Fl.
Arlington, VA 22203
Phone: 678-624-6210
Fax: 800-664-4641
Web: us.etrade.com/e/t/banking

CEO: Arlen W. Gelbard
CFO: Matthew J. Audette
HR: –
FYE: December 31
Type: Subsidiary

If you want to e-void e-nnoying trips to the bank, try e-banking with E*TRADE Bank. A subsidiary of online brokerage E*TRADE Financial, the bank is one of the largest electronic banks in the US. Its customers can access their accounts via the Internet, mail, phone, and ATMs, as well as through more than 20 bricks-and-mortar locations in major metropolitan areas. Like most traditional banks, E*TRADE Bank offers deposits, loans, credit cards, and other financial services. Unlike most traditional banks, however, E*TRADE Bank allows its customers to transfer funds between their banking and E*TRADE brokerage accounts in real time.

E*TRADE FINANCIAL CORPORATION

NASDAQ (GS): ETFC

135 E. 57th St.
New York, NY 10022
Phone: 646-521-4300
Fax: 212-826-2803
Web: www.etrade.com

CEO: Donald H. (Don) Layton
CFO: Matthew J. Audette
HR: –
FYE: December 31
Type: Public

E*TRADE wants you to use its services for E*VERYTHING financial. A top online brokerage, the company has more than 4.5 million retail account holders who can trade stock over the Internet (the majority of transactions) and by phone. It also offers mutual funds, options, fixed income products, exchange-traded funds, and portfolio management services. For corporate clients, the company performs market making, trade clearing, and employee stock option plan administration services. Subsidiary E*TRADE Bank offers deposits, loans, and credit cards online, as well as at more than 25 financial centers in major US cities; customers can transfer funds between their banking and brokerage accounts in real-time.

	Annual Growth	12/03	12/04	12/05	12/06	12/07
Sales ($ mil.)	15.5%	2,008.4	2,083.3	2,537.0	2,420.3	3,569.7
Net income ($ mil.)	—	203.0	380.5	430.4	628.9	(1,441.8)
Market value ($ mil.)	(23.0%)	4,642.7	5,525.9	8,689.9	9,557.7	1,636.2
Employees	5.7%	—	—	3,400	4,100	3,800

ETRIALS WORLDWIDE, INC.

NASDAQ (GM): ETWC

4000 Aerial Center Pkwy.
Morrisville, NC 27560
Phone: 919-653-3400
Fax: 919-653-3620
Web: www.etrials.com

CEO: Eugene E. (Chip) Jennings
CFO: Joseph Trepanier
HR: –
FYE: December 31
Type: Public

etrials Worldwide can make drug and device research much less of a difficult trial. Its eClinical software is used to manage clinical trials, integrating electronic data capture (EDC), interactive voice response (IVR), and electronic patient diaries (EPD) functions, as well as providing applications for data analytics. etrials' customers include pharmaceutical, biotechnology, and device and contract research organizations. The company also provides services such as project training, project implementation, project management, medical coding, and system and performance monitoring. etrials was founded in 1999.

	Annual Growth	12/03	12/04	12/05	12/06	12/07
Sales ($ mil.)	16.7%	—	—	—	19.2	22.4
Net income ($ mil.)	—	—	—	—	(0.6)	(6.2)
Market value ($ mil.)	(14.9%)	—	—	—	42.9	36.5
Employees	—	—	—	—	2	125

An in-depth profile of this company is available to Hoover's Online members at hoovers.com.

EURAMAX INTERNATIONAL, INC.

5445 Triangle Pkwy., Ste. 350
Norcross, GA 30092
Phone: 770-449-7066
Fax: 770-449-7354
Web: www.euramax.com

CEO: Mitchell B. Lewis
CFO: R. Scott Vansant
HR: –
FYE: Last Friday of December
Type: Holding company

When it comes to RV components and parts, Euramax International takes it to the max, both in Europe and the US. Through subsidiary holdings, the company produces aluminum, steel, vinyl, and fiberglass products for OEMs (commercial panel makers and RV and other transportation industry manufacturers), distributors, contractors, and home centers. The company has in-house coil-coating capabilities for supplying aluminum sidewalls to RV makers and steel siding to manufactured housing customers. Euramax makes a majority of the aluminum sidewalls used annually by RV makers in the US. Euramax International is controlled by Goldman Sachs & Co.

	Annual Growth	12/02	12/03	12/04	12/05	12/06
Sales ($ mil.)	17.3%	639.1	744.3	964.8	1,068.0	1,210.0
Employees	9.3%	2,312	2,600	2,700	3,200	3,300

EUREKA FINANCIAL CORPORATION

OTC: EKFC

3455 Forbes Ave.
Pittsburgh, PA 15213
Phone: 412-681-8400
Fax: 412-681-6625
Web: www.eurekabancorp.com

CEO: Edward F. Seserko
CFO: Gary B. Pepper
HR: –
FYE: September 30
Type: Public

Eureka will help you eke the most out of your income. Eureka Financial is the holding company of the single-branch Eureka Bank, a thrift serving Pittsburgh's Oakland neighborhood, near the University of Pittsburgh. Originally chartered in 1886, the bank offers standard personal and business deposit products including checking and savings accounts, CDs, and IRAs. Eureka Bank is focused on real estate lending: Real estate loans — mostly single-family mortgages — account for three-quarters of its total loan portfolio. It also offers commercial and consumer loans. Eureka Bancorp, MHC, owns a majority of Eureka Financial.

	Annual Growth	9/03	9/04	9/05	9/06	9/07
Est. sales ($ mil.)	—	—	—	—	—	4.8
Employees	—	—	—	—	—	15

EUROBANCSHARES, INC.

NASDAQ (GS): EUBK

Quebrada Arena Rd., 1 Km. 24.5
San Juan, PR 00926
Phone: 787-751-7340
Fax: 787-758-5611
Web: www.eurobankpr.com

CEO: Rafael Arrillaga-Torréns Jr.
CFO: Yadira R. Mercado Piñiero
HR: –
FYE: December 31
Type: Public

Far, far away from the old country is Puerto Rico-based EuroBancshares, which is the holding company for Eurobank. Through about 25 branches around the island, Eurobank targets small and midsized businesses, owners and employees of such firms, and professionals. The company focuses on commercial banking; auto and other leasing; mortgage banking; and trust and wealth management. Lending activities are concentrated on products related to real estate development, particularly on single-family homes and townhouses. Real estate-secured loans make up about 45% of a portfolio that also includes leases (about 25%) and business loans (more than 15%). Director Pedro Feliciano Benítez owns more than 25% of the company.

	Annual Growth	12/03	12/04	12/05	12/06	12/07
Assets ($ mil.)	20.1%	1,320.9	2,102.8	2,391.3	2,500.9	2,751.4
Net income ($ mil.)	(24.6%)	9.9	22.7	16.5	8.0	3.2
Market value ($ mil.)	(42.9%)	—	410.8	274.9	170.0	76.4
Employees	—	—	—	477	—	—

EUROMARKET DESIGNS, INC.

1250 Techny Rd.
Northbrook, IL 60062
Phone: 847-272-2888
Fax: 847-272-5366
Web: www.crateandbarrel.com

CEO: Barbara A. Turf
CFO: Diane Pearse
HR: Susie Muellman
FYE: Last day in February
Type: Private

Think you've never bought anything from Euromarket Designs? Think again. The retailer, which does business under the Crate & Barrel name, pioneered the fashionable-yet-homey look for contemporary interiors. It has some 160 stores (including nearly a dozen outlet stores) in about two dozen US states and the District of Columbia. About a third of the merchandise, which includes furniture and housewares, is unique to the chain. Crate & Barrel issues eight catalogs annually to some 15 million households and sells merchandise on its Web site. Germany-based Otto GmbH, the world's largest mail-order merchant, owns a majority stake in Euromarket Designs.

	Annual Growth	2/03	2/04	2/05	2/06	2/07
Est. sales ($ mil.)	—	—	—	—	—	401.3
Employees	—	—	—	—	—	6,000

EURONET WORLDWIDE, INC.

NASDAQ (GS): EEFT

4601 College Blvd., Ste. 300
Leawood, KS 66211
Phone: 913-327-4200
Fax: 913-327-1921
Web: www.euronetworldwide.com

CEO: Michael J. (Mike) Brown
CFO: Rick L. Weller
HR: –
FYE: December 31
Type: Public

Euronet Worldwide might soon have the whole world in its net — thanks to its network of ATMs and other electronic financial services. Banks, card issuers, and other institutions pay the firm for managing transactions at more than 11,000 ATMs and some 400,000 point-of-sale terminals in 100 countries across Africa, Europe, India, and the Middle East. The company operates in three segments: its aforementioned EFT (electronic funds transfer) services; its prepaid processing operations, which provide prepaid mobile phone cards and other prepaid products and collection services; and money transfer, which holds the operations of subsidiary Ria Envia and provides global money transfer and bill pay services.

	Annual Growth	12/03	12/04	12/05	12/06	12/07
Sales ($ mil.)	45.6%	204.4	381.1	531.2	629.2	917.6
Net income ($ mil.)	45.9%	11.8	18.4	27.4	46.3	53.5
Market value ($ mil.)	28.9%	532.6	861.9	994.6	1,111.6	1,468.6
Employees	64.3%	—	—	926	1,098	2,500

EV ENERGY PARTNERS, L.P.

NASDAQ (GS): EVEP

1001 Fannin St., Ste. 800
Houston, TX 77002
Phone: 713-651-1144
Fax: 713-651-1260
Web: www.evenergypartners.com

CEO: John B. Walker
CFO: Michael E. (Mike) Mercer
HR: –
FYE: December 31
Type: Public

EV Energy Partners is a natural gas and oil exploration and production company, which operates in the Appalachian Basin, primarily in West Virginia and Ohio, as well as in northern Louisiana and Michigan. EV Energy Partners has estimated proved reserves of about 183 billion cu. ft. of natural gas equivalent. Its base in the Appalachian Basin puts EV Energy Partners in close proximity to the nation's major consuming markets, allowing for stronger pricing power. The company acquired assets in Michigan in 2007. EV Energy Partners was formed in 2006 by Canadian energy industry investment group EnerVest, which owns 24.5% of the company, and 71% of EV Energy Partners' general partner.

	Annual Growth	12/03	12/04	12/05	12/06	12/07
Sales ($ mil.)	65.7%	13.8	30.1	46.3	47.9	104.0
Net income ($ mil.)	42.7%	2.7	8.4	15.1	19.9	11.2
Market value ($ mil.)	265.2%	—	—	—	105.4	384.8
Employees	8.4%	—	—	332	360	—

An in-depth profile of this company is available to Hoover's Online members at hoovers.com.

583

EV3 INC.

NASDAQ (GS): EVVV

9600 54th Ave. North, Ste. 100	CEO: Robert J. (Bob) Palmisano
Plymouth, MN 55442	CFO: Patrick D. Spangler
Phone: 763-398-7000	HR: Gregory Morrison
Fax: 763-398-7200	FYE: December 31
Web: www.ev3.net	Type: Public

Here's what the "ev" in ev3 stands for: *endovascular*. The "3" refers to the three systems the catheter maker targets: peripheral vascular, cardiovascular, and neurovascular. ev3 develops, manufactures, and sells catheter-based medical devices used to treat vascular diseases, especially disorders in the heart and brain. ev3's products include stents, microcatheters, guidewires, embolic coils, and stroke reduction devices. The company sells more than 100 products in more than 60 countries through a direct sales team and distributors. Among its customers are radiologists, cardiologists, neurosurgeons, and vascular surgeons.

	Annual Growth	12/03	12/04	12/05	12/06	12/07
Sales ($ mil.)	43.2%	67.6	86.3	133.7	202.4	284.2
Net income ($ mil.)	—	(106.9)	(99.3)	(110.0)	(52.4)	(165.7)
Market value ($ mil.)	35.5%	—	—	727.4	992.4	1,335.6
Employees	34.8%	—	—	880	—	1,600

EVANS & SUTHERLAND COMPUTER

NASDAQ (GM): ESCC

770 Komas Dr.	CEO: David H. Bateman
Salt Lake City, UT 84108	CFO: Paul L. Dailey Jr.
Phone: 801-588-1000	HR: Bob Morishita
Fax: 801-588-4500	FYE: December 31
Web: www.es.com	Type: Public

Evans & Sutherland Computer Corporation (E&S) makes products that can fairly be described as stellar. The company provides hardware and software used in digital planetariums and other theaters. Its products include laser projectors, domed projection screens, and complete planetarium packages. The company also produces planetarium content. E&S sells its visual systems to theaters and schools; its domes are additionally marketed to casinos, theme parks, and military defense contractors. The company counts Disney, Griffith Observatory, IMAX, Texas A&M University, and Universal Studios among its customers.

	Annual Growth	12/03	12/04	12/05	12/06	12/07
Sales ($ mil.)	(25.4%)	84.8	69.2	73.6	15.1	26.2
Net income ($ mil.)	—	(36.0)	(8.9)	(1.1)	22.0	(6.3)
Market value ($ mil.)	(27.3%)	47.2	73.3	51.6	46.6	13.2
Employees	(56.0%)	—	—	268	118	—

EVANS BANCORP, INC.

NASDAQ (GM): EVBN

1 Grimsby Dr.	CEO: David J. Nasca
Hamburg, NY 14075	CFO: Gary A. Kajtoch
Phone: 716-926-2000	HR: –
Fax: 716-926-2005	FYE: December 31
Web: www.evansbancorp.com	Type: Public

Evans National Bank wants to take care of Buffalo's bills. The Evans Bancorp subsidiary operates about a dozen branches in western New York (including Buffalo). The bank primarily uses funds gathered from deposits to originate commercial and residential real estate loans (more than 70% of its loan portfolio) and to invest in US government, state, and municipal securities. Subsidiaries include ENB Insurance Agency, which provides retail and commercial property and casualty insurance; ENB Associates, offering mutual funds and annuities to bank customers; real estate investment trust Evans National Holding; and Evans National Leasing, which provides financing for business equipment throughout the US.

	Annual Growth	12/03	12/04	12/05	12/06	12/07
Assets ($ mil.)	7.2%	334.7	429.0	468.5	473.9	442.7
Net income ($ mil.)	(4.6%)	4.1	4.5	4.8	4.9	3.4
Market value ($ mil.)	(4.4%)	51.9	61.1	56.4	53.7	43.3
Employees	—	—	—	186	—	—

EVANSTON NORTHWESTERN HEALTHCARE

1301 Central St.	CEO: Mark R. Neaman
Evanston, IL 60201	CFO: Thomas H. Hodges
Phone: 847-570-2000	HR: William R. (Bill) Luehrs
Fax: 847-570-2940	FYE: September 30
Web: www.enh.org	Type: Not-for-profit

Evanston Northwestern Healthcare (ENH) provides care to residents of Chicago's north side and its suburbs through hospitals, home services, and a medical group with more than 460 primary and specialty care physicians. With 476 beds flagship Evanston Hospital has teaching and research programs, as well as capabilities for trauma, cancer, perinatal, and women's health care. The smaller Glenbrook Hospital has about 140 beds and is also a teaching facility, while Highland Park Hospital has nearly 240 beds. The health care system is affiliated with Northwestern University's Feinberg School of Medicine.

	Annual Growth	9/03	9/04	9/05	9/06	9/07
Est. sales ($ mil.)	—	—	—	—	—	1,061.0
Employees	—	—	—	—	—	7,500

EVCI CAREER COLLEGES HOLDING CORP.

NASDAQ (CM): EVCI

1 Van Der Donck St., 2nd Fl.	CEO: John J. McGrath
Yonkers, NY 10701	CFO: Stephen Schwartz
Phone: 914-623-0700	HR: –
Fax: 914-964-8222	FYE: December 31
Web: www.evcinc.com	Type: Public

EVCI provides on-campus college education through three institutions: the Interboro Institute, Technical Career Institutes, and Pennsylvania School of Business. Interboro (2,700 students) offers associate degrees to students who have GEDs or did not graduate from high school. Students earn an associate of occupational studies degree in areas such as accounting, medical assistant, executive assistant, paralegal studies, ophthalmic dispensing, and security. Technical Career (3,000 students) degrees include office technology, facilities management technology, and industrial technology. The Pennsylvania School of Business (325 students) offers training in office and medical billing operations, among others.

	Annual Growth	12/02	12/03	12/04	12/05	*12/06
Sales ($ mil.)	43.6%	15.4	20.2	33.1	50.7	65.4
Net income ($ mil.)	—	(2.0)	3.4	6.3	0.4	(13.5)
Employees	31.1%	237	—	—	849	700

*Most recent year available

EVENFLO COMPANY, INC.

1801 Commerce Dr.	CEO: Robert S. (Rob) Matteucci
Piqua, OH 45356	CFO: Mike Katafiasz
Phone: 937-415-3300	HR: Dennis Pregent
Fax: 937-415-3112	FYE: December 31
Web: www.evenflo.com	Type: Private

Those having a baby say hello to Evenflo. Named for a nursing device patented in 1935, the veteran company offers hundreds of items for the well-equipped baby and tot, including car seats, strollers, cribs, bath items, baby monitors, and feeding and safety products under the names Evenflo, Exersaucer, Gerry, and Snugli. The company's Web site also provides parenting resources with safety recalls and child care information. Evenflo has international sales operations in Canada, Mexico, and the Philippines. The firm sells its products through specialty retailers and big box stores, such as Target and Wal-Mart. An affiliate of private equity firm Weston Presidio bought Evenflo from Harvest Partners in early 2007.

	Annual Growth	12/03	12/04	12/05	12/06	12/07
Est. sales ($ mil.)	—	—	—	—	—	124.3
Employees	—	—	—	—	—	1,500

EVERBANK FINANCIAL CORPORATION

501 Riverside Ave.
Jacksonville, FL 32202
Phone: 904-281-6000
Fax: 904-281-6165
Web: www.everbank.com

CEO: Robert M. Clements
CFO: W. Blake Wilson
HR: –
FYE: December 31
Type: Private

EverBank Financial helps bank accounts stay evergreen. The holding company owns home loan servicer EverHome Mortgage and EverBank, which offers community banking services through a handful of branches in northeastern Florida. The company has a mortgage production joint venture with priceline.com, and provides online banking through EverBank Direct. It also offers wholesale residential and commercial real estate lending. EverBank Financial is buying most of the assets of NetBank, including that company's direct banking, small business financing, and mortgage servicing operations.

	Annual Growth	12/03	12/04	12/05	12/06	12/07
Est. sales ($ mil.)	—	—	—	—	—	286.5
Employees	—	—	—	—	—	1,841

EVERCORE PARTNERS INC.

NYSE: EVR

55 E. 52nd St., 43rd Fl.
New York, NY 10055
Phone: 212-857-3100
Fax: 212-857-3101
Web: www.evercore.com

CEO: Roger C. Altman
CFO: Robert B. Walsh
HR: –
FYE: December 31
Type: Public

Evercore Partners provides financial, restructuring, and mergers and acquisitions advisory services to corporate clients. Subsidiary Evercore Asset Management serves institutional investors and focuses on small- and mid-cap equities. Subsidiary Protego, a boutique investment bank founded by Pedro Aspe, Mexico's former Minister of Finance, specializes in financing municipal infrastructure and energy projects in Mexico. Evercore Europe provides services from its London office. The company also has a venture capital fund. As a boutique investment firm, Evercore believes that it operates without the conflicts of interest that plague larger firms that both underwrite and invest in their clients.

	Annual Growth	12/03	12/04	12/05	12/06	12/07
Sales ($ mil.)	54.2%	60.1	86.3	125.6	216.5	340.0
Net income ($ mil.)	—	34.3	49.8	63.2	69.7	(34.5)
Market value ($ mil.)	3.3%	—	—	—	234.3	242.0
Employees	55.5%	—	—	120	247	290

EVEREST REINSURANCE COMPANY

477 Martinsville Rd.
Liberty Corner, NJ 07938
Phone: 908-604-3000
Fax: 908-604-3322
Web: www.everestre.com

CEO: Joseph V. (Joe) Taranto
CFO: –
HR: –
FYE: December 31
Type: Subsidiary

Everest Reinsurance, part of the Everest Re Group, provides property/casualty reinsurance and insurance in the US through a handful of subsidiaries. Its Everest National Insurance underwrites property/casualty insurance in 47 states. While not technically a niche provider, Everest Security Insurance sells auto insurance only in Georgia and Alabama. Everest Indemnity Insurance writes excess and surplus lines in 49 states, the District of Columbia, and Puerto Rico. Everest Insurance Company of Canada no longer writes new business, and is operating in run-off. Formed in 1973, the company also offers actuarial support, claims management, and loss control services.

	Annual Growth	12/03	12/04	12/05	12/06	12/07
Est. sales ($ mil.)	—	—	—	—	—	2,147.5
Employees	—	—	—	—	—	377

EVERETT SMITH GROUP, LTD.

330 Kilbourn Ave., Ste. 750
Milwaukee, WI 53202
Phone: 414-223-1560
Fax: 414-225-0025
Web: www.esmithgroup.com

CEO: J. Douglas Gray
CFO: James Orth
HR: –
FYE: November 30
Type: Private

From skins to steel, Everett Smith Group has you covered. The investment firm owns Albert Trostel & Sons and Eagle Ottawa Leather, which makes upholstery leather for major carmakers. Other Everett Smith portfolio companies include OEM Worldwide, which manufactures electronic assemblies for medical and industrial applications, and Maysteel, which makes power distribution equipment and sheet metal enclosures for the utility industry. Everett Smith typically invests up to $75 million per transaction and maintains a buy-and-hold philosophy.

EVERGREEN ENERGY INC.

NYSE Arca: EEE

55 Madison St., Ste. 745
Denver, CO 80206
Phone: 303-293-2992
Fax: 303-293-8430
Web: www.evgenergy.com

CEO: Kevin R. Collins
CFO: Diana L. Kubik
HR: Hubert R. Henderson
FYE: December 31
Type: Public

Evergreen Energy (formerly KFx) wants to fuel the advancement of efficient, environmentally friendly power generation. The company has patented a process, known as K-Fuel, that uses heat and pressure to transform low-energy value coal and other feedstocks into high-energy fuel for power plants. After low-grade coal has been through the K-Fuel process, it can be used without causing power plants to violate pollution standards. In 2005 Evergreen Energy began shipments from its first K-Fuel commercial plant in Gillette, Wyoming. The pilot plant can refine 750,000 tons of coal a year; plans call for the facility to be expanded to be able to produce 10 million tons annually.

	Annual Growth	12/03	12/04	12/05	12/06	12/07
Sales ($ mil.)	369.8%	0.1	0.0	1.0	36.7	48.7
Net income ($ mil.)	—	(8.3)	(10.6)	(23.3)	(51.5)	(204.7)
Employees	—	—	—	72	—	—

EVERGREEN HOLDINGS, INC.

3850 Three Mile Ln.
McMinnville, OR 97128
Phone: 503-472-9361
Fax: 503-472-1048
Web: www.evergreenaviation.com

CEO: Delford M. (Del) Smith
CFO: John A. Irwin
HR: Forrest Clayton
FYE: February 28
Type: Holding company

Through Evergreen International Aviation, Evergreen Holdings soars through blue skies and travels across green lands. Evergreen International Aviation itself operates through several subsidiaries, including Evergreen International Airlines, which transports cargo for government and commercial customers with a fleet of Boeing 747 freighters. Evergreen Aviation Ground Logistics Enterprise provides ground handling services at US airports. Other Evergreen units offer helicopter transportation services; maintain, repair, and overhaul aircraft; sell and lease aircraft; and engage in farming. Del Smith, a former Air Force pilot and crop duster, owns a controlling stake in the company, which he founded in 1960.

	Annual Growth	2/02	2/03	2/04	2/05	2/06
Sales ($ mil.)	14.1%	447.7	574.3	535.6	580.9	757.7
Net income ($ mil.)	—	(12.4)	31.8	(6.5)	(5.3)	26.1
Employees	0.2%	—	4,386	4,354	4,565	4,411

An in-depth profile of this company is available to Hoover's Online members at hoovers.com.

585

EVERGREEN SOLAR, INC.

NASDAQ (GM): ESLR

138 Bartlett St.
Marlboro, MA 01752
Phone: 508-357-2221
Fax: 508-357-0747
Web: www.evergreensolar.com

CEO: Richard M. Feldt
CFO: Michael (Mike) El-Hillow
HR: Gary T. Pollard
FYE: December 31
Type: Public

Evergreen Solar wants to be a star in solar power. Using its proprietary crystalline technology, called String Ribbon, the company develops and manufactures solar power cells and panels. Applications for Evergreen's solar cells and systems include highway call boxes, microwave stations, street and billboard lighting, and off-grid rural electrification. Once a novelty, solar power has become more efficient and is now targeted at both remote rural users and the clean-energy set. Leading customers include Krannich Solartechnik (20% of sales), Donauer Solartechnik (19%), and SunPower Systems. Evergreen Solar gets most of its sales in the US.

	Annual Growth	12/03	12/04	12/05	12/06	12/07
Sales ($ mil.)	65.6%	9.3	23.5	44.0	103.2	69.9
Net income ($ mil.)	—	(15.0)	(19.4)	(17.3)	(26.7)	(16.6)
Market value ($ mil.)	196.8%	27.0	266.4	659.9	549.9	2,097.4
Employees	27.6%	151	250	290	330	400

EVERGREENBANCORP, INC.

OTC: EVGG

1111 3rd Ave., Ste. 2100
Seattle, WA 98101
Phone: 206-628-4250
Fax: 206-628-4022
Web: www.evergreenbank.com

CEO: Gerald O. Hatler
CFO: Gordon D. Browning
HR: —
FYE: December 31
Type: Public

This company probably isn't named for its love of trees; EvergreenBancorp is into money. Its subsidiary, EvergreenBank, has branches that can be found in and around Seattle. The bank offers general commercial banking services such as checking and savings accounts, lending, and financial planning. Commercial real estate loans make up some 40% of the bank's loan portfolio; commercial loans constitute about one-third. Originally founded as Teacher's State Bank by English and math teacher and credit union founder Robert Handy, it adopted the Evergreen name in 1980.

	Annual Growth	12/03	12/04	12/05	12/06	12/07
Assets ($ mil.)	21.4%	194.6	209.6	249.2	343.5	422.8
Net income ($ mil.)	4.7%	1.0	1.3	1.0	1.8	1.2
Market value ($ mil.)	27.7%	13.4	19.9	28.2	35.3	35.6
Employees	—	—	—	—	—	70

EVERLAST WORLDWIDE INC.

1350 Broadway, Ste. 2300
New York, NY 10018
Phone: 212-239-0990
Fax: 212-239-4261
Web: www.everlast.com

CEO: Seth A. Horowitz
CFO: Gary J. Dailey
HR: Ronnie Kornblum
FYE: December 31
Type: Subsidiary

Everlast Worldwide has one foot in the ring and one foot in the closet. Everlast trunks and boxing gloves have outfitted pugilists from Jack Dempsey to Muhammad Ali. The company also licenses its name for distribution overseas and to makers of children's wear, footwear, watches, exercise equipment, gym bags, and more. Everlast sells its products in department and sporting goods stores, as well as through online and catalog retailers. The company was acquired by Brands Holdings, a unit of Sports Direct International, in 2007.

	Annual Growth	12/02	12/03	12/04	12/05	12/06
Sales ($ mil.)	(7.6%)	71.1	64.7	45.0	43.3	51.9
Net income ($ mil.)	17.1%	2.5	(0.9)	(1.0)	(0.9)	4.7
Employees	(14.2%)	269	215	188	170	—

EVITE

555 12th St., Ste. 500
Oakland, CA 94607
Phone: 510-985-7400
Fax: —
Web: www.evite.com

CEO: Rosanna McCollough
CFO: —
HR: —
FYE: December 31
Type: Business segment

An invite from Evite gets you in with the cyber in-crowd. The company offers registered users online tools for planning parties, activities, and other social events, both private and public. Services include e-mail invitations, calendars, photo sharing, and address books. Customized Web invitations allow guests to RSVP, post comments, view the names of other invitees, and get additional information (such as a map to the event or items to bring). Revenues are primarily generated through sponsorships and ads. Launched in 1998 by former company executives Adam Lieb and Selina Tobaccowala, Evite operates alongside IAC Search & Media as part of the Media & Advertising division of parent company IAC/InterActiveCorp.

EVOLUTION PETROLEUM CORPORATION

AMEX: EPM

820 Gessner, Ste. 1340
Houston, TX 77024
Phone: 713-935-0122
Fax: 713-935-0199
Web: www.evolutionpetroleum.com

CEO: Robert Stevens Herlin
CFO: Sterling H. McDonald
HR: —
FYE: June 30
Type: Public

Petroleum evolved from old living forms and Evolution Petroleum Corporation evolved from Natural Gas Systems (which was formed in 2003). The crude oil and natural gas exploration operates four oil and gas producing fields in Louisiana. Its strategy is to acquire already-established properties and to redevelop them, thereby making the fields more profitable. One method it uses is gas flooding, which uses carbon dioxide to free up trapped old deposits. In 2007 the company reported proved reserves of 1.7 million barrels of oil equivalent and probable reserves of up to 16 million barrels of oil equivalent.

	Annual Growth	6/03	6/04	6/05	6/06	6/07
Sales ($ mil.)	166.8%	—	0.1	1.6	2.9	1.9
Net income ($ mil.)	—	—	(1.0)	(2.2)	24.6	(1.8)
Market value ($ mil.)	15.5%	—	52.8	42.1	77.3	81.4
Employees	—	—	—	—	—	—

EVOLVING SYSTEMS, INC.

NASDAQ (CM): EVOL

9777 Pyramid Ct., Ste. 100
Englewood, CO 80112
Phone: 303-802-1000
Fax: 303-802-1420
Web: www.evolving.com

CEO: Thaddeus (Thad) Dupper
CFO: Brian R. Ervine Sr.
HR: —
FYE: December 31
Type: Public

Evolving Systems offers software for the ever-evolving telecommunications industry. The company provides applications used by telecom companies to automate and manage parts of their network operations, including tools for managing and monitoring number inventory, as well as applications that allow users to route calls and messages to various devices. The company also provides local number portability software that allows telephone customers to keep the same phone number when changing to a new carrier. Its services include such offerings as training, support, maintenance, integration, installation, and consulting.

	Annual Growth	12/03	12/04	12/05	12/06	12/07
Sales ($ mil.)	6.5%	28.0	26.3	39.5	33.8	36.0
Net income ($ mil.)	(45.7%)	6.9	0.4	(2.9)	(16.8)	0.6
Market value ($ mil.)	(29.0%)	209.9	72.1	34.1	19.0	53.4
Employees	—	—	—	227	—	—

EVONIK DEGUSSA CORPORATION

379 Interpace Pkwy.
Parsippany, NJ 07054
Phone: 973-541-8000
Fax: 973-541-8013
Web: www.degussa-nafta.com

CEO: John Rolando
CFO: James Hickey
HR: Thomas P. (Tom) Ayers
FYE: December 31
Type: Subsidiary

Evonik Degussa Corporation is the North American arm of German chemical giant Evonik Degussa AG. Like its parent, it operates through three divisions: specialty materials (acrylics, coatings), consumer solutions (additives for personal care products and feed), and technology specialties (basic building block chemicals, fillers, and pigments). Products range from amino acids and building protection coatings to another of its specialties, carbon black, which is used in automobile tires for abrasion resistance. Its North American operations include units in Canada and Mexico, as well as acrylics maker CYRO Industries. Degussa sold its construction chemicals unit to BASF in 2006.

EVRAZ OREGON STEEL MILLS, INC.

1000 SW Broadway, Ste. 2200
Portland, OR 97205
Phone: 503-240-5226
Fax: 503-240-5232
Web: www.osm.com

CEO: James E. (Jim) Declusin
CFO: L. Ray Adams
HR: Jennifer R. Murray
FYE: December 31
Type: Subsidiary

Evraz Oregon Steel Mills has pipe dreams. The company produces steel plate, coil, electric-resistance welded (ERW) pipe and structural tubing from plants in Colorado and Oregon, as well as Alberta, Canada. Evraz Oregon Steel's customers are primarily located west of the Mississippi River in the US and Canada and include railroad operators, oil and gas pipeline companies, construction companies, and steel products distributors. Russian steelmaker Evraz acquired what was then called simply Oregon Steel Mills for $2.3 billion in early 2007 and then added to its name. The next year, the parent company combined its North American operations under one unit called Evraz Inc. NA.

THE E. W. SCRIPPS COMPANY

NYSE: SSP

312 Walnut St.
Cincinnati, OH 45202
Phone: 513-977-3000
Fax: 513-977-3721
Web: www.scripps.com

CEO: Kenneth W. (Ken) Lowe
CFO: Joseph G. (Joe) NeCastro
HR: Jennifer L. Weber
FYE: December 31
Type: Public

There is a lot of TV watching going on at this newspaper business. The E. W. Scripps Company is a venerable newspaper publisher with a portfolio of about 20 dailies including *The Commercial Appeal* (Memphis, Tennessee) and the *Denver Rocky Mountain News* (operated through Denver Newspaper Agency, a joint venture with MediaNews). However, the biggest share of the company's sales comes from its Scripps Networks unit which operates such cable TV channels as Home & Garden Television (HGTV) and the Food Network (70%-owned). Scripps also owns 10 TV stations and syndicates newspaper content through its United Media subsidiary. Trusts benefiting the Scripps family own almost 90% of the company.

	Annual Growth	12/03	12/04	12/05	12/06	12/07
Sales ($ mil.)	7.6%	1,874.8	2,167.5	2,513.9	2,498.1	2,517.1
Net income ($ mil.)	—	270.8	303.8	249.1	353.2	(1.6)
Market value ($ mil.)	17.8%	679.3	1,407.3	1,404.9	1,460.8	1,308.9
Employees	(5.9%)	—	—	9,600	9,000	8,500

EXACT SCIENCES CORPORATION

NASDAQ (GM): EXAS

100 Campus Dr.
Marlborough, MA 01752
Phone: 508-683-1200
Fax: 508-683-1201
Web: www.exactlabs.com

CEO: Jeffrey R. Luber
CFO: Charles R. Carelli Jr.
HR: –
FYE: December 31
Type: Public

Guesstimates aren't good enough when diagnosing a deadly cancer, so EXACT Sciences aims for accuracy. The firm makes PreGen-Plus, a non-invasive test for the early detection of colorectal cancer and precancerous lesions. PreGen-Plus isolates DNA in stool samples, using its Effipure technology, then identifies genetic mutations associated with cancer. Colorectal cancer is a common (and deadly) cancer, and EXACT believes its method is superior to existing diagnostic methods because it may be able to discern colorectal cancer in its early stages, when it is most treatable. EXACT Sciences is also developing its genomics-based technology to detect other cancers.

	Annual Growth	12/03	12/04	12/05	12/06	12/07
Sales ($ mil.)	(11.2%)	2.9	4.9	4.3	4.8	1.8
Net income ($ mil.)	—	(28.3)	(18.5)	(14.5)	(12.9)	(12.0)
Market value ($ mil.)	(18.1%)	194.8	100.3	58.4	76.0	87.7
Employees	(46.5%)	—	—	49	—	14

EXACTECH, INC.

NASDAQ (GM): EXAC

2320 NW 66th Ct.
Gainesville, FL 32653
Phone: 352-377-1140
Fax: 352-378-2617
Web: www.exac.com

CEO: William (Bill) Petty
CFO: Joel C. Phillips
HR: Betty B. Petty
FYE: December 31
Type: Public

Back off, lawman — Exactech's joints are medicinal. Hospitals, surgeons, and clinics worldwide use the company's knee and hip devices to replace joints weakened by injury or disease. Its Optetrak knee implants and AcuMatch hip implant system either partially or totally replace patients' damaged joints. It also markets Opteform and Optefil, bone allograft materials used to correct bone defects and damage. Exactech markets its products through independent dealers in the US and primarily through distributors in some 25 other countries. Chairman, president, and CEO William Petty and his family own about a third of Exactech.

	Annual Growth	12/03	12/04	12/05	12/06	12/07
Sales ($ mil.)	14.9%	71.3	81.8	91.0	102.4	124.2
Net income ($ mil.)	6.9%	6.5	7.3	6.6	7.8	8.5
Market value ($ mil.)	10.5%	162.5	203.9	130.1	163.9	242.6
Employees	—	—	—	214	—	—

EXACTTARGET, INC.

20 N. Meridian St.
Indianapolis, IN 46204
Phone: 317-423-3928
Fax: 317-396-1592
Web: www.exacttarget.com

CEO: Scott D. Dorsey
CFO: Traci M. Dolan
HR: Traci M. Dolan
FYE: December 31
Type: Private

ExactTarget helps others get the word out. The company offers e-mail marketing software for marketing campaigns. Its agency and retailer software helps customers create and personalize e-mails, build lists, and track the results of their campaigns. ExactTarget serves some 2,800 clients directly and another 2,000 indirectly through its 400 customers who are marketing services providers. Its client base, which includes Charles Schwab, Wellpoint, CareerBuilder, and firms with fewer than 150 employees, spans many industries. ExactTarget, which filed for an initial public offering in December 2007, was founded in 2000 by president and CEO Scott Dorsey and VP Peter McCormick.

	Annual Growth	12/02	12/03	12/04	12/05	12/06
Sales ($ mil.)	64.0%	—	—	11.6	19.7	31.2
Net income ($ mil.)	—	—	—	(1.4)	(1.5)	6.5
Employees	34.0%	—	—	—	200	268

An in-depth profile of this company is available to Hoover's Online members at hoovers.com.

587

EXAR CORPORATION

NASDAQ (GM): EXAR

48720 Kato Rd.
Fremont, CA 94538
Phone: 510-668-7000
Fax: 510-668-7001
Web: www.exar.com

CEO: Pedro (Pete) Rodriguez
CFO: J. Scott Kamsler
HR: Diane Hill
FYE: March 31
Type: Public

Exar seeks excellence in the exacting world of high-speed communications chips. The fabless semiconductor company's digital, analog, and mixed-signal integrated circuits are used in broadband networking equipment — especially telecommunications infrastructure gear — as well as in video and imaging devices, such as medical instrumentation, digital still cameras, and scanners. Exar outsources most of its manufacturing to Chartered Semiconductor; its customers include Alcatel-Lucent, Apple, Cisco Systems, Fujitsu, Hewlett-Packard, IBM, LG Electronics, Motorola, NEC, Nokia Siemens Networks, and Samsung Electronics. The company derives about two-thirds of its sales outside the US.

	Annual Growth	3/04	3/05	3/06	3/07	3/08
Sales ($ mil.)	7.5%	67.2	57.4	67.0	68.5	89.7
Net income ($ mil.)	—	4.6	5.3	7.8	8.0	(195.9)
Market value ($ mil.)	(17.0%)	757.7	573.8	626.9	475.7	359.8
Employees	10.9%	267	268	255	234	404

EXCEL TECHNOLOGY, INC.

NASDAQ (GS): XLTC

41 Research Way
East Setauket, NY 11733
Phone: 631-784-6175
Fax: 631-784-6195
Web: www.exceltechinc.com

CEO: Antoine Dominic
CFO: Alice Varisano
HR: Alice Varisano
FYE: December 31
Type: Public

Excel Technology excels in photonics. Operating through a number of subsidiaries, the company makes electro-optical components and laser systems for the scientific, industrial, and medical markets. Excel's Baublys-Control Laser unit is a leading producer of lasers for marking and engraving industrial materials, while its Cambridge Technology subsidiary develops optical scanners for biomedical research. Other units produce photomask repair systems, precision photometers, diamond-cutting systems, and scientific and industrial lasers. Customers located in the US account for nearly 40% of sales.

	Annual Growth	12/03	12/04	12/05	12/06	12/07
Sales ($ mil.)	6.9%	122.7	136.6	137.7	154.5	160.0
Net income ($ mil.)	11.9%	11.3	14.8	15.2	14.0	17.7
Market value ($ mil.)	(6.9%)	392.4	313.4	286.9	311.2	294.3
Employees	3.8%	619	684	721	704	719

EXCHANGE BANK

OTC: EXSR

545 4th St.
Santa Rosa, CA 95401
Phone: 707-524-3000
Fax: 707-579-4745
Web: www.exchangebank.com

CEO: J. Barrie Graham
CFO: Bruce E. DeCrona
HR: Diane Franzese
FYE: December 31
Type: Public

In Santa Rosa there may be no refunds, but there *are* exchanges. Exchange Banks, that is. Serving personal and business customers throughout Sonoma County, California, Exchange Bank offers standard deposit products such as checking and savings accounts; Visa credit cards; online banking; a variety of loans including home, auto, and boat; and trust and investment management services. Representing more than 60% of the total, the bank's loan portfolio is dominated by real estate (both commercial and residential); business loans represent about 20%. The bank has had just six presidents since its inception in 1890.

	Annual Growth	12/03	12/04	12/05	12/06	12/07
Est. sales ($ mil.)	—	—	—	—	—	95.0
Employees	—	—	—	—	—	453

EXCLUSIVE RESORTS, LLC

1515 Arapahoe St., Tower 3, Ste. 300
Denver, CO 80202
Phone: 303-226-4900
Fax: 303-474-6990
Web: www.exclusiveresorts.com

CEO: Jeff S. Potter
CFO: Robert E. Parsons Jr.
HR: Trish Beck
FYE: December 31
Type: Private

Exclusive Resorts is time-share gone way way upscale. The 2,500-member company owns more than 300 luxury vacation homes in more than 30 locations worldwide divided into beach (Hawaii, Costa Rica, France), mountain (France, Canada, US), metropolitan (San Francisco, London, Paris), and leisure categories. Leisure locations include golf resorts in the US, an English castle, and a Tuscan villa. Members pay from $225,000 to $425,000 enrollment and between $12,900 and $29,000 per year to stay from 15 to 45 days in one of the $3 million, on average, homes. Exclusive Resorts was founded by brothers Brad (vice chairman) and Brent (president) Handler and EVP Tom Filippini; AOL co-founder Steve Case is the majority owner.

	Annual Growth	12/03	12/04	12/05	12/06	12/07
Est. sales ($ mil.)	—	—	—	—	—	7.4
Employees	—	—	—	—	—	275

EXCO RESOURCES, INC.

NYSE: XCO

12377 Merit Dr., Ste. 1700, LB 82
Dallas, TX 75251
Phone: 214-368-2084
Fax: 214-368-2087
Web: www.excoresources.com

CEO: Douglas H. Miller
CFO: J. Douglas Ramsey
HR: Joe D. Ford
FYE: December 31
Type: Public

EXCO Resources puts extra effort into oil and gas exploration and production operations in Colorado, Ohio, Oklahoma, Pennsylvania, Texas, and West Virginia. The company has pursued a strategy of growth through the drill bit coupled with selective acquisitions. In 2005 TXOK (a Boone Pickens-controlled affiliate) acquired ONEOK Energy. Following EXCO Resources' 2006 IPO, TXOK became a subsidiary of EXCO Resources in a move that added 223.3 billion cu. ft. of natural gas equivalent to the company's reserves. In 2007 the oil and gas explorer reported proved reserves of 1.9 trillion cu. ft. of natural gas equivalent. EXCO Resources holds stakes in 10,300 gross wells.

	Annual Growth	12/03	12/04	12/05	12/06	12/07
Sales ($ mil.)	130.5%	32.1	92.8	34.8	559.5	906.5
Net income ($ mil.)	75.8%	5.2	6.2	0.9	138.9	49.7
Market value ($ mil.)	(8.2%)	—	—	—	1,762.7	1,618.9
Employees	51.2%	132	—	314	471	689

EXEL TRANSPORTATION SERVICES, INC.

17330 Preston Rd., Ste. 200C
Dallas, TX 75252
Phone: 972-447-0075
Fax: –
Web: www.ets.exel.com

CEO: James J. (Jim) Damman
CFO: Andrew Hadland
HR: –
FYE: December 31
Type: Subsidiary

For Exel Transportation Services, the goal is to excel at expediting freight transportation. The company arranges for its customers' freight to be hauled in truckload and less-than-truckload (LTL) quantities; in addition, it oversees intermodal freight transportation, which involves the use of both trucks and trains. Through its numerous affiliates, Exel Transportation Services provides services such as international freight forwarding, warehousing, and package delivery. The company is part of the US arm of the DHL Exel Supply Chain business unit of DHL, the global express delivery and logistics giant. DHL itself is a subsidiary of Germany's Deutsche Post.

	Annual Growth	12/03	12/04	12/05	12/06	12/07
Est. sales ($ mil.)	—	—	—	—	—	714.8
Employees	—	—	—	—	—	320

EXELIXIS, INC.

NASDAQ (GS): EXEL

210 E. Grand Ave.
South San Francisco, CA 94083
Phone: 650-837-7000
Fax: 650-837-8300
Web: www.exelixis.com

CEO: George A. Scangos
CFO: Frank L. Karbe
HR: Lupe M. Rivera
FYE: December 31
Type: Public

We've come a long way, baby, but we still have a lot in common with the fruit fly. Exelixis got its start analyzing genetic data from fruit flies and other organisms as a means to speed the development of drugs, insecticides, and animal health products. Its early genomic work has yielded a pipeline of drug candidates primarily in the areas of cancer, but also metabolic and cardiovascular disease, among other things. One of the company's top drug candidates, XL647, is in clinical trials for the treatment of non-small cell lung cancer. Development partners include GlaxoSmithKline, Genentech, Wyeth, and Bristol-Myers Squibb.

	Annual Growth	12/03	12/04	12/05	12/06	12/07
Sales ($ mil.)	21.8%	51.5	52.9	76.0	98.7	113.5
Net income ($ mil.)	—	(94.8)	(137.2)	(84.4)	(101.5)	(86.4)
Market value ($ mil.)	15.8%	502.6	712.5	785.7	863.9	903.9
Employees	15.6%	—	—	550	651	735

EXELON CORPORATION

NYSE: EXC

10 S. Dearborn St., 37th Fl.
Chicago, IL 60680
Phone: 312-394-7398
Fax: 312-394-7945
Web: www.exeloncorp.com

CEO: John W. Rowe
CFO: Matthew F. Hilzinger
HR: Andrea L. Zopp
FYE: December 31
Type: Public

The City of Brotherly Love meets the Windy City in utility holding company Exelon. The company distributes electricity to 5.4 million customers in northern Illinois (including Chicago) and southeastern Pennsylvania (including Philadelphia) through subsidiaries Commonwealth Edison (ComEd) and PECO Energy. PECO also distributes natural gas to 480,000 customers. Subsidiary Exelon Generation holds the company's power plants, which produce 24,808 MW of capacity. Exelon Power Team is a top wholesale energy marketer, and Exelon Energy markets retail power and offers other energy-related services. In 2006 Exelon dropped its bid to buy New Jersey utility Public Service Enterprise Group (PSEG).

	Annual Growth	12/03	12/04	12/05	12/06	12/07
Sales ($ mil.)	4.6%	15,812.0	14,515.0	15,357.0	15,655.0	18,916.0
Net income ($ mil.)	31.9%	905.0	1,864.0	923.0	1,592.0	2,736.0
Market value ($ mil.)	49.2%	10,889.1	29,381.5	35,412.5	41,466.3	53,964.0
Employees	1.7%	—	—	17,200	17,200	17,800

EXIDE TECHNOLOGIES

NASDAQ (GM): XIDE

13000 Deerfield Pkwy., Bldg. 200
Alpharetta, GA 30004
Phone: 678-566-9000
Fax: 678-566-9188
Web: www.exide.com

CEO: Gordon A. Ulsh
CFO: Phillip A. Damaska
HR: George S. Jones Jr.
FYE: March 31
Type: Public

Exide Technologies hopes you'll get a charge out of its products. The company makes lead-acid automotive and industrial batteries with customers that include retailers such as Wal-Mart and NAPA, and transportation giants such as Ford and Toyota. The company also makes batteries for boats, farm equipment, golf carts, locomotives, and wheelchairs, as well as backup power supply batteries for telecommunications, computer, and power plant systems. Brand names include Classic, Marathon, NASCAR Extreme, Sunlyte, and Super Crank. The company is challenged by rising prices for lead and other raw materials. Operations outside the US account for more than half of sales.

	Annual Growth	3/04	3/05	3/06	3/07	3/08
Sales ($ mil.)	10.3%	2,500.5	2,476.3	2,819.9	2,939.8	3,696.7
Net income ($ mil.)	—	(114.1)	(466.9)	(172.7)	(105.9)	32.1
Market value ($ mil.)	46.1%	—	316.2	70.2	527.9	986.1
Employees	(3.9%)	15,300	14,268	13,982	13,862	13,027

EXLSERVICE HOLDINGS, INC.

NASDAQ (GS): EXLS

350 Park Ave., 10th Fl.
New York, NY 10022
Phone: 212-277-7100
Fax: 212-277-7111
Web: www.exlservice.com

CEO: Rohit Kapoor
CFO: Matt Appel
HR: Sanjay Gupta
FYE: December 31
Type: Public

Have an extra-large task you'd rather not take on? Outsource it to ExlService Holdings. The company, known as EXL, offers business process outsourcing (BPO), research and analytics, and consulting services. EXL's BPO offerings, which generate most of its sales, include claims processing, collections, customer support, and finance and accounting. Customers come mainly from the banking, financial services, and insurance industries, but also from sectors such as utilities and telecommunications. Two UK-based customers, insurer Norwich Union and natural gas supplier Centrica, together account for just over half of EXL's sales.

	Annual Growth	12/03	12/04	12/05	12/06	12/07
Sales ($ mil.)	59.5%	27.8	60.5	73.9	121.8	179.9
Net income ($ mil.)	—	(0.5)	5.4	7.1	14.1	27.0
Market value ($ mil.)	12.1%	—	—	—	594.6	666.8
Employees	46.2%	2,626	—	—	8,200	—

EXOPACK HOLDING CORP.

3070 Southport Rd.
Spartanburg, SC 29304
Phone: 877-447-3539
Fax: 864-596-7150
Web: www.exopack.com

CEO: Jack E. Knott II
CFO: Johnathan (John) Heard
HR: –
FYE: December 31
Type: Private

Rover loves Exopack. It is likely his dog food shows up in one of its bags. Exopack manufactures flexible packaging material for the pet food, lawn and garden, cement, and agricultural industries, among others. Key packaging products include plastic films (mono-layer, co-extruded or laminated), converted plastics (standup pouches and edge seam bags), consumer paper (popcorn, coffee, and pet food bags), and industrial paper (graphics and coated paper). The company, which is pursuing a strategy of growth through acquisition, has 14 manufacturing facilities across North America. In 2005 Exopack LLC merged with Cello-Foil and The Packaging Group to form Exopack Holding. Sun Capital Partners owns the company.

EXPEDIA, INC.

NASDAQ (GS): EXPE

3150 139th Ave. SE
Bellevue, WA 98005
Phone: 425-679-7200
Fax: 425-679-7240
Web: www.expediainc.com

CEO: Dara Khosrowshahi
CFO: Michael B. Adler
HR: Kathleen K. (Kathy) Dellplain
FYE: December 31
Type: Public

These days, expediting your vacation begins online. As the market leader in online travel services (ahead of rivals Orbitz, Priceline, and Travelocity), Expedia's travel-planning tools allow users to book airline tickets, hotel reservations, car rentals, vacation packages, and cruises online. Expedia's destination guides feature travel-related content, news, and maps. Its portfolio of brands includes Hotels.com, discount travel Web site Hotwire, travel search engine TripAdvisor, Chinese travel service company eLong (56% stake), and luxury travel segment Classic Vacations, among others. Chairman Barry Diller controls about 60% of the company.

	Annual Growth	12/03	12/04	12/05	12/06	12/07
Sales ($ mil.)	3.3%	2,339.8	1,843.0	2,119.5	2,237.6	2,665.3
Net income ($ mil.)	27.7%	111.4	163.5	228.7	244.9	295.9
Market value ($ mil.)	3.1%	—	—	7,714.6	6,417.8	8,205.0
Employees	17.6%	—	4,400	6,850	6,600	7,150

An in-depth profile of this company is available to Hoover's Online members at hoovers.com.

589

EXPEDITORS INTERNATIONAL

NASDAQ (GS): EXPD

1015 3rd Ave., 12th Fl.
Seattle, WA 98104
Phone: 206-674-3400
Fax: 206-682-9777
Web: www.expeditors.com

CEO: Peter J. Rose
CFO: R. Jordan Gates
HR: Samuel R. Bokor
FYE: December 31
Type: Public

Need your goods moved expeditiously? Freight forwarder Expeditors International of Washington, Inc., can help. As a freight forwarder, the company purchases air and ocean cargo space on a volume basis and resells that space to its customers at lower rates than they could obtain directly from the carriers. The company also acts as a customs broker for air and ocean freight shipped by its customers and offers supply chain management services. Expeditors operates from about 360 facilities in more than 50 countries worldwide. More than half of the company's sales come from the Asia/Pacific region.

	Annual Growth	12/03	12/04	12/05	12/06	12/07
Sales ($ mil.)	18.8%	2,624.9	3,317.5	3,901.8	4,626.0	5,235.2
Net income ($ mil.)	21.9%	121.9	156.1	218.6	235.1	269.1
Market value ($ mil.)	48.1%	1,978.2	2,979.6	3,598.7	8,629.8	9,516.7
Employees	9.4%	—	—	10,600	11,600	—

EXPERIAN AMERICAS

475 Anton Blvd.
Costa Mesa, CA 92626
Phone: 714-830-7000
Fax: 714-830-2449
Web: www.experian.com

CEO: Donald A. (Don) Robert
CFO: Paul Brooks
HR: –
FYE: March 31
Type: Subsidiary

Experian Americas is the US-based arm of Experian Group Limited. The unit performs credit reporting and lead generation services utilizing its database of more than 215 million US consumers and some 15 million US businesses. Clients include retailers, financial services firms, utilities, not-for-profits, and small businesses. It is responsible for providing addresses for more than 20 billion pieces of mail every year. Services include skip tracing and collections, direct marketing, sales prospecting, demographic information, and more. It has about a dozen offices across the US. Parent company Experian Group Limited became an independent entity when it was spun off from GUS plc in 2006.

	Annual Growth	3/03	3/04	3/05	3/06	3/07
Est. sales ($ mil.)	—	—	—	—	—	281.9
Employees	—	—	—	—	—	6,765

EXPONENT, INC.

NASDAQ (GS): EXPO

149 Commonwealth Dr.
Menlo Park, CA 94025
Phone: 650-326-9400
Fax: 650-326-8072
Web: www.exponent.com

CEO: Michael R. Gaulke
CFO: Richard L. Schlenker Jr.
HR: Gregory P. Klein
FYE: Friday nearest December 31
Type: Public

Exponent has found success in failure. The science and engineering consulting firm specializes in analyzing and solving complex problems and preventing disasters and product failures. Exponent's scientists, physicians, engineers, and business consultants assess environmental risks, regulatory issues, and workplace hazards for government agencies and clients from such industries as transportation, construction, and manufacturing. Established in 1967, its work has included analyzing such disasters as the Exxon Valdez oil spill and the bombing of the Murrah Federal Building in Oklahoma City. Exponent operates through more than 20 facilities in China, Germany, the UK, and the US.

	Annual Growth	12/03	12/04	12/05	12/06	12/07
Sales ($ mil.)	10.1%	139.7	151.5	155.2	168.5	205.1
Net income ($ mil.)	18.8%	10.2	12.0	14.2	14.2	20.3
Market value ($ mil.)	49.9%	77.7	110.0	114.9	274.5	392.6
Employees	5.6%	—	—	785	—	875

EXPRESS-1 EXPEDITED SOLUTIONS, INC.

AMEX: XPO

429 Post Rd.
Buchanan, MI 49107
Phone: 269-695-2700
Fax: 269-695-7458
Web: www.express-1.com

CEO: Michael R. (Mike) Welch
CFO: Mark K. Patterson
HR: –
FYE: December 31
Type: Public

Express-1 Expedited Solutions specializes in arranging expedited ground transportation. Customers' freight is transported throughout the US by independent contractors, who give the company's Express-1 unit access to a fleet of vehicles that includes cargo vans, trucks, and tractor-trailers. In addition to for-hire hauling, the company provides dedicated service — delivery of parts from a major Ford distribution facility in Evansville, Indiana, to dealers with a 250-mile radius. Express-1 Expedited offers domestic and international freight forwarding through Concert Group Logistics, which it acquired in 2008, as well as a variety of supply chain management services, through Bounce Logistics.

	Annual Growth	12/03	12/04	12/05	12/06	12/07
Sales ($ mil.)	37.7%	14.7	42.5	39.8	42.2	52.8
Net income ($ mil.)	82.1%	0.2	(3.2)	(5.8)	3.9	2.2
Market value ($ mil.)	8.8%	23.6	40.1	18.0	33.4	33.0
Employees	(23.4%)	—	294	127	—	132

EXPRESS EMPLOYMENT PROFESSIONALS

8516 Northwest Expwy.
Oklahoma City, OK 73162
Phone: 405-840-5000
Fax: 405-717-5669
Web: www.expresspros.com

CEO: Robert A. Funk
CFO: Thomas N. Richards
HR: Carol Lane
FYE: December 31
Type: Private

When you need a worker fast, Express Employment Professionals delivers. Formerly known as Express Personnel Services, the professional staffing company provides work for some 350,000 employees from about 600 offices across Australia, Canada, South Africa, and the US. In addition to temporary staffing, it provides professional placement and contract staffing through Express Professional Staffing and offers workplace services (consulting, training, development) through Express Business Solutions. Founded in 1983, the company is owned by founders William Stoller (vice chairman) and Robert Funk (CEO).

	Annual Growth	12/02	12/03	12/04	12/05	12/06
Est. sales ($ mil.)	16.1%	—	—	—	1,550.0	1,800.0
Employees	16.7%	—	—	—	300,000	350,000

EXPRESS, LLC

1 Limited Pkwy.
Columbus, OH 43230
Phone: 614-415-4000
Fax: 614-415-7440
Web: www.expressfashion.com

CEO: Michael A. Weiss
CFO: Matt Mollering
HR: –
FYE: Saturday nearest January 31
Type: Private

Right from the runway is the Express way. Express operates more than 620 men's, women's, and dual-gender stores in the US that sell trendy private-label apparel and accessories. (Its fashions are styled to have an international influence and modern appeal.) Express also sells denim and lingerie. Its brand was extended to menswear, again, when former parent company Limited Brands converted its Structure stores and reunited both labels to re-create Express Men's in 2002. More recently, amid declining sales, Express has been closing stores and converting its men's and women's stores to dual-gender outlets. Limited Brands, which launched Express in 1980, sold the chain to Golden Gate Capital in mid-2007.

	Annual Growth	1/03	1/04	1/05	1/06	1/07
Sales ($ mil.)	(4.2%)	2,073.0	2,071.0	1,913.0	1,794.0	1,749.0
Employees	—	20,000	—	—	—	—

EXPRESS SCRIPTS, INC.

NASDAQ (GS): ESRX

1 Express Way
St. Louis, MO 63121
Phone: 314-996-0900
Fax: –
Web: www.express-scripts.com

CEO: George Paz
CFO: Jeffrey L. Hall
HR: Karen Matteuzzi
FYE: December 31
Type: Public

Express Scripts knows its customers like their drugs fast. One of the largest pharmacy benefits management (PBM) companies in North America, Express Scripts administers the prescription drug benefit of millions of health plan members in the US and Canada. Members have access to a network of about 60,000 retail pharmacies, as well as the company's own mail order pharmacies. Express Scripts processes claims for more than 400 million prescriptions per year, designs formularies, and offers such services as disease management programs and consumer drug data analysis. Clients include HMOs and other health insurers, self-insured businesses, and union benefit plans.

	Annual Growth	12/03	12/04	12/05	12/06	12/07
Sales ($ mil.)	8.3%	13,294.5	15,114.7	16,266.0	17,660.0	18,273.6
Net income ($ mil.)	22.8%	249.6	278.2	400.0	474.4	567.8
Market value ($ mil.)	94.5%	1,288.3	1,411.4	6,132.9	4,856.3	18,423.1
Employees	3.2%	—	—	11,100	11,300	11,820

EXPRESSJET HOLDINGS, INC.

NYSE: XJT

700 N. Sam Houston Pkwy. West, Ste. 200
Houston, TX 77067
Phone: 832-353-1000
Fax: 832-353-1008
Web: www.expressjet.com

CEO: James B. (Jim) Ream
CFO: Frederick S. (Fred) Cromer
HR: Karen P. Miles
FYE: December 31
Type: Public

ExpressJet Holdings' main subsidiary, ExpressJet Airlines, helps link smaller cities to bigger ones and to one another. Operating as Continental Express, the regional airline enables Continental Airlines to reach markets that would be inefficient to serve with larger aircraft. It operates a fleet of more than 200 Embraer regional jets from Continental's hubs in Cleveland, Houston, and Newark, New Jersey, and serves about 175 destinations in the US, Canada, Mexico, and the Caribbean. Under its own brand, ExpressJet Airlines uses about 40 regional jets to serve about 30 US cities, mainly smaller markets. ExpressJet Holdings is considering options that could include a sale of the company.

	Annual Growth	12/03	12/04	12/05	12/06	12/07
Sales ($ mil.)	6.5%	1,311.4	1,507.5	1,562.8	1,679.6	1,685.5
Net income ($ mil.)	—	108.5	122.8	98.0	92.6	(70.3)
Market value ($ mil.)	(36.9%)	812.5	700.3	437.3	438.8	129.0
Employees	(25.7%)	—	—	6,700	4,980	—

EXTERRAN HOLDINGS, INC.

NYSE: EXH

4444 Brittmoore Rd.
Houston, TX 77041
Phone: 713-335-7000
Fax: 281-854-3051
Web: www.exterran.com

CEO: Stephen A. (Steve) Snider
CFO: J. Michael Anderson
HR: Stephen W. (Steve) Muck
FYE: December 31
Type: Public

Applying pressure is Exterran's forte — the company rents and repairs compressors and performs natural gas compression services for oil and gas companies. It has a fleet of about 12,950 mobile compressors ranging from 8 to 4,750 horsepower. The company's subsidiaries also provide fabrication services and equipment for oil and natural gas processing and transportation applications. Exterran's Aftermarket Services segment provides a full range of services to support the surface production and processing needs of customers. In 2007 Hanover Compressor merged with compression products provider Universal Compression Holdings to form Exterran Holdings.

	Annual Growth	12/03	12/04	12/05	12/06	12/07
Sales ($ mil.)	23.4%	1,095.3	1,188.6	1,375.6	1,670.7	2,540.5
Net income ($ mil.)	—	(208.3)	(44.0)	(38.0)	86.5	34.6
Market value ($ mil.)	55.5%	918.7	1,229.2	1,443.8	2,007.7	5,368.9
Employees	18.1%	5,500	5,900	6,650	8,800	10,700

EXTERRAN PARTNERS, L.P.

NASDAQ (GM): EXLP

4444 Brittmoore Rd.
Houston, TX 77041
Phone: 713-335-7000
Fax: 713-466-6720
Web: www.exterran.com

CEO: Stephen A. (Steve) Snider
CFO: J. Michael Anderson
HR: Angie Wilson
FYE: December 31
Type: Public

Exterran Partners provides natural gas contract compression services to customers nationwide. Its services include designing, installing, operating, repairing, and maintaining compression equipment. Following the company's 2006 IPO, it operated a fleet of 829 compressor units, comprising more than 343,000 horsepower, or some 17% of global compression services player Universal Compression Holdings' US contract compression business. Universal Compression held a 50% stake in the company until it merged with Hanover Compressors to form Exterran Holdings in 2007. Exterran Partners changed its name from Universal Compression Partners at that time.

	Annual Growth	3/04	3/05	*12/05	12/06	12/07
Sales ($ mil.)	(21.3%)	281.0	296.2	248.4	13.5	107.7
Net income ($ mil.)	(32.4%)	92.8	98.0	84.0	2.7	19.4
Market value ($ mil.)	—	—	—	—	—	331.3
Employees	—	—	—	—	0	—

*Fiscal year change

EXTRA SPACE STORAGE INC.

NYSE: EXR

2795 E. Cottonwood Pkwy., Ste. 400
Salt Lake City, UT 84121
Phone: 801-562-5556
Fax: 801-365-4801
Web: www.extraspace.com

CEO: Kenneth M. Woolley
CFO: Kent W. Christensen
HR: Bruce Boucher
FYE: December 31
Type: Public

Is your closet bursting at the seams? Looking for a little extra space? Extra Space Storage has your back. The self-administered, self-managed real estate investment trust (REIT) buys, develops, and manages self-storage properties. It wholly owns, owns in joint-venture partnerships, or operates for third parties more than 600 facilities totaling approximately 44 million sq. ft. of rentable space in about 33 states and Washington, DC. It offers both ground-floor and multi-floor facilities, and leases to approximately 300,000 tenants nationwide. Extra Space Storage operates in two segments: property management and rental operations.

	Annual Growth	12/03	12/04	12/05	12/06	12/07
Sales ($ mil.)	60.2%	36.3	66.0	134.7	197.3	238.9
Net income ($ mil.)	—	(17.9)	(18.5)	(5.0)	14.9	36.1
Market value ($ mil.)	31.3%	—	415.5	797.2	1,173.1	940.1
Employees	48.9%	377	469	1,943	1,835	1,853

EXTREME NETWORKS, INC.

NASDAQ (GM): EXTR

3585 Monroe St.
Santa Clara, CA 95051
Phone: 408-579-2800
Fax: 408-579-3000
Web: www.extremenetworks.com

CEO: Mark Canepa
CFO: Karen M. Rogge
HR: Rebecca Guerra
FYE: June 30
Type: Public

Extreme Networks hopes you switch to its products. The company designs and markets three switch families — Alpine, BlackDiamond, and Summit — using custom semiconductor components to address network switching needs from desktops to network cores. Designed to replace software-based routers, its Layer 3 switches are used by enterprise customers and network service providers to build and upgrade LANs, WANs, and metro-area networks. The company, which outsources the manufacturing of its products to Flextronics, also offers load-balancing Web switches and software for switch management and configuration. Extreme primarily sells through resellers and distributors such as Tech Data.

	Annual Growth	6/03	6/04	6/05	6/06	6/07
Sales ($ mil.)	(1.4%)	363.3	351.9	383.4	358.6	342.8
Net income ($ mil.)	—	(197.2)	(1.8)	12.9	8.5	(14.2)
Market value ($ mil.)	(5.5%)	634.1	637.0	498.6	517.8	506.7
Employees	—	—	—	834	—	—

An in-depth profile of this company is available to Hoover's Online members at hoovers.com.

EXX INC

AMEX: EXXA

1350 E. Flamingo Rd., Ste. 689
Las Vegas, NV 89119
Phone: 702-598-3223
Fax: –

CEO: David A. Segal
CFO: David A. Segal
HR: –
FYE: December 31
Type: Public

EXX marks the spot for this holding company. TX Technology makes cable pressurization equipment (used to prevent signal reductions) and related pressurization monitoring equipment for telecom firms. Henry Gordy International produces such impulse-buying items as toys, watches, and kites, which it sells mainly through toy and discount stores. Additionally, EXX owns auto parts manufacturer Newcor. Newcor sells and markets automotive and light truck products, which make up 73% of Newcor's sales; its remaining sales come from heavy-duty components, including over-the-highway trucks and agricultural and other equipment. Almost all sales are in the US, with some shipments to Canada and Mexico.

	Annual Growth	12/03	12/04	12/05	12/06	12/07
Sales ($ mil.)	(6.3%)	—	143.6	147.3	158.9	118.2
Net income ($ mil.)	(12.6%)	—	1.5	0.9	5.7	1.0
Market value ($ mil.)	21.9%	—	16.5	24.6	38.1	29.8
Employees	(12.3%)	—	1,000	1,100	825	675

EXXON MOBIL CORPORATION

NYSE: XOM

5959 Las Colinas Blvd.
Irving, TX 75039
Phone: 972-444-1000
Fax: 972-444-1350
Web: www.exxon.mobil.com

CEO: Rex W. Tillerson
CFO: Donald D. (Don) Humphreys
HR: Lucille J. Cavanaugh
FYE: December 31
Type: Public

It's not necessarily the oil standard, but Exxon Mobil is the world's largest integrated oil company (ahead of BP and Royal Dutch Shell). Exxon Mobil engages in oil and gas exploration, production, supply, transportation, and marketing worldwide. It has proved reserves of 13.2 billion barrels of oil equivalent. Exxon Mobil's 38 refineries in 21 countries have a throughput capacity of 6.3 million barrels per day. The company supplies refined products to nearly 34,000 service stations in 100 countries. It provides fuel to more than 600 airports and 200 seaports. Exxon Mobil is also a major petrochemical producer. The company posted consecutive US records for annual corporate earnings for 2005, 2006, and 2007.

	Annual Growth	12/03	12/04	12/05	12/06	12/07
Sales ($ mil.)	13.2%	246,738.0	298,035.0	370,680.0	377,635.0	404,552.0
Net income ($ mil.)	17.2%	21,510.0	25,330.0	36,130.0	39,500.0	40,610.0
Market value ($ mil.)	17.0%	269,288.0	328,115.2	344,490.6	439,013.3	504,239.6
Employees	(1.5%)	88,300	85,900	83,700	82,100	83,000

EXXONMOBIL CHEMICAL COMPANY

13501 Katy Fwy.
Houston, TX 77079
Phone: 281-870-6000
Fax: 281-870-6661
Web: www.exxonmobilchemical.com

CEO: Stephen D. (Steve) Pryor
CFO: –
HR: Maureen K. McGurk
FYE: December 31
Type: Subsidiary

No surprise that a subsidiary of the world's #1 oil company, Exxon Mobil, is among the world's top chemical companies. ExxonMobil Chemical ranks #1 or #2 in making many petrochemicals, including benzene and toluene, as well as polyolefins such as polypropylene (PP) and high-density and linear low-density polyethylene (HDPE and LLDPE, respectively). The company also is a major producer of olefins (such as ethylene and propylene, used to make polyolefins), aromatics (toluene and xylene used in paints and agrochemicals), and plastics (such as thermoplastic elastomers). ExxonMobil uses its polyolefins to make films for packaging and labeling and also licenses some of its process technology. It operates globally.

EYE CARE CENTERS OF AMERICA, INC.

11103 West Ave.
San Antonio, TX 78213
Phone: 210-340-3531
Fax: 210-524-6996
Web: www.ecca.com

CEO: David L. Holmberg
CFO: Jennifer L. Kelley
HR: Robert T. Cox
FYE: Saturday nearest December 31
Type: Subsidiary

Eye Care Centers of America is clearly focused on becoming the top eyewear chain. It owns or manages more than 400 optical stores in some 36 states. Its stores — operating under the EyeMasters name and a host of others (Binyon's, Hour Eyes, Stein Optical, Visionworks, and Vision World) — sell contact lenses, prescription eyewear, and sunglasses. The firm, founded in 1984, offers contacts and eyeglass frames under its own and designer brands, as well as one-hour service, onsite processing labs, and independent optometrists. In 2006 HVHC, Inc. (a vision subsidiary of health care provider Highmark) acquired Eye Care Centers of America for about $310 million.

	Annual Growth	12/03	12/04	12/05	12/06	12/07
Est. sales ($ mil.)	—	—	—	—	—	301.9
Employees	—	—	—	—	—	4,800

EYEMED VISION CARE LLC

4000 Luxottica Place
Mason, OH 45040
Phone: 513-765-4321
Fax: 513-765-6388
Web: www.eyemedvisioncare.com

CEO: Kerry Bradley
CFO: Jack Dennis
HR: Mildred Curtis
FYE: December 31
Type: Subsidiary

EyeMed Vision Care delivers the visuals. A subsidiary of Italian eyewear maker Luxottica, the company administers managed vision care plans to more than 120 million members through a nationwide network of providers that includes optometrists, ophthalmologists, opticians, and retailers (including Luxottica subsidiaries LensCrafters and Pearle Vision). EyeMed offers several different plans, all of which provide various levels of discounts on exams and vision products such as eyeglass frames and lenses, contact lenses, and other eye care services. The company has a diverse customer base that includes large corporations (Cintas), government entities (the State of New York), and health insurers (Health Net).

E-Z MART STORES, INC.

602 W. Falvey Ave.
Texarkana, TX 75504
Phone: 903-832-6502
Fax: 903-832-3731
Web: www.e-zmart.com

CEO: Sonja Yates Hubbard
CFO: Stacy Yates
HR: –
FYE: September 30
Type: Private

In 1970, when small-town America closed at 6 p.m., E-Z Mart Stores founder Jim Yates kept his first convenience store in Ashdown, Arkansas, open until 11. The company now boasts 300 outlets across five southern states (Arkansas, Louisiana, Missouri, Oklahoma, and Texas). Rather than build its own stores, the company usually expands through acquisitions. In addition to the standard hot dogs, chips, sodas, and cigarettes, most E-Z Mart locations also offer Shell, Conoco, Phillips 66, or CITGO gasoline. Yates died in late 1998 when the plane he was piloting crashed, leaving his daughter Sonja Hubbard at the company's helm as CEO.

	Annual Growth	9/03	9/04	9/05	9/06	9/07
Est. sales ($ mil.)	—	—	—	—	—	359.3
Employees	—	—	—	—	—	2,700

EZCORP, INC.

NASDAQ (GS): EZPW

1901 Capital Pkwy.
Austin, TX 78746
Phone: 512-314-3400
Fax: 512-314-3404
Web: www.ezcorp.com

CEO: Joseph L. (Joe) Rotunda
CFO: Daniel N. (Dan) Tonissen
HR: Robert A. Kasenter
FYE: September 30
Type: Public

No mere pawn in the game, EZCORP is one of the largest operators of pawnshops in the US. In addition to collecting interest from loans it makes, EZCORP also sells second-hand jewelry, tools, electronics, sports equipment, and musical instruments through more than 300 EZPAWN pawnshops in some 10 states and Mexico; most are in Texas. Its inventory is built from items forfeited by customers who used them as collateral and then failed to repay small, short-term, high-interest loans. EZCORP also offers customers unsecured loans, commonly referred to as payday loans or payroll advances, through about 75 of its pawnshops, as well as more than 430 EZMONEY payday loan stores in nearly a dozen states.

	Annual Growth	9/03	9/04	9/05	9/06	9/07
Assets ($ mil.)	13.1%	153.7	164.3	165.4	197.9	251.2
Net income ($ mil.)	212.0%	0.4	9.1	14.8	29.3	37.9
Market value ($ mil.)	119.4%	22.3	32.4	63.5	483.7	516.4
Employees	8.9%	—	—	2,700	—	3,200

EZENIA! INC.

OTC: EZEN

14 Celina Ave., Ste. 17-18
Nashua, NH 03063
Phone: 781-505-2100
Fax: –
Web: www.ezenia.com

CEO: Khoa D. Nguyen
CFO: Khoa D. Nguyen
HR: –
FYE: December 31
Type: Public

Ezenia! is thrilled to be making networked video and multimedia conferencing equipment and software. The company makes communications products that connect multiple users over both circuit-switched and Internet protocol networks, enabling them to interact as a group. Its InfoWorkSpace suite of software applications is used by the US military and intelligence community to facilitate communication and collaboration among far-flung locations. The company also sells systems for large enterprises and communications service providers that provide video-conferencing and Web collaboration capabilities. Ezenia! counts defense contractors General Dynamics and SAIC among its customers.

	Annual Growth	12/03	12/04	12/05	12/06	12/07
Sales ($ mil.)	2.4%	8.2	10.4	13.2	13.2	9.0
Net income ($ mil.)	—	(0.8)	3.2	3.8	3.9	(4.6)
Market value ($ mil.)	30.5%	3.4	14.6	35.2	29.7	9.9
Employees	—	—	—	—	—	—

THE F. DOHMEN CO.

W175 N11120 Stonewood Dr., Ste. 101
Germantown, WI 53022
Phone: 262-251-6420
Fax: 262-250-5062
Web: www.dohmen.com

CEO: John F. Dohmen
CFO: –
HR: Shannon Brown
FYE: April 30
Type: Private

The F. Dohmen Co. helps pharmacists with just about everything except interpreting handwriting. Its RESTAT subsidiary is a prescription benefits management company, handling the drug benefit plans of some 3 million covered members through a network of 54,000 pharmacies. RESTAT helps insurers, third-party administrators, self-insured employers and others with formulary design, claims services, and clinical management, among other things. F. Dohmen also provides pharmaceutical logistics services through DDN/Obergfel. In 2007 the company sold JASCORP, which provides pharmacy management software, to Arcadia Resources. It had previously sold its drug distribution business to Cardinal Health.

F. SCHUMACHER & CO.

79 Madison Ave.
New York, NY 10016
Phone: 212-213-7900
Fax: 212-213-7848
Web: www.fschumacher.com

CEO: Gerald W. Puschel
CFO: –
HR: –
FYE: December 31
Type: Private

The "F" is for fabrics. F. Schumacher & Co. is a top designer and marketer of fabrics, furnishings, wallpaper, rugs, and accessories. Its interior design brands include Greeff (fabrics and wall coverings); Patterson, Flynn & Martin (floor coverings); Rosecore (carpet); and Schumacher (high-end fine fabrics and wallpaper pieces). Its Gramercy brand for textiles and furniture is designed for the retail market. The Village brand is sold through home improvement retailers and features do-it-yourself wallpaper and decorative products. The firm has 18 showrooms across the US. It is owned and run by descendants of founder Frederic Schumacher. NexCen Brands bought the company's famed Waverly brand in 2007.

	Annual Growth	12/03	12/04	12/05	12/06	12/07
Est. sales ($ mil.)	—	—	—	—	—	50.5
Employees	—	—	—	—	—	325

F5 NETWORKS, INC.

NASDAQ (GS): FFIV

401 Elliott Ave. West
Seattle, WA 98119
Phone: 206-272-5555
Fax: 206-272-5556
Web: www.f5.com

CEO: John McAdam
CFO: Andy Reinland
HR: John Rodriguez
FYE: September 30
Type: Public

F5 Networks wants to help your network take a load off. The company's products include application delivery controllers and software that are used to manage and route network traffic. Companies including Microsoft and The Motley Fool use F5's products for tasks such as load balancing, availability assurance, and security assessment. Its customers come from a variety of industries, including telecommunication, financial services, manufacturing, and e-commerce. The company also offers services such as network monitoring, performance analysis, and training.

	Annual Growth	9/03	9/04	9/05	9/06	9/07
Sales ($ mil.)	45.9%	115.9	171.2	281.4	394.0	525.7
Net income ($ mil.)	108.2%	4.1	33.0	46.9	66.0	77.0
Market value ($ mil.)	85.5%	265.1	529.6	838.8	1,095.3	3,138.1
Employees	48.1%	—	—	—	1,068	1,582

FACEBOOK, INC.

156 University Ave.
Palo Alto, CA 94301
Phone: 650-543-4800
Fax: 650-543-4801
Web: www.facebook.com

CEO: Mark Zuckerberg
CFO: Gideon Yu
HR: –
FYE: –
Type: Private

When it comes to social networking, it's wise to put your best face forward. Online directory Facebook began by connecting students through social networks at schools, but has since opened its service to the general public. Users post photos and information about themselves through online profiles published on Facebook.com. The site was launched in 2004 by undergraduates at Harvard, led by Mark Zuckerberg, as an online version of the Harvard Facebook. (The name comes from books of freshmen's faces, majors, and hometowns that are distributed to incoming students.) Microsoft has a deal to be the exclusive provider of advertising to Facebook. Investors include Paypal co-founder Peter Thiel and Accel Partners.

An in-depth profile of this company is available to Hoover's Online members at hoovers.com.

593

FACTIVA

4300 Rte. 1 North, Bldg. 5, 2nd Fl.
Monmouth Junction, NJ 08852
Phone: 609-627-2000
Fax: 609-627-2310
Web: www.factiva.com

CEO: Claude Green
CFO: –
HR: Kristine Breuer
FYE: December 31
Type: Subsidiary

This company is helping people get their facts straight. Factiva, formerly Dow Jones Reuters Business Interactive, is a leading provider of news articles and business information. Its Web-based service aggregates information from more than 10,000 sources, including the *Financial Times, New York Times, Wall Street Journal,* and *Yomiuri Shimbun,* as well as 400 newswire services. It also offers business intelligence tools and provides corporate and industry information. Factiva has some 2 million paying subscribers. The company was formed in 1999. Previously a joint venture between news giants Dow Jones & Company and Reuters, in late 2006 Dow Jones bought out Reuters' stake in Factiva for about $160 million.

FACTORY CARD & PARTY OUTLET CORP.

2727 Diehl Rd.
Naperville, IL 60563
Phone: 630-579-2000
Fax: 630-579-2400
Web: www.factorycard.com

CEO: Gary W. Rada
CFO: Timothy J. (Tim) Benson
HR: Debra Smetana
FYE: Saturday nearest January 31
Type: Subsidiary

Factory Card & Party Outlet takes the work out of partying. The retailer operates about 185 discount stores in 20 states, primarily in the Midwest and along the eastern seaboard. Greeting cards, beginning at 49 cents apiece, account for only part of the company's offerings, which also include gift wrap and ribbon, party supplies (invitations, party favors, candles, and piñatas), balloons, and novelty and celebratory items for birthdays, holidays, weddings, graduations, and other special occasions. The company filed for bankruptcy in 1999 and emerged in April 2002. Amid slumping sales, in late 2007 Factory Card & Party Outlet agreed to be acquired by Amscan Holdings, which also owns Party City and Party America.

	Annual Growth	1/03	1/04	1/05	1/06	1/07
Sales ($ mil.)	7.1%	185.7	222.6	230.1	233.1	244.2
Net income ($ mil.)	(2.1%)	2.5	1.4	(0.2)	(1.0)	2.3
Employees	(7.4%)	—	—	—	2,700	2,500

FACTORY MUTUAL INSURANCE COMPANY

1301 Atwood Ave.
Johnston, RI 02919
Phone: 401-275-3000
Fax: 401-275-3029
Web: www.fmglobal.com

CEO: Shivan S. Subramaniam
CFO: Jeffrey A. Burchill
HR: Enzo Rebula
FYE: December 31
Type: Mutual company

If you're looking to protect your corporation, turn your insurance dial to FM Global. Factory Mutual Insurance (operating as FM Global) provides commercial and industrial property insurance and a variety of risk management services, ranging from all-risk programs to specialized products for ocean cargo and machinery equipment, as well as property loss prevention engineering and research. FM Global operates through such subsidiaries as Affiliated FM Insurance, FM Global Cargo, Mutual Boiler Re, and Bermuda-based New Providence Mutual (which offers alternative risk financing for hard-to-find coverage). In addition to the US, the company has offices in Asia, Australia, Canada, Europe, and South America.

	Annual Growth	12/03	12/04	12/05	12/06	12/07
Sales ($ mil.)	4.7%	2,789.1	2,700.4	3,053.3	3,321.7	3,355.8
Net income ($ mil.)	8.6%	666.2	557.7	634.6	736.9	927.8
Employees	0.6%	4,400	4,700	4,700	4,900	4,500

⊞ FACTSET RESEARCH SYSTEMS INC.

NYSE: FDS

601 Merritt 7
Norwalk, CT 06851
Phone: 203-810-1000
Fax: 203-810-1001
Web: www.factset.com

CEO: Philip A. Hadley
CFO: Peter G. Walsh
HR: –
FYE: August 31
Type: Public

Analysts, portfolio managers, and investment bankers know FactSet Research Systems has the scoop. The company offers financial information from more than 200 databases focusing on areas such as broker research data, financial information, and newswires. FactSet complements its databases with a variety of software for use in downloading and manipulating the data. Among the company's applications are tools for presentations, data warehousing, economic analysis, portfolio analysis, and report writing. Revenues are derived from month-to-month subscriptions to services, databases, and financial applications. About 75% of revenue comes from investment managers; investment banking clients account for the rest.

	Annual Growth	8/03	8/04	8/05	8/06	8/07
Sales ($ mil.)	21.0%	222.3	251.9	312.6	387.4	475.8
Net income ($ mil.)	20.8%	51.4	58.0	71.8	82.9	109.6
Market value ($ mil.)	27.7%	1,089.5	925.3	1,691.9	2,156.0	2,897.5
Employees	16.1%	—	—	1,226	1,431	1,653

FAGEN, INC.

501 W. Hwy. 212
Granite Falls, MN 56241
Phone: 320-564-3324
Fax: 320-564-3278
Web: www.fageninc.com

CEO: Ron Fagen
CFO: Jennifer A. Johnson
HR: –
FYE: September 30
Type: Private

Although Fagen knows what the *dickens* is going on in the construction industry, it should not be confused with the character in "Oliver!" The company offers a range of commercial and industrial contracting and engineering services, including design/build, project management, and general contracting. Affiliate Fagen Engineering performs civil, structural, electrical, and mechanical engineering services. The company works across a variety of heavy industries and has completed such projects as power generation plants, water and wastewater treatment plants, manufacturing facilities, and housing. Focusing on green energy, it also has constructed about two dozen ethanol plants. The Fagen family owns the company.

	Annual Growth	9/03	9/04	9/05	9/06	9/07
Est. sales ($ mil.)	—	—	—	—	—	95.4
Employees	—	—	—	—	—	750

⊞ FAIR ISAAC CORPORATION

NYSE: FIC

901 Marquette Ave., Ste. 3200
Minneapolis, MN 55402
Phone: 612-758-5200
Fax: 612-758-5201
Web: www.fairisaac.com

CEO: Mark N. Greene
CFO: Charles M. (Chuck) Osborne
HR: Richard S. Deal
FYE: September 30
Type: Public

Fair or not, Fair Isaac has a lot to say about whether you get a loan. A leading developer of credit scoring systems, the firm offers statistics-based predictive tools for the consumer credit industry. Customers include credit card companies, retailers, commercial lenders, insurers, and health care and telecommunications service providers in some 80 countries worldwide. Fair Isaac's analytic and decision-management products and services, used around the world, include applicant scoring for insurers, and financial risk and database management products for financial concerns.

	Annual Growth	9/03	9/04	9/05	9/06	9/07
Sales ($ mil.)	6.9%	629.3	706.2	798.7	825.4	822.2
Net income ($ mil.)	(0.6%)	107.2	102.8	134.6	103.5	104.7
Market value ($ mil.)	0.2%	1,830.8	2,031.7	2,859.9	2,171.1	1,843.9
Employees	(2.1%)	—	—	2,796	2,737	—

THE FAIRCHILD CORPORATION
NYSE: FA

1750 Tysons Blvd., Ste. 1400
McLean, VA 22102
Phone: 703-478-5800
Fax: 703-478-5775
Web: www.fairchild.com

CEO: Jeffrey J. Steiner
CFO: Michael L. McDonald
HR: –
FYE: September 30
Type: Public

The Fairchild Corporation is bucking for a banner year. Formerly focused on making aerospace fasteners, Fairchild now concentrates on its Banner Aerospace unit. Banner distributes aircraft products — including avionics, radar products, liquid crystal displays, GPS products, and communications systems — and offers aircraft repair, overhaul, sales, and inspection services. It bought Hein Gericke and PoloExpress and folded them into its sports and leisure segment, Fairchild Sports, which makes and distributes motorcycle clothing, helmets, and accessories. CEO Jeffrey Steiner and his family own about 47% of Fairchild. Steiner and Philip Sassower are seeking to take the company private.

	Annual Growth	6/03	*9/04	9/05	9/06	9/07
Sales ($ mil.)	46.4%	77.5	338.4	352.4	309.6	356.0
Net income ($ mil.)	—	(53.2)	3.4	(21.3)	(37.3)	(0.3)
Market value ($ mil.)	(16.0%)	90.9	89.8	52.4	58.8	45.2
Employees	—	—	—	550		

*Fiscal year change

FAIRCHILD SEMICONDUCTOR INTERNATIONAL, INC.
NYSE: FCS

82 Running Hill Rd.
South Portland, ME 04106
Phone: 207-775-8100
Fax: 207-761-6139
Web: www.fairchildsemi.com

CEO: Mark S. Thompson
CFO: Mark S. Frey
HR: Kevin B. London
FYE: Last Sunday in December
Type: Public

Fairchild Semiconductor International is hardly a babe in the woods when it comes to making chips. One of the world's oldest chip companies, Fairchild makes semiconductors for tens of thousands of customers in the automotive, computer, consumer electronics, industrial, and telecommunications markets. Its diversified product line includes logic chips, discrete power and signal components, optoelectronics, non-volatile memory chips, and many types of analog and mixed-signal chips. The company also provides foundry (contract semiconductor manufacturing) services for other chip makers, such as Samsung Electronics and National Semiconductor. Operations in Asia account for three-quarters of Fairchild's sales.

	Annual Growth	12/03	12/04	12/05	12/06	12/07
Sales ($ mil.)	4.6%	1,395.8	1,603.1	1,425.1	1,651.1	1,670.2
Net income ($ mil.)	—	(81.5)	59.2	(241.2)	83.4	64.0
Market value ($ mil.)	(11.0%)	2,854.2	1,945.5	2,121.3	2,063.1	1,788.8
Employees	(0.1%)	9,740	9,024	8,929	9,344	9,691

FAIRFIELD LANGUAGE TECHNOLOGIES

1101 Wilson Blvd., Ste. 1130
Arlington, VA 22209
Phone: 540-432-6166
Fax: 540-432-0953
Web: www.rosettastone.com

CEO: Tom Adams
CFO: Brian D. Helman
HR: –
FYE: December 31
Type: Private

Who needs translators when you have the Rosetta Stone? Founded in 1991, Fairfield Language Technologies provides language-learning software via CD-ROM and the Internet. The company's Rosetta Stone Language Library combines educational techniques and interactive technologies to replicate the way children learn their native languages, helping users learn new languages more quickly and effectively. With customers in more than 150 countries, Fairfield offers software for 28 languages, ranging from Pashto and Swahili to French, German, and English. The company sells to schools, corporate training departments, and individual consumers.

FAIRFIELD RESIDENTIAL LLC

5510 Morehouse Dr., Ste. 200
San Diego, CA 92121
Phone: 858-457-2123
Fax: 858-457-3982
Web: www.fairfield-residential.net

CEO: Christopher E. Hashioka
CFO: Glenn D. Jones
HR: Pat Etherton
FYE: December 31
Type: Private

Affordable housing need not look like affordable housing. That's the challenge for construction company Fairfield Residential, which renovates working-class apartments so that they mimic luxury complexes. The firm has built more than 73,000 multifamily residential units (both affordable and upscale), served as the general contractor for 66 million sq. ft. of residential property, and developed master-planned communities totaling 2,000 acres in Texas and California, where it develops the majority of its properties. It also builds university student housing in the Southeast and provides property management services to more than 130 properties across 14 states. Mitsubishi Corp. owns 17% of the firm.

	Annual Growth	12/03	12/04	12/05	12/06	12/07
Est. sales ($ mil.)	—	—	—	—	—	11.9
Employees	—	—	—	—	—	566

FAIRMONT HOMES, INC.

502 S. Oakland Ave.
Nappanee, IN 46550
Phone: 574-773-7941
Fax: 574-773-2185
Web: www.fairmonthomes.com

CEO: James Foster (Jim) Shea
CFO: –
HR: Rick Jones
FYE: December 31
Type: Private

As a maker of recreational vehicles as well as manufactured housing, Fairmont Homes puts the mobile in mobile homes. It produces both single- and multi-section homes with up to 2,340 sq. ft. from floor plans that feature two to five bedrooms. Brothers Jim and John Shea acquired Fairmont Homes in 1971. (Jim bought John's share in 1975 and founded subsidiary Gulfstream Coach, a builder of RVs, in 1983.) Gulf Stream offers around 20 models of luxury and economy travel trailers, toy haulers, and fifth-wheel towable vehicles. Fairmont's suppliers include Whirlpool (appliances), Georgia-Pacific (building materials), and Owens Corning (shingles and insulation).

	Annual Growth	12/03	12/04	12/05	12/06	12/07
Est. sales ($ mil.)	—	—	—	—	—	133.0
Employees	—	—	—	—	—	850

FAIRPOINT COMMUNICATIONS, INC.
NYSE: FRP

521 E. Morehead St., Ste. 250
Charlotte, NC 28202
Phone: 704-344-8150
Fax: 704-344-8121
Web: www.fairpoint.com

CEO: Eugene B. (Gene) Johnson
CFO: John P. Crowley
HR: –
FYE: December 31
Type: Public

When the country mouse calls the city mouse, she might just be using FairPoint Communications. Founded in 1991 as MJD Communications, the company serves nearly 2 million subscribers in more than 30 largely rural local-exchange carriers in 18 US states. It concentrates largely on small urban markets located mainly in the Northeast and the Midwest, but the company's service areas extend to the South and the Northwest. FairPoint provides local and long-distance phone services, as well as dial-up, wireless, and digital subscriber line (DSL) Internet access to residential and business customers. It also offers Web hosting and domain name registration.

	Annual Growth	12/03	12/04	12/05	12/06	12/07
Sales ($ mil.)	5.2%	231.4	252.6	262.8	270.1	283.5
Net income ($ mil.)	37.1%	1.7	(23.7)	28.9	31.1	6.0
Market value ($ mil.)	12.4%	—	—	362.8	667.4	458.6
Employees	9.9%	—	—	900	952	1,087

FAIRVIEW HEALTH SERVICES

2450 Riverside Ave.
Minneapolis, MN 55454
Phone: 612-672-6000
Fax: 612-672-7186
Web: www.fairview.org

CEO: David R. Page
CFO: James M. Fox
HR: Diane Iorfida
FYE: December 31
Type: Not-for-profit

Fairview Health Services is a not-for-profit health care system that serves Minnesota's Twin Cities and surrounding communities. Fairview Health Services is affiliated with the medical school of the University of Minnesota and counts among its seven hospitals the University of Minnesota Medical Center. All told, its hospitals house some 2,500 beds and provide comprehensive medical and surgical services. The integrated health system also operates a network of primary and specialty care clinics, retail pharmacies, and nursing homes; and it provides home health care and rehabilitation services.

	Annual Growth	12/03	12/04	12/05	12/06	12/07
Est. sales ($ mil.)	—	—	—	—	—	1,982.8
Employees	—	—	—	—	—	18,000

FALCON PHARMACEUTICALS, LTD.

6201 South Fwy.
Fort Worth, TX 76134
Phone: 817-293-0450
Fax: 800-777-2799
Web: www.falconpharma.com

CEO: Cary R. Rayment
CFO: —
HR: —
FYE: December 31
Type: Subsidiary

Falcon Pharmaceuticals has a keen eye for alternatives. The company specializes in making generic equivalents of ophthalmic and otic drugs (treating a variety of diseases related to eyes and ears). Its lead product, Timolol GFS, is the only generic equivalent on the market of Merck's glaucoma treatment Timoptic-XE gel. The company also offers anti-infective, steroid, anti-virals, anti-allergy, and anesthetic pharmaceutical products without the markup typically associated with brand names. Founded in 1995, Falcon Pharmaceuticals is a subsidiary of eye care products company Alcon.

	Annual Growth	12/03	12/04	12/05	12/06	12/07
Est. sales ($ mil.)	—	—	—	—	—	385.0
Employees	—	—	—	—	—	3,000

FALCON RIDGE DEVELOPMENT, INC.

OTC: FCNR

5111 Juan Tabo Blvd. NE
Albuquerque, NM 87111
Phone: 505-856-6043
Fax: —
Web: www.falconridgedev.com

CEO: Fred M Montaño
CFO: Karen Y. Duran
HR: —
FYE: September 30
Type: Public

Falcon Ridge Development acquires raw land and cooks up delectable communities. The acquired property — which the firm develops, operates, and resells — typically comprises residential, commercial, and retail spaces. Its Sierra Norte community, just northwest of Albuquerque, includes about 370 lots with entry-level to fully-custom homes, jogging trails, and a 7-acre park. Its Spanish Trails property, which includes more than 500 lots on 140 acres in Belen, New Mexico, is under development. Falcon Ridge plans to resell these lots to third-party builders, as well as offer its own homes built by newly acquired firm Nailman LLC. Falcon Ridge was founded in 2005 by CEO Fred Montaño and CFO Karen Duran.

	Annual Growth	1/03	1/04	1/05	*9/06	9/07
Sales ($ mil.)	—	0.1	0.2	0.3	0.0	0.0
Net income ($ mil.)	—	(1.2)	(2.7)	(0.5)	(0.4)	(1.3)
Employees	—	—	—	—	—	

*Fiscal year change

FALCONSTOR SOFTWARE, INC.

NASDAQ (GM): FALC

2 Huntington Quadrangle, Ste. 2S01
Melville, NY 11747
Phone: 631-777-5188
Fax: 631-501-7633
Web: www.falconstor.com

CEO: ReiJane Huai
CFO: James Weber
HR: —
FYE: December 31
Type: Public

FalconStor Software watches data like a hawk. The company provides network storage management software and related services. Its IPStor software is used to manage storage provisioning, data availability, replication, and disaster recovery functions. FalconStor also offers consulting, engineering, implementation, and maintenance services. The company's customers come from fields such as health care, financial services, education, and information technology. FalconStor sells predominantly through distributors, manufacturers, and resellers. Chairman and CEO ReiJane Huai owns about 20% of the company.

	Annual Growth	12/03	12/04	12/05	12/06	12/07
Sales ($ mil.)	46.3%	16.9	28.7	41.0	55.1	77.4
Net income ($ mil.)	—	(7.4)	(5.9)	2.3	(3.4)	12.7
Market value ($ mil.)	8.6%	406.5	454.5	353.9	417.1	564.8
Employees	21.8%	—	—	279	—	414

FALKEN TIRE CORPORATION

13649 Valley Blvd.
Fontana, CA 92335
Phone: 800-723-2553
Fax: 800-950-2561
Web: www.falkentire.com

CEO: Hideo Honda
CFO: Dan Sullivan
HR: —
FYE: December 31
Type: Subsidiary

Just like the theme song from *Rawhide*, Falken Tire keeps "rollin', rollin', rollin'." The company, a subsidiary of the Japan-based Sumitomo Rubber Industries, makes and distributes tires that run the gamut from original equipment replacement tires for passenger cars to those found on SUVs (including tires for off-road use), and even race cars. Falken's other product offerings include high-performance wheels geared for the consumer automotive aftermarket. Wheel brands include Torque 5, Atlantic City, Solaris, and Aviator. Falken tires are sold through independent dealers throughout the US and Canada.

	Annual Growth	12/03	12/04	12/05	12/06	12/07
Est. sales ($ mil.)	—	—	—	—	—	200.0
Employees	—	—	—	—	—	50

FALLON WORLDWIDE

901 Marquette Ave., Ste. 2400
Minneapolis, MN 55402
Phone: 612-758-2345
Fax: 612-758-2346
Web: www.fallon.com

CEO: Patrick (Pat) Fallon
CFO: Steve Waring
HR: —
FYE: December 31
Type: Subsidiary

This company might be able to lend a hand if your brand has fallen on hard times. Fallon Worldwide is a leading creative ad agency, serving such clients as Sony, Holiday Inn, Purina, and NBC, and operating through a network of offices in the US, Asia, and Europe. In addition to creative development, the firm offers marketing and branding services, brand and corporate identity consulting, and campaign planning services. Fallon also provides interactive marketing services and Web site development. The agency was founded as Fallon McElligott Rice in 1981 by partners Pat Fallon, Tom McElligott, and Nancy Rice. Fallon is a subsidiary of Paris-based advertising conglomerate Publicis.

FAMILY CHRISTIAN STORES, INC.

5300 Patterson Ave. SE
Grand Rapids, MI 49530
Phone: 616-554-8700
Fax: 616-554-8608
Web: www.familychristian.com

CEO: Cliff Bartow
CFO: –
HR: Steve Biondo
FYE: Last Sunday in January
Type: Private

The latest from John Grisham or Stephen King is no match for a perennial best-seller found in large supply at Family Christian Stores. The leading Christian retailer in the US, Family Christian Stores has more than 300 stores in some 40 states. The company sells a variety of Christian-themed merchandise, including Bibles and other books, music, software, gifts, cards, videos, apparel, and church supplies. Customers can also buy products through the company's catalog and Web site. Family Christian has grown through new store openings and acquisitions (including chains Joshua's Christian Stores and Shepherd Shoppe). Investment firm Madison Dearborn owns about 70% of Family Christian Stores.

	Annual Growth	1/03	1/04	1/05	1/06	1/07
Est. sales ($ mil.)	—	—	—	—	—	360.3
Employees	—	—	—	—	—	4,600

FAMILY DOLLAR STORES, INC.

NYSE: FDO

10401 Monroe Rd.
Matthews, NC 28105
Phone: 704-847-6961
Fax: 704-847-0189
Web: www.familydollar.com

CEO: Howard R. Levine
CFO: Kenneth T. (Ken) Smith
HR: Michael Lariosa
FYE: August 31
Type: Public

Penny-pinching moms are important to Family Dollar Stores. The nation's #2 dollar store (behind Dollar General) targets women shopping for a family that earns around $25,000 a year. Fast-growing Family Dollar operates more than 6,500 stores in 44 states and the District of Columbia. Consumables (food, health and beauty aids, and household products) account for about 60% of sales; the stores also sell apparel, shoes, and linens. Family Dollar emphasizes neighborhood stores near its low- and middle-income customers in rural and urban areas. Most merchandise (national brands, Family Dollar private labels, and unbranded items) is less than $10. Family Dollar was founded in 1959 by the father of CEO Howard Levine.

	Annual Growth	8/03	8/04	8/05	8/06	8/07
Sales ($ mil.)	9.5%	4,750.2	5,281.9	5,824.8	6,394.8	6,834.3
Net income ($ mil.)	(0.5%)	247.5	257.9	217.5	195.1	242.9
Market value ($ mil.)	(11.7%)	6,909.0	4,457.8	3,344.9	3,542.0	4,197.1
Employees	2.4%	—	—	42,000	44,000	44,000

FAMILY ROOM ENTERTAINMENT CORPORATION

OTC: FMYR

1438 N. Gower St., Bldg. 35, Ste. 555
Hollywood, CA 90028
Phone: 323-993-7310
Fax: –
Web: www.fmlyroom.com

CEO: George Furla
CFO: Stanley Tepper
HR: –
FYE: June 30
Type: Public

Family Room Entertainment, doing business as Emmett/Furla Films, provides movie production and development services to the motion picture industry. Services include seeking creative material, acquiring rights, arranging for writing the screenplay, and negotiating talent and distribution agreements. Family Room Entertainment has worked on several Steven Segal flicks (*Mercenary For Justice, Submerged, Today You Die*), as well as the 2008 release *Rambo* (the fourth film in the *Rambo* series, and the first to be directed by Sylvester Stallone).

	Annual Growth	6/03	6/04	6/05	6/06	6/07
Sales ($ mil.)	12.5%	1.0	0.8	2.3	3.4	1.6
Net income ($ mil.)	—	(2.3)	(4.3)	(1.3)	(1.3)	(3.2)
Market value ($ mil.)	(52.7%)	—	—	895.4	583.5	199.9
Employees	0.0%	—	—	7	7	—

FAMOUS DAVE'S OF AMERICA, INC.

NASDAQ (GM): DAVE

12701 Whitewater Dr., Ste. 200
Minnetonka, MN 55343
Phone: 952-294-1300
Fax: 952-294-1301
Web: www.famousdaves.com

CEO: Wilson L. Craft
CFO: Diana G. Purcel
HR: Joleen Flory-Lundgren
FYE: December 31
Type: Public

Barbecue made this Dave famous. Famous Dave's of America operates and franchises more than 160 barbecue restaurants in about 35 states, primarily Minnesota, Illinois, Michigan, and Wisconsin. The eateries serve St. Louis-style ribs, Georgia chopped pork, and Texas brisket. Most restaurants resemble 1930s-era roadhouse shacks, although others follow the decor of a hunting lodge or a Chicago-style blues club featuring live music. The company also distributes barbecue sauce, seasonings, and prepared meats through grocery stores and other retail outlets. Famous Dave's owns more than 40 of its restaurants and franchises the rest.

	Annual Growth	12/03	12/04	12/05	12/06	12/07
Sales ($ mil.)	6.5%	97.7	99.3	102.3	116.6	125.9
Net income ($ mil.)	—	(2.9)	3.5	4.4	4.9	6.1
Market value ($ mil.)	19.8%	60.1	144.6	119.5	167.0	123.6
Employees	30.0%	—	—	2,000	2,600	—

FAMOUS UNCLE AL'S HOT DOGS & GRILLE, INC.

OTC: FDOG

100 Mill Plain Rd.
Danbury, CT 06811
Phone: 203-791-0044
Fax: –
Web: www.famousunclealshotdogs.com

CEO: Paul Esposito
CFO: –
HR: –
FYE: December 31
Type: Public

Famous Uncle Al's Hot Dogs & Grille operates a chain of about 10 franchised quick-service restaurants in Arizona, Connecticut, Florida, Nevada, and Virginia that specialize in hot dogs and sausage sandwiches. The eateries also serve a variety of Italian-style sandwiches, burgers, and fries. CEO Paul Esposito and president Dean Valentino together control more than 30% of the company.

	Annual Growth	12/03	12/04	12/05	12/06	12/07
Est. sales ($ mil.)	—	—	—	—	—	0.2
Net income ($ mil.)	—	—	—	—	—	(1.5)
Market value ($ mil.)	—	—	—	—	—	3.8
Employees	—	—	—	—	—	—

FANDANGO INC.

12200 W. Olympic Blvd., Ste. 150
Los Angeles, CA 90064
Phone: 310-451-7690
Fax: 310-451-7861
Web: www.fandango.com

CEO: Chuck Davis
CFO: Daniel V. Murray
HR: Bethany Ellis
FYE: January 1
Type: Private

Better than cutting ahead in line, Fandango lets you skip the line. The firm provides advance movie tickets and show time information via the Internet (at Fandango.com), telephone (at 1-800-FANDANGO), and wireless mobile (mobile.fandango.com). Customers can use their credit cards to guarantee tickets, which they pick up at the theater. Fandango also offers print-at-home tickets and is supported by more than 20 US and Canadian movie exhibitors, including Cinemark USA and Regal Entertainment Group, providing tickets to some 15,000 screens. A group of exhibitors formed Fandango in 2000; cable TV firm Comcast purchased it in 2007.

An in-depth profile of this company is available to Hoover's Online members at hoovers.com.

597

F & M BANK CORP.

OTC: FMBM

205 S. Main St.
Timberville, VA 22853
Phone: 540-896-8941
Fax: 540-896-2840
Web: www.farmersandmerchants.biz

CEO: Dean W. Withers
CFO: Neil W. Hayslett
HR: Ellen C. Branner
FYE: December 31
Type: Public

F & M Bank has deep roots in Virginia's Shenandoah Valley. Founded in 1908, the holding company operates about 10 Farmers & Merchants Bank branches in the northern Virginia counties of Rockingham and Shenandoah. Farmers & Merchants provides typical deposit products, including checking and savings accounts, CDs, and IRAs. Some 45% of its loans are mortgages; it also writes agricultural, business, construction, and consumer loans. The company offers insurance, brokerage, and financial services through TEB Life Insurance and Farmers & Merchants Financial Services.

	Annual Growth	12/03	12/04	12/05	12/06	12/07
Assets ($ mil.)	5.8%	309.1	370.0	346.3	375.9	386.7
Net income ($ mil.)	2.4%	4.0	4.3	4.8	4.5	4.4
Market value ($ mil.)	7.8%	54.0	62.8	62.5	66.8	72.8
Employees	—	—	—	—	—	137

FANSTEEL INC.

Pink Sheets: FELI

570 Lake Cook Rd., Ste. 200
Deerfield, IL 60015
Phone: 847-689-4900
Fax: 847-689-0307
Web: www.fansteel.com

CEO: Gary L. Tessitore
CFO: R. Michael McEntee
HR: R. Michael McEntee
FYE: December 31
Type: Public

Fansteel is a big fan of steel and other performance metals. The specialty metalworker makes products from tungsten carbide, titanium, special alloys, and other metals. Its Industrial Metal Components segment makes wire forms, powdered metal components, and sand and investment castings. Its Advanced Structures unit makes wearable components, closed die forgings, and machined components. United Technologies represents nearly 25% of sales, while Navistar International accounts for 10%. Other customers include companies in the aerospace, automotive, construction, metalworking, plumbing and electrical, and petrochemicals industries.

	Annual Growth	12/03	12/04	12/05	12/06	12/07
Sales ($ mil.)	12.3%	47.1	52.1	56.3	67.5	74.8
Net income ($ mil.)	—	(14.9)	(3.8)	(1.4)	(5.3)	(2.5)
Employees	—	—	—	—	685	—

FAO SCHWARZ INC.

875 Avenue of the Americas, 20th Fl.
New York, NY 10001
Phone: 212-644-9400
Fax: 212-308-6094
Web: www.fao.com

CEO: Edward M. (Ed) Schmults
CFO: Erin Carachilo
HR: Tom Wheeland
FYE: January 31
Type: Private

Famed toy store FAO Schwarz is still in business, although in a much reduced capacity. The toy seller operates just two locations: its landmark store on New York's Fifth Avenue and a shop in Las Vegas. It also sells its unique, hard-to-find toys (such as life-size stuffed bears and $50,000 kid-size Ferraris) via its relaunched catalog and Web site. Founded in 1862 by Frederick August Otto Schwarz, F.A.O. (formerly The Right Start) bought most of the company's assets from European retailer Vendex in 2002 (taking the FAO name). After filing Chapter 11 bankruptcy twice in 2003, the company shuttered about a dozen stores. Parent company F.A.O. sold out to hedge fund D. E. Shaw in 2004 for $41 million.

	Annual Growth	1/03	1/04	1/05	1/06	1/07
Est. sales ($ mil.)	—	—	—	—	—	18.0
Employees	—	—	—	—	—	225

FAREWAY STORES, INC.

2300 E. 8th St.
Boone, IA 50036
Phone: 515-432-2623
Fax: 515-433-4416

CEO: F. William Beckwith
CFO: Craig A. Shepley
HR: Mike Mazour
FYE: March 31
Type: Private

Fareway Stores makes the green through groceries. The regional supermarket chain operates under the Fareway banner, primarily in Iowa but also in Illinois and Nebraska. Its 90-plus locations average about 25,000 sq. ft. Eschewing such amenities as video rentals and dry-cleaning services, Fareway Stores sticks to the basics — lots of meat (all cut to order) and groceries only. Former Safeway workers Paul Beckwith and Fred Vitt founded Fareway in 1938; the Beckwith family controls the company. Because of the founders' biblical beliefs, the stores are closed on Sundays, and if you've got a 2 a.m. brisket craving, you're out of luck: Not even shelf-stocking night crews can be found at the stores after hours.

FARGO ELECTRONICS, INC.

6533 Flying Cloud Dr.
Eden Prairie, MN 55344
Phone: 952-941-9470
Fax: 952-941-7836
Web: www.fargo.com

CEO: David M. (Dave) Sullivan
CFO: Tony J. Dick
HR: –
FYE: December 31
Type: Subsidiary

Fargo Electronics offers more than a carte blanche. The company makes desktop systems that print personalized plastic cards. Customers use Fargo's "instant-issue" card printers to make personalized bus and train passes, driver's licenses, hotel room access cards, library cards, membership cards, parking passes, retail loyalty and discount cards, and security and student identification cards. Users can print holograms, photographs, and bar codes on the cards and encode data on them with magnetic stripes or smart-card semiconductors. Fargo was acquired by ASSA ABLOY subsidiary HID Global in 2006.

	Annual Growth	12/03	12/04	12/05	12/06	12/07
Est. sales ($ mil.)	—	—	—	—	—	17.8
Employees	—	—	—	—	—	226

FARLEY'S & SATHERS CANDY COMPANY, INC.

1 Sather Plaza
Round Lake, MN 56167
Phone: 507-945-8181
Fax: 507-945-8343
Web: www.farleysandsathers.com

CEO: Keith Lively
CFO: Tammy Koller
HR: Theresa Neuberger
FYE: December 31
Type: Private

Farley's & Sathers Candy Company went on a buying spree. The company makes non-chocolate confections including Chuckles, JujyFruits, and Jujubes (all acquired from Hershey Foods in 2002), along with Now and Later, Mighty Bite, and Intense Fruit Chews candies (acquired from Kraft Foods in 2002 as well). Farley's also makes RainBlo, Jujyfruits, Super Bubble, and Hot Dog! bubble gums (which it bought from Hershey in 2003). Offering 900 different candy items, the company produces some 42 million pounds of confections a year, which are distributed throughout the US. It purchased Brach's Confections in 2007.

	Annual Growth	12/03	12/04	12/05	12/06	12/07
Est. sales ($ mil.)	—	—	—	—	—	200.0
Employees	—	—	—	—	—	1,200

FARM BUREAU MUTUAL INSURANCE COMPANY

5400 University Ave.
West Des Moines, IA 50266
Phone: 515-225-5400
Fax: 515-225-5419
Web: www.fbfs.com

CEO: James W. (Jim) Noyce
CFO: Jim Brannen
HR: Mark Mincks
FYE: December 31
Type: Private

Farm Bureau Mutual offers property/casualty insurance, life insurance, and investment products, primarily to farmers, ranchers, and agricultural businesses in the Midwest and West. Its lines of coverage include life, farmowners, commercial liability, crop, and workers' compensation. Based in Des Moines, Iowa, Farm Bureau Mutual is managed by FBL Financial Group. Farm Bureau Mutual operates in Arizona, Iowa, Kansas, Minnesota, Nebraska, New Mexico, South Dakota, and Utah.

	Annual Growth	12/03	12/04	12/05	12/06	12/07
Est. sales ($ mil.)	—	—	—	—	—	700.8
Employees	—	—	—	—	—	587

FARM FRESH

853 Chimney Hill Shopping Center
Virginia Beach, VA 23452
Phone: 757-306-7006
Fax: 757-306-2215
Web: www.farmfreshsupermarkets.com

CEO: Ron Dennis
CFO: –
HR: Mark Motsenbocker
FYE: Saturday nearest April 30
Type: Business segment

Farm Fresh stores serve up farm-fresh produce and lots more to shoppers in southeastern Virginia. The regional grocery chain operates about 40 supermarkets under the Farm Fresh Food & Pharmacy banner, primarily in the Hampton and Richmond areas. It also operates a supermarket in Elizabeth City, North Carolina. Farm Fresh moved from its roots in 1956 as an open-air fruit and vegetable stand in Norfolk, Virginia to upscale operations offering everything from catering services to fine wines. The firm declared bankruptcy in 1998. Soon after, food distributor Richfood Holdings bought it and began a cash infusion. SUPERVALU then acquired Richfood in 1999.

	Annual Growth	4/03	4/04	4/05	4/06	4/07
Est. sales ($ mil.)	—	—	—	—	—	542.2
Employees	—	—	—	—	—	5,000

FARM STORES CORPORATION

5800 NW 74th Ave.
Miami, FL 33166
Phone: 305-471-5141
Fax: –

CEO: Carlos Bared
CFO: –
HR: –
FYE: December 31
Type: Private

Forget the shopping cart. At Farm Stores Corporation's drive-thru markets, you never leave the car. With more than 100 Express Markets throughout Florida, Farm Stores is the nation's largest drive-thru grocery retailer. The chain's pre-paid Farm Stores Quick Card (think of it as a debit card for milk) allows customers to buy gallons more cheaply by paying in advance. The grocery chain's stores are supplied by Associated Grocers of Florida. The company is exploring plans to expand its concept nationally. Founded in 1937, the Bared family, fronted by company president and CEO Carlos Bared, bought Farm Stores out of bankruptcy in 1992.

	Annual Growth	12/03	12/04	12/05	12/06	12/07
Est. sales ($ mil.)	—	—	—	—	—	28.0
Employees	—	—	—	—	—	700

FARMER BROS. CO.

NASDAQ (GM): FARM

20333 S. Normandie Ave.
Torrance, CA 90502
Phone: 310-787-5200
Fax: 310-787-5246
Web: www.farmerbroscousa.com

CEO: Roger M. (Rocky) Laverty III
CFO: John E. Simmons
HR: Lori Brown
FYE: June 30
Type: Public

Farmer Bros. Co. knows beans about farming — coffee beans that is. Farmer Bros. roasts and packages coffee and sells it to restaurants, hotels, fast-food outlets, convenience stores, and hospitals. The company also distributes related or "allied" products such as filters, cups, creamers, teas, spices, and soup bases to those same customers. Farmer Bros. distributes more than 400 products from about 100 branch warehouses in major cities in more than a dozen US states. Its Brewmatic division makes coffee dispensers. The Farmer family founded Farmer Bros. in 1912 and controls nearly 40% of Farmer Bros.

	Annual Growth	6/03	6/04	6/05	6/06	6/07
Sales ($ mil.)	1.8%	201.6	193.6	198.4	207.4	216.3
Net income ($ mil.)	(26.7%)	23.6	12.7	(5.4)	4.8	6.8
Market value ($ mil.)	53.6%	65.4	431.3	357.8	348.5	363.8
Employees	6.7%	—	—	1,084	1,091	1,233

FARMERS CAPITAL BANK CORPORATION

NASDAQ (GS): FFKT

202 W. Main St.
Frankfort, KY 40601
Phone: 502-227-1600
Fax: 502-227-1692
Web: www.farmerscapital.com

CEO: G. Anthony (Tony) Busseni
CFO: C. Douglas Carpenter
HR: Linda L. Faulconer
FYE: December 31
Type: Public

Farmers Capital has found some green in the Bluegrass State. Its seven bank subsidiaries — Farmers Bank & Capital Trust, Farmers Bank and Trust, United Bank & Trust, Lawrenceburg Bank and Trust, First Citizens Bank, Citizens Bank of Northern Kentucky, and Citizens National Bank of Jessamine — operate more than 35 branches in northern and central Kentucky. Serving individuals and local businesses, they offer standard retail services such as checking and savings accounts, CDs, and trust activities. Residential mortgages and commercial real estate loans each account for around 80% of the company's loan portfolio. Nonbank subsidiaries of Farmers Capital provide insurance and data processing services.

	Annual Growth	12/03	12/04	12/05	12/06	12/07
Assets ($ mil.)	11.9%	1,318.6	1,397.1	1,672.6	1,824.4	2,068.3
Net income ($ mil.)	4.7%	13.0	13.4	15.8	21.4	15.6
Market value ($ mil.)	(3.3%)	228.4	279.5	227.1	269.5	199.4
Employees	0.7%	—	—	570	—	578

FARMERS GROUP, INC.

4680 Wilshire Blvd.
Los Angeles, CA 90010
Phone: 323-932-3200
Fax: –
Web: www.farmers.com

CEO: Paul N. Hopkins
CFO: Scott R. Lindquist
HR: –
FYE: December 31
Type: Subsidiary

Don't expect to see tractors in the parking lot of Farmers Group. The US subsidiary of Zurich Financial Services provides insurance management services to the members of the Farmers Insurance Exchange, Truck Insurance Exchange, and Fire Insurance Exchange — which are among the leading US property/casualty insurers. Farmers Group does not own the exchanges, but acts as the companies' attorneys-in-fact. It chooses risks, distributes policy statements to customers, collects premiums, and provides other non-claims related services. The Farmers Group also is the holding company of Farmers New World Life Insurance, and Foremost Insurance, a specialty insurer for mobile homes, motor homes, and specialty dwellings.

	Annual Growth	12/03	12/04	12/05	12/06	12/07
Est. sales ($ mil.)	—	—	—	—	—	2,147.5
Employees	—	—	—	—	—	25,935

An in-depth profile of this company is available to Hoover's Online members at hoovers.com.

599

FARMERS NATIONAL BANC CORP.

OTC: FMNB

20 S. Broad St.
Canfield, OH 44406
Phone: 330-533-3341
Fax: 330-533-0451
Web: www.fnbcanfield.com

CEO: Frank L. Paden
CFO: Carl D. Culp
HR: Anthony F. Peluso
FYE: December 31
Type: Public

Farmers National Banc is willing to help even nonfarmers to grow their seed income into thriving bounties of wealth. Farmers National Banc is the holding company for Farmers National Bank of Canfield, which provides commercial and personal banking from about 20 branches in northeastern Ohio. The bank offers traditional retail products and services including checking accounts, savings accounts, credit cards, and loans and mortgages. Farmers National Banc's lending portfolio comprises real estate mortgages, consumer loans, and commercial loans.

	Annual Growth	12/03	12/04	12/05	12/06	12/07
Assets ($ mil.)	(0.5%)	812.8	817.8	827.1	821.6	798.2
Net income ($ mil.)	(11.2%)	9.5	7.2	8.1	7.2	5.9
Market value ($ mil.)	(15.3%)	195.3	207.2	166.3	137.9	100.3
Employees	—	—	—	—	—	—

FARMLAND DAIRIES, LLC

520 Main Ave.
Wallington, NJ 07057
Phone: 973-777-2500
Fax: 973-777-7648
Web: www.farmlanddairies.com

CEO: Martin J. (Marty) Margherio
CFO: –
HR: Peter Clifford
FYE: December 31
Type: Private

Farmland Dairies, LLC (formerly Parmalat USA) has happy cows once again. The company got caught up in its then Italian parent Parmalat Finaziaria's bankruptcy scandal but emerged in 2005 hale and healthy as Farmland. Its brand names include Clinton's, Farmland, Parmalat, Lil' Milk, Pomi, and Welsh Farms. In addition to fresh and shelf-stable milk, Farmland also makes ice cream, cream, half & half, drinks, juices, and shelf-stable tomatoes and tomato sauces. The company's milk and milk products are market leaders in metro New Jersey and New York.

	Annual Growth	12/03	12/04	12/05	12/06	12/07
Est. sales ($ mil.)	—	—	—	—	—	49.0
Employees	—	—	—	—	—	490

FARO TECHNOLOGIES, INC.

NASDAQ (GM): FARO

125 Technology Park
Lake Mary, FL 32746
Phone: 407-333-9911
Fax: 407-333-4181
Web: www.faro.com

CEO: Jay W. Freeland
CFO: Keith S. Bair
HR: John E. Townsley
FYE: December 31
Type: Public

FARO Technologies is putting the Arm on companies around the world — and they like it. With the touch of its mechanical arm, FARO's Control Station measuring system can facilitate reverse engineering of an undocumented part or a competitor's product. The FARO Arm is a portable, jointed device that simulates the human arm's movement and works with FARO's CAM2 3-D software to take measurements, perform reverse engineering, and inspect parts by comparing them with digital designs. Aerospace, automotive, and heavy equipment companies such as Boeing, Caterpillar, General Motors, and Siemens use FARO Arm units in their factories. Customers located outside the Americas account for more than half of sales.

	Annual Growth	12/03	12/04	12/05	12/06	12/07
Sales ($ mil.)	27.8%	71.8	97.0	125.6	152.4	191.6
Net income ($ mil.)	21.5%	8.3	14.9	8.2	8.2	18.1
Market value ($ mil.)	7.6%	336.7	435.4	285.8	347.7	451.3
Employees	23.0%	341	453	657	641	780

FAROUK SYSTEMS, INC.

250 Pennbright
Houston, TX 77090
Phone: 281-876-2000
Fax: 281-876-1700
Web: www.farouk.com

CEO: Rami Shami
CFO: –
HR: –
FYE: December 31
Type: Private

Girlfriend, forget about bad hair days. Farouk Systems manufactures personal care products, including hair care and spa items. Farouk products include Biosilk hair care products, as well as CHI styling products and implements (hair dryers, curling irons, clippers, and hairstyling irons). The company also makes its own CHI men's and women's fragrances as well as CHI nail polish. Products are distributed by salons and beauty supply shops. The firm, founded by Palestinian immigrant Farouk Shami (chairman) in 1986, is owned and operated by professional hairdressers.

	Annual Growth	12/03	12/04	12/05	12/06	12/07
Est. sales ($ mil.)	—	—	—	—	—	15.3
Employees	—	—	—	—	—	150

FASTENAL COMPANY

NASDAQ (GS): FAST

2001 Theurer Blvd.
Winona, MN 55987
Phone: 507-454-5374
Fax: 507-453-8049
Web: www.fastenal.com

CEO: Willard D. (Will) Oberton
CFO: Daniel L. (Dan) Florness
HR: Reyne K. Wisecup
FYE: December 31
Type: Public

Some might say it has a screw loose, but things are really pretty snug at Fastenal. The company operates about 2,150 stores in all 50 US states, Canada, China, Mexico, the Netherlands, Puerto Rico, and Singapore. Its stores stock about 690,000 products in about a dozen categories, including threaded fasteners such as screws, nuts, and bolts. Other sales come from fluid-transfer parts for hydraulic and pneumatic power; janitorial, electrical, and welding supplies; material handling items; metal-cutting tool blades; and power tools. Its customers are typically construction, manufacturing, and other industrial professionals. Fastenal Company was founded by its chairman Bob Kierlin in 1967 and went public in 1987.

	Annual Growth	12/03	12/04	12/05	12/06	12/07
Sales ($ mil.)	20.0%	994.9	1,238.5	1,523.3	1,809.3	2,061.8
Net income ($ mil.)	29.0%	84.1	131.0	166.8	199.0	232.6
Market value ($ mil.)	33.7%	1,887.4	2,335.5	5,910.8	5,425.3	6,027.5
Employees	13.6%	—	—	9,306	10,415	12,013

FATBURGER CORPORATION

301 Arizona Ave., Ste. 200
Santa Monica, CA 90401
Phone: 310-319-1850
Fax: 310-319-1863
Web: www.fatburger.com

CEO: Donald J. Berchtold
CFO: Harold Fox
HR: Victor Santillan
FYE: June 30
Type: Private

It's a little more expensive than 99 cents, but you don't need to be a real fat cat to enjoy one of these burgers. Fatburger operates and franchises more than 90 hamburger stands known for their 1/3-pound signature sandwich. Located primarily in Southern California, the 1950s-style restaurants also offer a 1/2-pound Kingburger and 1/8-pound Baby Fat burger, as well as a variety of side orders and other sandwiches. Franchisees operate more than 50 of the chain's locations. Lovie Yancey opened the first Fatburger in 1952 when "fat" was used to describe the size, not the content, of the burger. Fog Cutter Capital Group owns more than 80% of the company; Former Fatburger CEO Keith Warlick also has a stake in the business.

FAUQUIER BANKSHARES, INC.

NASDAQ (CM): FBSS

10 Courthouse Sq.
Warrenton, VA 20186
Phone: 540-347-2700
Fax: 540-349-9533
Web: www.fauquierbank.com

CEO: Randy K. Ferrell
CFO: Eric P. Graap
HR: –
FYE: December 31
Type: Public

Fauquier Bankshares is the holding company for The Fauquier Bank, which operates about 10 branches in northern Virginia, southwest of Washington, DC. The bank targets individual and regional business customers, offering standard retail products such as checking, savings, and money market accounts, and CDs. Its lending activities consist mostly of residential and commercial mortgages (about 40% and 30% of its loan portfolio, respectively). Its wealth management division provides investment management, trust, estate, retirement, insurance, and brokerage services. Through subsidiary Fauquier Bank Services it has equity ownership in Bankers Insurance, Bankers Investments Group, and Bankers Title Shenandoah.

	Annual Growth	12/03	12/04	12/05	12/06	12/07
Assets ($ mil.)	6.7%	378.5	429.2	481.3	521.8	489.9
Net income ($ mil.)	3.3%	4.3	5.0	5.7	5.6	4.9
Market value ($ mil.)	(5.6%)	76.0	84.5	86.1	87.0	60.3
Employees	(6.7%)	—	—	147	147	128

FAYGO BEVERAGES, INC.

3579 Gratiot Ave.
Detroit, MI 48207
Phone: 313-925-1600
Fax: 313-571-7611
Web: www.faygo.com

CEO: Alan A. (Al) Chittaro
CFO: –
HR: –
FYE: April 30
Type: Subsidiary

Faygo Beverages believes in flavor. The beverage company offers an array of fruit sodas, ginger ale, root beer, and creme soda. It also offers sparkling water (flavors include orange and lemon lime), non-carbonated beverages (OHANA), energy drinks (RIP IT), and nonalcoholic mixers (club soda, tonic water), but it is best known for its "pop." The wide range of Faygo's pop flavors include Creme Soda, Dr. Faygo, Moon Mist Green, and Black Cherry. Faygo products and clothing are available via the company's Web site. National Beverage Corp purchased the company in 1987.

	Annual Growth	4/03	4/04	4/05	4/06	4/07
Est. sales ($ mil.)	—	—	—	—	—	67.5
Employees	—	—	—	—	—	450

FAZOLI'S RESTAURANTS, INC.

2470 Palumbo Dr.
Lexington, KY 40509
Phone: 859-268-1668
Fax: 859-268-2263
Web: www.fazolis.com

CEO: Robert T. (Bob) Weissmueller
CFO: David Smith
HR: Ann Tincher
FYE: March 31
Type: Private

The taste of Italy can be as close as your local shopping mall thanks to this company. Fazoli's Restaurants operates a leading quick-service Italian food chain with more than 300 locations in about 30 states. The eateries serve pasta, pizzas (whole pies and by the slice), and panini sandwiches, as well as soups, salads, and dessert items. Many Fazoli's locations can be found in shopping centers, highway service areas, and other high-traffic locations. About 45% of the restaurants are company-owned, while the rest are franchised. Fazoli's was started in 1988 by restaurant operator Jerrico (which also started the Long John Silver's chain). Private equity firm Sun Capital Partners acquired the company in 2006.

FBL FINANCIAL GROUP, INC.

NYSE: FFG

5400 University Ave.
West Des Moines, IA 50266
Phone: 515-225-5400
Fax: 515-226-6053
Web: www.fblfinancial.com

CEO: James W. (Jim) Noyce
CFO: James P. Brannen
HR: Mark Mincks
FYE: December 31
Type: Public

Insurance holding company FBL Financial Group is the parent of Farm Bureau Life and EquiTrust Life. Through these subsidiaries the firm sells property/casualty and life insurance including disability insurance, annuities, and mutual funds to farmers, ranchers, and agricultural businesses. Farm Bureau Life sells its insurance and annuities through an exclusive network of some 2,000 agents in the Midwest and West. EquiTrust Life's annuity products are sold through about 20,000 independent agents across the US. The company markets its products through an affiliation with the American Farm Bureau Federation. The Iowa Farm Bureau Federation owns a majority stake in the company.

	Annual Growth	12/03	12/04	12/05	12/06	12/07
Assets ($ mil.)	15.2%	7,949.1	9,100.7	10,153.9	12,154.0	14,003.0
Net income ($ mil.)	7.0%	65.9	66.1	72.8	90.1	86.3
Market value ($ mil.)	9.3%	696.5	786.3	916.7	1,112.6	995.4
Employees	(2.8%)	—	—	1,923	1,858	1,818

FBOP CORPORATION

11 W. Madison St.
Oak Park, IL 60302
Phone: 708-386-5000
Fax: 708-386-9980
Web: www.fbopcorporation.com

CEO: Michael E. (Mike) Kelly
CFO: Michael (Mike) Dunning
HR: Loraine Guse
FYE: December 31
Type: Private

When the IRA is DOA, or a CD is needed ASAP, try FBOP. Acquisitive FBOP Corporation owns eight community banks in California, Illinois, Texas, and Arizona. The largest of these is Los Angeles-based California National Bank, which has some 70 branches. FBOP's other primary markets include Chicago, Phoenix, San Diego, and San Francisco; all told, the company has more than 130 locations. The banks provide retail and commercial services including checking, savings, and money market accounts; credit cards; and cash management. They mainly specialize in real estate and construction lending. FBOP plans to acquire PFF Bancorp, which has some 40 branches in Southern California.

	Annual Growth	12/03	12/04	12/05	12/06	12/07
Est. sales ($ mil.)	—	—	—	—	—	194.6
Employees	—	—	—	—	—	1,452

FBR CAPITAL MARKETS CORPORATION

NASDAQ (GS): FBCM

1001 Nineteenth St. North, 18th Fl.
Arlington, VA 22209
Phone: 703-312-9500
Fax: 703-312-9501
Web: www.fbrcm.com

CEO: Eric F. Billings
CFO: Bradley J. Wright
HR: –
FYE: December 31
Type: Public

Don't confuse FDR and FBR: One was a beloved US president, while the other *loves* dead presidents. FBR Capital Markets provides investment banking, institutional brokerage, and fee-based asset management services for institutional and corporate clients and wealthy individuals. It also invests its own capital in merchant banking transactions alongside its clients and Friedman, Billings, Ramsey (FBR Group). The company focuses on the financial services, insurance, and energy industries as well as real estate and health care. FBR Group created FBR Capital Markets in 2006 and spun off some of its stake in an IPO the following year, but retains a controlling stake of around 50% in the firm.

	Annual Growth	12/03	12/04	12/05	12/06	12/07
Sales ($ mil.)	5.7%	392.4	582.4	575.4	418.6	489.4
Net income ($ mil.)	(48.1%)	71.4	89.8	48.1	(9.8)	5.2
Market value ($ mil.)	—	—	—	—	—	632.3
Employees	40.4%	473	664	—	—	—

An in-depth profile of this company is available to Hoover's Online members at hoovers.com.

601

FCSTONE GROUP, INC.

NASDAQ (GM): FCSX

2829 Westown Pkwy., Ste. 100
West Des Moines, IA 50266
Phone: 515-223-3788
Fax: 515-223-3765
Web: www.fcstone.com

CEO: Paul G. (Pete) Anderson
CFO: William J. Dunaway
HR: Kathy Holmes
FYE: August 31
Type: Public

No, Tom Cruise doesn't work there, but FCStone tries to make a risky business a little less so. The firm provides market intelligence and analysis to help companies manage the risks associated with commodities trading. Industries served include agriculture, energy, food service, forest products, livestock, and renewable fuels. Subsidiary FGDI offers grain merchandising services, connecting buyers and sellers in both US and international markets. The firm serves more than 7,500 customers from about a dozen US offices and four locations overseas. FCStone is a clearing member on all major US futures exchanges; it executes more than 70 million derivative contracts annually.

	Annual Growth	8/03	8/04	8/05	8/06	8/07
Sales ($ mil.)	2.1%	1,232.8	1,624.3	1,401.8	1,294.8	1,341.7
Net income ($ mil.)	66.8%	4.3	6.4	6.6	15.3	33.3
Market value ($ mil.)	—	—	—	—	—	854.3
Employees	(6.1%)	—	—	424	424	374

FEATHERLITE, INC.

Hwys. 63 and 9
Cresco, IA 52136
Phone: 563-547-6000
Fax: 563-547-6100
Web: www.featherliteinc.com

CEO: Eric P. Clement
CFO: –
HR: Rick Ruden
FYE: December 31
Type: Private

Featherlite belongs in the aluminum trailer industry's Haul of Fame. The company offers a line of standard and specialty trailer models. Featherlite's trailers are used to haul horses, racecars, livestock, construction equipment, ATVs, and motorcycles. The company also makes custom specialty trailers used for vending, offices, kitchens, passenger trams, and classrooms. Fellow trailer maker Universal Trailer bought Featherlite for $29 million in cash and the assumption of $109 million in debt late in 2006. Featherlite branded trailers are sold all across the US through a network of more than 200 dealers.

	Annual Growth	12/03	12/04	12/05	12/06	12/07
Est. sales ($ mil.)	—	—	—	—	—	162.5
Employees	—	—	—	—	—	1,300

FEDDERS CORPORATION

Pink Sheets: FJCC

Westgate Corporate Center, 505 Martinsville Rd.
Liberty Corner, NJ 07938
Phone: 908-604-8686
Fax: 908-604-0715
Web: www.fedders.com

CEO: Robert L. Laurent Jr.
CFO: Robert L. Laurent Jr.
HR: Michael W. Carr
FYE: December 31
Type: Public

A little hot under the collar? Fedders feels your pain. The company makes heating, ventilation, and air conditioning (HVAC) and engineered products, primarily for commercial and industrial use. Products include window and central air conditioners, gas furnaces, humidifiers, air cleaners, and dust collectors. Fedders sells its products to retailers, wholesalers, and OEMs under its own name, as well as under the Airtemp, Koppel, MAC-10, Sun, and Trion brands. It also licenses the Maytag name for air conditioners and produces private-label products. Feeling its own heat, Fedders and its North American subsidiaries filed for Chapter 11 bankruptcy protection in 2007; foreign operations were not included.

	Annual Growth	8/02	8/03	*12/04	12/05	†12/06
Sales ($ mil.)	(7.0%)	373.7	421.7	413.0	297.7	279.3
Net income ($ mil.)	—	8.0	(3.1)	(26.1)	(62.1)	(124.6)
Employees	3.4%	2,700	—	—	2,981	—

*Fiscal year change †Most recent year available

FEDERAL AGRICULTURAL MORTGAGE CORPORATION

NYSE: AGM

1133 21st St. NW, Ste. 600
Washington, DC 20036
Phone: 202-872-7700
Fax: 202-872-7713
Web: www.farmermac.com

CEO: Henry D. Edelman
CFO: Nancy E. Corsiglia
HR: –
FYE: December 31
Type: Public

Farmer Mac (Federal Agricultural Mortgage Corporation) is Fannie Mae and Freddie Mac's country cousin. Like its city-slicker kin, it provides liquidity in its markets (agricultural real estate and rural housing mortgages) by buying loans from lenders and then securitizing the loans into Farmer Mac Guaranteed Securities. Farmer Mac buys both conventional loans and those guaranteed by the US Department of Agriculture. About 40% of Farmer Mac's outstanding loans are secured by real estate in the southwestern US; the Northwest and the Upper Midwest account for nearly 20% apiece. More than 40% of its loans are for crops, some 25% for livestock facilities, and about another 20% for permanent plantings.

	Annual Growth	12/03	12/04	12/05	12/06	12/07
Assets ($ mil.)	3.7%	4,299.6	3,846.8	4,341.4	4,953.7	4,977.6
Net income ($ mil.)	(29.6%)	27.3	30.5	49.3	32.0	6.7
Market value ($ mil.)	(6.6%)	23.1	17.7	22.6	19.4	17.5
Employees	—	—	—	46	—	—

FEDERAL EXPRESS CORPORATION

3610 Hacks Cross Rd.
Memphis, TN 38125
Phone: 901-369-3600
Fax: 901-395-2000
Web: fedex.com/us

CEO: David J. Bronczek
CFO: Cathy D. Ross
HR: R. Larry Brown
FYE: May 31
Type: Subsidiary

You can't spell FedEx without Federal Express Corporation, which does business as FedEx Express. The largest subsidiary of FedEx, FedEx Express is responsible for its parent's namesake express delivery business, the world's largest. FedEx Express delivers about 3.5 million packages per day throughout the US and to some 220 countries and territories worldwide. Packages (from envelopes to boxes weighing up to 150 pounds) account for most of the company's sales; FedEx Express also delivers pallets of freight weighing from 151 pounds to 2,200 pounds. The company operates a fleet of about 670 aircraft and more than 44,500 motor vehicles.

	Annual Growth	5/03	5/04	5/05	5/06	5/07
Sales ($ mil.)	8.3%	16,351.0	17,383.0	19,364.0	21,296.0	22,527.0
Net income ($ mil.)	30.5%	431.0	360.0	823.0	1,086.0	1,251.0
Employees	1.6%	134,000	133,500	138,100	138,000	143,000

FEDERAL HOME LOAN MORTGAGE CORPORATION

NYSE: FRE

8200 Jones Branch Dr.
McLean, VA 22102
Phone: 703-903-2000
Fax: –
Web: www.freddiemac.com

CEO: Richard F. (Dick) Syron
CFO: Anthony S. (Buddy) Piszel
HR: Paul G. George
FYE: December 31
Type: Public

Uncle Sam's nephew is somewhat of a real estate tycoon. Freddie Mac (officially the Federal Home Loan Mortgage Corporation) is a shareholder-owned, government-sponsored enterprise that, along with sister Fannie Mae, creates liquidity in the residential mortgage market by guaranteeing, purchasing, securitizing, and investing in such loans. The company, which is prohibited from originating loans, buys conventional residential mortgages from mortgage bankers, transferring risk from them and allowing them to provide mortgages to those who otherwise wouldn't qualify. It also provides assistance for affordable rental housing. Freddie Mac indirectly finances one out of every six homes in the US.

	Annual Growth	12/03	12/04	12/05	12/06	12/07
Assets ($ mil.)	(0.0%)	—	795,284.0	806,222.0	813,081.0	794,368.0
Net income ($ mil.)	—	—	2,937.0	2,130.0	2,211.0	(3,094.0)
Employees	(9.7%)	—	—	—	5,535	5,000

FEDERAL NATIONAL MORTGAGE ASSOCIATION

NYSE: FNM

3900 Wisconsin Ave. NW
Washington, DC 20016
Phone: 202-752-7000
Fax: –
Web: www.fanniemae.com

CEO: Daniel H. (Dan) Mudd
CFO: Stephen M. (Steve) Swad
HR: Emmanuel Bailey
FYE: December 31
Type: Public

The Federal National Mortgage Association, or Fannie Mae, has helped more than 50 million low- to middle-income families realize the American Dream. A public company operating under federal charter, it is the US's #1 source for mortgage funding, financing one of every five home loans. The firm, like brother Freddie Mac, provides liquidity in the mortgage market by buying mortgages from lenders and packaging them for resale, transferring risk from lenders and allowing them to offer mortgages to those who may not otherwise qualify. Top customers include Countrywide Financial and Bank of America. As with its private-industry cohorts, the company was hit hard by the subprime mortgage crisis of 2007.

	Annual Growth	12/03	12/04	12/05	12/06	12/07
Sales ($ mil.)	(1.2%)	53,768.0	51,826.0	50,149.0	48,861.0	51,176.0
Net income ($ mil.)	—	7,905.0	4,967.0	6,347.0	4,059.0	(2,050.0)
Market value ($ mil.)	(14.5%)	72,808.2	69,007.9	47,371.7	57,733.7	38,944.7
Employees	1.8%	—	5,400	5,600	—	5,700

FEDERAL PRISON INDUSTRIES, INC.

320 1st St. NW, Bldg. 400
Washington, DC 20534
Phone: 202-305-3500
Fax: 202-305-7340
Web: www.unicor.gov

CEO: Harley G. Lappin
CFO: Bruce Long
HR: Keith Hall
FYE: September 30
Type: Government agency

Some businesses benefit from captive audiences; this company benefits from captive employees. Federal Prison Industries (FPI), known by its trade name UNICOR, uses prisoners to make products and provide services, mainly for the US government. More than 21,000 inmates (about 18% of the total eligible inmate population) are employed in nearly 110 FPI factories in prisons across the US. UNICOR, which is part of the Justice Department's Bureau of Prisons, manufactures products such as office furniture, clothing, beds and linens, electronics equipment, and eyewear. It also offers services including data entry, bulk mailing, laundry services, recycling, and refurbishing of vehicle components.

	Annual Growth	9/02	9/03	9/04	9/05	9/06
Sales ($ mil.)	1.9%	716.9	721.9	879.4	833.6	774.0
Net income ($ mil.)	16.9%	9.1	2.0	63.6	64.5	17.0
Employees	(0.7%)	21,778	20,274	19,337	19,720	21,205

FEDERAL REALTY INVESTMENT TRUST

NYSE: FRT

1626 E. Jefferson St.
Rockville, MD 20852
Phone: 301-998-8100
Fax: 301-998-3700
Web: www.federalrealty.com

CEO: Donald C. (Don) Wood
CFO: Joseph M. Squeri
HR: Philip E. Altschuler
FYE: December 31
Type: Public

It's a safe bet that Federal Realty Investment Trust makes a federal case of shopping centers. The real estate investment trust (REIT) owns or has majority interest in some 80 retail properties including community and neighborhood shopping centers and mixed-use complexes totaling more than 18 million sq. ft. The company's key markets are densely populated, affluent areas in the Mid-Atlantic and Northeast, but it also has properties in California and Texas. Tenants include Bed Bath & Beyond, Kohl's, and Whole Foods. Rather than acquiring other real estate firms, the REIT tends to grow by acquiring and renovating existing, primarily grocery-anchored shopping centers.

	Annual Growth	12/03	12/04	12/05	12/06	12/07
Sales ($ mil.)	7.9%	357.9	394.3	410.3	451.0	485.9
Net income ($ mil.)	19.9%	94.5	84.2	114.6	118.7	195.5
Market value ($ mil.)	26.4%	1,889.6	2,692.9	3,215.2	4,702.2	4,817.7
Employees	(37.3%)	—	—	394	—	155

FEDERAL SCREW WORKS

Pink Sheets: FSCR

20229 Nine Mile Rd.
St. Clair Shores, MI 48080
Phone: 586-443-4200
Fax: 586-443-4220
Web: www.federalscrew.com

CEO: Thomas ZurSchmiede
CFO: W. T. ZurSchmiede Jr.
HR: –
FYE: June 30
Type: Public

Although many US residents might think so, Federal Screw Works is not a division of the Internal Revenue Service. *This* Federal Screw Works is a manufacturer of fasteners and related items, primarily for the auto industry. The company produces high-volume lots to the specifications of manufacturers. Nonautomotive sales are mainly to makers of durable goods. Federal Screw Works' products include locknuts, bolts, piston pins, studs, bushings, shafts, and other machined, cold-formed, hardened, and ground-metal parts. It maintains five manufacturing facilities, all of which are located in Michigan. In 2005 the company delisted its shares from the Nasdaq.

	Annual Growth	6/03	6/04	6/05	6/06	6/07
Est. sales ($ mil.)	—	—	—	—	—	34.7
Employees	—	—	—	—	—	376

FEDERAL SIGNAL CORPORATION

NYSE: FSS

1415 W. 22nd St.
Oak Brook, IL 60523
Phone: 630-954-2000
Fax: 630-954-2030
Web: www.federalsignal.com

CEO: James E. Goodwin
CFO: Stephanie K. Kushner
HR: –
FYE: December 31
Type: Public

Stuff happens — and the need to prevent, respond to, warn others about, and clean up that stuff means business for Federal Signal. The company makes a range of goods, from fire safety equipment (E-One) to vacuum trucks (Elgin Sweeper). Its Fire Rescue Group manufactures fire trucks, rescue vehicles, and aerial access ladders, and its Environmental Products Group makes street and sewer cleaning vehicles. Its Safety & Security Systems Group makes signaling lights and sirens, and its Tool Group supplies industrial customers with die components and precision tools. Municipal and governmental customers account for some 35% of the company's sales.

	Annual Growth	12/03	12/04	12/05	12/06	12/07
Sales ($ mil.)	1.2%	1,206.8	1,139.0	1,156.9	1,211.6	1,268.1
Net income ($ mil.)	10.1%	37.3	(2.3)	(4.6)	22.7	54.9
Market value ($ mil.)	(10.6%)	839.5	851.2	722.0	763.5	537.4
Employees	0.0%	—	—	5,500	5,400	5,500

FEDERAL TRUST CORPORATION

AMEX: FDT

312 W. 1st St.
Sanford, FL 32771
Phone: 407-323-1833
Fax: 407-645-1501
Web: www.federaltrust.com

CEO: Dennis T. Ward
CFO: Gregory E. Smith
HR: –
FYE: December 31
Type: Public

This company would prefer it if you *did* make a federal case of things. Federal Trust Corporation is the holding company for Federal Trust Bank, which serves Central Florida with about a dozen branches. The bank provides traditional retail products including personal and business checking accounts, savings accounts, and CDs. Residential mortgages make up some 60% of the company's loan portfolio; other offerings include construction and land development loans, commercial mortgages, and (to a lesser extent) business and consumer loans. Subsidiary Federal Trust Mortgage, which began operating in 2006, handles most of the residential lending and servicing and trades mortgages in the secondary market.

	Annual Growth	12/03	12/04	12/05	12/06	12/07
Assets ($ mil.)	10.2%	468.2	603.1	735.4	723.0	690.3
Net income ($ mil.)	—	2.8	3.1	4.4	3.4	(14.2)
Market value ($ mil.)	(21.8%)	52.2	80.6	102.8	94.8	19.5
Employees	17.4%	—	—	87	100	120

An in-depth profile of this company is available to Hoover's Online members at hoovers.com.

603

FEDERAL-MOGUL CORPORATION

NASDAQ (GM): FDML

26555 Northwestern Hwy.
Southfield, MI 48033
Phone: 248-354-7700
Fax: 248-354-8950
Web: www.federal-mogul.com

CEO: José Maria Alapont
CFO: Jeff Kaminski
HR: Richard P. Randazzo
FYE: December 31
Type: Public

For Federal-Mogul, the sum of the parts is greater than the whole. The company makes components for cars, trucks, and construction vehicles. Its products include chassis and engine parts, pistons, and sealing systems sold under brand names such as Federal-Mogul, Fel-Pro, and Glyco. Federal-Mogul has manufacturing and distribution facilities primarily in the Americas and Europe; major customers include global automakers, such as General Motors, Ford, BMW, and Volkswagen. Federal-Mogul also distributes auto parts to aftermarket customers. The company entered Chapter 11 in late 2001 as a result of asbestos claims related to its acquisition of T&N plc. Federal-Mogul exited Chapter 11 in late 2007.

	Annual Growth	12/02	12/03	12/04	12/05	*12/06
Sales ($ mil.)	3.9%	5,422.4	5,546.0	6,174.1	6,286.0	6,326.4
Net income ($ mil.)	—	(1,628.9)	(189.5)	(334.0)	(334.2)	(549.6)
Employees	—	—	—	—	—	43,100

*Most recent year available

FEDERATED GROUP, INC.

3025 W. Salt Creek Ln.
Arlington Heights, IL 60005
Phone: 847-577-1200
Fax: 847-632-8204
Web: www.fedgroup.com

CEO: Dave LaPlante
CFO: Eileen Roman
HR: Eileen Roman
FYE: December 31
Type: Private

If "federate" means food distribution, supply chain management, branding solutions, design and labeling, and other sales and marketing services, then Federated Group is aptly named. The company serves manufacturers, retailers, distributors, and wholesalers in the nationwide grocery, drug store, and food service industries. In addition to providing private-label products, the company distributes items under its own brands including Hy-Top, Parade, and Red & White. Subsidiaries include Golden Bay (purchasing and redistribution) and SailPointe Creative (design services). Federated Group was founded in the early 1900s by S.M. Flickinger.

	Annual Growth	12/03	12/04	12/05	12/06	12/07
Est. sales ($ mil.)	—	—	—	—	—	83.5
Employees	—	—	—	—	—	240

FEDERATED INSURANCE COMPANIES

121 E. Park Sq.
Owatonna, MN 55060
Phone: 507-455-5200
Fax: 507-455-5452
Web: www.federatedinsurance.com

CEO: Al Annexstad
CFO: Raymond R. Stawarz
HR: Bryan Brose
FYE: December 31
Type: Mutual company

Federated Insurance is a mutual firm with a clear focus. The company provides multiple lines of business insurance coverage and risk management to employers in automotive repair and sales, building construction, printers, funeral homes, and jewelers, among others. Its products and services include workers' compensation, automotive, group life and health, and retirement planning. Federated Insurance markets its products both directly and through an independent sales force; it operates in 48 states and Washington, DC. Since its founding in 1904, the company has worked closely with trade associations to develop and endorse its insurance programs.

	Annual Growth	12/03	12/04	12/05	12/06	12/07
Est. sales ($ mil.)	—	—	—	—	—	1,515.5
Net income ($ mil.)	—	—	—	—	—	189.6
Employees	—	—	—	—	—	2,600

FEDERATED INVESTORS, INC.

NYSE: FII

Federated Investors Tower, 1001 Liberty Ave.
Pittsburgh, PA 15222
Phone: 412-288-1900
Fax: 412-288-1171
Web: www.federatedinvestors.com

CEO: J. Christopher Donahue
CFO: Thomas R. Donahue
HR: –
FYE: December 31
Type: Public

One of the country's largest money market fund managers, Federated Investors provides investment advisory and administrative services to nearly 150 mutual funds and to separate accounts. The company's products are distributed to more than 5,400 clients, including investment advisers, financial institutions, corporations, and government entities. The company primarily serves the wealth management, trust, and broker/dealer market sectors. Money market funds make up the majority of Federated Investors' more than $300 billion in assets under management. Chairman John Donahue and his family (including his son, president and CEO J. Christopher) own about 10% of Federated Investors, but control all of its votes.

	Annual Growth	12/03	12/04	12/05	12/06	12/07
Assets ($ mil.)	(1.1%)	879.2	954.7	896.6	810.3	841.0
Net income ($ mil.)	3.2%	191.5	181.2	160.3	197.7	217.5
Market value ($ mil.)	7.6%	3,190.1	3,252.8	3,964.5	3,508.2	4,274.7
Employees	(1.4%)	—	—	1,305	1,243	1,270

FEDEX CORPORATION

NYSE: FDX

942 S. Shady Grove Rd.
Memphis, TN 38120
Phone: 901-818-7500
Fax: 901-395-2000
Web: www.fedex.com

CEO: Frederick W. (Fred) Smith
CFO: Alan B. Graf Jr.
HR: –
FYE: May 31
Type: Public

Holding company FedEx hopes its package of subsidiaries will keep delivering significant market share. Its FedEx Express unit is the world's #1 express transportation provider, delivering some 3.3 million packages daily to more than 220 countries and territories. It maintains a fleet of about 670 aircraft and more than 43,000 motor vehicles. Complementing the express delivery business, FedEx Ground provides ground delivery of small packages in North America, and less-than-truckload (LTL) carrier FedEx Freight hauls larger shipments. FedEx Office stores, which are being rebranded from FedEx Kinko's, offer a variety of document-related and other business services and serve as retail hubs for other FedEx units.

	Annual Growth	5/03	5/04	5/05	5/06	5/07
Sales ($ mil.)	11.9%	22,487.0	24,710.0	29,363.0	32,294.0	35,214.0
Net income ($ mil.)	24.8%	830.0	838.0	1,449.0	1,806.0	2,016.0
Market value ($ mil.)	15.8%	19,130.0	21,880.9	27,004.8	33,436.6	34,379.0
Employees	(45.0%)	—	—	—	260,000	143,000

FEDEX FREIGHT CORPORATION

1715 Aaron Brenner Dr., Ste. 600
Memphis, TN 38120
Phone: 901-346-4400
Fax: 901-434-3118
Web: www.fedex.com/us/freight/main

CEO: Douglas G. Duncan
CFO: Donald C. (Don) Brown
HR: –
FYE: May 31
Type: Subsidiary

For overnight shipments that won't fit in an envelope, there's FedEx Freight. The company, a subsidiary of express delivery giant FedEx, provides less-than-truckload (LTL) transportation services throughout the US and in Canada. (LTL carriers consolidate freight from multiple shippers into a single truckload.) The company operates from about 470 terminals through two regional subsidiaries, FedEx Freight East and FedEx Freight West, plus long-haul unit FedEx National LTL (formerly Watkins Motor Lines) and FedEx Freight Canada. Altogether, the FedEx Freight carriers maintain a fleet of about 14,000 tractors and some 42,000 trailers and other pieces of equipment.

	Annual Growth	5/02	5/03	5/04	5/05	5/06
Sales ($ mil.)	16.8%	1,960.0	2,120.0	2,689.0	3,217.0	3,645.0
Employees	5.3%	22,000	21,800	24,000	26,500	27,000

FEDEX GROUND PACKAGE SYSTEM, INC.

1000 FedEx Dr.
Coraopolis, PA 15018
Phone: 412-269-1000
Fax: 412-747-4290
Web: www.fedex.com/us/ground/main

CEO: David F. (Dave) Rebholz
CFO: Gretchen G. Smarto
HR: Shannon A. Brown
FYE: May 31
Type: Subsidiary

When it doesn't absolutely, positively have to be there overnight, there's FedEx Ground Package System. A unit of air express giant FedEx, FedEx Ground provides ground delivery of small packages (up to 150 pounds) throughout the continental US and Canada. The company serves Alaska, Hawaii, and Puerto Rico through alliances. Deliveries are generally made within one to seven business days, depending on distance. The company offers both business-to-business and home delivery services with a fleet of about 20,000 motorized vehicles, most of which are operated by independent contractors. FedEx Ground handles more than 3 million shipments per day from a network of about 30 hubs.

	Annual Growth	5/02	5/03	5/04	5/05	5/06
Sales ($ mil.)	18.3%	2,711.0	3,413.0	3,910.0	4,680.0	5,306.0
Employees	10.7%	—	42,800	48,800	51,600	58,000

FEDEX OFFICE

13155 Noel Rd., Ste. 1600
Dallas, TX 75240
Phone: 214-550-7000
Fax: 214-550-7001
Web: www.fedex.com/us/officeprint/main

CEO: Brian D. Philips
CFO: Leslie Benners
HR: Tracy Brightman
FYE: May 31
Type: Subsidiary

A unit of express delivery giant FedEx, FedEx Office (formerly FedEx Kinko's Office and Print Services) has duplicated its business formula many times. The company operates about 1,900 business service centers in the US and about 10 other countries worldwide. FedEx Office offers a wide range of document services, including copying, printing, and graphic design. In addition, its locations serve as drop-off points for items to be delivered by sister companies FedEx Express and FedEx Ground. FedEx Office also sells office supplies and rents videoconferencing rooms. Primarily targeting small business and home office clients, the company also provides services to individuals and corporations.

	Annual Growth	6/02	6/03	*5/04	5/05	5/06
Sales ($ mil.)	(0.1%)	2,100.0	2,000.0	1,867.0	2,066.0	2,088.0
Employees	0.0%	20,000	20,000	20,000	22,000	20,000

*Fiscal year change

FEDFIRST FINANCIAL CORPORATION

NASDAQ (CM): FFCO

Donner at 6th St.
Monessen, PA 15062
Phone: 724-684-6800
Fax: 724-684-4851
Web: www.firstfederal-savings.com

CEO: John G. Robinson
CFO: Robert C. (Bob) Barry Jr.
HR: DaCosta Smith III
FYE: December 31
Type: Public

FedFirst Financial wants to be first in the hearts of its customers. It is the holding company for First Federal Savings Bank, a community-oriented thrift serving southwestern Pennsylvania. From eight locations in Fayette, Washington, and Westmoreland counties, the bank offers traditional deposit products and services, including checking and savings accounts, money markets accounts, and IRAs. Residential mortgages secured by homes in the Pittsburgh metropolitan area make up more than three-quarters of a lending portfolio that also includes multi-family and commercial mortgages and construction, business, and consumer loans. Mutual holding company FedFirst Financial MHC owns 55% of FedFirst Financial.

	Annual Growth	12/03	12/04	12/05	12/06	12/07
Assets ($ mil.)	4.2%	—	270.1	276.1	283.5	305.3
Net income ($ mil.)	—	—	(0.9)	(0.1)	0.3	(2.0)
Market value ($ mil.)	0.0%	—	—	58.8	65.1	58.8
Employees	—	—	—	94	—	—

FEED THE CHILDREN, INC.

333 N. Meridian Ave.
Oklahoma City, OK 73107
Phone: 405-942-0228
Fax: 405-945-4177
Web: www.feedthechildren.org

CEO: Larry Jones
CFO: Christy Tharp
HR: Richard Gray
FYE: June 30
Type: Not-for-profit

Tuppence a bag might feed some birds, but it takes more to feed growing children. Feed The Children (FTC) is a not-for-profit Christian charity that distributes food, medicine, and other items. In the US, FTC accepts bulk contributions of surplus food from businesses, packages it in various ways at six main facilities nationwide, and distributes it to food banks, homeless shelters, churches, and other organizations that help feed the hungry. Overseas, FTC works with organizations, such as schools, orphanages, and churches to provide food, medical supplies, clothing, and educational support to the needy. Larry and Frances Jones founded FTC in 1979.

	Annual Growth	6/02	6/03	6/04	6/05	6/06
Sales ($ mil.)	4.7%	553.4	575.9	967.1	861.4	663.9
Net income ($ mil.)	—	—	4.6	42.6	—	(11.1)
Employees	0.0%	160	160	160	—	—

FEI COMPANY

NASDAQ (GM): FEIC

5350 NE Dawson Creek Dr.
Hillsboro, OR 97124
Phone: 503-726-7500
Fax: 503-726-7509
Web: www.feicompany.com

CEO: Don R. Kania
CFO: Raymond A. (Ray) Link
HR: Jim D. Higgs
FYE: December 31
Type: Public

FEI finds defects PDQ. The company makes structural process management systems that use ion beams to analyze and diagnose submicron structures in semiconductors, data storage components, and biological and industrial compounds. FEI makes focused ion beam and dual beam electron microscopes that analyze integrated circuits (ICs). It also makes scanning and transmission electron microscopes that detect defects in ICs and analyze biological specimens and materials. FEI is targeting applications in nanotechnology R&D, while still getting sales from semiconductor and data storage companies. Customers outside of the US account for more than 60% of sales.

	Annual Growth	12/03	12/04	12/05	12/06	12/07
Sales ($ mil.)	13.2%	361.0	465.7	427.2	479.5	592.5
Net income ($ mil.)	68.7%	7.2	16.6	(78.2)	20.0	58.3
Market value ($ mil.)	4.9%	745.9	701.7	647.9	898.0	904.8
Employees	3.0%	1,656	1,757	1,674	1,683	1,866

FELCOR LODGING TRUST INCORPORATED

NYSE: FCH

545 E. John Carpenter Fwy., Ste. 1300
Irving, TX 75062
Phone: 972-444-4900
Fax: 972-444-4949
Web: www.felcor.com

CEO: Richard A. (Rick) Smith
CFO: Andrew J. Welch
HR: –
FYE: December 31
Type: Public

FelCor Lodging welcomes weary North American travelers. One of the top hotel real estate investment trusts (REIT) in the US, FelCor owns roughly 90 hotels in about two dozen states and Canada. Most are upscale hotels, with a concentration of its portfolio located in Florida, California, and Texas. Operating through its majority-owned partnership, FelCor buys, renovates, and rebrands its properties with such names as Embassy Suites, Doubletree, and Holiday Inn. (FelCor is the largest owner of these branded hotels in North America.) Most of the company's hotels are managed by Hilton Hotels, InterContinental Hotels, Marriott International, and Starwood Hotels & Resorts.

	Annual Growth	12/03	12/04	12/05	12/06	12/07
Sales ($ mil.)	(3.9%)	1,199.9	1,191.6	1,212.2	991.0	1,021.9
Net income ($ mil.)	—	(310.1)	(100.1)	(251.6)	51.0	89.0
Market value ($ mil.)	10.5%	655.0	876.3	1,036.2	1,516.5	977.6
Employees	(2.7%)	—	—	76	74	72

An in-depth profile of this company is available to Hoover's Online members at hoovers.com.

FELD ENTERTAINMENT, INC.

8607 Westwood Center Dr.	CEO: Kenneth J. (Ken) Feld
Vienna, VA 22182	CFO: Michael (Mike) Little
Phone: 703-448-4000	HR: Kirk McCoy
Fax: 703-448-4100	FYE: January 31
Web: www.feldentertainment.com	Type: Private

A lot of clowning around has helped Feld Entertainment become one of the largest live entertainment producers in the world. The company entertains people through its centerpiece, Ringling Bros. and Barnum & Bailey Circus, which visits about 90 locations. Feld also produces several touring ice shows, including Disney On Ice shows such as *Finding Nemo* and *High School Musical: The Ice Tour*. Chairman and CEO Kenneth Feld, whose father, Irvin, began managing the circus in 1956, owns the company and personally oversees most of its productions. Ringling Bros. and Barnum & Bailey Circus made its first performance in 1871.

FELDMAN MALL PROPERTIES, INC.

NYSE: FMP

1010 Northern Blvd., Ste. 314	CEO: Thomas E. Wirth
Great Neck, NY 11021	CFO: Thomas E. Wirth
Phone: 516-684-1239	HR: –
Fax: 516-684-1059	FYE: December 31
Web: www.feldmanmall.com	Type: Public

Even shopping malls in a slump can be whipped back into tip top shape. In fact, it's Feldman Mall Properties' specialty. The real estate investment trust (REIT) buys underperforming malls in an attempt to turn them into more attractive and profitable venues. Founded in 2004 to continue the business of mall management firm Feldman Equities of Arizona, the company owns or has stakes in about a half-dozen mall properties spanning 2.5 million rentable sq. ft. in Arizona, Florida, Illinois, Ohio, Pennsylvania, and Texas. Feldman's renovation techniques include architectural redesign, square footage increase, and the addition of more in-demand tenants. Its top tenant is Loews Cineplex.

	Annual Growth	12/03	12/04	12/05	12/06	12/07
Sales ($ mil.)	47.4%	11.7	12.3	55.2	65.3	55.3
Net income ($ mil.)	—	(0.7)	(3.5)	(2.6)	20.2	(16.3)
Market value ($ mil.)	(30.1%)	—	140.4	156.7	162.2	48.0
Employees	40.3%	75	—	210	207	—

FELLOWES, INC.

1789 Norwood Ave.	CEO: James (Jamie) Fellowes
Itasca, IL 60143	CFO: –
Phone: 630-893-1600	HR: Lyn Bulman
Fax: 630-893-1683	FYE: March 31
Web: www.fellowes.com	Type: Private

Fellowes (formerly Fellowes Manufacturing Company) produces office products that can organize or obliterate. The leading maker of paper shredders (Powershred, Micro-shred), it also makes computer and office accessories, such as ergonomic wrist rests, multimedia storage, and other accessories. As a licensee of Body Glove International (maker of high-tech surf and scuba gear), Fellowes offers fashionable Body Glove cases for mobile phones and iPods. Fellowes' products are sold through office retailers and mass merchants, as well as online. Still owned and run by the Fellowes family, the company was started in 1917 when Harry Fellowes paid $50 for Bankers Box, a maker of storage boxes for bank records.

THE FEMALE HEALTH COMPANY

AMEX: FHC

515 N. State St., Ste. 2225	CEO: O. B. Parrish
Chicago, IL 60610	CFO: Donna Felch
Phone: 312-595-9123	HR: –
Fax: 312-595-9122	FYE: September 30
Web: www.femalehealth.com	Type: Public

Move over, Trojan Man! Here comes The Female Health Company, maker of condoms for women. The polyurethane female condom is the only female contraceptive that is FDA-approved for preventing both pregnancy and sexually transmitted diseases. The firm's condoms are marketed in the US (under the FC Female Condom name), as well as Brazil and Venezuela and Asian and European countries such as China, India, Japan, and the UK. Outside the US, many of its products bear the Femidom name. Female Health also provides low-cost female condoms in Africa through an agreement with the Joint United Nations Programme on HIV/AIDS (UNAIDS). It sponsors the Female Health Foundation, which provides women with health education.

	Annual Growth	9/03	9/04	9/05	9/06	9/07
Sales ($ mil.)	20.7%	9.1	8.8	11.2	14.8	19.3
Net income ($ mil.)	—	(2.4)	(2.0)	(1.4)	0.3	1.7
Market value ($ mil.)	9.1%	43.9	31.1	39.0	32.3	62.1
Employees	—	—	—	—	—	166

FENDER MUSICAL INSTRUMENTS CORPORATION

8860 E. Chaparral Rd., Ste. 100	CEO: William (Bill) Mendello
Scottsdale, AZ 85250	CFO: Richard Kerley
Phone: 480-596-9690	HR: Beth McReynolds
Fax: 480-596-1384	FYE: December 31
Web: www.fender.com	Type: Private

Jimi Hendrix's electrified version of "The Star-Spangled Banner" shows what Fender guitars can do. Fender Musical Instruments is the world's #1 maker of stringed instruments (and the nation's #1 maker of solid-body electric guitars, including the Stratocaster and Telecaster lines that have made it a favorite of strummers). Fender also makes instruments such as acoustic guitars, electric basses, mandolins, banjos, and violins, as well as amplifiers, and PA equipment. Other notable brands include Guild (acoustic and electric guitars), Rodriguez (classical guitars), Benedetto (jazz guitars), and Squier (lower-priced guitars). A management group controls the firm, which acquired Kaman Music in late 2007.

	Annual Growth	12/03	12/04	12/05	12/06	12/07
Est. sales ($ mil.)	—	—	—	—	—	196.3
Employees	—	—	—	—	—	1,742

FENTURA FINANCIAL, INC.

OTC: FETM

175 N. Leroy St.	CEO: Donald L. Grill
Fenton, MI 48430	CFO: Douglas J. Kelley
Phone: 810-750-8725	HR: –
Fax: 810-629-3892	FYE: December 31
Web: www.fentura.com	Type: Public

It just makes *cents* to say that Fentura Financial has got its hands full. The financial institution is the holding company for The State Bank, Davison State Bank, and West Michigan Community Bank (acquired in 2004), which together offer traditional deposit, loan, investment, and trust services from some 15 branches and offices in eastern and southwestern Michigan. The State Bank, which was founded in 1898 as The Commercial Savings Bank of Fenton, was the holding company's first bank. In 1931 the bank became State Savings Bank, taking its current name in 1988.

	Annual Growth	12/03	12/04	12/05	12/06	12/07
Assets ($ mil.)	10.6%	420.0	584.9	619.1	622.3	628.0
Net income ($ mil.)	—	3.8	4.0	5.1	5.3	(0.5)
Market value ($ mil.)	(3.0%)	53.8	63.1	57.5	70.1	47.6
Employees	—	—	—	—	—	236

FENWAY PARTNERS, INC.

152 W. 57th St., 59th Fl.
New York, NY 10019
Phone: 212-698-9400
Fax: 212-581-1205
Web: www.fenwaypartners.com

CEO: Peter D. Lamm
CFO: Joseph Domonkos
HR: —
FYE: December 31
Type: Private

Let's go, team! Private equity firm Fenway Partners' portfolio boasts an eclectic roster of companies in the consumer products and transportation sectors; they produce high school class rings (American Achievement), official NFL football helmets (Easton-Bell Sports), laptop computer carrying cases (Targus), and home decor products (DCI Holdings). The investments, generally leveraged buyouts, vary in size and stage, from startups to long-established firms. Upon making its investment in a company, Fenway Partners provides management and strategy advice to boost performance. Despite its name, the company has offices in New York and Los Angeles, but not in Boston, home of baseball's Fenway Park.

	Annual Growth	12/03	12/04	12/05	12/06	12/07
Est. sales ($ mil.)	—	—	—	—	—	394.8
Employees	—	—	—	—	—	4,008

FERGUSON ENTERPRISES, INC.

12500 Jefferson Ave.
Newport News, VA 23602
Phone: 757-874-7795
Fax: 757-989-2501
Web: www.ferguson.com

CEO: John A. Stegeman
CFO: Braden L. (Brad) Miller
HR: Steven M. Roznowski
FYE: July 31
Type: Subsidiary

Ferguson Enterprises is part of the pipeline for pipes. It is the US's largest wholesale distributor of plumbing, heating, waterworks (water hydrants and meters), and piping products, as well as safety equipment and tools to professional contractors and industry. It has 1,400 locations throughout the US, Puerto Rico, Mexico, and the Caribbean. Ferguson's customers include plumbing contractors, utilities, air conditioning dealers, and irrigation and fire suppression equipment installers. Ferguson, which was formed in 1953, is growing rapidly through acquisitions. It is a subsidiary of Wolseley, the world's #1 plumbing and heating equipment distributor.

	Annual Growth	7/02	7/03	7/04	7/05	7/06
Sales ($ mil.)	17.9%	5,000.0	5,000.0	5,000.0	5,000.0	9,650.0
Employees	17.7%	12,000	12,000	13,000	18,500	23,000

THE FEROLIE GROUP

2 Van Riper Rd.
Montvale, NJ 07645
Phone: 201-307-9100
Fax: 201-782-0878
Web: www.feroliegroup.com

CEO: Lawrence J. Ferolie Sr.
CFO: Catherine (Cathy) Ross
HR: Julie Feroline
FYE: December 31
Type: Private

A food broker serving the entire US, The Ferolie Group broke into the business on the East Coast in 1948. The company provides sales and marketing services for packaged food and packaged goods companies. Through exclusive area and regional contracts, the group arranges distribution to warehouse stores, drugstores, supermarkets, and mass merchandisers. Some of Ferolie's biggest clients have included Duracell, Kraft Foods, and McCormick & Company. The company is affiliated with Advantage Sales & Marketing, a partnership of food brokerages operating across the US. Founded by Joseph Ferolie, the company remains family-owned.

FEROLITO, VULTAGGIO & SONS

644 Linn St., Ste. 318
Cincinnati, OH 45203
Phone: 516-812-0300
Fax: 516-326-4988
Web: www.arizonabev.com

CEO: Richard (Rick) Adonailo
CFO: Richard (Rick) Adonailo
HR: —
FYE: December 31
Type: Private

At Ferolito, Vultaggio & Sons, image is everything. Distinctive bottle and can designs distinguish the company's beverages — including AriZona iced teas, energy drinks, and fruit drinks — from the competition. The company's products are top sellers in the ready-to-drink iced tea sector in the US. Flavors include Green Tea, Botanical Black Tea, and RX Energy. Its other beverage products include energy drinks and juice. In addition to tea, its Hornell Brewing operation sells malt liquor and beer (Crazy Stallion, Mississippi Mud) and bottled water. Co-founders John Ferolito and Don Vultaggio own and run the company.

FERRARA PAN CANDY COMPANY

7301 W. Harrison St.
Forest Park, IL 60130
Phone: 708-366-0500
Fax: 708-366-5921
Web: www.ferrarapan.com

CEO: Salvatore (Sal) Ferrara II
CFO: James (Jim) Buffardi
HR: Angie Castejon
FYE: December 31
Type: Private

At Ferrara Pan Candy Company, a sour face is a happy face. Best known for its venerable, mouth-puckering Lemonhead candies (the company makes 4,800 Lemonheads a minute), Ferrara makes such familiar treats as Red Hots, Jaw Busters, Boston Baked Beans, and Atomic Fireballs. Panned candies, made in a rotating pan as the name implies, are the company's specialty; it also makes Black Forest Gummies and co-packs confections for other companies. Ferrara started out in business making those pastel-colored sugar-coated almonds served at Italian weddings and expanded to serve the candy appetites of kids.

FERRARI NORTH AMERICA INC.

250 Sylvan Ave.
Englewood Cliffs, NJ 07632
Phone: 201-816-2600
Fax: 201-816-2626
Web: www.ferrariusa.com

CEO: Maurizio Parlato
CFO: Joe Marsella
HR: —
FYE: December 31
Type: Subsidiary

Few automotive brands are as synonymous with speed as Ferrari. Ferrari North America is Ferrari's marketing, sales, and dealer network arm for the US and Canada. Its models, as expensive as they are fast, include the F430, the F430 Spider, the 599 GTB Fiorano, and the 612 Scaglietti. Ferrari and Ferrari North America are subsidiaries of Fiat. Although very small compared with corporate behemoths like GM and Ford, Ferrari is growing. The company added two new dealerships in 2005 — one in Las Vegas and another in Redwood City, California.

	Annual Growth	12/03	12/04	12/05	12/06	12/07
Est. sales ($ mil.)	—	—	—	—	—	27.3
Employees	—	—	—	—	—	200

An in-depth profile of this company is available to Hoover's Online members at hoovers.com.

607

FERRELLGAS PARTNERS, L.P.

NYSE: FGP

7500 College Blvd., Ste. 1000
Overland Park, KS 66210
Phone: 913-661-1500
Fax: −
Web: www.ferrellgas.com

CEO: James E. Ferrell
CFO: J. Ryan VanWinkle
HR: Eugene D. (Gene) Caresia
FYE: July 31
Type: Public

Ferrellgas Partners' flame is burning brightly as the second-largest US retail marketer of propane, behind AmeriGas. The company sells 805 million gallons of propane a year to more than 1 million industrial, commercial, and agricultural customers in 50 states, primarily in the Midwest and the Southeast. It operates about 886 retail outlets, and its delivery fleet includes 4,460 trucks and trailers. Ferrellgas also trades propane and natural gas, markets wholesale propane, provides liquid natural gas storage, and markets chemical feedstock. About 32% of the company's stock is held in trust for employees.

	Annual Growth	7/03	7/04	7/05	7/06	7/07
Sales ($ mil.)	13.0%	1,221.6	1,379.4	1,754.1	1,895.5	1,992.4
Net income ($ mil.)	(11.5%)	56.8	28.5	88.8	25.0	34.8
Market value ($ mil.)	14.6%	867.6	977.4	1,323.4	1,369.3	1,494.6
Employees	(0.9%)	—	—	3,704	3,669	—

FERRIS, BAKER WATTS, INCORPORATED

100 Light St.
Baltimore, MD 21202
Phone: 410-685-2600
Fax: 410-468-2746
Web: www.fbw.com

CEO: Roger L. Calvert
CFO: Craig Hartman
HR: Mary Mackinson
FYE: −
Type: Private

Ferris, Baker Watts makes money multiply. The retail brokerage and investment bank — the largest based in the Baltimore/Washington, DC, area — offers stock trading services, CDs, IRAs, tax-free bonds, and other investment vehicles to individuals and companies. The firm also provides access to capital markets for regional companies in a variety of industries, as well as for state and local governments. Ferris, Baker Watts has more than 40 branch offices, located primarily in the mid-Atlantic US. The employee-owned company was founded in 1900. Minneapolis-based RBC Dain Rauscher, a subsidiary of Royal Bank of Canada, is buying the company.

FERRO CORPORATION

NYSE: FOE

1000 Lakeside Ave.
Cleveland, OH 44114
Phone: 216-641-8580
Fax: 216-875-7205
Web: www.ferro.com

CEO: James F. Kirsch
CFO: Sallie Ballantine Bailey
HR: Ann E. Killian
FYE: December 31
Type: Public

Ferro is a quite colorful character. Ferro Corporation makes all kinds of colorants, including ceramic glazes, pigments, and porcelain enamels. The company's products are used in construction and by manufacturers of appliances, cars, electronics, and household furnishings. Ferro also produces fine and industrial chemicals (including stabilizers, plasticizers, and lubricants) used by makers of fuels, foods, cosmetics, pharmaceuticals, and plastics. With operations in more than 20 countries throughout the Americas, Asia, and Europe, Ferro is a global manufacturer and sells to customers in more than 100 countries.

	Annual Growth	12/03	12/04	12/05	12/06	12/07
Sales ($ mil.)	8.0%	1,622.4	1,843.7	1,882.3	2,041.5	2,204.8
Net income ($ mil.)	—	19.5	24.9	16.3	20.1	(94.5)
Market value ($ mil.)	(36.7%)	1,128.1	985.8	794.5	886.9	181.4
Employees	(5.8%)	—	—	—	6,660	6,275

FFD FINANCIAL CORPORATION

NASDAQ (CM): FFDF

321 N. Wooster Ave.
Dover, OH 44622
Phone: 330-364-7777
Fax: 330-364-7779
Web: www.onlinefirstfed.com

CEO: Trent B. Troyer
CFO: Robert R. Gerber
HR: −
FYE: June 30
Type: Public

FFD Financial is the holding company for First Federal Community Bank, which serves Tuscarawas County and contiguous portions of eastern Ohio through three branches. Founded in 1898, the bank offers a full range of retail products, including IRAs, passbook savings accounts, and NOW and money market accounts. The bank mainly uses these funds to originate one- to four-family residential mortgages, which make up nearly half of its loan portfolio, and nonresidential real estate and land loans (some 30% of all loans). First Federal Community Bank also originates business, consumer, and multifamily residential real estate loans.

	Annual Growth	6/03	6/04	6/05	6/06	6/07
Assets ($ mil.)	6.1%	136.4	135.9	148.6	161.2	173.0
Net income ($ mil.)	12.5%	1.0	0.7	1.1	1.4	1.6
Market value ($ mil.)	0.7%	17.0	16.6	20.2	20.3	17.5
Employees	5.7%	—	—	43	—	48

FHC HEALTH SYSTEMS, INC.

240 Corporate Blvd.
Norfolk, VA 23502
Phone: 757-459-5100
Fax: 757-459-5219
Web: www.fhchealthsystems.com

CEO: Ronald I. Dozoretz
CFO: −
HR: Carol Dalton Cash
FYE: December 31
Type: Private

FHC Health Systems makes life just a little bit easier, providing behavioral health care services to millions of people through its subsidiary companies. Its ValueOptions subsidiary offers managed behavioral care for companies, health plans, and state agencies, including employee assistance plans and mental health and substance abuse services. Rx Innovations provides institutional pharmacy services for long-term care facilities and other treatment centers. Its FirstLab subsidiary offers drug testing and employment screening. FHC sold its Alternative Behavioral Services subsidiary, which offered residential psychiatric care and case management services, to Psychiatric Solutions for about $200 million.

	Annual Growth	12/02	12/03	12/04	12/05	12/06
Sales ($ mil.)	4.2%	1,188.0	1,300.0	1,500.0	1,600.0	1,400.0
Employees	(13.6%)	8,169	8,198	8,500	8,100	4,549

FIBERLINK COMMUNICATIONS CORP.

1787 Sentry Pkwy. West, Bldg. 18, Ste. 200
Blue Bell, PA 19422
Phone: 215-664-1600
Fax: 215-664-1601
Web: www.fiberlink.com

CEO: James (Jim) Sheward
CFO: Mark W. Partin
HR: Penny Tizer
FYE: December 31
Type: Private

With Fiberlink, telecommuters will never feel disconnected from work, even when away from the office. Fiberlink's software is used to provide remote access to corporate networks, data, and applications. Its platform allows mobile employees and telecommuters to safely and securely connect to enterprise networks over the Internet. Its technology ensures that data is protected against hackers, viruses, loss, theft, and data leakage. Fiberlink also provides managed virtual private network (VPN) services to connect companies with branch offices. Some of Fiberlink's more than 700 clients are Bloomberg, Continental Airlines, General Electric, Grant Thornton, and Henkel.

	Annual Growth	12/03	12/04	12/05	12/06	12/07
Est. sales ($ mil.)	—	—	—	—	—	76.2
Employees	—	—	—	—	—	225

FIBERMARK, INC.

161 Wellington Rd.
Brattleboro, VT 05302
Phone: 802-257-0365
Fax: 802-257-5907
Web: www.fibermark.com

CEO: Anthony MacLaurin
CFO: John E. Hanley
HR: Stephen F. Pfistner
FYE: December 31
Type: Private

If it's made from flexible fibers, you can just about mark it down that FiberMark produces it. FiberMark offers many different types of fiber-based textiles and papers. The company's decorative specialties segment became its bread and butter after its purchase of Rexam DSI — a maker of latex-saturated decorative coverings for the book publishing and luxury packaging industries. The company's office products include binders and report covers, and it also makes tape products. FiberMark sells to various markets, especially the graphic arts and office supply industries. In 2004 the company filed for bankruptcy protection — from which it emerged in 2006.

	Annual Growth	12/03	12/04	12/05	12/06	12/07
Est. sales ($ mil.)	—	—	—	—	—	214.3
Employees	—	—	—	—	—	757

FIBERNET TELECOM GROUP, INC.

NASDAQ (CM): FTGX

570 Lexington Ave., 3rd Fl.
New York, NY 10022
Phone: 212-405-6200
Fax: 212-421-8860
Web: www.ftgx.com

CEO: Jon A. DeLuca
CFO: Charles Wiesenhart Jr.
HR: –
FYE: December 31
Type: Public

FiberNet Telecom Group is a carrier's carrier. The company's fiber-optic telecommunications networks bring bandwidth to corporate office buildings; it serves other telecom carriers that provide retail voice and data services. As a facilities-based operator, the company leases dark fiber and lights it with its own optical networking equipment. It also operates in-building riser networks and runs a "carrier hotel" facility for interconnecting carriers. Its customers include multi-tenant office properties, local-exchange carriers, ISPs, application service providers, storage service providers, and long-distance carriers.

	Annual Growth	12/03	12/04	12/05	12/06	12/07
Sales ($ mil.)	17.0%	26.6	34.6	33.8	40.1	49.8
Net income ($ mil.)	—	(27.8)	(18.4)	(13.9)	(6.9)	(4.9)
Market value ($ mil.)	(41.1%)	498.6	448.7	7.9	47.6	60.2
Employees	(1.5%)	—	—	68	67	—

FIBERTOWER CORPORATION

NASDAQ (GM): FTWR

185 Berry St., Ste. 4800
San Francisco, CA 94107
Phone: 415-659-3500
Fax: 415-659-0007
Web: www.fibertower.com

CEO: Thomas A. Scott
CFO: Thomas A. Scott
HR: –
FYE: December 31
Type: Public

FiberTower, formerly First Avenue Networks, rises to great heights to provide wireless backhaul and access services to mobile, fiber, and other high-speed telecommunications carriers, large-volume enterprise users, and government agencies. The company owns wireless spectrum licenses in high-frequency 24 GHz and 39 GHz bands that cover virtually all of the US. Its service offerings include leasing spectrum, backhauling mobile phone traffic, and providing broadband connectivity and extensions to fiber optic networks. Most of its operations cater to AT&T Mobility and are located in New York City.

	Annual Growth	12/03	12/04	12/05	12/06	12/07
Sales ($ mil.)	305.7%	0.1	0.1	1.3	13.8	27.1
Net income ($ mil.)	—	(4.2)	(14.5)	(11.3)	(57.3)	(272.1)
Employees	176.1%	—	—	29	219	221

FIDELITY BANCORP, INC.

NASDAQ (GM): FSBI

1009 Perry Hwy.
Pittsburgh, PA 15237
Phone: 412-367-3300
Fax: 412-364-6504
Web: www.fidelitybancorp-pa.com

CEO: Richard G. Spencer
CFO: Lisa L. Griffith
HR: Richard L. Barron
FYE: September 30
Type: Public

Fidelity Bancorp is the holding company for Fidelity Bank, which has faithfully served the Greater Pittsburgh area since 1927. The bank serves individuals and small business customers from about a dozen branch offices. Its deposit products include checking and savings accounts, CDs, IRAs, and money market accounts. Single-family residential mortgages make up nearly 40% of the bank's loan portfolio, which also includes installment loans (some 20% of all loans), commercial mortgages, construction loans, and business loans and leases. The bank also sells insurance; other investment products and services are available to customers through an agreement with Raymond James Financial.

	Annual Growth	9/03	9/04	9/05	9/06	9/07
Assets ($ mil.)	4.2%	617.5	627.7	677.8	730.7	726.6
Net income ($ mil.)	(2.5%)	4.1	4.3	3.9	4.2	3.7
Market value ($ mil.)	(0.6%)	47.5	53.3	56.6	56.2	46.3
Employees	—	—	—	—	—	162

FIDELITY D & D BANCORP, INC.

OTC: FDBC

Blakely and Drinker Sts.
Dunmore, PA 18512
Phone: 570-342-8281
Fax: 570-346-5724
Web: www.the-fidelity.com

CEO: Steven C. (Steve) Ackmann
CFO: Salvatore R. DeFrancesco Jr.
HR: Joyce Jones
FYE: December 31
Type: Public

Don't worry, eight-sided dice are not needed at Fidelity D & D Bancorp. The institution is the holding company for The Fidelity Deposit & Discount Bank, serving Lackawanna and Luzerne counties in northeastern Pennsylvania through about a dozen locations, including a full-service branch within a supermarket. The bank attracts local individuals and business customers by offering such services as checking and savings accounts, CDs, mortgages, and investment services. Commercial loans account for more than half of the company's loan portfolio; real estate loans make up about a quarter.

	Annual Growth	12/03	12/04	12/05	12/06	12/07
Assets ($ mil.)	0.5%	575.2	536.7	544.1	562.3	587.4
Net income ($ mil.)	30.2%	1.6	3.4	4.6	4.1	4.6
Market value ($ mil.)	(1.0%)	61.5	56.7	76.9	68.9	59.1
Employees	—	—	—	—	—	—

FIDELITY NATIONAL FINANCIAL, INC.

NYSE: FNF

601 Riverside Ave.
Jacksonville, FL 32204
Phone: 904-854-8100
Fax: 904-357-1007
Web: www.fnf.com

CEO: Alan L. (Al) Stinson
CFO: Anthony J. Park
HR: –
FYE: December 31
Type: Public

To make sure that buying a dream home doesn't become a nightmare, Fidelity National Financial provides title insurance, escrow, and other services related to real estate transactions. It's one of the big dogs in the title insurance sector, and accounts for more than 25% of all title insurance policies in the US. The company operates through its five underwriters: Fidelity National Title Company, Chicago Title, Ticor Title, Security Union Title, and Alamo Title. It sells its products both directly and through independent agents. Its direct operations include more than 1,000 offices. Fidelity National Financial also offers flood and home warranty insurance through its specialty lines business.

	Annual Growth	12/03	12/04	12/05	12/06	12/07
Assets ($ mil.)	13.2%	—	—	5,900.5	—	7,556.4
Net income ($ mil.)	(50.9%)	—	—	539.0	418.4	129.8
Market value ($ mil.)	—	—	—	—	—	3,112.5
Employees	(10.8%)	—	—	19,500	17,800	15,500

FIDELITY NATIONAL INFORMATION SERVICES, INC.
NYSE: FIS

601 Riverside Ave.
Jacksonville, FL 32204
Phone: 904-854-5000
Fax: 904-854-4124
Web: www.fidelityinfoservices.com

CEO: Lee A. Kennedy
CFO: Jeffrey S. Carbiener
HR: Kelly P. Feese
FYE: December 31
Type: Public

Fidelity National Information Services (FIS) provides software, outsourcing, and information technology consulting for the financial services and mortgage industries. For banks and other financial institutions, the division offers software for lending, community and wholesale banking, customer relationship management, data management, and e-business. For mortgage lenders, FIS offers billing and customer care, data and service order exchange, and mortgage servicing applications. FIS was formed in 2003, when Fidelity National Financial (FNF) bought ALLTEL's information services division. FNF merged FIS with credit and debit processor Certegy to form a publicly traded company in 2006.

	Annual Growth	12/03	12/04	12/05	12/06	12/07
Sales ($ mil.)	47.1%	1,015.5	1,039.5	1,117.1	4,132.6	4,758.0
Net income ($ mil.)	57.0%	92.4	111.8	130.3	259.1	561.2
Market value ($ mil.)	(24.6%)	—	—	7,765.7	4,312.6	4,412.9
Employees	24.6%	—	—	—	24,871	31,000

FIDELITY SOUTHERN CORPORATION
NASDAQ (GS): LION

3490 Piedmont Rd. NE, Ste. 1550
Atlanta, GA 30305
Phone: 404-639-6500
Fax: 404-814-8060
Web: www.lionbank.com

CEO: James B. Miller Jr.
CFO: B. Rodrick Marlow
HR: Stephanie Huckaby
FYE: December 31
Type: Public

Like a Georgia peach, Fidelity Southern Corporation has ripened in the South. Its subsidiary Fidelity Bank operates about two dozen branches, mostly in and around Atlanta, but also in Jacksonville, Florida. The bank offers traditional retail banking, as well as consumer installment, real estate, commercial, Small Business Administration, and other loans. It offers online banking through lionbank.com. The company's investment division partners with Raymond James Financial to provide financial and brokerage services. Subsidiary LionMark Insurance Company operates an office in Atlanta, through which it offers consumer credit related insurance products.

	Annual Growth	12/03	12/04	12/05	12/06	12/07
Assets ($ mil.)	11.5%	1,091.9	1,223.7	1,405.7	1,649.2	1,686.5
Net income ($ mil.)	14.8%	3.8	7.6	10.3	10.4	6.6
Market value ($ mil.)	(7.2%)	117.6	173.3	165.4	172.9	87.4
Employees	—	—	—	—	356	—

FIDUCIARY TRUST COMPANY INTERNATIONAL

600 5th Ave.
New York, NY 10020
Phone: 212-632-3000
Fax: –
Web: www.ftci.com

CEO: James C. (Jim) Goodfellow
CFO: Lawrence A. (Larry) Sternkopf
HR: –
FYE: September 30
Type: Subsidiary

A subsidiary of Franklin Resources, Fiduciary Trust Company International specializes in private banking and investment management for individuals and families; to a lesser extent, it serves institutional investors as well. The company caters to its target clientele of wealthy families by providing a range of integrated services (investments, trusts, estate planning, private banking, and more) under its Family Resource Management banner. It also offers trust and custody services. Fiduciary Trust, which has been increasingly involved in international investments since it entered that market in the 1960s, has some ten offices around the globe. Founded in 1931, it was acquired by Franklin Resources in 2001.

	Annual Growth	9/03	9/04	9/05	9/06	9/07
Est. sales ($ mil.)	—	—	—	—	—	27.0
Employees	—	—	—	—	—	704

FIELDPOINT PETROLEUM CORPORATION
AMEX: FPP

1703 Edelweiss Dr., Ste. 301
Cedar Park, TX 78613
Phone: 512-250-8692
Fax: 512-335-1294
Web: www.fppcorp.com

CEO: Ray D. Reaves
CFO: Ray D. Reaves
HR: –
FYE: December 31
Type: Public

Got oil and gas? FieldPoint Petroleum can point to its oil and gas fields and its interests in more than 340 productive oil and gas wells in Louisiana, New Mexico, Oklahoma, Texas, and Wyoming. The independent oil and gas exploration company operates some 61 of these wells. More than 200 of its gross productive oil wells are located in Oklahoma. FieldPoint Petroleum has proved reserves of more than 637,650 barrels of oil and 1.8 billion cu. ft. of natural gas. Chairman and CEO Ray Reaves, an oil and gas industry veteran, controls about 34% of the company.

	Annual Growth	12/03	12/04	12/05	12/06	12/07
Sales ($ mil.)	16.4%	2.4	3.0	4.0	4.1	4.4
Net income ($ mil.)	31.6%	0.2	0.5	1.0	1.2	0.6
Market value ($ mil.)	33.8%	3.3	9.9	58.3	20.5	10.7
Employees	0.0%	—	—	4	4	—

FIESTA MART, INC.

5235 Katy Fwy.
Houston, TX 77007
Phone: 713-869-5060
Fax: 713-869-6197
Web: www.fiestamart.com

CEO: Louis Katopodis
CFO: Vicki Baum
HR: Wanda Parish
FYE: May 31
Type: Subsidiary

Fiesta Mart celebrates food every day of the year. The company runs about 50 stores in Texas that sell ethnic and conventional groceries, including items popular with its target customers: Mexican- and Asian-Americans. Its stores are located mainly in the Houston area, but Fiesta also has stores in the Dallas/Fort Worth metroplex and Austin. Fiesta purchased three supermarkets from Winn-Dixie Stores when the grocer left Texas. At its supermarkets, Fiesta leases kiosks to vendors who offer such items as jewelry and cellular phones. The company also runs some 15 Fiesta liquor stores. Fiesta Mart, founded in 1972 by Donald Bonham and O. C. Mendenhall, was acquired by wholesaler Grocers Supply Co. in 2004.

	Annual Growth	5/03	5/04	5/05	5/06	5/07
Est. sales ($ mil.)	—	—	—	—	—	639.9
Employees	—	—	—	—	—	5,900

FIFTH THIRD BANCORP
NASDAQ (GS): FITB

38 Fountain Sq. Plaza, Fifth Third Center
Cincinnati, OH 45263
Phone: 513-579-5300
Fax: 513-534-0629
Web: www.53.com

CEO: Kevin T. Kabat
CFO: Daniel T. Poston
HR: Nancy R. Phillips
FYE: December 31
Type: Public

Fifth Third Bancorp wants to be first in the hearts and minds of its customers. The holding company operates more than 1,200 Fifth Third Bank branches in the Midwest and Southeast. It operates through five segments: branch banking, commercial banking, processing solutions, consumer lending, and investment advisors. It provides consumer and business banking (including deposit accounts, loans, and credit cards); investment advisory services (mutual funds, private banking, and securities brokerage); and ATM and merchant transaction processing. The company also runs the Jeanie ATM network. In 2008 Fifth Third entered the North Carolina market with its purchase of First Charter and some 60 branch offices.

	Annual Growth	12/03	12/04	12/05	12/06	12/07
Assets ($ mil.)	5.0%	91,143.0	94,456.0	105,225.0	100,669.0	110,962.0
Net income ($ mil.)	(11.5%)	1,755.0	1,525.0	1,549.0	1,188.0	1,076.0
Market value ($ mil.)	(20.5%)	33,491.1	26,376.8	20,958.1	22,767.4	13,386.0
Employees	(0.5%)	—	—	22,901	21,362	22,678

An in-depth profile of this company is available to Hoover's Online members at hoovers.com.

⊞ FILA USA, INC

1 Fila Way	CEO: Jon Epstein
Sparks, MD 21152	CFO: Y. C. Cho
Phone: 410-773-3000	HR: Angela Bass
Fax: 410-773-4989	FYE: December 31
Web: www.fila.com/us/eng/corporate	Type: Private

After tripping over a few hurdles, Fila is feeling nimble and virile again. With a history of high design in athletic shoes and sportswear, Fila had run down its image in lieu of a hodgepodge of athletic endorsements. Ready to throw in the towel, Fila's owner, RCS Media Group (formerly Holding di Partecipazioni), inked a deal with Sport Brands International (SBI; associated with private investment fund manager Cerberus). The resulting Fila remained intact until early 2007, when Fila Korea Ltd. acquired the global Fila footwear and apparel business from SBI. Fila also sold the subsidiaries for its European, Middle East, African, and Indian businesses in March 2008 and now licenses the Fila brand for the region.

⊞ FILEMAKER, INC.

5201 Patrick Henry Dr.	CEO: Dominique Phillipe Goupil
Santa Clara, CA 95054	CFO: Bill Epling
Phone: 408-987-7000	HR: John F. Pinheiro
Fax: 408-987-7105	FYE: September 30
Web: www.filemaker.com	Type: Subsidiary

FileMaker believes data's place is in the database. A subsidiary of Apple, the company provides its eponymous database software application that is compatible with the Apple Macintosh and Microsoft Windows operating systems. The company also offers FileMaker Mobile which runs on Windows and Palm-powered handhelds. FileMaker makes it possible for multiple users to access and exchange information instantaneously over corporate intranets or the Internet. The company markets to customers ranging from individual users and small businesses to universities and large corporations.

	Annual Growth	9/03	9/04	9/05	9/06	9/07
Est. sales ($ mil.)	—	—	—	—	—	41.1
Employees	—	—	—	—	—	407

⊞ FILENE'S BASEMENT, INC.

25 Corporate Dr., Ste. 400	CEO: Mark Shulman
Burlington, MA 01803	CFO: –
Phone: 617-348-7000	HR: Anne Keefe
Fax: 617-348-7128	FYE: Saturday nearest January 31
Web: www.filenesbasement.com	Type: Subsidiary

You don't have to go underground to get to Filene's Basement. The company runs its Boston flagship store and about 30 other Filene's Basement stores in eight states, including Massachusetts, New York, and Illinois, as well as Washington, DC. The stores offer off-price men's and women's apparel, home goods, and accessories. Filene's Basement buys most of its name-brand merchandise from department stores or apparel vendors with overruns or out-of-season stock. An original member of Federated Department Stores, the company began as a bargain basement of a Boston department store. Retail Ventures bought the company in 2000. (Filene's Basement is not related to Filene's, now owned by Federated Department Stores.)

	Annual Growth	1/02	1/03	1/04	1/05	1/06
Sales ($ mil.)	7.3%	293.4	303.2	316.9	371.7	389.3
Employees	—	—	—	—	—	1,000

⊞ FINANCIAL FEDERAL CORPORATION

NYSE: FIF

733 3rd Ave.	CEO: Paul R. Sinsheimer
New York, NY 10017	CFO: Steven F. (Steve) Groth
Phone: 212-599-8000	HR: –
Fax: 212-286-5885	FYE: July 31
Web: www.financialfederal.com	Type: Public

Has your crane been grounded, your Caterpillar lost its worm gear, or your bulldozer become hamburger? Financial Federal may be able to help. The company provides loans, leases, and installment sales plans for heavy-duty industrial and commercial equipment such as bulldozers, buses, cement mixers, cranes, earthmovers, trucks, recycling equipment, and machine tools. Financial Federal's customers are primarily construction firms, waste-disposal firms, and trucking companies in the US that have up to $25 million in annual sales. Virtually all of its finance receivables are secured by first liens on the equipment financed.

	Annual Growth	7/03	7/04	7/05	7/06	7/07
Sales ($ mil.)	10.1%	130.3	118.3	126.6	162.5	191.3
Net income ($ mil.)	13.5%	30.1	31.2	36.7	43.6	50.0
Market value ($ mil.)	18.3%	373.4	370.2	448.8	731.3	730.3
Employees	1.1%	—	—	225	—	230

FINANCIAL GUARANTY INSURANCE COMPANY

125 Park Ave.	CEO: Frank J. Bivona
New York, NY 10017	CFO: Donna J. Blank
Phone: 212-312-3000	HR: Sean N. Woodroffe
Fax: 212-312-3093	FYE: December 31
Web: www.fgic.com	Type: Private

Financial Guaranty Insurance Company (FGIC), like a superhero, secures the city . . . well, secures the city bonds, anyway. The company provides credit enhancement on public finance (including transportation, state and local leases, and municipal electric utility), structured finance (asset-backed securities including mortgage and consumer loans), and global infrastructure and utility securities. FGIC typically guarantees the scheduled payments of principal and interest on an issuer's obligation. Founded in 1983, the company is majority owned by mortgage guaranty insurer The PMI Group, which bought its stake from General Electric.

FINANCIAL INDUSTRIES CORPORATION

Pink Sheets: FNIN

6500 River Place Blvd., Bldg. 1	CEO: William B. (Bill) Prouty
Austin, TX 78730	CFO: Vincent L. Kasch
Phone: 512-404-5000	HR: –
Fax: 512-404-5210	FYE: December 31
Web: www.ficgroup.com	Type: Public

Financial Industries underwrites, markets, and services a variety of life insurance products and fixed annuities. The company has shrunk in size, but its remaining subsidiary, Investors Life, administers life, accident, and health insurance policies and annuities throughout the US. In 2004, Financial Industries stopped writing new annuities (it maintains a book of in-force annuities) but may resume that line of business. Financial Industries has seen shareholder protests, changes in management and directors, and a general reshuffling of its business in recent times.

	Annual Growth	12/03	12/04	12/05	12/06	12/07
Assets ($ mil.)	(6.4%)	1,286.1	1,240.8	1,175.4	1,038.3	987.5
Net income ($ mil.)	—	(22.5)	(14.3)	(0.2)	(24.8)	3.6
Employees	—	—	—	—	98	—

⊞ An in-depth profile of this company is available to Hoover's Online members at hoovers.com.

611

FINANCIAL INSTITUTIONS, INC.

NASDAQ (GS): FISI

220 Liberty St.
Warsaw, NY 14569
Phone: 585-786-1100
Fax: 585-786-5254
Web: www.fiiwarsaw.com

CEO: Peter G. Humphrey
CFO: Ronald A. Miller
HR: Bruce H. Nagle
FYE: December 31
Type: Public

Well, you certainly can't accuse Financial Institutions of wasting valuable company funds on creating a snazzy name. The holding company owns Five Star Bank, which serves western and central New York through some 50 branch offices. It offers standard products and services to consumers and small businesses, including checking and savings accounts, CDs, and IRAs. Residential real estate loans, consumer loans, and commercial mortgages each account for more than a quarter of Financial Institutions' loan portfolio. The bank also writes business and agricultural loans. Subsidiary Five Star Investment Services offers insurance brokerage, risk assessment, and financial management services.

	Annual Growth	12/03	12/04	12/05	12/06	12/07
Assets ($ mil.)	(3.8%)	2,173.7	2,156.3	2,022.4	1,907.6	1,857.9
Net income ($ mil.)	3.5%	14.3	12.5	2.2	17.4	16.4
Market value ($ mil.)	(11.2%)	315.3	261.5	222.4	261.5	196.2
Employees	—	—	—	700	—	—

FINANCIAL MEDIA GROUP, INC.

OTC: FNGP

2355 Main St., Ste. 120
Irvine, CA 92614
Phone: 949-486-3990
Fax: 949-486-3995
Web: www.financialmediagroupinc.com

CEO: Albert Aimers
CFO: Manu Ohri
HR: –
FYE: August 31
Type: Public

Financial Media Group is counting on Wall Street to keep it in the black. The company provides business and financial news through its WallSt.net Web site and business newspaper *WallSt.net Digest*. It also provides financial social networking through its MyWallStreet subsidiary, and more than 150 business and finance podcasts through its WallStRadio. In addition, Financial Media operates The Wealth Expo, a line of investment conferences, as well as subsidiary Financial Filings, which offers SEC document formatting and newswire services for small and mid-sized public companies. Chairman and CEO Albert Aimers owns 45% of the company.

	Annual Growth	8/03	8/04	8/05	8/06	8/07
Sales ($ mil.)	7.6%	—	—	—	6.6	7.1
Net income ($ mil.)	—	—	—	—	(1.6)	(5.9)
Market value ($ mil.)	(80.3%)	—	—	—	60.5	11.9
Employees	40.0%	—	—	—	30	42

FINANCIAL SECURITY ASSURANCE HOLDINGS LTD.

31 West 52nd St.
New York, NY 10019
Phone: 212-826-0100
Fax: 212-688-3101
Web: www.fsa.com

CEO: Robert P. (Bob) Cochran
CFO: Joseph W. (Joe) Simon
HR: –
FYE: December 31
Type: Subsidiary

Financial Security Assurance Holdings wants to make sure that cities pay off their bonds on time. Through its subsidiaries, Financial Security Assurance (FSA) provides guaranty insurance on municipal bonds and asset-backed obligations. The company insures new issues and those already trading in the secondary market; it also writes portfolio insurance for securities held by investment funds. The company operates primarily in the US, but also extends into Europe, Mexico, and the Pacific Rim. French-Belgian financial services company Dexia owns almost all of Financial Security Assurance Holdings.

	Annual Growth	12/03	12/04	12/05	12/06	12/07
Assets ($ mil.)	23.1%	12,304.5	17,081.0	22,001.6	25,773.6	28,230.9
Net income ($ mil.)	—	290.6	378.6	326.1	424.1	(65.7)
Employees	4.8%	326	345	373	375	—

FINANCIALCONTENT, INC.

OTC: FCON

101 Lincoln Centre Dr., Ste. 410
Foster City, CA 94404
Phone: 650-286-9702
Fax: 650-745-2677
Web: www.financialcontent.com

CEO: Wing Yu
CFO: Dave Neville
HR: –
FYE: June 30
Type: Public

It doesn't matter if it's a bear or bull market; FinancialContent puts financial data right in front of you. The company's software integrates financial data (including stock quotes, SEC filings, interest rates) and tools into Web sites, corporate intranets, and print media. It has content partnerships with companies such as Business Wire, Dow Jones, and PR Newswire, and its customers have included Adobe, Bayer, and WR Hambrecht.

	Annual Growth	6/03	6/04	6/05	6/06	6/07
Sales ($ mil.)	62.7%	0.4	1.0	1.3	1.8	2.8
Net income ($ mil.)	—	(1.2)	(1.6)	(0.9)	(0.5)	(1.4)
Market value ($ mil.)	9.5%	3.9	15.1	10.5	5.5	5.6
Employees	—	—	—	—	—	14

FINDEX.COM INC.

OTC: FIND

11204 Davenport St., Ste. 100
Omaha, NE 68154
Phone: 402-333-1900
Fax: 402-778-5763
Web: www.quickverse.com/shopfiles

CEO: Steven Malone
CFO: Kirk R. Rowland
HR: –
FYE: December 31
Type: Public

For churches not blessed with financial management skills, FindEx.com is an answer to prayers. The company develops, publishes, and distributes (through a license agreement) software for churches, ministries, and other Christian organizations. Its primary product is a search application called QuickVerse, which is designed to facilitate biblical research. Other offerings include publishing software for Christian-themed printed materials; applications that assist pastors in developing sermons; children's Christian entertainment software; and language tutorials for Greek and Hebrew. Investment firm Barron Partners owns about 60% of FindEx.com.

	Annual Growth	12/03	12/04	12/05	12/06	12/07
Sales ($ mil.)	(7.7%)	4.4	5.4	5.3	3.7	3.2
Net income ($ mil.)	—	1.8	1.0	(1.6)	0.6	(0.6)
Market value ($ mil.)	(10.5%)	—	4.4	4.9	1.7	3.1
Employees	—	—	—	—	—	—

FINGER FURNITURE COMPANY INC.

1601 Gillingham Ln.
Sugar Land, TX 77478
Phone: 713-221-4441
Fax: 713-221-4315
Web: www.fingerfurniture.com

CEO: Rodney S. Finger
CFO: Larry Hogue
HR: Jerry Labita
FYE: July 31
Type: Private

Finger Furniture (more commonly known as Fingers) is a home furnishings retailer. The chain operates about a half dozen locations in the Houston area, from which it sells furniture for the bedroom, dining room, and living room, as well as office and entertainment pieces. In addition Fingers sells mattresses under such brands as Sealy, Stearns & Foster, and Restonic. The company moved its headquarters from Houston to Sugar Land in mid-2007 as part of a three-year expansion plan, which includes increasing its presence in the Sugar Land area. In business since 1927, today Fingers is run by chairman and CEO Rodney Finger.

	Annual Growth	7/03	7/04	7/05	7/06	7/07
Est. sales ($ mil.)	—	—	—	—	—	65.5
Employees	—	—	—	—	—	600

FINGERHUT DIRECT MARKETING, INC.

7777 Golden Triangle Dr.
Eden Prairie, MN 55344
Phone: 952-656-3700
Fax: 952-656-4112
Web: www.fingerhut.com

CEO: Brian Smith
CFO: Karen Miller
HR: –
FYE: Saturday nearest January 31
Type: Subsidiary

You might say this company lets your fingers do the shopping. Fingerhut Direct Marketing is a leading catalog retailer offering a broad line of private-label and brand-name merchandise, including apparel, appliances, electronics, health and beauty products, home furnishings, jewelry, toys, kitchen wares, luggage, and sporting goods. In addition to the catalogs it mails to consumers once a month, the company sells its merchandise through an online store. Fingerhut also offers its customers credit through its Fingerhut Credit Account (issued by CIT Bank). Founded by William Fingerhut in 1948, Fingerhut Direct is owned by an affiliate of Petters Group Worldwide.

	Annual Growth	1/03	1/04	1/05	1/06	1/07
Est. sales ($ mil.)	—	—	—	—	—	25.8
Employees	—	—	—	—	—	400

FINISAR CORPORATION

NASDAQ (GS): FNSR

1389 Moffett Park Dr.
Sunnyvale, CA 94089
Phone: 408-548-1000
Fax: 408-745-6097
Web: www.finisar.com

CEO: Jerry S. Rawls
CFO: Stephen K. Workman
HR: –
FYE: April 30
Type: Public

Finisar helps put the "work" in network with equipment that enables high-speed data communications over LANs or metro-area and storage-area networks (MANs/SANs). Finisar's optical components and subsystems (more than 90% of sales) include data links (transmitters, receivers, and transceivers) and link extenders. The company's customers include EMC and Cisco (21% of sales). Finisar also works with such IT vendors as Hewlett-Packard, IBM, and NEC Corporation of America. The company gets nearly two-thirds of its sales from customers in the US. Finisar plans to merge with rival Optium in a stock-swap deal valued at about $212 million.

	Annual Growth	4/04	4/05	4/06	4/07	4/08
Sales ($ mil.)	24.1%	185.6	280.8	364.3	418.5	440.2
Net income ($ mil.)	—	(113.8)	(114.1)	(24.9)	(45.4)	(76.4)
Market value ($ mil.)	1.4%	393.9	326.3	1,435.9	1,117.2	416.9
Employees	12.2%	2,826	2,580	3,688	3,908	4,476

THE FINISH LINE, INC.

NASDAQ (GS): FINL

3308 N. Mitthoeffer Rd.
Indianapolis, IN 46235
Phone: 317-899-1022
Fax: 317-899-0237
Web: www.finishline.com

CEO: Alan H. Cohen
CFO: Kevin S. Wampler
HR: Cindy Lorentson Cook
FYE: Saturday nearest last day in February
Type: Public

Coming up from the rear, The Finish Line is beginning to break the pace in the race for athletic footwear customers. The company sells athletic and casual big-brand name (adidas, NIKE, PUMA) footwear through about 700 Finish Line stores in 47 states, and apparel at about 95 Man Alive hip-hop-inspired stores in some 20 states. Man Alive offers "urban street wear" apparel (Sean Jean, Baby Phat). Its stores are bigger than its competitors' and offer more apparel and accessories, including jackets, backpacks, warm-ups, sunglasses, and watches. Finish Line has shuttered all 15 of its Paiva women's athletic shoe stores to focus on its primary Finish Line and Man Alive locations.

	Annual Growth	2/04	2/05	2/06	2/07	2/08
Sales ($ mil.)	6.7%	985.9	1,166.8	1,306.0	1,338.2	1,277.2
Net income ($ mil.)	—	47.3	61.3	60.5	32.4	(60.8)
Market value ($ mil.)	(24.4%)	366.1	882.0	735.1	521.0	119.4
Employees	(0.4%)	—	—	13,200	13,200	13,100

FINISHMASTER, INC.

Pink Sheets: FMST

54 Monument Circle, Ste. 800
Indianapolis, IN 46204
Phone: 317-237-3678
Fax: 317-237-2150
Web: www.finishmaster.com

CEO: John A. Lacy
CFO: Robert R. (Bob) Millard
HR: Robert (Bob) Pruim
FYE: December 31
Type: Public

Accidents are why pencils have erasers and why FinishMaster sells tons of paint. The company is a top US distributor of automotive paints, coatings, and accessories, which it sells mainly to customers in the collision repair industry. FinishMaster distributes a wide variety of brand name products from such producers as BASF, DuPont, 3M, and PPG (its top suppliers accounting for 85% of sales). It also sells refinishing accessories under the FinishMaster private brand name. The firm's distribution network serves its customers from about 170 sales outlets in 28 states. Chairman emeritus Andre Lacy controls a three-quarters stake in FinishMaster through holding company LDI, Ltd.

	Annual Growth	12/03	12/04	12/05	12/06	12/07
Sales ($ mil.)	7.7%	347.0	386.4	423.8	450.5	466.6
Net income ($ mil.)	5.8%	11.9	13.3	15.6	22.5	14.9
Employees	7.2%	—	1,550	—	1,550	1,910

FINLAY ENTERPRISES, INC.

NASDAQ (GM): FNLY

529 5th Ave.
New York, NY 10017
Phone: 212-808-2800
Fax: 212-557-3848
Web: www.finlayenterprises.com

CEO: Arthur E. Reiner
CFO: Bruce E. Zurlnick
HR: Joyce Manning Magrini
FYE: Saturday nearest January 31
Type: Public

Finlay Enterprises is used to getting the most from the leased. Its Finlay Fine Jewelry unit is the top operator of leased jewelry departments in the US, selling moderately priced fine jewelry such as necklaces, earrings, bracelets, rings, and watches in host department store groups. The company's subsidiaries operate about 685 domestic jewelry departments that are leased from department store retailers, such as Macy's and Dillard's. As the department store industry consolidates, Finlay has looked to other channels, including stand-alone retail stores, to distribute its jewelry. To that end, Finlay has acquired the 70-store Bailey Banks & Biddle Fine Jewelry division from Zale for about $200 million.

	Annual Growth	1/04	1/05	1/06	1/07	1/08
Sales ($ mil.)	(1.9%)	902.4	923.6	990.1	761.8	835.9
Net income ($ mil.)	—	8.4	16.0	(55.7)	4.4	(10.1)
Market value ($ mil.)	(40.1%)	132.3	152.8	84.0	87.0	17.0
Employees	(25.0%)	—	—	6,000	4,500	—

FIREARMS TRAINING SYSTEMS, INC.

7340 McGinnis Ferry Rd.
Suwanee, GA 30024
Phone: 770-813-0180
Fax: 770-622-3505
Web: www.fatsinc.com

CEO: Ronavan R. (Ron) Mohling
CFO: Gregory A. Ton
HR: James (Jim) Hall
FYE: March 31
Type: Subsidiary

Firearms Training Systems (FATS) allows customers to practice gunplay without mortal consequences: The company uses digital technology and laser-emitting weapons to provide realistic weapons training. FATS' systems integrate video and digitized imagery with laser-emitting firearms that have the look and feel of the real thing — they even recoil and require loading. Simulated arms range from archery bows and semiautomatic pistols to anti-armor rocket launchers and cannons. FATS products are used by law enforcement, military, and security personnel in the US and overseas. UK-based defense concern Meggitt PLC owns FATS.

	Annual Growth	3/03	3/04	3/05	3/06	3/07
Est. sales ($ mil.)	—	—	—	—	—	32.1
Employees	—	—	—	—	—	395

An in-depth profile of this company is available to Hoover's Online members at hoovers.com.

613

FIRED UP, INC.

7500 Rialto Blvd., Bldg. 1, Ste. 250
Austin, TX 78735
Phone: 512-263-0800
Fax: 512-263-8055
Web: www.carinos.com

CEO: Creed L. Ford III
CFO: H.G. (Carey) Carrington Jr.
HR: Rodney Morris
FYE: December 31
Type: Private

Italian cooking and casual dining are two things that excite this company. Fired Up operates and franchises more than 170 Carino's Italian Grill restaurants in about 30 states. The full-service eateries offer pizza and freshly prepared pasta along with beef, chicken and pork dishes inspired by the cuisine of Southern Italy. The company owns about half the restaurants and franchises the rest. A handful of Carino's units are located in Bahrain, Egypt, Kuwait, and United Arab Emirates. Fired Up was founded in 1997 by partners and former Brinker International executives Norman Abdallah and Creed Ford. The company is backed by Rosewood Capital and U. S. Bancorp Piper Jaffray.

	Annual Growth	12/03	12/04	12/05	12/06	12/07
Est. sales ($ mil.)	—	—	—	—	—	89.0
Employees	—	—	—	—	—	415

FIREHOUSE RESTAURANT GROUP, INC.

3410 Kori Rd.
Jacksonville, FL 32257
Phone: 904-886-8300
Fax: 904-886-2111
Web: www.firehousesubs.com

CEO: Robin Sorensen
CFO: Stephen C. Joost
HR: –
FYE: December 31
Type: Private

Firehouse Restaurant Group operates and franchises more than 250 Firehouse Subs sandwich shops in a dozen southern states. The chain offers a variety of hot and cold sub-style sandwiches, as well as soups, salads, and sides. Brothers and fire fighters Robin and Chris Sorensen started Firehouse Subs in 1994 after gaining popularity as firehouse cooks.

	Annual Growth	12/03	12/04	12/05	12/06	12/07
Est. sales ($ mil.)	—	—	—	—	—	5.0
Employees	—	—	—	—	—	55

FIREMAN'S FUND INSURANCE COMPANY

777 San Marin Dr.
Novato, CA 94998
Phone: 415-899-2000
Fax: 415-899-3600
Web: www.firemansfund.com

CEO: Michael E. (Mike) LaRocco
CFO: Jill E. Paterson
HR: –
FYE: December 31
Type: Subsidiary

Lending a helping hand is more than a slogan for Fireman's Fund Insurance. Founded in 1863 in San Francisco, the company is named for a now-defunct arrangement that saw 10% of its profits supporting widows and orphans of firefighters. The property/casualty insurer sells commercial insurance for small and midsized businesses and personal lines focused on wealthy individuals. Its specialty insurance division sells insurance to protect overland and ocean cargo, as well as professional liability insurance, and excess and surplus casualty insurance. Affiliate Fireman's Fund AgriBusiness provides crop and livestock coverage. Fireman's Fund is a subsidiary of German insurance mammoth Allianz.

	Annual Growth	12/03	12/04	12/05	12/06	12/07
Est. sales ($ mil.)	—	—	—	—	—	2,147.5
Employees	—	—	—	—	—	7,900

FIRST ACCEPTANCE CORPORATION

NYSE: FAC

3813 Green Hills Village Dr.
Nashville, TN 37215
Phone: 615-327-4888
Fax: 615-327-9957
Web: www.firstacceptancecorp.com

CEO: Stephen J. (Steve) Harrison
CFO: Kevin P. Cohn
HR: –
FYE: June 30
Type: Public

First Acceptance sells car insurance to customers wanting to stay on the right side of the law. A personal auto insurer operating in about a dozen states, First Acceptance specializes in providing non-standard auto insurance — that is, insurance for drivers who have trouble getting coverage because of poor driving records or payment histories, but who must have the minimum coverage required by state laws. First Acceptance sells its policies, branded Acceptance Insurance, through about 450 retail offices staffed by its own employees. Chairman Gerald Ford owns one-third of the company.

	Annual Growth	6/03	6/04	6/05	6/06	6/07
Assets ($ mil.)	70.5%	59.0	285.7	330.7	434.3	498.9
Net income ($ mil.)	—	(1.9)	(3.8)	26.2	28.1	(16.7)
Market value ($ mil.)	44.2%	111.8	325.7	448.9	560.0	483.8
Employees	69.0%	—	—	725	1,225	—

FIRST ADVANTAGE CORPORATION

NASDAQ (GS): FADV

12395 First American Way
Poway, CA 92064
Phone: 727-214-3411
Fax: 727-214-3410
Web: www.fadv.com

CEO: Anand K. Nallathambi
CFO: John Lamson
HR: Anita Tefft
FYE: December 31
Type: Public

I screen, you screen, we all screen with First Advantage. Created after The First American Corporation acquired US SEARCH.com and merged it with its Screening Technology (FAST) Division, First Advantage provides such risk management services as employment background screening, occupational health (especially drug testing), tenant screening (credit history, eviction actions, and rental payment history), and motor vehicle reports. Additionally it offers automotive lead generation services to auto dealers and lenders, and provides specialized credit reports, as well as litigation and investigative services for detecting corporate fraud. First Advantage is an indirect subsidiary of The First American Corporation.

	Annual Growth	12/03	12/04	12/05	12/06	12/07
Sales ($ mil.)	50.0%	166.5	266.5	643.8	817.6	842.9
Net income ($ mil.)	165.0%	2.8	9.9	58.4	66.2	138.1
Market value ($ mil.)	16.9%	100.1	147.4	261.5	240.0	187.2
Employees	10.0%	—	—	3,800	4,400	4,600

🔲 THE FIRST AMERICAN CORPORATION

NYSE: FAF

1 First American Way
Santa Ana, CA 92707
Phone: 714-800-3000
Fax: –
Web: www.firstam.com

CEO: Parker S. Kennedy
CFO: Max O. Valdes
HR: Kelly J. Dunmore
FYE: December 31
Type: Public

The First American Corporation believes that when you're buying real estate, more information is better. Along with good old title insurance from its First American Title subsidiary, the company's financial services arm also provides specialty property/casualty insurance, escrow services, equity loans, and home warranties. First American's information technology arm provides real estate tax monitoring, flood-zone certification, appraisal services, and credit-reporting services for property buyers and mortgage lenders. The company is also making use of extensive databases from its holdings in First Advantage to offer employee screening and credit reporting for landlords and automotive lenders.

	Annual Growth	12/03	12/04	12/05	12/06	12/07
Assets ($ mil.)	15.3%	4,892.1	6,208.4	7,598.6	8,224.3	8,647.9
Net income ($ mil.)	—	451.0	349.1	485.3	287.7	(3.1)
Market value ($ mil.)	7.6%	2,346.7	3,164.6	4,342.5	3,925.0	3,150.1
Employees	2.7%	—	—	35,444	39,670	37,354

FIRST AVIATION SERVICES INC.

Pink Sheets: FAVS

15 Riverside Ave.
Westport, CT 06880
Phone: 203-291-3300
Fax: 203-291-3330
Web: www.favs.com

CEO: Aaron P. Hollander
CFO: James Howell
HR: –
FYE: Sunday nearest January 31
Type: Public

The Pep Boys of the aerospace world, First Aviation Services (FAvS) supplies the parts and components that keep aircraft flying high. The company sells about 200,000 different new and reconditioned parts to airlines, parts resellers, fixed-base operators (FBOs), and corporate aviation customers. Overall, FAvS has about 7,000 customers. The company obtains its parts from more than 170 manufacturers, including major OEMs such as General Electric, Goodrich, and Parker Hannifin. CEO Aaron Hollander and vice chairman Michael Culver (who are also co-CEOs of First Equity Group) together own about 52% of FAvS through First Equity.

	Annual Growth	1/04	1/05	1/06	1/07	1/08
Sales ($ mil.)	4.3%	105.8	124.3	131.5	119.4	125.2
Net income ($ mil.)	—	0.0	(2.2)	1.0	(14.5)	(3.7)
Employees	2.3%	198	196	204	212	—

FIRST BANCORP.

NYSE: FBP

1519 Ponce de León Ave., Stop 23
Santurce, PR 00908
Phone: 787-729-8200
Fax: 787-729-8205
Web: www.firstbankpr.com

CEO: Luis M. Beauchamp
CFO: Fernando Scherrer
HR: Aida M. Garcia
FYE: December 31
Type: Public

Not to be confused with North Carolina's First Bancorp, this First BanCorp is the holding company for FirstBank Puerto Rico and FirstBank Florida. The company offers banking, mortgage, insurance, and leasing services from around 150 locations on the island, the US, and the US and British Virgin Islands. Commercial lending represents more than half of First BanCorp's loan portfolio, including business loans and mortgages; residential mortgages make up another quarter of its lending. FirstBank owns Money Express La Financiera, a consumer loan company with about 40 offices throughout Puerto Rico, and car rental agency First Leasing and Rental, which has about 10 locations.

	Annual Growth	12/03	12/04	12/05	12/06	12/07
Assets ($ mil.)	7.9%	12,667.9	15,637.0	19,917.7	17,390.3	17,186.9
Net income ($ mil.)	(18.2%)	152.3	177.3	114.6	84.6	68.1
Market value ($ mil.)	(3.9%)	791.9	1,282.6	1,003.7	793.4	674.4
Employees	—	—	—	—	—	—

FIRST BANCORP

NASDAQ (GS): FBNC

341 N. Main St.
Troy, NC 27371
Phone: 910-576-6171
Fax: 910-576-1070
Web: www.firstbancorp.com

CEO: Jerry L. Ocheltree
CFO: Eric P. Credle
HR: Patricia McCormick
FYE: December 31
Type: Public

First Bancorp (not to be confused with First Bancorp in Virginia or First BanCorp in Puerto Rico) is the holding company for First Bank, which operates some 75 branches in east-central North Carolina, east South Carolina, and western Virginia. The bank offers checking, savings, money market, and NOW accounts; IRAs; investments; and discount brokerage services. It focuses lending on mortgage loans, which account for some three-quarters of its loan portfolio. The company also owns in-house and third-party data processor Montgomery Data Services, as well as a property/casualty insurance agency.

	Annual Growth	12/03	12/04	12/05	12/06	12/07
Assets ($ mil.)	11.9%	1,475.8	1,638.9	1,801.1	2,136.6	2,317.3
Net income ($ mil.)	3.0%	19.4	20.1	16.1	19.3	21.8
Market value ($ mil.)	8.5%	196.3	384.1	286.9	313.5	271.6
Employees	3.1%	—	—	616	—	655

FIRST BANCORP OF INDIANA, INC.

NASDAQ (GM): FBEI

5001 Davis Lant Dr.
Evansville, IN 47715
Phone: 812-492-8100
Fax: –
Web: www.firstfedevansville.com

CEO: Michael H. Head
CFO: George J. (Jeffrey) Smith
HR: –
FYE: June 30
Type: Public

First Bancorp of Indiana wants to be second to none. It's the holding company for First Federal Savings Bank, which serves individuals and local businesses through nine branches in the Evansville, Indiana, area. First Federal Savings Bank offers standard retail products and services like checking, savings, and money market accounts; certificates of deposit; and retirement savings plans. Mortgages account for more than half of the company's loan portfolio; it also makes business and consumer loans. In 2006 First Bancorp of Indiana bought Home Building Bancorp, which added two Washington, Indiana, branches to the company's network.

	Annual Growth	6/03	6/04	6/05	6/06	6/07
Assets ($ mil.)	17.8%	188.5	264.1	277.4	294.5	363.0
Net income ($ mil.)	(25.2%)	1.6	0.3	1.5	1.3	0.5
Employees	0.0%	—	—	83	—	83

FIRST BANCSHARES, INC.

NASDAQ (GM): FBSI

142 E. 1st St.
Mountain Grove, MO 65711
Phone: 417-926-5151
Fax: 417-926-4362
Web: www.firsthomesavingsbank.com

CEO: Daniel P. (Dan) Katzfey
CFO: Ronald J. (Ron) Walters
HR: –
FYE: June 30
Type: Public

First Bancshares is the holding company for First Home Savings Bank, which operates 10 branches serving south central Missouri. Founded in 1911 as Mountain Grove Building and Loan Association, First Home Savings offers a range of retail banking services, including checking and savings, as well as NOW accounts and CDs. Residential mortgage loans account for more than half of First Home Savings' portfolio; commercial real estate loans represent about a quarter. A unit of the bank, Fybar Service, owns a handful of rental properties, mostly commercial.

	Annual Growth	6/03	6/04	6/05	6/06	6/07
Assets ($ mil.)	(2.6%)	268.6	265.0	244.0	228.4	241.3
Net income ($ mil.)	(39.2%)	2.2	2.3	1.3	(0.2)	0.3
Market value ($ mil.)	(2.3%)	28.1	32.6	28.7	25.8	25.6
Employees	11.8%	—	—	100	—	125

THE FIRST BANCSHARES, INC.

NASDAQ (CM): FBMS

6480 US Hwy. 98 West
Hattiesburg, MS 39402
Phone: 601-268-8998
Fax: 601-268-8904
Web: www.thefirstbank.com

CEO: David E. Johnson
CFO: DeeDee Lowery
HR: Marsie H. White
FYE: December 31
Type: Public

Hoping to be first in the hearts of its customers, The First Bancshares is the holding company for The First, A National Banking Association, a community bank with nearly 10 branches in southern Mississippi. Customers are offered such standard deposit services as checking, savings, NOW, money market, and individual retirement accounts. The bank also offers commercial customers loans for working capital, business expansion, equipment, and machinery. Consumer loan products include auto, home, education, and equity lines of credit. Commercial and residential mortgages and construction loans make up the bulk (more than three-quarters) of the bank's total loan portfolio.

	Annual Growth	12/03	12/04	12/05	12/06	12/07
Assets ($ mil.)	31.7%	164.9	212.4	294.4	417.8	496.1
Net income ($ mil.)	39.6%	1.0	1.2	1.9	3.3	3.8
Market value ($ mil.)	61.1%	9.6	10.3	19.0	86.5	64.8
Employees	9.5%	—	—	168	—	184

An in-depth profile of this company is available to Hoover's Online members at hoovers.com.

615

FIRST BANCTRUST CORPORATION

NASDAQ (CM): FBTC

101 S. Central Ave.
Paris, IL 61944
Phone: 217-465-6381
Fax: −
Web: www.firstbanktrust.com

CEO: Terry J. Howard
CFO: Ellen M. Litteral
HR: −
FYE: December 31
Type: Public

You can *spend* your money along the banks of the Seine in Paris, but you can *save* your money at the First BancTrust Corporation in Paris (Illinois, that is). It's the holding company for First Bank & Trust, which has offices in the rural eastern Illinois towns of Marshall, Martinsville, Paris, Rantoul, and Savoy. Founded in 1887, the bank attracts deposits by offering such services as checking and savings accounts, CDs, and IRAs. The company's loan portfolio consists mostly of one- to four-family residential mortgages, vehicle and farmland loans, and agricultural production financing. First Bank subsidiaries offer title insurance and investment products.

	Annual Growth	12/03	12/04	12/05	12/06	12/07
Assets ($ mil.)	9.6%	226.2	230.9	273.9	311.1	326.9
Net income ($ mil.)	(13.9%)	2.0	1.2	1.3	1.1	1.1
Market value ($ mil.)	11.4%	15.2	29.6	29.0	27.4	23.4
Employees	0.9%	−	−	109	−	111

FIRST BANKS, INC.

135 N. Meramec Ave.
Clayton, MO 63105
Phone: 314-854-4600
Fax: 314-592-6840
Web: www.firstbanks.com

CEO: Terrance M. (Terry) McCarthy
CFO: Steven F. (Steve) Schepman
HR: John D. Kitson
FYE: December 31
Type: Private

First Banks keeps it in the family. The holding company for First Bank is owned by chairman James Dierberg and his family, and a number of its branches and ATMs are located in Dierbergs Markets, a Missouri-based grocery chain owned by relatives of the chairman. First Bank has about 215 branches in such metro markets as Chicago, Dallas, Houston, Los Angeles, Sacramento, St. Louis, San Diego, and San Francisco, as well as smaller communities in Florida, Illinois, and Missouri. The bank offers deposit products, mortgages, and business and consumer loans, as well as securities brokerage, insurance, trust, private banking, and institutional money management services.

	Annual Growth	12/03	12/04	12/05	12/06	12/07
Est. sales ($ mil.)	−	−	−	−	−	759.2
Employees	−	−	−	−	−	2,930

FIRST BUSEY CORPORATION

NASDAQ (GS): BUSE

201 W. Main St.
Urbana, IL 61801
Phone: 217-365-4528
Fax: 217-365-4592
Web: www.busey.com

CEO: Van A. Dukeman
CFO: Barbara J. Harrington
HR: Lisa A. Davis
FYE: December 31
Type: Public

First Busey Corporation sure stays busy. Its the holding company for several subsidiaries, including Busey Bank, which has nearly 50 branches, mostly in central Illinois, but also in Florida and Indiana. Another subsidiary, Busey Bank, N.A., operates about 10 offices in three southwest Florida counties. The banks provide traditional demand and savings deposit and loan products. Real estate lending accounts for more than 80% of the company's loan portfolio, which also includes agricultural, business, and consumer loans. First Busey offers trust and investment management services through Busey Wealth Management, and retail payment processing through FirsTech.

	Annual Growth	12/03	12/04	12/05	12/06	12/07
Assets ($ mil.)	28.8%	1,522.1	1,964.4	2,263.4	2,509.5	4,192.9
Net income ($ mil.)	12.2%	19.9	22.5	26.9	28.9	31.5
Market value ($ mil.)	30.9%	246.5	430.1	449.2	494.6	723.5
Employees	29.7%	−	−	608	−	1,023

FIRST BUSINESS FINANCIAL SERVICES, INC.

NASDAQ (GM): FBIZ

401 Charmany Dr.
Madison, WI 53719
Phone: 608-238-8008
Fax: 608-232-5920
Web: www.fbfinancial.net

CEO: Corey A. Chambas
CFO: James F. Ropella
HR: −
FYE: December 31
Type: Public

Business comes first at First Business Financial Services, which serves business customers through First Business Bank and First Business Bank-Milwaukee. The banks offer deposit products, cash management services, equipment leases, loans, and other products from a handful of offices in Madison and southeastern Wisconsin. About 40% of its loan portfolio is dedicated to commercial mortgages; business loans and leases add another 30%. Subsidiary First Business Capital specializes in asset-based lending. First Business Equipment Finance provides commercial equipment financing. First Business Trust & Investments offers investment management and retirement services.

	Annual Growth	12/03	12/04	12/05	12/06	12/07
Assets ($ mil.)	17.1%	−	−	669.2	788.3	918.4
Net income ($ mil.)	(17.1%)	−	−	4.8	3.8	3.3
Market value ($ mil.)	(12.8%)	−	−	57.7	56.9	43.9
Employees	9.2%	−	−	119	−	142

FIRST CALIFORNIA FINANCIAL GROUP, INC.

NASDAQ (GM): FCAL

1880 Century Park East, Ste. 800
Los Angeles, CA 90067
Phone: 310-277-2265
Fax: −
Web: www.fcalgroup.com

CEO: C. G. Kum
CFO: Romolo C. Santarosa
HR: −
FYE: December 31
Type: Public

First California Financial Group was formed in 2007 when it merged with FCB Bancorp and National Mercantile Bancorp. The holding company then combined its three existing banks (First California Bank, National Mercantile Bank, and South Bay Bank) to form First California Bank, which operates a dozen branches in Southern California's Los Angeles, Orange, and Ventura counties. The bank provides standard fare for mostly local small and midsized businesses, but also individuals, including checking and savings accounts, mortgages and other loans, and investment services. The Pohlad family (which also owns Marquette Financial Companies and the Minnesota Twins) is a major investor in First California.

	Annual Growth	12/03	12/04	12/05	12/06	12/07
Assets ($ mil.)	−	−	−	−	−	1,108.8
Net income ($ mil.)	−	−	−	−	−	7.1
Market value ($ mil.)	−	−	−	−	−	106.5
Employees	−	−	−	−	−	205

FIRST CAPITAL BANCORP, INC.

NASDAQ (CM): FCVA

4222 Cox Rd., Ste. 200
Glen Allen, VA 23060
Phone: 804-273-1160
Fax: 804-527-0195
Web: www.1capitalbank.com

CEO: Robert G. Watts Jr.
CFO: William W. Ranson
HR: −
FYE: December 31
Type: Public

Moolah, scratch, bread, chedda, bucks, dough, duckets, or skrilla, it all means business for First Capital Bank and its holding company, First Capital Bancorp. Founded in 1998, the bank provides general commercial banking services from more than six branches serving the Richmond, Virginia, area. First Capital Bank offers the usual array of personal and business banking services including credit cards, IRAs, consumer and commercial loans, Internet banking services, and deposit accounts. The bank has also cultivated its product and service offerings to focus on the needs of small to medium-sized businesses in the community and offers a number of investment products in association with brokerage firm BI Investments.

	Annual Growth	12/03	12/04	12/05	12/06	12/07
Assets ($ mil.)	29.6%	−	−	209.5	257.2	351.9
Net income ($ mil.)	14.4%	−	−	1.3	1.6	1.7
Market value ($ mil.)	6.4%	−	−	−	32.2	34.3
Employees	11.3%	−	−	−	62	69

FIRST CAPITAL, INC.

NASDAQ (GM): FCAP

220 Federal Dr. NW
Corydon, IN 47112
Phone: 812-738-2198
Fax: 812-738-2202
Web: www.firstharrison.com

CEO: William W. Harrod
CFO: Michael Chris Frederick
HR: Sherry LeClair
FYE: December 31
Type: Public

First Capital is the holding company for First Harrison Bank, which operates about a dozen branches in Clark, Floyd, Harrison, and Washington counties in southern Indiana. Targeting individuals and small to midsized businesses, First Harrison offers standard deposit products including checking, savings, NOW, and money market accounts, as well as certificates of deposit and retirement savings plans. Residential mortgages make up slightly more than half of the company's loan portfolio; consumer loans are almost 20%. First Harrison Bank also provides business, commercial real estate, construction, and land loans.

	Annual Growth	12/03	12/04	12/05	12/06	12/07
Assets ($ mil.)	2.6%	409.1	425.3	438.4	457.1	453.2
Net income ($ mil.)	(0.7%)	3.5	3.4	3.7	3.7	3.4
Market value ($ mil.)	(3.7%)	53.9	49.6	42.1	52.7	46.4
Employees	—	—	—	144	—	—

FIRST CAPITAL TRUST, INC.

Pink Sheets: APGO

181 Main St.
Peapack, NJ 07977
Phone: 973-467-9330
Fax: –

CEO: John F. Vitale
CFO: John F. Vitale
HR: –
FYE: December 31
Type: Public

First Capital Trust — which does business as the AAMPRO Group — amps it up whenever clients require human resources services. The group provides a broad range of services specializing in human resources consulting, payroll processing, and benefits administration. It also provides recruiting and temporary staffing services primarily to clients in the tri-state (New York, New Jersey, and Pennsylvania) area. The group zeroes in on small and midsized businesses residing in the legal, accounting, manufacturing, automobile, medical, and warehousing sectors. AAMPRO Group legally changed its name to First Capital Trust in October 2007.

	Annual Growth	12/02	12/03	12/04	12/05	*12/06
Sales ($ mil.)	(42.8%)	17.7	2.0	1.4	1.8	1.9
Net income ($ mil.)	—	(0.6)	(1.8)	(1.7)	(1.0)	(1.2)
Employees	—	—	—	—	—	—

*Most recent year available

FIRST CASH FINANCIAL SERVICES, INC.

NASDAQ (GS): FCFS

690 E. Lamar Blvd., Ste. 400
Arlington, TX 76011
Phone: 817-460-3947
Fax: 817-461-7019
Web: www.firstcash.com

CEO: Rick L. Wessel
CFO: R. Douglas (Doug) Orr
HR: Jan Hartz
FYE: December 31
Type: Public

Texas isn't just oil, land, and cattle. Since the 1980s, a new industry has found a home on the range: pawnshops. First Cash Financial Services operates about 250 pawnshops and cash advance stores there and in about a dozen other states and in Mexico (where it has more than 150 locations). The company lends money secured by such personal property as jewelry, electronics, tools, sporting goods, and musical equipment. First Cash Financial Services is also half-owner of Cash & Go, a partnership that operates about 40 check-cashing kiosks inside convenience stores. The company added auto loans to its offerings in 2006 by purchasing dealer and lender Auto Master, which has about 15 locations.

	Annual Growth	12/03	12/04	12/05	12/06	12/07
Assets ($ mil.)	20.1%	140.1	160.9	185.9	233.8	291.5
Net income ($ mil.)	23.9%	15.0	20.7	25.4	31.7	35.3
Market value ($ mil.)	51.1%	86.4	213.5	229.7	830.3	451.0
Employees	19.4%	—	—	2,314	2,900	3,300

FIRST CENTURY BANKSHARES, INC.

OTC: FCBS

500 Federal St.
Bluefield, WV 24701
Phone: 304-325-8181
Fax: 304-325-3727
Web: www.firstcentury.com

CEO: Richard W. Wilkinson
CFO: J. Ronald Hypes
HR: Lisa A. Huff
FYE: December 31
Type: Public

If you get a calendar from First Century Bankshares, be sure to check in which epoch it was published. The firm is the holding company for First Century Bank, which serves southern West Virginia and southwestern Virginia from about a dozen branch locations. The bank provides traditional time deposit accounts (such as NOW and money market accounts) and lending services, including checking and savings accounts, check cards, CDs, and IRAs. It uses funds from deposits to write commercial and consumer loans, primarily mortgages (which account for some 70% of the company's loan book).

	Annual Growth	12/03	12/04	12/05	12/06	12/07
Assets ($ mil.)	4.5%	363.7	378.1	390.8	411.0	433.9
Net income ($ mil.)	13.8%	2.8	3.1	4.0	4.5	4.7
Market value ($ mil.)	2.7%	43.8	47.8	45.6	55.0	48.7
Employees	—	—	—	—	—	180

FIRST CHESTER COUNTY CORPORATION

OTC: FCEC

9 N. High St.
West Chester, PA 19380
Phone: 484-881-4000
Fax: 484-881-4130
Web: www.fnbchestercounty.com

CEO: John A. Featherman III
CFO: John E. Balzarini
HR: Deborah R. Pierce
FYE: December 31
Type: Public

First Chester County Corporation hopes folks don't keep their cash in the chest of drawers or under the mattress, for that matter. It's the holding company of First National Bank of Chester County, which provides traditional banking services to individuals and businesses through about two dozen branches in southeastern Pennsylvania. Besides checking and savings accounts, the bank also offers money markets, IRAs, CDs, and trust and asset management services. The company is primarily a commercial lender, with business loans and commercial mortgages accounting for more than two-thirds of its loan portfolio. It also provides construction loans, consumer loans, residential mortgages, and lease financing.

	Annual Growth	12/03	12/04	12/05	12/06	12/07
Assets ($ mil.)	7.3%	689.2	805.5	845.1	872.1	914.8
Net income ($ mil.)	7.3%	5.8	6.2	6.5	7.3	7.7
Market value ($ mil.)	(4.2%)	108.0	118.0	101.1	110.9	91.1
Employees	—	—	—	—	—	—

FIRST CITIZENS BANC CORP.

NASDAQ (CM): FCZA

100 E. Water St.
Sandusky, OH 44870
Phone: 419-625-4121
Fax: 419-627-3359
Web: www.fcza.com

CEO: James O. Miller
CFO: –
HR: –
FYE: December 31
Type: Public

First Citizens Banc Corp. is the holding company for The Citizens Banking Company and its First Citizens Bank division, which together operate more than 20 branches in north-central Ohio. The banks concentrate on real estate lending, with residential mortgages and commercial mortgages each comprising approximately 40% of the company's loan portfolio. They offer such deposit products as checking and savings accounts and CDs, in addition to trust services. The Citizens Banking Company's First Citizens Advisors division provides investment management and retirement planning services through an agreement with third-party provider UVEST.

	Annual Growth	12/03	12/04	12/05	12/06	12/07
Assets ($ mil.)	15.2%	636.4	817.5	750.9	749.0	1,119.3
Net income ($ mil.)	5.4%	5.6	4.8	6.7	6.2	6.9
Market value ($ mil.)	(6.6%)	142.5	135.4	106.8	107.8	108.4
Employees	0.8%	—	—	259	—	263

An in-depth profile of this company is available to Hoover's Online members at hoovers.com.

617

FIRST CITIZENS BANCORPORATION, INC.

OTC: FCBN

1230 Main
Columbia, SC 29201
Phone: 803-733-2020
Fax: 803-733-2763
Web: www.firstcitizensonline.com

CEO: Jim B. Apple
CFO: Craig L. Nix
HR: Annette Rollins
FYE: December 31
Type: Public

First Citizens Bancorporation is the holding company for First Citizens Bank and Trust Company, which has more than 160 branches in South Carolina and Georgia, and The Exchange Bank of South Carolina, which has four branches. The banks provide standard products and services for individuals and businesses, including checking and savings accounts, credit cards, and online banking. Residential mortgages comprise the majority of the banks' loan portfolio. The company also has a wealth management division that offers investment management, trust, and private banking services. Formerly a publicly traded entity, First Citizens Bancorporation was taken private in early 2006.

	Annual Growth	12/03	12/04	12/05	12/06	12/07
Est. sales ($ mil.)	—	—	—	—	—	386.0
Employees	—	—	—	—	—	1,641

FIRST CITIZENS BANCSHARES, INC.

NASDAQ (GS): FCNCA

4300 Six Forks Rd.
Raleigh, NC 27609
Phone: 919-716-7000
Fax: 919-716-7074
Web: www.firstcitizens.com

CEO: Frank B. Holding Jr.
CFO: Kenneth A. Black
HR: Lou J. Davis
FYE: December 31
Type: Public

First Citizens BancShares knows the first thing about banking in several states. The company owns First-Citizens Bank & Trust, which operates some 340 branches in North Carolina, Maryland, Tennessee, Virginia, and West Virginia; it also owns IronStone Bank, which has about 55 branches in nine states primarily located in the Sun Belt and along the West Coast. In addition to deposit products, the banks also offer discount brokerage, trust, and investment services. Real estate loans (including commercial, residential, and revolving mortgages, and construction and land development loans) make up more than two-thirds of the company's lending portfolio.

	Annual Growth	12/03	12/04	12/05	12/06	12/07
Assets ($ mil.)	6.6%	12,559.9	13,258.7	14,639.4	15,729.7	16,212.1
Net income ($ mil.)	9.6%	75.2	74.8	112.9	126.5	108.6
Market value ($ mil.)	4.9%	1,055.4	1,298.2	1,527.4	1,774.5	1,277.2
Employees	(0.1%)	—	—	4,794	4,764	4,781

FIRST CLOVER LEAF FINANCIAL CORP.

NASDAQ (CM): FCLF

6814 Goshen Rd.
Edwardsville, IL 62025
Phone: 618-656-6122
Fax: –
Web: www.cloverleafbank.com

CEO: Dennis M. Terry
CFO: Darlene F. (Dee) McDonald
HR: –
FYE: December 31
Type: Public

First Clover Leaf Financial counts itself lucky to be in the banking business in the greater St. Louis area. The company (formerly First Federal Financial Services) is the holding company for three-branch First Clover Leaf Bank. Under its former name, the company in 2006 acquired Clover Leaf Financial and merged the acquisition's Clover Leaf Bank with First Federal Savings & Loan Association of Edwardsville to form First Clover Leaf Bank. The bank serves individuals and businesses in and around Edwardsville and Glen Carbon, offering such standard services as deposit accounts, credit cards, and loans, including real estate (about 85% of its total portfolio), business, and consumer loans.

	Annual Growth	12/03	12/04	12/05	12/06	12/07
Assets ($ mil.)	0.7%	—	—	—	410.3	413.3
Net income ($ mil.)	33.3%	—	—	—	1.8	2.4
Market value ($ mil.)	(16.5%)	—	—	—	104.4	87.1
Employees	—	—	—	—	—	—

FIRST COMMONWEALTH FINANCIAL CORPORATION

NYSE: FCF

22 N. 6th St.
Indiana, PA 15701
Phone: 724-349-7220
Fax: 888-711-2329
Web: www.fcbanking.com

CEO: John J. Dolan
CFO: Edward J. (Ed) Lipkus III
HR: –
FYE: December 31
Type: Public

First Commonwealth Financial is the holding company for First Commonwealth Bank, which operates more than 110 offices in 15 central and western Pennsylvania counties. The bank offers standard deposit products like checking and savings accounts and CDs; its loan book includes a mix of residential and commercial mortgages and business, construction, and consumer loans. Among First Commonwealth Financial's nonbanking subsidiaries are an insurance agency, a trust company, a financial planning company, a data processing firm, and a professional services organization.

	Annual Growth	12/03	12/04	12/05	12/06	12/07
Assets ($ mil.)	3.2%	5,189.2	6,198.5	6,026.3	6,043.9	5,883.6
Net income ($ mil.)	(3.5%)	53.3	38.7	57.8	53.0	46.3
Market value ($ mil.)	(2.6%)	865.8	1,075.8	910.0	992.7	778.8
Employees	1.6%	—	—	1,598	—	1,649

FIRST COMMUNITY BANCSHARES, INC.

NASDAQ (GS): FCBC

1 Community Place
Bluefield, VA 24605
Phone: 276-326-9000
Fax: 276-326-9010
Web: www.fcbinc.com

CEO: John M. Mendez
CFO: David D. Brown V
HR: Melissa Ward
FYE: December 31
Type: Public

First Community Bancshares doesn't play second fiddle to other area banks. The firm is the holding company for First Community Bank, which serves communities in North Carolina, Tennessee, Virginia, and West Virginia. Through some 60 branches, the bank provides traditional services such as checking and savings accounts, CDs, and trust services. The bank is mainly a real estate lender, with residential mortgages accounting for about 40% of its loan portfolio and commercial real estate loans comprising more than 30%. First Community Bancshares bought money manager Investment Planning Consultants in 2006 and insurance agency GreenPoint Insurance Group the following year.

	Annual Growth	12/03	12/04	12/05	12/06	12/07
Assets ($ mil.)	6.5%	1,672.7	1,830.8	1,952.5	2,033.7	2,149.8
Net income ($ mil.)	4.1%	25.2	22.4	26.3	29.0	29.6
Market value ($ mil.)	(1.4%)	372.8	405.9	350.6	444.9	353.0
Employees	(7.3%)	—	—	716	—	615

FIRST COMMUNITY BANK CORPORATION

NASDAQ (CM): FCFL

9001 Belcher Rd.
Pinellas Park, FL 33782
Phone: 727-520-0987
Fax: 727-471-0010
Web: www.efirstcommbank.com

CEO: Kenneth P. Cherven
CFO: Stan B. McClelland
HR: Patricia TC Daerda
FYE: December 31
Type: Public

Although not the first community bank *in* America, First Community Bank Corporation of America *is* the holding company for First Community Bank of America, which has about 10 branches in the Sunshine State's Tampa Bay area. The thrift concentrates on real estate lending, with commercial mortgages and residential mortgages representing the bulk of its activities. It also makes business and consumer installment loans. The company is eyeing growth and plans to expand through aquisitions of small banks or by opening new branches. Chairman Robert M. Menke owns 38% of First Community Bank Corporation of America; company officers and directors collectively own 51%.

	Annual Growth	12/03	12/04	12/05	12/06	12/07
Assets ($ mil.)	24.7%	180.4	241.8	324.8	390.9	436.5
Net income ($ mil.)	17.9%	1.5	2.0	2.9	3.7	2.9
Market value ($ mil.)	24.9%	18.4	37.1	64.7	69.1	44.9
Employees	21.4%	—	—	74	110	109

FIRST COMMUNITY CORPORATION

NASDAQ (CM): FCCO

5455 Sunset Blvd.
Lexington, SC 29072
Phone: 803-951-2265
Fax: 803-951-1722
Web: www.firstcommunitysc.com

CEO: Michael C. (Mike) Crapps
CFO: Joseph G. Sawyer
HR: −
FYE: December 31
Type: Public

Putting first things first, First Community is the holding company for First Community Bank, which serves individuals and smaller businesses in central South Carolina's Lexington, Richland, Kershaw and Newberry counties. Through about a dozen offices, the bank offers such products and services as checking and savings accounts, money market accounts, CDs, IRAs, credit cards, insurance, and investment services. Commercial mortgages make up about 40% of First Community Bank's loan portfolio, which also includes residential mortgages and business, consumer, and construction loans. The company bought DutchFork Bancshares in 2004 and DeKalb Bankshares (parent of The Bank of Camden) in 2006.

	Annual Growth	12/03	12/04	12/05	12/06	12/07
Assets ($ mil.)	27.4%	215.0	455.7	467.5	548.1	565.6
Net income ($ mil.)	22.1%	1.8	2.2	3.1	3.5	4.0
Market value ($ mil.)	4.5%	34.8	55.7	52.7	54.6	41.4
Employees	11.4%	—	—	123	137	—

FIRST DATA CORPORATION

6200 S. Quebec St.
Greenwood Village, CO 80111
Phone: 303-488-8000
Fax: 303-967-7000
Web: www.firstdatacorp.com

CEO: Michael D. Capellas
CFO: Philip M. Wall
HR: Peter W. Boucher
FYE: December 31
Type: Private

Paper, plastic, or Internet — First Data moves the money. The company covers virtually all the bases when it comes to transaction processing and funds transfer. Primary segments include commercial services and financial services, (merchant and debit network processing, check verification, prepaid cards, statement and card processing), and First Data International. Through its integrated payment segment, the company also provides official checks and money orders, remote clearing, and similar services. Subsidiary TeleCheck provides paper check processing services, although the use of paper checks has been dropping steadily. Investment firm KKR bought First Data in 2007.

	Annual Growth	12/02	12/03	12/04	12/05	12/06
Sales ($ mil.)	(1.9%)	7,636.2	8,400.2	10,013.2	10,568.2	7,076.4
Net income ($ mil.)	5.2%	1,237.9	1,408.7	1,875.2	1,717.4	1,513.4
Employees	0.0%	29,000	29,000	32,000	33,000	29,000

FIRST DEFIANCE FINANCIAL CORP.

NASDAQ (GS): FDEF

601 Clinton St.
Defiance, OH 43512
Phone: 419-782-5015
Fax: 419-782-5145
Web: www.fdef.com

CEO: William J. Small
CFO: John C. Wahl
HR: −
FYE: December 31
Type: Public

Named for its hometown, not its attitude, First Defiance Financial is the holding company for First Federal Bank of the Midwest, which operates more than 35 branches serving northwestern Ohio, western Indiana, and southern Michigan. The bank offers standard deposit products including checking, savings, and money market accounts and CDs. Commercial real estate loans account for about 40% of the bank's loan portfolio; residential mortgages make up about another 20%. The company's insurance agency subsidiary, First Insurance & Investments, provides life insurance, property/casualty coverage, and investment products. In 2008 First Defiance bought Pavilion Bancorp, giving the bank its first branches in Michigan.

	Annual Growth	12/03	12/04	12/05	12/06	12/07
Assets ($ mil.)	11.5%	1,040.6	1,126.7	1,461.1	1,527.9	1,609.4
Net income ($ mil.)	3.5%	12.1	10.8	12.0	15.6	13.9
Market value ($ mil.)	(1.3%)	163.9	181.2	191.9	216.0	155.4
Employees	3.5%	—	—	476	—	510

FIRST FEDERAL BANCSHARES OF ARKANSAS

NASDAQ (GM): FFBH

1401 Hwy. 62-65 North
Harrison, AR 72602
Phone: 870-741-7641
Fax: 870-365-8369
Web: www.ffbh.com

CEO: Larry J. Brandt
CFO: Sherri R. Billings
HR: −
FYE: December 31
Type: Public

If there's gold in them thar Ozark Mountains, it's probably tucked away in First Federal Bancshares of Arkansas, Inc. Its subsidiary — First Federal Bank of Arkansas — serves commercial and individual customers through some 20 branches in north central and northwestern portions of the state. The bank offers standard retail services such as savings, checking, and money market accounts, as well as certificates of deposit. Funds generated are largely used to write single-family residential mortgages (about one-third of the company's loan portfolio), real estate construction loans (a quarter), and commercial mortgages (nearly 20%). The bank also writes business and consumer loans. It was founded in 1934.

	Annual Growth	12/03	12/04	12/05	12/06	12/07
Assets ($ mil.)	3.5%	690.7	751.7	852.4	852.5	792.0
Net income ($ mil.)	(23.3%)	7.5	7.8	7.8	7.4	2.6
Market value ($ mil.)	(11.1%)	109.5	114.7	122.7	117.7	68.3
Employees	(0.6%)	—	—	333	—	329

FIRST FEDERAL BANKSHARES, INC.

NASDAQ (GM): FFSX

329 Pierce St.
Sioux City, IA 51101
Phone: 712-277-0200
Fax: 712-277-0369
Web: www.firstfederalbank.com

CEO: Michael W. (Mike) Dosland
CFO: Michael S. Moderski
HR: −
FYE: June 30
Type: Public

First Federal Bankshares is the holding company for Vantus Bank, which serves northwest and central Iowa, as well as contiguous parts of Nebraska and South Dakota, through about 15 branches. Founded in 1923, the bank emphasizes real estate lending, with one- to four-family residential mortgages, commercial mortgages, and multifamily residential mortgages comprising the bulk of its activities. It also writes consumer and business loans. Deposit products include CDs, IRAs, and checking, money market, and savings accounts. Other units offer financial planning and products and real estate development services.

	Annual Growth	6/03	6/04	6/05	6/06	6/07
Assets ($ mil.)	0.7%	627.9	615.5	586.8	612.5	645.8
Net income ($ mil.)	(13.7%)	5.6	5.6	4.2	3.3	3.1
Market value ($ mil.)	(0.5%)	67.2	84.6	72.8	73.3	65.9
Employees	—	—	—	201	—	—

FIRST FEDERAL OF NORTHERN MICHIGAN

NASDAQ (GM): FFNM

100 S. 2nd Ave.
Alpena, MI 49707
Phone: 989-356-9041
Fax: 989-354-8671
Web: www.first-federal.com

CEO: Martin A. Thomson
CFO: Amy E. Essex
HR: Joseph W. Gentry II
FYE: December 31
Type: Public

First Federal of Northern Michigan Bancorp, Inc., has an interest in geography. The institution is the holding company for First Federal of Northern Michigan, which offers financial services to residents and businesses from locations in the northern part of the state's lower peninsula. Deposit services include checking, savings, money market, and NOW accounts; IRAs; and CDs. Lending includes the issuance of credit cards and the origination of consumer and commercial loans, and residential mortgage loans (which makes up about 50% of its loan portfolio). First Federal's subsidiary InsuranCenter of Alpena (ICA) provides property, casualty, and health insurance.

	Annual Growth	12/03	12/04	12/05	12/06	12/07
Assets ($ mil.)	(1.5%)	—	262.8	282.8	281.0	250.8
Net income ($ mil.)	—	—	0.4	0.4	0.5	(1.6)
Market value ($ mil.)	(20.8%)	—	42.7	27.3	27.6	21.2
Employees	—	—	—	129	—	—

An in-depth profile of this company is available to Hoover's Online members at hoovers.com.

619

FIRST FINANCIAL BANCORP

NASDAQ (GS): FFBC

300 High St.
Hamilton, OH 45011
Phone: 513-867-4700
Fax: 513-867-3111
Web: bankatfirst.com

CEO: Claude E. Davis
CFO: J. Franklin (Frank) Hall
HR: –
FYE: December 31
Type: Public

First Financial spreads itself thick. The holding company's flagship subsidiary, First Financial Bank, operates through more than 80 branches in Ohio, Indiana, and Kentucky. First Financial's services include checking and savings accounts, money market accounts, CDs, credit cards, mutual funds, and trust and asset management services. Real estate (construction and mortgages, combined) make up about half of First Financial's total loan portfolio; the company also offers commercial loans (30% of total) and consumer loans. The company's nonbanking subsidiaries include First Financial Capital Advisors (investment advisory) and First Financial Insurance (formerly Flagstone Insurance and Financial Services).

	Annual Growth	12/03	12/04	12/05	12/06	12/07
Assets ($ mil.)	(3.9%)	3,956.1	3,916.7	3,690.8	3,301.6	3,369.3
Net income ($ mil.)	(1.5%)	37.9	41.1	37.9	21.3	35.7
Market value ($ mil.)	(11.7%)	700.8	764.4	693.2	651.9	426.0
Employees	—	—	—	1,604	—	—

FIRST FINANCIAL BANKSHARES, INC.

NASDAQ (GS): FFIN

400 Pine St.
Abilene, TX 79601
Phone: 325-627-7155
Fax: 325-627-7393
Web: www.ffin.com

CEO: F. Scott Dueser
CFO: J. Bruce Hildebrand
HR: Pamela (Pam) Mann
FYE: December 31
Type: Public

Texas hold 'em? Well, sort of. First Financial Bankshares is the Texas-based holding company for First Financial Bankshares of Delaware, which in turn owns 10 banks (most bear the First Financial Bank name) and a trust company, all of which are located in small and midsized markets in North and West Texas. Through about 45 offices, the banks offer traditional products such as checking and savings accounts, CDs, and loans. Real estate mortgages account for approximately 40% of the company's loan portfolio; commercial, financial, and agricultural loans are almost one third. The banks also offer construction and consumer loans.

	Annual Growth	12/03	12/04	12/05	12/06	12/07
Assets ($ mil.)	10.1%	2,092.6	2,315.2	2,733.8	2,850.2	3,070.3
Net income ($ mil.)	8.8%	35.3	39.2	44.0	46.0	49.5
Market value ($ mil.)	12.9%	477.4	521.3	726.3	861.7	776.0
Employees	0.0%	—	—	975	—	975

FIRST FINANCIAL CORPORATION

NASDAQ (GS): THFF

1 First Financial Plaza
Terre Haute, IN 47807
Phone: 812-238-6000
Fax: 812-238-6140
Web: www.first-online.com

CEO: Norman L. Lowery
CFO: Michael A. Carty
HR: Karen Stinson
FYE: December 31
Type: Public

Which came first . . . the First Financial in Indiana, Rhode Island, Tennessee, Texas, or Wisconsin? Regardless, this particular First Financial Corporation is the holding company for First Financial Bank, which operates about 50 branches in west-central Indiana and east-central Illinois. With roots dating back to 1834, the banks offer traditional deposit services such as CDs and checking and savings accounts, as well as Internet banking. Residential mortgages account for about half of the company's loan portfolio. First Financial also operates an insurance agency and two investment subsidiaries.

	Annual Growth	12/03	12/04	12/05	12/06	12/07
Assets ($ mil.)	0.1%	2,223.1	2,184.0	2,136.9	2,176.0	2,231.6
Net income ($ mil.)	(0.9%)	26.5	28.0	23.0	23.5	25.6
Market value ($ mil.)	(2.2%)	407.4	473.1	361.1	470.4	372.3
Employees	—	—	—	808	—	—

FIRST FINANCIAL HOLDINGS, INC.

NASDAQ (GS): FFCH

34 Broad St.
Charleston, SC 29401
Phone: 843-529-5933
Fax: 843-529-5883
Web: www.firstfinancialholdings.com

CEO: A. Thomas Hood
CFO: R. Wayne Hall
HR: Jerry P. Gazes
FYE: September 30
Type: Public

First Financial Holdings serves South Carolina through thrift subsidiary First Federal Savings and Loan of Charleston, established in 1934. With more than 50 branches (including one North Carolina office and about a dozen in-store locations in Wal-Mart Supercenters and Kroger groceries), the bank offers checking and savings accounts, retirement accounts, and credit cards. One- to four-family residential mortgages make up about 40% of the company's loan portfolio, followed by commercial mortgages and land, home equity, mobile home, and consumer loans. Subsidiaries provide insurance, trust, asset management, and securities brokerage services.

	Annual Growth	9/03	9/04	9/05	9/06	9/07
Assets ($ mil.)	3.9%	2,322.9	2,442.3	2,522.4	2,658.1	2,711.4
Net income ($ mil.)	(2.0%)	27.2	24.5	26.2	27.6	25.1
Market value ($ mil.)	(1.0%)	378.4	384.6	373.6	411.4	363.9
Employees	5.1%	—	—	791	847	873

FIRST FINANCIAL SERVICE CORPORATION

NASDAQ (GM): FFKY

2323 Ring Rd.
Elizabethtown, KY 42701
Phone: 270-765-2131
Fax: 270-765-2135
Web: www.ffsbky.com

CEO: B. Keith Johnson
CFO: Steven M. Zagar
HR: –
FYE: December 31
Type: Public

First Financial Service Corporation is the holding company for First Federal Savings Bank of Elizabethtown, which has about 15 branches in nine central Kentucky cities. Founded in 1923, the bank offers CDs, IRAs, and savings, NOW, and money market accounts, primarily using deposit funds to originate commercial real estate loans (about 60% of its loan portfolio) and residential mortgages (about 20%). Other loans include home equity, consumer, and business loans. First Service Corporation of Elizabethtown, a subsidiary of the bank, sells investment products to the bank's customers.

	Annual Growth	12/03	12/04	12/05	12/06	12/07
Assets ($ mil.)	6.6%	676.3	737.7	766.5	822.8	872.7
Net income ($ mil.)	4.1%	8.0	7.8	9.1	10.3	9.4
Market value ($ mil.)	12.8%	69.2	70.3	95.3	122.8	111.9
Employees	(87.6%)	—	—	262	—	4

FIRST FRANKLIN CORPORATION

NASDAQ (GM): FFHS

4750 Ashwood Dr.
Cincinnati, OH 45241
Phone: 513-469-8000
Fax: 513-469-5360
Web: www.franklinsavings.com

CEO: Thomas H. Siemers
CFO: Daniel T. Voelpel
HR: Robert (Rob) Snyder
FYE: December 31
Type: Public

This company is all about the Benjamins. First Franklin Corporation is the holding firm for The Franklin Savings and Loan Company, which serves individuals and small to midsized businesses through about 10 branches in Cincinnati. Established in 1883, The Franklin Savings and Loan offers such standard retail banking services as savings, checking, money market, and NOW accounts, as well as CDs and IRAs. Annuities, mutual funds, and discount brokerage services also are provided. Residential mortgage loans account for nearly three-quarters of the thrift's loan portfolio, which also includes business, construction, consumer, and nonresidential mortgage loans.

	Annual Growth	12/03	12/04	12/05	12/06	12/07
Assets ($ mil.)	3.9%	273.4	274.0	296.7	332.0	318.9
Net income ($ mil.)	(22.7%)	1.4	0.7	1.2	1.4	0.5
Market value ($ mil.)	(13.1%)	29.5	32.6	26.5	26.1	16.8
Employees	(1.6%)	—	—	64	—	62

FIRST HARTFORD CORPORATION

Pink Sheets: FHRT

149 Colonial Rd.
Manchester, CT 06040
Phone: 860-646-6555
Fax: 860-646-8572
Web: firsthartford.com

CEO: Neil H. Ellis
CFO: Stuart I. Greenwald
HR: –
FYE: April 30
Type: Public

First Hartford puts real estate first. The company, operating through subsidiary First Hartford Realty, invests in and develops commercial and other real estate. Its portfolio is located primarily in the Northeast and includes shopping centers, a restaurant, and a business and technology school campus. First Hartford has also built single-family homes, public housing units, government facilities, and several industrial properties. It is a preferred developer for CVS Corporation in West Texas, northern New Jersey, and Long Island, New York. The company's largest tenants are Stop & Shop, Big Y Foods, and Price Rite Pharmacy. Subsidiary Lead Tech provides lead and asbestos inspection and remediation services.

	Annual Growth	4/03	4/04	4/05	4/06	4/07
Sales ($ mil.)	19.9%	5.9	3.8	6.5	33.9	12.2
Net income ($ mil.)	—	0.1	4.6	(0.2)	0.7	0.0
Employees	11.8%	24	27	30	—	—

FIRST HEALTH GROUP CORP.

3200 Highland Ave.
Downers Grove, IL 60515
Phone: 630-737-7900
Fax: –
Web: www.firsthealth.com

CEO: Thomas P. McDonough
CFO: Dennis Meulemans
HR: –
FYE: December 31
Type: Subsidiary

First Health Group wants to have the last word on managed care. The company provides a dizzying array of services to commercial and public health plans, self-insured employers, and third-party administrators (TPAs). It provides administrative services, programs such as disease management and pharmacy benefit management, and a ready-made preferred provider organization. Clients such as large multi-state companies who self-insure their employees' health benefits use First Health's PPO and its other services to run their programs. The company also serves federal employee health plans, workers' compensation programs, and health insurers. First Health Group was acquired by Coventry Health Care in 2005.

	Annual Growth	12/03	12/04	12/05	12/06	12/07
Est. sales ($ mil.)	—	—	—	—	—	327.2
Employees	—	—	—	—	—	6,000

FIRST HORIZON NATIONAL CORPORATION

NYSE: FHN

165 Madison Ave.
Memphis, TN 38103
Phone: 901-523-4444
Fax: 901-523-4266
Web: www.fhnc.com

CEO: Gerald L. (Jerry) Baker
CFO: D. Bryan Jordan
HR: John M. Daniel
FYE: December 31
Type: Public

First Horizon would like to be the first bank people think of in the Volunteer State. The company operates more than 200 First Tennessee Bank branches in its home state and First Horizon Bank branches elsewhere in the South. It provides various financial services through three primary business segments: Retail and Commercial Banking, Mortgage Banking, and Capital Markets. In addition to general banking services, the company also offers securities underwriting, equipment leasing, brokerage services, investments, and insurance. Subsidiaries include investment bank FTN Financial, investment advisors Highland Capital and Martin & Company, and First Horizon Home Loans, which operates in some 40 states.

	Annual Growth	12/03	12/04	12/05	12/06	12/07
Assets ($ mil.)	10.9%	24,506.7	29,771.7	36,579.1	37,918.3	37,015.5
Net income ($ mil.)	—	473.3	454.4	438.0	462.9	(170.1)
Market value ($ mil.)	(19.7%)	5,505.2	5,325.5	4,852.0	5,216.9	2,293.5
Employees	(38.4%)	—	—	26,676	12,398	10,130

FIRST INDUSTRIAL REALTY TRUST, INC.

NYSE: FR

311 S. Wacker Dr., Ste. 4000
Chicago, IL 60606
Phone: 312-344-4300
Fax: 312-922-6320
Web: www.firstindustrial.com

CEO: Michael W. (Mike) Brennan
CFO: Michael J. Havala
HR: –
FYE: December 31
Type: Public

First Industrial wants to be the first and only stop for all of your industrial property needs. As its name suggests, the self-administered real estate investment trust (REIT) owns, manages, and develops industrial real estate. Its portfolio consists of some 800 properties in nearly 30 states and Canada, with the largest concentrations in Michigan, Texas, and Colorado. The REIT's more than 60 million sq. ft. of industrial space is weighted toward light industrial properties but also includes bulk and regional warehouses, research and development buildings, and manufacturing facilities. The company also builds to suit for companies that need customized industrial facilities.

	Annual Growth	12/03	12/04	12/05	12/06	12/07
Sales ($ mil.)	6.2%	341.4	319.7	367.1	396.0	434.9
Net income ($ mil.)	8.0%	113.8	110.6	87.1	112.1	155.1
Market value ($ mil.)	3.0%	1,345.0	1,744.6	1,711.1	2,110.5	1,511.1
Employees	—	—	—	441	—	—

FIRST INVESTORS CORPORATION

110 Wall St.
New York, NY 10005
Phone: 212-858-8000
Fax: 212-858-8014
Web: www.firstinvestors.com

CEO: Robert Flanagan
CFO: William Lipkus
HR: Karen Nelson
FYE: December 31
Type: Private

So maybe they weren't the very first investors, but they *have* been around for a while. Founded in 1930, First Investors oversees a variety of investment and insurance operations through its subsidiaries and affiliates, including First Investors Life Insurance Company. The company's products and services include mutual funds, college savings plans, insurance, and retirement planning. First Investors, which has more than $7 billion in assets under management, prides itself on offering a personal approach to investment management, employing advisers in some 25 states.

	Annual Growth	12/03	12/04	12/05	12/06	12/07
Est. sales ($ mil.)	—	—	—	—	—	83.0
Employees	—	—	—	—	—	460

FIRST INVESTORS FINANCIAL SERVICES

OTC: FIFS

675 Bering Dr., Ste. 710
Houston, TX 77057
Phone: 713-977-2600
Fax: 800-528-2384
Web: www.fifsg.com

CEO: Tommy A. Moore Jr.
CFO: Bennie H. Duck
HR: Mary Dela Cruz
FYE: April 30
Type: Public

They're not the first investors in the subprime auto loan market, but they're coming on. First Investors Financial Services Group, Inc., originates subprime auto loans (made to people with blemished or nonexistent credit) indirectly through auto dealers or directly to consumers; the latter accounts for nearly two thirds of all originations. The dealer indirect program consists of loans originated through more than 2,000 franchised auto dealers. First Investors Financial Services writes auto loans in more than 40 states. Texas represents its largest market, followed by Georgia; those two states are home to almost half of the company's receivables.

	Annual Growth	4/03	4/04	4/05	4/06	4/07
Assets ($ mil.)	17.3%	273.0	245.8	283.5	419.3	516.4
Net income ($ mil.)	80.7%	0.3	0.0	0.7	2.5	3.2
Market value ($ mil.)	11.5%	20.6	26.8	21.0	33.2	31.8
Employees	30.4%	—	—	148	193	—

An in-depth profile of this company is available to Hoover's Online members at hoovers.com.

621

FIRST KEYSTONE CORPORATION

OTC: FKYS

111 W. Front St.
Berwick, PA 18603
Phone: 570-752-3671
Fax: 570-752-4022
Web: www.fnbbwk.com

CEO: J. Gerald Bazewicz
CFO: Diane C. A. Rosler
HR: –
FYE: December 31
Type: Public

First Keystone Corporation, it's not a group of fumbling and bumbling cops. It's the holding company for First Keystone National Bank (formerly First National Bank of Berwick), which serves individuals and businesses in northeastern and central Pennsylvania. The bank provides traditional deposit products including checking and savings accounts, debit cards, and CDs; business, consumer, and real estate loans; and trust and estate planning services. Real estate mortgages constitute more than 80% of the bank's loan portfolio; business and consumer installment loans make up the remainder. The company acquired Pocono Community Bank, which still operates as a division of First Keystone National Bank, in 2007.

	Annual Growth	12/03	12/04	12/05	12/06	12/07
Assets ($ mil.)	9.0%	481.8	497.6	512.4	525.9	681.2
Net income ($ mil.)	(4.4%)	7.3	6.8	6.8	6.2	6.1
Market value ($ mil.)	17.8%	44.6	94.7	84.6	81.5	86.0
Employees	—	—	—	—	—	178

FIRST KEYSTONE FINANCIAL, INC.

NASDAQ (GM): FKFS

22 W. State St.
Media, PA 19063
Phone: 610-565-6210
Fax: 610-892-5150
Web: www.firstkeystone.com

CEO: Thomas M. Kelly
CFO: Thomas M. Kelly
HR: Carol Walsh
FYE: September 30
Type: Public

First Keystone wants to be the cornerstone of its Pennsylvania customers' financial security. It's the holding company for First Keystone Federal Savings Bank, which serves the Keystone State's Delaware and Chester counties from nearly 10 offices. The bank offers standard deposit products and services such as checking and savings accounts, CDs, IRAs, and money market accounts, as well as credit cards, insurance, and investments. Single-family residential mortgages and home equity loans account for nearly two-thirds of the company's loan portfolio.

	Annual Growth	9/03	9/04	9/05	9/06	9/07
Assets ($ mil.)	(1.5%)	558.7	571.9	518.1	523.0	524.9
Net income ($ mil.)	(34.4%)	2.7	2.2	0.6	1.0	0.5
Market value ($ mil.)	(10.8%)	51.0	42.9	44.5	40.0	32.4
Employees	(0.9%)	—	—	112	—	110

FIRST LITCHFIELD FINANCIAL CORPORATION

OTC: FLFL

13 North St.
Litchfield, CT 06759
Phone: 860-567-8752
Fax: 860-567-9326
Web: www.fnbl.com

CEO: Joseph J. Greco
CFO: Carroll A. Pereira
HR: Karen Laliberte
FYE: December 31
Type: Public

This bank was established even before the Federal Reserve System! First Litchfield Financial Corporation's subsidiary, First National Bank of Litchfield (FNBL), has served the communities of Litchfield County, Connecticut, since 1814. It's the state's oldest bank, not to mention one of the oldest in the nation. Through about 10 branches, FNBL provides standard retail products and services, including checking, savings, and money market accounts; IRAs; and CDs. It uses funds from deposits to originate business and consumer loans; residential mortgages make up the lion's share of FNBL's loan portfolio at nearly 60%. Additionally, the company provides trust, investment, and estate management services.

	Annual Growth	12/03	12/04	12/05	12/06	12/07
Assets ($ mil.)	6.6%	393.8	424.3	467.6	501.2	507.7
Net income ($ mil.)	(9.2%)	2.8	3.9	4.0	1.4	1.9
Employees	7.2%	—	99	105	126	122

FIRST LOOK STUDIOS, INC.

Pink Sheets: FRST

2000 Avenue of the Stars, Ste. 410
Century City, CA 90067
Phone: 424-202-5000
Fax: –
Web: www.firstlookmedia.com

CEO: Trevor Short
CFO: –
HR: Richard Shore
FYE: December 31
Type: Public

Turn to these guys for a first look at the latest art film or second go 'round at *Baywatch*. First Look Studios provides film development, production and distribution, and foreign sales of its extensive film and television library that includes *Waking Ned Devine* and *Baywatch*. The company's 2007 films include *Aqua Teen Hunger Force Colon Movie Film for Theaters* and *Paris, je t'aime*. First Look is shifting its focus away from production and instead concentrating on the financing, distribution, marketing, and acquisition of movies. The company operates in the home entertainment market through its First Look Home Entertainment subsidiary.

	Annual Growth	12/03	12/04	12/05	12/06	12/07
Est. sales ($ mil.)	—	—	—	—	—	5.3
Employees	—	—	—	—	—	47

FIRST M&F CORPORATION

NASDAQ (GS): FMFC

134 W. Washington St.
Kosciusko, MS 39090
Phone: 662-289-5121
Fax: 662-289-8084
Web: www.mfbank.com

CEO: Hugh S. Potts Jr.
CFO: John G. Copeland
HR: –
FYE: December 31
Type: Public

First M&F Corporation is the holding company for Merchants and Farmers Bank of Kosciusko, which operates nearly 50 branches in Alabama, Florida, Mississippi, and Tennessee. Merchants and Farmers offers a full range of commercial and consumer services, including trust services, credit cards, loans, and a variety of deposit products. Its lending activities consist of commercial real estate loans (60% of its loan book), residential mortgages, and consumer, business, and agricultural loans. First M&F also has subsidiaries, and affiliates that offer insurance and investment products, asset-based lending, property management, and factoring services. It provides investment services through UVEST Financial.

	Annual Growth	12/03	12/04	12/05	12/06	12/07
Assets ($ mil.)	11.3%	1,078.3	1,142.7	1,267.1	1,540.3	1,653.8
Net income ($ mil.)	7.4%	10.9	10.8	12.6	13.9	14.5
Market value ($ mil.)	13.4%	86.5	76.2	75.8	177.2	143.3
Employees	9.3%	—	—	472	—	564

THE FIRST MARBLEHEAD CORPORATION

NYSE: FMD

The Prudential Tower, 800 Boylston St., 34th Fl.
Boston, MA 02199
Phone: 617-638-2000
Fax: 617-638-2100
Web: www.firstmarblehead.com

CEO: Jack L. Kopnisky
CFO: John A. Hupalo
HR: –
FYE: June 30
Type: Public

With a Harvard education costing six figures, that government student loan just isn't going to cut it anymore. Enter First Marblehead. The company creates programs and provides services for lenders who offer private (not secured by the government) student loans for undergraduate, graduate, and professional education, and to a lesser extent primary and secondary education. First Marblehead provides marketing, servicing, processing, securitization, and guarantee services to national and regional lending institutions. In light of difficulties in the student loan industry, the company eliminated 500 jobs (more than half of its personnel) in 2008.

	Annual Growth	6/03	6/04	6/05	6/06	6/07
Assets ($ mil.)	93.2%	87.1	360.1	558.2	770.3	1,214.5
Net income ($ mil.)	85.3%	31.5	75.3	159.7	236.0	371.3
Market value ($ mil.)	28.1%	—	1,717.1	1,516.9	2,393.1	3,606.7
Employees	11.2%	—	—	842	932	1,042

FIRST MARINER BANCORP

NASDAQ (GM): FMAR

1501 S. Clinton St.
Baltimore, MD 21224
Phone: 410-342-2600
Fax: 410-563-1594
Web: www.1stmarinerbank.com

CEO: Edwin F. Hale Sr.
CFO: Mark A. Keidel
HR: Lorraine Ash
FYE: December 31
Type: Public

First Mariner Bancorp helps customers navigate banking seas (and fees). It's the holding company for First Mariner Bank, which operates more than two dozen branches along the Baltimore/Washington DC corridor. Targeting individuals and businesses, First Mariner Bank offers standard deposit products such as checking, savings, and money market accounts. Lending activities consist of commercial mortgages (more than 30% of all loans), as well as consumer (20%), residential construction (about 15%), residential mortgage, and business loans. Subsidiary First Mariner Mortgage originates mortgages for sale to secondary markets. First Mariner Bancorp also owns Mariner Finance, which offers consumer loans in five states.

	Annual Growth	12/03	12/04	12/05	12/06	12/07
Assets ($ mil.)	4.2%	1,057.8	1,250.5	1,362.5	1,263.3	1,246.8
Net income ($ mil.)	—	5.3	6.1	7.8	1.9	(10.1)
Market value ($ mil.)	(23.6%)	105.9	102.3	109.6	119.2	36.0
Employees	—	—	—	730	—	—

FIRST MERCHANTS CORPORATION

NASDAQ (GS): FRME

200 E. Jackson St.
Muncie, IN 47305
Phone: 765-747-1500
Fax: 765-747-1473
Web: www.firstmerchants.com

CEO: Michael C. (Mike) Rechin
CFO: Mark K. Hardwick
HR: Kimberly J. (Kim) Ellington
FYE: December 31
Type: Public

First Merchants makes community banking its first priority. The multibank holding company owns First Merchants Bank, First Merchants Bank of Central Indiana, Lafayette Bank and Trust, and Commerce National Bank, which together have more than 65 branches in Indiana and western Ohio. The banks provide standard consumer and commercial banking services, including checking and savings accounts, certificates of deposit, and check cards. Commercial real estate and farmland loans account for the largest portion of the company's loan portfolio (about 33%), followed by residential mortgages and business loans.

	Annual Growth	12/03	12/04	12/05	12/06	12/07
Assets ($ mil.)	5.3%	3,076.8	3,191.7	3,237.1	3,554.9	3,782.1
Net income ($ mil.)	3.4%	27.6	29.4	30.2	30.2	31.6
Market value ($ mil.)	(4.5%)	472.4	524.8	479.1	501.4	393.2
Employees	—	—	—	—	—	—

FIRST MERCURY FINANCIAL CORPORATION

NYSE: FMR

29621 Northwestern Hwy.
Southfield, MI 48034
Phone: 248-358-4010
Fax: 248-358-2459
Web: www.firstmercury.com

CEO: Richard H. Smith
CFO: John A. Marazza
HR: –
FYE: December 31
Type: Public

First Mercury Financial Corporation (FMFC) would like to take after its namesake, the Roman god of commerce and profit, by capitalizing on its expertise in niche insurance markets. Through its CoverX wholesale brokerage, the company underwrites general and professional liability policies for businesses, with a special focus on the security industry — private investigators, security guards, armored car units, and the like. It has also formed a special general liability unit that insures small to midsized builders, oil and gas contractors, and apartment building owners, among others.

	Annual Growth	12/03	12/04	12/05	12/06	12/07
Assets ($ mil.)	43.3%	—	254.0	365.6	512.9	747.3
Net income ($ mil.)	39.5%	11.0	17.7	22.8	21.9	41.7
Market value ($ mil.)	7.6%	—	—	—	407.6	438.5
Employees	19.7%	—	—	136	148	195

FIRST MID-ILLINOIS BANCSHARES, INC.

OTC: FMBH

1515 Charleston Ave.
Mattoon, IL 61938
Phone: 217-234-7454
Fax: 217-258-0426
Web: www.firstmid.com

CEO: William S. Rowland
CFO: Michael L. Taylor
HR: Kelly A. Downs
FYE: December 31
Type: Public

Money doesn't grow on trees, so when farmers in Central Illinois need a little cash, they turn to First Mid-Illinois Bancshares. Its primary subsidiary, First Mid-Illinois Bank & Trust, is the largest supplier of farm credit (including real estate, machinery, and production loans; inventory financing; and lines of credit) in its market area. In addition to agricultural loans, the bank also offers commercial, consumer, industrial, and real estate lending. Through its more than two dozen branches, it also provides standard deposit products such as savings and checking accounts, as well as trust and investment services.

	Annual Growth	12/03	12/04	12/05	12/06	12/07
Assets ($ mil.)	6.4%	793.6	826.7	850.6	980.6	1,016.3
Net income ($ mil.)	2.9%	9.1	9.8	9.8	10.0	10.2
Market value ($ mil.)	26.0%	64.8	112.9	118.7	116.6	163.5
Employees	—	—	—	—	—	—

FIRST MIDWEST BANCORP, INC.

NASDAQ (GS): FMBI

1 Pierce Place, Ste. 1500
Itasca, IL 60143
Phone: 630-875-7450
Fax: 630-875-7369
Web: www.firstmidwest.com

CEO: John M. O'Meara
CFO: Paul F. Clemens
HR: –
FYE: December 31
Type: Public

There's a lot of cabbage in corn country. Just ask First Midwest Bancorp, parent of First Midwest Bank. Through around 100 branches, the bank serves primarily the suburban Chicago area, including parts of Iowa and Indiana. Services include deposit products, loans, and trust and investment management services. Commercial real estate loans account for about 40% of the bank's portfolio; commercial and industrial loans are around 25%. Subsidiary FMB Investment Corporation manages investment securities and provides corporate management services. FMB Investment Trust manages the bank's real estate loans. First Midwest Insurance acts as a reinsurer of credit life, accident, and health coverage.

	Annual Growth	12/03	12/04	12/05	12/06	12/07
Assets ($ mil.)	4.0%	6,906.7	6,863.4	7,210.1	8,441.5	8,091.5
Net income ($ mil.)	(3.6%)	92.8	99.1	101.4	117.3	80.2
Market value ($ mil.)	(0.5%)	1,510.6	1,671.7	1,591.3	1,935.0	1,482.7
Employees	—	—	—	1,625	—	—

FIRST MONTAUK FINANCIAL CORP.

OTC: FMFK

Parkway 109 Office Center, 328 Newman Springs Rd.
Red Bank, NJ 07701
Phone: 732-842-4700
Fax: 732-842-9047
Web: www.montaukfinancial.com

CEO: Victor K. Kurylak
CFO: Mindy A. Horowitz
HR: Pat Pampel
FYE: December 31
Type: Public

First Montauk Financial offers financial services through a network of independent affiliates. Operating as Montauk Financial Group, the company offers securities brokerage services to retail and institutional clients. It recruits established broker/dealers and provides them with financial products and back-office administrative support in return for a percentage of commissions. The company has some 200 representatives in 24 states who handle about 45,000 accounts. All of the firm's branch offices are owned and operated by affiliates. First Montauk Financial also performs corporate finance and investment banking; its Montauk Insurance Services unit sells life insurance, health insurance, and annuities.

	Annual Growth	12/03	12/04	12/05	12/06	12/07
Sales ($ mil.)	(9.2%)	58.2	59.2	58.1	51.0	39.6
Net income ($ mil.)	—	(3.5)	0.7	2.4	(0.8)	(2.1)
Employees	(19.6%)	529	356	326	275	221

An in-depth profile of this company is available to Hoover's Online members at hoovers.com.

623

FIRST NATIONAL BANCSHARES, INC.

NASDAQ (GM): FNSC

215 N. Pine St.
Spartanburg, SC 29302
Phone: 864-948-9001
Fax: 864-281-0830
Web: www.firstnational-online.com

CEO: Jerry L. Calvert
CFO: Kitty B. Payne
HR: Van Clark
FYE: December 31
Type: Public

Do the East Lake High School Spartans bank at First National Bancshares' First National Bank of the South? Cheri Oteri and Will Ferrell might say, "Uh-huh, uh-huh, uh-huh!" Also known as First National Bank of Spartanburg, the bank operates more than a half-dozen offices in South Carolina, offering checking, savings, and money market accounts, as well as trust and investment management services. Commercial real estate loans make up more than half of the bank's loan portfolio. First National Bancshares also operates small business lending division, First National Business Capital. The company added four branches when it acquired Carolina National Corporation and its Carolina National Bank subsidiary in 2008.

	Annual Growth	12/03	12/04	12/05	12/06	12/07
Assets ($ mil.)	34.2%	180.6	236.3	328.7	465.4	586.5
Net income ($ mil.)	46.1%	0.9	1.8	2.8	4.1	4.1
Market value ($ mil.)	38.6%	13.2	28.1	55.1	55.3	48.9
Employees	32.9%	—	—	77	102	136

FIRST NATIONAL BANK ALASKA

OTC: FBAK

101 W. 36th Ave.
Anchorage, AK 99503
Phone: 907-777-4362
Fax: 907-777-4569
Web: www.fnbalaska.com

CEO: Daniel H. Cuddy
CFO: Jason L. Roth
HR: –
FYE: December 31
Type: Public

First National Bank Alaska is a financial anchor in Anchorage. Founded in 1922, the bank (formerly The First National Bank of Anchorage) is one of the state's oldest and largest financial institutions. With nearly 30 branches throughout The Last Frontier (and about 20 ATMs in rural communities), First National Bank Alaska offers traditional deposit products such as checking, savings, and money market accounts, as well as trust and escrow services. Commercial mortgages represent more than 35% of the bank's loan portfolio; commercial and industrial loans account for about another 25%. The family of longtime president Daniel Cuddy owns a majority of the company.

	Annual Growth	12/03	12/04	12/05	12/06	12/07
Est. sales ($ mil.)	—	—	—	—	—	146.5
Employees	—	—	—	—	—	738

FIRST NATIONAL COMMUNITY BANCORP, INC.

OTC: FNCB

102 E. Drinker St.
Dunmore, PA 18512
Phone: 570-346-7667
Fax: 570-348-6426
Web: www.fncb.com

CEO: J. David Lombardi
CFO: William S. Lance
HR: Robert J. Mancuso
FYE: December 31
Type: Public

First National Community Bancorp is the holding company for First National Community Bank, which has about 20 offices in Lackawanna, Luzerne, Wayne and Monroe counties in northeastern Pennsylvania. The bank offers standard retail services such as checking and savings accounts, credit cards, mortgages, and other loans. Real estate loans account for approximately 65% of its loan portfolio, while commercial and industrial loans make up another 20%. Executives and directors of First National Community Bancorp collectively own nearly 30% of the company.

	Annual Growth	12/03	12/04	12/05	12/06	12/07
Assets ($ mil.)	12.3%	816.3	907.5	1,008.1	1,184.8	1,296.2
Net income ($ mil.)	14.3%	8.6	9.3	11.2	13.5	14.7
Market value ($ mil.)	81.4%	27.6	198.2	237.1	287.0	299.0
Employees	—	—	—	—	—	302

FIRST NATIONAL CORPORATION

Pink Sheets: FXNC

112 W. King St.
Strasburg, VA 22657
Phone: 540-465-9121
Fax: 540-465-5946
Web: www.firstbank-va.com

CEO: Harry S. Smith
CFO: M. Shane Bell
HR: –
FYE: December 31
Type: Public

First National Corporation knows that being number one is always good. The financial institution is the holding company for First Bank, which has about a dozen branches in northern Virginia's Shenandoah Valley. The bank provides community-oriented deposit products and services, including checking and savings accounts, IRAs, money market accounts, CDs, and NOW accounts. Mortgages account for about 60% of the company's loan portfolio; the company also provides business, construction, and consumer loans. Additionally, First Bank provides trust and asset management services.

	Annual Growth	12/03	12/04	12/05	12/06	12/07
Assets ($ mil.)	12.0%	343.6	408.8	475.0	527.9	541.6
Net income ($ mil.)	15.1%	3.3	4.2	5.4	5.8	5.8
Market value ($ mil.)	28.0%	24.5	30.7	79.1	78.9	65.8
Employees	—	—	—	—	—	172

FIRST NATIONAL LINCOLN CORPORATION

NASDAQ (GS): FNLC

223 Main St.
Damariscotta, ME 04543
Phone: 207-563-3195
Fax: 207-563-6853
Web: www.the1st.com

CEO: Daniel R. Daigneault
CFO: F. Stephen Ward
HR: Susan A. Norton
FYE: December 31
Type: Public

First National Lincoln is the holding company for The First, a regional bank serving coastal Maine from about 15 branches. Tracing its roots to 1852, the bank offers traditional retail products and services, including checking and savings accounts, CDs, IRAs, and loans. Residential mortgages make up about half of the company's loan portfolio; business loans account for nearly 30%. Bank division First Advisors offers private banking and investment management services. First National Lincoln acquired competitor FNB Bankshares and its First National Bank of Bar Harbor subsidiary in early 2005.

	Annual Growth	12/03	12/04	12/05	12/06	12/07
Assets ($ mil.)	21.1%	568.8	634.2	1,042.2	1,104.9	1,223.3
Net income ($ mil.)	15.3%	7.4	8.5	12.8	12.3	13.1
Market value ($ mil.)	37.1%	40.3	128.4	172.9	163.4	142.5
Employees	(1.9%)	—	—	216	212	—

FIRST NATIONAL OF NEBRASKA, INC.

Pink Sheets: FINN

1620 Dodge St.
Omaha, NE 68197
Phone: 402-341-0500
Fax: 402-342-4332
Web: www.fnni.com

CEO: Bruce R. Lauritzen
CFO: Timothy D. (Tim) Hart
HR: –
FYE: December 31
Type: Public

It's not corny to say that First National of Nebraska is one of the largest community bank holding companies in the western US. It is the parent of several western and midwestern banks and nonbanking subsidiaries, including First National Bank Southwest, First National Bank of Colorado, First National Bank South Dakota, First National Bank Omaha, Castle Bank (Illinois), and First National Merchant Solutions, a credit card payment processor. All told, the company has about 90 banking locations and merchant sales operations nationwide. The banks offer savings, loans, and other banking services for individuals and businesses alike.

	Annual Growth	12/97	12/98	12/99	12/00	*12/01
Assets ($ mil.)	7.4%	7,332.0	7,465.2	8,560.4	9,283.3	9,752.3
Net income ($ mil.)	1.8%	75.2	86.5	92.4	105.5	80.8
Employees	13.5%	4,553	5,047	5,867	—	—

*Most recent year available

An in-depth profile of this company is available to Hoover's Online members at hoovers.com.

FIRST NIAGARA FINANCIAL GROUP, INC.

NASDAQ (GS): FNFG

6950 S. Transit Rd.
Lockport, NY 14095
Phone: 716-625-7500
Fax: 716-625-8405
Web: www.fnfg.com

CEO: John R. Koelmel
CFO: Michael W. Harrington
HR: Kathleen P. Monti
FYE: December 31
Type: Public

A lot of water and a few barrels have gone over Niagara Falls since First Niagara Bank was founded. Tracing its roots to 1870, the flagship subsidiary of acquisitive First Niagara Financial Group operates more than 100 offices in western and central New York, offering deposit and loan products, brokerage services, insurance, investments, and asset management. Residential mortgages comprise about 35% of the company's loan portfolio; commercial real estate loans are more than 30%. The company's First Niagara Commercial Bank subsidiary accepts municipal deposits. In 2008 First Niagara Financial bought Great Lakes Bancorp, the parent of Greater Buffalo Savings Bank.

	Annual Growth	12/03	12/04	12/05	12/06	12/07
Assets ($ mil.)	22.5%	3,589.5	5,078.4	8,064.8	7,945.5	8,096.2
Net income ($ mil.)	23.5%	36.1	51.8	92.9	91.9	84.1
Market value ($ mil.)	4.5%	1,058.9	1,151.1	1,632.3	1,645.3	1,261.4
Employees	(4.1%)	—	—	1,984	1,922	1,824

FIRST NORTHERN COMMUNITY BANCORP

OTC: FNRN

195 N. First St.
Dixon, CA 95620
Phone: 707-678-3041
Fax: 707-678-9734
Web: www.thatsmybank.com

CEO: Owen J. (John) Onsum
CFO: Louise A. Walker
HR: Larry Miller
FYE: December 31*
Type: Public

First Northern Community Bancorp is the holding company for First Northern Bank, which operates about 10 branches in the northern California counties of El Dorado, Placer, Sacramento, Solano, and Yolo. Founded in 1910, the bank offers community-oriented services such as checking, savings, and money market accounts, and certificates of deposit. Its loan products include real estate mortgages (which account for about half of the bank's portfolio), commercial and construction loans, and agricultural and installment loans. Investment products and services are available to customers via a pact with Raymond James Financial.

	Annual Growth	12/04	12/05	12/06	12/07	*3/08
Assets ($ mil.)	3.1%	628.7	660.7	685.2	709.9	709.9
Net income ($ mil.)	2.2%	6.7	8.7	8.8	7.3	7.3
Market value ($ mil.)	55.4%	20.3	155.5	161.6	121.4	118.5
Employees	—	—	—	—	—	—

*Fiscal year change

THE FIRST OF LONG ISLAND CORPORATION

NASDAQ (CM): FLIC

10 Glen Head Rd.
Glen Head, NY 11545
Phone: 516-671-4900
Fax: 516-676-7900
Web: www.fnbli.com

CEO: Michael N. Vittorio
CFO: Mark D. Curtis
HR: –
FYE: December 31
Type: Public

When it comes to banking, The First of Long Island wants to be the first thing on Long Islanders' minds. The company owns The First National Bank of Long Island, which offers a variety of lending, investment, and deposit services through about two dozen branches on New York's Long Island and in Manhattan. Loans secured by real estate, including residential and commercial mortgages, home equity loans, and construction loans, make up more than 85% of the bank's loan portfolio. To a lesser extent, the bank also writes business and consumer loans. Other services include checking and savings accounts, IRAs, CDs, and credit cards. Subsidiary The First of Long Island Agency sells mutual funds and annuities.

	Annual Growth	12/03	12/04	12/05	12/06	12/07
Assets ($ mil.)	4.0%	914.3	917.8	944.2	954.2	1,069.0
Net income ($ mil.)	0.2%	11.4	12.1	12.3	11.2	11.5
Market value ($ mil.)	12.0%	87.8	99.4	81.3	83.4	138.3
Employees	2.9%	—	—	203	—	215

FIRST PACTRUST BANCORP, INC.

NASDAQ (GM): FPTB

610 Bay Blvd.
Chula Vista, CA 91910
Phone: 619-691-1519
Fax: 619-691-1350
Web: www.pacifictrustbank.com

CEO: Hans R. Ganz
CFO: Regan J. Lauer
HR: Lisa Moss
FYE: December 31
Type: Public

First PacTrust Bancorp is the holding company for Pacific Trust Bank, which operates nearly 10 branches in Southern California's Riverside and San Diego counties. The community bank offers standard services such as deposit accounts and real estate loans, with mortgages secured by one-to four-family residences accounting for nearly 60% of its loan portfolio. Multifamily residential and commercial mortgages and business, construction, and consumer loans round out its lending activities. The bank was founded in 1941 as Rohr Employees Federal Credit Union; a handful of former Rohr executives remain on First PacTrust's board of directors.

	Annual Growth	12/03	12/04	12/05	12/06	12/07
Assets ($ mil.)	5.6%	624.0	674.5	755.2	808.3	774.7
Net income ($ mil.)	(7.5%)	4.1	5.1	4.8	4.7	3.0
Market value ($ mil.)	(8.2%)	113.0	127.0	120.0	122.1	80.1
Employees	—	—	—	114	—	—

FIRST PLACE FINANCIAL CORP.

NASDAQ (GS): FPFC

185 E. Market St.
Warren, OH 44481
Phone: 330-373-1221
Fax: 330-393-5578
Web: www.firstplacebank.net

CEO: Steven R. Lewis
CFO: David W. Gifford
HR: Robert J. Kowalski
FYE: June 30
Type: Public

First Place Financial is the holding company for First Place Bank, which serves businesses and consumers through about 25 branch offices in northeastern Ohio; Franklin Bank, a division of First Place bank, has about 15 branches in Michigan. The company also operates more than 10 loan production offices in Ohio, Michigan, and Indiana. First Place Financial also owns a real estate brokerage; a general insurance agency that sells life, health, and property/casualty coverage; a title insurance agency; and two employee benefits consulting firms. One- to four-family residential real estate loans make up almost half of First Place Financial's loan portfolio; commercial loans make up more than 35%.

	Annual Growth	6/03	6/04	6/05	6/06	6/07
Assets ($ mil.)	19.9%	1,558.6	2,247.1	2,498.9	3,113.2	3,226.2
Net income ($ mil.)	11.3%	16.7	14.1	18.9	23.0	25.6
Market value ($ mil.)	11.1%	232.9	281.5	301.9	401.1	355.1
Employees	—	—	—	—	868	—

FIRST POTOMAC REALTY TRUST

NYSE: FPO

7600 Wisconsin Ave., 11th Fl.
Bethesda, MD 20814
Phone: 301-986-9200
Fax: 301-986-5554
Web: www.first-potomac.com

CEO: Douglas J. (Doug) Donatelli
CFO: Barry H. Bass
HR: –
FYE: December 31
Type: Public

Will First Potomac Realty Trust build a portfolio as mighty as its namesake? The self-managed real estate investment trust (REIT) owns and manages more than 160 industrial properties and business parks in the Mid-Atlantic region, covering Washington, DC, Maryland, and Virginia. Its portfolio totals more than 11 million sq. ft. of space. As with many real estate firms located in the area, the REIT's largest tenant is the US government, which accounts for about 7% of its rental revenues; manufacturers account for about 25%. First Potomac Realty Trust generally purchases generous warehouse spaces and adds offices to add property value and increase revenue.

	Annual Growth	12/03	12/04	12/05	12/06	12/07
Sales ($ mil.)	61.3%	18.4	42.1	77.6	104.5	124.6
Net income ($ mil.)	—	(10.1)	2.6	1.4	10.0	0.5
Market value ($ mil.)	26.9%	161.8	322.7	533.9	702.3	419.3
Employees	15.0%	—	—	—	99	131

An in-depth profile of this company is available to Hoover's Online members at hoovers.com.

625

FIRST REGIONAL BANCORP

NASDAQ (GM): FRGB

1801 Century Park East, Ste. 800
Los Angeles, CA 90067
Phone: 310-552-1776
Fax: 310-552-1772
Web: www.firstregional.com

CEO: H. Anthony Gartshore
CFO: Elizabeth Thompson
HR: –
FYE: December 31
Type: Public

Wholesale banking company First Regional Bancorp caters to Southern California businesses through First Regional Bank. With about 10 locations, the bank mainly offers real estate loans (accounting for the majority of its portfolio), as well as commercial and construction loans. It specializes in equipment finance and midsized residential and commercial projects. Because of the bank's business focus, it has fewer customer deposit accounts than its competitors, but accounts typically have high balances. First Regional Bancorp also offers merchant credit card clearing and trust services, as well as administrative services for self-directed retirement plans.

	Annual Growth	12/03	12/04	12/05	12/06	12/07
Assets ($ mil.)	29.4%	775.3	1,306.1	1,811.7	2,074.6	2,174.3
Net income ($ mil.)	64.4%	4.6	11.1	26.5	38.3	33.6
Market value ($ mil.)	68.5%	27.9	71.9	91.9	418.7	224.6
Employees	16.1%	—	—	224	264	302

FIRST REPUBLIC BANK

111 Pine St.
San Francisco, CA 94111
Phone: 415-392-1400
Fax: 415-392-1413
Web: www.firstrepublic.com

CEO: James H. Herbert II
CFO: Willis H. Newton Jr.
HR: Esther Trillana
FYE: December 31
Type: Subsidiary

First Republic Bank is a trophy bank for people who build trophy homes. The company offers personal and business banking, trust, investment management, and brokerage services for wealthy clients. The bank operates about 50 branches mostly in California's Silicon Valley, Bay area, and the wine country, but also in the Northeast and the Pacific Northwest. The bank's lending focuses on financing the purchase, construction, and renovation of luxury homes. Merrill Lynch bought the bank for some $1.8 billion in 2007; First Republic Bank now operates as a division of Merrill Lynch Bank & Trust.

	Annual Growth	12/03	12/04	12/05	12/06	12/07
Est. sales ($ mil.)	—	—	—	—	—	685.7
Employees	—	—	—	—	—	1,500

FIRST REPUBLIC PREFERRED CAPITAL

NASDAQ (GM): FRCCO

111 Pine St., 2nd Fl.
San Francisco, CA 94111
Phone: 415-392-1400
Fax: 415-392-1413

CEO: James J. Baumberger
CFO: Willis H. Newton Jr.
HR: –
FYE: December 31
Type: Public

First Republic Preferred Capital Corporation prefers mortgages to almost any other type of investment. The company is a real estate investment trust (REIT) that invests in residential mortgages. Formed in 1999 by First Republic Bank, the REIT acquires its mortgages from its parent company (although it is not required to do so). Most of the single-family mortgages it invests in are nonconforming loans; multifamily mortgages are typically secured by urban properties in San Francisco, Los Angeles, and Las Vegas. California accounts for about 80% of its total portfolio. First Republic Preferred Capital is also open to investing in commercial mortgages. First Republic Bank owns 99.9% of the REIT's common shares.

	Annual Growth	12/03	12/04	12/05	12/06	12/07
Sales ($ mil.)	9.7%	13.6	16.5	16.5	18.7	19.7
Net income ($ mil.)	9.7%	13.4	16.2	16.2	18.5	19.4
Market value ($ mil.)	(1.4%)	49.8	61.5	59.5	60.4	47.0
Employees	—	—	—	—	—	0

FIRST RESERVE CORPORATION

1 Lafayette Place
Greenwich, CT 06830
Phone: 203-661-6601
Fax: 203-661-6729
Web: www.frcorp.com

CEO: William E. (Bill) Macaulay
CFO: Jennifer C. Zarrilli
HR: –
FYE: December 31
Type: Private

First Reserve Corporation fuels the companies that help fuel the world. The private equity firm invests in middle-market energy companies, and currently manages about $12.5 billion. Its typical investment ranges from $100 million to $500 million in enterprises involved in energy manufacturing and services, energy infrastructure, and energy reserves. The company's current portfolio includes stakes in some 20 firms, including Brand Energy & Infrastructure Services and Dresser. In 2008 the company offered to buy CHC Helicopter for some $1.5 billion. First Reserve's investor base is primarily composed of corporations, endowments, foundations, and public retirement funds.

	Annual Growth	12/03	12/04	12/05	12/06	12/07
Est. sales ($ mil.)	—	—	—	—	—	218.2
Employees	—	—	—	—	—	6,484

FIRST ROBINSON FINANCIAL CORPORATION

OTC: FRFC

501 E. Main St.
Robinson, IL 62454
Phone: 618-544-8621
Fax: 618-544-7506
Web: www.frsb.net

CEO: Rick L. Catt
CFO: Jamie E. McReynolds
HR: –
FYE: March 31
Type: Public

If heaven holds a place for those who pay, hey, hey, hey, then here's to you, First Robinson! First Robinson Financial is the holding company for First Robinson Savings Bank, which provides traditional banking services to individuals and businesses in eastern Illinois' Crawford County through four area locations. Deposit services include savings, checking, money market, and NOW accounts; IRAs; and CDs. The bank uses funds from deposits primarily to originate one- to four-family real estate loans (accounting for more than half of the bank's loan portfolio), and to a lesser extent, consumer, commercial, and agricultural loans.

	Annual Growth	3/04	3/05	3/06	3/07	3/08
Assets ($ mil.)	7.0%	101.9	111.4	109.4	112.3	133.8
Net income ($ mil.)	2.7%	0.9	0.9	1.0	1.0	1.0
Market value ($ mil.)	6.0%	12.8	12.8	12.6	16.7	16.2
Employees	—	—	—	—	—	—

FIRST SECURITY GROUP, INC.

NASDAQ (GS): FSGI

531 Broad St.
Chattanooga, TN 37402
Phone: 423-266-2000
Fax: 423-267-3383
Web: www.fsgbank.com

CEO: Rodger B. Holley
CFO: William L. (Chip) Lusk Jr.
HR: –
FYE: December 31
Type: Public

Pardon me boy, as Glenn Miller would say, but if you've got your fare and a trifle to spare, you might want to turn to First Security Group. The holding company for FSGBank operates about 40 branches in eastern and middle Tennessee (including Chattanooga) and northern Georgia; in addition to the FSGBank brand, the company also operates certain locations under the Dalton Whitfield Bank, Jackson Bank & Trust, and Primer Banco Seguro names. The bank offers standard deposit and lending services, including checking and savings accounts and CDs. Real estate loans and mortgages make up about three-quarters of First Security's loan portfolio, which also includes business, agricultural, and consumer loans.

	Annual Growth	12/03	12/04	12/05	12/06	12/07
Assets ($ mil.)	17.1%	644.8	766.7	1,040.7	1,129.8	1,212.0
Net income ($ mil.)	46.1%	2.5	4.3	9.6	11.1	11.4
Market value ($ mil.)	(6.4%)	—	—	171.9	204.8	150.6
Employees	(1.5%)	—	—	366	376	355

An in-depth profile of this company is available to Hoover's Online members at hoovers.com.

FIRST SOLAR, INC.

NASDAQ (GM): FSLR

350 W. Washington St., Ste. 600
Tempe, AZ 85281
Phone: 602-414-9300
Fax: 602-414-9400
Web: www.firstsolar.com

CEO: Michael J. Ahearn
CFO: Jens Meyerhoff
HR: –
FYE: Last Saturday in December
Type: Public

Ready to go solar? Maybe you should first get into film. First Solar makes solar-power modules with a thin-film semiconductor technology that doesn't use silicon. A worldwide shortage of polycrystalline silicon is holding back some producers of silicon-based solar cells, which can't get enough raw material to meet demand. First Solar uses a sheet of glass as a substrate, coated with a film of cadmium telluride, for its products. About 90% of the company's sales of solar modules are to six customers in Germany — Blitzstrom, Colexon Energy, Conergy, Gehrlicher Umweltschonende Energiesysteme, Juwi Solar, and Phoenix Solar.

	Annual Growth	12/03	12/04	12/05	12/06	12/07
Sales ($ mil.)	254.3%	3.2	13.5	48.1	135.0	504.0
Net income ($ mil.)	—	(28.0)	(16.8)	(6.5)	4.0	158.4
Market value ($ mil.)	868.5%	—	—	—	2,158.4	20,904.1
Employees	102.2%	—	—	—	723	1,462

FIRST SOUTH BANCORP, INC.

NASDAQ (GS): FSBK

1311 Carolina Ave.
Washington, NC 27889
Phone: 252-946-4178
Fax: 252-946-3873
Web: www.firstsouthnc.com

CEO: Thomas A. Vann
CFO: William L. Wall
HR: –
FYE: December 31
Type: Public

First South Bancorp (not to be confused with the South Carolina company of the same name) is the holding company for First South Bank. Founded in 1902, the bank has more than 25 offices throughout the eastern half of North Carolina. Its deposit products include checking, savings, and money market accounts; CDs; and IRAs; these are used to fund a variety of loans. Commercial real estate loans comprise more than 70% of the bank's loan portfolio, which is rounded out by single-family mortgages, home equity loans, and business, construction, and consumer loans. Bank subsidiary First South Leasing provides equipment lease financing; retail investment services are offered through a partnership with UVEST.

	Annual Growth	12/03	12/04	12/05	12/06	12/07
Assets ($ mil.)	7.7%	675.8	721.2	833.1	910.5	909.3
Net income ($ mil.)	10.5%	11.4	11.7	14.1	17.2	17.0
Market value ($ mil.)	33.8%	68.0	107.9	149.3	317.1	217.7
Employees	16.7%	—	—	252	294	—

FIRST SOUTH BANCORP, INC.

OTC: FSBS

1450 John B. White Sr. Blvd.
Spartanburg, SC 29306
Phone: 864-595-0455
Fax: 864-587-2781
Web: www.firstsouthbancorp.com

CEO: Barry L. Slider
CFO: V. Lewis Shuler
HR: –
FYE: December 31
Type: Public

First South Bancorp is full of firsts. It is the holding company for First South Bank (no relation to North Carolina's First South Bancorp) and serves the area around Spartanburg, South Carolina (a state that was among the first 13 American colonies and the first one to secede prior to the Civil War). The four-branch bank offers such traditional retail-banking products as checking and savings accounts, CDs, money market accounts, and IRAs. Funds from deposits are used to write real estate, business, and consumer installment loans. Mortgages account for more than three-quarters of the bank's loan portfolio. First South Bank also operates a loan production office in Asheville, North Carolina.

	Annual Growth	12/03	12/04	12/05	12/06	12/07
Assets ($ mil.)	10.8%	251.7	296.4	324.7	353.4	378.9
Net income ($ mil.)	11.1%	2.1	3.0	3.4	4.6	3.2
Market value ($ mil.)	12.7%	24.2	49.1	48.1	58.7	39.0
Employees	—	—	—	—	—	—

FIRST STATE BANCORPORATION

NASDAQ (GS): FSNM

7900 Jefferson NE
Albuquerque, NM 87109
Phone: 505-241-7500
Fax: 505-241-7572
Web: www.fsbnm.com

CEO: Michael R. Stanford
CFO: Christopher C. Spencer
HR: –
FYE: December 31
Type: Public

First State Bancorporation has cornered the Four Corners market. The bank is the holding company for First Community Bank, which operates about 60 branches in New Mexico, Colorado, Arizona, and Utah. Founded as First State Bank in 1922, First Community Bank provides retail services such as checking and savings accounts, money market accounts, CDs, and credit cards. Lending activities focus on residential real estate and construction, together accounting for about 75% of the bank's loan portfolio. First State Bancorporation is growing by acquiring other, smaller financial companies in the area.

	Annual Growth	12/03	12/04	12/05	12/06	12/07
Assets ($ mil.)	20.1%	1,646.7	1,815.5	2,157.6	2,801.6	3,424.2
Net income ($ mil.)	13.6%	14.9	15.2	21.4	22.8	24.8
Market value ($ mil.)	20.6%	132.1	281.7	369.3	514.2	279.3
Employees	16.7%	—	—	663	864	903

FIRST STATE FINANCIAL CORPORATION

NASDAQ (GM): FSTF

22 S. Links Ave.
Sarasota, FL 34236
Phone: 941-929-9000
Fax: 941-951-6189
Web: www.firststatefl.com

CEO: John E. (Jed) Wilkinson
CFO: Dennis Grinsteiner
HR: –
FYE: December 31
Type: Public

Florida certainly wasn't the first state, but First State Financial is the holding company for First State Bank, which serves individuals and small to midsized businesses in west-central Florida's Sarasota and Pinellas counties. Through more than a half-dozen branches, the bank offers such standard deposit services as checking and savings accounts, money market and retirement accounts, and certificates of deposit. Commercial real estate lending dominates First State Financial's loan portfolio, accounting for more than half of all loans written. The bank also makes business, construction, consumer, and residential mortgage loans.

	Annual Growth	12/03	12/04	12/05	12/06	12/07
Assets ($ mil.)	22.3%	212.3	274.0	372.7	453.5	474.9
Net income ($ mil.)	31.6%	0.8	2.1	3.8	5.3	2.4
Market value ($ mil.)	(8.5%)	—	76.2	89.5	99.3	58.4
Employees	17.2%	—	—	93	109	—

FIRST STUDENT INC.

705 Central Ave., Ste. 300
Cincinnati, OH 45202
Phone: 513-241-2200
Fax: 513-381-0149
Web: www.firststudentinc.com

CEO: Carey Paster
CFO: Gary Waites
HR: Rick Vilines
FYE: March 31
Type: Subsidiary

School bus operator First Student knows that a student's first assignment is to get to school. Together, First Student and sister company FirstBus Canada transports about 2.9 million students to and from their classrooms every day via a fleet of some 62,000 buses. Combined, the companies represent North America's #1 school bus business. First Student is a subsidiary of FirstGroup America, which in turn is a unit of UK-based FirstGroup. First Student's operations grew dramatically in 2007 when FirstGroup completed its acquisition of Laidlaw International, which had been the leading school bus company in North America.

	Annual Growth	3/03	3/04	3/05	3/06	3/07
Est. sales ($ mil.)	—	—	—	—	—	235.9
Employees	—	—	—	—	—	10,000

An in-depth profile of this company is available to Hoover's Online members at hoovers.com.

627

FIRST TRUST BANK

OTC: NCFT

1420 E. Third St.
Charlotte, NC 28204
Phone: 704-377-3936
Fax: 704-377-8869
Web: www.firsttrustnc.com

CEO: Jim Bolt
CFO: Jean Galloway
HR: –
FYE: December 31
Type: Public

Business-minded Tar Heels might put their trust in First Trust Bank. First Trust Bank provides banking services to the North Carolina communities of Charlotte, Concord, Monroe, and Mooresville. Operating three retail branches and two loan production offices, the bank serves primarily small to midsized businesses, as well as individuals. It offers standard deposit services and products, including checking and savings accounts, IRAs, CDs, and debit cards. Commercial mortgages make up slightly more than half of First Trust Bank's loan portfolio, followed by construction and land development loans (about 15%) and one- to four-family residential mortgages (about 10%).

	Annual Growth	12/03	12/04	12/05	12/06	12/07
Est. sales ($ mil.)	—	—	—	—	—	23.3
Employees	—	—	—	—	—	30

FIRST UNITED CORPORATION

NASDAQ (GM): FUNC

19 S. 2nd St.
Oakland, MD 21550
Phone: 301-334-9471
Fax: 301-334-2318
Web: www.mybankfirstunited.com

CEO: William B. Grant
CFO: Carissa L. Rodeheaver
HR: Jeannette R. Fitzwater
FYE: December 31
Type: Public

First United is the holding company for First United Bank & Trust and other financial services subsidiaries. Founded in 1900, the bank operates about 25 branches in the panhandles of western Maryland and eastern West Virginia, as well as the Morgantown, West Virginia area. The bank provides standard services such as checking and savings accounts, money market accounts, and CDs, as well as retirement and trust services. Commercial loans make up the largest portion of the company's loan portfolio (more than 45%), followed by real estate mortgages (more than 35%), consumer installment loans, and construction loans.

	Annual Growth	12/03	12/04	12/05	12/06	12/07
Assets ($ mil.)	7.5%	1,108.2	1,231.9	1,311.0	1,349.3	1,478.9
Net income ($ mil.)	4.3%	10.8	7.6	12.1	12.6	12.8
Market value ($ mil.)	(4.6%)	148.3	125.5	129.9	134.5	122.9
Employees	2.5%	—	—	449	—	472

FIRST WEST VIRGINIA BANCORP, INC.

AMEX: FWV

1701 Warwood Ave.
Wheeling, WV 26003
Phone: 304-277-1100
Fax: 304-277-4705
Web: www.progbank.com

CEO: Sylvan J. Dlesk
CFO: Francie P. Reppy
HR: Stephanie A. LaFlam
FYE: December 31
Type: Public

First West Virginia Bancorp is crossing state boundaries. The financial institution is the holding company for Progressive Bank, which operates about a dozen branches in the upper Ohio River valley of the Mountaineer State and eastern Ohio. Targeting individuals and local businesses, the bank offers standard retail products like checking and savings accounts, money market accounts, certificates of deposit, and individual retirement accounts. Lending activities consist primarily of commercial and residential real estate mortgages (which account for more than 75% of its loan portfolio), but Progressive Bank also originates business, construction, and consumer loans.

	Annual Growth	12/03	12/04	12/05	12/06	12/07
Assets ($ mil.)	(2.8%)	284.1	279.8	266.2	254.4	253.2
Net income ($ mil.)	(5.4%)	2.5	2.6	2.3	2.1	2.0
Market value ($ mil.)	(11.9%)	37.4	36.7	29.6	30.2	22.6
Employees	(2.3%)	—	—	111	—	106

THE FIRST YEARS INC.

100 Technology Center Dr., Ste. 2A
Stoughton, MA 02072
Phone: 781-341-6250
Fax: 781-341-6251
Web: www.thefirstyears.com

CEO: Curtis W. (Curt) Stoelting
CFO: Jody L. Taylor
HR: –
FYE: December 31
Type: Subsidiary

With a little help from Big Bird and Pooh, The First Years sees babies through plenty of "firsts." It manufactures bathing, childproofing, diapering, feeding, playing, sleeping, and transporting products for newborns up to 3-year-olds. Products, such as bottles, crib toys, teething rings, toilet trainers, and medicine dispensers, are available in nearly 50 countries and sold under its own label, as well as the *Winnie the Pooh* (licensed from The Walt Disney Company) and *Sesame Street* (from the Sesame Workshop) names. Products are sold at toy, mass merchandising, drug, and grocery store chains, as well as specialty and online retailers. Collectibles maker RC2 acquired The First Years in September 2004.

	Annual Growth	12/03	12/04	12/05	12/06	12/07
Est. sales ($ mil.)	—	—	—	—	—	36.4
Employees	—	—	—	—	—	201

FIRSTBANK CORPORATION

NASDAQ (GS): FBMI

311 Woodworth Ave.
Alma, MI 48801
Phone: 989-463-3131
Fax: 989-466-2042
Web: www.firstbank-corp.com

CEO: Thomas R. (Tom) Sullivan
CFO: Samuel G. Stone
HR: –
FYE: December 31
Type: Public

Firstbank Corporation is the holding company for six separately chartered subsidiary banks offering services under the Firstbank banner; it also owns Keystone Community Bank, which it acquired in 2005. Through more than 50 branches in Michigan's Lower Peninsula, the banks attract deposits from area residents and businesses by providing standard services such as checking and savings accounts and CDs. The company also owns subsidiaries that provide real estate appraisal services, armored car services, and title insurance. Firstbank bought another Michigan-based bank holding company, ICNB Financial, parent of Ionia County Community Bank (now Firstbank — West Michigan), in 2007.

	Annual Growth	12/03	12/04	12/05	12/06	12/07
Assets ($ mil.)	15.2%	776.5	806.1	1,061.1	1,095.1	1,365.7
Net income ($ mil.)	(8.7%)	12.1	10.4	10.1	10.2	8.4
Market value ($ mil.)	(9.4%)	151.9	139.7	138.8	138.2	102.4
Employees	10.2%	—	—	405	—	492

FIRSTCITY FINANCIAL CORPORATION

NASDAQ (GS): FCFC

6400 Imperial Dr.
Waco, TX 76712
Phone: 254-761-2800
Fax: –
Web: www.fcfc.com

CEO: James T. Sartain
CFO: J. Bryan Baker
HR: Teresa Kizer
FYE: December 31
Type: Public

FirstCity Financial is all about loans. Operating through subsidiaries, the company buys, manages, and sells portfolios of loans and other assets. FirstCity Financial mostly purchases nonperforming loans from banks, credit unions, and other financial institutions at a discount to their face value; its portfolio is worth some $10 billion. The company services all the loans it acquires. FirstCity Financial has an acquisition partnership with Cargill Financial, a unit of agricultural giant Cargill, to purchase distressed assets. In 2007, the company with Crestone Capital established the FirstCity Crestone platform which invests in special investments including restructurings, turnarounds, and executive buyouts.

	Annual Growth	12/03	12/04	12/05	12/06	12/07
Sales ($ mil.)	0.6%	42.7	36.0	24.1	28.4	43.7
Net income ($ mil.)	(30.1%)	9.2	63.6	8.2	9.8	2.2
Market value ($ mil.)	5.4%	68.3	113.6	130.4	119.5	84.4
Employees	—	—	—	214	—	—

FIRSTENERGY CORP.

NYSE: FE

76 S. Main St.
Akron, OH 44308
Phone: 800-633-4766
Fax: 330-384-3866
Web: www.firstenergycorp.com

CEO: Anthony J. Alexander
CFO: Richard H. (Rich) Marsh
HR: Lynn M. Cavalier
FYE: December 31
Type: Public

FirstEnergy's first goal is to deliver power, but its second goal is to survive deregulation. Its utilities provide electricity to 4.5 million customers in Ohio, Pennsylvania, and New Jersey, three states that are ushering in power-industry competition. The company's domestic power plants have a total generating capacity of more than 14,120 MW, most generated by coal-fired plants. Subsidiary FirstEnergy Solutions trades energy commodities in deregulated markets throughout the US. FirstEnergy's other nonregulated operations include electrical and mechanical contracting and energy planning and procurement.

	Annual Growth	12/03	12/04	12/05	12/06	12/07
Sales ($ mil.)	1.0%	12,307.0	12,453.0	11,989.0	11,501.0	12,802.0
Net income ($ mil.)	32.6%	422.8	878.2	861.0	1,254.0	1,309.0
Market value ($ mil.)	17.4%	11,610.2	13,031.8	16,158.7	19,248.1	22,051.8
Employees	(1.6%)	—	15,245	14,586	13,739	14,534

FIRSTFED FINANCIAL CORP.

NYSE: FED

401 Wilshire Blvd.
Santa Monica, CA 90401
Phone: 310-319-6000
Fax: 310-319-2100
Web: www.firstfedca.com

CEO: Babette E. Heimbuch
CFO: Douglas J. Goddard
HR: Caroline Galbraith
FYE: December 31
Type: Public

Southern Californians are on a first come, FirstFed basis. FirstFed Financial is the savings and loan holding company for First Federal Bank of California. Founded in 1929, First Federal serves consumers and businesses through more than 30 branches, two lending offices, and a call center. The bank uses funds from deposits mainly to finance residential real estate loans, which account for about 95% of FirstFed's total portfolio. It also writes other real estate loans, as well as business and consumer loans, and offers wealth management and trust services. Subsidiary Oceanside Insurance Agency sells annuities.

	Annual Growth	12/03	12/04	12/05	12/06	12/07
Assets ($ mil.)	10.6%	4,825.0	7,469.0	10,457.0	9,295.6	7,223.0
Net income ($ mil.)	9.6%	64.5	65.8	91.7	129.1	92.9
Market value ($ mil.)	(9.9%)	741.5	855.8	903.2	1,114.9	488.6
Employees	—	—	—	—	603	—

FIRSTGROUP AMERICA, INC

705 Central Ave., Ste. 300
Cincinnati, OH 45202
Phone: 513-241-2200
Fax: 513-419-3242
Web: www.firstgroupamerica.com

CEO: Phil Crookes
CFO: Phil Crookes
HR: Gayle Gray
FYE: March 31
Type: Subsidiary

Bus operator FirstGroup America aims to be the first option for school systems, public transit authorities, and fleet managers. Its First Student unit provides school bus services under contracts with districts throughout the US; together, First Student and sister company FirstBus Canada operate a fleet of about 62,000 buses. FirstGroup America's First Transit unit manages bus systems for transit agencies and private companies in the US, Canada, and Puerto Rico, and First Services provides maintenance and asset management for vehicle fleet operators. FirstGroup America expanded significantly in 2007 when its UK-based parent, FirstGroup plc, acquired Laidlaw International.

	Annual Growth	3/04	3/05	3/06	3/07	3/08
Est. sales ($ mil.)	—	—	—	—	—	3,319.0
Employees	—	—	—	—	—	—

FIRSTMERIT CORPORATION

NASDAQ (GS): FMER

3 Cascade Plaza, 7th Fl.
Akron, OH 44308
Phone: 330-996-6300
Fax: –
Web: www.firstmerit.com

CEO: Paul G. Greig
CFO: Terrence E. Bichsel
HR: Christopher J. Mauer
FYE: December 31
Type: Public

FirstMerit Corporation is the holding company of FirstMerit Bank, which provides retail and commercial banking services through more than 150 Ohio and Pennyslvania branch locations. It offers standard deposit and lending products for individuals and small to mid-sized businesses, commercial loans account for about half of the company's loan portfolio. the bank offers equipment leasing; credit life, accident, and health insurance sales; and securities brokerage. FirstMerit Bank and its subsidiaries also provide equipment leasing, credit life insurance, trust services, and securities brokerage.

	Annual Growth	12/03	12/04	12/05	12/06	12/07
Assets ($ mil.)	(0.2%)	10,473.6	10,122.6	10,161.3	10,252.6	10,400.7
Net income ($ mil.)	0.4%	121.0	103.2	130.5	94.9	123.0
Market value ($ mil.)	(8.5%)	2,296.9	2,382.1	2,068.8	1,933.7	1,610.5
Employees	(5.0%)	—	—	3,050	2,755	2,755

FIRSTWAVE TECHNOLOGIES, INC.

Pink Sheets: FSTW

7000 Central Pkwy. NE, Ste. 330
Atlanta, GA 30328
Phone: 678-672-3100
Fax: 678-672-3130
Web: www.firstwave.com

CEO: Richard T. Brock
CFO: –
HR: –
FYE: December 31
Type: Public

Firstwave Technologies doesn't want you using second-hand, antiquated methods of managing customers and relationships. The company provides customer relationship management (CRM) software that helps marketing, sales, and customer service personnel generate sales leads, manage marketing campaigns, collect customer information, and share account information securely over the Web. Firstwave also offers industry-specific versions of its products. Chairman and CEO Richard Brock owns about 25% of Firstwave.

	Annual Growth	12/02	12/03	12/04	12/05	*12/06
Sales ($ mil.)	(34.2%)	14.4	11.9	7.4	3.2	2.7
Net income ($ mil.)	(49.2%)	3.0	(0.8)	(4.6)	(1.7)	0.2
Employees	(32.9%)	79	65	40	5	16
					*Most recent year available	

FISERV, INC.

NASDAQ (GS): FISV

255 Fiserv Dr.
Brookfield, WI 53045
Phone: 262-879-5000
Fax: 262-879-5013
Web: www.fiserv.com

CEO: Jeffery W. (Jeff) Yabuki
CFO: Douglas J. (Doug) Craft
HR: Bridie A. Fanning
FYE: December 31
Type: Public

It's 10:30, America. Do you know where your money is? Fiserv does. A leading processor of financial data, Fiserv provides check processing, software development, business support, insurance claims and transaction processing, and other information management services to the financial industry. Its clients include banks, lenders, credit unions, insurance firms, health plan administrators, and leasing companies. The company operates in three business segments: financial institution services, insurance services, and payments and industry products (via its CheckFree business, acquired in 2007). The company has offices in the US and about 15 other countries.

	Annual Growth	12/03	12/04	12/05	12/06	12/07
Sales ($ mil.)	6.6%	3,033.7	3,729.8	4,059.5	4,544.1	3,922.0
Net income ($ mil.)	8.7%	315.0	377.6	516.4	449.9	439.0
Market value ($ mil.)	4.5%	7,681.0	7,806.9	7,864.5	8,968.6	9,161.4
Employees	6.6%	—	—	22,000	23,000	25,000

An in-depth profile of this company is available to Hoover's Online members at hoovers.com.

629

FISHER COMMUNICATIONS, INC.

NASDAQ (GM): FSCI

100 4th Ave. North, Ste. 510
Seattle, WA 98109
Phone: 206-404-7000
Fax: 206-404-6037
Web: www.fsci.com

CEO: Colleen B. Brown
CFO: Joseph L. (Joe) Lovejoy
HR: Karen L. Aliabadi
FYE: December 31
Type: Public

Fisher Communications not only broadcasts to the sleepless in Seattle, but also Oregon and Idaho. The company owns and operates more than a dozen full-power television stations serving markets in Idaho, Oregon, and Washington, including the Seattle metropolitan area. Its stations are affiliated with broadcast networks ABC and CBS, as well as Hispanic networks TeleFutura and Univision (both owned by Univision Communications). In addition to its portfolio of TV stations, Fisher owns three radio stations in Seattle and it owns and operates Fisher Plaza, a high-tech office plaza located near downtown Seattle.

	Annual Growth	12/03	12/04	12/05	12/06	12/07
Sales ($ mil.)	3.8%	138.4	153.9	149.3	154.7	160.4
Net income ($ mil.)	40.4%	8.2	(11.9)	(5.1)	16.8	31.9
Market value ($ mil.)	(6.6%)	435.2	421.3	360.6	385.5	331.2
Employees	—	—	—	931	—	—

FISK CORPORATION

111 T.C. Jester Blvd.
Houston, TX 77007
Phone: 713-868-6111
Fax: 713-880-2918
Web: www.fiskcorp.com

CEO: Larry C. Brookshire
CFO: Larry McTague
HR: Darcy Kazanecki
FYE: September 30
Type: Private

Long a specialist electrical contractor, Fisk added technology contracting and services to its portfolio when high-tech telecommunications and Internet installations became as ubiquitous as electrical power. Its electrical operations include preconstruction (estimating, design/assist, and value engineering), project execution (material management, scheduling/labor analysis, and contracts administration), and closeout (training and maintenance) services. Technology services include the installation and maintenance of structured cabling, electronic security systems, audio/visual setups, wireless LAN/WAN systems, telephony, and network services.

	Annual Growth	9/03	9/04	9/05	9/06	9/07
Est. sales ($ mil.)	—	—	—	—	—	250.0
Employees	—	—	—	—	—	2,300

FITCH RATINGS INC.

1 State Street Plaza
New York, NY 10004
Phone: 212-908-0500
Fax: 212-480-4435
Web: www.fitchratings.com

CEO: Stephen W. Joynt
CFO: David Kennedy
HR: Nancy Leinwand
FYE: December 31
Type: Subsidiary

Because governments can have lousy credit, too. Fitch Ratings, one of the top three credit rating agencies in the world (alongside Moody's and Standard & Poor's), issues ratings for thousands of banks, financial institutions, corporations, and governments. With dual headquarters in New York City and London and about 50 offices worldwide, Fitch Ratings engages in the politically charged business of rating the debt of nations; it covers companies and governments in more than 90 nations. The company is part of the Fitch Group, which is a subsidiary of France-based Fimalac.

FITNESS QUEST INC.

1400 Raff Rd. SW
Canton, OH 44750
Phone: 330-478-0755
Fax: 330-479-5075
Web: www.fitnessquest.com

CEO: Robert R. (Bob) Schnabel Jr.
CFO: –
HR: –
FYE: December 31
Type: Private

Fitness Quest wants to provide the tools for customers on a quest for improved fitness. The company manufactures and sells its exercise bikes, ellipticals, gliders, treadmills, rowers, and other fitness equipment under such brand names as Total Gym, Eclipse, and Easy Shaper. Its products are sold at retail stores such as Target and Sears, through catalogs like Spiegel and Sharper Image, and on home shopping TV channels, including QVC and HSN, and on the Fitness Quest Web site. The company's products are most notably seen via its infomercials such as Tony Little's Gazelle Freestyle machine. Fitness Quest was founded by president and CEO Bob Schnabel Jr.

	Annual Growth	12/03	12/04	12/05	12/06	12/07
Est. sales ($ mil.)	—	—	—	—	—	35.3
Employees	—	—	—	—	—	147

FITZ AND FLOYD, INC.

501 Corporate Dr.
Lewisville, TX 75057
Phone: 972-874-3480
Fax: 972-353-7718
Web: www.fitzandfloyd.com

CEO: Steve Baram
CFO: –
HR: –
FYE: December 31
Type: Private

Well-dressed tabletops thank company founders Pat Fitzpatrick and Bob Floyd. Fitz and Floyd is a leading manufacturer of giftware, dinnerware, and collectibles. The company also sells seasonal decorative items like cookie jars, Christmas ornaments, and Halloween candy plates. Fitz and Floyd operates retail locations in Texas and sells its products online through its company Web site.

	Annual Growth	12/03	12/04	12/05	12/06	12/07
Est. sales ($ mil.)	—	—	—	—	—	50.0
Employees	—	—	—	—	—	250

FIVE STAR PRODUCTS, INC.

OTC: FSPX

903 Murray Rd.
East Hanover, NJ 07936
Phone: 646-742-1600
Fax: –
Web: www.fivestargroup.com

CEO: John C. Belknap
CFO: Ira J. Sobotko
HR: Ann Sandau
FYE: December 31
Type: Public

Five Star Products helps homeowners brush up. Operating though its Five Star Group subsidiary, Five Star Products is a leading wholesale distributor of hardware, and finishing and home decorating products, such as paint, paint brushes, and stains. It distributes products from such manufacturers as 3M and Stanley to more than 3,500 independent retailers in a dozen states in the Northeast from warehouses in Connecticut and New Jersey. The company also sells its private-label Five Star line. National Patent Development owns about 70% of Five Star Products.

	Annual Growth	12/03	12/04	12/05	12/06	12/07
Sales ($ mil.)	6.8%	95.1	102.0	106.4	108.1	123.7
Net income ($ mil.)	18.9%	0.6	1.1	(0.3)	0.3	1.2
Market value ($ mil.)	50.5%	2.2	4.6	2.6	4.9	11.3
Employees	8.2%	—	—	—	219	237

An in-depth profile of this company is available to Hoover's Online members at hoovers.com.

FIVE STAR QUALITY CARE, INC.

AMEX: FVE

400 Centre St.
Newton, MA 02458
Phone: 617-796-8387
Fax: 617-796-8385
Web: www.fivestarqualitycare.com

CEO: Bruce J. Mackey Jr.
CFO: Francis R. Murphy III
HR: Maryann Hughes
FYE: December 31
Type: Public

Five Star Quality Care aims to become the long-term care industry's Five Star provider. Operating in 29 states, Five Star Quality Care runs more than 160 senior living facilities with around 18,000 living units. Five Star's facilities consist of nursing homes, senior apartments, independent living apartments, and assisted living suites. Services include skilled nursing, and hospice care, rehabilitation, occupational therapy, nutritional support, and social and recreational services. In addition, Five Star Quality Care operates a handful of pharmacies and two rehabilitation hospitals, as well as more than 20 affiliated rehabilitation clinics.

	Annual Growth	12/03	12/04	12/05	12/06	12/07
Sales ($ mil.)	14.0%	576.2	628.0	757.5	827.3	972.9
Net income ($ mil.)	—	(7.9)	3.3	(84.2)	(116.7)	23.3
Market value ($ mil.)	62.9%	37.5	102.5	158.1	353.3	264.1
Employees	52.7%	—	—	7,852	17,018	18,301

FLAGSTAR BANCORP, INC.

NYSE: FBC

5151 Corporate Dr.
Troy, MI 48098
Phone: 248-312-2000
Fax: –
Web: www.flagstar.com

CEO: Mark T. Hammond
CFO: Paul D. Borja
HR: Rebecca A. Lucci
FYE: December 31
Type: Public

Flagstar Bancorp is the holding company for Flagstar Bank, which operates some 150 branches in Michigan, Indiana, and Georgia (many inside big box retailers such as Wal-Mart). It also originates, purchases, and services residential mortgage loans through some 75 loan offices in 20 states, including top markets California, Michigan, Florida, Washington, Colorado, Texas, and Arizona. Almost all of its loans are mortgage or home equity loans. Flagstar offers standard retail banking services to individuals and small business customers. The bank also offers insurance through Douglas Insurance Agency.

	Annual Growth	12/03	12/04	12/05	12/06	12/07
Assets ($ mil.)	10.6%	10,570.2	13,125.5	15,075.4	15,497.2	15,792.7
Net income ($ mil.)	—	254.4	143.8	79.9	75.2	(39.2)
Market value ($ mil.)	(24.6%)	1,299.7	1,386.7	910.2	943.9	420.1
Employees	4.4%	—	—	2,405	2,510	—

FLANDERS CORPORATION

NASDAQ (GS): FLDR

2399 26th Ave. N.
St. Petersburg, FL 33734
Phone: 727-822-4411
Fax: 727-823-5510
Web: www.flanderscorp.com

CEO: Robert R. Amerson
CFO: Cully Bohush
HR: Brenda Davis
FYE: December 31
Type: Public

This Flanders handles flecks, fleas, flies, fluff, and other airborne flotsam. The company makes air filters under such brand names as Air Seal, Eco-Air, and Precisionaire. Its products include high-efficiency particulate air (HEPA) filters used in industrial cleanrooms, as well as standard residential and commercial heating, ventilation, and air-conditioning filters. The company makes most of its sales from aftermarket replacement filters that it sells directly to wholesalers, distributors, and retail outlets. Flanders' customers include Abbott Laboratories, The Home Depot, Motorola, and Wal-Mart. Chairman and CEO Robert Amerson owns about 30% of the company.

	Annual Growth	12/03	12/04	12/05	12/06	12/07
Sales ($ mil.)	7.6%	182.8	199.9	229.3	238.4	244.9
Net income ($ mil.)	—	7.8	9.8	12.5	2.0	(19.7)
Market value ($ mil.)	(4.3%)	171.6	252.5	320.0	260.9	144.1
Employees	—	—	—	2,743	—	—

FLANIGAN'S ENTERPRISES, INC.

AMEX: BDL

5059 NE 18th Ave.
Fort Lauderdale, FL 33334
Phone: 954-377-1961
Fax: 954-351-1245
Web: www.flanigans.net

CEO: James G. Flanigan II
CFO: Jeffrey D. Kastner
HR: –
FYE: Last Saturday in September
Type: Public

Seafood and sauce are the catch of the day at Flanigan's Enterprises. The company operates and manages about 15 restaurants that do business as Flanigan's Seafood Bar and Grill, along with a chain of eight package liquor stores called Big Daddy's Liquors. (Four properties have combination liquor store/restaurant operations.) Seven of its restaurants are franchised and owned primarily by family members of company executives. All of its lounges and liquor stores are located in Florida. In addition, Flanigan's owns the Mardi Gras adult entertainment club in Atlanta, which is operated by a third party. The family of former chairman and CEO Joseph "Big Daddy" Flanigan owns more than 50% of the company.

	Annual Growth	9/03	9/04	9/05	9/06	9/07
Sales ($ mil.)	11.0%	40.3	45.9	49.0	55.0	61.1
Net income ($ mil.)	9.6%	0.9	0.4	1.1	1.3	1.3
Market value ($ mil.)	9.1%	11.8	12.1	18.0	17.0	16.6
Employees	—	—	—	—	—	950

FLATBUSH FEDERAL BANCORP, INC.

OTC: FLTB

2146 Nostrand Ave.
Brooklyn, NY 11210
Phone: 718-859-6800
Fax: 718-421-3210
Web: www.flatbush.com

CEO: Jesus R. Adia
CFO: John S. Lotardo
HR: –
FYE: December 31
Type: Public

Flatbush residents looking to finance a new flat might turn to Flatbush Federal Bancorp, the holding company for Flatbush Federal Savings and Loan. The thrift has been serving the Flatbush neighborhood of Brooklyn, New York, since 1883. Through three branches, the bank offers checking and savings accounts, CDs, and a variety of loans. Residential mortgages account for most of its loan portfolio, or about 75% of all loans. The company also writes commercial mortgages, construction loans, and a small amount of Small Business Administration and other loans not secured by real estate. Mutual holding company Flatbush Federal Bancorp, MHC, owns 53% of Flatbush Federal Bancorp.

	Annual Growth	12/02	12/03	12/04	12/05	*12/06
Assets ($ mil.)	2.2%	141.5	142.9	134.3	143.9	154.4
Net income ($ mil.)	(9.6%)	0.3	0.1	0.3	0.4	0.2
Market value ($ mil.)	(4.9%)	—	24.4	23.6	19.9	21.0
Employees	—	—	—	—	—	—

*Most recent year available

FLEETCOR TECHNOLOGIES, INC.

655 Engineering Dr., Ste. 300
Norcross, GA 30092
Phone: 770-449-0479
Fax: 770-449-3471
Web: www.fleetcor.com

CEO: Ronald F. (Ron) Clarke
CFO: Eric Dey
HR: –
FYE: December 31
Type: Private

Fleetcor provides management services for business fleets of all sizes. The company issues fleet cards, which are accepted at more than 40,000 fueling stations across the US and Europe in more than 25 cities. When a fleet card is used by a driver, Fleetcor tracks fuel, maintenance work, and state-specific taxes — needed for company tax purposes. As part of its FleetNet Private Label Solutions group, the company provides major oil companies with branded fleet cards; it processes data for those cards as well. Overall Fleetcor sells its products under the CFN, CCS, Fuelman, Keyfuels, and Mannatec branded card names. Advent International, Summit Partners, and Bain Capital own a majority interest in Fleetcor.

	Annual Growth	12/03	12/04	12/05	12/06	12/07
Est. sales ($ mil.)	—	—	—	—	—	160.0
Employees	—	—	—	—	—	400

An in-depth profile of this company is available to Hoover's Online members at hoovers.com.

631

FLEETPRIDE, INC.

8708 Technology Forest Pl., Ste. 125
The Woodlands, TX 77381
Phone: 866-435-3387
Fax: 832-592-9970
Web: www.fleetpride.com

CEO: Todd A. Dunn
CFO: Timothy Gadus
HR: Benita I. Meads
FYE: December 31
Type: Private

For FleetPride bigger is better. It distributes heavy-duty parts for buses, tractor-trailers, waste-disposal trucks, and large off-road vehicles, as well as provides repair services. FleetPride, which is the largest independent heavy-duty truck parts distributor in the US, operates through more than 330 FleetPride parts and FleetCare services outlets. FleetCare locations are company owned. Some of the brands included among FleetPride's 20,000-plus SKUs are ArvinMeritor, Federal Signal, Ingersoll-Rand, and Tenneco. It also offers private label products and rebuilt (in-house) parts. Aurora Capital Group owned 80% of the firm until mid-2006, when Investcorp and other investors acquired it for some $506 million.

	Annual Growth	12/03	12/04	12/05	12/06	12/07
Est. sales ($ mil.)	—	—	—	—	—	280.8
Employees	—	—	—	—	—	2,197

FLEETWOOD ENTERPRISES, INC.

NYSE: FLE

3125 Myers St.
Riverside, CA 92503
Phone: 951-351-3500
Fax: 951-351-3312
Web: www.fleetwood.com

CEO: Elden L. Smith
CFO: Boyd R. Plowman
HR: Michael B. Shearin
FYE: Last Sunday in April
Type: Public

Fleetwood Enterprises gets revved up over recreational vehicles (RVs). The company is also a leading maker of manufactured housing. Fleetwood's RVs come in three types: motor homes (brands such as American Eagle, American Heritage, Southwind, and Tioga), travel trailers (Mallard, Pioneer, and Wilderness), and folding trailers. Fleetwood's manufactured homes feature vaulted ceilings, walk-in closets, and porches. Fleetwood operates manufacturing facilities in 14 US states and in Canada; sales are made through both company-owned outlets and independent distributors.

	Annual Growth	4/03	4/04	4/05	4/06	4/07
Sales ($ mil.)	(3.5%)	2,318.3	2,608.0	2,374.7	2,432.4	2,007.9
Net income ($ mil.)	—	(70.7)	(22.3)	(161.5)	(28.4)	(90.0)
Market value ($ mil.)	32.6%	179.0	813.4	456.2	600.5	553.3
Employees	(14.4%)	—	—	12,700	11,500	9,300

FLEISCHMANN'S YEAST

1350 Timberlake Manor Pkwy., Ste. 550
Chesterfield, MO 63017
Phone: 636-349-8800
Fax: 636-349-8825
Web: www.fleischmannsyeast.com

CEO: Andrew Armstrong
CFO: Christopher (Chris) Bohnert
HR: —
FYE: September 30
Type: Business segment

Fleischmann's Yeast manages to get a rise out of most folks — it is, after all, the world's leading maker of baker's yeast. The company makes fresh yeast cakes, traditional active dried, and quick-rise yeast for use by the baking industry and home bakers alike. Fleischmann's also makes specially designed yeasts for use in bread machines. The company was acquired by Associated British Foods in 2004. ABF then stirred Fleischmann's into its ACH Food Companies group of US businesses along with Mazola corn oil, Karo syrup, Argo corn starch, and Tone spices. Fleischmann's baking products are available in the US and Canada.

	Annual Growth	9/03	9/04	9/05	9/06	9/07
Est. sales ($ mil.)	—	—	—	—	—	130.0
Employees	—	—	—	—	—	300

FLEX-N-GATE CORPORATION

1306 E. University Ave.
Urbana, IL 61802
Phone: 217-278-2600
Fax: 217-278-2616
Web: www.flex-n-gate.com

CEO: Shahid Khan
CFO: —
HR: Linda Perez
FYE: June 30
Type: Private

Flex-N-Gate makes metal and plastic automotive components and assemblies, such as bumpers, grilles, hinges, instrument panels, pedal systems, and running boards. The company also offers prototyping, mechanical assembly, and sequencing services. Customers have included BMW, Chrysler, Ford, General Motors, and Toyota. Since 2000 Flex-N-Gate has been rapidly exanding its global manufacturing presence through acquisitions. The company has more than 45 manufacturing plants in Argentina, Canada, Mexico, Spain, and the US. Flex-N-Gate was founded in 1956.

	Annual Growth	6/03	6/04	6/05	6/06	6/07
Est. sales ($ mil.)	—	—	—	—	—	964.7
Employees	—	—	—	—	—	10,325

FLEXSTEEL INDUSTRIES, INC.

NASDAQ (GM): FLXS

3400 Jackson St.
Dubuque, IA 52001
Phone: 563-556-7730
Fax: 563-556-8345
Web: www.flexsteel.com

CEO: Ronald J. Klosterman
CFO: Timothy E. Hall
HR: —
FYE: June 30
Type: Public

Are you sitting down for this? If not, Flexsteel Industries might ask why. It's not as if the firm hasn't given you plenty of options. Flexsteel makes wood and upholstered furniture for the home, office, recreational vehicle, health care, and hotel markets. Most of its products — including recliners, swivel rockers, sofas, and sofa beds — incorporate a unique unitized spring for which the company is named. Flexsteel distributes its products, which are manufactured mostly in the US, throughout the country; it has minimal export sales. The company's retail operations were discontinued in 2003. That year Flexsteel acquired subsidiary DMI Furniture, which imports most of its products from Asia.

	Annual Growth	6/03	6/04	6/05	6/06	6/07
Sales ($ mil.)	9.9%	292.0	401.2	410.0	426.4	425.4
Net income ($ mil.)	2.9%	8.3	10.1	6.0	4.7	9.3
Market value ($ mil.)	(2.1%)	103.8	152.6	93.5	85.3	95.3
Employees	—	—	—	2,400	—	—

FLIGHT OPTIONS LLC

26180 Curtiss Wright Pkwy.
Cleveland, OH 44143
Phone: 216-261-3500
Fax: 216-261-3595
Web: www.flightoptions.com

CEO: S. Michael Scheeringa
CFO: Bruce C. Boyle
HR: Ralph Knull
FYE: December 31
Type: Private

When you want the comfort and privacy of a private jet, you have flight options. Flight Options is a leading provider of fractional jet ownership services, in which customers share ownership and are guaranteed access to a particular type of aircraft operated by the company. Its fleet of more than 130 aircraft includes Beechjet and Hawker models as well as Cessna Citation and Embraer Legacy jets. Besides fractional ownership, Flight Options offers aircraft leasing and management and a membership program, JetPASS, that gives customers access to a variety of aircraft. Investment firm H.I.G. Capital owns Flight Options, which it acquired in 2007 from defense contractor Raytheon.

	Annual Growth	12/03	12/04	12/05	12/06	12/07
Est. sales ($ mil.)	—	—	—	—	—	128.7
Employees	—	—	—	—	—	1,800

FLIGHT SAFETY TECHNOLOGIES, INC.

AMEX: FLT

28 Cottrell St.
Mystic, CT 06355
Phone: 860-245-0191
Fax: 860-437-4587
Web: www.flysafetech.com

CEO: William B. Cotton
CFO: David D. Cryer
HR: –
FYE: May 31
Type: Public

Flight Safety Technologies develops technologies to improve air travel safety. Major programs include SOCRATES (Sensor for Optically Characterizing Remote Atmospheric Turbulence Emanating Sound), which is intended to warn pilots of wake turbulence, and UNICORN (UNIversal Collision Obviation and Reduced Near-Miss), which uses radar to provide small aircraft pilots with warnings when other aircraft approach. The company also has begun work on TIICM (Tactical Integrated Illuminating CounterMeasure), which is intended to protect aircraft against shoulder-launched missiles.

	Annual Growth	5/03	5/04	5/05	5/06	5/07
Sales ($ mil.)	8.1%	1.1	3.6	3.3	3.9	1.5
Net income ($ mil.)	—	(0.9)	(0.4)	(1.4)	(2.3)	(2.8)
Market value ($ mil.)	6.2%	—	—	13.1	18.9	14.8
Employees	—	—	—	8	—	—

FLIGHTSAFETY INTERNATIONAL INC.

Marine Air Terminal, La Guardia Airport
Flushing, NY 11371
Phone: 718-565-4100
Fax: 718-565-4134
Web: www.flightsafety.com

CEO: Bruce N. Whitman
CFO: Kenneth W. Motschwiller
HR: Thomas (Tom) Eff
FYE: December 31
Type: Subsidiary

On-the-job training may work in some industries, but FlightSafety International helps train pilots before they ever step into a cabin. A subsidiary of Berkshire Hathaway, FlightSafety has the world's largest fleet of flight simulators, training more than 75,000 pilots and maintenance personnel per year for airlines and airplane manufacturers in some 230 simulators at 40 training centers in the US, Canada, France, and the UK. The company has a staff of 1,500 professional instructors and provides training for corporate, commercial, private, and military pilots. In addition, FlightSafety International offers training for flight attendants, maintenance technicians, and dispatchers.

	Annual Growth	12/03	12/04	12/05	12/06	12/07
Est. sales ($ mil.)	—	—	—	—	—	825.6
Employees	—	—	—	—	—	3,300

FLIR SYSTEMS, INC.

NASDAQ (GS): FLIR

27700A SW Parkway Ave.
Wilsonville, OR 97070
Phone: 503-498-3547
Fax: 503-498-3904
Web: www.flir.com

CEO: Earl R. Lewis
CFO: Stephen M. Bailey
HR: Paul T. Zaninovich
FYE: December 31
Type: Public

FLIR Systems can see through smoke screens. The company's thermal imaging and obscurant-proof camera systems detect heat and radiation, thus allowing operators to see objects through fog, darkness, or smoke. FLIR's imaging products enhance vision for military and commercial applications such as search and rescue, drug interdiction, border patrol, surveillance, navigation, and newsgathering. Industrial customers use FLIR's thermography products, which employ infrared cameras to measure temperatures from a distance for equipment monitoring, process control, product development, and other applications. US government agencies collectively account for about half of FLIR's sales.

	Annual Growth	12/03	12/04	12/05	12/06	12/07
Sales ($ mil.)	25.7%	312.0	482.6	508.6	575.0	779.4
Net income ($ mil.)	32.2%	44.7	71.5	90.8	100.9	136.7
Market value ($ mil.)	94.4%	299.9	1,102.3	772.8	1,047.8	4,280.9
Employees	14.9%	—	—	1,320	—	1,743

FLORIDA CRYSTALS CORPORATION

1 N. Clematis St., Ste. 200
West Palm Beach, FL 33401
Phone: 561-366-5100
Fax: 561-366-5158
Web: www.floridacrystals.com

CEO: Alfonso (Alfy) Fanjul Jr.
CFO: Luis J. Fernandez
HR: Jose Perez
FYE: March 31
Type: Private

Florida Crystals leans heavily on its cane. One of the top US sugar producers, the company, a unit of Flo-Sun, grows sugar cane and rice on its 180,000 acres. It operates two sugar mills, a rice mill, a refinery, a packaging and distribution center, and a renewable energy facility. The company's products include granulated, baking, powdered, and large- and fine-grain organic and regular sugars under the Natural Sugars name. With the Sugar Cane Growers Cooperative of Florida (SCGC), Florida Crystals jointly owns American Sugar Refining, the owner and producer of the Domino brand sugar.

	Annual Growth	3/03	3/04	3/05	3/06	3/07
Est. sales ($ mil.)	—	—	—	—	—	462.0
Employees	—	—	—	—	—	2,000

FLORIDA EAST COAST INDUSTRIES, INC.

10151 Deerwood Park Blvd., Bldg. 100, Ste. 360
Jacksonville, FL 32256
Phone: 904-996-2810
Fax: 904-256-0460
Web: www.feci.com

CEO: John D. McPherson
CFO: Daniel H. (Dan) Popky
HR: Edward Manno Shumsky
FYE: December 31
Type: Private

Where do you suppose Florida East Coast Industries (FECI) does business? The company's Florida East Coast Railway hauls crushed stone, motor vehicles, intermodal containers, and other goods along 351 miles of track between Jacksonville and Miami. Along the way it serves ports at Palm Beach and Ft. Lauderdale. Building materials supplier Rinker Materials has been a major customer. FECI's other main business is Florida real estate. The company's Flagler Development subsidiary oversees office and industrial buildings and raw land. Fortress Investment Group owns FECI.

	Annual Growth	12/02	12/03	12/04	12/05	12/06
Sales ($ mil.)	11.0%	301.5	339.0	378.2	362.4	458.2
Net income ($ mil.)	—	(107.8)	43.2	80.6	49.4	63.1
Employees	6.0%	834	873	865	903	1,053

FLORIDA GAMING CORPORATION

OTC: FGMG

3500 NW 37th Ave.
Miami, FL 33142
Phone: 305-633-6400
Fax: 305-638-1330
Web: www.fla-gaming.com

CEO: W. Bennett Collett
CFO: Kimberly R. (Kim) Tharp
HR: Yolande Coleman
FYE: December 31
Type: Public

Jai-alai is the high life for this company. Florida Gaming Corporation owns and operates two jai-alai frontons in Miami and Ft. Pierce, Florida, that feature live jai-alai competition with wagering. The gaming centers offer wagering on simulcast jai-alai from other locations, as well as simulcast horse racing and dog racing. In addition, its Miami location features a card room for poker. Florida Gaming also owns Tara Club Estates, a real estate development project near Atlanta. Chairman W. Bennett Collett owns more than 40% of the company, partially through his holding company Freedom Financial.

	Annual Growth	12/03	12/04	12/05	12/06	12/07
Sales ($ mil.)	2.1%	10.5	9.5	18.3	17.4	11.4
Net income ($ mil.)	—	(1.3)	(3.9)	(2.8)	(0.6)	(6.7)
Market value ($ mil.)	132.8%	2.4	18.3	46.1	44.2	71.8
Employees	—	—	—	—	—	—

An in-depth profile of this company is available to Hoover's Online members at hoovers.com.

633

FLORIDA POWER & LIGHT COMPANY

700 Universe Blvd.
Juno Beach, FL 33408
Phone: 561-694-4000
Fax: 561-694-4620
Web: www.fpl.com

CEO: Lewis (Lew) Hay III
CFO: Armando Pimentel Jr.
HR: Robert H. Escoto
FYE: December 31
Type: Subsidiary

Florida Power & Light (FPL) sheds extra light onto the Sunshine State. The company, a subsidiary of utility holding company FPL Group, serves some 4.5 million electricity customers in eastern and southern Florida. FPL has more than 73,380 miles of transmission and distribution lines, as well as interests in fossil-fueled and nuclear power plants that give it a generating capacity of more than 25,100 MW. FPL's Energy Marketing and Trading unit purchases and sells energy commodities (including electricity, natural gas, and oil) to wholesale customers. The company's primary fuel source in 2007 was natural gas (52% of total).

	Annual Growth	12/02	12/03	12/04	12/05	12/06
Sales ($ mil.)	20.8%	7,378.0	8,293.0	8,734.0	9,528.0	15,710.0
Net income ($ mil.)	15.0%	732.0	755.0	750.0	748.0	1,281.0
Employees	2.7%	—	9,600	10,000	10,200	10,400

FLORIDA POWER CORPORATION

299 First Ave. North
St. Petersburg, FL 33701
Phone: 727-820-5151
Fax: 727-384-7865
Web: www.progress-energy.com

CEO: Jeffrey J. (Jeff) Lyash
CFO: Peter M. Scott III
HR: –
FYE: December 31
Type: Subsidiary

Sometimes the sunshine state just isn't bright enough, and that's when Florida Power really shines. Incorporated in 1899 and operating as Progress Energy Florida since 2003, the utility transmits and distributes electricity to 1.6 million customers and oversees about 9,360 MW of generating capacity from interests in nuclear and coal-, oil-, and gas-fired power plants. Additionally, Florida Power purchases about 20% of the energy it provides. The utility, a subsidiary of holding company Progress Energy, also sells wholesale power to other utilities and marketers.

	Annual Growth	12/03	12/04	12/05	12/06	12/07
Sales ($ mil.)	10.8%	3,152.0	3,525.0	3,955.0	4,639.0	4,749.0
Net income ($ mil.)	1.6%	297.0	335.0	260.0	328.0	317.0
Employees	8.1%	—	—	3,700	4,000	—

FLORIDA PUBLIC UTILITIES COMPANY

AMEX: FPU

401 S. Dixie Hwy.
West Palm Beach, FL 33401
Phone: 561-832-2461
Fax: 561-833-8562
Web: www.fpuc.com

CEO: John T. (Jack) English
CFO: George M. Bachman
HR: Wayne C. Bonn
FYE: December 31
Type: Public

Electricity, natural gas, and propane are the right energy mix to keep the customers of Florida Public Utilities happy. The company serves approximately 83,000 natural gas and electricity customers, and 13,000 propane customers in southern, central, northwestern, and northeastern Florida. Florida Public Utilities buys its natural gas supply directly from marketers and producers and its electricity supply from nearby generating utilities; propane is purchased from wholesale suppliers. Florida Public Utilities has been expanding its operations through acquisitions.

	Annual Growth	12/03	12/04	12/05	12/06	12/07
Sales ($ mil.)	7.4%	102.7	110.0	130.0	134.4	136.5
Net income ($ mil.)	(28.2%)	12.4	3.6	4.3	4.2	3.3
Market value ($ mil.)	(6.5%)	—	—	81.4	79.6	71.1
Employees	—	—	—	352	—	—

FLORIDA ROCK INDUSTRIES, INC.

155 E. 21st St.
Jacksonville, FL 32206
Phone: 904-355-1781
Fax: 904-355-0817
Web: www.flarock.com

CEO: John D. Baker II
CFO: Wallace A. Patzke Jr.
HR: H. W. (Bill) Walton
FYE: September 30
Type: Subsidiary

Florida Rock Industries is a big star in the arena of the southern rock. The company provides sand, gravel, and crushed stone to the construction industry, and calcium products used in roofing and animal feeds. It also manufactures concrete block, ready mix concrete, and portland and masonry cements. Florida Rock operates quarries, plants, and distribution sites in the southeastern and mid-Atlantic US and serves commercial, industrial, residential, and governmental construction companies. It has joint ownership in a granite quarry and aggregates distribution venture in Canada. The Baker family owned about 25% of Florida Rock until rival Vulcan Materials acquired the company in late 2007.

	Annual Growth	9/03	9/04	9/05	9/06	9/07
Sales ($ mil.)	9.7%	746.1	948.5	1,153.4	1,367.8	1,080.8
Net income ($ mil.)	16.7%	75.9	113.7	157.6	211.4	141.0
Employees	(7.2%)	—	—	3,426	3,464	2,950

FLORIDA'S NATURAL GROWERS

20205 US Hwy. 27 North
Lake Wales, FL 33853
Phone: 863-676-1411
Fax: –
Web: floridanatural.com

CEO: Stephen Caruso
CFO: William (Chip) Hendry
HR: Susan Langley
FYE: August 31
Type: Cooperative

Florida's Natural Growers is known for squeezing out profits. The cooperative is one of the largest citrus juice sellers in the US; ranking right up there with the country's two giant brand names: PepsiCo's Tropicana and Coca-Cola's Minute Maid. Florida Natural 1,000 farmer/members harvest from more than 50,000 acres of citrus groves to make juice the co-ops products. The cooperative produces frozen concentrated and not-from-concentrate juices (orange, apple, grapefruit, lemonade, and fruit blends) under the Florida's Natural, Growers Pride, and Bluebird labels. The co-op's products are sold to customers in the food service, retail food, and vending industries, and are exported worldwide.

	Annual Growth	8/03	8/04	8/05	8/06	8/07
Est. sales ($ mil.)	—	—	—	—	—	360.0
Employees	—	—	—	—	—	800

FLOTEK INDUSTRIES, INC.

AMEX: FTK

2930 W. Sam Houston Pkwy. North, Ste. 300
Houston, TX 77043
Phone: 713-849-9911
Fax: 713-896-4511
Web: www.flotekind.com

CEO: Jerry D. Dumas Sr.
CFO: Lisa G. Meier
HR: –
FYE: December 31
Type: Public

Flotek Industries works to keep oil and gas flowing. The company gets half of its sales from chemicals used in the cementing and stimulation of oil and gas wells. (Cementing holds well casings in place; stimulation opens up cracks in the earth to allow for the easier flow of oil.) Flotek also makes the equipment used in cementing and stimulation, as well as Petrovalve downhole pump valves (used to pump off the liquids in gas wells) and Turbeco casing centralizers (used to center pipe). The company markets its products throughout the US and is expanding into international markets.

	Annual Growth	12/03	12/04	12/05	12/06	12/07
Sales ($ mil.)	80.8%	14.8	21.9	52.9	100.6	158.0
Net income ($ mil.)	—	(7.4)	2.2	7.7	11.4	16.7
Market value ($ mil.)	195.0%	—	—	77.6	123.8	675.1
Employees	68.9%	—	—	157	253	448

FLOW INTERNATIONAL CORPORATION

NASDAQ (GM): FLOW

23500 64th Ave. South
Kent, WA 98032
Phone: 253-850-3500
Fax: 253-813-9377
Web: www.flowcorp.com

CEO: Charles M. (Charley) Brown
CFO: Douglas P. Fletcher
HR: Theresa S. Treat
FYE: April 30
Type: Public

Don't use Flow International's products to wash the family dog. The company makes waterjet cutting and cleaning systems with ultrahigh pressure (UHP; up to 100,000 pounds per square inch). Its machines are used to cut metallic and non-metallic materials in the aerospace, automotive, and stonecutting industries. Flow International also manufactures automated assembly equipment, isostatic and flexform press systems, and consumable waterjet system parts, such as seals, garnet, and orifices. Sales from consumable replacement parts and services make up about one-quarter of Flow's revenues. The US accounts for more than half of the company's sales.

	Annual Growth	4/04	4/05	4/06	4/07	4/08
Sales ($ mil.)	8.3%	177.6	173.0	205.4	217.3	244.3
Net income ($ mil.)	—	(11.5)	(21.2)	7.4	3.7	22.4
Market value ($ mil.)	75.7%	39.6	198.3	499.5	434.5	377.0
Employees	(0.3%)	767	806	732	756	759

FLOWERS FOODS, INC.

NYSE: FLO

1919 Flowers Cir.
Thomasville, GA 31757
Phone: 229-226-9110
Fax: 229-225-3806
Web: www.flowersfoods.com

CEO: George E. Deese
CFO: R. Steve Kinsey
HR: Leny J. Garcia-Hill
FYE: Saturday nearest December 31
Type: Public

Look for Flowers Foods in your breadbox, not your garden — the company is one of the largest wholesale bakeries in the US. Its Flowers Bakeries unit produces, markets, and distributes fresh breads, buns, rolls, and bakery goodies to retail and foodservice customers throughout the southern US. The company's brand names include ButterKrust, Cobblestone Mill, and Nature's Own. The company's Flowers Specialty division makes snack cakes and frozen bread products for retail, vending, and co-pack customers nationwide. Flowers Bakeries also rolls out hamburger buns for foodservice chains such as Burger King, Hardee's, Outback Steakhouse, Wendy's, and Whataburger.

	Annual Growth	12/03	12/04	12/05	12/06	12/07
Sales ($ mil.)	8.8%	1,453.0	1,551.3	1,715.9	1,888.7	2,036.7
Net income ($ mil.)	59.3%	14.7	50.8	61.2	81.0	94.6
Market value ($ mil.)	44.2%	508.3	605.6	1,108.2	1,087.7	2,198.4
Employees	2.0%	—	—	7,500	7,800	7,800

FLOWSERVE CORPORATION

NYSE: FLS

5215 N. O'Connor Blvd., Ste. 2300
Irving, TX 75039
Phone: 972-443-6500
Fax: 972-443-6800
Web: www.flowserve.com

CEO: Lewis M. Kling
CFO: Mark A. Blinn
HR: Mark D. Dailey
FYE: December 31
Type: Public

Flowserve stays pumped up about fluid-handling equipment. The company makes pumps, valves, and mechanical seals. The acquisition of Ingersoll-Dresser Pumps (IDP) from Ingersoll-Rand made Flowserve the world's largest provider of pumps for the chemical, petroleum, and power industries. It provides its products and services to more than 10,000 customers around the globe. Flowserve's flow solutions division offers mechanical seals, sealing systems, and repair services to OEMs that make pumps, compressors, and mixers. Its flow control division makes valves, actuators, and related equipment that control the flow of liquids and gases.

	Annual Growth	12/03	12/04	12/05	12/06	12/07
Sales ($ mil.)	11.8%	2,404.4	2,638.2	2,695.3	3,061.1	3,762.7
Net income ($ mil.)	48.3%	52.9	24.2	11.8	115.0	255.8
Market value ($ mil.)	47.5%	1,145.0	1,527.6	2,214.3	2,827.4	5,416.9
Employees	7.1%	—	—	—	14,000	15,000

FLUOR CORPORATION

NYSE: FLR

6700 Las Colinas Blvd.
Irving, TX 75039
Phone: 469-398-7000
Fax: 469-398-7255
Web: www.fluor.com

CEO: Alan L. Boeckmann
CFO: D. Michael (Mike) Steuert
HR: H. Steven (Steve) Gilbert
FYE: December 31
Type: Public

Fluor ranks among the leading international design, engineering, and contracting firms. The company oversees construction projects for a large range of industrial sectors worldwide, focusing on its core strengths: engineering, procurement, construction, and maintenance. Its projects include designing and building manufacturing facilities, refineries, pharmaceutical facilities, health care buildings, power plants, and telecommunications and transportation infrastructure. The oil and gas sector accounts for about 50% of sales. Fluor also provides operations and maintenance services for its projects, as well as administrative and support services to the US government.

	Annual Growth	12/03	12/04	12/05	12/06	12/07
Sales ($ mil.)	17.3%	8,805.7	9,380.3	13,161.0	14,078.5	16,691.0
Net income ($ mil.)	35.7%	157.4	186.7	227.3	263.5	533.3
Market value ($ mil.)	41.2%	3,254.5	4,663.6	6,728.4	7,188.6	12,922.8
Employees	8.8%	—	—	34,836	37,560	41,260

FLUSHING FINANCIAL CORPORATION

NASDAQ (GS): FFIC

1979 Marcus Ave., Ste. E140
Lake Success, NY 11042
Phone: 718-961-5400
Fax: –
Web: www.flushingsavings.com

CEO: John R. Buran
CFO: David W. Fry
HR: Ruth Filiberto
FYE: December 31
Type: Public

Flush with cash? You could keep it at Flushing Financial. The holding company's Flushing Savings Bank operates about 15 branches in the Brooklyn, Manhattan, and Queens boroughs of New York City and in nearby Nassau County. Deposit products include CDs and checking, savings, passbook, money market, and NOW accounts. Multifamily residential and mixed-use real estate mortgage loans account for the majority of the bank's loan portfolio; other offerings include commercial mortgages and one- to four-family mortgages, construction loans, and SBA loans.

	Annual Growth	12/03	12/04	12/05	12/06	12/07
Assets ($ mil.)	15.1%	1,910.8	2,058.0	2,353.2	2,836.5	3,354.5
Net income ($ mil.)	(1.8%)	21.7	22.6	23.5	21.6	20.2
Market value ($ mil.)	(0.7%)	352.6	385.8	303.1	360.7	342.2
Employees	0.9%	—	—	264	—	269

FLYING FOOD GROUP, INC.

212 N. Sangamon St., Ste. 1-A
Chicago, IL 60607
Phone: 312-243-2882
Fax: 312-243-5088
Web: www.flyingfood.com

CEO: Sue Ling Gin
CFO: David L. Cotton
HR: Francine Smith
FYE: December 31
Type: Private

The food is really flying (or soon will be) in this company's kitchens. Flying Food Group is a leading provider of in-flight catering services in the US. It supplies prepared meals to more than 80 air carriers from about a dozen kitchens at 10 airports in the US and China. The company also supplies prepared snacks, salads, and meals to grocery store chains and specialty food retailers. Founded in 1983 by CEO Sue Ling Gin, Flying Food Group originally operated from Chicago's Midway Airport and provided in-flight catering services to now defunct Midway Airlines.

An in-depth profile of this company is available to Hoover's Online members at hoovers.com.

635

FLYING J INC.

1104 Country Hills Dr.
Ogden, UT 84403
Phone: 801-624-1000
Fax: 801-624-1587
Web: www.flyingj.com

CEO: J. Phillip (Phil) Adams
CFO: Robert L. Inkley
HR: Jerry Beckman
FYE: January 31
Type: Private

Flying J puts out a welcome mat for truckers in North America. From its beginnings in 1968 with four locations, the company is now the #1 distributor of diesel fuel and a leading truck-stop operator in the US — with 250-plus amenity-loaded Flying J Travel Plazas and fuel stops in about 40 US states and Canada. Flying J goes beyond the usual truck-stop fare (food, fuel, showers) by offering extra services, including banking, bulk-fuel programs, communications (wireless Internet connections), fuel cost analysis, insurance, and truck fleet sales. The company also owns Longhorn Pipeline Holdings, the operator of a 700-mile-long pipeline across Texas. Founder and chairman Jay Call died in a plane crash in 2003.

	Annual Growth	1/03	1/04	1/05	1/06	1/07
Sales ($ mil.)	25.1%	4,637.0	5,585.7	5,910.0	9,450.0	11,350.0
Employees	8.5%	11,750	12,000	13,000	14,600	16,300

FMC CORPORATION

NYSE: FMC

1735 Market St.
Philadelphia, PA 19103
Phone: 215-299-6000
Fax: 215-299-5998
Web: www.fmc.com

CEO: William G. (Bill) Walter
CFO: William K. Foster
HR: Kenneth R. Garrett
FYE: December 31
Type: Public

E may = mc^2, but FMC = chemicals. Once in areas as diverse as oil field equipment and food machinery, FMC Corporation now focuses on industrial, specialty, and agricultural chemicals. The company's industrial chemicals include soda ash (it's one of the largest producers), hydrogen peroxide, and phosphorus chemicals. The rest of its sales come from agricultural products (insecticides and herbicides) and specialty chemicals (food and pharmaceutical additives). FMC's equation lately has improved after a few years' effort to increase its efficiency, profitability, and credit rating. The company cut costs across the board and re-focused on strong growth areas, especially specialty chemicals.

	Annual Growth	12/03	12/04	12/05	12/06	12/07
Sales ($ mil.)	8.2%	1,921.4	2,051.2	2,150.2	2,347.0	2,632.9
Net income ($ mil.)	49.5%	26.5	160.2	116.6	132.0	132.4
Market value ($ mil.)	61.6%	600.6	894.2	1,028.4	1,466.6	4,098.3
Employees	0.0%	—	—	5,000	5,000	5,000

FMC TECHNOLOGIES, INC.

NYSE: FTI

1803 Gears Rd.
Houston, TX 77067
Phone: 281-591-4000
Fax: 281-591-4102
Web: www.fmctechnologies.com

CEO: Peter D. Kinnear
CFO: William H. (Bill) Schumann III
HR: –
FYE: December 31
Type: Public

Who says oil and orange juice won't mix? Through its energy systems unit, FMC Technologies offers subsea drilling and production systems for the exploration and production of oil and gas. Other oil and gas products include fluid control, measurement, loading, and blending systems. FMC Technologies' FoodTech makes food-handling and juice-extraction systems used by companies such as Pilgrim's Pride and Tyson Foods. The company's airport systems unit makes airline ground-support systems such as cargo loaders and boarding bridges. In 2006 FMC Technologies acquired Galaxy Oilfield Services (production equipment used for oil sands).

	Annual Growth	12/03	12/04	12/05	12/06	12/07
Sales ($ mil.)	18.9%	2,307.1	2,767.7	3,226.7	3,790.7	4,615.4
Net income ($ mil.)	41.5%	75.6	116.7	106.1	276.3	302.8
Market value ($ mil.)	87.8%	—	1,106.1	1,461.4	2,073.8	7,331.3
Employees	10.0%	—	—	10,000	11,000	

FMR LLC

82 Devonshire St.
Boston, MA 02109
Phone: 617-563-7000
Fax: 617-476-6150
Web: www.fidelity.com

CEO: Edward C. (Ned) Johnson III
CFO: Clare S. Richer
HR: D. Ellen Wilson
FYE: December 31
Type: Private

FMR is *semper fidelis* (ever faithful) to its core business. The financial services conglomerate, better known as Fidelity Investments, is one of the world's largest mutual fund firms. Serving more than 23 million individual and institutional clients, Fidelity manages more than 300 funds and has more than $1.5 trillion of assets under management. It also operates a leading online discount brokerage and has more than 100 investor centers in the US and Canada, as well as locations in Europe and Asia. The founding Johnson family controls FMR; Abigail Johnson, CEO Ned Johnson's daughter and perhaps his successor (not to mention one of the richest women in America), is the company's largest single shareholder.

	Annual Growth	12/03	12/04	12/05	12/06	12/07
Sales ($ mil.)	15.8%	—	—	—	12,870.0	14,900.0
Employees	10.7%	—	—	—	41,900	46,400

FNB BANCORP

OTC: FNBG

975 El Camino Real
South San Francisco, CA 94080
Phone: 650-588-6800
Fax: 650-588-9695
Web: www.fnbnorcal.com

CEO: Thomas C. (Tom) McGraw
CFO: David A. (Dave) Curtis
HR: –
FYE: December 31
Type: Public

To *be* or not to *FNB*? If that's your question, you might want to look into FNB Bancorp. It's the holding company for First National Bank of Northern California, which provides traditional deposit products and loan offerings to small to midsized businesses and individuals in California's San Mateo and San Francisco counties. Through more than a dozen branches, it offers deposit products including savings, checking, and money market accounts; IRAs; and CDs. Lending activities include credit card services and commercial, personal, and residential mortgage loans. First National Bank also offers cash management, financial planning, and merchant card services.

	Annual Growth	12/03	12/04	12/05	12/06	12/07
Assets ($ mil.)	10.7%	429.5	490.0	569.1	581.3	644.5
Net income ($ mil.)	13.1%	4.1	4.7	5.7	7.6	6.7
Market value ($ mil.)	1.9%	62.7	76.7	83.3	88.3	67.7
Employees	—	—	—	—	—	

F.N.B. CORPORATION

NYSE: FNB

1 F.N.B. Blvd.
Hermitage, PA 16148
Phone: 724-981-6000
Fax: 724-983-4873
Web: www.fnbcorporation.com

CEO: Robert V. New Jr.
CFO: Brian F. Lilly
HR: –
FYE: December 31
Type: Public

F.N.B. Corporation is the holding company for First National Bank of Pennsylvania, which operates about 220 bank branches in Pennsylvania and northeastern Ohio. The company also has more than 50 consumer finance offices in those states and Tennessee, plus a handful of loan production offices in Florida. It operates in four segments, providing community banking, wealth management, insurance, and consumer finance products and services to consumers and small businesses. Commercial loans make up about half of the company's loan portfolio. F.N.B. Corporation bought Omega Financial in 2008; a deal to buy another Pennsylvania-based bank, Iron and Glass Bancorp, is pending.

	Annual Growth	12/03	12/04	12/05	12/06	12/07
Assets ($ mil.)	(7.5%)	8,308.3	5,027.0	5,590.3	6,007.6	6,088.0
Net income ($ mil.)	4.3%	58.8	61.8	55.3	67.7	69.7
Market value ($ mil.)	0.6%	870.1	1,019.2	996.8	1,103.4	890.1
Employees	2.8%	—	—	1,793	—	1,893

FNB UNITED CORP.

NASDAQ (GS): FNBN

150 South Fayetteville St.
Asheboro, NC 27203
Phone: 336-626-8300
Fax: 336-625-2452
Web: www.myyesbank.com

CEO: Michael C. Miller
CFO: Mark A. Severson
HR: Deborah B. Auman
FYE: December 31
Type: Public

FNB United is the holding company for CommunityONE Bank (formerly First National Bank and Trust), which has about 45 branches in North Carolina. The bank's offerings include checking, savings, and money market accounts, CDs, IRAs, credit cards, and trust services. It concentrates on real estate lending: Commercial mortgages account for more than 35% of the company's loan portfolio, while residential mortgages and construction loans are about 25% apiece. The bank also makes business and consumer loans. Subsidiary Dover Mortgage Company originates mortgages for sale into the secondary market through about five loan production offices in its home state.

	Annual Growth	12/03	12/04	12/05	12/06	12/07
Assets ($ mil.)	25.3%	773.2	862.9	1,102.1	1,814.9	1,906.5
Net income ($ mil.)	10.2%	8.4	6.6	9.9	12.2	12.4
Market value ($ mil.)	3.6%	120.4	107.4	121.0	207.1	139.0
Employees	18.3%	—	—	350	584	490

FNBH BANCORP, INC.

OTC: FNHM

101 E. Grand River
Howell, MI 48843
Phone: 517-546-3150
Fax: 517-546-6275
Web: www.fnbsite.com

CEO: Ronald L. Long
CFO: –
HR: Nancy Morgan
FYE: December 31
Type: Public

If Thurston III and Lovey ever did get off that island, they might've stashed their fortune here. FNBH Bancorp is the holding company for First National Bank of Howell, which provides individual and local business customers with traditional deposit products and loans across Livingston County, Michigan. Business customers get additional perks, such as simplified employee pension management and investment services. Commercial loans comprise about 85% of the bank's loan portfolio. Founded in 1934, the bank traditionally served rural communities, but a growing suburban community has increased its customer base.

	Annual Growth	12/03	12/04	12/05	12/06	12/07
Assets ($ mil.)	(1.0%)	449.8	456.6	477.2	473.9	432.9
Net income ($ mil.)	—	5.9	6.3	6.5	5.6	(6.6)
Market value ($ mil.)	(16.7%)	85.6	101.0	80.5	81.5	41.1
Employees	—	—	—	—	—	—

FOAMEX INTERNATIONAL INC.

Pink Sheets: FMXI

1000 Columbia Ave.
Linwood, PA 19061
Phone: 610-859-3000
Fax: 610-859-3035
Web: www.foamex.com

CEO: John G. (Jack) Johnson Jr.
CFO: Robert M. Larney
HR: John G. (Jack) Johnson Jr.
FYE: Sunday nearest December 31
Type: Public

Foam sweet foam. Foamex International is one of North America's largest makers of polyurethane foam for carpets and furniture. Products made with Foamex's flexible polyurethane and polymer foams include mattresses, couches, car interior trim, and carpet cushions. Computer cabinets, industrial filters, and gaskets are but a few of the uses for the products made by the company's technical products division. Foamex's customers include auto supplier Johnson Controls, as well as other major automobile and bedding manufacturers. The company emerged from Chapter 11 bankruptcy protection in February 2007.

	Annual Growth	12/03	12/04	12/05	12/06	12/07
Sales ($ mil.)	(2.7%)	1,304.6	1,266.4	1,311.6	1,357.2	1,169.4
Net income ($ mil.)	—	(21.5)	(150.9)	(56.2)	12.4	(46.7)
Employees	—	—	—	—	4,000	—

FOCUS BRANDS INC.

200 Glenridge Point Pkwy., Ste. 200
Atlanta, GA 30342
Phone: 404-255-3250
Fax: 404-255-4978
Web: www.focusbrands.com

CEO: Steven (Steve) Romaniello
CFO: Lenore L. Krentz
HR: Jean Boland
FYE: December 31
Type: Private

The focus of this company is on coffee, sandwiches, spicy food, and sweets. FOCUS Brands is a leading multi-concept restaurant franchisor and operator, with more than 2,100 locations in the US and more than 30 other countries. Its businesses include Carvel, a leading chain of ice cream stores primarily in the Northeast, Cinnabon, a popular sweet snacks chain found in shopping malls and other high-traffic locations, and Schlotzsky's, a chain of sandwich outlets found mostly in Texas. FOCUS Brands also owns quick-casual Mexican chain Moe's Southwest Grill through subsidiary MSWG. The company was formed in 2004 by private equity firm Roark Capital Group.

	Annual Growth	12/03	12/04	12/05	12/06	12/07
Est. sales ($ mil.)	—	—	—	—	—	117.1
Employees	—	—	—	—	—	2,140

FOCUS ELECTRONICS GROUP

675 W. 14600 South
Bluffdale, UT 84065
Phone: 801-523-6600
Fax: 801-571-6061
Web: www.backtobasicsproducts.com

CEO: Mike Carpenter
CFO: Jack Theler
HR: Lecia Thornton
FYE: December 31
Type: Private

Focus Electronics Group (formerly Back to Basics) boasts products that help to make cooking fun again. It markets and retails household countertop appliances including blenders, ice shavers, nut roasters, food dehydrators, and juicers. It also sells Disney licensed appliances for kids and specialty items, such as wheat grass growing kits and juicers, cherry stoners, and egg and muffin toasters. The firm has a partnership with Food Network celebrity and cookbook author Paula Deen, granting Focus Electronics the exclusive license for a family of Paula Deen small appliances, both electric and non-electric. Focus Electronics was founded in 1971 as Back to Basics. Focus Products Group bought the company in 2007.

	Annual Growth	12/03	12/04	12/05	12/06	12/07
Est. sales ($ mil.)	—	—	—	—	—	10.6
Employees	—	—	—	—	—	85

FOCUS ENHANCEMENTS, INC.

NASDAQ (CM): FCSE

1370 Dell Ave.
Campbell, CA 95008
Phone: 408-866-8300
Fax: 408-866-4859
Web: www.focusinfo.com

CEO: Brett A. Moyer
CFO: Gary L. Williams
HR: Elizabeth Fisher
FYE: December 31
Type: Public

FOCUS Enhancements has a renewed focus. The 2001 acquisition of Videonics expanded FOCUS' offerings into digital video postproduction equipment and software with its FireStore product line. The company's established TView set-top, rackmount, and PC products modify PC video signals for viewing on television screens. FOCUS' converters are used for business presentations, videoconferencing, classroom activities, and gaming. The company also makes PC-to-TV video co-processor chips and digital video mixers. Products are sold to US resellers and distributors and directly to manufacturers.

	Annual Growth	12/03	12/04	12/05	12/06	12/07
Sales ($ mil.)	3.1%	26.6	20.0	24.5	37.5	30.0
Net income ($ mil.)	—	(1.7)	(11.0)	(15.4)	(15.9)	(17.4)
Market value ($ mil.)	(17.5%)	91.8	68.3	42.4	122.2	42.5
Employees	19.1%	77	126	132	143	155

An in-depth profile of this company is available to Hoover's Online members at hoovers.com.

637

FOG CUTTER CAPITAL GROUP INC.

OTC: FCCG

1410 SW Jefferson St.
Portland, OR 97201
Phone: 503-721-6500
Fax: 503-721-6501
Web: www.fccgi.com

CEO: Andrew A. (Andy) Wiederhorn
CFO: R. Scott Stevenson
HR: –
FYE: December 31
Type: Public

This company's beacon shines brightest on the fast-food business. Fog Cutter Capital Group has investments in a variety of enterprises, but its primary operating business is Fatburger. The 82%-owned hamburger chain, with more than 90 restaurants in California and more that a dozen other states, is popular for its gourmet burgers and retro-themed diner interiors. More than 50 Fatburger locations are franchised. In addition, Fog Cutter owns an industrial manufacturing business (DAC International) and has a number of real estate holdings. CEO Andrew Wiederhorn and his wife, Tiffany, own about 30% of the company.

	Annual Growth	12/03	12/04	12/05	12/06	12/07
Sales ($ mil.)	29.3%	15.6	47.0	31.9	44.9	43.6
Net income ($ mil.)	—	5.4	(3.9)	(6.9)	(10.1)	(10.2)
Employees	3.8%	624	599	659	676	724

FOLEY & LARDNER LLP

777 E. Wisconsin Ave.
Milwaukee, WI 53202
Phone: 414-271-2400
Fax: 414-297-4900
Web: www.foley.com

CEO: Ralf-Reinhard Böer
CFO: Tom L. Budde
HR: Marion E. Baker
FYE: January 31
Type: Partnership

Though most famous for its cheese, Wisconsin has another thing going for it: lawyers. Foley & Lardner, the largest and oldest law firm in Wisconsin, has nearly 1,000 lawyers and has expanded far beyond its Milwaukee base with offices in more than 15 other US cities (including four in Florida and six in California). In addition, Foley & Lardner has international offices in Brussels and Tokyo. The firm, founded in 1842, has one of the nation's leading health law practices and an increased focus on its intellectual property practice; other areas of expertise include business law, litigation, regulatory issues, and tax planning.

	Annual Growth	1/03	1/04	1/05	1/06	1/07
Sales ($ mil.)	8.1%	489.5	523.0	542.5	610.5	668.0
Employees	5.4%	—	—	2,334	2,461	—

▥ FOLLETT CORPORATION

2233 West St.
River Grove, IL 60171
Phone: 708-583-2000
Fax: 708-452-9347
Web: www.follett.com

CEO: Christopher D. (Chris) Traut
CFO: Kathryn A. Stanton
HR: Richard Ellspermann
FYE: March 31
Type: Private

Not all kids like to read, but (fortunately for Follett) by the time they reach college, they don't have a choice. Follett is the #1 operator of US college bookstores with more than 750 campus bookshops across the nation, as well as Canada. The company's business groups, which reach about 60 countries, also provide books and audiovisual materials to grade school and public libraries, library automation and management software, textbook reconditioning, and other services. Follett acquired its smaller online rival Varsity Group in 2008, complementing its own efollett.com Web site that sells new and used college textbooks. The Follett family has owned and managed the company for four generations.

	Annual Growth	3/02	3/03	3/04	3/05	3/06
Sales ($ mil.)	8.1%	1,733.0	1,851.0	1,899.0	2,000.0	2,370.0
Employees	(4.6%)	10,000	10,000	10,000	10,000	8,300

FONAR CORPORATION

NASDAQ (CM): FONR

110 Marcus Dr.
Melville, NY 11747
Phone: 631-694-2929
Fax: 631-753-5150
Web: www.fonar.com

CEO: Raymond V. Damadian
CFO: Raymond V. Damadian
HR: –
FYE: June 30
Type: Public

SONAR finds objects hidden under the water using sound waves; FONAR uses magnetic resonance imaging (MRI) to find disease or injury hidden inside the body. The company was the first to market a commercial MRI scanner in 1980, and it is trying to stay at the forefront of the field with its Upright MRI, which scans patients in sitting, standing, or bending positions. FONAR also makes the FONAR 360, a room-sized MRI that does away with the claustrophia-producing enclosed tubes of traditional machines. Additionally, FONAR's Health Management Corporation of America (HMCA) subsidiary provides management services to a dozen diagnostic imaging centers, primarily in Florida and New York.

	Annual Growth	6/03	6/04	6/05	6/06	6/07
Sales ($ mil.)	(11.0%)	52.9	71.6	104.9	33.1	33.2
Net income ($ mil.)	—	(15.0)	(9.5)	1.0	(30.0)	(25.5)
Market value ($ mil.)	—	—	—	—	—	24.2
Employees	(13.5%)	—	—	494	—	370

FONIX CORPORATION

OTC: FNIX

387 S. 520 West, Ste. 110
Linton, UT 84042
Phone: 801-553-6600
Fax: 801-553-6707
Web: www.fonix.com

CEO: Roger D. Dudley
CFO: Roger D. Dudley
HR: Stacy Hansen
FYE: December 31
Type: Public

Fonix hopes to get speech down pat. The company develops text-to-speech and automated speech recognition applications that are integrated into a variety of products, enabling such services as voice-activated telephone menus. Marketing its products primarily to software developers, consumer electronics manufacturers, and others who embed the software in their own products, Fonix also offers applications targeted to consumers. The company had offered VoIP services to business customers through subsidiaries, but those operations filed for bankruptcy in late 2006. Former CEO Thomas Murdock owns about 41% of the company; current CEO Roger Dudley holds a 32% stake.

	Annual Growth	12/03	12/04	12/05	12/06	12/07
Sales ($ mil.)	(6.9%)	2.4	14.9	16.2	1.3	1.8
Net income ($ mil.)	—	(13.5)	(15.1)	(22.6)	(21.9)	15.0
Market value ($ mil.)	(45.4%)	24.2	25.3	7.9	3.9	—
Employees	—	63	—	—	—	—

FOOD FOR THE POOR, INC.

6401 Lyons Rd., Dept. 9662
Coconut Creek, FL 33073
Phone: 954-427-2222
Fax: 954-570-7654
Web: www.foodforthepoor.org

CEO: Robin G. Mahfood
CFO: –
HR: –
FYE: December 31
Type: Not-for-profit

Food For The Poor wants to feed spiritual hunger. The Christian charity provides health, social, economic, and religious services for impoverished people in more than 15 countries in Latin America and the Caribbean. Food For The Poor believes its organization serves God by helping those most in need, distributing requested goods through local churches and charities. The group works through Caritas, the American-Nicaraguan Foundation, and others to provide vocational training, clinic and school construction, educational materials, feeding programs, and medical supplies. Food For The Poor has distributed more than $3 billion in goods since its 1982 inception; the group uses 96% of its funds on programs.

	Annual Growth	12/03	12/04	12/05	12/06	12/07
Est. sales ($ mil.)	—	—	—	—	—	861.9
Employees	—	—	—	—	—	232

An in-depth profile of this company is available to Hoover's Online members at hoovers.com.

FOOD TECHNOLOGY SERVICE, INC.

NASDAQ (CM): VIFL

502 Prairie Mine Rd.
Mulberry, FL 33860
Phone: 863-425-0039
Fax: 863-425-5526
Web: www.foodtechservice.com

CEO: Richard G. Hunter
CFO: Richard G. Hunter
HR: Richard G. Hunter
FYE: December 31
Type: Public

Food Technology Service is out to get Sal — *salmonella* that is. The firm operates a facility in Mulberry, Florida, that irradiates foods using gamma irradiation to kill insects and pathogens and to extend shelf life by retarding spoilage. It provides contract sterilization services to the medical-device, food and consumer-goods industries, and also irradiates packaging, cosmetic ingredients, spices, and horticultural items. Given that only three customers account for 60% of its sales, Food Technology is seeking to diversify its customer base. Canada-based MDS Inc., a life-science services company, owns about 31% of Food Technology Service.

	Annual Growth	12/03	12/04	12/05	12/06	12/07
Sales ($ mil.)	2.5%	1.9	1.3	1.7	1.8	2.1
Net income ($ mil.)	(15.9%)	0.4	(0.1)	0.1	0.7	0.2
Market value ($ mil.)	(10.3%)	11.7	14.0	9.2	6.9	7.5
Employees	—	—	—	10	—	—

FOODARAMA SUPERMARKETS, INC.

922 Hwy. 33, Bldg. 6, Ste. 1
Freehold, NJ 07728
Phone: 732-462-4700
Fax: 732-294-2322

CEO: Richard J. Saker
CFO: Thomas H. Flynn
HR: –
FYE: Saturday nearest October 31
Type: Private

Foodarama Supermarkets thinks its customers deserve world-class grocery stores. A member of the Wakefern Food purchasing and distribution cooperative, the company operates about 25 ShopRite supermarkets in central New Jersey. The majority of Foodarama's stores are classified by the company as World Class, meaning they are larger than 50,000 sq. ft. and offer amenities such as international foods, in-store bakeries, kosher sections, snack bars, and pharmacies. Foodarama also operates two liquor stores, a garden center, a food processing facility (which supplies its stores with meat and prepared foods), and a bakery. The founding Saker family took the company private in 2006.

	Annual Growth	10/02	10/03	10/04	10/05	10/06
Est. sales ($ mil.)	3.7%	—	—	—	1,215.0	1,260.0
Employees	0.0%	—	—	—	6,850	6,850

FOOT LOCKER, INC.

NYSE: FL

112 W. 34th St.
New York, NY 10120
Phone: 212-720-3700
Fax: 212-720-4397
Web: www.footlocker-inc.com

CEO: Matthew D. (Matt) Serra
CFO: Robert W. McHugh
HR: Laurie J. Petrucci
FYE: Saturday nearest January 31
Type: Public

Foot Locker leads the pack in the race to capture the biggest share of the athletic footwear market. The company is a leading retailer of athletic shoes and apparel. Foot Locker has about 3,800 specialty stores in some 20 countries in North America and Europe, as well as Australia and New Zealand, led by Foot Locker (the #1 athletic footwear retailer in the US). Foot Locker also operates Lady Foot Locker and Kids Foot Locker; Champs Sports, an athletic wear retail chain; Eastbay, a catalog retailer of athletic equipment and apparel; and the Footlocker.com Web site. The company also has about 355 Footaction stores in the US and Puerto Rico, which sell footwear and apparel to young urbanites.

	Annual Growth	1/04	1/05	1/06	1/07	1/08
Sales ($ mil.)	3.3%	4,779.0	5,355.0	5,653.0	5,750.0	5,437.0
Net income ($ mil.)	(29.5%)	207.0	293.0	264.0	251.0	51.0
Market value ($ mil.)	(11.8%)	3,561.4	4,083.3	3,481.7	3,528.2	2,153.4
Employees	2.6%	—	—	44,276	45,406	—

FOOTSTAR, INC.

Pink Sheets: FTAR

933 MacArthur Blvd.
Mahwah, NJ 07430
Phone: 201-934-2000
Fax: 201-934-0398
Web: www.footstar.com

CEO: Jeffrey A. (Jeff) Shepard
CFO: Michael J. (Mike) Lynch
HR: Dennis M. Lee
FYE: December 31
Type: Public

Footstar is losing its footing in the discount footwear arena. The firm operates leased footwear departments in about 1,390 Kmart and 860 Rite Aid stores on the West Coast. Footstar offers shoes under its own Cobbie Cuddlers, Texas Steer, and Thom McAn labels, as well as licensed brands Basic Editions, Route 66, Thalia, and Joe Boxer. Retail giant Wal-Mart no longer purchases Thom McAn brand footwear for its stores, leaving Kmart as Footstar's most valuable customer. Accounting issues led Footstar to file for Chapter 11 bankruptcy protection in 2004. Consequently, it sold its US-based Footaction retail stores to Foot Locker to focus on its wholesale business. The firm emerged from bankruptcy in February 2006 and has agreed to sell its footwear license.

	Annual Growth	12/03	12/04	12/05	12/06	12/07
Sales ($ mil.)	(11.0%)	1,015.6	800.2	715.4	666.7	637.0
Net income ($ mil.)	—	(54.4)	(70.0)	24.4	45.3	52.0
Market value ($ mil.)	(27.5%)	—	—	—	137.0	99.3
Employees	(34.8%)	14,087	4,460	—	3,901	—

FORBES INC.

60 5th Ave.
New York, NY 10011
Phone: 212-620-2200
Fax: 212-620-2245
Web: www.forbesinc.com

CEO: Malcolm S. (Steve) Forbes Jr.
CFO: Sean P. Hegarty
HR: Margaret W. Loftus
FYE: December 31
Type: Private

Repeat after Forbes: Capitalism is good! The family-owned company publishes the biweekly business magazine *Forbes*, long promoted as the "Capitalist Tool." It also publishes a handful of other magazines, including *ForbesLife*, *American Heritage*, and *American Legacy*, an African-American history quarterly that's a joint venture with RJR Communications. In addition, the company operates a Web site (Forbes.com), produces business-related conferences, and publishes newsletters and custom magazines for a variety of clients. Scottish immigrant and journalist B.C. Forbes launched *Forbes* in 1917. CEO Malcolm "Steve" Forbes (B.C.'s grandson) became known as a self-funded Republican presidential candidate in 1996 and 2000.

	Annual Growth	12/03	12/04	12/05	12/06	12/07
Est. sales ($ mil.)	—	—	—	—	—	78.8
Employees	—	—	—	—	—	700

FORCE PROTECTION, INC.

NASDAQ (CM): FRPT

9801 Hwy. 78, Bldg. 1
Ladson, SC 29456
Phone: 843-740-7015
Fax: 843-740-1973
Web: www.forceprotectioninc.com

CEO: Michael Moody
CFO: Francis E. (Frank) Scheuerell Jr.
HR: –
FYE: December 31
Type: Public

Force Protection's vehicles protect military forces from blast forces. The company makes armored land vehicles designed to protect troops from landmines, bombs, and hostile fire. Force Protection's products include the 22-ton Buffalo, which is designed for mine-clearing operations, and the Cougar, a lighter-weight vehicle with similar armoring that can be used for route clearance support, urban patrol, and other activities. The Cheetah is the smallest of the company's offerings. It is used for reconnaissance and other urban operations. While the US Marine Corps is Force Protection's largest single customer, the US Army and friendly foreign governments also purchase military vehicles from the company.

	Annual Growth	12/02	12/03	12/04	12/05	*12/06
Sales ($ mil.)	194.7%	2.6	6.3	10.3	49.7	196.0
Net income ($ mil.)	—	(5.4)	(5.3)	(10.3)	(14.4)	18.2
Market value ($ mil.)	83.3%	103.0	102.7	774.9	28.2	1,162.3
Employees	—	—	—	—	—	658

*Most recent year available

An in-depth profile of this company is available to Hoover's Online members at hoovers.com.

639

FORCE10 NETWORKS, INC.

350 Holger Way
San Jose, CA 95134
Phone: 408-571-3500
Fax: 408-571-3550
Web: www.force10networks.com

CEO: Mark Randall
CFO: Karen Blasing
HR: –
FYE: October 31
Type: Private

Force10 Networks develops communications network routing and switching equipment to be reckoned with. The company's E-series products, used in both enterprise and service provider networks, are designed for cutting-edge Ethernet technologies Gigabit and 10 Gigabit Ethernet. It has also developed its S-series switch specifically for data center applications. Force10 sells to large enterprises, carriers, and communications services providers; other customers include educational institutions and research labs. The company has received funding from venture firms New Enterprise Associates, US Venture Partners, and Worldview Technology Partners, among others.

	Annual Growth	10/03	10/04	10/05	10/06	10/07
Est. sales ($ mil.)	—	—	—	—	—	35.9
Employees	—	—	—	—	—	375

THE FORD FOUNDATION

320 E. 43rd St.
New York, NY 10017
Phone: 212-573-5000
Fax: 212-351-3677
Web: www.fordfound.org

CEO: Luis A. Ubiñas
CFO: Nicholas M. Gabriel
HR: Bruce D. Stuckey
FYE: September 30
Type: Foundation

As one of the US's largest philanthropic organizations, The Ford Foundation can afford to be generous. The foundation offers grants to individuals and institutions around the world that work to meet its goals of strengthening democratic values, reducing poverty and injustice, promoting international cooperation, and advancing human achievement. The Ford Foundation's charitable giving has run the gamut from A (Association for Asian Studies) to Z (Zanzibar International Film Festival). The foundation has an endowment of about $12 billion. It no longer has stock in Ford Motor Company or ties to the founding Ford family.

	Annual Growth	9/02	9/03	9/04	9/05	9/06
Sales ($ mil.)	46.0%	288.9	260.8	1,318.5	1,587.8	1,312.3
Employees	—	400	—	—	—	—

FORD MOTOR COMPANY

NYSE: F

1 American Rd.
Dearborn, MI 48126
Phone: 313-322-3000
Fax: 313-845-6073
Web: www.ford.com

CEO: Alan R. Mulally
CFO: Donat R. (Don) Leclair
HR: Felicia J. Fields
FYE: December 31
Type: Public

Ford Motor began a manufacturing revolution with its mass production assembly lines in the early 1900s. The company is now firmly entrenched in the status quo as one of the world's largest makers of cars and trucks. Its vehicles brands include Ford, Lincoln, and Mercury. Among its biggest successes are the redesigned Ford Mustang and F-Series pickup. Ford owns a 33% stake in Mazda and also controls the Volvo nameplate. Finance subsidiary Ford Motor Credit is the one of the US's leading auto finance companies. After clearing all of the antitrust and labor hurdles, Ford has sold Land Rover and Jaguar to India-based Tata Motors for a reported $2.3 billion.

	Annual Growth	12/03	12/04	12/05	12/06	12/07
Sales ($ mil.)	1.1%	165,066.0	171,652.0	176,896.0	160,123.0	172,455.0
Net income ($ mil.)	—	495.0	3,487.0	1,440.0	(12,613.0)	(2,723.0)
Market value ($ mil.)	(16.5%)	29,392.0	26,893.7	14,181.6	13,795.9	14,294.5
Employees	(9.4%)	—	—	—	300,000	283,000	246,000

FORD MOTOR CREDIT COMPANY LLC

1 American Rd.
Dearborn, MI 48126
Phone: 313-322-3000
Fax: 313-323-2959
Web: www.fordcredit.com

CEO: Michael E. (Mike) Bannister
CFO: Kenneth R. Kent
HR: –
FYE: December 31
Type: Subsidiary

Seems its trucks aren't the only things built Ford tough. The automaker's subsidiary, Ford Motor Credit, is proving to be pretty resilient, too. One of the world's largest auto financing companies, it funds autos for and through Ford, Lincoln, Mercury, Jaguar, Land Rover, Mazda, and Volvo dealerships in more than 35 countries. It finances new, used, and leased vehicles (including more than 40% of new Fords sold in the US) and provides wholesale financing, mortgages, and capital loans for dealers. The company also provides business fleet financing. It sold APCO, which provides extended-care warranties for new and used vehicles, to private equity firm Stone Point Capital and APCO's management in 2007.

	Annual Growth	12/03	12/04	12/05	12/06	12/07
Assets ($ mil.)	(1.4%)	178,829.0	172,621.0	162,262.0	167,332.0	169,023.0
Net income ($ mil.)	(19.2%)	1,817.0	2,862.0	1,904.0	1,283.0	775.0
Employees	(14.0%)	—	—	—	12,900	11,100

FOREMOST FARMS USA, COOPERATIVE

E10889A Penny Ln.
Baraboo, WI 53913
Phone: 608-355-8700
Fax: 608-355-8699
Web: www.foremostfarms.com

CEO: David E. (Dave) Fuhrmann
CFO: –
HR: Joe Chenoweth
FYE: December 31
Type: Cooperative

No jokes about "herd mentality," please. Foremost Farms USA (owned by some 3,000 dairy farmers in Wisconsin and six other Midwestern states) is a major dairy cooperative. From 20 plants, the co-op churns some 5 billion pounds of milk per year into solid and fluid dairy products for industrial, retail, and foodservice customers. Its biggest sector is cheese, with a 2006 production of almost 500 million pounds. Foremost's retail brands include Golden Guernsey Dairy and Morning Glory. The co-op also produces private-label products for retailers.

	Annual Growth	12/02	12/03	12/04	12/05	12/06
Sales ($ mil.)	(12.2%)	—	—	—	1,419.2	1,245.8
Net income ($ mil.)	—	—	—	—	4.8	(12.5)
Employees	(1.1%)	—	—	—	1,540	1,523

FOREST CITY ENTERPRISES, INC.

NYSE: FCE

1100 Terminal Tower, 50 Public Sq.
Cleveland, OH 44113
Phone: 216-621-6060
Fax: 216-263-4808
Web: www.forestcity.net

CEO: Charles A. Ratner
CFO: Robert G. O'Brien
HR: Minta A. Monchein
FYE: January 31
Type: Public

Forest City Enterprises has gone from treeline to skyline. Founded in 1920 as a lumber dealer, the company now focuses on real estate development in metropolitan areas across the US. Its commercial group develops and manages more than 90 retail and office properties, half a dozen hotels, and nearly 20 regional malls in about 15 states. The residential group owns and manages more than 110 upscale and middle-market apartments, condominiums, and military family housing units in 20 states. The company also owns some 10,500 acres of raw land, some of which it sells and some of which it plans to develop into master-planned communities. The interrelated Ratner, Miller, and Shafran families control Forest City.

	Annual Growth	1/04	1/05	1/06	1/07	1/08
Sales ($ mil.)	6.1%	1,021.6	1,041.8	1,200.8	1,168.8	1,295.6
Net income ($ mil.)	5.3%	42.7	85.2	83.5	177.3	52.4
Market value ($ mil.)	60.3%	471.5	537.6	2,866.6	4,632.2	3,116.3
Employees	4.8%	—	—	4,279	4,484	—

FOREST LABORATORIES, INC.

NYSE: FRX

909 3rd Ave.
New York, NY 10022
Phone: 212-421-7850
Fax: 212-750-9152
Web: www.frx.com

CEO: Howard Solomon
CFO: Francis I. Perier Jr.
HR: Bernard J. McGovern
FYE: March 31
Type: Public

Forest Laboratories doesn't just blend in with the trees. The company develops and manufactures name-brand as well as generic prescription and over-the-counter pharmaceutical products. The company's central nervous system pharmaceutical line includes antidepressants Celexa and Lexapro, as well as Namenda, which treats Alzheimer's disease. Other products include treatments for thyroid disease, hypertension, respiratory ailments, and pain. Forest Laboratories, which has subsidiaries in the UK and Ireland, markets directly to doctors, drugstore chains, managed care organizations, and distributors through its own sales force.

	Annual Growth	3/04	3/05	3/06	3/07	3/08
Sales ($ mil.)	9.4%	2,680.3	3,159.6	2,962.4	3,441.8	3,836.3
Net income ($ mil.)	7.1%	735.9	838.8	708.5	454.1	967.9
Market value ($ mil.)	(17.2%)	26,465.5	12,845.4	14,341.4	16,462.0	12,459.4
Employees	(0.1%)	—	5,136	5,050	5,126	—

FOREST OIL CORPORATION

NYSE: FST

707 - 17th St., Ste. 3600
Denver, CO 80202
Phone: 303-812-1400
Fax: 303-812-1602
Web: www.forestoil.com

CEO: H. Craig Clark
CFO: David H. Keyte
HR: Paul J. Dusha
FYE: December 31
Type: Public

Forest Oil hasn't gotten lost among the big trees of the oil and gas business as it squeezes hydrocarbons from old forests buried deep underground. While the independent exploration and production company explores outside of North America, Forest Oil is focusing on building additional reserves in the US and expanding in Canada. It holds substantial acreage in Canada (12% of total reserves) and also operates a marketing and trading unit in that country. The company reports proved reserves of about 2.1 trillion cu. ft. of natural gas equivalent. Once a major owner, billionaire Philip Anschutz controls about 9% of Forest Oil. In 2007 the company acquired Houston Exploration for $1.5 billion.

	Annual Growth	12/03	12/04	12/05	12/06	12/07
Sales ($ mil.)	13.3%	657.2	912.9	1,072.0	820.0	1,083.9
Net income ($ mil.)	17.7%	88.3	122.6	151.6	168.5	169.3
Market value ($ mil.)	44.2%	1,040.1	1,328.2	1,999.6	2,058.8	4,493.2
Employees	19.9%	—	—	506	585	728

FOREVER 21, INC.

2001 S. Alameda St.
Los Angeles, CA 90058
Phone: 213-741-5100
Fax: 213-741-5161
Web: www.forever21.com

CEO: Do Won (Don) Chang
CFO: Lawrence (Larry) Meyer
HR: Kate Chun
FYE: December 31
Type: Private

You don't have to be 21 or older to shop at Forever 21's stores — you just need your wallet. The retailer operates 400-plus mainly mall-based stores in the US and Canada under the Forever 21, Forever XXI, and For Love 21 and Gadzooks banners. The stores offer cheap and chic fashions and accessories for women and junior girls. Its trendy clothes are priced 2% lower than its competitors. Most of the retailer's apparel is private label and made in Southern California. Forever XXI stores are larger than classic Forever 21 shops and offer men's and women's fashions, as well as lingerie, footwear, cosmetic items, and other accessories. Owner and CEO Don Chang and his wife founded the company as Fashion 21 in 1984.

	Annual Growth	12/02	12/03	12/04	12/05	12/06
Sales ($ mil.)	—	—	—	—	—	1,050.0
Employees	—	—	—	—	—	12,500

FOREVER LIVING PRODUCTS INTERNATIONAL, INC.

7501 E. McCormick Pkwy.
Scottsdale, AZ 85258
Phone: 480-998-8888
Fax: 480-905-8451
Web: www.foreverliving.com

CEO: Rex Gene Maughan
CFO: Rjay Lloyd
HR: Glen B. Banks
FYE: December 31
Type: Private

Forever Living Products International might not lead you to immortality, but its aloe-vera-based health care products are intended to improve your well-being. The firm sells aloe vera drinks, as well as aloe-vera-based aromatherapy products, cosmetics, dietary and nutritional supplements, lotion, soap, and tooth gel products. Owner Rex Maughan also owns aloe vera plantations in the Dominican Republic, Mexico, and Texas; Aloe Vera of America, a processing plant; and Forever Resorts' US resorts and marinas, including Dallas-area Southfork Ranch (of *Dallas* TV show fame). Forever Living Products, founded in 1978, sells its goods through a global network of some 8.8 million independent distributors.

FOREVERGREEN WORLDWIDE CORPORATION

OTC: FVRG

972 N. 1430 West
Orem, UT 84057
Phone: 801-655-5500
Fax: 801-655-5505
Web: www.forevergreen.org

CEO: Ronald K. (Ron) Williams
CFO: Paul T. Frampton
HR: –
FYE: December 31
Type: Public

ForeverGreen Worldwide wants to give customers a piece of its mind, naturally. The company offers 100% natural foods and personal-care products. Its chemical-free goodies include salsas, snack packs (made up of seeds, nuts, fruits, and grains), body oils, creams, lotions, cleansers, and shampoos. Major brands include Pulse snack bars, FrequenSea drink, and 24 Karat Chocolate. The sales of products take place on the company's Web site but are mainly reliant on independent distributors who are part of a network marketing operation in Asia, Australia, Europe, and North America.

	Annual Growth	12/03	12/04	12/05	12/06	12/07
Sales ($ mil.)	16.6%	12.3	6.8	3.8	3.5	22.7
Net income ($ mil.)	—	(1.1)	(2.5)	(2.0)	(1.2)	0.1
Market value ($ mil.)	(53.7%)	387.7	179.2	150.1	20.8	17.8
Employees	—	—	—	—	—	—

FORGENT NETWORKS, INC.

NASDAQ (GM): ASUR

108 Wild Basin Dr.
Austin, TX 78746
Phone: 512-437-2700
Fax: 512-437-2365
Web: www.forgentnetworks.com

CEO: Richard N. (Dick) Snyder
CFO: Jay C. Peterson
HR: –
FYE: July 31
Type: Public

Forgent Networks (dba Asure Software) is forging new paths. The company has transitioned from being a manufacturer of videoconferencing equipment to providing scheduling software and licensing data compression intellectual property. Its Meeting Room Manager software offers scheduling functions that allow users to reserve meeting rooms, schedule equipment and resources, and track office assets. Forgent's data compression intellectual property portfolio addresses devices used to compress, store, manipulate, print, and transmit digital still images, including digital cameras, PDAs, cellular telephones, printers, and scanners. About 80% of the company's sales come from its intellectual property licensing efforts.

	Annual Growth	7/03	7/04	7/05	7/06	7/07
Sales ($ mil.)	(7.0%)	53.9	17.5	9.9	14.9	40.4
Net income ($ mil.)	11.4%	8.0	(20.6)	(6.6)	(3.6)	12.3
Market value ($ mil.)	(27.4%)	77.6	30.4	39.8	10.4	21.5
Employees	17.8%	98	34	33	37	189

An in-depth profile of this company is available to Hoover's Online members at hoovers.com.

641

FORMFACTOR, INC.

NASDAQ (GS): FORM

7005 Southfront Rd.
Livermore, CA 94551
Phone: 925-290-4000
Fax: 925-290-4010
Web: www.formfactor.com

CEO: Igor Y. Khandros
CFO: Jean Bernard Vernet
HR: Henry I. Feir
FYE: Last Saturday in December
Type: Public

Good evening, and welcome to FormFactor! On tonight's show, our contestants will dive off a high platform, retrieve a silicon wafer at the bottom of the water tank, and then run tests on the semiconductors! Using an interconnect technology it calls MicroSpring, FormFactor makes wafer probe cards that test semiconductor circuits (especially memory chips) while they are still part of semiconductor wafers — before the wafers are cut into individual chips. FormFactor touts the process for its cost-effectiveness, since it allows testing of many chips at once across a range of scales and temperatures. The company gets about three-fourths of revenues from the Asia/Pacific region.

	Annual Growth	12/03	12/04	12/05	12/06	12/07
Sales ($ mil.)	47.3%	98.3	177.8	237.5	369.2	462.2
Net income ($ mil.)	76.6%	7.5	25.2	30.2	57.2	72.9
Market value ($ mil.)	23.5%	699.4	1,044.5	983.0	1,745.6	1,628.1
Employees	34.7%	341	485	653	936	1,124

FORMICA CORPORATION

255 East 5th St., Ste. 200
Cincinnati, OH 45202
Phone: 513-744-8700
Fax: 513-744-8749
Web: www.formica.com

CEO: Mark Adamson
CFO: –
HR: Linda Farfsing
FYE: December 31
Type: Subsidiary

Where would the modern kitchen be without it? Formica Corporation makes the eponymous adhesive and surfacing materials used in products such as countertops, cabinets, and flooring. In addition to the traditional laminate, the company offers metal, wood veneers, and stone surfaces. Its commercial products include fire-rated wall panels, doors, and toilet partitions. A top laminate supplier, Formica offers its products globally. The company has offices in Asia, Europe, and North America. Formica emerged from Chapter 11 bankruptcy protection in 2004 after a two-year restructuring. The group is owned by New Zealand building materials company Fletcher Building and is part of that group's Laminates & Panels division.

	Annual Growth	12/03	12/04	12/05	12/06	12/07
Est. sales ($ mil.)	—	—	—	—	—	295.7
Employees	—	—	—	—	—	4,109

FORMOSA PLASTICS CORPORATION, U.S.A.

9 Peach Tree Hill Rd.
Livingston, NJ 07039
Phone: 973-992-2090
Fax: 973-992-9627
Web: www.fpcusa.com

CEO: Chih-Tsun Lee
CFO: D. Lin
HR: Martin Hass
FYE: December 31
Type: Subsidiary

Formosa Plastics Corp., U.S.A., is the prince of PVC. Part of Taiwan's Formosa Plastics Corporation (one of the world's largest PVC suppliers), the company produces suspension and specialty polyvinyl chloride (PVC) resins,the former for pipe and fencing the latter for florring and insect screening. Formosa's product roster of plastic resins and petrochemicals also includes polyethylene, polypropylene, vinyl, and chlor alkali products like caustic soda. Subsidiary J-M Manufacturing makes PVC pipe for sewer, water main, and other construction applications. Other Formosa products are used for packaging and chemical processing, and the company drills for natural gas and operates a rail fleet.

	Annual Growth	12/03	12/04	12/05	12/06	12/07
Est. sales ($ mil.)	—	—	—	—	—	2,147.5
Employees	—	—	—	—	—	4,000

FORREST GENERAL HOSPITAL

6051 Hwy. 49 South
Hattiesburg, MS 39404
Phone: 601-288-7000
Fax: 601-288-1202
Web: www.forrestgeneral.com

CEO: William C. (Bill) Oliver
CFO: Ed Tucker
HR: –
FYE: September 30
Type: Not-for-profit

Forrest General Hospital is the hub of health care in Hattiesburg, Mississippi, also known as the "Hub City." Founded in 1952, the regional medical center serves southern Mississippi with some 400 acute care beds and offers general medical and surgical care, as well as specialty care in areas such as heart disease, cancer, and women's health. Other facilities include Pine Grove, a behavioral health center offering psychiatric and substance abuse treatment, an inpatient rehabilitation facility, and an outpatient surgery center. The hospital system also operates a home health care agency and hospice.

	Annual Growth	9/03	9/04	9/05	9/06	9/07
Est. sales ($ mil.)	—	—	—	—	—	346.1
Employees	—	—	—	—	—	4,030

🔲 FORRESTER RESEARCH, INC.

NASDAQ (GS): FORR

400 Technology Sq.
Cambridge, MA 02139
Phone: 617-613-6000
Fax: 617-613-5000
Web: www.forrester.com

CEO: George F. Colony
CFO: Michael A. Doyle
HR: Elizabeth Lemons
FYE: December 31
Type: Public

Can't see the tech forest for the trees? Maybe a Forrester ranger can guide you through the technological timber. One of the leading market research firms focused on the Internet and technology, Forrester Research supplies reports and briefs to more than 2,000 corporate clients, providing insight into market forces, industry trends, and consumer behavior. Forrester also offers custom research and consulting services to give its clients additional understanding of the technology market. In addition, the company produces a number of events where its clients can network with each other as well as with players in the technology industry.

	Annual Growth	12/03	12/04	12/05	12/06	12/07
Sales ($ mil.)	13.9%	126.0	138.5	153.2	181.5	212.1
Net income ($ mil.)	71.2%	2.2	4.1	11.4	17.8	18.9
Market value ($ mil.)	12.9%	398.7	389.0	394.2	624.7	648.7
Employees	12.4%	—	—	693	779	—

FORSTMANN LITTLE & CO.

767 5th Ave.
New York, NY 10153
Phone: 212-355-5656
Fax: 212-759-9059

CEO: Theodore J. (Ted) Forstmann
CFO: Winston W. Hutchins
HR: –
FYE: December 31
Type: Private

Don't let the "Little" fool you: Buyout firm Forstmann Little & Co. has been home to some big names. The company, which specializes in telecommunications, technology, education, and health care investments, counts among its former advisory board members Donald Rumsfeld, Colin Powell, George Shultz, and Henry Kissinger. Since its founding in 1978, Forstmann Little has invested in about 30 companies, including former holdings Gulfstream Aerospace, General Instrument, and Revlon. Current holdings include IMG and 24 Hour Fitness. It is led by the surviving founding group member, Ted Forstmann.

	Annual Growth	12/03	12/04	12/05	12/06	12/07
Est. sales ($ mil.)	—	—	—	—	—	1,681.0
Employees	—	—	—	—	—	17,034

FORSYTHE TECHNOLOGY, INC.

7770 Frontage Rd.
Skokie, IL 60077
Phone: 847-213-7000
Fax: 847-213-7922
Web: www.forsythe.com

CEO: William P. (Bill) Brennan
CFO: Albert L. (Al) Weiss
HR: Julie A. Fusco
FYE: December 31
Type: Private

Forsythe Technology believes it has the foresight to provide valuable information technology (IT) consulting services. Its Forsythe Solutions Group works on companies' IT infrastructure elements, including servers, storage, and networks, and clients can lease computer equipment through the Forsythe McArthur subsidiary. Forsythe Technology customers have included Aflac, Outback Steakhouse, and TriZetto. In 2004 the company acquired security services firm National Business Group, which expanded Forsythe's offerings in the area of IT risk management.

	Annual Growth	12/02	12/03	12/04	12/05	12/06
Sales ($ mil.)	1.5%	568.2	444.3	449.3	517.6	604.0
Employees	10.6%	535	549	639	619	800

FORT DEARBORN COMPANY

1530 Morse Ave.
Elk Grove, IL 60007
Phone: 847-357-9500
Fax: 847-357-8726
Web: www.fortdearborn.com

CEO: Michael (Mike) Anderson
CFO: Timothy Trahey
HR: Bill Samuels
FYE: December 31
Type: Private

Fort Dearborn's forté is in packaging labels. Named for the outpost that predated Chicago, Fort Dearborn is one of the country's largest producers of labels for consumer goods packaging. It offers such products as flexible packaging, paper labels, and label substrates and services including graphic design, digital imaging, and computer-to-plate printing. The company, which has six production facilities in the US, has served customers as ConAgra (Peter Pan and Hunt's brands), Campbell Soup, and Tri Valley Growers (Libby and Redpack Tomatoes). Investment firm Genstar Capital acquired Fort Dearborn from the founding Adler family in 2006. The company was established in 1925.

FORT ORANGE FINANCIAL CORP.

OTC: FOFC

1375 Washington Ave.
Albany, NY 12206
Phone: 518-434-1212
Fax: 518-434-1242
Web: www.capitalbank.com

CEO: Peter D. Cureau
CFO: Steven J. Owens
HR: Victoria A. Harkins
FYE: December 31
Type: Public

Small businesses might find a veritable fortress in this orange. Fort Orange Financial (formerly Capital Bank & Trust) owns community bank Capital Bank, which operates three branch offices in and around Albany, New York. Capital Bank specializes in business banking, but also serves the general public. It offers checking and savings accounts, debit cards, IRAs, and CDs, among other traditional banking services. About half of the bank's lending portfolio is devoted to commercial mortgages, followed by business loans (one-third of loans), single- to four-family residential mortgages, construction loans, and multifamily mortgages.

	Annual Growth	12/03	12/04	12/05	12/06	12/07
Est. sales ($ mil.)	—	—	—	—	—	10.7
Employees	—	—	—	—	—	22

FORTINET, INC.

1090 Kifer Rd.
Sunnyvale, CA 94086
Phone: 408-235-7700
Fax: 408-235-7737
Web: www.fortinet.com

CEO: Ken Xie
CFO: Kenneth A. (Ken) Goldman
HR: Norma J. Lane
FYE: December 31
Type: Private

Fortinet develops and markets ASIC-accelerated security appliances that integrate antivirus, firewall, content filtering, VPN, intrusion prevention (IPS), antispam and traffic shaping to detect and eliminate the most damaging, content-based threats from e-mail and Web traffic, such as viruses, worms, intrusions, inappropriate Web content, and more — in real time. Continuous updates against all new threats are delivered by Fortinet's FortiGuard subscription services to provide real-time network protection. The company also offers complementary products that include its FortiMail e-mail security system, FortiManager security management system, and FortiAnalyzer logging, reporting and analysis systems.

	Annual Growth	12/03	12/04	12/05	12/06	12/07
Est. sales ($ mil.)	—	—	—	—	—	150.0
Employees	—	—	—	—	—	1,000

FORTRESS INVESTMENT GROUP LLC

NYSE: FIG

1345 Avenue of the Americas
New York, NY 10105
Phone: 212-798-6100
Fax: —
Web: www.fortressinv.com

CEO: Wesley R. (Wes) Edens
CFO: Daniel N. Bass
HR: —
FYE: December 31
Type: Public

Fortress Investment Group specializes in private equity funds, hedge funds, and publicly traded alternative investments. The company oversees about $33 billion of assets under management for institutional investors and high-net-worth individuals, as well as its own account. It also manages publicly traded real estate investment trust (REIT) Newcastle Investment Corporation and commercial property investment company Eurocastle, which trades on Euronext; both companies make real estate-related investments. Fortress Investment Group's private equity business focuses on acquiring long-term controlling stakes in undervalued enterprises in the US, Canada, and Western Europe. The company went public in 2007.

	Annual Growth	12/03	12/04	12/05	12/06	12/07
Sales ($ mil.)	53.9%	220.3	351.4	1,044.1	1,521.3	1,236.0
Net income ($ mil.)	—	40.3	114.4	192.7	442.9	(59.8)
Market value ($ mil.)	—	—	—	—	—	1,473.8
Employees	39.6%	—	257	400	550	699

🔲 FORTUNE BRANDS, INC.

NYSE: FO

520 Lake Cook Rd.
Deerfield, IL 60015
Phone: 847-484-4400
Fax: 847-478-0073
Web: www.fortunebrands.com

CEO: Bruce A. Carbonari
CFO: Craig P. Omtvedt
HR: Rosalyn D. Wesley
FYE: December 31
Type: Public

Execs at Fortune Brands have good reason to meet over a game of golf and a glass of bourbon. The holding company is a leading US producer and distributor of distilled spirits (Jim Beam, DeKuyper, Knob Creek, Maker's Mark) and golf equipment (Titleist, Cobra, FootJoy, Pinnacle). However, Fortune's largest segment is home products and hardware, where its holdings include Moen faucets, MasterBrand cabinets, Master Lock padlocks, and Therma-Tru doors. The firm added former Allied Domecq brands Sauza, Courvoisier, and Canadian Club to its stable of potent potables in 2005.

	Annual Growth	12/03	12/04	12/05	12/06	12/07
Sales ($ mil.)	8.3%	6,214.5	6,145.2	7,061.2	8,769.0	8,563.1
Net income ($ mil.)	7.1%	579.2	783.8	621.1	830.1	762.6
Market value ($ mil.)	14.3%	9,958.6	10,605.7	11,413.6	20,058.1	16,997.4
Employees	1.2%	—	—	30,298	36,251	31,027

🔲 An in-depth profile of this company is available to Hoover's Online members at hoovers.com.

643

FORTUNE INDUSTRIES, INC.

AMEX: FFI

6402 Corporate Dr.
Indianapolis, IN 46278
Phone: 317-532-1374
Fax: 317-235-1011
Web: www.fdvi.net

CEO: John F. Fisbeck
CFO: Garth D. Allred
HR: –
FYE: August 31
Type: Public

Through its operating subsidiaries, holding company Fortune Industries tries its luck in a number of markets. The company is active in business services, commercial real estate development, electronics distribution, and steel fabrication. Its largest segment provides outsourced HR services such as payroll and tax processing through its Professional Staff Management and Pro Staff subsidiaries. Through subsidiary J.H. Drew, the company also makes and installs roadway guardrails and structural steel for commercial buildings. Fortune's wireless infrastructure unit provides real estate acquisition, architectural design, and construction management services for the telecommunications industry.

	Annual Growth	8/03	8/04	8/05	8/06	8/07
Sales ($ mil.)	78.8%	15.5	66.9	113.1	157.1	158.4
Net income ($ mil.)	—	0.1	2.4	(2.3)	2.2	(7.3)
Market value ($ mil.)	(49.0%)	405.3	881.3	66.5	45.8	27.3
Employees	(2.0%)	—	—	524	—	503

FORTUNET, INC.

NASDAQ (GM): FNET

2950 S. Highland Dr., Ste. C
Las Vegas, NV 89109
Phone: 702-796-9090
Fax: 702-796-9069
Web: www.fortunet.com

CEO: Yuri Itkis
CFO: Kevin A. Karo
HR: –
FYE: December 31
Type: Public

FortuNet hopes to score "bingo" with the casino crowd. The company makes electronic gaming systems used in casinos and other gambling establishments, including its flagship FortuNet and BingoStar multi-game terminal systems. It allows gamblers to play a variety of games — bingo, keno, poker, and slots — using both stationary terminals and handheld wireless devices. FortuNet also makes accounting and casino management systems used for tracking players and payouts. The company generates revenue mostly by leasing equipment and software to gaming operators, generally for a percentage of gaming revenue. Chairman and CEO Yuri Itkis owns more than 70% of FortuNet.

	Annual Growth	12/03	12/04	12/05	12/06	12/07
Sales ($ mil.)	3.6%	14.3	14.3	14.7	16.5	16.5
Net income ($ mil.)	16.1%	2.2	2.3	2.2	2.0	4.0
Market value ($ mil.)	(20.4%)	—	—	—	114.8	91.4
Employees	—	—	—	—	—	—

FORTUNOFF

70 Charles Lindbergh Blvd.
Uniondale, NY 11553
Phone: 516-832-9000
Fax: 516-237-1703
Web: www.fortunoff.com

CEO: Charles (Charlie) Chinni
CFO: Michael J. (Mike) Geraghty
HR: Louis Fortunoff
FYE: January 31
Type: Private

Fortunoff wants to bedeck your body, as well as your home. The locally renowned jewelry and household goods selller operates about 20 stores in New York, New Jersey, Connecticut, and Pennsylvania. Fortunoff consists of two related firms, started by the Fortunoff family. Fortunoff Fine Jewelry & Silverware sells fine and antique jewelry, silver, and watches, plus housewares and cookware products. M. Fortunoff of Westbury sells home furnishings, small appliances, gifts, luggage, and more. The company was founded in 1922 by Max Fortunoff and family run until 2000. After filing for Chapter 11 bankruptcy protection in February 2008, Fortunoff was sold to Lord & Taylor owner NRDC Equity Partners.

	Annual Growth	1/03	1/04	1/05	1/06	1/07
Est. sales ($ mil.)	—	—	—	—	—	155.3
Employees	—	—	—	—	—	1,800

FORWARD AIR CORPORATION

NASDAQ (GS): FWRD

430 Airport Rd.
Greeneville, TN 37745
Phone: 423-636-7000
Fax: 423-636-7279
Web: www.forwardair.com

CEO: Bruce A. Campbell
CFO: Rodney L. Bell
HR: –
FYE: December 31
Type: Public

When it's time to haul freight, Forward Air never looks back. The company provides transportation of deferred airfreight — cargo that requires specific-time delivery but is less time-sensitive than airfreight. Forward Air typically receives freight that has been transported by plane, sends it to a sorting facility, then dispatches it by truck to a terminal near its destination. The company operates from about 85 terminals at or near airports in the US and Canada, including about 10 regional hubs. Forward Air contracts with owner-operator truckers for cargo hauling. Along with its main transportation offerings, Forward Air provides services such as warehousing and local pick-up and delivery.

	Annual Growth	12/03	12/04	12/05	12/06	12/07
Sales ($ mil.)	12.9%	241.5	282.2	320.9	352.8	392.7
Net income ($ mil.)	14.9%	25.8	34.4	44.9	48.9	44.9
Market value ($ mil.)	22.7%	394.1	965.5	1,149.4	878.7	893.0
Employees	—	—	—	1,134	—	—

FORWARD INDUSTRIES, INC.

NASDAQ (CM): FORD

1801 Green Rd., Ste. E
Pompano Beach, FL 33064
Phone: 954-419-9544
Fax: 954-419-9735
Web: www.forwardindustries.com

CEO: Douglas W. Sabra
CFO: James O. McKenna
HR: –
FYE: September 30
Type: Public

Forward Industries helps keep the gadget guy and gal on the go. The company designs and markets custom carrying cases, bags, clips, hand straps, and related accessories made of leather, nylon, vinyl, plastic, PVC, and other synthetic fibers. It sells its goods to makers of portable products such as cellular telephones, laptop computers, medical instruments (including products for blood glucose monitoring kits), cameras, and hand tools. Contractors in Asia make most of the company's products. Forward Industries has been distributing cell phone cases to Europe, the Middle East, and Africa (EMEA) through a licensing agreement with Motorola.

	Annual Growth	9/03	9/04	9/05	9/06	9/07
Sales ($ mil.)	4.0%	18.9	20.1	51.9	30.6	22.1
Net income ($ mil.)	—	1.5	1.9	9.4	1.5	(0.6)
Market value ($ mil.)	14.2%	14.2	14.2	183.9	40.3	24.2
Employees	(16.9%)	—	—	71	—	49

FOSSIL, INC.

NASDAQ (GS): FOSL

2280 N. Greenville Ave.
Richardson, TX 75082
Phone: 972-234-2525
Fax: 972-234-4669
Web: www.fossil.com

CEO: Kosta N. Kartsotis
CFO: Mike L. Kovar
HR: Dean Carter
FYE: December 31
Type: Public

Fossil digs the watch business while unearthing a place in the accessories and apparel niches. A leading mid-priced watchmaker in the US, it generates most of its sales from watches. Brands include its Fossil and Relic watches, as well as licensed names Giorgio Armani, Michael Kors, adidas, Burberry, Marc Jacobs, and Donna Karan and private-label watches for Target and Wal-Mart. Fossil also distributes fashion accessories, such as leather goods, sunglasses, and apparel. The firm sells through department stores and specialty shops in more than 90 countries and some 240 company-owned stores, as well as through its own catalog and Web site. Brothers and executives Tom and Kosta Kartsotis own about 32% of Fossil.

	Annual Growth	12/03	12/04	12/05	12/06	12/07
Sales ($ mil.)	16.4%	781.2	960.0	1,040.5	1,214.0	1,433.0
Net income ($ mil.)	15.9%	68.3	90.6	78.1	77.6	123.3
Market value ($ mil.)	30.3%	868.8	1,823.2	1,469.5	1,535.3	2,507.6
Employees	(8.5%)	—	—	7,160	—	6,000

FOSTER DAIRY FARMS OF CALIFORNIA

1707 McHenry Ave.
Modesto, CA 95350
Phone: 209-576-3400
Fax: 209-576-3437
Web: www.fosterfarmsdairy.com

CEO: Ron Foster
CFO: Dennis Lund
HR: Luis Miranda
FYE: December 31
Type: Private

The folks at Foster Farms know better than to try to milk a rooster, so they keep their dairy and meat businesses separate. While Foster Poultry Farms tends its chickens, its sister company, Foster Dairy Farms, is one of California's largest private dairy operations, milking more than 5,000 cows per week. The company processes 2.5 million gallons of milk a week at its three processing plants, and then distributes it to retailers and foodservice businesses throughout California. Along with retail fluid and cultured dairy products (milk, yogurt, ice cream, butter, cottage cheese, fruit juice, and more), the company produces powdered milk and bulk dairy products for food manufacturers, bakers, and confectioners.

	Annual Growth	12/03	12/04	12/05	12/06	12/07
Est. sales ($ mil.)	—	—	—	—	—	40.0
Employees	—	—	—	—	—	600

FOSTER POULTRY FARMS

1000 Davis St.
Livingston, CA 95334
Phone: 209-357-1121
Fax: 209-394-6342
Web: www.fosterfarms.com

CEO: Ron Foster
CFO: John Landis
HR: Tim Walsh
FYE: December 31
Type: Private

It doesn't matter if Henny Penny is having hot flashes, Foster Poultry Farms never uses hormones. The company's vertically integrated operations see chickens and turkeys from the incubator to grocers' meat cases, delis, and freezers (under the Foster Farms brand). In addition to hatching, raising, slaughtering, and processing chickens and turkeys for the grocery and foodservice industries, the company grinds its own feeds. Already #1 in its home state, Foster Poultry Farms grew larger when it bought the chicken operations of local rival, Zacky Farms. Max and Verda Foster founded the company in 1939; it is still owned by the Foster family, which also operates sister company Foster Dairy Farms.

	Annual Growth	12/02	12/03	12/04	12/05	12/06
Est. sales ($ mil.)	5.8%	1,434.0	1,520.0	1,660.0	1,730.0	1,800.0
Employees	(1.2%)	11,000	11,000	10,000	10,000	10,500

FOSTER WHEELER LTD.

NASDAQ (GS): FWLT

Perryville Corporate Park
Clinton, NJ 08809
Phone: 908-730-4000
Fax: 908-730-5315
Web: www.fwc.com

CEO: Raymond J. (Ray) Milchovich
CFO: Franco Baseotto
HR: –
FYE: Last Friday in December
Type: Public

Even state-of-the-art power plants need face lifts from time to time. That's where Foster Wheeler comes in. The international engineering and construction contractor designs, builds, and upgrades oil and gas processing facilities and manufactures power equipment through its two business units: Global Engineering & Construction and Global Power. Clients of its Global E&C group include companies in the oil and gas, chemical, pharmaceutical, and biotechnology markets. Its Global Power group serves energy, utility, and industrial clients. Foster Wheeler also offers construction management, environmental remediation services, and waste-to-energy conversion technologies. The majority of its revenues come from Europe.

	Annual Growth	12/03	12/04	12/05	12/06	12/07
Sales ($ mil.)	7.7%	3,801.3	2,661.3	2,200.0	3,495.1	5,107.2
Net income ($ mil.)	—	(157.1)	(285.3)	(109.8)	262.0	393.9
Market value ($ mil.)	87.3%	913.3	643.4	1,056.7	1,904.9	11,241.9
Employees	20.1%	6,661	6,723	8,953	11,992	13,859

FOSTER'S AMERICAS

610 Airpark Rd.
Napa, CA 94558
Phone: 707-259-4500
Fax: 707-259-4542

CEO: Scott A. Weiss
CFO: Andrew Leyden
HR: –
FYE: June 30
Type: Subsidiary

A name, give me a name. According to the Way Back Machine, this company was once called Beringer Blass Wine Estates but was given its first Foster moniker (Foster's Wine Estates) after Australia's Foster's Group bought it from Texas Pacific Group in 2001 and combined it with Mildara Blass. It was renamed again in 2006, when its parent combined it with its Southcorp Wines Americas group. Foster's Americas operates six wineries and owns 3,899 hectares of vineyards. It offers premium wines; its brands include Beringer, Lindemans, Wolf Blass, Penfolds, Rosemount, Stag's Leap, and Chateau St. Jean. It also distributes its parent company's Foster's Lager throughout the Americas.

	Annual Growth	6/03	6/04	6/05	6/06	6/07
Est. sales ($ mil.)	—	—	—	—	—	69.3
Employees	—	—	—	—	—	900

FOUNDATION COAL HOLDINGS, INC.

NYSE: FCL

999 Corporate Blvd., Ste. 300
Linthicum Heights, MD 21090
Phone: 410-689-7500
Fax: 410-689-7511
Web: www.foundationcoal.com

CEO: James F. Roberts
CFO: Frank J. Wood
HR: Michael R. Peelish
FYE: December 31
Type: Public

Foundation Coal Holdings has found a solid footing in the US. One of the largest coal miners in the country, Foundation Coal operates about a dozen surface and underground mines in Central Appalachia, Northern Appalachia, and the Powder River Basin. Foundation Coal produces and sells around 70 million tons of coal annually and has 1.5 billion tons of proved and probable coal reserves. Steam coal, produced for electric utilities, accounts for more than 90% of the company's sales. Foundation Coal also produces metallurgical coal (for steel manufacturers). Foundation Coal was formed in 2004 to buy RAG American Coal from German conglomerate RAG.

	Annual Growth	12/03	12/04	12/05	12/06	12/07
Sales ($ mil.)	10.9%	983.7	444.6	1,316.9	1,470.3	1,489.7
Net income ($ mil.)	0.1%	32.5	14.5	88.9	31.4	32.6
Market value ($ mil.)	35.3%	—	953.8	1,738.0	1,442.9	2,362.5
Employees	3.6%	2,600	—	2,900	3,150	3,000

FOUNDRY NETWORKS, INC.

NASDAQ (GS): FDRY

4980 Great America Pkwy.
Santa Clara, CA 95054
Phone: 408-207-1700
Fax: 408-207-1709
Web: www.foundrynet.com

CEO: Bobby R. Johnson Jr.
CFO: Daniel W. (Dan) Fairfax
HR: Lisa D. McGill
FYE: December 31
Type: Public

Foundry Networks casts better connections. Businesses, schools, government agencies, and communications service providers use the company's high-performance switches and routers (including Layer 2, Layer 3, and Layer 4-7 equipment) to build local-, metro-, and wide-area networks. Its wireless networking products include access points and controllers. Foundry also provides network management software and product support services. The company, which outsources its manufacturing to companies including Celestica and Sanmina-SCI, sells directly and through resellers worldwide.

	Annual Growth	12/03	12/04	12/05	12/06	12/07
Sales ($ mil.)	11.0%	399.6	409.1	403.9	473.3	607.2
Net income ($ mil.)	1.9%	75.1	48.0	56.0	38.7	81.1
Market value ($ mil.)	(7.7%)	3,597.3	1,805.9	1,949.3	2,202.6	2,605.2
Employees	13.5%	—	—	719	816	—

An in-depth profile of this company is available to Hoover's Online members at hoovers.com.

645

FOUNTAIN POWERBOAT INDUSTRIES, INC.

AMEX: FPB

1653 Whichards Beach Rd.
Washington, NC 27889
Phone: 252-975-2000
Fax: 252-975-6793
Web: www.fountainpowerboats.com

CEO: Reginald M. (Reggie) Fountain Jr.
CFO: Irving L. Smith
HR: Carol J. Price
FYE: June 30
Type: Public

Fountain Powerboat Industries builds sport boats, sport fishing boats, and express cruisers for aquatic speedracers with deep pockets. Overall, the company offers more than 20 models, which range in length from 27 feet to 47 feet and in price from about $70,000 to $500,000. The company sells its boats through a network of about 60 dealers worldwide. Fountain Powerboat does nearly 90% of its business in the US, but the company is expanding its dealer network in South America, Europe, and the Middle East. Founder Reggie Fountain, a professional speedboat racer, owns about 51% of the company.

	Annual Growth	6/03	6/04	6/05	6/06	6/07
Sales ($ mil.)	5.1%	—	59.3	71.2	79.2	68.8
Net income ($ mil.)	—	—	0.6	0.8	2.4	(5.1)
Market value ($ mil.)	(17.3%)	—	24.7	22.7	22.0	14.0
Employees	(11.5%)	—	—	419	—	328

FOUR OAKS FINCORP, INC.

OTC: FOFN

6114 US 301 South
Four Oaks, NC 27524
Phone: 919-963-2177
Fax: 919-963-4169
Web: portal.fxfn.com/zfobtnc

CEO: Ayden R. Lee Jr.
CFO: Nancy S. Wise
HR: —
FYE: December 31
Type: Public

There's no need to knock on wood when trusting your money to Four Oaks Fincorp. It's the holding company for Four Oaks Bank & Trust Company, which now (with the 2008 acquisition of LongLeaf Community Bank) operates 16 branches in eight central and eastern North Carolina counties. The bank offers standard retail products and services, including checking and savings accounts, CDs, IRAs, and money market accounts. It uses funds from deposits to originate mostly real estate loans, which account for nearly 90% of the company's loan book. To a lesser extent, it writes business, consumer, and farm loans. The bank also offers insurance and investment services.

	Annual Growth	12/03	12/04	12/05	12/06	12/07
Assets ($ mil.)	20.0%	341.7	398.5	522.9	608.1	708.3
Net income ($ mil.)	18.4%	2.9	4.4	5.0	7.0	5.7
Market value ($ mil.)	35.5%	28.8	44.0	72.0	135.6	97.1
Employees	—	—	—	—	—	177

FOX BROADCASTING COMPANY

10201 W. Pico Blvd.
Los Angeles, CA 90035
Phone: 310-369-1000
Fax: 310-369-1283
Web: www.fox.com

CEO: Ed Wilson
CFO: David F. DeVoe
HR: —
FYE: June 30
Type: Subsidiary

TV viewers worshiping the *Idol* have helped make FOX a ratings superstar. FOX Broadcasting is the #1 broadcast television network in the US, with more than 200 affiliate stations including 25 company-owned broadcast outlets. The network offers such hit shows as *American Idol, House,* and the reality show *Moment of Truth,* as well as its Saturday night lineup of crime reality shows *COPS* and *America's Most Wanted.* FOX, which was launched with only six stations in 1986, is a unit of Fox Entertainment Group. A subsidiary of Rupert Murdoch's News Corporation, Fox Entertainment oversees film and television production, as well as the regional cable sports channels of FOX Sports Net.

FOX CHASE BANCORP, INC.

NASDAQ (CM): FXCB

4390 Davisville Rd.
Hatboro, PA 19040
Phone: 215-682-7400
Fax: 215-682-4147
Web: www.foxchasebank.com

CEO: Thomas M. Petro
CFO: Roger Deacon
HR: —
FYE: December 31
Type: Public

Fox Chase Bancorp was formed in 2006 to be the holding company for Fox Chase Bank, which operates about a dozen locations in southeastern Pennsylvania and southern New Jersey. Founded in 1867, the bank serves area businesses and consumers by offering standard services such as checking and savings accounts, certificates of deposit, and money market accounts. One- to four-family residential mortgages make up around 60% of the bank's loan portfolio; home equity loans add almost another 20%. Fox Chase MHC, a mutual holding company, owns a majority of Fox Chase Bancorp, which went public in 2006.

	Annual Growth	12/03	12/04	12/05	12/06	12/07
Assets ($ mil.)	7.4%	—	—	—	757.0	812.9
Net income ($ mil.)	(47.2%)	—	—	—	3.6	1.9
Market value ($ mil.)	(17.4%)	—	—	—	198.2	163.6
Employees	—	—	—	—	—	—

FOX ENTERTAINMENT GROUP, INC.

10201 W. Pico Blvd.
Los Angeles, CA 90035
Phone: 310-369-1000
Fax: —
Web: www.fox.com

CEO: Peter Chernin
CFO: David F. DeVoe
HR: Mitsy Wilson
FYE: Sunday nearest June 30
Type: Subsidiary

This Fox has cunning ways to keep TV and movie fans entertained. Fox Entertainment Group (FEG) oversees a broad collection of entertainment assets owned by media giant News Corp. Its Fox Filmed Entertainment division includes such movie studios as Fox 2000, Fox Searchlight, and its flagship imprint Twentieth Century Fox. FEG also oversees the FOX television network, the upstart MyNetworkTV (launched in 2006), and about 35 broadcasting stations. In addition it runs a portfolio of cable channels, including FX and the regional sports stations of Fox Sports Net.

FOX RACING, INC.

18400 Sutter Blvd.
Morgan Hill, CA 95037
Phone: 408-776-8633
Fax: 408-776-8610
Web: www.foxracing.com

CEO: Peter Fox
CFO: —
HR: —
FYE: December 31
Type: Private

Fox Racing sells motocross apparel including motocross pants, jerseys, gloves, boots, and helmets. In addition the company sponsors many professional riders. Fox Racing also makes BMX and mountain bike apparel, T-shirts, hats, jeans, sweaters, sweatshirts, and jackets. The company's products are sold at sporting goods and cycle shops nationwide; it also operates a store in Santa Clara, California. Fox Racing is branching out into surfer wear and its products are also sold in surf shops. President and CEO Peter Fox founded the company, which is still family-owned and -operated, in 1974.

	Annual Growth	12/03	12/04	12/05	12/06	12/07
Est. sales ($ mil.)	—	—	—	—	—	172.1
Employees	—	—	—	—	—	420

FOX & HOUND RESTAURANT GROUP

1551 N. Waterfront Pkwy., Ste. 310
Wichita, KS 67206
Phone: 316-634-0505
Fax: 316-634-6060
Web: www.tentcorp.com

CEO: Stephen M. Johnson
CFO: James K. (Jim) Zielke
HR: Fran Vavala
FYE: Last Tuesday in December
Type: Private

You might say this bar & grill chain caters to the canine tooth. Fox & Hound Restaurant Group operates about 85 sports bars and pubs in 25 states under the banners Fox & Hound Pub & Grille and Bailey's Pub & Grille. Popular for their expansive TV installations and a menu heavy on burgers and other carnivorous cravings, the locations also offer a wide selection of beer, billiards, darts, and other entertainments. The company also operates the Champps family entertainment and dining chain. Restaurateur Jamie Coulter started the Fox & Hound chain in 1997; the company was taken private in 2006 by an investment group led by Dallas-based Newcastle Partners.

	Annual Growth	12/03	12/04	12/05	12/06	12/07
Est. sales ($ mil.)	—	—	—	—	—	149.2
Employees	—	—	—	—	—	4,800

FOXHOLLOW TECHNOLOGIES, INC.

740 Bay Rd.
Redwood City, CA 94063
Phone: 650-421-8400
Fax: 650-421-8781
Web: www.foxhollowtech.com

CEO: John B. Simpson
CFO: –
HR: –
FYE: December 31
Type: Subsidiary

Put in layman's terms, FoxHollow Technologies' main product works like a Roto-Rooter for your arteries after too many french fries. The company's FDA-approved medical devices are used to treat peripheral artery disease (PAD). PAD is caused by the build up of plaque in arteries of the leg and pelvis, resulting in reduced oxygen in the blood and increased risk of heart attacks and strokes. FoxHollow's flagship product, SilverHawk, is a disposable catheter system that removes plaque and reopens blocked arteries. SilverHawk is marketed to cardiologists and other surgeons in the US through a direct sales force and through distributors in Europe. FoxHollow Technologies is a subsidiary of ev3.

	Annual Growth	12/02	12/03	12/04	12/05	12/06
Sales ($ mil.)	—	0.0	2.6	38.5	128.2	193.1
Net income ($ mil.)	—	(8.2)	(14.4)	(29.9)	(11.6)	(12.2)
Employees	—	—	—	—	542	—

FOX-PITT KELTON COCHRAN CARONIA WALLER

420 Fifth Avenue, 5th Fl.
New York, NY 10018
Phone: 212-687-1105
Fax: 212-599-2723
Web: www.fpk.com

CEO: Giles Fitzpatrick
CFO: –
HR: –
FYE: December 31
Type: Private

Everyone knows Wall Street is full of bulls and bears, but there's at least one Fox roaming the financial markets landscape. Investment bank Fox-Pitt Kelton Cochran Caronia Waller specializes in banking, insurance, and related industries. The company serves up a smorgasbord of products and services, including equity brokerage and trading, capital markets services, and mergers and acquisitions advice. It also conducts equity research on more than 400 financial services companies around the globe. Its clients include pension funds, mutual fund managers, insurance firms, bank investment departments, hedge funds, and private client asset managers.

	Annual Growth	12/03	12/04	12/05	12/06	12/07
Est. sales ($ mil.)	—	—	—	—	—	17.4
Employees	—	—	—	—	—	153

FOXWORTH-GALBRAITH LUMBER COMPANY

17111 Waterview Pkwy.
Dallas, TX 75252
Phone: 972-437-6100
Fax: 972-454-4251
Web: www.foxgal.com

CEO: Walter L. Foxworth
CFO: –
HR: Eileen Nichols
FYE: December 31
Type: Private

Foxworth-Galbraith Lumber Company is helping build the Southwest. It sells hardware, lumber, paint, plumbing equipment, tools, and other building supplies through some 70 locations in Arizona, Colorado, New Mexico, and Texas. Foxworth-Galbraith's main customers are residential and commercial builders; other clients include do-it-yourselfers, specialty contractors, and federal and state agencies. The firm also provides installation services. Foxworth-Galbraith is still owned and operated by the families of W. L. Foxworth and H. W. Galbraith, who founded the company in Dalhart, Texas, in 1901, to take advantage of railroad construction.

	Annual Growth	12/02	12/03	12/04	12/05	12/06
Est. sales ($ mil.)	—	—	—	—	—	750.0
Employees	—	—	—	—	—	2,300

FPB BANCORP, INC.

NASDAQ (GM): FPBI

1301 SE Port St. Lucie Blvd.
Port St. Lucie, FL 34952
Phone: 772-398-1388
Fax: 772-398-1399
Web: www.1stpeoplesbank.com

CEO: David W. Skiles
CFO: Nancy E. Aumack
HR: Nancy E. Aumack
FYE: December 31
Type: Public

FPB Bancorp is for the birds. The *snow* birds, that is. It's the holding company for First Peoples Bank, which targets retired winter visitors, as well as year-round residents and small to midsized businesses primarily in the Florida counties of St. Lucie and Martin. The six-branch bank operates in Fort Pierce, Palm City, Port St. Lucie, Stuart, and Vero Beach, offering such standard deposit products as checking, savings, and money market accounts. Business loans and commercial real estate loans together account for more than three-quarters of the bank's loan portfolio, which is rounded out by construction, consumer, and residential real estate loans.

	Annual Growth	12/03	12/04	12/05	12/06	12/07
Assets ($ mil.)	29.4%	70.1	94.6	127.3	153.4	196.8
Net income ($ mil.)	0.0%	0.2	0.1	0.8	0.6	0.2
Market value ($ mil.)	(16.2%)	—	—	28.7	31.8	20.2
Employees	26.8%	—	—	56	71	—

FPIC INSURANCE GROUP, INC.

NASDAQ (GS): FPIC

225 Water St., Ste. 1400
Jacksonville, FL 32202
Phone: 904-354-2482
Fax: 904-475-1159
Web: www.fpic.com

CEO: John R. Byers
CFO: Charles Divita III
HR: –
FYE: December 31
Type: Public

Pulled the wrong tooth or read an X-ray backwards? FPIC Insurance Group knows that these things happen. Through its First Professionals Insurance subsidiary, the company sells medical professional liability (including medical error and malpractice) insurance to more than 13,000 physicians and dentists. Its Anesthesiologists Professional Assurance Company subsidiary serves that specialty market. Although the company is licensed in nearly 30 states, Florida accounts for more than 80% of its premiums written. FPIC's subsidiaries sell its policies through independent agents and First Professionals Insurance is an endorsed carrier for several local medical associations.

	Annual Growth	12/03	12/04	12/05	12/06	12/07
Assets ($ mil.)	(2.3%)	1,183.1	1,271.3	1,308.5	1,219.1	1,077.0
Net income ($ mil.)	32.3%	16.6	28.2	35.0	51.6	50.9
Market value ($ mil.)	11.9%	245.2	356.3	358.8	392.2	384.6
Employees	—	—	—	472	—	—

An in-depth profile of this company is available to Hoover's Online members at hoovers.com.

647

FPL GROUP, INC.

NYSE: FPL

700 Universe Blvd.
Juno Beach, FL 33408
Phone: 561-694-4000
Fax: 561-694-4620
Web: www.fplgroup.com

CEO: Lewis (Lew) Hay III
CFO: Armando Pimentel Jr.
HR: Robert H. Escoto
FYE: December 31
Type: Public

For a Florida company without any oranges, FPL Group produces a lot of juice. It has operations across the US, including independent power production and telecommunications businesses, but most of its revenues are produced by its utility subsidiary, Florida Power & Light (FPL). FPL distributes electricity to 4.5 million customers and has more than 25,100 MW of generating capacity from interests in nuclear and fossil-fueled power plants. Subsidiary FPL Group Capital owns nonutility businesses, including FPL Energy, an independent power producer and wholesale energy marketer. In 2007 the company acquired the Point Beach Nuclear Plant in Two Rivers from Wisconsin Energy for $924 million.

	Annual Growth	12/03	12/04	12/05	12/06	12/07
Sales ($ mil.)	12.2%	9,630.0	10,522.0	11,846.0	15,710.0	15,263.0
Net income ($ mil.)	10.2%	890.0	887.0	885.0	1,281.0	1,312.0
Market value ($ mil.)	46.3%	6,018.6	6,958.3	16,410.3	22,040.1	27,609.8
Employees	1.5%	—	—	10,200	10,400	10,500

FRAGRANCENET.COM, INC.

Pink Sheets: FGNT

104 Parkway Dr. South
Hauppauge, NY 11788
Phone: 631-582-5204
Fax: 631-582-8433
Web: www.fragrancenet.com

CEO: Dennis M. Apfel
CFO: Dennis M. Apfel
HR: –
FYE: March 31
Type: Public

FragranceNet.com has set its sights on the sweet smell of success through its fragrance site. Customers can buy — but not sample — more than 10,000 brand-name fragrances, aromatherapy and skin care products, and scented candles at FragranceNet.com. The company carries items under designer names Ralph Lauren, Christian Dior, Hermes, Nicole Miller, Yves Saint Laurent, Oscar de la Renta, Fendi, and others. In addition the fragrance firm operates a wholesale business called FragranceNet Wholesales. FragranceNet.com got its start in 1995 selling fragrances via an 800 number.

	Annual Growth	3/02	3/03	3/04	3/05	*3/06
Sales ($ mil.)	43.6%	7.5	10.5	14.7	23.3	31.9
Net income ($ mil.)	18.9%	0.2	0.1	0.4	0.3	0.4
Employees	—	—	—	—	—	

*Most recent year available

FRANCISCO PARTNERS MANAGEMENT LLC

2882 Sand Hill Rd., Ste. 280
Menlo Park, CA 94025
Phone: 650-233-2900
Fax: 650-233-2999
Web: www.franciscopartners.com

CEO: David Stanton
CFO: –
HR: –
FYE: December 31
Type: Partnership

Francisco Partners wants to be the patron saint of companies at a crossroads. The company invests in public and private technology companies that are past their start-up stage, but are at some transition point involving a product, management change, or a merger. Francisco works closely with venture capital firm Sequoia Capital, which provides investment brainstorming and strategic counsel to clients. Portfolio companies include Legerity, Attachmate, and WebTrends. Founder David Stanton previously led tech investing for Texas Pacific Group. Francisco Partners has some $5 billion in commited capital. Its investments range from $50 million to $2 billion.

	Annual Growth	12/03	12/04	12/05	12/06	12/07
Est. sales ($ mil.)	—	—	—	—	—	15.4
Employees	—	—	—	—	—	205

FRANCO MANUFACTURING COMPANY, INC.

555 Prospect St.
Metuchen, NJ 08840
Phone: 732-494-0500
Fax: 732-906-0591
Web: www.francomfg.com

CEO: Louis D. Franco
CFO: Michael Kaplan
HR: Dave Tutrone
FYE: December 31
Type: Private

If you go beyond the labels at Bed Bath & Beyond and other retailers you will find textile manufacturers, like Franco Manufacturing, that make the goods. Franco Manufacturing produces home furnishing textiles, including bedding, kitchen and bath towels, through facilities in New Jersey and South Carolina. One of the top US-based home textile companies, the firm makes a range of bedding and clothing products for both children and adults, as well as furnishings (including pillows and curtains) for many of the leading brands, including Bratz, Disney, Eddie Bauer, Nickelodeon, Paul Frank, Speedo, and Warner Bros. Products are sold through department stores, specialty stores, and mass market retailers.

	Annual Growth	12/03	12/04	12/05	12/06	12/07
Est. sales ($ mil.)	—	—	—	—	—	53.6
Employees	—	—	—	—	—	750

FRANK CONSOLIDATED ENTERPRISES, INC.

666 Garland Place
Des Plaines, IL 60016
Phone: 847-699-7000
Fax: 847-699-6494
Web: www.wheels.com

CEO: James S. (Jim) Frank
CFO: Mary Ann O'Dwyer
HR: Joan Richards
FYE: August 31
Type: Private

Frank Consolidated Enterprises has an old lease on life. A holding company for its Wheels subsidiary, the firm is a pioneer of the auto leasing concept, provides fleet management services — administrative, management, and financing services to help clients maintain vehicle fleets. Overall, the company manages more than 250,000 vehicles. It operates in the US as Wheels and in other countries through Fleet Synergy International, an alliance of international fleet management and leasing companies. Wheels was founded in 1939 by a Chicago auto dealer named Zollie Frank. The Frank family owns and runs the company.

	Annual Growth	8/02	8/03	8/04	8/05	8/06
Sales ($ mil.)	4.7%	1,575.0	1,500.0	1,600.0	1,733.0	1,890.0
Employees	2.3%	550	550	550	551	602

FRANK RUSSELL COMPANY

909 A St.
Tacoma, WA 98402
Phone: 253-572-9500
Fax: 253-439-3495
Web: www.russell.com

CEO: P. Craig Ueland
CFO: Hal Strong
HR: Ann Watson
FYE: December 31
Type: Subsidiary

No longer Frank Russell's company (it's a subsidiary of Northwestern Mutual), Frank Russell Company provides investment services to institutional clients in nearly 40 countries. The company (which markets itself as the Russell Investment Group, or just Russell) is best known for lending its name to equity indices, such as the Russell 2000 and others in the US, the UK (the FTSE indices), and Japan. Russell also provides asset management and securities research. It offers more than 280 multi-manager investment funds, as well as separate accounts.

	Annual Growth	12/03	12/04	12/05	12/06	12/07
Est. sales ($ mil.)	—	—	—	—	—	53.6
Employees	—	—	—	—	—	400

FRANKLIN BANK CORP.

NASDAQ (GS): FBTX

9800 Richmond Ave., Ste. 680
Houston, TX 77042
Phone: 713-339-8900
Fax: 713-343-8122
Web: www.bankfranklin.com

CEO: Lewis S. Ranieri
CFO: Russell McCann
HR: Glenn Mealey
FYE: December 31
Type: Public

Franklin Bank Corp. is the holding company for Franklin Bank, a thrift with about 50 branches in the Austin, Tyler, and Kingsland areas of central and east Texas. In addition to these locations, the company has more than 35 offices in some 20 states from which it originates residential mortgages and residential construction loans. It also purchases mortgages on the secondary market and provides financing to small and midsized mortgage banking companies. Franklin was founded in 2001 by executives of the former Bank United Corp. The institution acquired the six-branch First National Bank of Bryan in 2007.

	Annual Growth	12/02	12/03	12/04	12/05	*12/06
Assets ($ mil.)	97.3%	365.7	2,251.3	3,479.7	4,471.3	5,537.4
Net income ($ mil.)	—	(0.7)	3.2	23.1	26.3	19.4
Market value ($ mil.)	6.3%	—	403.3	399.6	421.0	484.9
Employees	(11.7%)	—	—	—	710	627

*Most recent year available

FRANKLIN COVEY CO.

NYSE: FC

2200 W. Parkway Blvd.
Salt Lake City, UT 84119
Phone: 801-817-1776
Fax: 801-817-8069
Web: www.franklincovey.com

CEO: Robert A. Whitman
CFO: Stephen D. (Steve) Young
HR: Lori Smith
FYE: August 31
Type: Public

"Never leave that till to-morrow which you can do to-day." Franklin Covey Co. offers products to help you — and more than 75% of the *FORTUNE* 500 companies — live up to Benjamin Franklin's admonition. A leader in productivity and time-management products and seminars, it sells audio- and videotapes, binders, books, planners, and software through about 90 stores, catalogs, online, and through licensed operations in about 140 countries. Franklin Covey was formed in 1997 when Franklin Quest acquired the firm created by productivity guru Stephen Covey (*The 7 Habits of Highly Effective People*). Peterson Partners is purchasing the company's Consumer Solutions Business Unit (CSBU) in 2008.

	Annual Growth	8/03	8/04	8/05	8/06	8/07
Sales ($ mil.)	(1.9%)	307.2	275.4	283.5	278.6	284.1
Net income ($ mil.)	—	(45.3)	(10.1)	10.2	28.6	7.6
Market value ($ mil.)	—	—	—	—	—	148.0
Employees	0.0%	1,425	1,349	1,333	—	1,425

FRANKLIN CREDIT MANAGEMENT

NASDAQ (GM): FCMC

101 Hudson St.
New Jersey, NJ 07302
Phone: 201-604-1800
Fax: 201-604-4400
Web: www.franklincredit.com

CEO: Alexander Gordon Jardin
CFO: Paul D. Colasono
HR: –
FYE: December 31
Type: Public

Franklin Credit Management Corporation bought discounted subprime mortgage assets (sometimes referred to as "scratch and dent" loans) in the secondary market, while subsidiary Tribeca Lending issued subprime residential mortgage loans to borrowers with poor or limited credit histories. However, the company, like many in its industry, has been hamstrung by the mortgage mess and in late 2007, ceased originating and acquiring loans under terms of restructuring agreements with creditors. The company is instead refocusing on servicing the existing residential loans in its portfolio and plans to provide similar services to other lenders.

	Annual Growth	12/03	12/04	12/05	12/06	12/07
Sales ($ mil.)	31.0%	57.6	80.5	121.4	163.8	169.6
Net income ($ mil.)	—	6.7	9.5	7.9	(1.8)	(8.6)
Market value ($ mil.)	(21.1%)	17.6	55.8	59.6	37.8	6.8
Employees	7.4%	—	—	216	232	—

FRANKLIN ELECTRIC CO., INC.

NASDAQ (GS): FELE

400 E. Spring St.
Bluffton, IN 46714
Phone: 260-824-2900
Fax: 260-824-2909
Web: www.franklinelect.com

CEO: R. Scott Trumbull
CFO: John J. Haines
HR: Gary D. Ward
FYE: Saturday nearest December 31
Type: Public

Franklin Electric would do Old Ben proud. The company keeps things flowing by making and distributing submersible and specialty electric motors, electronic drives and controls, and related items. Its fueling system products include electronic tank monitoring equipment, fittings, flexible piping, nozzles, and vapor recovery systems. Franklin Electric's products are used primarily by OEMs that incorporate them in underground petroleum pumping systems, sewage pumps, vacuum pumping systems, and fresh-water pumping systems. The US makes up more than half of sales. Major customers include ITT Corp. and Pentair.

	Annual Growth	12/03	12/04	12/05	12/06	12/07
Sales ($ mil.)	13.8%	359.5	404.3	439.6	558.0	602.0
Net income ($ mil.)	(4.5%)	34.5	38.1	46.0	57.0	28.7
Market value ($ mil.)	28.5%	328.7	931.5	889.1	1,182.5	896.9
Employees	6.4%	2,500	2,600	2,800	3,100	3,200

FRANKLIN ELECTRONIC PUBLISHERS

AMEX: FEP

1 Franklin Plaza
Burlington, NJ 08016
Phone: 609-386-2500
Fax: 609-387-1787
Web: www.franklin.com

CEO: Barry J. Lipsky
CFO: Frank A. Musto
HR: –
FYE: March 31
Type: Public

Like to read but hate turning those pesky pages? Franklin Electronic Publishers, Incorporated, may have a solution for you. The company markets handheld, battery-powered devices (which are made by third parties) that display the text of reference and entertainment publications. It owns or licenses more than 41,000 electronic book titles. Those titles run the gamut from *Merriam-Webster's Collegiate Dictionary*, to popular fiction, to the *Holy Bible*. Franklin also offers ROLODEX electronic organizers and selected Seiko products (dictionaries and translators). In addition, Franklin owns linguistic software maker Proximity Technology.

	Annual Growth	3/04	3/05	3/06	3/07	3/08
Sales ($ mil.)	(0.5%)	61.8	62.2	59.6	52.2	60.6
Net income ($ mil.)	11.8%	1.6	2.4	2.0	(3.2)	2.5
Market value ($ mil.)	(9.5%)	26.0	31.5	30.9	18.4	17.4
Employees	(7.5%)	—	200	185	—	—

FRANKLIN FINANCIAL SERVICES CORPORATION

OTC: FRAF

20 S. Main St.
Chambersburg, PA 17201
Phone: 717-264-6116
Fax: 717-261-3545
Web: www.fmtrustonline.com

CEO: William E. Snell Jr.
CFO: Mark R. Hollar
HR: Karen C. Carmack
FYE: December 31
Type: Public

Ben Franklin said, "A penny saved is a penny earned," but Franklin Financial might be able to convert those pennies into dollars. It's the holding company for F&M Trust, which serves south-central Pennsylvania (the heart of Ben Franklin country) from about 20 locations. Established in 1906, F&M Trust offers standard deposit products, including checking and savings accounts, IRAs, and CDs. It also provides securities and insurance brokerage, retirement planning, and other investment services. About half of its lending portfolio is represented by commercial, industrial, and agricultural loans; it also includes consumer loans and mortgages. The company bought area rival Fulton Bancshares in 2006.

	Annual Growth	12/03	12/04	12/05	12/06	12/07
Assets ($ mil.)	10.5%	549.7	563.3	621.4	799.3	820.4
Net income ($ mil.)	12.5%	5.8	5.2	6.1	7.6	9.3
Market value ($ mil.)	6.6%	74.3	91.9	84.6	104.8	95.9
Employees	—	—	—	—	—	254

An in-depth profile of this company is available to Hoover's Online members at hoovers.com.

649

THE FRANKLIN MINT

801 Springdale Dr., Ste. 200
Exton, PA 19341
Phone: 800-843-6468
Fax: –
Web: www.franklinmint.com

CEO: Steven J. Sisskind
CFO: David Pincus
HR: –
FYE: December 31
Type: Private

Not to be confused with the US Mint, The Franklin Mint was founded in 1964 by Joseph Segal (who later went on to found the QVC shopping network) and was initially known for making coins. Many of its wares — die-cast cars and airplanes, precision modeling, and its Harley-Davidson-branded items — are produced under licensing agreements. It also offers hand-painted collectibles, such as commemorative dolls (many made in the likeness of living and dead celebrities), as well as jewelry and seasonal giftware. Its goods are distributed via wholesale and the Internet. The Franklin Mint was bought in 1985 by Stewart and Lynda Resnick and sold in late 2006 to a group led by executives from The Morgan Mint.

FRANKLIN RESOURCES, INC.

NYSE: BEN

1 Franklin Pkwy., Bldg. 970, 1st Fl.
San Mateo, CA 94403
Phone: 650-312-2000
Fax: 650-312-5606
Web: www.franklintempleton.com

CEO: Gregory E. (Greg) Johnson
CFO: Kenneth A. Lewis
HR: Penelope S. Alexander
FYE: September 30
Type: Public

Franklin Resources believes a penny saved is a penny lost — if it's not invested. The firm manages a family of more than 300 mutual funds that invest in international and domestic stocks; taxable and tax-exempt money market instruments; and corporate, municipal, and US government bonds. The investment products are sold under the Franklin, Templeton, Mutual Series, Bissett, Darby Overseas, and Fiduciary Trust banners. Franklin Resources also offers separately managed accounts and insurance product funds. Descendants of founder Rupert Johnson Sr. and their families own more than a third of Franklin Resources.

	Annual Growth	9/03	9/04	9/05	9/06	9/07
Assets ($ mil.)	9.3%	6,970.8	8,228.1	8,893.9	9,499.9	9,943.3
Net income ($ mil.)	37.0%	502.8	706.7	1,057.6	1,267.6	1,772.9
Market value ($ mil.)	30.3%	10,872.6	13,922.2	21,220.5	26,781.1	31,297.4
Employees	11.1%	—	—	7,200	8,000	

FRANKLIN STREET PROPERTIES CORP.

AMEX: FSP

401 Edgewater Place, Ste. 200
Wakefield, MA 01880
Phone: 781-557-1300
Fax: 781-246-2807
Web: www.franklinstreetproperties.com

CEO: George J. Carter
CFO: John G. Demeritt
HR: –
FYE: December 31
Type: Public

A real estate investment trust (REIT), Franklin Street Properties acquires, finances, leases, and manages office properties throughout the US. It owns more than 25 properties located mainly in suburban areas; Dallas, Houston, Denver, and Atlanta are its largest markets. The company's FSP Management subsidiary manages the properties. Its FSP Investment unit is an investment bank and brokerage that organizes REITs that invest in single properties and raises equity for them through private placements. Franklin Street Properties acquired about 10 such REITs in 2005 and 2006.

	Annual Growth	12/03	12/04	12/05	12/06	12/07
Sales ($ mil.)	11.0%	83.8	100.1	96.4	114.4	127.0
Net income ($ mil.)	7.1%	46.4	47.8	75.1	110.9	61.1
Market value ($ mil.)	(8.7%)	—	—	1,252.7	1,489.6	1,043.1
Employees		—	—	39	—	—

FRANKLIN WIRELESS CORP.

OTC: FKWL

9853 Pacific Heights Blvd., Ste. J
San Diego, CA 92121
Phone: 858-623-0000
Fax: 858-623-0050
Web: www.fklt.com

CEO: O. C. Kim
CFO: O. C. Kim
HR: –
FYE: June 30
Type: Public

Franklin Wireless hopes to be a founding father of the mobile nation. The company, formerly Franklin Telecommunications, makes connectivity products for wireless devices. In 2003 it acquired Accetio, a designer and marketer of cell phones, but it has since shifted its focus to the development of wireless modems. Its products include USB, embedded, and standalone modems, as well as PC cards. The company sells directly and through distributors, primarily in the Americas. Its customers include consumer electronics makers, cellular operators, and end users.

	Annual Growth	6/03	6/04	6/05	6/06	6/07
Sales ($ mil.)	488.8%	—	—	0.3	1.0	10.4
Net income ($ mil.)	—	—	—	(0.6)	(0.3)	1.3
Market value ($ mil.)	39.5%	—	—	666.2	524.8	1,296.5
Employees	—	—	—	—	—	9

FRED ALGER MANAGEMENT, INC.

111 5th Ave.
New York, NY 10003
Phone: 212-806-8800
Fax: 212-806-2942
Web: www.alger.com

CEO: Daniel C. (Dan) Chung
CFO: Robert L. Kincel
HR: –
FYE: December 31
Type: Private

Growing money is a growing concern for Fred Alger Management. The company, which focuses on growth-stock investing, oversees investment portfolios for individuals and such entities as governments, corporate pensions, and foundations. Fred Alger Management manages a family of mutual funds with significant holdings in the health care, information technology, and financial sectors. It also subadvises other funds. Additional products include separately managed accounts. The firm has some $14 billion in assets under management. Fred Alger Management was founded in 1964 by Fred Alger.

	Annual Growth	12/03	12/04	12/05	12/06	12/07
Est. sales ($ mil.)	—	—	—	—	—	27.2
Employees	—	—	—	—	—	170

FREDERICK'S OF HOLLYWOOD GROUP INC.

AMEX: FOH

1115 Broadway
New York, NY 10010
Phone: 212-684-3400
Fax: 212-684-3295
Web: www.moviestarinc.com

CEO: Peter G. Cole
CFO: Thomas Rende
HR: –
FYE: June 30
Type: Public

Frederick's of Hollywood Group is making big business out of little somethings. Through the early 2008 merger of Frederick's of Hollywood and Movie Star Inc., the group pairs two of the top intimates makers and retailers. Its Movie Star unit designs intimate apparel, sleepwear, leisurewear, and loungewear under brands Movie Star, Cinema Etoile, Seductive Wear, Night Magic, and Meant To Be. It also makes Maidenform robes, sleepwear, and loungewear under license. Movie Star sells to discount, specialty, mass merchandise, and department stores and to catalog merchants. The group's Frederick's of Hollywood subsidiary peddles intimates, as well as wigs, hosiery, and dresses, and operates some 135 namesake stores.

	Annual Growth	6/03	6/04	6/05	6/06	6/07
Sales ($ mil.)	(0.5%)	64.9	53.7	58.5	51.6	63.5
Net income ($ mil.)	(50.8%)	3.4	0.1	(3.1)	(1.0)	0.2
Employees	3.9%	—	—	289	—	312

FREDERICK'S OF HOLLYWOOD, INC.

6255 W. Sunset Blvd., Suite 600
Hollywood, CA 90028
Phone: 323-466-5151
Fax: 323-464-5149
Web: www.fredericks.com

CEO: Linda LoRe
CFO: Thomas Rende
HR: –
FYE: December 31
Type: Subsidiary

Even in a town not known for modesty, Frederick's of Hollywood is an eye-opener. The firm, which operates some 135 women's intimate apparel stores in the US (primarily in malls), sells lingerie, bras, foundations, dresses, sportswear, swimwear, footwear, wigs, edible underwear, fragrances, and hosiery. Frederick's pioneered the push-up bra and other dainties designed from a man's point of view, but has been broadening its portfolio by adding apparel, jewelry, and perfume. It operates a mail-order catalog business in the US and Canada and an online shopping site. In January 2008 Frederick's merged with Movie Star Inc., which now trades as Frederick's of Hollywood Group Inc., and became a subsidiary.

	Annual Growth	12/03	12/04	12/05	12/06	12/07
Est. sales ($ mil.)	—	—	—	—	—	56.7
Employees	—	—	—	—	—	1,000

FRED'S, INC.

NASDAQ (GS): FRED

4300 New Getwell Rd.
Memphis, TN 38118
Phone: 901-365-8880
Fax: 901-328-0354
Web: www.fredsinc.com

CEO: Michael J. Hayes
CFO: Jerry A. Shore
HR: Jordan Resnick
FYE: January 31
Type: Public

Those whose greenbacks feature George and Abe rather than Andrew and Ulysses may very well shop at Fred's. Generally serving customers with modest incomes, Fred's runs about 700 discount stores in some 15 mostly southeastern states, primarily in small towns. Fred's stores carry more than 12,000 brand-name, off-brand, and private-label products, including pharmaceuticals, household goods, clothing and linens, food and tobacco items, health and beauty aids, and paper and cleaning supplies. About 40% of Fred's stores have full-service pharmacies; the company also fills mail-order prescriptions. It also provides goods and services to some two dozen franchised Fred's stores. Fred's was founded in 1947.

	Annual Growth	1/04	1/05	1/06	1/07	1/08
Sales ($ mil.)	8.1%	1,302.7	1,441.8	1,589.3	1,767.2	1,780.9
Net income ($ mil.)	(24.9%)	33.7	28.0	26.1	26.8	10.7
Market value ($ mil.)	(23.0%)	1,094.6	617.6	614.2	571.0	384.9
Employees	(1.1%)	—	—	10,370	10,010	10,150

FREEDOM COMMUNICATIONS, INC.

17666 Fitch Ave.
Irvine, CA 92614
Phone: 949-253-2300
Fax: 949-474-7675
Web: www.freedom.com

CEO: Scott N. Flanders
CFO: Douglas S. (Doug) Bennett
HR: Marcy E. Bruskin
FYE: December 31
Type: Private

You can say this company believes in freedom of the press. Freedom Communications is a leading newspaper publisher with more than 20 daily papers mostly in California, North Carolina, and Texas. Its portfolio includes *The Orange County Register* in California, which boasts a circulation of more than 250,000. Freedom Communications also publishes more than 15 weekly community papers and it owns nearly 10 TV stations mostly affiliated with CBS and ABC serving markets in a half dozen states. The family of founder R. C. Hoiles owns about 55% of the company. Private equity firms The Blackstone Group and Providence Equity Partners own the remaining 45%.

	Annual Growth	12/03	12/04	12/05	12/06	12/07
Est. sales ($ mil.)	—	—	—	—	—	866.0
Employees	—	—	—	—	—	7,540

FREEDOMROADS, L.L.C.

250 Parkway Dr., Ste. 320
Lincolnshire, IL 60069
Phone: 847-808-3000
Fax: 847-808-7015
Web: www.freedomroads.com

CEO: Marcus A. Lemonis
CFO: Roger Nuttall
HR: Benny Ball
FYE: December 31
Type: Private

Home, home on the road, where the semis and the SUVs play . . . that's how this company would sing it. The company sells about 20 brands of new and used RVs at some 60 FreedomRoads dealerships in nearly 30 states and online at RVs.com. Its Camping World unit runs 70-plus accessory stores for RV owners and camping buffs. FreedomRoads also provides financing and service for RVs. The firm grows by buying existing dealerships. To that end, the company acquired Sonny's Camp-N-Travel and in 2007 rebranded it as Camping World RV Sales. Chairman and CEO Marcus Lemonis founded FreedomRoads in 2003. It is owned, indirectly, by Steve Adams, chairman of RV products company Affinity Group.

	Annual Growth	12/02	12/03	12/04	12/05	12/06
Sales ($ mil.)	15.5%	—	—	1,200.0	1,500.0	1,600.0
Employees	9.4%	—	—	—	3,200	3,500

FREEMAN DECORATING SERVICES, INC.

1600 Viceroy, Ste. 100
Dallas, TX 75266
Phone: 214-445-1000
Fax: 214-445-0200
Web: www.freemanco.com

CEO: Joseph V. (Joe) Popolo Jr.
CFO: Ellis Moseley
HR: Albert Chew
FYE: June 30
Type: Private

Freeman Decorating Services knows there's no business like the trade show business. Doing business simply as "Freeman," the firm stages thousands of conventions, corporate meetings, expositions, and trade shows every year and prepares exhibits for its clients. Its operations include event design and production, Party Time Rentals (equipment rental for events in Canada), and Stage Rigging (theatrical rigging). The company's AVW/TELAV unit specializes in providing audio and visual technology and equipment used for meetings and events. Freeman was founded by D.S. "Buck" Freeman in 1927; the company is owned by the Freeman family (including chairman Donald Freeman) and company employees.

	Annual Growth	6/02	6/03	6/04	6/05	6/06
Sales ($ mil.)	8.3%	—	—	—	1,173.0	1,270.0
Employees	—	—	—	—	—	3,900

FREEMAN SPOGLI & CO. INCORPORATED

11100 Santa Monica Blvd., Ste. 1900
Los Angeles, CA 90025
Phone: 310-444-1822
Fax: 310-444-1870
Web: www.freemanspogli.com

CEO: Bradford M. Freeman
CFO: Lou A. Losorelli
HR: –
FYE: December 31
Type: Private

Freeman Spogli & Co. loves to hear those cash registers *rrring rrring rrring*. The private investment firm targets middle-market US companies in such industries as retail, direct marketing, and distribution. After investing in them, Freeman Spogli helps guide the growth of its portfolio companies via strategic planning: from identifying add-on acquisition opportunities to recruiting additional management personnel. Although it is generally not active in day-to-day operations, Freeman Spogli monitors a company's development by serving on its board of directors. Founded in 1983, the firm has pumped some $2.5 billion into more than 40 companies, including Bright Now! Dental, El Pollo Loco, PETCO, and Sur La Table.

	Annual Growth	12/03	12/04	12/05	12/06	12/07
Est. sales ($ mil.)	—	—	—	—	—	1,464.5
Employees	—	—	—	—	—	14,841

An in-depth profile of this company is available to Hoover's Online members at hoovers.com.

FREEPORT-MCMORAN COPPER & GOLD INC.

NYSE: FCX

1 North Central Ave.
Phoenix, AZ 85004
Phone: 602-366-8100
Fax: –
Web: www.fcx.com

CEO: Richard C. Adkerson
CFO: Kathleen L. Quirk
HR: –
FYE: December 31
Type: Public

Freeport-McMoRan Copper & Gold (FCX) really digs its profits. Its 91%-owned subsidiary, PT Freeport Indonesia (PT-FI), operates the vast open-pit Grasberg gold, copper, and silver mine in Indonesia, whose government owns the other 9%. FCX controls proved and probable reserves of about 90 billion pounds of copper, 40 million ounces of gold, and 2 billion pounds of molybdenum. Copper, in the form of concentrates and in refined products such as cathodes and anodes, accounts for most of FCX's sales. In 2007 the company acquired Phelps Dodge for $26 billion, creating the world's #2 copper company behind Codelco. That deal brought Phelps Dodge's global copper, gold, and molybdenum business into the fold.

	Annual Growth	12/03	12/04	12/05	12/06	12/07
Sales ($ mil.)	66.3%	2,212.2	2,371.9	4,179.1	5,790.5	16,939.0
Net income ($ mil.)	101.2%	181.7	202.3	995.1	1,456.5	2,977.0
Market value ($ mil.)	50.1%	7,725.3	6,842.8	10,050.2	21,225.7	39,234.5
Employees	(74.0%)	—	—	26,938	7,000	—

FREESCALE SEMICONDUCTOR, INC.

6501 William Cannon Dr. West
Austin, TX 78735
Phone: 512-895-2000
Fax: –
Web: www.freescale.com

CEO: Richard M. (Rich) Beyer
CFO: Alan Campbell
HR: Kurt Twining
FYE: December 31
Type: Private

Freescale Semiconductor just wants to be free. Freescale, formerly Motorola's Semiconductor Products Sector, is one of the oldest and most diverse makers of microchips in the world. It produces many different kinds of chips for use in automobiles, computers, industrial equipment, wireless communications and networking equipment, and other applications. The company's global client roster includes such blue-chip companies as Alcatel-Lucent, Cisco Systems, Fujitsu, Hewlett-Packard, QUALCOMM, Robert Bosch, and Siemens; former parent Motorola remains a substantial customer, representing around 24% of sales. Freescale gets about half of its sales from the Asia/Pacific region.

	Annual Growth	12/03	12/04	12/05	12/06	12/07
Sales ($ mil.)	4.1%	4,864.0	5,715.0	5,843.0	6,363.0	5,722.0
Net income ($ mil.)	—	(366.0)	211.0	563.0	—	(1,607.0)
Employees	1.0%	22,300	22,200	22,700	24,000	23,200

FREIGHTCAR AMERICA, INC.

NASDAQ (GS): RAIL

2 N. Riverside Plaza, Ste. 1250
Chicago, IL 60606
Phone: 312-928-0850
Fax: 814-533-5010
Web: www.freightcaramerica.com

CEO: Christian B. (Chris) Ragot
CFO: Kevin P. Bagby
HR: Tom McCarthy
FYE: December 31
Type: Public

Coal keeps FreightCar America in the black. The company designs and makes railroad freight cars, more than 95% of which are aluminum-bodied coal-carrying cars. FreightCar America claims leadership in the North American market for coal-carrying cars. Other products include coil steel cars, flatcars, intermodal cars, mill gondola cars, and motor vehicle carriers. FreightCar America also refurbishes and rebuilds railcars and supplies parts for railcars made by other companies. Customers include leasing companies, railroads, and utilities; Burlington Northern Santa Fe, Norfolk Southern, and TXU Energy accounted for 15%, 11%, and 11% of sales, respectively.

	Annual Growth	12/03	12/04	12/05	12/06	12/07
Sales ($ mil.)	35.2%	244.4	482.2	927.2	1,444.8	817.0
Net income ($ mil.)	—	(7.4)	(24.9)	45.7	128.7	26.5
Market value ($ mil.)	(17.3%)	—	—	604.4	703.2	413.5
Employees	10.9%	—	—	1,289	1,429	—

FREMONT GENERAL CORPORATION

NYSE: FMT

2425 Olympic Blvd., 3rd Fl.
Santa Monica, CA 90404
Phone: 310-315-5500
Fax: 310-315-5599
Web: www.fremontgeneral.com

CEO: Stephen H. Gordon
CFO: Thea Stuedli
HR: –
FYE: December 31
Type: Public

Fremont General owns Fremont Investment & Loan, which has more than 20 retail bank branches in California. Until 2007 the company wrote nonprime and subprime home mortgages nationwide and sold the loans into the secondary market, retaining the servicing. However, it has been hit hard by the housing bust, and sold its subprime lending unit to various investors, exiting the sector entirely. The company also sold its commercial real estate lending operations to iStar Financial in 2007, and is selling the retail deposits and branches of Fremont Investment and Loan to CapitalSource for approximately $170 million.

	Annual Growth	12/02	12/03	12/04	12/05	*12/06
Assets ($ mil.)	17.9%	6,668.7	9,521.9	10,106.0	11,484.1	12,890.5
Net income ($ mil.)	—	26.3	256.3	353.8	328.0	(202.3)
Employees	28.1%	1,300	—	—	3,200	3,500
					*Most recent year available	

FREQUENCY ELECTRONICS, INC.

NASDAQ (GM): FEIM

55 Charles Lindbergh Blvd.
Mitchel Field, NY 11553
Phone: 516-794-4500
Fax: 516-794-4340
Web: www.freqelec.com

CEO: Martin B. Bloch
CFO: Alan L. Miller
HR: –
FYE: April 30
Type: Public

Frequency Electronics, Inc. (FEI) lets the good times roll. The company makes quartz-, rubidium-, and cesium-based time and frequency control products, such as oscillators and amplifiers, used by commercial customers to synchronize voice, data, and video transmissions in satellite and wireless communications. The US military uses its products for navigation, communications, surveillance, and timing systems in aircraft, satellites, and missiles. While FEI was once primarily a military contractor, it has diversified and gets three-quarters of its sales from commercial clients. Top customers include Alcatel-Lucent, Belgacom, Computer Sciences, France Telecom, Space Systems/Loral, Motorola, and SI International.

	Annual Growth	4/03	4/04	4/05	4/06	4/07
Sales ($ mil.)	15.6%	31.5	50.1	55.2	52.8	56.2
Net income ($ mil.)	—	(8.9)	0.2	5.0	4.8	(0.3)
Market value ($ mil.)	—	—	—	—	—	94.1
Employees	13.3%	—	—	375	425	—

FRESH BRANDS, INC.

2215 Union Ave.
Sheboygan, WI 53081
Phone: 920-457-4433
Fax: –
Web: www.fresh-brands.com

CEO: Gary Suokko
CFO: Michael G. (Mike) Isken
HR: Nadine Becker
FYE: Saturday nearest December 31
Type: Private

You don't have to convince this company that fresh foods taste better. Fresh Brands is a leading food wholesaler serving independent and corner grocers primarily in rural and suburban Wisconsin, northern Illinois, and northeastern Iowa. It offers such private-label products as Springtime carbonated and fruit drinks, and drinking and distilled water. Fresh Brands also owns and operates about 25 Piggly Wiggly supermarkets and franchises some 70 Piggly Wiggly stores. The company is owned by the majority owner and chairman of Certifresh Holdings, Paul Butera. Certifresh is a holding company controlled by members of wholesale distribution cooperative, Certified Grocers Midwest, of which Butera is also chairman.

	Annual Growth	12/03	12/04	12/05	12/06	12/07
Est. sales ($ mil.)	—	—	—	—	—	260.1
Employees	—	—	—	—	—	2,400

FRESH CHOICE LLC

8371 Cental Ave., Ste. A
Newark, CA 94560
Phone: 510-857-1230
Fax: 510-857-1269
Web: www.freshchoice.com

CEO: Tim G. O'Shea
CFO: Mike Kfoury
HR: Jim Howell
FYE: Last Sunday in December
Type: Private

It's actually good for you to belly-up to this bar. Fresh Choice owns and operates more than 30 salad bar eateries, mostly located in California, featuring tossed and prepared salads along with more than 40 ingredients and toppings. In addition to greens, the restaurants offer soup, pasta, pizza, and dessert items, as well as breads and muffins. Fresh Choice's restaurants operate primarily under its signature brand; it also has a Zoopa location, a small number of dual-brand units, and Fresh Choice Express quick-service satellite locations. The company is owned by Crescent Real Estate Equities, Cedarlane Natural Foods, and certain members of the management team.

THE FRESH MARKET, INC.

628 Green Valley Rd., Ste. 500
Greensboro, NC 27408
Phone: 336-272-1338
Fax: 336-282-8176
Web: www.thefreshmarket.com

CEO: Brett Berry
CFO: Mike Berry
HR: Bill Bailey
FYE: December 31
Type: Private

When it comes to food, it is good to get fresh. The Fresh Market operates about 80 full-service upscale specialty grocery stores in more than 15 US states, from Florida to Wisconsin. As its name suggests, the company specializes in perishables goods, including fruits and vegetables, meat, and seafood. A typical store is 20,000 to 25,000 square feet, about half the size of a conventional supermarket. However, customers won't find non-food items sold in most grocery stores these days, such as cleaning and cooking supplies. The Fresh Market was founded by president Ray Berry and his wife, EVP Beverly Berry in 1982. In 2008 the grocery chain hired Goldman Sachs to explore a sale of the company.

	Annual Growth	12/03	12/04	12/05	12/06	12/07
Est. sales ($ mil.)	—	—	—	—	—	653.9
Employees	—	—	—	—	—	6,029

FRESH PRODUCE SPORTSWEAR INC.

5600 Flatiron Pkwy.
Boulder, CO 80301
Phone: 303-444-7573
Fax: 303-444-6919
Web: www.fresh-produce.biz

CEO: Mary Ellen Vernon
CFO: Peggy McNeal
HR: –
FYE: September 30
Type: Private

Fresh Produce Sportswear is feeling just beachy. The company designs, makes, and markets women's and children's casual apparel and swimwear, as well as related accessories. Its collections are sold in department stores such as Nordstrom, Walt Disney resorts and stores, and more than 800 specialty boutiques and resort retailers worldwide. In addition, Fresh Produce operates company-owned and outlet stores throughout the US. Company founders and husband-and-wife team Thom and Mary Ellen Vernon got their start in the fashion industry by designing and selling high-end screenprinted T-shirts and custom jewelry at the 1984 Summer Olympics in Los Angeles. Fresh Produce was born out of that first endeavor.

	Annual Growth	9/03	9/04	9/05	9/06	9/07
Est. sales ($ mil.)	—	—	—	—	—	35.8
Employees	—	—	—	—	—	90

FRESHDIRECT, LLC

23-30 Borden Ave.
Long Island City, NY 11101
Phone: 718-928-1000
Fax: 718-433-0648
Web: www.freshdirect.com

CEO: Steven W. (Steve) Michaelson
CFO: Jason Ackerman
HR: –
FYE: September 30
Type: Private

The emphasis is on fresh at online grocer FreshDirect. The Internet grocery shopping service delivers to most of Manhattan, and some neighborhoods in Brooklyn, the Bronx, and Queens. It has also expanded to serve parts of Long Island, New Jersey, and Westchester County. The company sells more than 3,000 fresh food and grocery items as well as kosher and organic products to more than 250,000-plus customers. With a business model similar to Dell's, FreshDirect deals directly with producers and makes food to order, which undercuts its rivals. Jason Ackerman founded the company in 1999. Since launching its delivery service in September 2002, FreshDirect has filled more than 6 million orders.

	Annual Growth	9/03	9/04	9/05	9/06	9/07
Est. sales ($ mil.)	—	—	—	—	—	200.0
Employees	—	—	—	—	—	1,800

FRIEDMAN, BILLINGS, RAMSEY GROUP, INC.

NYSE: FBR

1001 19th St. North
Arlington, VA 22209
Phone: 703-312-9500
Fax: 703-312-9501
Web: www.fbr.com

CEO: Eric F. Billings
CFO: Kurt R. Harrington
HR: –
FYE: December 31
Type: Public

Friedman, Billings, Ramsey (FBR) is a real estate investment trust (REIT) that invests in mortgages and related securities, equities, and other assets. But it is perhaps best known for its majority stake in FBR Capital Markets, which provides investment banking, institutional brokerage, and fee-based asset management services to corporations, institutions, and wealthy individuals. Focusing on such industries as financial services, technology, energy, real estate, and health care, FBR Capital Markets provides mergers and acquisitions advice, public offerings, and private placements. It is also a market-maker or dealer in about 900 securities and provides equity research on more than 500 securities.

	Annual Growth	12/03	12/04	12/05	12/06	12/07
Sales ($ mil.)	2.2%	630.1	1,052.1	995.3	1,007.9	687.0
Net income ($ mil.)	—	201.4	349.6	(170.9)	(67.3)	(660.3)
Market value ($ mil.)	(39.5%)	3,254.8	2,791.5	1,577.8	1,291.9	437.3
Employees	(35.3%)	—	—	2,449	3,019	1,025

FRIEDMAN INDUSTRIES, INCORPORATED

AMEX: FRD

4001 Homestead Rd.
Houston, TX 77028
Phone: 713-672-9433
Fax: 713-672-7043
Web: www.friedmanindustries.com

CEO: William E. Crow
CFO: Benny B. (Ben) Harper
HR: –
FYE: March 31
Type: Public

Steel processor Friedman Industries operates in two roughly equal business segments: coil products and tubular products. The company's coil products unit, the slightly larger of Friedman's segments, purchases hot-rolled steel coils and processes them into sheet and plate products. Friedman Industries' Texas Tubular Products unit buys pipe and coil material and processes it for use in pipelines, oil and gas drilling, and piling and structural applications. The company's XSCP unit inventories and sells Nucor's surplus prime, secondary, and transition steel coils. Friedman Industries' processing facilities are located near mills operated by Lone Star Steel (a unit of Lone Star Technologies) and Nucor.

	Annual Growth	3/04	3/05	3/06	3/07	3/08
Sales ($ mil.)	11.4%	116.2	188.0	181.9	199.7	178.8
Net income ($ mil.)	15.8%	2.5	6.3	6.4	7.0	4.5
Market value ($ mil.)	8.9%	24.8	48.8	62.0	62.0	34.9
Employees	—	—	—	140	—	—

An in-depth profile of this company is available to Hoover's Online members at hoovers.com.

653

⊞ FRIENDLY ICE CREAM CORPORATION

1855 Boston Rd.
Wilbraham, MA 01095
Phone: 413-731-4000
Fax: 413-731-4471
Web: www.friendlys.com

CEO: George M. Condos
CFO: Paul V. Hoagland
HR: Garrett J. Ulrich
FYE: Last Sunday in December
Type: Private

Screaming ice cream lovers can soothe their pipes at Friendly Ice Cream. The company operates a chain of more than 500 family-style restaurants in more than 15 states that specialize in frozen dairy dessert treats. Among fan favorites are Friendly's Fribble shakes, the Royal Banana Split Sundae, and Chocolate Covered Berry Patch desserts. In addition to ice cream, the restaurants serve breakfast, lunch, and dinner — mostly traditional American fare such as sandwiches and burgers. Most of the chain's locations are company-operated. Friendly's also distributes ice cream and other frozen desserts through some 4,000 supermarkets and other retail sites. The company was acquired by Sun Capital Partners in 2007.

	Annual Growth	12/02	12/03	12/04	12/05	12/06
Sales ($ mil.)	(1.8%)	570.4	579.8	574.5	531.3	531.5
Net income ($ mil.)	(5.7%)	6.2	10.2	(3.4)	(27.3)	4.9
Employees	(3.9%)	15,000	16,000	14,500	12,700	12,800

FRIENDSTER, INC.

568 Howard St.
San Francisco, CA 94105
Phone: 415-972-1400
Fax: 415-618-0074
Web: www.friendster.com

CEO: Kent Lindstrom
CFO: Kent Lindstrom
HR: –
FYE: –
Type: Private

Is everyone on Friendster connected to Kevin Bacon? Friendster hosts social networks of friends through Friendster.com. Members create profiles on Friendster.com through which they can trade messages, view each other's tastes and preferences, and write testimonials about friends. It also features a blogging service powered by software from Six Apart. Friendster has about 70 million members. Founded in 2002 by Jonathan Abrams, Friendster received considerable buzz in its first year, but the hype has since fizzled as a result of strong competition. Investors include Kleiner Perkins and Internet heavyweights such as former Yahoo! CEO Tim Koogle, former PayPal CEO Peter Thiel, and former Amazon.com VP Ram Shriram.

⊞ FRISCH'S RESTAURANTS, INC.

AMEX: FRS

2800 Gilbert Ave.
Cincinnati, OH 45206
Phone: 513-961-2660
Fax: 513-559-5160
Web: www.frischs.com

CEO: Craig F. Maier
CFO: Donald H. Walker
HR: Michael E. (Mike) Connor Sr.
FYE: Sunday nearest May 31
Type: Public

Buddie Boy, Big Boy, Super Big Boy, Brawny Lad — Frisch's burger menu reads like an arm wrestling contest marquee. Frisch's Restaurants operates and licenses about 115 Big Boy family-style restaurants in Indiana, Kentucky, and Ohio. Famous for its double-decker hamburgers, Big Boy also offers chicken, roast beef, pasta, beef, and seafood dinners, as well as a breakfast bar that converts to a soup and salad bar at lunch. About 30 locations are operated by licensees. Frisch's also operates about 35 buffet-style Golden Corral steak houses in many of the same areas. The family of president and CEO Craig Maier controls about 45% of the company.

	Annual Growth	5/03	5/04	5/05	5/06	5/07
Sales ($ mil.)	5.4%	234.9	260.9	279.3	292.2	289.9
Net income ($ mil.)	(1.3%)	9.8	10.5	14.7	9.2	9.3
Market value ($ mil.)	15.2%	92.8	143.7	123.9	130.4	163.7
Employees	—	—	—	—	—	—

⊞ FRITO-LAY, INC.

7701 Legacy Dr.
Plano, TX 75024
Phone: 972-334-7000
Fax: 972-334-2019
Web: www.fritolay.com

CEO: Albert P. (Al) Carey
CFO: Dave Rader
HR: Michele Thatcher
FYE: Last Saturday in December
Type: Subsidiary

Frito-Lay is the undisputed chip champ of North America. The company makes some of the best-known and top-selling snack-foods around, including Cheetos, Doritos, Fritos, Lay's, Rold Gold, Ruffles, SunChips, and Tostitos. Frito-Lay also makes Grandma's cookies, Funyuns onion-flavored rings, Cracker Jack candy-coated popcorn, and Smartfood popcorn. The company's offers a light line of chips (formerly WOW!) made with fat substitute olestra. Parent PepsiCo singles out and reports Frito-Lay's North American snack food sales only; they are a good part of the bottom line at about 30% of total PepsiCo sales. International sales of Frito-Lay products are combined with Pepsi's International division sales.

⊞ FRONTIER AIRLINES HOLDINGS, INC.

Pink Sheets: FRNT

7001 Tower Rd.
Denver, CO 80249
Phone: 720-374-4200
Fax: 720-374-4375
Web: www.frontierairlines.com

CEO: Sean E. Menke
CFO: Ted Christie
HR: Ann E. Block
FYE: March 31
Type: Public

Faster by far than covered wagons, Frontier Airlines Holdings jets part the clouds and ply the skies from the Mile High City. The company's primary subsidiary, Frontier Airlines, operates as a budget carrier from its hub at Denver International Airport. The airline maintains a fleet of about 60 Airbus 319 and 318 jets with onboard amenities that include satellite TV. Together with regional affiliate Frontier JetExpress and subsidiary Lynx Aviation, Frontier Airlines serves more than 60 cities, primarily in the US west of the Mississippi but also in Mexico, Canada, and Costa Rica. Frontier Airlines Holdings is operating under Chapter 11 bankruptcy protection, which the company sought in April 2008.

	Annual Growth	3/04	3/05	3/06	3/07	3/08
Sales ($ mil.)	21.4%	643.7	833.6	994.3	1,170.9	1,399.0
Net income ($ mil.)	—	12.6	(23.4)	(14.0)	(20.4)	(60.3)
Employees	8.9%	4,392	4,526	4,770	—	6,170

FRONTIER FINANCIAL CORPORATION

NASDAQ (GS): FTBK

332 SW Everett Mall Way
Everett, WA 98204
Phone: 425-514-0700
Fax: 425-514-0718
Web: www.frontierbank.com

CEO: John J. Dickson
CFO: Carol E. Wheeler
HR: Connie L. Pachek
FYE: December 31
Type: Public

Frontier Financial serves the part of the western frontier that includes Washington and Oregon. Its Frontier Bank subsidiary operates about 50 offices that offer standard retail products, including savings, checking, and money market accounts and certificates of deposit. Funds gathered are largely used to originate real estate construction and land development loans (more than 45% of the company's portfolio) and commercial mortgages (around 30%). Lending activities also include residential mortgage, business consumer loans. Other offerings include life insurance, annuities, mutual funds, and trust services.

	Annual Growth	12/03	12/04	12/05	12/06	12/07
Assets ($ mil.)	17.8%	2,075.4	2,243.4	2,637.0	3,238.5	3,995.7
Net income ($ mil.)	16.9%	39.6	43.0	51.6	68.9	73.9
Market value ($ mil.)	33.6%	273.7	321.7	606.7	1,325.6	871.9
Employees	10.5%	—	—	663	721	809

FRONTIER OIL CORPORATION

NYSE: FTO

10000 Memorial Dr., Ste. 600
Houston, TX 77024
Phone: 713-688-9600
Fax: 713-688-0616
Web: www.frontieroil.com

CEO: James R. (Jim) Gibbs
CFO: Michael C. (Mike) Jennings
HR: –
FYE: December 31
Type: Public

Frontier Oil's territory covers the old frontier of the Rocky Mountains and the Great Plains. The company refines crude oil and markets petroleum products. Frontier's Cheyenne, Wyoming, refinery can handle 52,000 barrels of heavy crude oil per day, and it processes 110,000 barrels of oil per day at its refinery in El Dorado, Kansas. The refineries' products include gasoline, diesel, and asphalt. It also owns a 25,000-barrels-per-day products terminal and blending facility located near Denver. Frontier held a 34.7% stake in a crude oil pipeline in Wyoming and a 50% stake in two crude oil tanks in Guernsey, Wyoming, but sold these assets in 2007.

	Annual Growth	12/03	12/04	12/05	12/06	12/07
Sales ($ mil.)	24.3%	2,170.5	2,861.7	4,001.2	4,796.0	5,188.7
Net income ($ mil.)	253.4%	3.2	69.8	272.5	379.3	499.1
Market value ($ mil.)	147.5%	113.6	180.2	1,057.4	3,171.3	4,259.1
Employees	4.9%	—	—	727	747	800

FRONTRANGE SOLUTIONS INC.

4120 Dublin Blvd., Ste. 200
Dublin, CA 94568
Phone: 925-404-1800
Fax: 925-404-1305
Web: www.frontrange.com

CEO: Michael J. McCloskey
CFO: Steve Baker
HR: –
FYE: June 30
Type: Subsidiary

FrontRange Solutions can solve all sorts of customer relationship problems. The company provides sales, marketing, and customer support software and services. Customers use FrontRange's software to maintain customer contacts, automate sales processes, manage documents, and provide help desk services. The company primarily targets small and midsized businesses. Originally founded as GoldMine Software in 1989, FrontRange Solutions was formed by the merger of GoldMine and the Bendata subsidiary of South Africa-based FrontRange Limited. In January 2006 FrontRange Solutions was acquired by Francisco Partners, a manager of technology-focused private equity funds.

	Annual Growth	6/03	6/04	6/05	6/06	6/07
Est. sales ($ mil.)	—	—	—	—	—	38.6
Employees	—	—	—	—	—	383

FROZEN FOOD EXPRESS INDUSTRIES, INC.

NASDAQ (GS): FFEX

1145 Empire Central Pl.
Dallas, TX 75247
Phone: 214-630-8090
Fax: 214-819-5559
Web: www.ffeinc.com

CEO: Stoney M. (Mit) Stubbs Jr.
CFO: Thomas G. Yetter
HR: Donna Mecom
FYE: December 31
Type: Public

The frozen assets of other companies mean big business for Frozen Food Express Industries, one of the largest temperature-controlled trucking companies in the US. Through its subsidiaries, which include FFE Transportation Services and Lisa Motor Lines, the company transports truckload and less-than-truckload (LTL) shipments in the US, Canada, and Mexico. Temperature-sensitive cargo accounts for most of the company's sales. Frozen Food Express Industries also hauls dry freight, under the American Eagle Lines brand, and offers logistics services. Overall, the company maintains a fleet of about 2,100 tractors and 4,000 trailers.

	Annual Growth	12/03	12/04	12/05	12/06	12/07
Sales ($ mil.)	2.8%	404.2	474.4	524.1	483.7	452.2
Net income ($ mil.)	—	4.3	10.8	20.4	11.2	(7.7)
Market value ($ mil.)	(4.0%)	115.7	226.0	196.4	149.7	98.2
Employees	(8.5%)	—	—	2,956	2,691	2,477

⊞ FRUIT OF THE LOOM, INC.

1 Fruit of the Loom Dr.
Bowling Green, KY 42103
Phone: 270-781-6400
Fax: 270-781-6588
Web: www.fruit.com

CEO: John B. Holland
CFO: G. William Newton
HR: Tony Pebski
FYE: First Saturday in January
Type: Subsidiary

Fruit of the Loom wants to be in your drawers. In addition to its namesake apparel — mostly basic underwear with brand names such as BVD, Fruit of the Loom, and Lofteez — the company's products include activewear, casual wear, and children's underwear sold under names Funpals, Fungals, and Underoos, which feature characters such as Batman, Scooby Doo, Pink Panther, and My Little Pony. Fruit of the Loom's products are sold primarily in North America through discount and mass merchandisers the likes of Wal-Mart and Target, as well as to department stores, wholesale clubs, and screen printers. To trim costs, Fruit of the Loom uses Latin American production. Warren Buffett's Berkshire Hathaway owns the company.

	Annual Growth	12/03	12/04	12/05	12/06	12/07
Est. sales ($ mil.)	—	—	—	—	—	983.1
Employees	—	—	—	—	—	23,000

FRY, INC.

650 Avis Dr.
Ann Arbor, MI 48108
Phone: 734-741-0640
Fax: 734-769-9918
Web: www.frymulti.com

CEO: David (Dave) Fry
CFO: Craig Camalo
HR: Deb Waldman
FYE: December 31
Type: Private

Fry cooks up e-commerce and corporate branding Web sites. The interactive marketing company designs online sites, including corporate intranets and extranets, and provides a host of marketing services, including brand design and multi-channel marketing campaign development. Additionally, Fry creates and integrates e-business applications, provides managed hosting services, and collects and analyzes Web traffic data. Clients include Brookstone, Eddie Bauer, and Godiva. The firm was founded in 1994 as part of printing company Fry Communications but was spun off as an independent enterprise in 1999. Fry has offices in California, Illinois, Michigan, and New York.

	Annual Growth	12/03	12/04	12/05	12/06	12/07
Est. sales ($ mil.)	—	—	—	—	—	24.2
Employees	—	—	—	—	—	175

⊞ FRY'S ELECTRONICS, INC.

600 E. Brokaw Rd.
San Jose, CA 95112
Phone: 408-487-4500
Fax: 408-487-4741
Web: www.frys.com

CEO: John Fry
CFO: –
HR: Karen Schultz
FYE: December 31
Type: Private

Trying to catalog all the things this superstore carries could fry your brain. Fry's Electronics is a leading big-box retailer of computers, consumer electronics, and appliances with 30-plus stores in about 10 states. The chain's extensive inventory includes computer software and components, magazines, movies and music, refigerators, small appliances, stereo equipment, and televisions. In addition, each store typically stocks a variety of snacks and other impulse items. The technogeek's dream store began in 1985 as the brainchild of CEO John Fry (with brothers Randy and Dave) and EVP Kathryn Kolder. The Fry brothers, who got their start at Fry's Food Stores, still own the company.

	Annual Growth	12/02	12/03	12/04	12/05	12/06
Est. sales ($ mil.)	6.9%	2,000.0	2,100.0	2,250.0	2,340.0	2,610.0
Employees	20.7%	5,650	6,000	6,500	12,000	12,000

⊞ An in-depth profile of this company is available to Hoover's Online members at hoovers.com.

655

FRY'S FOOD AND DRUG STORES

500 S. 99th Ave.
Tolleson, AZ 85353
Phone: 623-936-2100
Fax: 623-907-1910
Web: www.frysfood.com

CEO: Jon C. Flora
CFO: –
HR: –
FYE: January 31
Type: Subsidiary

Fry's Food and Drug Stores operates about 120 supermarkets under the Fry's Food & Drug banner, mostly in Phoenix but also in Tucson, Arizona. In addition to traditional supermarket fare, many Fry's stores have in-store pharmacies, and a third of its supermarkets offer full-service banking in partnership with Bank One. Fry's also operates more than 15 Fry's Marketplace stores, large (up to 120,000 sq. ft.) multi-department stores that offer full-service grocery and pharmacy departments as well as expanded general merchandise, electronics, home goods, and toy sections. Fry's Food and Drug Stores is owned by The Kroger Co., the #1 pure grocery chain in the US.

	Annual Growth	1/03	1/04	1/05	1/06	1/07
Est. sales ($ mil.)	—	—	—	—	—	1,084.8
Employees	—	—	—	—	—	10,000

FSI INTERNATIONAL, INC.

NASDAQ (GM): FSII

3455 Lyman Blvd.
Chaska, MN 55318
Phone: 952-448-5440
Fax: 952-448-2825
Web: www.fsi-intl.com

CEO: Donald S. (Don) Mitchell
CFO: Patricia M. (Pat) Hollister
HR: –
FYE: Last Saturday in August
Type: Public

FSI International stays focused on semiconductor wafers all around the world. The company's surface conditioning equipment performs key cleaning, etching, and stripping functions that remove contaminants from semiconductor wafers and prepare them for subsequent production steps. FSI's equipment is used by electronics manufacturers worldwide, such as Samsung Electronics (about 13% of sales), Intel (11%), STMicroelectronics, Texas Instruments, Seagate Technology, IBM Microelectronics, and NXP, as well as by other high-tech organizations, including Sandia National Laboratories. Customers outside the US account for about two-thirds of sales. South Korea and Israel are leading markets overseas.

	Annual Growth	8/03	8/04	8/05	8/06	8/07
Sales ($ mil.)	7.0%	88.8	114.4	86.4	113.2	116.2
Net income ($ mil.)	—	(78.6)	0.1	(3.3)	(7.3)	(14.6)
Market value ($ mil.)	(12.1%)	130.5	144.9	119.8	166.1	77.9
Employees	—	—	—	—	—	—

FTD GROUP, INC.

NYSE: FTD

3113 Woodcreek Dr.
Downers Grove, IL 60515
Phone: 630-719-7800
Fax: 630-719-6170
Web: www.ftd.com

CEO: Michael J. (Mike) Soenen
CFO: Becky A. Sheehan
HR: –
FYE: June 30
Type: Public

Mercury, the Roman god of speed and commerce with winged feet (and an icon for megaflorist FTD), comes bearing flowers. FTD Group (formerly Mercury Man Holdings) is the holding company for operating subsidiary FTD, Inc., which was established in 1910. Flowers, plants, gourmet foods, and gift baskets loaded with all of the above find their way to about 45,000 florist shops throughout North America and the UK. FTD Group was formed in 2003 when Green Equity Investors, a business unit of Leonard Green & Partners, acquired the company for about $420 million. FTD Group went public in early 2005. FTD Group has agreed to be acquired by Internet service provider United Online in a deal valued at $456 million.

	Annual Growth	6/03	6/04	6/05	6/06	6/07
Sales ($ mil.)	18.3%	—	—	437.8	465.1	613.0
Net income ($ mil.)	—	—	—	(22.6)	25.5	31.9
Market value ($ mil.)	27.4%	—	—	334.3	398.0	542.8
Employees	(3.5%)	—	—	772	745	

FTI CONSULTING, INC.

NYSE: FCN

500 E. Pratt St., Ste. 1400
Baltimore, MD 21202
Phone: 410-951-4800
Fax: 410-224-8378
Web: www.fticonsulting.com

CEO: Jack B. Dunn IV
CFO: Jorge A. Celaya
HR: Liz Behrmann
FYE: December 31
Type: Public

When someone has been cooking the books, FTI Consulting has a recipe for recovery. Established in 1982, the company is one of the leading providers of forensic accounting and litigation support services in the US. Its experts offer investigative services to companies confronted with problems such as fraud in order to assist them in their legal defense or pursuit of recoveries. FTI also provides consulting services related to corporate finance and restructuring, such as advice on mergers and acquisitions and performance improvement. Other consulting service areas include economics, strategic and financial communications, and technology. FTI's main clients are large business enterprises and major law firms.

	Annual Growth	12/03	12/04	12/05	12/06	12/07
Sales ($ mil.)	27.8%	375.7	427.0	539.5	707.9	1,001.3
Net income ($ mil.)	11.5%	59.5	42.9	56.4	42.0	92.1
Market value ($ mil.)	32.2%	987.5	895.2	1,070.4	1,168.3	3,019.1
Employees	38.0%	—	—	1,338	2,079	2,549

FTS GROUP, INC.

OTC: FLIP

7610 W. Hillsborough Ave.
Tampa, FL 33615
Phone: 813-868-3600
Fax: 215-689-2748
Web: www.ftsgroup.tv

CEO: Scott Gallagher
CFO: –
HR: –
FYE: December 31
Type: Public

FTS Group is a business development company that operates through its primary subsidiary FTS Wireless, which distributes wireless products and services from retail centers in Florida and online. FTS Wireless resells phone service from national operators AT&T Mobility (formerly Cingular) and Sprint Nextel, as well as mobile virtual network operators (MVNOs) like Virgin Mobile. Its e-commerce operations offer cellular phones and accessories and satellite phones from Globalstar. In 2006 the company acquired a 25% stake in privately held Internet advertising firm Elysium Internet (which became a subsidiary in 2007) and purchased See World Satellites, a regional service provider for Dish Networks.

	Annual Growth	12/03	12/04	12/05	12/06	12/07
Sales ($ mil.)	189.3%	0.1	0.7	1.3	6.7	7.0
Net income ($ mil.)	—	(0.9)	(2.3)	(3.6)	1.2	(0.6)
Market value ($ mil.)	0.8%	2.7	5.7	3.1	4.3	2.8
Employees	—	—	—	—	—	49

FUBU

350 5th Ave., Ste. 6617
New York, NY 10118
Phone: 212-273-3300
Fax: 212-273-3333
Web: www.fubu.com

CEO: Daymond John
CFO: Theresa Wang
HR: –
FYE: December 31
Type: Private

Urban youth and youthful are down with FUBU's hip-hop inspired sportswear. Besides making sportswear, FUBU (an acronym for "for us, by us") also licenses its name for men's, women's, and children's wear, as well as footwear and accessories such as watches, caps, and bags. Its FB Entertainment unit produces and promotes musical artists. FUBU's online retail site, Y2G.com, hosts channels on careers, personal success, and politics, primarily for Latino and African-American viewers. The company, which is expanding rapidly in Asia, has about 45 franchised stores worldwide. Founders Daymond John, Alexander Martin, Carl Brown, and Keith Perrin own FUBU.

	Annual Growth	12/03	12/04	12/05	12/06	12/07
Est. sales ($ mil.)	—	—	—	—	—	12.1
Employees	—	—	—	—	—	62

An in-depth profile of this company is available to Hoover's Online members at hoovers.com.

FUDDRUCKERS, INC.

5700 S. Mopac Expwy., Ste. 300
Austin, TX 78749
Phone: 512-275-0400
Fax: 512-275-0670
Web: www.fuddruckers.com

CEO: Peter Large
CFO: –
HR: –
FYE: September 30
Type: Private

You might say this company is raising a ruckus in the burger world. Fuddruckers operates and franchises about 250 fast-casual restaurants in more than 30 states that specialize in large portioned, made-to-order hamburgers and hot dogs, as well as chicken sandwiches, salads, soups, and sides. The company also operates a handful of Koo Koo Roo locations in California that offer rotisserie-cooked chicken along with chicken items. Restaurateur Phil Romano, the brainchild behind several casual dining chains such as Romano's Macaroni Grill (now owned by Brinker International), started Fuddruckers in 1980. The business was acquired eight years later by former CEO Bryce King and investor Michael Cannon.

	Annual Growth	9/03	9/04	9/05	9/06	9/07
Est. sales ($ mil.)	—	—	—	—	—	200.0
Employees	—	—	—	—	—	2,074

FUEL SYSTEMS SOLUTIONS, INC.

NASDAQ (GM): FSYS

3030 S. Susan St.
Santa Ana, CA 92704
Phone: 714-656-1300
Fax: 714-656-1401
Web: www.fuelsystemssolutions.com

CEO: Mariano Costamagna
CFO: Bill Larkin
HR: –
FYE: December 31
Type: Public

Fuel Systems Solutions was green before green was hip. Operating through two primary subsidiaries, the holding company (formerly IMPCO Technologies, Inc.) manufactures equipment that allows internal combustion engines to run cleaner by using alternative fuels. Fuel Systems Solutions' IMPCO Technologies subsidiary makes fuel systems that allow engines to burn gaseous fuels such as natural gas, propane, or biogas. IMPCO serves the heavy-duty, power generation, stationary power, and industrial markets. The company's BRC Gas Equipment subsidiary makes gaseous fuel conversion systems for vehicles so they can meet market requirements. Fuel Systems was formed in 1957 as IMPCO.

	Annual Growth	12/03	12/04	12/05	12/06	12/07
Sales ($ mil.)	37.3%	74.7	118.3	174.5	220.8	265.3
Net income ($ mil.)	—	(6.9)	(15.9)	(10.7)	6.9	5.9
Employees	28.0%	373	721	694	845	1,002

FUEL TECH, INC.

NASDAQ (GM): FTEK

512 Kingsland Dr.
Batavia, IL 60510
Phone: 630-845-4500
Fax: 630-845-4501
Web: www.fueltechnv.com

CEO: John F. Norris Jr.
CFO: John P. Graham
HR: –
FYE: December 31
Type: Public

Thanks in part to the Clean Air Act, Fuel Tech (formerly Fuel-Tech N.V.) is batting in the clean-up position. The company sells NOxOUT brand of products, equipped with a retrofittable system, for the reduction of nitrogen oxide in boilers, incinerators, furnaces, and other combustion sources. Fuel Tech's NOx reduction technologies are installed worldwide on more than 450 combustion units, including utility, industrial and municipal solid waste applications. The air pollution control company also makes FUEL CHEM to reduce slag formation and corrosion in boilers and furnaces. Fuel Tech owns about 4% of Clean Diesel Technologies. Chairman Ralph Bailey owns almost 20% of Fuel Tech.

	Annual Growth	12/03	12/04	12/05	12/06	12/07
Sales ($ mil.)	22.5%	35.7	30.8	52.9	75.1	80.3
Net income ($ mil.)	60.0%	1.1	1.6	7.6	6.8	7.2
Market value ($ mil.)	64.5%	69.2	91.2	185.2	544.2	507.6
Employees	31.7%	—	—	104	137	—

FUELCELL ENERGY, INC.

NASDAQ (GM): FCEL

3 Great Pasture Rd.
Danbury, CT 06813
Phone: 203-825-6000
Fax: 203-825-6100
Web: www.fuelcellenergy.com

CEO: R. Daniel Brdar
CFO: Joseph G. Mahler
HR: Joseph G. Mahler
FYE: October 31
Type: Public

FuelCell Energy engages in fuelish pursuits. The company develops electrochemical technologies such as carbonate fuel cells and electrochemical engines that generate electricity without combustion. FuelCell Energy's Direct FuelCell (DFC) does not need an external hydrogen supply and can be fed fuel directly without an external reactor; the equipment can be fired up with biogas, coal gas, coal-mine methane, diesel, methanol, natural gas, or propane. The company has operated a fuel cell power plant for the Los Angeles Department of Water and Power since 2001. FuelCell Energy operates more than 40 DFC power plants for customers around the world. The US market accounts for two-thirds of sales.

	Annual Growth	10/03	10/04	10/05	10/06	10/07
Sales ($ mil.)	9.3%	33.8	31.4	30.4	33.3	48.2
Net income ($ mil.)	—	(67.4)	(86.4)	(68.2)	(76.1)	(68.7)
Market value ($ mil.)	3.3%	602.4	594.0	424.8	351.7	684.9
Employees	4.5%	372	346	335	384	443

FUJIFILM MEDICAL SYSTEMS USA, INC.

419 West Ave.
Stamford, CT 06902
Phone: 203-324-2000
Fax: 203-327-6485
Web: www.fujimed.com

CEO: Makoto Kawaguchi
CFO: John Weber
HR: –
FYE: March 31
Type: Subsidiary

FUJIFILM Medical Systems USA wants to take snapshots of your heart. A division of Japanese camera and film company FUJIFILM, the company markets and sells FUJIFILM's imaging equipment and software in the US, Puerto Rico, and the Caribbean. It is one of the largest providers of machines utilizing digital X-ray technology (known as Computed Radiography, or CR). The company also makes picture archiving software (branded Synapse) and heads up Fuji's R&D operations for such software technology. Other products include conventional X-ray equipment, imaging printers, and mammography systems.

	Annual Growth	3/03	3/04	3/05	3/06	3/07
Est. sales ($ mil.)	—	—	—	—	—	63.8
Employees	—	—	—	—	—	425

FUJIFILM U.S.A., INC.

200 Summit Lake Dr.
Valhalla, NY 10595
Phone: 914-789-8100
Fax: 914-789-8295
Web: www.fujifilmusa.com

CEO: Hiro Sakai
CFO: –
HR: Joseph Convery
FYE: March 31
Type: Subsidiary

Smile, you've been captured on Fujifilm U.S.A. (formerly Fuji Photo Film U.S.A.). The marketing unit of Tokyo-based Fujifilm Holdings, Fujifilm also makes photographic products (film, paper, one-time cameras, and photographic equipment and chemicals), offers photo-finishing services, and makes such products as digital cameras and other digital imaging items, computer disks, and videocassettes. The firm operates a few subsidiaries: Fujifilm e-Systems, Fujicolor Processing, and Enovation Graphic Systems. Fujifilm and rival Eastman Kodak are racing to take advantage of the increasing number of cell phones that capture digital photos. AT&T customers can subscribe to Fujifilm's online photo printing service.

	Annual Growth	3/03	3/04	3/05	3/06	3/07
Est. sales ($ mil.)	—	—	—	—	—	703.5
Employees	—	—	—	—	—	3,500

An in-depth profile of this company is available to Hoover's Online members at hoovers.com.

FUJITSU COMPUTER PRODUCTS OF AMERICA, INC.

1255 E. Arques Ave.
Sunnyvale, CA 94085
Phone: 408-746-7000
Fax: –
Web: www.fcpa.fujitsu.com

CEO: Yoshihiko Masuda
CFO: Takeshi Moriguchi
HR: –
FYE: March 31
Type: Subsidiary

Fujitsu Computer Products of America (FCPA) sells Fujitsu computer products in — you guessed it — America. The company, a subsidiary of Japanese technology titan Fujitsu Limited, provides hard drives, high-definition video encoder/decoder hardware, and workgroup image scanners to customers in the US. FCPA's hard drives are used in notebook computers, servers, and workstations. The company's other products include Ethernet switches and biometric authentication systems, as well as degaussers (data disposal systems). Fujitsu founded FCPA in 1991.

	Annual Growth	3/03	3/04	3/05	3/06	3/07
Est. sales ($ mil.)	—	—	—	—	—	126.8
Employees	—	—	—	—	—	600

FUJITSU COMPUTER SYSTEMS CORPORATION

1250 E. Arques Ave.
Sunnyvale, CA 94085
Phone: 408-746-6000
Fax: 408-992-2674
Web: us.fujitsu.com/computers

CEO: Farhat Ali
CFO: Ari Hovsepyan
HR: Gloria Veon
FYE: March 31
Type: Subsidiary

Fujitsu Computer Systems provides customers in North America with desktop, notebook, and tablet PCs. The company also sells Intel and SPARC-based servers, as well as disk-based mass storage systems. Its service offerings range from product maintenance to managed operational support for enterprises. The company sells directly and through retailers and systems integrators. Fujitsu Computer Systems serves biotech and pharmaceutical researchers through its BioSciences Group. The unit provides hardware and software, including massively parallel servers and molecular modeling applications, designed specifically for life sciences research.

	Annual Growth	3/03	3/04	3/05	3/06	3/07
Est. sales ($ mil.)	—	—	—	—	—	149.2
Employees	—	—	—	—	—	750

FUJITSU NETWORK COMMUNICATIONS, INC.

2801 Telecom Pkwy.
Richardson, TX 75082
Phone: 972-690-6000
Fax: 972-479-4647
Web: www.fujitsu.com/us/services/telecom

CEO: Satoshi Ikeuchi
CFO: Hirofuma Shimmura
HR: Joe Snayd
FYE: March 31
Type: Subsidiary

Fujitsu Network Communications designs, manufactures, and maintains a variety of broadband transmission systems. The company supplies optical transport equipment to telecom carriers and cable TV service providers. Its products include multiplexers, switches, and transponders. The company also provides network design, deployment, maintenance, and testing services. Its customers have included AT&T Inc., BellSouth, Qwest Communications, and Verizon Communications. Fujitsu Network Communications is a subsidiary of the Japan-based electronics and computer systems giant Fujitsu Limited.

	Annual Growth	3/03	3/04	3/05	3/06	3/07
Est. sales ($ mil.)	—	—	—	—	—	543.4
Employees	—	—	—	—	—	1,450

FULL HOUSE RESORTS, INC.

AMEX: FLL

4670 S. Fort Apache Rd., Ste. 190
Las Vegas, NV 89147
Phone: 702-221-7800
Fax: 702-221-8101
Web: www.fullhouseresorts.com

CEO: Andre M. Hilliou
CFO: Mark J. Miller
HR: –
FYE: December 31
Type: Public

When it comes to gaming outside of Sin City, nothing beats a Full House. Full House Resorts owns 50% of Harrington Raceway and Casino (formerly called Midway Slots and Simulcast) in Delaware. Harrington offers more than 2,100 slot machines and gaming devices, a 450-seat buffet, a fine dining restaurant, a 50-seat diner, and an entertainment lounge area. The company also owns Stockman's Casino in Nevada, featuring 260 slot machines, 4 table games, and keno. In addition, Full House is collaborating with Native American tribes in Michigan and Montana to develop gaming enterprises.

	Annual Growth	12/03	12/04	12/05	12/06	12/07
Sales ($ mil.)	—	—	—	—	—	9.6
Net income ($ mil.)	—	—	—	—	—	0.9
Market value ($ mil.)	—	—	—	—	—	54.2
Employees	—	—	—	—	—	—

FULLNET COMMUNICATIONS, INC.

OTC: FULO

201 Robert S. Kerr Ave., Ste. 210
Oklahoma City, OK 73102
Phone: 405-236-8200
Fax: 405-236-8201
Web: web.fullnet.net

CEO: Timothy J. (Tim) Kilkenny
CFO: Roger P. Baresel
HR: –
FYE: December 31
Type: Public

FullNet Communications is trying to net as many Oklahoma Internet users as possible. Established in 1995, the company provides dial-up Internet access to the state's consumers and small to midsized businesses. It sells connectivity on a retail or wholesale basis, allowing other Internet service providers to resell the service under their own brand names. FullNet's wholly owned FullTel subsidiary is a competitive local-exchange carrier (CLEC) that provides the company with the local phone numbers necessary to offer dial-up service; it has points of presence in about 230 Oklahoma cities and plans to add voice service to its list of products.

	Annual Growth	12/03	12/04	12/05	12/06	12/07
Sales ($ mil.)	(2.5%)	2.1	2.3	2.4	1.8	1.9
Net income ($ mil.)	—	(0.7)	0.2	0.1	(0.5)	(0.3)
Market value ($ mil.)	—	—	—	—	—	—
Employees	—	—	—	—	—	—

FULTON FINANCIAL CORPORATION

NASDAQ (GS): FULT

1 Penn Sq., P.O. Box 4887
Lancaster, PA 17604
Phone: 717-291-2411
Fax: 717-295-4792
Web: www.fult.com

CEO: R. Scott Smith Jr.
CFO: Charles J. Nugent
HR: Craig H. Hill
FYE: December 31
Type: Public

Fulton Financial is simply full of banks. The multibank holding company owns 10 community banks, which together operate about 270 branches in Delaware, Maryland, New Jersey, Pennsylvania, and Virginia. Each bank retains a local identity. Personal banking products and services include checking and savings accounts, CDs, IRAs, and consumer loans. Residential mortgages are offered through Fulton Mortgage Company. Commercial loans (which account for 30% of the company's portfolio), equipment leasing, credit cards, cash management services, and traditional deposit products are offered to commercial customers.

	Annual Growth	12/03	12/04	12/05	12/06	12/07
Assets ($ mil.)	13.0%	9,767.3	11,158.3	12,401.6	14,919.0	15,923.1
Net income ($ mil.)	2.5%	138.2	152.9	166.1	185.5	152.7
Market value ($ mil.)	3.1%	1,722.6	2,232.4	2,631.6	2,900.8	1,946.7
Employees	51.7%	—	—	2,900	4,400	—

FURMANITE CORPORATION

NYSE: FRM

2435 N. Central Expwy.
Richardson, TX 75080
Phone: 972-699-4000
Fax: 972-644-3524
Web: www.furmanite.com

CEO: John R. Barnes
CFO: –
HR: –
FYE: December 31
Type: Public

Furmanite hopes its products stick. The specialty contractor provides on-site leak sealing, heat treating, and valve testing and repair primarily to the energy and power generation industries around the globe. Formerly called Xanser, Furmanite spun off its oil pipeline operations and wholesale fuel marketing services businesses to focus on its technical services. Customers include petroleum refineries, chemical plants, steel mills, nuclear power stations, pulp and paper mills, and food processing plants. Subsidiary Xtria also provides information technology services (including Web hosting and program and policy analysis) through contracts with state and federal government agencies.

	Annual Growth	12/03	12/04	12/05	12/06	12/07
Sales ($ mil.)	20.9%	135.7	145.7	153.9	246.4	290.3
Net income ($ mil.)	—	(13.1)	2.4	(4.3)	(3.4)	12.5
Market value ($ mil.)	54.3%	74.8	88.5	101.2	190.8	423.7
Employees	31.3%	—	—	1,047	1,647	1,805

FURNITURE BRANDS INTERNATIONAL, INC.

NYSE: FBN

101 S. Hanley Rd.
St. Louis, MO 63105
Phone: 314-863-1100
Fax: 314-863-5306
Web: www.furniturebrands.com

CEO: Ralph P. Scozzafava
CFO: Steven G. (Steve) Rolls
HR: Richard Lockard
FYE: December 31
Type: Public

Furniture Brands International runs a furniture-making empire. The company ranks as one of the top US makers of residential furniture. Furniture Brands' subsidiaries offer a line-up of nationally recognized brands, including Broyhill, Lane, Thomasville, and Drexel Heritage, among others. Broyhill makes medium-priced bedroom, dining room, and other furnishings. Lane (offering 18th-century reproductions and cedar chests) and Thomasville (wood and upholstered furniture) target the premium-priced furniture market. Furniture Brands distributes its products through a network of furniture centers, independent dealers, national and local chains, and department stores.

	Annual Growth	12/03	12/04	12/05	12/06	12/07
Sales ($ mil.)	(3.2%)	2,367.7	2,447.4	2,386.8	2,418.2	2,082.1
Net income ($ mil.)	—	94.6	91.6	61.4	55.1	(45.7)
Market value ($ mil.)	(26.2%)	1,640.9	1,333.1	1,109.1	784.5	487.9
Employees	(11.4%)	—	—	15,150	13,800	11,900

FURNITURE.COM, INC.

85 River St., Ste. 8
Waltham, MA 02453
Phone: 781-693-2100
Fax: 781-899-7160
Web: www.furniture.com

CEO: Carl E. Prindle
CFO: Miguel Contessi
HR: –
FYE: December 31
Type: Private

Furniture.com knows some people would rather bypass a visit to the furniture store when shopping for a sofa. The company sells furniture online through its partnership with major furniture retailers in North America including the RoomStore. Product lines include dining, bedroom, living room, entertainment centers, lighting, and mattresses. The company also provides retailers with e-commerce services and technologies, such as launching retailer-branded sites for its partners, including Levitz.com.

FURUKAWA ELECTRIC NORTH AMERICA, INC.

2000 Northeast Expwy.
Norcross, GA 30071
Phone: 770-798-2082
Fax: 770-798-2083

CEO: Yukimasa Shiga
CFO: Yukimasa Shiga
HR: Rena Uesaka
FYE: March 31
Type: Subsidiary

Furukawa Electric North America (FENA) has its hands in numerous businesses in the US. Like its Japan-based parent, The Furukawa Electric Co., the firm makes products ranging from automotive, architectural, and communications wiring to batteries, sheet metal, and semiconductor materials. FENA APD — the company's automotive division — designs, manufactures, and markets electrical devices such as steering roll connectors, fuse and relay boxes, terminals, and automotive wire harness systems for such customers as Honda, Toyota, Saturn, and General Motors.

	Annual Growth	3/03	3/04	3/05	3/06	3/07
Est. sales ($ mil.)	—	—	—	—	—	251.1
Employees	—	—	—	—	—	800

FUSION TELECOMMUNICATIONS INTERNATIONAL, INC.

AMEX: FSN

420 Lexington Ave., Ste. 1718
New York, NY 10170
Phone: 212-201-2400
Fax: 212-972-7884
Web: www.fusiontel.com

CEO: Matthew D. Rosen
CFO: Barbara Hughes
HR: –
FYE: December 31
Type: Public

Fusion Telecommunications International understands that modern communications is a blend of old and familiar processes with new technologies. Fusion provides VoIP (Voice over Internet Protocol) telephone and other Internet services primarily to other US communciations carriers. Fusion offers such services as voice calling and broadband Internet access. Top clients include communications services providers Qwest (40% of sales) and Telco Group (10%). The company also serves consumers through its Mobilink brand and offers ISP and hosted PBX services among others to enterprise customers.

	Annual Growth	12/03	12/04	12/05	12/06	12/07
Sales ($ mil.)	3.5%	—	49.6	49.4	47.1	55.0
Net income ($ mil.)	—	—	(5.0)	(9.4)	(13.4)	(12.7)
Market value ($ mil.)	(39.7%)	—	—	28.0	31.5	10.2
Employees	(6.5%)	—	—	92	86	—

FUZE BEVERAGE, LLC

140 Sylvan Ave., 3rd Fl.
Englewood Cliffs, NJ 07632
Phone: 201-461-6640
Fax: 201-461-1091
Web: www.fuzebev.com

CEO: Carl Sweat
CFO: John Petrizzo
HR: –
FYE: December 31
Type: Private

Fuze Beverage makes Fuze health drinks and teas, including the Vitalize, Refresh, Tea, and Slenderize brands. The drinks contain an array of vitamins and minerals. Cross-branding was its aim when Fuze teamed with Pentland Group's bathing suit brand Speedo to develop Speedo Sportswater, marketed through Fuze's Performance Waters division. The company works with more than 350 distributors in the US, the Bahamas, Bermuda, Guam, Puerto Rico, and the Virgin Islands. Started in 2001 by Lance Collins, the company was acquired by The Coca-Cola Company in 2007.

	Annual Growth	12/03	12/04	12/05	12/06	12/07
Est. sales ($ mil.)	—	—	—	—	—	7.1
Employees	—	—	—	—	—	47

An in-depth profile of this company is available to Hoover's Online members at hoovers.com.

659

F.W. WEBB COMPANY

160 Middlesex Tpke.
Bedford, MA 01730
Phone: 781-272-6600
Fax: 781-275-3354
Web: www.fwwebb.com

CEO: Jack Hester
CFO: Robert Mucciarone
HR: —
FYE: December 31
Type: Private

Since 1866 F.W. Webb has kept people warm in winter and cool in summer. One of the largest distributors of hardware products in the northeastern US, F.W. Webb offers products for residential and commercial markets through about 70 retail outlets and its own delivery fleet. The company sells piping and plumbing products (fountains, pumps), and heating, ventilation, and air conditioning (HVAC) equipment (air filters, furnaces). It also offers gas boilers and valves and biopharmaceutical equipment, as well as general industrial products such as adhesives and sealants. In addition, F.W. Webb offers customized fabrication and inventory programs. John Pope and his family own F.W. Webb, which they purchased in 1933.

	Annual Growth	12/03	12/04	12/05	12/06	12/07
Est. sales ($ mil.)	—	—	—	—	—	650.0
Employees	—	—	—	—	—	1,400

FX ENERGY, INC.

NASDAQ (GM): FXEN

3006 Highland Dr., Ste. 206
Salt Lake City, UT 84106
Phone: 801-486-5555
Fax: 801-486-5575
Web: www.fxenergy.com

CEO: David N. Pierce
CFO: Clay Newton
HR: —
FYE: December 31
Type: Public

FX Energy used to get its energy fix in the western US, but it is Poland that is fixing its attention today. The exploration and production company has proved reserves of 19.3 billion cu. ft. of natural gas and 202,000 barrels of oil in Poland, and 382,000 barrels of oil in the US. The company was founded in 1989 to concentrate on the northern Rocky Mountain states, but since 1993 FX Energy has focused on Poland. Partners include state-owned Polish Oil and Gas and CalEnergy Gas, which serve as operators for exploration wells. The company holds about 3.5 million acreas in western Poland.

	Annual Growth	12/03	12/04	12/05	12/06	12/07
Sales ($ mil.)	67.3%	2.3	3.8	5.9	8.2	18.0
Net income ($ mil.)	—	(2.9)	(12.6)	(11.4)	(13.8)	(11.7)
Market value ($ mil.)	12.3%	136.5	403.3	280.1	219.4	217.0
Employees	—	—	—	—	39	

G-III APPAREL GROUP, LTD.

NASDAQ (GM): GIII

512 7th Ave.
New York, NY 10018
Phone: 212-403-0500
Fax: 212-403-0551
Web: www.g-iii.com

CEO: Morris Goldfarb
CFO: Neal S. Nackman
HR: —
FYE: January 31
Type: Public

G-III Apparel Group has the leather part of Stevie Nicks' leather and lace wrapped up. It's best known for making leather jackets under the names G-III, Marvin Richards, Black Rivet, Winlit, Siena Studio, La Nouvelle Renaissance, and other labels (such as Andrew Marc), as well as under licensed names. It also makes leather and other pants, skirts, and sportswear. More of its sales are generated from licensed apparel it makes for the NFL, NBA, NHL, and MLB teams, as well as for Jones New York, Nine West, and Kenneth Cole. Its customers include department stores, such as Macy's, and mass merchants the likes of Wal-Mart. Father and son team Aron and Morris Goldfarb own some 20% of G-III Apparel.

	Annual Growth	1/04	1/05	1/06	1/07	1/08
Sales ($ mil.)	23.4%	224.1	214.3	324.1	427.0	518.9
Net income ($ mil.)	20.1%	8.4	0.7	7.1	13.2	17.5
Market value ($ mil.)	49.8%	43.7	39.1	117.6	307.3	220.2
Employees	0.0%	—	—	510	510	—

THE GAB ROBINS GROUP OF COMPANIES

9 Campus Dr., Ste. 7
Parsippany, NJ 07054
Phone: 973-993-3400
Fax: 973-993-9579
Web: www.gabrobins.com

CEO: Edward G. (Ed) Troy
CFO: Alan N. Mansfield
HR: Janet Turoff
FYE: December 31
Type: Private

GAB Robins knows all about risky business. The GAB Robins Group of Companies identifies insurance risk and provides loss adjusting services to property and casualty insurers. It helps self-insured companies and others implement and manage claims processes for workers' compensation, general liability, and property claims. Its MedInsights subsidiary covers workers' comp claims. GAB Robins also performs forensic analysis and investigation, surveillance, accident reconstruction, and other investigative services. The GAB Robins North America division combines the company's risk management and insurance services. The company has nearly 700 offices in around 60 countries. Brera Capital Partners controls the company.

	Annual Growth	12/03	12/04	12/05	12/06	12/07
Est. sales ($ mil.)	—	—	—	—	—	226.9
Employees	—	—	—	—	—	3,350

GABRIEL BROTHERS, INC.

55 Scott Ave.
Morgantown, WV 26508
Phone: 304-292-6965
Fax: 304-292-3874
Web: www.gabrielbrothers.com

CEO: Art Gabriel Sr.
CFO: —
HR: Don Mancini
FYE: January 31
Type: Private

Gabriel, blow your horn! Your magical, mystical discount horn, that is. Gabriel Brothers sells discounted brand-name clothing through about 100 stores, under the Gabriel Brothers and Rugged Wearhouse banners. Stores are located in nearly a dozen East Coast states and average about 50,000 to 55,000 sq. ft. Each store offers men's, women's, and children's apparel and footwear, as well as housewares, with markdowns as high as 70% off of their original retail prices. Brands include Anne Klein, Kenneth Cole, and Liz Claiborne. The family-run company was established in 1961 by James and Arthur Gabriel.

	Annual Growth	1/03	1/04	1/05	1/06	1/07
Est. sales ($ mil.)	—	—	—	—	—	263.5
Employees	—	—	—	—	—	3,500

GABRIEL TECHNOLOGIES CORPORATION

Pink Sheets: GWLK

4538 S. 140th St.
Omaha, NE 68137
Phone: 402-614-0258
Fax: 402-614-0498
Web: www.gabrieltechnologies.com

CEO: Ronald E. Gillum Jr.
CFO: —
HR: —
FYE: June 30
Type: Public

Gabriel Technologies has its place in business locked up. The company sells locking systems for truck trailers, railcars, and intermodal shipping containers under the WAR-LOK brand name. Its products are manufactured by contractors and distributed from Gabriel's assembly center. Gabriel also offers Trace Location Services, an asset-tracking system for vehicle fleet operators that is based on the Global Positioning System (GPS). The trucking industry accounts for more than 85% of the company's sales. Gabriel added biometric technology to its product mix in 2006 by acquiring a majority stake in Resilent, an Omaha, Nebraska-based company that does business as Digital Defense Group.

	Annual Growth	6/02	6/03	6/04	6/05	*6/06
Sales ($ mil.)	33.3%	—	—	—	0.9	1.2
Net income ($ mil.)	—	—	—	—	(3.5)	(14.6)
Employees	—	—	—	—	—	11

*Most recent year available

GAIAM, INC.

NASDAQ (GM): GAIA

360 Interlocken Blvd.
Broomfield, CO 80021
Phone: 303-222-3600
Fax: 303-222-3700
Web: www.gaiam.com

CEO: Jirka Rysavy
CFO: Vilia Valentine
HR: Jackie Abraham
FYE: December 31
Type: Public

If you're into living a healthy sustainable lifestyle, Gaiam is your kind of company. The name Gaiam (pronounced "guy-um") is a combination of Gaia (the Earth goddess) and "I am." The company's more than 10,000 products (7,000 are proprietary items) include environmentally friendly paraphernalia divided into five categories: Sustainable Economy, Healthy Living, Alternative Healthcare, Personal Development, and Ecological Lifestyles. Top sellers include solar panels, yoga and pilates DVDs, and natural cleaners. Gaiam markets through catalogs, its Web sites, and other retailers (including Costco and Target). CEO Jirka Rysavy, founder of Corporate Express, started Gaiam in 1988.

	Annual Growth	12/03	12/04	12/05	12/06	12/07
Sales ($ mil.)	26.7%	102.0	96.7	142.5	219.5	262.9
Net income ($ mil.)	—	(1.0)	(4.6)	1.3	5.6	8.5
Market value ($ mil.)	80.4%	54.8	57.9	202.8	297.5	580.4
Employees	12.3%	285	267	367	363	454

GAINEY CORPORATION, INC.

6000 Clay Ave. SW
Grand Rapids, MI 49548
Phone: 616-530-8558
Fax: 616-530-6064
Web: www.gaineycorp.com

CEO: Harvey N. Gainey Sr.
CFO: Mark Babin
HR: –
FYE: December 31
Type: Private

Gainey, through its Gainey Transportation Services and Super Service units, provides dry van and flat bed truckload freight transportation. Besides for-hire freight hauling, the company offers dedicated contract carriage, in which drivers and equipment are assigned to a customer long-term. Other Gainey units include Aero Bulk, which transports pressurized gases and liquid chemicals, LCT Transportation Services, which handles temperature-controlled freight, and Freight Brokers of America. Collectively, Gainey's transportation businesses operate about 2,700 tractors and 5,100 trailers. President Harvey Gainey founded the company in 1984.

	Annual Growth	12/03	12/04	12/05	12/06	12/07
Est. sales ($ mil.)	—	—	—	—	—	425.1
Employees	—	—	—	—	—	2,800

GAINSCO, INC.

AMEX: GAN

3333 Lee Pkwy., Ste. 1200
Dallas, TX 75219
Phone: 972-629-4301
Fax: 972-629-4302
Web: www.gainsco.com

CEO: Glenn W. Anderson
CFO: Daniel J. Coots
HR: Richard M. Buxton
FYE: December 31
Type: Public

Although at times it might be more appropriate, you wouldn't call an insurance company LOSSCO, would you? Through its MGA Insurance subsidiary, GAINSCO sells personal nonstandard auto insurance in over 40 states. The company does much of its business in Florida but has laid the groundwork for sales growth in Arizona, California, Nevada, New Mexico, South Carolina, and Texas. Its products are sold through more than 3,700 independent agencies. The company has also entered into the niche of marketing third party insurance to racecar operators through its GAINSCO Motorsports Insurance subsidiary. A handful of GAINSCO executives and directors collectively own 70% of the company.

	Annual Growth	12/03	12/04	12/05	12/06	12/07
Assets ($ mil.)	7.2%	185.7	164.6	212.2	289.3	245.3
Net income ($ mil.)	—	3.4	5.5	8.9	11.4	(18.5)
Market value ($ mil.)	51.8%	19.1	364.1	153.5	198.2	101.3
Employees	32.5%	—	—	295	391	—

GALARDI GROUP, INC.

4440 Von Karman Ave., Ste. 222
Newport Beach, CA 92660
Phone: 949-752-5800
Fax: 949-851-2618
Web: www.wienerschnitzel.com

CEO: John N. Galardi
CFO: –
HR: –
FYE: December 31
Type: Private

It's not Oscar Mayer, but Galardi Group is focused on wieners. The company operates and franchises about 350 Wienerschnitzel restaurants in California and a dozen other states. One of the largest hot dog chains, the restaurants offer a variety of toppings for its wieners, such as chili, cheese, and barbecued bacon, as well as alternative menu items including chicken sandwiches, Polish sausages, and hamburgers. About 90% of Wienerschnitzel locations are operated by franchisees. Galardi Group also owns Tastee Freez, a chain of more than 60 ice cream stands, and The Original Hamburger Stand. Owner, founder, and CEO John Galardi opened his first hot dog stand, called Der Wienerschnitzel, in 1961.

	Annual Growth	12/03	12/04	12/05	12/06	12/07
Est. sales ($ mil.)	—	—	—	—	—	38.0
Employees	—	—	—	—	—	45

GALAXY ENERGY CORPORATION

AMEX: GAX

1331 17th St., Ste. 1050
Denver, CO 80202
Phone: 303-293-2300
Fax: 303-293-2417
Web: www.galaxyenergy.com

CEO: Marc E. Bruner
CFO: Christopher S. Hardesty
HR: –
FYE: November 30
Type: Public

It's not Carl Sagan's "billions and billions of stars" that Galaxy Energy Corporation is looking for, but a few stellar finds in the oil and gas exploration and production business. The company focuses on acquiring and developing coalbed methane and other natural gas properties in Montana, Texas, Wyoming. In 2005 Galaxy Energy acquired 60% of a parcel of 4,000 undeveloped acres in the Piceance Basin in Colorado. In 2006 Galaxy Energy reported estimated proved reserves of 1 billion cu. ft. of natural gas and 320 barrels of oil. CEO Marc Bruner owns 14% of the company through his stake in PetroHunter Energy. In 2007 Galaxy Energy agreed to sell its Powder River Basin assets to PetroHunter Energy.

	Annual Growth	11/03	11/04	11/05	11/06	11/07
Sales ($ mil.)	71.0%	—	0.1	1.5	1.3	0.5
Net income ($ mil.)	—	—	(9.8)	(24.0)	(26.2)	(20.0)
Employees	—	—	—	—	—	—

GALAXY NUTRITIONAL FOODS, INC.

OTC: GXYF

2441 Viscount Row
Orlando, FL 32809
Phone: 407-855-5500
Fax: 407-855-7485
Web: www.galaxyfoods.com

CEO: Michael E. (Mike) Broll
CFO: Salvatore J. Furnari
HR: Christine Carlile
FYE: March 31
Type: Public

Never mind that the word "galaxy" is derived from the Latin word for "milk," Galaxy Nutritional Foods operates in an alternate dairy universe. The company's soy-based dairy "alternatives" include sliced cheese, butter, milk, and yogurt, all sold in supermarkets. Its other dairy-free brands include Rice, Rice Vegan, Vegan, Veggie, and Veggy. The company also offers Wholesome Valley Organic processed cheese made from organic milk and private-label cheese products. In 2005 Galaxy sold its supplies and equipment to Schreiber Foods and signed a renewable five-year supply agreement with Schreiber, which now maufactures, supplies, and delivers Galaxy's products.

	Annual Growth	3/04	3/05	3/06	3/07	3/08
Sales ($ mil.)	(8.7%)	36.2	44.5	37.8	27.2	25.2
Net income ($ mil.)	—	(3.0)	(3.9)	(24.1)	0.2	1.3
Market value ($ mil.)	(44.3%)	30.2	37.7	18.2	12.3	2.9
Employees	(57.4%)	—	143	—	26	—

An in-depth profile of this company is available to Hoover's Online members at hoovers.com.

661

GALDERMA LABORATORIES, L.P.

14501 N. Freeway
Fort Worth, TX 76177
Phone: 817-961-5000
Fax: 817-961-0041
Web: www.galdermausa.com

CEO: Albert Draaijer
CFO: –
HR: Chuck Paschke
FYE: December 31
Type: Private

Galderma Laboratories can't soothe all of the irritations of the world, but it can help with itchy, spotty, and sensitive skin. The company is the North American operation of Swiss firm Galderma, a joint venture between L'Oréal and Nestlé founded in 1981. The company focuses exclusively on developing over-the-counter and prescription dermatology products. In addition to such consumer brands as sensitive skin cleanser Cetaphil, the company offers treatments for skin conditions such as acne, rosacea, atopic dermatitis (eczema), psoriasis, and melasma. In 2008 Galderma acquired dermatology-focused drugmaker CollaGenex Pharmaceuticals.

	Annual Growth	12/03	12/04	12/05	12/06	12/07
Est. sales ($ mil.)	—	—	—	—	—	430.0
Employees	—	—	—	—	—	369

THE GALE COMPANY

100 Campus Dr., Ste. 200
Florham Park, NJ 07932
Phone: 973-301-9500
Fax: 973-301-9501
Web: www.thegalecompany.com

CEO: Stanley C. (Stan) Gale
CFO: Ron Gentile
HR: Philip Boffa
FYE: December 31
Type: Subsidiary

Real estate is a breeze for The Gale Company. Founded by former CEO Stanley Gale, the firm offers land development, property management, and asset management services. It also provides general contracting and construction management services through its Gale Construction division. Its property portfolio primarily consists of Class A office space in the Northeast, mainly in the *FORTUNE* 500 mecca of New Jersey. Tenants include the IRS and Deloitte & Touche USA. It has developed more than 20 million sq. ft. of commercial office and warehouse space and invests in property through joint ventures with such financiers as Morgan Stanley and J.P. Morgan. The Gale Company is a subsidiary of Mack-Cali Realty.

	Annual Growth	12/03	12/04	12/05	12/06	12/07
Est. sales ($ mil.)	—	—	—	—	—	22.9
Employees	—	—	—	—	—	450

GALLERY FURNITURE

6006 North Fwy.
Houston, TX 77076
Phone: 713-694-5570
Fax: 713-696-4524
Web: www.galleryfurniture.com

CEO: Jim (Mattress Mac) McIngvale
CFO: Dave Gardner
HR: –
FYE: December 31
Type: Private

Gallery Furniture and its founder, Jim "Mattress Mac" McIngvale, have become something of a Houston institution. McIngvale's animated television ads, which promise they "really will save you money," seemingly resonate with the masses; the company's single-site location has evolved into a leading furniture retailer in the region — out of some 150 furniture outlets, it accounts for some 18% of the market share in Houston. The company also ranks as one of the nation's top sellers in terms of sales-per-square-foot. In addition to its mattress offerings (Simmons Beautyrest and Tempur-Pedic brands), Gallery Furniture sells bedroom, dining room, home office, and living room furniture. The company was founded in 1981.

	Annual Growth	12/03	12/04	12/05	12/06	12/07
Est. sales ($ mil.)	—	—	—	—	—	130.4
Employees	—	—	—	—	—	400

GALLERY OF HISTORY, INC.

NASDAQ (CM): HIST

3601 W. Sahara Ave., Promenade Ste.
Las Vegas, NV 89102
Phone: 702-364-1000
Fax: 702-364-1285
Web: www.galleryofhistory.com

CEO: Todd M. Axelrod
CFO: Rod R. Lynam
HR: –
FYE: September 30
Type: Public

Those who don't know their Gallery of History are doomed to buy their memorabilia from another auction house. Gallery of History auctions autographs, memorabilia, and manuscripts from artists, authors, athletes, entertainers, politicians, and scientists. Items in its catalogs range from an autographed photo of poet Allen Ginsberg to letters from Albert Einstein. The company has turned to the Internet as its primary sales channel, virtually abandoning traditional auctions. Through its retail gallery located at its Las Vegas headquarters, the company also offers items from its inventory of more than 183,000 documents and autographs. Founder, chairman, and CEO Todd Axelrod and his wife own 82% of the company.

	Annual Growth	9/03	9/04	9/05	9/06	9/07
Sales ($ mil.)	(17.6%)	1.3	1.1	1.1	0.7	0.6
Net income ($ mil.)	—	(0.6)	(0.9)	(0.8)	(0.5)	(0.4)
Market value ($ mil.)	(23.9%)	22.5	21.1	8.4	11.4	7.5
Employees	(16.3%)	—	—	10	—	7

THE GALLUP ORGANIZATION

901 F Street, NW
Washington, DC 20004
Phone: 202-715-3030
Fax: 202-715-3041
Web: www.gallup.com

CEO: James K. (Jim) Clifton
CFO: James (Jim) Krieger
HR: Jacques Murphy
FYE: December 31
Type: Private

More than a pollster, The Gallup Organization draws from its research and behavioral studies to offer consulting services related to performance management. Other specialties include branding, marketing, and recruiting. The company delivers its services on the Web, through its Gallup University campuses, and through more than 40 global offices. It draws customers from a variety of industries, including automotive, business services, health care, hospitality, and retail. Despite its diversified business offerings, the company is still most famous for its Gallup Poll surveys. The company was founded in 1935 by Dr. George Gallup, a pioneer in the science of polling. It is owned by its employees.

THE GAMBRINUS COMPANY

14800 San Pedro Ave.
San Antonio, TX 78232
Phone: 210-490-9128
Fax: 210-490-9984
Web: www.gambrinusco.com

CEO: Carlos E. Alvarez
CFO: James J. Bolz
HR: Brad Kohanke
FYE: December 31
Type: Private

Named for a medieval royal credited with inventing the toast as a social custom, The Gambrinus Company brews and distributes a fine libation with which to toast: beer: Shiner Beer. In fact, the company sold about 5 million cases consumed in 35 US states in 2006. Shiner is brewed by Gambrinus' Spoetzl Brewery located in Shiner, Texas. It also owns BridgePort Brewing Company, Oregon's oldest microbrewery; and Pete's Brewing Company (Pete's Wicked Ale). Owner Carlos Alvarez founded Gambrinus in 1986 and serves as its president and CEO.

GAMBRO BCT, INC.

10810 W. Collins Ave.
Lakewood, CO 80215
Phone: 303-232-6800
Fax: 303-231-4160
Web: www.gambrobct.com

CEO: David B. Perez
CFO: Katie MacWilliams
HR: –
FYE: December 31
Type: Subsidiary

Gambro BCT knows that having blood in the bank is as good as gold, but only if it's clean and properly stored. The company develops and sells products used in hospitals and blood banks. It also offers products used for both clinical and in-home hemodialysis, peritoneal dialysis, renal intensive care systems, and for hepatic care. The company also develops and sells blood collection systems (including apheresis systems and cell processors) and blood products to hospitals and blood banks. Gambro BCT has operations in 30 countries and sells its products in nearly 100 countries. The Wallenberg family's Investor AB owns Gambro BCT and its Sweden-based sister company Gambro Renal Products.

	Annual Growth	12/03	12/04	12/05	12/06	12/07
Est. sales ($ mil.)	—	—	—	—	—	159.9
Employees	—	—	—	—	—	1,900

GAMCO INVESTORS, INC.

NYSE: GBL

1 Corporate Center
Rye, NY 10580
Phone: 914-921-5100
Fax: 914-921-5392
Web: www.gabelli.com

CEO: Mario J. Gabelli
CFO: Diane M. LaPointe
HR: –
FYE: December 31
Type: Public

Investments are anything but a game for "Super Mario" Gabelli, founder and CEO of GAMCO Investors (formerly Gabelli Asset Management). The company oversees the mutual fund- and securities-related portion of Gabelli's financial empire. GAMCO provides advisory services to more than 20 mutual funds under the Gabelli, GAMCO, and Comstock brands, as well as to separate accounts for wealthy individuals and, to a lesser extent, pension plans, trusts, and profit-sharing plans. Despite the renown of its founder, the company adopted the GAMCO Investors name from one of its subsidiaries, which changed its name to GAMCO Asset Management. Gabelli controls the company.

	Annual Growth	12/03	12/04	12/05	12/06	12/07
Assets ($ mil.)	0.7%	736.5	699.0	721.1	837.2	757.6
Net income ($ mil.)	12.4%	49.8	62.6	63.4	71.9	79.6
Market value ($ mil.)	15.3%	306.4	392.1	279.2	288.0	541.1
Employees	—	—	—	—	200	—

GAMESTOP CORP.

NYSE: GME

625 Westport Pkwy.
Grapevine, TX 76051
Phone: 817-424-2000
Fax: 817-424-2002
Web: www.gamestop.com

CEO: R. Richard (Dick) Fontaine
CFO: David W. Carlson
HR: Marissa Andrada
FYE: Saturday nearest January 31
Type: Public

GameStop holds the top score in the video game retailing industry. The company is the largest retailer of new and used games, hardware, entertainment software, and accessories through more than 5,260 stores located primarily in the US, with the balance of them in Canada, Australia, and Europe. A majority of sales come from new and used video games; stores branded as GameStop and EB Games carry an average of 1,000 new titles and 3,500 used ones. The company also operates e-commerce Web sites (GameStop.com, ebgames.com) and publishes *Game Informer*, a video game magazine that reaches more than 2.9 million subscribers. The company's 2005 purchase of rival Electronics Boutique doubled GameStop's size.

	Annual Growth	1/04	1/05	1/06	1/07	1/08
Sales ($ mil.)	45.6%	1,578.8	1,842.8	3,091.8	5,318.9	7,094.0
Net income ($ mil.)	46.0%	63.5	60.9	100.8	158.3	288.3
Market value ($ mil.)	164.9%	171.7	196.7	839.5	4,104.6	8,456.1
Employees	1.2%	—	—	42,000	32,000	43,000

GAMETECH INTERNATIONAL, INC.

NASDAQ (GM): GMTC

900 Sandhill Rd.
Reno, NV 89521
Phone: 775-850-6000
Fax: 775-850-6090
Web: www.gametech-inc.com

CEO: Jay M. Meilstrup
CFO: Marcia R. Martin
HR: Ellen Droog
FYE: October 31
Type: Public

Name an old-fashioned parlor game that could benefit from a high-tech makeover. Bingo! GameTech International designs and sells electronic handheld and fixed-base bingo systems that allow contestants to play up to 2,000 bingo cards at once. More than 500 commercial, charity, and Native American bingo halls in about 40 states use GameTech's bingo systems. The company also markets video lottery terminals and systems used by casinos, taverns, and truck stops in 15 states. GameTech generates revenue from the sale of software and equipment, as well as from maintenance and upgrade services.

	Annual Growth	10/03	10/04	10/05	10/06	10/07
Sales ($ mil.)	3.0%	52.3	51.5	49.7	49.3	58.8
Net income ($ mil.)	40.7%	1.2	(9.9)	1.3	4.4	4.7
Market value ($ mil.)	27.8%	41.1	47.3	47.4	124.5	109.6
Employees	(1.0%)	—	240	200	200	233

GAMING & ENTERTAINMENT GROUP, INC.

Pink Sheets: GMEI

4501 Hayvenhurst Ave.
Encino, CA 91436
Phone: 818-400-5930
Fax: 413-723-2141
Web: www.gaming-group.com

CEO: Tibor N. Vertes
CFO: –
HR: –
FYE: December 31
Type: Public

Gaming & Entertainment Group (G&EG) makes a variety of gaming machines specifically for UK casino market. Its products include slot machines, video poker, and video roulette games. G&EG has offices in the US, UK, and Australia. The company formerly produced Internet gaming systems, but sold those assets in 2006 to bond trader Cantor Fitzgerald, which owns about 40% of G&EG. Chairman and CEO Tibor Vertes owns about a third of the company.

	Annual Growth	12/02	12/03	12/04	12/05	*12/06
Sales ($ mil.)	(42.3%)	—	—	0.3	1.3	0.1
Net income ($ mil.)	—	—	—	(3.2)	(1.5)	(1.1)
Employees	(65.7%)	—	—	17	6	2

*Most recent year available

GAMING PARTNERS INTERNATIONAL

NASDAQ (GM): GPIC

1700 Industrial Rd.
Las Vegas, NV 89102
Phone: 702-384-2425
Fax: 702-384-1965
Web: www.gpigaming.com

CEO: Gérard P. Charlier
CFO: David W. Grimes
HR: Cynthia Allen
FYE: December 31
Type: Public

This company doesn't care if gamblers win or crap out, as long as they do it using its products. Gaming Partners International Corporation is a leading manufacturer of casino gaming products, including dealing shoes, dice, gaming chips, playing cards, and roulette wheels. It also supplies table furniture and layouts for blackjack, poker, baccarat, craps, and other casino games. With manufacturing facilities in the US, Mexico, and France, the company markets its products under the brands Bourgogne et Grasset, Bud Jones, and Paulson to casino operators around the world. French holding company Holding Wilson owns almost 50% of Gaming Partners International.

	Annual Growth	12/03	12/04	12/05	12/06	12/07
Sales ($ mil.)	12.9%	36.2	44.6	57.1	73.9	58.8
Net income ($ mil.)	(36.1%)	1.2	2.6	4.3	5.1	0.2
Market value ($ mil.)	6.8%	43.7	159.5	88.3	145.6	56.9
Employees	(12.6%)	—	—	870	760	—

An in-depth profile of this company is available to Hoover's Online members at hoovers.com.

GANDER MOUNTAIN COMPANY

NASDAQ (GM): GMTN

180 E. 5th St., Ste. 1300
St. Paul, MN 55101
Phone: 651-325-4300
Fax: 651-325-2003
Web: www.gandermountain.com

CEO: Mark R. Baker
CFO: Robert J. (Bob) Vold
HR: JoAnn B. Boldt
FYE: Saturday nearest January 31
Type: Public

Gander Mountain has got the gear to get you out of the office and up the mountain. The company operates about 115 outdoor sporting goods stores focused on hunting, camping, and fishing in some two dozen southern and midwestern states. In addition to outdoor equipment and related accessories, the stores also sell apparel and footwear, as well as all terrain vehicles (ATVs) and gear. The company began selling fishing and pontoon boats in 2007 in an arrangement with Tracker Marine Group (a division of Bass Pro Shops). Founded in 1960 as an outdoor catalog operation, Gander Mountain expanded its retail store presence beginning in 1987. It sold off its catalog operations in 1996 but resumed non-store sales in 2008.

	Annual Growth	1/04	1/05	1/06	1/07	1/08
Sales ($ mil.)	18.6%	489.4	642.1	804.5	911.4	969.4
Net income ($ mil.)	—	1.5	1.6	(13.3)	(13.2)	(31.8)
Market value ($ mil.)	(0.6%)	—	123.3	88.4	202.9	121.0
Employees	5.5%	—	—	5,600	6,000	6,238

G & J PEPSI-COLA BOTTLERS, INC.

9435 Waterstone Blvd., Ste. 390
Cincinnati, OH 45249
Phone: 513-785-6060
Fax: 513-683-9467

CEO: Timothy (Tim) Hardig
CFO: Dale Watkins
HR: T.R. Gross Jr.
FYE: December 31
Type: Private

Cincinnati-based G & J Pepsi-Cola Bottlers delivers. And it has done so for the more than 40 years that it has distributed Pepsi products in Ohio and Kentucky. The company is one of the larger Pepsi bottlers in the US, shipping the leading PepsiCo brands, including Pepsi-Cola, Mountain Dew, Gatorade, Slice, SoBe, and Aquafina to beverage retailers. The bottler was formerly named the Grandpop Bottling Co., and was under the management of Walter Gross and Isaac Jarson. The company's current chairman, Stanley Kaplan, was married to Jarson's daughter, Mickey, who died in 2003.

	Annual Growth	12/03	12/04	12/05	12/06	12/07
Est. sales ($ mil.)	—	—	—	—	—	244.7
Employees	—	—	—	—	—	1,612

G&K SERVICES, INC.

NASDAQ (GS): GKSR

5995 Opus Pkwy., Ste. 500
Minnetonka, MN 55343
Phone: 952-912-5500
Fax: 952-912-5999
Web: www.gkservices.com

CEO: Richard L. (Rick) Marcantonio
CFO: Jeffery L. (Jeff) Wright
HR: Jacqueline Tschida (Jackie) Punch
FYE: Saturday nearest June 30
Type: Public

G&K Services likes uniformity. The company is the third-largest uniform rental agency (behind #1 Cintas and #2 ARAMARK). G&K supplies uniforms for more than 160,000 customers in the automotive, manufacturing, hospitality, and technology industries, among others, from 160-plus locations throughout North America. Along with rental and sales, the company provides cleaning, repair, and replacement services for all of its uniforms. G&K also carries cleanroom garments used by the semiconductor industry. In addition, the company offers facility services, providing restroom supplies and renting items such as dust mops, floor mats, and towels.

	Annual Growth	6/03	6/04	6/05	6/06	6/07
Sales ($ mil.)	7.1%	705.6	733.5	788.8	880.8	929.5
Net income ($ mil.)	6.4%	33.7	35.4	39.9	41.8	43.2
Market value ($ mil.)	10.1%	572.4	783.5	750.0	730.0	841.2
Employees	(0.1%)	—	—	7,743	9,685	7,720

G&S MINERALS, INC.

Pink Sheets: GSML

723 S. Casino Center Blvd.
Las Vegas, NV 89101
Phone: 704-370-3430
Fax: —
Web: www.gold-silverco.com

CEO: Charles Brown
CFO: Ryan Kutty
HR: —
FYE: December 31
Type: Public

G&S Minerals is less interested in hot burgers and ready to focus on hot mineral assets. The company used to be called Hot Brands, when it owned and operated the Hot 'n Now Burgers fast food chain, which once had about 40 locations in Indiana, Michigan, and Wisconsin. The burger business went bankrupt, however, and was sold to STEN Corporation in 2005. The following year Hot Brands agreed to a reverse merger with Gold & Silver Minerals, a company focused on the mining industry and oil and gas exploration.

GANNETT CO., INC.

NYSE: GCI

7950 Jones Branch Dr.
McLean, VA 22107
Phone: 703-854-6000
Fax: 703-854-2053
Web: www.gannett.com

CEO: Craig A. Dubow
CFO: Gracia C. Martore
HR: Roxanne V. Horning
FYE: Last Sunday in December
Type: Public

Gannett satisfies news junkies with a stash of daily US papers. The company is the top newspaper publisher in the US with about 85 daily papers boasting a total circulation of 6.9 million. Its flagship *USA TODAY*, with a circulation of 2.3 million, is the nation's largest newspaper. Some other major papers in Gannett's holdings include *The Arizona Republic* and the *Detroit Free Press*. The company also owns about 900 non-daily publications, as well as about 300 papers in the UK (through subsidiary Newsquest). In addition, Gannett owns 23 television stations in 20 markets, publishes periodicals and inserts (including *USA WEEKEND*), and operates Web sites for many of its papers.

	Annual Growth	12/03	12/04	12/05	12/06	12/07
Sales ($ mil.)	2.6%	6,711.1	7,381.3	7,598.9	8,033.4	7,439.5
Net income ($ mil.)	(3.4%)	1,211.2	1,317.2	1,244.7	1,160.8	1,055.6
Market value ($ mil.)	(22.1%)	23,945.5	20,523.1	14,542.2	14,192.6	8,800.6
Employees	(6.4%)	—	—	52,600	49,675	46,100

THE GAP INC.

NYSE: GPS

2 Folsom St.
San Francisco, CA 94105
Phone: 650-952-4400
Fax: 415-427-2553
Web: www.gap.com

CEO: Glenn K. Murphy
CFO: Sabrina Simmons
HR: Eva Sage-Gavin
FYE: Saturday nearest January 31
Type: Public

The ubiquitous clothing retailer Gap has been filling closets with jeans and khakis, T-shirts and poplin since the Woodstock era. The company, which operates more than 3,150 stores worldwide, built its iconic casual brand on basics for men, women, and children, but over the years has expanded through the urban chic chain Banana Republic and fast-growing budgeteer Old Navy. Other brand extensions include GapBody, GapKids, and babyGap; each also has its own online incarnation. All Gap clothing is private-label merchandise made exclusively for the company. From the design board to store displays, Gap controls all aspects of its trademark casual look. The founding Fisher family owns about a third of Gap Inc.

	Annual Growth	1/04	1/05	1/06	1/07	1/08
Sales ($ mil.)	(0.1%)	15,854.0	16,267.0	16,023.0	15,943.0	15,763.0
Net income ($ mil.)	(5.2%)	1,030.0	1,150.0	1,113.0	778.0	833.0
Market value ($ mil.)	(3.9%)	16,670.0	18,768.8	14,894.4	15,846.1	14,195.6
Employees	(1.0%)	—	—	153,000	154,000	150,000

An in-depth profile of this company is available to Hoover's Online members at hoovers.com.

GARAN, INCORPORATED

350 Fifth Ave.
New York, NY 10118
Phone: 212-563-2000
Fax: 212-971-2250
Web: www.garanimals.com

CEO: Seymour Lichtenstein
CFO: –
HR: –
FYE: December 31
Type: Subsidiary

If you've ever enlisted the help of a monkey to match your shirt and shorts, you're likely to be familiar with Garan. The company designs, manufactures, and distributes apparel primarily for infants, toddlers, and children, but also for men and women. Products are sold under its customers' private labels, as well as its own brand, Garanimals. Characters like Charley Chimp help young children dress themselves with coordinated hang-tags. Most of Garan's products are sold through distribution centers in the US to major national chains such as Wal-Mart, department stores, and specialty stores. Founded in 1941, Garan is a subsidiary of Warren Buffett's Berkshire Hathaway.

	Annual Growth	12/03	12/04	12/05	12/06	12/07
Est. sales ($ mil.)	—	—	—	—	—	160.4
Employees	—	—	—	—	—	4,500

GARDEN CITY HOSPITAL, INC.

6245 Inkster Rd.
Garden City, MI 48135
Phone: 734-421-3300
Fax: 734-421-3530
Web: www.gchosp.org

CEO: Gary R. Ley
CFO: Robert Giddings
HR: Mitchell Nimmoor
FYE: September 30
Type: Not-for-profit

Garden City Hospital provides health care and osteopathic medical education services in western Wayne County, Michigan. With around 325 beds, some of the hospital's specialties include cardiology, women's health, and sports rehabilitation. Some of its more unusual services include clinical hypnotherapy and a massage clinic. The hospital has more than 350 physicians on its medical staff. Its emergency department treats nearly 45,000 patients each year. Garden City Hospital partners with Michigan State University's College of Osteopathic Medicine as well as Iowa's Health Sciences College of Osteopathic Medicine and Surgery.

	Annual Growth	9/03	9/04	9/05	9/06	9/07
Est. sales ($ mil.)	—	—	—	—	—	55.6
Employees	—	—	—	—	—	1,200

GARDEN FRESH RESTAURANT CORP.

15822 Bernardo Ctr. Dr., Ste. A
San Diego, CA 92127
Phone: 858-675-1600
Fax: 858-675-1617
Web: www.souplantation.com

CEO: Michael P. Mack
CFO: John D. Morberg
HR: –
FYE: September 30
Type: Private

This company's success proves that rabbit food is for people too. Garden Fresh Restaurant Corp. owns and operates about 100 salad-buffet restaurants under the names Souplantation and Sweet Tomatoes. Found in California and more than a dozen other US states, the eateries feature salad bars that include all the usual fixings, as well as specialty and prepared salads. The restaurants also feature self-serve bars for pasta, soups, breads, and fresh fruit. Garden Fresh supplies its restaurants through a network of centralized kitchens and distribution centers. Founded in 1983 by CEO Michael Mack and partner Anthony Brooke, the company is owned by private equity firm Sun Capital Partners.

	Annual Growth	9/03	9/04	9/05	9/06	9/07
Est. sales ($ mil.)	—	—	—	—	—	117.5
Employees	—	—	—	—	—	5,420

GARDEN RIDGE CORPORATION

19411 Atrium Place, Ste. 170
Houston, TX 77084
Phone: 281-579-7901
Fax: –
Web: www.gardenridge.com

CEO: Tom Kibarian
CFO: –
HR: –
FYE: Last Sunday in January
Type: Private

Megastore retailer Garden Ridge Corporation offers decorating accessories for more than just the garden. The company operates about 40 stores, each covering almost three acres and located off major highways in some 15 states (Texas has 15 stores). Its stores sell baskets, candles, crafts, home accents, home textiles, housewares, mirrors, party supplies, patio furniture, pictures and frames, pottery, seasonal items, and silk and dried flowers. Garden Ridge, which started as a single store outside of San Antonio in 1979, was bought by a group of investors led by Three Cities Research in 2000. In May 2005 Garden Ridge emerged from Chapter 11 bankruptcy protection (filed in February 2004).

	Annual Growth	1/03	1/04	1/05	1/06	1/07
Est. sales ($ mil.)	—	—	—	—	—	291.7
Employees	—	—	—	—	—	3,500

GARDERE WYNNE SEWELL LLP

1601 Elm St., Ste. 3000
Dallas, TX 75201
Phone: 214-999-3000
Fax: 214-999-4667
Web: www.gardere.com

CEO: Stephen D. (Steve) Good
CFO: –
HR: Tammy Patterson
FYE: March 31
Type: Private

Gardere Wynne Sewell is a mid-sized law firm with about 300 attorneys practicing from three offices in Texas and one in Mexico. The firm offers more than forty practice areas with specialized practices in such areas as antitrust and trade regulations, bankruptcy, intellectual property, and real estate. Gardere Wynne Sewell traces its roots back to 1909. The firm merged with Houston firm Sewell & Riggs in 1995 and added an office in Mexico in 1996.

	Annual Growth	3/03	3/04	3/05	3/06	3/07
Est. sales ($ mil.)	—	—	—	—	—	180.0
Employees	—	—	—	—	—	700

GARDNER DENVER, INC.

NYSE: GDI

1800 Gardner Expwy.
Quincy, IL 62305
Phone: 217-222-5400
Fax: 217-228-8247
Web: www.gardnerdenver.com

CEO: Barry L. Pennypacker
CFO: Helen W. Cornell
HR: –
FYE: December 31
Type: Public

Need air compressors, blowers, or petroleum pumps? Just ask Gardner Denver. The company makes a variety of compressors, such as reciprocating, rotary screw, and sliding vane compressors, as well as positive displacement and centrifugal blowers. Manufacturing plants and industrial facilities use the compressors to produce durable goods, process petroleum and pharmaceuticals, and to treat wastewater. Compressed air products are its principal product. Gardner Denver also makes well-servicing pumps for oil and natural gas companies, and it is adding new lines, such as water-jetting products. More than half of the company's sales comes from outside the US.

	Annual Growth	12/03	12/04	12/05	12/06	12/07
Sales ($ mil.)	43.6%	439.5	739.5	1,214.6	1,669.2	1,868.8
Net income ($ mil.)	77.6%	20.6	37.1	66.9	132.9	205.1
Market value ($ mil.)	74.1%	192.4	361.9	640.9	1,963.5	1,767.0
Employees	34.4%	1,900	3,800	6,200	6,000	6,200

An in-depth profile of this company is available to Hoover's Online members at hoovers.com.

665

GARTNER, INC.

NYSE: IT

56 Top Gallant Rd.
Stamford, CT 06902
Phone: 203-964-0096
Fax: 203-316-6488
Web: www.gartner.com

CEO: Eugene A. (Gene) Hall
CFO: Christopher J. (Chris) Lafond
HR: Michele E. Riess
FYE: December 31
Type: Public

You might not know IT, but Gartner does. The company is a leading provider of market research covering the information technology (IT) industry. It provides more than 10,000 client organizations with competitive analysis reports, industry overviews, market trend data, and product evaluation reports. Its GartnerG2, Gartner Dataquest, and other research services are made available through subscriptions, primarily to CIOs and other IT professionals. Gartner also offers technology and management consulting services, and it produces a number of conferences, seminars, and other events aimed at the technology sector. The company operates in more than 75 countries.

	Annual Growth	12/03	12/04	12/05	12/06	12/07
Sales ($ mil.)	8.5%	858.5	893.8	989.0	1,060.3	1,189.2
Net income ($ mil.)	32.7%	23.7	16.9	(2.4)	58.2	73.6
Market value ($ mil.)	10.9%	1,151.0	1,110.8	1,474.9	2,059.4	1,739.0
Employees	4.5%	—	—	3,622	3,784	—

GASCO ENERGY, INC.

AMEX: GSX

8 Inverness Dr. East, Ste. 100
Englewood, CO 80112
Phone: 303-483-0044
Fax: 303-483-0011
Web: www.gascoenergy.com

CEO: Mark A. Erickson
CFO: W. King Grant
HR: Suzie Wright
FYE: December 31
Type: Public

Gasco Energy is not your local gas company or energy provider. The exploration and production independent develops and explores for natural gas and crude petroleum primarily in the Rocky Mountains. The company's exploration activities are focused on Utah's Uinta Basin and Wyoming's Green River Basin. At the end of 2006 Gasco Energy's proved reserves stood at 42.2 billion cu. ft. of natural gas equivalent. The principal markets for its commodity products are natural gas transmission pipeline companies, private industrial companies, refining companies, and utilities. In 2007 the company acquired fellow explorer Brek Energy.

	Annual Growth	12/03	12/04	12/05	12/06	12/07
Sales ($ mil.)	103.3%	1.3	3.6	16.9	25.7	22.2
Net income ($ mil.)	—	(2.5)	(4.2)	0.0	(55.8)	(104.4)
Market value ($ mil.)	38.3%	58.4	303.9	554.8	210.9	213.4
Employees	—	—	—	17	—	—

GASTAR EXPLORATION LTD.

AMEX: GST

1331 Lamar St., Ste. 1080
Houston, TX 77010
Phone: 713-739-1800
Fax: 713-739-0458
Web: www.gastar.com

CEO: –
CFO: Michael A. Gerlich
HR: –
FYE: December 31
Type: Public

Gastar Exploration has hitched its star to exploring for natural gas in the US and Australia. Its primary areas of exploration and production are Deep Bossier (in East Texas), the Powder River Basin, and the Appalachian Basin. In Australia the company operates in Gippsland, Victoria, and in New South Wales and has ownership stakes in about 3 million gross acres. Gastar Exploration has interests in Wyoming's Powder River Basin, one of the most active coalbed methane plays in the US. It also operates in the San Joaquin Basin in California. The company has proved reserves of 31.2 billion cu. ft. of natural gas and 30,000 barrels of oil. Chesapeake Energy owns about 15% of the company.

	Annual Growth	12/03	12/04	12/05	12/06	12/07
Sales ($ mil.)	12.4%	—	—	27.4	26.8	34.6
Net income ($ mil.)	—	—	—	(25.7)	(84.8)	(30.5)
Market value ($ mil.)	(39.0%)	—	—	699.9	419.2	260.2
Employees	—	—	—	15	—	—

GATE PETROLEUM COMPANY

9540 San Jose Blvd.
Jacksonville, FL 32257
Phone: 904-737-7220
Fax: 904-732-7660
Web: www.gatepetro.com

CEO: Herbert H. (Herb) Peyton
CFO: P. Jeremy Smith
HR: Mary Ann Bright
FYE: June 30
Type: Private

Gate Petroleum swings many ways. It runs a chain of about 225 Gate Food Post stores in Florida, Georgia, Kentucky, Louisiana, North Carolina, South Carolina, and Virginia that sell gas and groceries and offer fleet management services. Gate is also a wholesale fuel distributor to customers throughout the Southeast and is also active in the real estate and construction materials businesses. In Florida Gate owns several private clubs, office buildings, and business parks. Subsidiary Gate Concrete has plants in six states that make and sell concrete and building materials. CEO Herbert Peyton, who founded the company in 1960, owns the majority of Gate Petroleum Company.

	Annual Growth	6/02	6/03	6/04	6/05	6/06
Est. sales ($ mil.)	9.4%	—	—	—	1,170.0	1,280.0
Employees	0.0%	—	—	—	3,500	3,500

GATEHOUSE MEDIA, INC.

NYSE: GHS

350 Willowbrook Office Park
Fairport, NY 14450
Phone: 585-598-0030
Fax: 585-248-2631
Web: gatehousemedia.com

CEO: Michael E. (Mike) Reed
CFO: Mark R. Thompson
HR: Amy V. Kahn
FYE: December 31
Type: Public

GateHouse Media lets the local news flow freely. The company is a leading community newspaper publisher with more than 500 publications in more than 20 states. Its portfolio includes about 100 daily newspapers, along with many more weeklies and shoppers that reach about 10 million readers. GateHouse generates revenue primarily through advertising; its papers serve ads from more than 230,000 business advertisers. In conjunction with its print publications, the company operates some 250 Web sites. GateHouse also produces a half dozen yellow page directories and it offers commercial printing services. Private equity firm Fortress Investment Group owns more than 40% of the company.

	Annual Growth	12/03	12/04	12/05	12/06	12/07
Sales ($ mil.)	32.9%	188.8	200.1	205.0	314.9	588.9
Net income ($ mil.)	—	(14.2)	(26.1)	(15.3)	(1.6)	(231.4)
Market value ($ mil.)	(30.0%)	—	—	—	726.5	508.3
Employees	5.6%	3,400	—	4,100	4,000	—

GATES CORPORATION

1551 Wewatta St.
Denver, CO 80202
Phone: 303-744-1911
Fax: 303-744-4443
Web: www.gates.com

CEO: Richard Bell
CFO: Jonathon Levine
HR: Mark Dutell
FYE: April 30
Type: Subsidiary

Success is no stretch for Gates Corporation (formerly The Gates Rubber Company), a leading manufacturer of automotive and industrial belts and hoses. A subsidiary of the UK's Tomkins plc, Gates has four product groups: Automotive OE (original equipment), automotive replacement, power transmission, and fluid power. The company's lines include specialty products for auto racing, marine, off-road, and snowmobile applications. Sister companies include Stant (engine and steering components), Trico (windshield wiper blades), and Schrader-Bridgeport (fluid-control components).

	Annual Growth	4/03	4/04	4/05	4/06	4/07
Est. sales ($ mil.)	—	—	—	—	—	1,175.3
Employees	—	—	—	—	—	13,496

An in-depth profile of this company is available to Hoover's Online members at hoovers.com.

GATEWAY ENERGY CORPORATION

OTC: GNRG

500 Dallas St., Ste. 2615
Houston, TX 77002
Phone: 713-336-0844
Fax: 713-336-0855
Web: www.gatewayenergy.com

CEO: Robert (Bob) Panico
CFO: Christopher M. Rasmussen
HR: –
FYE: December 31
Type: Public

The door swings both ways for Gateway Energy, which serves as a go-between for natural gas producers and customers. It owns natural gas gathering, transportation, and distribution systems (totaling more than 775 miles of pipeline) in Texas, Oklahoma, and in the Gulf of Mexico. The company gathers gas at the wellhead and transports it to distribution companies or its own processing facilities. Its Fort Cobb Fuel Authority subsidiary is a local distribution company which serves 2,300 customers in the Caddo and Washita counties in Oklahoma. Offshore holdings include pipelines in Galveston Bay, Texas.

	Annual Growth	12/03	12/04	12/05	12/06	12/07
Sales ($ mil.)	(6.9%)	15.2	23.0	10.5	10.2	11.4
Net income ($ mil.)	—	(1.0)	(0.8)	1.8	0.3	3.6
Market value ($ mil.)	22.8%	6.3	7.2	6.0	8.1	14.3
Employees	—	—	—	—	—	—

GATEWAY FINANCIAL HOLDINGS, INC.

NASDAQ (GM): GBTS

1580 Laskin Rd.
Virginia Beach, VA 23451
Phone: 757-422-4055
Fax: 757-422-4056
Web: www.trustgateway.com

CEO: Daniel B. (Ben) Berry
CFO: Theodore L. (Teddy) Salter
HR: –
FYE: December 31
Type: Public

Gateway Financial Holdings wants to be the portal to all things financial in northeastern North Carolina and Virginia's Tidewater region. Subsidiary Gateway Bank & Trust is a full-service bank with some 35 branches offering products including checking and savings accounts, CDs, IRAs, and merchant services. It primarily uses funds from deposits to write real estate loans: Construction and land development loans and commercial and residential mortgages account for more than 80% of its loan portfolio. It also offers business, consumer, and home equity loans. Bank subsidiaries Gateway Insurance Services and Gateway Investment Services offer insurance and investment products and services.

	Annual Growth	12/03	12/04	12/05	12/06	12/07
Assets ($ mil.)	56.1%	314.8	535.7	882.4	1,207.5	1,868.2
Net income ($ mil.)	74.0%	1.2	2.0	3.9	5.3	11.0
Market value ($ mil.)	49.5%	30.0	88.3	142.8	157.3	149.8
Employees	30.9%	—	—	245	327	420

GATEWAY, INC.

7565 Irvine Center Dr.
Irvine, CA 92618
Phone: 949-471-7000
Fax: 949-471-7041
Web: www.gateway.com

CEO: Rudi Schmidleithner
CFO: –
HR: Lazane Smith
FYE: December 31
Type: Subsidiary

Gateway decided to help Acer with an upgrade. The company provides desktop and portable PCs and displays. It also offers third-party consumer electronics and peripherals including printers, storage drives, and networking equipment. Its services include training, support, and financing. It sells directly by phone and through its Web site, and through electronics retailers including Best Buy and Circuit City. Gateway markets lower priced PCs under the eMachines brand. Gateway was acquired by Taiwan-based Acer for $710 million in 2007. The combined company ranks behind only Hewlett-Packard and Dell in global PC sales.

	Annual Growth	12/02	12/03	12/04	12/05	12/06
Sales ($ mil.)	(1.2%)	4,171.3	3,402.4	3,649.7	3,854.1	3,980.8
Net income ($ mil.)	—	(297.7)	(514.8)	(567.6)	6.2	9.6
Employees	(38.0%)	11,500	—	—	1,800	1,700

GATX CORPORATION

NYSE: GMT

500 W. Monroe St.
Chicago, IL 60661
Phone: 312-621-6200
Fax: 312-621-6648
Web: www.gatx.com

CEO: Brian A. Kenney
CFO: Robert C. Lyons
HR: Gail L. Duddy
FYE: December 31
Type: Public

GATX never tried to unite Georgia and Texas, but the holding company does bring together some diverse businesses. After reorganizing in late 2003, and selling nearly all its aircraft holdings in 2006, the company now operates three divisions: rail (tank and freight car and locomotive leasing), specialty (leases, affiliate investments, and loans), and American Steamship Company (a shipping company with a fleet of self-unloading ships operating on the Great Lakes for nearly 100 years). GATX sold its information technology leasing business to CIT Group in 2004. The company chose to exit the aircraft leasing business in late 2006.

	Annual Growth	12/03	12/04	12/05	12/06	12/07
Sales ($ mil.)	0.6%	1,314.5	1,231.4	1,134.6	1,229.1	1,346.0
Net income ($ mil.)	27.6%	76.9	169.6	(14.3)	111.7	203.7
Market value ($ mil.)	6.3%	1,377.9	1,464.1	1,826.3	2,253.0	1,757.0
Employees	5.8%	—	—	1,870	2,340	2,094

GAYLORD ENTERTAINMENT COMPANY

NYSE: GET

1 Gaylord Dr.
Nashville, TN 37214
Phone: 615-316-6000
Fax: 615-316-6555
Web: www.gaylordentertainment.com

CEO: Colin V. Reed
CFO: David C. Kloeppel
HR: Melissa J. Buffington
FYE: December 31
Type: Public

Gaylord Entertainment may be hollerin' for attention in the hospitality game, but it's no corporate hayseed. Its hospitality and attractions businesses, which cater to large meeting and event planners, include The Radisson Hotel at Opryland and the Gaylord Opryland Resort & Convention Center (home to the Gaylord Springs golf course), both in Nashville, Tennessee; the Gaylord Palms Resort in Florida; and the Gaylord Texan Resort near Dallas. The company's other holdings include the famous Grand Ole Opry and related attractions, as well as the Ryman Auditorium and the General Jackson Showboat. Gaylord sold ResortQuest in 2007.

	Annual Growth	12/03	12/04	12/05	12/06	12/07
Sales ($ mil.)	13.6%	448.8	749.5	868.8	947.9	747.7
Net income ($ mil.)	243.9%	0.8	(53.6)	(34.0)	(79.4)	111.9
Market value ($ mil.)	9.1%	1,176.2	1,658.3	1,757.0	2,078.1	1,668.8
Employees	(14.0%)	—	—	12,178	12,031	9,013

GC SERVICES LIMITED PARTNERSHIP

6330 Gulfton St., Ste. 400
Houston, TX 77081
Phone: 713-777-4441
Fax: 713-777-6641
Web: www.gcserv.com

CEO: J. B. Katz
CFO: –
HR: –
FYE: December 31
Type: Private

GC Services considers it a Good Call when it Gets Cash. The company, one of the nation's top five collection agencies, provides a wide range of services, including customer relations and receivables management, to clients throughout North America from about 35 US call centers. Its teleservices division provides inbound and outbound call center management services, including general reception and operator services, billing and payment assistance, and back-office processing of accounts. Its receivables management division provides such services as debt collection, and receivables processing and reporting. Clients include companies in the financial, retail, automotive, and telecommunications sectors.

	Annual Growth	12/03	12/04	12/05	12/06	12/07
Est. sales ($ mil.)	—	—	—	—	—	444.4
Employees	—	—	—	—	—	10,300

An in-depth profile of this company is available to Hoover's Online members at hoovers.com.

667

GEHL COMPANY

NASDAQ (GS): GEHL

143 Water St.
West Bend, WI 53095
Phone: 262-334-9461
Fax: 262-338-7517
Web: www.gehl.com

CEO: William D. (Bill) Gehl
CFO: Malcolm F. (Mac) Moore
HR: Brian L. Pearlman
FYE: December 31
Type: Public

Gehl Company asks the question, "Can you dig it?" The company manufactures light-construction equipment bearing the Gehl and Mustang brand names primarily used by building contractors. Products include mini-excavators, mini-loaders, and skid steer loaders for material handling; telescopic loaders; and asphalt pavers for building sidewalks, parking lots, trails, and driveways. The company has about 750 distributors all across the globe, but some 85% are located in North America. Gehl also offers financing to its dealers and their customers. In 2006 the company decided to exit the agricultural machinery business.

	Annual Growth	12/03	12/04	12/05	12/06	12/07
Sales ($ mil.)	17.0%	244.4	361.6	478.2	486.2	457.6
Net income ($ mil.)	75.0%	2.6	13.4	21.8	19.5	24.4
Market value ($ mil.)	40.2%	50.3	103.4	315.2	335.8	194.5
Employees	—	—	—	982	—	—

GEISINGER HEALTH SYSTEM

100 N. Academy Ave.
Danville, PA 17822
Phone: 570-271-6211
Fax: 570-271-7498
Web: www.geisinger.org

CEO: Glenn D. Steele Jr.
CFO: Kevin F. Brennan
HR: Richard Merkle
FYE: June 30
Type: Not-for-profit

Geisinger Health System provides health care to a large section of the Keystone State, serving residents of about 40 counties in the central and northeastern portions of Pennsylvania. Founded in 1915, the system's flagship facility is Geisinger Medical Center, a 400-bed medical-surgical hospital in Danville that includes the Janet Weis Children's Hospital. With joint venture partner HealthSouth, the organization runs a rehabilitation hospital in Danville. And two smaller hospitals in Wilkes-Barre, as well as outpatient facilities and doctors' offices throughout the region, are also part of the system. Additionally, Geisinger runs the Geisinger Health Plan, a not-for-profit HMO with more than 200,000 members.

	Annual Growth	6/03	6/04	6/05	6/06	6/07
Est. sales ($ mil.)	—	—	—	—	—	282.1
Employees	—	—	—	—	—	8,387

GELCO INFORMATION NETWORK, INC.

10700 Prairie Lakes Dr.
Eden Prairie, MN 55344
Phone: 952-947-1500
Fax: 952-947-8360
Web: www.gelco.com

CEO: Karen T. Beckwith
CFO: –
HR: –
FYE: December 31
Type: Subsidiary

Gelco Information Network is the penny-pinching businessperson's friend. The company's Gelco Expense Management unit helps public and private enterprises track travel expenses and reimbursement with Web-based programs. Its Gelco Trade Management group helps consumer goods retailers, manufacturers, and sales agents manage their trade relationships and promotions with Web-based software. Clients come from a wide range of industries such as travel, retail, health care, and consumer goods. Customers have included Novartis, Colony Capital, Expedia, Peace Corps, and Maple Leaf Foods.

GENAERA CORPORATION

NASDAQ (CM): GENR

5110 Campus Dr.
Plymouth Meeting, PA 19462
Phone: 610-941-4020
Fax: 610-941-5399
Web: www.genaera.com

CEO: John L. (Jack) Armstrong Jr.
CFO: Leanne M. Kelly
HR: Jennifer Bilotti
FYE: December 31
Type: Public

Genaera is learning the dangers of swimming with sharks. The biotechnology company scrapped development efforts on EVIZON, a potential age-related macular degeneration drug made from a compound (squalamine lactate) taken from sharks, in 2006. Recruiting difficulties and disappointing preliminary results in clinical trials led to the decision. Instead the company is focusing its resources on developing trodusquemine to treat obesity and metabolic disorders. MedImmune has teamed with Genaera to work on interleukin-9 as a possible treatment for asthma.

	Annual Growth	12/03	12/04	12/05	12/06	12/07
Sales ($ mil.)	25.2%	1.1	0.9	0.4	0.9	2.7
Net income ($ mil.)	—	(9.4)	(17.9)	(26.4)	(21.2)	(15.7)
Market value ($ mil.)	(55.9%)	922.6	1,171.1	618.3	238.6	34.9
Employees	—	—	—	46	—	—

GENCO DISTRIBUTION SYSTEM, INC.

100 Papercraft Park
Pittsburgh, PA 15238
Phone: 412-820-3700
Fax: 412-820-3689
Web: www.genco.com

CEO: Herbert S. (Herb) Shear
CFO: Rick Roadarmel
HR: –
FYE: December 31
Type: Private

GENCO Distribution System, which does business as GENCO Supply Chain Solutions, provides third-party logistics services. Among the company's offerings are warehousing and distribution services, reverse logistics and pharmaceutical returns (processing of returned goods), supply chain analysis, transportation management (including parcel management), and damage research (analyzing causes of damage to customers' unsaleable products). The company maintains about 37 million sq. ft. of warehouse space at about 120 locations in the US and Canada. Customers include manufacturers, retailers, and government agencies. CEO Herb Shear owns the company, which was founded in 1898 by his grandfather Hyman Shear.

GENCO SHIPPING & TRADING LIMITED

NASDAQ (GS): GNK

299 Park Ave., 20th Fl.
New York, NY 10171
Phone: 646-443-8550
Fax: 646-443-8551
Web: gencoshipping.com

CEO: Robert Gerald Buchanan
CFO: John C. Wobensmith
HR: –
FYE: December 31
Type: Public

Marine transportation company Genco Shipping & Trading transports dry cargo in a wet environment. The company maintains a fleet of about 30 oceangoing dry bulk carriers, which it charters mainly on long-term contracts to shippers of bulk commodities and marine transportation companies. Its fleet has an overall capacity of about 2 million deadweight tons (DWT). Genco Shipping's vessels transport cargo such as coal, grain, iron ore, and steel products. Customers have included shippers such as BHP Billiton and Cargill and shipping lines such as Lauritzen Bulkers and NYK.

	Annual Growth	12/03	12/04	12/05	12/06	12/07
Sales ($ mil.)	360.4%	—	1.9	116.9	133.2	185.4
Net income ($ mil.)	391.4%	—	0.9	54.5	63.5	106.8
Market value ($ mil.)	89.1%	—	—	443.6	712.6	1,586.2
Employees	84.2%	—	140	408	475	—

GENCOR INDUSTRIES, INC.

NASDAQ (GM): GENC

5201 N. Orange Blossom Trail
Orlando, FL 32810
Phone: 407-290-6000
Fax: 407-578-0577
Web: www.gencor.com

CEO: E. J. (Mike) Elliott
CFO: Scott W. Runkel
HR: –
FYE: September 30
Type: Public

Gencor Industries loves the smell of asphalt in the morning. The company makes industrial process equipment, such as machinery that makes hot-mix asphalt and other highway construction materials. Gencor's products include asphalt plants, combustion systems (large burners that transform various fuels into usable energy), and fluid heat transfer systems under the Hy-Way and Beverley names. It also produces soil decontamination machines and combustion systems for dryers, kilns, boilers, and tank heaters. Gencor operates offices and production plants in the US and the UK. Chairman and CEO E. J. "Mike" Elliott owns about 13% of Gencor; investor Harvey Houtkin owns about 27%.

	Annual Growth	9/03	9/04	9/05	9/06	9/07
Sales ($ mil.)	7.7%	55.9	54.1	48.1	67.1	75.3
Net income ($ mil.)	26.2%	7.3	2.6	31.3	11.6	18.5
Market value ($ mil.)	8.9%	—	—	66.5	76.8	78.9
Employees	8.2%	317	299	—	—	434

GENCORP INC.

NYSE: GY

Hwy. 50 and Aerojet Rd.
Rancho Cordova, CA 95742
Phone: 916-355-4000
Fax: 916-351-8668
Web: www.gencorp.com

CEO: J. Scott Neish
CFO: Yasmin R. Seyal
HR: Bryan Ramsey
FYE: November 30
Type: Public

GenCorp hopes to see its profits rise on a rocket-like trajectory. The company's main subsidiary, Aerojet-General, manufactures missile propulsion technologies for defense and space systems. Aerojet's defense-related products include liquid, solid, and air-breathing propulsion systems for missiles and for interceptors used for missile defense systems, as well as armament systems. Aerojet also makes liquid, solid, and electric propulsion systems for launch vehicles, transatmospheric vehicles, and spacecraft. Aerojet's products are sold to major defense contractors and directly to end users, which consist primarily of branches of the US military. Lockheed Martin accounts for 28% of the company's sales.

	Annual Growth	11/03	11/04	11/05	11/06	11/07
Sales ($ mil.)	(11.1%)	1,192.0	499.0	624.0	621.1	745.4
Net income ($ mil.)	33.1%	22.0	(398.0)	(230.0)	(38.5)	69.0
Market value ($ mil.)	11.8%	438.4	907.7	1,004.3	770.6	684.9
Employees	2.4%	—	—	3,101	3,144	3,252

GENELABS TECHNOLOGIES, INC.

NASDAQ (CM): GNLB

505 Penobscot Dr.
Redwood City, CA 94063
Phone: 650-369-9500
Fax: 650-368-0709
Web: www.genelabs.com

CEO: Irene A. Chow
CFO: Frederick W. (Fred) Driscoll
HR: –
FYE: December 31
Type: Public

Genelabs Technologies and lupus sufferers both believe 50 years is a long time to wait for a new drug. The company has developed Prestara to treat lupus, a condition for which a new drug has not been approved in the US for five decades. The company first submitted Prestara for FDA approval in 2000 and has been working with the agency ever since to gather enough clinical evidence to win a regulatory green light for the drug. The company is also developing hepatitis C and E therapies; its antiviral compounds stop the virus from reproducing. Genelabs has teamed with Gilead Sciences and Novartis to explore possible hepatitis C drugs.

	Annual Growth	12/03	12/04	12/05	12/06	12/07
Sales ($ mil.)	55.4%	2.9	5.6	6.8	11.2	16.9
Net income ($ mil.)	—	(19.8)	(13.5)	(10.8)	(8.7)	(2.3)
Market value ($ mil.)	(54.0%)	1,230.1	531.0	33.0	35.3	54.9
Employees	—	—	—	66	—	—

GENELINK, INC.

OTC: GNLK

Newport Financial Center, 113 Pavonia Ave., Ste. 313
Jersey City, NJ 07310
Phone: 609-823-6991
Fax: 509-352-1328
Web: www.bankdna.com

CEO: Monte E. Taylor Jr.
CFO: Monte E. Taylor Jr.
HR: –
FYE: December 31
Type: Public

Want to make sure long-lost Cousin Fred is really a member of the family before you share a portion of Granny's multimillion-dollar estate? Better do a little banking with Genelink. The company stores DNA samples taken with its collection kits at its facility at the University of North Texas Health Science Center. Customers and their progeny can use the samples taken with the self-administered kits to create genetic profiles for identifying lineage or risk factors for disease. Genelink markets its DNA collection kits to funeral homes; its kit can be used up to 40 hours after death. The company formed subsidiary Dermagenetics to create and distribute skin care products tailored to a patient's genetic make up.

	Annual Growth	12/03	12/04	12/05	12/06	12/07
Sales ($ mil.)	0.0%	0.1	0.3	0.4	0.2	0.1
Net income ($ mil.)	—	(1.2)	(2.1)	(1.0)	(0.6)	(1.6)
Market value ($ mil.)	(14.4%)	14.8	8.5	3.3	2.3	8.0
Employees	—	—	—	—	—	—

GENENCOR INTERNATIONAL, INC.

925 Page Mill Rd.
Palo Alto, CA 94304
Phone: 650-846-7500
Fax: 650-845-6500
Web: www.genencor.com

CEO: Tjerk de Ruiter
CFO: Andrew (Andy) Ashworth
HR: Jim Sjoerdsma
FYE: December 31
Type: Subsidiary

If you've got the money, honey, Genencor International's got the 'zyme. Genencor manufactures genetically modified enzymes for the industrial, agricultural, and consumer products markets. Using its biotechnology know-how, the company discovers useful enzymes (naturally occurring protein catalysts) and develops them for mass production; the enzymes are used in myriad ways, including as additives in animal feed and detergents, as a method of converting starch into ethanol, and in the production of textiles and paper. In 2005 Danisco, which previously owned about 40% of Genencor, acquired the remainder of the company, including a roughly 40% share from Eastman Chemical.

	Annual Growth	12/03	12/04	12/05	12/06	12/07
Est. sales ($ mil.)	—	—	—	—	—	90.7
Employees	—	—	—	—	—	1,098

GENENTECH, INC.

NYSE: DNA

1 DNA Way
South San Francisco, CA 94080
Phone: 650-225-1000
Fax: 650-225-6000
Web: www.gene.com

CEO: Arthur D. (Art) Levinson
CFO: David A. Ebersman
HR: Denise Smith-Hams
FYE: December 31
Type: Public

"The few, the proud, the profitable" could be Genentech's motto. One of the world's most successful biotechs (in an industry full of money-losers), the firm has three billion-dollar blockbusters: Rituxan, which fights non-Hodgkin's lymphoma; Avastin, a treatment for colorectal and non-small cell lung cancers; and Herceptin for breast cancer. Lung cancer drug Tarceva rounds out the company's oncology portfolio. Genentech's other marketed drugs include cardiovascular therapies Activase and TNKase, human growth hormone Nutropin, cystic fibrosis drug Pulmozyme, and asthma drug Xolair. Products are sold through direct marketing and large drug distributors including AmerisourceBergen. Roche owns 56% of the firm.

	Annual Growth	12/03	12/04	12/05	12/06	12/07
Sales ($ mil.)	37.3%	3,300.3	4,621.2	6,633.4	9,284.0	11,724.0
Net income ($ mil.)	49.0%	562.5	784.8	1,279.0	2,113.0	2,769.0
Market value ($ mil.)	30.2%	24,550.1	56,960.6	97,468.4	85,429.9	70,557.6
Employees	8.5%	—	—	9,500	10,533	11,174

An in-depth profile of this company is available to Hoover's Online members at hoovers.com.

GENER8XION ENTERTAINMENT, INC.

OTC: GNXE

3400 Cahuenga Blvd.
Hollywood, CA 90068
Phone: 323-874-9888
Fax: 323-876-5217
Web: www.8x.com

CEO: Matthew Crouch
CFO: Richard J. Cook
HR: –
FYE: October 31
Type: Public

Gener8Xion Entertainment is a family/faith-based genre film and TV production and distribution company. The company's first movie was the 2006 Biblical epic *One Night with the King*, a movie based on the novel *Hadassah* by Tommy Tenney. Gener8Xion released its second motion picture, *Noëlle*, in 2007. Other activities include distribution rights to the documentary film *Lord save Us From Your Followers*, well as the rights to the script for an animated feature-length project entitled *The Prodigal*, and the rights to *Omega Code* and *Omega Code 2*. In addition, Gener8Xion is engaged in the manufacture, sales, and rentals of film and video lighting equipment through its Cinemills division.

	Annual Growth	10/03	10/04	10/05	10/06	10/07
Sales ($ mil.)	362.6%	—	0.1	0.4	5.7	9.9
Net income ($ mil.)	—	—	(0.1)	(1.2)	(5.8)	(0.6)
Market value ($ mil.)	39.6%	—	3.3	28.1	14.8	9.1
Employees	—	—	—	—	—	17

GENERAL ATOMICS

3550 General Atomics Ct.
San Diego, CA 92121
Phone: 858-455-3000
Fax: 858-455-3621
Web: www.ga.com

CEO: James N. (Neal) Blue
CFO: Anthony G. Navarra
HR: Karin Yates
FYE: December 31
Type: Private

General Atomics has more than nuclear energy these days. The company, which was founded in 1955 to research atomic energy, continues to develop and operate nuclear power reactor systems, but may be finding more demand for its research and engineering expertise in areas such as unmanned military aircraft, airborne sensors, hazardous waste, superconducting magnets, and information technology. Through several divisions and subsidiaries, the company commercializes and develops its technology to customers worldwide. Customers have included the US Department of Defense, the US Department of Energy, and National Science Foundation. General Atomics was originally a division of defense titan General Dynamics.

	Annual Growth	12/03	12/04	12/05	12/06	12/07
Est. sales ($ mil.)	—	—	—	—	—	86.6
Employees	—	—	—	—	—	1,150

GENERAL BEARING CORPORATION

Pink Sheets: GNRL

44 High St.
West Nyack, NY 10994
Phone: 845-358-6000
Fax: 845-358-6277
Web: www.generalbearing.com

CEO: David L. Gussack
CFO: Rocky Cambrea
HR: Fran Garner
FYE: Saturday nearest December 31
Type: Public

General Bearing's business keeps on rolling. The company manufactures and distributes a variety of bearing products, including ball bearings, tapered roller bearings, spherical roller bearings, and cylindrical roller bearings and components, which it sells mainly to US and Canadian manufacturers and aftermarket distributors. General Bearing produces its bearing products in China (through joint ventures) and the US. Its brand names include The General and Hyatt. Chairman Seymour Gussack, David Gussack, Robert Baruc, and Nina Gussack together own more than half of the company, and they took General Bearing private in early 2005. Seymour Gussack founded the company in 1958.

	Annual Growth	12/03	12/04	12/05	12/06	12/07
Est. sales ($ mil.)	—	—	—	—	—	119.5
Employees	—	—	—	—	—	971

GENERAL CABLE CORPORATION

NYSE: BGC

4 Tesseneer Dr.
Highland Heights, KY 41076
Phone: 859-572-8000
Fax: 859-572-8458
Web: www.generalcable.com

CEO: Gregory B. Kenny
CFO: Brian J. Robinson
HR: Peter J. Olmsted
FYE: December 31
Type: Public

General Cable helps all sorts of companies get wired for business. The company makes aluminum, copper, and fiber-optic wire and cable, including electric utility (cables used for low-, medium- and high-voltage power distribution and power transmission), electrical infrastructure (for industrial and commercial power and control applications), and telecommunications products (low-voltage signal wire for voice, data, video, and control applications). Brand names include Carol, BICC, and Helix/HiTemp. General Cable also produces power cables, automotive wire, mining cables, and custom-designed cables for medical equipment and other products. It operates about 45 facilities worldwide.

	Annual Growth	12/03	12/04	12/05	12/06	12/07
Sales ($ mil.)	31.6%	1,538.4	1,970.7	2,380.8	3,665.1	4,614.8
Net income ($ mil.)	—	(4.8)	37.9	39.2	135.3	208.6
Market value ($ mil.)	86.6%	317.1	545.8	975.5	2,273.0	3,842.1
Employees	5.5%	—	—	7,300	7,700	—

GENERAL CASUALTY INSURANCE COMPANIES

1 General Dr.
Sun Prairie, WI 53596
Phone: 608-837-4440
Fax: 608-837-0583
Web: www.generalcasualty.com

CEO: Peter Christen
CFO: Laura Hinson
HR: Kip Kobussen
FYE: December 31
Type: Subsidiary

Despite its name General Casualty Insurance Companies gets very specific about its property/casualty products. The company sells personal and commercial auto, homeowners, liability, and workers' compensation coverage through regional offices. General Casualty sells its products through some 1,500 independent insurance agencies in 25 states. Two-thirds of the company's premiums come from commercial lines; personal auto and homeowners coverage make up the majority of the remaining revenue. General Casualty is a subsidiary of QBE Regional Insurance.

GENERAL COMMUNICATION, INC.

NASDAQ (GS): GNCMA

2550 Denali St., Ste. 1000
Anchorage, AK 99503
Phone: 907-868-5600
Fax: 907-868-5676
Web: www.gci.com

CEO: Ronald A. (Ron) Duncan
CFO: John M. Lowber
HR: –
FYE: December 31
Type: Public

Customers don't turn to General Communication for its catchy name, but through its operating subsidiaries, the company provides them with facilities-based phone services to about 100,000 long distance customers and 120,000 local callers in Anchorage, Fairbanks, and Juneau, Alaska. The competitive local-exchange carrier is also Alaska's leading cable television provider with than 140,000 basic cable subscribers; it provides wireless services to nearly 80,000 customers through a partnership with AT&T Mobility. Other services include dial-up and cable Internet access.

	Annual Growth	12/03	12/04	12/05	12/06	12/07
Sales ($ mil.)	7.4%	390.8	424.8	443.0	477.5	520.3
Net income ($ mil.)	(3.0%)	15.5	21.3	20.8	18.5	13.7
Market value ($ mil.)	(1.2%)	454.6	569.2	525.9	793.2	432.5
Employees	1.3%	—	—	1,262	—	1,295

THE GENERAL COUNCIL OF THE ASSEMBLIES OF GOD

1445 N. Boonville Ave.
Springfield, MO 65802
Phone: 417-862-2781
Fax: 417-862-8558
Web: ag.org

CEO: Rev Thomas E. Trask
CFO: George O. Wood
HR: James R. Stalnaker
FYE: March 31
Type: Private

The General Council of the Assemblies of God oversees the US activities of one of the world's largest Pentecostal churches. In the US, the Assemblies of God includes more than 12,000 churches that have about 2.8 million constituents. In addition, the group has some 236,000 churches and outstations and 48 million constituents in about 190 other countries. Its US-based Gospel Publishing House arm prints, sells, and distributes Bibles and other religious resources. The Assemblies of God traces its roots to a religious revival that began in the US during the late 1800s. The General Council of the Assemblies of God was founded in Hot Springs, Arkansas, in 1914.

	Annual Growth	3/03	3/04	3/05	3/06	3/07
Est. sales ($ mil.)	—	—	—	—	—	439.5
Employees	—	—	—	—	—	1,330

GENERAL DYNAMICS CORPORATION

NYSE: GD

2941 Fairview Park Dr., Ste. 100
Falls Church, VA 22042
Phone: 703-876-3000
Fax: 703-876-3125
Web: www.gendyn.com

CEO: Nicholas D. (Nick) Chabraja
CFO: L. Hugh Redd
HR: Walter M. Oliver
FYE: December 31
Type: Public

Defense contractor General Dynamics brings it on by land, air, and sea. It operates in four areas: Information Systems & Technology (command and control systems), Marine Systems (warships and nuclear submarines), Combat Systems (tanks, amphibious assault vehicles, and munitions), and Aerospace (business jets). General Dynamics' Electric Boat subsidiary builds nuclear submarines (Seawolf, Ohio, Los Angeles classes); Bath Iron Works builds DDG 51 destroyers and LPD 17 landing craft; Land Systems builds the Abrams M1A1 and M1A2 main battle tanks and Fox reconnaissance vehicles; and Gulfstream Aerospace makes business jets. The US government accounts for more than two-thirds of sales.

	Annual Growth	12/03	12/04	12/05	12/06	12/07
Sales ($ mil.)	13.2%	16,617.0	19,178.0	21,244.0	24,063.0	27,240.0
Net income ($ mil.)	19.9%	1,004.0	1,227.0	1,461.0	1,856.0	2,072.0
Market value ($ mil.)	41.5%	8,957.7	10,466.8	11,415.4	30,170.7	35,950.1
Employees	7.5%	—	—	72,200	81,000	83,500

GENERAL ELECTRIC CAPITAL CORPORATION

3135 Easton Turnpike
Fairfield, CT 06828
Phone: 203-373-2211
Fax: 203-373-2884
Web: www.gecapital.com

CEO: Jeffrey R. (Jeff) Immelt
CFO: Keith S. Sherin
HR: –
FYE: December 31
Type: Subsidiary

General Electric Capital (GE Capital) encompasses the consumer finance and commercial finance operations of sprawling conglomerate General Electric. It also provides equipment financing and leasing to the air and rail transportation, energy, and water and process technologies industries. Consumer services include private-label credit cards, personal loans, mortgages, deposit and savings products, and credit insurance. Focusing on middle-market companies, the commercial finance division provides commercial mortgages and loans, as well as loans and leases for premises and equipment. GE Capital and its divisions are active in more than 50 countries in North America, Europe, and Asia.

	Annual Growth	12/03	12/04	12/05	12/06	12/07
Assets ($ mil.)	5.2%	506,428.0	566,708.0	475,259.0	543,665.0	620,386.0
Net income ($ mil.)	—	—	—	—	—	9,815.0
Employees	—	—	—	—	—	80,500

GENERAL ELECTRIC COMPANY

NYSE: GE

3135 Easton Tpke.
Fairfield, CT 06828
Phone: 203-373-2211
Fax: 203-373-3131
Web: www.ge.com

CEO: Jeffrey R. (Jeff) Immelt
CFO: Keith S. Sherin
HR: John F. Lynch
FYE: December 31
Type: Public

From turbines to TV, from household appliances to power plants, General Electric (GE) is plugged in to most of the businesses that have shaped the modern world. The company produces — take a deep breath — aircraft engines, locomotives and other transportation equipment, kitchen and laundry appliances, lighting, electric distribution and control equipment, generators and turbines, and medical imaging equipment. GE is also one of the preeminent financial services companies in the US. Commercial finance, consumer finance, and equipment financing and leasing together comprise the company's largest segment. Other operations include the NBC television network.

	Annual Growth	12/03	12/04	12/05	12/06	12/07
Assets ($ mil.)	5.3%	647,483.0	750,507.0	673,321.0	697,239.0	795,337.0
Net income ($ mil.)	10.3%	15,002.0	16,819.0	16,711.0	20,829.0	22,208.0
Market value ($ mil.)	4.4%	311,755.5	386,402.1	367,473.6	382,421.0	370,240.3
Employees	1.7%	—	—	316,000	319,000	327,000

GENERAL EMPLOYMENT ENTERPRISES, INC.

AMEX: JOB

1 Tower Ln., Ste. 2200
Oakbrook Terrace, IL 60181
Phone: 630-954-0400
Fax: 630-954-0447
Web: www.generalemployment.com

CEO: Herbert F. (Corky) Imhoff Jr.
CFO: Kent M. Yauch
HR: –
FYE: September 30
Type: Public

Who's got jobs for information technology, engineering, and accounting professionals? General Employment Enterprises specializes in finding this group permanent and temporary employment. Most offices operate under the General Employment name and provide both full-time employee placement and contract staffing (other brand names include Triad Personnel Services, Business Management Personnel, Generation Technologies, and Omni One). The firm places permanent employees for a fee based on a percentage of their salaries. Contract workers remain employees of the company, which bills clients hourly for their services.

	Annual Growth	9/03	9/04	9/05	9/06	9/07
Sales ($ mil.)	1.4%	18.6	18.0	20.4	20.1	19.7
Net income ($ mil.)	—	(3.5)	(1.4)	0.7	1.0	0.9
Market value ($ mil.)	17.5%	4.4	10.7	10.7	8.7	8.3
Employees	(7.9%)	—	—	330	—	280

GENERAL GROWTH PROPERTIES, INC.

NYSE: GGP

110 N. Wacker Dr.
Chicago, IL 60606
Phone: 312-960-5000
Fax: 312-960-5475
Web: www.generalgrowth.com

CEO: John Bucksbaum
CFO: Bernard (Bernie) Freibaum
HR: –
FYE: December 31
Type: Public

General Growth Properties is a major player in the retail real estate sector. The real estate investment trust (REIT) is the second-largest owner/operator of malls in the US, behind Simon Property Group. It owns or operates more than 200 shopping malls in 44 states, encompassing about 200 million sq. ft. of space and housing retail tenants such as J. C. Penney, Sears, and Old Navy. Its merger with The Rouse Company gave it entree into the master-planned community business. General Growth also owns office, mixed-use, and industrial buildings, and it manages additional holdings for institutional owners. The founding Bucksbaum family owns about 25% of the company.

	Annual Growth	12/03	12/04	12/05	12/06	12/07
Sales ($ mil.)	26.6%	1,270.7	1,802.8	3,073.4	3,256.3	3,261.8
Net income ($ mil.)	2.3%	263.4	267.9	75.6	59.3	288.0
Market value ($ mil.)	13.6%	6,029.9	8,487.6	11,239.9	12,643.1	10,043.7
Employees	(5.5%)	—	—	4,700	4,700	4,200

GENERAL MARITIME CORPORATION

NYSE: GMR

299 Park Ave.
New York, NY 10171
Phone: 212-763-5600
Fax: 212-763-5602
Web: www.generalmaritimecorp.com

CEO: Peter C. Georgiopoulos
CFO: Jeffrey D. Pribor
HR: –
FYE: December 31
Type: Public

Black gold on the deep blue brings in the green for General Maritime. A leading operator of midsized tankers, General Maritime transports crude oil, primarily in the Atlantic Basin but also in the Black Sea. The company's fleet consists of about 20 double-hull Aframax and Suezmax tankers that have an overall capacity of about 2.7 million deadweight tons (DWT). General Maritime deploys its vessels both on the spot market (voyage by voyage) and under longer-term time-charter contracts. Customers have included major oil companies such as Chevron, CITGO, Exxon Mobil, Hess, and Shell.

	Annual Growth	12/03	12/04	12/05	12/06	12/07
Sales ($ mil.)	(13.5%)	454.5	701.3	567.9	326.0	255.0
Net income ($ mil.)	(14.8%)	84.5	315.1	212.4	156.8	44.5
Market value ($ mil.)	4.2%	664.7	1,513.9	1,409.0	1,152.1	783.1
Employees	—	—	—	349	—	—

GENERAL MILLS, INC.

NYSE: GIS

1 General Mills Blvd.
Minneapolis, MN 55426
Phone: 763-764-7600
Fax: 763-764-7384
Web: www.generalmills.com

CEO: Kendall J. (Ken) Powell
CFO: Donal Leo (Don) Mulligan
HR: Michael A. (Mike) Peel
FYE: Last Sunday in May
Type: Public

General Mills gets its Kix as the US's #2 cereal maker (behind *uber*-rival Kellogg). Among its Big G Cereals unit's brands are Cheerios, Chex, Total, Kix, and Wheaties. General Mills is also a brand leader in flour (Gold Medal), baking mixes (Betty Crocker, Bisquick), dinner mixes (Hamburger Helper), fruit snacks (Fruit Roll-Ups), and grain snacks (Chex Mix, Pop Secret). It is also a leader in branded yogurt (Colombo, Go-Gurt, and Yoplait). Through joint ventures, the company's products are available worldwide. Its 2001 acquisition of Pillsbury (refrigerated dough products, frozen vegetables) from Diageo doubled the company's size, making General Mills one of the world's largest food companies.

	Annual Growth	5/04	5/05	5/06	5/07	5/08
Sales ($ mil.)	5.4%	11,070.0	11,244.0	11,640.0	12,442.0	13,652.1
Net income ($ mil.)	5.3%	1,055.0	1,240.0	1,090.0	1,144.0	1,294.7
Market value ($ mil.)	4.3%	17,452.9	18,331.9	18,437.2	20,451.0	20,617.9
Employees	1.3%	—	27,800	28,100	28,500	

GENERAL MOTORS CORPORATION

NYSE: GM

300 Renaissance Center
Detroit, MI 48265
Phone: 313-556-5000
Fax: –
Web: www.gm.com

CEO: G. Richard (Rick) Wagoner Jr.
CFO: Ray G. Young
HR: Kathleen S. (Katy) Barclay
FYE: December 31
Type: Public

So far General Motors (GM) has steered around competitors to remain the world's #1 maker of cars and trucks, with brands such as Buick, Cadillac, Chevrolet, GMC, Pontiac, Saab, and Saturn. GM also produces cars through its Holden, Opel, and Vauxhall units. Financing and insurance business is primarily conducted by one-time wholly owned subsidiary GMAC (GM currently owns 49%). In addition, GM owns slightly more than 50% of South Korea's GM Daewoo Auto & Technology. Like its US counterparts Ford Motor and Chrysler, GM is in the midst of restructuring its North American operations.

	Annual Growth	12/03	12/04	12/05	12/06	12/07
Sales ($ mil.)	(0.6%)	185,524.0	193,517.0	192,604.0	207,349.0	181,122.0
Net income ($ mil.)	—	3,822.0	2,804.0	(10,567.0)	(1,978.0)	(38,732.0)
Market value ($ mil.)	(17.2%)	30,010.7	22,639.2	10,982.4	17,377.4	14,089.2
Employees	(10.9%)	—	—	335,000	280,000	266,000

GENERAL PARTS, INC.

2635 Millbrook Rd.
Raleigh, NC 27604
Phone: 919-573-3000
Fax: 919-573-3553

CEO: O. Temple Sloan Jr.
CFO: John Gardner
HR: John Dibenedetto
FYE: December 31
Type: Private

Feel free to salute General Parts, distributor of replacement automotive parts, supplies, and tools for every make and model of foreign and domestic car, truck, bus, and farm or industrial vehicle. The firm operates the CARQUEST auto parts distribution network of some 40 distribution centers, and owns about 1,400 of CARQUEST's 3,400 auto parts stores across the US, Canada, and Mexico. The company sells its parts to DIY mechanics, professional installers, body shops, farmers, and fleet owners (commercial customers account for most sales). General Parts has been growing through acquisitions. The company, founded in 1961 by college student Temple Sloan, owns CARQUEST Canada.

	Annual Growth	12/02	12/03	12/04	12/05	12/06
Est. sales ($ mil.)	9.8%	1,650.0	1,800.0	2,000.0	2,250.0	2,400.0
Employees	15.0%	14,000	13,500	20,000	23,000	24,500

GENERAL RE CORPORATION

695 E. Main St.
Stamford, CT 06904
Phone: 203-328-5000
Fax: 203-328-6423
Web: www.genre.com

CEO: Franklin (Tad) Montross IV
CFO: William G. Gasdaska Jr.
HR: Sandra Bell
FYE: December 31
Type: Subsidiary

General Re, or Gen Re to its friends, is a subsidiary of Berkshire Hathaway and one of the top four reinsurers in the world. The company's main subsidiary, General Reinsurance, is one of the biggest property & casualty reinsurers in the US. Its second-largest operating company is Germany's Kölnische Rückversicherungs-Gesellschaft (Cologne Re), the world's oldest reinsurer and a major force in international reinsurance. Its reinsurance business is divided into North American property & casualty, International property/casualty, life and health. Its international reinsurance is conducted through Cologne Re and its London market Faraday subsidiary.

	Annual Growth	12/03	12/04	12/05	12/06	12/07
Sales ($ mil.)	(12.9%)	10,548.0	7,245.0	6,435.0	6,075.0	6,076.0
Employees	(8.4%)	2,700	—	1,487	1,900	1,900

GENERAL RV CENTER

48500 W. 12 Mile Rd.
Wixom, MI 48393
Phone: 248-349-0900
Fax: 248-348-4150
Web: www.generalrv.com

CEO: Robert S. (Rob) Baidas
CFO: Katie Short
HR: –
FYE: May 31
Type: Private

General RV Center can get pretty specific about the traveling homes it offers for sale. Operating through about half a dozen locations in Michigan that include a total of 50-plus service bays, the #1 RV dealer in the nation (by volume) sells more than 5,000 new and used camping trailers, motor homes, RVs, travel trailers, and truck campers a year. Brands include Dutchmen, Forest River, Monaco, Newmar, and Winnebago. General RV Center also rents RVs at about five locations. Online, RV shoppers may search the company's inventory and owners may apply for insurance. Founded in 1962 by Abe Baidas, General RV Center is still owned by the Baidas family.

	Annual Growth	5/03	5/04	5/05	5/06	5/07
Est. sales ($ mil.)	—	—	—	—	—	180.0
Employees	—	—	—	—	—	300

THE GENERATIONS NETWORK, INC.

360 W. 4800 North
Provo, UT 84604
Phone: 801-705-7000
Fax: 801-705-7001
Web: www.myfamily.com

CEO: Timothy P. (Tim) Sullivan
CFO: David H. Rinn
HR: –
FYE: December 31
Type: Private

Can't stand your relatives? Try having a virtual relationship with them through The Generations Network. Formerly, MyFamily.com, the company operates a network of Web sites that help subscribers hold family discussions, create online family photo albums, maintain a calendar of family events, share family histories, and buy gifts for family members, among other things. Network sites include MyFamily.com, Ancestry.com (historical records), Genealogy.com (family histories), and RootsWeb.com (a genealogy community). The firm also publishes *Ancestry Magazine*, Family Tree Maker software, a variety of books, and databases on CD-ROM. Investors include firms such as Ventures, EsNet, Sorenson Media, and Spectrum Equity.

	Annual Growth	12/03	12/04	12/05	12/06	12/07
Est. sales ($ mil.)	—	—	—	—	—	140.3
Employees	—	—	—	—	—	760

GENESCO INC.

NYSE: GCO

Genesco Park, 1415 Murfreesboro Rd.
Nashville, TN 37217
Phone: 615-367-7000
Fax: 615-367-8278
Web: www.genesco.com

CEO: Hal N. Pennington
CFO: James S. Gulmi
HR: John W. Clinard
FYE: Saturday nearest January 31
Type: Public

Genesco's sole concern is nicely capped off, to boot (so to speak). It sells casual and dress shoes — primarily for men and boys — through its about 2,175 department, discount, and specialty stores in the US, Puerto Rico, and Canada. Genesco operates through five segments: Journeys, Underground Station (with Jarman), Hat World (including Lids, Hat Shack, Hat Zone, Head Quarters, Cap Connection, and Lids Kids), Johnston & Murphy, and Licensed Brands (Dockers footwear). Along with its Johnston & Murphy and Journeys shops, Genesco operates Underground Station shops, which target young urban men. Genesco and rival Finish Line, which offered to acquire the firm for about $1.5 billion in 2007, terminated the deal.

	Annual Growth	1/04	1/05	1/06	1/07	1/08
Sales ($ mil.)	15.7%	837.4	1,112.7	1,283.9	1,460.5	1,502.1
Net income ($ mil.)	(30.0%)	28.7	48.3	62.7	67.7	6.9
Market value ($ mil.)	19.4%	375.8	632.7	893.2	929.2	763.2
Employees	12.1%	—	—	11,100	12,750	13,950

GENESEE & WYOMING INC.

NYSE: GWR

66 Field Point Rd.
Greenwich, CT 06830
Phone: 203-629-3722
Fax: 203-661-4106
Web: www.gwrr.com

CEO: John C. Hellmann
CFO: Timothy J. Gallagher
HR: Shayne L. Magdoff
FYE: December 31
Type: Public

Genesee & Wyoming once relied on the salt of the earth — hauling salt on a 14-mile railroad for one customer. Now the company owns stakes in about 50 short-line and regional freight railroads that operate over a total of about 8,800 miles of track, including about 5,800 miles of track owned and leased by the company and another 3,000 miles belonging to other railroads. The company is North America's #2 operator of short-line railroads, behind RailAmerica. Freight transported by Genesee & Wyoming railroads includes coal; forest products; and pulp and paper. Outside the US and Canada, the company has operations in Australia and the Netherlands and a minority stake in a railroad in Bolivia.

	Annual Growth	12/03	12/04	12/05	12/06	12/07
Sales ($ mil.)	20.5%	244.8	303.8	385.4	478.9	516.2
Net income ($ mil.)	17.8%	28.7	37.6	50.1	134.0	55.2
Market value ($ mil.)	28.1%	282.4	457.5	931.1	987.5	759.8
Employees	(5.5%)	2,889	3,093	3,513	2,677	2,307

GENESIS ENERGY, L.P.

AMEX: GEL

500 Dallas St., Ste. 2500
Houston, TX 77002
Phone: 713-860-2500
Fax: 713-860-2640
Web: www.genesiscrudeoil.com

CEO: Grant E. Sims
CFO: Ross A. Benavides
HR: Joe Mueller
FYE: December 31
Type: Public

In the beginning was the oil. And on the third day (or thereabouts), there was oil gathering and marketing. Genesis Energy purchases and aggregates crude oil at the wellhead and makes bulk buys at pipeline and terminal facilities for resale. The company transports crude oil — more than 61,580 barrels per day — through three common carrier pipeline systems along the US Gulf Coast. Genesis Energy has a fleet of 48 tractor-trailers that carry oil from the wellhead to the pipelines, terminals, or refineries. The company is also engaged in wholesale carbon dioxide marketing. Denbury Resources indirectly owns Genesis Energy's general partner and a 9.25% ownership interest in the company.

	Annual Growth	12/03	12/04	12/05	12/06	12/07
Sales ($ mil.)	16.2%	657.9	927.1	1,078.7	918.4	1,199.7
Net income ($ mil.)	—	13.3	(1.4)	3.4	8.4	(13.6)
Market value ($ mil.)	77.2%	91.3	117.4	160.6	268.5	899.0
Employees	2.7%	—	—	185	190	—

GENESIS HEALTHCARE CORPORATION

101 E. State St.
Kennett Square, PA 19348
Phone: 610-444-6350
Fax: 610-925-4000
Web: www.genesishcc.com

CEO: George V. Hager Jr.
CFO: James V. (Jim) McKeon III
HR: Arthur T. (Bud) Locilento Jr.
FYE: September 30
Type: Private

Genesis HealthCare Corporation cares for people when care is what counts. The company operates about 200 assisted living and skilled nursing facilities in 13 states in the eastern US. Its facilities have about 26,000 beds total. Genesis HealthCare's rehabilitation division provides speech, physical, and occupational therapy services through contracts with health care providers in nearly 20 states. The company also offers respiratory therapy, adult day care, Alzheimer's care, dialysis, and home and hospice care. Genesis HealthCare was taken private in 2007 by a group of private equity investors from Formation Capital and the private equity arm of real estate investment firm J. E. Roberts.

	Annual Growth	9/02	9/03	9/04	9/05	9/06
Sales ($ mil.)	8.1%	—	1,403.3	1,529.9	1,711.4	1,770.3
Net income ($ mil.)	44.5%	—	11.9	29.1	46.1	35.9
Employees	0.5%	—	35,000	35,000	35,000	35,500

GENESIS MICROCHIP INC.

2525 Augustine Dr.
Santa Clara, CA 95054
Phone: 408-919-8400
Fax: 408-986-9644
Web: www.gnss.com

CEO: Elias (Elie) Antoun
CFO: Rick Martig
HR: Paula Ewanich
FYE: December 31*
Type: Subsidiary

While Genesis Microchip may not have created the video chip, it keeps coming up with new designs. The fabless semiconductor company designs integrated circuits (ICs) that translate video images for viewing in flat-panel displays, consumer video products, and digital TVs. Its chips filter and refresh images, process videos, and enhance high-volume displays. Clients include Samsung Electronics (16% of sales), Philips (10%), BenQ (also 10%), LG Electronics, and Sony. The company gets more than 80% of its sales from the Asia/Pacific region. Rival STMicroelectronics has acquired Genesis Microchip for about $336 million in cash.

	Annual Growth	3/03	3/04	3/05	3/06	3/07
Sales ($ mil.)	2.5%	194.3	213.4	204.1	269.5	214.6
Net income ($ mil.)	—	(14.6)	(4.2)	(9.4)	18.4	(144.3)
Employees	10.9%	393	431	476	563	595

*Fiscal year change

An in-depth profile of this company is available to Hoover's Online members at hoovers.com.

673

GENESIS PHARMACEUTICAL ENTERPRISES, INC.

OTC: GTEC

7900 Glades Rd., Ste. 420
Boca Raton, FL 33434
Phone: 561-988-9880
Fax: 561-988-9890
Web: www.genesis-technology.net

CEO: Cao Wubo
CFO: Elsa Sung
HR: –
FYE: September 30
Type: Public

Genesis Pharmaceutical Enterprises (formerly Genesis Technology Group) operates primarily through subsidiary Laiyang Jiangbo, a China-based contract pharmaceutical manufacturer. Genesis Technology became Genesis Pharmaceutical in October 2007 in conjunction with a reverse merger in which the controlling shareholders of Laiyang Jiangbo wound up with a 75% stake in the new company. Previously, Genesis Technology had offered consulting and investment services to companies wanting to do business in China. The company also had been seeking a merger partner.

	Annual Growth	9/03	9/04	9/05	9/06	9/07
Sales ($ mil.)	(40.3%)	23.6	23.4	0.2	6.8	3.0
Net income ($ mil.)	—	(3.1)	(1.6)	(3.7)	2.9	(5.8)
Market value ($ mil.)	16.2%	4.9	8.2	2.8	10.1	9.0
Employees	—	—	—	—	—	—

GENESYS TELECOMMUNICATIONS LABORATORIES INC.

2001 Junipero Serra Blvd.
Daly City, CA 94014
Phone: 650-466-1100
Fax: 650-466-1260
Web: www.genesyslab.com

CEO: Paul Segre
CFO: Stacey W. White
HR: Alexander Gressenich
FYE: December 31
Type: Subsidiary

The beginning of a beautiful customer relationship could be software to integrate your communications systems. Genesys Telecommunications Laboratories, a subsidiary of French telecom equipment giant Alcatel-Lucent, makes computer telephony integration software that brings together phones, computers, databases, and the Internet for customer contact centers and other call centers. Its software platforms identify callers, route calls and e-mail, and report caller statistics. Companies also use its voice portal system to offer self-service resources over the phone.

	Annual Growth	12/03	12/04	12/05	12/06	12/07
Est. sales ($ mil.)	—	—	—	—	—	85.5
Employees	—	—	—	—	—	1,100

GENETHERA, INC.

OTC: GTHA

3930 Youngfield St.
Wheat Ridge, CO 80033
Phone: 303-463-6371
Fax: 303-463-6377
Web: www.genethera.net

CEO: Antonio (Tony) Milici
CFO: Tannya L. Irizarry
HR: –
FYE: December 31
Type: Public

GeneThera does its part to protect the world's fauna. GeneThera, formerly called Hand Brand Distribution, develops genetic diagnostic assays for the agriculture and veterinary industries. The biotech company's assays have been developed that detect chronic wasting disease in elk and deer and mad cow disease in cattle. The company plans to develop a cancer detection test for animals and later develop a similar test for humans under two contracts with Xpention, a biotechnology company focused on cancer detection tests. The contracts mark a transition for GeneThera from a development company to a revenue-generating operation.

	Annual Growth	12/03	12/04	12/05	12/06	12/07
Sales ($ mil.)	0.0%	0.1	0.0	0.2	0.2	0.1
Net income ($ mil.)	—	(3.1)	(5.8)	(3.6)	(1.5)	(0.8)
Employees	—	—	—	—	—	—

GENIUS PRODUCTS, INC.

OTC: GNPI

2230 Broadway
Santa Monica, CA 90404
Phone: 310-453-1222
Fax: 310-453-0074
Web: www.geniusproducts.com

CEO: Trevor J. Drinkwater
CFO: Ed Byrnes
HR: –
FYE: December 31
Type: Public

Genius Products isn't just for geniuses. The company produces, licenses, and distributes videos and music titles in such genres as children's entertainment, fitness, holistic living collections, and classic and modern television and movie selections. Genius Products' licensed brands include titles from companies such as ESPN, Sesame Workshop, World Wrestling Entertainment (WWE), The Weinstein Company, and Discovery Communications. Genius Products owns American Vantage Media and its Wellspring Media unit, owner of a 700-title library of independent cinema, documentary, and health and wellness titles.

	Annual Growth	12/02	12/03	12/04	12/05	*12/06
Sales ($ mil.)	174.4%	2.1	3.1	16.6	22.3	119.0
Net income ($ mil.)	—	(2.8)	(2.7)	(6.1)	(17.2)	8.8
Market value ($ mil.)	89.6%	13.3	51.6	53.3	122.5	172.2
Employees	88.0%	12	18	41	93	150

*Most recent year available

THE GENLYTE GROUP INCORPORATED

10350 Ormsby Park Place, Ste. 601
Louisville, KY 40223
Phone: 502-420-9500
Fax: 502-420-9540
Web: www.genlyte.com

CEO: Larry K. Powers
CFO: William G. (Bill) Ferko
HR: Nancy Costa
FYE: December 31
Type: Subsidiary

The Genlyte Group wants everyone to lighten up. A leading lighting manufacturer in North America, the company produces a wide range of lighting fixtures and controls. Genlyte's indoor and outdoor lighting products include incandescent, fluorescent, and high-intensity discharge fixtures sold under such brand names as Bronzelite, Capri/Omega, Lightolier, and Wide-Lite. Between 1998 and 2004 the company had primarily operated through Genlyte Thomas Group LLC, its joint venture with Thomas Industries, but in 2004 Genlyte bought out Thomas Industries' 32% stake in the venture to assume full ownership. The Genlyte Group was purchased by Royal Philips Electronics in early 2008.

	Annual Growth	12/02	12/03	12/04	12/05	12/06
Sales ($ mil.)	11.2%	970.3	1,033.9	1,179.1	1,252.2	1,484.8
Net income ($ mil.)	39.2%	41.1	46.3	58.3	84.8	154.5
Employees	(6.4%)	5,073	—	—	5,485	3,891

GENMAR HOLDINGS, INC.

80 S. 8th St.
Minneapolis, MN 55402
Phone: 612-337-1965
Fax: 612-337-1994
Web: www.genmar.com

CEO: Roger R. Cloutier II
CFO: –
HR: –
FYE: June 30
Type: Private

Genmar Holdings trolls for sales by cruising the pleasure boat market with a line of luxury yachts, recreational powerboats, and fishing boats. The company builds more than 250 different boat models, ranging in size from 60-foot yachts (servants not included) to fishing skiffs. Its brands include Glastron, Ranger, and Wellcraft. Genmar markets its boats through more than 1,000 independent dealers in the US and 30 other countries. The company, which is a combination of 13 different boat manufacturing brands acquired over 25 years, is controlled by chairman Irwin Jacobs, an investor and former corporate raider.

	Annual Growth	6/02	6/03	6/04	6/05	6/06
Sales ($ mil.)	(2.2%)	1,200.0	1,100.0	1,100.0	1,100.0	1,100.0
Employees	(6.3%)	6,500	6,000	6,000	5,400	5,000

GENOMIC HEALTH, INC.

NASDAQ (GM): GHDX

301 Penobscot Dr.
Redwood City, CA 94063
Phone: 650-556-9300
Fax: 650-556-1132
Web: www.genomichealth.com

CEO: Randal W. (Randy) Scott
CFO: G. Bradley (Brad) Cole
HR: –
FYE: December 31
Type: Public

Genomic Health believes the genome is key to good health. The company conducts genomic research to develop molecular diagnostics and assays that can predict the likelihood of disease recurrence and response to therapy and treatments. Genomic Health's Onco*type* DX assay predicts the likelihood of chemotherapy effectiveness and breast cancer recurrence in women with newly diagnosed, early-stage invasive breast cancer. The company markets its products to oncologists and pathologists. Genomic Health's research efforts are targeted at providing a wider base of cancer-related tests.

	Annual Growth	12/03	12/04	12/05	12/06	12/07
Sales ($ mil.)	403.0%	0.1	0.3	5.2	29.2	64.0
Net income ($ mil.)	—	(15.3)	(25.0)	(31.4)	(28.9)	(27.3)
Market value ($ mil.)	69.2%	—	—	222.9	457.0	638.0
Employees	52.4%	—	—	124	—	288

GENOPTIX, INC.

NASDAQ (GM): GXDX

2110 Rutherford Rd.
Carlsbad, CA 92008
Phone: 760-268-6200
Fax: 760-268-6201
Web: www.genoptix.com

CEO: Tina S. Nova Bennett
CFO: Douglas A. Schuling
HR: Cheri Caviness
FYE: December 31
Type: Public

Genoptix is promoting optimal health. The biotechnology company is a specialized laboratory service provider founded in 1997. It analyzes blood and tissue samples in order to diagnose diseases and markets those services to community-based hematologists and oncologists treating malignancies of the blood and bone marrow, as well as other types of cancer. Its key service offerings are COMPASS (short for Comprehensive Assessment) and CHART (a service offering introduced in 2007). Genoptix was started by Dr. Tina Nova, who also co-founded San Diego-based life science companies Ligand Pharmaceuticals and Nanogen.

	Annual Growth	12/03	12/04	12/05	12/06	12/07
Sales ($ mil.)	339.2%	—	0.7	5.2	24.0	59.3
Net income ($ mil.)	—	—	(10.2)	(9.2)	(3.8)	13.4
Market value ($ mil.)	—	—	—	—	—	494.1
Employees	—	—	—	—	113	—

GEN-PROBE INCORPORATED

NASDAQ (GS): GPRO

10210 Genetic Center Dr.
San Diego, CA 92121
Phone: 858-410-8000
Fax: 858-410-8625
Web: www.gen-probe.com

CEO: Henry L. (Hank) Nordhoff
CFO: Herm Rosenman
HR: Diana De Walt
FYE: December 31
Type: Public

Gen-Probe knows the answer is flowing through your veins. The company is a leading provider of diagnostic tests to detect HIV, chlamydia, and other sexually transmitted diseases. Gen-Probe also makes diagnostics to detect a host of infectious, disease-causing bacteria and fungi, including tuberculosis and the streptococcus bacteria that causes strep throat. In addition, the company makes products that screen donated blood for these diseases. Gen-Probe's products are designed to provide results within hours, while traditional cultured tests can take days. Major blood suppliers, including The American Red Cross and America's Blood Centers, use its products to screen much of the US blood supply.

	Annual Growth	12/03	12/04	12/05	12/06	12/07
Sales ($ mil.)	18.1%	207.2	269.7	306.0	354.8	403.0
Net income ($ mil.)	25.0%	35.3	54.6	60.1	59.5	86.1
Market value ($ mil.)	17.6%	1,776.9	2,262.1	2,495.0	2,735.5	3,393.0
Employees	9.0%	—	809	866	—	1,049

GENSYM CORPORATION

Pink Sheets: GNSM

52 2nd Ave.
Burlington, MA 01803
Phone: 781-265-7100
Fax: 781-265-7101
Web: www.gensym.com

CEO: Robert B. Ashton
CFO: Stephen D. (Steve) Allison
HR: –
FYE: December 31
Type: Public

Gensym hopes to unlock the knowledge in your operations. The company's application development software is used to generate applications that analyze operational data in order to automate and optimize business processes. Gensym's software is used to develop applications for managing network operations, optimizing supply chains, and monitoring process manufacturing. The company also offers applications for automating business processes, as well as services such as application engineering, maintenance, and support.

	Annual Growth	12/02	12/03	12/04	12/05	*12/06
Sales ($ mil.)	(0.9%)	17.5	14.6	17.6	17.7	16.9
Net income ($ mil.)	—	1.6	(1.8)	0.9	(0.7)	(0.8)
Employees	—	—	—	—	—	65

*Most recent year available

GENTA INCORPORATED

OTC: GNTA

2 Connell Dr.
Berkeley Heights, NJ 07922
Phone: 908-286-9800
Fax: 908-464-1701
Web: www.genta.com

CEO: Raymond P. Warrell Jr.
CFO: Gary Siegel
HR: –
FYE: December 31
Type: Public

Genta plays rough with cancer. The firm develops drugs, including DNA/RNA medicines and more traditional small molecule drugs, for cancer and other diseases. Lead candidate Genasense blocks production of a protein that can cause resistance to cancer treatments. The company is hoping for marketing approval of Genasense to be used in conjunction with chemotherapy by patients with lymphocytic leukemia and malignant melanoma. Genasense is also in clinical trials for treatment of other diseases such as prostate and colon cancer. Its small molecule program yielded Ganite, an FDA-approved treatment for hypercalcemia (a potentially fatal side effect of cancer), but the company does not actively market the drug.

	Annual Growth	12/03	12/04	12/05	12/06	12/07
Sales ($ mil.)	(45.3%)	6.7	15.1	26.6	0.7	0.6
Net income ($ mil.)	—	(50.1)	(32.7)	(2.2)	(56.8)	(23.3)
Market value ($ mil.)	(60.6%)	791.9	167.8	167.2	67.6	19.1
Employees	—	—	—	59	—	—

GENTEK INC.

NASDAQ (GS): GETI

90 E. Halsey Rd.
Parsippany, NJ 07054
Phone: 973-515-3221
Fax: 973-515-3229
Web: www.gentek-global.com

CEO: William E. Redmond Jr.
CFO: Thomas B. Testa
HR: Robert D. (Rob) Novo
FYE: December 31
Type: Public

GenTek products can be found in your car, in your kitchen, and under your arms. Through its subsidiaries, GenTek manufactures performance chemicals for such industries as pharmaceuticals and personal care (active ingredients for antiperspirants), environmental services (water treatment), technology (chemicals for semiconductor manufacturing), and chemicals processing. Its other segment makes valve actuation products that include auto parts such as valve-train components. GenTek has been tweaking its business mix by exiting some manufacturing operations while adding bolt-on acquisitions that enhance its businesses.

	Annual Growth	12/03	12/04	12/05	12/06	12/07
Sales ($ mil.)	43.8%	142.2	843.9	920.0	611.4	608.2
Net income ($ mil.)	128.1%	1.1	195.3	(0.8)	(2.1)	29.8
Market value ($ mil.)	(3.3%)	354.0	453.4	182.2	358.4	309.4
Employees	(52.4%)	—	—	6,500	1,525	1,475

An in-depth profile of this company is available to Hoover's Online members at hoovers.com.

675

⊞ GENTEX CORPORATION

NASDAQ (GS): GNTX

600 N. Centennial St.
Zeeland, MI 49464
Phone: 616-772-1800
Fax: 616-772-7348
Web: www.gentex.com

CEO: Fred T. Bauer
CFO: Steve Dykman
HR: Bruce Los
FYE: December 31
Type: Public

To find competitors in the race for market share, Gentex can just check its rearview mirror. The company manufactures interior and exterior automotive mirrors based on electrochromic technology, which uses electricity to darken a mirror's surface. Its Night Vision Safety (NVS) automatic-dimming car mirrors are featured as standard or optional equipment on more than 200 vehicle models. Automotive products account for more than 95% of the company's sales; major customers include giants Chrysler, General Motors, and BMW. Gentex also manufactures more than 60 models of smoke detectors and 160 kinds of fire alarms and signaling devices.

	Annual Growth	12/03	12/04	12/05	12/06	12/07
Sales ($ mil.)	8.7%	469.0	505.7	536.5	572.3	653.9
Net income ($ mil.)	3.4%	106.8	112.7	109.5	108.8	122.1
Market value ($ mil.)	10.9%	1,701.1	1,441.3	3,042.9	2,216.9	2,572.3
Employees	5.7%	—	—	2,264	2,393	—

GENTIVA HEALTH SERVICES, INC.

NASDAQ (GS): GTIV

3 Huntington Quadrangle, Ste. 200S
Melville, NY 11747
Phone: 631-501-7000
Fax: 631-501-7148
Web: www.gentiva.com

CEO: Ronald A. (Ron) Malone
CFO: John R. Potapchuk
HR: Brian D. Silva
FYE: Sunday nearest December 31
Type: Public

Gentiva Health Services is a gentle giant. Gentiva is the nation's largest home health care services firm. The company provides home nursing care through a network of more than 300 locations in 37 states. Gentiva's home care nurses provide services ranging from acute care treatment to housekeeping for the elderly or disabled. Gentiva also manages the home health care operations of other managed care companies through its CareCentrix division. CareCentrix's services include benefits and care coordination, data analysis, and billing. Respiratory and infusion therapy, home medical equipment, and hospice care are among the company's other offerings.

	Annual Growth	12/03	12/04	12/05	12/06	12/07
Sales ($ mil.)	10.9%	814.0	845.8	868.8	1,106.6	1,229.3
Net income ($ mil.)	(12.8%)	56.8	26.5	23.4	20.8	32.8
Market value ($ mil.)	12.2%	332.0	396.6	339.5	523.8	525.8
Employees	5.3%	—	—	13,935	7,600	15,450

⊞ GENUINE PARTS COMPANY

NYSE: GPC

2999 Circle 75 Pkwy.
Atlanta, GA 30339
Phone: 770-953-1700
Fax: 770-956-2211
Web: www.genpt.com

CEO: Thomas C. (Tom) Gallagher
CFO: Jerry W. Nix
HR: R. Bruce Clayton
FYE: December 31
Type: Public

What do spark plugs, hydraulic hoses, note pads, and magnet wire have in common? They're all Genuine Parts. The diversified company is the largest member and majority owner of the National Automotive Parts Association (NAPA), a voluntary trade association that distributes auto parts nationwide. Genuine Parts Company (GPC) operates about 1,100 NAPA Auto Parts stores in more than 40 US states. North of the border, NAPA Canada runs more than 600 auto parts and TRACTION stores. GPC's Auto Todo subsidiary operates distribution centers and auto and tire stores in Mexico. Other subsidiaries include Balkamp, Motion Industries, S.P. Richards Company, and UAP Inc.

	Annual Growth	12/03	12/04	12/05	12/06	12/07
Sales ($ mil.)	6.4%	8,449.3	9,097.3	9,783.0	10,457.9	10,843.2
Net income ($ mil.)	11.0%	334.1	395.5	437.4	475.4	506.3
Market value ($ mil.)	7.4%	5,778.3	7,709.0	7,599.6	8,088.3	7,688.8
Employees	0.5%	—	—	31,700	32,000	32,000

GENVEC, INC.

NASDAQ (GM): GNVC

65 W. Watkins Mill Rd.
Gaithersburg, MD 20878
Phone: 240-632-0740
Fax: 240-632-0735
Web: www.genvec.com

CEO: Paul H. Fischer
CFO: Douglas J. Swirsky
HR: Margaret M. (Marge) Meyer
FYE: December 31
Type: Public

GenVec is all over the medical map. The clinical-stage biopharmaceutical firm develops gene-based drugs and vaccines for everything from cancer to HIV. Its lead candidate, TNFerade, may boost the effectiveness of chemotherapy used to treat pancreatic and other types of cancer. Another drug candidate, AdPEDF, is in early clinical testing to treat age-related macular degeneration, a leading cause of blindness. GenVec is also developing multiple vaccines for contagious diseases, such as HIV, malaria, and foot-and-mouth, through grants from and collaborations with several federal agencies: the National Institute of Allergy and Infectious Diseases, the US Department of Homeland Security, and the US Department of Agriculture.

	Annual Growth	12/03	12/04	12/05	12/06	12/07
Sales ($ mil.)	7.6%	10.5	11.9	26.5	18.9	14.1
Net income ($ mil.)	—	(21.3)	(18.9)	(14.0)	(19.3)	(18.7)
Market value ($ mil.)	(10.1%)	169.2	90.6	105.1	176.3	110.8
Employees	—	—	—	109	—	—

GENWORTH FINANCIAL, INC.

NYSE: GNW

6620 W. Broad St.
Richmond, VA 23230
Phone: 804-281-6000
Fax: 804-662-2414
Web: www.genworth.com

CEO: Michael D. (Mike) Fraizer
CFO: Patrick B. (Pat) Kelleher
HR: Michael S. Laming
FYE: December 31
Type: Public

What's a Genworth? Insurance and investment specialist Genworth might ask what your life or your nest egg is worth. Genworth specializes in long-term care insurance, as well as life insurance, retirement investments, and private mortgage insurance. The company also offers a variety of payment protection insurance products in international markets. Genworth focuses its retirement investment products, including individual and group annuities and mutual funds, on affluent individuals. Genworth serves over 15 million customers in 25 countries; its products are sold through independent distributors and financial advisors.

	Annual Growth	12/03	12/04	12/05	12/06	12/07
Assets ($ mil.)	3.2%	—	103,878.0	105,292.0	110,871.0	114,315.0
Net income ($ mil.)	1.8%	—	1,157.0	1,221.0	1,328.0	1,220.0
Market value ($ mil.)	41.0%	—	3,955.5	13,313.3	15,155.0	11,096.2
Employees	0.7%	—	—	6,900	7,200	7,000

⊞ GENZYME CORPORATION

NASDAQ (GS): GENZ

500 Kendall St.
Cambridge, MA 02142
Phone: 617-252-7500
Fax: 617-252-7600
Web: www.genzyme.com

CEO: Henri A. Termeer
CFO: Michael S. Wyzga
HR: Zoltan A. Csimma
FYE: December 31
Type: Public

Genzyme makes big money off small-time diseases. The company's product portfolio focuses on rare genetic disorders as well as organ transplant, cancer, and kidney disease. One of its main products, Cerezyme, is a leading (and pricey) treatment for Gaucher's disease, a rare enzyme-deficiency condition. Founded in 1981, Genzyme also is involved in drug development and genetic testing and other services. In addition, the company develops gene-based cancer diagnosis and treatment products and it makes orthopedic medical and surgical products. Genzyme's products are sold to health care professionals in some 90 countries, primarily through wholesale distributors.

	Annual Growth	12/03	12/04	12/05	12/06	12/07
Sales ($ mil.)	22.1%	1,713.9	2,201.1	2,734.8	3,187.0	3,813.5
Net income ($ mil.)	—	(67.6)	86.5	441.5	(16.8)	480.2
Market value ($ mil.)	15.6%	11,076.3	14,466.7	18,350.3	16,197.1	19,801.6
Employees	10.4%	—	—	8,200	9,000	10,000

THE GEO GROUP, INC.

NYSE: GEO

1 Park Place, 621 NW 53rd St., Ste. 700
Boca Raton, FL 33487
Phone: 561-893-0101
Fax: 561-999-7635
Web: www.thegeogroupinc.com

CEO: George C. Zoley
CFO: John G. O'Rourke
HR: Stephen V. (Steve) Fuller
FYE: Sunday nearest December 31
Type: Public

The GEO Group sticks to its convictions, and it relies on them to generate business. The company, one of the largest operators of private correctional facilities in the US (along with Corrections Corporation of America), operates about 60 correctional, detention, and mental health facilities with more than 50,000 beds. Besides incarceration, GEO offers educational, rehabilitative, and vocational training programs at its facilities. The firm offers mental health and residential treatment services through its GEO Care subsidiary. Most of the company's facilities are in the US; it also has operations in Australia, Canada, South Africa, and the UK.

	Annual Growth	12/03	12/04	12/05	12/06	12/07
Sales ($ mil.)	13.5%	617.5	614.5	612.9	860.9	1,024.8
Net income ($ mil.)	(2.0%)	45.3	16.8	7.0	30.0	41.8
Market value ($ mil.)	289.9%	—	—	—	370.5	1,444.6
Employees	14.2%	—	—	8,463	10,253	11,037

GEOBIO ENERGY, INC.

OTC: GBOE

601 Union St., Ste. 4500
Seattle, WA 98121
Phone: 206-838-9715
Fax: –
Web: www.geobioenergy.com

CEO: Kenneth R. (Ken) Bennett
CFO: Allen Perron
HR: –
FYE: September 30
Type: Public

Biodiesel is definitely the way of the future for GeoBio Energy; it's just taking a while to decide what it wants to do with the fuel. Formerly involved in developing a proprietary technology that reduces the costs of biodiesel production while accelerating the production timeline, the company has moved on from that business. In 2008, when it was called Better Biodiesel, it acquired GeoAlgae Technologies, which develops low-cost, renewable feedstock used for the production of biodiesel. Following that deal, it changed its name to GeoBio Energy. With the rising costs of raw materials, the company is hoping that its ability to keep feedstock prices low will allow it to succeed in the hyper-competitive industry.

	Annual Growth	12/02	12/03	12/04	12/05	*9/07
Sales ($ mil.)	—	1.1	1.0	0.6	0.4	0.0
Net income ($ mil.)	—	0.0	(0.2)	(0.2)	(0.2)	(2.4)
Employees	—	—	—	—	—	—

*Fiscal year change

GEOEYE, INC.

NASDAQ (GM): GEOY

21700 Atlantic Blvd.
Dulles, VA 20166
Phone: 703-480-7500
Fax: 703-450-9570
Web: www.geoeye.com

CEO: Matthew M. O'Connell
CFO: Henry E. Dubois
HR: Angela Galyean
FYE: December 31
Type: Public

GeoEye provides satellite-collected Earth imagery and geospatial information for commercial and government organizations. It operates high-resolution imaging satellites that collect detailed land, sea, and atmospheric images, which the company processes and distributes. The company's imagery and information is used for a variety of applications, including mapping, environmental monitoring, urban planning, resource management, homeland defense, national security, and emergency preparedness. GeoEye also offers advanced image processing and production software and services.

	Annual Growth	12/03	12/04	12/05	12/06	12/07
Sales ($ mil.)	81.0%	—	31.0	40.7	151.2	183.8
Net income ($ mil.)	—	—	(24.7)	(24.3)	23.4	42.4
Market value ($ mil.)	48.5%	—	183.5	191.0	338.1	601.3
Employees	45.5%	—	133	295	318	410

GEOLOGISTICS CORPORATION

1251 E. Dyer Rd., Ste. 200
Santa Ana, CA 92705
Phone: 714-513-3000
Fax: 714-513-3120
Web: www.geo-logistics.com

CEO: Charbel Abou-Jaoude
CFO: –
HR: Jane Loftus
FYE: December 31
Type: Subsidiary

GeoLogistics gets goods going, globally. The company's offerings include freight forwarding, customs brokerage, and supply chain management. As a freight forwarder, GeoLogistics buys transportation capacity from air, ocean, and over-the-road carriers and resells that capacity to customers. Together with its parent company, PWC Logistics, GeoLogistics does business from a network of some 450 offices in more than 100 countries. Operations outside the US account for most of the company's sales. Along with other PWC Logistics units, GeoLogistics is adopting a new brand: Agility.

GEOMET, INC.

NASDAQ (GM): GMET

909 Fannin, Ste. 1850
Houston, TX 77010
Phone: 713-659-3855
Fax: 713-571-6394
Web: www.geometinc.com

CEO: J. Darby Seré
CFO: William C. Rankin
HR: –
FYE: December 31
Type: Public

Hoping that high oil prices will drive its geometric financial growth, GeoMet is engaged in the exploration and production of natural gas from coal-bed methane properties in the Cahaba Basin in Alabama and the Appalachian Basin in West Virginia and Virginia. The methane gas explorer is developing 77,000 acres in the Gurnee field in the Cahaba Basin and in the Pond Creek field in the Appalachian Basin. GeoMet also controls 203,000 net acres of coal-bed methane assets in British Columbia, Colorado, Louisiana, and West Virginia. In 2006 the company reported 325.7 billion cu. ft. of estimated proved reserves. Director Howard Keenan, general partner of Yorktown Energy Partners, owns nearly 42% of GeoMet.

	Annual Growth	12/03	12/04	12/05	12/06	12/07
Sales ($ mil.)	43.6%	12.0	21.5	42.0	58.1	51.0
Net income ($ mil.)	20.1%	2.5	3.8	(1.6)	17.3	5.2
Market value ($ mil.)	(49.6%)	—	—	—	402.3	202.6
Employees	22.2%	—	—	63	77	—

GEOPETRO RESOURCES COMPANY

AMEX: GPR

1 Maritime Plaza, Ste. 700
San Francisco, CA 94111
Phone: 415-398-8186
Fax: 415-398-9227
Web: www.geopetro.com

CEO: Stuart J. Doshi
CFO: J. Chris Steinhauser
HR: –
FYE: December 31
Type: Public

You have to drill down deep to figure out exactly what GeoPetro Resources does. It's an oil and natural gas exploration and production company with projects in Australia, Canada, Indonesia, and the US. These sites cover about 1.6 million gross acres consisting of mineral leases, production sharing contracts, and exploration permits. GeoPetro operates one cash generating property in the Madisonville Project in Texas; almost all of the revenue from this project has been derived from sales to two clients: Atmos Pipeline-Texas and ETC Katy Pipeline. GeoPetro Resources also has put together a geographically diverse portfolio of exploratory and appraisal prospects with the potential for oil and natural gas reserves.

	Annual Growth	12/03	12/04	12/05	12/06	12/07
Sales ($ mil.)	(77.0%)	2,453.0	5.8	8.0	6.7	6.9
Net income ($ mil.)	—	(1.7)	(2.1)	2.6	(0.5)	(1.6)
Market value ($ mil.)	31.7%	—	—	—	85.1	112.1
Employees	11.1%	—	—	9	10	—

An in-depth profile of this company is available to Hoover's Online members at hoovers.com.

677

GEOPHARMA, INC.

NASDAQ (CM): GORX

6950 Bryan Dairy Rd.
Largo, FL 33777
Phone: 727-544-8866
Fax: 727-544-4386
Web: www.onlineihp.com

CEO: Mihir K. Taneja
CFO: Carol Dore-Falcone
HR: —
FYE: March 31
Type: Public

GeoPharma makes a world of health care products, from generic antibiotics to weight loss aids and nutritionals. Its main business — contract manufacturing of nutritional supplements — is done through subsidiary Innovative Health Products. Another subsidiary, Libi Labs, focuses on private-label nutraceutical and cosmeceutical manufacturing. GeoPharma also develops some of its own products, including dietary supplements through Breakthrough Engineered Nutrition (also known as DelMar Labs) and generic drugs through Belcher Pharmaceuticals. Its marketed diet products include appetite suppressants DEX-L10 and Cortiloss, which are distributed through mass retailers, drug stores, and health food stores.

	Annual Growth	3/04	3/05	3/06	3/07	3/08
Sales ($ mil.)	24.4%	23.0	28.2	49.7	59.8	55.0
Net income ($ mil.)	—	1.1	(0.9)	1.8	2.5	(7.0)
Market value ($ mil.)	(6.3%)	46.7	28.0	43.6	45.0	36.0
Employees	29.4%	83	103	150	180	—

GEORESOURCES, INC.

NASDAQ (GM): GEOI

1407 W. Dakota Pkwy., Ste. 1-B
Williston, ND 58801
Phone: 701-572-2020
Fax: 701-572-0277
Web: www.georesources.net

CEO: Frank A. Lodzinski
CFO: Howard E. Ehler
HR: —
FYE: December 31
Type: Public

Though most of GeoResources' products are wet and slippery, one of them is dry and powdery. The company's oil and gas operations in Montana and North Dakota generate the bulk of its revenues. It also has a contract drilling operation. GeoResources has proved reserves of 2.8 million barrels of oil and 1.4 billion cu. ft. of gas. It also mines leonardite, an oxidized lignite coal, which it processes into a powder used primarily as a dispersant or thinner in drilling mud, but the company is exiting this business in order to focus on oil and gas. In 2007 the company acquired Southern Bay Oil & Gas, L.P., and Chandler Energy, LLC, for $78 million.

	Annual Growth	12/03	12/04	12/05	12/06	12/07
Sales ($ mil.)	70.0%	4.8	6.8	8.0	8.9	40.1
Net income ($ mil.)	66.8%	0.4	1.1	2.2	1.7	3.1
Market value ($ mil.)	—	—	—	—	—	132.3
Employees	4.1%	12	11	13	—	—

GEORGE E. WARREN CORPORATION

3001 Ocean Dr.
Vero Beach, FL 32963
Phone: 772-778-7100
Fax: 772-778-7171
Web: www.gewarren.com

CEO: Thomas L. Corr
CFO: Michael E. George
HR: Cheryl Ernst
FYE: December 31
Type: Private

By barge, by pipeline, by tank truck, by George; George E. Warren is a major private wholesale distributor of petroleum in the eastern US. Founded in Boston by George E. Warren in 1907 as a coal and oil distributor, it moved to Florida in 1989. The company distributes products mostly by barge and pipeline, though it uses some tank trucks as well. Warren has distribution facilities in the southeastern and southwestern US. It distributes products including ethylene and heating oil to various industries. President and CEO Thomas Corr owns the company.

GEORGE P. JOHNSON COMPANY

3600 Giddings Rd.
Auburn Hills, MI 48326
Phone: 248-475-2500
Fax: 248-475-2325
Web: www.gpjco.com

CEO: Robert G. Vallee Jr.
CFO: David Drews
HR: Eva-Katerine Miller
FYE: December 31
Type: Private

The George P. Johnson Company (GPJ) is a leading event marketing company that helps businesses strut their stuff at more than 4,900 events each year. The company produces and markets the entire experience — from architectural engineering, graphic design, and lighting to scripting, storyboarding, and audience acquisition. Clients include such big names as IBM, Cisco Systems, and Toyota. Operating 20 offices worldwide, the company was founded by George P. Johnson in 1914 as a flag and decoration business.

	Annual Growth	12/03	12/04	12/05	12/06	12/07
Est. sales ($ mil.)	—	—	—	—	—	33.5
Employees	—	—	—	—	—	500

GEORGE RISK INDUSTRIES, INC.

OTC: RISKA

802 S. Elm St.
Kimball, NE 69145
Phone: 308-235-4645
Fax: 308-235-2609
Web: www.grisk.com

CEO: Ken R. Risk
CFO: Stephanie Risk
HR: —
FYE: April 30
Type: Public

George Risk Industries (GRI) wants customers to be able to manage risks. The company makes burglar alarm components and systems, including panic buttons (for direct access to alarm monitoring centers). In addition to security products, GRI manufactures pool alarms, which are designed to sound alerts when a pool or spa area has been entered. The company also makes thermostats, specialty computer keyboards and keypads, custom-engraved key caps, and push-button switches. Chairman and president Ken Risk, a son of founder George Risk, owns more than half of the company.

	Annual Growth	4/03	4/04	4/05	4/06	4/07
Sales ($ mil.)	1.0%	12.9	12.8	13.1	14.3	13.4
Net income ($ mil.)	6.9%	2.3	2.4	2.5	2.7	3.0
Market value ($ mil.)	30.1%	13.5	30.5	30.2	43.3	38.7
Employees	—	—	—	—	275	—

GEORGE WESTON BAKERIES INC.

55 Paradise Ln.
Bay Shore, NY 11706
Phone: 800-355-1260
Fax: 973-785-0009
Web: www.gwbakeries.com

CEO: Gary J. Prince
CFO: Stephen (Steve) Mollick
HR: Louis A. (Lou) Minella
FYE: December 31
Type: Subsidiary

George Weston Bakeries wants you to lay it on. What you should "lay on" is butter, jam, or any other yummy topping of your choice. What you should "lay it on" is one of Weston's many well-known brands of bagels, breads, English muffins, pitas, and pizza crusts. The company makes such branded baked-goods labels as Arnold, Boboli, Brownberry, Entenmann's, Freihofer's, Stroehmann, and Thomas'. The company's Interbake Foods division is a major supplier of Girl Scout cookies in the US. George Weston Bakeries is a subsidiary of Canadian giant George Weston Limited.

	Annual Growth	12/03	12/04	12/05	12/06	12/07
Est. sales ($ mil.)	—	—	—	—	—	1,165.9
Employees	—	—	—	—	—	15,000

GEORGIA CROWN DISTRIBUTING CO.

100 Georgia Crown Dr.
McDonough, GA 30253
Phone: 770-302-3000
Fax: 770-302-3080
Web: www.georgiacrown.com

CEO: Donald M. Leebern III
CFO: Orlene Bovaird
HR: Mary Beth Gibbon
FYE: July 31
Type: Private

Aptly named Fate Leebern may have died for Georgia Crown Distributing, a beverage bottler and distributor. He founded Georgia Crown as Columbus Wine Company Distributor in 1938, the same year Georgia prohibition was repealed. After the first rail shipment of legal liquor was received, someone — reportedly the Dixie Mafia — murdered Leebern. Today the family-owned company distributes beer, wine, liquor, bottled water, juices, and soft drinks to Georgia, Alabama, and Tennessee. The bottler also distributes its brand of bottled water, Melwood Springs. CEO Donald Leebern III is the grandson of the company's founder. The Leebern family owns the business.

	Annual Growth	7/03	7/04	7/05	7/06	7/07
Est. sales ($ mil.)	—	—	—	—	—	154.8
Employees	—	—	—	—	—	475

GEORGIA FARM BUREAU MUTUAL INSURANCE COMPANY

1620 Bass Rd.
Macon, GA 31209
Phone: 478-474-8411
Fax: 478-474-8869
Web: www.gfb.org/indexins.htm

CEO: Vincent (Zippy) Duvall
CFO: Wayne Daniel
HR: –
FYE: December 31
Type: Mutual company

You don't have to be a farmer to get insurance coverage here, but it helps. Georgia Farm Bureau Mutual and its affiliates provide a variety of commercial and individual property/casualty products to members of Georgia's Farm Bureau. Its offerings include automobile, farm, homeowners, and personal liability insurance. The company specializes in writing lower-cost, preferred risk policies (policies for customers that are less likely to file claims). A network of more than 550 company agents and representatives market Georgia Farm Bureau Mutual's products. A part of the Georgia Farm Bureau, the company was founded in 1959.

	Annual Growth	12/03	12/04	12/05	12/06	12/07
Est. sales ($ mil.)	—	—	—	—	—	534.5
Employees	—	—	—	—	—	1,210

GEORGIA GULF CORPORATION

NYSE: GGC

115 Perimeter Center Place, Ste. 460
Atlanta, GA 30346
Phone: 770-395-4500
Fax: 770-395-4529
Web: www.ggc.com

CEO: Paul D. Carrico
CFO: Gregory C. (Greg) Thompson
HR: James Worrell
FYE: December 31
Type: Public

It doesn't take an old sweet song to tell you what Georgia Gulf Corporation does. The company makes chlorovinyls and aromatics used by the construction and housing, plastics, pulp and paper, and pharmaceutical industries. Its primary chlorovinyl products are PVC (polyvinyl chloride) compounds and resins, caustic soda, and chlorine; this segment also makes vinyl chloride monomer (VCM), used by Georgia Gulf to manufacture PVC resins. Aromatics include phenol (sold to makers of wood adhesives and engineered plastics), acetone (sold to makers of acrylic resins), and cumene (used by the firm to make phenol and acetone). Much of Georgia Gulf's sales are to the housing and construction market.

	Annual Growth	12/03	12/04	12/05	12/06	12/07
Sales ($ mil.)	21.6%	1,444.5	2,206.2	2,273.7	2,427.8	3,157.3
Net income ($ mil.)	—	12.5	105.9	95.5	48.5	(266.0)
Market value ($ mil.)	(29.9%)	945.4	1,689.4	1,041.5	664.1	227.7
Employees	116.2%	—	—	1,123	6,654	5,249

GEORGIA LOTTERY CORPORATION

250 Williams St., Ste. 3000
Atlanta, GA 30303
Phone: 404-215-5000
Fax: 404-215-8983
Web: www.galottery.com

CEO: Margaret R. DeFrancisco
CFO: Joan Schoubert
HR: Doug Parker
FYE: June 30
Type: Government-owned

Lottery fans with an eye toward education may have Georgia on their minds. Established in 1993, the Georgia Lottery has contributed more than $9 billion to the state's education coffers. In addition to the HOPE program, which has helped some 1 million students attend college with lottery-funded scholarships, the lottery helps finance a pre-kindergarten program and public school capital improvements. More than 7,500 retailers throughout Georgia sell tickets for lottery games, including instant-ticket, online, and keno-style games, and a powerball-like game aptly named Mega Millions. In its first year the Georgia Lottery reached $1.1 billion in sales and has been growing ever since.

	Annual Growth	6/02	6/03	6/04	6/05	6/06
Sales ($ mil.)	6.1%	2,449.0	2,604.0	2,710.0	2,922.0	3,100.0
Employees	0.0%	250	250	—	—	—

GEORGIA POWER COMPANY

241 Ralph McGill Blvd. NE
Atlanta, GA 30308
Phone: 404-506-6526
Fax: 404-506-3771
Web: www.georgiapower.com

CEO: Michael D. (Mike) Garrett
CFO: Cliff S. Thrasher
HR: –
FYE: December 31
Type: Subsidiary

Bigger than a giant peach, Georgia Power is the largest subsidiary of US utility holding company Southern Company. The regulated utility provides electricity to more than 2.3 million residential, commercial, and industrial customers throughout most of Georgia. It has fossil-fueled, nuclear, and hydroelectric power plant interests that give it more than 14,500 MW of generating capacity. Georgia Power sells wholesale electricity to several cooperatives and municipalities in the region. The utility also offers energy efficiency, surge protection, and outdoor lighting products and services. In 2006 Georgia Power absorbed Southern Company subsidiary Savannah Electric.

	Annual Growth	12/03	12/04	12/05	12/06	12/07
Est. sales ($ mil.)	—	—	—	—	—	7,571.6
Net income ($ mil.)	—	—	—	—	—	842.1
Employees	—	—	—	—	—	—

GEORGIA-CAROLINA BANCSHARES, INC.

3527 Wheeler Rd.
Augusta, GA 30909
Phone: 706-731-6600
Fax: 706-731-0731
Web: www.firstbankofga.com

CEO: Remer Y. Brinson III
CFO: Bradley J. (Jack) Gregory
HR: Terra Lariscy
FYE: December 31
Type: Public

Georgia-Carolina Bancshares is holding the line on banking in and around Augusta, Georgia. The holding company owns First Bank of Georgia, which has about a half-dozen branches along the eastern edge of the Peach State. The company also owns First Bank Mortgage, which originates residential loans and other mortgage products through offices in Georgia and Florida. The bank focuses on real estate lending, in addition to providing such standard deposit products as checking and savings accounts. Other lending activities include business and consumer loans. The bank's FB Financial Services division offers investment products and financial management services through an agreement with brokerage Linsco/Private Ledger.

	Annual Growth	12/03	12/04	12/05	12/06	12/07
Assets ($ mil.)	13.9%	266.0	332.4	349.5	417.5	447.9
Net income ($ mil.)	(12.7%)	5.0	3.5	3.5	2.9	2.9
Market value ($ mil.)	(0.4%)	38.0	44.4	47.8	47.3	37.4
Employees	7.2%	148	149	170	—	—

An in-depth profile of this company is available to Hoover's Online members at hoovers.com.

679

GEORGIA-PACIFIC CORPORATION

133 Peachtree St., NE
Atlanta, GA 30303
Phone: 404-652-4000
Fax: 404-230-1674
Web: www.gp.com

CEO: James (Jim) Hannan
CFO: Tyler L. Woolson
HR: Julie Brehm
FYE: Saturday nearest December 31
Type: Subsidiary

Georgia-Pacific (GP) may be on your mind when you think about paper, but the world's #1 producer of tissue products (bath tissue, paper towels, and napkins) is also made of sturdier stuff such as building products (plywood, lumber, OSB, gypsum wallboard, particleboard, adhesives). Consumer products include bleached pulp and paper. Brawny paper towels and Quilted Northern bath tissue products are some of its top brands. The paper and building products giant, a subsidiary of Koch Industries, is the second-largest US forest products manufacturer behind International Paper. GP has more than 300 manufacturing facilities in North America, South America, and Europe.

	Annual Growth	12/03	12/04	12/05	12/06	12/07
Est. sales ($ mil.)	—	—	—	—	—	2,147.5
Employees	—	—	—	—	—	50,000

GERBER PRODUCTS COMPANY

200 Kimball Dr.
Parsippany, NJ 07054
Phone: 973-503-8000
Fax: 973-503-8400
Web: www.gerber.com

CEO: Kurt T. Schmidt
CFO: Andre Cadieux
HR: –
FYE: December 31
Type: Subsidiary

Gerber Products Company doesn't strain to make money. But it does strain to make its products. Gerber's more than 200 baby offerings include the almost ubiquitous glass jars of baby food. The company, which had its beginnings in 1927 in Dorothy Gerber's kitchen, also makes baby cereal, juices, and toddler food, along with baby bath and skin care products, bottles, teethers, breastfeeding accessories, spill-proof cups, and infant toys and clothing. Its Gerber Life Insurance Company offers various whole and term life products. Gerber feeds, soothes, and amuses babies worldwide. In 2007 Nestlé acquired the company from Novartis.

GERBER SCIENTIFIC, INC.

NYSE: GRB

83 Gerber Rd. West
South Windsor, CT 06074
Phone: 860-644-1551
Fax: 860-643-7039
Web: www.gerberscientific.com

CEO: Marc T. Giles
CFO: Michael R. Elia
HR: Jay Wickliff
FYE: April 30
Type: Public

Gerber Scientific began with baby steps. Now the company is an industry leader in making products for the specialty graphics, ophthalmic lens processing, and apparel and flexible materials industries. The company produces automated manufacturing systems for sign-making, industrial manufacturing, and eyeglass lens production. Its signage subsidiaries, Gerber Scientific Products and Spandex, make digital imaging systems, materials, cutting systems, and software. The company's Gerber Technology subsidiary provides CAD/CAM pattern-making and cutting systems for apparel, automotive, composite, furniture, and technical textile companies. The firm's Gerber Coburn Optical makes eyeglass lens manufacturing equipment.

	Annual Growth	4/04	4/05	4/06	4/07	4/08
Sales ($ mil.)	5.5%	516.8	517.3	530.4	574.8	640.0
Net income ($ mil.)	27.4%	5.5	(5.6)	2.6	13.5	14.5
Market value ($ mil.)	13.3%	133.3	157.9	234.5	232.1	219.8
Employees	2.7%	1,980	2,000	2,022	2,190	2,200

GERDAU AMERISTEEL CORPORATION

NYSE: GNA

4221 W. Boy Scout Blvd., Ste. 600
Tampa, FL 33607
Phone: 813-286-2300
Fax: 813-207-2328
Web: www.gerdauameristeel.com

CEO: Mario Longhi
CFO: Barbara R. Smith
HR: Terry K. Danahy
FYE: December 31
Type: Public

Gerdau Ameristeel is putting its stamp on the steel business in the US. The company is one of the largest minimill steel makers in North America, producing more than 8 million tons of finished steel annually. Through its 20 steel mills (mostly in the US), Gerdau Ameristeel primarily sells to the eastern two-thirds of North America. The company also operates scrap recycling operations, specialty processing centers, and rebar fabricating and coating plants. Its minimills produce beams, flat-rolled steel, merchant bar, rebar, and wire rod primarily used in the automotive, appliance, construction, machinery, and equipment industries. Brazilian steelmaker Gerdau owns approximately two-thirds of the company.

	Annual Growth	12/03	12/04	12/05	12/06	12/07
Sales ($ mil.)	24.5%	—	3,009.9	3,897.1	4,464.2	5,806.6
Net income ($ mil.)	16.8%	—	337.7	302.0	378.6	537.9
Market value ($ mil.)	44.1%	—	2,055.2	1,717.2	2,724.0	6,149.6
Employees	44.9%	—	—	7,000	10,140	—

GERMAN AMERICAN BANCORP

NASDAQ (GS): GABC

711 Main St.
Jasper, IN 47546
Phone: 812-482-1314
Fax: 812-482-0721
Web: www.germanamericanbancorp.com

CEO: Mark A. Schroeder
CFO: Bradley M. Rust
HR: Lisa A. Matheis
FYE: December 31
Type: Public

German American Bancorp is the holding company for German American Bank, which also operates under the brands Citizens State Bank, First American Bank, First State Bank, Peoples Bank, and Stone City Bank. The bank has some 30 branches in 10 southwestern Indiana counties and offers such standard retail products as checking and savings accounts, CDs, and IRAs. Commercial and industrial loans make up about half of the bank's loan portfolio; agricultural loans account for about 20%. Other offerings include residential mortgages and consumer loans. The company also operates insurance agencies and a trust, financial planning, and brokerage subsidiary.

	Annual Growth	12/03	12/04	12/05	12/06	12/07
Assets ($ mil.)	5.1%	926.0	942.1	946.5	1,093.4	1,131.7
Net income ($ mil.)	3.5%	8.2	7.2	9.7	10.2	9.4
Market value ($ mil.)	(7.4%)	191.3	175.5	140.1	158.3	140.5
Employees	(4.7%)	—	—	402	—	365

GERON CORPORATION

NASDAQ (GM): GERN

230 Constitution Dr.
Menlo Park, CA 94025
Phone: 650-473-7700
Fax: 650-473-7750
Web: www.geron.com

CEO: Thomas B. Okarma
CFO: David L. Greenwood
HR: –
FYE: December 31
Type: Public

Not far from the center of the controversy over human embryonic stem cell (hESC) research is Geron. The company hopes to parlay its work into viable therapies for various diseases and conditions. It is focused on lead anticancer drug candidate GRN163L, which inhibits telomerase, an enzyme that may prolong cellular life and prevents apoptosis (programmed cell death). The company is also continuing its work with hESCs to develop neural cells that could be implanted to treat spinal cord injury and other neurological disorders, heart muscle cells that could treat various cardiovascular conditions, and pancreatic islet cells that may restore insulin production in patients suffering from type I diabetes.

	Annual Growth	12/03	12/04	12/05	12/06	12/07
Sales ($ mil.)	58.6%	1.2	1.0	6.2	3.3	7.6
Net income ($ mil.)	—	(29.9)	(80.4)	(33.5)	(31.4)	(36.7)
Market value ($ mil.)	2.5%	392.0	416.2	558.2	618.5	432.0
Employees	—	—	—	90	—	—

GES EXPOSITION SERVICES, INC.

950 Grier Dr.
Las Vegas, NV 89119
Phone: 702-263-1500
Fax: 702-263-1520
Web: www.gesexpo.com

CEO: Kevin M. Rabbitt
CFO: Dave Hall
HR: Anne Hanson
FYE: December 31
Type: Subsidiary

GES Exposition Services provides exhibition and event services to conventions across North America. Producing all manner of trade shows, the company provides planning, design, logistics, and graphics production services in addition to preparation, installation, and dismantling of exhibits and displays. The company is a key subsidiary of Viad Corp, a leader in convention and event services, and serves more than 250,000 exhibitor customers through its offices across more than 15 US and seven Canadian cities. GES is quite the breadwinner for its parent company, representing almost 70% of Viad's total revenue each year. GES expanded in 2007 when it bought Melville Exhibition and Event Services, based in the UK.

GETTY IMAGES, INC.

NYSE: GYI

601 N. 34th St.
Seattle, WA 98103
Phone: 206-925-5000
Fax: 206-925-5001
Web: www.gettyimages.com

CEO: Jonathan D. Klein
CFO: Thomas (Tom) Oberdorf
HR: James C. (Jim) Gurke
FYE: December 31
Type: Public

With an eye out for the big picture, visual content provider Getty Images is a major supplier of creative (stock) and editorial still and moving images and illustrations, as well as music. It also offers photo services for corporate clients. The company targets four main markets: advertising and graphic design firms; editorial organizations, such as newspapers, magazines, and online publishers; corporate communications departments; and film and broadcast producers. Getty Images, which distributes its products online, has customers in more than 100 countries around the world; most of its sales come from outside the US. In 2008 Getty Images agreed to be acquired by private equity firm Hellman & Friedman.

	Annual Growth	12/03	12/04	12/05	12/06	12/07
Sales ($ mil.)	13.1%	523.2	622.4	733.7	806.6	857.6
Net income ($ mil.)	18.4%	64.0	106.7	149.7	130.4	125.9
Market value ($ mil.)	(11.9%)	2,873.7	4,181.6	5,558.4	2,535.9	1,727.5
Employees	(4.0%)	—	—	1,823	1,750	—

GETTY PETROLEUM MARKETING INC.

1500 Hempstead Tpke.
East Meadow, NY 11554
Phone: 516-542-4900
Fax: 516-832-8272
Web: www.getty.com

CEO: Vadim Gluzman
CFO: Michael K. Hantman
HR: –
FYE: December 31
Type: Subsidiary

A remnant of J. Paul Getty's oil empire, Getty Petroleum Marketing distributes gasoline and heating fuels. The company, which became a subsidiary of Russian oil giant LUKOIL in 2001, has about 2,100 gas stations (some of which maintain convenience stores, auto repair centers, or car washes) in 13 northeastern and mid-Atlantic US states. Originally a part of Getty Petroleum (now Getty Realty), the company sells heating oil through its KOSCO subsidiary. Getty Petroleum Marketing expanded its US retail chain by acquiring 779 gas stations in New Jersey and Pennsylvania from ConocoPhillips.

	Annual Growth	12/03	12/04	12/05	12/06	12/07
Est. sales ($ mil.)	—	—	—	—	—	180.6
Employees	—	—	—	—	—	624

GETTY REALTY CORP.

NYSE: GTY

125 Jericho Tpke., Ste. 103
Jericho, NY 11753
Phone: 516-478-5400
Fax: 516-478-5476
Web: www.gettyrealty.com

CEO: Leo Liebowitz
CFO: Thomas J. Stirnweis
HR: –
FYE: December 31
Type: Public

Some black gold is sold on property owned by Getty Realty Corp. The self-administered real estate investment trust (REIT) owns and leases about 1,100 gas service stations, adjacent convenience stores, and petroleum distribution terminals, primarily in the Northeast and Mid-Atlantic. One-third of its properties reside in New York; about 80% of its properties are leased to one tenant, Getty Petroleum Marketing Inc., which is responsible for operating and maintaining its property, as well as the remediation of any environmental contamination it causes. Getty Realty was formed in 1997 when it spun off Getty Petroleum Marketing and sold its heating oil distribution business.

	Annual Growth	12/03	12/04	12/05	12/06	12/07
Sales ($ mil.)	3.5%	68.3	66.3	71.4	72.4	78.5
Net income ($ mil.)	(2.1%)	36.9	39.3	45.5	42.7	33.9
Market value ($ mil.)	0.6%	645.0	709.5	649.8	765.2	660.7
Employees	0.0%	—	—	16	—	16

GEVITY HR, INC.

NASDAQ (GS): GVHR

9000 Town Center Pkwy.
Bradenton, FL 34202
Phone: 941-741-4300
Fax: 941-744-8030
Web: www.gevityhr.com

CEO: Garry J. Welsh
CFO: Garry J. Welsh
HR: Clifford M. Sladnick
FYE: December 31
Type: Public

Gevity HR runs on people power — and lots of it. The company, a professional employer organization, or PEO, has about 6,900 clients and more than 130,000 worksite employees throughout the US. Gevity acts as a full-service human resources department, providing recruiting, payroll administration, risk management, benefits administration, and human resources consultation to small and medium-size businesses. Gevity Edge, which offers these services together, is the company's flagship product. Gevity operates through more than 40 offices in nearly 20 states and delivers its products and services through human resources consultants and through an online payroll and human resources portal.

	Annual Growth	12/03	12/04	12/05	12/06	12/07
Sales ($ mil.)	9.2%	425.8	585.5	608.8	648.0	605.0
Net income ($ mil.)	(10.2%)	15.4	34.6	37.4	35.3	10.0
Market value ($ mil.)	(19.5%)	426.8	625.2	678.3	585.2	179.1
Employees	(1.4%)	954	993	1,050	1,000	900

GFI GROUP INC.

NASDAQ (GS): GFIG

100 Wall St.
New York, NY 10005
Phone: 212-968-4100
Fax: 212-968-4124
Web: www.gfigroup.com

CEO: Michael Gooch
CFO: James A. Peers
HR: Sheena Griffiths
FYE: December 31
Type: Public

A financial matchmaker, GFI Group is an inter-dealer electronic brokerage that acts as an intermediary for more than 2,000 institutional clients such as banks, large corporations, insurance companies, and hedge funds. The firm deals primarily in over-the-counter derivatives, which tend to be less liquid and thus harder to trade than other assets. It also offers market data and analysis on credit, equity, commodity, and currency derivatives, and other financial instruments. Other products include foreign exchange options, freight, and other energy derivatives, including electric power, coal, and carbon emissions options. GFI has about a dozen offices in North America, Europe, and Asia.

	Annual Growth	12/03	12/04	12/05	12/06	12/07
Sales ($ mil.)	38.2%	265.8	385.0	533.6	747.2	970.5
Net income ($ mil.)	59.9%	14.5	23.1	48.1	61.1	94.9
Market value ($ mil.)	45.9%	—	—	330.9	446.7	704.7
Employees	24.9%	—	—	1,151	1,438	—

An in-depth profile of this company is available to Hoover's Online members at hoovers.com.

681

GGNSC HOLDINGS LLC

1000 Fianna Way
Fort Smith, AR 72919
Phone: 479-201-2000
Fax: 479-201-1101
Web: www.goldenliving.com/Golden+Ventures

CEO: –
CFO: Richard D. Skelly Jr.
HR: Michael Karicher
FYE: December 31
Type: Private

GGNSC Holdings is a holding company doing business as Golden Horizons. The firm operates hundreds of nursing homes and assisted living facilities across the US, most of them company-owned and others leased. Its company-owned facilities go by the name Golden Living, while its leased ones operate under the Beverly brand, a nod to the company's former existence as Beverly Enterprises. All told, Golden Horizons runs about 350 nursing homes and 20 assisted living centers. It was taken private in 2006, when private investor Fillmore Capital Partners bought it for more than $2 billion. It subsequently changed its name to Golden Horizons and rebranded all its company-owned operations under the "Golden" moniker.

	Annual Growth	12/02	12/03	12/04	12/05	12/06
Est. sales ($ mil.)	—	—	—	—	—	2,500.0
Employees	—	—	—	—	—	40,000

GHIRARDELLI CHOCOLATE COMPANY

1111 139th Ave.
San Leandro, CA 94578
Phone: 510-483-6970
Fax: 510-297-2649
Web: www.ghirardelli.com

CEO: Fabrizio Parini
CFO: –
HR: Leslie Yewell
FYE: December 31
Type: Subsidiary

With boxes, bars, and business gifts, Ghirardelli Chocolate Company speaks to American chocolate lovers on many levels. Established in 1852, the company makes premium chocolate products such as its signature chocolate squares, baking chocolate, and chocolate beverage mixes. Ghirardelli controls the entire manufacturing process and distributes its products nationwide. Its chocolate products are available at retail outlets including grocery, drug, mass-merchandise, and specialty stores. The company operates about a dozen Ghirardelli Soda Fountain and Chocolate Shops aimed at the tourist and local-community markets.

	Annual Growth	12/03	12/04	12/05	12/06	12/07
Est. sales ($ mil.)	—	—	—	—	—	35.8
Employees	—	—	—	—	—	650

G-I HOLDINGS INC.

1361 Alps Rd.
Wayne, NJ 07470
Phone: 973-628-3000
Fax: –

CEO: Samuel J. (Sam) Heyman
CFO: John Rebele
HR: Gary Schneid
FYE: December 31
Type: Private

G-I Holdings has a kung-fu grip on the roofing materials business. Also known under its former name GAF Corporation, G-I Holdings and its subsidiary Building Materials Corporation of America make flashing, vents, and complete roofing systems. G-I Holdings makes residential shingles and commercial asphalt roofing under the Timberline, Everguard, and Ruberoid brands. Other products include natural stone, ornamental ironwork, and ducting. G-I Holdings is in bankruptcy protection due to asbestos liability claims. Chairman Samuel Heyman owns the company and affiliate specialty chemicals manufacturer International Specialty Products Inc.

	Annual Growth	12/02	12/03	12/04	12/05	12/06
Sales ($ mil.)	9.7%	1,361.0	1,608.0	1,770.0	1,956.0	1,970.0
Employees	1.4%	3,400	3,500	3,700	3,700	3,600

GIANT EAGLE, INC.

101 Kappa Dr.
Pittsburgh, PA 15238
Phone: 412-963-6200
Fax: 412-968-1617
Web: www.gianteagle.com

CEO: David S. (Dave) Shapira
CFO: Mark Minnaugh
HR: Vicki Clites
FYE: June 30
Type: Private

Giant Eagle has its talons firmly wrapped around parts of Pennsylvania and Ohio. The grocery chain, #1 in Pittsburgh and eastern Ohio, operates more than 150 corporate and some 70 franchised supermarkets, as well as about 130 GetGo convenience stores (which feature fresh foods and sell gas at discounted prices through the fuelperks! program). Many Giant Eagle stores feature video rental, banking, photo processing, dry cleaning services, and ready-to-eat meals. Giant Eagle is also a wholesaler to licensed stores and sells groceries to other retail chains. CEO David Shapira is the grandson of one of the men who founded the company in 1931. The founders' families own Giant Eagle.

	Annual Growth	6/02	6/03	6/04	6/05	6/06
Sales ($ mil.)	12.7%	4,415.0	4,739.0	5,100.0	5,500.0	7,130.0
Employees	8.5%	26,000	26,000	28,000	36,000	36,000

GIANT FOOD LLC

8301 Professional Place, Ste. 115
Landover, MD 20785
Phone: 301-341-4100
Fax: 301-618-4998
Web: www.giantfood.com

CEO: Jose B. Alvarez
CFO: James K. Rojas
HR: Ira Kress
FYE: Sunday nearest December 31
Type: Subsidiary

A monster among mid-Atlantic grocers, Giant Food (dba Giant-Landover) operates about 185 Giant Food and Super G supermarkets. It's #1 in the Baltimore and Washington, DC, markets; it also operates in the most populous areas of Delaware, Maryland, and Virginia. Most of its supermarkets house full-service pharmacies, and some have Toys "R" Us toy departments. The company also operates its own dairy, beverage bottling, and ice cream plants. Founded in 1936, Giant was acquired in 1998 by Ahold USA, which owns about 825 supermarkets in the US, including the New England-based Stop & Shop chain, Giant Food's sister company. The two regional grocery chains have been jointly managed since 2004.

GIANT FOOD STORES, LLC

1149 Harrisburg Pike
Carlisle, PA 17013
Phone: 717-249-4000
Fax: 717-960-1327
Web: www.giantpa.com

CEO: Carl Schlicker
CFO: Rick Herring
HR: John Bussenger
FYE: December 31
Type: Subsidiary

Giant Food Stores (aka Giant-Carlisle) operates about 140 supermarkets under the Giant and Martin's Food Markets banners in Pennsylvania, and in Maryland, Virginia, and West Virginia. Giant Food Stores and its Landover, Maryland-based sister company Giant Food are units of Ahold USA, which operates some 700 supermarkets in the US. Giant Food Stores was founded in 1923 and acquired by Ahold USA in 1981. In 2003 the parent company integrated administrative and other functions at the chain with New York-based TOPS Markets. However, Ahold USA's parent company, Dutch grocer Royal Ahold, sold TOPS Markets to the private equity arm of Morgan Stanley in late 2007.

GIANT MOTORSPORTS, INC.

OTC: GMOS

13134 State Rte. 62
Salem, OH 44460
Phone: 440-439-9480
Fax: 440-439-9253
Web: www.giantcorporate.com

CEO: Russell A. Haehn
CFO: –
HR: –
FYE: December 31
Type: Public

Giant Motorsports believes in thinking big when it comes to fun. Tne company is a leading motorsports dealer in the US. The company sells new and used motorcycles, ATVs, motor scooters, and personal watercraft, as well as related parts and accessories. It operates through two subsidiaries, W. W. Cycles (which does business in Ohio as Andrews Cycles) and Chicago Cycles. Giant plans to grow in the future by acquiring other underperforming dealerships and integrating them into its business model. It has been expanding and updating showrooms in hopes of becoming a shopping destination for those in the market for big, noisy toys.

	Annual Growth	8/03	*12/04	12/05	12/06	12/07
Sales ($ mil.)	460.5%	0.1	79.9	105.6	100.8	98.7
Net income ($ mil.)	—	0.0	1.0	0.0	(0.2)	0.8
Market value ($ mil.)	(45.1%)	—	18.8	7.2	2.6	3.1
Employees	—	—	—	—	136	—

*Fiscal year change

GIBRALTAR INDUSTRIES, INC.

NASDAQ (GS): ROCK

3556 Lake Shore Rd.
Buffalo, NY 14219
Phone: 716-826-6500
Fax: 716-826-1589
Web: www.gibraltar1.com

CEO: Brian J. Lipke
CFO: Kenneth W. (Ken) Smith
HR: Paul M. Murray
FYE: December 31
Type: Public

When it comes to metal products, Gibraltar Industries is rock solid. The company makes building products such as roofing, vents, gutters, steel framing, and hardware. It's one of the leading mailbox makers in the US. Gibraltar Industries also is one of the country's largest providers of cold-rolled strip steel, which it processes into a variety of products for companies in the automotive and hardware industries. The company's processing businesses also offer coated sheet steel and powdered metal. Gibraltar has been adjusting its business mix by selling off noncore operations and acquiring others that are a better strategic fit.

	Annual Growth	12/03	12/04	12/05	12/06	12/07
Sales ($ mil.)	14.7%	758.3	1,014.7	1,178.2	1,303.4	1,311.8
Net income ($ mil.)	(16.4%)	27.0	50.8	43.5	57.3	13.2
Market value ($ mil.)	9.3%	323.1	699.7	681.2	701.6	460.9
Employees	(5.8%)	—	—	4,450	3,460	3,950

GIBSON, DUNN & CRUTCHER LLP

333 S. Grand Ave.
Los Angeles, CA 90071
Phone: 213-229-7000
Fax: 213-229-7520
Web: www.gibsondunn.com

CEO: Kenneth M. (Ken) Doran
CFO: –
HR: Stacy Glover
FYE: October 31
Type: Partnership

One of the top corporate transactions law firms in the US, Gibson, Dunn & Crutcher also practices in such areas as labor and employment, litigation, public policy, real estate, and tax. The firm has about 900 lawyers in more than a dozen offices, not only in California but also elsewhere in the US and in Europe and the Middle East. It has a significant presence in Washington, DC. Along with multinational companies, Gibson Dunn clients include commercial and investment banks, government entities, individuals, and startups. The firm was founded in 1890.

	Annual Growth	10/03	10/04	10/05	10/06	10/07
Est. sales ($ mil.)	—	—	—	—	—	147.3
Employees	—	—	—	—	—	1,700

GIBSON GUITAR CORP.

309 Plus Park Blvd.
Nashville, TN 37217
Phone: 615-871-4500
Fax: 615-889-5509
Web: www.gibson.com

CEO: Henry E. Juszkiewicz
CFO: –
HR: Michael L. Allen
FYE: December 31
Type: Private

Real pickers put Gibson Guitar on a pedestal. Though it trails top guitar maker Fender, Gibson builds instruments that are held in unparalleled esteem by many guitarists, including top professional musicians. The company's most popular guitar is the legendary Les Paul. Gibson also makes guitars under such brands as Epiphone, Kramer, and Steinberger. In addition to guitars, the company makes pianos through its Baldwin unit, Slingerland drums, Tobias bass, Wurlitzer vending machines and jukeboxes, and Echoplex amplifiers, as well as many accessory items. Company namesake Orville Gibson began making mandolins in the late 1890s. Gibson Guitar is owned by executives Henry Juszkiewicz and David Berryman.

GIDDINGS & LEWIS MACHINE TOOLS, LLC

142 Doty St.
Fond du Lac, WI 54936
Phone: 920-921-9400
Fax: 920-906-2522
Web: www.giddings.com

CEO: Marty Lakes
CFO: –
HR: –
FYE: September 30
Type: Private

Giddings & Lewis Machine Tools (G&L) hopes your business is boring. The company manufactures (naturally enough) machine tools, such as boring mills, drill grinders, servomotors, measurement machines, flexible machining systems, and metal castings (ranging in size from 250 pounds to 35 tons). Brand names include Giddings & Lewis, Kearney & Trecker, Gisholt, Gray, Bickford, and Warner & Swasey. Clients come from the appliance, automotive, construction, military, and aerospace industries. G&L also offers contract machining services. It had been a subsidiary of Germany's ThyssenKrupp until it was bought by private equity group Maxcor in 2005.

	Annual Growth	9/03	9/04	9/05	9/06	9/07
Est. sales ($ mil.)	—	—	—	—	—	93.1
Employees	—	—	—	—	—	1,000

GIGABEAM CORPORATION

NASDAQ (CM): GGBM

4021 Stirrup Creek Dr., Ste. 400
Druham, NC 27703
Phone: 571-283-6200
Fax: 571-283-6203
Web: www.gigabeam.com

CEO: Samuel J. (Jay) Lawrence
CFO: Mark Hahn
HR: –
FYE: December 31
Type: Public

GigaBeam won't teleport your crew, but it can provide communications at transmission rates that approach "warp speed." Under the trade name WiFiber, the company offers line-of-sight point-to-point wireless communications transmission at a gigabit per second or faster. Its network operates in the 71-to-76-GHz and 81-to-86-GHz spectrum, which provides ample bandwidth and high quality. The "virtual fiber" links between GigaBeam transceivers offers a high-speed alternative to the "last mile" communications network connection. The company was founded in 2004 by chairman Lou Slaughter and CTO Douglas Lockie; each owns about 17% of the company.

	Annual Growth	12/02	12/03	12/04	12/05	*12/06
Sales ($ mil.)	300.0%	—	—	—	1.2	4.8
Net income ($ mil.)	—	—	—	—	(15.3)	(20.2)
Employees	(45.7%)	—	—	—	46	25

*Most recent year available

GIGA-TRONICS INCORPORATED

NASDAQ (CM): GIGA

4650 Norris Canyon Rd.
San Ramon, CA 94583
Phone: 925-328-4650
Fax: 925-328-4700
Web: www.gigatronics.com

CEO: John R. Regazzi
CFO: Patrick J. Lawlor
HR: –
FYE: Saturday before March 31
Type: Public

Giga-tronics has a cool gig in electronics. Its three units — Giga-tronics Instruments, Microsource, and ASCOR — make test, measurement, and control equipment for both commercial and military customers. The units make synthesizers and power measurement instruments used in electronic warfare, radar, satellite, and telecommunications devices; switching systems for aircraft and automated test equipment; and oscillators and filters used in microwave instruments. Top customers include the US Department of Defense and its prime contractors (62% of sales). More than three-fifths of the company's sales are to customers located in the US.

	Annual Growth	3/04	3/05	3/06	3/07	3/08
Sales ($ mil.)	1.1%	17.5	21.5	20.6	18.0	18.3
Net income ($ mil.)	—	(6.8)	0.6	(1.0)	(1.9)	(0.2)
Market value ($ mil.)	(11.8%)	11.3	22.7	12.6	9.5	6.9
Employees	(8.0%)	130	120	120	117	93

GILBANE, INC.

7 Jackson Walkway
Providence, RI 02903
Phone: 401-456-5800
Fax: 401-456-5936
Web: www.gilbaneinc.com

CEO: Paul J. Choquette Jr.
CFO: John T. Ruggieri
HR: –
FYE: December 31
Type: Private

Family-owned Gilbane has been the bane of its rivals for four generations. Subsidiary Gilbane Building provides construction management, contracting, and design and build services to construct office buildings, manufacturing plants, schools, prisons, and more for the firm's governmental, commercial, and industrial clients. Landmark projects include work on the National Air and Space Museum, Lake Placid's 1980 Winter Olympics facilities, and the WWII memorial in Washington, DC. Another subsidiary, Gilbane Development Company, develops and finances public and private projects and acts as a property manager. William Gilbane founded the firm in 1873.

	Annual Growth	12/02	12/03	12/04	12/05	12/06
Sales ($ mil.)	0.2%	2,771.3	2,100.0	2,580.0	2,832.0	2,790.0
Employees	4.5%	1,700	1,700	1,757	1,800	2,024

GILEAD SCIENCES, INC.

NASDAQ (GS): GILD

333 Lakeside Dr.
Foster City, CA 94404
Phone: 650-574-3000
Fax: 650-578-9264
Web: www.gilead.com

CEO: John C. Martin
CFO: Robin L. Washington
HR: Kristen M. Metza
FYE: December 31
Type: Public

Gilead Sciences has biotech balms for infectious diseases, including hepatitis, HIV, and infections related to AIDS. The company's HIV franchise includes blockbuster Truvada, a combination of two of its other drugs, Viread and Emtriva. It co-promotes another HIV treatment, called Atripla, in the US and Europe with Bristol-Myers Squibb. Other products on the market include AmBisome, used to treat systemic fungal infections such as those that accompany AIDS; Vistide, for AIDS-related eye infections; and hepatitis B antiviral Hepsera. Outside of the infectious disease realm, Gilead has won FDA approval for Letairis, a treatment for pulmonary arterial hypertension.

	Annual Growth	12/03	12/04	12/05	12/06	12/07
Sales ($ mil.)	48.6%	867.9	1,324.6	2,028.4	3,026.1	4,230.0
Net income ($ mil.)	—	(72.0)	449.4	813.9	(1,190.0)	1,615.3
Market value ($ mil.)	92.8%	3,107.1	7,852.1	12,083.9	14,970.4	42,903.6
Employees	20.2%	1,425	1,654	1,900	2,515	2,979

GILMAN + CIOCIA, INC.

Pink Sheets: GTAX

11 Raymond Ave.
Poughkeepsie, NY 12603
Phone: 845-486-0900
Fax: 845-483-9332
Web: www.gilcio.com

CEO: Michael P. Ryan
CFO: Karen Fisher
HR: Shannon Whitlow
FYE: June 30
Type: Public

Gilman + Ciocia aims to make money management less taxing for middle- and upper-income Americans. The firm's financial planning services (which generate about 90% of its revenue) include assisting individuals with investment management, securities brokerage, insurance, and mortgage services. Gilman + Ciocia also provides accounting services to small and middle-market businesses and prepares federal, state, and local tax returns for individuals; some returns are prepared online. The company markets its efforts via direct mail as well as tradtional channels including print, broadcast, and online media.

	Annual Growth	6/03	6/04	6/05	6/06	6/07
Assets ($ mil.)	(1.8%)	—	—	17.1	16.6	16.5
Net income ($ mil.)	—	—	—	(1.8)	(2.6)	0.8
Employees	—	—	—	—	—	227

GILSTER-MARY LEE CORPORATION

1037 State St.
Chester, IL 62233
Phone: 618-826-2361
Fax: 618-826-2973
Web: www.gilstermarylee.com

CEO: Donald Welge
CFO: Michael Welge
HR: Robert Welge
FYE: December 31
Type: Private

Breakfast is the most important meal of the day, especially at Gilster-Mary Lee. One of the largest private-label cereal manufacturers in the US (along with Ralcorp Holdings), Gilster-Mary Lee makes some 8,000 products under 500 private labels, including breakfast cereal, cake, baking mixes, cocoa, drink mixes, pasta, and more. The company's customers include major US grocery chains and food wholesalers. It also offers products under its own Hospitality brand. Gilster-Mary Lee owns 14 manufacturing operations located in Arkansas, Illinois, and Missouri. Its products are available worldwide.

GIRL SCOUTS OF THE UNITED STATES OF AMERICA

420 5th Ave.
New York, NY 10018
Phone: 212-852-8000
Fax: 212-852-6514
Web: www.girlscouts.org

CEO: Kathy Cloninger
CFO: Florence Corsello
HR: Michael Watson
FYE: September 30
Type: Not-for-profit

For the Girl Scouts of the United States of America, the calendar includes one month of cookie sales and 12 months of character-building. The group, one of the largest devoted to girls, counts about 2.7 million girl members, plus more than 900,000 adult volunteers. Girl Scouts of the USA is open to girls between ages 5 and 17 and strives to develop character and leadership skills through projects involving technology, sports, the environment, literacy, the arts, and the sciences. It operates through about 300 regional councils, which oversee cookie sales and keep most of the proceeds for local use. Girl Scouts of the USA was founded in 1912.

	Annual Growth	9/03	9/04	9/05	9/06	9/07
Est. sales ($ mil.)	—	—	—	—	—	123.0
Employees	—	—	—	—	—	500

GIRLING HEALTH CARE, INC.

4902 Grover Ave.
Austin, TX 78756
Phone: 512-452-5781
Fax: 512-451-0620
Web: www.girling.com

CEO: Lew Little
CFO: −
HR: −
FYE: December 31
Type: Private

Girling Health Care provides a variety of home health, personal care, home-maker, and hospice services for clients in Florida, Illinois, New York, Oklahoma, Tennessee, and Texas. Services include skilled nursing, hospice, occupational therapy, medication management, and cardiac pulmonary care. Girling's largest market is Texas, where it operates in more than 20 cities throughout the state. The family-owned company was founded in 1967 by Bob and Bettie Girling. In 2007 Girling was acquired by another Austin-based health care company, privately held Harden Healthcare.

	Annual Growth	12/03	12/04	12/05	12/06	12/07
Est. sales ($ mil.)	—	—	—	—	—	237.2
Employees	—	—	—	—	—	15,000

GIRLS INCORPORATED

120 Wall St.
New York, NY 10005
Phone: 212-509-2000
Fax: 212-509-8708
Web: www.girlsinc.org

CEO: Joyce M. Roché
CFO: Anna Gross
HR: Robin Robin
FYE: September 30
Type: Not-for-profit

Girls Incorporated's going concern is giving girls a chance. Begun in 1864 during the Industrial Revolution, it's a national organization that supports girls and young women age 6 to 18 living in high-risk or underserved areas. Girls Incorporated is a not-for-profit group that provides educational programs for girls in areas such as math and science, sports, money management, and leadership. Its programs are implemented through partner entities including schools and youth-service organizations nationwide. Programs encourage girls to master challenges, while the group lobbies lawmakers to promote girls' needs. Girls Incorporated was formally founded in 1945 as Girls Clubs of America.

	Annual Growth	9/03	9/04	9/05	9/06	9/07
Est. sales ($ mil.)	—	—	—	—	—	11.8
Employees	—	—	—	—	—	189

GKN SINTER METALS, INC.

3300 University Dr.
Auburn Hills, MI 48326
Phone: 248-371-0800
Fax: 248-371-0809
Web: www.gknsintermetals.com

CEO: Andrew Reynolds Smith
CFO: Chris Granger
HR: −
FYE: December 31
Type: Subsidiary

GKN Sinter Metals makes precision pressed-powder metal components for use principally in the automotive, lawn and garden, power tool, and home appliance industries. The company uses a process known as powder metallurgy to make intricate and complex parts with performance attributes comparable to components produced through such processes as forging and casting. Its metal components include gears, bearings, and pulleys, primarily for use in engines, transmissions, and other drive mechanisms. Customers have included Volkswagen, Volvo, and Deere & Co. GKN Sinter Metals is a subsidiary of UK-based automotive components and aerospace concern GKN plc.

GLACIER BANCORP, INC.

NASDAQ (GS): GBCI

49 Commons Loop
Kalispell, MT 59901
Phone: 406-751-4200
Fax: 406-751-4729
Web: www.glacierbancorp.com

CEO: Michael J. (Mick) Blodnick
CFO: Ronald J. (Ron) Copher
HR: Robin S. Roush
FYE: December 31
Type: Public

Glacier Bancorp serves Big Sky Country. The company owns about a dozen community banks, including Glacier Bank, Western Security Bank, Big Sky Western Bank, Citizens State Bank, and 1st Bank. Together they serve individuals, small to midsized businesses, not-for-profits, and public entities in Montana, Idaho, Utah, Washington, and Wyoming through more than 90 branches. Glacier Bancorp offers traditional transaction and savings deposit products. Its lending activities consist mostly of commercial real estate loans (about 45% of the banks' portfolio) and residential mortgages (nearly 20%). Investment services are offered through Raymond James Financial.

	Annual Growth	12/03	12/04	12/05	12/06	12/07
Assets ($ mil.)	15.2%	2,739.6	3,010.7	3,706.3	4,467.7	4,817.3
Net income ($ mil.)	15.9%	38.0	44.6	52.4	61.1	68.6
Market value ($ mil.)	39.1%	268.3	445.7	644.5	1,278.3	1,005.3
Employees	(20.5%)	885	935	1,125	1,356	354

GLACIER WATER SERVICES, INC.

Pink Sheets: GWSV

1385 Park Center Dr.
Vista, CA 92081
Phone: 760-560-1111
Fax: 760-560-3333
Web: www.glacierwater.com

CEO: Brian H. McInerney
CFO: Steve Stringer
HR: Luz E. Gonzales
FYE: Sunday nearest December 31
Type: Public

Glacier Water Services serves those who shun the tap. The company operates more than 15,000 self-service vending machines that dispense filtered drinking water. Its machines are in 40 states, with the majority in California, Florida, and Texas. The machines are connected to municipal water sources and are designed to reduce impurities in the water through processes such as micron filtration, reverse osmosis, carbon absorption, and ultraviolet disinfection. Glacier Water's machines are placed outside supermarkets and other stores; it uses indoor models in colder climates.

	Annual Growth	12/03	12/04	12/05	12/06	12/07
Sales ($ mil.)	5.7%	72.3	76.3	76.3	87.2	90.4
Net income ($ mil.)	—	(1.4)	(2.4)	(2.4)	(4.7)	(4.9)
Employees	7.5%	301	331	348	—	—

GLADSTONE CAPITAL CORPORATION

NASDAQ (GS): GLAD

1521 Westbranch Dr., Ste. 200
McLean, VA 22102
Phone: 703-287-5800
Fax: 703-287-5801
Web: www.gladstonecapital.com

CEO: David Gladstone
CFO: Gresford Gray
HR: −
FYE: September 30
Type: Public

If your fledgling company shows promise, Gladstone Capital might be glad to provide some capital. The business development company (BDC) provides loans (generally $3 million — $15 million) to small and medium-sized family-owned companies or firms backed by leveraged buyout funds or venture capital outfits. Gladstone Capital particularly targets firms undergoing ownership transitions. The firm then shepherds its portfolio companies towards merger or acquisition transactions or initial public offerings. Company affiliate Gladstone Management Corporation provides management services to the firm's portfolio companies. Subsidiary Gladstone Business Loan holds the loan investment portfolio.

	Annual Growth	9/03	9/04	9/05	9/06	9/07
Sales ($ mil.)	24.9%	15.1	20.4	24.0	32.9	36.7
Net income ($ mil.)	7.6%	11.1	10.6	15.5	24.4	14.9
Market value ($ mil.)	10.1%	196.1	256.1	254.9	270.8	288.2
Employees		—	—	—	0	0	0

An in-depth profile of this company is available to Hoover's Online members at hoovers.com.

685

GLADSTONE COMMERCIAL CORPORATION

NASDAQ (GM): GOOD

1521 Westbranch Dr., Ste. 200
McLean, VA 22102
Phone: 703-287-5800
Fax: 703-287-5801
Web: www.gladstonecommercial.com

CEO: David Gladstone
CFO: Harry Brill
HR: Paula Novara
FYE: December 31
Type: Public

Gladstone Commercial will gladly buy your commercial property, or lease you some if you need a business home. A real estate investment trust (REIT), Gladstone invests in commercial and industrial real estate properties and long-term commercial mortgages. The company owns more than 50 properties across the US with assets that include office buildings, warehouses, retail, and manufacturing facilities. Gladstone predominantly leases to small and midsized businesses; most properties carry triple-net leases. The firm is closely affiliated with management investment firm Gladstone Capital, which is also headed by chairman and CEO David Gladstone.

	Annual Growth	12/03	12/04	12/05	12/06	12/07
Sales ($ mil.)	—	0.0	4.3	13.5	26.0	32.8
Net income ($ mil.)	—	(0.2)	1.6	3.6	4.4	6.1
Market value ($ mil.)	3.9%	128.8	131.1	126.6	172.5	150.2
Employees	—	—	—	33	—	0

GLAXOSMITHKLINE RESEARCH & DEVELOPMENT

5 Moore Dr.
Research Triangle Park, NC 27709
Phone: 919-483-2100
Fax: 919-549-7459
Web: www.gsk.com/research

CEO: Moncef Slaoui
CFO: Julian Heslop
HR: Daniel J. (Dan) Phelan
FYE: —
Type: Business segment

GlaxoSmithKline Research & Development is the actual pipeline filled with products in various stages of completion for pharmaceutical giant GlaxoSmithKline. With multiple locations in the US, across Europe, and Japan, the company has treatments in the works for therapies such as infectious diseases, neuroscientific requirements, cardiovascular ailments, oncology, and respiratory needs. It has approximately 150 products in clinical trial stages. The organization's facilities are grouped into Molecular Discovery Research (preclinical), Centres of Excellence for Drug Discovery (early-stage clinical), and Medicine Development Centres (late-stage clinical).

GLAZER'S WHOLESALE DRUG COMPANY, INC.

14911 Quorum Dr., Ste. 400
Dallas, TX 75254
Phone: 972-392-8200
Fax: 972-702-8508
Web: www.glazers.com

CEO: Bennett J. Glazer
CFO: Cary Rossel
HR: Gregg Mitchell
FYE: December 31
Type: Private

Glazer's Wholesale Drug, named during Prohibition when only drugstores and drug wholesalers could deal in liquor, is a wholesale distributor of alcoholic beverages. In Texas it is the largest company of its kind and one of the largest wine and spirits distributors in the US. The company distributes Robert Mondavi wines, Brown-Forman and Bacardi spirits, and Diageo products. CEO Bennett Glazer and his family own Glazer's. The company's origins date back to the early 1900s when the Glazer family sold flavored soda water, which it distributed using horse-drawn wagons.

	Annual Growth	12/02	12/03	12/04	12/05	12/06
Sales ($ mil.)	14.4%	1,750.0	2,200.0	2,800.0	2,900.0	3,000.0
Employees	10.4%	3,900	5,500	5,800	5,800	5,800

GLAZIER FOODS COMPANY

11303 Antoine
Houston, TX 77066
Phone: 713-869-6411
Fax: —
Web: www.glazierfoods.com

CEO: Bill Mathis
CFO: John Miller
HR: —
FYE: June 30
Type: Private

Glazier Foods supplies a full line of food products to day-care centers, entertainment and sporting complexes, governmental agencies, hospitals, nursing homes, schools, and restaurants. It also supplies food service equipment. The company provides private-label and nationally branded products to more than 4,300 customers. Glazier Foods was founded in 1936.

	Annual Growth	6/03	6/04	6/05	6/06	6/07
Est. sales ($ mil.)	—	—	—	—	—	252.8
Employees	—	—	—	—	—	500

GLEASON CORPORATION

1000 University Ave.
Rochester, NY 14692
Phone: 585-473-1000
Fax: 585-461-4348
Web: www.gleason.com

CEO: John J. Perrotti
CFO: John W. Pysnack
HR: —
FYE: December 31
Type: Private

If you love the v-v-vrooom, 0-to-60-in-a-few-seconds experience, then you can thank Gleason Corporation. The company designs, manufactures, and sells the machines that make, test, and finish the gears used in drive shafts. Gleason sells to makers of cars, trucks, SUVs, buses, aircraft, boats, and agricultural and construction machinery. The company also provides replacement parts for the aftermarket, and inspection software and training programs for its customers. Gleason was founded in 1865. In 2005 the company acquired M&M Precision Systems, a supplier of gear inspection and manufacturing process control systems. In early 2007 Gleason bought the assets of LeCount, Inc., a producer of expanding mandrels.

	Annual Growth	12/03	12/04	12/05	12/06	12/07
Est. sales ($ mil.)	—	—	—	—	—	235.0
Employees	—	—	—	—	—	2,508

GLEN BURNIE BANCORP

NASDAQ (CM): GLBZ

101 Crain Hwy. SE
Glen Burnie, MD 21061
Phone: 410-766-3300
Fax: 410-787-8581
Web: www.thebankofglenburnie.com

CEO: Michael G. Livingston
CFO: John E. Porter
HR: —
FYE: December 31
Type: Public

Glen Burnie Bancorp has an interest in the Old Line State. The institution is the holding company for Bank of Glen Burnie, which has branches in central Maryland's Anne Arundel County, south of Baltimore. The bank offers such services as checking and savings accounts, money market and individual retirement accounts, certificates of deposit, ATM and debit cards, and remote banking services. It focuses on consumer banking, with residential mortgages accounting for the largest portion of its loan portfolio, followed by commercial mortgages and indirect automobile loans. The latter are usually originated through area car dealers who have agreements with the bank.

	Annual Growth	12/03	12/04	12/05	12/06	12/07
Assets ($ mil.)	0.4%	302.3	302.3	306.6	317.8	307.3
Net income ($ mil.)	(2.5%)	3.1	3.1	2.8	2.7	2.8
Market value ($ mil.)	2.0%	29.9	34.3	30.7	35.3	32.4
Employees	(2.8%)	—	—	125	—	118

GLIDEWELL LABORATORIES

4141 MacArthur Blvd.
Newport Beach, CA 92660
Phone: 949-440-2600
Fax: 800-411-9722
Web: www.glidewell-lab.com

CEO: Jim Glidewell
CFO: Rob Grice
HR: Stephanie Goddard
FYE: December 31
Type: Private

Glidewell Laboratories makes a wide range of restorative, reconstructive, and cosmetic dental products, including systems using porcelain fused to metal, ceramic, and zirconia materials. Its products include impression systems, nightguards and other bitesplints, implants, bridges, and dentures. The company also provides continuing education programs. Established in 1970, Glidewell Laboratories has eight locations.

	Annual Growth	12/03	12/04	12/05	12/06	12/07
Est. sales ($ mil.)	—	—	—	—	—	66.5
Employees	—	—	—	—	—	1,900

GLIMCHER REALTY TRUST

NYSE: GRT

150 E. Gay St.
Columbus, OH 43215
Phone: 614-621-9000
Fax: 614-621-9321
Web: www.glimcher.com

CEO: Michael P. Glimcher
CFO: Mark E. Yale
HR: –
FYE: December 31
Type: Public

In Glimcher's ideal world, we'd all be glimmering and glamourous shopaholics. A self-administered and self-managed real estate investment trust (REIT), Glimcher acquires, develops, and manages retail real estate. Its portfolio includes approximately 25 enclosed shopping malls (a couple owned through a joint venture) and about five strip shopping centers for a total of some 21.6 million sq. ft. of space. Properties are located in about 15 states, primarily in the East and Midwest. Major tenants include Limited Brands, The Gap, and Foot Locker. Glimcher has spent several years divesting its shopping centers so it can focus on its mall properties.

	Annual Growth	12/03	12/04	12/05	12/06	12/07
Sales ($ mil.)	(1.2%)	316.9	345.1	334.9	309.3	302.2
Net income ($ mil.)	12.7%	23.8	51.8	20.9	(77.2)	38.4
Market value ($ mil.)	(9.0%)	784.8	988.8	889.2	982.3	538.5
Employees	(3.9%)	—	—	1,128	—	1,042

GLOBAL 360, INC.

2911 Turtle Creek Blvd., Ste. 1100
Dallas, TX 75235
Phone: 214-520-1660
Fax: 214-219-0476
Web: www.global360.com

CEO: David Mitchell
CFO: George H. Ellis
HR: –
FYE: December 31
Type: Private

Global 360 (formerly eiStream) can help you globally view all of your business processes. The company provides business process management software and services that customers use to monitor, manage, and analyze their operations and decision-making processes. Global 360's products enable users to create, share, analyze and deploy business processes within units and across an entire enterprise, addressing tasks such as accounting, claims management, reporting, and compliance. Global 360 also offers services such as consulting, support, and training. The company was founded in 2000.

	Annual Growth	12/03	12/04	12/05	12/06	12/07
Est. sales ($ mil.)	—	—	—	—	—	23.5
Employees	—	—	—	—	—	300

GLOBAL AXCESS CORP

OTC: GAXC

7800 Belfort Pkwy., Ste. 165
Jacksonville, FL 32256
Phone: 904-280-3950
Fax: 904-280-8588
Web: www.glxs.biz

CEO: George A. McQuain
CFO: Michael J. Loiacono
HR: –
FYE: December 31
Type: Public

Global Axcess has no ax to grind, just a bunch of ATMs to manage. Through subsidiaries, the company provides products, software, and services for about 4,300 ATMs it owns or operates in more than 40 states across the country. Through subsidiary Nationwide Money Services, the company provides full-service management of its ATM network. Global Axcess ATMs are placed in areas with high pedestrian traffic, including grocery and convenience stores, major retailers, malls, colleges, and sports arenas. Its network is concentrated in the South (Georgia has more of its ATMs than any other state) and on the East Coast.

	Annual Growth	12/03	12/04	12/05	12/06	12/07
Sales ($ mil.)	20.9%	10.2	13.9	19.6	21.4	21.8
Net income ($ mil.)	7.5%	0.3	1.1	(0.7)	(4.9)	0.4
Market value ($ mil.)	(45.9%)	83.3	158.2	25.0	7.8	7.1
Employees	—	—	—	—	—	—

GLOBAL CASH ACCESS HOLDINGS, INC.

NYSE: GCA

3525 E. Post Rd., Ste. 120
Las Vegas, NV 89120
Phone: 702-855-3000
Fax: 866-672-4371
Web: www.globalcashaccess.com

CEO: Scott H. Betts
CFO: George W. Gresham
HR: –
FYE: December 31
Type: Public

If you're losing your shirt at the tables in Atlantic City, Las Vegas, or London, Global Cash Access can get you more money on the spot. The growing company provides such services and products as ATMs, credit- and debit-card advances, and check guarantee to the gaming industry in the US, Asia, Canada, the Caribbean, South Africa, and Europe. A joint venture with International Game Technology has developed a cashless gaming system that allows slots players to access funds without leaving their machines. Global Cash Access also offers patron information to gaming establishments that provide credit to customers through its Central Credit database and reports.

	Annual Growth	12/03	12/04	12/05	12/06	12/07
Sales ($ mil.)	14.0%	355.7	403.0	454.1	548.2	600.9
Net income ($ mil.)	(20.2%)	58.4	254.6	22.6	26.6	23.7
Market value ($ mil.)	(35.0%)	—	—	1,189.9	1,335.9	502.9
Employees	12.6%	—	—	279	—	354

GLOBAL CASINOS, INC.

OTC: GBCS

5455 Spine Rd., Ste. C
Boulder, CO 80301
Phone: 303-527-2903
Fax: 303-527-2916

CEO: Clifford L. Neuman
CFO: Todd Huss
HR: –
FYE: June 30
Type: Public

Global Casinos doesn't have the whole world in its hands, but it does enjoy gaming in Colorado. The company's Bull Durham Saloon and Casino in Black Hawk, Colorado, has more than 180 slot machines. Bull Durham's customer base consists primarily of day visitors from Denver. The company also owns a second property, the Doc Holliday Casino, in Central City, Colorado. Not as large as its competitors, Global Casinos focuses on customer service and gaming equipment, regularly upgrading its machines.

	Annual Growth	6/03	6/04	6/05	6/06	6/07
Sales ($ mil.)	6.5%	2.8	3.1	3.9	4.0	3.6
Net income ($ mil.)	(33.1%)	0.5	0.3	0.9	0.1	0.1
Market value ($ mil.)	15.3%	—	—	3.7	4.7	4.9
Employees	(4.3%)	37	39	—	34	31

An in-depth profile of this company is available to Hoover's Online members at hoovers.com.

687

GLOBAL DIVERSIFIED INDUSTRIES, INC.

OTC: GDIV

1200 Airport Dr.
Chowchilla, CA 93610
Phone: 559-665-5800
Fax: 559-665-5700
Web: www.gdvi.net

CEO: Phillip (Phil) Hamilton
CFO: Adam N. DeBard
HR: –
FYE: April 30
Type: Public

Global Diversified Industries is the new mod squad. Through its Global Modular subsidiary, the company makes prefabricated portable modular buildings, mainly for use as classrooms. It also constructs permanent one- and two-story structures. Clients include public and private schools, universities, child-care facilities, and municipalities. The company is active throughout California. Global Diversified divested its MBS Construction subsidiary, which provided construction site management services, in 2006. Company president Phil Hamilton has voting control of more than 20% of Global Diversified's stock.

	Annual Growth	4/03	4/04	4/05	4/06	4/07
Sales ($ mil.)	—	0.0	3.8	9.2	14.9	6.6
Net income ($ mil.)	—	(0.5)	(0.4)	0.5	0.6	(1.3)
Market value ($ mil.)	(54.0%)	—	514.3	271.7	224.2	50.2
Employees	—	—	—	—	—	—

GLOBAL EARTH ENERGY, INC.

OTC: GEEG

534 Delaware Ave., Ste. 412
Buffalo, NY 14202
Phone: 716-332-7150
Fax: –

CEO: Sydney A. Harland
CFO: Edmund Gorman
HR: –
FYE: August 31
Type: Public

Global Earth Energy (formerly Global Wataire) is angling for business in Fresh Water. Through subsidiary Fresh Water Technologies, Global Earth Energy markets water purification systems using ultraviolet, ozone and water activator technology. Products include the industry-leading Sterilight ultraviolet systems plus reverse osmosis, ozone systems, and the Impression Water Softener Series. Customers include water-regulatory agencies, schools, and golf courses, as well as such large water users as IBM, Xerox, and General Motors. Chairman Betty-Ann Harland is Global Earth Energy's largest shareholder.

	Annual Growth	8/03	8/04	8/05	8/06	8/07
Sales ($ mil.)	—	—	—	—	—	0.1
Net income ($ mil.)	—	—	—	—	—	(1.4)
Market value ($ mil.)	—	—	—	—	—	2.6
Employees	—	—	—	—	—	—

GLOBAL ENTERTAINMENT CORPORATION

AMEX: GEE

4909 E. McDowell Rd., Ste. 104
Phoenix, AZ 85008
Phone: 480-994-0772
Fax: 480-994-0759
Web: www.globalentertainment2000.com

CEO: Richard (Rick) Kozuback
CFO: James C. Yeager
HR: –
FYE: May 31
Type: Public

Global Entertainment Corporation is helping to bring sports to the hinterlands. The company, through its subsidiaries, offers project management services to small communities looking to develop event centers and sports facilities. It also offers facilities management services, as well as sponsorship and marketing consulting. Through its WPHL (Western Professional Hockey League) subsidiary, Global Entertainment manages Central Hockey League, a development league affiliated with the National Hockey League. Its Cragar Industries licenses the Cragar brand to automobile aftermarket manufacturers. WPHL Holdings, which includes chairman James Treliving and his son Brad Treliving, controls more than 40% of the company.

	Annual Growth	5/03	5/04	5/05	5/06	5/07
Sales ($ mil.)	62.5%	3.8	5.3	13.5	14.3	26.5
Net income ($ mil.)	—	0.6	0.9	0.4	0.3	(4.1)
Market value ($ mil.)	7.6%	—	—	27.5	44.8	31.9
Employees	311.8%	—	—	110	453	—

GLOBAL EPOINT, INC.

Pink Sheets: GEPT

339 S. Cheryl Ln.
City of Industry, CA 91789
Phone: 909-869-1688
Fax: 909-598-5808
Web: www.globalepoint.com

CEO: Daryl F. Gates
CFO: John Pan
HR: –
FYE: December 31
Type: Public

Global ePoint hopes to make the world secure through digital video surveillance. The company makes products and technologies for law enforcement, homeland security, the military, transportation, and other commercial and industrial security applications. Its digital security products are marketed under the Perpetual Digital, Sequent Mobile, and Tops brands. Its Global Airworks aviation division, acquired through the purchase of Greenick (did business as AirWorks), supplies surveillance systems for commercial aircraft, in-flight entertainment systems, and communications systems. Global ePoint also makes customized security systems for clients. Chairman John Pan owns about 30% of the company.

	Annual Growth	12/02	12/03	12/04	12/05	*12/06
Sales ($ mil.)	184.8%	0.5	21.4	21.1	32.8	32.9
Net income ($ mil.)	—	(1.7)	(0.4)	(5.0)	(7.3)	(11.2)
Employees	(37.2%)	—	—	—	145	91

*Most recent year available

GLOBAL HEALTHCARE EXCHANGE, LLC

11000 Westmoor Cir., Ste. 400
Westminster, CO 80021
Phone: 720-887-7000
Fax: 720-887-7200
Web: www.ghx.com

CEO: Michael F. Mahoney
CFO: Stephen Waters
HR: –
FYE: December 31
Type: Private

Global Healthcare Exchange (GHX) provides an electronic trading exchange open to all health care providers, suppliers, and manufacturers that offers a forum to buy and sell supplies online. GHX aims to lower supply chain costs for its users by allowing them to perform transactions with multiple parties over one Internet connection, as well as by automating the purchasing process and reducing purchase order errors. The firm was founded in 2000 by an initial group of five health care manufacturers: Abbott Labs, Baxter International, GE Medical Systems, Johnson & Johnson, and Medtronic. Other companies — including wholesalers, health care providers, and purchasing organizations — have since become equity owners.

	Annual Growth	12/03	12/04	12/05	12/06	12/07
Est. sales ($ mil.)	—	—	—	—	—	48.5
Employees	—	—	—	—	—	500

⊞ GLOBAL HYATT CORPORATION

71 S. Wacker Dr.
Chicago, IL 60606
Phone: 312-750-1234
Fax: 312-750-8550
Web: www.hyatt.com

CEO: Mark S. Hoplamazian
CFO: Harmit Singh
HR: Doug Patrick
FYE: January 31
Type: Private

Travelers interested in luxury lodgings can check in for the Hyatt touch. Global Hyatt is one of the world's top operators of full-service luxury hotels and resorts with more than 700 locations in some 40 countries. Its core Hyatt Regency brand offers hospitality services targeted primarily to business travelers and upscale vacationers. The firm also operates properties under the names Grand Hyatt, Park Hyatt, Hyatt Place, Hyatt Summerfield Suites, Hyatt Resorts, and Andaz. Its resort destinations offer golf, spas, and other upmarket rest and relaxation activities. Although Global Hyatt was formed in 2004, the Hyatt chain traces its roots back to 1957. It is owned by the wealthy Pritzker family of Chicago.

	Annual Growth	1/02	1/03	1/04	1/05	1/06
Sales ($ mil.)	0.7%	3,400.0	3,600.0	5,812.0	6,438.0	3,500.0
Employees	23.1%	37,000	40,000	—	88,647	85,000

GLOBAL IMAGING SYSTEMS, INC.

3820 Northdale Blvd., Ste. 200A
Tampa, FL 33624
Phone: 813-960-5508
Fax: 813-264-7877
Web: www.global-imaging.com

CEO: Thomas S. (Tom) Johnson
CFO: Raymond (Ray) Schilling
HR: Cecil A. McClary
FYE: March 31
Type: Subsidiary

Global Imaging Systems (GIS) is consolidating the fragmented office equipment industry one acquisition at a time. The company sells and services products such as copiers, fax machines, printers, projectors, and videoconferencing equipment under brands that include Canon, Hewlett-Packard, InFocus, Konica, and Sharp. It also provides its customers — principally businesses with fewer than 1,000 employees — with network integration services and systems (network design, software, and hardware). GIS operates from more than 180 locations in 32 states and the District of Columbia. The acquisitive company purchased more than 80 firms before it was purchased in 2007 by technology products giant Xerox for about $1.5 billion.

	Annual Growth	3/02	3/03	3/04	3/05	3/06
Sales ($ mil.)	13.7%	616.4	679.4	750.7	926.5	1,030.6
Net income ($ mil.)	22.8%	27.2	34.2	39.8	57.0	61.9
Employees	10.9%	2,800	3,150	3,200	3,970	4,230

GLOBAL INDUSTRIES, LTD.

NASDAQ (GS): GLBL

8000 Global Dr.
Carlyss, LA 70665
Phone: 337-583-5000
Fax: 337-583-5100
Web: www.globalind.com

CEO: B. K. Chin
CFO: Jeffrey B. (Jeff) Levos
HR: William A. Cummings
FYE: December 31
Type: Public

Global Industries industriously provides global offshore construction and support services, including pipeline construction, platform installation and removal, and diving services to the oil and gas industry in the all of the world's major offshore oil patches. Global's services include pipeline installation pipelay, simultaneous multiple pipeline laying, pipeline burial, and pipeline maintenance and repair. Global installs pipelines, insulated pipe-in-pipe, and bundled flowlines. Its barge fleet provides derrick services and heavy-lift capabilities for installation and removal of offshore platforms, and drilling and workover rigs. Petróleos Mexicanos (PEMEX) accounted for 23% of the company's revenue in 2007.

	Annual Growth	12/03	12/04	12/05	12/06	12/07
Sales ($ mil.)	19.4%	488.7	463.3	688.6	1,234.8	992.5
Net income ($ mil.)	—	(68.3)	22.4	34.8	199.7	160.0
Market value ($ mil.)	47.6%	519.6	932.8	1,297.8	1,515.9	2,465.4
Employees	(0.2%)	—	—	3,024	3,279	3,009

GLOBAL KNOWLEDGE TRAINING LLC

9000 Regency Pkwy., Ste. 500
Cary, NC 27518
Phone: 919-461-8600
Fax: 919-461-8646
Web: www.globalknowledge.com

CEO: Joseph W. Cece
CFO: Brian K. Branson
HR: Donna B. Peffley
FYE: December 31
Type: Private

Companies keep employee skills up-to-date with Global Knowledge. The company provides technical training services to the employees of clients such as the Netherlands Ministry of Defence, Sabre, and ACTS Retirement-Life Communities. Specializing in networking systems and telecommunications, the education company offers about 700 vendor-authorized and proprietary courses covering the products of specific manufacturers, including Microsoft and Cisco. Global Knowledge also provides custom integration and training services, training software, and outsourced education management services. New York-based investment firm Welsh, Carson, Anderson, and Stowe owns the company, which has around 170 offices worldwide.

	Annual Growth	12/03	12/04	12/05	12/06	12/07
Est. sales ($ mil.)	—	—	—	—	—	49.0
Employees	—	—	—	—	—	1,050

GLOBAL MED TECHNOLOGIES, INC.

OTC: GLOB

12600 W. Colfax, Ste. C-420
Lakewood, CO 80215
Phone: 303-238-2000
Fax: 303-238-3368

CEO: Michael I. Ruxin
CFO: Michael I. Ruxin
HR: –
FYE: December 31
Type: Public

Global Med Technologies doesn't shrink from the sight of blood. Through subsidiary Wyndgate Technologies, the company develops information management software that tracks blood donations and manages information for blood banks, transfusion centers, hospitals, clinics, and other health care facilities. Global Med's SafeTrace software keeps track of blood products from donor recruitment through shipment, and its SafeTrace Tx software is a transfusion management system. PeopleMed.com, an 83%-owned subsidiary of Global Med, offers Internet-based applications that help provide disease management for patients with chronic diseases. Director Fai Chan controls a 65% stake in Global Med.

	Annual Growth	12/03	12/04	12/05	12/06	12/07
Sales ($ mil.)	25.5%	6.5	6.9	11.2	12.4	16.1
Net income ($ mil.)	—	(0.9)	(0.8)	(10.8)	1.4	2.0
Market value ($ mil.)	34.4%	8.8	33.8	23.6	16.2	28.8
Employees	—	—	—	—	—	—

GLOBAL MOTORSPORT GROUP, INC.

16100 Jacqueline Ct.
Morgan Hill, CA 95037
Phone: 408-778-0500
Fax: 408-782-6603
Web: www.customchrome.com

CEO: John Lott
CFO: Dan Cook
HR: –
FYE: January 31
Type: Private

Global Motorsport Group deals in quality hog parts, but it isn't in the butcher business. Through its Custom Chrome subsidiary the company is one of the world's largest independent providers of aftermarket parts and accessories for Harley-Davidson motorcycles. It sells parts through its catalog and via a network of motorcycle dealers and repair shops worldwide. Products (transmission assemblies and gear sets, wheels and tires, engines, frames, and headlight kits) are sold under such brands as RevTech, Santee, and Jammer Cycle Products. The company filed for Chapter 11 in early 2008 and has agreed to be acquired by Dae IL USA, the North American arm of Korea-based car parts manufacturer Dae IL Corp.

	Annual Growth	1/03	1/04	1/05	1/06	1/07
Est. sales ($ mil.)	—	—	—	—	—	39.5
Employees	—	—	—	—	—	680

GLOBAL PARTNERS LP

NYSE: GLP

800 South St.
Waltham, MA 02454
Phone: 781-894-8800
Fax: 781-398-4160
Web: www.globalp.com

CEO: Eric Slifka
CFO: Thomas J. (Tom) Hollister
HR: Barbara E. Rosenbloom
FYE: December 31
Type: Public

Global Partners (formerly Global Companies) imports petroleum products from global sources, but its marketing is strictly regional. The company wholesales heating oil, residual fuel oil, diesel oil, kerosene, and gasoline to commercial, retail, and wholesale customers in New England. A major player in the regional home heating oil wholesale market, Global Partners operates storage facilities at 20 bulk terminals with a total storage capacity of 9.3 million barrels. Global Partners was founded in 1933 as a one-truck heating oil retailer by current CEO Eric Slifka's grandfather, Abraham Slifka. The Slifka family owns 42.6% of the company.

	Annual Growth	12/03	12/04	12/05	12/06	12/07
Sales ($ mil.)	29.2%	—	—	4,045.9	4,472.4	6,757.8
Net income ($ mil.)	61.1%	—	—	18.1	33.5	47.0
Market value ($ mil.)	35.4%	—	—	105.5	146.6	193.5
Employees	15.6%	—	—	172	180	230

An in-depth profile of this company is available to Hoover's Online members at hoovers.com.

689

GLOBAL PAYMENT TECHNOLOGIES, INC.

NASDAQ (GM): GPTX

170 Wilbur Place
Bohemia, NY 11716
Phone: 631-563-2500
Fax: 631-563-2630
Web: www.gptx.com

CEO: Andre Soussa
CFO: William McMahon
HR: –
FYE: September 30
Type: Public

GPT's advice: Don't take any wooden nickels (or counterfeit dollar bills). Global Payment Technologies (GPT) makes systems that detect counterfeit paper currency. The gaming industry accounts for most of GPT's sales, but the company also makes products for vending machines, beverage dispensers, and other devices. GPT's basic currency validators accept, count, and store legal tender. Its advanced Generation II and Argus systems recognize coins and paper denominations from more than 50 countries and incorporate bar-code readers, security sensors, and other features.

	Annual Growth	9/03	9/04	9/05	9/06	9/07
Sales ($ mil.)	(18.4%)	26.1	24.4	25.9	14.3	11.6
Net income ($ mil.)	—	(5.7)	(1.7)	(0.6)	(4.1)	(5.6)
Market value ($ mil.)	(42.8%)	18.3	22.4	22.4	8.0	1.9
Employees	—	—	—	—	—	71

GLOBAL PAYMENTS INC.

NYSE: GPN

10 Glenlake Pkwy. NE, North Tower
Atlanta, GA 30328
Phone: 770-829-8000
Fax: 770-829-8224
Web: www.globalpaymentsinc.com

CEO: Paul R. Garcia
CFO: Joseph C. (Joe) Hyde
HR: Morgan M. (Mac) Schuessler Jr.
FYE: May 31
Type: Public

Charge! And when you do, there's a good chance that Global Payments will be right there too, making sure your transaction is successful. Global Payments offers credit and debit card processing, check authorization, and other functions for merchants and financial institutions; it also offers corporate and government clients a variety of services, including electronic tax payment services and electronic benefits transfer processing. Global Payments markets to retailers, financial institutions, independent sales organizations (ISOs), and government agencies. The company also offers consumer money transfer services from the US and Europe, primarily targeting immigrants who send money to their home countries.

	Annual Growth	5/03	5/04	5/05	5/06	5/07
Sales ($ mil.)	19.8%	516.1	629.3	784.3	908.1	1,061.5
Net income ($ mil.)	28.0%	53.3	62.4	92.9	125.5	143.0
Market value ($ mil.)	50.5%	631.2	888.1	1,354.7	3,717.7	3,238.3
Employees	—	—	—	—	4,277	

GLOBAL POWER EQUIPMENT GROUP INC.

6120 S. Yale St., Ste. 1480
Tulsa, OK 74136
Phone: 918-488-0828
Fax: 918-488-8389
Web: www.globalpower.com

CEO: John M. Matheson
CFO: David Willis
HR: –
FYE: December 30
Type: Private

Global Power Equipment Group (GPEG) doesn't let global power go to its head, but to its bottom line. The company has two business segments: heat recovery equipment and auxiliary power equipment for gas turbine power plants. GPEG's heat recovery equipment, including heat recovery steam generators and specialty boilers, is marketed under the Deltak brand. Its auxiliary power equipment (filter houses, inlet systems, exhaust systems, and diverter dampers) is sold under the Braden and Consolidated Fabricators brands. GPEG's largest customer is General Electric. In 2006 GPEG and its US subsidiaries filed for Chapter 11 protection from creditors. The company emerged from Chapter 11 in early 2008.

GLOBAL TELECOM & TECHNOLOGY, INC.

OTC: GTLT

8484 Westpark Dr., Ste. 720
McLean, VA 22102
Phone: 703-442-5500
Fax: 703-442-5501
Web: www.gt-t.net

CEO: Richard D. (Rick) Calder Jr.
CFO: Kevin J. Welch
HR: –
FYE: December 31
Type: Public

Global Telecom & Technology offers businesses a choice of ways to phone home. The company provides data and telecommunications network design and integration, network monitoring, and support services to customers in about 50 countries. It also provides consulting, network security evaluation, and project management services. The company has distribution partnerships with technology suppliers including iPass. Global Telecom & Technology serves customers in such industries as industrial manufacturing, banking, and wireless communications. Clients have included Airbus, Comsat, and Equant. Executive chairman H. Brian Thompson owns one third of the company.

	Annual Growth	12/03	12/04	12/05	12/06	12/07
Sales ($ mil.)	448.6%	—	—	—	10.5	57.6
Net income ($ mil.)	—	—	—	—	(1.9)	(4.3)
Market value ($ mil.)	(60.3%)	—	—	—	38.3	15.2
Employees	—	—	—	—	—	—

GLOBAL TRAFFIC NETWORK, INC.

NASDAQ (GM): GNET

800 2nd Ave., 5th Fl.
New York, NY 10017
Phone: 212-896-1255
Fax: –
Web: www.globaltrafficnetwork.com

CEO: William L. Yde III
CFO: Scott Cody
HR: –
FYE: June 30
Type: Public

Great, just what we need: more traffic. Global Traffic Network (GTN) provides customized traffic reports to some 70 radio stations in nearly 20 markets in Australia. In exchange for its content, GTN receives commercial airtime from the stations, which the company sells to advertisers. In addition, the firm produces radio and TV news reports in Australia. GTN also does business in the US through a deal with Metro Networks. It provides traffic reports in Canada through an agreement with Corus Entertainment, and provides news, weather, sports, and business reports in Canada through subsidiary Wise Broadcasting Network. Chairman and CEO William Yde and director Dale Arfman together own more than a third of GTN.

	Annual Growth	6/03	6/04	6/05	6/06	6/07
Sales ($ mil.)	69.9%	3.8	7.7	11.7	19.5	31.7
Net income ($ mil.)	—	0.6	0.1	1.2	(3.0)	(2.0)
Market value ($ mil.)	25.3%	—	—	—	70.8	88.7
Employees	82.5%	—	—	63	115	

GLOBALSCAPE, INC.

AMEX: GSB

4500 Lockhill-Selma, Ste. 150
San Antonio, TX 78249
Phone: 210-308-8267
Fax: 210-293-8003
Web: www.globalscape.com

CEO: Kelly E. Simmons
CFO: Kelly E. Simmons
HR: –
FYE: December 31
Type: Public

GlobalSCAPE is pretty cute, for a software company. With packages like CuteFTP and CuteSITE Builder, GlobalSCAPE provides content management, file management, and Web site development tools for businesses and individuals. GlobalSCAPE's software can be downloaded from its Web site, and the company sells CD-ROM versions at Fry's and other retail stores. Its CuteFTP and CuteFTP Pro products, which enable file transfers via the Internet and other networks, account for a majority of sales. Formed in 1996 as the Internet subsidiary of ATSI Communications, GlobalSCAPE became independent in 2002, when investors Thomas Brown and David Mann (who collectively own 45% of the company) acquired a controlling interest.

	Annual Growth	12/03	12/04	12/05	12/06	12/07
Sales ($ mil.)	39.9%	4.8	4.9	6.7	11.0	18.4
Net income ($ mil.)	—	(0.6)	0.2	1.5	2.0	3.9
Market value ($ mil.)	158.2%	2.2	2.2	15.3	48.0	95.9
Employees	17.2%	35	39	41	56	66

GLOBALSTAR, INC.

NASDAQ (GM): GSAT

461 S. Milpitas Blvd.
Milpitas, CA 95035
Phone: 408-933-4000
Fax: 408-933-4100
Web: www.globalstar.com

CEO: James (Jay) Monroe III
CFO: Fuad Ahmad
HR: Carla Filipe
FYE: December 31
Type: Public

Is the success of another mobile phone network written in the stars? Globalstar hopes so. The satellite communications company bets on simplicity with a "bent pipe" design: Because its earthbound gateways connect to terrestrial phone networks, the system avoids complex in-orbit switching and satellite-to-satellite transmissions envisioned for other networks. It serves up voice and data using digital CDMA (code division multiple access) technology developed by Globalstar co-founder QUALCOMM. The firm's satellites bounce calls from special mobile phones back to ground-based gateways connected to traditional phone networks. Private equity firm Thermo Capital Partners owns 63% of Globalstar; QUALCOMM owns 7%.

	Annual Growth	12/03	12/04	12/05	12/06	12/07
Sales ($ mil.)	13.1%	60.2	84.4	127.2	136.7	98.4
Net income ($ mil.)	—	(266.4)	0.4	18.7	23.6	(27.9)
Market value ($ mil.)	(33.6%)	—	—	—	1,009.1	669.5
Employees	—	—	—	—	349	—

GLOBECOMM SYSTEMS INC.

NASDAQ (GM): GCOM

45 Oser Ave.
Hauppauge, NY 11788
Phone: 631-231-9800
Fax: 631-231-1557
Web: www.globecommsystems.com

CEO: David E. Hershberg
CFO: Andrew C. Melfi
HR: Paul Eterno
FYE: June 30
Type: Public

Globecomm Systems sends data flying. The company designs, assembles, and installs satellite earth stations, complete uplink centers, and media broadcast centers. It also builds IP-based communications networks. Its Globecomm Network Services subsidiary provides broadband satellite-delivered Internet and intranet access, Web hosting, video broadcasting, and network management services. Globecomm markets to communications carriers, government agencies, equipment makers, content providers, and broadcasters. Customers have included CBS, Nortel Networks, Reuters, and the United Nations.

	Annual Growth	6/03	6/04	6/05	6/06	6/07
Sales ($ mil.)	29.2%	54.0	87.2	109.6	126.0	150.7
Net income ($ mil.)	—	(19.6)	(1.3)	4.8	4.5	8.3
Market value ($ mil.)	55.8%	40.9	74.2	88.0	113.2	240.9
Employees	—	—	—	163	—	—

GLOWPOINT, INC.

OTC: GLOW

225 Long Ave.
Hillside, NJ 07205
Phone: 973-282-2000
Fax: 973-391-1901
Web: www.glowpoint.com

CEO: Michael Brandofino
CFO: Edwin F. Heinen
HR: –
FYE: December 31
Type: Public

Glowpoint adds a little light to virtual meeting rooms, providing subscription-based video-conferencing services that enable businesses, government offices, educational institutions, and other customers to engage in video communications over an Internet protocol-based network. The company also offers Webcasting services, streaming live and recorded video via standard video-conferencing systems. Glowpoint operates 11 network points of presence (POPs) around the globe. The company counts government agencies, corporations, and not-for-profits among its customers.

	Annual Growth	12/03	12/04	12/05	12/06	12/07
Sales ($ mil.)	16.9%	—	—	—	19.5	22.8
Net income ($ mil.)	—	—	—	—	(10.8)	(5.5)
Market value ($ mil.)	25.5%	—	—	—	17.6	22.1
Employees	—	—	—	—	59	—

GLU MOBILE INC.

NASDAQ (GM): GLUU

1800 Gateway Dr., 2nd Fl.
San Mateo, CA 94404
Phone: 650-571-1550
Fax: 650-571-5698
Web: www.glu.com

CEO: L. Gregory (Greg) Ballard
CFO: Eric R. Ludwig
HR: Rocky Francis
FYE: December 31
Type: Public

Glu Mobile hopes to get your phone stuck permanently to your hand. The company (formerly called Sorrent) develops and publishes video games for wireless devices. Glu Mobile's portfolio includes more than 100 games, including original titles, as well as applications based on licensed, third-party brands such as *Sonic the Hedgehog*. It also produces ring tones and wallpapers. Glu Mobile brings its applications to the mobile masses through wireless service providers such as Sprint Nextel, T-Mobile USA, Verizon Wireless, and Vodaphone.

	Annual Growth	12/03	12/04	12/05	12/06	12/07
Sales ($ mil.)	146.9%	1.8	7.0	25.6	46.2	66.9
Net income ($ mil.)	—	(3.8)	(8.3)	(17.9)	(12.3)	(3.3)
Market value ($ mil.)	—	—	—	—	—	151.5
Employees	—	—	—	—	—	—

GMAC INSURANCE HOLDINGS, INC.

13736 River Port Dr., Ste. 700
Maryland Heights, MO 63043
Phone: 314-493-8000
Fax: 314-493-8114
Web: www.gmacinsurance.com

CEO: Arturo M. (Art) Raschbaum
CFO: Bernard J. (Bernie) Buselmeier
HR: John C. Beattie
FYE: December 31
Type: Subsidiary

GMAC Insurance Holdings is there for the careful as well as the accident prone. A subsidiary of General Motors Acceptance Corporation (GMAC), the financial services unit of General Motors, GMAC Insurance is an underwriter of preferred and nonstandard automobile insurance. The company focuses on its consumer insurance products for cars, recreational vehicles, and motorcycles, but also offers homeowners insurance. Its commercial products cover a range of industries, starting with car dealerships. The company also sells automobile extended service contracts through GM car dealers. GMAC Insurance operates primarily in the US, but also has operations in Canada, Mexico, the UK, and other countries.

	Annual Growth	12/02	12/03	12/04	12/05	12/06
Sales ($ mil.)	18.2%	2,874.0	3,420.0	3,983.0	4,259.0	5,616.0
Net income ($ mil.)	89.7%	87.0	179.0	329.0	417.0	1,127.0
Employees	0.0%	—	3,800	3,800	3,800	3,800

GMAC LLC

200 Renaissance Center
Detroit, MI 48265
Phone: 313-556-5000
Fax: 815-282-6156
Web: www.gmacfs.com

CEO: Alvaro G. (Al) de Molina
CFO: Michael P. McCarthy
HR: –
FYE: December 31
Type: Subsidiary

GMAC aims to be the MAC Daddy of global finance firms. With operations in 40 countries, GMAC offers financing to General Motors dealerships and their customers and has begun diversifying to include other dealer franchises. It is also one of the largest mortgage issuers and servicers in the US, originating residential real estate loans, investing in mortgage-backed securities, and packaging nonconforming single-family home loans for sale to investors through Residential Capital. GMAC Insurance offers vehicle service contracts and home and auto coverage. Its commercial finance arm offers financing to middle-market businesses, as well as factoring and accounts receivable financing. GMAC was founded in 1919.

	Annual Growth	12/03	12/04	12/05	12/06	12/07
Assets ($ mil.)	(3.7%)	288,163.0	324,139.0	320,516.0	287,439.0	247,710.0
Net income ($ mil.)	—	2,793.0	2,913.0	2,394.0	2,125.0	(2,332.0)
Employees	(15.0%)	—	—	—	31,400	26,700

An in-depth profile of this company is available to Hoover's Online members at hoovers.com.

691

GMR MARKETING LLC

5000 S. Towne Dr.
New Berlin, WI 53151
Phone: 262-786-5600
Fax: 262-786-0697
Web: www.gmrlive.com

CEO: Gary M. Reynolds
CFO: Virginia Geraghty
HR: Brian Kramer
FYE: December 31
Type: Subsidiary

GMR Marketing brings products to the people. The company produces product promotions at shopping malls, temporary retail locations, concerts, sports, and lifestyle events such as car shows and Spring Break — as well as "virtual" events tied in with video games and online spaces. It provides all-inclusive services — from concept and design to construction and site management. GMR productions include the Microsoft Xbox Odyssey, the Kraft Food and Family Show, and the Miller Lite Racing Garage. CEO Gary Reynolds founded the company in 1979. It is a part of The Radiate Group, a unit of advertising giant Omnicom.

GMX RESOURCES INC.

NASDAQ (GM): GMXR

9400 N. Broadway, Ste. 600
Oklahoma City, OK 73114
Phone: 405-600-0711
Fax: 405-600-0600
Web: www.gmxresources.com

CEO: Ken L. Kenworthy Jr.
CFO: James A. (Jim) Merrill
HR: –
FYE: December 31
Type: Public

The natural resources in productive, hydrocarbon-rich geological basins are the target for GMX Resources. The Oklahoma-based independent oil and natural gas company explores on more than 19,244 combined net acres located in the Sabine Uplift in Texas and Louisiana, and the Tatum basin in New Mexico. With 96 net producing wells, in 2006 GMX Resources reported proved reserves of 258.4 billion cu. ft. of natural gas equivalent. It has a large inventory of drilling and recompletion projects with an estimated 181.9 billion cu. ft. of natural gas equivalent of proved undeveloped reserves. Ken L. Kenworthy Jr. and Ken L. Kenworthy Sr. each own about 6% of the company.

	Annual Growth	12/03	12/04	12/05	12/06	12/07
Sales ($ mil.)	88.4%	5.4	7.8	19.2	32.0	68.1
Net income ($ mil.)	141.1%	0.5	1.4	7.2	9.0	16.9
Market value ($ mil.)	100.8%	26.4	56.1	359.1	399.1	428.3
Employees	131.3%	8	11	16	99	—

🏢 GNC CORPORATION

300 6th Ave.
Pittsburgh, PA 15222
Phone: 412-288-4600
Fax: 412-288-4764
Web: www.gnc.com

CEO: Joseph (Joe) Fortunato
CFO: Curtis J. Larrimer
HR: Eileen D. Scott
FYE: December 31
Type: Private

What's good for the customer is good for GNC Corporation (formerly General Nutrition Centers). With more than 6,150 company-owned and franchised outlets in all 50 US states and Canada and franchised stores in some 50 foreign markets, GNC is the leading nutritional-supplements retail chain devoted solely to items such as vitamins and dietary products. The company also has about 1,350 stores within Rite Aid drugstores and makes Rite Aid private-label products. GNC has been closing underperforming stores located in the US. GNC's online partner is drugstore.com. In 2007 Apollo Advisors sold the firm to Ontario Teachers' Pension Plan and Ares Management, a US private equity firm, for about $1.6 billion.

	Annual Growth	12/02	12/03	12/04	12/05	12/06
Sales ($ mil.)	1.1%	1,425.0	1,429.5	1,344.7	1,317.7	1,490.0
Employees	(3.8%)	—	14,251	13,618	12,415	12,707

GOAMERICA, INC.

NASDAQ (CM): GOAM

433 Hackensack Ave., 3rd Fl.
Hackensack, NJ 07601
Phone: 201-996-1717
Fax: 201-996-1772
Web: www.goamerica.com

CEO: Daniel R. (Dan) Luis
CFO: John R. Ferron
HR: –
FYE: December 31
Type: Public

GoAmerica is on a quest to provide assistance for people who are hearing impaired. The company's Wynd Communications subsidiary offers wireless subscription services primarily for people with hearing loss (it has more than 7,000 subscribers). Customers can send and receive text telephone (TTY/TDD) messages, as well as faxes and e-mail. Additionally, GoAmerica partners with EarthLink to provide its Go.Web software to enterprises. The program allows subscribers to access corporate networks using wireless handheld devices. Faced with a shortage of operating cash, the company has refocused its efforts behind the development of Wynd Communications.

	Annual Growth	12/03	12/04	12/05	12/06	12/07
Sales ($ mil.)	11.8%	11.9	6.2	8.1	12.8	18.6
Net income ($ mil.)	—	(8.2)	(4.4)	(4.4)	(2.0)	(3.7)
Market value ($ mil.)	(68.0%)	4,775.4	20.6	9.0	20.1	50.4
Employees	245.1%	—	—	33	—	393

GODFATHER'S PIZZA, INC.

2808 N. 108th St.
Omaha, NE 68114
Phone: 402-391-1452
Fax: 402-255-2687
Web: www.godfathers.com

CEO: Ronald B. (Ron) Gartlan
CFO: Annette M. Sneckenberg
HR: Kathleen M. (Kathy) Johnson
FYE: May 31
Type: Private

This Godfather will make you a pizza you can't refuse. Godfather's Pizza operates a leading quick-service restaurant chain with more than 600 family-oriented pizza joints in about 45 states. The parlors offer a crew of pizzas and a mob of topping choices — as well as appetizers, salads, and sandwiches. The company typically offers dine-in, delivery, and carry-out service. The chain operates mostly in such Midwestern states as Iowa, Illinois, Minnesota, and Nebraska, as well as in New York and Florida; about 45 locations are company-owned. Founded by Nebraska native Willy Theisen in 1973, the business is owned by a group led by CEO Ron Gartlan.

	Annual Growth	5/03	5/04	5/05	5/06	5/07
Est. sales ($ mil.)	—	—	—	—	—	54.2
Employees	—	—	—	—	—	2,500

GOFISH CORPORATION

OTC: GOFH

706 Mission St., 10th Fl.
San Francisco, CA 94103
Phone: 415-738-8706
Fax: –
Web: www.gofish.com

CEO: Matt Freeman
CFO: Lennox L. Vernon
HR: –
FYE: December 31
Type: Public

If you decide to "Go Fish" on this company's Web site, there's no telling what you might find. GoFish Corporation operates The GoFish Network, a group of Web sites aimed at six-to-17 year-olds. The company earns money through advertising. GoFish was founded in 2003 by former CEO Michael Downing and Pierce Ledbetter, CEO of LEDIC Management Group; the firm evolved from a music sharing program called Musicbank that Downing and Ledbetter created in 2001. After receiving funding from Global Asset Capital, the company went public through a reverse merger with GoFish Technologies in 2006. It terminated plans to acquire the youth-oriented Web site Bolt in 2007.

	Annual Growth	12/03	12/04	12/05	12/06	12/07
Sales ($ mil.)	—	—	—	—	0.0	2.1
Net income ($ mil.)	—	—	—	—	(5.3)	(16.4)
Market value ($ mil.)	(93.4%)	—	—	—	90.5	6.0
Employees	—	—	—	—	—	—

GOJO INDUSTRIES

1 GOJO Plaza, Ste. 500
Akron, OH 44311
Phone: 330-255-6000
Fax: 330-255-6119
Web: www.gojo.com

CEO: Joe Kanfer
CFO: –
HR: –
FYE: December 31
Type: Private

GOJO Industries believes in the importance of good hygiene. The company makes hand cleaners for professional and consumer use for clients, such as automotive, food service, education, government, and health care facilities, and its product dispensers are seen in many public restrooms. The company also offers a line of health care products under the PROVON brand; its waterless hand sanitizer PURELL is sold through retail channels. GOJO Industries, which sells its products around the globe, has offices in Brazil, Japan, the UK, and the US. The company is named after its heavy-duty hand cleaner, which was formulated by GOJO founder Jerome Lippman.

	Annual Growth	12/03	12/04	12/05	12/06	12/07
Est. sales ($ mil.)	—	—	—	—	—	83.3
Employees	—	—	—	—	—	700

GOLD RESERVE INC.

AMEX: GRZ

926 W. Sprague Ave., Ste. 200
Spokane, WA 99201
Phone: 509-623-1500
Fax: 509-623-1634
Web: www.goldreserveinc.com

CEO: Rockne J. Timm
CFO: Robert A. McGuinness
HR: Mary E. Smith
FYE: December 31
Type: Public

Gold Reserve's primary asset is the Brisas project in Venezuela, which contains estimated reserves of about 10 million ounces of gold and 1.4 billion pounds of copper. Gold Reserve has been developing Brisas since 1992, and it is still working to raise money to begin mining. The company also owns the rights to another minerals property in Venzuela, called Choco 5, and which is adjacent to gold properties owned by Hecla and Gold Fields.

	Annual Growth	12/03	12/04	12/05	12/06	12/07
Sales ($ mil.)	68.8%	0.8	0.9	1.4	8.3	6.5
Net income ($ mil.)	—	(11.4)	(10.4)	(5.9)	(7.0)	(13.8)
Market value ($ mil.)	20.8%	133.7	149.4	102.3	190.4	285.0
Employees	—	—	—	—	65	—

THE GOLDEN 1 CREDIT UNION

8945 Cal Center Dr.
Sacramento, CA 95826
Phone: 916-732-2900
Fax: 916-451-8214
Web: www.golden1.com

CEO: Teresa A. Halleck
CFO: Donna A. Bland
HR: Tammy A. Davis
FYE: December 31
Type: Not-for-profit

The Golden 1 Credit Union wants to be the 1 you bank with in the Golden State. It's California's leading membership financial cooperative, not to mention one of the largest credit unions in the US. The member-owned organization serves communities throughout the state, offering a range of consumer financial products and services through a network of some 75 branches and more than 270 ATMs. The credit union also provides members full-service banking via telephone and the Internet. The Golden 1 offers savings, checking, and money market accounts, IRAs, and credit/check cards. It also provides a variety of personal, real estate, and commercial loans, as well as financial planning and insurance services.

	Annual Growth	12/03	12/04	12/05	12/06	12/07
Est. sales ($ mil.)	—	—	—	—	—	331.3
Employees	—	—	—	—	—	1,292

GOLDEN CORRAL CORPORATION

5151 Glenwood Ave., Ste. 300
Raleigh, NC 27612
Phone: 919-781-9310
Fax: 919-881-4686
Web: www.goldencorral.net

CEO: Theodore M. (Ted) Fowler
CFO: Lamar Bell
HR: Judith (Judy) Irwin
FYE: December 31
Type: Private

If you're so hungry you could eat a horse, ride into the Golden Corral. The company operates and franchises more than 480 family dining restaurants throughout the US. The chain serves a variety of steak, chicken, and pork entrees along with its Golden Choice Buffet, which offers a plethora of hot meats, pasta, pizza, and fresh vegetables. Golden Corral units also feature a Brass Bell Bakery serving fresh-baked breads, rolls, cookies, and brownies. About 120 of the restaurants are company-owned, while the rest are operated by franchisees. Chairman James Maynard, who controls Golden Corral through his holding company Investors Management Corp., founded the chain with partner Bill Carl in 1973.

	Annual Growth	12/03	12/04	12/05	12/06	12/07
Est. sales ($ mil.)	—	—	—	—	—	195.1
Employees	—	—	—	—	—	9,000

GOLDEN ENTERPRISES, INC.

NASDAQ (GM): GLDC

1 Golden Flake Dr.
Birmingham, AL 35205
Phone: 205-458-7316
Fax: 205-458-7327
Web: www.goldenflake.com

CEO: Mark W. McCutcheon
CFO: Patty Townsend
HR: David Jones
FYE: May 31
Type: Public

Located in Birmingham, Alabama, Golden Enterprises (dba Golden Flake Snack Foods) is a true southern source for pork rinds and vinegar- and salt-flavored potato chips. The holding company's Golden Flake Snack Foods makes and distributes salty snacks to food retailers in 12 states throughout the South. The company's lineup includes regular, Cajun hot, and deli ranch potato chips; corn chips; cheese curls; fried pork skins; onion rings; and popcorn. It also sells Golden Flake cakes, dips, dried meat products, pretzels, and nuts packaged by other manufacturers.

	Annual Growth	5/03	5/04	5/05	5/06	5/07
Sales ($ mil.)	3.5%	96.6	97.6	103.1	106.6	110.8
Net income ($ mil.)	—	(0.9)	(0.1)	0.0	0.3	1.2
Market value ($ mil.)	9.0%	26.1	34.4	42.1	33.5	36.9
Employees	(4.0%)	—	—	1,032	991	—

GOLDEN STAR RESOURCES LTD.

AMEX: GSS

10901 W. Toller Dr., Ste. 300
Littleton, CO 80127
Phone: 303-830-9000
Fax: 303-830-9094
Web: www.gsr.com

CEO: Thomas G. (Tom) Mair
CFO: Roger Palmer
HR: –
FYE: December 31
Type: Public

Gold gets top billing at Golden Star Resources. The company's main assets are in Ghana, in West Africa's Ashanti gold belt, and include the Bogoso, Prestea, and Wassa properties. (The Ghanaian government owns 10% of each of those properties.) The company has proved and probable reserves of about 5 million ounces of gold. It also explores other mineral properties elsewhere in Africa and South America. In 2005 Golden Star expanded in Africa by acquiring St. Jude Resources for $118 million. Golden Star had owned a controlling stake in EURO Ressources until late 2006, when it sold most of its stake in the company. The company's goal is to produce half a million ounces annually, a mark it expects to achieve by 2009.

	Annual Growth	12/03	12/04	12/05	12/06	12/07
Sales ($ mil.)	28.5%	64.4	65.0	95.5	128.7	175.6
Net income ($ mil.)	—	13.4	2.6	(13.5)	57.9	(41.8)
Market value ($ mil.)	(5.5%)	926.5	570.4	543.7	613.3	738.5
Employees	21.6%	1,000	1,150	1,500	1,800	—

An in-depth profile of this company is available to Hoover's Online members at hoovers.com.

693

GOLDEN STATE FOODS CORP.

18301 Von Karman Ave., Ste. 1100
Irvine, CA 92612
Phone: 949-252-2000
Fax: 949-252-2080
Web: www.goldenstatefoods.com

CEO: Mark S. Wetterau
CFO: Richard D. (Rich) Moretti
HR: Steve Becker
FYE: December 31
Type: Private

You might say this company helps make the Golden Arches shine. Golden State Foods is a leading food-service supplier that primarily supplies McDonald's restaurants with more than 130 products, including beef patties, Big Mac sauce (which it helped formulate), buns, ketchup, and mayonnaise. It distributes goods to more than 20,000 quick-service eateries from more than a dozen distribution centers, including one in Egypt. In addition, the company runs a non-profit organization, the GSF Foundation, that supports local charities focused on helping children and families. Founded in 1947 by the late William Moore, Golden State Foods is controlled by Wetterau Associates, an investment group led by CEO Mark Wetterau.

	Annual Growth	12/02	12/03	12/04	12/05	12/06
Sales ($ mil.)	11.2%	1,700.0	2,100.0	2,200.0	2,375.0	2,600.0
Employees	8.8%	2,000	2,500	2,500	2,500	2,800

THE GOLDFIELD CORPORATION

AMEX: GV

1684 W. Hibiscus Blvd.
Melbourne, FL 32901
Phone: 321-724-1700
Fax: 321-724-1163
Web: www.goldfieldcorp.com

CEO: John H. Sottile
CFO: Stephen R. Wherry
HR: –
FYE: December 31
Type: Public

The Goldfield Corporation now earns more laying cable than it did digging for mother lodes. Through its Southeast Power subsidiary, Goldfield builds and maintains electrical facilities in the Southeast and Mid-Atlantic regions for utilities and industrial customers, including Florida Power & Light Company and Progress Energy. The unit also installs transmission lines and fiber-optic cable. Goldfield's Bayswater Development subsidiary maintains real estate operations in Florida, specializing in developing waterfront condominiums for retirees. The company, which had been in the mining industry since 1906, divested those operations in 2002 after deciding that it had become economically unfeasible.

	Annual Growth	12/03	12/04	12/05	12/06	12/07
Sales ($ mil.)	(4.6%)	33.0	32.7	39.3	47.5	27.3
Net income ($ mil.)	—	0.4	(0.4)	2.3	3.0	(2.3)
Market value ($ mil.)	2.7%	16.5	15.0	22.0	30.3	18.3
Employees	(1.6%)	—	—	123	—	119

GOLDLEAF FINANCIAL SOLUTIONS, INC.

NASDAQ (CM): GFSI

9020 Overlook Blvd., 3rd Fl.
Brentwood, TN 37027
Phone: 615-250-2100
Fax: 615-373-3421
Web: www.goldleaf.com

CEO: G. Lynn Boggs
CFO: Scott R. Meyerhoff
HR: –
FYE: December 31
Type: Public

Goldleaf Financial Solutions says you can take its products to the bank. Formerly known as Private Business, the company provides a bankroll of outsourced technology-based products and services, including data processing, item processing, and check imaging, to small and midsized community banks. Its BusinessManager product automates the buying, processing, billing, and tracking of accounts receivable that banks purchase from small businesses. Goldleaf's Retail Merchandising Service Automation (RMSA) division helps retailers forecast and track inventories through its Freedom product. Goldleaf Financial Solutions serves more than 2,500 financial institutions nationwide.

	Annual Growth	12/03	12/04	12/05	12/06	12/07
Sales ($ mil.)	7.0%	43.2	39.7	38.3	55.7	56.7
Net income ($ mil.)	—	1.8	2.6	2.3	(3.0)	(0.6)
Market value ($ mil.)	(24.6%)	85.1	175.5	93.3	99.6	27.5
Employees	13.7%	—	—	377	—	487

THE GOLDMAN SACHS GROUP, INC.

NYSE: GS

85 Broad St.
New York, NY 10004
Phone: 212-902-1000
Fax: 212-902-3000
Web: www.goldmansachs.com

CEO: Lloyd C. Blankfein
CFO: David A. Viniar
HR: Kevin W. Kennedy
FYE: Last Friday in November
Type: Public

Goldman Sachs has traditionally possessed the Midas touch in the investment banking world. A global leader in mergers and acquisitions advice and securities underwriting, Goldman offers a gamut of investment banking and asset management services to corporate and government clients, as well as institutional and individual investors. Goldman's business falls into three segments: Investment Banking, Trading and Principal Investments, and Asset Management and Securities Services. It owns Goldman Sachs Execution & Clearing (formerly Spear, Leeds & Kellogg Specialists), one of the largest market makers on the NYSE, and is also a leading market maker for fixed income products, currencies, and commodities.

	Annual Growth	11/03	11/04	11/05	11/06	11/07
Sales ($ mil.)	38.9%	23,623.0	29,839.0	43,391.0	69,353.0	87,968.0
Net income ($ mil.)	40.2%	3,005.0	4,553.0	5,626.0	9,537.0	11,599.0
Market value ($ mil.)	18.1%	45,447.3	50,423.8	58,633.3	83,193.5	88,544.2
Employees	(0.8%)	—	—	31,005	26,467	30,522

GOLD'S GYM INTERNATIONAL, INC.

125 E. John Carpenter Fwy, Ste. 1300
Irving, TX 75062
Phone: 214-574-4653
Fax: 214-296-5000
Web: www.goldsgym.com

CEO: David A. (Dave) Schnabel
CFO: Randall R. (Randy) Schultz
HR: TJ Carter
FYE: February 28
Type: Private

The site of America's most famous muscle beach is the birthplace of one of the world's best-known muscle makers. Gold's Gym, which first opened in Venice Beach, California, in 1965, franchises more than 620 gyms in more than 25 countries, with franchises accounting for most of the company's locations. The company boasts nearly 3 million members. In addition to opening franchises, the firm buys smaller regional health clubs and converts them to Gold's Gyms. The company also licenses the Gold's Gym name for products such as fitness equipment and accessories, luggage, T-shirts, and men's and women's sportswear. Gold's Gym was acquired by TRT Holdings in 2004 for about $158 million.

	Annual Growth	2/03	2/04	2/05	2/06	2/07
Est. sales ($ mil.)	—	—	—	—	—	48.6
Employees	—	—	—	—	—	2,000

GOLF GALAXY, INC.

7275 Flying Cloud Dr.
Eden Prairie, MN 55344
Phone: 952-941-8848
Fax: 952-941-8846
Web: www.golfgalaxy.com

CEO: Randall K. (Randy) Zanatta
CFO: Richard C. (Rick) Nordvold
HR: –
FYE: Saturday nearest February 28
Type: Subsidiary

Let Golf Galaxy help with your galactic battle to break par. It operates more than 75 golf superstores in about 35 states. Its stores offer equipment, apparel and shoes, gifts, accessories, books, and videos. Golf Galaxy also sells pre-owned clubs and has a trade-in program. In-store amenities include computer video swing analysis, on-site certified club technicians, indoor driving bays, full-sized putting greens, and advice on equipment from a staff that includes PGA and LPGA professionals. Golf Galaxy also operates a Web site (golfgalaxy.com) and catalog. Founded in 1997 by executives Randy Zanatta and Greg Maanum, the firm went public in mid-2005 and was acquired by Dick's Sporting Goods in 2007.

	Annual Growth	2/02	2/03	2/04	2/05	2/06
Sales ($ mil.)	41.7%	—	—	99.6	133.1	200.1
Net income ($ mil.)	(16.5%)	—	—	7.6	7.5	5.3
Employees	143.3%	—	—	—	600	1,460

GOLFSMITH INTERNATIONAL HOLDINGS, INC.
NASDAQ (GM): GOLF

11000 N. IH-35
Austin, TX 78753
Phone: 512-837-8810
Fax: 512-837-1245
Web: www.golfsmith.com

CEO: Martin E. (Marty) Hanaka
CFO: Virginia (Ginger) Bunte
HR: Gillian (Gill) Felix
FYE: December 31
Type: Public

You might not be so quick to wrap that 5-iron around a tree if you'd made it yourself. Golfsmith International was founded in 1967 as a mail-order seller of custom-made golf clubs, and it still teaches golfers how to assemble their own irons, woods, and putters. The company sells its products through its catalogs, Web site, and more than 70 golf superstores in about 20 states. The company's stores — averaging about 20,000 sq. ft. — sell private-label and brand-name golf equipment, accessories, and related paraphernalia and offer such services as swing analysis. Golfsmith also operates the Harvey Penick Golf Academy, an instructional school for golfers.

	Annual Growth	12/03	12/04	12/05	12/06	12/07
Sales ($ mil.)	9.4%	—	296.2	323.8	357.9	388.2
Net income ($ mil.)	—	—	(4.8)	3.0	(7.0)	(40.8)
Market value ($ mil.)	(59.2%)	—	—	—	151.7	61.8
Employees	11.9%	—	—	1,330	—	1,665

THE GOLUB CORPORATION

501 Duanesburg Rd.
Schenectady, NY 12306
Phone: 518-355-5000
Fax: 518-379-3536
Web: www.pricechopper.com

CEO: Neil M. Golub
CFO: John Endres
HR: Margaret Davenport
FYE: April 30
Type: Private

Supermarket operator The Golub Corporation offers tasty come-ons such as table-ready meals, gift certificates, automatic discount cards, and a hotline where cooks answer food-related queries. Golub operates about 115 Price Chopper supermarkets in Connecticut, Massachusetts, New Hampshire, upstate New York, northeastern Pennsylvania, and Vermont. It also runs Mini Chopper service stations and convenience stores. Golub discontinued its HouseCalls home delivery service in 2001 but is giving home delivery another try. Brothers Bill and Ben Golub founded the company in 1932. Today the Golub family runs the company and owns 45% of the regional grocery chain; employees own slightly more than 50%.

	Annual Growth	4/02	4/03	4/04	4/05	4/06
Est. sales ($ mil.)	9.4%	2,100.0	2,100.0	2,500.0	2,700.0	3,010.0
Employees	3.9%	19,700	20,000	22,000	22,000	22,970

GOMEZ, INC.

10 Maguire Rd., Ste. 330
Lexington, MA 02421
Phone: 781-778-2700
Fax: 781-778-2799
Web: www.gomez.com

CEO: Jaime W. Ellertson
CFO: Richard M. (Rick) Darer
HR: —
FYE: December 31
Type: Private

Performance is the true measure of a Web site, according to Gomez. The company provides Web site testing and management services primarily to companies in the financial services, retail, and travel industries. Its ExperienceFirst product helps companies measure performance outside of a firewall in order to stay ahead of potential data bottlenecks and other network problems that can interfere with their online operations. Serving more than 2,000 customers worldwide, including such big names as DoubleClick, Expedia, Facebook, and Home Depot, Gomez also offers consulting services to help guide companies as they build and expand their online footprint. Founded in 1997, Gomez filed for an IPO in mid-2008.

	Annual Growth	12/03	12/04	12/05	12/06	12/07
Sales ($ mil.)	48.4%	—	—	14.8	21.7	32.6
Net income ($ mil.)	—	—	—	0.1	0.6	(2.3)
Employees	—	—	—	—	—	237

GOOD SAMARITAN HOSPITAL

2222 Philadelphia Dr.
Dayton, OH 45406
Phone: 937-278-2612
Fax: 937-276-8337
Web: www.goodsamdayton.org

CEO: James R. (Jim) Pancoast
CFO: Scott Shelton
HR: William Linesch
FYE: December 31
Type: Subsidiary

Good Samaritan Hospital offers a caring hand to the residents of Dayton, Ohio, and the surrounding areas. The hospital has some 560 beds and offers a mix of services, including primary and emergency care, pediatric specialties, and a family birthing center. Good Samaritan also runs the Samaritan North Health Center, an outpatient health center that offers outpatient surgery, rehab and sports medicine, diagnostic imaging, and cancer care, among other services. Other operations include the Maria-Joseph Living Care Center, a long-term care facility with some 400 beds, and Samaritan Family Care, a primary care physicians' network. Good Samaritan Hospital is part of Premier Health Partners.

	Annual Growth	12/03	12/04	12/05	12/06	12/07
Est. sales ($ mil.)	—	—	—	—	—	307.2
Employees	—	—	—	—	—	221

GOOD TIMES RESTAURANTS, INC.
NASDAQ (CM): GTIM

601 Corporate Cir.
Golden, CO 80401
Phone: 303-384-1400
Fax: 303-273-0177
Web: www.goodtimesburgers.com

CEO: Boyd E. Hoback
CFO: Susan M. Knutson
HR: Gary Staton
FYE: September 30
Type: Public

Hot eats and cold treats are a "Dyn-o-mite!" combination for this company. Good Times Restaurants operates and franchises more than 50 Good Times Drive Thru hamburger joints located primarily in the Denver area. The chain is made up mostly of double drive-through and walk-up eateries that feature a menu of burgers, fries, and frozen custard. A limited number of Good Times outlets also offer dine-in seating. More than 25 of the locations are operated by franchisees, while the rest are either company-owned or operated under joint venture agreements. The family of director Geoffrey Bailey owns almost 30% of the company.

	Annual Growth	9/03	9/04	9/05	9/06	9/07
Sales ($ mil.)	12.7%	15.5	15.8	17.0	20.9	25.0
Net income ($ mil.)	—	(0.2)	(0.7)	(0.4)	0.0	0.0
Market value ($ mil.)	26.4%	8.3	7.3	14.2	23.6	21.2
Employees	18.3%	—	—	394	—	551

GOODBY, SILVERSTEIN & PARTNERS

720 California St.
San Francisco, CA 94108
Phone: 415-392-0669
Fax: 415-788-4303
Web: www.goodbysilverstein.com

CEO: Jeffrey (Jeff) Goodby
CFO: Rich Dizon
HR: Jill Sammons
FYE: December 31
Type: Subsidiary

Just making good ads doesn't seem to be enough for this firm. Goodby, Silverstein & Partners is one of the premier names in advertising with a long heritage of cutting-edge and effective creative work. Perhaps best known for the "Got Milk" campaign (produced for the California Milk Processors), the agency has also worked for blue-chip brands such as Häagen-Dazs, Hewlett-Packard, and Saturn. In addition to traditional ad work, Goodby, Silverstein offers interactive and brand promotion services. Co-chairmen Rich Silverstein and Jeff Goodby started the company in 1983; it operates today as a subsidiary of advertising services conglomerate Omnicom Group.

THE GOODHEART-WILLCOX CO., INC.

Pink Sheets: GWOX

18604 W. Creek Dr.
Tinley Park, IL 60477
Phone: 708-687-5000
Fax: 708-687-0315
Web: www.g-w.com

CEO: John F. Flanagan
CFO: –
HR: –
FYE: April 30
Type: Public

Goodheart-Willcox's educational textbooks run more toward HVAC than Homer. The company publishes textbooks, workbooks, computer software supplements, and instructor's guides for junior and senior high schools, vocational schools, technical and private trade schools, and colleges. Its titles cover industrial and technical topics (AutoCAD, drafting) and family and consumer topics (child care, nutrition). Apprentice trainers, educators, and do-it-yourselfers also use the company's books. Goodheart-Willcox hires authors and designs, edits, illustrates, and sells its books directly to schools or through bookstores. The company was founded in 1921.

	Annual Growth	4/03	4/04	4/05	4/06	4/07
Est. sales ($ mil.)	—	—	—	—	—	26.5
Employees	—	—	—	—	—	65

GOODMAN GLOBAL, INC.

5151 San Felipe, Ste. 500
Houston, TX 77056
Phone: 713-861-2500
Fax: 713-861-3207
Web: www.goodmanmfg.com

CEO: David L. (Dave) Swift
CFO: Lawrence M. Blackburn
HR: Donald R. King
FYE: December 31
Type: Private

While a good man may be hard to find, *this* Goodman makes it easy to find comfort with its residential and light commercial HVAC products. The company manufactures heating, ventilation, and air conditioning (HVAC) products, including split-system air conditioners and heat pumps, gas furnaces, packaged units, air handlers, and evaporator coils. It sells products under the Goodman, Amana, and Quietflex brands through some 150 company-operated distribution centers and about 700 independent distributor locations throughout North America. Investment firm Hellman & Friedman bought the company in 2008.

	Annual Growth	12/02	12/03	12/04	12/05	12/06
Sales ($ mil.)	12.1%	1,136.2	1,192.7	1,317.6	1,565.4	1,794.8
Net income ($ mil.)	(0.6%)	65.8	87.4	47.7	24.9	64.2
Employees	0.6%	—	—	4,816	4,997	4,878

GOODMAN MANUFACTURING COMPANY, L.P.

5151 San Felipe St., Ste. 500
Houston, TX 77056
Phone: 713-861-2500
Fax: 713-861-0772
Web: www.goodmanmfg.com

CEO: David L. (Dave) Swift
CFO: Lawrence M. (Larry) Blackburn
HR: Donald R. King
FYE: December 31
Type: Subsidiary

Goodman Manufacturing knows how to cool off a hot situation. The company makes heating, ventilation, and air conditioning (HVAC) equipment for residential and commercial use in North America. Goodman, which sells its products through about 700 independent installers and dealers, is the #2 domestic maker of air conditioners, humidifiers, gas furnaces, heat pumps, and other products. It manufactures its products (predominantly marketed under the Goodman, Amana, and Quietflex brand names) at facilities in Texas, Tennessee, Arizona, and Florida. Founded by Harold Goodman in 1982, the company is a subsidiary of Goodman Global, Inc., which merged with an affiliate of Hellman & Friedman LLC in early 2008.

GOODRICH CORPORATION

NYSE: GR

Four Coliseum Centre, 2730 W. Tyvola Rd.
Charlotte, NC 28217
Phone: 704-423-7000
Fax: 704-423-5540
Web: www.goodrich.com

CEO: Marshall O. Larsen
CFO: Scott E. Kuechle
HR: Terrence G. Linnert
FYE: December 31
Type: Public

Goodrich Corporation is a tireless leader in aerospace systems. The company, formerly tire maker BFGoodrich, is now focused on its three aerospace divisions. Goodrich's largest unit, Actuation and Landing Systems, makes fuel systems, aircraft wheels, brakes, landing gear, and flight control and actuation systems. Next largest is Nacelles and Interior Systems which makes aerostructures (nacelles, pylons, and thrust reversers) as well as aircraft seats, cargo, and lighting systems. Finally, Goodrich's Electronics Systems division makes fuel controls, flight management systems, and reconnaissance and surveillance systems.

	Annual Growth	12/03	12/04	12/05	12/06	12/07
Sales ($ mil.)	9.9%	4,382.9	4,724.5	5,396.5	5,878.3	6,392.2
Net income ($ mil.)	48.1%	100.4	172.2	263.6	482.1	482.6
Market value ($ mil.)	26.0%	3,495.3	3,888.8	5,059.7	5,691.5	8,798.7
Employees	1.8%	—	—	22,600	23,400	23,400

GOODRICH PETROLEUM CORPORATION

NYSE: GDP

808 Travis St., Ste. 1320
Houston, TX 77002
Phone: 713-780-9494
Fax: 713-780-9254
Web: www.goodrichpetroleum.com

CEO: Walter G. (Gil) Goodrich
CFO: David R. Looney
HR: –
FYE: December 31
Type: Public

From deep in the mystic Miocene sands and the good rich rocks of ancient Mother Earth, Goodrich Petroleum brings forth oil and gas. The independent exploration and production company delves into formations dating to the Miocene and Frio Age in southern Louisiana, where it has most of its proved reserves. The company also operates in the Cotton Valley trend in Texas and Louisiana, and it leases acreage in Michigan. Goodrich Petroleum owns interests in more than 300 active oil and gas wells and has estimated proved reserves of 357.8 billion cu. ft. of natural gas equivalent. Chairman Patrick Malloy owns 16% of the company; director Josiah Austin, 18%.

	Annual Growth	12/03	12/04	12/05	12/06	12/07
Sales ($ mil.)	35.8%	32.7	47.3	68.3	116.2	111.3
Net income ($ mil.)	—	3.7	18.5	(17.5)	1.6	(45.0)
Market value ($ mil.)	68.9%	96.8	333.7	623.8	1,020.9	787.7
Employees	31.4%	37	52	64	84	—

GOODWILL INDUSTRIES INTERNATIONAL, INC.

15810 Indianola Dr.
Rockville, MD 20855
Phone: 301-530-6500
Fax: 301-530-1516
Web: www.goodwill.org

CEO: Jim Gibbons
CFO: –
HR: Miriam Johnson
FYE: December 31
Type: Not-for-profit

Goodwill Industries International supports the operations of more than 185 independent Goodwill chapters worldwide. Though known mainly for its 2,100-plus thrift stores, the organization focuses on providing rehabilitation, job training, placement, and employment services for people with disabilities and others. Goodwill is one of the world's largest providers of such services, as well as one of the world's largest employers of the physically, mentally, and emotionally disabled. Support for the organization's programs comes mainly from sales of donated goods, both at the retail stores and through an online auction site, as well as from contract work and from government grants. Goodwill was founded in 1902.

	Annual Growth	12/02	12/03	12/04	12/05	12/06
Sales ($ mil.)	9.0%	2,055.0	2,210.0	2,390.0	2,650.0	2,903.2
Employees	(41.2%)	140,023	82,370	—	—	—

An in-depth profile of this company is available to Hoover's Online members at hoovers.com.

GOODY PRODUCTS, INC.

400 Galleria Pkwy., Ste. 1100
Atlanta, GA 30339
Phone: 770-615-4700
Fax: 770-615-4740
Web: www.goody.com

CEO: A.J. Ross
CFO: Dale Metz
HR: Nicole Leiter
FYE: December 31
Type: Subsidiary

Goody has the tools to help even the Bride of Frankenstein have a good hair day. Goody Products manufactures hair care accessories, brushes, combs, and travel storage products and sells them through food, drug, and discount stores, such as Target and Wal-Mart. The firm makes products under the Goody, Ace, Stayput, Ouchless, TherapySolutions, Styling Therapy, ColourCollection, and StylingSolutions trademarks. The Goody brand set root in 1907 when Henry Goodman and his son, Abraham, began selling rhinestone-studded hair combs off a pushcart in New York City. Since 1993 it has been owned by Newell Rubbermaid. Goody Products is a subsidiary in its parent's home and family segment.

	Annual Growth	12/03	12/04	12/05	12/06	12/07
Est. sales ($ mil.)	—	—	—	—	—	45.5
Employees	—	—	—	—	—	800

THE GOODYEAR TIRE & RUBBER COMPANY

NYSE: GT

1144 E. Market St.
Akron, OH 44316
Phone: 330-796-2121
Fax: 330-796-2222
Web: www.goodyear.com

CEO: Robert (Bob) Keegan
CFO: W. Mark Schmitz
HR: Kathleen T. Geier
FYE: December 31
Type: Public

Despite a worldwide alliance with Sumitomo Rubber Industries designed to dominate the tire industry, The Goodyear Tire & Rubber Company is the #3 tire maker in the world, behind Bridgestone and Michelin. The company operates more than 50 plants worldwide, and has nearly 1,800 retail tire and auto centers. Goodyear sells tires for the replacement market as well as to the world's automakers. In addition to its own brand of tires, Goodyear makes Dunlop tires for sale in North America and Europe through its alliance with Japan's Sumitomo. The company has sold its Engineered Products division to The Carlyle Group.

	Annual Growth	12/03	12/04	12/05	12/06	12/07
Sales ($ mil.)	6.8%	15,119.0	18,370.4	19,723.0	20,258.0	19,644.0
Net income ($ mil.)	—	(802.1)	114.8	228.0	(330.0)	602.0
Market value ($ mil.)	48.9%	1,378.1	2,574.6	3,067.7	3,740.8	6,776.3
Employees	(5.1%)	—	—	80,000	77,000	72,000

GOODY'S FAMILY CLOTHING, INC.

400 Goody's Ln.
Knoxville, TN 37922
Phone: 865-966-2000
Fax: 865-777-4220
Web: www.goodysonline.com

CEO: Paul G. White
CFO: David G. Peek
HR: Thomas Hughes
FYE: Saturday nearest January 31
Type: Private

Goody's Family Clothing doesn't believe big national chains beat out small-town department stores. Goody's operates about 350 small department stores in about 20 states, mainly in strip malls in the southeastern and midwestern US. The stores sell clothes, shoes, accessories, and gift items. Goody's sticks to smaller towns where budget-minded shoppers may be hungry for popular brand names. It sells Dockers, Levi's, NIKE, Reebok, and Skechers, as well as its own labels (Ashley Judd line), which account for about a third of sales. Founded as Athens Outlet Stores in 1953, Goody's Family Clothing was taken private by two investment firms in early 2006. The company filed for Chapter 11 bankruptcy protection in June 2008.

	Annual Growth	1/02	1/03	1/04	1/05	1/06
Sales ($ mil.)	4.8%	1,192.5	1,193.4	1,227.0	1,267.0	1,440.0
Employees	5.7%	10,000	10,000	10,000	10,000	12,480

GOOGLE INC.

NASDAQ (GS): GOOG

1600 Amphitheatre Pkwy.
Mountain View, CA 94043
Phone: 650-253-0000
Fax: 650-253-0001
Web: www.google.com

CEO: Eric E. Schmidt
CFO: George Reyes
HR: Stacy Sullivan
FYE: December 31
Type: Public

If you've never Googled, you probably aren't finding what you want online. Google operates the leading Internet search engine, offering targeted search results from billions of Web pages. Results are based on a proprietary algorithm — Google's technology for ranking Web pages is called PageRank. The company generates nearly all of its revenue through ad sales. Advertisers can deliver relevant ads targeted to search queries or Web content. Google also operates the Google Network, a network of third-party customers that use Google's advertising programs to deliver relevant ads to their own Web sites. Founders Sergey Brin and Larry Page each have nearly 30% voting control of the company.

	Annual Growth	12/03	12/04	12/05	12/06	12/07
Sales ($ mil.)	83.4%	1,465.9	3,189.2	6,138.6	10,604.9	16,594.0
Net income ($ mil.)	151.1%	105.7	399.1	1,465.4	3,077.4	4,203.7
Market value ($ mil.)	106.9%	—	18,419.5	121,565.2	104,837.5	163,256.3
Employees	64.6%	2,292	3,021	5,680	10,674	16,805

GORDON BROTHERS GROUP, LLC

101 Huntington Ave., 10th Fl.
Boston, MA 02199
Phone: 617-426-3233
Fax: 617-422-6222
Web: www.gordonbrothers.com

CEO: Mark J. Schwartz
CFO: Alan R. Goldstein
HR: Karen A. Meier
FYE: December 31
Type: Private

Gordon Brothers Group organizes the sale of assets, including retail inventories, overstocks, real estate, industrial assets, accounts receivable, and intellectual property. The company, which prides itself on discretion and speed, also manages closings of underperforming stores for top retailers. Its GB Merchant Partners affiliate takes equity positions in retail and consumer products firms such as Laura Secord, Spencer Gifts, and Things Remembered. Gordon Brothers Group was founded in 1903 by Jacob Gordon, whose grandson Michael Frieze serves as chairman of the company. It has about 20 offices in North America, Asia, and Europe.

	Annual Growth	12/03	12/04	12/05	12/06	12/07
Est. sales ($ mil.)	—	—	—	—	—	104.9
Employees	—	—	—	—	—	1,800

GORDON FOOD SERVICE

333 50th St. SW
Grand Rapids, MI 49501
Phone: 616-530-7000
Fax: 616-717-7600
Web: www.gfs.com

CEO: Dan Gordon
CFO: Jeff Maddox
HR: –
FYE: October 31
Type: Private

This company caters to the tastes of American and Canadian food-service operators alike. Gordon Food Service (GFS) is a leading food-service supplier in North America with more than a dozen distribution centers in the US and Canada. It offers more than 15,000 food and nonfood products (both nationally branded and private-label items) to some 45,000 customers in 15 US states and throughout Canada. It serves schools, restaurants, and other institutions. The company also sells food and supplies through more than 100 GFS Marketplace stores, which are open to the public, in five midwestern states and Florida. Tracing its roots back to 1897, GFS is owned by the Gordon family.

	Annual Growth	10/02	10/03	10/04	10/05	10/06
Est. sales ($ mil.)	21.0%	2,750.0	3,000.0	3,300.0	3,915.0	5,900.0
Employees	21.8%	5,000	5,750	33,000	7,050	11,000

An in-depth profile of this company is available to Hoover's Online members at hoovers.com.

THE GORES GROUP, LLC

10877 Wilshire Blvd., 18th Fl.
Los Angeles, CA 90024
Phone: 310-209-3010
Fax: 310-209-3310
Web: www.gores.com

CEO: Vance W. Diggins
CFO: Catherine Babon Scanlon
HR: –
FYE: December 31
Type: Private

In the gory aftermath of the tech wreck, Gores Group looks for survivors to nurse back to health. Formerly known as Gores Technology Group, the private investment company buys and manages technology (software, hardware, technology services) and telecommunications companies. Gores Group does its own due diligence, usually takes full ownership, and sets its experts to work to turn around the company. Since its founding by chairman Alec Gores in 1992, it has bought more than 40 companies around the world. Typical targets have revenues between $30 million and more than $1 billion and are often spinoffs of noncore operations from large corporate parents.

	Annual Growth	12/03	12/04	12/05	12/06	12/07
Est. sales ($ mil.)	—	—	—	—	—	386.7
Employees	—	—	—	—	—	3,789

THE GORMAN-RUPP COMPANY

AMEX: GRC

305 Bowman St.
Mansfield, OH 44903
Phone: 419-755-1011
Fax: 419-755-1233
Web: www.gormanrupp.com

CEO: Jeffrey S. Gorman
CFO: Robert E. Kirkendall
HR: Lee A. Wilkins
FYE: December 31
Type: Public

Gorman-Rupp keeps pumping out pumps. The company, founded in 1933 by engineers J.C. Gorman and H.E. Rupp, makes a range of pump models used in construction work, sewage treatment, petroleum refining, agriculture, and fire fighting, as well as for HVAC and military applications. Gorman-Rupp's pumps range in size from 1/4-inch (one gallon per minute) to 84-inch (500,000 gallons per minute). Smaller pumps are used for dispensing soft drinks and making ice cubes, while large pumps find use in the refueling of aircraft and boosting low water pressure in municipal fresh water markets. Gorman-Rupp sells its products through distributors and representatives in over 100 countries.

	Annual Growth	12/03	12/04	12/05	12/06	12/07
Sales ($ mil.)	11.8%	195.8	203.6	231.3	270.9	305.6
Net income ($ mil.)	23.6%	9.8	9.3	10.9	19.1	22.9
Market value ($ mil.)	45.7%	115.5	157.2	151.2	395.1	521.1
Employees	—	—	—	1,021	—	—

GOSS INTERNATIONAL CORPORATION

3 Territorial Ct.
Bolingbrook, IL 60440
Phone: 630-755-9300
Fax: 630-755-9301
Web: www.gossinternational.com

CEO: Bob Brown
CFO: Joseph P. Gaynor III
HR: Angela Lewis
FYE: December 31
Type: Private

Goss International always has some pressing news. The company operates through its Goss Graphic Systems subsidiary, making web-offset printing presses for newspapers and commercial printers. Goss offers its presses, related parts, and services (sensitive to publishing schedules) through sales offices and plants in North America, Europe, and Asia. The company serves newspaper publishers in more than 120 countries. Customers include *The Asahi Shimbun* (Japan), *The People's Daily* (China), and *The Financial Times* (UK). Investment firm Stonington Partners controls the company.

	Annual Growth	12/02	12/03	12/04	12/05	12/06
Est. sales ($ mil.)	3.6%	—	—	—	1,100.0	1,140.0
Employees	0.0%	—	—	—	4,100	4,100

GOTTSCHALKS INC.

NYSE: GOT

7 River Park Place East
Fresno, CA 93720
Phone: 559-434-4800
Fax: 559-434-4666
Web: www.gottschalks.com

CEO: James R. (Jim) Famalette
CFO: Daniel T. Warzenski
HR: –
FYE: Saturday nearest January 31
Type: Public

Californians don't look for Gottschalks department stores on Rodeo Drive. The company's stores anchor smaller city malls and offer moderately priced and better name-brand consumer goods (clothes, shoes, housewares, and accessories). Gottschalks operates about 60 department stores, mostly in California, but also in Alaska, Idaho, Nevada, Oregon, and Washington. It also sells plus-sized women's clothing in its Village East specialty stores. Gottschalks bought the nine-store Harris chain in 1998 from Spanish retailer El Corte Inglés, which owns about 15% of the firm through The Harris Company. Founded by Emil Gottschalk in 1904, the regional department store chain has rejected plans to sell the company.

	Annual Growth	1/04	1/05	1/06	1/07	1/08
Sales ($ mil.)	(1.2%)	667.8	668.6	676.8	687.5	636.4
Net income ($ mil.)	—	1.9	5.3	5.2	2.7	(12.4)
Market value ($ mil.)	(12.5%)	60.3	104.8	129.7	150.9	35.3
Employees	0.0%	—	—	5,800	5,800	—

GOULD PAPER CORPORATION

11 Madison Ave.
New York, NY 10010
Phone: 212-301-0000
Fax: 212-481-0067
Web: www.gouldpaper.com

CEO: Harry E. Gould Jr.
CFO: Carl Matthews
HR: Barbara O'Grady
FYE: December 31
Type: Private

Paper is as good as gold for Gould Paper, one of the largest privately owned distributors of printing and fine papers in the US. The company, owned by the Gould family, distributes and sells paper for multiple markets, including fine papers, commercial printing, lithography, newsprint, direct mail, catalogs, envelopes, and specialty papers. Gould also supplies paperboard and packaging grades, and it has paper converting operations. The company sells 2 million tons of paper products annually. It operates from about 20 locations in Canada and the US; subsidiaries P3/Saleshurst, WWF, and Price & Pierce focus on sales in Europe and the Asia/Pacific.

	Annual Growth	12/02	12/03	12/04	12/05	12/06
Sales ($ mil.)	0.6%	1,125.0	1,100.0	1,210.0	1,240.0	1,150.0
Employees	(1.1%)	485	400	410	374	464

GOUVERNEUR BANCORP, INC.

AMEX: GOV

42 Church St.
Gouverneur, NY 13642
Phone: 315-287-2600
Fax: 315-287-3340
Web: www.gouverneurbank.com

CEO: Richard F. Bennett
CFO: Robert J. Twyman
HR: –
FYE: September 30
Type: Public

Gouverneur Bancorp is the holding company for Gouverneur Savings and Loan, which serves upstate New York from two full-service branches and a loan production office. Chartered in 1892, the thrift offers deposit products including checking and savings accounts, NOW accounts, CDs, and money market accounts. Gouverneur Savings and Loan primarily uses funds from deposits to originate residential mortgages, which account for more than 80% of its loan portfolio. It also offers commercial mortgages and consumer loans (mostly automobile loans). Cambray Mutual Holding Company owns 57% of Gouverneur Bancorp.

	Annual Growth	9/03	9/04	9/05	9/06	9/07
Assets ($ mil.)	10.2%	90.0	104.2	122.2	130.1	132.6
Net income ($ mil.)	10.7%	0.6	0.9	1.0	1.3	0.9
Market value ($ mil.)	0.8%	25.1	32.0	28.2	32.2	25.9
Employees	1.5%	—	—	33	34	34

GOVERNMENT EMPLOYEES INSURANCE COMPANY

5260 Western Ave.
Chevy Chase, MD 20815
Phone: 301-986-3000
Fax: 301-986-2888
Web: www.geico.com

CEO: Olza M. (Tony) Nicely
CFO: Mike Campbell
HR: Jan Stewart
FYE: December 31
Type: Subsidiary

The Government Employees Insurance Company, widely known as GEICO, has found that driving down costs brings drivers by the droves into its fold. GEICO has traditionally provided auto and other insurance to preferred low-risk demographic groups (such as government and military employees) but has also begun to sell to nonstandard (high-risk) drivers. In addition to auto coverage, the company's offerings include motorcycle insurance and emergency road service. GEICO eschews agents in favor of direct marketing through such vehicles as direct mail, TV, radio, and the Internet. Its gecko mascot is one of the most recognized marketing icons. The company is a subsidiary of Warren Buffett's Berkshire Hathaway.

GOYA FOODS, INC.

100 Seaview Dr.
Secaucus, NJ 07096
Phone: 201-348-4900
Fax: 201-348-6609
Web: www.goya.com

CEO: Robert I. (Bob) Unanue
CFO: Miguel Lugo
HR: Tony Rico
FYE: December 31
Type: Private

Whether you call 'em *frijoles* or *habichuelas*, beans are beans, and Goya's got 'em. Goya Foods produces approximately 1,500 Hispanic and Caribbean grocery items, including canned and dried beans, canned meats, fruit nectars, oils, olives, rice, seasonings and sauces, plantain and yucca chips, and frozen entrees. It sells many different types of rice and some 30 types of beans and peas. The company's brands include Goya and Canilla. It also sells beverages such as tropical fruit nectars and juices, tropical sodas, and coffee. Goya is owned by one of the richest Hispanic *familias* in the US, the Unanues, who founded the company in 1936.

	Annual Growth	5/02	5/03	5/04	5/05	*12/06
Est. sales ($ mil.)	12.2%	750.0	750.0	850.0	750.0	1,190.0
Employees	4.7%	2,500	2,500	2,500	2,500	3,000

*Fiscal year change

GP STRATEGIES CORPORATION

NYSE: GPX

6095 Marshalee Dr., Ste. 300
Elkridge, MD 21075
Phone: 410-379-3600
Fax: 410-540-5311
Web: www.gpstrategies.com

CEO: Scott N. Greenberg
CFO: Sharon Esposito-Mayer
HR: Lydia M. DeSantis
FYE: December 31
Type: Public

GP Strategies, through its General Physics subsidiary, offers a broad range of consulting, engineering, staffing, and training services. The company divides its offerings into three main categories: manufacturing and business process outsourcing (BPO), which accounts for more than 45% of sales; process, energy, and government; and training and marketing. General Physics has more than 500 clients, including auto manufacturers, electric utilities, government agencies and contractors, and technology companies. US government agencies, led by the Department of the Army, account for about 18% of the company's sales; General Motors and its various affiliates, 21%.

	Annual Growth	12/03	12/04	12/05	12/06	12/07
Sales ($ mil.)	10.2%	168.7	194.0	175.6	178.8	248.4
Net income ($ mil.)	—	(8.3)	22.5	7.2	6.6	9.7
Market value ($ mil.)	12.4%	111.8	121.9	128.1	136.3	178.4
Employees	5.2%	—	—	1,580	—	1,747

GPM INVESTMENTS, LLC.

7443 Lee Davis Rd., Ste. 301
Mechanicsville, VA 23111
Phone: 804-730-1568
Fax: 804-746-1669
Web: www.fasmart.com

CEO: Dave McComas
CFO: Don Bassell
HR: Allan Ritchie
FYE: December 31
Type: Private

GPM Investments is where it's at for convenience store operators Fas Mart and Shore Stop. The Israeli investment firm operates about 280 convenience stores in Connecticut, Delaware, Maryland, New Jersey, North Carolina, Pennsylvania, Rhode Island, and Virginia. GPM also owns and operates the Shore Stop network of convenience stores along the Eastern Shore of Maryland and Virginia. In 2004 Fas Mart acquired New England chain DB Mart (36 stores) and converted them all to the Fas Mart banner. The company also supplies petroleum products to a network of about 60 independent third-party dealers. GPM Investments is majority owned by Israel's Gmul Energy Ltd.

	Annual Growth	12/03	12/04	12/05	12/06	12/07
Est. sales ($ mil.)	—	—	—	—	—	703.9
Employees	—	—	—	—	—	1,300

GRACO INC.

NYSE: GGG

88 11th Ave. NE
Minneapolis, MN 55413
Phone: 612-623-6000
Fax: 612-378-3505
Web: www.graco.com

CEO: Patrick J. McHale
CFO: James A. Graner
HR: –
FYE: Last Friday in December
Type: Public

To state the obvious, Graco has fluid management skills. The company, which was founded in 1926 as Gray Company, manufactures equipment designed to move, measure, control, dispense, and apply fluid materials. Products include pumps, applicators, spray guns, pressure washers, filters, valves, and accessories; these goods are used in industrial and commercial applications to handle paints, adhesives, sealants, and lubricants. In addition to painting contractors, Graco's customers include automotive, construction equipment, and vehicle lubrication companies. Graco sells its products globally through independent distributors.

	Annual Growth	12/03	12/04	12/05	12/06	12/07
Sales ($ mil.)	12.0%	535.1	605.0	731.7	816.5	841.3
Net income ($ mil.)	15.2%	86.7	108.7	125.8	149.8	152.8
Market value ($ mil.)	17.3%	1,229.3	2,576.4	2,494.8	2,646.8	2,326.7
Employees	2.4%	—	—	2,100	2,300	2,200

GRAEBEL COMPANIES, INC.

16346 E. Airport Cir.
Aurora, CO 80011
Phone: 303-214-6683
Fax: 303-214-2156
Web: www.graebel.com

CEO: William (Bill) Graebel
CFO: Brad Siler
HR: Mary Dymond
FYE: December 31
Type: Private

Graebel Companies grapples for market share in the moving business. The company provides household and commercial relocation services in the US and internationally. It gets most of its business from companies that need to arrange the transfers of their employees, but it also provides individual household moving services. Graebel operates from service centers located throughout the US and from international forwarding offices at major US ports. It provides transportation services on its own in the US and via partners in other countries. The family-run company was founded by chairman Dave Graebel in 1950.

	Annual Growth	12/03	12/04	12/05	12/06	12/07
Est. sales ($ mil.)	—	—	—	—	—	334.2
Employees	—	—	—	—	—	1,771

An in-depth profile of this company is available to Hoover's Online members at hoovers.com.

GRAFTECH INTERNATIONAL LTD.

NYSE: GTI

12900 Snow Rd.	CEO: Craig S. Shular
Parma, OH 44130	CFO: Mark R. Widmar
Phone: 216-676-2000	HR: –
Fax: 216-676-2526	FYE: December 31
Web: www.graftech.com	Type: Public

If GrafTech International were a bard, it could wax poetic in an ode to the electrode. The company is the US's largest maker of graphite electrodes. GrafTech's synthetic graphite division makes graphite electrodes and cathodes that are used as components in conductive power systems used to produce steel, aluminum, and other non-ferrous metals. It also makes specialty products for transportation and semiconductor applications. GrafTech's other division makes flexible graphite products, flow field plates, gas diffusion layers, and carbon electrodes and refractories. Customers include Alcoa, Ballard Power Systems, Cisco, MEMC Electronic Materials, and Nucor. The US represents around one-quarter of sales.

	Annual Growth	12/03	12/04	12/05	12/06	12/07
Sales ($ mil.)	9.0%	712.0	848.0	886.7	855.4	1,004.8
Net income ($ mil.)	—	(24.0)	17.0	(125.2)	91.3	153.7
Market value ($ mil.)	9.5%	1,268.3	927.7	611.8	684.6	1,822.4
Employees	(9.2%)	3,762	3,872	3,851	2,757	2,554

GRAHAM CORPORATION

AMEX: GHM

20 Florence Ave.	CEO: James R. Lines
Batavia, NY 14020	CFO: J. Ronald Hansen
Phone: 585-343-2216	HR: –
Fax: 585-343-1177	FYE: March 31
Web: www.graham-mfg.com	Type: Public

You're not crackers if you know that Graham Corporation takes the biscuit when it comes to helping companies make beer, soap, and other products. The company makes vacuum systems, pumps, compressors, and heat exchangers designed to create vacuums, condense steam, or produce heat. Graham sells its equipment to manufacturers in the petroleum, plastics, chemicals, food processing, and other industries, where its gear is used in processes ranging from power generation to brewing beer and making soap. The company sells its products directly and through independent sales representatives worldwide.

	Annual Growth	3/04	3/05	3/06	3/07	3/08
Sales ($ mil.)	18.9%	43.3	41.3	55.2	65.8	86.4
Net income ($ mil.)	—	(1.1)	(2.9)	3.6	5.8	15.0
Market value ($ mil.)	124.2%	7.0	12.4	59.8	51.2	177.7
Employees	4.4%	—	243	250	265	—

GRAHAM PACKAGING HOLDINGS COMPANY

2401 Pleasant Valley Rd.	CEO: Warren D. Knowlton
York, PA 17402	CFO: Mark S. Burgess
Phone: 717-849-8500	HR: –
Fax: 717-848-4836	FYE: December 31
Web: www.grahampackaging.com	Type: Private

Grocery stockers and mechanics handle Graham Packaging's products every day. The company makes blow-molded plastic containers for food and beverages, automotive lubricants, household products, and personal care and specialty products. Major customers include large global companies such as BP, Clorox, Danone, Heinz, and PepsiCo. Graham Packaging operates more than 80 manufacturing plants across the Americas and Europe, many of which are located on the grounds of its customers' production facilities. The company sells its products through its direct-sales force and brokers in the US and abroad.

	Annual Growth	12/02	12/03	12/04	12/05	12/06
Sales ($ mil.)	29.1%	906.7	978.7	1,353.0	2,473.4	2,520.9
Net income ($ mil.)	—	7.6	9.8	(40.6)	(52.6)	(120.4)
Employees	21.1%	3,900	3,900	8,600	8,900	8,400

GRAMERCY CAPITAL CORP.

NYSE: GKK

420 Lexington Ave.	CEO: Marc Holliday
New York, NY 10170	CFO: John B. Roche
Phone: 212-297-1000	HR: –
Fax: 212-297-1090	FYE: December 31
Web: www.gramercycapitalcorp.com	Type: Public

Gramercy Capital, a real estate investment trust (REIT), invests in commercial real estate and real estate loans secured by commercial properties throughout the US. The company's portfolio includes mezzanine financing, bridge loans, interests in whole loans, preferred equity, private equity investments, and mortgage-backed securities. The REIT also owns more than 1,000 properties primarily leased to banks and other financial institutions; Bank of America and Wachovia are its largest tenants and together account for about half of all rental revenues. The REIT is externally managed and advised by a subsidiary of SL Green Realty, which owns about 20% of Gramercy Capital.

	Annual Growth	12/03	12/04	12/05	12/06	12/07
Sales ($ mil.)	256.9%	—	7.2	88.1	198.2	327.3
Net income ($ mil.)	332.3%	—	2.0	31.4	55.9	161.6
Market value ($ mil.)	29.8%	—	387.5	519.4	799.4	847.2
Employees	—	—	—	0	—	—

GRAND CIRCLE CORPORATION

347 Congress St.	CEO: Alan E. Lewis
Boston, MA 02210	CFO: –
Phone: 617-350-7500	HR: –
Fax: 617-346-6030	FYE: December 31
Web: www.gct.com	Type: Private

Grand Circle wants to take your grandparents there and back again. Through its fleet of 50 ships, the travel services company provides leisurely-paced tour services primarily to customers over 50 years old. Its Grand Circle Travel division offers all-inclusive package tours at a relaxed pace, while its Overseas Adventure subsidiary organizes small groups for land, canal barge, and small ship journeys of the more rugged variety. Grand Circle's 45 offices are located in Africa, North and South America, Asia, and Europe. It began life in 1958 as part of a plan by AARP founder Ethel Andrus to help older Americans be more active. In late 2007, Grand Circle agreed to be acquired by Court Square Capital Partners.

GRANDE COMMUNICATIONS HOLDINGS, INC.

401 Carlson Cir.	CEO: Roy H. Chestnutt
San Marcos, TX 78666	CFO: Michael L. (Mike) Wilfley
Phone: 512-878-4000	HR: Kay Stroman
Fax: 512-878-4010	FYE: December 31
Web: www.grandecom.com	Type: Private

Grande Communications' grand vision is to become a big player in Texas telecommunications. The company provides bundled telephone services, Internet access, and cable television to more than 140,000 residential and business customers over its own fiber-optic network. Grande Communications also provides wholesale communications services to other telecoms and ISPs. The company has operations in Austin-San Marcos, Corpus Christi, Dallas, Houston, Midland-Odessa, San Antonio, and Waco. Grande's investors include Whitney & Co. (22% of voting power), The Centennial Funds (17%), and Austin Ventures (7%).

	Annual Growth	12/02	12/03	12/04	12/05	12/06
Sales ($ mil.)	6.5%	147.4	181.5	179.0	194.7	189.9
Net income ($ mil.)	—	(28.8)	(37.5)	(55.0)	(89.8)	(141.6)
Employees	3.7%	700	811	873	835	810

An in-depth profile of this company is available to Hoover's Online members at hoovers.com.

GRANDSOUTH BANCORPORATION

OTC: GRRB

381 Halton Rd.
Greenville, SC 29607
Phone: 864-770-1000
Fax: 864-770-1081
Web: www.grandsouth.com

CEO: Mason Y. Garrett
CFO: J. B. Garrett
HR: –
FYE: December 31
Type: Public

GrandSouth Bancorporation likes to do things in a big way, down past the Mason-Dixon line. The institution is the holding company for GrandSouth Bank, a local thrift serving northwestern South Carolina's Greenville area. Established in 1998, GrandSouth Bancorporation offers standard retail services and products including checking and savings accounts, IRAs, CDs, and money markets. Real estate mortgages (residential and commercial) account for some 80% of the bank's total loan book. GrandSouth Bank has locations in Anderson, Fountain Inn, and Greenville, South Carolina.

	Annual Growth	12/03	12/04	12/05	12/06	12/07
Assets ($ mil.)	18.9%	172.5	207.9	251.9	300.3	345.1
Net income ($ mil.)	47.0%	0.6	1.3	2.4	3.3	2.8
Market value ($ mil.)	32.6%	11.8	15.4	33.4	84.3	36.4
Employees	—	—	—	—	—	—

GRANGE MUTUAL CASUALTY COMPANY

650 S. Front St.
Columbus, OH 43206
Phone: 614-445-2900
Fax: 614-445-2337
Web: www.grangeinsurance.com

CEO: Philip H. Urban
CFO: Randall J. Montelone
HR: Robert Rissmeyer
FYE: December 31
Type: Mutual company

Grange offers many breeds of insurance and financial products to grangers and others. Founded in 1935, Grange Insurance and Grange Life offer auto, commercial, farm, homeowners, life, and marine insurance to customers in 12 US states, mostly in the farm belt. The company targets small to midsized businesses for its commercial policies; offerings include workers' compensation, commercial auto, and umbrella insurance. It sells its products through a network of independent agents. The company has agreed to sell its Grange Bank subsidiary to American Bank Holdings; the Grange Bank operates one branch office in Ohio and offers financial products and services, including credit cards and mortgages.

	Annual Growth	12/03	12/04	12/05	12/06	12/07
Est. sales ($ mil.)	—	—	—	—	—	350.2
Employees	—	—	—	—	—	1,450

GRANITE BROADCASTING CORPORATION

767 3rd Ave., 34th Fl.
New York, NY 10017
Phone: 212-826-2530
Fax: 212-826-2858
Web: www.granitetv.com

CEO: W. Don Cornwell
CFO: Lawrence I. Wills
HR: –
FYE: December 31
Type: Private

Television really rocks the world of this company. Granite Broadcasting owns, jointly operates, or provides programming to more than 20 TV stations in about a dozen markets in California, Illinois, Indiana, Michigan, Minnesota, New York, and Wisconsin. Its stations have network affiliations with NBC, ABC, and CBS, as well as smaller networks The CW and MyNetworkTV. The company also operates Internet sites for most of its properties. Founded by CEO W. Don Cornwell in 1988, Granite Broadcasting emerged from bankruptcy in 2007 and is owned by Silver Point Capital.

GRANITE CITY FOOD & BREWERY LTD.

NASDAQ (CM): GCFB

5402 Parkdale Dr., Ste. 101
Minneapolis, MN 55416
Phone: 952-215-0660
Fax: 952-525-2021
Web: www.gcfb.net

CEO: Steven J. (Steve) Wagenheim
CFO: James G. (Jim) Gilbertson
HR: Liz Severance
FYE: Last Tuesday in December
Type: Public

Drinking and dining form the bedrock of this small restaurant chain. Granite City Food & Brewery operates about 25 brewpubs in a dozen Midwestern states, mostly in Minnesota, Kansas, Illinois, and Iowa. The restaurants offer a variety of handcrafted beers that are brewed on-site, including Brother Benedict's Mai Bock, Duke of Wellington (English ale), and Victory Lager. The menu features chicken and steak, as well as appetizers, burgers, salads, and sandwiches. CEO Steve Wagenheim and director Arthur Pew own about 10% of the company through investment vehicle Brewing Ventures.

	Annual Growth	12/03	12/04	12/05	12/06	12/07
Sales ($ mil.)	51.0%	14.6	30.8	36.2	58.3	75.9
Net income ($ mil.)	—	(1.5)	(0.7)	(3.7)	(5.5)	(9.6)
Market value ($ mil.)	30.8%	15.2	56.7	61.8	81.6	44.5
Employees	—	—	—	1,955	—	—

GRANITE CONSTRUCTION INCORPORATED

NYSE: GVA

585 W. Beach St.
Watsonville, CA 95076
Phone: 831-724-1011
Fax: 831-722-9657
Web: www.graniteconstruction.com

CEO: William G. (Bill) Dorey
CFO: LeAnne M. Stewart
HR: Brian R. Dowd
FYE: December 31
Type: Public

Granite Construction is paving its way coast to coast. The holding company operates through its main subsidiary, Granite Construction Company, a transportation and heavy construction contractor that works on public infrastructure projects, ranging from airports, bridges, and dams to highways, mass transit systems, and tunnels. For private-sector firms, it performs site preparation for residential and commercial development. The company is aligned geographically into two divisions: Granite West and Granite East. One of its biggest customers is the California Department of Transportation, which accounts for 10% of revenues. Public sector projects in California account for nearly a quarter of its total revenues.

	Annual Growth	12/03	12/04	12/05	12/06	12/07
Sales ($ mil.)	10.4%	1,844.5	2,136.2	2,641.4	2,969.6	2,737.9
Net income ($ mil.)	16.7%	60.5	57.0	83.2	80.5	112.1
Market value ($ mil.)	10.0%	973.2	1,106.8	1,496.8	2,105.1	1,427.3
Employees	(36.5%)	—	—	5,200	5,200	2,100

⊞ GRANT THORNTON INTERNATIONAL

175 W. Jackson Blvd., 20th Fl.
Chicago, IL 60604
Phone: 312-856-0200
Fax: 312-602-8099
Web: www.gti.org

CEO: David C. McDonnell
CFO: Barry Barber
HR: Annemarie Wade
FYE: September 30
Type: Not-for-profit

Grant Thornton International is a kid brother to the Big Four. The umbrella organization of accounting and management consulting firms operates from more than 520 offices in more than 110 countries, making it one of the top second-tier companies that trail behind the biggest of the big guys (Deloitte Touche Tohmatsu, Ernst & Young Global, KPMG International, and PricewaterhouseCoopers). More than 60% of its member firms' clients are private companies. The company offers assurance, tax, business risk, corporate advisory, and other services to public and private companies. By virtue of the consolidation in the industry, Grant Thornton is the longest-lived, same-name organization in the world.

	Annual Growth	9/02	9/03	9/04	9/05	9/06
Sales ($ mil.)	16.7%	—	1,742.0	2,092.0	2,740.0	2,772.0
Employees	5.2%	—	21,500	22,000	22,000	25,000

GRANT THORNTON LLP

175 W. Jackson Blvd., 20th Fl.
Chicago, IL 60604
Phone: 312-856-0200
Fax: 312-602-8099
Web: www.grantthornton.com

CEO: Edward E. (Ed) Nusbaum
CFO: William E. (Bill) Schultz
HR: Anne M. Lang
FYE: July 31
Type: Partnership

Grant Thornton grants accounting wishes to US clients. The firm encompasses the US operations of Grant Thornton International, one of the largest accountancies outside of the Big Four (Deloitte Touche Tohmatsu, Ernst & Young, KPMG, and PricewaterhouseCoopers). The firm has some 50 US offices. In addition to auditing, Grant Thornton provides its customers with such services as Sarbanes-Oxley expertise, mergers and acquisitions advice, tax services, and business valuations. Target industries include construction, consumer goods, financial services, health care, and technology. Founded as Alexander Richardson in 1924, the firm took its current name in 1986 when it joined with the UK firm Thornton Baker.

	Annual Growth	12/02	12/03	*7/04	7/05	7/06
Sales ($ mil.)	22.0%	400.0	485.0	564.3	728.0	886.0
Employees	10.7%	2,900	3,127	3,555	—	—
						*Fiscal year change

GRAPHIC CONTROLS LLC

400 Exchange St.
Buffalo, NY 14204
Phone: 716-853-7500
Fax: 716-849-7551
Web: www.graphiccontrols.com

CEO: Sam Heleba
CFO: Gary Toomey
HR: –
FYE: September 30
Type: Private

Graphic Controls has printing under control. The company manufactures precision charts and pens for hundreds of models of industrial recording instruments. Other products include ink jet fluids, pressure-sensitive bar code label printers, case coding printers, and continuous ink jet printers. It also offers thermal printing and papers used for ticketing, as well as plastic magnetic-strip cards. After Graphic Controls was acquired by Tyco International in 2002, its key medical products business was sold off; the company was resold to Strategic Investments and Holdings in late 2005.

	Annual Growth	9/03	9/04	9/05	9/06	9/07
Est. sales ($ mil.)	—	—	—	—	—	54.0
Employees	—	—	—	—	—	275

GRAPHIC PACKAGING HOLDING COMPANY

NYSE: GPK

814 Livingston Ct.
Marietta, GA 30067
Phone: 770-644-3000
Fax: 770-644-2962
Web: www.graphicpkg.com

CEO: David W. Scheible
CFO: Daniel J. (Dan) Blount
HR: James Aikins
FYE: December 31
Type: Public

If you've ever toted home a 12-pack, then you might be familiar with Graphic Packaging. Doing business through subsidiary Graphic Packaging International, the company is a leading maker of cartons for beverages, food, and household products. Most of the company's sales come from its paperboard unit, which makes paperboard at its mills and then converts it into laminated, coated, and printed packaging products such as beverage carriers, cereal boxes, and detergent containers. Customers include Kraft Foods, Anheuser-Busch, Molson Coors Brewing, General Mills, SABMiller, and various Coca-Cola and Pepsi bottlers. In 2008 Graphic Packaging merged with Altivity Packaging in a $1.75 billion deal.

	Annual Growth	12/03	12/04	12/05	12/06	12/07
Sales ($ mil.)	9.5%	1,683.3	2,386.5	2,384.0	2,413.0	2,421.2
Net income ($ mil.)	—	(82.9)	(60.9)	(91.1)	(100.5)	(74.6)
Market value ($ mil.)	2.5%	805.4	1,429.9	453.0	868.5	—
Employees	(1.3%)	—	—	7,800	7,700	

GRAPHON CORPORATION

OTC: GOJO

5400 Soquel Ave., Ste. A2
Santa Cruz, CA 95062
Phone: 603-225-3525
Fax: 831-475-3017
Web: www.graphon.com

CEO: Robert P. (Bob) Dilworth
CFO: William (Bill) Swain
HR: –
FYE: December 31
Type: Public

GraphOn keeps its thin clients on a diet. The company provides business connectivity software that delivers applications to PCs and workstations from a host computer. The company's products enable clients to relocate desktop software to centralized servers and deploy and manage applications when needed, thus conserving computing resources. GraphOn's software can be used to provide access to applications through Linux, UNIX, and Windows platforms. The company serves clients in a variety of industries, including telecommunications, software development, manufacturing, financial services, and electronics.

	Annual Growth	12/03	12/04	12/05	12/06	12/07
Sales ($ mil.)	28.6%	4.2	3.5	5.2	5.2	11.5
Net income ($ mil.)	—	(1.9)	(1.4)	(1.1)	(3.0)	0.2
Market value ($ mil.)	54.7%	3.3	11.3	8.8	7.0	19.0
Employees	—	—	—	—	—	—

GRAY TELEVISION, INC.

NYSE: GTN

4370 Peachtree Rd. NE
Atlanta, GA 30319
Phone: 404-504-9828
Fax: 404-261-9607
Web: www.graycommunications.com

CEO: J. Mack Robinson
CFO: James C. (Jim) Ryan
HR: –
FYE: December 31
Type: Public

Gray Television has The Eye for local television markets. The company is the largest independent operator of TV stations affiliated with the CBS network, with 17 stations in more than a dozen states. In total the company operates more than 35 stations in 30 midsized and smaller markets mostly in the Midwest and South. Its other stations are affiliated with ABC, NBC, and FOX. In addition to traditional analog signals, it broadcasts an additional 40 digital channels mostly carrying programming from The CW and MyNetworkTV. Chairman and CEO J. Mack Robinson and his family have more than 35% voting control of the company.

	Annual Growth	12/03	12/04	12/05	12/06	12/07
Sales ($ mil.)	1.0%	295.4	346.6	261.5	332.1	307.3
Net income ($ mil.)	—	14.0	44.3	3.4	11.7	(23.1)
Market value ($ mil.)	(12.7%)	586.4	588.5	372.4	312.0	340.1
Employees	—	—	—	2,113	—	—

▥ GRAYBAR ELECTRIC COMPANY, INC.

34 N. Meramec Ave.
St. Louis, MO 63105
Phone: 314-573-9200
Fax: 314-573-9455
Web: www.graybar.com

CEO: Robert A. Reynolds Jr.
CFO: D. Beatty D'Alessandro
HR: Jack F. Van Pelt
FYE: December 31
Type: Private

There's no gray area when it comes to describing Graybar Electric's main business: it's one of the largest distributors of electrical products in the US. Purchasing from thousands of manufacturers, the employee-owned company distributes more than 1 million types of electrical and communications components, including wire, cable, and lighting products. Its customers include electrical contractors, industrial plants, power utilities, and telecommunications providers. Subsidiary Graybar Financial Services offers equipment leasing and financing, as well as complete project funding. Graybar Electric gets most of its sales in the US, with a small portion derived from Canada, Mexico, and Puerto Rico.

	Annual Growth	12/02	12/03	12/04	12/05	12/06
Sales ($ mil.)	6.0%	3,974.9	3,802.5	4,079.6	4,288.0	5,009.1
Net income ($ mil.)	49.8%	11.4	8.5	14.0	16.8	57.4
Employees	0.3%	8,300	7,900	7,700	7,800	8,400

GREAT AMERICAN BANCORP, INC.

OTC: GTPS

1311 S. Neil St.
Champaign, IL 61820
Phone: 217-356-2265
Fax: 217-356-2502
Web: www.greatamericanbancorp.com

CEO: George R. Rouse
CFO: Jane F. Adams
HR: Ata M. Durukan
FYE: December 31
Type: Public

Great American Bancorp is the holding company for First Federal Savings Bank of Champaign-Urbana, which operates two branches in Champaign and one in Urbana, Illinois. Targeting individuals and local businesses, First Federal provides retail banking products such as checking, savings, and money market accounts, credit cards, and CDs. Lending activities consist primarily of residential mortgages, as well as commercial real estate, construction, business, and consumer loans. The bank was founded in 1908. Through a partnership with UMB Financial Corporation subsidiary UMB Financial Services, First Federal Savings Bank also offers investment services.

	Annual Growth	12/02	12/03	12/04	12/05	*12/06
Assets ($ mil.)	(1.5%)	—	—	—	144.2	142.1
Net income ($ mil.)	—	—	—	—	—	1.5
Employees	—	—	—	—	—	72

*Most recent year available

GREAT AMERICAN FINANCIAL RESOURCES, INC.

525 Vine St.
Cincinnati, OH 45202
Phone: 513-333-5300
Fax: 513-412-3777
Web: www.gafri.com

CEO: S. Craig Lindner
CFO: Christopher P. Miliano
HR: –
FYE: December 31
Type: Subsidiary

Great American Financial Resources (GAFRI) flies the patriotic banners of retirement products and insurance. Its principal subsidiary, Great American Life Insurance Company, has marketed insurance products since 1959. The company also sells retirement products, primarily fixed and variable annuities, and offers supplemental health and life insurance (through Loyal American Life Insurance) and supplemental coverage (through United Teacher Associates Insurance). The company has seen growth from the introduction of fixed annuity products targeted at public school teachers. GAFRI is owned by chairman Carl Lindner's American Financial Group.

	Annual Growth	12/02	12/03	12/04	12/05	12/06
Assets ($ mil.)	9.2%	9,362.6	10,194.3	11,722.0	11,922.0	13,335.4
Net income ($ mil.)	57.2%	16.2	49.7	101.8	69.9	98.9
Employees	(11.1%)	1,600	—	—	815	1,000

⊞ THE GREAT ATLANTIC & PACIFIC TEA COMPANY

NYSE: GAP

2 Paragon Dr.
Montvale, NJ 07645
Phone: 201-573-9700
Fax: 201-505-3054
Web: www.aptea.com

CEO: Eric Claus
CFO: Brenda M. Galgano
HR: Allan Richards
FYE: Last Saturday in February
Type: Public

Once the biggest bagger of groceries in the US, The Great Atlantic & Pacific Tea Company, Inc., (A&P) had been reduced to a handful of regional grocery chains but is moving toward filling up its bag again. It runs some 450 supermarkets in eight eastern states and the District of Columbia. In addition to its mainstay A&P chain, the firm now operates seven others, including Super Fresh along the East Coast from New Jersey to Virginia and The Food Emporium and Waldbaum chains in the New York and New Jersey area. A&P acquired its rival in the Northeast, Pathmark Stores, for about $1.4 billion in December 2007, reversing years of decline at the grocery company.

	Annual Growth	2/04	2/05	2/06	2/07	2/08
Sales ($ mil.)	(12.3%)	10,812.5	10,854.9	8,740.3	6,850.3	6,401.1
Net income ($ mil.)	—	(147.0)	(188.1)	392.6	26.9	(160.7)
Market value ($ mil.)	51.2%	306.2	447.0	1,332.8	1,298.6	1,602.1
Employees	(8.9%)	74,000	73,000	38,000	38,000	51,000

GREAT DANE LIMITED PARTNERSHIP

602 E. Lathrop Ave.
Savannah, GA 31415
Phone: 912-644-2100
Fax: 912-644-2166
Web: www.greatdanetrailers.com

CEO: Phillip (Phill) Pines
CFO: John J. Sobota
HR: Butch Krishnamurti
FYE: December 31
Type: Partnership

Some Great Danes have an all-American heritage. Great Dane is one of the largest manufacturers of truck trailers in North America. The company makes standard dry freight trailers, refrigerated trailers (reefers), and platform, or flatbed, trailers. Great Dane has manufacturing plants in the US and sales, parts, and service centers across the US, Canada, Mexico, and South America. The company also sells used trailers. Great Dane is a unit of Chicago-based investment group CC Industries, which is controlled by Henry Crown and Company. The company that became Great Dane started in 1900 as a maker of sheet metal blowpipe systems and switched to trailers in 1931.

GREAT LAKES AVIATION, LTD.

OTC: GLUX

1022 Airport Pkwy.
Cheyenne, WY 82001
Phone: 307-432-7000
Fax: 307-432-7001
Web: www.greatlakesav.com

CEO: Charles R. Howell IV
CFO: Michael O. Matthews
HR: Christine Gervais
FYE: December 31
Type: Public

Great Lakes Aviation goes to great lengths to get people where they need to be, even if it's far from the big city. Flying as Great Lakes Airlines, the regional carrier transports passengers to more than 40 destinations in the western and midwestern US, mainly from Denver, but also from markets such as Phoenix, St. Louis, Kansas City, and Albuquerque, New Mexico. It maintains codesharing agreements with Frontier Airlines and United Airlines. (Code-sharing enables carriers to sell tickets on one another's flights and thus extend their networks.) Great Lakes operates a fleet of about 30 turboprop aircraft, consisting mostly of 19-passenger Beechcraft 1900Ds, but also including 30-passenger Embraer Brasilia 120s.

	Annual Growth	12/03	12/04	12/05	12/06	12/07
Sales ($ mil.)	6.7%	75.8	76.3	76.4	87.6	98.2
Net income ($ mil.)	80.7%	1.8	5.6	1.2	15.7	19.2
Market value ($ mil.)	51.8%	6.2	14.1	14.1	31.9	32.9
Employees	—	—	—	—	845	—

GREAT LAKES CHEESE COMPANY, INC.

17825 Great Lakes Pkwy.
Hiram, OH 44234
Phone: 440-834-2500
Fax: 440-834-1002
Web: www.greatlakescheese.com

CEO: Gary Vanic
CFO: Russell (Russ) Mullins
HR: Beth Wendell
FYE: December 31
Type: Private

Great Lakes Cheese understands the power of provolone, the charm of cheddar, and the goodness of gruyere. The firm manufactures and distributes natural and processed cheeses and cheese spreads, including varieties such as cheddar, colby, Swiss, mozzarella, and provolone. It also sells imported cheeses. Great Lakes packages shredded, chunked, and sliced cheese for deli, bulk, and food-service sale under the Great Lakes, Adams Reserve, and private-label and store brands. With seven manufacturing plants, the firm distributes its products, which are sold in deli and dairy cases, throughout the US.

	Annual Growth	12/02	12/03	12/04	12/05	12/06
Sales ($ mil.)	18.9%	851.0	965.0	1,375.0	1,375.0	1,700.0
Employees	6.9%	1,300	1,700	1,700	1,700	1,700

⊞ An in-depth profile of this company is available to Hoover's Online members at hoovers.com.

703

GREAT LAKES DREDGE & DOCK CORPORATION   NASDAQ (GS): GLDD

2122 York Rd.
Oak Brook, IL 60523
Phone: 630-574-3000
Fax: 630-574-2909
Web: www.gldd.com

CEO: Douglas B. (Doug) Mackie
CFO: Deborah A. (Deb) Wensel
HR: –
FYE: December 31
Type: Public

Dig this: Great Lakes Dredge & Dock (GLDD) provides dredging services around the world. The company's services include beach improvement or renourishment, rock dredging, harbor excavation, land reclamation, demolition, and restoration of aquatic and wetland habitats. Among GLDD's projects are maintenance dredging at the Miami Harbor, nourishing San Diego beaches, and expanding Pier J in Long Beach, California. GLDD also owns an 85% stake in North American Site Developers, a commercial/industrial demolition firm. The company was founded in 1890 as the partnership of William A. Lydon & Fred C. Drews.

	Annual Growth	12/03	12/04	12/05	12/06	12/07
Est. sales ($ mil.)	—	—	—	—	—	377.2
Employees	—	—	—	—	—	875

GREAT LAKES GAS TRANSMISSION COMPANY

5250 Corporate Dr.
Troy, MI 48098
Phone: 248-205-7400
Fax: 248-205-7517
Web: www.glgt.com

CEO: Lee G. Hobbs
CFO: Julie E. Willett
HR: Norma N. Kolasa
FYE: December 31
Type: Private

Great Lakes Gas Transmission transports great amounts of natural gas — 2.2 billion cu. ft. per day, to be exact. With a pipeline spanning 2,100 miles, the company supplies gas to major urban markets in Michigan, Minnesota, Wisconsin, and parts of southern Canada. Its customers include a number of regional natural gas transporters, local gas distributors, and energy trading firms including Alliance Energy Services, ANR Pipeline, Michigan Consolidated Gas, Northern States Power, and Sempra Energy Trading. Great Lakes Gas Transmission was founded in 1967 and is controlled by TransCanada Corp.

	Annual Growth	12/03	12/04	12/05	12/06	12/07
Est. sales ($ mil.)	—	—	—	—	—	8.7
Employees	—	—	—	—	—	172

GREAT NORTHERN IRON ORE PROPERTIES   NYSE: GNI

W-1290 First National Bank Bldg., 332 Minnesota St.
St. Paul, MN 55101
Phone: 651-224-2385
Fax: 651-224-2387

CEO: Joseph S. Micallef
CFO: Thomas A. Janochoski
HR: Thomas A. Janochoski
FYE: December 31
Type: Public

Great Northern Iron Ore Properties is the landlord of one big iron formation. The trust gets income from royalties on iron ore minerals (principally taconite) taken from its more than 12,000 acres on the Mesabi Iron Formation in Minnesota. The trust was formed in 1906 to own the properties of an affiliate of Burlington Northern Santa Fe (formerly Great Northern Railway). The trust's beneficiaries were the heirs of railroad founder James Hill; however, the last survivor, his grandson Louis Hill, died in 1995. In 2015 (20 years after Louis Hill's death) the land will be transferred to a unit of Burlington Resources, which is a spinoff of Burlington Northern.

	Annual Growth	12/03	12/04	12/05	12/06	12/07
Sales ($ mil.)	9.0%	12.2	14.4	18.4	17.5	17.2
Net income ($ mil.)	9.5%	10.0	12.2	15.7	14.8	14.4
Market value ($ mil.)	8.3%	139.2	175.5	208.9	179.2	191.6
Employees	—	—	—	10		

GREAT PLAINS COCA-COLA BOTTLING COMPANY

600 N. May Ave.
Oklahoma City, OK 73107
Phone: 405-280-2000
Fax: 405-946-5739
Web: www.greatplainscocacola.com

CEO: Robert F. (Bob) Browne
CFO: Clayton Sliger
HR: Mario Nunez
FYE: January 31
Type: Private

Great Plains Coca-Cola Bottling Company is one of the largest Coca-Cola bottling companies in the US, distributing Coke products throughout central and northeast Oklahoma and northwest Arkansas. It also operates a vending machine service under the name Snappy Snack Vending that supplies coffee, food, soft drinks, and snacks. Great Plains Coca-Cola Bottling was founded by the family of CEO Robert Browne in 1922.

	Annual Growth	1/03	1/04	1/05	1/06	1/07
Est. sales ($ mil.)	—	—	—	—	—	281.5
Employees	—	—	—	—	—	1,200

GREAT PLAINS ENERGY INCORPORATED   NYSE: GXP

1201 Walnut St.
Kansas City, MO 64106
Phone: 816-556-2200
Fax: 816-556-2992
Web: www.greatplainsenergy.com

CEO: Michael J. Chesser
CFO: Terry Bassham
HR: Marvin L. Rollinson
FYE: December 31
Type: Public

Great Plains Energy is sweeping the plains with electric light. The holding company serves 506,000 electricity customers in western Missouri and eastern Kansas through regulated utility Kansas City Power & Light (KCP&L). KCP&L has more than 4,000 MW of primarily coal-fired generating capacity. The company has exited most of its deregulated businesses in order to focus on its utility operations. In 2007 the company agreed to acquire Aquila's utility operations in Missouri, consisting of the Missouri Public Service and St. Joseph Light & Power divisions, as well as Aquila's merchant service operations.

	Annual Growth	12/03	12/04	12/05	12/06	12/07
Sales ($ mil.)	11.0%	2,149.5	2,464.0	2,604.9	2,675.4	3,267.1
Net income ($ mil.)	2.4%	144.9	180.8	162.3	127.6	159.2
Market value ($ mil.)	3.5%	2,203.7	2,251.8	2,089.7	2,555.2	2,528.4
Employees	2.5%	—	—	2,382	2,470	2,504

GREAT SOUTHERN BANCORP, INC.   NASDAQ (GS): GSBC

1451 E. Battlefield
Springfield, MO 65804
Phone: 417-887-4400
Fax: –
Web: www.greatsouthernbank.com

CEO: Joseph W. (Joe) Turner
CFO: –
HR: Matt Snyder
FYE: December 31
Type: Public

What do Babe Ruth, Elvis Presley, Rosa Parks, Woody Guthrie, and a bank have in common? They're all great southerners. Great Southern Bancorp is the holding company for Great Southern Bank, which operates about 40 branches in 16 central, southwestern, and western Missouri counties (including the Kansas City, Joplin, and Springfield metropolitan areas). Founded in 1923, the bank offers checking and savings accounts, CDs, IRAs, and credit cards. Its lending activities include commercial and industrial revenue bonds (about 25% of its loan portfolio), commercial construction loans (another 25%), and residential construction loans (20%). It also writes consumer loans and residential mortgages.

	Annual Growth	12/03	12/04	12/05	12/06	12/07
Assets ($ mil.)	12.1%	1,540.7	1,845.7	2,081.2	2,240.3	2,431.7
Net income ($ mil.)	6.1%	23.1	26.9	22.7	30.7	29.3
Market value ($ mil.)	16.7%	158.8	480.0	378.9	403.6	294.3
Employees	6.7%	—	—	681		775

GREAT-WEST LIFE & ANNUITY INSURANCE COMPANY

8515 E. Orchard Rd.
Greenwood Village, CO 80111
Phone: 303-737-3000
Fax: 303-737-4861
Web: www.greatwest.com

CEO: Mitchell T. G. Graye
CFO: James L. McCallen
HR: George C. Bogdewiecz
FYE: December 31
Type: Subsidiary

Great-West Life & Annuity Insurance is the southern arm of a northern parent. The company, a subsidiary of Canada's Great-West Lifeco and a member of the Power Financial family, represents the Great-West group's primary US operations. The company's Financial Services segment offers life insurance and annuities to individuals and, under the Great-West Retirement Services brand, administers employer-sponsored retirement products, including defined-benefit and 401(k) plans. In 2008 the company sold its Healthcare division to CIGNA for $1.5 billion; the segment offered group life and medical insurance products to US businesses, with an emphasis on self-funded programs for small and midsized employers.

	Annual Growth	12/02	12/03	12/04	12/05	12/06
Assets ($ mil.)	10.7%	27,656.1	36,610.1	37,065.9	37,779.4	41,481.9
Net income ($ mil.)	4.4%	283.5	318.0	326.4	371.6	337.2
Employees	(0.7%)	6,800	6,200	6,200	6,600	6,600

GREAT WOLF RESORTS, INC.

NASDAQ (GM): WOLF

122 W. Washington Ave.
Madison, WI 53703
Phone: 608-661-4700
Fax: 608-661-4701
Web: greatwolfresorts.com

CEO: Randall L. (Randy) Churchey
CFO: James A. (Jim) Calder
HR: −
FYE: December 31
Type: Public

Great Wolf Resorts has its customers muttering "Great Scott!" as they pull up to the company's drive-to family resorts. Great Wolf owns and operates a handful of resorts under the Great Wolf Lodge name in mostly midwestern states. It also operates the Blue Harbor Resort, which features a conference center and a nautical theme. Great Wolf's properties are open year-round and include lodging, indoor water parks, themed restaurants, and other diversions such as arcades, spas, and organized children's activities. The company is growing quickly and plans to open at least two new resorts each year. Great Wolf was formed in 2004 to succeed the properties' previous owner, The Great Lakes Companies.

	Annual Growth	12/03	12/04	12/05	12/06	12/07
Sales ($ mil.)	40.8%	47.8	69.9	139.4	148.6	187.6
Net income ($ mil.)	—	(4.3)	(16.8)	(24.4)	(49.3)	(9.6)
Market value ($ mil.)	(23.4%)	—	676.1	312.2	425.9	303.8
Employees	33.8%	1,430	—	2,560	—	—

GREATBATCH, INC.

NYSE: GB

9645 Wehrle Dr.
Clarence, NY 14031
Phone: 716-759-5600
Fax: 716-759-5660
Web: www.greatbatch.com

CEO: Thomas J. Hook
CFO: Thomas J. Mazza
HR: Barbara Davis
FYE: Friday nearest December 31
Type: Public

Greatbatch likes to keep its business close to the heart. The company is a leading maker of batteries used in implantable medical devices such as pacemakers and implantable cardioverter defibrillators (ICDs). Other medical components include electrodes, capacitors, and feedthroughs (used to deliver electrical signals from an implantable medical device to an electrode). Greatbatch also makes batteries for demanding industrial applications, such as oil and gas exploration, and supplies power sources for space shuttle missions. Boston Scientific, Medtronic, and St. Jude Medical are the company's top customers; together, they account for about two-thirds of its sales. About half of Greatbatch's sales are in the US.

	Annual Growth	12/03	12/04	12/05	12/06	12/07
Sales ($ mil.)	10.2%	216.4	200.1	241.1	271.1	318.8
Net income ($ mil.)	(10.3%)	23.3	16.3	10.1	16.1	15.1
Market value ($ mil.)	(16.3%)	909.5	483.5	563.3	595.2	447.4
Employees	14.3%	1,431	1,225	1,338	1,835	2,445

GREATER ATLANTIC FINANCIAL CORP.

Pink Sheets: GAFC

10700 Parkridge Blvd., Ste. P50
Reston, VA 20191
Phone: 703-391-1300
Fax: 703-391-1506
Web: www.gab.com

CEO: Carroll E. Amos
CFO: David E. Ritter
HR: −
FYE: September 30
Type: Public

Greater Atlantic Financial owns Greater Atlantic Bank, a thrift with six locations in the Washington, DC, metropolitan area. Serving consumers and small to midsized businesses, the bank offers standard deposit products and services including checking, savings, and money market accounts; certificates of deposit; and IRAs. Single-family residential mortgages and home equity loans account for nearly half of the company's loan portfolio; business loans and commercial mortgages, about 20% apiece. Summit Financial Group is buying Greater Atlantic Financial.

	Annual Growth	9/03	9/04	9/05	9/06	9/07
Assets ($ mil.)	(16.2%)	499.4	434.4	340.8	305.2	246.0
Net income ($ mil.)	(20.9%)	2.3	(3.2)	(1.6)	(5.6)	0.9
Employees	—	—	—	129	—	—

GREATER COMMUNITY BANCORP

NASDAQ (GM): GFLS

55 Union Blvd.
Totowa, NJ 07512
Phone: 973-942-1111
Fax: 973-942-9816
Web: www.greatercommunity.com

CEO: Anthony M. Bruno Jr.
CFO: Stephen J. Mauger
HR: −
FYE: December 31
Type: Public

Greater Community Bancorp has in interest in being a good neighbor in northern New Jersey. The holding company offers community-oriented financial services through Greater Community Bank and its Rock Community Bank division. Through about 15 branches in Bergen, Morris, and Passaic counties, the banks offer standard services such as checking and savings accounts, CDs, IRAs, and debit and ATM cards. More than half of the company's loan portfolio is devoted to commercial mortgages; residential mortgages account for another 20% of loans. Other subsidiaries of Greater Community Bancorp include medical equipment financier Highland Capital and securities brokerage Greater Community Financial.

	Annual Growth	12/03	12/04	12/05	12/06	12/07
Assets ($ mil.)	6.7%	753.1	825.4	925.8	951.0	976.0
Net income ($ mil.)	7.4%	6.7	7.8	8.9	5.6	8.9
Market value ($ mil.)	7.4%	107.2	115.4	113.3	146.8	142.4
Employees	(1.5%)	—	—	203	—	197

GREATWIDE LOGISTICS SERVICES, INC.

12404 Park Central Dr., Ste. 300S
Dallas, TX 75251
Phone: 972-228-7300
Fax: 972-228-7328
Web: www.greatwide.com

CEO: Raymond B. (Ray) Greer
CFO: Stephen P. (Steve) Bishop
HR: Kyle Killingsworth
FYE: December 31
Type: Private

Greatwide Logistics Services has brought together a world of freight transportation and logistics companies. Greatwide's operating units, assembled through a series of acquisitions, provide dedicated transportation, in which drivers and equipment are assigned to a customer long-term; distribution logistics; truckload freight brokerage; and truckload freight transportation, largely via independent owner-operators. Overall, Greatwide can call upon a fleet of some 5,500 tractors and 1,700 trailers, and the company maintains about 3.6 million sq. ft. of warehouse space at facilities throughout the US. Investcorp owns a majority interest in Greatwide.

	Annual Growth	12/02	12/03	12/04	12/05	12/06
Est. sales ($ mil.)	10.4%	—	—	—	1,087.0	1,200.0
Employees	7.1%	—	—	—	2,800	3,000

GREDE FOUNDRIES, INC.

9898 W. Bluemound Rd.
Milwaukee, WI 53226
Phone: 414-257-3600
Fax: 414-256-9399
Web: www.grede.com

CEO: Bruce E. Jacobs
CFO: Raymond F. Lowry
HR: W. Stewart (Stew) Davis
FYE: December 31
Type: Private

To paraphrase Gordon Gecko from the movie *Wall Street*, "Grede is good for America." Grede Foundries that is. The company produces gray iron, ductile iron, and steel castings for use in farm and construction equipment, motor vehicles, and a host of other products. Grede Foundries' cast products include axles, brackets, crankshafts, hydraulic end caps, and sprockets. The company also offers services such as design assistance, painting, machining, and sub-assembly. William Grede founded the company as Liberty Foundry in 1920. The business is still owned by Grede's descendants, including chairman Burleigh Jacobs.

	Annual Growth	12/03	12/04	12/05	12/06	12/07
Est. sales ($ mil.)	—	—	—	—	—	604.7
Employees	—	—	—	—	—	4,000

GREEN BANKSHARES, INC

NASDAQ (GS): GCBS

100 N. Main St.
Greeneville, TN 37743
Phone: 423-639-5111
Fax: 423-787-1235
Web: www.mybankconnection.com

CEO: R. Stan Puckett
CFO: James E. Adams
HR: Steve D. Ottinger
FYE: December 31
Type: Public

This bank was Green before "going green" was cool. Green Bankshares (formerly Greene County Bancshares) is the holding company for GreenBank (the erstwhile Greene County Bank), which operates more than 60 branches in some 20 counties, mostly in eastern and central Tennessee, but also in North Carolina and Virginia. The bank focuses on real estate lending, with commercial mortgages making up approximately 65% of its loan portfolio and residential mortgages adding almost another 20%. Its deposit products include checking and savings accounts and CDs. In 2007 the company bought Civitas BancGroup and its Cumberland Bank subsidiary, which added about a dozen branches in the Nashville area.

	Annual Growth	12/03	12/04	12/05	12/06	12/07
Assets ($ mil.)	27.7%	1,108.5	1,233.4	1,620.0	1,772.7	2,947.7
Net income ($ mil.)	24.4%	10.2	12.0	14.2	21.3	24.4
Market value ($ mil.)	—	—	—	—	—	248.3
Employees	15.0%	451	474	561	609	789

GREEN BAY PACKAGING INC.

1700 N. Webster Ct.
Green Bay, WI 54307
Phone: 920-433-5111
Fax: 920-433-5471
Web: www.gbp.com

CEO: William F. Kress
CFO: Joseph Baemmert
HR: –
FYE: December 31
Type: Private

Green Bay Packaging is the other Green Bay packers' enterprise. The integrated and diversified paperboard packaging manufacturer operates through 30 divisions in 15 states. In addition to corrugated containers, the company makes pressure-sensitive label stock, folding cartons, linerboard, and lumber products. Its Fiber Resources division in Arkansas manages more than 210,000 acres of company-owned forests and produces lumber, wood chips, recycled paper, and wood fuel. Family-owned Green Bay Packaging also offers fiber procurement, wastepaper brokerage, and paper-slitting services.

THE GREEN BAY PACKERS, INC.

Lambeau Field Atrium, 1265 Lombardi Ave.
Green Bay, WI 54304
Phone: 920-569-7500
Fax: 920-569-7301
Web: www.packers.com

CEO: Mark H. Murphy
CFO: Vicki Vannieuwenhoven
HR: –
FYE: March 31
Type: Not-for-profit

On the frozen tundra of Lambeau Field, the Green Bay Packers battle for pride in the National Football League. The team, founded in 1919 by Earl "Curly" Lambeau, has been home to such football icons as Bart Starr, Ray Nitschke, and legendary coach Vince Lombardi. The Packers boast a record 12 championship titles, including three Super Bowl victories (its last in Super Bowl XXXI after the 1996 season). The team is also the only community-owned franchise in American professional sports, being a not-for-profit corporation with about 112,000 shareholders. The shares do not increase in value nor pay dividends, and can only be sold back to the team. No individual is allowed to own more than 200,000 shares.

	Annual Growth	3/04	3/05	3/06	3/07	3/08
Sales ($ mil.)	7.7%	179.2	200.0	208.4	218.1	241.0
Employees	10.1%	150	150	150	200	—

GREEN MOUNTAIN COFFEE ROASTERS, INC.

NASDAQ (GS): GMCR

33 Coffee Ln.
Waterbury, VT 05676
Phone: 802-244-5621
Fax: 802-244-5436
Web: www.greenmountaincoffee.com

CEO: Lawrence J. (Larry) Blanford
CFO: Frances G. (Fran) Rathke
HR: Kathryn S. (Kathy) Brooks
FYE: Last Saturday in September
Type: Public

Green Mountain Coffee Roasters' business amounts to more than a hill of beans. The company offers about 180 varieties of coffee, cocoa, and tea, which it sells to wholesale customers including supermarkets, convenience stores, resorts, and office-delivery services. Among its customers are ExxonMobil's convenience stores nationwide and McDonalds restaurants in New England and the Albany, New York area. Green Mountain's coffee is also sold under the Newman's Own Organics brand, as well as its namesake Green Mountain Coffee label. The company also sells the Keurig single-cup brewing systems for office and home use.

	Annual Growth	9/03	9/04	9/05	9/06	9/07
Sales ($ mil.)	30.8%	116.7	137.4	161.5	225.3	341.6
Net income ($ mil.)	19.4%	6.3	7.8	9.0	8.4	12.8
Market value ($ mil.)	101.9%	47.1	46.9	85.3	93.6	781.3
Employees	14.8%	573	608	676	849	995

GREEN MOUNTAIN ENERGY COMPANY

3815 Capital of Texas Hwy. South, Ste. 100
Austin, TX 78704
Phone: 512-691-6100
Fax: 512-691-6151
Web: www.greenmountain.com

CEO: Paul D. Thomas
CFO: Bryan M. DeCordova
HR: Bob Penico
FYE: December 31
Type: Private

The power is always greener on this side of the mountain. Green Mountain Energy buys and resells "green" power generated from hydroelectric, solar, wind, geothermal, and natural and landfill gas facilities. It has helped develop 14 wind and solar renewable facilities around the US and offset more than 2.5 million tons of carbon dioxide pollution. In 2005 the company (which operates in Florida, New Jersey, New York, Oregon, and Texas) suffered a setback when it withdrew from Ohio, which had accounted for half of its sales. Dutch utility Nuon and oil giant BP have invested heavily in the firm.

	Annual Growth	12/03	12/04	12/05	12/06	12/07
Est. sales ($ mil.)	—	—	—	—	—	65.9
Employees	—	—	—	—	—	240

GREEN MOUNTAIN POWER CORPORATION

163 Acorn Ln.
Colchester, VT 05446
Phone: 802-864-5731
Fax: 802-655-8419
Web: www.gmpvt.com

CEO: Christopher L. (Chris) Dutton
CFO: Dawn D. Bugbee
HR: –
FYE: December 31
Type: Private

Public utility Green Mountain Power (GMP) lights up the hills of Vermont, supplying electricity to 90,000 customers in the state. The company operates more than 4,700 miles of transmission and distribution lines and owns 29% of high-voltage transmission operator Vermont Electric Power (VELCO). GMP serves residential, commercial, and industrial customers; its largest business customer is IBM (15% of sales). The utility also markets wholesale electricity in New England. GMP owns about 150 MW of capacity from hydroelectric and fossil-fueled power plants, but it purchases most of its power from other utilities. In 2007 GMP was acquired by Gaz Metro LP's Northern New England Energy Corp. for $187 million.

	Annual Growth	12/02	12/03	12/04	12/05	12/06
Sales ($ mil.)	(3.3%)	274.6	280.5	228.8	245.9	240.5
Net income ($ mil.)	(3.2%)	11.5	10.4	11.6	11.2	10.1
Employees	0.2%	194	196	192	195	—

GREEN PLAINS RENEWABLE ENERGY, INC.

NASDAQ (CM): GPRE

4124 Airport Rd.
Shenandoah, IA 51601
Phone: 712-246-2932
Fax: 712-246-2610
Web: www.gpreethanol.com

CEO: Wayne B. Hoovestol
CFO: Jerry L. Peters
HR: Ellen DeWitt
FYE: November 30
Type: Public

It's plain to Green Plains Renewable Energy that with stratospheric oil prices there is green to be made in ethanol production. Formed in 2004, the company has built and operates an ethanol plant in Iowa, and is in the process of constructing another. Completed in 2007, the first plant annually processes 18 million bushels of corn into 50 million gallons of ethanol that can be used as an alternative fuel additive to mix with petroleum. In addition, Green Plains Renewable Energy's plant produces 160,000 tons of animal feed known as distillers grains, the primary by-product of ethanol production. In 2008 the company agreed to acquire ethanol producer VBV LLC.

	Annual Growth	11/03	11/04	11/05	11/06	11/07
Sales ($ mil.)	—	—	—	—	—	24.2
Net income ($ mil.)	—	—	—	—	—	(7.1)
Market value ($ mil.)	—	—	—	—	—	72.4
Employees	—	—	—	—	—	—

GREEN TREE SERVICING LLC

345 St. Peter St.
St. Paul, MN 55102
Phone: 651-293-3400
Fax: 651-293-3622
Web: www.gtservicing.com

CEO: Keith A. Anderson
CFO: Cheryl Collins
HR: –
FYE: December 31
Type: Joint venture

Money might not grow on trees, but the green does grow on this tree. Green Tree Servicing is one of the largest servicers of manufactured home loans in the US; it also services home equity, home improvement, and consumer installment loans. The company originates manufactured home loans, securitizes and sells loans into the secondary market, and sells insurance, as well. All told, the company services some 700,000 accounts worth about $20 billion. A consortium that includes private equity firm Centerbridge Partners and Green Tree's management acquired the company in 2007.

	Annual Growth	12/03	12/04	12/05	12/06	12/07
Est. sales ($ mil.)	—	—	—	—	—	194.8
Employees	—	—	—	—	—	2,500

GREENBERG TRAURIG, LLP

1221 Brickell Ave.
Miami, FL 33131
Phone: 305-579-0500
Fax: 305-579-0717
Web: www.gtlaw.com

CEO: Cesar L. Alvarez
CFO: Larry Harris
HR: Lauren Center
FYE: December 31
Type: Partnership

Greenberg Traurig is known for its entertainment practice, but show business isn't the firm's only legal business. Its 1,750-plus lawyers maintain a wide range of practices, including corporate and securities, intellectual property, labor and employment, litigation, and real estate. Clients have included Delta Air Lines, Lorimar Pictures, and Metromedia Company. The firm has about 30 offices, mainly in the US but also in Europe and the Asia/Pacific region. It extends its network in Europe and Asia via strategic alliances. Greenberg Traurig was founded in 1967 by Mel Greenberg.

	Annual Growth	12/03	12/04	12/05	12/06	12/07
Est. sales ($ mil.)	—	—	—	—	—	190.8
Employees	—	—	—	—	—	2,200

THE GREENBRIER COMPANIES, INC.

NYSE: GBX

1 Centerpointe Dr., Ste. 200
Lake Oswego, OR 97035
Phone: 503-684-7000
Fax: 503-684-7553
Web: www.gbrx.com

CEO: William A. Furman
CFO: Mark J. Rittenbaum
HR: Jeannie Wakayama-Onchi
FYE: August 31
Type: Public

Greenbrier has been working for the railroads all the livelong day. The company manufactures, repairs, and refurbishes railcars. Its railcar line includes 100-ton-capacity boxcars, intermodal railcars, tank cars, and conventional railcars such as gondolas, center-partition cars, and flat cars. The company maintains manufacturing facilities in North America and Europe. Greenbrier's leasing unit owns and manages a fleet of about 8,500 railcars and manages another 136,000 railcars on behalf of railroads and other transportation and leasing companies in North America. Greenbrier also makes marine vessels, primarily ocean-going barges.

	Annual Growth	8/03	8/04	8/05	8/06	8/07
Sales ($ mil.)	28.3%	—	—	—	953.8	1,223.8
Net income ($ mil.)	(44.4%)	—	—	—	39.6	22.0
Market value ($ mil.)	7.2%	—	—	—	443.2	475.0
Employees	15.8%	—	—	—	3,661	4,239

GREENE COUNTY BANCORP, INC.

NASDAQ (CM): GCBC

302 Main St.
Catskill, NY 12414
Phone: 518-943-2600
Fax: 518-943-4431
Web: www.thebankofgreenecounty.com

CEO: Donald E. Gibson
CFO: Michelle M. Plummer
HR: Rebecca R. Main
FYE: June 30
Type: Public

This company helps put the "green" in Greene. Greene County Bancorp is the holding company for The Bank of Greene County, serving upstate New York's Catskill Mountains region from about 10 branches. Founded in 1889 as a building and loan association, the bank offers traditional retail products such as savings, NOW, checking, and money market accounts; IRAs; and CDs. Real estate loans make up nearly 85% of the bank's lending activities; it also writes business and consumer loans. Through affiliations with Fenimore Asset Management and Essex Corp., Greene County Bancorp offers investment products to existing customers. Subsidiary Greene County Commercial Bank is a state-chartered limited-purpose commercial bank.

	Annual Growth	6/03	6/04	6/05	6/06	6/07
Assets ($ mil.)	6.1%	257.0	284.6	294.7	307.6	325.8
Net income ($ mil.)	1.1%	2.2	2.9	3.0	2.2	2.3
Market value ($ mil.)	26.6%	21.9	33.0	73.6	61.3	56.5
Employees	5.5%	—	—	106	—	118

An in-depth profile of this company is available to Hoover's Online members at hoovers.com.

GREENE, TWEED & CO., INC.

1510 Gehman Rd.
Kulpsville, PA 19443
Phone: 215-256-9521
Fax: 215-513-9411
Web: www.gtweed.com

CEO: Michael Delfiner
CFO: Kevin Lukiewski
HR: Donna Grantland
FYE: December 31
Type: Private

Like a political enforcer in a presidential administration, Greene, Tweed & Co.'s job is to stop leaks from happening. Founded in 1863, the company manufactures specialty seals, gaskets, and engineered plastic components for applications in the aerospace and defense, pharmaceutical, chemical, petrochemical, oil field equipment manufacturing, industrial hydraulics, and semiconductor industries. Greene, Tweed's products are used in a variety of applications, from brakes on earthmoving equipment and jets to machinery used to process chemicals and make semiconductors. The company's customers include companies such as Airbus, Boeing, and Bayer.

	Annual Growth	12/03	12/04	12/05	12/06	12/07
Est. sales ($ mil.)	—	—	—	—	—	100.1
Employees	—	—	—	—	—	1,300

GREENFIELD ONLINE, INC.

NASDAQ (GM): SRVY

21 River Rd.
Wilton, CT 06897
Phone: 203-834-8585
Fax: 203-834-8686
Web: www.greenfield.com

CEO: Albert Angrisani
CFO: Robert E. (Bob) Bies
HR: –
FYE: December 31
Type: Public

Greenfield Online harvests marketing data using the Internet. The company provides survey research services, gathering demographic data over the Web from its panel of more than 1 million people. It performs surveys to track brand awareness and test new advertising campaigns for its clients, as well as to measure consumer interest in new products and services. Its Ciao subsidiary provides comparison shopping services featuring consumer products such as computers, electronics, and vehicles, primarily to the European market. Greenfield's clients mostly include consulting and market research firms such as Taylor Nelson Sofres and GfK. In mid-2008 the company agreed to be acquired by buyout firm Quadrangle Group.

	Annual Growth	12/03	12/04	12/05	12/06	12/07
Sales ($ mil.)	49.4%	25.9	44.4	89.2	100.3	129.0
Net income ($ mil.)	68.5%	1.6	5.7	(66.0)	8.4	12.9
Market value ($ mil.)	(5.9%)	—	461.8	148.3	364.5	384.4
Employees	42.3%	190	281	584	675	778

GREENHECK FAN CORPORATION

P.O. Box 410
Schofield, WI 54476
Phone: 715-359-6171
Fax: 715-355-2444
Web: www.greenheck.com

CEO: Dwight E. Davis
CFO: Chet Kwasniak
HR: Jon Krueger
FYE: March 31
Type: Private

Greenheck Fan offers products that help its customers feel a heck of lot cooler and breathe more easily. The employee-owned company, one of central Wisconsin's largest manufacturers, makes a variety of ventilation equipment, including fans, ventilators, dampers, and louvers. Greenheck Fan has manufacturing plants in Schofield, Wisconsin; Frankfort, Kentucky; and Rocklin, California; and overseas in Kunshan, China. It also has eight distribution centers across the US and sales representation throughout the world. Bernie and Bob Greenheck founded the company as a small sheet metal shop in 1947. Bernie Greenheck died in 2003; his brother Bob continues to serve as the company's chairman.

GREENHILL & CO, INC.

NYSE: GHL

300 Park Ave., 23rd Fl.
New York, NY 10022
Phone: 212-389-1500
Fax: 212-389-1700
Web: www.greenhill-co.com

CEO: Scott L. Bok
CFO: Richard Lieb
HR: Julie Kaeli
FYE: December 31
Type: Public

It's no secret what the favorite color is around the offices of Greenhill & Co. The investment bank specializes in mergers and acquisitions, corporate restructurings, venture capital, and merchant banking for clients worldwide. Merchant banking activities are conducted through the firm's Greenhill Capital Partners unit, which makes private equity investments, typically in the $10 million to $75 million range. Its Barrow Street Capital unit invests in real estate funds. Greenhill's high-profile transactions have included advising on the recapitalization of Ambac Financial and Nikko Cordial's share exchange with Citigroup.

	Annual Growth	12/03	12/04	12/05	12/06	12/07
Sales ($ mil.)	33.3%	126.7	151.9	221.1	290.6	400.4
Net income ($ mil.)	26.2%	45.4	38.3	55.5	75.7	115.3
Market value ($ mil.)	33.0%	—	882.5	1,734.2	2,100.9	2,076.3
Employees	19.0%	—	—	151	201	214

GREENLIGHT CAPITAL, INC.

2 Grand Central Tower, 140 E. 45th St., 24th Fl.
New York, NY 10017
Phone: 212-973-1900
Fax: 212-973-9219
Web: www.greenlightcapital.com

CEO: David Einhorn
CFO: Harry Brandler
HR: –
FYE: –
Type: Private

Red means stop, and green means . . . more capital? Greenlight Capital is a hedge fund firm that invests primarily in publicly traded North American corporate debt offerings and equities. Founded in 1996, Greenlight Capital also manages a fund of funds and a private equity fund through its affiliates, Greenlight Masters and Greenlight Private Equity Partners. It also operates Greenlight Capital Re, a property/casualty reinsurer. The company is led by activist investor David Einhorn, who has made a name for himself both in the boardroom and at the card table (as a finalist in the World Series of Poker).

GREENMAN TECHNOLOGIES, INC.

OTC: GMTI

12498 Wyoming Ave. South
Savage, MN 55378
Phone: 781-224-2411
Fax: 781-224-0114
Web: www.greenman.biz

CEO: Lyle E. Jensen
CFO: Charles E. (Chuck) Coppa
HR: –
FYE: September 30
Type: Public

Old tires are black gold for GreenMan Technologies. The company collects and processes the equivalent of about 13 million passenger tires a year. Whole tires go to cement kilns to be used as fuel, and the shredded rubber from recycled tires is used in the construction of landfills, roads, and septic fields. When granulated, the recycled rubber can be used as playground turf. GreenMan recovers about 60% of each tire through its processing operations; it extracts steel in addition to the rubber. The company obtains its raw material from tire stores, tire manufacturing plants, and government agencies that clean up piles of tires. Director Allen Kahn owns about 21% of GreenMan.

	Annual Growth	9/03	9/04	9/05	9/06	9/07
Sales ($ mil.)	(9.2%)	29.7	30.8	22.1	17.6	20.2
Net income ($ mil.)	—	(2.9)	(2.6)	(15.2)	(3.7)	0.3
Market value ($ mil.)	(26.0%)	26.7	23.3	4.4	7.1	8.0
Employees	—	—	—	159	—	—

GREENSHIFT CORPORATION

OTC: GSHF

1 Penn Plaza, Ste. 1612
New York, NY 10119
Phone: 888-895-3585
Fax: 646-572-6336
Web: greenshift.com

CEO: Kevin E. Kreisler
CFO: Jacqueline Flynn
HR: –
FYE: December 31
Type: Public

Altruism is all well and good, but GreenShift Corporation knows that being green can be good business too. Greenshift invests in companies that practice the efficient and sustainable use of resources and technology to support the environment. Its portfolio of companies hold some 20 patents in environmentally sound technologies. The company's strategy is to find and eliminate inefficiencies in the way society uses natural resources. GreenShift has stakes in environmentally proactive companies, including GS CleanTech (clean technology engineering and processes), GS Agrifuels (biodiesel and other fuels), and GS EnviroServices (industrial and hazardous waste management and site remediation services).

	Annual Growth	12/03	12/04	12/05	12/06	12/07
Est. sales ($ mil.)	—	—	—	—	—	17.9
Employees	—	—	—	—	—	133

GREENVILLE HOSPITAL SYSTEM

701 Grove Rd.
Greenville, SC 29605
Phone: 864-455-7000
Fax: 864-455-6218
Web: www.ghs.org

CEO: Michael C. (Mike) Riordan
CFO: Susan J. Bichel
HR: D. Douglas Dorman
FYE: September 30
Type: Not-for-profit

Greenville Hospital System is a not-for-profit community hospital system serving South Carolina's "Golden Strip" (the I-85 corridor connecting Charlotte, North Carolina, and Atlanta). Founded in 1912 as a community hospital, the system today includes four acute-care hospitals (with more than 1,100 beds), as well as a children's hospital, a cancer center, and a nursing home. Greenville Hospital System offers a full range of services, including a primary-care physician network and outpatient care. The company has teaching affiliations with the Medical University of South Carolina and the University of South Carolina Medical School, and nursing school affiliations with Clemson University and Bob Jones University.

GREENWICH CAPITAL MARKETS, INC.

600 Steamboat Rd.
Greenwich, CT 06830
Phone: 203-625-2700
Fax: –
Web: www.rbsgc.com

CEO: Jay Levine
CFO: Carol P. Mathis
HR: David MacWilliams
FYE: December 31
Type: Subsidiary

Greenwich Capital Markets (doing business as RBS Greenwich Capital) is a leading underwriter, trader, and distributor of fixed-income investment products. The company specializes in US dollar derivatives, asset-based securities, corporate debt, and prime and subprime mortgage-backed securities. It also is active in corporate banking, commercial real estate finance, foreign exchange, futures trading, and financing of mergers and acquisitions. RBS Greenwich Capital is a subsidiary of Royal Bank of Scotland. The firm and its affiliates have about 10 US offices.

	Annual Growth	12/03	12/04	12/05	12/06	12/07
Est. sales ($ mil.)	—	—	—	—	—	54.7
Employees	—	—	—	—	—	563

GREIF, INC.

NYSE: GEF

425 Winter Rd.
Delaware, OH 43015
Phone: 740-549-6000
Fax: 740-549-6100
Web: www.greif.com

CEO: Michael J. Gasser
CFO: Donald S. (Don) Huml
HR: Michael L. Roane
FYE: October 31
Type: Public

Good Greif! Greif (rhymes with "life") produces containers and container-board, mainly for bulk shippers in the chemical, food, petroleum, and pharmaceutical industries. The firm's industrial shipping products include shipping drums, drum closure systems, and pallets, while its containerboard segment makes containerboard, corrugated sheets and containers, and multi-wall packaging. Greif's multiwall bag products are used to ship a wide range of industrial and consumer products, such as chemicals, flour, pet foods, seed, and sugar. Greif also manages timber properties in the US and Canada. Michael Dempsey, the son of former company chairman Jack Dempsey (not the boxer), owns about 55% of Greif.

	Annual Growth	10/03	10/04	10/05	10/06	10/07
Sales ($ mil.)	14.7%	1,916.4	2,209.3	2,424.3	2,628.5	3,322.3
Net income ($ mil.)	101.4%	9.5	47.8	104.7	142.1	156.4
Market value ($ mil.)	72.1%	172.4	229.1	351.7	545.1	1,510.8
Employees	—	—	—	—	9,025	—

GREY GROUP INC.

777 3rd Ave.
New York, NY 10017
Phone: 212-546-2000
Fax: 212-546-1538
Web: www.grey.com

CEO: James R. (Jim) Heekin III
CFO: Lester M. Feintuck
HR: –
FYE: December 31
Type: Subsidiary

This company colors its advertising clients impressed. A unit of UK-based conglomerate WPP Group, Grey Group is a leading provider of advertising and marketing services through offices in more than 80 countries. Its flagship agency network, Grey Worldwide, offers creative ad development and campaign management services along with a variety of other marketing disciplines. The company also offers specialized public relations and communications services through GCI and Grey Healthcare. Smaller agencies such as G2 Branding & Design and G2 Direct & Digital (formerly Grey Direct) provide brand promotion and direct marketing services.

	Annual Growth	12/03	12/04	12/05	12/06	12/07
Est. sales ($ mil.)	—	—	—	—	—	2,147.5
Employees	—	—	—	—	—	10,500

GREY WOLF, INC.

AMEX: GW

10370 Richmond Ave., Ste. 600
Houston, TX 77042
Phone: 713-435-6100
Fax: 713-435-6180
Web: www.gwdrilling.com

CEO: Thomas P. (Tom) Richards
CFO: David W. Wehlmann
HR: Robert J. Proffit
FYE: December 31
Type: Public

Grey Wolf makes its living hunting down onshore oil and gas drilling contracts. The company performs onshore contract drilling, primarily for natural gas, using a US-based fleet of 121 marketed rigs that can reach depths of up to 40,000 ft. Grey Wolf's operations are focused on six regions: Mid-Continent; South Texas; the Gulf Coast (Texas and Louisiana); Ark-La-Tex (northeastern Texas, northern Louisiana, and southern Arkansas); southern Mississippi and Alabama; and the Rocky Mountains. The company provides rigs, related equipment, and field personnel to customers on a turnkey, footage, or day-work basis. In 2008 Grey Wolf agreed to acquire Basic Energy Services.

	Annual Growth	12/03	12/04	12/05	12/06	12/07
Sales ($ mil.)	33.4%	286.0	424.6	697.0	945.5	906.6
Net income ($ mil.)	—	(30.2)	8.1	120.6	219.9	169.9
Market value ($ mil.)	8.8%	678.0	1,002.0	1,489.0	1,275.5	950.6
Employees	(6.5%)	—	—	3,200	3,400	2,800

⊞ GREYHOUND LINES, INC.

15110 N. Dallas Pkwy., 1st Fl.
Dallas, TX 75248
Phone: 972-789-7000
Fax: 972-387-1874
Web: www.greyhound.com

CEO: Dave Leach
CFO: Cheryl W. Farmer
HR: Rhonda Piar MacAndrew
FYE: December 31
Type: Subsidiary

If you're going by bus, the old grey dog is likely to be the only one on the track. The only US bus company with a regular nationwide intercity schedule, Greyhound Lines carries some 21 million passengers yearly to about 1,700 destinations. Some markets are served via partnerships with regional bus lines. The company's fleet includes about 1,500 buses. In conjunction with its intercity passenger service, Greyhound offers express package delivery. It also provides charter bus services. Affiliates operate under the Greyhound brand in Canada and Mexico. The company is a unit of FirstGroup America.

GREYSTONE LOGISTICS, INC.

OTC: GLGI

1613 E. 15th St.
Tulsa, OK 74120
Phone: 918-583-7441
Fax: 918-583-7442
Web: www.greystonelogistics-glgi.com

CEO: Warren F. Kruger
CFO: Robert H. Nelson
HR: –
FYE: May 31
Type: Public

If you need plastic pallets, then (ironically) Greystone is your answer — Greystone Logistics, that is. The company (formerly known as PalWeb) manufactures and sells plastic pallets for various commercial applications. Its products include the Greystone Beverage Pallet, Hawker Series fire retardant plastic pallets, Tank picture frame pallets, and the Granada Series (including nestable and flat deck plastic pallets). Greystone Logistics also offers multi-station plastic injection molding systems. The company uses a proprietary recycled resin mix and manufacturing process to produce its plastics. It serves customers in the pharmaceutical, beverage, and other industries, primarily in the US.

	Annual Growth	5/03	5/04	5/05	5/06	5/07
Sales ($ mil.)	75.7%	1.3	7.0	9.3	16.0	12.4
Net income ($ mil.)	—	(3.2)	(3.0)	(10.4)	(2.3)	(2.6)
Market value ($ mil.)	5.8%	4.2	6.8	7.0	2.9	5.2
Employees	—	—	—	—	75	—

GRIFFIN LAND & NURSERIES, INC.

NASDAQ (GM): GRIF

1 Rockefeller Plaza
New York, NY 10020
Phone: 212-218-7910
Fax: 212-218-7917
Web: www.imperialnurseries.com

CEO: Frederick M. Danziger
CFO: Anthony J. Galici
HR: Tammy Pollack
FYE: Saturday nearest November 30
Type: Public

Griffin Land & Nurseries aims to reshape the suburban landscape. Through subsidiary Imperial Nurseries, it grows and distributes container-based plants, mostly broadleaf evergreens such as rhododendrons, to garden center operators and the garden departments of retail chain stores. Griffin also has real estate operations, including developing tracts of land in Connecticut and Massachusetts for light industrial and residential use. Griffin owns small percentages of a nursery distributor and a business magazine publisher. The Cullman and Ernst families together own about 49% of Griffin.

	Annual Growth	11/03	11/04	11/05	11/06	11/07
Sales ($ mil.)	11.7%	38.2	41.3	41.9	53.2	59.4
Net income ($ mil.)	—	(2.3)	31.0	(1.4)	(0.4)	8.3
Market value ($ mil.)	26.6%	72.7	129.2	120.0	161.2	186.6
Employees	(4.1%)	—	—	223	—	205

GRIFFITH LABORATORIES INC.

1 Griffith Center
Alsip, IL 60803
Phone: 708-371-0900
Fax: 708-597-3294
Web: www.griffithlaboratories.com

CEO: Hervé de la Vauvre
CFO: Joseph (Joe) Maslick
HR: Stephen (Steve) Lee
FYE: September 30
Type: Private

A little pinch here, a little pinch there, pretty soon you have a business. Griffith Laboratories is a food-ingredient manufacturer with operations worldwide. The company's customers range from food processors to restaurants and grocery retailers. Its products include seasonings, sauce and soup mixes, condiments, texturizers, and bakery blends. Griffith's subsidiaries include Custom Culinary (food bases and mixes for food service) and Innova (meat flavors). The company also offers customized-ingredient services and operates consumerquiz.com, a Web site that offers consumer research assistance for food and beverage manufacturers.

	Annual Growth	9/03	9/04	9/05	9/06	9/07
Est. sales ($ mil.)	—	—	—	—	—	520.4
Employees	—	—	—	—	—	2,500

⊞ GRIFFON CORPORATION

NYSE: GFF

100 Jericho Quadrangle
Jericho, NY 11753
Phone: 516-938-5544
Fax: 516-938-5644
Web: www.griffoncorp.com

CEO: Ronald J. Kramer
CFO: Patrick L. Alesia
HR: –
FYE: September 30
Type: Public

Like its mythical namesake, Griffon is wonderfully varied and more than the sum of its parts. The company has four major divisions. Its Clopay unit, which makes up about one-third of sales, is the US's leading garage-door maker. Telephonics makes advanced information and communications products used in radar, air-traffic control, and defense systems. Clopay Plastic Products manufactures specialty plastic films used in disposable diapers, adult incontinence products, medical garments, and surgical drapes. Clopay Service provides installation services for such products as garage doors and fireplaces. More than 75% of Griffon's sales are attributable to the US.

	Annual Growth	9/03	9/04	9/05	9/06	9/07
Sales ($ mil.)	6.5%	1,254.7	1,393.8	1,402.0	1,636.6	1,616.6
Net income ($ mil.)	(15.3%)	43.0	53.9	48.8	51.8	22.1
Market value ($ mil.)	(3.9%)	529.1	611.7	743.9	712.5	451.9
Employees	(3.6%)	—	—	5,700	5,700	5,300

GRILL CONCEPTS, INC.

NASDAQ (CM): GRIL

11661 San Vicente Blvd., Ste. 404
Los Angeles, CA 90049
Phone: 310-820-5559
Fax: 310-820-6530
Web: www.dailygrill.com

CEO: Philip Gay
CFO: Wayne Lipschitz
HR: Chris Gehrke
FYE: Sunday nearest December 31
Type: Public

Can a Daily Grill help ease the daily grind? Grill Concepts operates a chain of more than 20 Daily Grill restaurants offering upscale casual dining in a setting reminiscent of a classic American grill from the 1930s and 1940s. Located primarily in California, the restaurants feature such fare as chicken pot pie, meatloaf, and cobbler, as well as steak, seafood, and pasta. In addition to its company-owned locations, Grill Concepts has nearly 10 licensed and managed units operating in shopping areas and hotels. The Daily Grill concept is based on the company's five Grill on the Alley fine dining restaurants.

	Annual Growth	12/03	12/04	12/05	12/06	12/07
Sales ($ mil.)	12.3%	58.3	63.7	70.7	80.8	92.8
Net income ($ mil.)	—	0.1	0.0	0.9	1.3	(1.3)
Market value ($ mil.)	28.2%	14.0	12.4	17.2	19.3	37.8
Employees	—	—	—	1,656	—	—

GRIMMWAY ENTERPRISES INC.

14141 Di Giorgio Rd.
Di Giorgio, CA 93203
Phone: 661-854-6270
Fax: 661-854-4137
Web: www.grimmway.com

CEO: Jeff Meger
CFO: Steve Barnes
HR: Sean K. McNally
FYE: December 31
Type: Private

If Bugs Bunny were to visit Grimmway Enterprises, he would think he'd died and gone to heaven. Grimmway produces everything carrot — from bagged baby carrots, to carrot coins, to carrot juice, to carrot sticks, to good old carrot bunches. The produce firm processes 40,000 acres of California farmland per year. Grimmway's fresh carrots are available in retail stores worldwide; it also sells potatoes, citrus fruits, and juices, and it provides products to foodservice customers. Subsidiary Cal Organics offers 75 organic fruit and vegetable product lines. The family-owned company was formed by Rod and Bob Grimm in 1968.

	Annual Growth	12/03	12/04	12/05	12/06	12/07
Est. sales ($ mil.)	—	—	—	—	—	254.2
Employees	—	—	—	—	—	4,000

GRISTEDE'S FOODS, INC.

823 11th Ave.
New York, NY 10019
Phone: 212-956-5803
Fax: 212-247-4509
Web: www.gristedes.com

CEO: John A. Catsimatidis
CFO: –
HR: –
FYE: November 30
Type: Private

New York City never sleeps, but eating is another matter. Gristede's Foods feeds hungry New Yorkers from more than 35 area supermarkets (most are located in Manhattan), including new Gristede's Mega Stores. The stores offer fresh meats, produce, dairy products, baked goods, frozen foods, gourmet foods, and nonfood items. Gristede's also operates three stand-alone pharmacies and XpressGrocer.com, for online grocery shopping. The company owns City Produce Operating, which supplies the supermarkets with groceries and produce and sells wholesale fresh produce to third parties. Chairman and CEO John Catsimatidis and Gristede's other major shareholders took the grocery chain private in November 2004.

THE GROCERS SUPPLY CO., INC.

3131 E. Holcombe Blvd.
Houston, TX 77221
Phone: 713-747-5000
Fax: 713-746-5611
Web: www.grocerssupply.com

CEO: Max S. Levit
CFO: Michael (Mike) Castleberry
HR: Deborah Howard
FYE: December 31
Type: Private

Need crackers in Caracas or vanilla in Manila? Grocers Supply Co. distributes groceries near and far. The company (not to be confused with fellow Texas distributor GSC Enterprises) supplies food, health and beauty items, household products, and school and office supplies to nearly 2,000 convenience stores and grocery retailers, as well as some 200 schools, within a 350-mile radius of Houston. The company's international division, meanwhile, ships supplies to oil company operations, US embassies, and other customers around the world. It also owns Fiesta Mart, a chain of ethnic food stores. Grocers Supply was founded by Joe Levit in 1923; his family, led by president Max Levit, continues to own the company.

	Annual Growth	12/02	12/03	12/04	12/05	12/06
Est. sales ($ mil.)	32.1%	—	—	—	1,900.0	2,510.0
Employees	340.0%	—	—	—	2,000	8,800

GROCERY OUTLET INC.

2000 Fifth St.
Berkeley, CA 94710
Phone: 510-845-1999
Fax: 510-845-7869
Web: www.groceryoutlets.com

CEO: Eric Lindberg
CFO: Mike Ward
HR: Frank Bilbao
FYE: December 31
Type: Private

Grocery Outlet operates about 125 deep-discount supermarkets in a half dozen western states, primarily California, Oregon, Washington, and Hawaii. The stores average about 20,000 sq. ft. and sell a wide range of name-brand products, including groceries, wine and beer, household items, health and beauty care products, and over-the-counter drugs. More than 50 of Grocery Outlet's stores are located in California. The chain purchased 17 Yes!Less stores in Texas and Louisiana from defunct grocery distributor Fleming in mid-2003, but closed all of those stores in 2004. Founded in 1946, the privately held, extreme-value retailer is expanding in the Seattle-Tacoma, Washington, area.

GROEN BROTHERS AVIATION, INC.

OTC: GNBA

2640 W. California Ave.
Salt Lake City, UT 84104
Phone: 801-973-0177
Fax: 801-973-4027
Web: www.groenbros.com

CEO: David L. Groen
CFO: David L. Groen
HR: –
FYE: June 30
Type: Public

A centaur is part man, part horse; a griffin is part eagle, part lion; and a gyroplane is part helicopter, part airplane. Groen Brothers Aviation's Hawk series gyroplanes are designed to be safer in low and slow flight than either an airplane or a helicopter. Gyroplanes, also known as autogyros or gyrocopters, derive lift from rotary blades and thrust from a propeller. Potential applications for the Hawk series include commercial surveying, fire patrol, law enforcement, and military surveillance. Flight testing of the Hawk 4 for FAA certification was halted because of a lack of money; however, the company has teamed with the government of Aragon, Spain, to fund a Hawk 5 through FAA certification.

	Annual Growth	6/03	6/04	6/05	6/06	6/07
Sales ($ mil.)	141.5%	0.1	0.5	0.9	3.1	3.4
Net income ($ mil.)	—	(4.7)	(12.5)	(13.4)	(20.1)	(25.4)
Market value ($ mil.)	1.0%	23.7	22.1	24.8	23.9	24.7
Employees	27.8%	—	—	—	72	92

GROUP 1 AUTOMOTIVE, INC.

NYSE: GPI

950 Echo Ln., Ste. 100
Houston, TX 77024
Phone: 713-647-5700
Fax: 713-647-5858
Web: www.group1auto.com

CEO: Earl J. Hesterberg
CFO: John C. Rickel
HR: J. Brooks O'Hara
FYE: December 31
Type: Public

Group 1 Automotive is only one in a group of firms (AutoNation and Penske Automotive Group are the largest) striving to consolidate US auto sales. The company owns and operates about 140 franchises at some 100 dealerships, as well as about 25 collision service centers in more than a dozen states. These dealerships offer new and used cars and light trucks under more than 30 different brands. (New cars account for more than 60% of sales.) The company also offers financing, provides maintenance and repair services, and sells replacement parts. Group 1 Automotive, which sells both US-made cars and imports, has been on a major shopping spree, acquiring more than two dozen dealerships in recent years.

	Annual Growth	12/03	12/04	12/05	12/06	12/07
Sales ($ mil.)	9.1%	4,518.6	5,435.0	5,969.6	6,083.5	6,393.0
Net income ($ mil.)	(2.8%)	76.1	27.8	54.2	88.4	67.9
Market value ($ mil.)	(9.5%)	817.9	734.3	754.8	1,254.8	548.7
Employees	3.1%	—	—	8,400	8,785	8,932

An in-depth profile of this company is available to Hoover's Online members at hoovers.com.

711

GROUP 1 SOFTWARE, INC.

4200 Parliament Place, Ste. 600
Lanham, MD 20706
Phone: 301-731-2300
Fax: 301-731-0360
Web: www.g1.com

CEO: Christopher (Chris) Baker
CFO: Scott Landers
HR: –
FYE: December 31
Type: Subsidiary

Group 1 Software knows that marketing and customer management is not only a top priority, but a group effort. The company provides a variety of direct marketing and customer communications management applications. Group 1's software helps businesses create documents, verify list addresses and eliminate duplications, and format databases. Group 1 also offers data quality software for verifying customer data, as well as services such as data migration, consulting, and document analysis. In 2004 the company was acquired by Pitney Bowes for about $321 million. In 2007 Pitney Bowes announced plans to merge the company with Pitney Bowes MapInfo to create a new business unit called Pitney Bowes Software.

	Annual Growth	12/03	12/04	12/05	12/06	12/07
Est. sales ($ mil.)	—	—	—	—	—	37.8
Employees	—	—	—	—	—	485

GROUP HEALTH COOPERATIVE

521 Wall St.
Seattle, WA 98121
Phone: 206-448-5600
Fax: 206-448-4010
Web: www.ghc.org

CEO: Scott Armstrong
CFO: –
HR: Brenda Tolbert
FYE: December 31
Type: Cooperative

Group Health Cooperative gives new meaning to the term "consumer-driven health care." The organization is a not-for-profit managed health care group serving some half a million residents of Washington and Idaho. Governed by a board that its members elect, the co-op offers health insurance through its Group Health Options and KPS Health Plans subsidiaries, but it also provides medical care at its own facilities. It maintains a partnership with Group Health Permanente, a multi-specialty medical group that provides care in those facilities. The co-op also partners with Kaiser Permanente to market its services, share knowledge, and offer reciprocal membership benefits.

GROUP HEALTH INCORPORATED

441 9th Ave.
New York, NY 10001
Phone: 212-615-0000
Fax: 212-563-8561
Web: www.ghi.com

CEO: Frank J. Branchini
CFO: Michael (Mike) Palmateer
HR: Thomas Nemeth
FYE: December 31
Type: Not-for-profit

Group Health Incorporated is a not-for-profit health benefits company that provides managed health care coverage and related services to more than 2.5 million members in New York State. Established in 1937, the company offers a wide range of medical, dental, and prescription drug plans to individuals, businesses, and government agencies. For businesses, it provides fully insured coverage or administrative services for self-insured employers. The firm also provides Medicare Advantage plans and manages care for recipients of Medicaid and other state-sponsored programs in some counties. Group Health became affiliated with Health Insurance Plan of Greater New York (HIP) late in 2006.

	Annual Growth	12/03	12/04	12/05	12/06	12/07
Est. sales ($ mil.)	—	—	—	—	—	2,147.5
Employees	—	—	—	—	—	2,354

GROWMARK, INC.

1701 Towanda Ave.
Bloomington, IL 61701
Phone: 309-557-6000
Fax: 309-829-8532
Web: www.growmark.com

CEO: William Davisson
CFO: Jeff Solberg
HR: –
FYE: August 31
Type: Cooperative

Retail farm-supply and grain-marketing cooperative GROWMARK can mark its growth by the grain. A member-owed co-op, GROWMARK serves farmers in the midwestern US and Ontario, Canada. Under the Fast Stop name, the co-op runs fuel stations and convenience stores. Its FS- and NK-brand grains include alfalfa, corn, wheat, and soybeans. GROWMARK also offers fertilizer and buildings such as grain bins. Its Seedway subsidiary markets farm and turf seed. GROWMARK partners with ag giant Archer Daniels Midland, fertilizer maker and distributor CF Industries, pet-food producer PRO-PET, Land O'Lakes, and agribusiness company Syngenta.

GRUBB & ELLIS COMPANY

NYSE: GBE

1551 N. Tustin Ave., Ste. 300
Santa Ana, CA 92705
Phone: 714-667-8252
Fax: 877-888-7348
Web: www.grubb-ellis.com

CEO: Scott D. Peters
CFO: Richard W. (Rich) Pehlke
HR: Amanda Piwonka
FYE: December 31
Type: Public

Want to swap that dingy old office building for a shiny glass skyscraper? Call Grubb & Ellis. Through a network of some 115 owned and affiliated offices, the company provides commercial real estate services to property owners, institutional investors, and tenants. Its 1,800 brokers and some 5,500 affiliated real estate professionals offer advisory and brokerage, property management, construction consultation, and other services. The company operates in two segments: transaction services, which comprise its brokerage operations, and management services, including facilities and project management. In 2007 Grubb & Ellis merged with NNN Realty Advisors, a commercial real estate management and investment firm.

	Annual Growth	6/04	6/05	6/06	6/07	*12/07
Sales ($ mil.)	(14.9%)	440.6	463.5	490.1	513.3	231.4
Net income ($ mil.)	10.0%	14.2	13.3	4.9	3.0	20.8
Market value ($ mil.)	116.6%	—	—	88.6	300.6	415.5
Employees	0.0%	4,100	4,100	—	—	

*Fiscal year change

GRUMA CORPORATION

1159 Cottonwood Ln., Ste. 200
Irving, TX 75038
Phone: 972-232-5000
Fax: 972-232-5176
Web: www.gruma.com/vlng

CEO: Jairo Senise
CFO: Joel Suarez
HR: Valina Ussery
FYE: December 31
Type: Subsidiary

Gruma Corporation has it all wrapped up. With operations in just about every corner of the world, the company manufactures and distributes more than 20 varieties of corn flour, corn tortillas, and related products throughout the US and Europe. Gruma's brand names include Mission and Guerrero tortillas and Maseca corn flour. The company is a wholly owned subsidiary of Mexican food company Gruma, S.A.B. de C.V. Although continually forced to raise its prices due to the increased costs of raw materials, ingredients, energy, packaging, and fuel prices, Gruma Corporation continues to do well.

	Annual Growth	12/03	12/04	12/05	12/06	12/07
Est. sales ($ mil.)	—	—	—	—	—	1,500.0
Employees	—	—	—	—	—	4,900

GRYPHON INVESTORS, INC.

1 Market Plaza, Steuart Tower, 24th Fl.
San Francisco, CA 94105
Phone: 415-217-7400
Fax: 415-217-7447
Web: www.gryphon-inv.com

CEO: R. David Andrews
CFO: –
HR: –
FYE: December 31
Type: Private

Gryphon Investors is on the hunt for hidden treasures among middle-market companies. The private equity firm pursues investments in companies in the business services, consumer goods, general industry, and retail sectors with annual sales of $25 million to $250 million. Seeking to take a controlling interest in its target firms, it typically invests between $25 million and $75 million per transaction and holds on to its investments for three to seven years. Its current portfolio includes stakes in Celerity and MSD Ignition. Founded in 1995, Gryphon Investors has completed more than 50 acquisitions and has some $900 million in capital under management.

	Annual Growth	12/03	12/04	12/05	12/06	12/07
Est. sales ($ mil.)	—	—	—	—	—	729.7
Employees	—	—	—	—	—	10,275

GS ENVIROSERVICES, INC.

Pink Sheets: GSEN

One Penn Plaza, Ste. 1612
New York, NY 10119
Phone: 212-994-5374
Fax: –

CEO: James F. Green
CFO: Doris Christiani
HR: –
FYE: December 31
Type: Public

GS EnviroServices (formerly TDS Telemedicine) is a development-stage company that plans to grow through acquisitions. The company discontinued its diagnostic services to physicians via telemedicine, the practice of medicine over phone lines or broadband connections. It no longer specializes in providing dermatology (skin) images and retina images that are used to monitor the condition of diabetics. In 2007 the company moved into the environmental services sector through the acquisition of GS EnviroServices.

	Annual Growth	12/03	12/04	12/05	12/06	12/07
Sales ($ mil.)	—	—	—	—	—	15.3
Net income ($ mil.)	—	—	—	—	—	0.1
Market value ($ mil.)	—	—	—	—	—	2.6
Employees	—	—	—	—	—	—

GS CAPITAL PARTNERS, L.P.

85 Broad St.
New York, NY 10004
Phone: 212-902-1000
Fax: 212-902-3000
Web: www.gs.com/client_services/merchant_banking/pia/capital

CEO: Joseph H. Gleberman
CFO: –
HR: –
FYE: November 30
Type: Partnership

GS Capital Partners makes private equity investments on behalf of Goldman Sachs and others. It participates in a range of transactions, including leveraged buyouts, recapitalizations, acquisitions, and build-outs. An active investor that partners with its portfolio companies, GS Capital Partners typically invests in middle-market or large firms in a variety of industries. In 2007 the firm closed its latest fund, GS Capital Partners VI, which raised some $20 billion, including more than $7 billion from Goldman Sachs; it is one of the largest private equity funds ever. That year, GS Capital Partners teamed up with TPG Capital in an offer to buy telecommunications giant ALLTEL for nearly $25 billion.

GS CLEANTECH CORPORATION

OTC: GSCT

1 Penn Plaza, Ste. 1612
New York, NY 10119
Phone: 212-994-5374
Fax: 646-572-6336
Web: www.gs-cleantech.com

CEO: David Winsness
CFO: Kevin E. Kreisler
HR: –
FYE: December 31
Type: Public

In a case of modern alchemy, GS CleanTech (formerly Veridium) is working overtime to turn trash into cash. The company recycles industrial hazardous wastes and converts them into usable commodities. GS CleanTech also provides site-based remedial, industrial cleaning, and other related services for its clients. The engineering and recycling company operates primarily in the northeastern US. In 2006 it discontinued its environmental engineering division (Enviro-Sciences of Delaware) and has a new focus on developing process innovations for the ethanol industry. Chairman Kevin Kreisler owns an 80% voting stake in GS CleanTech through his GreenShift company, which is seeking to acquire GS CleanTech.

	Annual Growth	12/03	12/04	12/05	12/06	12/07
Sales ($ mil.)	23.3%	13.0	13.2	14.0	14.4	30.0
Net income ($ mil.)	—	(14.2)	(7.0)	(5.7)	(9.9)	(24.3)
Market value ($ mil.)	(98.4%)	—	—	—	559.8	9.2
Employees	—	—	—	—	—	—

GS FINANCIAL CORP.

NASDAQ (GM): GSLA

3798 Veterans Blvd.
Metairie, LA 70002
Phone: 504-457-6220
Fax: 504-457-6227
Web: www.gsfinancialcorp.com

CEO: Stephen E. Wessel
CFO: J. Andrew (Andy) Bower
HR: Bruce A. Scott
FYE: December 31
Type: Public

GS Financial wants to make banking easy in The Big Easy. It's the holding company for Guaranty Savings Bank, which operates about five branches in and around New Orleans. Founded in 1937, it mainly targets small business owners and individual consumers, offering such traditional retail services as checking and savings accounts, individual retirement accounts, and certificates of deposit. Lending activities consist mainly of one- to four-family residential mortgages, as well as commercial mortgages and construction loans.

	Annual Growth	12/03	12/04	12/05	12/06	12/07
Assets ($ mil.)	(3.5%)	214.7	200.1	177.6	168.4	186.5
Net income ($ mil.)	0.0%	0.7	0.2	(3.7)	2.1	0.7
Market value ($ mil.)	(1.0%)	25.4	23.2	19.3	25.1	24.4
Employees	10.0%	—	—	38	43	46

GSC ENTERPRISES, INC.

130 Hillcrest Dr.
Sulphur Springs, TX 75482
Phone: 903-885-0829
Fax: 903-885-6928
Web: www.grocerysupply.com

CEO: Michael J. Bain
CFO: Kerry Law
HR: Janet Price
FYE: Saturday nearest December 31
Type: Private

GSC Enterprises brings the groceries to the grocery store. Doing business as Grocery Supply Company (not to be confused with Grocers Supply Co.), the wholesale distributor supplies more than 4,500 independently owned convenience stores, grocers, discounters, and other retailers and wholesalers in about 15 states, mostly in the Southwest, Southeast, and Midwest. GSC stocks and distributes tobacco, grocery items, prepared foods (Chicago Style Pizza, Chester Fried Chicken, Deli-Fast Foods), and other items. In addition, its Fidelity Express subsidiary sells money orders in retail stores. Ken McKenzie, Curtis McKenzie, and Woodrow Brittain started GSC in 1947; the McKenzie family continues to own the company.

	Annual Growth	12/02	12/03	12/04	12/05	12/06
Sales ($ mil.)	4.8%	—	—	—	1,174.0	1,230.0
Employees	4.3%	—	—	—	1,150	1,200

An in-depth profile of this company is available to Hoover's Online members at hoovers.com.

713

GSC GROUP

500 Campus Dr., Ste. 220
Florham Park, NJ 07932
Phone: 973-437-1000
Fax: 973-437-1037
Web: www.gscpartners.com

CEO: Alfred C. Eckert III
CFO: Andrew J. Wagner
HR: David L. Goret
FYE: December 31
Type: Private

Got Some Cash? GSC does. Investment firm GSC Group (formerly GSC Partners) manages assets for pension funds, foundations, universities, and wealthy individual investors in Europe and the US. It specializes in distressed debt investing and mezzanine lending, as well as high-yield bonds and other opportunities. The company has more than $24 billion under management. It has a stake in real estate investment trust GSC Capital. The company was founded in 1994 as Greenwich Street Capital and spun off from the Travelers Group in 1999.

GSE SYSTEMS, INC.

AMEX: GVP

7133 Rutherford Rd., Ste. 200
Baltimore, MD 21244
Phone: 410-277-3740
Fax: 410-277-5287
Web: www.gses.com

CEO: John V. Moran
CFO: Jeffery G. Hough
HR: Terri DiBella
FYE: December 31
Type: Public

GSE Systems is into power and control. The company provides simulation software to train power plant operators, engineers, and managers. Its systems, used primarily for the nuclear power, fossil energy, and chemical industries, can also be used to test new plant systems before they are installed. The company also offers training services through a partnership with General Physics. Customers have included Archer Daniels Midland Company; BASF Corporation; Cargill Incorporated; Merck & Co., Inc.; and Miller Brewing Company.

	Annual Growth	12/03	12/04	12/05	12/06	12/07
Sales ($ mil.)	2.0%	—	29.5	22.0	27.5	31.9
Net income ($ mil.)	86.1%	—	0.1	(4.8)	(0.3)	1.2
Market value ($ mil.)	87.0%	—	24.3	11.2	73.2	158.8
Employees	9.8%	—	—	123	135	—

GSI COMMERCE, INC.

NASDAQ (GS): GSIC

935 1st Ave.
King of Prussia, PA 19406
Phone: 610-491-7000
Fax: –
Web: www.gsicommerce.com

CEO: Michael G. Rubin
CFO: Michael R. Conn
HR: James (Jim) Flanagan
FYE: December 31
Type: Public

GSI Commerce offers e-commerce packages organized across three categories: technology, logistics and customer care, and marketing. It creates and operates Web sites for about 60 retailers and consumer goods manufacturers in addition to its own fogdog.com sporting goods retail operation. The company offers Web site design and hosting services as well as merchandising for such clients as palmOne, Polo Ralph Lauren, Reebok, and Sport Chalet. GSI also offers outsourced order fulfillment, customer service, and Web analytics services. In addition to retailers and manufacturers, the company serves media outlets such as HBO, Nickelodeon, and PBS, as well as professional sports teams.

	Annual Growth	12/03	12/04	12/05	12/06	12/07
Sales ($ mil.)	32.7%	241.9	335.1	440.4	609.5	750.0
Net income ($ mil.)	—	(12.1)	(0.3)	2.7	53.7	3.0
Market value ($ mil.)	23.8%	389.4	739.3	674.1	860.2	915.4
Employees	64.5%	—	—	1,729	2,521	4,679

GSI GROUP INC.

NASDAQ (GS): GSIG

39 Manning Rd.
Billerica, MA 01821
Phone: 978-439-5511
Fax: 978-663-0044
Web: www.gsig.com

CEO: Sergio Edelstein
CFO: Robert L. Bowen
HR: Anthony J. (Tony) Bellantuoni
FYE: December 31
Type: Public

GSI Group has its laser sights set on manufacturing. Formed by the 1999 merger of General Scanning and Lumonics, the global company makes components for precision motion and motion control products for niche markets, and laser-based manufacturing systems with a focus on the semiconductor, telecommunications, and electronics industries. Laser functions include marking, tuning, drilling, placement, and inspection, and are also used in lithography, industrial processing, medical, and military applications. GSI has divested its noncore operations and acquired several companies. Customers in the Asia/Pacific region account for more than half of the company's sales.

	Annual Growth	12/03	12/04	12/05	12/06	12/07
Sales ($ mil.)	14.4%	185.6	330.0	260.8	313.6	317.8
Net income ($ mil.)	—	(2.2)	41.5	9.7	21.7	19.0
Market value ($ mil.)	(11.0%)	622.1	568.7	452.1	405.9	389.6
Employees	6.3%	1,067	1,175	1,167	1,347	1,363

GSI TECHNOLOGY, INC.

NASDAQ (GM): GSIT

2360 Owen St.
Santa Clara, CA 95054
Phone: 408-980-8388
Fax: 408-980-8377
Web: www.gsitechnology.com

CEO: Lee-Lean Shu
CFO: Douglas Schirle
HR: –
FYE: March 31
Type: Public

Gee whiz, GSI makes some fast chips. GSI Technology designs and markets specialized SRAM (static random-access memory) integrated circuits used in high-speed networking equipment. Its chips allow routers, switches, and other gear from the likes of Alcatel-Lucent and Cisco Systems to retrieve data at the speeds needed for broadband transmission. The fabless semiconductor company does most of its business through contract manufacturers, such as Celestica, and through distributors, including Avnet (about one-quarter of sales) and Nu Horizons. Other customers include SMART Modular Technologies (nearly 30% of sales), which buys memory chips for products it makes on behalf of Cisco.

	Annual Growth	3/04	3/05	3/06	3/07	3/08
Sales ($ mil.)	10.7%	35.4	45.7	43.1	58.2	53.2
Net income ($ mil.)	—	(0.7)	4.8	4.3	7.4	6.8
Market value ($ mil.)	120.9%	—	—	—	33.3	73.6
Employees	1.3%	98	99	100	100	103

GSV, INC.

OTC: GSVI

191 Post Rd. West
Westport, CT 06880
Phone: 203-221-2690
Fax: 203-221-2691
Web: www.gsv.com

CEO: Gilad Gat
CFO: Gilad Gat
HR: –
FYE: December 31
Type: Public

GSV (Grove Strategic Ventures) should know more about weeding out good and bad business plans since trashing its own. The firm operated consumer products e-tailers CyberShop.com and electronics.net. It opted out of those businesses and reinvented itself as an Internet startup incubator. Investments included Weema Technologies and Telephone.com. After the dot-com bust, the value of GSV's investments plummeted. GSV gets about half of its revenues from an interest in two Louisiana oil and gas wells. The company sublet offices in New Jersey. Since the tenant defaulted on the lease, insurance covered the payments, and GSV ceased those operations. Chairman Sagi Matza controls 77% of GSV.

	Annual Growth	12/03	12/04	12/05	12/06	12/07
Sales ($ mil.)	27.8%	0.3	0.4	0.7	0.3	0.8
Net income ($ mil.)	—	(0.7)	(0.5)	(0.2)	(0.2)	0.2
Market value ($ mil.)	(17.1%)	—	2.2	1.1	—	1.3
Employees	—	1	—	—	—	—

GTC BIOTHERAPEUTICS, INC.

NASDAQ (GM): GTCB

175 Crossing Blvd., Ste. 410
Framingham, MA 01702
Phone: 508-620-9700
Fax: 508-370-3797
Web: www.gtc-bio.com

CEO: Geoffrey F. Cox
CFO: John B. Green
HR: Patricia (Pat) Nagle
FYE: Last Sunday in December
Type: Public

Transgenic manipulation is the name of the game at GTC Biotherapeutics. The firm makes its products by inserting human DNA into animals who then produce the protein in their milk; the proteins are purified from the milk and used for human treatments. This process of creating what are known as recombinant proteins makes it easier and cheaper to produce large quantities of certain therapeutic proteins. The company's lead candidate, ATryn, received European regulatory approval in 2006; the product is a recombinant human antithrombin, which has anticoagulant and anti-inflammatory properties. It is in late-stage clinical trials in the US. French firm LFB Biotechnologies owns about 20% of GTC.

	Annual Growth	12/03	12/04	12/05	12/06	12/07
Sales ($ mil.)	9.1%	9.8	6.6	4.2	6.1	13.9
Net income ($ mil.)	—	(29.5)	(29.5)	(30.1)	(35.3)	(36.3)
Market value ($ mil.)	(5.7%)	95.8	59.0	99.5	81.7	75.9
Employees	—	—	—	130	—	—

GTC TELECOM CORP.

OTC: GTCC

3151 Airway Ave., Ste. P-3
Costa Mesa, CA 92626
Phone: 714-549-7700
Fax: 714-549-7707
Web: www.gtctelecom.com

CEO: S. Paul Sandhu
CFO: –
HR: –
FYE: June 30
Type: Public

GTC Telecom provides a variety of telecommunications, Internet, and business process outsourcing (BPO) services. These include the resale of long-distance service and calling cards, as well as dial-up Internet access. It had begun reselling local service in some markets but ceased the service after regulatory changes made leasing lines from incumbent carriers like BellSouth and Verizon too costly. The company's Perfexa Solutions unit, operating in India, provides call center outsourcing and IT development services.

	Annual Growth	6/02	6/03	6/04	6/05	*6/06
Sales ($ mil.)	(21.7%)	17.8	15.1	11.0	9.0	6.7
Net income ($ mil.)	—	(1.3)	0.0	(0.6)	3.7	(3.4)
Employees	—	—	—	—	—	—

*Most recent year available

GTCR GOLDER RAUNER, LLC

6100 Sears Tower
Chicago, IL 60606
Phone: 312-382-2200
Fax: 312-382-2201
Web: www.gtcr.com

CEO: Bruce V. Rauner
CFO: Anna May L. Trala
HR: –
FYE: December 31
Type: Partnership

GTCR Golder Rauner is a privately held investment firm that manages some $8 billion in capital on behalf of institutional investors and its own account. Specializing in management-led industry consolidation deals, the firm has invested in more than 125 companies. It focuses on such industries as business services, health care, technology, financial services, and consumer products. Holdings include Coinmach, HealthSpring, Prestige Brands, Syniverse, and VeriFone. Founded in 1980 as Golder Thoma Cressey, the firm is now headed by Stanley Golder's protege Bruce Rauner; Carl Thoma and Bryan Cressey founded another private equity firm, Thoma Cressey Equity Partners (now Thoma Cressey Bravo).

	Annual Growth	12/03	12/04	12/05	12/06	12/07
Est. sales ($ mil.)	—	—	—	—	—	325.9
Employees	—	—	—	—	—	2,541

GTECH HOLDINGS CORPORATION

10 Memorial Blvd.
Providence, RI 02903
Phone: 401-392-1000
Fax: 401-392-1234
Web: www.gtech.com

CEO: Jaymin B. Patel
CFO: Stefano Bortoli
HR: John L. Pothin
FYE: Last Saturday in February
Type: Subsidiary

Believe it or not, GTECH Holdings will make you happy when your number comes up. One of the world's leading operators of lottery systems, GTECH supplies or operates lotteries for customers in more than 50 countries. It designs, installs, operates, and maintains lottery and instant ticket systems and furnishes the hardware and software to keep lotteries humming. GTECH also offers other services, like electronic bill payments that can be sold in outlets along with lottery tickets, as well as debit and credit card merchant transaction services. In addition, GTECH has expanded into online and video lottery products. Italian lottery giant Lottomatica acquired the company in 2006.

	Annual Growth	2/03	2/04	2/05	2/06	2/07
Est. sales ($ mil.)	—	—	—	—	—	183.2
Employees	—	—	—	—	—	5,300

GTSI CORP.

NASDAQ (GM): GTSI

3901 Stonecroft Blvd.
Chantilly, VA 20151
Phone: 703-502-2000
Fax: 703-222-5204
Web: www.gtsi.com

CEO: James J. Leto
CFO: Joseph D. (Joe) Ragan III
HR: Bridget Atkinson
FYE: December 31
Type: Public

GTSI supplies the goods when the government goes shopping. The company resells computers, software, and networking products to US federal, state, and local governments. GTSI offers products from vendors including Cisco Systems (19% of revenues in 2007), Hewlett-Packard (15%), Panasonic (15%), IBM, and Microsoft. GTSI also provides asset management, consulting, design, integration, maintenance, procurement, and support services. The company offers financing through its GTSI Financial Services subsidiary. It also has a unit devoted to logistics services.

	Annual Growth	12/03	12/04	12/05	12/06	12/07
Sales ($ mil.)	(6.7%)	954.1	1,076.2	882.0	850.2	723.5
Net income ($ mil.)	—	3.2	10.3	(13.7)	(3.0)	(1.8)
Market value ($ mil.)	(5.1%)	117.8	94.5	65.2	87.8	95.7
Employees	(3.7%)	—	—	732	719	679

GTX, INC.

NASDAQ (GM): GTXI

3 N. Dunlap St., Van Vleet Bldg.
Memphis, TN 38163
Phone: 901-523-9700
Fax: 901-523-9772
Web: www.gtxinc.com

CEO: Mitchell S. Steiner
CFO: Mark E. Mosteller
HR: –
FYE: December 31
Type: Public

GTx knows hormones are just as important to men as they are to women. The company develops therapies targeting estrogens and androgens for prostate cancer and other diseases in the arena of men's health. GTx's lead drug candidate, Acapodene, could prevent men who have been identified with certain precancerous conditions from developing prostate cancer. The drug may also be useful in treating osteoporosis, hot flashes, and other side effects of androgen-deprivation therapy (a treatment for advanced prostate cancer). To fund its work, GTx sells Fareston, a drug for metastatic breast cancer. Chairman J.R. Hyde owns nearly one-third of the company.

	Annual Growth	12/03	12/04	12/05	12/06	12/07
Sales ($ mil.)	55.2%	—	1.9	3.8	7.5	7.1
Net income ($ mil.)	—	—	(22.4)	(36.8)	(35.5)	(40.4)
Market value ($ mil.)	16.0%	—	332.7	234.3	621.2	519.7
Employees	15.0%	—	—	84	—	111

An in-depth profile of this company is available to Hoover's Online members at hoovers.com.

715

GUARANTY BANCORP

NASDAQ (GS): GBNK

1331 17th St., Ste. 300
Denver, CO 80202
Phone: 303-296-9600
Fax: –
Web: www.gbnk.com

CEO: Daniel M. (Dan) Quinn
CFO: Paul W. Taylor
HR: Sherri L. Heronema
FYE: December 31
Type: Public

Guaranty Bancorp (formerly Centennial Bank Holdings) knows a thing or two about dollars and cents. After all, it's the holding company for Colorado's Guaranty Bank and Trust. The bank operates about 30 branches, primarily in the metropolitan Denver and North Front Range areas. Guaranty Bank and Trust offers traditional checking, savings, money market, and NOW accounts as well as IRAs. Real estate mortgages and business loans each make up more than one-third of a loan portfolio that also includes construction and other types of consumer and business loans. In 2008 the company merged subsidiary Centennial Bank of the West into Guaranty Bank and Trust and, following suit, changed its own name.

	Annual Growth	12/03	12/04	12/05	12/06	12/07
Assets ($ mil.)	(10.8%)	—	—	2,980.8	2,720.6	2,371.7
Net income ($ mil.)	—	—	—	14.7	24.4	(138.1)
Market value ($ mil.)	(36.2%)	—	—	747.2	541.5	304.1
Employees	(16.0%)	—	—	617	518	—

GUARANTY FEDERAL BANCSHARES, INC.

NASDAQ (GM): GFED

1341 W. Battlefield
Springfield, MO 65807
Phone: 417-520-4333
Fax: 417-520-3607
Web: www.gfed.com

CEO: Shaun A. Burke
CFO: Carter M. Peters
HR: –
FYE: December 31
Type: Public

Like the Simpsons, Guaranty Bank calls Springfield home. The flagship subsidiary of Guaranty Federal Bancshares has six branches in Springfield, Missouri, and two more, including a branch inside a Wal-Mart, in nearby Nixa. The bank offers CDs and checking, savings, money market, and retirement accounts, mainly using deposit funds to originate commercial mortgages (more than 30% of the company's loan portfolio) and business loans (around 20%), as well as residential mortgages, consumer loans, and construction loans. Guaranty Bank also invests in mortgage-backed, US government, and other securities.

	Annual Growth	12/03	12/04	12/05	12/06	12/07
Assets ($ mil.)	10.0%	386.8	440.6	481.0	524.8	565.8
Net income ($ mil.)	42.0%	1.5	4.3	5.9	6.5	6.1
Market value ($ mil.)	7.9%	57.6	72.2	81.8	82.9	78.1
Employees	26.9%	—	—	105	—	169

GUARANTY FINANCIAL GROUP INC.

NYSE: GFG

1300 S. Mopac Expwy.
Austin, TX 78746
Phone: 512-434-1000
Fax: 512-434-8680
Web: www.guarantygroup.com

CEO: Kenneth R. Dubuque
CFO: Ronald D. Murff
HR: Karen J. Hartnett
FYE: December 31
Type: Public

Guaranty Financial Group (formerly Temple-Inland Financial Services) is the holding company for Guaranty Bank. The bank has approximately 100 Texas offices in and around the metropolitan areas of Austin, Dallas/Ft. Worth, Houston, and San Antonio, and about 50 offices in the Inland Empire and Central Valley regions of California. It provides individuals and businesses with the usual variety of deposit, lending, and investment products and services. Bank subsidiary Guaranty Insurance Services sells annuities and personal and commercial coverage. Packaging and building materials manufacturer Temple-Inland spun off Guaranty Financial Group at the end of 2007.

	Annual Growth	12/03	12/04	12/05	12/06	12/07
Assets ($ mil.)	—	—	—	—	—	16,796.0
Net income ($ mil.)	—	—	—	—	—	78.0
Market value ($ mil.)	—	—	—	—	—	566.4
Employees	—	—	—	—	—	—

GUARDIAN GLASS COMPANY

2300 Harmon Rd
Auburn Hills, MI 48326
Phone: 248-340-1800
Fax: 248-340-9988

CEO: William M. (Bill) Davidson
CFO: Ann Waichunas
HR: Bruce Cummings
FYE: December 31
Type: Private

The old saying about rocks and glass houses holds no power over Guardian Glass — more than a few of its products can easily handle a rock or two. A business unit of Guardian Industries, Guardian Glass produces glass for automotive, construction, and decorative applications. The company's products include architectural glass, auto glass replacement products, and a variety of glass for use in residential applications such as windows, mirrors, and patterned specialty glass. Guardian Glass serves clients around the globe with operations in more than 20 countries. The company markets its architectural glass products under the SunGuard brand.

	Annual Growth	12/03	12/04	12/05	12/06	12/07
Est. sales ($ mil.)	—	—	—	—	—	13.8
Employees	—	—	—	—	—	275

▣ GUARDIAN INDUSTRIES CORP.

2300 Harmon Rd.
Auburn Hills, MI 48326
Phone: 248-340-1800
Fax: 248-340-9988
Web: www.guardian.com

CEO: William M. (Bill) Davidson
CFO: Jeffrey A. Knight
HR: Bruce Cummings
FYE: December 31
Type: Private

Giving its customers a break would never occur to Guardian Industries, one of the world's largest glassmakers. With more than 60 facilities on five continents, Guardian primarily produces float glass and fabricated glass products for the automobile and construction markets. It also makes architectural glass, fiberglass, and automotive trim parts. Through its Guardian Building Products Distribution division, the company operates building supply distribution centers throughout North America. President and CEO William Davidson took Guardian Industries public in 1968 and bought it back for himself in 1985. Davidson is also the managing partner of the Detroit Pistons NBA team.

	Annual Growth	12/02	12/03	12/04	12/05	12/06
Est. sales ($ mil.)	6.6%	—	—	—	5,000.0	5,330.0
Employees	0.0%	—	—	—	19,000	19,000

▣ THE GUARDIAN LIFE INSURANCE COMPANY OF AMERICA

7 Hanover Sq.
New York, NY 10004
Phone: 212-598-8000
Fax: 212-919-2170
Web: www.guardianlife.com

CEO: Dennis J. Manning
CFO: Robert E. Broatch
HR: James D. (Jim) Ranton
FYE: December 31
Type: Mutual company

When your guardian angel fails you, there's Guardian Life Insurance Company of America. The mutual company, owned by its policy holders, offers life insurance, disability income insurance, and — more recently — retirement programs to individuals and businesses. Guardian's employee health indemnity plans provide HMO, PPO, and dental and vision plans, as well as disability plans. In the retirement area, the company offers the Park Avenue group of mutual funds and annuity products, managed by its Guardian Investor Services. Guardian also offers estate planning and education savings programs.

	Annual Growth	12/02	12/03	12/04	12/05	12/06
Sales ($ mil.)	1.0%	7,192.0	6,732.0	7,021.0	7,396.0	7,491.0
Employees	(2.4%)	5,500	5,500	5,000	5,000	5,000

GUARDIAN TECHNOLOGIES INTERNATIONAL, INC.

OTC: GDTI

516 Herndon Pkwy., Ste. A
Herndon, VA 20170
Phone: 703-464-5495
Fax: 703-464-8530
Web: www.guardiantechintl.com

CEO: Michael W. Trudnak
CFO: Gregory E. Hare
HR: –
FYE: December 31
Type: Public

Guardian Technologies (formerly RJL Marketing Services) might consider itself a protector of sorts. The company provides software to help medical personnel identify health threats and airport security workers detect explosives. Guardian's FlowPoint products are used by hospitals, radiology centers, and clinics to create and archive diagnostic images. Its PinPoint Threat Identification software is used in aviation security to help screen baggage.

	Annual Growth	12/03	12/04	12/05	12/06	12/07
Sales ($ mil.)	44.2%	—	0.1	0.4	0.5	0.3
Net income ($ mil.)	—	—	(29.2)	(13.1)	(10.1)	(10.5)
Market value ($ mil.)	(45.7%)	—	129.0	76.8	29.0	20.7
Employees	—	—	—	—	—	—

GUARDSMARK, LLC

10 Rockefeller Plaza
New York, NY 10020
Phone: 212-765-8226
Fax: 212-603-3854
Web: www.guardsmark.com

CEO: Ira A. Lipman
CFO: Jeffrey B. Westcott
HR: –
FYE: June 30
Type: Private

When FBI agents leave Quantico, they go to Guardsmark. The company, a leading employer of former FBI agents, provides security services to companies in the financial, health care, transportation, and utility industries. Guardsmark offers security guards, private investigation, and drug testing services. The company also conducts background checks (employment, education, and criminal history) and consults with architects and builders to design security programs. Guardsmark operates in some 400 cities. Chairman and president Ira Lipman owns the company, which he founded in 1963.

GUESS?, INC.

NYSE: GES

1444 S. Alameda St.
Los Angeles, CA 90021
Phone: 213-765-3100
Fax: 213-744-7838
Web: www.guess.com

CEO: Paul Marciano
CFO: Dennis R. Secor
HR: Susan Tenney
FYE: Saturday nearest January 31
Type: Public

Guess? wants you to get in its pants. Founded as a designer jeans maker, the company makes trendy, upscale apparel and accessories for men, women, and children under brand names GUESS, GUESS Kids, Baby GUESS, and GUESS by MARCIANO, among others. Its trademark sexy ads, featuring the likes of Claudia Schiffer and Drew Barrymore, are designed in-house. Guess? sells its lines through a Web site, some 370 retail locations in the US and Canada, and more than 120 stores in Europe, Asia, and Mexico. Guess? licenses its name for accessories (eyewear, footwear, jewelry, watches). Chairman Maurice Marciano, who with his brother Paul runs the company founded by their father, controls about 37% of Guess's shares.

	Annual Growth	12/03	12/04	12/05	12/06	*1/08
Sales ($ mil.)	28.8%	636.6	729.3	936.1	1,185.2	1,749.9
Net income ($ mil.)	124.8%	7.3	29.6	58.8	123.2	186.5
Market value ($ mil.)	91.3%	263.6	277.2	800.5	2,920.6	3,528.2
Employees	16.5%	—	—	7,300	8,800	9,900

*Fiscal year change

GUIDANCE SOFTWARE, INC.

NASDAQ (GM): GUID

215 N. Marengo Ave., 2nd Fl.
Pasadena, CA 91101
Phone: 626-229-9191
Fax: 626-229-9199
Web: www.guidancesoftware.com

CEO: Victor Limongelli
CFO: Frank J. Sansone
HR: Sandy Gyenes
FYE: December 31
Type: Public

Guidance Software leads investigators down the right path. The company provides applications that government authorities, police agencies, and corporate investigators use for functions such as digital forensic investigations, information auditing, and information technology threat assessment and response. The company's software is a forensics platform that helps organizations respond quickly to threats and analyze information, including court-validated forensics tools for government and corporate investigations. Chairman and CTO Shawn McCreight owns about 47% of the company.

	Annual Growth	12/03	12/04	12/05	12/06	12/07
Sales ($ mil.)	45.3%	17.7	27.6	39.5	55.9	78.9
Net income ($ mil.)	—	(1.7)	(0.8)	1.6	(3.1)	(2.9)
Market value ($ mil.)	(6.6%)	—	—	—	345.1	322.4
Employees	23.6%	150	—	—	346	350

GUIDED THERAPEUTICS, INC.

Pink Sheets: GTHP

4955 Avalon Ridge Pkwy., Ste. 300
Norcross, GA 30071
Phone: 770-242-8723
Fax: 770-242-8639
Web: www.spectrx.com

CEO: Mark L. Faupel
CFO: Mark L. Faupel
HR: –
FYE: December 31
Type: Public

Guided Therapeutics (formerly SpectRx) can shed some light on your condition. The firm is developing diagnostic products, including a cervical cancer detection device, using its proprietary biophotonic technology known as LightTouch. The technology uses optics and spectroscopy to provide doctors with non-invasive diagnostic methods for finding cancer. In order to zero in on its diagnostic business, the company in 2007 sold its SimpleChoice line of insulin pumps, which diabetics use to control blood glucose levels, to ICU Medical; it changed its name to Guided Therapeutics the following year to reflect its new focus.

	Annual Growth	12/02	12/03	12/04	12/05	*12/06
Sales ($ mil.)	(28.4%)	3.8	1.6	1.1	1.0	1.0
Net income ($ mil.)	—	(8.5)	(2.6)	(9.2)	(2.2)	(4.9)
Employees	(23.5%)	76	59	43	39	26

*Most recent year available

GUIDELINE, INC.

625 Avenue of the Americas
New York, NY 10011
Phone: 212-645-4500
Fax: 212-645-7681
Web: www.guideline.com

CEO: Marc C. Litvinoff
CFO: Peter M. Stone
HR: Tom McGillis
FYE: December 31
Type: Subsidiary

Guideline has found its niche in the consulting business. The company (formerly Find/SVP) provides rapid-turnaround consulting and research services to 1,700 small and midsized clients. Its consultants and researchers typically handle day-to-day research requests in three hours or less. Guideline offers strategic consulting and research services that cover more in-depth issues such as industry studies and market surveys. Its Guideline Group subsidiary offers traditional market research and consumer survey services, and its Product Development Intelligence unit provides technology market research. Guideline is a subsidiary of information services giant infoGROUP (formerly infoUSA).

	Annual Growth	12/02	12/03	12/04	12/05	12/06
Sales ($ mil.)	22.1%	20.8	31.6	38.4	43.0	46.3
Net income ($ mil.)	—	(1.1)	(0.9)	(1.9)	0.4	1.0
Employees	—	—	—	—	—	239

An in-depth profile of this company is available to Hoover's Online members at hoovers.com.

717

GUILFORD MILLS, INC.

127 Racine Dr., Ste. 201
Wilmington, NC 28403
Phone: 910-794-5800
Fax: 336-316-4057
Web: www.guilfordproducts.com

CEO: Shannon M. White
CFO: Marc Bourhis
HR: Elizabeth (Beth) Patrick
FYE: Sunday nearest September 30
Type: Private

Guilford Mills makes fabrics to cover your ride *and* your hide. The company produces textiles used in automobiles and apparel. With the textile industry in turmoil though, Guilford Mills has drastically cut production of apparel textiles to focus on more lucrative automotive fabrics. Johnson Controls and Lear Corporation have been major customers. Burdened with $275 million in debt, the company filed for Chapter 11 bankruptcy protection in early 2002. It emerged about six months later with its debt reduced to $135 million. In 2004 New York-based private equity firm Cerberus Capital Management, L.P., purchased the company for around $98 million.

	Annual Growth	9/03	9/04	9/05	9/06	9/07
Est. sales ($ mil.)	—	—	—	—	—	199.3
Employees	—	—	—	—	—	2,600

GUITAR CENTER, INC.

5795 Lindero Canyon Rd.
Westlake Village, CA 91362
Phone: 818-735-8800
Fax: 818-735-8822
Web: www.guitarcenter.com

CEO: Marty P. Albertson
CFO: Erick Mason
HR: Dennis Haffeman
FYE: December 31
Type: Private

What AutoZone is to the garage, Guitar Center is to the garage band. The nation's #1 retailer of guitars, amplifiers, drums, keyboards, and pro-audio equipment operates more than 210 stores in more than 40 US states. Brands include Fender, Roland, Yamaha, and Sony. Guitar Center stores also sell music-related computer hardware and software and used instruments. Its American Music Group division operates about 95 Music & Arts Center stores that specialize in the sale and rental of band and orchestral instruments. The music retailer acquired ailing Dennis Bamber in early 2007. Later that same year Guitar Center was taken private by the investment firm Bain Capital Partners (BCP) for about $2.1 billion.

	Annual Growth	12/02	12/03	12/04	12/05	12/06
Sales ($ mil.)	16.5%	1,100.9	1,275.1	1,513.2	1,782.5	2,030.0
Net income ($ mil.)	(64.5%)	25.3	36.9	63.4	76.7	0.4
Employees	(47.9%)	5,003	—	—	8,154	370

GULF ISLAND FABRICATION, INC.

NASDAQ (GS): GIFI

583 Thompson Rd.
Houma, LA 70363
Phone: 985-872-2100
Fax: 985-872-2129
Web: www.gulfisland.com

CEO: Kerry J. Chauvin
CFO: Robin A. Seibert
HR: Herb Ledet
FYE: December 31
Type: Public

Through its subsidiaries, holding company Gulf Island Fabrication makes islands in the stream — the Gulf Stream, that is. Its subsidiaries make offshore drilling and production platforms for use mainly in the Gulf of Mexico. Products include jackets and deck sections of fixed production platforms, hull and deck sections of floating production platforms, piles, subsea templates, wellhead protectors, and various production, compressor, and utility modules. Gulf Island also produces and repairs pressure vessels and refurbishes existing platforms. Chevron accounted for some 42% of Gulf Island's sales in 2006.

	Annual Growth	12/03	12/04	12/05	12/06	12/07
Sales ($ mil.)	23.4%	203.7	173.9	188.5	312.2	472.7
Net income ($ mil.)	18.5%	15.8	12.0	13.0	21.3	31.2
Market value ($ mil.)	22.4%	201.0	265.3	298.5	520.9	450.7
Employees	26.8%	—	—	1,150	1,800	1,850

GULF OIL LIMITED PARTNERSHIP

275 Washington St., Ste. 300
Newton, MA 02458
Phone: 617-454-9300
Fax: 617-884-0637
Web: www.gulfoil.com

CEO: Joseph H. (Joe) Petrowski
CFO: Jayne Fitzpatrick
HR: Karen Channel
FYE: September 30
Type: Partnership

Gulf Oil bridges the gap between petroleum producers and retail sales outlets. The petroleum wholesaler distributes gasoline and diesel fuel to about 2,400 Gulf-brand stations in 11 northeastern states. Gulf Oil, which owns and operates 12 storage terminals, also distributes motor oils, lubricants, and heating oil to commercial, industrial, and utility customers. The company has alliances with terminal operators in areas in the Northeast where it does not have a proprietary terminal. Gulf Oil boasts one of the oldest and most recognizable brands in the oil business.

GULF POWER COMPANY

1 Energy Place
Pensacola, FL 32520
Phone: 850-444-6111
Fax: 850-444-6448
Web: www.gulfpower.com

CEO: Susan N. Story
CFO: Philip C. Raymond
HR: –
FYE: December 31
Type: Subsidiary

Pensacola power patrons presently put Gulf Power to work. The regulated utility, a subsidiary of Southern Company, transmits and distributes electricity to 427,660 customers in northwestern Florida. Gulf Power generates 2,660 MW of capacity from its fossil-fueled power plants, and it operates 1,600 miles of transmission lines and 7,500 miles of distribution lines in its service territory. The utility also provides wholesale electricity to two distributors in Florida, and it offers conservation, outdoor lighting, surge protection, and other energy-related products and services.

	Annual Growth	12/03	12/04	12/05	12/06	12/07
Est. sales ($ mil.)	—	—	—	—	—	1,259.8
Net income ($ mil.)	—	—	—	—	—	88.0
Employees	—	—	—	—	—	1,324

GULF STATES TOYOTA, INC.

7701 Wilshire Place Dr.
Houston, TX 77040
Phone: 713-580-3300
Fax: 713-580-3332

CEO: Toby Hynes
CFO: Frank Gruen
HR: Dominic Gallo
FYE: December 31
Type: Private

Even good ol' boys buy foreign cars from Gulf States Toyota (GST). One of only two US Toyota distributors not owned by Toyota Motor Sales (the other is JM Family Enterprises' Southeast Toyota Distributors), the company distributes Toyota cars, trucks, and sport utility vehicles in Arkansas, Louisiana, Mississippi, Oklahoma, and Texas. GST has expanded its vehicle processing center in Houston to handle Toyota Tundra pickup trucks built in nearby San Antonio. Founded in 1969 by Thomas Friedkin and still owned by The Friedkin Companies, GST distributes new Toyotas, parts, and accessories to around 145 dealers in Texas and other states in the region. GST plans to move to a new headquarters in west Houston.

	Annual Growth	12/02	12/03	12/04	12/05	12/06
Est. sales ($ mil.)	5.6%	3,700.0	3,800.0	4,000.0	4,600.0	4,600.0
Employees	(20.5%)	3,000	3,100	3,500	1,200	1,200

GULFMARK OFFSHORE, INC.

NYSE: GLF

10111 Richmond Ave., Ste. 340
Houston, TX 77042
Phone: 713-963-9522
Fax: 713-963-9796
Web: www.gulfmark.com

CEO: Bruce A. Streeter
CFO: Edward A. (Ed) Guthrie
HR: –
FYE: December 31
Type: Public

GulfMark Offshore makes its mark on the high seas. The company offers support services for the construction, positioning, and operation of offshore oil and natural gas rigs and platforms. It owns, manages, or charters 62 vessels located primarily in the North Sea (35 vessels), Southeast Asia (13), and offshore Brazil (4). Marine services include anchor handling; cargo, supply, and crew transportation; towing; and emergency services. Some of its ships conduct seismic data gathering and provide diving support. GulfMark Offshore serves both oil majors and smaller independents. Lehman Brothers owns 9.6% of the company. In 2008 the company agreed to acquire Rigdone Marine.

	Annual Growth	12/03	12/04	12/05	12/06	12/07
Sales ($ mil.)	23.9%	129.9	139.3	204.0	250.9	306.0
Net income ($ mil.)	275.1%	0.5	(4.6)	38.4	89.7	99.0
Market value ($ mil.)	40.0%	280.2	448.4	603.4	848.5	1,075.4
Employees	1.9%	1,175	1,085	1,212	1,243	—

GULFPORT ENERGY CORPORATION

NASDAQ (GS): GPOR

14313 N. May Ave., Ste. 100
Oklahoma City, OK 73134
Phone: 405-848-8807
Fax: 405-848-8816
Web: www.gulfportenergy.com

CEO: James D. (Jim) Palm
CFO: Michael G. (Mike) Moore
HR: –
FYE: December 31
Type: Public

Gulfport Energy puts most of its eggs into just a couple of baskets. The exploration and production company sells 100% of its oil to Shell and 96% of its gas to Chevron. It operates off the Gulf Coast of Louisiana, with a heavy concentration on two fields: West Cote Blanche Bay and Hackberry Fields. Gulfport operates about 90 producing wells and has proved reserves of nearly 25 million barrels of oil equivalent. The company emerged from the ashes of WRT Energy, which filed for bankruptcy in 1996 amid allegations of fraud. Gulfport emerged from Chapter 11 bankruptcy protection in 1997.

	Annual Growth	12/03	12/04	12/05	12/06	12/07
Sales ($ mil.)	60.6%	15.9	23.2	27.6	60.4	105.8
Net income ($ mil.)	181.7%	0.6	4.3	10.9	27.8	37.8
Market value ($ mil.)	126.6%	29.4	105.7	387.6	477.0	775.2
Employees	82.1%	25	40	63	151	—

GULFSTREAM AEROSPACE CORPORATION

500 Gulfstream Rd.
Savannah, GA 31407
Phone: 912-965-3000
Fax: 912-965-3084
Web: www.gulfstream.com

CEO: Joseph T. (Joe) Lombardo
CFO: Dan Clare
HR: Jennifer Giffen
FYE: December 31
Type: Subsidiary

Prom-goers may prefer limos, but grown-ups who've really made it — executives, celebrities, and heads of state — arrive in jets (and rarely rent tuxes). Gulfstream Aerospace Corporation, a General Dynamics subsidiary, is the largest maker of private jets in the world, ahead of Bombardier. The company's smallest plane (G150) seats up to eight and has a range of 2,950 nautical miles (nm); its largest (G550) offering seats up to 19, cruises at Mach 0.885, and has a range of 6,750 nm. To help market its new aircraft, the company's Gulfstream Financial Services unit helps arrange financing. Gulfstream also provides aftermarket maintenance services and sells used Gulfstream aircraft.

	Annual Growth	12/03	12/04	12/05	12/06	12/07
Est. sales ($ mil.)	—	—	—	—	—	498.6
Employees	—	—	—	—	—	6,800

GULFSTREAM INTERNATIONAL GROUP, INC.

AMEX: GIA

3201 Griffin Rd., 4th Fl.
Fort Lauderdale, FL 33312
Phone: 954-985-1500
Fax: 954-985-5245

CEO: David F. Hackett
CFO: Robert M. Brown
HR: –
FYE: December 31
Type: Public

Going to the Bahamas on a Gulfstream isn't just for the jet set. Gulfstream International Group, through its Gulfstream International Airlines subsidiary, provides service between Florida and the Bahamas with a fleet of about 35 turboprop aircraft. It serves about two dozen destinations overall. The regional airline, no relation to high-end business jet manufacturer Gulfstream Aerospace, flies primarily under the Continental Connection brand on behalf of Continental Airlines. It also operates as a code-sharing partner of carriers such as United, Northwest, and Copa Airlines and provides charter services. In addition to its airline operations, Gulfstream International Group runs a pilot-training school.

	Annual Growth	12/03	12/04	12/05	12/06	12/07
Sales ($ mil.)	15.8%	—	72.3	92.0	105.1	112.3
Net income ($ mil.)	—	—	2.0	0.9	1.2	(3.1)
Market value ($ mil.)	—	—	—	—	—	25.0
Employees	—	—	—	—	629	—

GUNDLE/SLT ENVIRONMENTAL, INC.

19103 Gundle Rd.
Houston, TX 77073
Phone: 281-443-8564
Fax: 281-230-2504
Web: www.gseworld.com

CEO: Samir T. Badawi
CFO: Ernest C. (Ernie) English Jr.
HR: –
FYE: December 31
Type: Private

Oil and water don't mix, and Gundle/SLT Environmental (GSE) plans to keep it that way. The company makes and installs synthetic liners designed to prevent groundwater contamination. Waste-management firms, industrial businesses, and mining companies, among others, use these liners at garbage dumps and water-containment facilities. Its solid waste containment services generate more than half of its revenue. The company makes high-density polyethylene smooth-sheet liners, as well as textured sheets and geosynthetic clay liners. The US accounts for about half of sales. Private equity firm Code Hennessy & Simmons bought GSE and took it private in 2004.

	Annual Growth	12/02	12/03	12/04	12/05	12/06
Sales ($ mil.)	13.9%	—	—	287.9	317.6	373.3
Net income ($ mil.)	11.8%	—	—	2.0	0.7	2.5
Employees	(5.8%)	—	—	1,045	1,033	928

GUTHY-RENKER CORPORATION

41-550 Eclectic St., Ste. 200
Palm Desert, CA 92260
Phone: 760-773-9022
Fax: 760-733-9016
Web: www.guthy-renker.com

CEO: William (Bill) Guthy
CFO: William (Bill) Guthy
HR: –
FYE: December 31
Type: Private

What do Kathie Lee Gifford, Cindy Crawford, Victoria Principal, and Tony Robbins have in common? Each has starred in a program produced by Guthy-Renker, one of the largest infomercial producers in the US. The electronic retailing company pursues marketing opportunities through direct TV, cable and satellite, mail, and telemarketing. Its pitch people hawk a variety of goods and services, including skin care products and cosmetics such as Proactive Solution (the company's primary category), fitness equipment, and motivational tapes. Guthy-Renker was founded in 1988 by co-CEOs Bill Guthy and Greg Renker, after being spun off from Guthy's Cassette Productions Unlimited (CPU).

	Annual Growth	12/02	12/03	12/04	12/05	12/06
Est. sales ($ mil.)	0.0%	—	—	—	1,500.0	1,500.0
Employees	0.0%	—	—	—	825	825

An in-depth profile of this company is available to Hoover's Online members at hoovers.com.

719

GXS, INC.

100 Edison Park Dr.
Gaithersburg, MD 20878
Phone: 301-340-4000
Fax: 301-340-5299
Web: www.gxs.com

CEO: Bob Segert
CFO: John Duvall
HR: Ann Addison
FYE: December 31
Type: Private

Global eXchange Services (GXS) wants the world to transact. The company operates one of the world's largest business-to-business (B2B) e-commerce networks, connecting 100,000 trading partners and managing more than a billion transactions each year. It also offers electronic data interchange (EDI) software and services, helping trading partners exchange electronic documents that are essential for business transactions. Other applications address shipping and labeling, product information management, order management, and logistics functions. Founded in the early 1960s as the information technology division of General Electric (GE), GXS was later sold to technology turnaround specialist Francisco Partners.

	Annual Growth	12/03	12/04	12/05	12/06	12/07
Est. sales ($ mil.)	—	—	—	—	—	434.3
Employees	—	—	—	—	—	1,600

THE GYMBOREE CORPORATION

NASDAQ (GS): GYMB

500 Howard St.
San Francisco, CA 94105
Phone: 415-278-7000
Fax: 707-678-1315
Web: www.gymboree.com

CEO: Matthew K. (Matt) McCauley
CFO: Blair W. Lambert
HR: Marina Armstrong
FYE: Sunday nearest January 31
Type: Public

Despite being more than a quarter-of-a-century old, The Gymboree Corporation is still a retail toddler, stumbling periodically, learning quickly, and growing fast. The Gymboree Corporation sells clothes and accessories for kids in the US and Canada. About 600 Gymboree stores carry colorful, fashionable playsuits and rompers for kids up to 12 years old. Gymboree also operates 90-plus Janie and Jack stores (newborn and toddler apparel), about 80 Gymboree Outlet stores, and two online stores: gymboree.com and janieandjack.com. The firm also provides parent-child play programs (designed to enhance child development) at some 555 franchised and three company-operated centers in the US and about 30 other countries.

	Annual Growth	1/04	1/05	1/06	1/07	1/08
Sales ($ mil.)	12.3%	578.0	594.5	678.5	791.6	920.8
Net income ($ mil.)	33.0%	25.7	8.6	33.7	60.3	80.3
Market value ($ mil.)	25.6%	441.6	389.8	814.5	1,435.4	1,100.0
Employees	4.1%	—	—	9,600	9,500	10,400

GYRODYNE COMPANY OF AMERICA, INC.

NASDAQ (CM): GYRO

1 Flowerfield, Ste. 24
St. James, NY 11780
Phone: 631-584-5400
Fax: 631-584-7075
Web: www.gyrodyne.com

CEO: Stephen V. Maroney
CFO: Stephen V. Maroney
HR: —
FYE: December 31
Type: Public

Gyrodyne spins in the direction of real estate development. The former helicopter maker's 70-acre Flowerfield development in Long Island contains about 127,000 sq. ft. of light industrial space for rent. About 50 tenants occupy the buildings set up for office, engineering, manufacturing, and warehouse use. Gyrodyne, which completed its conversion into a real estate investment trust (REIT), also has an interest in a citrus grove in Florida. Details of plans for a mixed-use residential and commercial development on the grove land are being considered by county commissioners in Palm Beach, where the Callery-Judge Grove is located.

	Annual Growth	4/04	4/05	4/06	*12/06	12/07
Sales ($ mil.)	8.4%	2.1	2.0	1.6	1.8	2.9
Net income ($ mil.)	—	(0.1)	(0.1)	13.1	(0.4)	(1.5)
Market value ($ mil.)	16.2%	32.5	49.5	58.6	80.0	59.3
Employees	—	—	—	—	—	7

*Fiscal year change

H GROUP HOLDING, INC.

71 S. Wacker Dr.
Chicago, IL 60606
Phone: 312-873-4900
Fax: 312-873-4983

CEO: Daniel Azark
CFO: —
HR: —
FYE: December 31
Type: Private

Owned and operated by the Pritzkers, Chicago's financial super-family, H Group Holding is the holding company for Global Hyatt Corporation (hospitality operations) and Classic Residence senior communities. Since the death of Jay Pritzker in 1999, family squabbles over their vast (estimated $20 billion) fortune have led to talks of breaking up the empire and taking Hyatt public. The Pritzker portfolio also includes the manufacturing conglomerate Marmon Group, credit bureau Trans Union, Pritzker Realty, and a stake in the Royal Caribbean cruise ship line. The family is active in philanthropic circles through the Pritzker Foundation.

	Annual Growth	12/03	12/04	12/05	12/06	12/07
Est. sales ($ mil.)	—	—	—	—	—	2,147.5
Employees	—	—	—	—	—	42,000

H. MUEHLSTEIN & CO., INC.

800 Connecticut Ave.
Norwalk, CT 06854
Phone: 203-855-6000
Fax: 203-855-6221
Web: www.muehlstein.com

CEO: J. Kevin Donohue
CFO: Ron J. Restivo
HR: —
FYE: December 31
Type: Private

H. Muehlstein & Co. has been bouncing around the plastic and rubber distribution business since the early 20th century. The company distributes polymers manufactured by the likes of Dow, Exxon Mobil, and BP. Its products include engineering resins, polyethylene, polypropylene, and polystyrene. Muehlstein claims the title of the world's largest polymer distributor, selling 3 billion pounds of plastic and rubber products to about 6,000 manufacturers in 75 countries. Herman Muehlstein founded the company to trade rubber raw materials in 1911; he retired and sold his stake to the company's employees in the 1960s.

	Annual Growth	12/03	12/04	12/05	12/06	12/07
Est. sales ($ mil.)	—	—	—	—	—	1,200.0
Employees	—	—	—	—	—	500

HABASIT HOLDING USA, INC.

825 Morgantown Rd.
Reading, PA 19607
Phone: 610-373-1400
Fax: 610-373-7448
Web: www.habasitholdingusa.com

CEO: James R. (Jim) Swartwout
CFO: James R. (Jim) Swartwout
HR: Miriam C. Rivera
FYE: August 31
Type: Private

Mixing some of this with some of that pretty well sums up how Habasit (formerly Summa Industries) has molded its plastics business. Its operating units make plastic components for the electronics, lighting, and materials-handling industries, among others. Habasit's units include LexaLite (optical lenses and HID fixtures), Plastic Specialties, Inc. (plastic lenses for fluorescent fixtures), Genesta Manufacturing (extruded and formed plastic lenses), KVP Holdings (parts for conveyor belts used in food processing), and Aquarius Brands (plastic fittings and valves for irrigation systems). In 2006 Habasit Holding bought Summa for some $60 million; it announced that Summa would operate under the Habasit name.

	Annual Growth	8/03	8/04	8/05	8/06	8/07
Est. sales ($ mil.)	—	—	—	—	—	39.5
Employees	—	—	—	—	—	528

An in-depth profile of this company is available to Hoover's Online members at hoovers.com.

HABERSHAM BANCORP

NASDAQ (GM): HABC

282 Historic Hwy. 441 North
Cornelia, GA 30531
Phone: 706-778-1000
Fax: 706-778-6886
Web: www.habcorp.com

CEO: David D. Stovall
CFO: Annette Banks
HR: –
FYE: December 31
Type: Public

Habersham Bancorp is the holding company for Habersham Bank, which serves northern Georgia from some 10 branch locations. The bank offers checking and savings accounts, IRAs, CDs, and NOW accounts. It also provides trust and asset management services. Real estate loans — primarily commercial real estate mortgages — account for 90% of Habersham Bank's loan portfolio. Other offerings include commercial and agricultural loans. Bank subsidiary Advantage Insurers sells property/casualty and life insurance. Habersham Bancorp is active in Forsyth, Cherokee, Gwinnett, Habersham, Stephens, Warren, and White counties. The family of chairman Thomas Arrendale controls about a third of Habersham Bancorp.

	Annual Growth	12/03	12/04	12/05	12/06	12/07
Assets ($ mil.)	8.2%	374.7	385.9	478.4	555.7	514.2
Net income ($ mil.)	6.0%	2.3	2.3	3.8	5.3	2.9
Market value ($ mil.)	(11.0%)	70.3	59.7	67.0	71.2	44.0
Employees	—	—	—	162	—	—

HABITAT FOR HUMANITY INTERNATIONAL, INC.

270 Peachtree St.
Atlanta, GA 30303
Phone: 404-924-6935
Fax: –
Web: www.habitat.org

CEO: Jonathan T.M. Reckford
CFO: –
HR: Marian Cooper
FYE: June 30
Type: Not-for-profit

Thanks to Habitat for Humanity International, more than 1 million people around the globe know there's no place like home. The not-for-profit, ecumenical Christian organization has built more than 225,000 houses at cost for families who demonstrate a need and are willing to invest several hundred hours of "sweat equity" during construction. The new homeowners also make payments on no-interest mortgages, and Habitat funnels the money back into the construction of houses for others. The organization operates through some 2,300 affiliates in more than 90 countries, including all 50 US states, the District of Columbia, Guam, and Puerto Rico. Habitat was founded in 1976 by Millard and Linda Fuller.

HACHETTE BOOK GROUP USA

237 Park Ave.
New York, NY 10017
Phone: 212-364-1200
Fax: 212-364-0930
Web: www.hachettebookgroupusa.com

CEO: David Young
CFO: Thomas (Tom) Maciag
HR: Andrea Weinzimer
FYE: December 31
Type: Subsidiary

Hachette Book Group USA (formerly Time Warner Book Group) goes by the book. The company is home to book publisher Little, Brown and hardcover, mass market, and trade paperback publisher Grand Central Publishing (formerly Warner Books). Other divisions include FaithWords (religious books) and Center Street (for readers in America's heartland). The company's best sellers have included books by James Patterson (*Lifeguard*), Malcolm Gladwell (*The Tipping Point*), and Jon Stewart and the *Daily Show* writers (*America*). Previously housed under media giant Time Warner's Time Inc. unit, Lagardère acquired Time Warner Book Group in 2006 and changed its name to Hachette Book Group USA.

HACKENSACK UNIVERSITY MEDICAL CENTER

30 Prospect Ave.
Hackensack, NJ 07601
Phone: 201-996-2000
Fax: 201-489-1766
Web: www.humed.com

CEO: John P. Ferguson
CFO: Harold P. Hogstrom
HR: –
FYE: December 31
Type: Not-for-profit

Serving the residents of northern New Jersey and parts of New York, Hackensack University Medical Center has more than 780 beds. The acute care facility doesn't forget about its young patients: The medical center includes The Joseph M. Sanzari Children's Hospital and the Tomorrows Children's Institute, which specializes in pediatric cancer and blood disorders. The teaching and research hospital is affiliated with the University of Medicine and Dentistry of New Jersey. The medical center, founded in 1988, has more than 1,400 physicians and dentists on its medical staff.

	Annual Growth	12/03	12/04	12/05	12/06	12/07
Est. sales ($ mil.)	—	—	—	—	—	281.9
Employees	—	—	—	—	—	5,988

THE HACKETT GROUP

NASDAQ (GM): HCKT

1001 Brickell Bay Dr., Ste. 3000
Miami, FL 33131
Phone: 305-375-8005
Fax: 305-379-8810
Web: www.thehackettgroup.com

CEO: Ted A. Fernandez
CFO: Robert A. Ramirez
HR: –
FYE: Friday nearest December 31
Type: Public

Business and technology consultancy The Hackett Group (formerly Answerthink) provides corporations with such services as advisory programs, benchmarking, business transformation services, working capital management, and more. The company's services span myriad company functions, including information technology, human resources, accounting, customer service, and supply chain management. The Hackett Group also provides services related to best practice research with a focus on sales, general and administrative (SG&A) and supply chain services, among other areas.

	Annual Growth	12/03	12/04	12/05	12/06	12/07
Sales ($ mil.)	7.5%	132.4	143.6	163.3	180.6	177.0
Net income ($ mil.)	—	(4.8)	(0.2)	0.6	(5.1)	9.0
Market value ($ mil.)	(6.2%)	250.1	202.5	189.1	137.6	193.8
Employees	5.4%	—	720	800	800	—

HADDON HOUSE FOOD PRODUCTS, INC.

250 Old Marlton Pike
Medford, NJ 08055
Phone: 609-654-7901
Fax: 609-654-8533
Web: www.haddonhouse.com

CEO: David Anderson
CFO: –
HR: –
FYE: December 31
Type: Private

Haddon House Food Products is a leading wholesale grocery distributor that specializes in ethnic food, gourmet ingredients, and organic products. It supplies more than 15,000 items covering more than 1,000 brands, including such in-house brands as Asian Gourmet, Jane's Krazy Mixed-Up Seasonings, Medford Farms, and Twin Tree Gardens. Haddon House serves specialty food retailers and other retail grocers nationwide.

	Annual Growth	12/03	12/04	12/05	12/06	12/07
Est. sales ($ mil.)	—	—	—	—	—	137.1
Employees	—	—	—	—	—	700

An in-depth profile of this company is available to Hoover's Online members at hoovers.com.

721

HAEMONETICS CORPORATION

NYSE: HAE

400 Wood Rd.
Braintree, MA 02184
Phone: 781-848-7100
Fax: 781-356-3558
Web: www.haemonetics.com

CEO: Brad Nutter
CFO: Christopher J. (Chris) Lindop
HR: Joseph J. Forish
FYE: Saturday nearest March 31
Type: Public

Haemonetics helps health care providers hold on to blood. The company develops and produces blood recovery systems that automate the collection of blood products from donors. Its donor systems allow blood banks to collect and process whole blood, taking only the components (such as plasma or red blood cells) that they might need. Haemonetics also makes systems that collect and re-infuse a patient's own blood during surgery; these surgical blood salvage systems are sold under the OrthoPAT, cardioPAT, and Cell Saver brand names. Additionally, the company sells information management software and provides consulting services to blood banks and hospitals.

	Annual Growth	3/04	3/05	3/06	3/07	3/08
Sales ($ mil.)	9.1%	364.2	383.6	419.7	449.6	516.4
Net income ($ mil.)	15.4%	29.3	39.6	69.1	49.1	52.0
Market value ($ mil.)	17.7%	786.7	1,084.3	1,362.1	1,239.7	1,508.3
Employees	8.7%	—	1,546	1,661	1,826	—

HAGEMEYER NORTH AMERICA, INC.

1460 Tobias Gadson Blvd.
Charleston, SC 29407
Phone: 843-745-2400
Fax: 843-745-6942
Web: www.hagemeyerna.com

CEO: David G. (Dave) Gabriel
CFO: Andros Neocleous
HR: Janine M. McManus
FYE: December 31
Type: Subsidiary

Hagemeyer North America (HNA) gets a charge out of spreading things around. The company distributes electrical, industrial, safety and other maintenance, repair, and operations (MRO) products. It also performs safety services and manufactures industrial safety equipment. The company, a subsidiary of Dutch distribution giant Hagemeyer NV, was formed after the acquisition of three US subsidiaries: Cameron & Barkley, Vallen, and Tristate Electrical and Electronic Supply Company. As its name implies, however, HNA also operates in Canada and Mexico.

HAGGAR CLOTHING CO.

11511 Luna Rd.
Dallas, TX 75234
Phone: 214-352-8481
Fax: –
Web: www.haggar.com

CEO: Terry L. Lay
CFO: John W. Feray
HR: –
FYE: September 30
Type: Private

Haggar is hooked on classics. A leading maker of men's apparel, the company's products include pants, sport coats, suits, shirts, and shorts. Haggar's clothes (including its "wrinkle-free" shirts and tab-waist expandable pants) are sold through about 10,000 stores in the US. Its Haggar brand is sold through department stores such as J. C. Penney, Kohl's, and Beall's and at more than 70 Haggar outlet stores. The company makes lower-priced brands for mass merchandisers and offers private-label clothing.

HAGGEN, INC.

2211 Rimland Dr.
Bellingham, WA 98226
Phone: 360-733-8720
Fax: 360-650-8235
Web: www.haggen.com

CEO: Dale C. Henley
CFO: Tom Kenney
HR: Derrick Anderson
FYE: December 31
Type: Private

Haggen showers shoppers in the Pacific Northwest with salmon, coffee, and other essentials. The area's largest independent grocer, Haggen operates 30-plus combination supermarkets and one drugstore in Washington and Oregon. Most upscale Haggen Food & Pharmacy stores feature specialty departments, while the TOP Food & Drug outlets emphasize savings; however, both may offer such amenities as Starbucks coffee shops, Blockbuster video outlets, or child-care centers. To keep up with the Joneses of supermarket fame and fortune, Haggen partnered with ShopEaze.com (an e-commerce service provider), which failed, leaving Haggen without an online store. Brothers and co-chairmen Don and Rick Haggen own the chain.

	Annual Growth	12/03	12/04	12/05	12/06	12/07
Est. sales ($ mil.)	—	—	—	—	—	758.7
Employees	—	—	—	—	—	3,900

HAHN AUTOMOTIVE WAREHOUSE, INC.

415 W. Main St.
Rochester, NY 14608
Phone: 585-235-1595
Fax: 585-235-8615
Web: www.hahnauto.com

CEO: Daniel J. (Dan) Chessin
CFO: Albert J. Van Erp
HR: –
FYE: September 30
Type: Private

You rely on your mechanic and your mechanic relies on Hahn Automotive Warehouse. The company distributes aftermarket auto parts to independent jobbers (middlemen who buy from distributors and sell to retailers), about 90 company-owned Advantage Auto, Nu-Way Auto, and Genuine Auto Parts stores, as well as professional installers. Hahn Automotive runs more than 20 distribution centers in the East, Mid-Atlantic, and Midwest. Eli Futerman and his son-in-law Daniel Chessin, who are both co-president and CEO, own the company after taking it private in 2001. Hahn Automotive Warehouse (formerly Hahn Tire and Battery) was purchased in 1958 by Futerman's father, Mike, and a partner.

	Annual Growth	9/03	9/04	9/05	9/06	9/07
Est. sales ($ mil.)	—	—	—	—	—	140.3
Employees	—	—	—	—	—	1,100

HAIER AMERICA TRADING LLC

1356 Broadway
New York, NY 10018
Phone: 212-594-3330
Fax: 212-594-9667
Web: www.haieramerica.com

CEO: Michael Jemal
CFO: Shirley Sun
HR: –
FYE: December 31
Type: Subsidiary

Haier America is the US sales and marketing arm of Chinese home appliance and consumer electronics giant Haier Group. Haier Group makes refrigerators, freezers, air conditioners, dishwashers, laundry machines, and small appliances, as well as mobile phones and plasma and flat-screen televisions. Its newest products are wine cellars and beer dispensers. Its products are sold through retailers such as Wal-mart, Bed Bath & Beyond, Home Depot, Lowe's, and Target. The division was founded in 1999 and has operations in New York and South Carolina.

	Annual Growth	12/03	12/04	12/05	12/06	12/07
Est. sales ($ mil.)	—	—	—	—	—	9.0
Employees	—	—	—	—	—	105

HAIGHTS CROSS COMMUNICATIONS, INC.

10 New King St., Ste. 102
White Plains, NY 10604
Phone: 914-289-9400
Fax: 914-289-9401
Web: www.haightscross.com

CEO: Paul J. Crecca
CFO: Paul J. Crecca
HR: –
FYE: December 31
Type: Private

Haights Cross Communications wants to see students buckle down on their studies. A leading publisher of test preparation and supplemental education materials, the company's imprints include Buckle Down, Sundance Publishing, and Triumph Learning. Materials, which are aimed at the K-12 market, cover competency tests, supplemental reading instruction, and skills assessment. Haights Cross also publishes audio books for libraries through its Recorded Books business, as well as continuing medical education (CME) products through its Oakstone imprint. The company has announced plans to sell all of its assets.

	Annual Growth	12/02	12/03	12/04	12/05	12/06
Sales ($ mil.)	8.0%	163.1	162.0	170.9	210.5	222.0
Net income ($ mil.)	—	(27.8)	(1.9)	(26.4)	(44.4)	(72.9)
Employees	8.4%	—	645	700	822	821

THE HAIN CELESTIAL GROUP, INC.

NASDAQ (GS): HAIN

58 S. Service Rd.
Melville, NY 11747
Phone: 631-730-2200
Fax: 631-730-2550
Web: www.hain-celestial.com

CEO: Irwin David Simon
CFO: Ira J. Lamel
HR: Maureen Paradine
FYE: June 30
Type: Public

The Hain Celestial Group serves up guiltless eating. It sells specialty foods in the kosher, sugar-free and low-salt, natural and organic, snack, and weight-management categories. The company's products are mainstays in natural foods stores and are increasingly available in mainstream supermarkets; club, mass-market, and drug stores, as well as through foodservice channels. Hain is also a player in the personal care market, offering disposable diapers and shampoo; its JĀSÖN Natural Products makes personal care items for adults, including items such as skin and hair care products.

	Annual Growth	6/03	6/04	6/05	6/06	6/07
Sales ($ mil.)	17.9%	466.5	544.1	620.0	738.6	900.4
Net income ($ mil.)	14.6%	27.5	27.0	21.9	37.1	47.5
Market value ($ mil.)	18.8%	546.2	658.7	714.0	997.5	1,088.0
Employees	19.7%	—	—	1,487	2,074	2,131

HAJOCA CORPORATION

127 Coulter Ave.
Ardmore, PA 19003
Phone: 610-649-1430
Fax: 610-649-1798
Web: www.hajoca.com

CEO: Richard Klau
CFO: –
HR: –
FYE: December 31
Type: Private

Sinks from Hajoca wash off grease from Philly cheese steaks just as well as sauce from Texas barbecue. One of the nation's leading plumbing and heating wholesalers, Hajoca operates through some 230 locations primarily in Texas, Florida, California, and Pennsylvania, but also in more than 30 other states. Hajoca wholesales plumbing, HVAC, swimming-pool, and industrial supplies for commercial and residential customers. The company has expanded through acquisitions of other distributors that continue to operate under their original names. Founded in 1858, the company takes its current name from the cable address for Haines, Jones, & Cadbury Exports. Hajoca went public in 1927, but was taken private in 1981.

	Annual Growth	12/03	12/04	12/05	12/06	12/07
Est. sales ($ mil.)	—	—	—	—	—	775.2
Employees	—	—	—	—	—	3,500

HALF PRICE BOOKS, RECORDS, MAGAZINES, INCORPORATED

5803 E. Northwest Hwy.
Dallas, TX 75231
Phone: 214-360-0833
Fax: 214-379-8010
Web: www.halfpricebooks.com

CEO: Sharon Anderson Wright
CFO: Nando Arduini
HR: Tim Jernigan
FYE: June 30
Type: Private

Half Price Books tries to live up to its name and its hippie roots. The bookstore chain sells used and new books, magazines, videos, DVDs, and recorded music. Only about half of the merchandise it sells is new. Its more than 90 stores are located in about 15 states, primarily in Texas. Its wholesale catalog division, Texas Bookman, reprints classics and other public domain works. Half Price Books has grown slowly but steadily; its stores keep a small company look with secondhand and employee-made furnishings. The company was started by Ken Gjemre and Pat Anderson (late mom of CEO Sharon Anderson Wright) in 1972 to save trees by recycling unwanted books. The Anderson family owns most of the company.

	Annual Growth	6/03	6/04	6/05	6/06	6/07
Est. sales ($ mil.)	—	—	—	—	—	136.1
Employees	—	—	—	—	—	1,740

HALIFAX CORPORATION

AMEX: HX

5250 Cherokee Ave.
Alexandria, VA 22312
Phone: 703-750-2202
Fax: 703-658-2444
Web: www.hxcorp.com

CEO: Charles L. McNew
CFO: Joseph Sciacca
HR: –
FYE: March 31
Type: Public

Halifax keeps the fax machine and other office equipment up and running in tip-top shape. The company's divisions offer information technology (IT), computer maintenance, support, training, installation, and other related services. Halifax, an authorized service provider for manufacturers including IBM, Lexmark, and Nokia, provides support and on-site computer repair to government and commercial customers throughout the US. The company's five largest customers account for more than half of sales including top client IBM.

	Annual Growth	3/04	3/05	3/06	3/07	3/08
Sales ($ mil.)	(3.0%)	49.5	62.0	54.9	50.7	43.9
Net income ($ mil.)	—	4.2	(1.4)	1.5	(2.8)	(2.5)
Market value ($ mil.)	(21.1%)	12.7	13.2	9.7	9.7	4.9
Employees	(10.5%)	—	581	520	—	—

HALLADOR PETROLEUM COMPANY

OTC: HPCO

1660 Lincoln St., Ste. 2700
Denver, CO 80264
Phone: 303-839-5504
Fax: 303-832-3013

CEO: Victor P. Stabio
CFO: Victor P. Stabio
HR: –
FYE: December 31
Type: Public

Despite its *Harry Potter*-like name, Hallador Petroleum could find no magic in oil and natural gas exploration and production, just a lot of hard and dirty work. It has therefore decided to focus on its coal operations. Hallador Petroleum sells coal from its Carlisle Mine in Indiana to two utilities in the Midwest. It has proved reserves of 17.4 million tons. The company has oil and gas assets in the San Juan Basin of New Mexico. In 2005 Hallador Petroleum sold its stake in the South Cuyama oil and gas field and adjacent exploration areas, all located in Santa Barbara County, California, to E&B Natural Resources, for $23 million. It also sold its North Dakota oil and gas assets.

	Annual Growth	12/03	12/04	12/05	12/06	12/07
Sales ($ mil.)	32.6%	9.6	1.1	1.6	2.5	29.7
Net income ($ mil.)	—	0.7	9.9	0.2	(0.8)	(2.4)
Market value ($ mil.)	61.1%	8.5	14.9	29.2	36.5	57.3
Employees	—	—	—	—	—	148

HALLIBURTON COMPANY

NYSE: HAL

5 Houston Center, 1401 McKinney St., Ste. 2400
Houston, TX 77010
Phone: 713-759-2600
Fax: 713-759-2635
Web: www.halliburton.com

CEO: David J. (Dave) Lesar
CFO: Mark A. McCollum
HR: Lawrence J. Pope
FYE: December 31
Type: Public

Ah, that feels better. Oilfield services giant Halliburton is feeling a lot lighter now that it has divested its KBR engineering and military contracts division. The company made the move so it can concentrate on its own dream — to be the largest oilfield services company in the world. Halliburton provides production optimization, drilling evaluation, fluid services, and oilfield drilling software and consulting. It combines tried and true well drilling and optimization techniques with high-tech analysis and modeling software and services. Halliburton works in established oilfields from the North Sea to the Middle East as well as in newer sites in Southeast Asia and Africa.

	Annual Growth	12/03	12/04	12/05	12/06	12/07
Sales ($ mil.)	(1.6%)	16,271.0	20,466.0	20,994.0	22,576.0	15,264.0
Net income ($ mil.)	—	(820.0)	(979.0)	2,358.0	2,348.0	3,499.0
Market value ($ mil.)	55.5%	5,707.0	8,672.0	15,923.7	30,987.9	33,360.8
Employees	(30.6%)	—	—	106,000	104,000	51,000

HALLMARK CARDS, INC.

2501 McGee St.
Kansas City, MO 64108
Phone: 816-274-5111
Fax: 816-274-5061
Web: www.hallmark.com

CEO: Donald J. (Don) Hall Jr.
CFO: –
HR: Tom Wright
FYE: December 31
Type: Private

As the #1 producer of warm fuzzies, Hallmark Cards is the Goliath of greeting cards. The company's cards are sold under brand names such as Hallmark, Shoebox, and Ambassador and can be found in more than 43,000 US retail stores. (About 3,700 stores bear the Hallmark Gold Crown name; the majority of these stores are independently owned.) Hallmark also offers electronic greeting cards, gifts, and flowers through its Web site. In addition to greeting cards, the company owns crayon manufacturer Crayola (formerly Binney & Smith), a controlling stake in cable broadcaster Crown Media, and Kansas City's Crown Center real estate development. Members of the founding Hall family own two-thirds of Hallmark.

	Annual Growth	12/03	12/04	12/05	12/06	12/07
Sales ($ mil.)	0.6%	4,300.0	4,400.0	4,200.0	4,100.0	4,400.0
Employees	(3.1%)	18,000	18,000	18,000	16,000	15,900

HALLMARK FINANCIAL SERVICES, INC.

NASDAQ (GM): HALL

777 Main St., Ste. 1000
Fort Worth, TX 76102
Phone: 817-348-1600
Fax: 817-348-1815
Web: www.hallmarkgrp.com

CEO: Mark J. Morrison
CFO: Jeffrey R. Passmore
HR: –
FYE: December 31
Type: Public

Personal or commercial, on the ground or in the air, Hallmark Financial sells insurance to cover risks both general and exceptional. Its Hallmark General Agency unit provides general commercial property/casualty insurance while its Texas General Agency sells specialty property/casualty coverage to businesses that don't fit into standard coverage. Its Aerospace unit provides general and specialty aviation insurance to both commercial and private pilots and small airports. Hallmark's Phoenix unit writes higher-risk non-standard personal auto insurance to folks in the southwestern and northwestern US. Chairman Mark Schwarz owns about 70% of the company, primarily through his investment firm, Newcastle Partners.

	Annual Growth	12/03	12/04	12/05	12/06	12/07
Assets ($ mil.)	64.0%	83.8	82.5	208.9	416.0	606.3
Net income ($ mil.)	33.2%	8.7	5.8	9.2	9.2	27.4
Market value ($ mil.)	17.6%	172.4	262.6	708.6	205.8	329.4
Employees	23.1%	186	179	165	347	—

THE HALLWOOD GROUP INCORPORATED

AMEX: HWG

3710 Rawlins, Ste. 1500
Dallas, TX 75219
Phone: 214-528-5588
Fax: 214-522-9254
Web: www.hallwood.com

CEO: Anthony J. Gumbiner
CFO: Melvin J. Melle
HR: –
FYE: December 31
Type: Public

What do a soldier's parachute and a Texas oil patch have in common? The Hallwood Group, a holding company with interests in both textiles and energy. Its Brookwood Companies subsidiary, which accounts for all of its revenue, develops and produces high-tech coated nylon fabric for the outdoors and sportswear industries. It is also a major supplier of specialty fabrics (including camouflage and waterproof items) to the US military, which is its largest customer. The Hallwood Group also owns less than a quarter of Hallwood Energy, which is involved in oil and gas exploration in Texas, Louisiana, and Arkansas. CEO Anthony Gumbiner owns about two-thirds of The Hallwood Group.

	Annual Growth	12/03	12/04	12/05	12/06	12/07
Sales ($ mil.)	4.5%	111.2	137.3	134.6	112.2	132.5
Net income ($ mil.)	—	7.4	94.5	26.3	(6.7)	(32.8)
Market value ($ mil.)	46.0%	26.1	141.3	117.7	185.6	118.6
Employees	—	—	—	462	—	—

HALO TECHNOLOGY HOLDINGS, INC.

Pink Sheets: HTHO

200 Railroad Ave.
Greenwich, CT 06830
Phone: 203-422-2950
Fax: 203-422-5329
Web: www.haloholdings.com

CEO: Rodney A. (Ron) Bienvenu Jr.
CFO: Mark S. Finkel
HR: –
FYE: June 30
Type: Public

Halo Technology Holdings (also known as Warp Technology Holdings) owns and operates a portfolio of enterprise software and information technology companies. Halo, which overhauled its management team in 2004 in connection with a funding deal, acquired relational database software maker Gupta Technologies from Platinum Equity in January 2005. Gupta offers a relational database software product that helps companies capture and manage customer-related data, and it also provides application development tools that help software developers create enterprise applications. In July 2005 Halo bought Kenosia and its DataAlchemy line of sales and marketing analytics software from Bristol Technology.

	Annual Growth	6/02	6/03	6/04	6/05	*6/06
Sales ($ mil.)	—	0.0	0.3	0.9	5.1	25.2
Net income ($ mil.)	—	(1.6)	(13.1)	(11.1)	(51.3)	19.4
Employees	—	—	—	—	—	—

*Most recent year available

HALOZYME THERAPEUTICS, INC.

NASDAQ (GM): HALO

11388 Sorrento Valley Rd.
San Diego, CA 92121
Phone: 858-794-8889
Fax: 858-704-8311
Web: www.halozyme.com

CEO: Jonathan E. Lim
CFO: David A. Ramsay
HR: –
FYE: December 31
Type: Public

Halozyme Therapeutics makes enzymes for infertility, cancer, and eye surgery applications. The company's products are based on recombinant human PH20, a human synthetic enzyme it hopes will offer safety benefits over animal-derived versions. The development-stage firm launched its first commercial product, Cumulase (in-vitro fertilization), in 2005. Halozyme's other products include Hylenex (infusion agent), Enhanze SC (ophthalmic surgery anesthesia) and Chemophase (solid tumor treatment). Its manufacturing and distribution partners include Avid Bioservices (a subsidiary of Peregrine Pharmaceuticals), Baxter International, MediCult, and MidAtlantic Diagnostics.

	Annual Growth	12/03	12/04	12/05	12/06	12/07
Sales ($ mil.)	516.4%	—	—	0.1	1.0	3.8
Net income ($ mil.)	—	—	—	(13.3)	(14.8)	(23.9)
Market value ($ mil.)	124.7%	—	—	109.7	41.2	553.9
Employees	17.6%	—	—	34	40	—

HAMILTON BEACH BRANDS, INC.

4421 Waterfront Dr.
Glen Allen, VA 23060
Phone: 804-273-9777
Fax: 804-527-7142
Web: www.hamiltonbeach.com

CEO: Michael J. Morecroft
CFO: James H. Taylor
HR: Kathleen L. Diller
FYE: December 31
Type: Subsidiary

Hamilton Beach Brands (formerly Hamilton Beach/Procter-Silex) peddles the products that blend strawberry daiquiris and brew the piping hot coffee that's necessary the morning after. The firm is a leading maker of household appliances (blenders, coffeemakers, air purifiers, food processors, humidifiers, and toasters) under the Hamilton Beach, Proctor-Silex, eclectrics, and TruAir brands. It also makes General Electric-branded appliances for Wal-Mart. It caters to the foodservice and hospitality markets with appliances such as drink mixers, glass washers, and hair dryers. Citing unfavorable market conditions, parent company NACCO Industries has reversed its decision to spin off Hamilton Beach Brands (HBB).

	Annual Growth	12/02	12/03	12/04	12/05	12/06
Sales ($ mil.)	2.1%	503.9	492.8	507.2	527.7	546.7
Net income ($ mil.)	13.5%	13.4	16.1	15.2	20.3	22.2
Employees	—	—	—	—	—	545

HAMILTON FIXTURE COMPANY

3550 Symmes Rd.
Hamilton, OH 45015
Phone: 513-874-2016
Fax: 513-870-8741
Web: www.hamiltonfixture.com

CEO: John Schlegal
CFO: –
HR: –
FYE: December 31
Type: Private

Hamilton Fixture is in business to see and be seen. One of the nation's largest store fixture manufacturers, the company designs and makes custom display cases and other fixtures for retailers. The company uses materials such as wood, metal, wire, and acrylic. Its customers include Barnes & Noble, Hollywood Video, Starbucks, T.J. Maxx, and Wal-Mart Stores. Hamilton Fixture manufactures, warehouses, and distributes its products through 750,000 sq. ft. of facilities in Ontario, California, and Hamilton, Ohio. The company was founded in 1959, providing counters to banks, post offices, and other retailers.

	Annual Growth	12/03	12/04	12/05	12/06	12/07
Est. sales ($ mil.)	—	—	—	—	—	35.7
Employees	—	—	—	—	—	500

HAMILTON SUNDSTRAND CORPORATION

1 Hamilton Rd.
Windsor Locks, CT 06095
Phone: 860-654-6000
Fax: –
Web: www.hamiltonsundstrandcorp.com

CEO: David P. Hess
CFO: Peter Longo
HR: Tatsuo Shirane
FYE: December 31
Type: Subsidiary

Out in space, yet down-to-earth, Hamilton Sundstrand manufactures aerospace systems and industrial products. A unit of United Technologies, Hamilton Sundstrand's aerospace offerings include electric power-generation, distribution, and control systems; fuel and special fluid pumps; and propeller and engine-control systems. Aerospace customers include NASA, as well as commercial airlines and the US military. The company's industrial products division manufactures air compressors, fluid handling equipment, and metering pumps used in construction, mining, chemical production, water and waste treatment, and agriculture. Hamilton Sundstrand accounts for more than 10% of United Technologies' sales.

	Annual Growth	12/03	12/04	12/05	12/06	12/07
Sales ($ mil.)	16.1%	—	3,600.0	4,300.0	5,000.0	5,636.0
Employees	5.1%	—	16,000	16,500	17,000	18,600

HAMMACHER SCHLEMMER & CO., INC.

9307 N. Milwaukee Ave.
Niles, IL 60714
Phone: 847-581-8600
Fax: 847-581-8616
Web: www.hammacher.com

CEO: Richard (Rich) Tinberg
CFO: Barry Orr
HR: Ken Gustin
FYE: December 31
Type: Private

It may not roll off the tongue, but the Hammacher Schlemmer name has been around for nearly 160 years. Founded as a New York hardware store, it's one of the nation's most seasoned retailers, producing the longest continually published catalog in the US. Offering a pricey lineup it calls "the Best, the Only and the Unexpected," the retailer sells innovative, upscale gifts, gadgets, and housewares. The firm has been the first to sell a number of cutting-edge products, including the pop-up toaster (1930), steam iron (1948), microwave oven (1968), portable DVD player (1998), and robotic lawnmower (2000). It operates a flagship store in New York City and a Web site. Heirs of J. Roderick MacArthur own the company.

HAMPSHIRE GROUP, LIMITED

Pink Sheets: HAMP

1924 Pearman Dairy Rd.
Anderson, SC 29625
Phone: 864-231-1200
Fax: 864-231-1201
Web: www.hamp.com

CEO: Michael S. Culang
CFO: Jonathan W. Norwood
HR: Horace D. Padgett Jr.
FYE: December 31
Type: Public

The Hampshire Group has warmed to the sweater business. It's a holding company that operates through several wholly owned subsidiaries including Hampshire Designers and Item-Eyes. As one of the largest US makers and marketers of sweaters, Hampshire Group peddles its Designers Originals-brand sweaters to department stores (Kohl's, May, J. C. Penney) and makes private-label items, as well. The firm is licensed to manufacture men's sweaters by Geoffrey Beene, Dockers, and Levi's. Its Item-Eyes unit makes women's woven and knit separates under the Requirements and Nouveaux labels, among others. Former CEO Ludwig Kuttner and his family own about 33% of Hampshire Group.

	Annual Growth	12/03	12/04	12/05	12/06	12/07
Sales ($ mil.)	1.5%	292.6	302.0	324.3	347.9	310.8
Net income ($ mil.)	—	5.6	13.7	11.4	4.3	0.0
Employees	—	—	—	370	—	—

HAMPTON AFFILIATES

9600 SW Barnes Rd., Ste. 200
Portland, OR 97225
Phone: 503-297-7691
Fax: 503-203-6607
Web: www.hamptonaffiliates.com

CEO: Steven J. (Steve) Zika
CFO: Robert Bluhm
HR: Dave Salmon
FYE: January 31
Type: Private

As a vertically integrated lumber company, Hampton Affiliates knows trees from the seedling to the stud. One of Oregon's top timber firms, Hampton produces about 1.4 billion board feet of softwood lumber annually through five sawmills. The company has nearly 170,000 acres of timberland and owns tree farms and mills in Oregon and Washington. Through its Hampton Distribution Companies division, it distributes doors, windows, and other building materials. Hampton supplies homebuilding centers through its stud lumber and distribution operations. The company has its own railcar fleet to transport its products. L. M. "Bud" Hampton founded the company in 1942, and the Hampton family continues to own the enterprise.

	Annual Growth	1/02	1/03	1/04	1/05	1/06
Sales ($ mil.)	9.3%	700.0	700.0	700.0	1,300.0	1,000.0
Employees	8.5%	1,300	1,300	1,300	1,500	1,800

HAMPTON ROADS BANKSHARES, INC.

NASDAQ (GS): HMPR

999 Waterside Dr., Ste. 200
Norfolk, VA 23510
Phone: 757-217-1000
Fax: 757-217-3656
Web: www.bankofhamptonroads.com

CEO: Jack W. Gibson
CFO: Donald W. Fulton Jr.
HR: –
FYE: December 31
Type: Public

Hampton Roads Bankshares probably wasn't the inspiration for a Willie Nelson song. The institution is, however, the holding company for the Bank of Hampton Roads, which has about 20 offices in southeastern Virginia. The bank offers standard retail services such as checking and savings accounts and consumer and business loans. Commercial mortgages account for about 40% of the bank's loan portfolio and business loans make up about 20%. Construction loans make up some 30%, which is not surprising considering some company board members also run construction companies. The company acquired Shore Financial and its Shore Bank subsidiary in 2008.

	Annual Growth	12/03	12/04	12/05	12/06	12/07
Assets ($ mil.)	15.5%	316.5	345.0	409.5	476.3	563.8
Net income ($ mil.)	14.2%	4.0	4.1	5.5	6.0	6.8
Market value ($ mil.)	6.0%	102.8	93.5	87.8	123.0	129.6
Employees	—	—	—	—	—	182

HANA BIOSCIENCES, INC.

NASDAQ (GM): HNAB

7000 Shoreline Ct., Ste. 370
South San Francisco, CA 94080
Phone: 650-588-6404
Fax: 650-588-2787
Web: www.hanabiosciences.com

CEO: Steven R. Deitcher
CFO: John P. Iparraguirre
HR: –
FYE: December 31
Type: Public

Hana Biosciences is fighting the good fight against the big "C." The development stage pharmaceutical company is looking to acquire and develop new drugs with a focus on cancer treatments. Its lead product PT-523 treats solid tumors by preventing DNA synthesis in target cells thereby preventing tumor growth. Its product Zensana is a spray that delivers drugs that ease the side effects of chemotherapy. IPdR is being developed to treat brain, liver, pancreatic, and colorectal cancers. In addition to these products, Hana is actively looking to acquire new candidates that it can further develop and commercialize.

	Annual Growth	12/03	12/04	12/05	12/06	12/07
Sales ($ mil.)	—	—	—	—	—	1.1
Net income ($ mil.)	—	—	—	—	—	(26.0)
Market value ($ mil.)	—	—	—	—	—	34.1
Employees	—	—	—	—	—	—

HANCOCK FABRICS, INC.

Pink Sheets: HKFI

1 Fashion Way
Baldwyn, MS 38824
Phone: 662-365-6000
Fax: –
Web: www.hancockfabrics.com

CEO: Jane F. Aggers
CFO: Robert Driskell
HR: James Britz
FYE: Sunday nearest January 31
Type: Public

Through careful piecing and pinning, Hancock Fabrics has become a leading nationwide fabric chain (far behind Jo-Ann Stores). The company caters to customers who sew by offering fabrics, crafts, and sewing machines and accessories through some 270 stores (down from nearly 450 in 2004) in more than 35 states. Hancock Fabrics also operates an online store. To compensate for the waning popularity of sewing clothes, the company has expanded its selection of home decorating products, including drapery and upholstery fabrics and home accent pieces. Still, slumping sales led the firm to file for Chapter 11 bankruptcy protection in March 2007 and shutter many stores while it tries to mend its fraying business.

	Annual Growth	1/04	1/05	1/06	1/07	1/08
Sales ($ mil.)	(11.2%)	443.6	426.7	403.2	376.2	276.3
Net income ($ mil.)	—	17.4	1.8	(30.3)	(45.9)	(28.0)
Employees	(13.3%)	—	—	6,000	5,200	—

HANCOCK HOLDING COMPANY

NASDAQ (GS): HBHC

1 Hancock Plaza, 2510 14th St.
Gulfport, MS 39501
Phone: 228-868-4000
Fax: 228-563-5673
Web: www.hancockbank.com

CEO: Carl J. Chaney
CFO: Carl J. Chaney
HR: D. Shane Loper
FYE: December 31
Type: Public

Hancock Holding holds its own as a Gulf Coast financial force. It is the holding company of the Mississippi-based Hancock Bank, Hancock Bank of Louisiana, Hancock Bank of Florida, and Hancock Bank of Alabama, which together operate more than 160 offices. The community-oriented banks offer traditional products and services, including deposit accounts; trust services; residential mortgages; and business, consumer, and construction loans. Hancock Holding also has subsidiaries or business units offering insurance, discount brokerage services, mutual funds, and consumer financing.

	Annual Growth	12/03	12/04	12/05	12/06	12/07
Assets ($ mil.)	9.9%	4,150.4	4,664.7	5,950.2	5,964.6	6,056.0
Net income ($ mil.)	7.7%	55.0	61.7	54.0	101.8	73.9
Market value ($ mil.)	29.6%	423.3	1,085.4	1,221.3	1,726.1	1,195.5
Employees	4.3%	—	—	1,735	—	1,888

H&E EQUIPMENT SERVICES, INC.

NASDAQ (GS): HEES

11100 Mead Rd., Ste. 200
Baton Rouge, LA 70816
Phone: 225-298-5200
Fax: 225-298-5377
Web: www.he-equipment.com

CEO: John M. Engquist
CFO: Leslie S. Magee
HR: –
FYE: December 31
Type: Public

Whether you're a he or a she, if you have a project that requires heavy lifting, H&E Equipment Services can help. The company sells and rents new and used equipment for construction, earthmoving, and material handling. H&E Equipment also offers parts and services such as planned maintenance, mobile service, repair, fleet management, and crane remanufacturing. The company markets its products and services throughout the US and represents lift, crane, and truck manufacturers such as JLG, Bobcat, and Komatsu. Private equity firm Bruckmann, Rosser, Sherrill & Co. and its members own nearly 40% of the company.

	Annual Growth	12/03	12/04	12/05	12/06	12/07
Sales ($ mil.)	24.8%	414.0	478.2	600.2	804.4	1,003.1
Net income ($ mil.)	—	(46.0)	(13.7)	28.2	32.7	64.6
Market value ($ mil.)	(25.2%)	—	—	—	946.0	707.4
Employees	9.1%	1,293	1,318	1,448	1,677	—

HANDLEMAN COMPANY

NYSE: HDL

500 Kirts Blvd.
Troy, MI 48084
Phone: 248-362-4400
Fax: 248-362-0718
Web: www.handleman.com

CEO: Albert A. (Al) Koch
CFO: Khaled Haram
HR: Mark J. Albrecht
FYE: Saturday nearest April 30
Type: Public

Handleman Company looks for the hits to keep itself at the top of the charts. One of the world's largest music distributors (annual sales routinely surpass $1.2 billion), the company serves mass retailers by supplying CDs and cassettes and providing display cases and advertising services. Amid slumping CD sales, the company is exiting the music distribution business in North America. Its Handleman Entertainment Resources unit distributes to Argentina, Brazil, Mexico, and the UK. Handleman moved into video games through its purchase of game and accessory distributor Crave Entertainment in late 2005. Handleman was originally founded as a distributor of drug sundries in 1934 by Philip Handleman and his four sons.

	Annual Growth	4/03	4/04	4/05	4/06	4/07
Sales ($ mil.)	(0.6%)	1,357.9	1,216.3	1,260.6	1,312.4	1,324.5
Net income ($ mil.)	—	27.7	35.8	34.2	13.6	(53.4)
Employees	—	—	—	—	2,600	—

H&R BLOCK, INC.   NYSE: HRB

1 H&R Block Way
Kansas City, MO 64105
Phone: 816-854-3000
Fax: 816-854-8500
Web: www.hrblock.com

CEO: Alan M. Bennett
CFO: Becky S. Shulman
HR: Tammy S. Serati
FYE: April 30
Type: Public

Only two things are certain in this life, and H&R Block has a stranglehold on one. The company, which boasts nearly 23 million tax customers, is the leading tax return preparer in the US with 12,000-plus national retail offices; it also prepares tax returns in Canada, Australia, and the UK through some 1,400 offices. A third of its network is franchised. H&R Block also operates nearly 1,500 shared locations in Wal-Mart, Sears, and other stores. Average fee per client is $165. In addition to its ubiquitous tax-preparation services, the company provides a number of other products and services; these include tax-preparation software and residential mortgage loans.

	Annual Growth	4/04	4/05	4/06	4/07	4/08
Sales ($ mil.)	1.2%	4,205.6	4,420.0	4,872.8	4,021.3	4,403.9
Net income ($ mil.)	—	697.9	623.9	490.4	(433.6)	(308.6)
Market value ($ mil.)	16.2%	3,904.2	8,249.6	7,499.9	9,852.9	7,129.9
Employees	1.6%	—	—	134,500	136,600	—

HANDS-ON MOBILE, INC.

580 California St., Ste. 600
San Francisco, CA 94104
Phone: 415-848-0400
Fax: 415-399-1666
Web: www.mforma.com

CEO: David White
CFO: Addo Barrows III
HR: Paul Bianchi
FYE: December 31
Type: Private

Hands-On Mobile (formerly called MFORMA) can help customers capitalize on all sorts of wireless entertainment and content. The company sells games and subscription information services to customers such as AT&T Wireless, Orange, T-Mobile, and Verizon Wireless. The company has partnerships with Activision, Atari, and Marvel, among others. In 2004 Hands-On Mobile acquired porting specialist FingerTwitch and UK-based mobile games developer Blue Beck. Venture capital investors in the company include Bessemer Venture Partners, Draper Fisher Jurvetson, eFund, and General Catalyst Partners.

	Annual Growth	12/03	12/04	12/05	12/06	12/07
Est. sales ($ mil.)	—	—	—	—	—	70.2
Employees	—	—	—	—	—	817

HANDY & HARMAN

555 Theodore Fremd Ave.
Rye, NY 10580
Phone: 914-921-5200
Fax: 914-925-4496
Web: www.handyharman.com

CEO: Jeffrey A. Svoboda
CFO: Robert K. Hynes
HR: —
FYE: December 31
Type: Subsidiary

Many industries find Handy & Harman's (H&H) specialized metal products very handy. The company's subsidiaries operate through three main business units: Precious Metals (fabrication, brazing, and electroplating with precious metals and alloys), Tubing (small-diameter fabricated tubing), and Engineered Materials (specialty roofing and construction fasteners). H&H also owns Canfield Metal Coating Corporation (electrogalvanized products for use in the construction and appliance industries). H&H sells its products to construction firms, steel converters and processors, and steel service centers. The company is a subsidiary of WHX.

	Annual Growth	12/03	12/04	12/05	12/06	12/07
Est. sales ($ mil.)	—	—	—	—	—	243.0
Employees	—	—	—	—	—	2,025

HANESBRANDS INC.   NYSE: HBI

1000 E. Hanes Mill Rd.
Winston-Salem, NC 27105
Phone: 336-519-4400
Fax: —
Web: www.hanesbrands.com

CEO: Richard A. (Rich) Noll
CFO: E. Lee Wyatt Jr.
HR: Kevin W. Oliver
FYE: Saturday nearest December 31
Type: Public

Hanesbrands can't wait until it gets its Hanes on you. Formerly Sara Lee Branded Apparel, the firm makes bras, boxers, hosiery, socks, and other unmentionables under top-brand names, including Bali, Champion, Barely There, Just My Size, Hanes, Hanes Her Way, L'eggs, Playtex, and Wonderbra. Its bras are tops in the US; its underwear, legwear, and activewear (T-shirts, fleece, and sport shirts) units are leaders as well. It also makes legwear under the licensed Donna Karan and DKNY names. Former parent Sara Lee spun off the division in September 2006 to form Hanesbrands Inc. After the spinoff, Hanesbrands announced plans to shutter several plants and eliminate up to 5,300 jobs or some 10% of its workforce.

	Annual Growth	6/04	6/05	6/06	*12/06	12/07
Sales ($ mil.)	(8.7%)	6,449.0	6,426.0	4,472.8	2,250.5	4,474.5
Net income ($ mil.)	(37.5%)	—	—	322.5	74.1	126.1
Market value ($ mil.)	16.5%	—	—	—	2,274.9	2,651.3
Employees	(1.4%)	—	—	49,000	—	47,600

*Fiscal year change

HANGER ORTHOPEDIC GROUP, INC.   NYSE: HGR

2 Bethesda Metro Center, Ste. 1200
Bethesda, MD 20814
Phone: 301-986-0701
Fax: 301-986-0702
Web: www.hanger.com

CEO: Thomas F. Kirk
CFO: George E. McHenry
HR: Brian A. Wheeler
FYE: December 31
Type: Public

No hanger-on here. Hanger Orthopedic Group is one of the US's leading operators of orthotic and prosthetic (O&P) rehabilitation centers, with some 640 facilities nationwide. The company's Southern Prosthetic Supply subsidiary designs, fits, and fabricates standard and custom-made braces and prosthetic devices. Its Innovative Neurotronics subsidiary makes products for patients with a loss of mobility. The company also has programs to manage patient care for private payers through subsidiary Linkia. Hanger Orthopedic Group has custom-fabrication, distribution, and corporate facilities across the US.

	Annual Growth	12/03	12/04	12/05	12/06	12/07
Sales ($ mil.)	3.9%	547.9	568.7	578.2	598.8	637.3
Net income ($ mil.)	5.5%	15.6	(23.4)	17.8	3.4	19.3
Market value ($ mil.)	(5.3%)	334.6	176.3	126.9	168.5	269.0
Employees	0.4%	—	—	3,290	3,303	—

HANLEY WOOD, LLC

1 Thomas Cir. NW, Ste. 600
Washington, DC 20005
Phone: 202-452-0800
Fax: 202-785-1974
Web: www.hanleywood.com

CEO: Frank Anton
CFO: Matthew A. (Matt) Flynn
HR: Wendy Entwistle
FYE: December 31
Type: Private

Devotees of the PBS program This Old House might like Hanley-Wood. Through its Business Media division, the company publishes trade journals for the residential and commercial construction markets, including Builder and residential architect, and consumer magazines such as Luxury Home Design. The unit also publishes related Web sites, including Builder Online. Hanley-Wood's Exhibition unit produces trade shows, conferences, and other industry events such as World of Concrete. The company additionally offers marketing communication services (Hanley Wood Marketing) and real estate research and information (Hanley Wood Market Intelligence).

	Annual Growth	12/03	12/04	12/05	12/06	12/07
Est. sales ($ mil.)	—	—	—	—	—	70.9
Employees	—	—	—	—	—	630

HANMI FINANCIAL CORPORATION

NASDAQ (GS): HAFC

3660 Wilshire Blvd., Penthouse Ste. A
Los Angeles, CA 90010
Phone: 213-382-2200
Fax: 213-384-0990
Web: www.hanmifinancial.com

CEO: Chung Hoon Youk
CFO: Brian E. Cho
HR: Miung Kim
FYE: December 31
Type: Public

No hand-me-down operation, Hanmi Financial is headquartered in a penthouse suite along Los Angeles' Wilshire Boulevard. It's the holding company for Hanmi Bank, which serves California's Korean-American communities in Los Angeles, Orange, San Diego, San Francisco, and Santa Clara counties. Through about two dozen branches and nearly 10 loan offices, the bank offers retail and small business banking, with an emphasis on the latter. Commercial and industrial loans, including Small Business Administration and international loans, account for more than 60% of Hanmi Financial's loan portfolio. Commercial real estate loans account for about 30%.

	Annual Growth	12/03	12/04	12/05	12/06	12/07
Assets ($ mil.)	22.2%	1,785.8	3,104.2	3,414.3	3,725.2	3,983.8
Net income ($ mil.)	—	19.2	36.7	58.2	65.7	(60.5)
Market value ($ mil.)	29.6%	140.0	886.5	869.0	1,105.7	395.3
Employees	6.7%	—	—	552	589	—

HANNAFORD BROS. CO.

145 Pleasant Hill Rd.
Scarborough, ME 04074
Phone: 207-883-2911
Fax: 207-885-2859
Web: www.hannaford.com

CEO: Ronald C. (Ron) Hodge
CFO: Greg Amoroso
HR: Bradford A. (Brad) Wise
FYE: Saturday nearest December 31
Type: Subsidiary

Hannaford Bros. may have started as a fruit and vegetable stand in 1883, but it has expanded from its Maine roots to become an upscale grocer with about 165 stores under the Hannaford Supermarkets banner throughout Maine, Massachusetts, New Hampshire, upstate New York, and Vermont. Still, produce continues to be a major focus at the Hannaford supermarkets, as are expansive meat selections and natural food products. More than 75% of the Hannaford stores are combination grocery stores and pharmacies. The stores average about 48,500 sq. ft. Maine's largest supermarket chain, Hannaford Bros. is owned by Delhaize America (parent of Food Lion), which in turn is owned by Belgium's Delhaize "Le Lion."

	Annual Growth	12/03	12/04	12/05	12/06	12/07
Est. sales ($ mil.)	—	—	—	—	—	2,147.5
Employees	—	—	—	—	—	26,000

HANNOUSH JEWELERS

134 Capital Dr.
West Springfield, MA 01089
Phone: 413-846-4640
Fax: 413-788-7588
Web: www.hannoush.com

CEO: Anthony Hannoush
CFO: Norman Hannoush
HR: –
FYE: March 31
Type: Private

It may not involve Adam Rich, but it turns out that eight really is enough. Founded by the Hannoush brothers (all eight of them) in 1980 and now operated by various family members, Hannoush Jewelers is both a jewelry manufacturer and retailer. The company's products (diamond- and gem-encrusted necklaces, earrings, bracelets, timepieces) are sold through about 80 retail stores, including several franchises, located in the Midwest and northeastern US, as well as through its company Web site.

	Annual Growth	3/03	3/04	3/05	3/06	3/07
Est. sales ($ mil.)	—	—	—	—	—	49.3
Employees	—	—	—	—	—	575

HANOVER CAPITAL MORTGAGE HOLDINGS, INC.

AMEX: HCM

200 Metroplex Dr., Ste. 100
Edison, NJ 08817
Phone: 732-548-0101
Fax: 732-548-0286
Web: www.hanovercapitalholdings.com

CEO: John A. Burchett
CFO: Harold F. McElraft
HR: –
FYE: December 31
Type: Public

After you hand over the down payment for your family home, Hanover Capital Mortgage might just enter the picture. A real estate investment trust (REIT), the company invests in acquiring single- to four-family mortgages. It specializes in mortgage loan pools and subordinate mortgage-backed securities; it occasionally buys and securitizes mortgage loans itself. Hanover Capital Mortgage is streamlining its operations by selling on noncore segments. In 2007 the REIT sold its HanoverTrade unit, which provided Web-based mortgage pool trading and loan sale advisory. It also sold its Hanover Capital Partners subsidiary (consulting, due diligence, and document processing services) was sold to Edison Mortgage.

	Annual Growth	12/03	12/04	12/05	12/06	12/07
Sales ($ mil.)	(6.7%)	36.0	36.6	42.0	25.8	27.3
Net income ($ mil.)	—	8.0	8.1	1.4	(2.9)	(80.0)
Market value ($ mil.)	(57.5%)	101.1	90.5	56.8	40.9	3.3
Employees	(48.5%)	—	—	64	—	17

HANOVER DIRECT, INC.

1500 Harbor Blvd.
Weehawken, NJ 07086
Phone: 201-863-7300
Fax: 201-272-3280
Web: www.hanoverdirect.com

CEO: Wayne P. Garten
CFO: –
HR: Jordan Vargas
FYE: Last Saturday in December
Type: Private

If catalogs are junk mail, then Hanover Direct is the junkyard dog. Mailing more than 180 million catalogs a year, the company sells home fashions (The Company Store, Domestications), as well as men's and women's apparel (International Male, Silhouettes, and Undergear). Each catalog has a corresponding Web site. In addition to its own sites, Hanover Direct also sells its products through affiliated third-party Web sites such as Amazon.com. The company makes Scandia Down brand comforters and pillows for sale in its catalogs, Web sites, and at its three retail outlets. Majority stockholder Chelsey Direct LLC, controlled by Hanover director Stuart Feldman, took the company private in 2007.

	Annual Growth	12/02	12/03	12/04	12/05	12/06
Sales ($ mil.)	(2.4%)	457.6	414.9	403.2	407.4	415.7
Net income ($ mil.)	—	(9.1)	(15.4)	5.0	12.0	(6.2)
Employees	(3.5%)	2,121	1,914	—	2,350	1,840

HANOVER FOODS CORPORATION

1486 York St.
Hanover, PA 17331
Phone: 717-632-6000
Fax: 717-637-2890
Web: hanoverfoods.com

CEO: John A. Warehime
CFO: Gary T. Knisely
HR: William (Bill) Gaugler
FYE: Sunday nearest May 31
Type: Private

Hanover Foods manufactures canned and frozen foods hand over fist. The company produces more than 40 million cases of food products per year. Its offerings include bean and pasta items, a full range of vegetables and vegetable blends, meat and seafood, juice, and snack foods. Expansion into value-added refrigerated, deli, and snack foods has helped Hanover Foods diversify beyond the narrow margins of vegetables. The company's customers consist of US businesses in the retail-food, food service, private-label, military, club-store, and industrials sectors.

	Annual Growth	5/03	5/04	5/05	5/06	5/07
Est. sales ($ mil.)	—	—	—	—	—	290.3
Employees	—	—	—	—	—	2,205

THE HANOVER INSURANCE GROUP, INC.

NYSE: THG

440 Lincoln St.
Worcester, MA 01653
Phone: 508-855-1000
Fax: 508-853-6332
Web: www.hanover.com

CEO: Frederick H. (Fred) Eppinger
CFO: Eugene M. (Gene) Bullis
HR: Bryan D. Allen
FYE: December 31
Type: Public

The Hanover Insurance Group is an all-around property/casualty insurance holding company. Through its Hanover Insurance Company, it provides personal and commercial automobile, homeowners, workers' compensation, and commercial multiple-peril insurance and professional liability coverage. In Michigan, it operates as Citizens Insurance Company. The group sells its products through a network of about 2,000 independent agents in the midwestern, northeastern, and southeastern US, but Michigan and Massachusetts furnish more than 40% of its business. Hanover Insurance also holds its AMGRO commercial-property finance company and Opus Investment Management, which provides institutional investment-management services.

	Annual Growth	12/03	12/04	12/05	12/06	12/07
Assets ($ mil.)	(20.9%)	25,112.5	23,719.2	10,634.0	9,856.6	9,815.6
Net income ($ mil.)	30.6%	86.9	125.3	(325.2)	170.3	253.1
Market value ($ mil.)	9.8%	1,630.8	1,746.6	2,243.0	2,493.7	2,372.4
Employees	(2.5%)	—	—	4,100	4,000	3,900

HANSEN MEDICAL, INC.

NASDAQ (GM): HNSN

308 N. Bernardo Ave.
Mountain View, CA 94043
Phone: 650-404-5800
Fax: 650-404-5901
Web: www.hansenmedical.com

CEO: Frederic H. Moll
CFO: Steven M. (Steve) Van Dick
HR: –
FYE: December 31
Type: Public

Hansen Medical helps doctors maneuver catheters within tricky parts of the heart. The company's portable Sensei system incorporates advanced robotics to assist in guiding the movement of flexible catheters in such places as the atria and ventricles. The system is designed to work along with its Artisan control catheters. Sensei has received FDA and European regulatory approval for the manipulation, positioning, and control of mapping catheters in electrophysiology procedures (designed to diagnose irregular electrical impulses in the heart). The product is awaiting clearance for use in more highly sensitive ablation procedures in the treatment of cardiac arrhythmia.

	Annual Growth	12/03	12/04	12/05	12/06	12/07
Sales ($ mil.)	—	—	—	—	—	10.1
Net income ($ mil.)	—	—	—	—	—	(50.4)
Market value ($ mil.)	—	—	—	—	—	657.5
Employees	—	—	—	—	—	—

HANSEN NATURAL CORPORATION

NASDAQ (GS): HANS

1010 Railroad St.
Corona, CA 92882
Phone: 951-739-6200
Fax: 951-739-6220
Web: www.hansens.com

CEO: Rodney C. Sacks
CFO: Hilton H. Schlosberg
HR: Linda Lopez
FYE: December 31
Type: Public

No matter the weather, Hansen Natural always has the energy to reach even higher than the blue sky. Adding to its Blue Sky energy drink, the company has expanded its stable of "alternative" sodas, juices, and teas to include a wide variety of energy beverages such as the popular Monster brand. Other products made by Hansen include fruit juice, smoothies, iced tea, and dry juice mixes — most of which are sold under the Hansen's brand. The company sells its products to grocery chains, wholesale clubs, and distributors, mainly in the US and Canada. Through Branded Limited Partnership, Hansen chairman and CEO Rodney Sacks and vice chairman and president Hilton Schlosberg own approximately 18% of the company.

	Annual Growth	12/03	12/04	12/05	12/06	12/07
Sales ($ mil.)	69.2%	110.3	180.3	348.9	605.8	904.5
Net income ($ mil.)	124.3%	5.9	20.4	62.8	97.9	149.4
Market value ($ mil.)	340.4%	11.0	49.8	437.3	3,033.2	4,127.4
Employees	40.1%	—	—	363	748	713

HANSON AGGREGATES NORTH AMERICA

8505 Freeport Pkwy.
Irving, TX 75063
Phone: 972-621-0345
Fax: 469-417-1438
Web: www.hansonaggeast.com

CEO: James (Jim) Kitzmiller
CFO: Tim McHugh
HR: Van Waldrop
FYE: December 31
Type: Subsidiary

Hanson Aggregates North America (HANA) mixes together a lot of ingredients, but instead of blenders and bowls it uses dump trucks and cement mixers. A subsidiary of UK-based Hanson PLC (itself a subsidiary of HeidelbergCement), HANA's ingredients include granite, limestone, asphalt, ready-mix concrete, concrete products, gravel, and sand. It also offers distribution and construction services for its customers in North America. HANA operates in about 20 US states as well as Mexico.

	Annual Growth	12/03	12/04	12/05	12/06	12/07
Est. sales ($ mil.)	—	—	—	—	—	132.8
Employees	—	—	—	—	—	1,000

HANSON BUILDING PRODUCTS NORTH AMERICA

300 E. John Carpenter Fwy.
Irving, TX 75062
Phone: 972-653-5500
Fax: 972-653-6146
Web: www.hanson.biz/us/pipe

CEO: Richard Manning
CFO: –
HR: –
FYE: December 31
Type: Subsidiary

Hanson Building Products North America has a big crush on the concrete materials business. A subsidiary of HeidelbergCement, the company is made up of two divisions: Pipe & Precast (about 75% of sales) Concrete Paving, and Brick & Tile (nearly 20%). Its Pipe & Precast unit is a leading US manufacturer of concrete pipes, manholes, drainage products, and precast concrete products. The company's Brick & Tile unit, the largest brick manufacturer in North America, primarily manufactures clay brick and roofing tiles from plants in Florida, California, North Carolina, and Canada. Hanson Building Products North America accounts for around 15% of its parent's total sales.

	Annual Growth	12/03	12/04	12/05	12/06	12/07
Est. sales ($ mil.)	—	—	—	—	—	2,147.5
Employees	—	—	—	—	—	14,920

HAPPY KIDS INC.

100 W. 33rd St., Ste. 1100
New York, NY 10001
Phone: 212-736-9266
Fax: –

CEO: Jack M. Benun
CFO: Stuart Bender
HR: –
FYE: December 31
Type: Private

Kids bedecked in apparel featuring their favorite *Rugrats* or *Looney Tunes* characters are Happy Kids. The company designs and markets apparel for newborns, infants, toddlers, boys, and girls through department stores, specialty and mass-market retailers, and mid-tier distributors. Designs are based on characters from popular children's TV shows (think Nickelodeon and Warner Bros.), books and movies (*Harry Potter*), and logos from professional sports teams. Investment firm H.I.G. Capital is a majority owner. The company filed for Chapter 11 bankruptcy protection in early 2005. Wear Me Apparel added Happy Kids' assets to its closet for a price tag of more than $26 million.

An in-depth profile of this company is available to Hoover's Online members at hoovers.com.

729

HARBOUR GROUP INDUSTRIES, INC.

7701 Forsyth Blvd., Ste. 600
St. Louis, MO 63105
Phone: 314-727-5550
Fax: 314-727-9912
Web: www.harbourgroup.com

CEO: Jeffrey L. (Jeff) Fox
CFO: William (Bill) Willhite
HR: –
FYE: December 31
Type: Private

Harbour Group Industries acquires and consolidates manufacturing companies in fragmented industries. The company's current portfolio includes companies in several diverse sectors such as auto accessories, plastic-processing equipment, and music and entertainment products. Since its founding in 1976, Harbour Group has acquired more than 140 companies. In 2005 Harbour Group acquired Lincoln Industrial, a provider of lubrication systems and equipment and related products; it bought another industrial lubricant company, Alemite, from Sentinel Capital Partners the following year. The Fox family controls Harbour Group Industries.

	Annual Growth	12/03	12/04	12/05	12/06	12/07
Est. sales ($ mil.)	—	—	—	—	—	234.4
Employees	—	—	—	—	—	3,282

HARD ROCK CAFE INTERNATIONAL, INC.

6100 Old Park Ln.
Orlando, FL 32835
Phone: 407-445-7625
Fax: 407-445-9709
Web: www.hardrock.com

CEO: Hamish Dodds
CFO: Thomas (Tom) Gispanski
HR: Kim Creighton
FYE: December 31
Type: Subsidiary

You can rock hard, eat hard, buy merchandise hard, even sleep hard with Hard Rock Cafe International. The company operates the Hard Rock Cafe chain of theme restaurants, which serve up typical American food, as well as rock-music memorabilia and plenty of Hard Rock-branded merchandise. It has more than 120 company-owned and franchised locations in more than 45 countries. The company also has about a half-dozen branded hotels and hotel casinos operated by third parties, as well as three concert venues in the US, Canada, and Mexico. Its collection of rock n' roll memorabilia boasts more than 60,000 items. The Hard Rock chain was acquired in 2007 by the Seminole Tribe of Florida.

HARD ROCK HOTEL, INC.

4455 Paradise Rd.
Las Vegas, NV 89109
Phone: 702-693-5000
Fax: 702-693-5021
Web: www.hardrockhotel.com

CEO: Peter A. Morton
CFO: James D. (Jim) Bowen
HR: –
FYE: December 31
Type: Subsidiary

This might be one of the only times in your life that you can find a Rolling Stone pinned to *The Wall* as you contemplate the glamour of Ziggy Stardust. Hard Rock Hotel, Inc. owns and operates the Hard Rock Hotel and Casino in Las Vegas. Using the successful cafe with the same name as its inspiration, the hotel boasts a collection of rock memorabilia as well as the giant outside guitar synonymous with the Hark Rock name. The hotel and casino is also home to a nightclub, concert hall, five restaurants, and a spa, as well as several other retail establishments. Chairman and CEO Peter Morton previously owned more than 90% of Hard Rock Hotel; Morgans Hotel Group purchased the company for $770 million.

HARDEE'S FOOD SYSTEMS, INC.

100 N. Broadway, Ste. 1200
St. Louis, MO 63102
Phone: 314-259-6200
Fax: 314-621-1778
Web: www.hardees.com

CEO: Andrew F. Puzder
CFO: Theodore (Ted) Abajian
HR: Victoria Straschil
FYE: Last Monday in January
Type: Subsidiary

This might be the right place if you have a hearty appetite for burgers. Hardee's Food Systems is a leading fast food chain operator, with more than 1,900 locations in some 30 states. The chain offers a variety of premium-priced Angus beef hamburgers under such names as Thickburger, Six Dollar Burger, and the Monster Thickburger. Hardee's also serves up chicken sandwiches, salads, fries, and beverages, as well as dessert items. The chain is located primarily in the Midwest and Southeast; about a third of the restaurants are operated by the company, while the rest are franchised. Hardee's is a subsidiary of fast food giant CKE Restaurants.

	Annual Growth	1/03	1/04	1/05	1/06	1/07
Est. sales ($ mil.)	—	—	—	—	—	361.6
Employees	—	—	—	—	—	16,680

HARDINGE INC.

NASDAQ (GS): HDNG

1 Hardinge Dr.
Elmira, NY 14902
Phone: 607-734-2281
Fax: 607-732-4925
Web: www.hardinge.com

CEO: Richard L. Simons
CFO: Edward J. Gaio
HR: –
FYE: December 31
Type: Public

Here's a company that keeps on turning. Hardinge makes industrial machine tools for small and mid-sized shops that turn out machined parts for the automotive, medical equipment, and farm equipment industries. The company's precision turning machine tools shape metal, composites, and plastics. Its computer-controlled machines cut either horizontally or vertically and can be connected to automatic material feeders for unattended machining. The Cobra line of lathes is marketed as an inexpensive alternative for smaller shops. Hardinge also offers a line of work- and tool-holding devices. The company gets about two-thirds of its sales outside of North America, predominantly in Western Europe.

	Annual Growth	12/03	12/04	12/05	12/06	12/07
Sales ($ mil.)	17.8%	185.3	232.1	289.9	326.6	356.3
Net income ($ mil.)	—	(11.3)	4.4	7.0	13.9	14.9
Market value ($ mil.)	17.1%	102.5	117.5	153.4	133.1	192.6
Employees	6.4%	1,187	1,354	1,429	1,457	1,519

HARLAN SPRAGUE DAWLEY, INC.

8520 Allison Pointe Blvd., Ste. 400
Indianapolis, IN 46250
Phone: 317-894-7025
Fax: 317-806-6090
Web: www.harlan.com

CEO: Stephen J. (Steve) Sullivan
CFO: Peter J. Mariani
HR: –
FYE: December 31
Type: Private

Harlan Sprague Dawley is where scientists go when they need rats for the maze. The research company sells laboratory animals and food and bedding for them. Its Harlan Bioproducts for Science supplies gerbils, hamsters, mice, rabbits, rats, and other animals to pharmaceutical and biotech companies, universities, and government agencies. The Harlan Bioproducts for Science division provides researchers with antibodies and sera while the Harlan Teklad division makes laboratory animal bedding and feed, including diets tailored to specified research projects. The company was found in 1931 by Howard Harlan.

	Annual Growth	12/03	12/04	12/05	12/06	12/07
Est. sales ($ mil.)	—	—	—	—	—	51.0
Employees	—	—	—	—	—	1,700

HARLAND FINANCIAL SOLUTIONS, INC.

605 Crescent Executive Ct., Ste. 600
Lake Mary, FL 32746
Phone: 407-804-6600
Fax: 407-829-6702
Web: www.harlandfs.com

CEO: John O'Malley
CFO: Jeff Groh
HR: Barbara Brescia
FYE: December 31
Type: Subsidiary

Harland Financial Solutions supplies software and services for financial institutions. The company's software offerings include applications for lending and account origination, financial institution customer relationship management, business intelligence, bank and credit union core processing systems, teller and call center platforms, mortgage lending and servicing, and regulatory compliance training. Harland Financial Solutions also offers a service bureau for outsourced core processing, as well as document imaging and electronic statement processing services.

HARLEM FURNITURE

1000-46 Rohlwing Rd.
Lombard, IL 60148
Phone: 630-261-1600
Fax: 630-261-1080
Web: www.harlemfurniture.com

CEO: Bruce Berman
CFO: Steven Kuptsis
HR: –
FYE: December 31
Type: Private

You'd best reserve a U-haul if you're trying to get your new furniture back to the *real* Harlem. Named Harlem Furniture because of its flagship location on Harlem Avenue, the company was founded by Sam Berman in 1912 in downtown Chicago. The family-run furniture retailer (Berman's grandson, Bruce, is president and CEO) sells furniture by the room at a discount and operates about 15 retail stores, primarily in Illinois. In 2005 Berman joined with private equity firms Pouschine Cook Capital, Bear Growth Capital, and Mercantile Capital, to buy a controlling stake in Harlem Furniture. With the increased funding, the company plans to open three to four new stores a year with openings in Illinois and Indiana in 2007.

	Annual Growth	12/03	12/04	12/05	12/06	12/07
Est. sales ($ mil.)	—	—	—	—	—	76.4
Employees	—	—	—	—	—	700

⊞ HARLEY-DAVIDSON, INC.　　NYSE: HOG

3700 W. Juneau Ave.
Milwaukee, WI 53208
Phone: 414-342-4680
Fax: 414-343-8230
Web: www.harley-davidson.com

CEO: James L. Ziemer
CFO: Thomas E. (Tom) Bergmann
HR: Harold A. Scott
FYE: December 31
Type: Public

"Put your a** on some class," reads one (not necessarily official) Harley-Davidson T-shirt. Harley-Davidson is the only major US maker of motorcycles and the nation's #1 seller of heavyweight motorcycles. The company offers 35 models of touring and custom Harleys through a worldwide network of more than 1,500 dealers. Harley models include the Electra Glide, the Sportster, and the Fat Boy. The company also makes motorcycles under the Buell nameplate. Besides its bikes, Harley-Davidson sells attitude — goods licensed with the company name include a line of clothing and accessories (MotorClothes). Harley-Davidson Financial Services offers financing to dealers and consumers in the US and Canada.

	Annual Growth	12/03	12/04	12/05	12/06	12/07
Sales ($ mil.)	5.8%	4,903.7	5,320.5	5,673.8	6,185.6	6,143.0
Net income ($ mil.)	5.3%	760.9	889.8	959.6	1,043.2	933.8
Market value ($ mil.)	(38.7%)	—	—	—	18,185.0	11,139.7
Employees	(3.7%)	—	—	9,700	9,000	9,000

HARLEYSVILLE GROUP INC.　　NASDAQ (GS): HGIC

355 Maple Ave.
Harleysville, PA 19438
Phone: 215-256-5000
Fax: 215-256-5799
Web: www.harleysvillegroup.com

CEO: Michael L. Browne
CFO: Arthur E. (Art) Chandler
HR: Jenifer L. Rinehart
FYE: December 31
Type: Public

The reckless, the accident-prone, or the just plain apprehensive take heed: Harleysville Group (also known as Harleysville Insurance) hopes to extend a safety net for all of you. A regional insurance holding company, Harleysville Group sells a broad line of personal and commercial property and casualty insurance. The company offers homeowners, auto, commercial multi-peril, and workers' compensation coverage. With its products marketed through about 1,500 independent agencies, the company maintains regional offices in 13 states, primarily in the eastern and midwestern US. Harleysville Mutual Insurance Company owns 53% of Harleysville Group.

	Annual Growth	12/03	12/04	12/05	12/06	12/07
Assets ($ mil.)	3.5%	2,680.4	2,718.1	2,905.3	2,991.0	3,072.4
Net income ($ mil.)	—	(47.6)	46.9	61.4	111.1	100.1
Market value ($ mil.)	15.9%	594.7	723.1	811.2	1,102.5	1,072.8
Employees	(6.5%)	—	—	2,029	1,898	—

HARLEYSVILLE NATIONAL CORPORATION　　NASDAQ (GS): HNBC

483 Main St.
Harleysville, PA 19438
Phone: 215-256-8851
Fax: 215-256-3065
Web: www.harleysvillebank.com

CEO: Paul D. Geraghty
CFO: George S. Rapp
HR: Robert L. Reiley
FYE: December 31
Type: Public

Harleysville National Corporation is all revved up about being the holding company for Harleysville National Bank and Trust. Established in 1909, the bank operates about 55 branches in more than a half dozen eastern Pennsylvania counties. The bank offers such products as checking and savings accounts and CDs, as well as corporate pension and personal trust services. Real estate loans dominate the bank's loan portfolio, making up about 40% of its lending activities; the portfolio also includes consumer and business loans, as well as lease financing. The company's Millennium Wealth Management & Private Banking unit focuses on serving wealthy individuals, as well as institutional clients.

	Annual Growth	12/03	12/04	12/05	12/06	12/07
Assets ($ mil.)	11.7%	2,510.9	3,024.5	3,117.4	3,249.8	3,903.0
Net income ($ mil.)	(6.8%)	35.3	38.6	38.8	39.4	26.6
Market value ($ mil.)	(7.4%)	620.0	634.0	499.1	559.3	456.5
Employees	—	—	—	665	—	—

HARLEYSVILLE SAVINGS FINANCIAL　　NASDAQ (GM): HARL

271 Main St.
Harleysville, PA 19438
Phone: 215-256-8828
Fax: 215-513-9393
Web: www.harleysvillesavings.com

CEO: Ronald B. Geib
CFO: Brendan J. McGill
HR: Diane M. Carlson
FYE: September 30
Type: Public

Get your moola runnin'! Harleysville Savings Financial Corporation is the holding company of Harleysville Savings Bank, which operates about a half-dozen branches in southeastern Pennsylvania's Montgomery County. The bank offers standard retail products, including checking, savings, and money market accounts, as well as CDs and IRAs. The company's loan portfolio is composed primarily of single-family residential mortgages (about 45%) and mortgage-backed securities (more than 35%); Harleysville Savings Bank also offers multifamily mortgages and construction, consumer, and business loans.

	Annual Growth	9/03	9/04	9/05	9/06	9/07
Assets ($ mil.)	4.3%	653.3	718.2	767.0	775.6	773.5
Net income ($ mil.)	(8.0%)	4.6	4.8	5.0	4.2	3.3
Market value ($ mil.)	8.6%	36.7	40.0	67.0	66.3	51.0
Employees	—	—	—	98	—	—

HARMAN INTERNATIONAL INDUSTRIES

NYSE: HAR

1101 Pennsylvania Ave. NW, Ste. 1010
Washington, DC 20004
Phone: 202-393-1101
Fax: 202-393-3064
Web: www.harman.com

CEO: Dinesh C. Paliwal
CFO: Herbert K. Parker
HR: John Stacey
FYE: June 30
Type: Public

Harman International Industries, Incorporated, is loud and clear. It makes high-end stereo and audio equipment for consumer and professional markets. Its consumer group makes loudspeakers, CD and DVD players, CD recorders, and amplifiers under brands Harman/Kardon, Infinity, Logic, JBL, Mark Levinson, and others. Harman's auto unit sells branded audio systems through carmakers, including Toyota/Lexus and General Motors. Its professional unit makes audio equipment, such as studio monitors, amplifiers, microphones, and mixing consoles for recording studios, cinemas, touring performers, and others. KKR & Co. and Goldman Sachs abandoned an $8 billion leveraged buyout of Harman in September 2007.

	Annual Growth	6/03	6/04	6/05	6/06	6/07
Sales ($ mil.)	12.4%	2,228.5	2,711.4	3,030.9	3,247.9	3,551.1
Net income ($ mil.)	31.4%	105.4	157.9	232.9	255.3	314.0
Market value ($ mil.)	55.9%	1,290.4	6,014.2	5,423.7	5,639.9	7,619.9
Employees	3.7%	—	—	10,845	11,246	—

HARMAN MANAGEMENT CORPORATION

199 1st St., Ste. 212
Los Altos, CA 94022
Phone: 650-941-5681
Fax: 650-948-7532

CEO: James D. (Jim) Olson
CFO: James S. Jackson
HR: Shawn Brady
FYE: June 30
Type: Private

This company helped a colonel get started in the chicken business. Harman Management, one of the largest franchisees of KFC (a division of YUM! Brands), was founded by Leon Harman — the first person to buy a franchise from the chain's founder, Colonel Sanders. The company now has more than 340 fried chicken units in California, Colorado, Utah, and Washington, along with several locations co-branded with Taco Bell, Pizza Hut, and A&W units. Harman, who ran a cafe in Salt Lake City, was awarded his franchise in 1952. He coined the name Kentucky Fried Chicken and popularized the concept of selling the chicken in a bucket.

	Annual Growth	6/03	6/04	6/05	6/06	6/07
Sales ($ mil.)	4.5%	377.3	391.4	411.0	437.0	450.0
Employees	3.8%	13,000	13,500	—	—	—

HARMONIC INC.

NASDAQ (GM): HLIT

549 Baltic Way
Sunnyvale, CA 94089
Phone: 408-542-2500
Fax: 408-542-2511
Web: www.harmonicinc.com

CEO: Patrick J. Harshman
CFO: Robin N. Dickson
HR: Anne Lynch
FYE: December 31
Type: Public

Harmonic answers the demand for advanced television features. The company provides fiber optic and wireless network transmission products used to enable video-on-demand services. Its video transmission equipment includes digital headend systems, digital signal encoders, and complete provider-to-subscriber delivery systems. Harmonic also supplies multiplexers, optical nodes, transmitters, optical amplifiers, and other broadband network access equipment. The company sells directly and through distributors and systems integrators, primarily to cable and satellite TV providers. Its customers include Cablevision, Charter Communications, Comcast, and Time Warner Cable.

	Annual Growth	12/03	12/04	12/05	12/06	12/07
Sales ($ mil.)	14.3%	182.3	248.3	257.4	247.7	311.2
Net income ($ mil.)	—	(29.4)	1.6	(5.7)	1.0	23.4
Market value ($ mil.)	17.4%	516.5	602.9	359.7	569.9	982.7
Employees	3.2%	—	—	618	639	658

HAROLD'S STORES, INC.

Pink Sheets: HRLS

5919 Maple Ave.
Dallas, TX 75235
Phone: 214-366-0600
Fax: 214-366-1061
Web: www.harolds.com

CEO: Ronald S. (Ron) Staffieri
CFO: Robert P. Cole
HR: Jeffrey T. Morrell
FYE: Saturday nearest January 31
Type: Public

Harold Powell founded his first store in 1948 to bring Ivy League fashions to Oklahoma. More than 50 years later, Harold's Stores — with nearly 45 stores and two outlets in some 20 states — still sells upscale, conservatively-styled men's and women's apparel. More than 80% of sales come from women's sportswear, dresses, shoes, and accessories, mostly sold under the company's private labels. Men's apparel (Old School Company and Harold Powell Clothing brands) and shoes account for the rest. Harold's discontinued direct sales efforts (including its Web site and mail-order catalog) were revived in 2003.

	Annual Growth	1/04	1/05	1/06	1/07	1/08
Sales ($ mil.)	(2.8%)	91.7	89.4	88.3	86.3	81.7
Net income ($ mil.)	—	(6.2)	0.1	(6.0)	(11.2)	(9.7)
Employees	—	—	—	—	785	—

HARPERCOLLINS PUBLISHERS, INC.

10 E. 53rd St.
New York, NY 10022
Phone: 212-207-7000
Fax: 212-207-7145
Web: www.harpercollins.com

CEO: Brian Murray
CFO: Janet Gervasio
HR: –
FYE: June 30
Type: Subsidiary

HarperCollins Publishers has a real page-turner on its hands. The book-publishing subsidiary of Rupert Murdoch's News Corp., HarperCollins is the publisher of best-sellers including *At the Center of the Storm* by George Tenet, Scott Adams' *Dilbert* books, and Michael Crichton's *State of Fear*. The company's publishing groups include HarperCollins General Books (imprints such as Perennial, Quill), HarperCollins Children's Book Group, HarperCollins UK, HarperCollins Canada, HarperCollins India, and HarperCollins Australia/New Zealand. Its Zondervan unit publishes bibles and Christian books. The company's e-book imprint is PerfectBound. HarperCollins provides about 5% of parent News Corp.'s sales.

	Annual Growth	6/03	6/04	6/05	6/06	6/07
Est. sales ($ mil.)	—	—	—	—	—	165.2
Employees	—	—	—	—	—	1,425

HARPO, INC.

110 N. Carpenter St.
Chicago, IL 60607
Phone: 312-633-1000
Fax: 312-633-1976
Web: www.oprah.com

CEO: Oprah G. Winfrey
CFO: Douglas J. (Doug) Pattison
HR: –
FYE: December 31
Type: Private

Everyone knows Oprah Winfrey is an exceptional businesswoman; there's no need to Harpo on it. Unrelated to the silent Marx brother, Harpo controls the entertainment interests of talk show host/actress/producer Oprah Winfrey. *The Oprah Winfrey Show* is the highest-rated TV talk show in history, seen in almost every US market and in 120 countries. Harpo also produces feature films (*Beloved*, which also starred Winfrey) and made-for-TV movies (*Their Eyes Were Watching God*), as well as radio content distributed by XM Satellite Radio. In print, the company publishes *O, The Oprah Magazine* with Hearst Magazines, which boasts a circulation of about 2.4 million. Winfrey founded Harpo in 1986.

	Annual Growth	12/02	12/03	12/04	12/05	12/06
Sales ($ mil.)	9.6%	225.0	275.0	275.0	290.0	325.0
Employees	12.4%	240	250	—	341	—

HARP'S FOOD STORES, INC.

918 S. Gutensohn Rd.
Springdale, AR 72762
Phone: 479-751-7601
Fax: 479-751-3625
Web: www.harpsfood.com

CEO: Roger Collins
CFO: Jim Antz
HR: Frank Ray
FYE: December 31
Type: Private

It's tough to survive in the face of Arkansas giant Wal-Mart, but Harp's Food Stores (founded when Sam Walton was 12 years old) is putting up a fight. The company, which got its start when Floy and Harvard Harp put down $500 cash and opened the first Harp's Cash Grocery in 1930, operates 50-plus grocery stores, mostly in Arkansas but also in Missouri and Oklahoma. Its stores, operating under the Harp's Food Stores and Price Cutter Food Warehouse banners, range in size from 13,000 to 63,000 square feet and often feature bakeries, pharmacies, and meat departments on site. Harp's operated as a family-run chain until 2001 when it transitioned into an employee-owned business.

	Annual Growth	12/03	12/04	12/05	12/06	12/07
Est. sales ($ mil.)	—	—	—	—	—	914.3
Employees	—	—	—	—	—	3,000

HARRAH'S ENTERTAINMENT, INC.

1 Caesars Palace Dr.
Las Vegas, NV 89109
Phone: 702-407-6000
Fax: 702-407-6037
Web: www.harrahs.com

CEO: Gary W. Loveman
CFO: Jonathan S. Halkyard
HR: Mary H. Thomas
FYE: December 31
Type: Private

Harrah's Entertainment likes to spread its bets. The world's largest gaming company, Harrah's owns, operates, and/or manages about 50 casinos (under such names as Bally's, Caesars, Harrah's, Horseshoe, and Rio), primarily in the US and the UK. Operations include casino hotels, dockside and riverboat casinos, and Native American gaming establishments. Harrah's acquired rival Caesars Entertainment for $9.4 billion in cash, stock, and debt. The deal cemented Harrah's as the world's #1 gaming company, jumping over the merged MGM MIRAGE/Mandalay combination. To appease regulators, Harrah's sold its Harrah's Tunica and East Chicago casinos to Colony Capital. The firm is owned by Apollo Advisors and TPG Capital.

	Annual Growth	12/03	12/04	12/05	12/06	12/07
Sales ($ mil.)	25.8%	4,322.7	4,548.3	7,111.0	9,673.9	10,825.2
Net income ($ mil.)	20.6%	292.6	367.7	236.4	535.8	619.4
Employees	20.7%	41,000	46,600	85,000	85,000	87,000

HARRINGTON WEST FINANCIAL GROUP, INC.

NASDAQ (GM): HWFG

610 Alamo Pintado Rd.
Solvang, CA 93463
Phone: 805-688-6644
Fax: 805-688-4959
Web: www.lospadresbank.com

CEO: Craig J. Cerny
CFO: Kerril K. (Kerry) Steele
HR: –
FYE: December 31
Type: Public

This is not your father's bank. It's Los Padres Bank, the flagship subsidiary of Harrington West Financial Group. The bank has about a dozen branches along California's central coast between San Francisco and Los Angeles, as well as the Phoenix metropolitan area. Its Harrington Bank division operates three branches in the Kansas City area. The banks serve individuals and small businesses, offering standard services such as deposit products and loans. Commercial mortgages make up about a third of its portfolio; business loans, residential mortgages, and construction loans each comprise about 15%. Los Padre Bank's Harrington Wealth Management unit provides trust and investment services.

	Annual Growth	12/03	12/04	12/05	12/06	12/07
Assets ($ mil.)	5.8%	974.8	1,081.3	1,140.2	1,154.5	1,223.4
Net income ($ mil.)	(13.2%)	7.4	8.2	8.3	8.2	4.2
Market value ($ mil.)	1.0%	60.0	99.5	89.3	94.2	62.5
Employees	3.2%	—	—	186	—	198

HARRIS & HARRIS GROUP, INC.

NASDAQ (GM): TINY

111 W. 57th St., Ste. 1100
New York, NY 10019
Phone: 212-582-0900
Fax: 212-582-9563
Web: www.tinytechvc.com

CEO: Charles E. Harris
CFO: Daniel B. Wolfe
HR: Sandra M. Forman
FYE: December 31
Type: Public

Harris & Harris Group likes to think small. The business development company (BDC) invests mostly in startup firms developing so-called "tiny technology" — microsystems, microelectromechanical systems, and nanotechnology. The company identifies small, thinly capitalized firms lacking operating history or experienced management. An active investor, it provides assistance such as strategic development and executive recruiting to its portfolio companies. Harris & Harris holds stakes in some 30 firms. It has made about 80 venture capital investments since it was founded, including investment in Molecular Imprints, NanoOpto, and Nanosys.

	Annual Growth	12/03	12/04	12/05	12/06	12/07
Sales ($ mil.)	52.4%	0.5	0.6	15.8	3.0	2.7
Net income ($ mil.)	—	(3.2)	(2.1)	6.7	(11.8)	(6.7)
Market value ($ mil.)	6.5%	159.1	282.5	288.5	254.1	204.9
Employees	—	—	—	11	—	—

HARRIS BANKCORP, INC.

111 W. Monroe St.
Chicago, IL 60603
Phone: 312-461-2121
Fax: 312-461-7869
Web: www.harrisbank.com

CEO: Ellen M. Costello
CFO: –
HR: Deirdre Drake
FYE: October 31
Type: Subsidiary

The US banking arm of Bank of Montreal (BMO), Harris Bankcorp offers financial services through Harris Bank and other subsidiaries. As BMO's US Personal and Commercial Banking segment, Harris has more than 270 branches in the Midwest (centered around Chicago) as well as in Arizona, California, Florida, Indiana, and major American cities. In addition to deposit and lending services, other operations include investment management (Harris Investment Management), middle-market investment bank BMO Capital Markets, and private bank and wealth management unit Harris Private Banking.

HARRIS CONNECT, INC.

1400-A Crossways Blvd.
Chesapeake, VA 10577
Phone: 914-641-3500
Fax: 914-641-3501
Web: www.harrisconnect.com

CEO: William K. (Bill) Harris
CFO: Thomas (Tom) Burke
HR: –
FYE: December 31
Type: Private

Bernard Harris would hate for you to miss a class reunion. Harris Connect, founded by Bernard Harris in 1963, maintains membership databases for more than 4,000 institutions such as schools, alumni associations, and trade organizations, and produces more than 600 directories a year both in print and CD-ROM formats. Among its clients are colleges and universities, fraternities and sororities, and many private and public high schools. The company has built more than 300 online communities for alumni groups and professional organizations to network and organize. The information hubs offer message boards, online chat, and e-mail services. The company is led by Bernard's eldest son Bill.

	Annual Growth	12/03	12/04	12/05	12/06	12/07
Est. sales ($ mil.)	—	—	—	—	—	67.8
Employees	—	—	—	—	—	900

An in-depth profile of this company is available to Hoover's Online members at hoovers.com.

733

HARRIS CORPORATION

NYSE: HRS

1025 W. NASA Blvd.
Melbourne, FL 32919
Phone: 321-727-9100
Fax: 321-674-4740
Web: www.harris.com

CEO: Howard L. Lance
CFO: Gary L. McArthur
HR: Jeffrey S. (Jeff) Shuman
FYE: Friday nearest June 30
Type: Public

Hail Harris for a high-flying, high-tech hookup. The company, which develops communications products for government and commercial customers worldwide, makes microwave, satellite, and other wireless network transmission equipment; air traffic control systems; mobile radio systems; and digital network broadcasting and management systems. The company's largest customer is the US government. Harris' commercial clients include radio and TV broadcasters, utilities providers, construction companies, and oil producers. Customers have included Clear Channel Communications, Sony, and Lockheed Martin.

	Annual Growth	6/03	6/04	6/05	6/06	6/07
Sales ($ mil.)	19.3%	2,092.7	2,518.6	3,000.6	3,474.8	4,243.0
Net income ($ mil.)	68.6%	59.5	132.8	202.2	237.9	480.4
Market value ($ mil.)	62.5%	1,014.8	1,650.6	4,215.5	5,514.3	7,068.5
Employees	12.7%	—	—	12,600	13,900	16,000

HARRIS INTERACTIVE INC.

NASDAQ (GS): HPOL

60 Corporate Woods
Rochester, NY 14623
Phone: 585-272-8400
Fax: 585-272-8680
Web: www.harrisinteractive.com

CEO: Gregory T. Novak
CFO: Ronald E. (Ron) Salluzzo
HR: Dennis K. Bhame
FYE: June 30
Type: Public

Harris Interactive has a high opinion of polling data. The company is a leading market research and opinion polling firm best known for its *Harris Poll*, which takes the pulse of public opinion on various topics each week. Harris conducts its market research and polling primarily through an Internet panel consisting of more than 6 million people from around the world. It offers research services to companies in such industries as consumer goods, health care, transportation, and technology; its Harris Interactive Service Bureau provides market research services to other market research firms. Harris traces its roots back to 1956, with the founding of Louis Harris & Associates.

	Annual Growth	6/03	6/04	6/05	6/06	6/07
Sales ($ mil.)	12.8%	130.6	146.0	197.0	216.0	211.8
Net income ($ mil.)	(4.8%)	11.1	29.9	1.6	9.5	9.1
Market value ($ mil.)	(5.3%)	352.1	383.1	299.1	346.7	282.7
Employees	(27.2%)	—	—	1,763	1,283	—

HARRIS PUBLICATIONS, INC.

1115 Broadway
New York, NY 10010
Phone: 212-807-7100
Fax: 212-924-2352
Web: www.harris-pub.com

CEO: Stanley R. Harris
CFO: Warren Sherman
HR: –
FYE: December 31
Type: Private

Harris Publications publishes a variety of magazines including *King* (a men's magazine aimed at African-Americans) and *XXL* (a hip-hop music magazine). Publications in its Outdoor Group unit are focused on hunting and weaponry, with titles such as *Sportsman's Bowhunting, Whitetail Hunting, Tactical Knives,* and *Combat Handguns*. In contrast to its testosterone-laden titles, Harris Publications also publishes craft magazine *Quilt*. The company sold its *Revolver* music magazine to special-interest magazine publisher Future US in 2006.

	Annual Growth	12/03	12/04	12/05	12/06	12/07
Est. sales ($ mil.)	—	—	—	—	—	14.6
Employees	—	—	—	—	—	125

HARRIS STRATEX NETWORKS, INC.

NASDAQ (GM): HSTX

Research Triangle Park, 637 Davis Dr.
Morrisville, NC 27560
Phone: 919-767-3230
Fax: 919-767-3233
Web: www.harrisstratex.com

CEO: Guy M. Campbell
CFO: Sally A. Dudash
HR: Stephen J. (Steve) Gilmore
FYE: Friday nearest June 30
Type: Public

Harris Stratex Networks makes data fly. The company designs and manufactures wireless network transmission equipment used to link and manage both fixed and wireless voice and data networks. Customers include mobile network operators, public safety agencies, private network operators, and utility and transportation companies in about 130 countries worldwide. Sold under the Eclipse and Constellation brands among others, the company's core products are microwave radios that enable network access and interconnection. Harris Stratex also sells a range of software applications used to monitor and manage network performance; brands include NetBoss, ProVision, and StarView.

	Annual Growth	6/03	6/04	6/05	6/06	6/07
Sales ($ mil.)	—	—	—	—	—	507.9
Net income ($ mil.)	—	—	—	—	—	(17.9)
Market value ($ mil.)	—	—	—	—	—	456.7
Employees	—	—	—	—	—	—

HARRY AND DAVID DIRECT MARKETING

2500 S. Pacific Hwy.
Medford, OR 97501
Phone: 541-864-2362
Fax: 541-864-2194
Web: www.harryanddavid.com

CEO: William H. (Bill) Williams
CFO: Stephen V. (Steve) O'Connell
HR: Rudd C. Johnson
FYE: Last Saturday in June
Type: Business segment

Not only were Harry and David Holmes brothers, but they also founded and gave their names to the company that was a pioneer in selling fruit, and later other specialty foods and gift items, through catalogs, the Internet, and business-to-business and consumer telemarketing. The multi-channel marketer mails about 100 million Harry and David catalogs each year. The Internet is a growing sales channel for the company and accounts for about 45% of all orders. A unit of Harry & David Holdings, which was acquired by New York investment firm Wasserstein & Co. in 2004, Harry and David Direct Marketing (famous for its Royal Riviera pears and Moose Munch chocolates) accounts for nearly 70% of its parent company's sales.

	Annual Growth	6/02	6/03	6/04	6/05	6/06
Sales ($ mil.)	—	—	—	—	—	369.8
Employees	—	—	—	—	—	—

HARRY & DAVID HOLDINGS, INC.

2500 S. Pacific Hwy.
Medford, OR 97501
Phone: 541-864-2362
Fax: 541-864-2742
Web: www.hndcorp.com

CEO: William H. (Bill) Williams
CFO: Stephen V. (Steve) O'Connell
HR: Rudd C. Johnson
FYE: Last Saturday in June
Type: Private

Harry & David Holdings (HDH) wants customers to enjoy the fruits — and flowers — of its labors. Its Harry and David Direct Marketing catalog and Internet unit offers gift baskets filled with gourmet foods, most notably its Royal Riviera pears and chocolates. Harry and David Stores sell fruit and flowers at 135 factory outlet and specialty shops in 35 US states. HDH has sold its mail-order nursery and wholesale business Jackson & Perkins. HDH (formerly Bear Creek Holdings) had been owned by Yamanouchi (now Astellas), but was sold in 2004 to New York investment firm Wasserstein & Co. for about $260 million. In 2005 HDH's new owners filed to take the company public, but eventually withdrew the offering in 2008.

HARRY WINSTON INC.

718 5th Ave.
New York, NY 10019
Phone: 212-245-2000
Fax: 212-765-8809
Web: www.harrywinston.com

CEO: Robert A. Gannicott
CFO: Alan S. Mayne
HR: Joanne Gendelman
FYE: August 31
Type: Subsidiary

Diamonds are Harry Winston's best friend. The retail arm of Canada's Harry Winston Diamond Corp. (formerly Aber Diamond Corp.), Harry Winston company buys, designs, and sells diamonds and gems. With about a dozen salons in locales including Beijing, London, New York, and Paris, the company's clientele includes sultans, starlets, and other affluent types who can afford the average $100,000 price tag for a Winston bauble. To broaden its clientele, Harry Winston is shedding some of its exclusive aura in favor of a more approachable image. The House of Harry Winston was established in 1932 by Harry Winston, the son of a New York jeweler. Harry's son Ronald retired as an executive of the company in 2008.

	Annual Growth	8/03	8/04	8/05	8/06	8/07
Est. sales ($ mil.)	—	—	—	—	—	20.1
Employees	—	—	—	—	—	200

HARSCO CORPORATION

NYSE: HSC

350 Poplar Church Rd.
Camp Hill, PA 17011
Phone: 717-763-7064
Fax: 717-763-6424
Web: www.harsco.com

CEO: Salvatore D. Fazzolari
CFO: Stephen J. Schnoor
HR: Gerald F. (Gerry) Vinci
FYE: December 31
Type: Public

If you're a metal producer or a construction company, Harsco is at your service. Its mill services unit, MultiServ, offers metal reclamation, slag processing, scrap management, and other services for steel and nonferrous metals producers. Harsco's Access Services businesses, SGB Group, Hünnebeck Group, and Patent Construction Systems, rent and sell concrete-forming equipment, scaffolding, and bridge-decking products, primarily to companies in the industrial maintenance and nonresidential construction industries. Other Harsco units make railway track, industrial grating, and heat exchangers.

	Annual Growth	12/03	12/04	12/05	12/06	12/07
Sales ($ mil.)	14.9%	2,118.5	2,502.1	2,766.2	3,423.3	3,688.2
Net income ($ mil.)	34.3%	92.2	121.2	156.7	196.4	299.5
Market value ($ mil.)	56.8%	895.4	1,154.7	1,410.4	1,598.8	5,411.3
Employees	1.2%	—	—	21,000	21,500	21,500

HARTE-HANKS, INC.

NYSE: HHS

200 Concord Plaza Dr., Suite 800
San Antonio, TX 78216
Phone: 210-829-9000
Fax: 210-829-9403
Web: www.harte-hanks.com

CEO: Dean H. Blythe
CFO: Douglas (Doug) Shepard
HR: Andrew Harrison
FYE: December 31
Type: Public

Harte-Hanks is a leading direct marketing services company and one of the largest producers of shoppers (advertising circulars sent by mail) in the US. The company provides integrated direct marketing services, ranging from market research and analytics to building contact databases and tracking leads. It also provides telephone, e-mail, and printing and mailing services designed to connect customers with their potential clients. Harte-Hanks' customers include major retailers and companies from the financial services, health care, and technology industries. The company's shopper division boasts a weekly circulation of about 13 million in key markets in California and Florida.

	Annual Growth	12/03	12/04	12/05	12/06	12/07
Sales ($ mil.)	5.3%	944.6	1,030.5	1,135.0	1,184.7	1,162.9
Net income ($ mil.)	1.5%	87.4	97.6	114.5	111.8	92.6
Market value ($ mil.)	(11.3%)	1,903.0	2,207.8	2,150.5	2,084.2	1,175.3
Employees	(0.6%)	—	—	7,106	6,338	7,026

THE HARTFORD FINANCIAL SERVICES GROUP, INC.

NYSE: HIG

One Hartford Plaza
Hartford, CT 06155
Phone: 860-547-5000
Fax: 860-547-2680
Web: www.thehartford.com

CEO: Ramani Ayer
CFO: Lizabeth H. (Liz) Zlatkus
HR: Eileen G. Whelley
FYE: December 31
Type: Public

This buck makes bucks by offering a variety of personal and commercial life and property/casualty insurance products, including homeowners, auto, and workers' compensation. Through its Hartford Life subsidiary, the company offers individual and group life insurance, annuities, employee benefits administration, asset management, and mutual funds (managed both in-house and by other groups including Wellington Management). Its property/casualty operations include both personal and business coverage, including specialty commercial coverage for large companies. The Hartford, in business since 1810, sells its products through about 11,000 independent agencies and more than 100,000 registered broker-dealers.

	Annual Growth	12/03	12/04	12/05	12/06	12/07
Assets ($ mil.)	12.4%	225,853.0	259,735.0	285,557.0	326,710.0	360,361.0
Net income ($ mil.)	—	(91.0)	2,115.0	2,274.0	2,745.0	2,949.0
Market value ($ mil.)	13.1%	16,727.9	20,391.6	25,951.9	30,168.6	27,363.9
Employees	1.7%	—	—	30,000	31,000	31,000

HARTFORD LIFE, INC.

200 Hopmeadow St.
Simsbury, CT 06089
Phone: 860-547-5000
Fax: 860-843-3528

CEO: John C. Walters
CFO: Glenn D. Lammey
HR: Jennifer Geisler
FYE: December 31
Type: Subsidiary

When choosing life insurance, you might find yourself having a heart-to-hart conversation with Hartford Life. As the life insurance arm of, The Hartford Financial Services Group, Hartford Life provides retail and institutional investment products such as annuities, mutual funds, and private placement life insurance. Hartford Life also provides life insurance for wealth protection, accumulation, and transfer, and offers group benefits, as well as fixed and variable annuity products via international operations. The company also operates through subsidiary Hartford Life and Accident Insurance Company.

HARTMARX CORPORATION

NYSE: HMX

101 N. Wacker Dr.
Chicago, IL 60606
Phone: 312-372-6300
Fax: 312-444-2710
Web: www.hartmarx.com

CEO: Homi B. Patel
CFO: Glenn R. Morgan
HR: Michael Pickelny
FYE: November 30
Type: Public

Hartmarx fills its pockets by outfitting well-heeled customers with its tailored clothing and sportswear. It's a top maker of men's suits and sports coats under the Hart Schaffner & Marx and Hickey-Freeman labels, as well as Austin Reed- and Barrie Pace-branded women's suits and separates. Best known for its tailored items, the firm also makes and markets Bobby Jones golfwear and Sansabelt slacks. It manufactures clothing under license from Tommy Hilfiger and other designers. Hartmarx sells its suits and sport coats primarily to upscale retailers; the balance is distributed to department and specialty stores, pro shops, resorts, and catalogs in the US and more than a dozen other countries.

	Annual Growth	11/03	11/04	11/05	11/06	11/07
Sales ($ mil.)	0.0%	563.8	588.9	600.3	600.5	564.9
Net income ($ mil.)	—	8.7	15.9	23.6	7.3	(4.2)
Market value ($ mil.)	(1.4%)	150.8	291.9	272.7	240.7	142.8
Employees	(3.7%)	—	—	4,100	4,000	3,800

An in-depth profile of this company is available to Hoover's Online members at hoovers.com.

735

HARTVILLE GROUP, INC.

OTC: HVLL

3840 Greentree Ave. SW
Canton, OH 44706
Phone: 330-484-8080
Fax: 330-484-8081
Web: www.hartvillegroup.com

CEO: Dennis C. Rushovich
CFO: Christopher R. Sachs
HR: Donna L. Killean Smith
FYE: December 31
Type: Public

Whether your heart belongs to a Fluffy or a Duke, Hartville can serve your pet insurance needs. Its Petsmarketing Insurance.com Agency subsidiary markets and sells health coverage for household pets across the US on behalf of insurance underwriters. Another unit, Hartville Re, provides reinsurance for pet health policies. Petsmarketing's products cover only cats and dogs, but range from the basic (illnesses, injuries, and neutering) to the deluxe (long-term and chronic illnesses, dental cleanings, and vaccinations). Proving itself no mere runt, Hartville insures over 60,000 pets and has been in business since 1997. The company sells its products by telephone and online.

	Annual Growth	12/03	12/04	12/05	12/06	12/07
Assets ($ mil.)	(10.2%)	10.6	14.9	9.4	6.2	6.9
Net income ($ mil.)	—	0.9	(8.1)	(8.0)	(11.2)	(21.1)
Market value ($ mil.)	(64.2%)	943.5	380.4	33.5	115.1	15.4
Employees	—	—	—	—	—	—

THE HARTZ MOUNTAIN CORPORATION

400 Plaza Dr.
Secaucus, NJ 07094
Phone: 201-271-4800
Fax: 201-271-0164
Web: www.hartz.com

CEO: William D. (Bill) Ecker
CFO: Chris Bridgnell
HR: Kelly Shevlin
FYE: March 31
Type: Subsidiary

Hartz Mountain has something for pets of all sizes. It markets more than 1,500 pet care products including nutritional items for small pets, birds, and fish; over-the-counter animal health products; and toys and accessories for dogs, cats, and birds. German immigrant Max Stern founded Hartz in 1926. His family operated the firm for more than 75 years under the Hartz Group umbrella along with the family's real estate operations. Investment group J.W. Childs and Hartz management bought the company in 2000, then sold it to the Sumitomo Corporation in 2004.

	Annual Growth	3/03	3/04	3/05	3/06	3/07
Est. sales ($ mil.)	—	—	—	—	—	189.3
Employees	—	—	—	—	—	1,600

HARVARD BIOSCIENCE, INC.

NASDAQ (GM): HBIO

84 October Hill Rd., Ste. 7
Holliston, MA 01746
Phone: 508-893-8999
Fax: 508-429-5732
Web: www.harvardbioscience.com

CEO: Chane Graziano
CFO: Susan M. Luscinski
HR: –
FYE: December 31
Type: Public

Toss a Harvard Bioscience catalog to a bioscience researcher and it will keep him busy for hours. The company develops, manufactures, and markets the scientific gizmos and instruments used in pharmaceutical, biotechnology, academic, and government labs around the world. Its 11,000 item-strong product line is focused on molecular biology and ADMET (absorption, distribution, metabolism, elimination, and toxicology); Harvard Bioscience sells tests to screen drug candidates for these qualities. Other products include spectrophotometers, analyzers, ventilators, and protein calculators. Customers can shop directly online, from its printed Harvard Apparatus catalog, or through distributors.

	Annual Growth	12/03	12/04	12/05	12/06	12/07
Sales ($ mil.)	(1.1%)	87.1	92.6	67.4	76.2	83.4
Net income ($ mil.)	—	4.3	2.3	(31.9)	(2.3)	(1.4)
Market value ($ mil.)	(14.8%)	268.2	140.7	135.6	156.8	141.3
Employees	—	—	—	269	—	—

THE HARVARD DRUG GROUP, L.L.C.

31778 Enterprise Dr.
Livonia, MI 48150
Phone: 734-743-6000
Fax: 734-743-7000
Web: www.theharvarddruggroup.com

CEO: Randolph J. Friedman
CFO: David F. Liming
HR: –
FYE: June 30
Type: Private

Drugs, not scholars, are what come out of this Harvard. The Harvard Drug Group distributes branded and generic prescription and OTC drugs, vitamins, and consumer products to retailers, medical and veterinary professionals, hospitals, and nursing homes. Its in-house generics are sold under the Major brand. The company distributes veterinary products through its RS Veterinary Supply subsidiary. The firm also offers manufacturing services through its partnership with Canadian drugmaker Apotex. Founded as Great Lakes Wholesale Drug in 1967, the company transformed itself into The Harvard Drug Group in 1997 after a steady regimen of acquisitions. Chairman and CEO Randolf Friedman and president and COO Jay Levine own the company.

	Annual Growth	6/03	6/04	6/05	6/06	6/07
Est. sales ($ mil.)	—	—	—	—	—	336.9
Employees	—	—	—	—	—	300

HARVARD PILGRIM HEALTH CARE, INC.

93 Worcester St.
Wellesley, MA 02481
Phone: 617-509-1000
Fax: 617-509-7590
Web: www.harvardpilgrim.org

CEO: Charles D. (Charlie) Baker Jr.
CFO: James M. DuCharme
HR: Deborah Hicks
FYE: December 31
Type: Not-for-profit

If Harvard Pilgrim Health Care were any more New England-centric, it would have to be located on Plymouth Rock. A leading provider of health benefits in Massachusetts, the not-for-profit organization also offers plans to residents of New Hampshire and Maine. It has about 1 million members enrolled in its HMO, PPO, point-of-service, and Medicare Advantage plans. Those members have access to a regional network of about 135 hospitals and 28,000 doctors and other providers. Harvard Pilgrim Health Care also targets multi-state employers with its Choice Plus and Options PPO plans, offered through a partnership with UnitedHealth.

HARVARD UNIVERSITY

University Hall
Cambridge, MA 02138
Phone: 617-495-1000
Fax: 617-495-0754
Web: www.harvard.edu

CEO: Drew Gilpin Faust
CFO: Elizabeth Mora
HR: Marilyn M. Hausammann
FYE: June 30
Type: School

Many parents dream of sending their children to Harvard; and at more than $30,000 a year (undergraduate), some even dream of being able to afford it. Harvard, the oldest institution of higher learning in the US, is home to Harvard College (undergraduate studies) and 10 graduate schools including the Harvard Business, Law, and Medical schools. The Radcliffe Institute for Advanced Study at Harvard was created when Radcliffe College and Harvard University merged in 1999. Harvard has about 20,000 students, about half of whom are enrolled in graduate programs. Harvard's endowment of more than $29 billion is the largest of any university in the world. (Yale ranks #2.)

	Annual Growth	6/02	6/03	6/04	6/05	6/06
Sales ($ mil.)	6.2%	2,357.0	2,472.7	2,597.7	2,800.9	2,999.6
Employees	(3.5%)	15,000	15,000	15,000	18,000	13,000

HARVEST NATURAL RESOURCES, INC.

NYSE: HNR

1177 Enclave Pkwy., Ste. 300
Houston, TX 77077
Phone: 281-899-5700
Fax: 281-899-5702
Web: www.harvestnr.com

CEO: James A. Edmiston
CFO: Stephen C. Haynes
HR: –
FYE: December 31
Type: Public

Harvest Natural Resources is keen to harvest the natural resources of oil and gas. The independent's main exploration and production work takes place in Venezuela, where it operates through its 80%-owned subsidiary, Harvest Vinccler. Harvest's operations hit a snag in 2005, due to Venezuela's difficult political climate, which has restricted the company's contracts and production activities. Founded in 1989, the company sold its stakes in Siberian ventures Arctic Gas and Geoilbent to Yukos in 2003. The company still has an interest in developing Russian and Chinese oil assets.

	Annual Growth	12/03	12/04	12/05	12/06	12/07
Sales ($ mil.)	(43.0%)	106.1	186.1	236.9	59.5	11.2
Net income ($ mil.)	20.3%	27.3	34.4	50.8	(58.6)	57.2
Market value ($ mil.)	5.4%	355.0	635.2	328.4	395.5	438.1
Employees	—	—	—	252	—	—

HARVEY ELECTRONICS, INC.

Pink Sheets: HRVE

205 Chubb Ave.
Lyndhurst, NJ 07071
Phone: 201-842-0078
Fax: 201-842-0660
Web: www.harveyonline.com

CEO: Michael E. Recca
CFO: Joseph J. Calabrese
HR: Janina Majchrzak
FYE: Saturday nearest October 31
Type: Public

Harvey Electronics gives serious audiophiles their stereo fix. The company offers esoteric (read: expensive) audio and video products at nine stores in the New York metropolitan area. It sells, repairs, and installs home theater and multi-room audio systems — including such big-ticket items as plasma flat-screen TVs — made by electronics giants such as Sony and Samsung and specialty manufacturers such as Boston Acoustics and Marantz. Installations can cost its clients more than $100,000. Two of Harvey Electronics' stores operate under the Bang & Olufsen brand name; those stores specialize in the Danish vendor's high-end products. The company has filed for Chapter 11 bankruptcy protection.

	Annual Growth	10/02	10/03	10/04	10/05	*10/06
Sales ($ mil.)	(3.5%)	41.6	42.5	43.2	40.4	36.1
Net income ($ mil.)	—	0.2	0.3	1.3	(0.8)	(3.2)
Employees	(5.0%)	157	147	153	152	128

*Most recent year available

HARVEY INDUSTRIES, INC.

1400 Main St.
Waltham, MA 02451
Phone: 781-899-3500
Fax: 781-398-7826
Web: www.harveyind.com

CEO: Alan Marlow
CFO: Frances E. (Frank) Martel
HR: –
FYE: February 28
Type: Private

At Harvey Industries the window of opportunity is always open. The company, incorporated in 1961, designs and manufactures its own line of vinyl and wood windows, as well as storm windows and doors. Harvey Industries also distributes brand-name exterior building products such as vinyl siding, roofing materials, and windows made by other manufacturers. It operates a network of nearly 30 warehouses in Connecticut, Maine, Massachusetts, New Hampshire, New York, Pennsylvania, Rhode Island, and Vermont that mainly serve professional contractors and builders. Harvey Industries operates three plants and two new-construction set-up shops. Co-founders and chairmen Fred Bigony and Bob Morrison control the company.

	Annual Growth	2/03	2/04	2/05	2/06	2/07
Est. sales ($ mil.)	—	—	—	—	—	481.2
Employees	—	—	—	—	—	2,000

HASBRO, INC.

NYSE: HAS

1027 Newport Ave.
Pawtucket, RI 02862
Phone: 401-431-8697
Fax: 401-431-8535
Web: www.hasbro.com

CEO: Brian Goldner
CFO: David D. R. Hargreaves
HR: Bob Carniaux
FYE: Last Sunday in December
Type: Public

It's all fun and games at Hasbro, the #2 toy maker in the US (after Mattel) and the producer of such childhood favorites as G.I. Joe, Play-Doh, Tonka toys, Nerf balls, and Weebles. Besides toys, Hasbro makes board games under its Milton Bradley (*Scrabble*, *Candy Land*) and Parker Brothers (*Monopoly*, *Trivial Pursuit*) brands, as well as trading cards such as *Pokémon*, *Harry Potter*, and *Magic: The Gathering* (through its Wizards of the Coast unit). Hasbro also makes *Star Wars* action figures and is the licensee of action figures and games for the prequels, as well as toys related to Disney and other movie and television characters.

	Annual Growth	12/03	12/04	12/05	12/06	12/07
Sales ($ mil.)	5.2%	3,138.7	2,997.5	3,087.6	3,151.5	3,837.6
Net income ($ mil.)	20.5%	157.7	196.0	212.1	230.1	333.0
Market value ($ mil.)	0.3%	3,724.1	3,402.7	3,623.1	4,376.9	3,762.3
Employees	0.0%	—	—	5,900	5,800	5,900

THE HASKELL COMPANY

111 Riverside Ave.
Jacksonville, FL 32202
Phone: 904-791-4500
Fax: 904-475-7681
Web: www.thehaskellco.com

CEO: Steven T. (Steve) Halverson
CFO: Edward W. Mullinix Jr.
HR: David I. Bogage
FYE: December 31
Type: Private

If a construction firm is what you need, don't *Leave it to Beaver*, try Haskell (tell 'em Eddie sent you). The company ranks among the US's top design/build firms, which oversee not only the architectural and engineering design but also the construction of a project. Haskell also offers construction management, facility management, interior design, steel fabrication, infrastructure, and real estate services. Projects include industrial, commercial, and institutional facilities and range from a Krispy Kreme Doughnuts factory to a federal medium-security prison. Chairman Preston Haskell founded the employee-owned firm in 1965 and also led the establishment of the Design-Build Institute of America in 1993.

HASTINGS ENTERTAINMENT, INC.

NASDAQ (GM): HAST

3601 Plains Blvd.
Amarillo, TX 79102
Phone: 806-351-2300
Fax: 806-467-8330
Web: www.gohastings.com

CEO: John H. Marmaduke
CFO: Dan Crow
HR: Lisa Hallett
FYE: January 31
Type: Public

Hastings Entertainment has it all for a small-town Saturday night. The company operates some 150 multimedia stores in about 20 Midwestern and Western US states, mostly in small and medium-sized towns. Its stores and Web site sell new and used music, videos, DVDs, books, games, and magazines, in addition to related electronics such as video game consoles and DVD players. Many of Hastings' locations are "superstores" averaging about 20,000 sq. ft. and offering such amenities as music listening stations, reading chairs, coffee bars, snacks, and kids' play areas. The founding Marmaduke family, including CEO John and director Stephen, owns about 42% of Hastings.

	Annual Growth	1/04	1/05	1/06	1/07	1/08
Sales ($ mil.)	1.9%	508.3	542.0	537.9	548.3	547.7
Net income ($ mil.)	6.9%	7.8	5.8	5.7	5.0	10.2
Market value ($ mil.)	13.9%	54.0	94.5	60.9	65.0	90.8
Employees	(2.1%)	—	—	6,344	5,962	6,080

An in-depth profile of this company is available to Hoover's Online members at hoovers.com.

737

HASTINGS MANUFACTURING COMPANY

Pink Sheets: HGMG

325 N. Hanover St.
Hastings, MI 49058
Phone: 269-945-2491
Fax: 269-945-4667
Web: www.hastingsmanufacturing.com

CEO: Fred Cook
CFO: Richard L. (Rick) Zwiernikowski
HR: –
FYE: December 31
Type: Public

Hastings Manufacturing is one of the automotive industry's ring leaders. The company's main business is making piston rings for the automotive aftermarket. Customers include engine rebuilders, retail outlets, and warehouse distributors. Hastings Manufacturing also makes piston rings for OEMs. Through a joint venture, the company sells additives for engines, transmissions, and cooling systems under the Casite brand name. Hastings Manufacturing distributes its products throughout the US and Canada. Chairman and CEO Mark Johnson and his family control the company, which was formed in 1915.

	Annual Growth	12/03	12/04	12/05	12/06	12/07
Est. sales ($ mil.)	—	—	—	—	—	13.4
Employees	—	—	—	—	—	215

HAT WORLD CORPORATION

7555 Woodland Dr.
Indianapolis, IN 46278
Phone: 317-334-9428
Fax: 317-337-1428
Web: www.hatworld.com

CEO: Kenneth J. (Ken) Kocher
CFO: Rick Cramer
HR: Carla Rodecap
FYE: January 31
Type: Subsidiary

Hat World tells its customers to put a lid on it. The largely mall-based retailer specializes in caps featuring licensed logos of pro (MLB, NBA, NFL, and NHL) and college sports teams. With nearly 800 stores in the US, Puerto Rico, and Canada, Hat World is the biggest licensed headwear company in the US. It opened its first store in 1995; six years later, Hat World bought bankrupt rival Lids and tripled in size. Stores and Web sites operate under both names and stock caps with regional team favorites. Hat World was acquired by footwear retailer Genesco in 2004 for $165 million; the company also signed a licensing agreement with industry big-head Mainland Headwear Holdings.

	Annual Growth	1/02	1/03	1/04	1/05	1/06
Sales ($ mil.)	37.4%	—	—	—	216.3	297.3
Net income ($ mil.)	—	—	—	—	—	40.1
Employees	—	—	—	—	—	—

HATTERAS FINANCIAL CORP.

NYSE: HTS

3288 Robinhood Rd., Ste. 100
Winston-Salem, NC 27106
Phone: 336-760-9347
Fax: –
Web: hatfin.com

CEO: Michael R. Hough
CFO: Kenneth A. Steele
HR: –
FYE: December 31
Type: Public

Hatteras Financial hopes for smooth sailing on the sometimes tumultuous seas of mortgage investing. The company is a mortgage real estate investment trust (REIT) that invests in adjustable rate (ARM) and hybrid adjustable rate single-family residential mortgages guaranteed by a US government agency or a government-backed company such as Ginnie Mae, Fannie Mae, or Freddie Mac. Hatteras' nearly $2 billion portfolio includes three-, five- (the majority), and seven-year hybrid ARM loans backed by Fannie Mae, mostly, and Freddie Mac. Hybrids start with a fixed rate for a set period (three, five, seven, or 10 years) and then become adjustable. Hatteras Financial is externally managed by Atlantic Capital Advisors.

	Annual Growth	12/03	12/04	12/05	12/06	12/07
Sales ($ mil.)	—	—	—	—	—	7.3
Net income ($ mil.)	—	—	—	—	—	1.2
Employees	—	—	—	—	—	6

HAUPPAUGE DIGITAL, INC.

NASDAQ (GM): HAUP

91 Cabot Ct.
Hauppauge, NY 11788
Phone: 631-434-1600
Fax: 631-434-3198
Web: www.hauppauge.com

CEO: Kenneth H. (Ken) Plotkin
CFO: Gerald (Jerry) Tucciarone
HR: Cheryl Willins
FYE: September 30
Type: Public

Wanna watch TV at work? Hauppauge Digital's WinTV analog and digital video boards let viewers videoconference, watch TV, and view input from VCRs and camcorders in a resizable window on a PC monitor. Hauppauge (pronounced "HAW-pog") also offers boards that accommodate radio and Internet broadcasts, and makes a line of PC video editing boards. The company outsources its manufacturing to companies in Europe and Asia. The company sells its products to manufacturers, including ASUSTeK Computer and Hon Hai Precision Industry (Foxconn), and has partnered with companies such as Intel and Microsoft. Customers outside the US make up more than 40% of sales.

	Annual Growth	9/03	9/04	9/05	9/06	9/07
Sales ($ mil.)	21.4%	51.0	65.3	78.5	97.7	110.9
Net income ($ mil.)	—	(0.8)	1.8	1.4	2.4	5.3
Market value ($ mil.)	15.8%	24.1	29.9	32.2	52.0	43.2
Employees	6.4%	113	135	138	141	145

HAVERTY FURNITURE COMPANIES, INC.

NYSE: HVT

780 Johnson Ferry Rd. NE, Ste. 800
Atlanta, GA 30342
Phone: 404-443-2900
Fax: 404-443-4180
Web: www.havertys.com

CEO: Clarence H. Smith
CFO: Dennis L. Fink
HR: Allan J. DeNiro
FYE: December 31
Type: Public

A table for dining, a chair to recline in — Haverty Furniture Companies fills the bill. Better known as Havertys, the company sells its own brand of furniture (launched 2000) as well as name-brand home furnishings and accessories in the middle to upper-middle price range. Private-label Havertys Collections and Havertys Premium Collections carry higher margins. The furniture seller has 120 showrooms in about 20 southern and central US states. Havertys is growing by enlarging or replacing smaller stores in high-growth markets. The retailer also sells bedding products in its showrooms from Sealy, Serta, and Tempur-Pedic. Furniture accounts for about 80% of the company's sales.

	Annual Growth	12/03	12/04	12/05	12/06	12/07
Sales ($ mil.)	1.2%	751.0	788.7	831.2	859.1	787.1
Net income ($ mil.)	(48.4%)	25.3	22.6	15.1	16.0	1.8
Market value ($ mil.)	(18.8%)	357.8	339.6	233.7	273.4	155.6
Employees	2.3%	—	—	4,400	4,500	—

HAWAIIAN ELECTRIC INDUSTRIES, INC.

NYSE: HE

900 Richards St.
Honolulu, HI 96813
Phone: 808-543-5662
Fax: 808-543-7602
Web: www.hei.com

CEO: Constance H. (Connie) Lau
CFO: Curtis Y. Harada
HR: –
FYE: December 31
Type: Public

When the luau bonfires go out, Hawaiian Electric Industries (HEI) keeps the islands lit up. HEI is the holding company for Hawaiian Electric Company (HECO) and some nonutility businesses. HECO (along with its utility subsidiaries Maui Electric and Hawaii Electric Light) serves about 440,000 customers as the sole public electricity provider on the islands of Hawaii, Lanai, Maui, Molokai, and Oahu. The utilities account for 83% of HEI's sales and have a generating capacity of about 1,670 MW. Nonutility businesses include American Savings Bank (with 63 retail branches in the state), investment firms, and energy-related services providers.

	Annual Growth	12/03	12/04	12/05	12/06	12/07
Sales ($ mil.)	9.5%	1,781.3	1,924.1	2,215.6	2,460.9	2,563.4
Net income ($ mil.)	(7.2%)	114.2	109.7	126.7	108.0	84.8
Employees	2.4%	3,197	3,354	3,383	3,447	3,520

HAWAIIAN HOLDINGS, INC.

AMEX: HA

3375 Koapaka St., Ste. G-350
Honolulu, HI 96819
Phone: 808-835-3700
Fax: 808-835-3690
Web: www.hawaiianair.com

CEO: Mark B. Dunkerley
CFO: Peter R. Ingram
HR: Barbara D. Falvey
FYE: December 31
Type: Public

Luaus, leis, and lazing in the sun — Hawaiian Holdings knows how to get you there. The company's main subsidiary, Hawaiian Airlines, transports passengers and cargo between Honolulu and major cities in the western US. Transpacific routes account for more than two-thirds of the carrier's revenue. Hawaiian Airlines also serves four of the six main Hawaiian islands and destinations in the South Pacific such as American Samoa, Australia, and Tahiti. It operates a fleet of about 30 Boeing aircraft. In addition to its scheduled passenger and cargo operations, Hawaiian Airlines provides charter services.

	Annual Growth	12/03	12/04	12/05	12/06	12/07
Sales ($ mil.)	39.6%	—	—	504.3	888.0	982.6
Net income ($ mil.)	—	—	—	(12.4)	(40.5)	7.1
Market value ($ mil.)	14.6%	—	—	183.3	228.3	240.9
Employees	1.5%	—	—	3,317	3,454	3,415

HAWAIIAN TELCOM COMMUNICATIONS, INC.

1177 Bishop St.
Honolulu, HI 96813
Phone: 808-546-4511
Fax: 808-546-6194
Web: hawaiiantel.com

CEO: Eric K. Yeaman
CFO: Robert F. (Bob) Reich
HR: Claire Cooper
FYE: December 31
Type: Private

No "coconut telegraph," Hawaiian Telcom Communications provides modern telecommunications services to residential and business customers in the island state. Hawaiian Telcom serves all of Hawaii's main island and has more than 550,000 local access lines in service. It also provides about 260,000 long-distance lines and about 93,000 broadband (DSL) Internet access lines. The company resells wireless communications services through an agreement with Sprint Nextel. Hawaiian Telcom, the state's incumbent local exchange carrier, has been in operation since 1883.

	Annual Growth	12/02	12/03	12/04	12/05	12/06
Sales ($ mil.)	69.0%	—	—	—	337.4	570.2
Net income ($ mil.)	—	—	—	—	(175.7)	(144.6)
Employees	(3.2%)	—	—	—	1,760	1,704

HAWK CORPORATION

AMEX: HWK

200 Public Square, Ste. 1500
Cleveland, OH 44114
Phone: 216-861-3553
Fax: 216-861-4546
Web: www.hawkcorp.com

CEO: Ronald E. Weinberg
CFO: Joseph J. Levanduski
HR: –
FYE: December 31
Type: Public

Whether you're flying an airplane or driving a tractor, Hawk wants to help put a stop to it. The company's friction products segment manufactures components used in brakes, clutches, and transmissions for off-highway vehicles, motorcycles, and trucks, along with brake parts for commercial and general aircraft landing systems. The company has announced it plans to sell its performance racing division that makes racecar clutches, transmissions, and driveline systems. Founded in 1989, Hawk operates more than 10 manufacturing facilities in six countries.

	Annual Growth	12/03	12/04	12/05	12/06	12/07
Sales ($ mil.)	3.1%	202.6	241.2	265.4	212.1	228.7
Net income ($ mil.)	—	(5.4)	1.1	(1.3)	3.0	17.3
Market value ($ mil.)	50.7%	31.3	75.9	131.1	107.9	161.6
Employees	(36.3%)	—	—	1,800	1,115	730

HAWKER BEECHCRAFT CORPORATION

10511 E. Central
Wichita, KS 67206
Phone: 316-676-7111
Fax: 316-676-6614
Web: www.hawkerbeechcraft.com

CEO: James E. (Jim) Schuster
CFO: James K. Sanders
HR: Sharad (Rich) Jiwanlal
FYE: December 31
Type: Private

Hawker Beechcraft (formerly Raytheon Aircraft) is flying solo now. The company manufactures passenger planes, and offers service and support as well as aircraft management and charter services. The company manufactures business jets (including Hawker 400XP, Hawker 850XP, Hawker 4000, Beechjet Premier IA), turboprops (King Air 350/B200GT/C90GTi), and piston-powered aircraft (Baron G58, Bonanza G36). The company handles mainteence orders through some 100 authorized and factory-owned sevice centers. Defense giant Raytheon Company sold Raytheon Aircraft in 2007 in order to focus on defense operations. The new owners changed the name to Hawker Beechcraft.

	Annual Growth	12/03	12/04	12/05	12/06	12/07
Est. sales ($ mil.)	—	—	—	—	—	586.5
Employees	—	—	—	—	—	7,999

HAWKINS, INC.

NASDAQ (GM): HWKN

3100 E. Hennepin Ave.
Minneapolis, MN 55413
Phone: 612-331-6910
Fax: 612-331-5304
Web: www.hawkinschemical.com

CEO: John R. Hawkins
CFO: Kathleen P. Pepski
HR: Tom Walters
FYE: Sunday nearest March 31
Type: Public

Hawkins processes and distributes bulk specialty chemicals. Its industrial chemicals segment stores and distributes caustic soda, phosphoric acid, and aqua ammonia, among many others. The segment also makes bleach (sodium hypochlorite), repackages liquid chlorine, and custom blends other chemicals. Hawkins' water treatment group distributes products and equipment used to treat drinking water, municipal and industrial wastewater, and public swimming pools. It also distributes laboratory-grade chemicals for the pharmaceutical industry. Through its fleet of trucks and tankers, the company operates facilities and serves customers throughout the midwestern US.

	Annual Growth	3/04	3/05	3/06	3/07	3/08
Sales ($ mil.)	16.4%	107.0	115.3	143.3	160.4	196.4
Net income ($ mil.)	11.9%	5.8	8.1	8.9	8.1	9.1
Market value ($ mil.)	6.7%	120.6	123.3	143.1	150.1	156.2
Employees	3.4%	—	—	235	243	

HAWORTH, INC.

1 Haworth Center
Holland, MI 49423
Phone: 616-393-3000
Fax: 616-393-1570
Web: www.haworth.com

CEO: Franco Bianchi
CFO: John Mooney
HR: Pamela Wright Armstrong
FYE: December 31
Type: Private

Designers at Haworth sit at their cubicles and think about . . . more cubicles. The company is one of the top office furniture manufacturers in the US, competing with top rivals Steelcase and HNI Corporation. Haworth offers a full range of furniture known for its innovative design, including partitions, desks, chairs, tables, and storage products. Brands include Monaco, Patterns, PLACES, and X99. Dilbert and other long-suffering office drones have Haworth to thank for inventing the pre-wired partitions that make today's cubicled workplace possible. Haworth is owned by the family of Gerrard Haworth, who founded the company in 1948.

	Annual Growth	12/02	12/03	12/04	12/05	12/06
Sales ($ mil.)	2.9%	1,320.0	1,230.0	1,260.0	1,400.0	1,480.0
Employees	(4.2%)	9,500	9,000	7,500	7,500	8,000

An in-depth profile of this company is available to Hoover's Online members at hoovers.com.

739

HAWTHORN BANCSHARES, INC.

NASDAQ (GM): HWBK

300 SW Longview Blvd.	CEO: James E. Smith
Lee's Summit, MO 64081	CFO: Richard G. Rose
Phone: 816-347-8100	HR: –
Fax: 816-268-6318	FYE: December 31
Web: www.exchangebancshares.com	Type: Public

Hawthorn Bancshares — through its subsidiary Hawthorn Bank — keeps a hawk eye on its clients' money. With more than two dozen branches in Missouri, the bank offers such deposit products as checking, savings, and money market accounts, CDs, and IRAs, as well as lending, trust, and brokerage services. Real estate mortgages account for more than 60% of Hawthorn Bancshares' loan portfolio, followed by real estate construction and commercial loans (more than 15% each) and, to a lesser extent, consumer loans. The company in 2007 consolidated four banks under the Hawthorn Bank charter and changed the holding company's name from Exchange National Bancshares to its current moniker.

	Annual Growth	12/03	12/04	12/05	12/06	12/07
Assets ($ mil.)	8.1%	875.6	923.9	1,126.5	1,142.7	1,195.8
Net income ($ mil.)	(3.5%)	9.0	8.3	9.9	10.9	7.8
Market value ($ mil.)	(8.8%)	150.9	120.4	123.1	131.4	104.2
Employees	7.8%	280	292	377	389	378

⊞ HAYES LEMMERZ INTERNATIONAL, INC.

NASDAQ (GM): HAYZ

15300 Centennial Dr.	CEO: Curtis J. Clawson
Northville, MI 48168	CFO: –
Phone: 734-737-5000	HR: Larry Karenko
Fax: 734-737-2198	FYE: January 31
Web: www.hayes-lemmerz.com	Type: Public

Steel Wheels is more than a Stones album — it's a living for Hayes Lemmerz. The company rolls along as the world's #1 maker of steel and aluminum wheels for automobiles. The company has structured its operations into two segments: automotive wheels and other products. It has divested most of its components segment, which included automotive brakes and suspensions. Its wheel segment makes steel and aluminum wheels for cars and light trucks. The company's other products include powertrain components. Major customers include GM, Ford, Honda, Nissan, and Toyota.

	Annual Growth	1/04	1/05	1/06	1/07	1/08
Sales ($ mil.)	0.8%	2,056.4	2,244.5	2,277.2	2,056.2	2,126.7
Net income ($ mil.)	—	996.5	(62.3)	(457.5)	(166.9)	(194.4)
Market value ($ mil.)	(10.3%)	550.5	303.7	141.7	175.8	355.7
Employees	(7.9%)	—	—	10,500	8,500	8,900

HAYNES INTERNATIONAL, INC.

NASDAQ (GS): HAYN

1020 W. Park Ave.	CEO: Francis J. Petro
Kokomo, IN 46904	CFO: Marcel Martin
Phone: 765-456-6012	HR: –
Fax: 765-456-6905	FYE: September 30
Web: www.haynesintl.com	Type: Public

Haynes International is an ally of companies that use alloys. Haynes develops and manufactures nickel- and cobalt-based alloys. The company specializes in high-temperature alloys (HTAs) able to withstand extreme temperatures and corrosion-resistant alloys (CRAs) that stand up to corrosive substances and processes. HTAs are used in jet engines, gas turbines used for power generation, and waste incinerators, while CRAs have applications in chemical processing, power plant emissions control, and hazardous waste treatment. HTAs account for about three-quarters of the company's sales. The aerospace industry is the biggest market for Haynes, accounting for more than a third of its business.

	Annual Growth	9/03	9/04	9/05	9/06	9/07
Est. sales ($ mil.)	—	—	—	—	—	434.4
Employees	—	—	—	—	—	1,072

HAYWARD INDUSTRIES, INC.

620 Division St.	CEO: Robert Davis
Elizabeth, NJ 07207	CFO: Andrew Diamond
Phone: 908-351-5400	HR: –
Fax: 908-351-5675	FYE: December 31
Web: www.haywardnet.com	Type: Private

Hayward Industries wants everyone to take the plunge! Hayward makes fluid-control and related equipment for the pool and spa market. Hayward Pool Products is a leader in its industry, and manufactures automatic cleaning systems, filters, heaters, pool pumps, and other pool-related accessories and equipment. The company also distributes fiber-optic lighting designed to illuminate pools and backyards. Hayward has operations in North America, Europe, and Australia. Chairman Oscar Davis owns Hayward, which traces its roots to a company founded in 1923.

	Annual Growth	12/03	12/04	12/05	12/06	12/07
Est. sales ($ mil.)	—	—	—	—	—	199.5
Employees	—	—	—	—	—	1,600

⊞ H.B. FULLER COMPANY

NYSE: FUL

1200 Willow Lake Blvd.	CEO: Michele Volpi
St. Paul, MN 55110	CFO: James R. (Jim) Giertz
Phone: 651-236-5900	HR: Ann B. Parriott
Fax: 651-236-5426	FYE: Saturday nearest November 30
Web: www.hbfuller.com	Type: Public

H.B. Fuller has stuck with glue for more than a century. Long known for making adhesives, the company also makes sealants, powder coatings for metals (office furniture, appliances), and liquid paints (in Latin America). Its industrial and performance adhesives customers include companies in the packaging, graphic arts, automotive, woodworking, and nonwoven textiles industries. In addition to metal coatings and paints, the company also produces construction products, principally ceramic tile installation products (TEC specialty products) and HVAC insulating coatings (through Foster products). Fuller sold its powder coatings business to Valspar in 2006 and its interest in EFTEC to partner EMS-CHEMIE in 2007.

	Annual Growth	11/03	11/04	11/05	11/06	11/07
Sales ($ mil.)	2.1%	1,287.3	1,409.6	1,512.2	1,472.4	1,400.3
Net income ($ mil.)	27.6%	38.6	35.6	61.6	134.2	102.2
Market value ($ mil.)	39.9%	379.2	406.1	465.2	1,552.8	1,452.6
Employees	(10.6%)	—	—	4,000	3,700	3,200

HBE CORPORATION

11330 Olive Blvd.	CEO: Fred S. Kummer
St. Louis, MO 63141	CFO: Dale Musick
Phone: 314-567-9000	HR: Jim O'Daniel
Fax: 314-567-0602	FYE: December 31
Web: www.hbecorp.com	Type: Private

HBE derives a healthy business out of designing and building health care facilities. The firm provides planning and conceptual design, financing, architectural, engineering, management, interior design, and construction services. It has designed and built hospitals, surgical and critical care facilities, and medical office buildings throughout the US for some 1,000 health care providers. HBE is owned by chairman, president, and CEO Fred Kummer, who founded the design/build firm as a small construction company in 1960. In 2008 Kummer planned to spin off the company as HBE Design-Build. The new entity would be owned by key employees.

	Annual Growth	12/03	12/04	12/05	12/06	12/07
Est. sales ($ mil.)	—	—	—	—	—	298.4
Employees	—	—	—	—	—	4,500

HCA INC.

1 Park Plaza
Nashville, TN 37203
Phone: 615-344-9551
Fax: 615-344-2266
Web: www.hcahealthcare.com

CEO: Jack O. Bovender Jr.
CFO: R. Milton Johnson
HR: John M. Steele
FYE: December 31
Type: Private

The largest for-profit hospital operator in the US, HCA (also known as Hospital Corporation of America) operates about 170 acute care, psychiatric, and rehabilitation hospitals in the US and abroad. It also runs about 100 ambulatory surgery centers, as well as diagnostic imaging, cancer treatment, and outpatient rehab centers that form health care networks in many of the communities it serves. The company has facilities in about 20 states, with about three-quarters of its hospitals located in the southern US. (About 70 are in Florida and Texas.) The hospital giant's HCA International operates six hospitals in the UK. In 2006 a group of investors took the company private in a $30 billion leveraged buyout.

	Annual Growth	12/03	12/04	12/05	12/06	12/07
Sales ($ mil.)	5.4%	21,808.0	23,502.0	24,455.0	25,477.0	26,900.0
Employees	(3.8%)	188,000	191,400	191,100	186,000	161,000

HCC INSURANCE HOLDINGS, INC.

NYSE: HCC

13403 Northwest Fwy.
Houston, TX 77040
Phone: 713-690-7300
Fax: 713-462-2401
Web: www.hcch.com

CEO: Frank J. Bramanti
CFO: Edward H. Ellis Jr.
HR: Farid F. Nagji
FYE: December 31
Type: Public

From skyway to waterway, HCC Insurance Holdings sells specialized property/casualty insurance, underwrites for its own and other insurance companies, and provides related services for commercial and individual customers. Its largest subsidiary is Houston Casualty Corporation. The company's products include direct and reinsurance policies for the aviation, marine, and offshore energy industries; property/casualty and health policies; medical stop-loss; directors' and officers' liability coverage, and workers' compensation and occupational accident insurance. HCC Insurance Holdings subsidiaries also offer surety and life coverage. The company operates in Belgium, Bermuda, Ireland, Spain, the UK, and the US.

	Annual Growth	12/03	12/04	12/05	12/06	12/07
Assets ($ mil.)	13.5%	4,864.3	5,933.4	7,028.8	7,630.1	8,074.6
Net income ($ mil.)	28.8%	143.6	163.0	191.2	342.3	395.4
Market value ($ mil.)	24.9%	1,356.0	1,502.3	3,288.6	3,585.4	3,300.2
Employees	7.8%	—	—	1,448	1,660	1,682

HCI DIRECT, INC.

3050 Tillman Dr., Ste. 101
Bensalem, PA 19020
Phone: 215-244-9600
Fax: 215-244-0328
Web: www.silkies.com

CEO: Jean P. Vernor
CFO: William J. Kelly
HR: –
FYE: December 31
Type: Private

HCI Direct shapes and colors millions of pairs of legs. The company sells women's sheer and opaque hosiery under the Silkies brand in more than a dozen styles and nearly as many colors. It also sells knee-highs, socks, and tights for girls. The firm manufactures its own products, including personal care items. Other brands include Sculptz, Silkies Enriche Anti-Aging Skincare, and a pain-relieving cream named PainVanish. Founded in 1974, HCI Direct sells its hosiery primarily by direct mail (typically offering a free pair as an enticement). It also sells through its Web site. A fund managed by Kelso & Company, Bennett Management, owns a majority stake in HCI Direct.

	Annual Growth	12/03	12/04	12/05	12/06	12/07
Est. sales ($ mil.)	—	—	—	—	—	53.1
Employees	—	—	—	—	—	1,108

HCP, INC.

NYSE: HCP

3760 Kilroy Airport Way, Ste. 300
Long Beach, CA 90806
Phone: 562-733-5100
Fax: 562-733-5200
Web: www.hcpi.com

CEO: James F. (Jay) Flaherty III
CFO: Mark A. Wallace
HR: William J. Budzinski
FYE: December 31
Type: Public

Old age isn't for sissies, but as far as HCP (formerly Health Care Property Investors) is concerned, it is for making money. HCP is a real estate investment trust (REIT) that invests in, develops, and manages health care facilities, including senior living facilities. It owns or has stakes in some 750 properties throughout the US; holdings also include medical offices, physician group practice clinics, hospitals, and health care laboratories. The company also provides mortgage financing on health care properties. HCP concentrates on health care real estate because it is one of the largest sectors of the US economy. As the US population ages the need for medical treatment and senior living facilities grows.

	Annual Growth	12/03	12/04	12/05	12/06	12/07
Sales ($ mil.)	25.2%	400.2	428.7	477.3	619.1	982.5
Net income ($ mil.)	38.8%	158.6	169.0	173.1	417.5	589.0
Market value ($ mil.)	22.8%	3,328.4	3,701.0	3,481.1	7,312.4	7,559.5
Employees	34.9%	—	—	83	165	151

HCSB FINANCIAL CORPORATION

OTC: HCFB

5201 Broad St.
Loris, SC 29569
Phone: 843-756-6333
Fax: 843-716-6136
Web: www.horrycountystatebank.com

CEO: James R. Clarkson
CFO: Edward L. Loehr Jr.
HR: Denise Floyd
FYE: December 31
Type: Public

HCSB Financial has erased the state lines in the Carolinas. The institution is the holding company for Horry County State Bank, which operates branches that serve Horry and Marion counties in South Carolina and Columbus and Brunswick counties in North Carolina. Horry County State Bank offers traditional deposit products including checking and savings accounts, CDs, money markets, and IRAs. The bank originates primarily real estate loans (more than half of its loan portfolio), followed by business loans, consumer loans, and other types of loans. The bank also offers investment services.

	Annual Growth	12/03	12/04	12/05	12/06	12/07
Assets ($ mil.)	12.9%	269.7	296.8	331.7	359.5	438.4
Net income ($ mil.)	5.7%	1.6	2.1	2.4	2.8	2.0
Market value ($ mil.)	24.7%	32.5	49.4	26.9	66.0	78.6
Employees	—	—	—	—	—	154

H. D. SMITH WHOLESALE DRUG COMPANY

3063 Fiat Ave.
Springfield, IL 62703
Phone: 217-753-1688
Fax: 217-467-8299
Web: www.hdsmith.com

CEO: Henry Dale (Dale) Smith Jr.
CFO: John D'Amaro
HR: –
FYE: December 31
Type: Private

With a name like Smith you might think it's all about generics, but H. D. Smith Wholesale Drug is more than that. The company supplies pharmaceuticals (brand name and generic), over-the-counter supplements, and other health care products to pharmacies, hospitals, and retailers. It also provides inventory management services for government agencies, including most branches of the military, veterans clinics, and federal prisons. In addition to supplying drugs, H. D. Smith offers a variety of marketing and merchandising services including point-of-purchase signage, store design, direct-to-consumer advertising programs, and loyalty program implementation. Henry Dale Smith founded the company in 1954.

	Annual Growth	12/03	12/04	12/05	12/06	12/07
Est. sales ($ mil.)	—	—	—	—	—	200.0
Employees	—	—	—	—	—	600

An in-depth profile of this company is available to Hoover's Online members at hoovers.com.

HD SUPPLY, INC.

3100 Cumberland Blvd., Ste. 1700
Atlanta, GA 30339
Phone: 770-852-9000
Fax: –
Web: www.hdsupplyinc.com

CEO: Joseph J. (Joe) DeAngelo
CFO: Mark T. Jamieson
HR: Jennifer Williams
FYE: Last Saturday in January
Type: Holding company

Do-it-yourselfers shop Home Depot or Lowe's, but the pros do business at HD Supply. Formerly the professional services division of Home Depot, HD Supply operates about 1,000 locations throughout North America that distribute building materials and tools and provide installation services to businesses and the government. The holding company operates about a dozen business units, including its Canadian arm HD Supply Canada. HD Supply was formed in 1997 when big-box retailer Home Depot bought Maintenance Warehouse and the firm has since grown aggressively by acquiring other supply businesses. HD Supply's struggling parent company Home Depot sold the business in 2007 to three private equity firms.

	Annual Growth	1/03	1/04	1/05	1/06	1/07
Est. sales ($ mil.)	—	—	—	—	—	475.5
Employees	—	—	—	—	—	3,946

HD SUPPLY WATERWORKS

1001 Washington Ave.
Waco, TX 76701
Phone: 254-772-5355
Fax: 254-772-5716
Web: waterworks.hdsupply.com

CEO: Jerry L. Webb
CFO: David Bearman
HR: J. L. Walker
FYE: December 31
Type: Subsidiary

It's not Niagara Falls or a Disney theme park; HD Supply Waterworks (formerly National Waterworks) is a top US distributor of water and wastewater transmission products. The company supplies items such as pipes, fittings, meters, valves, and hydrants to water and wastewater management facilities. The firm operates nearly 140 branches across US. It buys from about 3,500 suppliers and sells to more than 26,000 customers. Municipal clients and the contractors who work for them account for the largest part of the company's customer base. The company was acquired in 2007 from Home Depot by a group of private equity firms comprised of Bain Capital, The Carlyle Group, and Clayton, Dubilier & Rice.

HDR, INC.

8404 Indian Hills Dr.
Omaha, NE 68114
Phone: 402-399-1000
Fax: 402-399-1238
Web: www.hdrinc.com

CEO: Richard R. (Dick) Bell
CFO: Terrence C. (Terry) Cox
HR: Judy Webster
FYE: December 31
Type: Private

From restoring the Pentagon and the Everglades to the Hoover Dam Bypass project, HDR has left its mark on the US. HDR has grown from the civil engineering firm formed in 1917 for municipal plants in the rural Midwest to become a leading architecture and engineering consulting firm with experience worldwide. Engineers Charles Durham and Willard Richardson provided the "R" and the "D" to add to the "H" for Henningson in the firm's name. The employee-owned group offers design/build services from nearly 150 locations around the globe and works on projects such as bridges, hospitals, and water and wastewater-treatment plants.

	Annual Growth	12/03	12/04	12/05	12/06	12/07
Est. sales ($ mil.)	—	—	—	—	—	994.6
Employees	—	—	—	—	—	6,553

🔲 H. E. BUTT GROCERY COMPANY

646 S. Main Ave.
San Antonio, TX 78204
Phone: 210-938-8000
Fax: 210-938-8169
Web: www.heb.com

CEO: Charles C. Butt
CFO: –
HR: Kathy Durbin
FYE: October 31
Type: Private

The Muzak bounces between Tejano and country, and the warm tortillas and marinated fajita meat are big sellers at H. E. Butt Grocery (H-E-B). Texas' largest private company and the #1 food retailer in South and Central Texas, H-E-B owns more than 300 supermarkets, including a growing number of large (70,000 sq. ft.) gourmet Central Market stores in major metropolitan areas and more than 80 smaller (24,000-30,000 sq. ft.) Pantry Foods stores, often in more rural areas. H-E-B also has about 30 upscale and discount stores in Mexico. H-E-B processes some of its own bread, dairy products, meat, and tortillas. The 100-year-old company is owned by the Butt family, which founded H-E-B in Kerrville, Texas, in 1905.

	Annual Growth	10/03	10/04	10/05	10/06	10/07
Sales ($ mil.)	6.0%	10,700.0	10,500.0	11,500.0	12,400.0	13,500.0
Employees	3.0%	56,000	60,000	60,000	60,000	63,000

HEADSTRONG INC.

4035 Ridge Top Rd., Ste. 300
Fairfax, VA 22030
Phone: 703-272-6700
Fax: 703-272-2000
Web: www.headstrong.com

CEO: Arjun Malhotra
CFO: Adarsh Mehra
HR: Nicki Mehra
FYE: December 31
Type: Private

Headstrong is stubborn when it comes to competing in the crowded global IT services market. Headstrong is a management and technology consulting company that helps companies manage customer relationships, develop and maintain applications, develop products (including risk assessment and engineering), and handle business processes like help desks and back office services. Subsidiary gantthead.com also offers an online membership-based portal for IT project managers. The company primarily serves the financial services (75% of sales), public sector, and service industries from offices in North America, Europe, and Asia. Headstrong was founded in 1981 as James Martin Associates; it took the new name in 2000.

	Annual Growth	12/03	12/04	12/05	12/06	12/07
Est. sales ($ mil.)	—	—	—	—	—	113.1
Employees	—	—	—	—	—	1,015

HEADWATERS INCORPORATED

NYSE: HW

10653 S. River Front Pkwy., Ste. 300
South Jordan, UT 84095
Phone: 801-984-9400
Fax: 801-984-9410
Web: www.headwaters.com

CEO: Kirk A. Benson
CFO: Steven G. (Steve) Stewart
HR: Sandra Pearson
FYE: September 30
Type: Public

Headwaters is a modern day alchemist, turning coal into clean. The company operates in three business segments: construction materials, coal combustion products (CCPs), and alternative energy. Headwaters Construction Materials makes stone veneer, concrete blocks, mortar and stucco. Headwater Resources markets fly ash and CCPs, which improve the performance of building materials, to the building products industry. Headwaters Energy Services develops technology for the synthetic fuels, alternative energy, and clean coal industries. In addition, Headwaters Technology Innovations Group develops technology to improve natural resource usage.

	Annual Growth	9/03	9/04	9/05	9/06	9/07
Sales ($ mil.)	32.9%	387.6	554.0	1,064.6	1,121.4	1,207.8
Net income ($ mil.)	(14.0%)	36.6	64.3	121.3	102.1	20.0
Market value ($ mil.)	9.2%	441.9	1,029.5	1,551.9	987.8	628.3
Employees	(4.4%)	—	—	4,500	4,300	—

An in-depth profile of this company is available to Hoover's Online members at hoovers.com. 🔲

HEALTH CARE REIT, INC.

NYSE: HCN

1 SeaGate, Ste. 1500
Toledo, OH 43603
Phone: 419-247-2800
Fax: 419-247-2826
Web: www.hcreit.com

CEO: George L. Chapman
CFO: Scott A. Estes
HR: –
FYE: December 31
Type: Public

Health Care REIT invests in old age. The company is a real estate investment trust (REIT) that invests in health care facilities, primarily skilled nursing and assisted-living facilities designed for older people needing help with everyday living. The trust owns about 650 facilities leased to health care operators in about 40 states. Its largest tenants include Emeritus Corporation, Brookdale Senior Living, and Home Quality Management, which combined make up for about a fifth of the REIT's sales. Health Care REIT also has investments in independent living facilities, medical office buildings, and specialty care facilities.. Additionally, the company invests in mortgage loans and provides financing.

	Annual Growth	12/03	12/04	12/05	12/06	12/07
Sales ($ mil.)	24.7%	201.0	251.4	281.9	322.8	486.0
Net income ($ mil.)	14.3%	82.7	85.4	84.3	102.8	141.4
Market value ($ mil.)	20.5%	1,813.0	2,019.1	1,970.4	3,148.7	3,820.8
Employees	55.3%	34	39	42	113	198

HEALTH CARE SERVICE CORPORATION

300 E. Randolph St.
Chicago, IL 60601
Phone: 312-653-6000
Fax: 312-819-1220
Web: www.hcsc.com

CEO: Raymond F. McCaskey
CFO: Denise A. Bujack
HR: Patrick F. O'Conner
FYE: December 31
Type: Mutual company

Health Care Service Corporation (HCSC) has the Blues in Chicago and the Southwest. A licensee of the Blue Cross and Blue Shield Association, HCSC consists of four regional Blue health plans: Blue Cross Blue Shield of Illinois, Blue Cross and Blue Shield of Texas, Blue Cross and Blue Shield of New Mexico, and Blue Cross Blue Shield of Oklahoma. The mutually owned company provides group and individual health plans — including traditional indemnity plans, managed care programs, and Medicare supplemental coverage — to more than 11 million members, a majority of them in Illinois. Through some non-blue subsidiaries, HCSC sells life and disability insurance and annuities.

	Annual Growth	12/03	12/04	12/05	12/06	12/07
Sales ($ mil.)	15.0%	8,190.4	10,629.1	11,713.9	12,971.6	14,348.4
Employees	6.1%	13,000	—	14,000	16,500	16,500

HEALTH FIRST, INC.

6450 US Hwy. 1
Rockledge, FL 32955
Phone: 321-434-4300
Fax: 321-434-4272
Web: www.health-first.org

CEO: Michael D. Means
CFO: Robert C. Galloway
HR: Robert W. Suttles
FYE: December 31
Type: Not-for-profit

Health First is a not-for-profit health care system that serves Brevard County, Florida, located along the state's Space Coast. The not-for-profit Health First system includes three hospitals, the largest of which is Holmes Regional Medical Center in Melbourne, with more than 500 beds. The two other acute care facilities, Cape Canaveral Hospital and Palm Bay Community Hospital, have 150 and 60 beds, respectively. Additionally, Health First runs outpatient clinics and a home health service, as well as its own physicians group. Its for-profit subsidiary Health First Health Plans is the county's largest insurer, with some 70,000 members.

	Annual Growth	12/03	12/04	12/05	12/06	12/07
Est. sales ($ mil.)	—	—	—	—	—	869.0
Employees	—	—	—	—	—	6,000

HEALTH FITNESS CORPORATION

OTC: HFIT

3600 American Blvd. West, Ste. 560
Bloomington, MN 55431
Phone: 952-831-6830
Fax: 952-897-5173
Web: www.hfit.com

CEO: Gregg O. Lehman
CFO: Wesley W. (Wes) Winnekins
HR: Jeanne C. Crawford
FYE: December 31
Type: Public

Health Fitness reckons employers are willing to pay for healthier workers. The firm develops, manages, and markets fitness centers and health management services for corporations, hospitals, universities, and communities across the US and Canada. Health Fitness manages about 230 corporate fitness centers and some 170 corporate health improvement programs. It additionally provides about 100 unstaffed health management programs. Health Fitness has introduced more fee-for-service offerings, including personal training. Health Fitness also offers staffing services, online fitness, health management, and wellness programs.

	Annual Growth	12/03	12/04	12/05	12/06	12/07
Sales ($ mil.)	22.1%	31.5	52.5	54.9	63.6	70.0
Net income ($ mil.)	10.7%	0.6	1.7	1.4	3.0	0.9
Market value ($ mil.)	36.5%	15.2	36.5	36.3	50.9	52.8
Employees	—	—	—	—	—	—

HEALTH GRADES, INC.

NASDAQ (CM): HGRD

500 Golden Ridge Rd.
Golden, CO 80401
Phone: 303-716-0041
Fax: 303-716-1298
Web: www.healthgrades.com

CEO: Kerry R. Hicks
CFO: Allen Dodge
HR: Carolyne Petty
FYE: December 31
Type: Public

Health Grades (which does business as HealthGrades) takes the health care industry to school. The company offers report cards on hospitals, physicians, nursing homes, home health agencies, hospice programs, and other health care providers. It sells the quality and patient safety information to a number of constituencies, including consumers, health plans, employers, and liability insurance companies. Hospitals themselves represent its biggest customer base, however; providers can license HealthGrades' ratings and trademarks (its Distinguished Hospital Award, for instance) to use in their marketing campaigns. They also come to the company for quality improvement consulting.

	Annual Growth	12/03	12/04	12/05	12/06	12/07
Sales ($ mil.)	42.4%	8.8	14.5	20.8	27.8	36.2
Net income ($ mil.)	—	(1.3)	1.8	4.1	3.2	6.8
Market value ($ mil.)	82.2%	15.0	76.7	179.0	127.8	165.3
Employees	30.0%	56	67	106	123	—

HEALTH INSURANCE PLAN OF GREATER NEW YORK

55 Water St.
New York, NY 10041
Phone: 646-447-5000
Fax: 646-447-3011
Web: www.hipusa.com

CEO: Anthony L. Watson
CFO: Michael D. Fullwood
HR: Fred Blickman
FYE: December 31
Type: Not-for-profit

This firm says it's HIP to be healthy. Health Insurance Plan of Greater New York (HIP) is a not-for-profit HMO founded in 1947 to provide low-cost health care to New York City employees. HIP now boasts more than 1 million members and is the largest HMO in the New York metro area, as well as New York state's biggest Medicare provider. The organization also provides access to medical, lab, and pharmacy services through some 43,000 physicians and more than 72,000 locations in New York, Connecticut, and Massachusetts. HIP serves employer groups ranging from small firms to *FORTUNE* 500 companies.

	Annual Growth	12/02	12/03	12/04	12/05	12/06
Sales ($ mil.)	14.8%	2,901.7	3,369.9	3,654.2	4,599.8	5,039.7
Employees	22.5%	2,000	2,000	3,000	—	—

An in-depth profile of this company is available to Hoover's Online members at hoovers.com.

743

⊞ HEALTH MANAGEMENT ASSOCIATES, INC.

NYSE: HMA

5811 Pelican Bay Blvd., Ste. 500	CEO: Burke W. Whitman
Naples, FL 34108	CFO: Robert E. Farnham
Phone: 239-598-3131	HR: Frederick L. Drow
Fax: 239-598-2705	FYE: December 31
Web: www.hma-corp.com	Type: Public

William Schoen, chairman of Health Management Associates (HMA) once described his company as the "Wal-Mart of the hospital business" because, like Sam Walton's empire, HMA thrives in small-town America. The company operates a network of about 60 acute care and psychiatric hospitals in 15 mainly southern states (although it also has facilities in Washington and Pennsylvania). Combined, the facilities have about 8,500 beds. HMA's hospitals provide general medical and surgical care, along with outpatient and emergency room services and specialty care in some areas such as cancer care and obstetrics.

	Annual Growth	9/03	9/04	9/05	*12/06	12/07
Sales ($ mil.)	14.4%	2,560.6	3,205.9	3,588.8	4,056.6	4,392.1
Net income ($ mil.)	(19.3%)	283.4	325.1	353.1	182.8	119.9
Market value ($ mil.)	(27.4%)	5,238.9	4,974.3	5,745.1	5,081.3	1,452.3
Employees	7.2%	—	—	31,000	34,500	35,645

*Fiscal year change

⊞ HEALTH MANAGEMENT SYSTEMS, INC.

401 Park Ave. South	CEO: William C. (Bill) Lucia
New York, NY 10016	CFO: –
Phone: 212-725-7965	HR: –
Fax: 212-857-5973	FYE: December 31
Web: www.hmsy.com	Type: Subsidiary

Health Management Systems (HMS) specializes in squeezing more money out of health insurers. The company supplies information management services and software used by government health agencies to recover money from health care providers that were either overpaid or paid in error. The company provides retroactive insurance claims reprocessing and third-party liability recovery through its COBConnect service. Overpayment for Medicare funded pharmaceuticals is recovered through the company's COBPlus Pharmacy services. Health Management Systems is a subsidiary of HMS Holdings Corp.

	Annual Growth	12/03	12/04	12/05	12/06	12/07
Est. sales ($ mil.)	—	—	—	—	—	10.1
Employees	—	—	—	—	—	150

⊞ HEALTH NET, INC.

NYSE: HNT

21650 Oxnard St.	CEO: Jay M. Gellert
Woodland Hills, CA 91367	CFO: Joseph C. Capezza
Phone: 818-676-6000	HR: Karin D. Mayhew
Fax: 818-676-8591	FYE: December 31
Web: www.healthnet.com	Type: Public

Health Net is not another Web site trying to give you health advice, it's a web of health services. The company provides managed health care medical coverage to some 6.6 million members across the US. Health Net's health plan services unit offers HMO, PPO, Medicare, Medicaid, and TRICARE plans, as well as vision, dental care, and pharmacy benefit programs. The Managed Health Network subsidiary provides behavioral health and employee assistance to 7 million individuals, including some traditional health plan customers. Health Net's products are marketed to commercial clients through its sales force and external brokers; individual plans are sold mostly through independents.

	Annual Growth	12/03	12/04	12/05	12/06	12/07
Sales ($ mil.)	6.3%	11,064.7	11,646.4	11,940.5	12,908.3	14,108.3
Net income ($ mil.)	(4.6%)	234.0	42.6	229.8	329.3	193.7
Market value ($ mil.)	9.5%	3,709.1	3,212.6	5,913.6	5,443.8	5,327.4
Employees	3.3%	—	—	9,286	10,068	9,910

HEALTH PARTNERS, INC.

833 Chestnut St., Ste. 900	CEO: William George
Philadelphia, PA 19107	CFO: William George
Phone: 215-849-9606	HR: Vicki Sessoms
Fax: 215-991-4159	FYE: December 31
Web: www.healthpart.com	Type: Not-for-profit

Health Partners is a not-for-profit health plan that provides health benefits to some 150,000 Medicaid and Medicare recipients in the Philadelphia area. Its Medical Assistance plans for Medicaid participants covers medical, dental, prescription, and vision costs through a network of about 1,000 doctors and 60 hospitals in the region. Nearly 20,000 seniors subscribe to its Medicare Advantage plan, branded Senior Partners. Health Partners is owned by a group of hospitals in the Philadelphia area that includes Albert Einstein Medical Center, Temple University Hospital, the Hospital of the University of Pennsylvania, and St. Christopher's Hospital for Children. The company was founded in 1985.

	Annual Growth	12/03	12/04	12/05	12/06	12/07
Est. sales ($ mil.)	—	—	—	—	—	608.2
Employees	—	—	—	—	—	500

HEALTHAXIS INC.

NASDAQ (CM): HAXS

7301 N. State Hwy. 161, Ste. 300	CEO: John M. Carradine
Irving, TX 75039	CFO: Ronald K. (Ron) Herbert
Phone: 972-443-5000	HR: Tina Jennings
Fax: 972-556-0572	FYE: December 31
Web: www.healthaxis.com	Type: Public

Healthaxis puts a healthy spin on e-commerce. The company offers hosted, Internet-based benefits distribution and administration applications, along with professional and business process outsourcing services, to health insurance payers, preferred provider organizations, and third-party health plan administrators. Clients use the company's applications to streamline health insurance plan distribution, enrollment, and claims processing. Service offerings include application management, computing services, data conversion, image storage and retrieval, image scanning, graphic design, and systems integration. Tak Investments controls 59% of the company.

	Annual Growth	12/03	12/04	12/05	12/06	12/07
Sales ($ mil.)	(6.5%)	20.9	16.2	15.7	16.7	16.0
Net income ($ mil.)	—	(4.3)	(6.0)	(2.3)	(0.5)	(1.0)
Market value ($ mil.)	7.7%	8.5	7.9	7.5	11.4	11.5
Employees	(7.2%)	—	—	210	—	181

HEALTHCARE REALTY TRUST INCORPORATED

NYSE: HR

3310 West End Ave., Ste. 700	CEO: David R. Emery
Nashville, TN 37203	CFO: Scott W. Holmes
Phone: 615-269-8175	HR: –
Fax: 615-269-8461	FYE: December 31
Web: www.healthcarerealty.com	Type: Public

Healthcare Realty Trust has the prescription for health care providers. The self-managed and self-administered real estate investment trust (REIT) invests in, develops, and manages inpatient and outpatient health care facilities, medical office buildings, and physician clinics. It owns about 180 properties with some 11 million sq. ft. of space in nearly 25 states. Healthcare Realty Trust also invests in mortgages backed by health care properties and provides property management services for about 100 health care facilities. The REIT's largest tenant is HealthSouth, which accounts for more than 10% of the company's revenues.

	Annual Growth	12/03	12/04	12/05	12/06	12/07
Sales ($ mil.)	2.6%	192.0	234.1	254.5	264.9	212.6
Net income ($ mil.)	(3.9%)	70.5	55.5	52.7	39.7	60.1
Market value ($ mil.)	(4.2%)	1,531.0	1,941.4	1,589.2	1,890.2	1,287.1
Employees	(1.6%)	—	—	215	—	208

HEALTHCARE SERVICES GROUP, INC.

NASDAQ (GS): HCSG

3220 Tillman Dr., Ste. 300
Bensalem, PA 19020
Phone: 215-639-4274
Fax: 215-639-2152
Web: www.hcsgcorp.com

CEO: Daniel P. McCartney
CFO: Richard W. Hudson
HR: Nicholas R. (Nick) Marino
FYE: December 31
Type: Public

Healthcare Services Group gets swept up in its work every day. The company provides housekeeping, laundry and linen, food, and maintenance services to hospitals, nursing homes, rehabilitation centers, and retirement facilities. It tidies up some 2,100 long-term care facilities in more than 45 states and Canada. Housekeeping and laundry and linen services are the company's top revenue generators. The company's food services division prepares food for residents and monitors nutritional needs. Healthcare Services Group was established in 1977.

	Annual Growth	12/03	12/04	12/05	12/06	12/07
Sales ($ mil.)	11.1%	379.7	442.6	466.3	511.6	577.7
Net income ($ mil.)	28.4%	10.9	14.7	19.1	25.5	29.6
Market value ($ mil.)	92.5%	65.7	162.2	373.6	530.6	902.2
Employees	(54.4%)	—	—	20,400	4,200	4,250

HEALTHEXTRAS, INC.

NASDAQ (GS): HLEX

800 King Farm Blvd.
Rockville, MD 20850
Phone: 301-548-2900
Fax: 301-548-2991
Web: www.healthextras.com

CEO: David T. Blair
CFO: Michael P. (Mike) Donovan
HR: Monica Wolfe
FYE: December 31
Type: Public

Extra, extra! Read all about it: HealthExtras provides pharmacy benefit management (PBM) services to managed care organizations, self-insured employers, and third-party administrators. Its PBM business, known as Catalyst Rx, helps clients design drug benefit plans that encourage the use of preferred prescriptions bought from one of about 60,000 pharmacies (including contracted mail order pharmacies) in the company's nationwide network. It also provides customized reporting and data analysis services. The State of Louisiana and Wellmark Blue Cross Blue Shield of Iowa are its largest customers.

	Annual Growth	12/03	12/04	12/05	12/06	12/07
Sales ($ mil.)	48.3%	384.1	521.3	694.5	1,271.0	1,857.7
Net income ($ mil.)	39.8%	10.3	16.4	23.0	31.6	39.3
Market value ($ mil.)	26.2%	436.9	614.7	999.7	996.4	1,109.7
Employees	44.4%	—	—	284	410	—

HEALTHFIRST

25 Broadway
New York, NY 10004
Phone: 212-801-6000
Fax: 212-801-3245
Web: www.healthfirstny.com

CEO: Paul Dickstein
CFO: Daniel Phillips
HR: Andrea Forino
FYE: December 31
Type: Not-for-profit

Healthfirst is a hospital-owned, not-for-profit health care management organization that serves nearly 500,000 members throughout New York City and Long Island, as well as northern New Jersey. The company offers a variety of free or low cost health insurance programs, including PPO, Medicaid, Medicare, Family Health Plus, and Child Health Plus health plans. The company was formed in 1993 and is owned by 39 New York-area hospitals and medical centers, including Beth Israel Medical Center, Mount Sinai Hospital, the Long Island Jewish Medical Center, and New York City Health and Hospitals. Its plans are administered by HF Management Services.

HEALTHGATE DATA CORP.

Pink Sheets: HGAT

25 Corporate Dr., Ste. 310
Burlington, MA 01803
Phone: 781-685-4000
Fax: 781-685-4050
Web: www.healthgate.com

CEO: William S. Reece
CFO: Julie Furrier
HR: –
FYE: December 31
Type: Public

HealthGate Data wants to be a gateway to better health. The company provides quality improvement and risk management products designed to help hospitals and other health care providers reduce costs and increase efficency. HealthGate sold its patient education and consumer health content products — which account for the majority of sales — to EBSCO Publishing for about $8 million in 2005. As a result, the company is phasing out its medical information business in order to focus on developing, marketing, and licensing its Collaboration Architect and InteractiveIC product lines, which provide quality measures, decision support tools, error prevention checklists, and interactive patient education tutorials.

	Annual Growth	12/03	12/04	12/05	12/06	12/07
Sales ($ mil.)	(49.4%)	6.1	5.9	1.9	0.2	0.4
Net income ($ mil.)	—	(1.4)	(0.3)	6.5	(3.3)	(2.6)
Employees	—	—	—	—	—	—

HEALTHMARKETS, INC.

9151 Boulevard 26
North Richland Hills, TX 76180
Phone: 817-255-5200
Fax: 817-255-5390
Web: www.healthmarkets.com

CEO: Phillip J. (Phil) Hildebrand
CFO: Michael E. Boxer
HR: –
FYE: December 31
Type: Private

HealthMarkets lets the self-employed shop for better insurance. The company offers health and life insurance through its MEGA Life and Health Insurance, Chesapeake Life Insurance Company, and other subsidiaries. Its targeted customers are the self-employed, association groups, and small businesses. Other services include third-party administrative and distribution services for health care providers and other insurers. HealthMarkets is expanding its product line to include health spending accounts (HSAs), high deductible health plans (HDHPs), and Medicare supplemental insurance. The company changed its name from UICI to Health Markets in 2006 after being acquired by a consortium led by the Blackstone Group.

	Annual Growth	12/02	12/03	12/04	12/05	12/06
Sales ($ mil.)	1.2%	—	—	—	2,121.0	2,146.6
Employees	(33.3%)	—	—	—	2,700	1,800

HEALTHNOW NEW YORK, INC.

1901 Main St.
Buffalo, NY 14240
Phone: 716-887-6900
Fax: 716-887-8981
Web: www.healthnowny.com

CEO: Alphonso O'Neil-White
CFO: James H. Dickerson
HR: Thomas A. Fentner
FYE: December 31
Type: Not-for-profit

HealthNow New York provides health insurance and related services to about 1 million members in more than 50 counties in New York state. The company offers a wide range of Blue Cross and Blue Shield-branded products, including PPO, HMO, POS, and traditional indemnity health plans, primarily through its Blue Cross Blue Shield of Western New York and BlueShield of Northeastern New York subsidiaries. HealthNow also provides resources to help its members maintain and improve their health and avoid the pitfalls associated with unhealthy lifestyles. The company serves businesses large and small as well as individuals.

	Annual Growth	12/03	12/04	12/05	12/06	12/07
Est. sales ($ mil.)	—	—	—	—	—	2,110.5
Employees	—	—	—	—	—	2,200

An in-depth profile of this company is available to Hoover's Online members at hoovers.com.

745

HEALTHPOINT, LTD.

3909 Hulen St.
Fort Worth, TX 76107
Phone: 817-900-4000
Fax: 817-900-4100
Web: www.healthpoint.com

CEO: Michael E. Steadman
CFO: –
HR: –
FYE: December 31
Type: Subsidiary

Healthpoint believes that everyone should make it a point to strive for good health, especially the unfortunate wounded. The company provides a variety of pharmaceutical products through three operating divisions: tissue management; dermatology; and surgical. Healthpoint markets its products to hospitals, nursing homes, home health services, and office practices. Products include antiseptics and wound cleaners and come in the form of sprays, ointments, and gels. The company was founded in 1992 and is an operating company of DFB Pharmaceuticals. Healthpoint sells its products in Canada, Mexico, Puerto Rico, and the US; it plans to expand sales in other regions abroad through strategic partnerships.

	Annual Growth	12/03	12/04	12/05	12/06	12/07
Est. sales ($ mil.)	—	—	—	—	—	119.0
Employees	—	—	—	—	—	220

HEALTHSOUTH CORPORATION

NYSE: HLS

1 HealthSouth Pkwy.
Birmingham, AL 35243
Phone: 205-967-7116
Fax: 205-969-3543
Web: www.healthsouth.com

CEO: Jay Grinney
CFO: John L. Workman
HR: Cheryl Levy
FYE: December 31
Type: Public

Embattled HealthSouth is looking for a way to rehabilitate its own fortunes. Hoping for a full recovery in the wake of accounting scandals that rocked the company beginning in 2003, it has shed its outpatient surgery, outpatient rehab, and diagnostic imaging divisions. What remains is its inpatient rehabilitation business, which operates about 90 wholly- or jointly-owned facilities in 27 states, with the largest concentrations in Alabama, Florida, Pennsylvania, Tennessee, and Texas. The rehab and long-term acute care facilities provide nursing and therapy to patients who have experienced significant disabilities as a result of stroke, spinal cord injury, neuromuscular disease, and other conditions.

	Annual Growth	12/03	12/04	12/05	12/06	12/07
Sales ($ mil.)	(18.4%)	3,957.6	3,753.8	3,207.7	3,000.1	1,752.5
Net income ($ mil.)	—	(434.6)	(174.5)	(446.0)	(625.0)	653.4
Market value ($ mil.)	(7.3%)	—	—	—	1,782.2	1,653.0
Employees	(13.9%)	40,000	40,000	37,000	33,000	22,000

HEALTHSPORT, INC.

OTC: HSPO

7633 E. 63rd Place, Ste. 220
Tulsa, OK 74133
Phone: 877-570-4776
Fax: –
Web: www.healthsportinc.com

CEO: Robert Kusher
CFO: Mark Udell
HR: –
FYE: December 31
Type: Public

When swigging a liquid is too complicated, HealthSport hopes you'll slip its products in your mouth. The company has developed a dissolving edible thin-strip product containing electrolytes equivalent to one fluid ounce of most recognized sports drinks. Its products, sold under the Enlyten Sport Strips brand, are designed to replenish the body's stores of electrolytes. HealthSport itself is boosting its performance through acquisitions, specifically Cooley Nutraceuticals and its nutritional supplement formula, and InnoZen. InnoZen introduced dissolving strips as a drug delivery system, primarily used for over-the-counter remedies for sore throats and coughs. InnoZen brought with it a manufacturing facility.

	Annual Growth	12/03	12/04	12/05	12/06	12/07
Sales ($ mil.)	—	—	—	—	0.0	0.4
Net income ($ mil.)	—	—	—	—	(1.4)	(9.9)
Market value ($ mil.)	(48.7%)	—	—	—	43.5	22.3
Employees	—	—	—	—	4	—

HEALTHSPRING, INC.

NYSE: HS

9009 Carothers Pkwy., Ste. 501
Franklin, TN 37067
Phone: 615-291-7000
Fax: 615-401-4566
Web: www.myhealthspring.com

CEO: Herbert A. (Herb) Fritch
CFO: Kevin M. McNamara
HR: –
FYE: December 31
Type: Public

Aging ain't for sissies, but HealthSpring wants to give seniors a little advantage. The company is a managed-care organization that focuses on providing supplemental Medicare plans to more than 150,000 members in Alabama, Florida, Illinois, Mississippi, Tennessee, and Texas. Its Medicare Advantage plans offer the support of Medicare with additional benefits such as Medicare Part D prescription benefits, vision and hearing benefits, and transportation programs. HealthSpring also provides HMO, PPO, and other commercial health plans for employer groups. In addition, the company offers management services to independent physician associations.

	Annual Growth	12/03	12/04	12/05	12/06	12/07
Sales ($ mil.)	43.4%	372.7	599.4	856.8	1,309.0	1,574.8
Net income ($ mil.)	39.4%	22.9	23.7	29.3	80.8	86.5
Market value ($ mil.)	(6.3%)	—	—	—	1,165.3	1,091.4
Employees	19.2%	—	780	900	1,200	1,320

HEALTHSTREAM, INC.

NASDAQ (GM): HSTM

209 10th Ave. South, Ste. 450
Nashville, TN 37203
Phone: 615-301-3100
Fax: 615-301-3200
Web: www.healthstream.com

CEO: Robert A. Frist Jr.
CFO: Gerard M. (Gerry) Hayden Jr.
HR: Meredith Hawn
FYE: December 31
Type: Public

HealthStream replenishes the well of knowledge for medical workers. The company offers Internet-based educational and training content for health care professionals. Courses train employees on new equipment, introduce new pharmaceuticals, provide continuing education credits, and disseminate regulatory information. The company's flagship Healthstream Learning Center has more than 1.7 million subscribers. HealthStream generates sales from subscription fees based on the number of users and type of content provided. Clients include health care organizations, pharmaceutical companies, and medical device firms. The company also provides data management and research products including surveys and results analysis.

	Annual Growth	12/03	12/04	12/05	12/06	12/07
Sales ($ mil.)	24.7%	18.2	20.1	27.4	31.8	44.0
Net income ($ mil.)	—	(3.4)	(1.0)	1.9	2.5	4.1
Market value ($ mil.)	10.1%	53.2	55.4	50.3	86.6	78.1
Employees	30.9%	143	146	160	160	420

HEALTHTRONICS, INC.

NASDAQ (GS): HTRN

1301 Capital of Texas Hwy., Ste. 200B
Austin, TX 78746
Phone: 512-328-2892
Fax: 512-328-8510
Web: www.healthtronics.com

CEO: James S. B. Whittenburg
CFO: Ross A. Goolsby
HR: –
FYE: December 31
Type: Public

HealthTronics is sending shock waves through urology patients across the nation . . . literally. The company makes and sells lithotripters, which use extracorporeal shock waves to break up kidney and gall-bladder stones. HealthTronics contracts with medical facilities to provide lithotripsy services including the provision of equipment, scheduling, training, and clinical technicians to help physicians run the equipment. It also offers other urology-related services, including urological laboratory testing and treatments for enlarged prostate and prostate cancer, as well as equipment such as patient tables and X-ray imaging systems.

	Annual Growth	12/03	12/04	12/05	12/06	12/07
Sales ($ mil.)	12.3%	88.4	193.1	267.7	142.9	140.4
Net income ($ mil.)	—	5.3	0.9	9.2	8.7	(14.6)
Market value ($ mil.)	22.3%	73.0	352.9	266.7	236.0	163.2
Employees	—	—	—	930	—	—

HEALTHWAYS, INC.

NASDAQ (GS): HWAY

3841 Green Hills Village Dr.
Nashville, TN 37215
Phone: 615-665-1122
Fax: 615-665-7697
Web: www.healthways.com

CEO: Ben R. Leedle Jr.
CFO: Mary A. Chaput
HR: Christopher Cigarran
FYE: August 31
Type: Public

Healthways (formerly American Healthways) paves the way for disease management. The company provides care management, as well as wellness programs, for health plans, hospitals, and self-insured employers nationwide. Its services help plan members with diabetes, respiratory diseases, cancer, and other chronic and serious diseases to coordinate their health care, keep up with treatment plans, and maintain healthy behaviors. The company also has screening and prevention programs to find people who are at risk for various diseases and to promote healthy living. Through a partnership with Medco Health, it helps users manage their prescription drugs.

	Annual Growth	8/03	8/04	8/05	8/06	8/07
Sales ($ mil.)	38.9%	165.5	245.4	312.5	412.3	615.6
Net income ($ mil.)	25.0%	18.5	26.1	33.1	37.2	45.1
Market value ($ mil.)	59.1%	277.1	890.3	1,477.4	1,785.9	1,773.2
Employees	25.9%	1,511	1,875	2,231	2,855	3,800

HEALTHY FAST FOOD, INC.

OTC: HFFIU

1075 American Pacific, Ste. C
Henderson, NV 89074
Phone: 702-448-5301
Fax: –

CEO: Henry E. (Hank) Cartwright
CFO: Brad Beckstead
HR: –
FYE: December 31
Type: Public

Is America ready for fast food without extra helpings of clowns, cartoons, and calories? Healthy Fast Food, Inc., is going to find out. A franchisee of EVOS USA, the company operates an EVOS restaurant in Henderson, Nevada, and has exclusive rights to develop EVOS restaurants in a 12-state territory. Serving burgers, fries, wraps, and salads, EVOS restaurants feature healthier foods with less fat and fewer calories than traditional quick fare. The restaurants' high-quality ingredients include naturally raised, hormone-free beef, organic field greens, organic milk (for shakes), and smoothies made from fresh fruit. The restaurant also utilizes innovative cooking processes to ensure a healthier product.

	Annual Growth	12/03	12/04	12/05	12/06	12/07
Sales ($ mil.)	900.0%	—	—	—	0.1	1.0
Net income ($ mil.)	—	—	—	—	(0.3)	(0.7)
Employees	3.2%	—	—	—	31	32

THE HEARST CORPORATION

300 W. 57th St.
New York, NY 10019
Phone: 212-649-2000
Fax: 212-649-2108
Web: www.hearstcorp.com

CEO: Victor F. Ganzi
CFO: Ronald J. Doerfler
HR: –
FYE: December 31
Type: Private

Like founder William Randolph Hearst's castle, The Hearst Corporation is sprawling. Through Hearst Newspapers, the company owns 12 daily newspapers (such as the *San Francisco Chronicle* and the *Houston Chronicle*) and 31 weekly newspapers. Its Hearst Magazines publishes some 20 US consumer magazines (*Cosmopolitan, Esquire*) with nearly 200 international editions. Hearst has broadcasting operations through majority-owned Hearst Argyle Television. Its Hearst Entertainment & Syndication unit includes a syndication service (King Features), a newspaper production service (Reed Brennan), and stakes in cable networks (A&E, ESPN). The Hearst Corporation is owned by the Hearst family, but managed by a board of trustees.

	Annual Growth	12/02	12/03	12/04	12/05	12/06
Est. sales ($ mil.)	6.1%	3,565.0	4,100.0	4,000.0	4,550.0	4,520.0
Employees	(0.4%)	17,320	20,000	16,667	17,016	17,062

HEARST-ARGYLE TELEVISION, INC.

NYSE: HTV

300 West 57th St.
New York, NY 10019
Phone: 212-887-6800
Fax: 212-887-6855
Web: www.hearstargyle.com

CEO: David J. Barrett
CFO: Harry T. Hawks
HR: –
FYE: December 31
Type: Public

One might wonder whether or not Hearst-Argyle Television ever shows *Citizen Kane* on its stations. The company, which is more than 75%-controlled by Hearst Corporation (Hearst family patriarch William Randolph Hearst was the inspiration for the 1941 film), is one of the leading TV groups in the US with about 30 stations (both owned and managed) serving more than two dozen markets around the country. The stations reach nearly 20% of US households and are primarily affiliated with the ABC and NBC networks. The firm also operates the digital NBC Weather Plus Network channel, a joint venture with NBC Universal, and it manages two Hearst radio stations in Baltimore.

	Annual Growth	12/03	12/04	12/05	12/06	12/07
Sales ($ mil.)	2.4%	686.8	779.9	706.9	785.4	755.7
Net income ($ mil.)	(9.0%)	94.2	123.9	100.2	98.7	64.7
Market value ($ mil.)	(4.3%)	1,506.6	1,456.5	1,327.9	1,436.8	1,266.3
Employees	(2.0%)	—	—	3,380	3,312	—

HEARTLAND EXPRESS, INC.

NASDAQ (GS): HTLD

901 North Kansas Ave.
North Liberty, IA 52317
Phone: 319-626-3600
Fax: 319-626-3355
Web: www.heartlandexpress.com

CEO: Russell A. Gerdin
CFO: John P. Cosaert
HR: –
FYE: December 31
Type: Public

Home is where the heart is, and Heartland Express stays close to home as a short- to medium-haul truckload carrier (average trip about 510 miles). The company mainly operates east of the Rockies; it also offers service in the southwestern US. Although most of its loads go directly from origin to destination, Heartland also operates from regional distribution hubs that are located near major customers. The regional hubs focus on short-haul freight movements (less than 400 miles). Heartland transports general commodities, including appliances, auto parts, consumer products, food, and paper products.

	Annual Growth	12/03	12/04	12/05	12/06	12/07
Sales ($ mil.)	9.9%	405.1	457.1	523.8	571.9	591.9
Net income ($ mil.)	7.4%	57.2	62.5	71.9	87.2	76.2
Market value ($ mil.)	22.8%	604.9	1,264.3	1,123.6	1,475.7	1,374.7
Employees	4.2%	—	—	3,029	—	3,291

HEARTLAND FINANCIAL USA, INC.

NASDAQ (GS): HTLF

1398 Central Ave.
Dubuque, IA 52001
Phone: 563-589-2100
Fax: 563-589-2011
Web: www.htlf.com

CEO: Lynn B. Fuller
CFO: John K. Schmidt
HR: Nancy Wilson
FYE: December 31
Type: Public

Heartland Financial USA's heart is in the right place. The holding company operates flagship subsidiary Dubuque Bank & Trust and eight other banks that together operate more than 60 branches in the Midwest and western regions of the US. Heartland Financial USA also operates eight nonbank subsidiaries including consumer lender Citizens Finance which operates offices in Illinois, Iowa, and Wisconsin. Approximately 70% of the company's loan portfolio comes from commercial loans, but, in keeping with the bank's midwestern identity, it also makes agricultural, residential mortgage, and consumer loans, each around 10% of its loan book.

	Annual Growth	12/03	12/04	12/05	12/06	12/07
Assets ($ mil.)	12.8%	2,018.4	2,629.1	2,818.3	3,058.2	3,264.1
Net income ($ mil.)	9.7%	17.7	20.3	22.7	25.1	25.6
Market value ($ mil.)	2.0%	282.0	330.6	355.7	478.1	305.0
Employees	3.9%	—	—	909	—	982

HEARTLAND INDUSTRIAL PARTNERS LP

55 Railroad Ave.
Greenwich, CT 06830
Phone: 203-861-2622
Fax: 203-861-2722
Web: www.heartlandpartners.com

CEO: Daniel P. Tredwell
CFO: Steve Lamb
HR: –
FYE: December 31
Type: Private

Heartland Industrial Partners is an investment firm that primarily targets industrial and auto parts companies. The company's holdings include a more than 40% stake in vehicle component maker TriMas. It sold auto parts maker Metaldyne to an affiliate of Ripplewood Holdings in early 2007. David Stockman, who co-founded Heartland Industrial Partners in 1999, is a former Michigan congressman and was director of the Office of Management and Budget during the Reagan administration. He was also chairman and CEO of one of Heartland Industrial's former portfolio companies, auto fabrics company Collins & Aikman, but was ousted in 2005.

	Annual Growth	12/03	12/04	12/05	12/06	12/07
Est. sales ($ mil.)	—	—	—	—	—	364.8
Employees	—	—	—	—	—	5,130

HEARTLAND PAYMENT SYSTEMS, INC.

NYSE: HPY

90 Nassau St.
Princeton, NJ 08542
Phone: 609-683-3831
Fax: 609-683-3815
Web: www.heartlandpaymentsystems.com

CEO: Robert O. (Bob) Carr
CFO: Robert H. B. (Bob) Baldwin Jr.
HR: –
FYE: December 31
Type: Public

If you're using your card to charge throughout the heartland, Heartland Payment Systems makes sure the transactions don't get lost along the way. The company provides credit card, debit card, and payroll processing services to more than 165,000 small and midsized merchants in the US and Canada, including retailers, hotels, and restaurants. (The latter account for about one-third of Heartland Payment Systems' customer base and about 40% of its processing volume.) The company also processes merchant-issued gift cards, sells and rents point-of-sale card processing equipment, and provides electronic check processing services.

	Annual Growth	12/03	12/04	12/05	12/06	12/07
Sales ($ mil.)	32.8%	422.2	602.8	834.6	1,097.0	1,313.8
Net income ($ mil.)	15.6%	20.1	8.9	19.1	28.5	35.9
Market value ($ mil.)	17.2%	—	—	740.8	1,056.7	1,018.1
Employees	23.1%	—	1,336	1,616	2,026	—

HEARUSA, INC.

AMEX: EAR

1250 Northpoint Pkwy.
West Palm Beach, FL 33407
Phone: 561-478-8770
Fax: 561-478-9603
Web: www.hearx.com

CEO: Stephen J. Hansbrough
CFO: Gino Chouinard
HR: Robert C. Packard
FYE: Last Friday in December
Type: Public

Have you heard of HearUSA? The company operates a network of hearing care centers that offer hearing aids, testing, diagnosis, and rehabilitation services for the hearing impaired. More than 185 centers operate under names such as HearUSA, HEARx, Helix Hearing Care, and National Ear Care Plan, with centers located in about nine states and in Ontario, Canada. HearUSA caters primarily to managed care and health insurance providers, but the company also markets to the general public. In addition, it offers products and services nationwide through affiliated providers, and it has a network of about 1,900 contracted audiologists across the US.

	Annual Growth	12/03	12/04	12/05	12/06	12/07
Sales ($ mil.)	9.8%	70.6	72.3	76.7	88.8	102.8
Net income ($ mil.)	—	(1.1)	(2.8)	(0.6)	(3.2)	(3.3)
Market value ($ mil.)	(7.2%)	67.4	47.0	42.7	41.6	49.9
Employees	55.0%	—	—	422	654	—

HECLA MINING COMPANY

NYSE: HL

6500 N. Mineral Dr., Ste. 200
Coeur d'Alene, ID 83815
Phone: 208-769-4100
Fax: 208-769-7612
Web: www.hecla-mining.com

CEO: Phillips S. Baker Jr.
CFO: James A. (Jim) Sabala
HR: George Lytle
FYE: December 31
Type: Public

Not all that glitters at Hecla Mining is gold — in fact, most of it is silver. Hecla explores for and mines gold, silver, lead, and zinc. It produces about 6 million ounces of silver and 175,000 ounces of gold annually; silver accounts for more than half of sales. The company operates mines in the US (Alaska and Idaho), Mexico, and Venezuela. Hecla's Greens Creek gold/silver/zinc/lead mine in Alaska is managed by Kennecott Greens Creek Mining. Hecla is focusing its exploration and development efforts on its properties in Venezuela.

	Annual Growth	12/03	12/04	12/05	12/06	12/07
Sales ($ mil.)	17.6%	116.3	130.8	110.2	217.4	222.6
Net income ($ mil.)	—	(6.0)	(6.1)	(25.4)	69.1	53.2
Market value ($ mil.)	—	—	—	—	—	1,134.9
Employees	(5.1%)	1,074	1,417	1,191	1,163	871

HEELYS, INC.

NASDAQ (GM): HLYS

3200 Belmeade Dr., Ste. 100
Carrollton, TX 75006
Phone: 214-390-1831
Fax: 214-390-1661
Web: www.heelys.com

CEO: Donald K. (Don) Carroll
CFO: –
HR: –
FYE: December 31
Type: Public

Heelys can't touch Elvis as The King of Rock 'n' Roll but the company has made a name for itself with those who walk and roll. Its flagship product, HEELYS wheeled footwear, includes a wheel in the heel that enables the user to transition from walking to skating. The company also sells helmets and other protective gear, as well as replacement wheels. Founded in 2000, Heelys has been on a roll since and sells its products at big box retailers nationwide, including Dick's Sporting Goods, Journeys, and Sports Authority, as well as online sites such as Zappos.com. The company also has independent distributors in Japan, South Korea, China, and Southeast Asia.

	Annual Growth	12/03	12/04	12/05	12/06	12/07
Sales ($ mil.)	69.6%	22.2	21.3	44.0	188.2	183.5
Net income ($ mil.)	112.2%	1.1	0.8	4.3	29.2	22.3
Market value ($ mil.)	(78.3%)	—	—	—	868.3	188.4
Employees	—	—	—	—	41	—

HEI, INC.

Pink Sheets: HEII

1495 Steiger Lake Ln.
Victoria, MN 55386
Phone: 952-443-2500
Fax: 952-443-2668
Web: www.heii.com

CEO: Mark B. Thomas
CFO: Mark B. Thomas
HR: Nina A. Anderson
FYE: August 31
Type: Public

For HEI, it's a small world after all. The company manufactures ultraminiature microelectronic components and products that use those components for the medical, communications, and wireless markets. HEI offers other services common to contract electronics manufacturers, including chip packaging, assembly, and testing, as well as high-density interconnect design and fabrication. The company's tiny products are found in such devices as hearing aids, implantable defibrillators, and mobile phones. HEI also provides medical imaging software and hardware development. Customers located in the US account for about three-quarters of sales.

	Annual Growth	8/03	8/04	8/05	8/06	8/07
Sales ($ mil.)	0.0%	38.4	43.3	56.6	52.6	38.4
Net income ($ mil.)	—	(4.6)	(7.0)	0.4	(6.1)	(5.7)
Employees	(1.3%)	285	299	454	466	270

HEICO COMPANIES LLC

70 W. Madison St., Ste. 5600
Chicago, IL 60602
Phone: 312-419-8220
Fax: 312-419-9417

CEO: E. A. (El) Roskovensky
CFO: Lawrence G. Wolski
HR: –
FYE: December 31
Type: Private

Heico Companies specializes in buying distressed companies and turning them around. The firm, which typically invests for the long haul, owns interests in about 40 companies, several of them Rust Belt-based manufacturing concerns that founder Michael Heisley acquired during the 1980s. Heico's holdings include CopperCom, Davis Wire, Canadian steelmaker Ivaco, and heavy industrial equipment maker Pettibone. Heico also has interests in companies in the plastics, food, and telecommunications industries. Heisley, who launched Heico in 1979, also controls the NBA's Memphis Grizzlies but is looking to sell his stake.

	Annual Growth	12/02	12/03	12/04	12/05	12/06
Est. sales ($ mil.)	12.6%	—	1,470.0	1,750.0	2,500.0	2,100.0
Employees	0.0%	—	8,000	9,500	11,000	8,000

HEICO CORPORATION

NYSE: HEI

3000 Taft St.
Hollywood, FL 33021
Phone: 954-987-4000
Fax: 954-987-8228
Web: www.heico.com

CEO: Laurans A. Mendelson
CFO: Thomas S. Irwin
HR: –
FYE: October 31
Type: Public

Here's a HEICO haiku: HEICO companies/ Providing for jet engines/ In flight or on land. Through the subsidiaries that make up the company's Flight Support Group, HEICO manufactures parts for jet engines that can be substituted for original parts. Products include combustion chambers and compressor blades. Flight Support operations, which include repair and overhaul services, account for more than 75% of HEICO's sales. Subsidiaries in HEICO's Electronic Technologies Group make a variety of electro-optical, electronic, and microwave products, primarily for defense applications.

	Annual Growth	10/03	10/04	10/05	10/06	10/07
Sales ($ mil.)	30.3%	176.4	215.7	269.6	392.2	507.9
Net income ($ mil.)	33.7%	12.2	20.6	22.8	31.9	39.0
Market value ($ mil.)	40.3%	148.3	179.2	223.0	374.1	573.7
Employees	21.2%	1,011	1,263	1,556	1,843	2,185

HEIDELBERG USA, INC.

1000 Gutenberg Dr.
Kennesaw, GA 30144
Phone: 770-419-6600
Fax: 770-419-6550
Web: www.us.heidelberg.com

CEO: James P. Dunn
CFO: Thomas Topp
HR: Susan P. Nofi
FYE: March 31
Type: Business segment

Heidelberg USA is a manufacturer of sheetfed printing presses and prepress, printing, and binding equipment for customers in the printing industry. The company also sells such consumables as plates and film and resells products made by other manufacturers, including Kodak. Through its Print Media Academy program, Heidelberg USA offers product training at locations in Canada and the US. The company, a US business segment of German printing giant Heidelberger Druckmaschinen (Heidelberg), operates from regional offices in Atlanta, Baltimore, Boston, Chicago, Dallas, Detroit, Los Angeles, Minneapolis, San Francisco, and Cranbury, New Jersey.

	Annual Growth	3/03	3/04	3/05	3/06	3/07
Est. sales ($ mil.)	—	—	—	—	—	154.1
Employees	—	—	—	—	—	1,000

HEIDRICK & STRUGGLES

NASDAQ (GS): HSII

233 S. Wacker Dr., Ste. 4200
Chicago, IL 60606
Phone: 312-496-1200
Fax: 312-496-1290
Web: www.heidrick.com

CEO: L. Kevin Kelly
CFO: Scott J. Krenz
HR: Patricia R. (Pat) Willard
FYE: December 31
Type: Public

Finding top dogs for clients in many industries, Heidrick & Struggles International, Inc., is one of the largest global recruiting firms. The company has more than 380 headhunters filling CEO, CFO, director, and other high-level positions for companies that range from start-up ventures to established *FORTUNE* 500 firms. It is divided into search groups that specialize by industry, such as financial services and consumer, which together account for half of sales. The company's fees are generally equal to one-third of a hired executive's first-year compensation. Heidrick & Struggles also provides temporary placement, management assessment, and professional development services.

	Annual Growth	12/03	12/04	12/05	12/06	12/07
Sales ($ mil.)	17.5%	340.6	398.2	432.9	502.0	648.3
Net income ($ mil.)	—	(80.7)	82.3	39.2	34.2	56.5
Market value ($ mil.)	12.5%	399.8	656.6	595.6	751.7	641.0
Employees	13.2%	—	—	1,286	1,550	1,647

HEINEKEN USA INC.

360 Hamilton Ave., Ste. 1103
White Plains, NY 10601
Phone: 914-681-4100
Fax: 914-681-1900
Web: www.heinekenusa.com

CEO: Donald J. (Don) Blaustein
CFO: Daniel Sullivan
HR: –
FYE: December 31
Type: Subsidiary

Americans love their green Heinies. Heineken USA is a subsidiary of one of the world's largest brewers, Netherlands-based Heineken. The company distributes brews such as Heineken, Amstel Light, Buckler (nonalcoholic), Murphy's Irish Stout, and Irish Amber. Heineken USA's sales are growing, partly due to the increased market share of imports, and Heineken is always ranked as one of the US's top imported beers. It had been the leading imported beer since its introduction in 1933 following Prohibition; however, Modelo's Corona now holds the crown. Not content to be left in the dust, Heineken has scored a hit with Amstel Light, one of the US's largest-selling imported light beers.

	Annual Growth	12/03	12/04	12/05	12/06	12/07
Est. sales ($ mil.)	—	—	—	—	—	112.6
Employees	—	—	—	—	—	400

HELICOS BIOSCIENCES CORPORATION

NASDAQ (GM): HLCS

1 Kendall Sq., Bldg. 700
Cambridge, MA 02139
Phone: 617-264-1800
Fax: –
Web: www.helicosbio.com

CEO: Stanley N. Lapidus
CFO: Stephen P. (Steve) Hall
HR: Jo Norton
FYE: December 31
Type: Public

Helicos BioSciences is in the business of developing genetic analysis technologies. Its True Single Molecule Sequencing (tSMS) platform allows for the direct analysis of DNA and RNA samples without amplification, cloning, or other time-consuming preparation techniques. The company serves the research, clinical diagnostic, and drug discovery markets and aims to provide customers with the ability to compare thousands of samples. Its HeliScope genetic analysis system can be integrated into existing laboratories and consists of a computer-controlled instrument and related supplies and reagents.

	Annual Growth	12/03	12/04	12/05	12/06	12/07
Sales ($ mil.)	200.0%	—	—	—	0.2	0.6
Net income ($ mil.)	—	—	—	—	(20.6)	(36.8)
Market value ($ mil.)	—	—	—	—	—	219.1
Employees						

An in-depth profile of this company is available to Hoover's Online members at hoovers.com.

749

HELIOS & MATHESON NORTH AMERICA INC.

NASDAQ (CM): HMNA

200 Park Ave. South, Ste. 901
New York, NY 10003
Phone: 212-979-8228
Fax: 212-979-8003
Web: www.tact.com

CEO: Salvatore M. (Sal) Quadrino
CFO: Salvatore M. (Sal) Quadrino
HR: –
FYE: December 31
Type: Public

Helios & Matheson North America (HMNA) offers information technology (IT) services and distributes software. The majority of sales come from IT consulting services, which include database management, project management, network design and implementation, application development, and Web enablement and related e-business services. The company also markets and distributes third-party software products. HMNA primarily serves global corporations and larger organizations in the automotive, banking, insurance, and publishing industries, among others.

	Annual Growth	12/03	12/04	12/05	12/06	12/07
Sales ($ mil.)	(0.9%)	21.6	25.0	26.4	24.9	20.8
Net income ($ mil.)	—	(0.1)	1.2	(0.5)	0.9	(0.8)
Market value ($ mil.)	(12.2%)	7.7	15.1	10.9	7.6	4.6
Employees	—	—	—	90	—	—

HELIX BIOMEDIX, INC.

OTC: HXBM

22122 20th Ave. SE, Ste. 204
Bothell, WA 98021
Phone: 425-402-8400
Fax: 425-806-2999
Web: www.helixbiomedix.com

CEO: R. Stephen Beatty
CFO: David H. Kirske
HR: –
FYE: December 31
Type: Public

Helix BioMedix wants to remove wrinkles and acne without leaving red, itchy skin. The company has a library of bioactive peptides with antimicrobial properties it hopes to exploit as it works to formulate wrinkle- and acne-fighting creams, along with topical treatments for skin and wound infections and sexually transmitted diseases, including HIV. The firm also hopes to use its peptides to develop a therapy for cystic fibrosis and a treatment that will speed the healing of wounds with minimal scarring. Helix is looking to partner with large, better-funded drugmakers to develop some of its product candidates. It has teamed with Body Blue to market its peptides to consumer products makers.

	Annual Growth	12/03	12/04	12/05	12/06	12/07
Sales ($ mil.)	49.5%	0.1	0.1	0.1	0.1	0.5
Net income ($ mil.)	—	(3.2)	(3.1)	(3.3)	(3.8)	(3.4)
Market value ($ mil.)	(13.9%)	23.3	23.7	15.7	19.8	12.8
Employees	—	—	—	—	—	—

HELIX ENERGY SOLUTIONS GROUP, INC.

NYSE: HLX

400 N. Sam Houston Pkwy. East, Ste. 400
Houston, TX 77060
Phone: 281-618-0400
Fax: 281-618-0501
Web: www.helixesg.com

CEO: Owen E. Kratz
CFO: A. Wade Pursell
HR: –
FYE: December 31
Type: Public

Helix Energy Solutions is in the energy services mix as a top marine shallow and deepwater contractor and operator of offshore oil and gas properties and production facilities. Its Contracting Deepwater unit primarily works in water depths greater than 1,000 feet, using dynamically positioned and remotely operated vehicles that offer a range of engineering, repair, maintenance, and pipe and cable burial services in global offshore markets. Subsidiary Energy Resource Technology buys and operates mature fields in the Gulf of Mexico, controlling proved reserves of 677 billion cu. ft. of natural gas equivalent.

	Annual Growth	12/03	12/04	12/05	12/06	12/07
Sales ($ mil.)	45.3%	396.3	543.4	799.5	1,366.9	1,767.4
Net income ($ mil.)	75.0%	34.2	82.7	152.6	347.4	320.5
Market value ($ mil.)	69.8%	456.6	782.8	2,788.4	2,843.0	3,792.5
Employees	36.8%	—	—	1,800	2,300	3,370

HELLER EHRMAN LLP

333 Bush St.
San Francisco, CA 94104
Phone: 415-772-6000
Fax: 415-772-6268
Web: www.hewm.com

CEO: Robert B. Hubell
CFO: Richard F. Holdrup
HR: David B. Sanders
FYE: December 31
Type: Partnership

Focusing on litigation and business transactions, Heller Ehrman provides legal services to clients ranging from *FORTUNE* 100 companies to startups. The firm's specialties include antitrust, corporate securities, intellectual property, and mergers and acquisitions. Its clients have come from industries such as accounting, energy, financial services, life sciences, and software and electronics and have included the likes of 3M, BP, and Microsoft. Heller Ehrman's 700-plus lawyers practice from more than a dozen offices, mainly in the western US but also in the Asia/Pacific region and in Europe. Emanuel Heller founded the firm in 1890.

	Annual Growth	12/02	12/03	12/04	12/05	12/06
Sales ($ mil.)	9.4%	354.0	430.0	430.0	475.0	507.0
Employees	(12.3%)	—	2,000	—	—	1,350

HELLMAN & FRIEDMAN LLC

1 Maritime Plaza, 12th Fl.
San Francisco, CA 94111
Phone: 415-788-5111
Fax: 415-788-0176
Web: www.hf.com

CEO: Brian M. Powers
CFO: Georgia Lee
HR: –
FYE: December 31
Type: Private

Hellman & Friedman has no trouble finding businesses to invest in. The private equity investment firm, which has raised more than $16 billion in capital and has invested in more than 50 companies, has put money into many industries, including financial services, professional services, information services, software, and media. It typically invests between $200 and $750 million per target; investments have included Nasdaq (stock market), DoubleClick (Internet marketing), and Vertafore (insurance industry software and services). It acquired Catalina Marketing in 2007 and Goodman Global the following year; it plans to buy Sheridan Healthcare.

	Annual Growth	12/03	12/04	12/05	12/06	12/07
Est. sales ($ mil.)	—	—	—	—	—	199.0
Employees	—	—	—	—	—	804

HELLMANN WORLDWIDE LOGISTICS, INC.

10450 Doral Blvd.
Doral, FL 33178
Phone: 305-406-4500
Fax: 305-406-4519
Web: www.hellmann.net

CEO: Frank Scheibner
CFO: Julian M. Riches
HR: Kenneth Finneran
FYE: December 31
Type: Private

Hellmann Worldwide Logistics, the US branch of a German logistics company with the same name, can arrange the transportation of freight by air or sea. As a freight forwarder, Hellmann buys transportation capacity from carriers and resells it to shippers. Related services include customs brokerage, supply chain management, and warehousing. The company's US network of about 30 offices includes facilities in major trade gateways such as Atlanta, Chicago, Houston, New York, Los Angeles, and Miami. Overall, Hellman operates in more than 130 countries. Carl Heinrich Hellmann founded the parent company in 1871; the Hellman family still owns the company.

	Annual Growth	12/03	12/04	12/05	12/06	12/07
Est. sales ($ mil.)	—	—	—	—	—	339.5
Employees	—	—	—	—	—	550

HELMERICH & PAYNE, INC.   NYSE: HP

1437 S. Boulder Ave.   CEO: Hans Helmerich
Tulsa, OK 74119   CFO: Douglas E. Fears
Phone: 918-742-5531   HR: –
Fax: 918-742-0237   FYE: September 30
Web: www.hpinc.com   Type: Public

In the oil and gas industry, Helmerich & Payne knows the drill. The contract driller operates almost 150 land and offshore platform rigs, mostly for industry giants such as BP, PDVSA, and Marathon Oil. Its contract drilling operations are conducted mainly in Louisiana, Oklahoma, Texas, and Wyoming, as well as offshore California, in the Gulf of Mexico, in South America, and in North and West Africa. Helmerich & Payne operates 156 FlexRigs (drilling rigs equipped with new technologies, environmental and safety design, and the capability of simultaneous crew activity). The company also has real estate operations, including a shopping center, residential buildings, and office buildings, in Tulsa.

	Annual Growth	9/03	9/04	9/05	9/06	9/07
Sales ($ mil.)	33.4%	515.3	620.9	800.7	1,224.8	1,629.7
Net income ($ mil.)	123.8%	17.9	4.4	127.6	293.9	449.3
Market value ($ mil.)	52.2%	655.3	723.6	1,568.2	2,465.5	3,514.7
Employees	16.0%	—	—	4,801	5,705	6,456

HELMSLEY ENTERPRISES, INC.

230 Park Ave.   CEO: –
New York, NY 10169   CFO: Abe Wolf
Phone: 212-679-3600   HR: Yogesh Mathur
Fax: 212-953-2810   FYE: December 31
                                              Type: Private

"Infamous" doesn't begin to cover Helmsley Enterprises and its former chairman, the late Leona Helmsley. The company holds the real estate empire amassed by the late Harry Helmsley over a period of 50 years. Leona, who was dubbed the "Queen of Mean" in her heyday, served time for tax evasion and had interests in such high-profile properties as the Helmsley Park Lane and the Helmsley Windsor. Other holdings include apartment buildings and millions of square feet of New York real estate, as well as a lease on the Empire State Building. The portfolio was valued at $5 billion before Harry Helmsley's death in 1997. Leona Helmsley sold more than $2 billion worth of property between 1997 and her death in 2007.

HELZBERG DIAMONDS

1825 Swift Ave.   CEO: H. Marvin Beasley
North Kansas City, MO 64116   CFO: Lonnie Lawton
Phone: 816-842-7780   HR: J. Kevin Fitzpatrick
Fax: 816-480-0294   FYE: December 31
Web: www.helzberg.com   Type: Subsidiary

Helzberg Diamonds is into hard rocks. The company sells a wide selection of diamonds and precious gems, mostly set into rings and other jewelry. It also sells men's and women's watches. One of the largest national jewelry chains, the company operates more than 260 stores nationwide. Helzberg Diamonds was founded in 1915 by Morris Helzberg and remained in his family until 1995, when it was acquired by investment guru Warren Buffett's Berkshire Hathaway. Long a mall-based chain, the company opened more than 45 free-standing locations in the 1990s. Helzberg Diamonds offers a 60-day return or exchange option and free jewelry repairs for 12 months after purchase.

	Annual Growth	12/03	12/04	12/05	12/06	12/07
Est. sales ($ mil.)	—	—	—	—	—	479.7
Employees	—	—	—	—	—	2,500

HEMACARE CORPORATION   OTC: HEMA

15350 Sherman Way, Ste. 350   CEO: Julian L. Steffenhagen
Van Nuys, CA 91406   CFO: Robert S. Chilton
Phone: 818-226-1968   HR: Annabelle Valtierra
Fax: 818-251-5300   FYE: December 31
Web: www.hemacare.com   Type: Public

HemaCare Corporation is a supplier of blood products and services to hospitals and researchers. The company collects whole blood from donors at donor centers and mobile donor vehicles and processes it into red blood cells, plasma, and other products used by hospitals for blood transfusion. HemaCare has blood collection centers in California and Maine; it operates under the name Coral Blood Services at its East Coast facilities. The company also provides therapeutic apheresis, a kind of blood treatment used for patients with autoimmune and other conditions, for hospitals in California and some mid-Atlantic states, including New York.

	Annual Growth	12/03	12/04	12/05	12/06	12/07
Sales ($ mil.)	5.6%	27.5	26.8	31.2	36.5	34.2
Net income ($ mil.)	—	(4.7)	1.5	1.7	1.9	(7.8)
Market value ($ mil.)	(13.2%)	6.0	12.5	12.5	23.8	3.4
Employees	(11.8%)	—	—	—	271	239

HEMAGEN DIAGNOSTICS, INC.   OTC: HMGN

9033 Red Branch Rd.   CEO: William P. Hales
Columbia, MD 21045   CFO: Catherine M. Davidson
Phone: 443-367-5500   HR: –
Fax: 410-997-7812   FYE: September 30
Web: www.hemagen.com   Type: Public

Hemagen Diagnostics lets no disease go undetected. The company makes diagnostic kits and related components. Its Virgo product line is used to identify infectious and autoimmune diseases such as rheumatoid arthritis, lupus, measles, and syphilis. Physicians and veterinarians use its Analyst reagent system and related components to test blood for substances like cholesterol, glucose, and triglycerides. Hemagen sells products internationally primarily through distributors; its Brazilian subsidiary markets its products in South America.

	Annual Growth	9/03	9/04	9/05	9/06	9/07
Sales ($ mil.)	(14.7%)	8.5	7.5	7.6	7.3	4.5
Net income ($ mil.)	—	(1.3)	(3.6)	(1.3)	0.3	(0.9)
Market value ($ mil.)	(4.8%)	3.1	5.8	3.8	4.6	2.5
Employees	—	—	—	—	—	—

HEMISPHERX BIOPHARMA, INC.   AMEX: HEB

1 Penn Center, 1617 JFK Blvd., 6th Fl.   CEO: William A. Carter
Philadelphia, PA 19103   CFO: Robert E. Peterson
Phone: 215-988-0080   HR: –
Fax: 215-988-1739   FYE: December 31
Web: www.hemispherx.net   Type: Public

Targeting chronic viral diseases and immune disorders, Hemispherx Biopharma hopes to do a world of good with its RNA (ribonucleic acid) and other drugs. The company has acquired the rights to Alferon N, an FDA-approved drug for genital warts that the company is developing to fight other viral diseases, such as multiple sclerosis and West Nile virus. Hemispherx also is developing Ampligen, an intravenously administered RNA drug that is in clinical trials to treat HIV and chronic fatigue syndrome (CFS). The compound has received orphan status from the FDA for kidney cancer, melanoma, CFS, and HIV.

	Annual Growth	12/03	12/04	12/05	12/06	12/07
Sales ($ mil.)	12.0%	0.7	1.2	1.1	0.9	1.1
Net income ($ mil.)	—	(14.8)	(24.1)	(12.4)	(19.4)	(18.1)
Market value ($ mil.)	(10.7%)	88.3	94.3	122.1	153.2	56.1
Employees	—	—	—	43	—	—

HENDRICK AUTOMOTIVE GROUP

6000 Monroe Rd., Ste. 100
Charlotte, NC 28212
Phone: 704-568-5550
Fax: 704-566-3295
Web: www.hendrickauto.com

CEO: James F. (Jim) Huzl
CFO: Veronica Zayatz
HR: Tim Taylor
FYE: December 31
Type: Private

For megadealer Hendrick Automotive Group, variety is the spice of life. The second-largest privately owned dealership group in the US, Hendrick Automotive sells new and used cars and light trucks from more than 20 automakers, from Hyundai to Hummer. Hendrick has a network of about 65 dealerships in some 10 states from the Carolinas to California. The company also offers financing, as well as automobile parts, accessories, service, and body repair. Founder Rick Hendrick pleaded guilty in 1997 to mail fraud relating to alleged bribes of American Honda executives; he was later pardoned by President Bill Clinton. Hendrick owns the company, which began in 1976 as a single dealership in Bennettsville, South Carolina.

HENDRICK MOTORSPORTS, INC.

4400 Papa Joe Hendrick Blvd.
Charlotte, NC 28262
Phone: 704-455-3400
Fax: 704-455-0346
Web: www.hendrickmotorsports.com

CEO: J. Richard (Rick) Hendrick III
CFO: Scott Lampe
HR: –
FYE: December 31
Type: Private

Stock car racing runs in the family at Hendrick Motorsports. The company is a major force in NASCAR Sprint Cup auto racing, with four teams competing for the checkered flag. Its top drivers include Jeff Gordon, Dale Earnhardt Jr., Casey Mears, and Jimmie Johnson. Hendrick Motorsports designs and builds its race cars at its 90-acre complex where it also builds and rebuilds some 700 engines. It also handles marketing and licensing for its racing teams. In addition to Sprint Cup racing, Hendrick Motorsports has teams competing in NASCAR's Nationwide Series and Craftsman Truck Series. Rick Hendrick and veteran driver Harry Hyde started the company in 1984 to compete in select races.

	Annual Growth	12/03	12/04	12/05	12/06	12/07
Est. sales ($ mil.)	—	—	—	—	—	44.3
Employees	—	—	—	—	—	500

HENKEL CORPORATION

2200 Renaissance Blvd., Ste. 200
Gulph Mills, PA 19406
Phone: 610-270-8100
Fax: 610-270-8103
Web: www.henkelcorp.com

CEO: John Knudson
CFO: John Knudson
HR: William (Bill) Read
FYE: December 31
Type: Subsidiary

The US subsidiary of German giant Henkel KGaA, Henkel Corporation helps consumers stick to it. The company operates through three business sectors: laundry and home care, personal care, and adhesives technologies. Some of its well known brands are Dial soap, Duck duct tape, Right Guard antiperspirant, LA LOOKS hair gel, Soft Scrub cleaner, and Purex laundry detergent. Henkel manufactures and markets industrial and engineering adhesives and surface technologies. The founding Henkel family controls the firm.

HENKELS & MCCOY, INC.

985 Jolly Rd.
Blue Bell, PA 19422
Phone: 215-283-7600
Fax: 215-283-7659
Web: www.henkels.com

CEO: Kenneth L. Rose
CFO: Robert J. Delark
HR: Vincent Benedict
FYE: September 30
Type: Private

When utilities, communications companies, or governments need the real McCoy to install or repair their transmission networks, they can call on specialty contractor Henkels & McCoy (H&M). The firm provides engineering, construction, and network development services globally. H&M also installs aerial and underground electrical distribution systems, gas transmission lines, and fiber-optic networks on electric transmission towers or along railroad rights-of-way. John Henkels Jr. and John McCoy founded H&M in Philadelphia in 1923 as a tree-trimming and landscaping firm. Employees and the Henkels family own H&M.

HENNIGES AUTOMOTIVE

36600 Corporate Dr.
Farmington Hills, MI 48331
Phone: 248-553-5300
Fax: 248-553-5105
Web: www.gdxautomotive.com

CEO: Robert DePierre
CFO: –
HR: –
FYE: December 31
Type: Private

Henniges Automotive wants the end users of its products to be able to listen to the radio instead of road noise. The company's sealing systems unit makes weatherstrips, moldings, beltstrips, and other seals. Henniges' anti-vibration division offers exhaust hangar systems, bearings and bushings, and dampening systems. The company also offers complete automotive glass modules including windows, windshields, and sunroofs. In 2007 Cerberus Capital Management sold GDX Automotive to MAPS Holdings, an affiliate of Wynnchurch Capital. MAPS and GDX were then merged, and the new entity was renamed Henniges Automotive.

	Annual Growth	12/03	12/04	12/05	12/06	12/07
Est. sales ($ mil.)	—	—	—	—	—	554.5
Employees	—	—	—	—	—	7,200

HENRY BROS. ELECTRONICS, INC.

AMEX: HBE

17-01 Pollitt Dr.
Fair Lawn, NJ 07410
Phone: 201-794-6500
Fax: 201-794-8341
Web: www.hbe-inc.com

CEO: James E. (Jim) Henry
CFO: John P. Hopkins
HR: T. Robert (Bob) Hodgson
FYE: December 31
Type: Public

Security systems integrator Henry Bros. Electronics (formerly Diversified Security Solutions) designs, installs, and maintains closed-circuit television (CCTV) and access control systems. The company also installs system components such as CCTVs, intercoms, alarm monitors, video recorders, and card access controls. Henry Bros. Electronics markets its services to large and midsized businesses and to government agencies. Revenues from the government represent about 40% of the company's sales. New York, New Jersey, and California account for two-thirds of business.

	Annual Growth	12/03	12/04	12/05	12/06	12/07
Sales ($ mil.)	33.3%	18.3	29.7	42.2	42.1	57.8
Net income ($ mil.)	—	(3.0)	0.0	1.1	(2.3)	(0.3)
Market value ($ mil.)	(2.6%)	29.1	28.4	26.4	22.4	26.3
Employees	15.1%	—	—	172	198	—

HENRY COMPANY

909 N. Sepulveda Blvd., Ste. 650
El Segundo, CA 90245
Phone: 310-955-9200
Fax: 310-640-7663
Web: www.henry.com

CEO: Warner W. Henry
CFO: –
HR: George Priggins
FYE: December 31
Type: Private

Henry Company can put a roof over your head and pavement under your feet. It operates in the US through three divisions: Henry Building Products (roofing systems, driveway maintenance products, vapor barriers); Bakor (commercial envelope systems and residential roofing and driveway maintenance products); and Resin Technology (polyurethane roof systems and insulation). Specialty products include undercoating for mobile homes, rust-proofing products for the auto industry, and protective coatings for industrial and commercial applications. Although it also operates in the US, Bakor has been a fixture in Canada for well over 60 years.

	Annual Growth	12/03	12/04	12/05	12/06	12/07
Est. sales ($ mil.)	—	—	—	—	—	84.0
Employees	—	—	—	—	—	560

HENRY CROWN AND COMPANY

222 N. LaSalle St.
Chicago, IL 60601
Phone: 312-236-6300
Fax: 312-899-5039

CEO: James S. Crown
CFO: –
HR: –
FYE: December 31
Type: Private

The jewels of Henry Crown and Company shine on like crazy diamonds. Controlled by Chicago's Crown family, Henry Crown and Company is an investment firm that owns or has interests in a variety of business assets. These holdings include stakes in sports teams (the Chicago Bulls and the New York Yankees), manufacturing, banking, and real estate (Rockefeller Center). The company also has a stake in General Dynamics; after once controlling the company outright, it still has a seat on the board. The Crown family, worth an estimated $4.5 billion, is on the *Forbes'* list of richest Americans, and its members are prominent Chicago-area philanthropists.

	Annual Growth	12/03	12/04	12/05	12/06	12/07
Est. sales ($ mil.)	—	—	—	—	—	59.9
Employees	—	—	—	—	—	783

HENRY FORD HEALTH SYSTEM

1 Ford Place
Detroit, MI 48202
Phone: 313-876-8700
Fax: 313-876-9243
Web: www.henryfordhealth.org

CEO: Nancy M. Schlichting
CFO: James M. Connelly
HR: Ronald Waetzman
FYE: December 31
Type: Not-for-profit

In 1915 automaker Henry Ford founded the hospital that forms the cornerstone of southeastern Michigan's not-for-profit Henry Ford Health System (HFHS), a hospital network that is also involved in medical research and education. The system's hospital network, which all together has nearly 2,000 beds, includes the flagship Henry Ford Hospital, the Henry Ford Wyandotte Hospital, and mental health facility Kingswood Hospital. HFHS also operates a 900-doctor medical group, nursing homes, hospice and home health care providers, and a medical supply retailer. The system's Health Alliance Plan of Michigan provides managed care and health insurance to more than 550,000 members.

	Annual Growth	12/02	12/03	12/04	12/05	12/06
Sales ($ mil.)	7.9%	2,400.0	2,600.0	2,846.3	3,049.1	3,250.0
Employees	5.7%	12,600	12,700	—	14,900	—

HENRY MODELL & COMPANY, INC.

498 7th Ave., 20th Fl.
New York, NY 10018
Phone: 212-822-1000
Fax: 212-822-1025
Web: www.modells.com

CEO: Mitchell B. Modell
CFO: Joseph Quinn
HR: Phyllis Siegel
FYE: January 31
Type: Private

Modell's colors change from city to city. Henry Modell & Company sells sporting goods, apparel (including local team apparel), and brand-name athletic footwear at about 135 Modell's Sporting Goods stores in about 10 states in the Northeast. Best known for offering branded products at reasonable prices, Modell has stores in malls, regional shopping centers, and busy urban areas. Founded in 1889 by Morris Modell (who first sold menswear from a Lower East Side pushcart in New York City), the chain is the oldest family-owned and -operated sports retailer in the country; it is in its fourth generation of Modell management.

	Annual Growth	1/03	1/04	1/05	1/06	1/07
Est. sales ($ mil.)	—	—	—	—	—	636.5
Employees	—	—	—	—	—	5,430

HENRY SCHEIN, INC.

NASDAQ (GS): HSIC

135 Duryea Rd.
Melville, NY 11747
Phone: 631-843-5500
Fax: 631-843-5658
Web: www.henryschein.com

CEO: Stanley M. Bergman
CFO: Steven Paladino
HR: Jan Ushioko
FYE: Last Saturday in December
Type: Public

Whether you're in Poughkeepsie or Prague, Henry Schein will help your dentist get those sparkly whites to shine. The company is a leading global distributor of dental supplies and equipment, with operations in North America, Europe, and Asia/Pacific. Henry Schein provides such items as impression materials, X-ray equipment, and anesthetics. But the company isn't only interested in teeth; it also supplies doctors' offices, veterinarians, and other office-based health care providers with diagnostic kits, surgical tools, drugs, vaccines, and animal health products. Additionally, its technology division offers practice management software and other services to dental, medical, and veterinary offices.

	Annual Growth	12/03	12/04	12/05	12/06	12/07
Sales ($ mil.)	15.3%	3,353.8	4,060.3	4,635.9	5,153.1	5,920.2
Net income ($ mil.)	11.8%	137.5	128.2	151.3	163.8	215.2
Market value ($ mil.)	39.2%	1,480.7	2,928.5	3,800.7	4,334.7	5,559.9
Employees	4.4%	—	—	11,000	11,000	12,000

HENSEL PHELPS CONSTRUCTION CO.

420 6th Ave.
Greeley, CO 80632
Phone: 970-352-6565
Fax: 970-352-9311
Web: www.henselphelps.com

CEO: Jerry L. Morgensen
CFO: Stephen J. (Steve) Carrico
HR: Charles Eaton
FYE: December 31
Type: Private

Hensel Phelps Construction builds it all, from the courthouse to the Big House. Launched as a homebuilder by founder Hensel Phelps in 1937, the employee-owned general contractor focuses on design/build and construction management services for institutional and commercial projects, including prisons, airport facilities, hotels, government and corporate complexes, convention centers, sport arenas, and more. It also works on transportation, educational, residential, and health care projects. Major clients have included the US Army Corps of Engineers, IBM, Computer Sciences Corporation, United Airlines, and Whole Foods. Hansel Phelps has eight regional offices throughout the US.

	Annual Growth	5/02	5/03	5/04	5/05	*12/06
Sales ($ mil.)	4.7%	1,771.0	1,872.0	1,800.0	1,728.0	2,130.0
Employees	3.6%	2,200	2,500	2,500	2,324	2,534

*Fiscal year change

An in-depth profile of this company is available to Hoover's Online members at hoovers.com.

753

THE HERB CHAMBERS COMPANIES

259 McGrath Hwy.
Somerville, MA 02145
Phone: 617-666-8333
Fax: 617-666-8448
Web: www.chamberscars.com

CEO: Herbert G. (Herb) Chambers
CFO: Bruce Spatz
HR: −
FYE: December 31
Type: Private

Step into the chambers of Herb Chambers Companies and you'll find a wide range of cars. The acquisitive company runs nearly 40 dealerships in southern New England that sell just about everything from pricey new cars by BMW, Cadillac, Lexus, Mercedes-Benz, and Porsche to more affordable offerings by Honda, Hyundai, Scion, Saturn, and Toyota. Dealerships also offer used cars, and one offers Vespa scooters. All of its vehicles are available online. Herb Chambers also offers parts and service and runs four body shops. Owner and CEO Herb Chambers started his automotive empire with a Cadillac/Oldsmobile dealership in New London, Connecticut, in 1985.

	Annual Growth	12/03	12/04	12/05	12/06	12/07
Est. sales ($ mil.)	—	—	—	—	—	70.8
Employees	—	—	—	—	—	164

HERBALIFE LTD.

NYSE: HLF

1800 Century Park East
Los Angeles, CA 90067
Phone: 310-410-9600
Fax: 310-258-7019
Web: www.herbalifeww.com

CEO: Michael O. Johnson
CFO: Richard (Rich) Goudis
HR: Patrick R. Dailey
FYE: December 31
Type: Public

Is it a weight-loss supplement or a way of life? Only Herbalife Ltd. knows for sure. Formerly known as WH Holdings (Cayman Islands), this holding company operates through Herbalife International, which manufactures and distributes weight control products such as meal replacements, snacks, and "enhancers." The company also offers nutritional supplements, energy drinks, and skin care products. The company has international subsidiaries in more than 60 countries. Herbalife's multi-level marketing program involves more than 1.5 million independent distributors throughout the world.

	Annual Growth	12/03	12/04	12/05	12/06	12/07
Sales ($ mil.)	17.9%	—	1,309.7	1,566.8	1,885.5	2,145.8
Net income ($ mil.)	—	—	(14.3)	93.1	143.1	191.4
Market value ($ mil.)	33.0%	—	1,115.3	2,273.1	2,875.5	2,622.8
Employees	(3.8%)	—	—	3,788	3,644	—

HERBORIUM GROUP, INC.

OTC: HBRM

3 Oak St.
Teaneck, NJ 07666
Phone: 888-836-2424
Fax: 800-813-4080
Web: www.herborium.com

CEO: Agnes P. Olszewski
CFO: Agnes P. Olszewski
HR: −
FYE: November 30
Type: Public

When Pacific Magtron International (PMIC) couldn't get its sales up, it sought relief with an herbal remedy from Herborium Group. Its previous business of distributing computer hardware, software, and peripherals failed to the point that it filed for Chapter 11 bankruptcy protection in 2005. What remained was a shell with one director who oversaw its 2006 reverse merger with Herborium, a developer and marketer of herbal nutritional supplements. Herborium's current and proposed product line includes Chinese medical herbal blends marketed to clear up acne, boost energy, and heighten sexual functioning. CEO and president Agnes Olszewski and director James Gilligan each hold some 40% of the company's shares.

	Annual Growth	12/03	12/04	12/05	*11/06	11/07
Sales ($ mil.)	(67.8%)	74.3	71.5	10.0	0.8	0.8
Net income ($ mil.)	—	(2.1)	(1.1)	(1.7)	(0.3)	(0.6)
Market value ($ mil.)	19.9%	1.6	—	—	2.7	—
Employees	—	—	—	—	1	—
*Fiscal year change						

H.E.R.C. PRODUCTS INCORPORATED

OTC: HERC

1420 Columbus Ave.
Portsmouth, VA 23704
Phone: 757-393-0002
Fax: 757-393-1651
Web: www.hercprod.com

CEO: C. Clifford (Cliff) Wright Jr.
CFO: −
HR: −
FYE: December 31
Type: Public

H.E.R.C. likes to run a clean ship. The company makes chemicals for treating water scale and corrosion on ship surfaces and in pipeline systems, and provides marine tank cleaning services. H.E.R.C. products such as Pipe-Klean and Well-Klean are combined with water and flushed through water delivery systems, sprinkler systems, waste systems, and water wells. Many of H.E.R.C.'s products are biodegradable and don't require the expensive clean-up that more toxic chemicals do. H.E.R.C. also sells products for use in cleaning industrial systems. The US Navy and Coast Guard are important customers. In 2007 H.E.R.C. bought Simplex Building, and in 2008 agreed to acquire Marine Environmental Services.

	Annual Growth	12/03	12/04	12/05	12/06	12/07
Est. sales ($ mil.)	—	—	—	—	—	4.0
Employees	—	—	—	—	—	100

HERCULES INCORPORATED

NYSE: HPC

Hercules Plaza, 1313 N. Market St.
Wilmington, DE 19894
Phone: 302-594-5000
Fax: 302-594-5400
Web: www.herc.com

CEO: Craig A. Rogerson
CFO: Allen A. Spizzo
HR: Edward V. (Ed) Carrington
FYE: December 31
Type: Public

Hercules labors to strengthen products such as paper, paint, and textiles. The company's paper technologies division supplies water-treatment and functional performance chemicals and services to the pulp and paper industry. Its Aqualon subsidiary makes thickeners for water-based products such as latex paints, printing inks, and oral hygiene products. The company's former Pinova unit, which makes wood and gum rosin resins for adhesives, food and beverages, and construction materials, was moved within Aqualon in 2006. Hercules owns a minority stake in FiberVisions, a business that makes staple fibers used in disposable diapers and automotive textiles.

	Annual Growth	12/03	12/04	12/05	12/06	12/07
Sales ($ mil.)	3.7%	1,846.0	1,997.0	2,068.8	2,035.3	2,136.2
Net income ($ mil.)	41.2%	45.0	27.0	(41.1)	238.7	178.9
Market value ($ mil.)	3.1%	1,951.8	1,665.3	1,273.9	2,240.5	2,205.9
Employees	0.1%	—	—	4,650	4,430	4,660

HERCULES OFFSHORE, INC.

NASDAQ (GS): HERO

9 Greenway Plaza, Ste. 2200
Houston, TX 77046
Phone: 713-350-5100
Fax: 713-350-5105
Web: www.herculesoffshore.com

CEO: Randall D. (Randy) Stilley
CFO: Lisa W. Rodriguez
HR: Laura D. Guthrie
FYE: December 31
Type: Public

"With the strength of 10, ordinary men . . . " Hercules Offshore, through its subsidiaries, provides shallow-water drilling and liftboat services to major integrated energy companies and independent oil and natural gas exploration and production companies. It owns and operates a fleet of 24 jackup rigs and three submersible rigs in the Gulf of Mexico; nine jackup rigs and one platform rig outside of the Gulf of Mexico; 12 conventional and 15 posted barge rigs that operate inland; and 65 self-propelled, self-elevating liftboats. Its Delta Towing business operates a fleet of 33 inland tugs, 17 offshore tugs, 34 crew boats, 45 deck barges, 17 shale barges, and four spud barges.

	Annual Growth	12/03	12/04	12/05	12/06	12/07
Sales ($ mil.)	118.0%	—	—	161.3	344.3	766.8
Net income ($ mil.)	122.8%	—	—	27.5	119.1	136.5
Market value ($ mil.)	56.8%	—	—	859.2	932.3	2,113.0
Employees	(33.7%)	—	—	750	920	330

An in-depth profile of this company is available to Hoover's Online members at hoovers.com.

HERCULES TECHNOLOGY GROWTH CAPITAL

NASDAQ (GM): HTGC

400 Hamilton Ave., Ste. 310
Palo Alto, CA 94301
Phone: 650-289-3060
Fax: 650-473-9194
Web: www.herculestech.com

CEO: Manuel A. Henriquez
CFO: David M. Lund
HR: –
FYE: December 31
Type: Public

Hercules Technology Growth Capital, Inc., (HTGC) performs its feats of strength with money. The closed-end investment firm offers financing vehicles to companies in the technology and life sciences sectors. HTCG provides primarily private companies (as well as some public ones) with such products as mezzanine loans, senior secured loans, and select private equity investments. Loans typically range from $1 million to $30 million. HTGC's portfolio includes some 95 companies; the biopharmaceuticals industry represents about half of all investments. Portfolio companies include data network provider IKANO Communications and software company Talisma. CEO Manuel Henriquez co-founded HTCG in 2003.

	Annual Growth	12/03	12/04	12/05	12/06	12/07
Sales ($ mil.)	545.9%	—	0.2	10.7	29.5	53.9
Net income ($ mil.)	—	—	(2.0)	2.1	11.4	42.4
Market value ($ mil.)	85.4%	—	—	117.5	327.6	404.2
Employees	51.2%	—	11	19	26	38

HERFF JONES COMPANY OF INDIANA, INC.

4501 W. 62nd St.
Indianapolis, IN 46268
Phone: 317-297-3740
Fax: 317-329-3308
Web: www.herff-jones.com

CEO: Joe Slaughter
CFO: Michael J. Cheek
HR: –
FYE: June 30
Type: Private

Herff Jones Company wants its products to play an integral part in all noteworthy achievements, ceremonies, and traditions. It makes commemorative items for educational and athletic institutions, including caps, gowns, diplomas, awards, rings, medals, and yearbooks. The firm, founded in 1920, also makes and markets robes to religious and judicial entities, including those for the Supreme Court. Its education division, Nystrom, makes and publishes classroom materials for history and social studies classes, including globes, maps, atlases, and other items. As part of the same educational unit, It's About Time publishes programs for math and science study that are supported by the National Science Foundation.

	Annual Growth	6/03	6/04	6/05	6/06	6/07
Est. sales ($ mil.)	—	—	—	—	—	506.1
Employees	—	—	—	—	—	3,000

HERITAGE BANKSHARES, INC.

OTC: HBKS

150 Granby St.
Norfolk, VA 23510
Phone: 757-648-1700
Fax: 757-626-0064
Web: www.heritagenorfolk.com

CEO: Michael S. (Mike) Ives
CFO: John O. Guthrie
HR: –
FYE: December 31
Type: Public

Heritage Bankshares comes from a long line of money. Heritage Bankshares is the holding company for Heritage Bank & Trust, a community-based institution in Virginia with branches in Chesapeake, Norfolk, and Virginia Beach. The bank offers standard banking products and services, including checking and savings accounts, debit cards, CDs, and IRAs. Real estate loans, primarily mortgages, account for the largest portion of its loan portfolio; the bank also originates loans for businesses, individuals, and municipalities. The company also sells insurance and annuities.

	Annual Growth	12/03	12/04	12/05	12/06	12/07
Assets ($ mil.)	11.1%	145.0	153.8	204.6	222.9	221.3
Net income ($ mil.)	(14.7%)	1.7	1.7	0.8	0.2	0.9
Market value ($ mil.)	0.6%	—	—	25.1	36.4	25.4
Employees	—	—	—	—	—	71

HERITAGE COMMERCE CORP

NASDAQ (GS): HTBK

150 Almaden Blvd.
San Jose, CA 95113
Phone: 408-947-6900
Fax: 408-947-6910
Web: www.heritagecommercecorp.com

CEO: Walter T. (Walt) Kaczmarek
CFO: Lawrence D. McGovern
HR: Janice Mizota
FYE: December 31
Type: Public

If you know the way to San Jose, you may also know the way to Heritage Commerce. It is the holding company for Heritage Bank of Commerce, which operates more than 10 branches in the South Bay region of the San Francisco Bay area. Serving consumers and small to midsized businesses and their owners and managers, the bank offers savings and checking accounts, NOW and money market accounts, and CDs, as well as cash management services and loans. Commercial, construction, land, and mortgage loans make up most of the company's loan portfolio, which is rounded out by home equity and consumer loans. Heritage Commerce was established in 1998.

	Annual Growth	12/03	12/04	12/05	12/06	12/07
Assets ($ mil.)	7.7%	1,003.2	1,108.2	1,130.5	1,037.1	1,347.5
Net income ($ mil.)	16.0%	7.8	8.5	14.4	17.3	14.1
Market value ($ mil.)	13.8%	140.0	222.0	253.9	310.5	234.9
Employees	—	—	—	188	—	—

HERITAGE FINANCIAL CORPORATION

NASDAQ (GS): HFWA

201 5th Ave. SW
Olympia, WA 98501
Phone: 360-943-1500
Fax: 360-943-8046
Web: www.heritagebankwa.com

CEO: Brian L. Vance
CFO: Donald J. Hinson
HR: Sabrina Robisson
FYE: December 31
Type: Public

Heritage Financial is the bank holding company for Heritage Bank and Central Valley Bank, which together operate some 20 branches in Washington in the southern Puget Sound area and the central part of the state, respectively. The banks offer a full range of consumer deposit services such as CDs, IRAs, and checking, savings, NOW, and money market accounts. Commercial loans account for more than half of Heritage Financial's loan portfolio; mortgages secured by multifamily real estate account for about 20%. The banks also write single-family mortgages, construction loans, and consumer loans.

	Annual Growth	12/03	12/04	12/05	12/06	12/07
Assets ($ mil.)	8.4%	640.9	697.3	751.2	852.9	886.1
Net income ($ mil.)	4.7%	8.9	9.6	10.5	10.6	10.7
Market value ($ mil.)	1.0%	127.0	125.3	152.7	162.7	132.2
Employees	3.0%	—	—	211	—	224

HERITAGE FINANCIAL GROUP

NASDAQ (GM): HBOS

721 North Westover Blvd.
Albany, GA 31707
Phone: 229-420-0000
Fax: 229-878-2054
Web: www.eheritagebank.com

CEO: O. Leonard (Len) Dorminey
CFO: T. Heath Fountain
HR: –
FYE: December 31
Type: Public

Chartered in the 1950s to serve its hometown Marine base, HeritageBank of the South has remained "forever faithful" to its local customers. Heritage Financial Group, through subsidiary HeritageBank of the South, serves individuals and small to midsized businesses in the Georgia counties of Dougherty, Lee, Mitchell, and Worth. It operates some 10 branches offering traditional deposit and loan products. Consumer loans and residential mortgage loans each account for about 26% of the thrift's total portfolio, which also includes business loans and commercial property loans. Mutual holding company Heritage MHC owns some 70% of Heritage Financial.

	Annual Growth	12/03	12/04	12/05	12/06	12/07
Assets ($ mil.)	8.7%	335.7	343.5	363.8	413.3	468.7
Net income ($ mil.)	6.0%	2.3	3.5	3.0	2.3	2.9
Market value ($ mil.)	(3.0%)	—	—	129.5	190.6	121.8
Employees	—	—	—	122	—	—

An in-depth profile of this company is available to Hoover's Online members at hoovers.com.

755

HERITAGE OAKS BANCORP

NASDAQ (CM): HEOP

545 12th St.
Paso Robles, CA 93446
Phone: 805-239-5200
Fax: 805-238-6257
Web: www.heritageoaksbancorp.com

CEO: Lawrence P. Ward
CFO: Margaret A. Torres
HR: Joni Watson
FYE: December 31
Type: Public

Stash your acorns at Heritage Oaks Bancorp. It's the holding company for Heritage Oaks Bank, which serves primarily retail customers, farmers, and small to midsized businesses in California's San Luis Obispo and northern Santa Barbara counties. The bank offers standard deposit products such as checking, savings, and money market accounts, and loan products such as agricultural, commercial, consumer, real estate, and SBA loans. Commercial real estate accounts for more than 50% of its loan portfolio; construction loans make up nearly 25%. The company provides investment and financial planning through the bank's division Heritage Oaks Financial Services.

	Annual Growth	12/03	12/04	12/05	12/06	12/07
Assets ($ mil.)	14.0%	442.0	448.0	488.5	541.8	745.5
Net income ($ mil.)	17.7%	3.6	4.6	6.6	6.7	6.9
Market value ($ mil.)	24.7%	36.3	48.0	121.7	103.9	87.8
Employees	10.2%	164	170	190	—	242

HERITAGE-CRYSTAL CLEAN, LLC

NASDAQ (GM): HCCI

2175 Point Blvd., Ste. 375
Elgin, IL 60123
Phone: 847-836-5670
Fax: 847-836-5677
Web: www.crystal-clean.com

CEO: Joseph Chalhoub
CFO: Gregory Ray
HR: –
FYE: Saturday nearest December 31
Type: Public

It's a dirty job, but somebody's gotta do it, and that "somebody" might be Heritage-Crystal Clean. The company helps businesses clean parts and dispose of highly regulated waste materials such as cleaning solvents, used oil, and paint that can't be discarded through municipal trash systems or standard drains. Customers are primarily small to midsized businesses and include car dealerships, auto repair shops, trucking firms, and manufacturers, such as metal fabricators and printers. Heritage-Crystal Clean regularly services more than 30,000 client sites from some 50 branches in nearly 40 states. President and CEO Joseph Chalhoub founded Heritage-Crystal Clean in 1999.

	Annual Growth	12/03	12/04	12/05	12/06	12/07
Sales ($ mil.)	22.8%	—	48.4	59.2	73.7	89.7
Net income ($ mil.)	116.5%	—	0.7	2.0	4.3	7.1
Employees	9.9%	—	—	—	423	465

HERLEY INDUSTRIES, INC.

NASDAQ (GM): HRLY

101 N. Pointe Blvd.
Lancaster, PA 17601
Phone: 717-735-8117
Fax: 717-397-9503
Web: www.herley.com

CEO: Myron Levy
CFO: Kevin J. Purcell
HR: John A. Carroll
FYE: Sunday nearest July 31
Type: Public

Herley Industries makes microwave products for aerospace, defense, and commercial customers. Defense and aerospace offerings include flight instruments such as transponders and flight telemetry systems, navigation system components, missile guidance systems, unmanned vehicle command-and-control systems, and flight-termination receivers (used to trigger explosives to destroy a craft if something goes wrong). The company sells its products to US and overseas military organizations and defense contractors. Herley's commercial products include amplifiers for nuclear magnetic resonance systems (used by researchers and scientists) and amplifiers and components used in medical magnetic resonance imaging (MRI) systems.

	Annual Growth	7/03	7/04	7/05	7/06	7/07
Sales ($ mil.)	10.3%	110.2	122.2	151.4	176.3	163.1
Net income ($ mil.)	(31.3%)	13.9	13.7	10.8	10.4	3.1
Market value ($ mil.)	(4.0%)	254.2	267.3	281.2	150.7	215.8
Employees	(5.0%)	—	—	1,026	1,014	926

HERMAN MILLER, INC.

NASDAQ (GS): MLHR

855 E. Main Ave.
Zeeland, MI 49464
Phone: 616-654-3000
Fax: 616-654-5234
Web: www.hermanmiller.com

CEO: Brian C. Walker
CFO: Curt Pullen
HR: Andrew J. (Andy) Lock
FYE: Saturday nearest May 31
Type: Public

Desk jockeys can ride Herman Miller's products all the way up the corporate ladder and home again. A top US manufacturer of office furniture, the firm is known for developing designs for corporate, government, home office and leisure, and health care environments. Herman Miller's products include ergonomic devices, filing and storage systems, freestanding furniture, lighting, seating, textiles, and wooden casegoods. It manufactures its products in the UK and the US and sells worldwide through its sales staff and dealer network, as well as through independent dealers and the Internet. Ariel Capital Management owns about 11% of capital stock.

	Annual Growth	5/03	5/04	5/05	5/06	5/07
Sales ($ mil.)	9.5%	1,336.5	1,338.3	1,515.6	1,737.2	1,918.9
Net income ($ mil.)	53.4%	23.3	42.3	68.0	99.2	129.1
Market value ($ mil.)	13.0%	1,408.5	1,727.8	2,073.7	2,003.5	2,298.4
Employees	2.7%	—	—	6,234	6,242	6,574

HERSHA HOSPITALITY TRUST

AMEX: HT

44 Hersha Dr.
Harrisburg, PA 17102
Phone: 717-236-4400
Fax: 717-774-7383
Web: www.hersha.com

CEO: Jay H. Shah
CFO: Ashish R. Parikh
HR: –
FYE: December 31
Type: Public

Hersha Hospitality's fortune is in hotels, not chocolate. The self-advised real estate investment trust (REIT) invests in hotel properties, primarily mid-scale, upscale, and extended-stay properties in central business districts. It owns or co-owns about 75 hotels containing a total of more than 9,100 rooms in the northeastern and western US. The properties are operated under such brand names as Comfort Inn, Fairfield Inn, Hampton Inn, Hilton Garden Inn, and Holiday Inn Express. Hersha Hospitality owns its hotels and leases them to subsidiary 44 New England Management Company. The properties are managed by Hersha Hospitality Management, a private affiliate.

	Annual Growth	12/03	12/04	12/05	12/06	12/07
Sales ($ mil.)	88.0%	19.4	50.6	80.9	147.9	242.1
Net income ($ mil.)	117.5%	0.8	2.0	3.3	5.1	17.9
Market value ($ mil.)	33.1%	124.8	232.4	182.9	461.3	391.4
Employees	—	—	13	—	—	—

THE HERSHEY COMPANY

NYSE: HSY

100 Crystal A Dr.
Hershey, PA 17033
Phone: 717-534-4200
Fax: –
Web: www.thehersheycompany.com

CEO: David J. (Dave) West
CFO: Humberto P. (Bert) Alfonso
HR: Kathryn M. McGrath
FYE: December 31
Type: Public

The Hershey Company (formerly Hershey Foods) will cover you in Kisses and bring you Almond Joy. Hershey makes such well-known chocolate and candy brands as Hershey's Kisses, Reese's peanut butter cups, Swizzles licorice, Mounds, York Peppermint Patty, and Kit Kat (licensed from Nestlé). The company also makes grocery goods such as baking chocolate, ice-cream toppings, chocolate syrup, cocoa mix, cookies, snack nuts, hard candies, lollipops, and peanut butter. Its products are sold throughout North America and exported overseas. The Hershey Trust, which benefits the Milton Hershey School for disadvantaged children, controls approximately 99% of Hershey's voting power.

	Annual Growth	12/03	12/04	12/05	12/06	12/07
Sales ($ mil.)	4.3%	4,172.5	4,429.3	4,836.0	4,944.2	4,946.7
Net income ($ mil.)	(17.3%)	457.6	590.9	493.2	559.1	214.1
Market value ($ mil.)	14.5%	3,815.1	10,316.4	9,928.7	8,438.5	6,550.0
Employees	(3.5%)	—	—	13,750	15,000	12,800

HERSHEY ENTERTAINMENT & RESORTS COMPANY

27 W. Chocolate Ave.	CEO: Theodore J. (Ted) Kleisner
Hershey, PA 17033	CFO: Dave Lavery
Phone: 717-534-3090	HR: –
Fax: 717-534-8991	FYE: December 31
Web: www.hersheypa.com	Type: Private

Life is sweet for Hershey Entertainment & Resorts. The company owns the many chocolate-related entertainment destinations in Hershey, Pennsylvania. Its holdings include HERSHEYPARK, one of the US's top amusement parks, HERSHEYPARK Stadium, The Star Pavilion, ZOOAMERICA wildlife park, THE HOTEL HERSHEY, and the HERSHEY Lodge. Hershey Entertainment's other holdings include a golf club, a minor league hockey team, RV campgrounds, and a spa with chocolate treatments. It also owns the DUTCH WONDERLAND Family Amusement Park in nearby Lancaster. The Hershey Trust, which controls a majority voting stake in candy firm Hershey Foods, owns the company.

	Annual Growth	12/03	12/04	12/05	12/06	12/07
Est. sales ($ mil.)	—	—	—	—	—	238.5
Employees	—	—	—	—	—	7,500

HERTZ GLOBAL HOLDINGS, INC.

NYSE: HTZ

225 Brae Blvd.	CEO: Mark P. Frissora
Park Ridge, NJ 07656	CFO: Elyse Douglas
Phone: 201-307-2000	HR: LeighAnne Baker
Fax: 201-307-2644	FYE: December 31
Web: www.hertz.com	Type: Public

If you've ever said, "Don't worry about it, it's just a rental," guess who hurts: Hertz Global Holdings, one of the world's leading car rental companies. On its own and through agents and licensees, Hertz operates about 8,000 rental locations, including more than 1,500 at US airports, in 145 countries worldwide. The company's fleet includes more than 500,000 cars from Ford, General Motors, Toyota, and other manufacturers. Car rentals account for about 80% of the company's sales. Hertz also rents a variety of heavy equipment through some 375 locations in North America and Europe. Investment firms Clayton Dubilier & Rice, The Carlyle Group, and Merrill Lynch Global Private Equity own some 55% of Hertz.

	Annual Growth	12/03	12/04	12/05	12/06	12/07
Sales ($ mil.)	13.6%	5,207.9	6,676.0	7,469.2	8,058.4	8,685.6
Net income ($ mil.)	13.7%	158.6	365.5	350.0	115.9	264.6
Market value ($ mil.)	(8.3%)	—	—	—	5,575.6	5,114.4
Employees	0.0%	29,300	31,400	32,200	31,500	29,350

HESKA CORPORATION

NASDAQ (CM): HSKA

3760 Rocky Mountain Ave.	CEO: Robert B. Grieve
Loveland, CO 80538	CFO: Jason A. Napolitano
Phone: 970-493-7272	HR: Mark D. Cicotello
Fax: 970-619-3003	FYE: December 31
Web: www.heska.com	Type: Public

If you lie down with dogs, Heska makes sure you don't get up with fleas. The company makes diagnostic products, vaccines, and pharmaceuticals for domestic animals. Products on the market and in development include diagnostics and treatments for allergies, arthritis, cancer, fleas, heartworms, skin problems, thyroid problems, and viral infections. The company also operates a diagnostic lab and makes veterinary diagnostic and monitoring devices. Subsidiary Diamond Animal Health also manufactures livestock vaccines. Heska's products are sold through direct representatives and independent distributors.

	Annual Growth	12/03	12/04	12/05	12/06	12/07
Sales ($ mil.)	6.0%	65.3	67.7	69.4	75.1	82.3
Net income ($ mil.)	—	(3.5)	(4.8)	0.3	1.8	34.8
Market value ($ mil.)	(4.3%)	112.3	57.7	66.1	85.3	94.1
Employees	—	—	—	286	—	—

HESS CORPORATION

NYSE: HES

1185 Avenue of the Americas	CEO: John B. Hess
New York, NY 10036	CFO: John P. Rielly
Phone: 212-997-8500	HR: Brian J. Bohling
Fax: 212-536-8593	FYE: December 31
Web: www.hess.com	Type: Public

Hess Corporation (formerly Amerada Hess) has what it takes. The integrated oil and gas company conducts exploration and production in Denmark, Gabon, Norway, the UK, and the US. It also operates in Indonesia, Thailand, and other countries. In 2007 Hess reported proved reserves totaling more than 1.3 billion barrels of oil equivalent. It operates a 50%-owned refinery (HOVENSA) in the US Virgin Islands and a smaller one in New Jersey, and it markets gasoline through more than 1,370 HESS gas stations, chiefly in the eastern US. CEO John Hess owns about 14% of the company.

	Annual Growth	12/03	12/04	12/05	12/06	12/07
Sales ($ mil.)	21.6%	14,480.0	17,126.0	23,255.0	28,720.0	31,647.0
Net income ($ mil.)	29.9%	643.0	977.0	1,242.0	1,916.0	1,832.0
Market value ($ mil.)	107.1%	—	—	—	15,615.4	32,335.7
Employees	7.0%	—	—	11,610	13,700	13,300

HEWITT ASSOCIATES, INC.

NYSE: HEW

100 Half Day Rd.	CEO: Russell P. (Russ) Fradin
Lincolnshire, IL 60069	CFO: John J. Park
Phone: 847-295-5000	HR: Andrés Tapia
Fax: 847-295-7634	FYE: September 30
Web: www.hewittassociates.com	Type: Public

If any of a company's resources are human, chances are it'll need the assistance of Hewitt Associates. As one of the primary leaders in its industry, the company provides a variety of HR related services including payroll, organizational change management, talent and reward consulting, and the largest portion of the company's business — benefits outsourcing. Hewitt Associates administers medical, 401(k), and pension plans on an outsourced basis for mainly larger companies with complex benefit programs. The company also provides consulting for the design, implementation, and operation of many of the same human resources programs. Hewitt Associates was founded by Ted Hewitt in 1940.

	Annual Growth	9/03	9/04	9/05	9/06	9/07
Sales ($ mil.)	10.2%	2,031.3	2,262.2	2,898.4	2,857.2	2,990.3
Net income ($ mil.)	—	94.3	122.8	134.7	(115.9)	(175.1)
Market value ($ mil.)	50.0%	741.8	859.4	1,622.0	2,688.6	3,754.8
Employees	2.2%	—	—	22,000	24,000	23,000

HEWLETT-PACKARD COMPANY

NYSE: HPQ

3000 Hanover St.	CEO: Mark V. Hurd
Palo Alto, CA 94304	CFO: Catherine A. (Cathie) Lesjak
Phone: 650-857-1501	HR: Marcela Perez de Alonso
Fax: 650-857-5518	FYE: October 31
Web: www.hp.com	Type: Public

While Hewlett-Packard may be known for product innovation, the company's corporate development is a tale of reinvention. HP provides enterprise and consumer customers a full range of high-tech equipment, including personal computers, servers, storage devices, printers, and networking equipment. Its software portfolio includes operating systems, print management tools, and OpenView, a suite that encompasses application, business, network infrastructure, and product lifecycle management. HP, which already boasts an IT service organization that is among the world's largest, agreed to acquire Electronic Data Systems (EDS) for about $13.9 billion in cash in 2008.

	Annual Growth	10/03	10/04	10/05	10/06	10/07
Sales ($ mil.)	9.3%	73,061.0	79,905.0	86,696.0	91,658.0	104,286.0
Net income ($ mil.)	30.1%	2,539.0	3,497.0	2,398.0	6,198.0	7,264.0
Market value ($ mil.)	18.4%	67,889.3	54,319.3	79,549.5	105,839.0	133,334.4
Employees	4.0%	—	—	150,000	156,000	—

An in-depth profile of this company is available to Hoover's Online members at hoovers.com.

757

▣ HEXCEL CORPORATION

NYSE: HXL

281 Tresser Blvd., 2 Stamford Plaza, 16th Fl.
Stamford, CT 06901
Phone: 203-969-0666
Fax: 203-358-3972
Web: www.hexcel.com

CEO: David E. Berges
CFO: Wayne C. Pensky
HR: Robert G. Hennemuth
FYE: December 31
Type: Public

The first footprints on the moon didn't come from Neil Armstrong, but from Hexcel, a maker of composite materials. Back then Hexcel made the footpads on the Apollo 11 lunar module; today the company makes advanced structural materials used in everything from aircraft components to bullet-resistant vests. Its composite materials include structural adhesives and honeycomb panels used in products like helicopter blades, auto parts, golf clubs, and even window blinds. Commercial aerospace companies account for more than half of Hexcel's sales; military and other governmental aerospace sales add up to another 20%.

	Annual Growth	12/03	12/04	12/05	12/06	12/07
Sales ($ mil.)	6.9%	896.9	1,074.5	1,161.4	1,193.1	1,171.1
Net income ($ mil.)	—	(11.1)	28.8	141.3	65.9	61.3
Market value ($ mil.)	68.8%	286.8	777.2	1,698.5	1,633.1	2,326.0
Employees	(4.3%)	—	—	4,460	4,459	4,081

HEXION SPECIALTY CHEMICALS, INC.

180 E. Broad St.
Columbus, OH 43215
Phone: 614-225-4000
Fax: –
Web: www.hexionchem.com

CEO: Craig O. Morrison
CFO: William H. (Bill) Carter
HR: Richard L. Monty
FYE: December 31
Type: Private

Hexion Specialty Chemicals is the world's largest thermosetting resins (or thermosets) maker, ahead of Georgia-Pacific. Thermosets add a desired quality (heat resistance, gloss, adhesion, etc.) to a number of different paints and adhesives. Hexion also is among the largest makers of formaldehyde and other forest product resins, epoxy resins, and raw materials for coatings and inks. In 2007 the company offered to buy Huntsman for $10.5 billion. The move came soon after LyondellBasell had bid $9.5 billion for Huntsman. Basell eventually backed down, and Huntsman and Hexion agreed to the deal. Apollo Management controls more than 90% of Hexion.

	Annual Growth	12/02	12/03	12/04	12/05	12/06
Sales ($ mil.)	62.9%	740.0	782.0	2,019.0	4,470.0	5,205.0
Net income ($ mil.)	—	(14.0)	(83.0)	(114.0)	(87.0)	(109.0)
Employees	0.0%	—	—	6,900	7,000	6,900

HF FINANCIAL CORP.

NASDAQ (GM): HFFC

225 S. Main Ave.
Sioux Falls, SD 57104
Phone: 605-333-7556
Fax: 605-333-7621
Web: www.homefederal.com

CEO: Curtis L. Hage
CFO: Darrel L. Posegate
HR: Mary F. Hitzemann
FYE: June 30
Type: Public

Those in South Dakota who want their finances to go north might turn to HF Financial. It's the holding company for Home Federal Bank, which serves consumers and businesses through more than 30 branches in eastern and central South Dakota, as well as one branch in Minnesota. Commercial real estate and business loans account for the largest portion of the bank's loan portfolio (about 35%). It also offers agriculture, consumer, and residential mortgage loans. Deposit products include checking and savings accounts and CDs. Founded in 1929, the bank also offers investment and trust services. Subsidiary Hometown Insurors sells insurance and annuities; another unit, Mid-America Capital, provides equipment financing.

	Annual Growth	6/03	6/04	6/05	6/06	6/07
Assets ($ mil.)	5.8%	800.5	847.1	897.9	961.3	1,001.5
Net income ($ mil.)	1.9%	5.0	5.2	5.2	4.5	5.4
Market value ($ mil.)	10.4%	47.3	49.3	69.2	67.5	70.3
Employees	1.0%	—	—	309	—	315

HFF, INC.

NYSE: HF

One Oxford Centre, 301 Grant St., Ste. 600
Pittsburgh, PA 15219
Phone: 412-281-8714
Fax: 412-281-2792
Web: www.hfflp.com

CEO: John H. Pelusi Jr.
CFO: Gregory R. Conley
HR: –
FYE: December 31
Type: Public

HFF (also known as Holliday Fenoglio Fowler) is keeping it real as one of the nation's largest companies providing capital markets services related to commercial real estate. With nearly 20 offices across the country, HFF helps clients find lenders for their commercial mortgage needs (including Fannie Mae and Freddie Mac), select joint venture capital partners, and find buyers for their commercial properties. Capital markets services include debt placement, investment sales, and commercial loan servicing; its biggest capital services market is Texas, about one-quarter of its revenues. Annually, HFF advises on more than $43 billion of completed commercial real estate transactions. HFF went public in 2007.

	Annual Growth	12/03	12/04	12/05	12/06	12/07
Assets ($ mil.)	62.4%	—	56.1	89.9	154.3	240.5
Net income ($ mil.)	(20.0%)	—	28.1	46.8	51.5	14.4
Market value ($ mil.)	—	—	—	—	—	127.3
Employees	13.2%	—	312	355	400	—

HHGREGG, INC.

NYSE: HGG

4151 E. 96th St.
Indianapolis, IN 46240
Phone: 317-848-8710
Fax: 317-848-8723
Web: www.hhgregg.com

CEO: Gerald W. (Jerry) Throgmartin
CFO: Donald J.B. Van der Wiel
HR: Thomas W. Westcott
FYE: March 31
Type: Public

hhgregg has evolved from black-and-white to digital. The appliance and electronics retailer began as a small storefront selling washing machines, refrigerators, and black-and-white TVs. Today the fast-growing company sells its premium, name-brand products at about 100 hhgregg and Fine Lines stores in 10 mostly southern states and online. Its offerings include TV and video products (LCD and plasma TVs, DVD players and recorders) as well as home and car audio (CD players, home theater, and satellite radio systems), appliances (air conditioners, refrigerators, washers and dryers), laptop computers, digital cameras, phones, and even mattresses. Founded in 1955, hhgregg went public in 2007.

	Annual Growth	3/04	3/05	3/06	3/07	3/08
Sales ($ mil.)	13.7%	753.2	803.2	900.4	1,059.4	1,256.7
Net income ($ mil.)	(6.7%)	28.2	29.2	22.2	21.4	21.4
Market value ($ mil.)	—	—	—	—	—	363.2
Employees	4.6%	—	2,900	3,171	3,171	—

▣ HIBBETT SPORTS, INC.

NASDAQ (GS): HIBB

451 Industrial Ln.
Birmingham, AL 35211
Phone: 205-942-4292
Fax: 205-912-7290
Web: www.hibbett.com

CEO: Michael J. (Mickey) Newsome
CFO: Gary A. Smith
HR: –
FYE: Saturday nearest January 31
Type: Public

Small-town southern sports fans are the bread and butter for fast-growing Hibbett Sports. Operating as Hibbett Sporting Goods, the firm sells sporting equipment, footwear, and apparel through more than 680 stores in small to midsized markets in more than 20 states, mainly in the southeast. Hibbett Sports stores, the firm's flagship chain, are located primarily in malls and strip centers anchored by a Wal-Mart store. It also operates a handful of larger format stores (25,000 sq. ft.) called Sports & Co. that offer in-store putting greens, basketball hoops, and special event appearances by famous athletes. Its approximately 20 Sports Additions shoe stores are in malls that also have Hibbett Sports stores.

	Annual Growth	1/04	1/05	1/06	1/07	1/08
Sales ($ mil.)	12.9%	321.0	377.5	440.3	512.1	520.7
Net income ($ mil.)	10.4%	20.4	25.1	33.6	38.1	30.3
Market value ($ mil.)	27.0%	215.5	372.5	1,010.2	1,015.4	561.4
Employees	9.5%	—	—	4,500	5,200	5,400

HICKOK INCORPORATED

OTC: HICKA

10514 Dupont Ave.
Cleveland, OH 44108
Phone: 216-541-8060
Fax: 216-761-9879
Web: www.hickok-inc.com

CEO: Robert L. Bauman
CFO: Gregory M. Zoloty
HR: Carmelita Gerome
FYE: September 30
Type: Public

Like "Wild Bill" of Wild West lore, Hickok is quite comfortable shooting it out with competitors on its own measured road to success. The company manufactures testing equipment used by automotive technicians to repair cars. Hickok also makes instruments, indicators, and gauges for manufacturers of aircraft and locomotives. Traditionally, Ford and General Motors (29% of sales) have been the company's two largest customers. Hickok operates production facilities in Mississippi and Ohio, and it sells products primarily in the US. President and CEO Robert Bauman and the three daughters of founder Robert D. Hickok, including chairman Janet Slade, control the company.

	Annual Growth	9/03	9/04	9/05	9/06	9/07
Sales ($ mil.)	3.2%	11.0	15.7	9.7	15.9	12.5
Net income ($ mil.)	—	(1.8)	0.7	(1.6)	0.8	(0.6)
Market value ($ mil.)	32.9%	3.1	4.0	3.6	4.5	9.8
Employees	—	—	—	—	—	160

HICKORY FARMS, INC.

1505 Holland Rd.
Maumee, OH 43537
Phone: 419-893-7611
Fax: 419-893-0164
Web: www.hickoryfarms.com

CEO: John J. Langdon
CFO: Mark J. Wagner
HR: Amy Eaton
FYE: January 31
Type: Private

Before your relationship goes to hell in a *gift* basket, try delighting your honey with a ham from Hickory Farms. The gift-food company sells high-end beef and cheese, chocolates, desserts, fresh fruits and nuts, seafood, and other delectables. Prices range from about $10 to more than $200. Gift-givers may order through catalogs and the company's Web site. In addition, Hickory Farms sells direct through about 600 shopping-mall kiosks that are deployed during the holiday season, and it retails at discount merchandisers (Target) and grocers (Safeway). The company once operated 550 mall stores but closed them all by 2000. Founded in 1960, Hickory Farms was bought by an affiliate of Sun Capital Partners in mid-2007.

	Annual Growth	1/03	1/04	1/05	1/06	1/07
Est. sales ($ mil.)	—	—	—	—	—	16.3
Employees	—	—	—	—	—	250

HICKORY TECH CORPORATION

NASDAQ (GM): HTCO

221 E. Hickory St.
Mankato, MN 56002
Phone: 507-387-1151
Fax: 507-625-9191
Web: www.hickorytech.com

CEO: John W. Finke
CFO: David A. Christensen
HR: Mary T. Jacobs
FYE: December 31
Type: Public

Its name sounds like a Division II college, but Hickory Tech's field of play is telecommunications. HickoryTech operates two business segments: Telecom and Enventis (Internet protocol, telephony, and data services). Through its subsidiaries, the company provides 64,000 residential and business customers with access lines in Iowa and Minnesota. It also offers long-distance services to 40,000 customers, broadband Internet access services to 17,000 customers, and digital television service to about 6,000 customers. Its National Independent Billing unit, which is part of the Telecom segment, provides data processing services to other telecommunications companies.

	Annual Growth	12/03	12/04	12/05	12/06	12/07
Sales ($ mil.)	13.9%	92.9	90.5	92.5	132.9	156.6
Net income ($ mil.)	—	(12.8)	7.6	8.5	2.3	8.6
Market value ($ mil.)	(4.5%)	148.7	139.6	103.6	94.4	123.8
Employees	—	—	—	460	—	—

HICKS SPORTS GROUP HOLDINGS LLC

1000 Ballpark Way, Ste. 400
Arlington, TX 76011
Phone: 817-273-5222
Fax: 817-273-5174

CEO: Thomas O. (Tom) Hicks
CFO: Robert Hutson
HR: Casey Shilts
FYE: December 31
Type: Holding company

Football might reign supreme in Texas, but there's plenty of other Lone Star state sports teams to go around. Hicks Sports Group is the holding company formed by Texas billionaire Thomas Hicks to oversee his interests in the Texas Rangers professional baseball team and the Dallas Stars hockey team. The company also owns a 50% stake in Center Operating Company, a joint venture with Dallas Mavericks owner Mark Cuban that runs the American Airlines Center in Dallas. Other interests include the Mesquite Championship Rodeo in Dallas, ice-skating rinks, and various real estate properties in the Dallas area. Hicks Sports Group also owns half of the Frisco RoughRiders minor league baseball team.

HID CORPORATION

9292 Jeronimo Rd.
Irvine, CA 92618
Phone: 949-598-1600
Fax: 949-598-1619
Web: www.hidcorp.com

CEO: Denis Hébert
CFO: Will West
HR: Michelle DeWitt
FYE: December 31
Type: Subsidiary

HID Corporation doesn't have to keep things hidden; instead, it keeps things under restricted access. The company makes contactless cards and readers for access control systems. HID uses radio-frequency identification (RFID) technology in electronic locks, alarms, biometric devices, and other systems that use encrypted access control. The company also makes parking area and vehicle access control systems. Its card and reader technologies are also used for network log-on security and biometric verification. With locations worldwide, the company serves retail, industrial, commercial, governmental, and institutional customers. HID Corporation is a subsidiary of the world's largest lock maker, Sweden's ASSA ABLOY.

	Annual Growth	12/03	12/04	12/05	12/06	12/07
Est. sales ($ mil.)	—	—	—	—	—	51.4
Employees	—	—	—	—	—	600

HI/FN, INC.

NASDAQ (GM): HIFN

750 University Ave.
Los Gatos, CA 95032
Phone: 408-399-3500
Fax: 408-399-3501
Web: www.hifn.com

CEO: Albert E. (Al) Sisto
CFO: William R. (Bill) Walker
HR: –
FYE: September 30
Type: Public

What is HIPP? Tell me, tell me, if you think you know. For this company, it's the Hifn Intelligent Packet Processing architecture. Semiconductor developer hi/fn (pronounced "hyphen" and usually styled "Hifn") offers data compression and encryption processors; it also licenses related software libraries. The company's compression products enhance the bandwidth of network equipment and expand the capacity of tape drive data backup systems. Its encryption processors enable network equipment vendors to add virtual private network capabilities to their products. The company's major customers include networking equipment makers Cisco Systems (53% of sales) and Huawei (12%) and tape drive maker Quantum.

	Annual Growth	9/03	9/04	9/05	9/06	9/07
Sales ($ mil.)	20.3%	20.5	42.1	46.4	43.8	43.0
Net income ($ mil.)	—	(20.3)	(10.9)	(5.2)	(8.7)	(2.5)
Market value ($ mil.)	9.5%	83.1	121.6	75.0	65.5	119.4
Employees	—	—	—	—	—	—

An in-depth profile of this company is available to Hoover's Online members at hoovers.com.

759

H.I.G. CAPITAL MANAGEMENT INC.

1001 Brickell Bay Dr., Fl. 27
Miami, FL 33131
Phone: 305-379-2322
Fax: 305-379-2013
Web: www.higcapital.com

CEO: Sami W. Mnaymneh
CFO: –
HR: –
FYE: December 31
Type: Private

H.I.G. Capital keeps an eye out for good deals. The private equity firm specializes in management buyouts or recapitalizations, with a focus on small and midsized companies in the US and Europe. An active investor, the company typically works alongside management of its portfolio companies. Holdings include stakes in marketing firm Thane International, customer service outsourcing concern Stream, window maker Thermal Industries, and Warrantech (acquired in 2007). H. I. G. Capital also provides development capital to young high-tech companies through its H.I.G Ventures division.

	Annual Growth	12/03	12/04	12/05	12/06	12/07
Est. sales ($ mil.)	—	—	—	—	—	918.3
Employees	—	—	—	—	—	9,310

HIGH INDUSTRIES, INC.

1853 William Penn Way
Lancaster, PA 17605
Phone: 717-293-4444
Fax: 717-293-4416
Web: www.high.net

CEO: W. Thomas Kennedy III
CFO: Michael W. Van Belle
HR: Larry Brown
FYE: December 31
Type: Private

It's not really the High Way or the highway, but more like the High Way *for* the highway. The company's largest division, High Steel Structures, is one of the largest steel bridge fabricators in North America. Other members of the High Industries stable of companies include High Steel Service Center, High Concrete Group (precast concrete components), High Construction (commercial and institutional). Greenfield Architectural, and High Hotels (Hilton and Marriott branded hotels). High Industries, founded as High Welding Co. in 1931, is controlled by founder Sanford High's son, chairman Dale High, and family.

	Annual Growth	12/03	12/04	12/05	12/06	12/07
Est. sales ($ mil.)	—	—	—	—	—	290.4
Employees	—	—	—	—	—	2,479

HIGHLAND CAPITAL MANAGEMENT, L.P.

13455 Noel Rd., 8th Fl.
Dallas, TX 75240
Phone: 972-628-4100
Fax: 972-628-4147
Web: www.hcmlp.com

CEO: James D. Dondero
CFO: Kenneth McGovern
HR: –
FYE: December 31
Type: Private

Highland Capital Management specializes in alternative fixed-income investments. Founded in 1993, the employee-owned firm manages more than $40 billion in senior secured loans, collateralized loan obligations, structured investment vehicles, mezzanine debt, high-yield bonds, equities, and more on behalf of financial institutions, pension plans, foundations, and wealthy individuals. Highland Capital Management has offices in Dallas and New York. From a location in London, Highland Capital Management Europe manages more than €3.5 billion of credit investments.

	Annual Growth	12/03	12/04	12/05	12/06	12/07
Est. sales ($ mil.)	—	—	—	—	—	10.1
Employees	—	—	—	—	—	280

HIGHLAND CAPITAL PARTNERS, INC.

92 Hayden Ave.
Lexington, MA 02421
Phone: 781-861-5500
Fax: 781-861-5499
Web: www.hcp.com

CEO: Sean M. Dalton
CFO: Kathy Barry
HR: –
FYE: January 1
Type: Private

Highland Capital Partners hopes to elevate promising entrepreneurs to new heights. The venture capital firm specializes in funding development-stage companies in the information technology and digital media, communications, health care, and consumer industries. Founded in 1988, the company is an active investor that takes a seat on the boards of most of its holdings. Highland Capital Partners has stakes in approximately 70 portfolio companies; some of the firms it has previously backed include AskJeeves, CheckFree, EXACT Sciences, and Odyssey HealthCare. The company has invested some $1.8 billion in more than 170 companies since its founding.

	Annual Growth	1/03	1/04	1/05	1/06	1/07
Est. sales ($ mil.)	—	—	—	—	—	3.7
Employees	—	—	—	—	—	31

HIGHLAND FINANCIAL TRUST

13455 Noel Rd., Ste. 800
Dallas, TX 75240
Phone: 972-628-4100
Fax: 972-628-4147

CEO: Todd Travers
CFO: Clifford (Cliff) Stoops
HR: –
FYE: December 31
Type: Holding company

Highland Financial Trust has a few ideas about how to make use of the family fortune you have squirreled away in that mattress. The investment trust operates primarily through subsidiaries (Highland CDO Holding, Highland Financial Real Estate, Highland Financial, and Highland Special Opportunities) which provide structured financing services to both institutional and retail investors. The investment options offered by Highland Financial Trust include asset-backed securities, bonds, commercial real estate, and corporate leveraged loans. The trust serves mutual funds and individuals among others. Highland Financial Trust was established and is managed by Dallas-based investment firm Highland Capital Management.

HIGHLANDS BANKSHARES, INC.

OTC: HBKA

340 W. Main St.
Abingdon, VA 24210
Phone: 276-628-9181
Fax: 276-619-2101
Web: www.hubank.com

CEO: James D. Moore Jr.
CFO: Robert M. (Rusty) Little
HR: –
FYE: December 31
Type: Public

Highlands Bankshares is not going to be left holding the bag(pipe). The firm (not to be confused with Highlands Bankshares in West Virginia) is the holding company for Highlands Union Bank, which operates about a dozen branches in Virginia, North Carolina, and Tennessee. The bank offers checking and savings accounts, money market accounts, IRAs, and CDs. The bank has two other subsidiaries, Highlands Union Insurance Services and Highlands Union Financial Services, the latter of which provides third-party mutual funds, annuities, and other investment services.

	Annual Growth	12/03	12/04	12/05	12/06	12/07
Assets ($ mil.)	5.0%	543.4	567.1	599.3	632.7	660.8
Net income ($ mil.)	2.2%	4.5	4.7	5.0	5.2	4.9
Market value ($ mil.)	28.1%	—	34.6	87.1	85.6	72.8
Employees	—	—	—	—	—	239

HIGHLANDS BANKSHARES, INC.

OTC: HBSI

3 N. Main St.
Petersburg, WV 26847
Phone: 304-257-4111
Fax: 304-257-4386
Web: grantcountybank.com

CEO: Clarence E. Porter
CFO: R. Alan Miller
HR: –
FYE: December 31
Type: Public

No matter if you take the high road or the low road, Highlands Bankshares will take of your money *afore ye*. The company (not to be confused with Highlands Bankshares, headquartered in Virginia) is the holding company for The Grant County Bank and Capon Valley Bank, which serves eastern West Virginia and western Virginia and Maryland. The banks offer standard retail products and services, including demand and time deposit accounts and business and consumer loans. The company focuses on real estate lending; mortgages account for the bulk of its loan book.

	Annual Growth	12/03	12/04	12/05	12/06	12/07
Assets ($ mil.)	6.0%	301.2	300.0	337.6	357.3	380.9
Net income ($ mil.)	20.9%	2.2	3.2	3.8	4.5	4.7
Market value ($ mil.)	0.6%	41.7	37.4	45.3	46.7	42.7
Employees	—	—	—	—	—	—

HIGHMARK INC.

CEO: Kenneth R. Melani
CFO: Nanette P. (Nan) DeTurk
HR: S. Tyrone Alexander
FYE: December 31
Type: Not-for-profit

Fifth Avenue Place, 120 5th Ave.
Pittsburgh, PA 15222
Phone: 412-544-7000
Fax: 412-544-8368
Web: www.highmark.com/hmk2

Highmark has staked its claim as the largest health insurer in the Keystone state. A licensee of the Blue Cross and Blue Shield Association, the firm covers some 4 million people in central and western Pennsylvania and the Lehigh Valley. It operates elsewhere in the state through partnerships with other insurers and provides administrative and network access services nationally. In Pennsylvania and neighboring West Virginia, Highmark sells Medicare Advantage and prescription drug plans to seniors. Other subsidiaries (not operating under the BCBS license) provide dental insurance, vision care, and other products and services nationwide. The firm agreed to merge with Independence Blue Cross in 2007.

	Annual Growth	12/03	12/04	12/05	12/06	12/07
Sales ($ mil.)	11.0%	8,140.0	9,118.4	9,847.3	11,083.8	12,352.6
Net income ($ mil.)	49.2%	75.7	310.5	341.6	398.3	375.4
Employees	13.9%	11,000	11,000	12,000	18,500	18,500

HIGHWOODS PROPERTIES, INC.

NYSE: HIW

3100 Smoketree Ct., Ste. 600
Raleigh, NC 27604
Phone: 919-872-4924
Fax: 919-873-0088
Web: www.highwoods.com

CEO: Edward J. (Ed) Fritsch
CFO: Terry L. Stevens
HR: Bob Albert
FYE: December 31
Type: Public

When it comes to office space, Highwoods Properties takes the road most traveled, especially if it runs through the Southeast. A self-administered real estate investment trust (REIT), Highwoods Properties owns and manages commercial property. Its holdings include suburban office, industrial, and retail properties focused on about a dozen core markets from Florida to the Midwest. The REIT owns or partially owns nearly 400 commercial properties (some 35 million sq. ft.). The company's stronghold is office holdings, which bring in some 80% of its revenues. The REIT also has residential apartment holdings and owns more than 600 acres of undeveloped land.

	Annual Growth	12/03	12/04	12/05	12/06	12/07
Sales ($ mil.)	(3.5%)	504.7	464.7	410.7	416.8	437.1
Net income ($ mil.)	17.3%	47.9	41.6	62.5	53.7	90.7
Market value ($ mil.)	5.5%	1,358.2	1,490.6	1,537.1	2,291.2	1,679.6
Employees	(10.7%)	—	553	494	—	—

HILAND HOLDINGS GP, LP

NASDAQ (GM): HPGP

205 W. Maple, Ste. 1100
Enid, OK 73701
Phone: 580-242-6040
Fax: 580-548-5188
Web: www.hilandpartners.com

CEO: Joseph L. (Joe) Griffin
CFO: Matthew S. (Matt) Harrison
HR: –
FYE: December 31
Type: Public

Hiland Holdings lets Hiland Partners do all the work. The company owns a 2% general partner interest and 57.8% limited partner interest in the natural gas gathering and processing company. Hiland Partners serves primarily the Mid-Continent and Rocky Mountain regions of the US. It maintains natural gas gathering systems, processing plants, treating facilities, and NGL fractionation facilities. Essentially Hiland Partners takes natural gas from production companies, processes it, removes impurities, and removes natural gas liquids (NGLs), which it fractionates into NGL products. After the various processes, Hiland Partners supplies natural gas and NGL products to transmission pipelines and various markets.

	Annual Growth	12/03	12/04	12/05	12/06	12/07
Sales ($ mil.)	38.3%	76.0	98.3	166.6	219.7	278.0
Net income ($ mil.)	51.0%	1.0	4.9	0.9	2.4	5.2
Market value ($ mil.)	(5.4%)	—	—	—	624.2	590.8
Employees	—	—	—	89	—	—

HILAND PARTNERS, LP

NASDAQ (GS): HLND

205 W. Maple, Ste. 1100
Enid, OK 73701
Phone: 580-242-6040
Fax: 580-548-5188
Web: www.hilandpartners.com

CEO: Joseph L. (Joe) Griffin
CFO: Matthew S. (Matt) Harrison
HR: –
FYE: December 31
Type: Public

Hiland Partners is looking for the higher ground of increased profits. The company, which went public in 2005, is a combination of Hiland Partners LLC and Continental Gas, a former subsidiary of Continental Resources. Hiland provides natural gas gathering and processing services to customers in the Mid-Continent and Rocky Mountain regions of the US through 13 gas gathering systems with 1,844 miles of pipeline, five natural gas processing plants, three natural gas treating facilities, and three NGL fractionation plants. It also provides air compression and water injection services for oil and gas recovery operations in North Dakota. Chairman Harold Hamm owns 57.8% of the company.

	Annual Growth	12/03	12/04	12/05	12/06	12/07
Sales ($ mil.)	126.3%	10.6	98.3	166.6	219.7	278.0
Net income ($ mil.)	33.5%	3.4	4.9	10.3	14.7	10.8
Market value ($ mil.)	28.2%	—	—	160.4	282.6	263.6
Employees	31.3%	42	51	67	95	—

HILB ROGAL & HOBBS COMPANY

NYSE: HRH

4951 Lake Brook Dr., Ste. 500
Glen Allen, VA 23060
Phone: 804-747-6500
Fax: 804-747-6046
Web: www.hrh.com

CEO: Martin L. (Mell) Vaughan III
CFO: Michael Dinkins
HR: Joseph W.G. Birriel
FYE: December 31
Type: Public

HRH denotes royalty in England. In the US it stands for Hilb Rogal & Hobbs, which plans to rule the insurance roost. With more than 100 offices in about 30 states, HRH places general and specialty insurance (including property/casualty, aviation, and employee benefits) with major underwriters on behalf of its targeted clients (middle-market businesses), as well as individuals and national corporations. Commissions account for the majority of HRH's sales, but it also offers risk management and loss-control consulting services. With additional operations in Europe and the Asia/Pacific region, HRH is a top 10 insurance broker worldwide and in the US. The company has agreed to be acquired by rival Willis Group.

	Annual Growth	12/03	12/04	12/05	12/06	12/07
Sales ($ mil.)	9.1%	563.7	619.6	673.9	710.8	799.7
Net income ($ mil.)	1.1%	74.9	81.4	56.2	87.0	78.1
Market value ($ mil.)	7.0%	1,136.8	1,300.5	1,392.7	1,529.5	1,490.9
Employees	8.0%	—	—	3,600	3,700	4,200

An in-depth profile of this company is available to Hoover's Online members at hoovers.com.

761

HILCO TRADING, LLC

5 Revere Dr., Ste. 206
Northbrook, IL 60062
Phone: 847-509-1100
Fax: 847-509-1150
Web: www.hilcotrading.com

CEO: Jeffrey B. Hecktman
CFO: Mark A. Smiley
HR: –
FYE: December 31
Type: Private

Businesses having trouble seeing over the next hill (or around the bend) might seek some input from Hilco Trading. Through its various operating units and subsidiaries, the company provides strategic financial services such as asset appraisals and liquidations; auctions and bulk dispositions of inventory and equipment; debt and equity capital financing; real estate disposition and lease restructuring services; accounts receivable acquisitions; and other business consulting services. Its clients include retailers, distributors, and manufacturers. Hilco operates in the US and Europe.

	Annual Growth	12/03	12/04	12/05	12/06	12/07
Est. sales ($ mil.)	—	—	—	—	—	8.2
Employees	—	—	—	—	—	250

HILL INTERNATIONAL, INC.

NASDAQ (GM): HINT

303 Lippincott Centre
Marlton, NJ 08053
Phone: 856-810-6200
Fax: 856-810-1309
Web: www.hillintl.com

CEO: Irvin E. Richter
CFO: John Fanelli III
HR: Catherine H. (Cathy) Emma
FYE: December 31
Type: Public

Hill International, a leader in the construction advice business, is far from over the hill. The company offers project management and construction claims consulting services worldwide. It manages all aspects of the construction process, from pre-design through completion, and even troubled project turnaround. Construction claims services include expert witness testimony and litigation support. The company provides its services for such clients as the Arizona Diamondbacks, Consolidated Edison, Kimpton Hotel & Restaurant Group, and Walt Disney. It also counts US government agencies and international governments among its clients, although the private sector accounts for more than half of its revenues.

	Annual Growth	12/03	12/04	12/05	12/06	12/07
Est. sales ($ mil.)	—	—	—	—	—	290.3
Net income ($ mil.)	—	—	—	—	—	14.1
Market value ($ mil.)	—	—	—	—	—	543.5
Employees	—	—	—	—	—	—

THE HILLMAN COMPANIES, INC.

10590 Hamilton Ave.
Cincinnati, OH 45231
Phone: 513-851-4900
Fax: 513-851-4997
Web: www.hillmangroup.com

CEO: Max W. Hillman Jr.
CFO: James P. Waters
HR: –
FYE: December 31
Type: Private

If you were to *label* it, the *key* to success, according to distributor The Hillman Companies, is doing things by the *numbers*. Operating through subsidiary The Hillman Group, it distributes small hardware such as fasteners, keys, signs, letters, numbers, and identification tags to home centers, hardware stores, pet stores, and grocery stores. Hillman distributes items from about 600 suppliers through nearly a dozen distribution centers in the US and Canada. It also makes and distributes its own key duplication and engraving systems. Customers include Wal-Mart, Home Depot, Lowe's, Sears, and PetSmart.

	Annual Growth	12/02	12/03	12/04	12/05	12/06
Sales ($ mil.)	10.3%	286.8	318.4	351.6	382.5	423.9
Net income ($ mil.)	—	6.1	(4.6)	(18.7)	(3.7)	(7.6)
Employees	1.3%	1,800	1,760	1,794	1,853	1,897

THE HILLMAN COMPANY

310 Grant St., 1900 Grant Bldg.
Pittsburgh, PA 15219
Phone: 412-281-2620
Fax: 412-338-3520

CEO: Joseph Manzinger
CFO: Eric C. (Rick) Johnson
HR: Vicky J. Brilmyer
FYE: December 31
Type: Private

Shhh! The Hillman Company is making money. The publicity-shy investment firm quietly has holdings primarily in real estate, including Pittsburgh's PPG Place and luxury resorts in California. The company also has invested in medical technology and other high-tech companies. Hillman was an early backer of investment firm Kohlberg Kravis Roberts (KKR). Billionaire philanthropist Henry Hillman (who once told *FORTUNE* magazine that "a whale is harpooned only when it spouts" when asked why he eschews interviews) stepped down as chairman in 2004, but continues to steer the firm's executive committee.

	Annual Growth	12/03	12/04	12/05	12/06	12/07
Est. sales ($ mil.)	—	—	—	—	—	12.4
Employees	—	—	—	—	—	200

HILL-ROM HOLDINGS, INC.

NYSE: HRC

700 State Rte. 46 East
Batesville, IN 47006
Phone: 812-934-7000
Fax: 812-931-3533
Web: www.hillenbrand.com

CEO: Peter H. Soderberg
CFO: Gregory N. Miller
HR: John H. Dickey
FYE: September 30
Type: Public

No longer torn between the quick and the dead, Hill-Rom Holdings (formerly Hillenbrand Industries) has cast its lot with the living. In 2008 the holding company spun off its funeral services business Batesville Casket into a separate entity owned by newly created holding company Hillenbrand Inc. That separation left Hill-Rom Holdings focused on its other operating unit, Hill-Rom, which makes, sells, and rents hospital beds and other patient-room furniture and equipment, along with stretchers, surgical table accessories, health care software, and non-invasive equipment for pulmonary and circulatory conditions and wounds. Its customers are acute and long-term care facilities around the world.

	Annual Growth	9/03	9/04	9/05	9/06	9/07
Sales ($ mil.)	(0.2%)	2,042.0	1,829.0	1,938.1	1,962.9	2,023.7
Net income ($ mil.)	8.4%	138.0	143.0	(94.1)	221.2	190.6
Employees	0.5%	—	—	9,800	9,300	9,900

HILL'S PET NUTRITION, INC.

400 SW 8th St.
Topeka, KS 66603
Phone: 785-354-8523
Fax: 785-368-5786
Web: www.hillspet.com

CEO: Robert C. Wheeler
CFO: –
HR: –
FYE: December 31
Type: Subsidiary

Hill's Pet Nutrition is barking up the right tree as one of the leading producers of premium pet food worldwide. The company's Science Diet pet food is available in pet stores and other retail outlets. Its Prescription Diet products are sold only through breeders, veterinarians, and authorized pet-supply retailers. The firm's cat and dog foods are produced in varieties geared to a pet's dietary requirements, medical condition, and age. Hill's also makes animal treats. Its products are sold in the US, Japan, and more than 80 other countries around the world. This subsidiary of Colgate-Palmolive was founded in 1948, after a veterinarian cooked up a special food to treat a guide dog's kidney problems.

HILLSTONE RESTAURANT GROUP, INC.

147 S. Beverly Dr.
Los Angeles, CA 90212
Phone: 310-385-7343
Fax: 310-385-7119
Web: www.hillstone.com

CEO: George Williams Biel
CFO: R. Scott Ashby
HR: Jeff Bell
FYE: December 31
Type: Private

Thanks to this company, you don't have to travel to Texas to get some Houston flavor. Hillstone Restaurant Group operates a small portfolio of about 50 upscale casual dining restaurants, including its flagship Houston's chain. With more than 30 locations around the country, Houston's offers a menu of classic American foods, including burgers, ribs, and seafood dishes. The restaurants are also distinct from one another by utilizing different exterior and interior designs. Hillstone also operates about a dozen other eateries under such names as Bandera, Gulfstream, and Rutherford Grill. CEO George Biel opened the first Houston's in 1977.

	Annual Growth	12/03	12/04	12/05	12/06	12/07
Est. sales ($ mil.)	—	—	—	—	—	97.6
Employees	—	—	—	—	—	4,500

HILLTOP HOLDINGS INC.

NYSE: HTH

7887 E. Belleview Ave., Ste. 200
Englewood, CO 80111
Phone: 303-291-0222
Fax: 303-294-9946
Web: www.aboutarc.com

CEO: Larry D. Willard
CFO: Darren Parmenter
HR: –
FYE: December 31
Type: Public

Manufactured housing communities by any other name are no longer called trailer parks, and Hilltop Holdings Inc. is no longer Affordable Residential Communities (ARC). In 2007 Farallon Capital Management and partners acquired the majority of Hilltop's business, comprising 275 residential communities with more than 57,000 home sites in some two dozen states. What's left? Hilltop Holdings is a property and casualty insurance provider that offers coverage for low-value homes through its NLASCO subsidiary. It sells its insurance through some 6,600 independent agents in more than 20 states. NLASCO operates primarily in the southern US through subsidiaries National Lloyds Insurance and American Summit Insurance.

	Annual Growth	12/03	12/04	12/05	12/06	12/07
Assets ($ mil.)	(0.9%)	1,125.8	1,813.0	1,728.5	1,542.7	1,085.5
Net income ($ mil.)	—	(34.4)	(85.7)	(184.5)	(17.4)	293.2
Market value ($ mil.)	—	—	—	—	—	616.6
Employees	—	—	—	960	—	—

HILTI, INC.

5400 S. 122nd East Ave.
Tulsa, OK 74146
Phone: 918-252-6000
Fax: 800-879-7000
Web: www.us.hilti.com

CEO: Cary R. Evert
CFO: Eugene Hodel
HR: Marcus Oden
FYE: December 31
Type: Subsidiary

Hilti, Inc., makes drills that cut through brick like buttah. A subsidiary of Liechtenstein-based Hilti Corporation, it manufactures tools and related items, including adhesives, blades, compressors, drills, fastening systems, foam, saws, screws, and studs for the construction and building-maintenance industries. To attract on-the-job contractors and effectively compete against other tool brands available at big box stores, Hilti has opened some 300 Pro Shops inside Home Depot stores, with plans to open more. Hilti Tool Fleet Management provides maintenance, repair, and replacement services for the construction industry. The Tulsa-based company accounts for about a quarter of its parent's annual sales.

	Annual Growth	12/03	12/04	12/05	12/06	12/07
Est. sales ($ mil.)	—	—	—	—	—	124.2
Employees	—	—	—	—	—	800

⊞ HILTON HOTELS CORPORATION

9336 Civic Center Dr.
Beverly Hills, CA 90210
Phone: 310-278-4321
Fax: 310-205-7678
Web: www.hiltonworldwide.com

CEO: Christopher J. (Chris) Nassetta
CFO: Robert M. La Forgia
HR: Molly McKenzie-Swarts
FYE: December 31
Type: Private

If you need a bed for the night, Hilton Hotels has a few hundred thousand of them. One of the largest hoteliers in the world, the company's lodging empire includes about 2,800 hotels and resorts in more than 80 countries operating under such names as Doubletree, Embassy Suites, and Hampton, as well as its flagship Hilton brand. Many of its hotels serve the mid-market segment, though its Hilton and Conrad hotels offer full-service, upscale lodging. In addition, its Homewood Suites chain offers extended-stay services. The company franchises many of its hotels; it owns the Waldorf-Astoria and the New York Hilton. Private equity firm The Blackstone Group bought Hilton in 2007 for about $20 billion plus debt.

	Annual Growth	12/02	12/03	12/04	12/05	12/06
Sales ($ mil.)	20.7%	3,847.0	3,819.0	4,146.0	4,437.0	8,162.0
Net income ($ mil.)	30.4%	198.0	164.0	238.0	460.0	572.0
Employees	9.1%	74,000	—	—	61,000	105,000

HINES

Williams Tower, 2800 Post Oak Blvd.
Houston, TX 77056
Phone: 713-621-8000
Fax: 713-966-2053
Web: www.hines.com

CEO: Gerald D. Hines
CFO: C. Hastings (Hasty) Johnson
HR: David LeVrier
FYE: December 31
Type: Private

Hines has been involved in many developments, but none of them involve ketchup. Founded by chairman Gerald Hines in 1957, the company is a private commercial real estate development firm that builds and finances corporate offices, mixed-used centers, industrial parks, medical facilities, and master-planned residential communities. Its portfolio consists of more than 1,000 properties completed or under development in the Americas, Europe, and Asia. Hines also manages real estate in the US and 16 other countries. Management services include public relations, tenant relations, and vendor contract-negotiation services. Appropriately enough, Hines is controlled by the Hines family.

	Annual Growth	12/03	12/04	12/05	12/06	12/07
Est. sales ($ mil.)	—	—	—	—	—	216.3
Employees	—	—	—	—	—	2,900

HINES HORTICULTURE, INC.

Pink Sheets: HORT

12621 Jeffrey Rd.
Irvine, CA 92620
Phone: 949-559-4444
Fax: 949-786-0968
Web: www.hineshorticulture.com

CEO: James R. Tennant
CFO: Claudia M. Pieropan
HR: Naomi Sullivan
FYE: December 31
Type: Public

With a little rain and a little sun (not to mention a lot of acquisitions), Hines Horticulture has grown into a national producer and supplier of plants. Through its Hines Nurseries subsidiary it grows about 5,700 varieties of ornamental shrubs and plants, which it sells to home centers (The Home Depot, Lowe's), mass merchandisers (Wal-Mart, Target), and independent garden centers in the US and Canada. Most plants carry the Hines Nurseries or Iverson brand names. Investment firm Madison Dearborn Partners owns 53% of Hines' shares.

	Annual Growth	12/02	12/03	12/04	12/05	*12/06
Sales ($ mil.)	(8.8%)	336.5	338.3	335.2	327.9	232.6
Net income ($ mil.)	—	(52.7)	9.7	8.2	(2.6)	(46.5)
Employees	(4.9%)	5,140	—	—	4,420	—

*Most recent year available

⊞ An in-depth profile of this company is available to Hoover's Online members at hoovers.com.

763

HINGHAM INSTITUTION FOR SAVINGS

NASDAQ (GM): HIFS

55 Main St.
Hingham, MA 02043
Phone: 781-749-2200
Fax: 781-749-7835
Web: www.hinghamsavings.com

CEO: Robert H. Gaughen Jr.
CFO: Deborah J. Jackson
HR: –
FYE: December 31
Type: Public

The Hingham Institution for Savings is a haven for wayward cash. The company has a handful of branches in Boston's south shore communities, operating in Boston, Cohasset, Hingham, Hull, Scituate, and South Weymouth, Massachusetts. Founded in 1834, the bank offers a wide variety of checking and savings products for individuals and businesses. Commercial mortgages make up about half of the bank's loan portfolio; residential mortgages represent about 40%. Hingham Institution for Savings also provides construction, business, and personal loans.

	Annual Growth	12/03	12/04	12/05	12/06	12/07
Est. sales ($ mil.)	—	—	—	—	—	38.8
Employees	—	—	—	—	—	53

HIRERIGHT, INC.

NASDAQ (GM): HIRE

5151 California Ave.
Irvine, CA 92617
Phone: 949-428-5800
Fax: 949-428-5801
Web: www.hireright.com

CEO: Eric J. Boden
CFO: Jeffrey A. (Jeff) Wahba
HR: Barbara M. Nieto
FYE: December 31
Type: Public

Because it would just be plain silly to hire wrong. HireRight provides Web-based pre-employment screening services for human resources and security professionals. The company helps businesses perform background verification, drug screening, and skills and behavioral assessment for prospective new hires. Serving more than 2,000 customers, HireRight's main product offering includes its Extended Workforce Screening Solution suite of software applications. It offers its products and services to more than 200 countries around the globe. Each year, HireRight processes almost 6 million record searches and candidate screenings. In June 2008, HireRight agreed to be bought by US Investigations Services for $195 million.

	Annual Growth	12/03	12/04	12/05	12/06	12/07
Sales ($ mil.)	34.7%	21.1	31.8	43.0	58.1	69.4
Net income ($ mil.)	—	—	(1.7)	(0.3)	0.0	10.9	6.2
Market value ($ mil.)	—	—	—	—	—	140.0
Employees	23.5%	175	—	367	390	407

🔲 HIRSCH INTERNATIONAL CORP.

NASDAQ (CM): HRSH

50 Engineers Rd.
Hauppauge, NY 11788
Phone: 631-436-7100
Fax: 631-436-7054
Web: www.tajima-hirsch.com

CEO: Paul Gallagher
CFO: Beverly Eichel
HR: –
FYE: December 31
Type: Public

Hirsch International will happily keep you in stitches. The company distributes single- and multi-head embroidery machines, embroidery supplies, embroidery application software, and used embroidery machines and parts. Although Hirsch sold its stake in Tajima USA, a joint venture that assembled 2-, 4-, 6-, and 8-head Tajima embroidery machines in the US, it remains the exclusive distributor of Tajima equipment in most of the US. The company also distributes screenprinting machines and laser application equipment for the apparel industry. Chairman Henry Arnberg holds special shares that allow him to elect two-thirds of Hirsch's board.

	Annual Growth	1/04	1/05	1/06	*12/06	12/07
Sales ($ mil.)	2.3%	48.1	43.6	51.1	49.9	52.6
Net income ($ mil.)	51.4%	0.4	(1.8)	0.5	1.3	2.1
Market value ($ mil.)	5.9%	13.5	9.5	10.7	17.1	17.0
Employees	1.0%	—	—	98	99	—

*Fiscal year change

HI-SHEAR TECHNOLOGY CORPORATION

AMEX: HSR

24225 Garnier St.
Torrance, CA 90505
Phone: 310-784-2100
Fax: 310-325-5354
Web: www.hstc.com

CEO: George W. Trahan
CFO: Jan L. Hauhe
HR: Linda A. Nespole
FYE: May 31
Type: Public

Hi-Shear Technology cuts loose with electronic, pyrotechnic, and mechanical devices for the aerospace industry. The company's power cartridges and separation devices provide release on command for structures designed to hold together under rigorous conditions. The devices are used in space vehicles such as the Space Shuttle and in airplane ejector seats. Major customers include the US government (16% of sales) and Lockheed Martin (37%). Hi-Shear also makes pyrotechnic-powered LifeShear cutters (for slicing through steel and other materials to free trapped victims).

	Annual Growth	5/03	5/04	5/05	5/06	5/07
Sales ($ mil.)	5.9%	16.3	16.4	16.1	21.0	20.5
Net income ($ mil.)	20.7%	1.6	1.9	0.2	2.3	3.4
Market value ($ mil.)	47.5%	15.0	21.0	24.4	62.9	71.0
Employees	14.9%	—	—	87	100	—

HITACHI AMERICA, LTD.

2000 Sierra Point Pkwy.
Brisbane, CA 94005
Phone: 650-589-8300
Fax: 650-583-4207
Web: www.hitachi.us

CEO: Masahide Tanigaki
CFO: Hiroshi Maruta
HR: Tetsuya Yamada
FYE: March 31
Type: Subsidiary

Hitachi America supplies North America with a broad range of high-tech products. The subsidiary of the Hitachi conglomerate makes and sells consumer electronics, computing products, telecom equipment, and industrial equipment. The company's home electronics offerings include TVs, camcorders, and DVD players; its computer-related products range from data storage systems to semiconductor manufacturing equipment; and its industrial products include such diverse lines as automotive components, power tools, and nuclear steam turbines. Hitachi America also offers a wide array of services, including business process consulting, financing, and travel arrangement.

HITACHI DATA SYSTEMS CORPORATION

750 Central Expwy.
Santa Clara, CA 95050
Phone: 408-970-1000
Fax: 408-727-8036
Web: www.hds.com

CEO: Minoru Kosuge
CFO: Susan Lynch
HR: –
FYE: March 31
Type: Subsidiary

Hitachi Data Systems (HDS) has mounted a raid on the data storage market. A subsidiary of Hitachi, Ltd., HDS contends with the likes of EMC and IBM in the market for high-end RAID (redundant array of independent disks) storage devices and software. Its storage systems range in size from PC-sized units to massive cabinets that can manage more than 30 petabytes of data. The company also sells network-attached storage (NAS) servers, and its software portfolio encompasses backup and recovery, content archiving, replication, and storage resource management applications. HDS services include training, support, and financing.

HITACHI GLOBAL STORAGE TECHNOLOGIES

3403 Yerba Buena Rd.	CEO: Hiroaki Nakanishi
San Jose, CA 95135	CFO: Stephen D. (Steve) Milligan
Phone: 408-717-5000	HR: –
Fax: –	FYE: December 31
Web: www.hitachigst.com	Type: Subsidiary

Hitachi Global Storage Technologies manufactures hard disk drives and components for PCs, servers, and electronic devices such as handheld computers and digital cameras. Its data storage product portfolio ranges from 3.5 inch computer drives to miniature drives used in digital music players. The company also provides consulting and hard drive integration services to consumer electronics manufacturers through five design studios. Hitachi Global Storage Technologies operates multiple development and manufacturing operations in Asia and North America.

	Annual Growth	12/03	12/04	12/05	12/06	12/07
Est. sales ($ mil.)	—	—	—	—	—	2,147.5
Employees	—	—	—	—	—	21,000

HI-TECH PHARMACAL CO., INC.

NASDAQ (GS): HITK

369 Bayview Ave.	CEO: David S. Seltzer
Amityville, NY 11701	CFO: William Peters
Phone: 631-789-8228	HR: –
Fax: 631-789-8429	FYE: April 30
Web: www.hitechpharm.com	Type: Public

Hi-Tech Pharmacal combines imitation with innovation, making and distributing dozens of liquid and semi-solid prescription, over-the-counter, and nutritional products. The company primarily produces generic forms of prescription drugs, including off-brand versions of antibiotic Bactrim (made by Roche) and antihistamine Phenergan (Wyeth), as well as prescription skin creams, mouthwashes, and pediatric multivitamins. Hi-Tech also makes branded over-the-counter products, mostly for diabetes patients. It has one branded prescription product, allergy medication Tanafed DMX, which it acquired from First Horizon Pharmaceutical in 2006.

	Annual Growth	4/04	4/05	4/06	4/07	4/08
Sales ($ mil.)	2.4%	56.4	67.7	78.0	58.9	62.0
Net income ($ mil.)	—	6.6	8.3	11.4	(2.0)	(5.1)
Market value ($ mil.)	(2.8%)	111.8	121.1	324.4	151.3	99.8
Employees	6.0%	—	232	246	—	—

HITTITE MICROWAVE CORPORATION

NASDAQ (GS): HITT

20 Alpha Rd.	CEO: Stephen G. Daly
Chelmsford, MA 01824	CFO: William W. Boecke
Phone: 978-250-3343	HR: –
Fax: 978-250-3373	FYE: December 31
Web: www.hittite.com	Type: Public

And lo, the Hittites did rise up out of their land, and they sacked Babylon. Actually, these Hittites rise up out of the Commonwealth of Massachusetts, and they're out to sell semiconductors. Hittite Microwave designs and develops microwave, millimeter-wave, and radio-frequency (RF) chips for aerospace, broadband, cellular, and military applications. In addition to amplifiers, frequency multipliers, mixers, modulators, switches, and other components, the company provides custom RF integrated circuits (ICs). Boeing and Motorola are among Hittite's 2,700 customers. More than half of the company's sales are outside the US.

	Annual Growth	12/03	12/04	12/05	12/06	12/07
Sales ($ mil.)	38.9%	42.0	61.7	80.7	130.3	156.4
Net income ($ mil.)	63.3%	7.2	13.4	21.1	42.7	51.2
Market value ($ mil.)	49.5%	—	—	663.7	992.5	1,484.2
Employees	19.2%	—	186	220	267	315

H. J. HEINZ COMPANY

NYSE: HNZ

1 PPG Place, Ste. 3100	CEO: William R. Johnson
Pittsburgh, PA 15222	CFO: Arthur B. (Art) Winkleblack
Phone: 412-456-5700	HR: Steve Clark
Fax: 412-456-6128	FYE: Wednesday nearest April 30
Web: www.heinz.com	Type: Public

Forget those original 57 varieties: H. J. Heinz now has thousands of products. One of the world's largest food producers, Heinz produces ketchup, condiments, sauces, frozen foods, beans, pasta meals, infant food, and other processed food products. Its flagship product is ketchup, of course, and the company dominates the US ketchup market. The company's customers include food retailers, the food service industry, and the US military. Its leading brands include the aforementioned ketchup, Lea & Perrins sauces, Ore-Ida frozen potatoes, Boston Market, T.G.I. Friday's, and Weight Watchers foods.

	Annual Growth	4/04	4/05	4/06	4/07	4/08
Sales ($ mil.)	4.6%	8,414.5	8,912.3	8,643.4	9,001.6	10,070.8
Net income ($ mil.)	1.2%	804.3	752.7	645.6	785.8	844.9
Market value ($ mil.)	2.2%	13,402.5	12,818.9	13,852.1	14,998.1	14,648.3
Employees	(8.3%)	—	—	36,000	33,000	—

H.J. RUSSELL & COMPANY

504 Fair St. SW	CEO: Michael B. Russell
Atlanta, GA 30313	CFO: Eddie Bradford
Phone: 404-330-1000	HR: Robelyn Witt
Fax: 404-330-0922	FYE: December 31
Web: www.hjrussell.com	Type: Private

H.J. Russell & Company, one of the US's largest minority-owned enterprises, helps shape Southeastern cities. The firm is a general contractor, construction manager, property manager, and developer that specializes in affordable multi-family housing and mixed-use communities. It also has expertise in building airports, hospitals, office towers, retail stores, and schools. Its development arm, Russell New Urban Development, offers such services as feasibility analysis, land development, and asset management; it has more than $500 million in development under way. H.J. Russell also manages more than 6,000 apartment and public housing units. The family-owned company was founded by chairman Herman J. Russell in 1952.

	Annual Growth	12/03	12/04	12/05	12/06	12/07
Est. sales ($ mil.)	—	—	—	—	—	171.5
Employees	—	—	—	—	—	733

HK SYSTEMS, INC.

2855 S. James Dr.	CEO: John W. Splude
New Berlin, WI 53151	CFO: James Purko
Phone: 262-860-7000	HR: Sharon Czerwinski
Fax: 262-860-7010	FYE: December 31
Web: www.hksystems.com	Type: Private

If your problems seem too big to handle, try HK Systems. The company makes material-handling systems, including automated guided vehicles, conveyors, palletizers (product binding machines), storage and retrieval machinery, and sortation equipment to manage warehouse items. It also provides customer support, consulting, aftermarket, and outsourcing services to maintain its systems. HK Systems serves industrial clients throughout North America. The company also hosts a suite of supply chain management software for use with both Windows and UNIX platforms.

	Annual Growth	12/03	12/04	12/05	12/06	12/07
Est. sales ($ mil.)	—	—	—	—	—	204.8
Employees	—	—	—	—	—	1,200

An in-depth profile of this company is available to Hoover's Online members at hoovers.com.

765

HKN, INC.

AMEX: HKN

180 State St., Ste. 200
Southlake, TX 76092
Phone: 817-424-2424
Fax: –
Web: www.harkenenergy.com

CEO: Mikel D. Faulkner
CFO: Anna M. Williams
HR: –
FYE: December 31
Type: Public

HKN (formerly Harken Energy) harkens back to the days when a certain President George W. Bush was an oil man. HKN, which bought Bush's small oil company more than a decade ago, explores for and produces oil and gas in the US and Latin America. It has interests in oil and gas wells in the Gulf Coast region of Texas and Louisiana. Internationally, it has exploration and development operations in Colombia, Panama, and Peru. The company, which is striving to put some unprofitable years behind it, in 2006 reported proved reserves (all in the US) of 7 billion cu. ft. of gas and 1.8 million barrels of oil. Lyford Investments Enterprises owns 30% of the voting stock of HKN.

	Annual Growth	12/03	12/04	12/05	12/06	12/07
Sales ($ mil.)	(3.0%)	27.4	29.7	40.1	29.0	24.3
Net income ($ mil.)	—	(1.0)	(17.9)	43.0	(0.9)	3.2
Market value ($ mil.)	—	—	—	—	—	78.6
Employees	—	—	—	46	—	—

HKS, INC.

1919 McKinney Ave.
Dallas, TX 75201
Phone: 214-969-5599
Fax: 214-969-3397
Web: www.hksinc.com

CEO: H. Ralph Hawkins
CFO: –
HR: –
FYE: December 31
Type: Private

HKS is a good sport when it comes to architectural, planning, structural engineering, interior architecture, and graphic design services. One of the leading design firms in the US, it serves several commercial and institutional building markets, including sports and entertainment, health care, aviation, education, hospitality, and government. HKS helped design the Frost Bank Tower, the tallest office building in Austin, Texas, and the American Airlines Center arena in Dallas, as well as the new football stadium for the Dallas Cowboys. Clients include the Texas Rangers, J. C. Penney, Walt Disney, and Whole Foods Market. Harwood K. Smith founded the firm in 1939.

	Annual Growth	12/03	12/04	12/05	12/06	12/07
Est. sales ($ mil.)	—	—	—	—	—	59.5
Employees	—	—	—	—	—	825

HLTH CORPORATION

NASDAQ (GS): HLTH

669 River Dr., Center 2
Elmwood Park, NJ 07407
Phone: 201-703-3400
Fax: 201-703-3401
Web: www.hlth.com

CEO: Martin J. (Marty) Wygod
CFO: Mark D. Funston
HR: –
FYE: December 31
Type: Public

HLTH hooks up patients with health information. The company controls WebMD Health, an online portal offering health information, including data on diseases, fitness, and diet, to both consumers and health care providers. HLTH, formerly known as Emdeon, has been selling off many of its other business units to more closely align itself with its WebMD operations. In 2008 it sold its remaining stake in Emdeon Business Services, which helped automate administrative tasks such as patient billing and manage clinical information, to private equity firm General Atlantic; it had previously sold a majority stake in the unit in 2006. It has also sold its Practice Services division to Sage Software.

	Annual Growth	12/03	12/04	12/05	12/06	12/07
Sales ($ mil.)	(14.0%)	964.0	1,160.3	1,276.9	1,098.6	527.1
Net income ($ mil.)	—	(17.0)	39.3	73.0	771.9	19.9
Market value ($ mil.)	(3.1%)	2,782.1	2,568.6	2,354.7	2,005.1	2,457.1
Employees	(36.6%)	—	—	6,100	2,260	2,450

HM CAPITAL PARTNERS LLC

200 Crescent Ct., Ste. 1600
Dallas, TX 75201
Phone: 214-740-7300
Fax: 214-720-7888
Web: www.hmcapital.com

CEO: John R. Muse
CFO: David (Dave) Knickel
HR: –
FYE: December 31
Type: Private

"Simplify, simplify." Name-wise, HM Capital — formerly Hicks, Muse, Tate & Furst — seems to have taken Thoreau's advice to heart. HM Capital creates investment pools from investors (pension funds, financial institutions, and wealthy private investors) in the form of limited partnerships. The leveraged buyout firm typically targets underperforming companies in specific niches (including cable TV, radio, gas production and transmission, and branded foods), builds them up, and sells them or spins them off in IPOs. HM Capital also has holdings in manufacturing.

	Annual Growth	12/03	12/04	12/05	12/06	12/07
Est. sales ($ mil.)	—	—	—	—	—	245.9
Employees	—	—	—	—	—	2,500

HMG/COURTLAND PROPERTIES, INC.

AMEX: HMG

1870 S. Bayshore Dr.
Coconut Grove, FL 33133
Phone: 305-854-6803
Fax: 305-856-7342

CEO: Maurice Wiener
CFO: Carlos Camarotti
HR: –
FYE: December 31
Type: Public

Sun, sea, and sand are key parts of the business mix for HMG/Courtland Properties, a real estate investment trust (REIT) that owns and manages commercial real estate in the Miami area. The company owns the Grove Isle luxury resort, which includes a hotel, restaurant, spa, and marina, and accounts for more than 70% of HMG/Courtland's rental income. Grive Isle is managed by Noble House Resorts. The REIT also holds a 50% interest in another retail, restaurant, and marina property and a 5,000 sq. ft. corporate office building. It has two properties held for development in Rhode Island and Vermont and has equity interests in other commercial real estate operations.

	Annual Growth	12/03	12/04	12/05	12/06	12/07
Sales ($ mil.)	32.9%	3.3	5.5	9.6	11.3	10.3
Net income ($ mil.)	—	0.2	1.5	(0.4)	(0.7)	(0.4)
Market value ($ mil.)	(2.1%)	11.4	15.0	13.8	14.5	10.4
Employees	—	—	—	1	—	0

HMN FINANCIAL, INC.

NASDAQ (GM): HMNF

1016 Civic Center Dr. NW
Rochester, MN 55901
Phone: 507-535-1200
Fax: 507-535-1300
Web: www.hmnf.com

CEO: Michael McNeil
CFO: Jon J. Eberle
HR: –
FYE: December 31
Type: Public

HMN Financial is the holding company for Home Federal Savings Bank, which operates about a dozen branches in southern Minnesota and central Iowa. Serving individuals and local businesses, the bank offers such deposit products as checking and savings accounts, CDs, and IRAs. Its lending activities include commercial mortgages (more than 30% of the company's loan portfolio), business loans (about 25%), residential mortgages, and construction, development, and consumer loans. The bank provides financial planning, investment management, and investment products through its Osterud Insurance Agency subsidiary and Home Federal Investment Management.

	Annual Growth	12/03	12/04	12/05	12/06	12/07
Assets ($ mil.)	6.6%	866.4	960.7	991.2	977.8	1,117.1
Net income ($ mil.)	7.1%	8.6	9.3	11.1	8.4	11.3
Market value ($ mil.)	(1.7%)	109.6	145.8	130.0	148.9	102.5
Employees	(0.7%)	—	—	224	—	221

HMS HOLDINGS CORP.

NASDAQ (GS): HMSY

401 Park Ave. South
New York, NY 10016
Phone: 212-725-7965
Fax: 212-857-5973
Web: www.hmsholdings.com

CEO: Robert M. Holster
CFO: Walter D. Hosp
HR: John D. Schmid
FYE: December 31
Type: Public

HMS Holdings makes sure government health providers are paying only as much as they have to. Through its Health Management Systems subsidiary, the company specializes in helping public programs (such as state Medicaid and child support agencies) identify and recover costs that should have been paid by a third party or that were paid in error. It serves Medicaid programs in some 40 states, as well as Medicaid managed care plans, SCHIP programs, and veterans' health care facilities. Its Reimbursement Services Group subsidiary offers Medicare reimbursement services for hospitals. HMS Holdings has operations throughout the US.

	Annual Growth	12/03	12/04	12/05	12/06	12/07
Sales ($ mil.)	18.5%	74.4	85.2	60.0	87.9	146.6
Net income ($ mil.)	59.8%	2.3	7.7	8.0	5.3	15.0
Market value ($ mil.)	82.7%	73.8	174.0	154.6	354.0	821.8
Employees	—	—	—	331	—	—

HMSHOST CORPORATION

6905 Rockledge Dr.
Bethesda, MD 20817
Phone: 240-694-4100
Fax: 240-694-4790
Web: www.hmshost.com

CEO: Elie W. Maalouf
CFO: Giorgio Spagliardi
HR: Chuck Powers
FYE: Friday nearest December 31
Type: Subsidiary

This company might be the last thing between you and airline food. HMSHost is a leading food service operator focused on travelers, with restaurants and eateries in airports, travel plazas, and other locations mostly in North America. It serves air travelers at more than 70 airports and feeds motorists at more than 100 rest areas along many of the major turnpikes and thruways in the US and Canada. HMSHost also operates restaurants at several shopping centers and at such destinations as the Empire State Building. It primarily operates quick-service locations franchised from Starbucks, Burger King, and Quiznos. Italian food service and restaurant operator Autogrill owns the company.

HNI CORPORATION

NYSE: HNI

408 E. 2nd St.
Muscatine, IA 52761
Phone: 563-272-7400
Fax: 563-272-7655
Web: www.hnicorp.com

CEO: Stanley A. (Stan) Askren
CFO: Stanley A. (Stan) Askren
HR: –
FYE: Saturday nearest December 31
Type: Public

Tired of your office furniture? HNI Corporation can supply you with replacements, along with a fireplace to burn the old set. HNI is a leading US manufacturer of office furniture. More than 80% of the firm's sales come from its office furniture. It sells primarily to furniture dealers, wholesalers, and retail superstores (OfficeMax, Corporate Express, Office Depot, and Staples). True to its name, the company's Hearth & Home subsidiary makes fireplaces. HNI also has a division devoted to international marketing and distribution. The company sells its products primarily in Canada and the US. State Farm Insurance Companies owns more than 16% of the company.

	Annual Growth	12/03	12/04	12/05	12/06	12/07
Sales ($ mil.)	10.0%	1,755.7	2,093.4	2,450.6	2,679.8	2,570.5
Net income ($ mil.)	5.3%	98.1	113.6	137.4	123.4	120.4
Market value ($ mil.)	(10.8%)	2,523.5	2,380.8	2,848.1	2,127.5	1,594.3
Employees	8.5%	—	—	11,304	14,200	13,300

HNTB COMPANIES

715 Kirk Dr.
Kansas City, MO 64105
Phone: 816-472-1201
Fax: 816-472-4060
Web: www.hntb.com

CEO: Paul A. Yarossi
CFO: Terry M. Campbell
HR: –
FYE: December 31
Type: Private

HNTB knows the ABCs of A/E. The company ranks among the pack of "pure designers," firms that derive most of their revenues from architecture, engineering, or environmental design operations. HNTB's operations are carried out by three companies — HNTB Corporation (transportation infrastructure), HNTB Architecture, and HNTB Federal Services (government contracts). The company is best-known for its highway and transit system design (New Jersey Turnpike) as well as airports (Midway) and sports arenas (Invesco Field). HNTB has about 75 locations in the US. Employee-owned HNTB (which once stood for Howard Needles Tammen & Berendoff) traces its roots to 1914.

	Annual Growth	12/03	12/04	12/05	12/06	12/07
Est. sales ($ mil.)	—	—	—	—	—	175.8
Employees	—	—	—	—	—	2,748

HOB ENTERTAINMENT, INC.

6255 Sunset Blvd., 16th Fl.
Hollywood, CA 90028
Phone: 323-769-4600
Fax: 323-769-4787
Web: www.hob.com

CEO: Joseph C. (Joe) Kaczorowski
CFO: Peter J. Cyffka
HR: Kimberly Hunt
FYE: December 31
Type: Subsidiary

HOB Entertainment has the low-down, dirty blues — and that's a good thing. The company owns and operates 10 House of Blues clubs that offer food, drinks, and live music from some of the top blues and rock performers in the country. Its House of Blues Concerts subsidiary owns, operates, or exclusively books more than 15 venues across North America and promotes several national tours. In addition, HOB owns The Commodore Ballroom, a small music venue in Vancouver; and eight amphitheaters in cities that include Seattle, Los Angeles, and Cleveland. The company is backed by several investment groups, including CCMP Capital. Concert promoter Live Nation acquired HOB in 2006 for $354 million.

	Annual Growth	12/03	12/04	12/05	12/06	12/07
Est. sales ($ mil.)	—	—	—	—	—	71.6
Employees	—	—	—	—	—	3,300

HOBBY LOBBY STORES, INC.

7707 SW 44th St.
Oklahoma City, OK 73179
Phone: 405-745-1100
Fax: 405-745-1547
Web: www.hobbylobby.com

CEO: David Green
CFO: John Cargill
HR: Bill Owens
FYE: December 31
Type: Private

If something wicker this way comes, Hobby Lobby Stores may be the source. The firm operates about 400 stores in more than 30 states and sells arts and crafts supplies, baskets, beads, candles, frames, home-decorating accessories, and silk flowers. The #3 craft and fabric retailer (behind Michaels Stores and Jo-Ann Stores), it prefers to set up shop in second-generation retail sites (such as vacated supermarkets and superstores). Sister companies supply Hobby Lobby stores with merchandise, received from its Oklahoma distribution facility. CEO David Green, who owns the company with his wife Barbara, founded Hobby Lobby in 1972 and operates it according to biblical principles, including closing stores on Sunday.

	Annual Growth	12/02	12/03	12/04	12/05	12/06
Sales ($ mil.)	8.6%	1,164.0	1,300.0	1,400.0	1,500.0	1,620.0
Employees	6.7%	13,500	15,000	16,000	—	17,500

An in-depth profile of this company is available to Hoover's Online members at hoovers.com.

767

HOFFMAN CORPORATION

805 SW Broadway, Ste. 2100
Portland, OR 97205
Phone: 503-221-8811
Fax: 503-221-8934
Web: www.hoffmancorp.com

CEO: Wayne A. Drinkward
CFO: Scott W. Fredricks
HR: Sheri Sundstrom
FYE: December 31
Type: Private

Hoffman cherishes a challenge — such as building the nation's deepest subway station in Portland, Oregon, or the snakelike, metal-clad Experience Music Project in Seattle. Through several subsidiaries (including flagship Hoffman Construction) the general contractor and construction manager builds civic, commercial, and industrial facilities, primarily in the northwestern US. It is a leading builder of semiconductor facilities and serves such sectors as education, health care, sports, transportation, and government. The group also provides electrical, surveying, concrete, and other services. Employees own the company, which was founded in 1922.

	Annual Growth	12/02	12/03	12/04	12/05	12/06
Sales ($ mil.)	—	—	—	—	—	1,600.0
Employees	—	—	—	—	—	920

HOFFMANN-LA ROCHE INC.

340 Kingsland St.
Nutley, NJ 07110
Phone: 973-235-5000
Fax: 973-777-3327
Web: www.rocheusa.com

CEO: George B. Abercrombie
CFO: Ivor MacLeod
HR: Stephen D. Grossman
FYE: December 31
Type: Subsidiary

Hoffmann-La Roche is the US prescription pharmaceuticals unit of Roche. The company develops, manufactures, and markets drugs to treat such life-threatening conditions as AIDS, cancer, and heart disease. Other product categories include central nervous system disorders, organ transplant rejection, and skin conditions. Hoffmann-La Roche's products include influenza fighter Tamiflu, controversial acne medication Accutane, HIV inhibitor Fuzeon (co-marketed with Trimeris), obesity drug Xenical, and hepatitis B and C therapy Pegasys. Hoffmann-La Roche's R&D is focused on oncology and metabolic, inflammatory, respiratory, and autoimmune diseases.

HOGAN & HARTSON LLP

555 13th St. NW
Washington, DC 20004
Phone: 202-637-5600
Fax: 202-637-5910
Web: www.hhlaw.com

CEO: J. Warren Gorrell Jr.
CFO: Robert (Bob) Bolton
HR: Martha K. Williams
FYE: December 31
Type: Partnership

Long known as a go-to law firm in Washington, DC, Hogan & Hartson can now be found in the capitals of several other nations as well. The firm's 1,000-plus lawyers practice from more than 20 offices, more than half of which are overseas. Outside the US, Hogan & Hartson has offices in the Asia/Pacific region, Europe, and South America. In addition, it has an alliance with business advisory firm Stonebridge International. Hogan & Hartson maintains a wide range of practice areas, mainly related to business transactions and government regulation. Specialties include litigation and intellectual property. Frank Hogan founded the firm as a solo practice in 1904.

	Annual Growth	12/03	12/04	12/05	12/06	12/07
Est. sales ($ mil.)	—	—	—	—	—	192.7
Employees	—	—	—	—	—	2,222

HOK GROUP, INC.

211 N. Broadway, Ste. 700
St. Louis, MO 63102
Phone: 314-421-2000
Fax: 314-421-2152
Web: www.hok.com

CEO: Patrick MacLeamy
CFO: Robert M. (Bob) Pratzel
HR: John Mahon
FYE: December 31
Type: Private

HOK is OK with St. Louis and beyond. The HOK Group, or Hellmuth, Obata + Kassabaum (HOK), has graduated from its 1955 beginnings as an architectural designer of schools in the St. Louis area to become one of the world's largest architecture/engineering design firms. It offers design/build, planning, and program management services. HOK also ranks among the world's top interior design firms. Its projects include St. Louis' Priory Chapel, San Francisco's Moscone Convention Center, and the National Air and Space Museum in Washington, DC. HOK's Kansas City-based sports unit (HOK Sport + Venue + Event) designs sports complexes throughout the US. The company has some 30 offices worldwide.

	Annual Growth	12/03	12/04	12/05	12/06	12/07
Est. sales ($ mil.)	—	—	—	—	—	100.7
Employees	—	—	—	—	—	1,839

HOKU SCIENTIFIC, INC.

NASDAQ (GM): HOKU

1075 Opakapaka St.
Kapolei, HI 96707
Phone: 808-682-7800
Fax: 808-682-7807
Web: www.hokuscientific.com

CEO: Dustin M. Shindo
CFO: Darryl S. Nakamoto
HR: –
FYE: March 31
Type: Public

Hoku Scientific doesn't fight the power — it wants to provide the power. The company is riding the wave of alternative energy technologies on a variety of fronts. Hoku originally developed fuel cells using membrane electrode assemblies, or MEAs. The company is winding down its activities in that technology, however, and moving into manufacturing polysilicon and reselling photovoltaic solar modules made by other companies. The US Navy's Naval Air Warfare Center Weapons Division and Hawaii's Paradise Beverages are leading customers. Chairman, president, and CEO Dustin Shindo owns about 18% of Hoku, whose name means "star" in the Hawaiian language.

	Annual Growth	3/04	3/05	3/06	3/07	3/08
Sales ($ mil.)	137.8%	0.1	2.9	5.5	5.4	3.2
Net income ($ mil.)	—	(2.9)	(0.7)	1.3	(2.8)	(4.3)
Market value ($ mil.)	23.6%	—	—	105.2	97.4	160.7
Employees	1.6%	—	20	27	17	21

HOLCIM (US) INC.

201 Jones Rd.
Waltham, MA 02451
Phone: 781-647-2501
Fax: 781-647-2516
Web: www.holcim.com/USA

CEO: Patrick Dolberg
CFO: Thomas Aebischer
HR: Scott Greenhouse
FYE: December 31
Type: Subsidiary

There's nothing abstract about Holcim (US) Inc.'s position as a leading US concrete manufacturer. Holcim (US) produces and sells both ready-mix concrete and aggregates. Its customers include manufacturers of concrete products and dealers of ready-mixed concrete and building materials in more than a dozen sales regions throughout the country. Holcim (US) has a production capacity of 15 million tons of cement through 14 cement-production plants and more than 70 distribution terminals; it also imports cement from overseas affiliates. The company is a subsidiary of Switzerland-based Holcim Ltd.

	Annual Growth	12/03	12/04	12/05	12/06	12/07
Est. sales ($ mil.)	—	—	—	—	—	479.8
Employees	—	—	—	—	—	2,400

HOLIDAY COMPANIES

4567 American Blvd. West	CEO: Ronald A. (Ron) Erickson
Bloomington, MN 55437	CFO: –
Phone: 952-830-8700	HR: Robert S. (Bob) Nye
Fax: 952-830-8864	FYE: December 31
Web: holidaystationstores.com	Type: Private

Wholesaling and sporting goods retailing have both taken a vacation at Holiday Companies. The firm sold its Fairway Foods distribution business in 2000; its Gander Mountain sporting goods chain went public in 2004. Today, Holiday Companies operates about 400 Holiday Stationstores (about 100 of which are franchised) in a dozen states, from Michigan west to Washington and Alaska. These stores sell gas supplied by the company's Erickson Petroleum subsidiary as well as Blue Planet gasoline (low-sulfur fuel available in Minnesota). The company was founded in 1928 as a general store in a small Wisconsin town by two Erickson brothers, whose descendants still own and run the company.

	Annual Growth	12/02	12/03	12/04	12/05	12/06
Est. sales ($ mil.)	9.8%	1,250.0	1,200.0	1,310.0	1,742.0	1,820.0
Employees	(7.4%)	6,000	4,000	4,000	4,200	4,410

HOLLAND & KNIGHT LLP

195 Broadway, 24th Fl.	CEO: Steve Sonberg
New York, NY 10007	CFO: Michael R. Marget
Phone: 212-513-3200	HR: Andrew Petterson
Fax: 212-385-9010	FYE: December 31
Web: www.hklaw.com	Type: Partnership

Your legal knight in shining armor might be just around the corner. Holland & Knight maintains more than 15 offices throughout the US, plus another half-dozen in other countries, including representative offices. It has more than 1,100 lawyers overall. The firm maintains more than 100 practice areas and draws clients from a wide range of industries; it has been recognized for its work in such areas as corporate transactions, litigation, maritime law, and real estate. Holland & Knight traces its roots to a law office opened by Peter Knight in Florida in 1889; it took its current shape in 1968 when Knight's firm was combined with one led by US Senator Spessard Holland.

HOLLANDER HOME FASHIONS CORP.

6560 W. Rogers Circle, Ste. 19	CEO: Jeff Hollander
Boca Raton, FL 33487	CFO: Michael E. Ricozzi
Phone: 561-997-6900	HR: Michelle Eisner
Fax: 561-997-8738	FYE: December 31
Web: www.hollander.com	Type: Private

Hollander Home Fashions may not come to mind as you lie in bed counting Little Bo Peep's flock, but perhaps it should. The company, a national leader in textile manufacturing, produces about 30 million pillows a year. In addition, Hollander makes blankets, comforters, sheets, shams, and other bedding products for the likes of Laura Ashley, Simmons Beautyrest, and Karen Neuberger. For years the firm has generated private-label store brands for well-known retailers, including Wal-Mart and J. C. Penney. In 2001 it began manufacturing in China, and the next year it launched its own Hollander brand. Founded in 1953 by Bernard Hollander, the company is still run by his grandson, Jeff (CEO).

HOLLINGSWORTH & VOSE COMPANY

112 Washington St.	CEO: Valentine (Val) Hollingsworth III
East Walpole, MA 02032	CFO: Jeff Sherer
Phone: 508-668-0295	HR: –
Fax: 508-668-6526	FYE: December 31
Web: hollingsworth-vose.com	Type: Private

The unfiltered truth: Hollingsworth & Vose Company produces engine filtration, air and liquid filtration, battery separators, and other specialty products using nonwoven materials; technical, filter, and specialty papers; and advanced composites. The company's engine and industrial filtration products are made to perform in harsh environments, and are used in automotive air, automotive lubrication, diesel, fuel, hydraulic, oil, and other specialty filtration applications. Hollingsworth & Vose's battery separators are made with uniform pore structure, chemical stability, and high wicking and absorbency. The company has plants in Germany and the UK, as well as in the US.

	Annual Growth	12/03	12/04	12/05	12/06	12/07
Est. sales ($ mil.)	—	—	—	—	—	250.7
Employees	—	—	—	—	—	1,700

HOLLIS-EDEN PHARMACEUTICALS, INC.

NASDAQ (GM): HEPH

4435 Eastgate Mall, Ste. 400	CEO: Richard B. Hollis
San Diego, CA 92121	CFO: –
Phone: 858-587-9333	HR: –
Fax: 858-558-6470	FYE: December 31
Web: www.holliseden.com	Type: Public

Hollis-Eden Pharmaceuticals knows that balancing hormones can heal. The company focuses on developing adrenal steroid hormones, which reduce inflammation, regulate immunity, and stimulate cell growth, for treating a variety of diseases. Levels of adrenal steroid hormones can decline as a result of aging, stress, trauma, and other conditions and lead to disease. Hollis-Eden Pharmaceuticals' current drug candidates in clinical trials provide treatment for type 2 diabetes, rheumatoid arthritis, and types of cancer such as prostate and breast cancer. Founded in 1994, the company is currently conducting research for treating other ailments.

	Annual Growth	12/03	12/04	12/05	12/06	12/07
Sales ($ mil.)	81.7%	—	0.1	0.1	0.4	0.6
Net income ($ mil.)	—	—	(24.8)	(29.4)	(30.2)	(23.1)
Market value ($ mil.)	(37.0%)	—	181.7	100.3	152.1	45.5
Employees	—	—	—	64	—	—

HOLLISTER INCORPORATED

2000 Hollister Dr.	CEO: Alan F. Herbert
Libertyville, IL 60048	CFO: Samuel P. (Sam) Brilliant
Phone: 847-680-1000	HR: –
Fax: 847-680-2123	FYE: December 31
Web: www.hollister.com	Type: Private

Hollister makes and then distributes a variety of specialty medical products throughout more than 90 countries. The employee-owned company concentrates on products for wound care, continence care, mother and baby care, pelvic floor therapy, and ostomy care. Hollister has operations worldwide. Products include catheters and wound dressings, among other items. The company has two US manufacturing centers located in Missouri and Virginia, as well as European facilities in Denmark and Ireland. John Dickinson Schneider founded Hollister in 1921 as JDS Printer Craftsman.

	Annual Growth	12/03	12/04	12/05	12/06	12/07
Est. sales ($ mil.)	—	—	—	—	—	183.3
Employees	—	—	—	—	—	2,400

An in-depth profile of this company is available to Hoover's Online members at hoovers.com.

769

HOLLY CORPORATION

NYSE: HOC

100 Crescent Ct., Ste. 1600
Dallas, TX 75201
Phone: 214-871-3555
Fax: 214-871-3560
Web: www.hollycorp.com

CEO: Matthew P. (Matt) Clifton
CFO: Bruce R. Shaw
HR: Nancy F. Hartmann
FYE: December 31
Type: Public

Holly Corporation refines crude oil to produce gasoline, diesel fuel, and jet fuel, which it sells in the southwestern US, northern Mexico, and Montana. Subsidiary Navajo Refining (New Mexico) has a refining capacity of 85,000 barrels a day. Holly's Woods Cross refinery (Utah) has a crude oil capacity of 26,000 barrels per day. Its owns 900 miles of crude oil pipelines located primarily in west Texas and New Mexico, and a 45% stake in Holly Energy Partners, which operates 1,700 miles of petroleum product pipelines. Holly also owns and operates Holly Asphalt Company, which manufactures and markets asphalt products from various terminals in Arizona and New Mexico.

	Annual Growth	12/03	12/04	12/05	12/06	12/07
Sales ($ mil.)	35.9%	1,403.2	2,246.4	3,212.7	4,023.2	4,791.7
Net income ($ mil.)	64.2%	46.0	83.9	167.7	266.6	334.1
Market value ($ mil.)	83.1%	—	436.1	864.7	2,843.3	2,677.6
Employees	(2.5%)	—	—	881	859	—

HOLLY ENERGY PARTNERS, L.P.

NYSE: HEP

100 Crescent Ct., Ste. 1600
Dallas, TX 75201
Phone: 214-871-3555
Fax: 214-871-3560
Web: www.hollyenergy.com

CEO: Matthew P. (Matt) Clifton
CFO: Bruce R. Shaw
HR: Nancy F. Hartmann
FYE: December 31
Type: Public

Holly Energy Partners is having a jolly good time piping petroleum. The company transports refined petroleum products from Holly Corporation's Navajo refinery in New Mexico and Alon USA's Big Spring refinery in Texas, to customers located in the southwestern US. It operates 1,290 miles of refined petroleum pipelines (including 340 miles of leased pipelines), 11 distribution terminals, and two truck-loading facilities used to transport gasoline, diesel, and jet fuel. The company also owns 70% of Rio Grande Pipeline Company. Holly Corporation, the parent of the company's general partner (Holly Logistics), holds a 45% stake in Holly Energy Partners.

	Annual Growth	12/03	12/04	12/05	12/06	12/07
Sales ($ mil.)	15.8%	—	67.8	80.1	89.2	105.4
Net income ($ mil.)	6.5%	—	32.5	26.8	27.5	39.3
Market value ($ mil.)	14.0%	—	241.2	301.4	328.8	357.4
Employees	13.7%	—	—	82	—	106

HOLLYWOOD ENTERTAINMENT CORPORATION

9275 SW Peyton Ln.
Wilsonville, OR 97070
Phone: 503-570-1600
Fax: 503-570-1680
Web: www.hollywoodvideo.com

CEO: Clarence J. (Gabe) Gabriel Jr.
CFO: Thomas Johnson
HR: –
FYE: December 31
Type: Subsidiary

Like a Jessica Simpson flick, Hollywood Entertainment hopes you'll skip the theaters and go straight to video. The #2 US video chain, behind Blockbuster, it runs more than 2,000 Hollywood Video rental superstores in 47 states and the District of Columbia. Hollywood Video stores also rent video games and game players, VCRs, and DVD players. In-store video game department Game Crazy (in about 700 stores) buys, sells, and trades used and new game software, hardware, and accessories. The stores are primarily located in strip malls or other high-traffic locales. The company is a subsidiary of Movie Gallery, which filed for bankruptcy protection in late 2007.

HOLLYWOOD MEDIA CORP.

NASDAQ (GM): HOLL

2255 Glades Rd., Ste. 221 A.
Boca Raton, FL 33431
Phone: 561-998-8000
Fax: 561-998-2974
Web: www.hollywood.com

CEO: Mitchell (Mitch) Rubenstein
CFO: Scott A. Gomez
HR: –
FYE: December 31
Type: Public

This company helps get people to the theatre and the local multiplex. Hollywood Media Corp. is a leading provider of live theater tickets, including Broadway and off-Broadway productions, as well as performances in London's West End district, through Broadway.com, Theatre.com, and its 1-800-BROADWAY phone service. Its Theatre Direct International subsidiary provides wholesale tickets to groups and travel agents. Hollywood Media also operates Hollywood.com (movie reviews, trailers, and show times) and CinemasOnline (Web site maintenance for cinemas and live theaters in the UK), which earn revenue via ad sales. The company additionally has a 26% stake in MovieTickets.com.

	Annual Growth	12/03	12/04	12/05	12/06	12/07
Sales ($ mil.)	17.5%	64.9	73.0	95.6	115.9	123.9
Net income ($ mil.)	—	(7.4)	(11.6)	(8.9)	9.5	1.7
Market value ($ mil.)	12.5%	58.0	153.5	141.0	141.2	92.8
Employees	4.4%	202	271	271	230	—

HOLLYWOOD PRESBYTERIAN MEDICAL CENTER, INC.

1300 N. Vermont Ave.
Los Angeles, CA 90027
Phone: 213-413-3000
Fax: 323-644-7613
Web: www.hollywoodpresbyterian.com

CEO: Shawn Bolouki
CFO: Robert Allen
HR: Norma Braun
FYE: December 31
Type: Not-for-profit

In addition to nurses and doctors, the staff at Hollywood Presbyterian Medical Center (HPMC) includes bellmen, concierges, and parking valets. Aiming to blur the lines between acute care hospital and hotel, HPMC serves the community of Hollywood, California. Its health care services include a cancer treatment center; physical, speech, and occupational therapy; and the Institute of Maternal Fetal Health which performs fetal surgeries. Other services include community health outreach programs and The Chalet, a skilled nursing facility. The 430-bed hospital was a subsidiary of Tenet until 2005 when it was sold to CHA Health Systems, headed by fertility specialist Dr. Kwang Yul Cha.

	Annual Growth	12/03	12/04	12/05	12/06	12/07
Est. sales ($ mil.)	—	—	—	—	—	55.6
Employees	—	—	—	—	—	1,200

HOLMAN ENTERPRISES

7411 Maple Ave.
Pennsauken, NJ 08109
Phone: 856-663-5200
Fax: 856-665-3444
Web: www.holmanenterprises.com

CEO: Melinda (Mindy) Holman
CFO: Robert Campbell
HR: –
FYE: December 31
Type: Private

Holman sells a whole lot of cars. Family-owned Holman Enterprises owns about a dozen car and truck dealerships in southern New Jersey and another 10 or so in southern Florida. The company sells BMW, Ford, Infiniti, Jaguar, Lincoln, Mercury, Rolls-Royce, and Saturn cars, as well as Ford and Sterling trucks. Homan also offers collision repair services and operates a sunroof installation service and a pair of leasing companies. Its Automotive Resources International unit is one of the largest independently owned fleet leasing groups in the world. Holman's RMP engine and parts distributor sells small parts and engines authorized by Ford. The company was founded by Steward C. Holman in 1924 as a single dealership.

	Annual Growth	12/03	12/04	12/05	12/06	12/07
Est. sales ($ mil.)	—	—	—	—	—	915.3
Employees	—	—	—	—	—	2,751

HOLOBEAM, INC.

Pink Sheets: HOOB

217 1st St.
Ho-Ho-Kus, NJ 07423
Phone: 201-445-2420
Fax: 201-445-2421

CEO: Melvin S. Cook
CFO: –
HR: –
FYE: September 30
Type: Public

Holobeam doesn't just give its investors hollow promises. Rather, the company is involved in the development and leasing of commercial real estate. Holobeam owns 95,000 sq. ft. of space in Paramus, New Jersey, comprising two buildings that house retailers The Sports Authority and CompUSA. Befitting its scientific-sounding name, Holobeam developed and was granted several patents for a new type of surgical staple. It ditched that venture in 2003 after finding the demand wasn't strong enough to pursue. Chairman Melvin Cook and family (including his wife and company secretary, Beverly) own more than 80% of Holobeam.

	Annual Growth	9/02	9/03	9/04	9/05	*9/06
Sales ($ mil.)	0.0%	2.1	2.1	2.1	2.1	2.1
Net income ($ mil.)	18.9%	0.2	0.2	0.2	0.5	0.4
Employees	—	—	—	—	—	—

*Most recent year available

HOLOGIC, INC.

NASDAQ (GS): HOLX

35 Crosby Dr.
Bedford, MA 01730
Phone: 781-999-7300
Fax: 781-280-0669
Web: www.hologic.com

CEO: John W. (Jack) Cumming
CFO: Glenn P. Muir
HR: David J. Brady
FYE: Last Saturday in September
Type: Public

With its mammography and breast biopsy systems, Hologic puts the squeeze on women to help save their lives. Its mammography products include film-based and digital systems, as well as the workstations and computer-aided detection systems that interpret the images. Additional products include X-ray and ultrasound bone densitometers, which detect and monitor osteoporosis, and breast biopsy collection systems (branded ATEC) sold by its Suros division. With its 2007 merger with women's health firm Cytyc, Hologic gained several other product lines, including tests to screen for cervical cancer. The company markets its products to hospitals and clinical labs worldwide through distributors and a direct sales force.

	Annual Growth	9/03	9/04	9/05	9/06	9/07
Sales ($ mil.)	37.9%	204.0	228.7	287.7	462.7	738.4
Net income ($ mil.)	139.0%	2.9	12.2	28.3	27.4	94.6
Market value ($ mil.)	123.0%	135.7	195.7	1,188.2	2,287.2	3,357.6
Employees	49.2%	722	761	870	1,617	3,580

HOLT CAT

3302 South W. W. White Rd.
San Antonio, TX 78222
Phone: 210-648-1111
Fax: 210-648-0079
Web: www.holtcat.com

CEO: Peter M. Holt
CFO: David (Dave) Hennessee
HR: Guy Clumpner
FYE: December 31
Type: Private

With cat-like reflexes, Caterpillar dealership Holt CAT sells, leases, and services new and used Caterpillar equipment and engines through 35 locations across Texas. The family-owned dealership also carries parts and represents Challenger tractors, Lexion combines, and Olympian generators. Holt CAT buys and sells used equipment around the world, and it produces its own land-clearing equipment (Holt Land Management) and water tankers (Spray King). The company provides financing options that include rental programs and lease/purchase plans (for both short and long terms) for its products.

	Annual Growth	12/03	12/04	12/05	12/06	12/07
Est. sales ($ mil.)	—	—	—	—	—	500.0
Employees	—	—	—	—	—	1,700

HOM FURNITURE, INC.

10301 Woodcrest Dr. NW
Minneapolis, MN 55433
Phone: 763-767-3600
Fax: 763-767-3760
Web: www.homfurniture.com

CEO: Wayne Johansen
CFO: Laurie Johnston
HR: –
FYE: December 31
Type: Private

HOM Furniture is a mid- to high-end home furnishings retailer operating about a dozen stores located in Iowa, Minnesota, North and South Dakota, and Wisconsin. In addition to its wooden (cherry, maple, oak, pine), upholstered (including leather), and patio furniture, store offerings include rugs, clocks, mattresses, and related accessories. Many of HOM's locations also offer free certified design consultants to help customers with decisions. The company is updating many of its stores as well as expanding product categories, such as its new World Rugs showroom. CEO Wayne Johansen established the forerunner of HOM Furniture in 1973.

	Annual Growth	12/03	12/04	12/05	12/06	12/07
Est. sales ($ mil.)	—	—	—	—	—	109.2
Employees	—	—	—	—	—	1,000

HOME BANCSHARES, INC.

NASDAQ (GS): HOMB

719 Harkrider
Conway, AR 72032
Phone: 501-328-4770
Fax: 501-329-9139
Web: www.homebancshares.com

CEO: John W. Allison
CFO: Randy E. Mayor
HR: –
FYE: December 31
Type: Public

At this Home, you don't have to stash your cash under the mattress. Instead, you can choose from a half-dozen bank subsidiaries in Arkansas and Florida. Home BancShares serves central and north central Arkansas through Bank of Mountain View, Centennial Bank, Community Bank, First State Bank, and Twin City Bank; it serves the Florida Keys and southwestern Florida through Marine Bank. With a combined network of some 50 branches, the banks offer checking, savings, NOW and money market accounts, and CDs. The banks focus on commercial real estate and development loans, which make up more than 60% of a lending portfolio that also includes residential mortgage, business, and other loans.

	Annual Growth	12/03	12/04	12/05	12/06	12/07
Assets ($ mil.)	41.7%	—	805.2	1,911.5	2,190.6	2,291.6
Net income ($ mil.)	52.2%	3.8	9.2	11.4	15.9	20.4
Market value ($ mil.)	(12.5%)	—	—	—	413.6	361.7
Employees	3.3%	—	—	544	562	—

HOME BOX OFFICE, INC.

1100 Avenue of the Americas
New York, NY 10036
Phone: 212-512-1000
Fax: 212-512-1182
Web: www.hbo.com

CEO: Bill Nelson
CFO: Rob Roth
HR: Shelley Fischel
FYE: December 31
Type: Subsidiary

Crime *does* pay for Home Box Office (HBO). Boffo Mafia hit *The Sopranos* has brought more viewers to the pay-TV channel than ever before. More than 40 million subscribers (including those for sister pay-TV station Cinemax) pay about $12 monthly to watch original series such as *Entourage* and *Curb Your Enthusiasm*. Its HBO Films unit produces original movies. HBO also broadcasts concerts, stand-up comedy, theatrical movies, and sports. Known for its broadcasting freedom — more blue language, nudity, and violence than traditional networks — the commercial-free HBO is a critical favorite. A unit of Time Warner, HBO began in Wilkes-Barre, Pennsylvania, in 1972 as a pay-TV channel with a sports focus.

An in-depth profile of this company is available to Hoover's Online members at hoovers.com.

771

HOME BUYERS WARRANTY CORPORATION

1 Denver Highlands, 10375 E. Harvard Ave., Ste. 100
Denver, CO 80231
Phone: 303-368-4805
Fax: 303-750-3970
Web: www.2-10.com

CEO: Emory (Em) Fluhr
CFO: Mark Lewis
HR: John Bushore
FYE: March 31
Type: Private

It's like WD-40 for your home: Home Buyers Warranty (better known as 2-10 HBW) eases the pain of home systems repair. Home Buyers Warranty provides builders, manufacturers, homeowners, and real estate professionals with warranty products for new, manufactured, and modular homes. The company sells its warranties nationally through some 15,000 builders and 60,000 realtors; it has covered more than 3 million new and pre-owned homes across the country. 2-10 HBW also sells home service contracts.

	Annual Growth	3/03	3/04	3/05	3/06	3/07
Est. sales ($ mil.)	—	—	—	—	—	178.2
Employees	—	—	—	—	—	600

THE HOME DEPOT, INC.

NYSE: HD

2455 Paces Ferry Rd. NW
Atlanta, GA 30339
Phone: 770-433-8211
Fax: 770-384-2356
Web: www.homedepot.com

CEO: Francis S. (Frank) Blake
CFO: Carol B. Tomé
HR: Gloria Johnson Goins
FYE: Sunday nearest January 31
Type: Public

Lots of folks embark on household projects from The Home Depot. As the world's largest home improvement chain and second-largest retailer in the US after Wal-Mart, the firm operates more than 2,230 stores in all 50 US states, the District of Columbia, Canada, Mexico, and Puerto Rico. It targets the do-it-yourself and professional markets with a broad product assortment (up to 45,000 items, including lumber, floor and wall coverings, plumbing, gardening supplies, tools, paint, and even appliances). Home Depot has reshuffled its top management in response to angry shareholders and sold its construction supply business, HD Supply, in 2007.

	Annual Growth	1/04	1/05	1/06	1/07	1/08
Sales ($ mil.)	4.5%	64,816.0	73,094.0	81,511.0	90,837.0	77,349.0
Net income ($ mil.)	0.5%	4,304.0	5,001.0	5,838.0	5,761.0	4,395.0
Market value ($ mil.)	(11.6%)	84,170.3	88,295.8	84,960.0	78,681.8	51,460.5
Employees	(2.0%)	—	—	345,000	364,000	331,000

HOME DIAGNOSTICS, INC.

NASDAQ (GM): HDIX

2400 NW 55th Ct.
Fort Lauderdale, FL 33309
Phone: 954-677-9201
Fax: 954-739-8506
Web: www.homediagnostics.com

CEO: J. Richard Damron, Jr.
CFO: Ronald L. (Ron) Rubin
HR: Kim Zeltwanger
FYE: December 31
Type: Public

Home Diagnostics makes blood glucose monitoring systems and disposable supplies for diabetics. The company sells its products through retail pharmacies, mass merchandisers, managed care companies, mail service providers, and distributors around the globe. Home Diagnostics markets its testing systems and blood monitors through these distribution channels in two ways, under its own brand names — including Sidekick, TrueTrack Smart System, TRUEread, and Prestige IQ — and through co-branded partnerships in which the company's customers market its products under their brand names alongside Home Diagnostics brands.

	Annual Growth	12/03	12/04	12/05	12/06	12/07
Sales ($ mil.)	11.9%	73.7	85.1	100.2	112.6	115.6
Net income ($ mil.)	5.0%	7.9	2.0	5.9	10.3	9.6
Market value ($ mil.)	(22.1%)	—	—	—	187.6	146.1
Employees	—	—	—	—	500	—

HOME FEDERAL BANCORP, INC.

NASDAQ (GS): HOME

500 12th Ave. South
Nampa, ID 83651
Phone: 208-468-5189
Fax: 208-468-5001
Web: www.myhomefed.com

CEO: Len E. Williams
CFO: Eric S. Nadeau
HR: Denis J. Trom
FYE: September 30
Type: Public

Home Federal Bancorp's location provides it with a treasure trove of opportunity. Its subsidiary, Home Federal Bank (formerly Home Federal Savings and Loan Association of Nampa), serves the Treasure Valley region of southwestern Idaho, which includes Ada, Canyon, Elmore, and Gem counties (where nearly 40% of the state's population resides). Home Federal serves the banking needs of area residents and businesses through 15 branches (six of which are located in Wal-Mart stores), two loan centers, an ATM network, and the Internet. Its primary business is attracting deposits and using them to originate loans. In 2007 Home Federal Bancorp converted from a mutual holding company to a stock ownership company.

	Annual Growth	9/03	9/04	9/05	9/06	9/07
Assets ($ mil.)	12.1%	450.2	743.9	689.6	761.3	710.0
Net income ($ mil.)	(0.9%)	5.5	4.7	5.3	6.2	5.3
Employees	(3.6%)	—	—	240	—	223

HOME INSTEAD, INC.

13330 California St., Ste. 200
Omaha, NE 68154
Phone: 402-498-4466
Fax: 402-498-5757
Web: www.homeinstead.com

CEO: Paul Hogan
CFO: Richard Phillis
HR: –
FYE: December 31
Type: Private

Home Instead is a provider of non-medical home care services for the elderly. The company offers services designed for people who are capable of managing their physical needs but require assistance, supervision, light housework, errands, or simply companionship in order to remain in their homes. Founded in 1994, Home Instead has a network of more than 600 franchises operating in 47 states, as well as Canada, Japan, western Europe, New Zealand, and Taiwan. Employees known as CAREGivers provide the elderly with one-on-one human contact to reduce isolation and improve their quality of life in the comfort of their own homes.

	Annual Growth	12/03	12/04	12/05	12/06	12/07
Est. sales ($ mil.)	—	—	—	—	—	24.8
Employees	—	—	—	—	—	203

HOME INTERIORS & GIFTS, INC.

1649 Frankford Rd. West
Carrollton, TX 75007
Phone: 972-695-1000
Fax: 972-695-1112
Web: www.homeinteriors.com

CEO: Robin Crossman
CFO: Mary-Knight Tyler
HR: Carla Fulton
FYE: December 31
Type: Private

Home Interiors & Gifts is knocking. The company makes decorating accessories that are sold by more than 140,000 representatives through home parties in the US, Canada, Mexico, and Puerto Rico. Its product lines include artificial flowers, candles, framed artwork, mirrors, sconces, small furniture, and shelves. The company buys many of its products from its own manufacturing subsidiaries such as Laredo Candle Company. The late Mary Crowley, sister-in-law of makeup maven Mary Kay Ash, founded Home Interiors in 1957. Highland Capital Management owns a majority interest in the company, which filed for Chapter 11 bankruptcy protection in 2008 and is reorganizing.

An in-depth profile of this company is available to Hoover's Online members at hoovers.com.

HOME MERIDIAN INTERNATIONAL

1 Pulaski Sq.
Pulaski, VA 24301
Phone: 540-980-7330
Fax: 540-994-5756
Web: www.pulaskifurniture.com

CEO: George Revington
CFO: –
HR: –
FYE: Sunday nearest October 31
Type: Private

Home Meridian International is the new group home for furniture companies Pulaski Furniture and SLF (formerly Samuel Lawrence Furniture). Pulaski Furniture is known for its high-end curio cabinets, but both companies sell wooden bedroom, dining room, occasional (credenzas and chests; home entertainment centers; and desks, bookcases, and consoles for the home office), and youth furniture. Pulaski and SLF both import furniture from Asia. (Pulaski closed its its last curios plant in Virginia in 2007.) The companies merged to form Home Meridian, which is majority owned by private equity firm Quad-C Management, in 2006. Combined they ring up about $270 million in annual sales.

	Annual Growth	10/03	10/04	10/05	10/06	10/07
Est. sales ($ mil.)	—	—	—	—	—	23.3
Employees	—	—	—	—	—	420

HOME PRODUCTS INTERNATIONAL, INC.

4501 W. 47th St.
Chicago, IL 60632
Phone: 773-890-1010
Fax: 773-890-0523
Web: www.hpii.com

CEO: George Hamilton
CFO: Don Hotz
HR: John Pugh Jr.
FYE: Last Saturday in December
Type: Private

Home Products International (HPI) helps folks get it together — and it has done the same for itself. HPI filed for Chapter 11 bankruptcy protection in late 2006. The company makes ironing boards and their covers in the US. It also makes other laundry products, plastic containers and carts, clothes hangers, shower organizers, food storage items, and organizers. HPI products are sold under the HOMZ brand name in more than 50 countries. HPI sells to hotels, discounters, and other retailers such as Wal-Mart, Kmart, and Target. In 2004 HPI was acquired by Storage Acquisition Company, which comprises a group of investors including chairman Joseph Gantz.

	Annual Growth	12/03	12/04	12/05	12/06	12/07
Est. sales ($ mil.)	—	—	—	—	—	260.3
Employees	—	—	—	—	—	750

HOME PROPERTIES, INC.

NYSE: HME

850 Clinton Sq.
Rochester, NY 14604
Phone: 585-546-4900
Fax: 585-546-5433
Web: www.homeproperties.com

CEO: Edward J. Pettinella
CFO: David P. Gardner
HR: Lisa M. Critchley
FYE: December 31
Type: Public

Even homes need facelifts from time to time. Home Properties provides that proverbial Botox shot by renovating and rehabilitating multi-family apartments that are in need of both interior and exterior maintenance, from new flooring and bathroom repair to roofing and landscaping. Formerly Home Properties of New York, the real estate investment trust (REIT) focuses on suburban areas in metropolitan markets in the northeastern and mid-Atlantic states and in southeast Florida. Home Properties owns and manages a portfolio of about 120 apartment communities with nearly 40,000 units.

	Annual Growth	12/03	12/04	12/05	12/06	12/07
Sales ($ mil.)	3.8%	434.5	458.3	443.8	454.0	505.2
Net income ($ mil.)	10.1%	41.8	47.0	81.5	110.5	61.5
Market value ($ mil.)	3.2%	1,291.1	1,402.9	1,272.3	1,962.0	1,462.1
Employees	—	—	—	1,500	—	—

HOME SHOPPING NETWORK, INC.

1 HSN Dr.
St. Petersburg, FL 33729
Phone: 727-872-1000
Fax: –
Web: www.hsn.com

CEO: Mindy F. Grossman
CFO: –
HR: Lisa Letizio
FYE: December 31
Type: Subsidiary

There's no need to worry about normal business hours when shopping from this retailer. Home Shopping Network (HSN) operates a leading home shopping television channel that reaches nearly 90 million homes in the US offering computers and electronics, fashion items, home and kitchen goods, jewelry, and health, beauty, and fitness products. The company also sells products through its Web site, HSN.com, and catalogs. In addition, HSN operates shopping channels in China and Japan. About 80% of the company's customers are female. Its fulfillment centers handle more than 50 million calls and deliver more than 50 million packages a year. Founded in 1977, HSN is a subsidiary of Barry Diller's IAC/InterActiveCorp.

HOME SOLUTIONS OF AMERICA, INC.

NASDAQ (GM): HSOA

1500 Dragon St., Ste. B
Dallas, TX 75207
Phone: 214-623-8446
Fax: 214-333-9435
Web: www.hsoacorp.com

CEO: Frank J. Fradella
CFO: James M. Grady
HR: –
FYE: December 31
Type: Public

Home Solutions of America can't solve the problems of hurricanes and flooding in coastal areas, but the company *can* do something about the aftermath. It provides specialty interior services through a number of subsidiaries. Home Solutions Restoration of Louisiana and PW Stephens provide recovery services (debris removal, dehumidification); the latter firm, along with Fiber Seal Systems, also provides such restoration services as air decontamination and removal of mold and asbestos. The company's rebuilding and remodeling operations include kitchen cabinet and counter construction and installation performed by subsidiaries Southern Exposure, SouthernStone Cabinets, and Cornerstone Building and Remodeling.

	Annual Growth	12/02	12/03	12/04	12/05	*12/06
Sales ($ mil.)	164.5%	2.6	14.0	31.1	68.1	127.2
Net income ($ mil.)	—	(0.5)	(0.7)	2.6	7.2	17.9
Employees	28.9%	166	195	186	483	458

*Most recent year available

HOMEFED CORPORATION

OTC: HOFD

1903 Wright Place, Ste. 220
Carlsbad, CA 92008
Phone: 760-918-8200
Fax: 760-918-8210

CEO: Paul J. Borden
CFO: Erin N. Ruhe
HR: –
FYE: December 31
Type: Public

HomeFed won't provide you with room and board, but it can help you get a home. The company earns *its* keep by investing in and developing residential real estate in California. Through subsidiaries, HomeFed is developing a master-planned community in San Diego County called San Elijo Hills, which is expected to contain approximately 3,500 residences. The company is responsible for design engineering, infrastructure, and finishing individual lots. HomeFed also owns a portion of another community under development, Otay Ranch, as well as some 1,500 acres of a grape vineyard in California.

	Annual Growth	12/03	12/04	12/05	12/06	12/07
Sales ($ mil.)	(36.8%)	148.3	81.7	107.9	69.4	23.7
Net income ($ mil.)	(45.0%)	74.1	36.8	31.8	17.2	6.8
Market value ($ mil.)	21.0%	239.4	413.1	553.8	546.1	513.0
Employees	—	—	—	—	—	24

An in-depth profile of this company is available to Hoover's Online members at hoovers.com.

773

HOMELAND SECURITY CAPITAL CORPORATION

OTC: HOMS

1005 N. Globe Rd., Ste. 550
Arlington, VA 22201
Phone: 703-528-7073
Fax: –
Web: www.hscapcorp.com

CEO: C. Thomas McMillen
CFO: Michael T. (Mike) Brigante
HR: –
FYE: December 31
Type: Public

Homeland Security Capital stakes its financial security on the nation's security. The investment company acquires, consolidates, and provides management assistance for companies that offer homeland security services and products. The firm hopes to capitalize on the highly fragmented nature of the young industry, which brings potential customers in the government and private sectors. In 2006 it acquired Nexus Technologies Group, which designs, builds, and installs closed-circuit security systems in the mid-Atlantic. It also holds a 51%-stake in detection equipment maker Polimatrix. Homeland Security Capital puts its platform companies up for partial or complete sale as they no longer fit its strategic criteria.

	Annual Growth	12/03	12/04	12/05	12/06	12/07
Sales ($ mil.)	132.7%	—	1.0	0.1	8.7	12.6
Net income ($ mil.)	—	—	(0.3)	(1.3)	(6.5)	(3.0)
Market value ($ mil.)	(92.8%)	—	—	703.6	375.8	3.7
Employees	—	—	—	—	—	27

HOMELAND STORES, INC.

28 E. 33rd St.
Edmond, OK 73013
Phone: 405-216-2200
Fax: 405-216-2282
Web: www.homelandstores.com

CEO: Darryl Fitzgerald
CFO: Deborah A. (Debbie) Brown
HR: Jim Kern
FYE: Saturday nearest December 31
Type: Subsidiary

Homeland Stores has a home with Associated Wholesale Grocers. The regional supermarket chain emerged from Chapter 11 bankruptcy protection in 2002 as a wholly owned subsidiary of Kansas City-based cooperative AWG. (AWG operates the Homeland stores through its Associated Retail Grocers subsidiary.) AWG supplies more than 70% of the products sold in Homeland stores. Its 70 supermarkets — mostly in Oklahoma, but also in Kansas and Missouri — offer groceries and general merchandise; most have delicatessens, pharmacies, and some have specialty departments (ethnic foods, floral services, seafood). Homeland still faces the same stiff competition from Wal-Mart and others that it did prior to filing for bankruptcy.

	Annual Growth	12/03	12/04	12/05	12/06	12/07
Est. sales ($ mil.)	—	—	—	—	—	96.3
Employees	—	—	—	—	—	890

HOMESERVICES OF AMERICA, INC.

333 S. 7th St., 27th Fl.
Minneapolis, MN 55402
Phone: 888-485-0018
Fax: 612-336-5590
Web: www.homeservices.com

CEO: Ronald J. (Ron) Peltier
CFO: Cynthia L. (Cindy) Sattler
HR: –
FYE: December 31
Type: Subsidiary

HomeServices of America knows bricks and mortar. The company is one of the largest residential real estate brokerages in the US, operating more than 375 offices under various brand names in some 20 states in the Midwest, Southeast, and West Coast. It also offers mortgages (through an agreement with Wells Fargo Home Mortgage), property/casualty insurance, home warranties, relocation assistance, and title and closing services. The company books approximately $70 billion worth of transactions annually. Warren Buffett's Berkshire Hathaway owns HomeServices of America through MidAmerican Energy Holdings.

	Annual Growth	12/03	12/04	12/05	12/06	12/07
Est. sales ($ mil.)	—	—	—	—	—	1,868.5
Employees	—	—	—	—	—	1,992

HOMESTEAD TECHNOLOGIES, INC.

3375 Edison Way
Menlo Park, CA 94025
Phone: 650-549-3100
Fax: 650-364-7329
Web: www.homestead.com

CEO: Justin S. Kitch
CFO: –
HR: Mona Bergevin
FYE: December 31
Type: Private

Homestead Technologies offers its members services and tools to build their own Web sites. Its drag-and-drop authoring software (SiteBuilder) allows small business owners, non-profit administrators, retailers, and hobbyists to create Web pages without knowledge of HTML coding. In 2003 the firm launched PhotoSite, for posting photos on the Web. Homestead sold PhotoSite in 2005 to United Online for about $10 million in cash. Investors in Homestead include CEO Justin Kitch, who co-founded the company as Kartoffelsoft in 1994, in addition to investment firms such as Draper Fisher Jurvetson, Goldman Sachs, and Redpoint Ventures.

	Annual Growth	12/03	12/04	12/05	12/06	12/07
Est. sales ($ mil.)	—	—	—	—	—	7.7
Employees	—	—	—	—	—	75

HOMETOWN AMERICA L.L.C.

150 N. Wacker Dr., Ste. 2800
Chicago, IL 60606
Phone: 312-604-7500
Fax: 312-604-7501
Web: www.hometownamerica.com

CEO: Richard Rich Cline
CFO: –
HR: –
FYE: December 31
Type: Private

There's no place like home for Hometown America. The company invests in and manages manufactured home parks throughout the US. It owns approximately 140 communities (many of which feature recreational facilities such as swimming pools, clubhouses, and basketball courts) consisting of more than 54,000 home sites in nearly 20 states. About a third of its properties — carrying the Providence brand — are targeted towards active seniors; more than half of these are located in Florida. The company also offers home financing and insurance through agreements with third-party providers.

	Annual Growth	12/03	12/04	12/05	12/06	12/07
Est. sales ($ mil.)	—	—	—	—	—	231.0
Employees	—	—	—	—	—	1,000

HONDA OF AMERICA MFG., INC.

24000 Honda Pkwy.
Marysville, OH 43040
Phone: 937-642-5000
Fax: 937-644-6575
Web: www.ohio.honda.com

CEO: Tsuneo Tanai
CFO: –
HR: –
FYE: March 31
Type: Subsidiary

Honda of America Mfg. operates five Ohio plants where Honda automobiles, engines, transmissions, and motorcycles are manufactured for the North American market, as well as others. The company's Marysville auto plant builds 440,000 vehicles per year, and was the first US auto plant to build both right- and left-hand drive cars on the same assembly line. Honda of America Mfg.'s other plants build cars, engines, and motorcycles. Vehicles made by Honda of America Mfg. include the Accord coupe and sedan, the Acura TL and RDX, the Civic Sedan, CR-V, and the Element. The vehicles built at Honda's Ohio plants are sold in more than 100 countries worldwide.

	Annual Growth	3/03	3/04	3/05	3/06	3/07
Est. sales ($ mil.)	—	—	—	—	—	1,889.2
Employees	—	—	—	—	—	13,500

⊞ HONEYWELL INTERNATIONAL INC.
NYSE: HON

101 Columbia Rd.
Morristown, NJ 07962
Phone: 973-455-2000
Fax: 973-455-4807
Web: www.honeywell.com

CEO: David M. Cote
CFO: David J. (Dave) Anderson
HR: Mark James
FYE: December 31
Type: Public

Jet engines and thermostats seem worlds apart, but they're Honeywell International's bread and butter. The company's largest business segment, Automation and Control, includes home and industrial heating, ventilation, and manufacturing process products. Close behind is Honeywell Aerospace, which makes products such as turbofan and turboprop engines and flight safety and landing systems. Honeywell, through its Specialty Materials segment, also makes performance materials used in semiconductors, polymers for electronics and fibers, and specialty friction materials. Lastly, the company turns out consumer car care products (Prestone, FRAM brands) through its Transportation Systems segment.

	Annual Growth	12/03	12/04	12/05	12/06	12/07
Sales ($ mil.)	10.6%	23,103.0	25,601.0	27,653.0	31,367.0	34,589.0
Net income ($ mil.)	16.6%	1,324.0	1,281.0	1,655.0	2,083.0	2,444.0
Market value ($ mil.)	12.4%	28,827.7	30,099.0	30,898.2	36,218.8	45,965.3
Employees	2.6%	—	—	116,000	118,000	122,000

HONICKMAN AFFILIATES

8275 Rte. 130
Pennsauken, NJ 08110
Phone: 856-665-6200
Fax: 856-661-4684

CEO: Jeffrey A. (Jeff) Honickman
CFO: Walt Wilkinson
HR: June Raufer
FYE: December 31
Type: Private

Honickman Affiliates doesn't mind bottling its creative juices. The firm is one of the nation's largest privately owned bottlers — bottling and distributing soft drinks primarily in Maryland, New Jersey, New York, Ohio, and Virginia. A major bottler of Pepsi-Cola and Dr Pepper Snapple Group brands including 7 UP, it also sells Canada Dry, Mott's, Snapple, and South Beach Beverage Company's SoBe beverages. It distributes Coors beers in New York and brews up private-label soft drinks. Chairman and owner Harold Honickman started the company in 1957, when his father-in-law built a bottling plant for him.

	Annual Growth	12/02	12/03	12/04	12/05	12/06
Est. sales ($ mil.)	6.8%	983.0	1,100.0	1,130.0	1,215.0	1,280.0
Employees	0.0%	5,000	5,000	5,000	5,000	5,000

HOOD INDUSTRIES, INC.

15 Professional Pkwy.
Hattiesburg, MS 39402
Phone: 601-264-2559
Fax: 601-296-4766
Web: www.hoodindustries.com

CEO: Don Grimm
CFO: Bill Wislocki
HR: Terry Lawhead
FYE: December 31
Type: Private

From deep in the forest to a place in your 'hood. That's the promise made by Hood Industries, a company that manufactures forest products from its mills in Beaumont, Waynesboro, and Wiggins, Mississippi and in Coushatta, Louisiana. The company's products include dimension lumber, decking, and plywood made from southern yellow pines. Hood Industries operates distribution centers in the eastern and southern US. The centers, operating under the McQuesten Lumber and McEwen Lumber names, serve the OEM, millwork, cabinet, and retail markets by supplying such products as hardwood lumber and plywood. The company offers truck and rail transportation services, paper-wrapping, and half-packs.

	Annual Growth	12/03	12/04	12/05	12/06	12/07
Est. sales ($ mil.)	—	—	—	—	—	130.1
Employees	—	—	—	—	—	1,150

HOOKER FURNITURE CORPORATION
NASDAQ (CM): HOFT

440 E. Commonwealth Blvd.
Martinsville, VA 24112
Phone: 276-632-0459
Fax: 276-632-0026
Web: www.hookerfurniture.com

CEO: Paul B. Toms Jr.
CFO: E. Larry Ryder
HR: Jack R. Palmer
FYE: Sunday nearest January 31
Type: Public

Hooker Furniture wants to sell you the pieces that will turn your house into a home. It offers hardwood and metal furniture including wall units, home office furniture, home theater cabinets, living and dining room tables, adult and children's bedroom furniture, and accent pieces. Its Bradington-Young line of residential upholstered furniture features leather reclining chairs and sofas, desk chairs, and more. Its Sam Moore unit makes upscale chairs. Hooker Furniture also produces a line of PGA TOUR golf-themed pieces. Its products are sold through specialty dealers (Star Furniture, Nebraska Furniture Mart) and department stores (Dillard's). Hooker Furniture executives hold about 14% of the company.

	Annual Growth	11/03	11/04	11/05	11/06	*1/08
Sales ($ mil.)	0.6%	309.0	345.9	341.8	350.0	316.8
Net income ($ mil.)	7.6%	14.7	18.2	12.5	14.1	19.7
Market value ($ mil.)	(4.5%)	303.9	338.0	223.9	214.4	253.2
Employees	—	—	—	1,400	—	—

*Fiscal year change

HOOPER HOLMES, INC.
AMEX: HH

170 Mount Airy Rd.
Basking Ridge, NJ 07920
Phone: 908-766-5000
Fax: 908-953-6304
Web: www.hooperholmes.com

CEO: Roy H. Bubbs
CFO: Michael J. Shea
HR: –
FYE: December 31
Type: Public

Talk about a high-pressure exam. Through its Health Information Division, Hooper Holmes arranges physical examinations of life insurance applicants for insurance carriers nationwide; it also performs phone interviews to collect medical records and tests blood and urine samples. The unit operates under the names Portamedic, Infolink, and Heritage Labs. Hooper Holmes' Claims Evaluation Division helps property/casualty insurers evaluate personal injury claims by arranging independent medical examinations; it operates primarily in the Northeast and Midwest as Hooper Evaluations. In 2007 the company sold its UK life insurance exams provider, Medicals Direct, to the unit's management.

	Annual Growth	12/03	12/04	12/05	12/06	12/07
Sales ($ mil.)	(5.7%)	300.2	327.8	320.4	293.9	237.7
Net income ($ mil.)	—	15.9	10.7	(96.6)	(85.2)	(7.3)
Market value ($ mil.)	(26.3%)	400.7	386.0	168.7	224.8	118.1
Employees	(3.8%)	—	—	3,275	3,150	—

⊞ HOOTERS OF AMERICA, INC.

1815 The Exchange
Atlanta, GA 30339
Phone: 770-951-2040
Fax: 770-618-7032
Web: www.hooters.com

CEO: Coby G. Brooks
CFO: Rodney Foster
HR: Doug White
FYE: December 31
Type: Private

The chicken wings aren't the only spicy items at Hooters. Hooters of America operates and franchises about 440 Hooters restaurants in about 45 states and approximately 20 other countries. The beach-themed bar-and-grills cater to sports fans and are known for their spicy chicken wings as well as their hostesses, who dress in the chain's trademark bright orange short shorts and tight T-shirts. Hooters also serves chili, sandwiches, and beer. The company operates more than 120 locations and franchises the rest. Hooters of America is controlled by CEO Coby Brooks, the son of the late Robert Brooks who built the chain. Six friends, none of whom had any restaurant experience, opened the first Hooters in 1983.

	Annual Growth	12/03	12/04	12/05	12/06	12/07
Est. sales ($ mil.)	—	—	—	—	—	121.4
Employees	—	—	—	—	—	5,600

⊞ An in-depth profile of this company is available to Hoover's Online members at hoovers.com.

775

HOOVER'S, INC.

5800 Airport Blvd.
Austin, TX 78752
Phone: 512-374-4500
Fax: 512-374-4501
Web: www.hoovers.com

CEO: David Mather
CFO: Michael (Mike) Clark
HR: Robin Pfahler
FYE: December 31
Type: Subsidiary

Hoover's offers proprietary business information through the Internet, data feeds, wireless devices, and co-branding agreements with other online services. Its Web site, Hoover's Online, features a database of information on more than 25 million corporations and organizations. Offering both free and for-pay content, the firm focuses on selling subscriptions (the majority of its revenues) to marketing, sales, and business development professionals. Hoover's also publishes its information in books. The company is a subsidiary of Dun & Bradstreet.

	Annual Growth	12/03	12/04	12/05	12/06	12/07
Sales ($ mil.)	38.8%	29.0	50.0	70.0	90.0	107.5
Employees	—	—	—	—	—	—

HOP ENERGY, LLC

4 W. Red Oak Ln., 3rd Fl.
White Plains, NY 10604
Phone: 914-304-1300
Fax: 914-644-7500
Web: www.hopheat.com

CEO: Michael Anton
CFO: Richard (Rick) Nota
HR: –
FYE: September 30
Type: Private

HOP Energy (formerly Heating Oil Partners) hops to it when it comes to serving customers in a six-state region from Boston to Philadelphia with heating oil, central air conditioning, commercial fuels, and heating/air conditioning equipment services. The environmentally conscious company carefully maintains its own bulk storage fuel facilities. HOP Energy, which emerged from bankruptcy protection in 2006, also conducts inspections and performs preventative maintenance on its customers' heating equipment to help improve fuel efficiency and reduce particulate emissions. The company is controlled by a private investment group led by Longroad Asset Management.

	Annual Growth	9/03	9/04	9/05	9/06	9/07
Est. sales ($ mil.)	—	—	—	—	—	215.9
Employees	—	—	—	—	—	1,000

HOPFED BANCORP, INC.

4155 Lafayette Rd.
Hopkinsville, KY 42240
Phone: 270-885-1171
Fax: 270-889-0313
Web: www.bankwithheritage.com

NASDAQ (GM): HFBC

CEO: John E. Peck
CFO: Billy C. Duvall
HR: –
FYE: December 31
Type: Public

HopFed Bancorp is the holding company for Heritage Bank (formerly Hopkinsville Federal Savings Bank), which started operations in 1879 as a building and loan association. The bank has about a dozen branches in southwestern Kentucky, with its market area extending into northwestern Tennessee. It offers standard products like checking, savings, money market, and NOW accounts, as well as CDs, IRAs, property/casualty insurance, and annuities. One- to four-family residential mortgages account for about 50% of its loan portfolio. To a lesser extent, Heritage Bank also writes multifamily residential, construction, commercial, and consumer loans. Directors and executives control 12% of the bank.

	Annual Growth	12/03	12/04	12/05	12/06	12/07
Assets ($ mil.)	11.0%	531.5	579.7	639.6	770.9	808.3
Net income ($ mil.)	4.0%	3.5	4.0	4.1	3.9	4.1
Market value ($ mil.)	(4.1%)	62.6	62.3	57.8	58.2	52.9
Employees	38.6%	—	—	126	—	242

HORACE MANN EDUCATORS CORPORATION

NYSE: HMN

1 Horace Mann Plaza
Springfield, IL 62715
Phone: 217-789-2500
Fax: 217-788-5161
Web: www.horacemann.com

CEO: Louis G. (Lou) Lower II
CFO: Peter H. (Pete) Heckman
HR: –
FYE: December 31
Type: Public

Naming itself in honor of Horace Mann, considered the father of public education, Horace Mann Educators is an insurance holding company that targets K-12 school teachers and other public school employees throughout the US. The company and its subsidiaries offer homeowners, auto, and individual and group life insurance, as well as retirement annuities. Horace Mann employs some 800 agents, many of whom are former teachers themselves. Writing business in 48 states and Washington, DC, the company derives a third of its premiums from five states — California, Florida, Illinois, Minnesota, and North Carolina.

	Annual Growth	12/03	12/04	12/05	12/06	12/07
Assets ($ mil.)	5.9%	4,973.0	5,371.9	5,840.6	6,329.7	6,259.3
Net income ($ mil.)	44.5%	19.0	56.3	77.3	98.7	82.8
Market value ($ mil.)	7.6%	596.8	817.5	814.7	870.4	800.0
Employees	(2.1%)	—	—	2,400	2,400	2,300

HORIZON AIR INDUSTRIES, INC.

19300 International Blvd.
Seattle, WA 98188
Phone: 206-241-6757
Fax: 206-431-4624
Web: www.alaskaair.com

CEO: Jeffrey D. Pinneo
CFO: Rudi H. Schmidt
HR: Marne K. McCluskey
FYE: December 31
Type: Subsidiary

Regional carrier Horizon Air Industries brings together the earth and sky in about 40 cities in the western US and Canada. A subsidiary of Alaska Air Group, Horizon does much of its flying from airports in Boise, Idaho; Portland, Oregon; Seattle; and Spokane, Washington. The carrier operates a fleet of about 70 aircraft, including some 50 turboprops and 20 regional jets. Horizon provides connecting service for sister company Alaska Airlines, and the carriers share several code-sharing partners, including American Airlines, Continental Airlines, and KLM.

	Annual Growth	12/03	12/04	12/05	12/06	12/07
Sales ($ mil.)	11.2%	463.8	503.2	556.4	633.1	709.2
Employees	2.8%	3,742	3,734	3,902	4,031	4,184

HORIZON BANCORP

NASDAQ (CM): HBNC

515 Franklin Square
Michigan City, IN 46360
Phone: 219-879-0211
Fax: 219-874-9305
Web: www.accesshorizon.com

CEO: Craig M. Dwight
CFO: James H. Foglesong
HR: –
FYE: December 31
Type: Public

Despite its name, Horizon Bancorp is on the up-and-up. It's the holding company for Horizon Bank, which serves northwest Indiana and southwest Michigan through about 20 branches. It provides local individuals and businesses such standard services as checking and savings accounts, IRAs, CDs, and credit cards. Commercial, financial, and agricultural loans make up the largest segment of Horizon's loan portfolio, which also includes mortgage warehouse loans (loans earmarked for sale into the secondary market), consumer installment loans, and residential mortgages. Through subsidiaries, the bank offers trust and investment management services, life and health insurance, property/casualty coverage, and annuities.

	Annual Growth	12/03	12/04	12/05	12/06	12/07
Assets ($ mil.)	13.6%	757.1	913.8	1,127.9	1,222.4	1,258.9
Net income ($ mil.)	5.7%	6.5	6.9	7.1	7.5	8.1
Market value ($ mil.)	0.4%	82.2	82.1	82.7	88.8	83.4
Employees	(3.2%)	—	—	283	—	265

An in-depth profile of this company is available to Hoover's Online members at hoovers.com.

HORIZON BAY MANAGEMENT, L.L.C

5102 W. Laurel St., Ste. 700
Tampa, FL 33607
Phone: 813-287-3900
Fax: 813-287-3914
Web: www.horizonbay.com

CEO: Thilo D. Best
CFO: Jon A. DeLuca
HR: Don Rath
FYE: December 31
Type: Private

Horizon Bay invests in and manages senior housing communities. Operating as Horizon Bay Senior Communities, the company manages independent- and assisted-living residential facilities, primarily targeting the higher-end market. It operates more than 40 senior housing communities, which are located in 12 states across the US. The company's *LiveWell!* program, which promotes health and well-being among residences, offers educational classes and activities. Horizon Bay was founded in 2001.

	Annual Growth	12/03	12/04	12/05	12/06	12/07
Est. sales ($ mil.)	—	—	—	—	—	277.8
Employees	—	—	—	—	—	3,500

HORIZON FINANCIAL CORP.

NASDAQ (GS): HRZB

1500 Cornwall Ave.
Bellingham, WA 98225
Phone: 360-733-3050
Fax: 360-733-7019
Web: www.horizonbank.com

CEO: Richard P. (Rich) Jacobson
CFO: –
HR: Christine Anderson
FYE: March 31
Type: Public

Horizon Financial is the holding company for Horizon Bank, which serves Skagit, Snohomish, Pierce, and Whatcom counties along Puget Sound in northwestern Washington. Founded in 1922, the bank offers traditional products and services through more than 25 branches and loan centers. Funds from deposits, such as CDs and checking, savings, and money market accounts, are primarily used to originate loans secured by real estate. Commercial mortgages make up about 25% of the bank's loan portfolio; construction and land development loans are around 40%. Horizon Bank also issues home equity, business, commercial construction, and consumer loans.

	Annual Growth	3/04	3/05	3/06	3/07	3/08
Assets ($ mil.)	12.8%	858.9	997.6	1,116.7	1,270.3	1,392.2
Net income ($ mil.)	9.3%	12.9	13.1	15.7	19.0	18.4
Market value ($ mil.)	1.7%	153.4	150.8	202.4	270.6	164.2
Employees	4.3%	—	—	276	288	

HORIZON FOOD GROUP, INC.

3 Embarcadero Ctr., Ste. 2360
San Francisco, CA 94111
Phone: 415-394-9700
Fax: –
Web: www.horizonfoodgroup.com

CEO: Phillip S. Estes
CFO: Lee Rucker
HR: –
FYE: December 31
Type: Subsidiary

If you scan this Horizon, you'll find snacks and baked goods. Horizon Food Group makes muffins, snack foods, and gourmet baked goods through three subsidiaries. Its Ne-Mo's Bakery unit makes cake squares, Danishes, and muffins that sold primarily through convenience stores, quick service restaurants, and vending machines. The company's Horizon Snack Foods subsidiary, meanwhile, is known for its Cutie Pie and Home Run Pie brand fruit pies. It also manufactures and distributes private label snacks for other customers. Horizon's La Tempesta Bakery unit makes fine cookies and candy, as well as Italian-style biscotti. The company is owned by private investment firm Horizon Holdings.

	Annual Growth	12/03	12/04	12/05	12/06	12/07
Est. sales ($ mil.)	—	—	—	—	—	51.9
Employees	—	—	—	—	—	350

HORIZON GROUP PROPERTIES, INC.

Pink Sheets: HGPI

1 O'Hare Center, 6250 N. River Rd., Ste. 10400
Rosemont, IL 60018
Phone: 847-292-1870
Fax: 847-292-1879
Web: www.horizongroup.com

CEO: Gary J. Skoien
CFO: David R. Tinkham
HR: –
FYE: December 31
Type: Public

Horizon Group Properties owns, develops, renovates, and operates shopping properties. It owns about a dozen factory outlet centers totaling almost 2 million sq. ft. of retail space. About half of the company's properties are located in Michigan and Texas; the rest are scattered among California, Minnesota, Missouri, Nebraska, and Nevada. They are occupied by tenants such as clothiers Polo Ralph Lauren, Tommy Hilfiger, and The Gap. Horizon Group Properties is also developing a master-planned community in suburban Chicago. The company is the product of a spinoff of properties left over from the 1998 merger of Prime Retail and Horizon Group.

	Annual Growth	12/03	12/04	12/05	12/06	12/07
Est. sales ($ mil.)	—	—	—	—	—	14.4
Employees	—	—	—	—	—	129

HORIZON HEALTH CORPORATION

2941 S. Lake Vista Dr.
Lewisville, TX 75067
Phone: 972-420-8200
Fax: 972-420-8252
Web: www.horz.com

CEO: Joey A. Jacobs
CFO: Jack E. Polson
HR: –
FYE: August 31
Type: Subsidiary

Horizon Health sees hope on the horizon for those in need of psychiatric care and physical rehabilitation. Operating as Horizon Health Behavioral Health Services, the firm provides contract psychiatric and rehabilitation management services to hospitals across the country, running its clients' inpatient and outpatient mental health programs and rehab departments. Horizon Health's EAP Services unit runs employee assistance programs for large employers, offering telephone counseling, doctor referrals, and other behavioral health services to employees. Horizon Health was acquired by psychiatric hospital operator Psychiatric Solutions in 2007.

	Annual Growth	8/02	8/03	8/04	8/05	8/06
Sales ($ mil.)	17.6%	143.7	166.3	180.3	207.4	275.0
Net income ($ mil.)	8.0%	8.9	9.6	10.8	5.2	12.1
Employees	14.3%	1,876	1,371	1,964	2,804	—

HORIZON HEALTHCARE SERVICES, INC.

3 Penn Plaza East
Newark, NJ 07101
Phone: 973-466-4000
Fax: 973-466-4317
Web: www.horizon-bcbsnj.com

CEO: William J. Marino
CFO: Robert J. Pures
HR: Margaret Coons
FYE: December 31
Type: Not-for-profit

Horizon Healthcare Services (dba Horizon Blue Cross Blue Shield of New Jersey) is New Jersey's top health insurance provider, serving more than 3 million members. The not-for-profit company offers traditional indemnity and managed care plans, including HMO, PPO, POS, and Medicare Advantage plans. It also provides dental and behavioral health coverage and, through subsidiary Horizon Casualty Services, manages workers' compensation claims. The company's Horizon Healthcare Insurance Agency sells life, long-term disability, and long-term care coverage. Its Horizon NJ Health subsidiary participates in the state of New Jersey's Medicaid program.

	Annual Growth	12/02	12/03	12/04	12/05	12/06
Sales ($ mil.)	13.2%	4,097.5	5,082.4	5,504.2	6,025.3	6,730.3
Net income ($ mil.)	12.1%	114.1	171.1	172.8	213.8	180.1
Employees	0.5%	4,600	4,600	4,400	4,400	4,700

HORIZON LINES, INC.

NYSE: HRZ

4064 Colony Rd., Ste. 200
Charlotte, NC 28211
Phone: 704-973-7000
Fax: 704-973-7075
Web: www.horizonlines.com

CEO: Charles G. (Chuck) Raymond
CFO: Michael T. (Mike) Avara
HR: Mark R. Blankenship
FYE: Sunday before last Friday in December
Type: Public

Horizon Lines rides the waves to connect the mainland US with its far-flung states and territories. The container shipping company transports cargo such as building materials, consumer goods, and food to and from the continental US and Alaska, Hawaii, Guam, and Puerto Rico. It maintains a fleet of more than 20 containerships, plus about 22,000 cargo containers. More than 85% of Horizon Lines' revenue comes from operations subject to the Jones Act, which restricts marine shipping between US ports to US-owned companies operating US-built vessels. Horizon Lines traces its roots back to 1956, when it was initially established as Sea-Land Service.

	Annual Growth	12/03	12/04	12/05	12/06	12/07
Sales ($ mil.)	8.0%	886.0	980.3	1,096.2	1,156.9	1,206.5
Net income ($ mil.)	17.6%	15.1	13.6	(18.3)	72.4	28.9
Market value ($ mil.)	19.6%	—	—	418.6	927.1	598.9
Employees	5.5%	—	1,843	1,881	1,878	2,162

HORIZON MEDIA, INC.

630 3rd Ave.
New York, NY 10017
Phone: 212-916-8600
Fax: 212-916-1180
Web: www.horizonmedia.com

CEO: Bill Koenigsberg
CFO: Stewart Linder
HR: Eileen Benwitt
FYE: December 31
Type: Private

Anxious to boost your media's magnitude? Horizon Media, one of the larger independent media buying shops, plans, coordinates, and negotiates deals across the media spectrum (television, newspapers, billboards, Internet). The television market (network, spot, and cable) accounts for more than half the agency's billings. The company's Eurizon subsidiary provides media services to European clients through offices in Amsterdam, and its Columbus Media International partnership extends its reach to the Asia Pacific. Horizon Media's client list has included heavy hitters such as NBC, Harrah's Entertainment Group, Panasonic, and Telemundo. President and founder Bill Koenigsberg established the company in 1989.

	Annual Growth	12/03	12/04	12/05	12/06	12/07
Est. sales ($ mil.)	—	—	—	—	—	21.2
Employees	—	—	—	—	—	283

⊞ HORMEL FOODS CORPORATION

NYSE: HRL

1 Hormel Place
Austin, MN 55912
Phone: 507-437-5611
Fax: 507-437-5129
Web: www.hormel.com

CEO: Jeffrey M. Ettinger
CFO: Jody H. Feragen
HR: David P. Juhlke
FYE: Last Saturday in October
Type: Public

Now that Hormel Foods has stocked its pantry with ethnic convenience foods, can we look forward to SPAM enchiladas or SPAM curry? Along with its famous canned "spiced ham," SPAM, Hormel is a top US turkey processor and a major pork processor, making Jennie-O turkey products, Cure 81 hams, and Always Tender fresh pork, as well as canned Stagg chili and Dinty Moore beef stews. Hormel has branched into convenience, ethnic, and frozen foods such as Chi-Chi's Mexican, Patak's Indian, and House of Tsang Asian products. As more people eat out, sales of Hormel's foodservice products have increased as well.

	Annual Growth	10/03	10/04	10/05	10/06	10/07
Sales ($ mil.)	10.2%	4,200.3	4,779.9	5,414.0	5,745.5	6,193.0
Net income ($ mil.)	12.9%	185.8	231.7	253.5	286.1	301.9
Market value ($ mil.)	11.2%	3,268.1	3,875.7	4,346.2	4,951.1	4,991.6
Employees	2.5%	—	—	17,600	18,100	18,500

HORNBECK OFFSHORE SERVICES, INC.

NYSE: HOS

103 Northpark Blvd., Ste. 300
Covington, LA 70433
Phone: 985-727-2000
Fax: 985-727-2006
Web: www.hornbeckoffshore.com

CEO: Todd M. Hornbeck
CFO: James O. Harp Jr.
HR: –
FYE: December 31
Type: Public

At the beck and call of oil companies, Hornbeck Offshore Services provides marine transportation of oil field equipment and supplies and petroleum products. The company operates offshore supply vessels (OSVs) that support offshore oil and gas drilling and production in the deepwater regions of the Gulf of Mexico. The company's fleet of about 45 OSVs transports cargo such as pipe and drilling mud, as well as rig crew members. In addition, Hornbeck Offshore operates oceangoing tug and tank barge units that transport crude and refined petroleum products in the northeastern US and in Puerto Rico. Its fleet includes about 15 tugs and 20 barges.

	Annual Growth	12/03	12/04	12/05	12/06	12/07
Sales ($ mil.)	32.3%	110.8	132.3	182.6	274.5	339.0
Net income ($ mil.)	70.6%	11.2	(2.5)	37.4	75.7	94.8
Market value ($ mil.)	42.3%	—	401.9	844.0	912.5	1,157.9
Employees	10.1%	556	601	657	742	—

HORNE INTERNATIONAL, INC.

OTC: HNIN

2677 Prosperity Ave., Ste. 300
Fairfax, VA 22031
Phone: 703-641-1100
Fax: 703-641-0440
Web: www.horne.com

CEO: Darryl K. Horne
CFO: John E. Krobath
HR: –
FYE: December 31
Type: Public

You'd get straight to the *point* if you said Horne International (formerly Spectrum Sciences & Software) once specialized in defense and homeland security, environment and energy services, and transportation. The company has announced that its Spectrum Sciences and Software unit (SSSI — military aircraft and munitions support equipment) and Coast Engine and Equipment Company (CEECO — ship repair and metal fabrication services for the US Navy) will cease operations in 2008. That leaves Horne Engineering Services (base and homeland security, missile defense, ecosystems management and restoration, and aviation navigation) as Horne's primary operating unit.

	Annual Growth	12/03	12/04	12/05	12/06	12/07
Sales ($ mil.)	7.4%	13.3	11.1	53.7	28.3	17.7
Net income ($ mil.)	—	0.2	(40.3)	(4.0)	(8.6)	(19.1)
Market value ($ mil.)	(23.9%)	21.2	—	—	19.4	7.1
Employees						

HORRY TELEPHONE COOPERATIVE, INC.

3480 Hwy. 701 North
Conway, SC 29528
Phone: 843-365-2154
Fax: –
Web: www.htcinc.net

CEO: Curley P. Huggins
CFO: O'Neal Miller
HR: –
FYE: December 31
Type: Cooperative

Horry Telephone Cooperative (HTC) is the incumbent local exchange carrier (ILEC) serving rural Horry County in South Carolina and the largest phone co-op in the country. HTC offers local-exchange and long-distance voice service, Internet access, cable TV, and mobile phone service (through AT&T Mobility, formerly Cingular) and maintains more than 80,000 access lines. The company first brought phone services to the coastal area in 1954 with help from the Horry Electric Cooperative and the Rural Electrification Administration. In 1998 the company created subsidiary HTC Communications as a competitive local-exchange carrier (CLEC) offering communications services in Georgetown county.

	Annual Growth	12/03	12/04	12/05	12/06	12/07
Est. sales ($ mil.)	—	—	—	—	—	144.0
Employees	—	—	—	—	—	700

HORSEHEAD HOLDING CORP.

NASDAQ (GM): ZINC

300 Frankfort Rd.
Monaca, PA 15061
Phone: 724-774-1020
Fax: 724-774-4348
Web: www.horseheadcorp.com

CEO: James M. Hensler
CFO: Robert D. (Bob) Scherich
HR: Daryl K. Fox
FYE: December 31
Type: Public

Bearing out the adage that one person's trash is another's treasure, Horsehead turns zinc-containing dust into zinc and value-added zinc products. (Yes, "value-added zinc products.") Key raw materials for the company include dust from the electric-arc furnaces used at steel minimills and residue from the galvanizing of metals. Besides zinc metal (used in galvanizing and alloying), Horsehead's products include zinc oxide (used in the agricultural, chemical, and pharmaceutical industries) and zinc dust (used in corrosion-resistant coatings). The company operates from facilities in Illinois, Oklahoma, Pennsylvania, Tennessee, and Texas. Investment firm Sun Capital Partners owned Horsehead before its 2007 IPO.

	Annual Growth	12/03	12/04	12/05	12/06	12/07
Sales ($ mil.)	36.2%	—	216.0	273.8	496.4	545.6
Net income ($ mil.)	—	—	(2.0)	3.2	54.5	90.7
Market value ($ mil.)	—	—	—	—	—	590.1
Employees	—	—	—	—	—	—

HOSPIRA, INC.

NYSE: HSP

275 N. Field Dr.
Lake Forest, IL 60045
Phone: 224-212-2000
Fax: 224-212-3350
Web: www.hospira.com

CEO: Christopher B. Begley
CFO: Thomas E. Werner
HR: Henry Weishaar
FYE: December 31
Type: Public

Hospira helps hospitals help the hurting. The company, a spinoff of drug manufacturer Abbott Laboratories, makes specialty injectable pharmaceuticals (primarily generics) and drug delivery equipment. Its medication delivery systems include drug pumps, infusion therapy devices, and related medication management software. Its injectable drugs include cardiovascular, anesthesia, and anti-infective therapies. In addition, Hospira offers critical care monitoring systems, such as angiography kits and cardiac catheters, and it provides contract manufacturing services for injectable pharmaceuticals. About 50% of Hospira's sales are to group purchasing organizations (GPOs), including Broadlane, Novation, and Premier.

	Annual Growth	12/03	12/04	12/05	12/06	12/07
Sales ($ mil.)	9.4%	2,400.2	2,645.0	2,626.7	2,688.5	3,436.2
Net income ($ mil.)	(14.9%)	260.4	301.5	235.6	237.7	136.8
Market value ($ mil.)	8.8%	—	5,258.5	6,916.2	5,234.6	6,766.5
Employees	0.0%	14,000	—	14,000	13,000	14,000

HOSPITALITY PROPERTIES TRUST

NYSE: HPT

400 Centre St.
Newton, MA 02458
Phone: 617-964-8389
Fax: 617-969-5730
Web: www.hptreit.com

CEO: John G. Murray
CFO: Mark L. Kleifges
HR: –
FYE: December 31
Type: Public

Hospitality Properties Trust (HPT) rolls out the welcome mat for the road-weary. The real estate investment trust (REIT) owns some 300 hotels throughout the US and in Canada and Puerto Rico, as well as more than 180 full-service truck stops operating as TravelCenters of America and Petro Stopping Centers. Unlike other hospitality REITs, HPT invests in hotels but does control the operations of those properties. Rather, it leases them to operating companies (usually former owners). Its hotels target different markets, from upscale (Crowne Plaza Hotels & Resorts) to business and family (Residence Inn by Marriott). Also unlike some hospitality REITs, HPT is not affiliated with any one branded hotel company.

	Annual Growth	12/03	12/04	12/05	12/06	12/07
Sales ($ mil.)	23.5%	552.8	645.4	834.4	1,039.4	1,285.5
Net income ($ mil.)	8.6%	238.2	127.1	129.9	169.0	331.0
Market value ($ mil.)	5.3%	2,460.5	2,944.2	2,746.6	3,905.8	3,025.2
Employees	—	—	—	0	0	500

HOST HOTELS & RESORTS, INC.

NYSE: HST

6903 Rockledge Dr., Ste. 1500
Bethesda, MD 20817
Phone: 240-744-1000
Fax: 240-744-5125
Web: hosthotels.com

CEO: W. Edward (Ed) Walter
CFO: Larry K. Harvey
HR: Pamela K. Wagoner
FYE: Friday nearest December 31
Type: Public

Host Hotels & Resorts will leave the chandelier on for you. It is the largest real estate investment trust (REIT) in the US and owns some 120 luxury and upscale hotels in North America and Mexico. Most of its hotels operate under the Marriott and Ritz-Carlton brands and are managed by sister firm Marriott International. Other brands include Four Seasons and Hyatt. To maintain its REIT status, the company operates through majority-owned Host LP. All properties are leased to management firms. Host Hotels & Resorts holds interests in several partnerships, including its leasehold interest in 53 Courtyard by Marriott hotels and a 49% stake in Tiburon Golf Ventures, which operates a golf course in Florida.

	Annual Growth	12/03	12/04	12/05	12/06	12/07
Sales ($ mil.)	12.0%	3,448.0	3,640.0	3,881.0	4,888.0	5,426.0
Net income ($ mil.)	168.4%	14.0	—	166.0	738.0	727.0
Market value ($ mil.)	(30.4%)	—	—	—	12,793.0	8,905.1
Employees	8.9%	—	—	205	229	243

HOSTWAY CORPORATION

1 N. State St., Ste. 1200
Chicago, IL 60602
Phone: 312-236-2125
Fax: 312-236-1958
Web: www.hostway.com

CEO: Lucas Roh
CFO: Donald K. (Don) Eldert
HR: –
FYE: December 31
Type: Private

Thousands of businesses worldwide follow Hostway's path to the Internet. The Web hosting company offers managed site hosting on shared or dedicated servers, as well as colocation and domain name registration services. It also sells a Web-based e-mail service and a hosted Web site design application called SiteBuilder. Hostway's customers include Disney, Tribune Company, Coca-Cola, and Bank of Montreal. Founded in 1998, the company has offices in Asia, Australia, Europe, and North America and provides services to more than 600,000 customers. Hostway acquired rival Affinity Internet in 2007, adding some 200,000 customers to its roster.

	Annual Growth	12/03	12/04	12/05	12/06	12/07
Est. sales ($ mil.)	—	—	—	—	—	16.4
Employees	—	—	—	—	—	347

HOT STUFF FOODS

2930 W. Maple St.
Sioux Falls, SD 57107
Phone: 605-330-7531
Fax: 605-336-0141
Web: www.hotstufffoods.com

CEO: John Fontana
CFO: Steve Watkins
HR: Sheryl Fox
FYE: December 31
Type: Private

Hungry shoppers making a stop at the convenience store might think this company is the cat's meow. Hot Stuff Foods franchises self-serve food kiosks at more than 2,200 convenience stores and other high-traffic locations offering customers a variety of ready-to-eat meals. Its flagship Hot Stuff Food on the Go concept offers hot, personal-sized pizzas, sandwiches, and breakfast items, along with appetizers, sides, and dessert items. The company's other concepts include C-Street Bakery, Eddie Pepper's (Mexican food), and Smash Hit Subs. Founded as Orion Food Systems in 1984, the management-owned company is backed by Allied Capital.

	Annual Growth	12/03	12/04	12/05	12/06	12/07
Est. sales ($ mil.)	—	—	—	—	—	21.6
Employees	—	—	—	—	—	380

An in-depth profile of this company is available to Hoover's Online members at hoovers.com.

779

HOT TOPIC, INC.

NASDAQ (GS): HOTT

18305 E. San Jose Ave.
City of Industry, CA 91748
Phone: 626-839-4681
Fax: 626-839-4686
Web: www.hottopic.com

CEO: Elizabeth M. (Betsy) McLaughlin
CFO: James J. (Jim) McGinty
HR: Robin L. Elledge
FYE: Saturday nearest January 31
Type: Public

What's the Hot Topic? "Everything About the Music," according to this punk-ish, teen-oriented retailer. Hot Topic's 690 mall-based stores in the US and Puerto Rico sell rock-inspired clothing and accessories in settings resembling industrial clubs where teens party. The retailer also runs about 150 Torrid shops for plus-sized girls (as old as 29!). Teens can buy T-shirts from TV shows, such as *SpongeBob SquarePants,* and licensed concert apparel from current and classic rockers including AFI, Slipknot, Nirvana, and Metallica. Hot Topic also produces private-label Morbid-brand products (including Morbid Threads and Morbid Metals). Hot Topic was founded in 1989 with the MTV generation in mind.

	Annual Growth	1/04	1/05	1/06	1/07	1/08
Sales ($ mil.)	6.2%	572.0	656.5	725.1	751.6	728.1
Net income ($ mil.)	(24.0%)	48.0	39.7	22.4	13.6	16.0
Market value ($ mil.)	(36.3%)	1,466.2	843.7	623.8	472.8	241.2
Employees	(0.8%)	—	—	9,871	9,794	—

HOUCHENS INDUSTRIES INC.

700 Church St.
Bowling Green, KY 42102
Phone: 270-843-3252
Fax: 270-780-2877

CEO: James (Jimmie) Gipson
CFO: Gordon Minter
HR: Sharon Grooms
FYE: September 30
Type: Private

Houchens Industries is a supermarket of businesses as well as an operator of supermarkets. The diversified company runs about 175 grocery stores under the Houchens, Food Giant, IGA, Piggly Wiggly, and Mad Butcher banners. Its 220-plus Save-A-Lot discount grocery stores in 13 states offer limited selections and cover 15,000 sq. ft. or less. Houchens also owns about 40 Jr. Foods convenience stores and 23 Tobacco Shoppe discount cigarette outlets, mostly in Kentucky and Tennessee. It sold cigarette maker Commonwealth Brands in 2007. Other businesses include construction, financial services, real estate, and recycling. Founded as BG Wholesale in 1918 by Ervin Houchens, the firm is 100% owned by its employees.

	Annual Growth	9/02	9/03	9/04	9/05	9/06
Sales ($ mil.)	2.3%	1,727.0	1,913.0	2,005.0	2,360.0	1,890.0
Employees	15.7%	5,850	7,760	9,229	11,487	10,500

HOUGHTON INTERNATIONAL INC.

Madison and Van Buren Aves.
Valley Forge, PA 19482
Phone: 610-666-4000
Fax: 610-666-1376
Web: www.houghtonintl.com

CEO: William F. (Bill) MacDonald Jr.
CFO: David H. Hays
HR: Wesley D. (Wes) Warner
FYE: December 31
Type: Private

It wouldn't have been called the Rust Belt if they'd used Houghton International's products more often. Houghton manufactures oils and specialty chemicals for lubrication in most of the big Midwestern industries: metal-working, automotive, and steel as well as offshore deep-water oil drilling. Its products range from aluminum and steel rolling lubricants to rust preventatives to fire-resistant hydraulic fluids. Its FLUIDCARE system helps manufacturers reduce costs through chemical management and recycling. Houghton maintains sales and manufacturing facilities throughout the world. The company was founded in 1865. In 2007 AEA Investors reached an agreement to buy Houghton.

	Annual Growth	12/03	12/04	12/05	12/06	12/07
Est. sales ($ mil.)	—	—	—	—	—	467.1
Employees	—	—	—	—	—	1,600

HOUGHTON MIFFLIN COMPANY

222 Berkeley St.
Boston, MA 02116
Phone: 617-351-5000
Fax: 617-351-1105
Web: www.hmco.com

CEO: Anthony (Tony) Lucki
CFO: Michael Muldowney
HR: Ciara Smyth
FYE: December 31
Type: Private

Alice Cooper's 1972 album *School's Out* probably doesn't get much play around the offices of Houghton Mifflin. A top publisher of textbooks for the K-12 markets, the company also offers trade and reference books for adults and children, such as the *American Heritage Dictionary.* Divisions include McDougal Littell (textbooks), Riverside Publishing (educational testing), and Great Source (supplemental school materials). In 2007 it acquired several businesses from Harcourt, another K-12 publisher, creating subsidiary Houghton Mifflin Harcourt Publishing Company. Houghton Mifflin sold its College Division in 2008. Houghton Mifflin is owned by Irish holding company Houghton Mifflin Riverdeep Group PLC.

HOUGHTON MIFFLIN HARCOURT PUBLISHING COMPANY

6277 Sea Harbor Dr.
Orlando, FL 32887
Phone: 407-345-2000
Fax: 407-345-8388
Web: www.hmco.com

CEO: Anthony (Tony) Lucki
CFO: Michael Muldowney
HR: Ciara Smyth
FYE: December 31
Type: Subsidiary

Houghton Mifflin Harcourt Publishing Company would like to thank all the professional students out there. The firm is a top publisher of educational material, covering areas from pre-K through grade 12, as well as adult learners. It publishes textbooks and printed materials, and provides digital content on the Web and CD-ROM. The company additionally publishes fiction and nonfiction titles under its Harcourt Trade Publishers unit, and operates reference title publisher Greenwood Publishing Group. In 2007 educational publisher Houghton Mifflin purchased several Harcourt brands from Reed Elsevier to form Houghton Mifflin Harcourt.

	Annual Growth	12/02	12/03	12/04	12/05	12/06
Sales ($ mil.)	2.2%	1,592.7	1,596.6	1,671.9	1,550.1	1,740.8
Employees	(2.2%)	5,800	5,400	5,400	5,400	5,300

HOULIHAN, LOKEY, HOWARD & ZUKIN, INC.

1930 Century Park West
Los Angeles, CA 90067
Phone: 310-553-8871
Fax: 310-553-2173
Web: www.hlhz.com

CEO: Scott L. Beiser
CFO: Gary E. Meek
HR: –
FYE: December 31
Type: Subsidiary

Investment banker Houlihan, Lokey, Howard & Zukin has hot lips for mergers on the economic front. Operating as Houlihan Lokey, the firm provides advisory services for (primarily mid-market) companies involved in mergers and acquisitions and corporate restructurings, including the sale of distressed assets and other turnaround situations. Houlihan Lokey also raises private and public equity for mid-sized private and small-cap public companies. The company has ranked among the country's top 20 M&A advisors for more than a decade; in 2006 it ranked first among US investment banks for M&A deals under $1 billion. Early that year Japanese financial services company ORIX acquired control of the company.

HOULIHAN'S RESTAURANTS, INC.

8700 State Line Rd., Ste. 100
Leawood, KS 66206
Phone: 913-901-2500
Fax: 913-901-2666
Web: www.houlihans.com

CEO: Robert M. (Bob) Hartnett
CFO: Robert (Rob) Ellis
HR: Francis King
FYE: Last Monday in December
Type: Private

Casual dining has been on Houlihan's menu for more than 30 years. Houlihan's Restaurants operates and franchises more than 90 casual eateries in about 20 states and in Mexico, most of them operating under the Houlihan's Restaurant & Bar name. The restaurants offer a variety of main dishes, including burgers, pasta, and steaks, as well as several appetizers and salads. About 60 Houlihan's locations are franchised. In addition to its flagship chain, the company operates a small number of other dining concepts, including Bristol Seafood Grill and J. Gilbert's Wood-Fired Steaks. Restaurant firm Gilbert-Robinson opened the first Houlihan's restaurant in 1972. A management group owns 51% of the company.

HOUSE OF RAEFORD FARMS, INC.

520 E. Central Ave.
Raeford, NC 28376
Phone: 910-875-5161
Fax: 910-875-8300
Web: www.houseofraeford.com

CEO: Robert C. (Bob) Johnson
CFO: Mike McLeod
HR: –
FYE: May 31
Type: Private

At House of Raeford Farms, a turkey can become a meatloaf, a pot roast, or a ham; a chicken can be transformed into fajitas, lunch meat, or a breaded dog-on-a-stick. The vertically-integrated North Carolina poultry processor supplies fresh, frozen, and value-added chicken and turkey products to retail food, in-store deli, and foodservice operators. The company has expanded its line of whole, cut-up, ground, boneless and bone-in meat to include fully-cooked, ready-to-heat entrees, as well as appetizers, smoked and breaded poultry products, sausage, and other deli offerings.

HOUSE OF TAYLOR JEWELRY, INC.

NASDAQ (CM): HOTJ

9200 Sunset Blvd., Ste. 425
West Hollywood, CA 90069
Phone: 310-860-2660
Fax: 310-860-2661
Web: www.hotj.com

CEO: Lyle M. Rose
CFO: Robert (Bob) Rankin
HR: –
FYE: December 31
Type: Public

Dames wild about white diamonds know that a true lady need not only smell divine, but must also bedeck herself in jewels befitting Dame Elizabeth Taylor. House of Taylor Jewelry designs and markets the House of Taylor, Elizabeth (luxury), and Kathy Ireland (upscale) brands of jewelry, found at retailers across the US, as well as in Mexico and the Caribbean. Most of the company's products are manufactured by third-party contractors in China. Through her licensing company Interplanet Productions, Elizabeth Taylor owns about 35% of the company. Kathy Ireland owns about 15% through her licensing firm, called Sandbox Jewelry.

	Annual Growth	3/02	*12/03	12/04	12/05	†12/06
Sales ($ mil.)	—	0.0	8.4	6.4	5.6	31.8
Net income ($ mil.)	—	(2.3)	0.4	0.4	(3.5)	(8.4)
Market value ($ mil.)	(20.3%)	273.0	—	—	267.6	110.3
Employees	18.2%				11	13

*Fiscal year change †Most recent year available

HOUSEVALUES, INC.

NASDAQ (GS): SOLD

11332 NE 122nd Way
Kirkland, WA 98034
Phone: 425-952-5500
Fax: 425-952-5809
Web: www.housevalues.com

CEO: Ian Morris
CFO: Jacqueline L. (Jackie) Davidson
HR: Jill M. Maguire-Ward
FYE: December 31
Type: Public

HouseValues doesn't give your residence a lesson in ethics, but the company can assess your home's market value. The company offers a bevy of services to aid real estate agents, home buyers, and home sellers. Its HouseValues.com targets home sellers; the site assigns a suggested listing price to a house based on property information and connects local real estate agents with buyers and sellers. The company's JustListed.com site targets home buyers by e-mailing listings to them based on personalized requests. HouseValues also provides real estate agents with an online prospect management system called Market Leader.

	Annual Growth	12/03	12/04	12/05	12/06	12/07
Sales ($ mil.)	24.2%	25.1	47.7	86.7	98.2	59.8
Net income ($ mil.)	—	3.8	7.5	15.0	(3.1)	(12.4)
Market value ($ mil.)	(41.2%)	—	374.5	336.2	137.4	76.0
Employees	—	—	—	507	—	—

HOUSTON AMERICAN ENERGY CORP.

NASDAQ (CM): HUSA

801 Travis St., Ste. 2020
Houston, TX 77002
Phone: 713-222-6966
Fax: 713-222-6440
Web: www.houstonamericanenergy.com

CEO: John F. Terwilliger
CFO: James (Jay) Jacobs
HR: –
FYE: December 31
Type: Public

Houston-based, with North and South American properties, and energy focused, Houston American Energy explores for and produces oil and natural gas, primarily in the US Gulf Coast and Colombia. The company has proved reserves of 425.8 million cu. ft. of natural gas and 392,366 barrels of oil. Of its 6,500 gross acres of proved developed leasehold, some 98% is in Colombia. The bulk of the balance is in Louisiana and Texas, although the oil and gas independent also holds some acreage in Oklahoma. President and CEO John Terwilliger owns about 31% of the company; director Orrie Tawes, 12%.

	Annual Growth	12/03	12/04	12/05	12/06	12/07
Sales ($ mil.)	123.6%	0.2	1.2	2.9	3.2	5.0
Net income ($ mil.)	—	(0.3)	0.1	(0.5)	(0.5)	0.5
Market value ($ mil.)	56.8%	14.1	19.6	62.9	205.5	85.2
Employees	—	—	—	—	—	—

HOUSTON WIRE & CABLE COMPANY

NASDAQ (GM): HWCC

10201 North Loop East
Houston, TX 77029
Phone: 713-609-2100
Fax: 713-609-2101
Web: www.houwire.com

CEO: Charles A. Sorrentino
CFO: Nicol G. (Nic) Graham
HR: Carol M. Sims
FYE: December 31
Type: Public

Houston Wire & Cable may have a Texas name, but it can keep customers wired from Seattle to Tampa. The company distributes specialty wire and cable products such as cable terminators, fiber-optic cables, and bare copper and building wire, as well as voice, data, and premise wire. It also provides cable management services (a custom program designed for wire and cable requirements) and an asset-management program (for the development and management of inventory). Houston Wire & Cable operates 11 regional distribution centers and sells primarily to electrical distributors.

	Annual Growth	12/03	12/04	12/05	12/06	12/07
Sales ($ mil.)	24.6%	149.1	172.7	214.0	323.5	359.1
Net income ($ mil.)	250.5%	0.2	4.8	12.5	30.7	30.2
Market value ($ mil.)	(39.8%)	—	—	—	436.1	262.7
Employees	—	—	—	—	293	—

An in-depth profile of this company is available to Hoover's Online members at hoovers.com.

781

HOVNANIAN ENTERPRISES, INC.

NYSE: HOV

110 W. Front St.
Red Bank, NJ 07701
Phone: 732-747-7800
Fax: 732-747-6835
Web: www.khov.com

CEO: Ara K. Hovnanian
CFO: J. Larry Sorsby
HR: Robyn T. Mingle
FYE: October 31
Type: Public

Gimme shelter. Hovnanian Enterprises designs, builds, and markets single-family detached homes, condominiums, and townhomes for first-time, move-up, and luxury buyers as well as for empty-nesters and active adults. Hovnanian builds about 15,000 homes a year, with base prices ranging from $36,000 to $3 million and averaging about $338,000. The company operates in about 20 states, primarily operating along the East Coast and in the Midwest, California, and Texas. Its K. Hovnanian American Mortgage unit offers mortgage financing and title services. Members of the Hovnanian family control more than 90% of Hovnanian Enterprises.

	Annual Growth	10/03	10/04	10/05	10/06	10/07
Sales ($ mil.)	10.6%	3,201.9	4,160.4	5,348.4	6,148.2	4,798.9
Net income ($ mil.)	—	257.4	348.7	471.9	149.5	(627.1)
Market value ($ mil.)	(12.4%)	919.5	1,741.9	2,113.7	1,454.9	540.9
Employees	(15.8%)	—	—	6,084	6,239	4,318

HP HOOD LLC

6 Kimball Ln.
Lynnfield, MA 01940
Phone: 617-887-3000
Fax: 617-887-8484
Web: www.hphood.com

CEO: John A. Kaneb
CFO: Gary R. Kaneb
HR: Bruce W. Bacon
FYE: December 31
Type: Private

HP Hood is busily trying to cream its competition — with coffee cream, ice cream, sour cream, and whipping cream. The company, a leading US dairy, also produces fluid milk, cottage cheese, and juices. Its home turf is New England, where it is one of the few remaining dairies to offer home milk delivery. Hood's products are available at chain and independent food retailers, convenience, stores, and to foodservice purveyors. In addition to its own brands, the company makes private-label, licensed, and franchise dairy products. It specializes in extended-shelf-life products, which are distributed nationally under licensing agreements. Hood operates 23 manufacturing plants throughout the US.

	Annual Growth	12/02	12/03	12/04	12/05	12/06
Sales ($ mil.)	25.7%	1,000.0	2,200.0	2,300.0	2,300.0	2,500.0
Employees	33.5%	1,700	5,000	4,850	5,000	5,400

HRPT PROPERTIES TRUST

NYSE: HRP

400 Centre St.
Newton, MA 02458
Phone: 617-332-3990
Fax: 617-332-2261
Web: www.hrpreit.com

CEO: John A. Mannix
CFO: John C. Popeo
HR: –
FYE: December 31
Type: Public

This real estate investment trust (REIT) pared down its name and its focus. The former Health and Retirement Properties Trust abbreviated its name and portfolio when in 1999 it spun off Senior Housing Properties Trust. HRPT no longer focuses on assisted living facilities but rather on office and industrial real estate. Its more than 500-property portfolio (some 65 million sq. ft.) is dominated by offices but also includes some 150 industrial properties. They are located in nearly 40 states but are concentrated in the metro markets of Austin, Texas; Boston; Oahu, Hawaii; Philadelphia; Southern California; and Washington, DC. Major tenants include the US government, GlaxoSmithKline, and Flextronics International.

	Annual Growth	12/03	12/04	12/05	12/06	12/07
Sales ($ mil.)	13.8%	500.7	603.2	710.8	795.8	840.0
Net income ($ mil.)	2.1%	114.4	162.8	165.0	250.6	124.3
Market value ($ mil.)	4.9%	1,440.6	2,275.0	2,172.1	2,594.1	1,742.7
Employees	—	—	—	0	0	—

HSBC FINANCE CORPORATION

2700 Sanders Rd.
Prospect Heights, IL 60070
Phone: 847-564-5000
Fax: 847-205-7401
Web: www.hsbcusa.com/hsbc_finance

CEO: Niall S. K. Booker
CFO: Beverley A. Sibblies
HR: Jon N. Couture
FYE: December 31
Type: Subsidiary

HSBC Finance (formerly Household International) is the consumer lending arm of gigantic British bank HSBC Holdings. The company caters to middle-class clients in the US, the UK, Canada, and Ireland, with a focus on serving customers with less-than-stellar credit. Its offerings include home mortgages, automobile loans, and personal loans; the company's subprime mortgage lending business has about 1,000 offices in more than 45 states. HSBC Finance also issues Visa, MasterCard, American Express, and Discover credit cards, as well as private-label cards for third parties such as General Motors and the AFL-CIO. It also sells specialty insurance in the US and Canada.

	Annual Growth	12/03	12/04	12/05	12/06	12/07
Assets ($ mil.)	8.6%	119,153.9	130,190.0	156,669.0	179,459.0	165,504.0
Net income ($ mil.)	—	1,665.2	1,940.0	1,772.0	1,443.0	(4,906.0)
Employees	2.9%	33,000	31,500	35,000	36,000	—

HSBC NORTH AMERICA HOLDINGS INC.

26525 N. Riverwoods Blvd.
Mettawa, IL 60045
Phone: 224-554-2000
Fax: 224-552-4400
Web: www.hsbcnorthamerica.com

CEO: Brendan P. McDonagh
CFO: Iain J. Mackay
HR: Jon N. Couture
FYE: December 31
Type: Subsidiary

Atlas may hold the world on his shoulders, but this company holds most of the North American continent. HSBC North America Holdings, a subsidiary of giant British bank HSBC Holdings, was formed in 2004 to comprise all of HSBC's US and Canadian operations, including HSBC USA, HSBC Bank Canada, and HSBC Finance. HSBC North America's subsidiaries offer personal and commercial banking services, mortgage services, consumer finance, private banking, insurance, trust services, and corporate investment banking under the HSBC, HFC, and Beneficial brands to more than 60 million customers.

	Annual Growth	12/03	12/04	12/05	12/06	12/07
Est. sales ($ mil.)	—	—	—	—	—	2,147.5
Employees	—	—	—	—	—	53,000

HSBC USA INC.

452 5th Ave.
New York, NY 10018
Phone: 212-525-5000
Fax: –
Web: www.us.hsbc.com

CEO: Paul J. Lawrence
CFO: Gerard Mattia
HR: Jeanne G. Ebersole
FYE: December 31
Type: Subsidiary

HSBC USA, a subsidiary of British banking behemoth HSBC Holdings, operates HSBC Bank USA. With some 400 offices, the bank has one of the largest branch networks in New York State, plus more than 50 additional locations in about a dozen other states and Washington, DC. It offers personal, commercial, and mortgage banking services, with a loan portfolio dominated by residential mortgages, commercial loans, and credit card loans. HSBC Bank USA's personal financial services segment also provides mutual funds, investments, and insurance. The company performs investment banking and private banking services as well.

	Annual Growth	12/03	12/04	12/05	12/06	12/07
Assets ($ mil.)	18.5%	95,561.7	141,050.0	153,859.0	168,957.0	188,373.0
Net income ($ mil.)	(38.1%)	940.7	1,258.0	976.0	1,036.0	138.0
Employees	(3.6%)	13,400	10,800	12,000	12,000	—

HSW INTERNATIONAL, INC.

NASDAQ (GM): HSWI

One Capital City Plaza, 3350 Peachtree Rd., Ste. 1150
Atlanta, GA 30326
Phone: 404-760-4729
Fax: –
Web: www.hswinternational.com

CEO: Gregory Swayne
CFO: J. David Darnell
HR: –
FYE: December 31
Type: Public

HSW International knows how stuff works, and it wants to tell the world. The online publishing firm offers translated versions of the US-based site HowStuffWorks.com to viewers in China and Brazil, two emerging markets for digital technology. The site provides information, buying guides, and informational videos on science, health, travel, consumer products, and other topics. HSW International also owns career development training and educational software businesses in China through its 2007 merger with computer software maker INTAC International. HSW International is 43% owned by HowStuffWorks. Formerly owned by The Convex Group, HowStuffWorks was acquired by Discovery Communications in 2007.

	Annual Growth	12/03	12/04	12/05	12/06	12/07
Sales ($ mil.)	—	—	—	—	—	0.3
Net income ($ mil.)	—	—	—	—	—	(39.5)
Market value ($ mil.)	—	—	—	—	—	288.5
Employees	—	—	—	—	—	—

H.T. HACKNEY COMPANY

502 S. Gay St.
Knoxville, TN 37902
Phone: 865-546-1291
Fax: 865-546-1501
Web: www.hthackney.com

CEO: William B. (Bill) Sansom
CFO: Mike Morton
HR: –
FYE: March 31
Type: Private

The H.T. Hackney Company began delivering goods to small grocers by horse and buggy in 1891; it now supplies more than 20,000 independent grocers and convenience stores in about 20 states east of the Mississippi. H.T. Hackney distributes more than 25,000 items, including frozen food, tobacco products, health and beauty items, and deli products. In addition, it owns bottled water producer Natural Springs Water Group, and the company is involved in furniture manufacturing through subsidiaries Holland House and Volunteer Fabricators. H.T. Hackney is owned by chairman and CEO Bill Sansom.

	Annual Growth	12/01	*3/03	3/04	3/05	3/06
Sales ($ mil.)	9.5%	2,500.0	3,300.0	3,500.0	3,550.0	3,600.0
Employees	2.7%	3,100	3,500	3,600	3,600	3,450

*Fiscal year change

⊞ HUB GROUP, INC.

NASDAQ (GS): HUBG

3050 Highland Pkwy., Ste. 100
Downers Grove, IL 60515
Phone: 630-271-3600
Fax: 630-964-6475
Web: www.hubgroup.com

CEO: David P. Yeager
CFO: Terri A. Pizzuto
HR: Brigitte Slaker
FYE: December 31
Type: Public

Hub Group helps its clients by handling the hubbub of freight movement throughout North America. An intermodal marketing company, Hub Group specializes in arranging the transportation of freight by a combination of rail and truck. A customer's freight is loaded into a container or trailer and transported by rail from one Hub Group operating center to another, then taken to its destination by a local trucking company, which in some cases is operated by a Hub Group unit. The company also provides truck brokerage and logistics services. It operates from about 20 main offices, each located near one or more railheads. The family of founder Phillip Yeager owns a controlling stake in Hub Group.

	Annual Growth	12/03	12/04	12/05	12/06	12/07
Sales ($ mil.)	5.1%	1,359.6	1,426.8	1,531.5	1,609.5	1,658.2
Net income ($ mil.)	63.3%	8.4	17.3	33.0	48.7	59.8
Market value ($ mil.)	122.5%	39.8	125.8	347.3	1,072.9	974.6
Employees	4.2%	1,197	1,172	1,184	1,513	1,412

HUB INTERNATIONAL LIMITED

55 E. Jackson Blvd.
Chicago, IL 60604
Phone: 877-402-6601
Fax: 877-402-6606
Web: www.hubinternational.com

CEO: Martin P. Hughes
CFO: Daniel (Dani) Goldsmith
HR: W. Kirk James
FYE: December 31
Type: Private

Shouldn't it be Hub North American? Hub International is an insurance broker that provides property/casualty, life and health, employee benefits, and investment products in the US and Canada. Focusing on midsized commercial clients, Hub operates primarily in the northeastern, northwestern, and midwestern US and in the Canadian provinces of British Columbia, Ontario, and Quebec. It operates under an organizational structure comprised of a head office and regional brokerages called "hub" brokerages. The company was acquired by private equity firm Apax Partners, along with Morgan Stanley Principal Investments, in 2007.

	Annual Growth	12/02	12/03	12/04	12/05	12/06
Sales ($ mil.)	25.4%	220.0	286.4	360.9	442.6	543.9
Net income ($ mil.)	17.8%	26.4	36.4	26.2	25.7	50.9
Employees	13.6%	2,294	2,500	3,170	3,200	3,820

HUBBARD BROADCASTING, INC.

3415 University Ave.
St. Paul, MN 55114
Phone: 651-646-5555
Fax: 651-642-4103

CEO: Stanley S. Hubbard
CFO: Gerald D. Deeney
HR: Suzanne Cook
FYE: December 31
Type: Private

This company's cupboard of media assets is hardly bare. Hubbard Broadcasting is a leading operator of television stations in Minnesota, New York, and New Mexico. Its portfolio of a dozen TV stations includes ABC affiliate KSTP (Minneapolis/St. Paul) and NBC affiliates KOB and WHEC (Albuquerque, New Mexico, and Rochester, New York, respectively). Its Hubbard Media Group operates entertainment network ReelzChannel and has a majority stake in the arts and leisure channel Ovation. Stanley E. Hubbard started the family-owned broadcasting empire with a single Minneapolis radio station in 1923.

HUBBELL INCORPORATED

NYSE: HUB-B

584 Derby Milford Rd.
Orange, CT 06477
Phone: 203-799-4100
Fax: 203-799-4205
Web: www.hubbell.com

CEO: Timothy H. (Tim) Powers
CFO: David G. Nord
HR: Stephen M. Mais
FYE: December 31
Type: Public

The Hubble telescope and Hubbell Incorporated both feature lots of modern electrical equipment — but you don't have to go into space to check out Hubbell's wares. The company's three operating segments — electrical, power, and industrial technology — make electrical and electronic products for commercial, industrial, telecom, and utility applications. Hubbell's products include lighting fixtures, outlet boxes, enclosures and fittings, wire and cable, insulators and surge arresters, and test and measurement equipment. As trustees for Hubbell family interests, general counsel Richard Davies and directors Andrew McNally and Jackson Ratcliffe together control nearly half of Hubbell.

	Annual Growth	12/03	12/04	12/05	12/06	12/07
Sales ($ mil.)	9.4%	1,770.7	1,993.0	2,104.9	2,414.3	2,533.9
Net income ($ mil.)	16.0%	115.1	154.7	165.1	158.1	208.3
Market value ($ mil.)	0.5%	399.2	452.2	377.2	363.9	406.6
Employees	0.9%	—	—	11,300	12,000	11,500

An in-depth profile of this company is available to Hoover's Online members at hoovers.com.

783

HUDDLE HOUSE, INC.

5901-B Peachtree Dunwoody Rd. Northeast
Atlanta, GA 30328
Phone: 707-325-1300
Fax: –
Web: www.huddlehouse.com

CEO: Philip M. (Phil) Greifeld
CFO: Tom Cossuto
HR: Claudia Koeppel Levitas
FYE: April 30
Type: Private

Bacon and eggs, hash browns, and toast, on three. Break! Huddle House operates and franchises more than 400 family-style restaurants that are popular spots for breakfast and coffee in more than 15 southern and Midwestern states. In addition to their morning menu, the classic coffee shops serve standard American fare (burgers, fried chicken, and steak) for lunch and dinner. The restaurants are mostly run by franchisees and are typically open 24 hours a day. John Sparks opened the first Huddle House in 1964. The company is owned by private equity firm Allied Capital.

	Annual Growth	4/03	4/04	4/05	4/06	4/07
Est. sales ($ mil.)	—	—	—	—	—	196.7
Employees	—	—	—	—	—	550

HUDSON CITY BANCORP, INC.

NASDAQ (GS): HCBK

W. 80 Century Rd.
Paramus, NJ 07652
Phone: 201-967-1900
Fax: 201-967-0332
Web: www.hcsbonline.com

CEO: Ronald E. Hermance Jr.
CFO: James C. Kranz
HR: J. Christopher Nettleton
FYE: December 31
Type: Public

Hudson City Bancorp is the holding company for Hudson City Savings Bank. Founded in 1868, the bank has about 120 branches in the New York City metropolitan area, including northern New Jersey, Long Island, and Fairfield County, Connecticut. It also has locations in coastal portions of New Jersey and that state's Philadelphia suburbs. The bank offers checking and savings accounts, money market and NOW accounts, CDs, and IRAs. First mortgages on one- to four-family residences account for more than 98% of the bank's loan portfolio; the balance consists of home equity loans, second mortgages, and other consumer and real estate loans. Bank subsidiary HC Value Broker Services sells life insurance and annuities.

	Annual Growth	12/03	12/04	12/05	12/06	12/07
Assets ($ mil.)	27.1%	17,033.4	20,146.0	28,075.3	35,506.6	44,424.0
Net income ($ mil.)	9.3%	207.4	239.3	276.1	288.6	295.9
Market value ($ mil.)	34.0%	2,416.0	2,284.6	7,137.5	7,742.1	7,788.9
Employees	8.8%	—	—	1,150	1,319	1,362

HUDSON HIGHLAND GROUP, INC.

NASDAQ (GM): HHGP

560 Lexington Ave.
New York, NY 10022
Phone: 212-351-7300
Fax: 917-256-8592
Web: www.hhgroup.com

CEO: Jon F. Chait
CFO: Mary Jane Raymond
HR: Robert W. Morgan
FYE: December 31
Type: Public

Hudson Highland Group offers specialty staffing and related consulting services through the three regional businesses of Hudson Global Resources, which target the Americas, the Asia/Pacific region, and Europe. Hudson Global Resources provides temporary and contract personnel as well as permanent recruitment services. Among the company's clients are small and large businesses, government agencies, and educational institutions. The company serves more than 10,000 clients across 100 offices in over 20 countries. All of Hudson Highland's revenue is generated from its three Hudson Global Resources staffing segments. A fourth business line, executive search service Highland Partners, was sold in late 2006.

	Annual Growth	12/03	12/04	12/05	12/06	12/07
Sales ($ mil.)	2.1%	1,085.3	1,256.3	1,428.3	1,373.5	1,179.1
Net income ($ mil.)	—	(328.8)	(26.8)	5.3	22.1	15.0
Market value ($ mil.)	20.7%	101.6	296.6	422.3	416.0	215.9
Employees	(2.7%)	—	—	3,800	3,600	3,600

HUDSON NEWS COMPANY

1305 Paterson Plank Rd.
North Bergen, NJ 07047
Phone: 201-867-3600
Fax: 201-867-0067
Web: www.hudsongroupusa.com

CEO: James Cohen
CFO: Catherine Oberg
HR: Rick Yockelson
FYE: December 31
Type: Private

Hudson News Company doesn't care if you're traveling to Pasadena, California, or Poughkeepsie, New York, as long as you stop over in one of its shops. The company operates more than 500 newsstands and specialty shops in airports and other transportation terminals across the US. Its shops offer books, magazines, apparel, souvenirs, snacks, and beverages. In addition to its airport locations, Hudson News partners with other major retailers (Crabtree & Evelyn, Godiva, Quiznos) in cross-selling ventures. It is also one of the largest distributors of books and magazines in the US. The company is owned by chairman Robert Cohen.

	Annual Growth	12/03	12/04	12/05	12/06	12/07
Est. sales ($ mil.)	—	—	—	—	—	282.3
Employees	—	—	—	—	—	2,000

HUDSON TECHNOLOGIES, INC.

NASDAQ (CM): HDSN

1 Blue Hill Plaza
Pearl River, NY 10965
Phone: 845-735-6000
Fax: 845-512-6070
Web: www.hudsontech.com

CEO: Kevin J. Zugibe
CFO: James R. Buscemi
HR: –
FYE: December 31
Type: Public

Hudson Technologies defends the ozone. Using proprietary reclamation technology to remove moisture and impurities from refrigeration systems, it recovers and reclaims chlorofluorocarbons (CFCs) used in commercial air-conditioning and refrigeration systems. The company sells both reclaimed and new refrigerants and also buys used refrigerants for reclamation and sale. In addition, Hudson Technologies offers services designed to improve the efficiency of customers' refrigeration systems. Customers include commercial and industrial enterprises and government entities, along with refrigerant contractors, distributors, and wholesalers and makers of refrigeration equipment.

	Annual Growth	12/03	12/04	12/05	12/06	12/07
Sales ($ mil.)	10.6%	18.0	14.6	19.2	23.5	26.9
Net income ($ mil.)	—	(2.4)	0.3	2.3	2.1	(2.0)
Market value ($ mil.)	15.6%	10.3	23.0	44.8	29.0	18.5
Employees	—	—	—	60	—	—

HUDSON VALLEY HOLDING CORP.

OTC: HUVL

21 Scarsdale Rd.
Yonkers, NY 10707
Phone: 914-961-6100
Fax: 914-961-7378
Web: www.hudsonvalleybank.com

CEO: James J. Landy
CFO: Stephen R. Brown
HR: –
FYE: December 31
Type: Public

Hudson Valley Holding is the parent company of Hudson Valley Bank and New York National Bank (dba NYNB Bank), which serve individuals, businesses, municipalities, and not-for-profit organizations from about 30 locations in New York City and surrounding areas. The banks focus on real estate lending, which accounts for more than two-thirds of the company's loan portfolio. Other products and services include savings, checking, and money market accounts; commercial and industrial loans; consumer loans; credit cards; CDs; and IRAs. Hudson Valley Bank provides investment management, trust, and fiduciary services, as well.

	Annual Growth	12/03	12/04	12/05	12/06	12/07
Assets ($ mil.)	8.7%	1,669.5	1,840.9	2,032.7	2,291.7	2,330.8
Net income ($ mil.)	9.3%	24.2	27.5	30.9	34.1	34.5
Market value ($ mil.)	12.2%	359.9	387.6	369.9	424.1	570.8
Employees	—	—	—	—	—	421

HUDSON'S GRILL INTERNATIONAL, INC.

Pink Sheets: HGII

16970 Dallas Pkwy., Ste. 402
Dallas, TX 75248
Phone: 972-931-9237
Fax: 972-931-1326
Web: www.hudsonsgrill.com

CEO: David L. Osborn
CFO: –
HR: –
FYE: December 31
Type: Public

Hudson's Grill International is the franchisor of Hudson's Grill, a 1950s-themed full-service restaurant chain. The diners serve mostly hamburgers and other sandwiches, along with appetizers, salads, and desserts. The company has about 10 franchised locations in Iowa, Michigan, Texas, and Wisconsin. Company president David Osborn owns more than 25% of Hudson's Grill.

	Annual Growth	12/03	12/04	12/05	12/06	12/07
Sales ($ mil.)	0.0%	0.3	0.3	0.4	0.5	0.3
Net income ($ mil.)	—	0.1	0.0	0.3	(0.1)	(0.3)
Employees	—	—	—	—	1	—

HUFFY CORPORATION

225 Byers Rd.
Miamisburg, OH 45342
Phone: 937-865-2800
Fax: 937-865-2887
Web: www.huffy.com

CEO: Michael Buenzow
CFO: –
HR: –
FYE: December 31
Type: Private

Huffy would like to peddle your kid's next bike. The company is best known for its all-purpose bikes, which are sold through national and regional chains. Its Huffy, Micro, and Royce Union bikes include kids' bikes and tricycles, comfort cruisers, mountain bikes, and BMX racing bikes (which are bought from makers in Asia). Most of the company's products are sold through mass marketers such as Wal-Mart and Kmart. The company also makes playground equipment and golf products under the Tommy Armour and Ram brand names.

	Annual Growth	12/03	12/04	12/05	12/06	12/07
Est. sales ($ mil.)	—	—	—	—	—	9.3
Employees	—	—	—	—	—	106

HUGHES COMMUNICATIONS, INC.

NASDAQ (GM): HUGH

11717 Exploration Ln.
Germantown, MD 20876
Phone: 301-428-5500
Fax: 301-428-1868
Web: www.hughes.com

CEO: Pradman P. Kaul
CFO: Grant A. Barber
HR: –
FYE: December 31
Type: Public

Hughes Communications keeps its principal assets even higher than visionary Howard Hughes could have imagined. Through its operating subsidiary, Hughes Network Systems, the company provides broadband satellite products and services. It uses its very small aperture terminal (VSAT) equipment and satellite network to provide consumers and businesses with broadband Internet access. The company's network also enables network applications ranging from voice services to credit authorization. In addition to its services, the company provides equipment used by fixed and mobile communication systems operators.

	Annual Growth	12/03	12/04	12/05	12/06	12/07
Sales ($ mil.)	3,922.2%	—	—	0.6	858.7	970.7
Net income ($ mil.)	(20.5%)	—	—	68.8	(39.1)	43.5
Market value ($ mil.)	18.3%	—	—	—	885.8	1,048.3
Employees	—	—	—	—	1,828	—

HUGOTON ROYALTY TRUST

NYSE: HGT

901 Main St., 17th Fl.
Dallas, TX 75283
Phone: 877-228-5083
Fax: 214-209-2431
Web: www.hugotontrust.com

CEO: Nancy G. Willis
CFO: Louis G. Baldwin
HR: –
FYE: December 31
Type: Public

Hugoton Royalty Trust was formed by Cross Timbers Oil Company (now XTO Energy) to pay royalties to shareholders based on the proceeds of sales from its oil and gas holdings. Payouts depend on oil and gas prices, the volume of gas and oil produced, and production and other costs. The trust receives 80% of the net proceeds from XTO Energy's properties, located in the Hugoton fields of Kansas, Oklahoma, and Texas; the Anadarko Basin of Oklahoma; and the Green River Basin of Wyoming. In 2007 the trust reported proved reserves of 3.6 million barrels of oil and 405.5 billion cu. ft. of natural gas. XTO Energy controls the trust, which is administered through Bank of America and has no officers.

	Annual Growth	12/03	12/04	12/05	12/06	12/07
Sales ($ mil.)	(3.3%)	80.7	81.9	105.2	91.4	70.6
Net income ($ mil.)	(3.6%)	80.4	81.6	104.8	90.9	69.4
Market value ($ mil.)	0.6%	875.2	1,048.0	1,516.4	984.0	897.2
Employees	—	—	—	0	—	0

HUISH DETERGENTS, INC.

3540 W. 1987 South
Salt Lake City, UT 84104
Phone: 801-975-3100
Fax: 801-975-3249
Web: www.huish.com

CEO: Paul Huish
CFO: –
HR: –
FYE: December 31
Type: Private

Huish Detergents tries its darndest to wash an unwanted hue of just about any color right out of your favorite shirt. The company manufactures laundry detergents and household cleaning products, such as floor and glass cleaners, oxygenated stain removers, prewash formulas, antibacterial soaps, bleach, and fabric softeners. Huish, which produces enough products to be second to behemoth Procter & Gamble, makes most of its own products under the Sun label. It's also one of the largest US contract manufacturers of laundry detergents and fabric softeners. Huish operates manufacturing plants in Kentucky, Tennessee, Texas, and Utah. In April 2007 Vestar Capital Partners bought Huish.

	Annual Growth	12/03	12/04	12/05	12/06	12/07
Est. sales ($ mil.)	—	—	—	—	—	167.1
Employees	—	—	—	—	—	1,300

HUMAN GENOME SCIENCES, INC.

NASDAQ (GM): HGSI

14200 Shady Grove Rd.
Rockville, MD 20850
Phone: 301-309-8504
Fax: 301-309-8512
Web: www.hgsi.com

CEO: H. Thomas (Tom) Watkins
CFO: Timothy C. Barabe
HR: Susan Bateson McKay
FYE: December 31
Type: Public

Human Genome Sciences (HGS) knows that the fault lies within ourselves, not in the stars. Using its expertise in human genetics, the firm is working on therapies for infectious and autoimmune diseases and cancer. One of its lead candidates is Albuferon, a long-acting version of protein therapy interferon alpha, that it is developing with Novartis to treat hepatitis C. Monoclonal antibody LymphoStat-B is also in later stages of clinical testing; GlaxoSmithKline is HGS' partner on the drug. With funding from the US government, HGS is developing an antibody that fights anthrax infection, and it has several anticancer antibodies at earlier stages of development.

	Annual Growth	12/03	12/04	12/05	12/06	12/07
Sales ($ mil.)	50.3%	8.2	3.8	19.1	25.8	41.8
Net income ($ mil.)	—	(185.3)	(242.9)	(239.4)	(251.2)	(262.5)
Market value ($ mil.)	(4.8%)	1,715.0	1,568.9	1,121.8	1,664.7	1,408.7
Employees	(12.5%)	—	—	880	770	—

An in-depth profile of this company is available to Hoover's Online members at hoovers.com.

HUMAN PHEROMONE SCIENCES, INC.

OTC: EROX

84 W. Santa Clara St., Ste. 720
San Jose, CA 95113
Phone: 408-938-3030
Fax: 408-938-3025
Web: www.naturalattraction.com

CEO: William P. Horgan
CFO: Gregory S. Fredrick
HR: –
FYE: December 31
Type: Public

Human Pheromone Sciences (HPS) hopes its animal magnetism makes consumers hot under the collar and jonesing for its scents. HPS makes fragrances for men and women that contain a patented synthetic version of a pheromone produced by the human body to stimulate the senses. It also licenses its technology to partners in the personal care products industry. The company's products are sold through its Web site and through direct marketing under the Natural Attraction name. The company has granted non-exclusive rights to the Natural Attraction brand in US, Europe, and Japan. HPS also partners with consumer products companies to license its patented technology.

	Annual Growth	12/03	12/04	12/05	12/06	12/07
Sales ($ mil.)	21.3%	0.6	1.1	0.4	1.2	1.3
Net income ($ mil.)	—	0.7	(0.5)	(0.9)	(0.1)	0.0
Employees	(9.1%)	—	4	3	3	3

HUMAN RIGHTS WATCH

350 5th Ave., 34th Fl.
New York, NY 10118
Phone: 212-290-4700
Fax: 212-736-1300
Web: www.hrw.org

CEO: Kenneth Roth
CFO: Barbara Guglielmo
HR: Maria Pignataro Nielsen
FYE: March 31
Type: Not-for-profit

Human Rights Watch (HRW) is watching out for everyone. The organization's mission is to prevent discrimination, uphold political freedom, protect people during wartime, and bring offenders to justice. HRW researches human rights violations around the world and publishes its findings to help generate publicity about the atrocities it uncovers. It also meets with national and international governing officials to help steer policy change. Along with partner organizations, HRW won the 1997 Nobel Peace Prize for its International Campaign to Ban Landmines. HRW is an independent organization; all funds come from private contributors.

	Annual Growth	3/03	3/04	3/05	3/06	3/07
Est. sales ($ mil.)	—	—	—	—	—	39.8
Employees	—	—	—	—	—	115

HUMANA INC.

NYSE: HUM

500 W. Main St.
Louisville, KY 40202
Phone: 502-580-1000
Fax: 502-580-3677
Web: www.humana.com

CEO: Michael B. (Mike) McCallister
CFO: James H. (Jim) Bloem
HR: Bonita C. (Bonnie) Hathcock
FYE: December 31
Type: Public

Humana is counting on Medicare to make it a big-time player in the health insurance game. One of the country's largest health insurers, Humana provides Medicare Advantage health plans and prescription drug coverage to more than 4.5 million members in all 50 states and Puerto Rico. It also administers managed care plans for other government programs, including Medicaid plans in Florida and Puerto Rico and TRICARE (a program for military personnel) in 10 southern states. Additionally, Humana offers health plans and some specialty products (group life and disability insurance, for example) to commercial employers and individuals. All told, it covers more than 18 million members in the US.

	Annual Growth	12/03	12/04	12/05	12/06	12/07
Sales ($ mil.)	19.9%	12,226.3	13,104.3	14,418.1	21,416.5	25,290.0
Net income ($ mil.)	38.1%	228.9	280.0	308.5	487.4	833.7
Market value ($ mil.)	36.4%	3,699.2	4,758.3	8,867.5	9,216.5	12,804.1
Employees	15.6%	—	—	18,700	22,300	25,000

THE HUMANE SOCIETY OF THE UNITED STATES

2100 L St. NW
Washington, DC 20037
Phone: 202-452-1100
Fax: 202-778-6132
Web: www.hsus.org

CEO: Wayne Pacelle
CFO: G. Thomas Waite III
HR: Robert G. Roop
FYE: December 31
Type: Not-for-profit

The Humane Society of the United States (HSUS) is a watchdog for, well, watchdogs, along with all sorts of other domestic and wild animals. A leading animal protection organization, HSUS has more than 10 million human members and constituents. The organization supports the work of local humane societies and implements a variety of investigative, educational, advocacy, and legislative programs to promote animal welfare. Its campaigns have addressed issues such as animal fighting, factory farming, the fur trade, and hunting practices. Most of its revenue comes from contributions and grants. An affiliate, Humane Society International, operates in other countries. HSUS was founded in 1954.

	Annual Growth	12/03	12/04	12/05	12/06	12/07
Est. sales ($ mil.)	—	—	—	—	—	5.1
Employees	—	—	—	—	—	375

HUMATECH, INC.

Pink Sheets: HUMT

4710 E. Falcon Dr., Ste. 101
Mesa, AZ 85215
Phone: 480-813-8484
Fax: 480-813-8485
Web: humatech.com

CEO: David G. Williams
CFO: John D. (J. D.) Rottweiler
HR: –
FYE: April 30
Type: Public

Humatech turns organic matter into food for plants and animals. Humatech claims that its line of organic, humate-based fertilizers, feed additives, and plant nutrients are safer for the environment and channel nutrients to the plants more efficiently. The company markets its products to commercial growers, independent garden consumers, and animal feeders throughout the US; it also has a 20% stake in its UK distributor, Humatech, Ltd. Chairman and CEO David Williams and his family, though its ownership of Willow Capital, controls 27% of Humatech, and fellow officer and director J. D. Rottweiler owns 13%.

	Annual Growth	4/02	4/03	4/04	4/05	*4/06
Sales ($ mil.)	52.0%	0.3	0.2	0.3	0.7	1.6
Net income ($ mil.)	—	(2.1)	(2.2)	(1.9)	(1.0)	(0.7)
Employees	6.9%	—	9	6	11	11

*Most recent year available

HUNGARIAN TELEPHONE AND CABLE CORP.

AMEX: HTC

1201 Third Ave., Ste. 3400
Seattle, WA 98101
Phone: 206-654-0204
Fax: 206-652-2911
Web: www.htcc.hu

CEO: Martin Lea
CFO: Robert Bowker
HR: –
FYE: December 31
Type: Public

Hungarian Telephone and Cable (HTCC) has stretched across the Atlantic to provide fixed-line local phone service in three regions of Hungary. Created in 1992 on the heels of the privatization of Hungarian telecom monopoly Magyar Telekom, HTCC operates through its subsidiaries Invitel Távközlési Zrt., Invitel Technocom Kft. and Invitel Telecom Kft. In 2007 the company acquired telecom carrier PanTel (which provides voice and data services to businesses throughout Hungary and into other European countries) and purchased Invitel. Denmark's TDC owns about 65% of HTCC.

	Annual Growth	12/03	12/04	12/05	12/06	12/07
Sales ($ mil.)	59.4%	59.6	60.3	110.2	193.7	385.2
Net income ($ mil.)	—	12.5	16.2	2.9	21.1	(96.5)
Market value ($ mil.)	22.7%	120.6	182.6	199.0	193.5	273.7
Employees	23.9%	600	900	700	700	1,412

HUNT BUILDING COMPANY, LTD.

4401 N. Mesa
El Paso, TX 79902
Phone: 915-533-1122
Fax: 915-545-2631
Web: www.huntbuilding.com

CEO: Woody L. Hunt
CFO: William Kell
HR: Patricia (Tricia) Westbrook
FYE: December 31
Type: Private

When sailors, soldiers, and pilots come home to roost, some seek the refuge of Hunt Building Company's homes. The firm is a design/build and construction management company that oversees the building of multifamily housing primarily for members of the US military. It typically converts old military housing into modern homes. It has completed projects in roughly 40 states, and in Puerto Rico and Guantanamo Bay, Cuba. Projects include building units at Camp Pendleton in California and Fort Lee in Virginia. Hunt Building also develops private commercial and residential properties. The company was founded in 1947 and is wholly owned by chairman Woody Hunt and president Mike Hunt, descendants of founder Marion Hunt.

	Annual Growth	12/03	12/04	12/05	12/06	12/07
Est. sales ($ mil.)	—	—	—	—	—	40.3
Employees	—	—	—	—	—	416

HUNT CONSOLIDATED INC.

Fountain Place, 1445 Ross at Field, Ste. 1400
Dallas, TX 75202
Phone: 214-978-8000
Fax: 214-978-8888
Web: www.huntoil.com

CEO: Ray L. Hunt
CFO: Donald (Don) Robillard
HR: Paul Hoffman
FYE: December 31
Type: Private

Hunt Consolidated is a holding company for the oil and real estate businesses of Ray Hunt, son of legendary Texas wildcatter and company founder H.L. Hunt. Founded in 1934 (reportedly with H.L.'s poker winnings), Hunt Oil is an oil and gas production and exploration company with primary interests in North and South America. Hoping to repeat huge discoveries in Yemen, Hunt is exploring in Canada, Ghana, Madagascar, and Oman. It has also teamed up with Repsol YPF and SK Corporation on an exploration project in Peru, and has expanded its Canadian operations through the acquisition of Chieftain International. Hunt Realty handles commercial and residential real estate investment management activities.

	Annual Growth	12/02	12/03	12/04	12/05	12/06
Est. sales ($ mil.)	(7.4%)	—	—	—	2,300.0	2,130.0
Employees	0.0%	—	—	—	3,000	3,000

THE HUNT CORPORATION

6720 N. Scottsdale Rd., Ste. 300
Scottsdale, AZ 85253
Phone: 480-368-4700
Fax: 480-368-4747
Web: www.thehuntcorp.com

CEO: Robert G. Hunt
CFO: Stephen E. (Steve) Atkins
HR: –
FYE: December 31
Type: Private

The Hunt Corporation doesn't have to prowl around for a good source of revenue. The company was created in 1974 as a holding company for primary subsidiary Hunt Construction Group, a high-ranking US construction contractor and the #1 builder of sports facilities in the country, according to *Engineering News-Record*. It regularly takes on stadium projects for professional and collegiate football and baseball teams, including the Arizona Cardinals and Washington Nationals. The firm provides general contracting, design/build, construction management, and environmental services. Other Hunt Corporation divisions include Hunt Paving, Hunt Sports, HuntCor, and Hunt International.

	Annual Growth	12/03	12/04	12/05	12/06	12/07
Est. sales ($ mil.)	—	—	—	—	—	1,663.2
Employees	—	—	—	—	—	600

HUNTER DOUGLAS INC.

2 Park Way & Rte. 17 South
Upper Saddle River, NJ 07458
Phone: 201-327-8200
Fax: 201-327-7938
Web: www.hunterdouglas.com

CEO: Marvin B. (Marv) Hopkins
CFO: Gordon Khan
HR: Betty Lou Smith
FYE: December 31
Type: Subsidiary

Don't move, Hunter Douglas has got you covered — well, at least it has your *windows* covered. Hunter Douglas, the North American subsidiary of Netherlands-based Hunter Douglas N.V., makes a variety of blinds, shades, and shutters. The company markets its window coverings under such names as Country Woods and Chalet Woods (wood blinds), Silhouette (shades), Palm Beach (custom shutters), Jubilance (Roman shades), Luminette (privacy sheers), Duette (honeycomb shades), and PowerRise (battery-operated window blinds). In addition to its own sales outlets, Hunter Douglas sells its products to retailers including Home Depot, Fortunoff, and J. C. Penney.

[H] HUNTINGTON BANCSHARES

NASDAQ (GS): HBAN

Huntington Center, 41 S. High St.
Columbus, OH 43287
Phone: 614-480-8300
Fax: 614-480-5284
Web: www.huntington.com

CEO: Thomas E. Hoaglin
CFO: Donald R. Kimble
HR: Melinda S. Ackerman
FYE: December 31
Type: Public

Huntington Bancshares Incorporated is the holding company for The Huntington National Bank, which operates more than 600 offices, mainly in Ohio and Michigan, but also in Indiana, Kentucky, Pennsylvania, and West Virginia. Huntington Bancshares operates in two other segments besides regional banking. Its Dealer Sales unit finances auto sales and leases through some 3,500 car dealerships throughout the Midwest and other states, while its Private Financial and Capital Markets Group provides asset management, private banking, and brokerage services to wealthy customers. Huntington Bancshares also offers trust and insurance services.

	Annual Growth	12/03	12/04	12/05	12/06	12/07
Assets ($ mil.)	15.7%	30,483.8	32,565.5	32,764.8	35,329.0	54,697.5
Net income ($ mil.)	(33.0%)	372.4	398.9	412.1	461.2	75.2
Market value ($ mil.)	1.2%	5,152.7	5,729.9	5,305.8	5,592.5	5,406.0
Employees	25.2%	—	—	7,602	8,081	11,925

HUNTINGTON LEARNING CENTERS, INC.

496 Kinderkamack Rd.
Oradell, NJ 07649
Phone: 201-261-8400
Fax: 201-261-3233
Web: www.huntingtonlearning.com

CEO: Raymond J. Huntington
CFO: Jim Emmerson
HR: –
FYE: December 31
Type: Private

No need to hunt for that A+. Huntington Learning Centers provides tutoring services to students from kindergarten through 12th grade (ages 5 to 17) to help them get better grades, raise their test scores, and improve their study skills. Each enrolled student is first given a series of diagnostic tests to discover his or her abilities, isolate problem areas, and develop an individualized instruction program based on the test results. The company franchises locations across the US; it has more than 400 learning centers in almost every state. Huntington Learning was founded in 1977 by Dr. Raymond and Eileen Huntington.

	Annual Growth	12/03	12/04	12/05	12/06	12/07
Est. sales ($ mil.)	—	—	—	—	—	33.9
Employees	—	—	—	—	—	1,000

[H] An in-depth profile of this company is available to Hoover's Online members at hoovers.com.

787

HUNTINGTON PREFERRED CAPITAL, INC.

NASDAQ (GM): HPCCP

41 S. High St.
Columbus, OH 43287
Phone: 614-480-8300
Fax: 614-480-5284
Web: www.investquest.com/iq/h/hpci

CEO: Donald R. Kimble
CFO: Thomas P. Reed
HR: –
FYE: December 31
Type: Public

Huntington Preferred Capital prefers investing in midwestern properties. The company is a real estate investment trust (REIT) that invests in residential and commercial real estate loans and mortgage-backed securities. Most of the firm's assets are secured by properties in the Midwest, primarily in Ohio and Michigan. (The REIT also holds some non-real estate related loans.) Huntington Preferred Capital generates income in the form of dividends from the acquisition and management of mortgage assets. Huntington Bancshares and its subsidiaries control Huntington Preferred Capital.

	Annual Growth	12/03	12/04	12/05	12/06	12/07
Sales ($ mil.)	4.6%	281.3	269.5	312.1	338.8	336.9
Net income ($ mil.)	0.6%	308.5	284.5	314.3	344.2	316.3
Market value ($ mil.)	(4.2%)	56.5	56.5	55.1	57.3	47.6
Employees	—	—	—	—	—	0

HUNTSMAN CORPORATION

NYSE: HUN

500 Huntsman Way
Salt Lake City, UT 84108
Phone: 801-584-5700
Fax: 801-584-5781
Web: www.huntsman.com

CEO: Peter R. Huntsman
CFO: J. Kimo Esplin
HR: R. Wade Rogers
FYE: December 31
Type: Public

Huntsman Corporation is no longer in the family way. The global chemical manufacturer supplies products through four segments. Its products include MDI, amines, surfactants, and epoxy-based polymers, as well as polyurethanes. Huntsman's chemicals are sold in more than 100 countries to a variety of customers in the adhesives, construction products, electronics, medical, and packaging industries. Private investment group Matlin Patterson and the founding Huntsman family still control a quarter stake in Huntsman, though, in 2007, US specialty chemicals company Hexion agreed to buy Huntsman for more than $10.5 billion.

	Annual Growth	12/03	12/04	12/05	12/06	12/07
Sales ($ mil.)	(5.6%)	—	11,485.8	12,961.6	10,623.6	9,650.8
Net income ($ mil.)	—	—	(227.7)	(34.6)	229.8	(172.1)
Employees	9.3%	—	—	10,800	15,000	12,900

HUNTSMAN INTERNATIONAL LLC

500 Huntsman Way
Salt Lake City, UT 84108
Phone: 801-584-5700
Fax: 801-584-5781
Web: www.huntsman.com

CEO: Peter R. Huntsman
CFO: J. Kimo Esplin
HR: R. Wade Rogers
FYE: December 31
Type: Subsidiary

Not that it can't keep a secret, but Huntsman International is no longer private about its business. Huntsman manufactures surfactants (used in cleaning and personal care products) and performance chemicals like polyurethanes, propylene oxides, and propylene glycol. It had been among the world's largest makers of basic chemicals and petrochemicals like ethylene and propylene until it began to sell off that business in 2006. Huntsman remains among the largest makers of titanium dioxide, the most commonly used white pigment, with 15% of the world market. Huntsman International operates the business of Huntsman Corporation, which in 2007 reached an agreement to be acquired by Hexion for about $10.5 billion.

HURCO COMPANIES, INC.

NASDAQ (GS): HURC

1 Technology Way
Indianapolis, IN 46268
Phone: 317-293-5309
Fax: 317-328-2811
Web: www.hurco.com

CEO: Michael Doar
CFO: John G. Oblazney
HR: Judy Summers
FYE: October 31
Type: Public

Hurco produces PC-based computer control systems and software and computerized machining tools designed to increase efficiencies in metal component production for the metalworking industry. Its products include computerized machine tools with integrated software and computer control systems that allow production floor operators to create programs for making new parts from a blueprint or electronic design in order to begin production quickly. Products include vertical machining and turning centers for metal-cutting and metal-forming applications. Europe is Hurco's largest market, generating about two-thirds of sales.

	Annual Growth	10/03	10/04	10/05	10/06	10/07
Sales ($ mil.)	25.6%	75.5	99.6	125.5	148.5	188.1
Net income ($ mil.)	154.3%	0.5	6.3	16.4	15.5	20.9
Market value ($ mil.)	124.7%	14.3	86.3	110.9	165.4	365.0
Employees	13.1%	232	250	284	320	380

HURON CONSULTING GROUP INC.

NASDAQ (GS): HURN

550 W. Van Buren St.
Chicago, IL 60607
Phone: 312-583-8700
Fax: 312-583-8701
Web: www.huronconsultinggroup.com

CEO: Gary E. Holdren
CFO: Gary L. Burge
HR: Mary M. Sawall
FYE: December 31
Type: Public

Huron Consulting Group aims to help keep companies sailing smoothly, but the firm also will dredge through financial statements to address issues that cause businesses to sink. The firm provides a variety of financial consulting services to corporate clients that are in financial distress or involved in other legal and regulatory disputes. Its consultants offer forensic accounting and economic analysis expertise and often serve as expert witnesses. The firm's operational consulting services are delivered primarily to health care and education enterprises and to law firms. Huron Consulting operates from a network of about 15 facilities, primarily in the US but also in the Asia/Pacific region and in Europe.

	Annual Growth	12/03	12/04	12/05	12/06	12/07
Sales ($ mil.)	49.3%	110.3	173.9	226.0	321.9	548.0
Net income ($ mil.)	—	(1.1)	10.9	17.8	26.7	41.9
Market value ($ mil.)	60.7%	—	363.3	413.8	819.4	1,506.9
Employees	37.8%	—	612	773	1,035	1,600

HUTCHINSON TECHNOLOGY INCORPORATED

NASDAQ (GS): HTCH

40 W. Highland Park
Hutchinson, MN 55350
Phone: 320-587-3797
Fax: 320-587-1404
Web: www.htch.com

CEO: Wayne M. Fortun
CFO: John A. Ingleman
HR: Rebecca A. (Becky) Albrecht
FYE: Last Sunday in September
Type: Public

Suspensions at Hutchinson Technology have nothing to do with getting kicked out of school. The company is a top global maker of disk drive suspension assemblies. These support the read-write head above the spinning magnetic disk in hard drives, typically at a height of about a millionth of an inch — 3,000 times thinner than a piece of paper. The company's products include conventional assemblies, trace suspension assemblies, and accessories such as base plates and flexures. Customers in Asia account for more than 95% of sales. Hutchinson supplies a select number of large disk drive makers; its top five customers (TDK, Alps Electric, Western Digital, Innovex, and Seagate) account for more than 85% of sales.

	Annual Growth	9/03	9/04	9/05	9/06	9/07
Sales ($ mil.)	9.5%	499.0	469.7	631.6	721.5	716.1
Net income ($ mil.)	(42.0%)	64.5	73.1	54.9	20.5	7.3
Market value ($ mil.)	(6.8%)	849.6	637.9	674.2	554.8	641.4
Employees	6.5%	3,656	3,911	5,458	5,433	4,698

An in-depth profile of this company is available to Hoover's Online members at hoovers.com.

HUTTIG BUILDING PRODUCTS, INC.

NYSE: HBP

555 Maryville University Dr., Ste. 240
St. Louis, MO 63141
Phone: 314-216-2600
Fax: 314-216-2601
Web: www.huttig.com

CEO: Jon P. Vrabely
CFO: David L. Fleisher
HR: David L. Fleisher
FYE: December 31
Type: Public

Hut one! Hut two! Huttig Building Products works to make buying building supplies a snap. The company is one of the US's largest distributors of millwork, building materials, and wood products. Huttig sells doors, windows, moldings, trusses, wall panels, lumber, and other supplies through about 435 centers throughout the US. The centers primarily sell to building materials dealers (84 Lumber, Stock Building Supply), buying groups, home centers, and industrial users. Products typically end up in the hands of professional builders and contractors. Doors (interior, exterior, patio) account for the majority of Huttig's sales. Mexico's CEMEX owns more than 25% of Huttig through the UK's Rugby Group.

	Annual Growth	12/03	12/04	12/05	12/06	12/07
Sales ($ mil.)	(1.0%)	909.3	938.4	1,097.2	1,102.7	874.8
Net income ($ mil.)	—	3.4	18.9	18.4	(7.7)	(8.2)
Market value ($ mil.)	5.8%	58.3	205.4	169.4	108.6	73.1
Employees	(11.5%)	—	—	2,146	1,900	—

HVM L.L.C.

100 Dunbar St.
Spartanburg, SC 29306
Phone: 864-573-1600
Fax: 864-573-1695
Web: www.extendedstayhotels.com

CEO: Gary A. DeLapp
CFO: Joseph Rogers
HR: Marshall L. Dildy
FYE: December 31
Type: Private

HVM's guests need not worry about wearing out their welcome. The company, which operates as Extended Stay Hotels, owns and operates more than 680 extended-stay properties throughout the US. Its lodgings offer all-suite accommodations targeting both business and leisure travelers looking for a temporary place to call home. Some properties feature exercise centers, swimming pools, and wireless Internet access. HVM's various hotel brands include Extended Stay America Efficiency Studios, Homestead Studio Suites, StudioPLUS Deluxe Studios, and Crossland Economy Studios. The firm was formed in 2004 by The Blackstone Group after its acquisitions of Extended Stay America and Homestead Village.

	Annual Growth	12/03	12/04	12/05	12/06	12/07
Est. sales ($ mil.)	—	—	—	—	—	101.0
Employees	—	—	—	—	—	3,000

HYDRO ALUMINUM NORTH AMERICA

801 International Dr., Ste. 200
Linthicum, MD 21090
Phone: 410-487-4500
Fax: 410-487-8053
Web: www4.hydro.com/northamerica/en

CEO: Fernando Simões Henriques
CFO: Frankie Winfield
HR: Sally Hobbs
FYE: December 31
Type: Business segment

Hydro Aluminum North America conducts its parent company's aluminum production throughout North America. The company divides its business into two units: Aluminum Products and Aluminum Metal. The former handles the company's extrusion operations, while the Aluminum Metal division produces aluminum billet. Its primary operations include aluminum extruded products, precision tubing, and products for the automotive industry. Norwegian metals giant Norsk Hydro is among the world's top 5 aluminum producers, and North America makes up a significant part of that business. The US is Norsk Hydro's largest market outside Europe.

HYDROMER, INC.

OTC: HYDI

35 Industrial Pkwy.
Branchburg, NJ 08876
Phone: 908-722-5000
Fax: 908-526-3633
Web: www.hydromer.com

CEO: Manfred F. Dyck
CFO: Robert Y. Lee
HR: John Konar
FYE: June 30
Type: Public

Hydromer likes to say its products become lubricious when wet. Bon Jovi preferred the term *slippery*, but it amounts to the same thing. The polymer research and development company makes lubricating and water-resistant coatings for use in medical, pharmaceutical, cosmetic, industrial, and veterinary markets. Its products include lubricated medical devices, hydro-gels for drugs, anti-fog coatings, marine hull protective coatings, barrier dips for dairy cows, and intermediaries for hair and skin care products. Hydromer's services include research and development, medical device manufacturing (through subsidiary Biosearch Medical Products), and contract coating. Chairman Manfred Dyck owns 35% of the company.

	Annual Growth	6/03	6/04	6/05	6/06	6/07
Sales ($ mil.)	6.1%	6.4	8.7	8.5	7.9	8.1
Net income ($ mil.)	—	0.1	0.2	0.3	(0.8)	(0.1)
Market value ($ mil.)	43.1%	2.6	6.9	4.1	4.6	10.8
Employees	—	—	—	—	—	—

HYDRON TECHNOLOGIES, INC.

OTC: HTEC

4400 34th St. North, Ste. F
St. Petersburg, FL 33714
Phone: 727-342-5050
Fax: 727-344-3920
Web: www.hydron.com

CEO: David Pollock
CFO: David Pollock
HR: –
FYE: September 30
Type: Public

The magic is in the moisture at Hydron Technologies. The company's personal health care products use patented polymers that help deliver moisturizers to the skin and are designed to keep active ingredients in contact with the skin longer. Hydron distributes its more than 40 individual skin care, hair care, sun care, and bath and body products through its own catalog and on its Web site, after abandoning its sales over television shopping channels. The company also makes private-label skin care products for Reliv International (13% of sales) and polymer-based products for use by dental professionals. Chairman and interim president Richard Banakus owns nearly a quarter of Hydron Technologies.

	Annual Growth	12/03	12/04	12/05	12/06	*9/07
Sales ($ mil.)	(6.9%)	1.2	1.2	1.5	1.5	0.9
Net income ($ mil.)	—	(0.9)	(0.9)	(0.8)	(0.6)	(0.5)
Employees	—	—	—	—	—	17

*Fiscal year change

HYLAND SOFTWARE, INC.

28500 Clemens Rd.
Westlake, OH 44145
Phone: 440-788-5000
Fax: 440-788-5100
Web: www.onbase.com

CEO: Anthony J. (A.J.) Hyland
CFO: Christopher J. (Chris) Hyland
HR: Debbie Connelly
FYE: December 31
Type: Private

Too many cooks in your company's kitchen? Founded in 1991, Hyland Software provides enterprise content management (ECM) software designed to help organizations streamline their document and content management processes and share information among employees, partners, and customers. The company's OnBase software, which electronically captures and manages everything from paper reports to Web content, is used by customers in industries ranging from financial services and government to manufacturing and health care.

	Annual Growth	12/03	12/04	12/05	12/06	12/07
Est. sales ($ mil.)	—	—	—	—	—	23.6
Employees	—	—	—	—	—	302

An in-depth profile of this company is available to Hoover's Online members at hoovers.com.

789

⊞ HYPERCOM CORPORATION

NYSE: HYC

2851 W. Kathleen Rd.
Phoenix, AZ 85053
Phone: 602-504-5000
Fax: 602-504-4655
Web: www.hypercom.com

CEO: Philippe Tartavull
CFO: Robert M. Vreeland
HR: Thomas A. (Tim) Jones
FYE: December 31
Type: Public

Hypercom is all worked up over transaction processing. The company jockeys with VeriFone and Ingenico to be the largest maker of point-of-sale (POS) and network payment systems. Retailers, financial institutions, electronic payment processors, and other businesses use Hypercom's products to swipe credit, debit, and smart cards. In addition to card swiping equipment, Hypercom products include printers, keypads, and POS software. It also provides consulting, system design and integration, and software development services. The company sells through distributors, financial institutions, payment processors, resellers, and retail chains.

	Annual Growth	12/03	12/04	12/05	12/06	12/07
Sales ($ mil.)	6.1%	231.5	255.2	245.2	248.6	293.8
Net income ($ mil.)	—	11.2	(8.7)	(33.4)	7.0	(7.5)
Market value ($ mil.)	2.7%	237.7	309.3	338.6	336.9	264.8
Employees	(5.6%)	—	—	1,452	1,358	1,295

HYPERDYNAMICS CORPORATION

AMEX: HDY

1 Sugar Creek Center Blvd., Ste. 125
Sugar Land, TX 77478
Phone: 713-353-9400
Fax: 713-353-9421
Web: www.hypd.com

CEO: Kent P. Watts
CFO: Steven M. Plumb
HR: –
FYE: June 30
Type: Public

Not as hyper as it was, but still dynamic, Hyperdynamics has shifted its business focus from IT consulting services to oil and gas exploration. Its SCS Corporation subsidiary concentrates on developing an oil and gas concession located offshore the Republic of Guinea in West Africa. It also develops and provides cutting-edge seismic data management services. Hyperdynamics' HYD Resources subsidiary and gas exploration and production company focuses on low-risk shallow exploration projects in Louisiana, where in 2007 it held proved reserves of 25,133 barrels of oil. Hyperdynamics' Trendsetter Production company holds oil and gas leases across the southern US. CEO Kent Watts owns 15% of Hyperdynamics.

	Annual Growth	6/03	6/04	6/05	6/06	6/07
Sales ($ mil.)	18.9%	0.5	0.0	0.2	0.7	1.0
Net income ($ mil.)	—	(4.2)	(3.5)	(5.2)	(7.1)	(23.2)
Market value ($ mil.)	66.8%	22.1	103.8	108.8	96.9	171.0
Employees	149.0%	5	30	31		

HYPERTENSION DIAGNOSTICS, INC.

OTC: HDII

2915 Waters Rd., Ste. 108
Eagan, MN 55121
Phone: 651-687-9999
Fax: 651-687-0485
Web: www.hdi-pulsewave.com

CEO: Mark N. Schwartz
CFO: –
HR: –
FYE: June 30
Type: Public

Hypertension Diagnostics can tell if your cardiovascular system is about to go snap, crackle, and pop. The company's noninvasive instruments measure the elasticity of arteries, helping physicians assess patients' risk for cardiovascular disease. Its CR-2000 Research System is marketed for research purposes to the US government, drug companies, academic research centers, and cardiovascular research centers worldwide; drug heavyweights AstraZeneca and Pfizer are among the system's users. The CVProfilor DO-2020, measuring heart rate and blood pressure, is intended for general practitioners, cardiologists, nephrologists, and other physicians. CEO Mark Schwartz controls more than two-thirds of the firm.

	Annual Growth	6/03	6/04	6/05	6/06	6/07
Sales ($ mil.)	24.1%	0.8	1.1	1.2	1.8	1.9
Net income ($ mil.)	—	(3.8)	(1.8)	(1.5)	(1.3)	(0.5)
Market value ($ mil.)	(11.9%)	7.6	4.0	5.6	10.4	4.6
Employees						

HYTHIAM, INC.

NASDAQ (GM): HYTM

11150 Santa Monica Blvd., Ste. 1500
Los Angeles, CA 90025
Phone: 310-444-4300
Fax: 310-444-5300
Web: www.hythiam.com

CEO: Terren S. Peizer
CFO: Chuck Timpe
HR: –
FYE: December 31
Type: Public

Hythiam specializes in researching, developing, and licensing medical protocols for the treatment of alcohol and drug addiction. The company's PROMETA Treatment Protocol utilizes a combination of medication, nutritional supplements, and counseling to treat drug and alcohol addiction. PROMETA also provides maintenance support by offering individualized care programs following medically supervised treatment. Hythiam has opened three PROMETA Centers and has licensing agreements with more than 30 health care providers in the US. CEO Terren Peizer owns about 35% of the company.

	Annual Growth	12/03	12/04	12/05	12/06	12/07
Sales ($ mil.)	358.0%	0.1	0.2	1.2	3.9	44.0
Net income ($ mil.)	—	(3.5)	(11.8)	(24.0)	(38.3)	(45.5)
Market value ($ mil.)	(2.5%)	176.2	183.9	240.7	402.5	159.2
Employees	—	—	—	90	—	—

HYUNDAI MOTOR AMERICA

10550 Talbert Ave.
Fountain Valley, CA 92708
Phone: 714-965-3000
Fax: 714-965-3149
Web: www.hyundaiusa.com

CEO: Jong Eun Kim
CFO: J.S. Choi
HR: Kathy Parker
FYE: December 31
Type: Subsidiary

The Accent is on US sales for Hyundai Motor America. The subsidiary of Hyundai Motor distributes Hyundai cars and SUVs in the United States, serving more than 600 Hyundai dealers. The Hyundai Advantage, which includes a variety of warranties, covers all Hyundai cars sold in the US. Hyundai Motor Finance provides financing for car buyers and for dealer inventory. The company operates an engineering facility in Michigan as well as a proving grounds and a research and design center in California. It opened its first US Hyundai auto-assembly plant in 2005. The Alabama facility's maximum capacity will be 300,000 vehicles a year. Hyundai Motor America plans to increase its number of dealerships to 1,000 by 2010.

	Annual Growth	12/03	12/04	12/05	12/06	12/07
Est. sales ($ mil.)	—	—	—	—	—	2,147.5
Employees	—	—	—	—	—	879

HY-VEE, INC.

5820 Westown Pkwy.
West Des Moines, IA 50266
Phone: 515-267-2800
Fax: 515-267-2817
Web: www.hy-vee.com

CEO: Richard N. (Ric) Jurgens
CFO: John Briggs
HR: Jane Knaack-Esbeck
FYE: September 30
Type: Private

Give Hy-Vee a high five for being one of the largest privately owned US supermarket chains, despite serving some modestly sized towns in the Midwest. The company runs about 225 Hy-Vee supermarkets in Illinois, Iowa, Kansas, Minnesota, Missouri, Nebraska, and South Dakota. About half of its supermarkets are in Iowa, as are most of its 25-plus Hy-Vee (formerly Drug Town) drugstores. It distributes products to its stores through several subsidiaries, including Lomar Distributing (specialty foods), Perishable Distributors of Iowa (fresh foods), and Florist Distributing (flowers). Charles Hyde and David Vredenburg founded the employee-owned firm in 1930. The company name is a combination of the founders' names.

	Annual Growth	9/02	9/03	9/04	9/05	9/06
Est. sales ($ mil.)	—	—	—	—	—	5,840.0
Employees	—	—	—	—	—	52,000

I2 TECHNOLOGIES, INC.

NASDAQ (GM): ITWO

1 i2 Place, 11701 Luna Rd.
Dallas, TX 75234
Phone: 469-357-1000
Fax: 469-357-1798
Web: www.i2.com

CEO: Pallab K. Chatterjee
CFO: Michael J. (Mike) Berry
HR: R. Robin M. Huss
FYE: December 31
Type: Public

i2 Technologies knows a thing or two about supply and demand. The company makes supply chain management software used by manufacturers to boost operating efficiency, schedule production and the delivery of raw materials, and collaborate with customers and suppliers. i2's software suites also include applications for related functions such as procurement, customer relationship management, and the integration and administration of public and private electronic marketplaces. In addition to software, i2 offers a number of professional services such as consulting, maintenance, and training. Company founder Sanjiv Sidhu owns about 20% of i2.

	Annual Growth	12/03	12/04	12/05	12/06	12/07
Sales ($ mil.)	(14.8%)	494.9	389.3	336.9	279.7	260.3
Net income ($ mil.)	143.9%	0.5	(1.4)	87.3	24.2	17.7
Market value ($ mil.)	(5.6%)	—	321.0	292.1	479.3	270.2
Employees	(14.9%)	2,452	—	1,250	1,340	1,285

I2 TELECOM INTERNATIONAL, INC.

OTC: ITUI

5070 Old Ellis Point, Ste. 110
Roswell, GA 30076
Phone: 404-567-4750
Fax: –
Web: www.i2telecom.com

CEO: Paul R. Arena
CFO: –
HR: –
FYE: December 31
Type: Public

i2 Telecom International enables its customers to let their virtual fingers do the talking. The Voice over Internet Protocol (VoIP) service and technology provider offers domestic and international long-distance calling over the Internet. The company operates switching centers in Atlanta and in Foshan, China, and offers VoIP service in the UK through an agreement with Touch Group. i2 has developed a software-based Internet phone device called VoiceStick, which plugs into any computer's USB port and allows phone calls over the Internet. Using the VoiceStick device and software, subscribers can call from their computers or from home and mobile phones through the company's i2Bridge service.

	Annual Growth	12/03	12/04	12/05	12/06	12/07
Sales ($ mil.)	3.0%	0.8	0.6	0.5	0.8	0.9
Net income ($ mil.)	—	0.0	(6.7)	(8.0)	(5.8)	(9.1)
Market value ($ mil.)	(18.8%)	—	25.8	2.4	8.1	13.8
Employees	—	—	—	—	—	—

IA GLOBAL, INC.

AMEX: IAO

101 California St., Ste. 2450
San Francisco, CA 94111
Phone: 415-946-8828
Fax: 415-946-8801
Web: www.iaglobalinc.com

CEO: Derek Schneideman
CFO: Mark E. Scott
HR: –
FYE: December 31
Type: Public

IA Global has made the call to the Pacific Rim region. The holding company is focused on growing its existing businesses and making strategic acquisitions in Asia. Its primary holdings revolve around Global Hotline, a Japanese business process outsourcing (BPO) company that owns two call centers and offers telemarketing services, medical insurance, and other products to customers in Japan. IA Global also owns call center operations in the Philippines along with parts of Japanese firms GPlus Media (online media), Slate Consulting (executive search), and Taicom Securities (financial services), and Australian Secured Financial Limited (private loans and real estate investment). IA Global was formed in 1998.

	Annual Growth	12/03	12/04	12/05	12/06	12/07
Sales ($ mil.)	126.8%	1.1	31.5	45.1	19.1	29.1
Net income ($ mil.)	—	(2.2)	(1.4)	(2.1)	(3.8)	(8.3)
Market value ($ mil.)	25.3%	19.4	32.1	34.6	21.4	47.8
Employees	309.2%	3	61	436	469	841

IAC/INTERACTIVECORP

NASDAQ (GS): IACI

555 West 18th St.
New York, NY 10011
Phone: 212-314-7300
Fax: –
Web: www.iac.com

CEO: Barry Diller
CFO: Thomas J. (Tom) McInerney
HR: –
FYE: December 31
Type: Public

IAC/InterActiveCorp (IAC) satisfies shop-a-holics who fantasize about taking in a show, meeting the right partner, and financing a home. The Internet conglomerate owns more than 60 interactive brands including HSN (formerly Home Shopping Network), which pipes on-air sales reps into more than 90 million US homes; US ticket seller Ticketmaster; and Match.com and LendingTree, the online dating and loan Web sites, respectively. Surrounded by billion-dollar media conglomerates, IAC once coveted a spot with the big shot entertainment companies, but it has since sold out to selling and now is pushing into the market for online content. Controlled by its CEO Barry Diller, IAC is splitting into five public companies.

	Annual Growth	12/03	12/04	12/05	12/06	12/07
Sales ($ mil.)	0.2%	6,328.1	4,188.3	5,753.7	6,277.6	6,373.4
Net income ($ mil.)	—	167.4	164.9	876.2	192.6	(144.1)
Market value ($ mil.)	(26.7%)	23,572.7	9,605.8	8,272.8	9,930.4	6,794.4
Employees	(13.4%)	—	—	28,000	20,000	21,000

IAC SEARCH & MEDIA, INC.

555 12th St., Ste. 500
Oakland, CA 94607
Phone: 510-985-7400
Fax: 510-985-7412
Web: www.iacsearchandmedia.com

CEO: Mark J. Stein
CFO: Dominic Butera
HR: Juanita Lott
FYE: December 31
Type: Subsidiary

If you'd rather NOT use Boolean logic OR key words AND want a different way to search the Internet, just Ask. IAC Search & Media (formerly Ask Jeeves) operates Ask.com, a search engine that allows users to pose questions in plain language instead of using key words. In addition to its US site, IAC Search & Media operates sites for six European countries, as well as a Japanese site, through its Ask-Global operations. The business generates most revenue through ads, but also syndicates its search technology and offers paid search services. IAC Search & Media is part of Internet giant IAC/InterActiveCorp, which has announced plans to split into five companies. IAC Search & Media properties will remain part of IAC.

THE IAMS COMPANY

7250 Poe Ave.
Dayton, OH 45414
Phone: 937-898-7387
Fax: 937-264-7264
Web: www.iams.com

CEO: Dan Rajczak
CFO: Jack Lucas
HR: –
FYE: June 30
Type: Subsidiary

As Iams tells it, Old Mother Hubbard went to the cupboard to fetch her portly pooch a bag of Eukanuba Large Breed Weight Control food. The Iams Company makes Eukanuba and Iams dry and canned versions of premium dog and cat foods and sells them in pet supply stores and veterinarians' offices in more than 70 countries. Founded by Paul Iams in 1946, Iams also funds research efforts related to animal dermatology, geriatrics, allergies, and nutrition through its Paul F. Iams Technical Center. Former chairman Clayton Mathile acquired the company in 1982 and sold it to consumer products giant Procter & Gamble in 1999.

	Annual Growth	6/03	6/04	6/05	6/06	6/07
Est. sales ($ mil.)	—	—	—	—	—	118.3
Employees	—	—	—	—	—	1,000

An in-depth profile of this company is available to Hoover's Online members at hoovers.com.

791

IAP WORLDWIDE SERVICES, INC.

7315 N. Atlantic Ave.
Cape Canaveral, FL 32920
Phone: 321-784-7100
Fax: 321-784-7336
Web: www.iapws.com

CEO: Michael S. Williams
CFO: James W. Jennings Jr.
HR: David B. Warhol
FYE: December 31
Type: Private

In many places where US troops are on the ground, IAP Worldwide Services is there to support them. The company provides a variety of logistics and support services, chiefly for the US Department of Defense and other government customers, including US states and other countries; it also undertakes work for commercial enterprises. IAP's offerings include base camp facilities support; disaster relief; logistics planning; and temporary staffing. Investment firm Cerberus Capital Management owns a controlling interest in IAP, which was founded in 1989.

	Annual Growth	12/03	12/04	12/05	12/06	12/07
Est. sales ($ mil.)	—	—	—	—	—	266.3
Employees	—	—	—	—	—	5,354

IASIS HEALTHCARE LLC

117 Seaboard Ln., Bldg. E
Franklin, TN 37067
Phone: 615-844-2747
Fax: 615-846-3006
Web: www.iasishealthcare.com

CEO: David R. White
CFO: W. Carl Whitmer
HR: Russ Follis
FYE: September 30
Type: Private

If you're sick in the suburbs, IASIS Healthcare provides a medical oasis. The company owns and operates about 15 acute care hospitals and one behavioral health facility (more than 2,600 beds total) in Arizona, Florida, Louisiana, Nevada, Texas, and Utah. IASIS also operates several outpatient facilities and other centers providing ancillary services, such as radiation therapy, diagnostic imaging, and ambulatory surgery. Its Health Choice Arizona subsidiary is a Medicaid managed health plan that serves about 125,000 individuals in Arizona. An investor group led by Texas Pacific Group owns the company.

	Annual Growth	9/02	9/03	9/04	9/05	9/06
Sales ($ mil.)	14.4%	949.9	1,088.2	1,386.6	1,523.7	1,626.0
Net income ($ mil.)	—	(11.0)	20.6	(32.4)	40.6	39.5
Employees	2.6%	8,000	8,200	9,000	8,800	8,877

IBASIS, INC.

NASDAQ (GM): IBAS

20 2nd Ave.
Burlington, MA 01803
Phone: 781-505-7500
Fax: 781-505-7300
Web: www.ibasis.net

CEO: Ofer Gneezy
CFO: Richard G. Tennant
HR: Tamah Solomon Rosker
FYE: December 31
Type: Public

Communications company iBasis is laying the foundation for Internet telephony. The company sells access to its international Voice over Internet Protocol (VoIP) network to telecommunications carriers and resellers. The company — which has more than 290 carrier clients including Cable and Wireless, Sprint Nextel, and Telenor — manages connection to its network and has agreements with local providers worldwide who handle termination of calls. In addition to its wholesale business, iBasis offers retail prepaid calling services through calling cards and on the Web.

	Annual Growth	12/03	12/04	12/05	12/06	12/07
Sales ($ mil.)	51.5%	178.2	263.7	385.5	511.1	938.6
Net income ($ mil.)	—	(9.7)	(17.5)	(1.7)	(2.2)	16.1
Market value ($ mil.)	52.4%	71.2	156.6	183.5	282.3	383.9
Employees	—	—	—	—	251	—

IBERDROLA RENEWABLES, INC.

1125 NW Couch, Ste. 700
Portland, OR 97209
Phone: 503-796-7000
Fax: 503-796-6901
Web: www.iberdrolarenewables.com

CEO: Terry F. Hudgens
CFO: Trevor Mihalik
HR: Linda Wah
FYE: March 31
Type: Subsidiary

IBERDROLA RENEWABLES (formerly PPM Energy) is a real power player in the energy industry. The company holds the nonregulated North American operations of Scottish Power (which was acquired by IBERDROLA in 2007). IBERDROLA RENEWABLES develops and operates cogeneration power plants and wind farms; it has generating capacity of more than 2,000 MW in operation or under construction in the Midwest and western US. IBERDROLA RENEWABLES also markets and trades wholesale energy and offers risk and asset management services. It has natural gas storage and hub operations through its ENSTOR affiliate. The company's customers include public and private utilities, large industrial companies, and other energy marketers.

	Annual Growth	3/03	3/04	3/05	3/06	3/07
Est. sales ($ mil.)	—	—	—	—	—	42.2
Employees	—	—	—	—	—	168

IBERIA TILES CORPORATION

2975 NW 77 Ave.
Miami, FL 33122
Phone: 305-591-3880
Fax: 305-591-4341
Web: www.iberiatiles.com

CEO: Fernando Rodriguez-Vila
CFO: –
HR: Nina Vidal
FYE: December 31
Type: Private

Carrying on the Spanish tile-making traditions of Barcelona's artisans, Iberia Tiles distributes ceramic tile, marble, and stone and wood products primarily in the southeastern US. The company has four showrooms in Florida (in Miami, Coral Gables, and Pompano Beach) and another in Norcross, Georgia. It also has an export division. Iberia Tiles' wholesale distribution subsidiary, Cypress Trading Company, was founded in 1989, to serve customers in the southeastern US. Chairman Rosa Sugrañes and her husband, Fernando Rodriguez-Vila, independently own and manage the company. Sugrañes brought the company to the US in 1979 as an expansion of Ceramica Sugrañes, her father's tile and marble business in Spain.

	Annual Growth	12/03	12/04	12/05	12/06	12/07
Sales ($ mil.)	—	—	—	—	—	25.0
Employees	—	—	—	—	—	—

IBERIABANK CORPORATION

NASDAQ (GS): IBKC

200 W. Congress St.
Lafayette, LA 70501
Phone: 337-521-4012
Fax: 337-364-1171
Web: www.iberiabank.com

CEO: Daryl G. Byrd
CFO: Anthony J. Restel
HR: –
FYE: December 31
Type: Public

IBERIABANK Corporation is a multi-bank holding company with 150 offices, including about 80 bank branches, 30 title insurance offices, and some 40 mortgage locations primarily in Louisiana, but also in Arkansas, Tennessee, and Oklahoma. Its primary bank subsidiary, IBERIABANK, offers passbook and NOW accounts, CDs, and IRAs through about 50 offices in 16 Louisiana parishes. IBERIABANK uses funds from deposits to make loans, focusing on business loans, which make up nearly 60% of a portfolio that also includes consumer loans (about 25%) and residential mortgages (15%). Expanding headlong into Arkansas, IBERIABANK Corporation acquired Pulaski Investment Corporation and Pocahontas Bancorp in 2007.

	Annual Growth	12/03	12/04	12/05	12/06	12/07
Assets ($ mil.)	23.5%	2,115.8	2,448.6	2,852.6	3,203.1	4,917.0
Net income ($ mil.)	15.1%	23.5	27.3	22.0	35.7	41.3
Market value ($ mil.)	17.4%	317.1	365.5	487.1	607.4	601.8
Employees	42.5%	—	—	650	—	1,319

IBIS TECHNOLOGY CORPORATION

NASDAQ (GM): IBIS

32 Cherry Hill Dr.
Danvers, MA 01923
Phone: 978-777-4247
Fax: 978-777-6570
Web: www.ibis.com

CEO: Martin J. Reid
CFO: William J. Schmidt
HR: Peg Donovan
FYE: December 31
Type: Public

Ibis Technology wants semiconductors to take flight. The company makes oxygen ion implanters used to produce specialized, silicon-based wafers through a process called separation by implantation of oxygen, silicon-on-insulator (SIMOX-SOI). SIMOX-SOI integrated circuits (ICs), which are faster and consume less power than conventional silicon chips, are used in auto electronics, cell phones, computer servers and workstations, game consoles, telecommunications networking gear, and TVs. Among Ibis Technology's leading customers are Axcelis Technologies, Nissin Electric (39% of sales), SUMCO (19%), and Tokyo Iovenus (28%).

	Annual Growth	12/03	12/04	12/05	12/06	12/07
Sales ($ mil.)	(53.0%)	18.4	7.9	0.6	14.0	0.9
Net income ($ mil.)	—	(21.5)	(10.9)	(9.3)	0.4	(8.5)
Market value ($ mil.)	(52.4%)	119.8	39.9	37.9	16.2	6.2
Employees	(29.5%)	81	59	45	45	20

I.C. ISAACS & COMPANY, INC.

OTC: ISAC

3840 Bank St.
Baltimore, MD 21224
Phone: 410-342-8200
Fax: 410-276-4087
Web: www.icisaacs.com

CEO: Robert Stephen Stec
CFO: Timothy J. Tumminello
HR: –
FYE: December 31
Type: Public

I.C. Isaacs & Company is putting all of its jeans in one laundry basket. A leading US licensee for French designer Girbaud, the company designs and makes jeans and sportswear targeting a young, fashionable urban market. It has otherwise cleaned out its closet to focus entirely on its Girbaud brand. (In 2001 I.C. Isaacs terminated its licenses with BOSS and Beverly Hills Polo Club and discontinued its own Urban Expedition and Isaacs lines.) The company's clothes are sold in about 1,500 specialty and department stores. Designers Marithé and François Girbaud have increased their stake in I.C. Isaacs to nearly 34%, making them the company's biggest shareholders.

	Annual Growth	12/03	12/04	12/05	12/06	12/07
Sales ($ mil.)	(13.4%)	66.2	80.7	83.3	82.2	37.2
Net income ($ mil.)	—	(1.7)	6.2	6.4	2.6	(15.6)
Employees	(11.6%)	—	100	110	110	69

ICAD, INC.

NASDAQ (CM): ICAD

98 Spit Brook Rd., Ste. 100
Nashua, NH 03063
Phone: 603-882-5200
Fax: 603-880-3843
Web: www.icadmed.com

CEO: Kenneth M. (Ken) Ferry
CFO: Darlene M. Deptula-Hicks
HR: –
FYE: December 31
Type: Public

Early detection is the best prevention in iCAD's eyes. The company targets the breast cancer detection market with its SecondLook computer-aided detection (CAD) systems. The systems include workstations and analytical software that help radiologists better identify potential cancers in mammography images. iCAD sells models that can be used with both film-based and digital mammography systems and offers film digitizers for radiology practices making the film-to-digital transition. SecondLook also provides image storage and patient tracking capabilities. iCAD markets its products directly and through sales partnerships with the likes of GE Healthcare, Siemens Medical Solutions, and Agfa.

	Annual Growth	12/03	12/04	12/05	12/06	12/07
Sales ($ mil.)	42.2%	6.5	23.3	19.8	19.7	26.6
Net income ($ mil.)	—	(8.2)	(0.8)	(4.8)	(6.6)	(1.5)
Market value ($ mil.)	(18.3%)	177.6	162.5	43.1	112.2	79.1
Employees	—	—	—	86		

ICAGEN, INC.

NASDAQ (GM): ICGN

4222 Emperor Blvd., Ste. 350
Durham, NC 27703
Phone: 919-941-5206
Fax: 919-941-0813
Web: www.icagen.com

CEO: P. Kay Wagoner
CFO: Richard D. Katz
HR: –
FYE: December 31
Type: Public

Icagen wants to set the market for ion channel modulators on fire. The development-stage biotech focuses on treatments for epilepsy, dementia, and atrial fibrillation by regulating the inflow into cells of such ions as calcium, potassium, and sodium. Bristol-Myers Squibb is developing one of Icagen's candidates to treat atrial fibrillation. Icagen's lead candidate, senicapoc for sickle cell disease, died in 2007 following lackluster Phase III clinical trial results. The drug was being developed in a partnership with Johnson & Johnson subsidiary McNeil Consumer & Specialty Pharmaceuticals. Shortly thereafter Icagen announced a deal collaborating with Pfizer on the development of pain treatments.

	Annual Growth	12/03	12/04	12/05	12/06	12/07
Sales ($ mil.)	40.0%	5.5	6.5	8.8	8.4	21.1
Net income ($ mil.)	—	(14.2)	(16.7)	(20.3)	(24.8)	(10.9)
Market value ($ mil.)	(30.4%)	—	—	141.8	38.2	68.7
Employees	—	—	—	72	—	—

ICAHN ENTERPRISES L.P.

NYSE: IEP

767 5th Ave., Ste. 4700
New York, NY 10153
Phone: 212-702-4300
Fax: 914-242-9282
Web: www.icahnenterprises.com

CEO: Keith A. Meister
CFO: Andrew R. Skobe
HR: –
FYE: December 31
Type: Public

Icahn Enterprises, formerly American Real Estate Partners, goes beneath the glitz and the glamour and invests in the dirt. The diversified holding company develops real estate, primarily single- and multifamily homes and residential lots. Real estate operations also include condos, hotels, and golf courses. Its PSC Metals subsidiary is one of the largest scrapyard operators in the US. The company also owns WestPoint International, a US maker of bed, bath, and other home products. Icahn sold its casino holdings, which included the Stratosphere Casino, Hotel, and Tower in Las Vegas, in 2008. Icahn and Company, the hedge fund of billionaire corporate raider Carl Icahn, owns around 90% of the company.

	Annual Growth	12/03	12/04	12/05	12/06	12/07
Sales ($ mil.)	72.1%	283.8	453.6	1,262.5	1,477.9	2,487.6
Net income ($ mil.)	45.9%	68.1	161.0	(27.0)	798.8	308.3
Market value ($ mil.)	—	—	—	—	—	9,143.9
Employees	(13.8%)	—	—	6,060	5,340	4,500

ICC INDUSTRIES INC.

460 Park Ave.
New York, NY 10022
Phone: 212-521-1700
Fax: 212-521-1970
Web: www.iccchem.com

CEO: John Oram
CFO: Blaise Sarcone
HR: –
FYE: December 31
Type: Private

ICC Industries supplies the dealers who supply the public with drugs. ICC makes the raw materials that pharmaceutical companies use to manufacture drugs and trades basic and specialty chemicals around the world. An international maker of chemicals (Dover Chemical), plastics (Primex), and pharmaceutical products, ICC also trades and distributes nutritional supplements and food ingredients. Its main subsidiary, ICC Chemical, maintains trading and marketing offices throughout the world. ICC Industries owns a majority of Pharmaceutical Formulations, a manufacturer and distributor of generic over-the-counter drugs. The Farber family, including chairman John Farber, owns ICC.

	Annual Growth	12/02	12/03	12/04	12/05	12/06
Sales ($ mil.)	2.1%	—	—	—	1,342.0	1,370.0
Employees	(10.3%)	—	—	—	1,700	1,525

An in-depth profile of this company is available to Hoover's Online members at hoovers.com.

793

ICEWEB, INC.

OTC: IWEB

205 Van Buren St., Ste. 150
Herndon, VA 20170
Phone: 703-964-8000
Fax: 703-964-0160
Web: www.iceweb.com

CEO: John R. Signorello
CFO: Mark B. Lucky
HR: –
FYE: September 30
Type: Public

IceWEB helps its customers spin a security web. The company generates the majority of its revenues from its Solutions Group, which provides network security products to local, state, and federal government agencies. Specializing in such applications as content filtering, e-mail security, intrusion detection, and network optimization, the unit implements products from partners including Blue Coat Systems, Cisco Systems, F5 Networks, McAfee, and RSA Security. The company also provides small and medium sized businesses with hosted e-mail server and security applications.

	Annual Growth	9/03	9/04	9/05	9/06	9/07
Sales ($ mil.)	82.1%	1.7	6.7	6.8	4.8	18.7
Net income ($ mil.)	—	(0.1)	(2.0)	(0.9)	(3.9)	(2.8)
Market value ($ mil.)	(49.0%)	115.5	1,247.3	5.7	3.9	7.8
Employees	—	—	—	—	—	18

ICF INTERNATIONAL, INC.

NASDAQ (GM): ICFI

9300 Lee Hwy.
Fairfax, VA 22031
Phone: 703-934-3000
Fax: 703-934-3740
Web: www.icfi.com

CEO: Sudhakar Kesavan
CFO: Alan Stewart
HR: Miriam Wardak
FYE: December 31
Type: Public

Consultant ICF International (formerly ICF Consulting) sees opportunity in government spending. The firm advises government entities and businesses on issues related to health, human services, and social programs, as well as defense and homeland security, energy and climate change, and the environment. It groups its consulting and information technology services into three main categories: advice, implementation, and evaluation and improvement. A contract with the State of Louisiana related to the resettlement of people displaced by hurricanes accounts for about two-thirds of the firm's sales.

	Annual Growth	12/03	12/04	12/05	12/06	12/07
Sales ($ mil.)	49.4%	145.8	139.5	177.2	331.3	727.1
Net income ($ mil.)	102.8%	2.4	3.0	2.0	11.9	40.6
Market value ($ mil.)	82.2%	—	—	—	201.5	367.1
Employees	31.6%	1,000	—	—	2,000	3,000

ICG COMMERCE, INC.

2520 Renaissance Blvd.
King of Prussia, PA 19406
Phone: 484-690-5000
Fax: 877-424-2339
Web: www.icgcommerce.com

CEO: Carl A. Guarino
CFO: –
HR: –
FYE: December 31
Type: Private

ICG Commerce wants to eliminate the extensive paperwork and never-ending phone calls that some people associate with traditional corporate buying. The company oversees the purchasing process for its customers by identifying suppliers, managing lists of preferred providers, and ensuring that items are properly shipped and paid for. ICG Commerce's customers have included telecommunications service provider Avaya, aircraft component manufacturer Vought, and upscale department store Nordstrom. Investment firm Internet Capital Group owns a controlling stake in ICG Commerce, which was founded in 1992.

	Annual Growth	12/03	12/04	12/05	12/06	12/07
Est. sales ($ mil.)	—	—	—	—	—	21.1
Employees	—	—	—	—	—	335

ICG COMMUNICATIONS, INC.

1025 Eldorado Blvd.
Broomfield, CO 80021
Phone: 888-424-4440
Fax: –
Web: www.icgcomm.com

CEO: Daniel P. (Dan) Caruso
CFO: Rob Schmiedeler
HR: –
FYE: December 31
Type: Subsidiary

Down from the Rocky Mountains and up from bankruptcy, ICG Communications hopes its roller coaster existence is a thing of the past. The facilities-based communications carrier, which emerged from bankruptcy in 2002 only to find itself on the brink again two years later, has refocused its business on providing wholesale access and corporate phone and data services over its fiber-optic networks in Colorado and Ohio. The company was acquired in 2004 by investment firms Columbia Capital and M/C Venture Partners (saving ICG from its second bankruptcy). It subsequently reduced its debt by shedding some businesses and concentrating on select markets. In 2006 ICG was acquired by Level 3 Communications.

	Annual Growth	12/03	12/04	12/05	12/06	12/07
Est. sales ($ mil.)	—	—	—	—	—	26.7
Employees	—	—	—	—	—	213

ICI PAINTS IN NORTH AMERICA

15885 W. Sprague Rd.
Strongsville, OH 44136
Phone: 440-297-8000
Fax: 440-297-8900
Web: www.icipaintsinna.com

CEO: David Hamill
CFO: Cathie McKinley
HR: Marguerite Walz
FYE: December 31
Type: Business segment

You might not readily recognize ICI Paints in North America by its name, but you know its brands. One of the largest North American makers of paints, the unit of Akzo Nobel is best known for Glidden paints and stores. Other well-known brands include ICI Dulux, Ralph Lauren paints, Fuller O'Brien, and Liquid Nails caulks and adhesives. Professionals are the primary buyers of ICI's DeVoe industrial coatings and its Ultra-Hide primers and paints. While just about all of its sales come from architectural and decorative paints and coatings, the division also makes coatings for packaging (cans and closures). In 2008 Akzo Nobel acquired former parent company Imperial Chemical Industries (ICI).

ICICLE SEAFOODS, INC.

4019 21st Ave. W
Seattle, WA 98199
Phone: 206-282-0988
Fax: 206-282-7222
Web: www.icicleseafoods.com

CEO: Don Giles
CFO: Dennis Guhlke
HR: Leauri Lopes
FYE: December 31
Type: Private

Forget about curling up for a nice long hibernation during the winter months at this company — Icicle Seafoods is hard at work even when icicles are forming outside. The fishery and seafood-processing company distributes fresh, canned, and frozen fish including cod, herring, pollock, halibut, salmon, crab, salmon caviar, and more to food retail, industrial, wholesale, and foodservice operations throughout the world. It maintains floating seafood processing plants, shoreline plants, and other facilities located in Alaska, Oregon, and Washington state, as well as in Japan and Chile. Its Alaskan cannery has been in operation since 1899. In 2007 the company was acquired by private investment firm Paine & Partners.

	Annual Growth	12/03	12/04	12/05	12/06	12/07
Est. sales ($ mil.)	—	—	—	—	—	272.6
Employees	—	—	—	—	—	500

ICL PERFORMANCE PRODUCTS LP

622 Emerson Rd., Ste. 500
St. Louis, MO 63141
Phone: 314-983-7500
Fax: 314-983-7638
Web: www.icl-pplp.com

CEO: Charles M. Weidhas
CFO: Paul M. Schlessman
HR: Michael (Mike) Bork
FYE: December 31
Type: Subsidiary

ICL Performance Products LP is phosphorific! The North American unit of Israel Chemicals Limited's performance products segment produces phosphorus chemicals, phosphoric acid, and phosphate salts. The chemicals are used in foods, cleaners, water treatment, flat panel displays, oral care products, paints and coatings, and pharmaceuticals. ICL Performance Products was formed at the turn of this century as a joint venture of FMC and Solutia called Astaris. ICL, wanting to expand its operations in North America, bought Astaris from the two US companies in late 2005.

ICO GLOBAL COMMUNICATIONS

NASDAQ (GM): ICOG

11700 Plaza America Dr., Ste. 1010
Reston, VA 20190
Phone: 703-964-1400
Fax: 703-964-1401
Web: www.ico.com

CEO: J. Timothy (Tim) Bryan
CFO: Dennis Schmitt
HR: –
FYE: December 31
Type: Public

When it gets off the ground, ICO Global Communications (Holdings) Limited will be a satellite-based communications system with global coverage. Operating through its principal operating subsidiary, ICO North America, ICO (pronounced Eye-Co) is authorized to operate a medium-Earth-orbit (MEO) mobile satellite service (MSS) to provide mobile voice, data, and Internet services. It is gearing its service primarily for customers in the transportation, oil and gas, and construction industries. The company was formed when the former ICO Global Communications emerged from bankruptcy protection in 2000, thanks to a $1.2 billion investment from a group led by US telecommunications entrepreneur Craig McCaw, who is now chairman.

	Annual Growth	12/01	12/02	12/03	12/04	*12/05
Sales ($ mil.)	—	—	—	—	—	0.0
Net income ($ mil.)	—	—	—	—	—	33.4
Employees	—	—	—	—	—	22

*Most recent year available

ICO, INC.

NASDAQ (GM): ICOC

1811 Bering Dr., Ste. 200
Houston, TX 77057
Phone: 713-351-4100
Fax: 713-335-2201
Web: www.icopolymers.com

CEO: A. John Knapp Jr.
CFO: Bradley T. (Brad) Leuschner
HR: Keith Haddock
FYE: September 30
Type: Public

I see, oh, a bunch of paint- and plastic-producing polymers over at ICO. The company, formerly an oilfield services provider, focuses now on its global polymers processing business. That business is to grind, blend, and compound polymer resin pellets (primarily polyethylene) into powders that are used to make paint and plastic products such as toys, garbage bags, and plastic film. The company also processes resins for desired characteristics such as color and UV protection. ICO's customers include chemical companies and plastics and polymers manufacturers.

	Annual Growth	9/03	9/04	9/05	9/06	9/07
Sales ($ mil.)	19.3%	206.6	257.5	296.6	324.3	417.9
Net income ($ mil.)	—	(50.1)	0.3	4.5	12.0	21.1
Market value ($ mil.)	100.3%	23.4	74.0	74.8	170.7	376.1
Employees	6.2%	—	—	825	—	931

ICON HEALTH & FITNESS, INC.

1500 S. 1000 West
Logan, UT 84321
Phone: 435-750-5000
Fax: 435-750-3917
Web: www.iconfitness.com

CEO: David J. Watterson
CFO: S. Fred Beck
HR: –
FYE: May 31
Type: Private

ICON Health & Fitness has brawn as one of the leading US makers of home fitness equipment. Its products primarily include treadmills, elliptical trainers, and weight benches. Brands include HealthRider, NordicTrack, and ProForm. ICON also offers fitness accessories and commercial fitness gear. It makes most of its products in Utah and sells them through retailers, infomercials, the Web, and its catalog Workout Warehouse. Sears has an exclusive license to sell NordicTrack brand products and apparel. The company was founded as a housewares importer in 1977.

	Annual Growth	5/02	5/03	5/04	5/05	5/06
Sales ($ mil.)	(0.6%)	871.4	1,011.5	1,095.7	898.1	852.2
Net income ($ mil.)	—	19.6	28.1	23.4	(110.0)	(49.7)
Employees	(9.2%)	4,800	4,569	5,142	3,467	3,263

ICON PRODUCTIONS, INC.

808 Wilshire Blvd., 4th Fl.
Santa Monica, CA 90401
Phone: 310-434-7300
Fax: 310-434-7377
Web: www.iconmovies.com

CEO: Mel Gibson
CFO: –
HR: –
FYE: –
Type: Private

A passionate story helped resurrect Icon Productions. Mel Gibson's movie production company Icon Productions independently financed *The Passion of the Christ* after Fox passed on theatrically distributing the surprise box office hit. The controversial interpretation of the final 12 hours in the life of Jesus Christ cost about $30 million to make and earned more than $150 million in its first eight days of release. (Independent distributor Newmarket released the film in the US, and Fox subsequently secured distribution rights in Latin America.) Other Icon films include 2006's *Apocalypto*, released by Disney and 2007's *Seraphim Falls*, as well as the Gibson vehicles *Braveheart, Payback*, and *What Women Want*.

ICONIX BRAND GROUP, INC.

NASDAQ (GS): ICON

1450 Broadway, 4th Fl.
New York, NY 10018
Phone: 212-730-0030
Fax: 212-391-2057
Web: iconixbrand.com

CEO: Neil Cole
CFO: Warren Clamen
HR: –
FYE: December 31
Type: Public

Once a shoemaker, Iconix Brand Group has stepped forward as a licensing and brand management company. Its company-owned consumer and home brands are licensed to third parties that make and sell apparel, footwear, and a variety of other fashion and home products. Consumer brands in the Iconix stable include Badgley Mischka, Danskin, Mossimo, Mudd, and Rocawear; among the company's home brands are Cannon and Fieldcrest. Along with licensing the brands, Iconix markets and promotes them through its in-house advertising and public relations services.

	Annual Growth	1/04	*12/04	12/05	12/06	12/07
Sales ($ mil.)	5.0%	131.4	69.0	30.2	80.7	160.0
Net income ($ mil.)	—	(11.3)	0.2	15.9	32.5	63.8
Market value ($ mil.)	113.6%	54.0	151.7	360.1	1,086.4	1,123.2
Employees	(17.2%)	200	—	39	46	94

*Fiscal year change

ICOP DIGITAL, INC.

NASDAQ (CM): ICOP

16801 W. 116th St.
Lenexa, KS 66219
Phone: 913-338-5550
Fax: –
Web: icopdigital.com

CEO: David C. Owen
CFO: Derick D. Shupe
HR: –
FYE: December 31
Type: Public

What happens in a police car doesn't necessarily stay in a police car — sometimes, it becomes a matter of considerable controversy. In those cases, accurate evidence is vital, and that's where ICOP Digital comes in. The company designs, engineers, and markets an in-car digital video system, including cameras and a hard disk drive, that is intended for use primarily by law enforcement agencies. Applications include portrayal of traffic stops and other contacts between police officers and the public, as well as officer performance monitoring. Besides law enforcement agencies, potential users of the ICOP Digital system include fire departments, emergency medical services, and public transportation systems.

	Annual Growth	12/03	12/04	12/05	12/06	12/07
Sales ($ mil.)	390.5%	—	0.1	1.8	6.6	11.8
Net income ($ mil.)	—	—	(2.4)	(2.9)	(3.5)	(5.5)
Market value ($ mil.)	34.9%	—	12.3	37.5	39.8	30.2
Employees	—	—	—	31	—	—

ICT GROUP, INC.

NASDAQ (GM): ICTG

100 Brandywine Blvd.
Newtown, PA 18940
Phone: 267-685-5000
Fax: 267-685-5705
Web: www.ictgroup.com

CEO: John J. Brennan
CFO: Vincent A. Paccapaniccia
HR: Gail Lebel
FYE: December 31
Type: Public

Who's that calling during supper? Could be ICT Group. The global customer management company handles outgoing and incoming calls from more than 40 contact centers in the Americas, Europe, and the Asia/Pacific region. Services include customer care, market research, telesales, technical support, database marketing, data collection, and e-commerce support for clients in such fields as insurance and financial services, as well as information technology, pharmaceuticals, and telecommunications. ICT's clients have included Capital One, Pfizer, and Virgin Mobile USA.

	Annual Growth	12/03	12/04	12/05	12/06	12/07
Sales ($ mil.)	11.1%	298.1	325.5	401.3	447.9	453.6
Net income ($ mil.)	—	(1.1)	(2.7)	12.2	16.8	(11.8)
Market value ($ mil.)	6.5%	146.6	122.8	216.8	497.0	188.7
Employees	8.4%	—	—	16,174	20,019	19,006

ICU MEDICAL, INC.

NASDAQ (GS): ICUI

951 Calle Amanecer
San Clemente, CA 92673
Phone: 949-366-2183
Fax: 949-366-8368
Web: www.icumed.com

CEO: George A. Lopez
CFO: Scott E. Lamb
HR: James J. (Jim) Reitz
FYE: December 31
Type: Public

ICU Medical sees the future of infection prevention. The company's devices protect health care workers and patients from the spread of diseases such as HIV and hepatitis. Its primary products are intravenous (IV) connection devices, called Clave needleless connectors, that reduce the risk of needle sticks and disconnections. The firm also makes custom IV sets, many of which use Clave connectors and other ICU products, for third parties. Additionally, ICU Medical makes critical care equipment, such as angiography kits and heart monitors, through a manufacturing agreement with Hospira, its largest customer. ICU Medical also sells its product to other equipment makers and distributors.

	Annual Growth	12/03	12/04	12/05	12/06	12/07
Sales ($ mil.)	15.1%	107.3	75.6	157.5	201.6	188.1
Net income ($ mil.)	0.9%	22.3	5.0	20.3	25.7	23.1
Market value ($ mil.)	1.2%	469.5	371.1	554.3	595.4	493.0
Employees	14.4%	—	—	1,373	1,819	1,796

ICX TECHNOLOGIES, INC.

NASDAQ (GM): ICXT

2100 Crystal Dr., Ste. 650
Arlington, VA 22202
Phone: 703-678-2111
Fax: 703-678-2112
Web: www.icxt.com

CEO: Hans C. Kobler
CFO: Deborah D. (Debbie) Mosier
HR: –
FYE: December 31
Type: Public

Constant vigilance may be the mantra and the mission of ICx Technologies. The firm develops high precision products used in the detection, identification, and prevention of chemical, biological, radiation, and explosive security threats. Other products offer perimeter security and wide area surveillance. Organized in three divisions — Detection, Surveillance, and Solutions (offering integrated systems, maintenance, and training services) — ICx has a primary customer base of government agencies such as DHS and DOD. Other clients include security and defense firms that integrate ICx products into their own systems. Private equity firm Wexford Capital owns about 65% of the company.

	Annual Growth	12/03	12/04	12/05	12/06	12/07
Sales ($ mil.)	252.9%	—	3.1	31.4	90.2	136.2
Net income ($ mil.)	—	—	(5.1)	(14.8)	(127.5)	(29.9)
Market value ($ mil.)	—	—	—	—	—	324.3
Employees	—	—	—	—	752	—

I.D. SYSTEMS, INC.

NASDAQ (GM): IDSY

1 University Plaza, 6th Fl.
Hackensack, NJ 07601
Phone: 201-996-9000
Fax: 201-996-9144
Web: www.id-systems.com

CEO: Jeffrey M. Jagid
CFO: Ned Mavrommatis
HR: –
FYE: December 31
Type: Public

I.D. Systems is trying to get its tracking business on the road. The company's Wireless Asset Net systems track, analyze, and control the movements of objects such as packages and vehicles. Its systems use radio-frequency identification (RFID) technology and tiny computers attached to the object to be monitored, and users can access tracking data via the Internet. The company is focused on vehicle management, rental car, package tracking, and airport ground security applications. Customers include 3M, the FAA, Ford, Hallmark Cards, Target, the US Postal Service (37% of sales), and Wal-Mart Stores (32%).

	Annual Growth	12/03	12/04	12/05	12/06	12/07
Sales ($ mil.)	20.9%	8.0	13.7	19.0	24.7	17.1
Net income ($ mil.)	—	(1.2)	0.4	0.9	(1.6)	(7.3)
Market value ($ mil.)	28.0%	49.6	143.5	187.2	213.4	133.2
Employees	27.9%	37	55	61	89	99

IDACORP, INC.

NYSE: IDA

1221 W. Idaho St.
Boise, ID 83702
Phone: 208-388-2200
Fax: 208-388-6955
Web: www.idacorpinc.com

CEO: J. LaMont Keen
CFO: Darrel T. Anderson
HR: Luci K. McDonald
FYE: December 31
Type: Public

Energy is more than small potatoes for IDACORP. The holding company's regulated utility, Idaho Power, distributes electricity to approximately 482,000 customers in 71 cities in Idaho and nine in Oregon. The utility's generation assets include 17 hydroelectric plants, two gas-fired plants, and interests in three coal-fired plants. Other IDACORP businesses include coal mining and affordable housing investments. The company has exited its energy trading business and independent power production business due to poor market conditions. It has also discontinued its fuel cell and telecommunications businesses.

	Annual Growth	12/03	12/04	12/05	12/06	12/07
Sales ($ mil.)	1.7%	823.0	844.5	859.5	926.3	879.4
Net income ($ mil.)	15.3%	46.6	73.0	63.7	107.4	82.3
Market value ($ mil.)	8.5%	1,143.1	1,290.6	1,242.8	1,694.2	1,587.1
Employees	1.8%	—	1,940	1,993	1,976	2,044

IDAHO POWER COMPANY

1221 W. Idaho St.
Boise, ID 83702
Phone: 208-388-2200
Fax: 208-388-6955
Web: www.idahopower.com

CEO: J. LaMont Keen
CFO: Darrel T. Anderson
HR: Luci K. McDonald
FYE: December 31
Type: Subsidiary

Idaho Power lights up spud farms and factories in southern Idaho and eastern Oregon. The utility provides electricity to 482,000 residential, commercial, and industrial customers over nearly 30,000 miles of transmission and distribution lines. Idaho Power holds franchises in 71 cities in Idaho and nine in Oregon. It also owns power plant interests that give it a generating capacity of more than 3,000 MW. In addition, the company, a subsidiary of IDACORP, has a 33% stake in the Bridger Coal Company, which supplies fuel to the Jim Bridger generating plant in Wyoming.

	Annual Growth	12/03	12/04	12/05	12/06	12/07
Sales ($ mil.)	2.9%	780.4	819.5	837.7	920.5	875.4
Net income ($ mil.)	6.9%	58.6	70.6	71.8	93.9	76.6
Employees	4.5%	1,713	1,757	1,821	1,927	2,044

IDEA SPHERE INC.

3133 Orchard Vista Dr. SE
Grand Rapids, MI 49546
Phone: 616-464-5000
Fax: –
Web: www.ideasphereinc.com

CEO: Bill Nicholson
CFO: Robert Conologue
HR: Justin Tomorello
FYE: December 31
Type: Private

Some people will tell you it's a good idea to take your vitamins, but Idea Sphere thinks its an even better idea to sell them. The company makes more than 200 natural and organic vitamins and other supplements. It produces tablets, capsules, drink mixes, and snack bars. In 2006 it added calcium-fortified spring water to its roster of products. Idea Sphere makes its products through its main operating subsidiaries, Twinlab Corporation, Metabolife, Nature's Herb, and Alvita Teas. Idea Sphere also provides health and wellness information guides and brochures through health education publisher Rebus.

	Annual Growth	12/03	12/04	12/05	12/06	12/07
Est. sales ($ mil.)	—	—	—	—	—	63.5
Employees	—	—	—	—	—	500

▣ IDEALAB

130 W. Union St.
Pasadena, CA 91103
Phone: 626-585-6900
Fax: 626-535-2701
Web: www.idealab.com

CEO: William (Bill) Gross
CFO: Craig Chrisney
HR: –
FYE: January 31
Type: Private

When entrepreneur Bill Gross wanted to coddle his Internet-related brainchildren, he created Idealab. The company, which once teetered on the brink of bankruptcy amid the flame-outs of its former dot-com progeny, nurtures business ideas (several generated by Gross) with the hopes of growing them into full-fledged companies by providing money, office space, and other resources. Its current portfolio is made up of more than a dozen firms involved in robotics, wireless communications, renewable energy, electric and hybrid vehicles, and more, in addition to its traditional Internet focus.

	Annual Growth	1/03	1/04	1/05	1/06	1/07
Est. sales ($ mil.)	—	—	—	—	—	9.5
Employees	—	—	—	—	—	90

IDEARC INC.

NYSE: IAR

2200 W. Airfield Dr.
Dallas/Fort Worth Airport, TX 75261
Phone: 972-453-7000
Fax: 972-453-3969
Web: www.idearc.com

CEO: Scott W. Klein
CFO: Samuel D. (Dee) Jones
HR: Michael D. (Mike) Pawlowski
FYE: December 31
Type: Public

Idearc (formerly Verizon Information Services) is a publisher of print and electronic directory information. Idearc publishes yellow and white pages, business to business directories, and neighborhood directories, and is the exclusive publisher of Verizon branded yellow and white pages. It also operates online local search products such as Superpages.com, Switchboard.com, and LocalSearch.com. The company additionally operates Superpages Mobile, an information directory for wireless subscribers, and provides direct and database marketing services. Most of the company's revenues come from print directory advertising. Idearc was spun off from Verizon Communications in 2006.

	Annual Growth	12/03	12/04	12/05	12/06	12/07
Sales ($ mil.)	(1.0%)	—	—	—	3,221.0	3,189.0
Net income ($ mil.)	(44.4%)	—	—	—	772.0	429.0
Market value ($ mil.)	(38.3%)	—	—	—	4,178.7	2,577.7
Employees	(2.7%)	—	—	—	7,400	7,200

IDENIX PHARMACEUTICALS, INC.

NASDAQ (GM): IDIX

60 Hampshire St.
Cambridge, MA 02139
Phone: 617-995-9800
Fax: 617-995-9801
Web: www.idenix.com

CEO: Jean-Pierre Sommadossi
CFO: Ronald C. (Ron) Renaud Jr.
HR: Paul J. Fanning
FYE: December 31
Type: Public

Idenix Pharmaceuticals is not suffering from any identity crisis — it is clear in its focus on identifying treatments for life-threatening viruses. The biopharmaceutical firm is developing orally-administered drugs to combat chronic hepatitis C (HCV) and HIV. Its lead HIV product candidate is in early clinical stages; its HCV candidates are in preclinical testing. Most are intended to be taken in combination with other therapeutic agents to improve efficacy and convenience. Under a development and commercialization agreement, Novartis has the option to license any of the product candidates developed by Idenix. Novartis owns 56% of Idenix.

	Annual Growth	12/03	12/04	12/05	12/06	12/07
Sales ($ mil.)	23.1%	29.6	95.4	64.7	67.4	68.0
Net income ($ mil.)	—	(41.9)	(6.2)	(50.8)	(75.1)	(82.5)
Market value ($ mil.)	(43.2%)	—	825.8	955.0	487.4	151.7
Employees	—	—	—	218	—	—

IDENTIPHI, INC.

OTC: IDPI

13809 Research Blvd., Ste. 275
Austin, TX 78750
Phone: 512-492-6220
Fax: 512-492-6225
Web: www.identiphi.net

CEO: Steven M. (Steve) Oyer
CFO: Jeffrey T. (Jeff) Dick
HR: –
FYE: December 31
Type: Public

IdentiPHI identified a new name, a new business model, and a new home. Specializing in biometric authentication systems, IdentiPHI provides enterprise network security consulting and systems integration services. Its products include software designed to secure computers and networks. The company also sells third-party hardware. Formerly called Saflink, the company has long developed and licensed biometric systems — technology that recognizes unique physical characteristics such as fingerprints, voice patterns, or facial features — used in security products. It merged with Austin, Texas-based IdentiPHI, changed its name, and moved its headquarters to Austin in 2008.

	Annual Growth	12/03	12/04	12/05	12/06	12/07
Sales ($ mil.)	15.0%	2.0	6.4	7.1	4.2	3.5
Net income ($ mil.)	—	(10.7)	(15.9)	(47.0)	(120.1)	(2.0)
Market value ($ mil.)	(62.8%)	1,399.4	3,702.1	1,170.6	283.1	26.7
Employees	(23.5%)	79	143	122	20	27

▣ An in-depth profile of this company is available to Hoover's Online members at hoovers.com.

797

IDEO

100 Forest Ave.
Palo Alto, CA 94301
Phone: 650-289-3400
Fax: 650-289-3707
Web: www.ideo.com

CEO: Tim Brown
CFO: David (Dave) Strong
HR: –
FYE: Last day in February
Type: Subsidiary

Ideas are IDEO's stock-in-trade. The company provides product development and branding services for a wide range of clients. It also offers packaging design, product research, and strategic consulting services. Its work has included contributions to TiVo's digital video recorder and the Palm V for Palm. In addition, IDEO (pronounced EYE-dee-oh) provides executive training and education services to help enterprises become more innovative. It operates from a network of several offices in the US, Europe, and the Asia/Pacific region. IDEO is a subsidiary of office furniture manufacturer Steelcase. Chairman David Kelley, whose design credits include the first mouse for Apple, and Bill Moggridge formed IDEO in 1991.

IDERA PHARMACEUTICALS, INC.

NASDAQ (GM): IDRA

345 Vassar St.
Cambridge, MA 02139
Phone: 617-679-5500
Fax: 617-679-5592
Web: www.iderapharma.com

CEO: Sudhir Agrawal
CFO: Louis J. (Lou) Arcudi III
HR: –
FYE: December 31
Type: Public

Idera Pharmaceuticals may try to manipulate you, but it's all for your own good. The biotech firm is developing DNA and RNA therapies that manipulate the immune system's response to disease. It is focused on Toll-Like Receptors (TLRs), immune cell receptors that recognize and respond to viral and bacterial invaders. Some of Idera's drugs (such as treatments for infectious disease and cancer) mimic those invaders to stimulate an immune response; others (including treatments for autoimmune diseases) target TLRs to suppress the immune response. The company's lead candidate is a potential treatment for hepatitis C. Idera has partnered some other programs with the likes of Merck & Co., Merck KGaA, and Novartis.

	Annual Growth	12/03	12/04	12/05	12/06	12/07
Sales ($ mil.)	72.7%	0.9	0.9	2.5	2.4	8.0
Net income ($ mil.)	—	(17.2)	(12.7)	(13.7)	(16.5)	(13.2)
Market value ($ mil.)	—	—	—	—	—	282.6
Employees	—	—	—	27	—	—

IDEX CORPORATION

NYSE: IEX

630 Dundee Rd., Ste. 400
Northbrook, IL 60062
Phone: 847-498-7070
Fax: 847-498-3940
Web: www.idexcorp.com

CEO: Lawrence D. Kingsley
CFO: Dominic A. Romeo
HR: Kimberly K. Bors
FYE: December 31
Type: Public

The big idea at IDEX is to dispense with inefficiencies and pump out profits. IDEX is a leading manufacturer of pump products, dispensing equipment, and other engineered products. Its fluid and metering segment includes industrial pumps, injectors, compressors, and flow meters that move chemicals, fuels, and similar fluids. Its health and science segment consists of low-flow pumps and equipment for analytical and clinical applications. The company's dispensing equipment includes gear for dispensing, metering, and mixing dyes, inks, and paints. IDEX's fire and safety/diversified products segment manufactures banding and clamping equipment, fire-fighting pumps, and rescue tools, including the Jaws of Life.

	Annual Growth	12/03	12/04	12/05	12/06	12/07
Sales ($ mil.)	14.2%	797.9	928.3	1,043.3	1,154.9	1,358.6
Net income ($ mil.)	25.6%	62.3	86.4	109.8	146.7	155.1
Market value ($ mil.)	48.2%	611.4	1,376.9	1,446.9	1,701.2	2,947.5
Employees	13.1%	—	—	4,300	4,863	—

IDEXX LABORATORIES, INC.

NASDAQ (GS): IDXX

1 IDEXX Dr.
Westbrook, ME 04092
Phone: 207-556-0300
Fax: 207-556-4286
Web: www.idexx.com

CEO: Jonathan W. (Jon) Ayers
CFO: Merilee Raines
HR: –
FYE: December 31
Type: Public

If IDEXX Laboratories had been on the scene, Old Yeller might have had a happier ending. A leading animal health care company, IDEXX makes diagnostic testing systems and drugs for pets and livestock. Veterinarians use the company's VetTest analyzers for blood and urine chemistry and its SNAP and PetChek point-of-care test kits to detect heartworms, feline leukemia, and other diseases. The company also provides veterinary lab testing services and practice management software. In addition, IDEXX makes diagnostic products to detect livestock diseases (such as mad cow disease) and to test systems for contaminants in water and antibiotics in milk.

	Annual Growth	12/03	12/04	12/05	12/06	12/07
Sales ($ mil.)	18.0%	476.0	549.2	638.1	739.1	922.6
Net income ($ mil.)	13.3%	57.1	78.3	78.3	93.7	94.0
Market value ($ mil.)	45.3%	802.5	903.2	1,145.2	1,235.7	3,576.7
Employees	19.3%	—	—	3,300	3,900	4,700

IDI GLOBAL, INC.

OTC: IDIB

462 E. 800 North
Orem, UT 84097
Phone: 801-224-4444
Fax: 801-224-4457
Web: www.idiglobal.com

CEO: Kevin R. Griffith
CFO: Steven Weatherly
HR: –
FYE: December 31
Type: Public

IDI Global has an idea or two about doing business on the Internet. Through its Internet Development subsidiary, the company offers Web development applications services and software for creating Web sites, as well as consulting and Web hosting. In April 2006 the company filed for Chapter 11 bankruptcy protection for the company and two of IDI Global's wholly owned subsidiaries, Chief Financial and IDI Small Business; its other operations continue to operate outside of bankruptcy protection.

	Annual Growth	12/02	12/03	12/04	12/05	*12/06
Sales ($ mil.)	(10.2%)	12.3	13.3	27.7	21.1	8.0
Net income ($ mil.)	—	(0.3)	0.3	(0.8)	(5.9)	(1.5)
Employees	—	—	—	—	—	25

*Most recent year available

IDM PHARMA, INC.

NASDAQ (GM): IDMI

9 Parker, Ste. 100
Irvine, CA 92618
Phone: 949-470-4751
Fax: 949-470-6470
Web: www.idm-biotech.com

CEO: Timothy P. (Tim) Walbert
CFO: Robert J. (Bob) De Vaere
HR: –
FYE: December 31
Type: Public

IDM Pharma has your immune system's back. The biopharmaceutical company is developing therapies that stimulate a patient's immune system to fight cancer. Its lead product, L-MTP-PE, aims to fight osteosarcoma, the most common form of bone cancer. IDM licensed the drug from Novartis. It is intended to be used in combination with chemotherapy. A second line of candidates includes synthetic and cell-based vaccines that may prevent tumor recurrence. One candidate, Uvidem, was being co-developed with Sanofi-Aventis for the treatment of melanoma. However, IDM halted development on this and two other products — colorectal cancer treatment Collidem and bladder cancer drug Bexidem — to focus on L-MTP-PE.

	Annual Growth	12/03	12/04	12/05	12/06	12/07
Sales ($ mil.)	15.0%	—	9.6	8.5	11.3	14.6
Net income ($ mil.)	—	—	(3.9)	(39.2)	(23.5)	(18.4)
Market value ($ mil.)	(52.6%)	—	186.1	34.4	34.8	19.9
Employees	—	—	—	103	—	—

IDNA, INC.

OTC: IDAI

415 Madison Ave., 7th Fl.
New York, NY 10017
Phone: 212-644-1400
Fax: 212-644-7070
Web: www.idnausa.com

CEO: James J. McNamara
CFO: Robert V. Cuddihy Jr.
HR: –
FYE: January 31
Type: Public

iDNA (formerly National Auto Credit) has left the auto financing business to focus on corporate communications. Through its Campus Group Companies, iDNA Healthcare, and OMI Business Communications subsidiaries, iDNA offers content development, management, and broadcast services for corporate events and meetings. iDNA's Audience Response Systems and Option Technologies Interactive subsidiaries provide software and services for corporate data collection, testing, and analysis that let clients respond in real-time to feedback from audiences. The company also owns 50% of the art film cineplex the Angelika Film Center (Reading International owns the rest). Chairman and CEO James McNamara owns 32% of iDNA.

	Annual Growth	1/04	1/05	1/06	1/07	1/08
Sales ($ mil.)	19.7%	7.1	11.3	14.1	15.4	14.6
Net income ($ mil.)	—	(3.0)	(3.2)	(0.5)	(7.6)	(11.8)
Market value ($ mil.)	(28.7%)	5.4	3.2	3.3	8.0	1.4
Employees	—	—	—	—	80	—

IDT CORPORATION

NYSE: IDT

520 Broad St.
Newark, NJ 07102
Phone: 973-438-1000
Fax: 973-482-3971
Web: www.idt.net

CEO: James A. (Jim) Courter
CFO: Stephen R. Brown
HR: –
FYE: July 31
Type: Public

IDT keeps a corporate finger in several pies. The company makes most of its money through IDT Telecom, which provides retail domestic and international long-distance access mainly in the US as well as wholesale voice and data services. IDT also offers wireless service and pre-paid calling cards. The company's international business, consisting of calling card sales to customers primarily in Europe, accounts for nearly one third of revenue. IDT's other operations include a capital division, which acquires and manages media and broadcast properties, and an energy services unit (ESCO), which resells natural gas and electric power in New York state. Founder and chairman Howard Jonas controls IDT with 40% ownership.

	Annual Growth	7/03	7/04	7/05	7/06	7/07
Sales ($ mil.)	2.3%	1,834.6	2,216.9	2,468.5	2,226.4	2,012.7
Net income ($ mil.)	—	(17.5)	(95.7)	(43.8)	(178.6)	58.6
Market value ($ mil.)	(11.3%)	905.3	1,057.1	955.4	955.4	559.3
Employees	(37.0%)	—	—	5,951	3,000	2,360

IEC ELECTRONICS CORP.

OTC: IECE

105 Norton St.
Newark, NY 14513
Phone: 315-331-7742
Fax: 315-331-3547
Web: www.iec-electronics.com

CEO: W. Barry Gilbert
CFO: Michael (Mike) Schlehr
HR: Tina DeVey
FYE: September 30
Type: Public

IEC makes products you may never see. Most of IEC Electronics' sales come from the contract manufacturing of printed circuit boards. The company makes a mix of boards, including models that use surface-mount technology, pin-through-hole connections, and more advanced interconnection techniques. Like many contract electronics manufacturers, IEC also offers a variety of auxiliary services, including design and prototyping, materials procurement and management, engineering, testing, packaging, and distribution. Nearly all sales are to customers located in the US.

	Annual Growth	9/03	9/04	9/05	9/06	9/07
Sales ($ mil.)	(4.0%)	48.2	27.7	19.1	22.6	40.9
Net income ($ mil.)	(23.3%)	2.6	(0.8)	0.3	0.2	0.9
Market value ($ mil.)	17.0%	8.8	5.8	6.1	8.7	16.5
Employees	5.9%	182	164	118	240	229

IESI CORPORATION

2301 Eagle Pkwy., Ste. 200
Fort Worth, TX 76177
Phone: 817-632-4000
Fax: 817-632-4540
Web: www.iesi.com

CEO: Charles F. (Mickey) Flood
CFO: Thomas J. (Tom) Cowee
HR: –
FYE: December 31
Type: Private

IESI collects, transports, and disposes of nonhazardous residential, commercial, and industrial waste and provides recycling services for more customers in two regions of the US. The company's northeastern region includes Maryland, New Jersey, New York, and Pennsylvania; its southern region includes Arkansas, Louisiana, Missouri, Oklahoma, and Texas. IESI operates a network of collection operations, transfer stations, landfills, and recycling facilities. BFI Canada Income Fund, owner of nonhazardous solid waste management company BFI Canada, bought IESI in 2005. IESI and BFI Canada together serve 1.8 million customers in five Canadian provinces and 10 US states.

	Annual Growth	12/03	12/04	12/05	12/06	12/07
Est. sales ($ mil.)	—	—	—	—	—	50.0
Employees	—	—	—	—	—	500

I-FLOW CORPORATION

NASDAQ (GM): IFLO

20202 Windrow Dr.
Lake Forest, CA 92630
Phone: 949-206-2700
Fax: 949-206-2600
Web: www.i-flowcorp.com

CEO: Donald M. Earhart
CFO: James R. Talevich
HR: –
FYE: December 31
Type: Public

I-Flow lets it, well, you know . . . The company makes mobile infusion systems used at home, in hospitals, and in other settings to administer non-narcotic acute pain treatments and a variety of other drugs, including antibiotics, chemotherapies, and nutrients. I-Flow's product line includes portable infusion pumps and catheters that deliver pain medications directly to wound sites, as well as disposable products for administration of chemotherapies and antibiotics. Products are marketed through direct sales representatives and international distributors. In 2008 I-Flow acquired AcryMed, a maker of infection control products and wound dressings, for $25 million.

	Annual Growth	12/03	12/04	12/05	12/06	12/07
Sales ($ mil.)	25.5%	47.0	71.1	100.6	93.6	116.5
Net income ($ mil.)	201.3%	0.5	(17.1)	(8.4)	13.7	41.2
Market value ($ mil.)	11.5%	254.8	405.1	330.8	357.3	394.1
Employees	—	—	—	810	—	—

IGA, INC.

8725 W. Higgins Rd.
Chicago, IL 60631
Phone: 773-693-4520
Fax: 773-693-4532
Web: www.igainc.com

CEO: Thomas S. Haggai
CFO: John Collins
HR: Barbara G. Wiest
FYE: December 31
Type: Holding company

IGA grocers are independent, but not alone. The world's largest voluntary supermarket network, IGA has more than 4,000 stores, including members in about 45 US states and more than 40 other countries, including China. Collectively, its members are among North America's leaders in terms of supermarket sales. IGA (for either International or Independent Grocers Alliance, the company says) is owned by about 50 worldwide distribution companies, including SUPERVALU. Members can sell IGA Brand private-label products (some 2,300 items) and take advantage of joint operations and services, such as advertising and volume buying. Some stores in the IGA alliance, which primarily caters to smaller towns, also sell gas.

	Annual Growth	12/02	12/03	12/04	12/05	12/06
Est. sales ($ mil.)	—	—	—	—	—	21,000.0
Employees	—	—	—	—	—	92,000

An in-depth profile of this company is available to Hoover's Online members at hoovers.com.

⊞ IGATE CORPORATION

NASDAQ (GM): IGTE

1000 Commerce Dr., Ste. 500	CEO: Phaneesh Murthy
Pittsburgh, PA 15275	CFO: N. (Ram) Ramachandran
Phone: 412-787-2100	HR: –
Fax: 412-494-9272	FYE: December 31
Web: www.igatecorp.com	Type: Public

iGate is the doorway to all things IT. The holding company oversees several independently operated information technology (IT) businesses that offer business process outsourcing (BPO) and offshore development. Subsidiary iGATE Global Solutions (formerly Mascot Systems) provides offshore software development and maintenance outsourcing. The company's iGATE Professional Services business, which includes iGATE Mastech, provides custom application and design and, in the US, offers project management services. Cofounders Sunil Wadhwani (co-chairman) and Ashok Trivedi (co-chairman and president) each own 30% of iGate.

	Annual Growth	12/03	12/04	12/05	12/06	12/07
Sales ($ mil.)	1.7%	287.8	264.6	276.0	283.6	307.3
Net income ($ mil.)	—	(9.0)	(18.2)	7.0	8.7	15.6
Market value ($ mil.)	2.8%	406.8	212.7	256.4	364.9	454.2
Employees	3.1%	—	—	5,890	6,900	6,260

IGENE BIOTECHNOLOGY, INC.

Pink Sheets: IGNE

9110 Red Branch Rd.	CEO: Stephen F. Hiu
Columbia, MD 21045	CFO: Edward J. Weisberger
Phone: 410-997-2599	HR: –
Fax: 410-730-0540	FYE: December 31
Web: www.igene.com	Type: Public

Some would say IGENE Biotechnology has some ingenious ideas about the way things should be. The company manufactures biochemical products for the human and animal nutrition industry. Among its products are natural astaxanthin, a feed nutrient which is used as a coloring agent in farm salmon, under the AstaXin brand. Other uses for astaxanthin include feed for shrimp and poultry and for coloring egg yolks. The company's proprietary fermentation of a yeast called Phaffia rhodozyma naturally extracts the nutrient, which is a potent antioxidant several times stronger than vitamin E. IGENE is trying to further develop the commercial applications of its astaxanthin as an ingredient in consumer health foods.

	Annual Growth	12/03	12/04	12/05	12/06	12/07
Sales ($ mil.)	—	—	—	—	—	2.3
Net income ($ mil.)	—	—	—	—	—	(1.9)
Employees	—	—	—	—	—	—

IGI, INC.

AMEX: IG

105 Lincoln Ave.	CEO: Rajiv Mathur
Buena, NJ 08310	CFO: Carlene Lloyd
Phone: 856-697-1441	HR: –
Fax: 856-697-2259	FYE: December 31
Web: www.askigi.com	Type: Public

IGI is betting big on small things. The company manufactures creams, liquids, and other topical products for drug and cosmetics companies using its microencapsulation technology. It originally licensed the technology, dubbed Novasome, from drug firm Novovax. The Novasome process entraps and protects the active ingredients of various skin care products, moisturizers, shampoos, and fragrances, allowing for greater stability during storage and a more controlled release when used. The company is examining further applications of the Novasome technology in food, personal care products, and pharmaceuticals.

	Annual Growth	12/03	12/04	12/05	12/06	12/07
Sales ($ mil.)	6.3%	3.6	3.6	2.9	2.6	4.6
Net income ($ mil.)	—	(0.3)	(0.9)	(1.3)	(1.7)	(0.3)
Market value ($ mil.)	4.0%	17.9	14.7	11.0	15.2	20.9
Employees	—	—	—	18	—	—

IGIA, INC.

OTC: IGAI

16 E. 40th St., 12th Fl.	CEO: Avi Sivan
New York, NY 10016	CFO: Prem Ramchandani
Phone: 212-575-0500	HR: –
Fax: 212-354-5323	FYE: February 28
Web: www.igia.com	Type: Public

Through its operating subsidiaries, chiefly Tactica International, IGIA has marketed and distributed a variety of branded personal care and skin care products. Tactica used television infomercials to sell products directly to consumers; however, the company has been forced to stop running the informercials because of a lack of working capital. IGIA is pursuing new sources of financing, but in the meantime, its auditors have questioned whether the company will be able to remain in business, given its history of operating losses. Besides Tactica, which emerged from bankruptcy protection in 2006, IGIA's businesses include Kleenfast and Shopflash.

	Annual Growth	6/02	6/03	*2/05	2/06	†2/07
Sales ($ mil.)	31.6%	2.0	1.9	11.3	25.5	6.0
Net income ($ mil.)	—	(0.4)	0.0	(16.2)	(17.2)	0.7
Employees	—	18	—	—	—	—

*Fiscal year change †Most recent year available

IGLOO PRODUCTS CORP.

777 Igloo Rd.	CEO: Jim Morley
Katy, TX 77494	CFO: Roy Bowman
Phone: 713-584-6800	HR: Mike Clark
Fax: 713-935-7763	FYE: December 31
Web: www.igloocoolers.com	Type: Private

Started in 1947 as a small metalworking shop that made metal water coolers for blue collar workers, Igloo Products is now a leading ice chest and beverage dispenser manufacturer, perhaps known best for its Playmate brand. The company's first all-plastic ice chest was introduced in 1962. Igloo makes the coolers for personal and industrial use and claims that nearly three in every four US households owns an Igloo cooler. The company's more than 500 products (including personal, beverage, and full-sized coolers) are sold through more than 250 retailers in the US and abroad. Private investment firm Westar Capital purchased Igloo from Brunswick in 2001.

	Annual Growth	12/03	12/04	12/05	12/06	12/07
Est. sales ($ mil.)	—	—	—	—	—	102.7
Employees	—	—	—	—	—	1,000

⊞ IHS INC.

NYSE: IHS

15 Inverness Way East	CEO: Jerre L. Stead
Englewood, CO 80112	CFO: Michael J. (Mike) Sullivan
Phone: 303-790-0600	HR: Jeffrey (Jeff) Sisson
Fax: 303-754-3940	FYE: November 30
Web: www.ihs.com	Type: Public

IHS Inc. (Information Handling Services Inc.) handles the hottest commodity around: information. A publisher of technical documents for clients in the energy, defense, aerospace, construction, electronics, and automotive industries, the company distributes its data in several electronic formats (Internet, intranet, extranet, CD-ROM). Products such as collections of technical specifications and standards, regulations, parts data, and design guides are sold through its IHS Engineering unit. IHS also has an Energy segment that develops and delivers oil and gas industry data on exploration, development, production, and transportation activities. The Thyssen-Bornemisza family controls about 75% of IHS.

	Annual Growth	11/03	11/04	11/05	11/06	11/07
Sales ($ mil.)	18.8%	345.8	394.0	476.1	550.8	688.4
Net income ($ mil.)	18.4%	42.6	61.3	41.8	56.3	83.8
Market value ($ mil.)	100.7%	—	—	848.9	1,668.7	3,419.9
Employees	236.5%	—	—	265	2,500	3,000

IKANOS COMMUNICATIONS, INC.

NASDAQ (GM): IKAN

47669 Fremont Blvd.
Fremont, CA 94538
Phone: 510-979-0400
Fax: 510-438-5377
Web: www.ikanos.com

CEO: Michael A. Ricci
CFO: Cory Sindelar
HR: Pam Kaur Gosal
FYE: December 31
Type: Public

Ikanos Communications hopes to become an icon in the field of networking semiconductors. The fabless semiconductor company designs high-speed programmable single- and multi-port chipsets that allow networks to achieve broadband transmission speeds over existing copper wires. Its SmartLeap and CleverConnect chipsets enable such high speeds over a few thousand feet of wire; this allows network access equipment makers to join multitenant units to the edge of fiber-optic networks, and enables broadband connections between neighboring buildings. Ikanos derives about 29% of sales from NEC, and 20% from Sagem (part of SAFRAN). Japanese customers provide nearly half of the company's sales.

	Annual Growth	12/03	12/04	12/05	12/06	12/07
Sales ($ mil.)	38.8%	29.0	66.7	85.1	134.7	107.5
Net income ($ mil.)	—	(29.9)	(8.5)	2.7	(22.8)	(33.3)
Market value ($ mil.)	(32.9%)	—	—	349.6	240.8	157.4
Employees	22.2%	—	154	178	—	281

IKON OFFICE SOLUTIONS, INC.

NYSE: IKN

70 Valley Stream Pkwy.
Malvern, PA 19355
Phone: 610-296-8000
Fax: 610-408-7025
Web: www.ikon.com

CEO: Matthew J. (Matt) Espe
CFO: Robert F. Woods
HR: Donna Venable
FYE: September 30
Type: Public

This company works to ensure that when it comes to buying business equipment, its customers say, "I can and I will." IKON Office Solutions sells and leases Canon, Ricoh, Hewlett-Packard, and other brands of copiers, printers, fax machines, and additional office equipment. It also provides an assortment of related office supplies, such as ink and toner cartridges, labels, paper, document management software, and mailroom supplies. In addition, the company offers such services as document management outsourcing, electronic file conversions, facilities management, and training. IKON serves primarily large and small businesses and government entities throughout North America and Western Europe.

	Annual Growth	9/03	9/04	9/05	9/06	9/07
Sales ($ mil.)	(3.0%)	4,710.9	4,613.5	4,377.3	4,228.3	4,168.3
Net income ($ mil.)	(0.3%)	116.0	83.7	60.7	106.2	114.5
Market value ($ mil.)	9.0%	1,070.0	1,708.4	1,354.8	1,732.8	1,510.8
Employees	(24.0%)	—	—	26,000	25,000	15,000

IKONICS CORPORATION

NASDAQ (CM): IKNX

4832 Grand Ave.
Duluth, MN 55807
Phone: 218-628-2217
Fax: 218-628-3245
Web: www.ikonics.com

CEO: William C. (Bill) Ulland
CFO: Jon Gerlach
HR: Molly Haugen
FYE: December 31
Type: Public

IKONICS makes light-sensitive coatings (emulsions) and films, used primarily by the screen printing and abrasive etching markets (to create stencil images for the one and to create architectural glass and art pieces for the other). Screen printing products represent IKONICS' largest product line. The company also makes photoresist films and metal etching materials for sign making and ink jet receptive films for creating photopositives and photonegatives. IKONICS sells its products through about 180 distributors worldwide, although the US accounts for two thirds of sales.

	Annual Growth	12/03	12/04	12/05	12/06	12/07
Sales ($ mil.)	6.9%	12.1	13.7	14.0	14.9	15.8
Net income ($ mil.)	24.5%	0.5	0.8	0.9	1.1	1.2
Market value ($ mil.)	38.0%	5.2	14.2	12.5	15.1	19.0
Employees	—	—	—	68	—	—

IL FORNAIO (AMERICA) CORPORATION

770 Tamalpais Dr., Ste. 400
Corte Madera, CA 94925
Phone: 415-945-0500
Fax: 415-924-0906
Web: www.ilfornaio.com

CEO: Michael J. (Mike) Hislop
CFO: Sean Maloney
HR: Mim McNulty
FYE: Last Sunday in December
Type: Private

Cooking up some Old World flavors is bringing in the dough for Il Fornaio (America). The company operates a chain of more than 20 upscale Italian restaurants under the Il Fornaio (Italian for "the baker") banner. The dining spots, located mostly in California, offer authentic regional cuisine for lunch and dinner (some locations also feature a breakfast menu), along with catering and banquet services. Many of the locations also sport an in-restaurant market offering baked goods, coffee, and other food items. In addition, the company owns Corner Baker Cafe operator CBC Restaurant Corp. Il Fornaio was established in Italy in 1972; the company is owned by private equity firm Bruckmann, Rosser, Sherrill, & Co.

	Annual Growth	12/03	12/04	12/05	12/06	12/07
Est. sales ($ mil.)	—	—	—	—	—	139.5
Employees	—	—	—	—	—	6,600

ILINC COMMUNICATIONS, INC.

AMEX: ILC

2999 N. 44th St., Ste. 650
Phoenix, AZ 85018
Phone: 602-952-1200
Fax: 602-952-0544
Web: www.ilinc.com

CEO: James M. Powers Jr.
CFO: James L. Dunn Jr.
HR: –
FYE: March 31
Type: Public

iLinc Communications provides Web-based voice and video conferencing and collaboration software and services. Companies use its products to handle meetings among co-workers at different locations, share documents and deliver corporate presentations, facilitate communications with customers, and offer remote training and education courses. iLinc Communications also offers implementation, technical support, and training services. Clients have included California Software, Cypress MicroSystems, Maximizer Software, National University, and QUALCOMM.

	Annual Growth	3/03	3/04	3/05	3/06	3/07
Sales ($ mil.)	18.5%	7.2	5.9	10.4	12.5	14.2
Net income ($ mil.)	—	(3.8)	(2.0)	(5.3)	(1.2)	0.1
Market value ($ mil.)	40.6%	5.7	24.3	8.9	11.3	22.2
Employees	—	—	—	—	78	—

ILITCH HOLDINGS, INC.

2211 Woodward Ave.
Detroit, MI 48201
Phone: 313-983-6600
Fax: 313-983-6094
Web: www.ilitchholdings.com

CEO: Christopher (Chris) Ilitch
CFO: Scott Fisher
HR: Joni C. Nelson
FYE: December 31
Type: Holding company

This holding company rules over a Caesar, tames Tigers, and takes flight on the ice. Ilitch Holdings controls the business interests of Mike and Marian Ilitch and their family, which includes the Little Caesars pizza chain, the Detroit Tigers baseball team, and the Detroit Red Wings hockey team. The holding company also oversees Olympia Entertainment, an entertainment company that owns Detroit's Fox Theatre and operates Comerica Park, Joe Louis Arena, and Cobo Arena. The Ilitches started Little Caesars in 1959, acquired control of the Red Wings in 1982, and bought the Tigers in 1992. They formed Ilitch Holdings in 1999.

	Annual Growth	12/02	12/03	12/04	12/05	12/06
Est. sales ($ mil.)	(1.3%)	—	—	—	1,500.0	1,480.0
Employees	41.7%	—	—	—	12,000	17,000

🔲 An in-depth profile of this company is available to Hoover's Online members at hoovers.com.

801

ILLINOIS POWER COMPANY

370 S. Main St.
Decatur, IL 62523
Phone: 217-424-6600
Fax: –
Web: www.illinoispower.com

CEO: Scott A. Cisel
CFO: Martin J. Lyons
HR: Donna K. Martin
FYE: December 31
Type: Subsidiary

Illinois Power, a unit of Ameren, lights up homes and businesses in the Land of Lincoln. The regulated utility, which operates as AmerenIP, serves 626,000 electricity customers and 427,000 natural gas customers. Illinois Power owns 23,390 circuit miles of electric transmission and distribution lines and more than 8,720 miles of gas transmission and distribution mains. To prepare for deregulation, the company has divested its fossil-fueled and nuclear power plant interests; it receives its power supply through contracts with generation companies and other utilities.

	Annual Growth	12/03	12/04	12/05	12/06	12/07
Sales ($ mil.)	—	—	—	—	—	1,646.0
Net income ($ mil.)	—	—	—	—	—	26.0
Employees	—	—	—	—	—	1,165

⊞ ILLINOIS TOOL WORKS INC.

NYSE: ITW

3600 W. Lake Ave.
Glenview, IL 60026
Phone: 847-724-7500
Fax: 847-657-4261
Web: www.itw.com

CEO: David B. Speer
CFO: Ronald D. Kropp
HR: Sharon M. Brady
FYE: December 31
Type: Public

Don't let the name fool you — Illinois Tool Works (ITW) hammers out a lot more than just tools, and it operates well beyond the Land of Lincoln. Doing business through more than 800 separate companies in about 50 nations, ITW makes a range of products used in the automotive, construction, electronics, food and beverage, paper products, and pharmaceuticals industries. The company's engineered products segment offers fasteners, nail guns, industrial adhesives, and automotive transmission components. The specialty systems segment's products include paint application equipment and welding machines. ITW gets about half of its sales in North America.

	Annual Growth	12/03	12/04	12/05	12/06	12/07
Sales ($ mil.)	12.7%	10,035.6	11,731.4	12,921.8	14,055.0	16,170.6
Net income ($ mil.)	16.3%	1,023.7	1,338.7	1,494.9	1,717.8	1,869.9
Market value ($ mil.)	21.7%	12,958.9	14,429.1	12,354.4	25,812.0	28,381.4
Employees	6.0%	47,500	49,000	50,000	55,000	60,000

ILLUMINA, INC.

NASDAQ (GM): ILMN

9885 Towne Centre Dr.
San Diego, CA 92121
Phone: 858-202-4500
Fax: 858-202-4545
Web: www.illumina.com

CEO: Jay T. Flatley
CFO: Christian O. Henry
HR: Kevin Harley
FYE: December 31
Type: Public

Illumina elucidates the human genome. The firm makes instruments used by life sciences and pharmaceutical researchers to test and analyze genes. With its Oligator technology, Illumina makes short pieces of DNA and with partner Invitrogen markets the products to researchers. Illumina also sells systems (based on its proprietary BeadArray technology) that facilitate large-scale testing of genetic variation and function in groups of people. The tests allow medical researchers to determine what genetic combinations are associated with various diseases, enabling faster diagnosis, better drugs, and individualized treatment. Customers include pharma and biotech companies, research centers, and academic institutions.

	Annual Growth	12/03	12/04	12/05	12/06	12/07
Sales ($ mil.)	90.2%	28.0	50.6	73.5	184.6	366.8
Net income ($ mil.)	—	(27.1)	(6.2)	(20.9)	40.0	(278.4)
Market value ($ mil.)	101.1%	230.5	361.4	582.2	1,842.0	3,773.9
Employees	66.6%	—	—	375	596	1,041

ILX RESORTS INCORPORATED

AMEX: ILX

2111 E. Highland Ave., Ste. 200
Phoenix, AZ 85016
Phone: 602-957-2777
Fax: 602-957-2780
Web: www.ilxresorts.com

CEO: Joseph P. Martori
CFO: Margaret M. Eardley
HR: Mary Kay Porter
FYE: December 31
Type: Public

ILX Resorts wants to take you away. The company develops, owns, operates, and markets timeshare resorts, primarily in the Western US. Its portfolio includes about a dozen vacation resorts located near major cities or in top vacation spots in Arizona, Colorado, Indiana, Nevada, and Mexico. Resort properties are sold, fully furnished, for one-week time units. The company's Varsity Club resorts are located near major universities and offer flexible ownership packages. (Think: football season.) ILX Resorts also provides timeshare financing and markets resorts owned by other parties. Chairman and CEO Joseph Martori and his family own about 20% of ILX Resorts.

	Annual Growth	12/03	12/04	12/05	12/06	12/07
Sales ($ mil.)	(7.2%)	65.4	60.1	56.9	54.5	48.6
Net income ($ mil.)	—	0.9	2.7	6.2	2.2	(0.7)
Market value ($ mil.)	(1.7%)	20.5	35.6	36.2	50.3	19.2
Employees	0.0%	—	—	840	840	—

IMAGE COMICS, INC.

1942 University Ave., Ste. 305
Berkeley, CA 94704
Phone: 510-644-4980
Fax: 510-644-4988
Web: www.imagecomics.com

CEO: Marc Silvestri
CFO: –
HR: –
FYE: December 31
Type: Private

Image Comics knows a lot about black ink figures. One of the largest comic book publishers in the US, its comics and graphic novels feature more risqué content than the traditional super hero-based books of its competitors. Titles include *Spawn*, *Violent Messiahs*, and *Hawaiian Dick*. The company's comics are owned solely by their creators — Image merely provides publishing, promotion, and distribution services. Image consists of three autonomous houses: Image Central, Todd McFarlane Productions, and Top Cow. Founded in 1992 by seven of Marvel's artists, the company is owned by partners Jim Valentino, Todd McFarlane (*Spawn* creator), Erik Larsen (*Savage Dragon*), and Marc Silvestri (*Witchblade*).

IMAGE ENTERTAINMENT, INC.

NASDAQ (GM): DISK

20525 Nordhoff St., Ste. 200
Chatsworth, CA 91311
Phone: 818-407-9100
Fax: 818-407-9151
Web: www.image-entertainment.com

CEO: David A. Borshell
CFO: Jeff M. Framer
HR: –
FYE: March 31
Type: Public

This Image has been altered to fit the format of your home entertainment center. Image Entertainment acquires rights to film and video titles and distributes them primarily in DVD format to US retailers. Customers include Amazon.com and Wal-Mart supplier Anderson Merchandisers. Its library contains nearly 3,000 DVD titles. The company also sells broadcast rights to cable and satellite channels and produces original programming of live musical performances. Its Egami Media subsidiary acquires and distributes digital content through video on demand, streaming video, and download channels. Image had agreed to be acquired by a group led by film financier David Bergstein. The deal, however, was terminated in 2008.

	Annual Growth	3/04	3/05	3/06	3/07	3/08
Sales ($ mil.)	3.1%	84.8	118.4	111.9	99.8	95.8
Net income ($ mil.)	—	(9.6)	5.1	(0.2)	(12.6)	(23.0)
Market value ($ mil.)	(11.7%)	60.3	116.2	78.8	91.1	36.7
Employees	—	—	—	195	—	—

IMAGE SENSING SYSTEMS, INC.

NASDAQ (CM): ISNS

500 Spruce Tree Centre, 1600 University Ave. West
St. Paul, MN 55104
Phone: 651-603-7700
Fax: 651-603-7795
Web: www.imagesensing.com

CEO: Ken R. Aubrey
CFO: Gregory R. L. Smith
HR: –
FYE: December 31
Type: Public

If you're stuck in traffic, you can't blame Image Sensing Systems (ISS). ISS's Autoscope vehicle detection system converts video images into digitized traffic data for traffic management. Unlike traditional embedded wire loop detectors, which are buried in the pavement, Autoscope enables wide-area detection using video cameras, a microprocessor, software, and a PC. The systems help users to design roads, manage traffic signals, and determine the environmental impact of gridlock. Royalty income from traffic management company Econolite Control Products accounts for nearly three-quarters of sales.

	Annual Growth	12/03	12/04	12/05	12/06	12/07
Sales ($ mil.)	12.9%	9.3	10.8	11.0	13.1	15.1
Net income ($ mil.)	(19.1%)	2.1	2.7	2.8	3.1	0.9
Market value ($ mil.)	19.7%	33.2	59.8	49.4	53.9	68.3
Employees	25.7%	32	38	49	53	80

IMAGE TECHNOLOGY LABORATORIES, INC.

OTC: IMTL

602 Enterprise Dr.
Kingston, NY 12401
Phone: 845-338-3366
Fax: 845-338-8880
Web: www.imagetechlabs.com

CEO: Lewis M. (Lew) Edwards
CFO: –
HR: –
FYE: December 31
Type: Public

Image Technology Laboratories provides medical image and information management software for radiologists and physicians. The company's WarpSpeed software includes a picture archiving and communication system, which stores and distributes medical images such as CAT scans, MRI images, and ultrasounds, and a radiology information system, which manages patient, insurance, billing, and scheduling information.

	Annual Growth	12/03	12/04	12/05	12/06	12/07
Sales ($ mil.)	(11.1%)	0.8	0.9	0.7	0.7	0.5
Net income ($ mil.)	—	(0.3)	(0.6)	(0.4)	(0.1)	(0.3)
Employees	—	—	—	—	—	—

IMAGEWARE SYSTEMS, INC.

AMEX: IWSY

10883 Thornmint Rd., Ste. A
San Diego, CA 92127
Phone: 858-673-8600
Fax: 858-673-1770
Web: www.iwsinc.com

CEO: S. James (Jim) Miller Jr.
CFO: Wayne G. Wetherell
HR: –
FYE: December 31
Type: Public

Even if your face won't launch a thousand ships, ImageWare Systems will remember it. The company's identification products are used to manage and issue secure credentials, including national IDs, passports, driver's licenses, smart cards, and access-control credentials. Its software creates secure digital images and enables the enrollment and management of unlimited population sizes. Its digital booking products provide law enforcement with integrated mug shot, fingerprint, and investigative capabilities. The company markets its products to governments, public safety agencies, and commercial enterprises.

	Annual Growth	12/03	12/04	12/05	12/06	12/07
Sales ($ mil.)	(14.9%)	16.2	10.5	9.5	10.2	8.5
Net income ($ mil.)	—	(10.7)	(9.6)	(8.4)	(5.9)	(4.7)
Market value ($ mil.)	—	—	—	—	—	27.7
Employees	(12.0%)	—	—	93	74	72

IMAGING DIAGNOSTIC SYSTEMS, INC.

OTC: IMDS

6531 NW 18th Ct.
Plantation, FL 33313
Phone: 954-581-9800
Fax: 954-581-0555
Web: www.imds.com

CEO: Linda B. Grable
CFO: Allan L. Schwartz
HR: Elizabeth Poveda
FYE: June 30
Type: Public

Imaging Diagnostic Systems is a medical technology company involved in the research and development of breast-imaging devices used for detecting cancer. Using laser-based technology, the company has created a more comfortable, radiation-free breast examination that does not require breast compression. Its CTLM (Computed Tomography Laser Mammography) system, used in conjuction with X-ray mammography, may help improve early diagnosis of cancer. The company is also researching other breast screening systems using fluorescence imaging. It had been developing laser imaging products for research with lab animals, but it has licensed the technology to Bioscan in order to focus on the women's health market.

	Annual Growth	6/03	6/04	6/05	6/06	6/07
Sales ($ mil.)	(15.9%)	0.2	0.7	0.4	0.7	0.1
Net income ($ mil.)	—	(8.2)	(8.4)	(7.3)	(7.2)	(7.2)
Market value ($ mil.)	(45.2%)	131.2	69.3	44.0	35.9	11.8
Employees	—	—	—	—	—	—

I-MANY, INC.

NASDAQ (GM): IMNY

399 Thornall St., 12th Fl.
Edison, NJ 08837
Phone: 800-832-0228
Fax: –
Web: www.imany.com

CEO: John A. Rade
CFO: Kevin M. Harris
HR: –
FYE: December 31
Type: Public

I-many isn't afraid of dealing with the fine print found in most contracts. The company provides contract management software and services, primarily to the health care, life sciences, and pharmaceuticals industries. Its enterprise contract management software helps companies create and manage contracts, track incentive programs and rebates, verify contract compliance, negotiate terms and conditions, and handle cash collection and dispute resolution. The company also provides a price management system for health and life sciences companies, and it offers a variety of related services.

	Annual Growth	12/03	12/04	12/05	12/06	12/07
Sales ($ mil.)	0.7%	39.4	38.4	32.6	29.6	40.5
Net income ($ mil.)	—	(39.5)	(7.3)	(9.3)	(15.8)	(9.8)
Market value ($ mil.)	41.5%	40.6	64.1	65.6	85.3	162.4
Employees	—	—	—	164	—	—

IMARX THERAPEUTICS, INC.

NASDAQ (CM): IMRX

1635 E. 18th St.
Tucson, AZ 85719
Phone: 520-770-1259
Fax: 520-791-2437
Web: www.imarx.com

CEO: Bradford A. Zakes
CFO: Greg Cobb
HR: –
FYE: December 31
Type: Public

Tiiiiiinny bubbles. It's not just a song. For ImaRx, they are a potential weapon against deadly blood clots and stroke. Under its SonoLysis program, the biopharmaceutical company is developing therapies for vascular disorders, such as ischemic stroke, based on its microbubble technology. Used in conjunction with ultrasound, the microbubbles break up blood clots and restore blood flow to oxygen-deprived tissues. ImaRx's commercial product, urokinase (formerly marketed as Abbokinase), is FDA approved for the treatment of pulmonary embolism. Urokinase was acquired from Abbott Laboratories in 2006 and since changing hands is being rebranded as Kinlytic. It is used in hundreds of acute care hospitals throughout the US.

	Annual Growth	12/03	12/04	12/05	12/06	12/07
Sales ($ mil.)	154.6%	0.2	0.6	0.6	1.3	8.4
Net income ($ mil.)	—	(3.8)	(5.7)	(27.9)	(0.7)	(8.8)
Market value ($ mil.)	—	—	—	—	—	19.4
Employees	(26.2%)	—	—	42	31	—

An in-depth profile of this company is available to Hoover's Online members at hoovers.com.

803

IMATION CORP.

NYSE: IMN

1 Imation Place
Oakdale, MN 55128
Phone: 651-704-4000
Fax: 651-704-4200
Web: www.imation.com

CEO: Frank P. Russomanno
CFO: Paul R. Zeller
HR: Jacqueline A. (Jackie) Chase
FYE: December 31
Type: Public

Imation wants to start fresh with a blank disk. The company is one of the world's top makers of media used to capture, process, store, and distribute information on computers and other electronic devices. Its removable data storage media products include optical disks (CD-R, CD-RW, DVD) and magnetic storage tapes. It also offers flash memory drives. Imation sells its products directly and through distributors to customers ranging from personal computer owners to large corporations. Imation has used acquisitions to dramatically expand its recording media product lines.

	Annual Growth	12/03	12/04	12/05	12/06	12/07
Sales ($ mil.)	15.4%	1,163.5	1,219.3	1,258.1	1,584.7	2,062.0
Net income ($ mil.)	—	82.0	29.9	87.9	76.4	(50.4)
Market value ($ mil.)	(7.8%)	1,244.3	1,072.7	1,589.4	1,625.1	900.9
Employees	3.5%	—	—	2,100	2,070	2,250

IMCLONE SYSTEMS INCORPORATED

NASDAQ (GS): IMCL

180 Varick St.
New York, NY 10014
Phone: 212-645-1405
Fax: 212-645-2054
Web: www.imclone.com

CEO: John H. Johnson
CFO: Kenneth J. Zuerblis
HR: David Schloss
FYE: December 31
Type: Public

ImClone Systems has got it in for the big "C." The biotechnology firm is focused on developing monoclonal antibody therapies that treat various forms of cancer. Its only product on the market is Erbitux, a treatment for colorectal cancer, as well as head and neck cancers; Imclone Systems co-promotes the drug with Bristol-Myers Squibb in North America and with Merck KGaA elsewhere. ImClone is developing Erbitux as a possible treatment for other kinds of cancer, including lung cancer; the company is also working on additional oncology-related antibody therapies.

	Annual Growth	12/03	12/04	12/05	12/06	12/07
Sales ($ mil.)	64.4%	80.8	388.7	383.7	677.8	590.8
Net income ($ mil.)	—	(112.5)	113.7	86.5	370.7	39.8
Market value ($ mil.)	5.7%	2,978.7	3,827.3	2,876.3	2,288.2	3,717.1
Employees	6.7%	—	—	991	993	1,128

IMCOR PHARMACEUTICAL CO.

Pink Sheets: ICRP

4660 La Jolla Dr., Ste. 500
San Diego, CA 92122
Phone: 858-546-2955
Fax: 858-410-5602

CEO: B. Jack DeFranco
CFO: –
HR: –
FYE: December 31
Type: Public

IMCOR Pharmaceutical is not quite the dynamic firm it once was. The company sold to the company's founders its core photodynamic therapies and changed its focus to concentrate on developing imaging agents. In 2003 it bought from Alliance Pharmaceutical a product to sell: Imagent, an ultrasound contrast agent, but it found little success with sales. The company has shut down its manufacturing operations and laid off its employees, and it is looking into ways to either license the technology, sell it, or engage in a merger. Oxford Bioscience Partners, which is controlled by IMCOR director Jonathan Fleming, owns two-thirds of the company.

	Annual Growth	12/02	12/03	12/04	12/05	*12/06
Sales ($ mil.)	100.0%	—	—	0.3	0.7	1.2
Net income ($ mil.)	—	—	—	(21.7)	(17.7)	(0.3)
Employees	—	—	—	—	—	—

*Most recent year available

IMERGENT, INC.

AMEX: IIG

754 E. Technology Ave.
Orem, UT 84097
Phone: 801-227-0004
Fax: 801-226-8848
Web: www.imergentinc.com

CEO: Donald L. (Don) Danks
CFO: Robert Lewis
HR: –
FYE: June 30
Type: Public

iMergent helps you cast a wide net for Internet shoppers. The company provides software and e-commerce services that enable small businesses to establish online storefronts. Its software helps merchants to create and maintain their e-commerce site and process orders. The company promotes seminars around the country to sell its products to aspiring e-commerce mavens. iMergent also offers related services such as consulting, creative design, transaction processing, data warehousing, and help desk support.

	Annual Growth	6/03	6/04	6/05	6/06	6/07
Sales ($ mil.)	29.9%	53.2	81.0	39.1	185.1	151.6
Net income ($ mil.)	48.0%	5.0	21.9	(29.5)	110.6	24.0
Market value ($ mil.)	58.0%	47.6	80.5	128.6	160.9	296.1
Employees	—	—	—	221	—	—

IMERYS PIGMENTS FOR PAPER

100 Mansell Ct. East, Ste. 300
Roswell, GA 30076
Phone: 770-594-0660
Fax: 770-645-3391
Web: www.imerys-paper.com

CEO: Jens Birgersson
CFO: Eric Borne
HR: –
FYE: December 31
Type: Business segment

You didn't think paper just came out that brightly white, did you? Imerys Pigments for Paper develops the pigments that render that paper in front of you so very white. It produces white mineral pigments, manufacturing kaolin, ground calcium carbonate, and precipitated calcium carbonate, which are used by paper manufacturers for coating and filling applications to improve the quality of paper and paperboard. The division of French chemical company Imerys pulls in about a quarter of the parent company's annual sales and operates globally. Imerys Pigments for Paper was created in 2003.

	Annual Growth	12/03	12/04	12/05	12/06	12/07
Est. sales ($ mil.)	—	—	—	—	—	125.0
Employees	—	—	—	—	—	1,000

IMG

1360 E. 9th St., Ste. 100
Cleveland, OH 44114
Phone: 216-522-1200
Fax: 216-522-1145
Web: www.imgworld.com

CEO: Theodore J. (Ted) Forstmann
CFO: Terri M. Santisi
HR: –
FYE: December 31
Type: Subsidiary

Show me the money! Founded by the late pioneer of sports marketing Mark McCormack, IMG (previously International Management Group) is the world's largest sports talent and marketing agency, operating in some 30 countries. The firm's clients include the hippest athletes of the day, including Tiger Woods, Annika Sorenstam, and Venus Williams. In addition to sports idols, IMG represents models and other stars including Giselle Bundchen and Liv Tyler. IMG also represents corporate clients, acts as a literary agent, is active in real estate and golf course design, and produces TV programming through its IMG Media division. Investment firm Forstmann Little & Co. purchased IMG in 2004 for $750 million.

IMMERSION CORPORATION

NASDAQ (GM): IMMR

801 Fox Ln.
San Jose, CA 95131
Phone: 408-467-1900
Fax: 408-467-1901
Web: www.immersion.com

CEO: Ralph Edward Clenton (Clent) Richardson
CFO: Stephen M. Ambler
HR: Janice Passarello
FYE: December 31
Type: Public

Immersion isn't afraid to get touchy-feely when doing business. The company develops hardware and software for simulating tactile experiences — such as the feel of an object or the jolt of an explosion during a video game — in order to enhance on-screen events. Immersion licenses its TouchSense technology to companies such as Logitech International and Microsoft, which use TouchSense in joysticks, mice, steering wheels, and other peripherals. In addition to computing and gaming applications, Immersion serves the medical (medical procedure simulation products) and automotive (control knobs) markets. Mazama Capital Management owns about 24% of Immersion.

	Annual Growth	12/03	12/04	12/05	12/06	12/07
Sales ($ mil.)	14.5%	20.2	23.8	24.3	27.9	34.7
Net income ($ mil.)	—	(17.0)	(20.7)	(13.1)	(10.4)	117.0
Market value ($ mil.)	33.7%	123.0	171.5	160.8	179.8	393.5
Employees	6.9%	—	—	133	—	152

IMMTECH PHARMACEUTICALS, INC.

AMEX: IMM

1 North End Ave., Ste. 1111
New York, NY 10282
Phone: 212-791-2911
Fax: 212-791-2917
Web: www.immtech-international.com

CEO: Eric L. (Rick) Sorkin
CFO: Gary C. Parks
HR: Helen Reese
FYE: March 31
Type: Public

Immtech Pharmaceuticals' products stunt growth, but that's the whole idea. Formerly Immtech International, the firm develops dications, compounds that inhibit the growth of such unpleasant guests as bacteria, viruses, and parasites. Targets include leishmaniasis (a liver-destroying parasite found in tropical and arid climates), drug-resistant tuberculosis, and fungal infections. Lead candidate DB289 may treat malaria and combat African sleeping sickness as well as certain kinds of pneumonia. It might also have anti-cancer properties. An alliance with a consortium of universities led by the University of North Carolina gives Immtech access to technology.

	Annual Growth	3/04	3/05	3/06	3/07	3/08
Sales ($ mil.)	41.8%	2.4	5.9	3.6	4.3	9.7
Net income ($ mil.)	—	(12.9)	(13.4)	(15.5)	(11.1)	(10.5)
Market value ($ mil.)	(48.5%)	182.1	140.7	106.6	88.2	12.8
Employees	3.8%	—	—	26	27	—

IMMUCELL CORPORATION

NASDAQ (CM): ICCC

56 Evergreen Dr.
Portland, ME 04103
Phone: 207-878-2770
Fax: 207-878-2117
Web: www.immucell.com

CEO: Michael F. Brigham
CFO: Michael F. Brigham
HR: –
FYE: December 31
Type: Public

While many biotech companies focus on human health, ImmuCell has udder pursuits. The firm develops products to help the dairy and beef farmers maintain the health of their livestock. The company's animal-health products include First Defense, which prevents diarrhea in calves; MASTiK, which diagnoses bovine mammary gland inflammation; and Wipe Out Dairy Wipes, towelettes used to prepare the teat area of cows prior to milking. ImmuCell also has products for people problems: the company has developed the human diarrhea treatment DiffGAM and Crypto-Scan, a test for *cryptosporidium* infections in humans. *Cryptosporidium* is a leading cause of diarrheal disease.

	Annual Growth	12/03	12/04	12/05	12/06	12/07
Sales ($ mil.)	15.7%	3.4	3.7	5.0	4.8	6.1
Net income ($ mil.)	15.0%	0.4	0.1	0.7	0.6	0.7
Market value ($ mil.)	18.0%	5.3	20.0	15.0	17.2	10.3
Employees	—	—	—	23	—	—

IMMUCOR, INC.

NASDAQ (GS): BLUD

3130 Gateway Dr.
Norcross, GA 30091
Phone: 770-441-2051
Fax: 770-441-3807
Web: www.immucor.com

CEO: Gioacchino (Nino) De Chirico
CFO: Richard A. Flynt
HR: Wayne Guthrie
FYE: May 31
Type: Public

Immucor makes sure you can feel good about getting a blood transfusion. The company makes automated analyzers and reagents used by blood banks, hospital, and clinical laboratories to test blood prior to transfusions. Its Galileo and Galileo Echo systems perform multiple routine blood tests, including blood type and group matching, antibody detection, and infectious disease screening. Its Capture Workstation is a semi-automated system that the company markets to smaller laboratories or as a back-up system for the Galileo analyzers. Immucor sells its systems and reagent tests directly in North America, Western Europe, and Japan.

	Annual Growth	5/03	5/04	5/05	5/06	5/07
Sales ($ mil.)	22.8%	98.3	112.6	144.8	183.5	223.7
Net income ($ mil.)	42.9%	14.4	12.5	23.9	39.8	60.1
Market value ($ mil.)	151.7%	54.4	635.9	1,017.0	1,234.9	2,181.8
Employees	7.0%	—	—	526	563	—

IMMUNOGEN, INC.

NASDAQ (GM): IMGN

128 Sidney St.
Cambridge, MA 02139
Phone: 617-995-2500
Fax: 617-995-2510
Web: www.immunogen.com

CEO: Mitchel Sayare
CFO: Daniel M. Junius
HR: Linda Buono
FYE: June 30
Type: Public

ImmunoGen is TAPping into cancer research. The firm's product candidates are TAPs, or tumor-activated prodrugs, that combine cancer-killing drugs with monoclonal antibodies and attach only to tumor cells. On its own, ImmunoGen is developing two clinical-stage compounds: HuC242-DM4, a TAP drug candidate to treat gastrointestinal cancers and some non-small-cell lung cancers; and HuN901-DM1, which targets small-cell lung cancer and multiple myeloma. The firm has additional candidates in clinical trials through partnerships with Genentech and Sanofi-Aventis, and it has outli-censed its TAP technology to the likes of Biogen Idec and Centocor.

	Annual Growth	6/03	6/04	6/05	6/06	6/07
Sales ($ mil.)	49.7%	7.6	26.0	35.7	32.1	38.2
Net income ($ mil.)	—	(20.0)	(5.9)	(10.9)	(17.8)	(19.0)
Market value ($ mil.)	7.9%	173.3	247.6	258.8	129.8	235.0
Employees	11.6%	—	—	172	192	—

IMMUNOMEDICS, INC.

NASDAQ (GM): IMMU

300 American Rd.
Morris Plains, NJ 07950
Phone: 973-605-8200
Fax: 973-605-8282
Web: www.immunomedics.com

CEO: Cynthia L. Sullivan
CFO: Gerard G. (Gerry) Gorman
HR: –
FYE: June 30
Type: Public

Drug firm Immunomedics is focused on developing humanized monoclonal antibodies (MAbs) to treat cancer and other serious diseases. Its lead product, epratuzumab, is in late-stage development for the treatment of lupus; UCB has licensed the drug for further applications in autoimmune diseases. Immunomedics is also conducting clinical trials for epratuzumab as an oncology treatment for non-Hodgkin's lymphoma and leukemia. The company has other drugs in clinical trials to treat various cancers, including veltuzumab (lymphoma) and milatuzumab (multiple myeloma). Immunomedics also makes diagnostic imaging products, and subsidiary IBC Pharmaceuticals develops radiotherapeutics for applications in oncology treatments.

	Annual Growth	6/03	6/04	6/05	6/06	6/07
Sales ($ mil.)	(11.2%)	13.7	4.3	3.8	4.3	8.5
Net income ($ mil.)	—	(7.9)	(22.4)	(26.8)	(28.8)	(16.7)
Market value ($ mil.)	(0.3%)	315.7	243.0	92.5	151.9	311.5
Employees	—	—	—	118	—	—

An in-depth profile of this company is available to Hoover's Online members at hoovers.com.

805

IMPAC MEDICAL SYSTEMS, INC.

100 Mathilda Place, 5th Fl.
Sunnyvale, CA 94086
Phone: 408-830-8000
Fax: 408-830-8003
Web: www.impac.com

CEO: James P. (Jay) Hoey
CFO: –
HR: –
FYE: September 30
Type: Private

IMPAC Medical Systems packs a technological punch. Founded in 1990, the company provides clinical and administrative management systems for cancer care facilities. Its products combine business functions such as scheduling, billing, and records management with specialized features for chemotherapy and radiation therapy treatment. IMPAC's clients include hospitals, cancer care centers, private practices, and government entities in some 55 countries; the company markets both directly and through a distribution relationship with Siemens Medical Solutions. IMPAC, which offers maintenance and support services, was acquired in 2005 by Sweden-based Elekta Group, a provider of clinical systems for radiation treatment.

	Annual Growth	9/03	9/04	9/05	9/06	9/07
Est. sales ($ mil.)	—	—	—	—	—	43.4
Employees	—	—	—	—	—	430

IMPAC MORTGAGE HOLDINGS, INC.

NYSE: IMH

19500 Jamboree Rd.
Irvine, CA 92612
Phone: 949-475-3600
Fax: 949-475-3969
Web: www.impaccompanies.com

CEO: Joseph R. Tomkinson
CFO: Todd R. Taylor
HR: Sheralee Urbano
FYE: December 31
Type: Public

Freddie Mac isn't looking so stodgy anymore. Impac Mortgage Holdings, which used to invest in loans considered unpalatable by Freddie Mac and Fannie Mae, was impacted by the subprime mortgage bust of 2007 and has ceased all lending activities of nonconforming loans. It will concentrate on conforming loans going forward — a reversal of its previous strategy, in which the real estate investment trust (REIT) primarily invested in Alt-A (one step above subprime) residential mortgages, second mortgages, and mortgage-backed securities. The REIT has also ceased its warehouse and commercial lending activities. Impac Mortgage Holdings is also considering new lines of business including asset management services.

	Annual Growth	12/03	12/04	12/05	12/06	12/07
Sales ($ mil.)	31.6%	447.3	796.4	1,472.9	1,558.7	1,342.8
Net income ($ mil.)	—	149.0	257.6	270.3	(75.3)	(2,047.1)
Market value ($ mil.)	(54.9%)	1,026.5	1,705.9	716.2	669.5	42.6
Employees	11.8%	529	752	989	827	827

IMPAX LABORATORIES, INC.

Pink Sheets: IPXL

30831 Huntwood Ave.
Hayward, CA 94544
Phone: 510-476-2000
Fax: 510-471-3200
Web: www.impaxlabs.com

CEO: Larry Hsu
CFO: Arthur A. Koch Jr.
HR: –
FYE: December 31
Type: Public

IMPAX Laboratories hopes that its combination of generic and branded pharmaceuticals will make an impact on its financial health. The company makes specialty generic pharmaceuticals, which it markets through its Global Pharmaceuticals division and through marketing alliances with other firms, such as Teva and Novartis. It concentrates on controlled-release versions of branded pharmaceuticals and niche pharmaceuticals that require difficult-to-obtain raw materials or specialized expertise. The company's branded pharmaceuticals business (called IMPAX Pharmaceuticals) is developing drugs that target Parkinson's disease, epilepsy, and other central nervous system disorders.

	Annual Growth	12/99	12/00	12/01	12/02	*12/03
Sales ($ mil.)	159.3%	1.3	10.2	6.6	24.5	58.8
Net income ($ mil.)	—	(8.9)	(25.0)	(25.1)	(20.0)	(14.2)
Employees	29.7%	125	112	150	273	—

*Most recent year available

IMPERIAL CAPITAL BANCORP, INC.

NYSE: IMP

888 Prospect St., Ste. 110
La Jolla, CA 92037
Phone: 858-551-0511
Fax: 858-551-1212
Web: www.imperialcapitalbancorp.com

CEO: George W. Haligowski
CFO: Timothy M. (Tim) Doyle
HR: –
FYE: December 31
Type: Public

This company is not part of the British Imperial System, but it can weigh and measure your wealth. Imperial Capital Bancorp (formerly ITLA Capital) is the holding company for Imperial Capital Bank, which serves individuals and businesses in Southern California, the San Francisco Bay area, Baltimore, and Carson City, Nevada, through about ten branches. It also has some two dozen loan production offices scattered throughout the US. The company attracts deposits by offering checking, savings, and money market accounts, and certificates of deposit.

	Annual Growth	12/03	12/04	12/05	12/06	12/07
Assets ($ mil.)	18.2%	1,818.2	2,318.1	3,051.2	3,415.5	3,551.2
Net income ($ mil.)	(14.8%)	29.6	30.6	24.1	26.9	15.6
Market value ($ mil.)	(25.1%)	299.2	326.3	263.9	304.7	94.2
Employees	—	—	—	253	—	—

IMPERIAL INDUSTRIES, INC.

NASDAQ (CM): IPII

3790 Park Central Blvd. North
Pompano Beach, FL 33064
Phone: 954-917-4114
Fax: 954-970-6565
Web: www.imperialindustries.com

CEO: Howard L. Ehler Jr.
CFO: Steven M. Healy
HR: –
FYE: December 31
Type: Public

Imperial Industries manufactures and distributes building materials to building materials dealers, real estate developers, and contractors primarily in the southeastern US. The company's Premix-Marbletite Manufacturing subsidiary manufactures roof tile mortar, stucco and plaster, adhesive, and pool finish products. Imperial Industries' Just-Rite Supply subsidiary distributes the company's products and such products as gypsum, roofing, insulation, and masonry materials made by other companies; it brings in two-thirds of Imperial Industries' sales. Just-Rite operates about a dozen distribution centers in Alabama, Florida, Georgia, and Mississippi.

	Annual Growth	12/03	12/04	12/05	12/06	12/07
Sales ($ mil.)	7.0%	41.1	55.3	72.3	75.6	53.8
Net income ($ mil.)	—	0.6	2.5	3.4	2.9	(1.3)
Market value ($ mil.)	(2.1%)	11.1	14.8	31.9	20.4	10.2
Employees	—	—	—	148	—	—

IMPERIAL SUGAR COMPANY

NASDAQ (GM): IPSU

1 Imperial Sq., 8016 Hwy. 90-A
Sugar Land, TX 77487
Phone: 281-491-9181
Fax: 281-490-9530
Web: www.imperialsugar.com

CEO: John C. Sheptor
CFO: Hal P. Mechler
HR: T. Kay Hastings
FYE: September 30
Type: Public

Imperial Sugar occupies a sweet spot in its field, manufacturing such well-known brands as Dixie Crystals, Holly, and Imperial. In addition to branded and private-label consumer products (white, brown, and powdered sugars), the company sells bulk sugar to industrial and foodservice customers. Its Savannah Gold brown sugar, syrup and molasses, and specialty sugars are used by Imperial's industrial customers in confections and icings. The company also sells sugar-production by-products. It operates two cane sugar refineries, one in Georgia, the other in Louisiana.

	Annual Growth	9/03	9/04	9/05	9/06	9/07
Sales ($ mil.)	(5.8%)	1,110.8	963.6	803.8	946.8	875.5
Net income ($ mil.)	(14.9%)	76.7	15.0	(19.3)	50.1	40.2
Market value ($ mil.)	32.2%	100.9	144.5	143.2	351.4	308.6
Employees	0.7%	—	—	827	842	839

IMPLANT SCIENCES CORPORATION

AMEX: IMX

107 Audubon Rd., Ste. 5
Wakefield, MA 01880
Phone: 781-246-0700
Fax: 781-246-1167
Web: www.implantsciences.com

CEO: Phillip C. Thomas
CFO: Diane J. Ryan
HR: –
FYE: June 30
Type: Public

Q: What do semiconductors, radiation treatments, and bomb-detectors have in common? A: The ion implantation and thin-film coating technologies used by Implant Sciences. The company's original products were implantable radioactive seeds used to treat prostate cancer, but its medical unit has taken a back seat to faster-growing parts of the business, including its handheld and tabletop trace explosives detectors, used to find bombs in airports and other public places. The firm is developing a walk-through portal through a contract with the Transportation Security Administration and has been expanding its security unit. It also provides ion implantation services for semiconductor makers and laboratories.

	Annual Growth	6/03	6/04	6/05	6/06	6/07
Sales ($ mil.)	23.1%	6.7	8.6	12.3	26.4	15.4
Net income ($ mil.)	—	(2.8)	(4.0)	(7.4)	(7.1)	(10.7)
Market value ($ mil.)	(14.1%)	35.6	93.1	31.9	38.7	19.4
Employees	—	—	—	112	—	—

IMPRESO, INC.

Pink Sheets: ZCOM

652 Southwestern Blvd.
Coppell, TX 75019
Phone: 972-462-0100
Fax: 972-462-7764
Web: www.tstimpreso.com

CEO: Marshall D. Sorokwasz
CFO: Susan M. Atkins
HR: –
FYE: August 31
Type: Public

Money is just paper to Impreso. Through its primary subsidiary TST/Impreso, the company makes and distributes specialty paper and film imaging products. Its paper products include thermal fax, copier, wide-format, continuous-feed, and special surface papers such as film transparencies. Impreso has six manufacturing plants and distributes in North America through more than 50 warehouses to dealers and other resellers. Impreso also owns two other subsidiaries: Hotsheet.com, which provides links to popular Web sites, and Alexa Springs, a natural spring water bottling company. Chairman, president, and CEO Marshall Sorokwasz took the company private in 2006.

	Annual Growth	8/03	8/04	8/05	8/06	8/07
Sales ($ mil.)	(12.2%)	120.5	104.0	77.7	70.3	71.6
Net income ($ mil.)	—	0.6	1.0	(2.9)	(0.8)	(0.3)
Employees	(19.5%)	295	295	191	—	—

IMPULSE ENERGY USA

3553 NW 50th St.
Miami, FL 33172
Phone: 305-593-5330
Fax: 305-593-5312
Web: www.impulseenergy.com

CEO: Harold Miller
CFO: –
HR: –
FYE: December 31
Type: Private

Gatorade may be the granddaddy of energy drinks and Red Bull may be the world's best seller, but Impulse Energy USA says it's steering the industry in a whole new direction. Impulse Energy has embraced the increasing use of energy drinks as cocktail mixers. The company launched its Impulse Energy drink in 2001 on the beaches of South Florida. In 2004 Impulse Energy introduced Impulse Zero, a zero-carb, zero-calorie version of its energy drink. Also available is Impulse Extreme, a sugar-free energy drink that triples the blend of taurine, caffeine, and other ingredients found in Impulse Energy.

IMS HEALTH INCORPORATED

NYSE: RX

901 Main Ave., Ste. 612
Norwalk, CT 06851
Phone: 203-845-5200
Fax: 203-845-5304
Web: www.imshealth.com

CEO: David R. (Dave) Carlucci
CFO: Leslye G. Katz
HR: Karla L. Packer
FYE: December 31
Type: Public

IMS Health has the dope on drugs. The company is a leading provider of sales management and market research services to clients in the pharmaceutical and health care industries. It tracks not only the sale of prescription drugs and over-the-counter products but also the productivity of individual sales representatives that work for its client companies. It offers market forecasts and surveys physicians and hospitals about drugs they are prescribing to patients. In addition, IMS Health offers consulting and other professional services. The company serves clients worldwide and operates through about 100 offices in more than 75 countries.

	Annual Growth	12/03	12/04	12/05	12/06	12/07
Sales ($ mil.)	12.2%	1,381.8	1,569.0	1,754.8	1,958.6	2,192.6
Net income ($ mil.)	(22.2%)	638.9	285.4	284.1	315.5	234.0
Market value ($ mil.)	(7.1%)	5,925.1	5,318.1	5,681.0	5,514.6	4,405.9
Employees	7.2%	—	—	6,900	7,400	—

INCA DESIGNS, INC.

Pink Sheets: IDGI

53 W. 36th St., Ste. 906
New York, NY 10018
Phone: 212-967-5212
Fax: 212-967-5218
Web: www.incagirl.com

CEO: Stacy Josloff
CFO: Stacy Josloff
HR: –
FYE: December 31
Type: Public

Who says being fashion-forward requires abandoning the pre-Columbian era? Not INCA Designs. The company, formerly Transportation Safety Technology, switched gears in 2007, exiting the security business in favor of high fashion. The company changed its name to INCA Designs after acquiring S2 New York Design, the owner of the INCA line of bags, swimwear, and resort wear. INCA clothes can be found in stores such as Barney's, NY and Bergdorf Goodman, and have been featured on *The Oprah Winfrey Show* and in *Vogue*. The label was launched by Stephanie Hirsch in 1998 after her return from hiking the Inca Trail in Peru.

	Annual Growth	12/03	12/04	12/05	12/06	12/07
Sales ($ mil.)	—	—	—	—	—	0.2
Net income ($ mil.)	—	—	—	—	—	(0.3)
Employees	—	—	—	—	—	—

INCENTRA SOLUTIONS INC.

OTC: ICNS

1140 Pearl St.
Boulder, CO 80302
Phone: 303-449-8279
Fax: 856-439-9960
Web: www.incentrasolutions.com

CEO: Thomas P. (Tom) Sweeney III
CFO: Anthony M. (Tony) DiPaolo
HR: –
FYE: December 31
Type: Public

Managing storage services is a cinch for Incentra Solutions. The company provides IT services for enterprises and service providers in North America and Europe. Specializing in infrastructure and data protection, it resells storage systems, servers, data protection software, and networking and security products from such vendors as Cisco Systems, Dell, EMC, and Symantec. It also resells third-party maintenance contracts. The company's professional and managed service offerings include systems design and integration, project management, financing, and remote monitoring. Incentra primarily targets mid-tier enterprises.

	Annual Growth	12/03	12/04	12/05	12/06	12/07
Sales ($ mil.)	166.3%	2.9	13.3	50.8	66.6	145.8
Net income ($ mil.)	—	(7.4)	(10.4)	(14.2)	(2.8)	(9.3)
Employees	78.7%	26	134	168	195	265

An in-depth profile of this company is available to Hoover's Online members at hoovers.com.

807

INCOME OPPORTUNITY REALTY INVESTORS, INC.

AMEX: IOT

1755 Wittington Place, Ste. 340
Dallas, TX 75234
Phone: 972-407-8400
Fax: 972-407-8436
Web: www.incomeopp-realty.com

CEO: R. Neil Crouch II
CFO: David R. Fletcher
HR: Michael K. Lane
FYE: December 31
Type: Public

When opportunity knocks, Income Opportunity Realty Investors (IORI) is there to answer. The real estate investment firm owns six apartment complexes, office buildings, a shopping center, a warehouse, and two parcels of land in Texas, as well as an apartment complex in Indiana. Syntek West, which oversees IORI's daily activities, owns 57% of the firm; Transcontinental Realty Investors (TRI) owns 25%. Another player in this game of six degrees of investment is American Realty Investors: It shares executive officers and board members with both IORI and TRI. Affiliates of Prime Income Asset Management manage IORI's properties, as well as those of TRI.

	Annual Growth	12/03	12/04	12/05	12/06	12/07
Sales ($ mil.)	(26.3%)	7.8	5.9	6.4	7.7	2.3
Net income ($ mil.)	—	1.4	5.4	1.4	0.2	(0.7)
Market value ($ mil.)	32.0%	7.4	5.2	26.3	27.7	22.5
Employees	—	—	—	—	—	—

INCYTE CORPORATION

NASDAQ (GM): INCY

Experimental Station, Route 141 & Henry Clay Road, Bldg. E336
Wilmington, DE 19880
Phone: 302-498-6700
Fax: 302-425-2750
Web: www.incyte.com

CEO: Paul A. Friedman
CFO: David C. Hastings
HR: Paula J. Swain
FYE: December 31
Type: Public

Incyte hopes its success with inhibitors is uninhibited. The biotechnology company is focused on discovering and developing drugs that inhibit specific enzymes associated with cancer, diabetes, HIV, and inflammatory diseases. The company's lede program is its JAK kinase inhibitor program, which covers treatments for inflammatory diseases and cancers, including rheumatoid arthritis, myelofibrosis, psoriasis, multiple myeloma, and prostate cancer. Incyte has several other products in clinical trial stages, including a CCR5 antagonist designed to prevent the entry of HIV into target cells.

	Annual Growth	12/03	12/04	12/05	12/06	12/07
Sales ($ mil.)	(7.6%)	47.1	14.1	7.8	27.6	34.4
Net income ($ mil.)	—	(166.5)	(164.8)	(103.0)	(74.2)	(86.9)
Market value ($ mil.)	14.4%	496.2	829.4	446.4	490.4	849.6
Employees	—	—	—	177	—	—

INDALEX HOLDINGS FINANCE, INC.

75 Tristate International, Ste. 450
Lincolnshire, IL 60069
Phone: 847-810-3000
Fax: 847-295-3851
Web: www.indalex.com

CEO: Timothy R.J. (Tim) Stubbs
CFO: Patrick Lawlor
HR: Dale Tabinowski
FYE: December 31
Type: Private

Its alloys may be soft, but don't try to muscle in on Indalex's business. Operating as Indalex Aluminum Solutions, the company manufactures soft alloy aluminum products such as fabricated aluminum conduit, aluminum profiles, and secondary aluminum billets, which in turn are sold to the automotive, construction, consumer durables, and electrical industries. (Some 95% of the products made by Indalex are custom orders.) Indalex operates extrusion facilities and cast houses across Canada and the US. Formerly a subsidiary of Honeywell, Indalex was acquired by Sun Capital Partners in 2006.

	Annual Growth	12/02	12/03	12/04	12/05	12/06
Sales ($ mil.)	—	—	—	—	—	1,242.9
Employees	—	—	—	—	—	3,000

INDEL, INC.

10 Indel Ave.
Rancocas, NJ 08073
Phone: 609-267-9000
Fax: 609-267-5705
Web: www.indelinc.com

CEO: Henry M. Rowan
CFO: Frank D. Manley
HR: David L. Braddock
FYE: April 30
Type: Private

The heat is on at Indel. The company is the parent of an international group of more than 50 engineering and technology companies that produce a variety of products, primarily for the metals industry. It operates through two groups. Its Inductotherm Group makes induction heating equipment and has more than 10,000 units installed worldwide. Its Diversified Technology Group manufactures metal products and components, welding equipment, electrical components and systems engineering electronics, engineering products, plastic products, and network communications products. Services range from metal fabrication to silkscreen printing.

	Annual Growth	4/03	4/04	4/05	4/06	4/07
Est. sales ($ mil.)	—	—	—	—	—	19.9
Employees	—	—	—	—	—	185

INDEPENDENCE BLUE CROSS

1901 Market St.
Philadelphia, PA 19103
Phone: 215-636-9559
Fax: 215-241-0403
Web: www.ibx.com

CEO: Joseph A. (Joe) Frick
CFO: John G. Foos
HR: Kathleen A. McEndy
FYE: December 31
Type: Not-for-profit

Independence Blue Cross provides health insurance and related services to more than 3 million members in the Philadelphia area. The company's plans include traditional indemnity, Keystone Health Plan East (HMO), Keystone Point of Service (POS), and Personal Choice (PPO). Independence Blue Cross also offers dental, vision, and Medicare supplement coverage, as well as workers' compensation, life, and disability insurance. Through its subsidiaries the company also provides assisted living, third-party administration, and umbilical cord blood services. Independence Blue Cross was founded as the Associated Hospital Service of Philadelphia in 1938; it agreed to merge with Pennsylvania insurer Highmark in 2007.

	Annual Growth	12/03	12/04	12/05	12/06	12/07
Est. sales ($ mil.)	—	—	—	—	—	1,038.5
Employees	—	—	—	—	—	6,000

INDEPENDENCE FEDERAL SAVINGS BANK

NASDAQ (CM): IFSB

1229 Connecticut Ave. NW
Washington, DC 20046
Phone: 202-628-5500
Fax: 202-626-7106
Web: www.ifsb.com

CEO: John A. Hall
CFO: Brenda Watkins Noel
HR: –
FYE: December 31
Type: Public

Founded in 1968 to provide loans to African-Americans living in Washington, DC, Independence Federal Savings Bank continues that mission today. The African-American-owned bank operates four branches in the US capital and nearby in Maryland. Although most of its loan portfolio consists of mortgages secured by single-family homes, the bank also focuses on providing guaranteed student loans through Sallie Mae. Its deposit products include checking and savings accounts, money market accounts, and CDs. Morton Bender, Independence Federal's largest shareholder with a 21% stake, has received regulatory approval to acquire a majority interest in the bank.

	Annual Growth	12/03	12/04	12/05	12/06	12/07
Assets ($ mil.)	(8.1%)	211.6	177.3	167.1	160.8	150.9
Net income ($ mil.)	—	(2.8)	(2.1)	(1.0)	(2.8)	(3.3)
Employees	(27.1%)	—	—	—	48	35

INDEPENDENCE HOLDING COMPANY
NYSE: IHC

96 Cummings Point Rd.
Stamford, CT 06902
Phone: 203-358-8000
Fax: 203-348-3103
Web: www.independenceholding.com

CEO: Roy T. K. Thung
CFO: Teresa A. Herbert
HR: –
FYE: December 31
Type: Public

Independence Holding wants to hold insurance policies. Through subsidiaries (including Madison National Life Insurance and Standard Security Life Insurance Company of New York), it sells and reinsures health and life insurance to groups and individuals. Instead of offering big major medical plans, the company prefers to offer niche coverage such as medical stop-loss insurance (which allows employers to limit their exposure to high health insurance claims), student health insurance, short-term medical coverage, and small-group major medical. In addition, the company provides disability products and group life insurance. Independence Holding does business throughout the US, and its protectorates.

	Annual Growth	12/03	12/04	12/05	12/06	12/07
Assets ($ mil.)	9.9%	898.3	968.5	1,150.9	1,259.7	1,308.1
Net income ($ mil.)	—	18.6	22.9	17.3	14.1	(2.3)
Market value ($ mil.)	16.9%	103.0	260.2	276.3	331.3	192.6
Employees	60.7%	—	—	264	652	682

INDEPENDENT BANK CORP.
NASDAQ (GS): INDB

288 Union St.
Rockland, MA 02370
Phone: 781-878-6100
Fax: 781-982-6130
Web: www.rocklandtrust.com

CEO: Christopher (Chris) Oddleifson
CFO: Denis K. Sheahan
HR: Raymond G. Fuerschbach
FYE: December 31
Type: Public

Independent Bank wants to rock your financial world. Its banking subsidiary, Rockland Trust, operates more than 50 branches, as well as several commercial lending centers, investment management offices, and mortgage banking centers in southeastern Massachusetts and Cape Cod. Serving individuals and small to mid-sized businesses, the bank offers such deposit products as checking and savings accounts, money market accounts, and CDs. Its lending activities mainly consist of commercial real estate loans (around 40% of its loan portfolio), residential mortgages, and home equity, consumer, business, and construction loans.

	Annual Growth	12/03	12/04	12/05	12/06	12/07
Assets ($ mil.)	3.2%	2,436.8	2,943.9	3,041.7	2,828.9	2,768.4
Net income ($ mil.)	1.8%	26.4	30.8	33.2	32.8	28.4
Market value ($ mil.)	(2.8%)	414.0	517.3	439.8	529.2	369.6
Employees	1.4%	—	—	722	—	742

INDEPENDENT BANK CORPORATION
NASDAQ (GS): IBCP

230 W. Main St.
Ionia, MI 48846
Phone: 616-527-9450
Fax: 616-527-4004
Web: www.ibcp.com

CEO: Michael M. Magee Jr.
CFO: Robert N. Shuster
HR: Laurinda M. Neve
FYE: December 31
Type: Public

Independent Bank Corporation is the holding company for Independent Bank, which serves customers in rural and suburban communities of Michigan's Lower Peninsula from about more than 100 branches and about 10 loan production offices. The bank offers traditional retail products, including checking and savings accounts and certificates of deposit; its Independent Financial and Insurance Services subsidiary offers investment products and services. Commercial loans make up more than 40% of the company's loan portfolio, followed by real estate mortgages and consumer installment loans.

	Annual Growth	12/03	12/04	12/05	12/06	12/07
Assets ($ mil.)	8.6%	2,358.6	3,094.0	3,355.9	3,429.9	3,276.1
Net income ($ mil.)	(27.5%)	37.6	38.6	46.9	33.2	10.4
Market value ($ mil.)	(19.1%)	503.4	573.5	570.3	578.2	215.2
Employees	—	—	—	1,111	—	—

INDEPENDENT HEALTH ASSOCIATION INC.

511 Farber Lakes Dr.
Buffalo, NY 14221
Phone: 716-631-5392
Fax: 716-631-0430
Web: www.independenthealth.com

CEO: Michael W. Cropp
CFO: Mark Johnson
HR: Gord Cumming
FYE: December 31
Type: Not-for-profit

Independent Health is a not-for-profit organization that provides a variety of health insurance products and related services to some 400,000 members in western New York. Independent Health's insurance plans include HMO, PPO, traditional indemnity, and Medicare Advantage plans. The company also provides dental and vision coverage, as well as a health plan for Medicaid recipients called MediSource. Through its NOVA Healthcare Administrators subsidiary, Independent Health manages the health benefits of some 45,000 employees who are part of employer-funded plans. And the firm strives to keep its members healthy with a variety of worksite and community-based fitness and health education programs.

	Annual Growth	12/03	12/04	12/05	12/06	12/07
Est. sales ($ mil.)	—	—	—	—	—	800.0
Employees	—	—	—	—	—	841

INDEVUS PHARMACEUTICALS, INC.
NASDAQ (GM): IDEV

33 Hayden Ave.
Lexington, MA 02421
Phone: 781-861-8444
Fax: 781-861-3830
Web: www.indevus.com

CEO: Glenn L. Cooper
CFO: Michael W. Rogers
HR: Tessa Cooper
FYE: September 30
Type: Public

When you gotta go, you gotta go. But when you gotta go too often, you may need Indevus Pharmaceuticals. With its partner Allergan, the drug firm markets Sanctura, a treatment for overactive bladder, in the US. Indevus has developed a once-daily version of the drug (Sanctura XR) and also has US marketing rights to hypogonadism treatment Delatestryl. With its 2007 acquisition of Valera Pharmaceuticals, the company added two other marketed products: prostate cancer drug Vantas and a treatment for early-onset puberty called Supprelin LA. Indevus Pharmaceuticals has built its product portfolio by acquiring clinical stage candidates and already approved drugs, primarily in the areas of urology and endocrinology.

	Annual Growth	9/03	9/04	9/05	9/06	9/07
Sales ($ mil.)	88.8%	5.2	18.7	33.3	50.5	66.1
Net income ($ mil.)	—	(31.8)	(68.2)	(53.2)	(50.5)	(103.8)
Market value ($ mil.)	20.2%	252.4	334.5	135.8	332.5	527.6
Employees	30.7%	—	—	147	250	251

INDIAN VILLAGE BANCORP, INC.
OTC: IDVB

100 S. Walnut St.
Gnadenhutten, OH 44629
Phone: 740-254-4313
Fax: 740-254-9555
Web: www.ivcbank.com

CEO: Ken Koher
CFO: Andrea R. Miley
HR: –
FYE: June 30
Type: Public

Indian Village Bancorp is the holding company for Indian Village Community Bank, a thrift that operates three branches in eastern Ohio's Amish country. Targeting individuals and small to midsized local businesses, the bank offers such standard retail services as checking and savings accounts, NOW and money market accounts, and CDs. Lending activities consist mostly of one- to four-family mortgage loans (approximiately three-quarters of the bank's portfolio). The bank also writes multifamily residential mortgage, commercial real estate, construction, consumer, business, and municipal loans. Indian Village Bancorp has agreed to be acquired by CSB Bancorp, parent of Ohio's The Commercial & Savings Bank.

	Annual Growth	6/03	6/04	6/05	6/06	6/07
Est. sales ($ mil.)	—	—	—	—	—	5.3
Employees	—	—	—	—	—	27

An in-depth profile of this company is available to Hoover's Online members at hoovers.com.

809

INDIANA COMMUNITY BANCORP

NASDAQ (GM): INCB

501 Washington St.
Columbus, IN 47201
Phone: 812-522-1592
Fax: 812-522-1611
Web: www.myindianabank.com

CEO: John K. Keach Jr.
CFO: Mark T. Gorski
HR: Pennie Stancombe
FYE: December 31
Type: Public

Indiana Community Bancorp (formerly Home Federal Bancorp) is the holding company for Indiana Bank and Trust (the former HomeFederal Bank), which operates around 20 offices in south-central Indiana. The bank offers such standard retail services as checking and savings accounts, NOW accounts, CDs, and IRAs. Commercial and residential mortgages account for more than half of the company's loan portfolio. Indiana Bank and Trust also writes mobile home, consumer, construction, and other loans. The holding company and the bank changed their names in 2008 in honor of the bank's 100th birthday.

	Annual Growth	12/03	12/04	12/05	12/06	12/07
Assets ($ mil.)	1.6%	853.3	868.2	850.7	904.5	908.8
Net income ($ mil.)	(10.7%)	9.6	5.2	6.1	6.4	6.1
Employees	(5.5%)	—	—	288	—	257

INDIANA MICHIGAN POWER COMPANY

1 Riverside Plaza
Columbus, OH 43215
Phone: 614-716-1000
Fax: 614-716-1823
Web: www.indianamichiganpower.com

CEO: Helen J. Murray
CFO: –
HR: David Ackerman
FYE: December 31
Type: Subsidiary

Indiana Michigan Power flips the switch where the Hoosiers and the Wolverines dare to tread. Founded in 1925, the geographically inclined utility serves approximately 575,000 electricity customers over its 22,000-mile transmission and distribution system in eastern and northern Indiana and southwestern Michigan. The American Electric Power subsidiary also sells power wholesale to other energy market participants, and it has some 5,500 MW of capacity from its primarily fossil-fueled and nuclear power plants. Indiana Michigan has operated the assets of Fort Wayne, Indiana's municipal system since 1975.

	Annual Growth	12/03	12/04	12/05	12/06	12/07
Est. sales ($ mil.)	—	—	—	—	—	2,043.2
Net income ($ mil.)	—	—	—	—	—	136.9
Employees	—	—	—	—	—	2,687

INDUSTRIAL DISTRIBUTION GROUP, INC.

NASDAQ (GM): IDGR

950 E. Paces Ferry Rd., Ste. 1575
Atlanta, GA 30326
Phone: 404-949-2100
Fax: 404-949-2040
Web: www.idglink.com

CEO: Charles A. Lingenfelter
CFO: Jack P. Healey
HR: Laura Wright
FYE: December 31
Type: Public

If it ain't broke, don't fix it. But if it is broke, you can call Industrial Distribution Group (IDG), a supplier of maintenance, repair, operating, and production products (including abrasives, cutting tools, hand and power tools, lubricants, and adhesives) to industrial, commercial, and institutional manufacturers. IDG has a portfolio of more than 300,000 different products drawn from more than 30,000 vendors; it sells these goods to an active customer base of 12,000 companies, including Ford, Borg Warner, and Danaher Coporation. IDG operates dozens of distribution locations in the US, as well as facilities in China and Mexico. IDG has attracted a flurry of offers to buy the company.

	Annual Growth	12/03	12/04	12/05	12/06	12/07
Sales ($ mil.)	2.7%	483.4	529.2	538.8	547.9	537.5
Net income ($ mil.)	12.1%	2.6	7.3	5.4	6.8	4.1
Market value ($ mil.)	20.6%	51.1	77.6	75.8	92.4	108.0
Employees	(0.4%)	1,260	1,325	1,300	1,300	1,240

INDUSTRIAL RUBBER PRODUCTS, INC.

Pink Sheets: INRB

3516 E. 13th Ave.
Hibbing, MN 55746
Phone: 218-262-5211
Fax: 218-262-4103
Web: www.irproducts.com

CEO: Daniel O. Burkes
CFO: Jim Skalski
HR: –
FYE: December 31
Type: Public

Smoothing the rough and tumble of industrial processes is the aim of Industrial Rubber Products. The company manufactures and supplies protective materials to the mineral-processing, power, pulp and paper processing, and other heavy industries. Operating through four subsidiaries (Irathane/Elliot, Industrial Rubber Applicators, Irathane Systems, and TJ Products), the company makes urethane cast parts, pipe and pipe-lining products (protective rubber lining for overland slurry pipes and other pipes used in mineral processing to remove tailings), standard rubber products, and engineered replacement parts (grinding-mill parts). CEO Daniel Burkes controls the company.

	Annual Growth	12/03	12/04	12/05	12/06	12/07
Est. sales ($ mil.)	—	—	—	—	—	7.3
Employees	—	—	—	—	—	96

INDUSTRIAL SERVICES OF AMERICA, INC.

NASDAQ (CM): IDSA

7100 Grade Ln.
Louisville, KY 40232
Phone: 502-368-1661
Fax: 502-368-1440
Web: www.isa-inc.com

CEO: Harry Kletter
CFO: Alan L. Schroering
HR: Marjorie Brian
FYE: December 31
Type: Public

Industrial Services of America manages solid waste so its customers won't have to. The company's largest unit, Computerized Waste Systems (CWS), doesn't pick up trash but instead arranges waste disposal services for its commercial and industrial customers. CWS negotiates contracts with service providers and offers centralized billing and dispatching and invoice auditing services. Industrial Services of America's ISA Recycling unit handles ferrous and nonferrous metals and fiber products, and the company's Waste Equipment Sales & Service (WESSCO) unit sells, leases, and services waste handling and recycling equipment. Chairman and CEO Harry Kletter owns 37% of the company; his wife, Roberta, owns 10%.

	Annual Growth	12/03	12/04	12/05	12/06	12/07
Sales ($ mil.)	(10.2%)	118.5	139.6	117.4	62.1	77.0
Net income ($ mil.)	38.8%	0.7	1.5	1.1	2.2	2.6
Market value ($ mil.)	67.6%	3.5	28.1	11.1	19.8	27.3
Employees	—	—	—	103		

INDYMAC BANCORP, INC.

NYSE: IMB

888 E. Walnut St.
Pasadena, CA 91101
Phone: 626-535-5901
Fax: 626-535-8203
Web: www.indymacbank.com

CEO: Michael W. Perry
CFO: A. Scott Keys
HR: Rayman K. Mathoda
FYE: December 31
Type: Public

IndyMac Bancorp says: Drivers, start your mortgages. The company, through its savings and loan/mortgage banker subsidiary IndyMac Bank, is one of the largest residential mortgage lenders in the country. The bank offers retail banking services through more than 30 Southern California branches, but the heart of its operations is its mortgage professionals group (about 60% of its annual mortgage production), which originates and buys mortgages through third parties such as mortgage brokers and homebuilders throughout the US. The company also markets mortgage products directly to consumers nationwide via direct mail, the Web, outbound telesales, and referral programs, as well as its branch network.

	Annual Growth	12/03	12/04	12/05	12/06	12/07
Assets ($ mil.)	25.4%	13,240.4	16,825.6	21,452.3	29,495.3	32,734.5
Net income ($ mil.)	—	171.3	170.5	300.2	342.9	(614.8)
Employees	24.0%	—	—	6,441	8,630	9,907

INERGY HOLDINGS, L.P.

NASDAQ (GS): NRGP

2 Brush Creek Blvd., Ste. 200
Kansas City, MO 64112
Phone: 816-842-8181
Fax: 816-842-1904
Web: www.inergypropane.com

CEO: John J. Sherman
CFO: R. Brooks Sherman Jr.
HR: –
FYE: September 30
Type: Public

Inergy Holdings is committed to putting all its energy into managing Inergy, L.P. This operating company retails about 362.2 million gallons of propane a year and wholesales 383.9 million gallons under such names as Bradley Propane, Country Gas, Direct Propane, Hoosier Propane, Independent Propane, McCracken, Pro Gas, and Star Gas Propane. It serves a retail base of 700,000 customers through 331 service centers in 28 states. Inergy provides wholesale services to distributors in 40 states and Canada. Inergy also owns natural gas storage facilities, liquefied petroleum gas (LPG) and natural gas liquids (NGL) businesses, and sells and leases propane equipment.

	Annual Growth	9/03	9/04	9/05	9/06	9/07
Sales ($ mil.)	42.1%	363.4	482.5	1,050.1	1,387.6	1,483.1
Net income ($ mil.)	90.4%	7.8	9.5	8.3	14.4	102.6
Market value ($ mil.)	19.4%	—	—	669.0	688.0	954.4
Employees	(1.7%)	—	—	—	3,021	2,971

INERGY, L.P.

NASDAQ (GS): NRGY

2 Brush Creek Blvd., Ste. 200
Kansas City, MO 64112
Phone: 816-842-8181
Fax: 816-842-1904
Web: www.inergypropane.com

CEO: John J. Sherman
CFO: R. Brooks Sherman Jr.
HR: –
FYE: September 30
Type: Public

Inergy has put its energy into acquiring propane companies (more than 60 purchases since its founding in 1996). The company retails about 362 million gallons of propane a year and wholesales about 384 million gallons under such names as Bradley Propane, Country Gas, Direct Propane, Hoosier Propane, Independent Propane, McCracken, Pro Gas, and Star Gas Propane. It serves a retail base of 700,000 customers through 321 service centers in 28 states. Inergy provides wholesale services to about 350 distributors in 40 states and Canada. Inergy also owns natural gas storage facilities, liquefied petroleum gas (LPG) and natural gas liquids (NGL) businesses, and sells and leases propane equipment.

	Annual Growth	9/03	9/04	9/05	9/06	9/07
Sales ($ mil.)	42.1%	363.4	482.5	1,050.1	1,387.6	1,483.1
Net income ($ mil.)	49.3%	13.5	(4.6)	38.6	9.8	67.0
Market value ($ mil.)	92.9%	113.8	481.9	995.8	1,225.9	1,573.6
Employees	1.9%	—	—	2,862	3,021	2,971

INFINERA CORPORATION

NASDAQ (GM): INFN

169 Java Dr.
Sunnyvale, CA 94089
Phone: 408-572-5200
Fax: 408-572-5343
Web: www.infinera.com

CEO: Jagdeep Singh
CFO: Duston M. Williams
HR: Paul M. Whitney
FYE: December 31
Type: Public

To Infinera, and beyond! The buzz on this company is that it designs photonic integrated circuits (PICs) intended to replace much larger components within optical networks. It also offers networking equipment built around these chips. Infinera's chips are made from indium phosphide, a specialized compound semiconductor material that offers light-years faster performance than standard silicon. Customers include cable system operators, Internet service providers, and telecommunications carriers, such as Cox Communications, freenet, Global Crossing, Level 3 Communications (47% of sales), Qwest Communications, and XO Communications. Infinera gets most of its sales in North America.

	Annual Growth	12/03	12/04	12/05	12/06	12/07
Sales ($ mil.)	642.8%	—	0.6	4.1	58.2	245.9
Net income ($ mil.)	—	—	(66.5)	(64.8)	(89.9)	(55.3)
Market value ($ mil.)	2,159.6%	—	—	2.5	8.0	1,286.7
Employees	—	—	—	—	—	711

INFINITE GROUP, INC.

OTC: IMCI

60 Office Park Way
Pittsford, NY 14534
Phone: 585-385-0610
Fax: 585-385-0614
Web: www.us-igi.com

CEO: Michael S. Smith
CFO: Michael S. Smith
HR: Michael Amici
FYE: December 31
Type: Public

Infinite Group, Inc. (IGI) has endless ways to develop its customers' high technology. Once a provider of laser applications, the company has moved its focus to providing information technology (IT) services, such as systems integration, e-commerce portal development, and application implementation, as well as biometrics services to corporate as well as federal, state, and local government customers. Clients include Unisys, the United States Air Force Research Laboratory, and the US Department of Homeland Security. Through its Laser Fare division, the company provides laser-based material processing services.

	Annual Growth	12/03	12/04	12/05	12/06	12/07
Sales ($ mil.)	102.5%	0.5	5.7	8.5	6.4	8.4
Net income ($ mil.)	—	(1.2)	0.6	0.0	(1.6)	(0.8)
Market value ($ mil.)	73.7%	—	3.5	5.0	11.9	18.4
Employees	—	—	—	—	—	—

INFINITY ENERGY RESOURCES, INC.

NASDAQ (GM): IFNY

633 17th St., Ste. 1800
Denver, CO 80202
Phone: 720-932-7800
Fax: 720-932-5409
Web: www.infinity-res.com

CEO: Stanton E. Ross
CFO: Daniel F. Hutchins
HR: –
FYE: December 31
Type: Public

Maybe nothing lasts forever, but Infinity Energy Resources hopes that US demand for fossil fuels won't go away for a long, long time. The company focuses its oil exploration and production operations in the Fort Worth Basin of Texas and in the Rocky Mountain region in the Greater Green River Basin in Wyoming and the Sand Wash and Piceance Basins Colorado. It is also pursuing an opportunity in offshore Nicaragua. The company has proved reserves of 16.1 billion cu. ft. of natural gas equivalent. Infinity Energy Resources has exited the oil services business. In 2006 it sold its Consolidated Oil Well Services subsidiary (cementing, acidizing, and fracturing services) and CIS-Oklahoma Inc.

	Annual Growth	12/03	12/04	12/05	12/06	12/07
Sales ($ mil.)	(15.2%)	18.2	21.0	30.8	12.3	9.4
Net income ($ mil.)	—	(9.9)	(4.6)	(13.6)	(12.7)	(30.8)
Market value ($ mil.)	(25.2%)	37.0	108.5	97.5	60.7	11.6
Employees	—	—	—	143	—	—

INFINITY PHARMACEUTICALS, INC.

NASDAQ (GM): INFI

780 Memorial Dr.
Cambridge, MA 02139
Phone: 617-453-1000
Fax: 617-453-1001
Web: www.ipi.com

CEO: Steven H. Holtzman
CFO: Adelene Q. Perkins
HR: –
FYE: December 31
Type: Public

Infinity Pharmaceuticals acts on the endless possibilities for new cancer treatments. The firm develops small-molecule anti-cancer drugs for applications in many types of cancer therapy. Its most advanced candidate is retaspimycin, which is in clinical trials for gastrointestinal, lung, and prostate cancers. Other cancer drugs in the pipeline are in discovery or early development phases. Infinity Pharmaceuticals has development partnerships with Novartis, Amgen, and Johnson & Johnson Pharmaceutical Research & Development. In 2006 Infinity merged with Discovery Partners International (DPI) in a reverse merger that made Infinity a public company.

	Annual Growth	12/03	12/04	12/05	12/06	12/07
Est. sales ($ mil.)	—	—	—	—	—	24.5
Net income ($ mil.)	—	—	—	—	—	(16.9)
Market value ($ mil.)	(22.3%)	—	—	—	242.3	188.2
Employees	—	—	—	—	—	—

An in-depth profile of this company is available to Hoover's Online members at hoovers.com.

INFINITY PROPERTY AND CASUALTY

NASDAQ (GS): IPCC

3700 Colonnade Pkwy.
Birmingham, AL 35243
Phone: 205-870-4000
Fax: 205-803-8231
Web: www.ipacc.com

CEO: James R. Gober
CFO: Roger Smith
HR: –
FYE: December 31
Type: Public

Infinity Property and Casualty Corporation covers all types of drivers, with emphasis on the infinitely bad ones. The insurer primarily provides personal nonstandard auto policies — Infinity is a leading writer of policies for high-risk drivers in the US. The company also offers standard and preferred personal auto, commercial nonstandard, and classic collector auto insurance. Licensed in all 50 states, the company currently focuses its business in 18 states, of which five — California, Florida, Georgia, Texas, and Pennsylvania — are key markets.

	Annual Growth	12/03	12/04	12/05	12/06	12/07
Assets ($ mil.)	0.2%	1,900.1	1,944.9	1,971.7	2,014.3	1,916.6
Net income ($ mil.)	5.4%	58.2	96.4	106.3	87.3	71.9
Market value ($ mil.)	(3.6%)	677.0	727.6	770.0	949.3	585.3
Employees	0.0%	—	—	2,100	2,100	2,100

INFLUENT INC.

565 Metro Place South, Ste. 250
Dublin, OH 43017
Phone: 614-280-1600
Fax: 614-280-1610
Web: www.influentinc.com

CEO: Andrew C. (Andy) Jacobs
CFO: Roger E. Jacobs
HR: –
FYE: December 31
Type: Private

Whatever you want to say to customers, Influent knows how to say it. Influent (formerly Interactive Teleservices Corporation) provides outsourced customer care services through its 10 contact centers located in the US and Asia. The company provides inbound, outbound, Web- or phone-based customer service and sales, serving such industries as financial services, insurance, telecommunications, and publishing. It is able to provide its outsourced services in English, Japanese, Spanish, and Portuguese. In early 2008, Influent agreed to be acquired by IPVG, an information technology outsourcer based in the Philippines.

	Annual Growth	12/03	12/04	12/05	12/06	12/07
Est. sales ($ mil.)	—	—	—	—	—	41.0
Employees	—	—	—	—	—	1,300

INFOCROSSING, INC.

2 Christie Heights St.
Leonia, NJ 07605
Phone: 201-840-4700
Fax: 201-840-7250
Web: www.infocrossing.com

CEO: Zach Lonstein
CFO: William J. McHale Jr.
HR: –
FYE: December 31
Type: Subsidiary

Infocrossing dots the i's and crosses the t's when it comes to managing your information technology services. The company provides a variety of outsourced IT services for customers, including ADT Security Services, Alicomp, IBM, and Elementis. Strategic partners include CA, Cisco, and Sun Microsystems. Infocrossing's services include computer facilities management, application development, remote monitoring, data center and data processing outsourcing, and network management. The company also offers infrastructure management consulting, mainframe and open system outsourcing, managed hosting, and disaster recovery services. Infocrossing was acquired by Wipro in 2007.

	Annual Growth	12/02	12/03	12/04	12/05	12/06
Sales ($ mil.)	45.7%	50.8	55.2	104.9	148.0	229.2
Net income ($ mil.)	66.7%	1.1	1.4	20.0	2.6	8.5
Employees	39.0%	236	257	553	838	882

INFOCUS CORPORATION

NASDAQ (GM): INFS

27500 SW Parkway Ave.
Wilsonville, OR 97070
Phone: 503-685-8888
Fax: 503-685-8887
Web: www.infocus.com

CEO: Robert G. (Bob) O'Malley
CFO: Lisa K. Prentice
HR: –
FYE: December 31
Type: Public

InFocus' projections are right on target. The company is a leading maker of projectors that can present output from computers, VCRs, and DVD and laserdisc players. Its products include portable projectors, projectors for conference rooms and auditoriums, and home theater models. Larger models are used to make business presentations and double as big-screen TVs when connected to a VCR or DVD player. InFocus sells its products through distributors such as Ingram Micro (about 22% of sales in 2007) and Tech Data, resellers that brand the projectors under their own labels, and directly to retailers and corporations.

	Annual Growth	12/03	12/04	12/05	12/06	12/07
Sales ($ mil.)	(15.5%)	604.5	648.9	532.1	374.8	308.2
Net income ($ mil.)	—	(109.5)	7.6	(79.8)	(61.9)	(25.6)
Market value ($ mil.)	(33.6%)	382.6	363.1	159.2	106.1	74.2
Employees	(22.0%)	—	—	554	456	337

INFOGROUP INC.

NASDAQ (GS): IUSA

5711 S. 86th Circle
Omaha, NE 68127
Phone: 402-593-4500
Fax: 402-596-8902
Web: www.infogroup.com

CEO: Vinod (Vin) Gupta
CFO: Stormy L. Dean
HR: Jim Stultz
FYE: December 31
Type: Public

Huddled masses yearning for information can immigrate to infoGROUP (formerly infoUSA). The company is a leading provider of business and consumer information and research services for direct marketing, sales prospecting, and business intelligence. Its Data Group has 12 databases with contact and credit information covering some 15 million businesses. The Data Group also includes Web-based information firm OneSource Information Services. The firm licenses its data to third parties such as Google, Yahoo!, and AOL. infoGROUP also has divisions devoted to services (infoUSA Services Group) and marketing. Chairman and CEO Vinod Gupta owns more than 35% of the company, which changed its name from infoUSA in 2008.

	Annual Growth	12/02	12/03	12/04	12/05	*12/06
Sales ($ mil.)	9.5%	302.5	311.3	344.9	383.2	434.9
Net income ($ mil.)	13.0%	20.4	19.7	17.8	31.5	33.3
Market value ($ mil.)	27.0%	254.0	387.3	595.1	587.5	660.5
Employees	19.6%	2,000	2,400	2,332	2,695	4,089

*Most recent year available

INFOLOGIX, INC.

OTC: IFLG

101 E. County Line Rd.
Hatboro, PA 19040
Phone: 215-604-0691
Fax: 215-604-0695
Web: www.infologixsys.com

CEO: David T. Gulian
CFO: John A. Roberts
HR: –
FYE: December 31
Type: Public

InfoLogix works the hard and soft sides of logistics problems. The company, which is divided into health care and enterprise divisions, provides hardware, software, wireless communications infrastructure, and consulting to give hospitals and large companies mobile computer access. It uses RFID systems and runs proprietary software on handheld computers, cell phones, and mobile workstations to create networks that connect with existing business software. Services include online training, technical support and maintenance, project management, and system configuration.

	Annual Growth	12/03	12/04	12/05	12/06	12/07
Sales ($ mil.)	19.6%	—	46.1	55.5	60.8	78.8
Net income ($ mil.)	—	—	—	—	(1.9)	(3.2)
Market value ($ mil.)	(55.6%)	—	—	—	123.4	54.8
Employees	800.0%	—	1	1	81	—

INFOR GLOBAL SOLUTIONS, INC.

13560 Morris Rd., Ste. 4100
Alpharetta, GA 30004
Phone: 678-319-8000
Fax: 678-319-8682
Web: www.infor.com

CEO: C. James (Jim) Schaper
CFO: Raghavan (Raj) Rajaji
HR: Glenn Goldberg
FYE: May 31
Type: Private

Before manufacturers and distributors get products to the shelf, Infor gets software to their computers. Infor Global Solutions supplies customers with enterprise resource planning, business intelligence, relationship management, demand management, supply chain planning, and warehouse management software. Infor targets customers in such industries as automotive, chemicals, consumer packaged goods, food and beverage processing, metal fabrication, and pharmaceuticals. Its client list includes Bristol-Myers Squibb, Cargill, Coca-Cola Enterprises, GlaxoSmithKline, Grohe, Heinz, and TRW. Infor is backed by Golden Gate Capital and Summit Partners.

	Annual Growth	5/02	5/03	5/04	5/05	5/06
Est. sales ($ mil.)	—	—	—	—	—	2,080.0
Employees	—	—	—	—	—	9,200

INFORMATICA CORPORATION

NASDAQ (GS): INFA

100 Cardinal Way
Redwood City, CA 94063
Phone: 650-385-5000
Fax: 650-385-5500
Web: www.informatica.com

CEO: Sohaib Abbasi
CFO: Earl E. Fry
HR: –
FYE: December 31
Type: Public

Thinking about data? Think Informatica. The company provides enterprise data integration software that enables companies to access, integrate, and consolidate their data across a variety of systems and users. Informatica's PowerCenter platform consolidates, codes, and moves large data warehouses, and its PowerExchange software enables access to bulk or changed data. Other products include PowerAnalyzer, an application for improving data performance and efficiency, and SuperGlue, a metadata tool that creates data about data, integrating information from different databases to identify redundancies and analyze how the data is being used. Informatica's more than 2,700 customers include ABN AMRO, Avnet, and CVS.

	Annual Growth	12/03	12/04	12/05	12/06	12/07
Sales ($ mil.)	17.5%	205.5	219.7	267.4	324.6	391.3
Net income ($ mil.)	65.4%	7.3	(104.4)	33.8	36.2	54.6
Market value ($ mil.)	16.0%	871.7	704.6	1,048.1	1,049.2	1,576.3
Employees	16.3%	—	—	1,010	1,221	1,365

INFORMATION ANALYSIS INCORPORATED

OTC: IAIC

11240 Waples Mill Rd., Ste. 201
Fairfax, VA 22030
Phone: 703-383-3000
Fax: 703-293-7979
Web: www.infoa.com

CEO: Sandor Rosenberg
CFO: Richard S. (Rich) DeRose
HR: –
FYE: December 31
Type: Public

Information Analysis Incorporated (IAI) gets info across. The company's software and services help enterprises and government agencies migrate from older, mainframe-based computer systems to client-server and Web-based applications. IAI offers services such as programming, platform migration, systems analysis, staffing, and maintenance to corporate and government clients. Its customers have included Citibank, Computer Sciences Corporation, the US Department of Energy, US Army, and US Air Force. The federal government accounted for about 90% of the company's sales in 2007.

	Annual Growth	12/03	12/04	12/05	12/06	12/07
Sales ($ mil.)	16.4%	5.4	9.3	10.8	9.5	9.9
Net income ($ mil.)	—	(0.2)	0.6	0.7	0.5	0.2
Market value ($ mil.)	16.6%	2.1	4.1	7.3	4.5	3.8
Employees	—	—	—	—	—	—

INFORMATION BUILDERS, INC.

2 Penn Plaza
New York, NY 10121
Phone: 212-736-4433
Fax: 212-967-6406
Web: www.informationbuilders.com

CEO: Gerald D. Cohen
CFO: Harry Lerner
HR: Lila Goldberg
FYE: December 31
Type: Private

Information Builders, Inc. (IBI) wants to help you grow your business intelligently. The company's flagship WebFOCUS software makes it easier to conduct data integration and business intelligence analysis over the Internet, intranets, and extranets. Customers use IBI's products to collect, analyze, and distribute a variety of enterprise data. The company also offers middleware technology through its subsidiary iWay Software, as well as providing consulting, training, and support services. The company was founded in 1975.

INFORMATION RESOURCES, INC.

150 N. Clinton St.
Chicago, IL 60661
Phone: 312-726-1221
Fax: 312-474-2714
Web: www.infores.com

CEO: John Freeland
CFO: Michael S. (Mike) Duffey
HR: Jane Altobelli
FYE: December 31
Type: Private

When products fly off the shelves, Information Resources, Inc. (IRI) is watching — and counting. One of the world's leading market research firms, IRI provides sales data for consumer packaged goods gathered from checkout scanners at more than 35,000 locations (excluding Wal-Mart, which doesn't release data). The company sells the data through subscriptions to its InfoScan service, which offers access to the data as well as analytical software tools. In addition to checkout scanner data, IRI gathers information via consumer panels and offers test marketing services. The company is owned by Symphony Technology Group and Tennenbaum Capital Partners, two private investment firms.

INFORTE CORP.

500 N. Dearborn St., Ste. 1200
Chicago, IL 60601
Phone: 312-540-0900
Fax: 312-540-0855
Web: www.inforte.com

CEO: Stephen C. P. Mack
CFO: William (Bill) Nurthen
HR: Ronald J. (Ron) Scheuman
FYE: December 31
Type: Private

Inforte's strong point is helping its customers manage relationships with their customers. Founded in 1993, the company offers management consulting and systems integration services to help clients forecast demand for their products or services and manage customer relationships accordingly. It also provides business intelligence insight, data analysis, and strategy consulting services. The company's clients have included AOL, Kimberly-Clark, and Vodafone. Inforte has offices in Atlanta, Chicago, and internationally in New Delhi. Inforte is a unit of France-based consulting firm Business & Decision, which bought the company for $50 million in July 2007.

	Annual Growth	12/02	12/03	12/04	12/05	12/06
Sales ($ mil.)	(1.5%)	46.0	37.4	50.0	41.7	43.3
Net income ($ mil.)	—	1.7	1.8	(0.6)	0.5	(3.6)
Employees	0.6%	229	189	250	233	—

An in-depth profile of this company is available to Hoover's Online members at hoovers.com.

813

INFOSONICS CORPORATION

NASDAQ (GM): IFON

4350 Executive Drive, Ste. 100
San Diego, CA 92121
Phone: 858-373-1600
Fax: 858-373-1505
Web: www.infosonics.com

CEO: Joseph Ram
CFO: Jeffrey A. (Jeff) Klausner
HR: –
FYE: December 31
Type: Public

InfoSonics answers the call for phone fulfillment. The company distributes wireless handsets and accessories from manufacturers such as LG Electronics, Novatel Wireless, and Samsung. It supplies retailers, wireless carriers, and distributors in the Americas from distribution centers in San Diego and Miami. InfoSonics' services include programming, software loading, and light assembly. Its logistics business includes outsourced supply-chain services such as inventory management and customized packaging. InfoSonics also sells its own line of phones under the verykool brand. CEO Joseph Ram owns almost a third of the company.

	Annual Growth	12/03	12/04	12/05	12/06	12/07
Sales ($ mil.)	39.2%	65.1	73.4	145.8	240.9	244.7
Net income ($ mil.)	—	1.1	0.0	2.7	2.5	(1.6)
Market value ($ mil.)	30.9%	—	9.3	45.7	69.6	20.9
Employees	85.7%	—	—	28	52	

⊞ INFOSPACE, INC.

NASDAQ (GS): INSP

601 108th Ave. NE, Ste. 1200
Bellevue, WA 98004
Phone: 425-201-6100
Fax: 425-201-6150
Web: www.infospaceinc.com

CEO: James F. (Jim) Voelker
CFO: David B. Binder
HR: –
FYE: December 31
Type: Public

Why crawl the Web when others have done it for you? InfoSpace operates a portfolio of online search services that rely on metasearch search technology. Its Web sites, including Dogpile.com, WebFetch.com, MetaCrawler.com, and WebCrawler.com, query such leading search engines as Google, Yahoo!, and MSN, and then collates and ranks those search results. Its metasearch technology also powers third-party search services, such as Info.com. InfoSpace in 2007 sold its mobile services business and its online directory and yellow pages business, including Switchboard.com, in order to focus on its search offerings.

	Annual Growth	12/03	12/04	12/05	12/06	12/07
Sales ($ mil.)	(3.2%)	160.1	249.4	340.0	371.7	140.5
Net income ($ mil.)	—	(6.3)	82.4	159.4	(15.1)	14.6
Market value ($ mil.)	(2.9%)	725.4	1,564.1	800.9	643.9	645.3
Employees	(47.6%)	—	—	620	530	170

INFOSYS CONSULTING, INC.

6607 Kaiser Dr.
Fremont, CA 94555
Phone: 510-742-3000
Fax: 510-742-3090
Web: www.infosysconsulting.com

CEO: Stephen R. (Steve) Pratt
CFO: –
HR: –
FYE: March 31
Type: Subsidiary

Infosys Consulting has a word or two of advice to offer about outsourcing. The company, a unit of India-based information technology services and business process outsourcing giant Infosys Technologies, consults with companies from a variety of industries on issues such as customer and product operations, enterprise systems, and IT strategy. Infosys Consulting aims to combine the disciplines of management consulting and IT consulting, and it works with its parent to facilitate the movement of work to countries outside the US when that makes sense for its customers. Infosys Consulting was established in 2004.

INFOUSA SERVICES GROUP

470 Chestnut Ridge Rd.
Woodcliff Lake, NJ 07677
Phone: 201-476-2000
Fax: –
Web: www.dblink.com

CEO: Edward C. (Ed) Mallin
CFO: –
HR: –
FYE: December 31
Type: Business segment

Mail carriers wouldn't have as much to carry if not for infoUSA Services Group. A division of infoGROUP (formerly infoUSA), the company (formerly The Donnelley Group) is a leading provider of direct mail services and consumer database information. Its infoUSA National Accounts (formerly Donnelley Marketing) unit offers traditional direct marketing services to such customers as catalog companies, fund raising organizations, and packaged goods manufacturers utilizing its database of more than 200 million names. List management unit Walter Karl markets mailing lists and database marketing services for use in direct marketing efforts while Yesmail offers e-mail marketing tools and campaigns.

INFRASOURCE SERVICES, INC.

100 W. 6th St., Ste. 300
Media, PA 19063
Phone: 610-480-8000
Fax: 610-480-8096
Web: www.infrasourceinc.com

CEO: David R. (Dave) Helwig
CFO: Terence R. (Terry) Montgomery
HR: Martha Christinziano
FYE: December 31
Type: Subsidiary

InfraSource Services is a source of comprehensive infrastructure services for electric, gas, telecommunications, and other clients throughout the US. The company designs, builds, and maintains utilities' transmission and distribution systems. InfraSource Services operates through subsidiaries including Dashiell, M. J. Electric, Transmission Services, Underground Services, REALTime Utility Engineers and Technology, and Blair Park/Sunesys. InfraSource Services is a subsidiary of Quanta Services, which acquired it in 2007.

	Annual Growth	12/02	12/03	12/04	12/05	12/06
Sales ($ mil.)	93.0%	—	138.0	651.0	865.5	992.3
Net income ($ mil.)	171.8%	—	1.3	9.6	13.7	26.1
Employees	11.3%	—	2,900	4,200	3,920	4,000

INFRASTRUX GROUP, INC.

10900 NE 4th St., Ste. 1900
Bellevue, WA 98004
Phone: 425-463-1010
Fax: 425-463-1011
Web: www.infrastrux.com

CEO: Michael T. Lennon
CFO: Douglas (Doug) Madison
HR: –
FYE: December 31
Type: Subsidiary

InfrastruX Group has the "X factor" when it comes to providing infrastructure construction services to the electric, gas, water/sewer, and telecommunications industries in the US and Canada. The group also provides design, engineering, and maintenance services through its network of infrastructure contractors (primarily for gas and electric utilities) that include Hawkeye, InterCon Construction, UtilX, and Texas Electric Utility Construction. Operations include installing overhead and underground power and transmission lines. It also provides water and sewer services on main lines, wet wells, and pump stations. Puget Energy sold InfrastruX to a unit of Tenaska in 2006.

	Annual Growth	12/03	12/04	12/05	12/06	12/07
Est. sales ($ mil.)	—	—	—	—	—	225.3
Employees	—	—	—	—	—	3,000

ING CLARION PARTNERS, LLC

230 Park Ave.
New York, NY 10169
Phone: 212-883-2500
Fax: 212-883-2700
Web: www.ingclarion.com/INGClarion/Clarion+Partners

CEO: Stephen J. (Steve) Furnary
CFO: Patrick J. Tully Jr.
HR: David J. Makowicz
FYE: December 31
Type: Subsidiary

ING Clarion Partners values properties and property values. The company provides private equity real estate investment management services to institutional investors. The firm manages about $24 billion in commercial and residential assets, primarily multi-family, office, industrial, and retail. The company manages its assets through separate accounts and commingled strategies. Property management affiliate ING Clarion Realty Services operates from more than 50 regional and branch offices across the US. The firm was established in 1982 and became part of the Netherlands' ING Groep in 1998.

	Annual Growth	12/03	12/04	12/05	12/06	12/07
Est. sales ($ mil.)	—	—	—	—	—	17.4
Employees	—	—	—	—	—	175

ING INVESTMENT MANAGEMENT AMERICAS

10 State House Sq.
Hartford, CT 06103
Phone: 860-275-3720
Fax: –
Web: www.inginvestment.com

CEO: Robert G. Leary
CFO: Jeffrey T. Becker
HR: –
FYE: December 31
Type: Business segment

ING Investment Management Americas is all about the Benjamins. The unit of Dutch financial services giant ING Groep administers approximately $197 billion for more than 500 institutional investors, such as corporations, pension funds, mutual funds, health care organizations, and insurance firms. The company also manages accounts for endowments and foundations, religious institutions, and other non-profit organizations. It employs a variety of investment styles such as private equity, growth and value equity, hedge funds, core fixed income, and multi-asset strategies.

	Annual Growth	12/03	12/04	12/05	12/06	12/07
Est. sales ($ mil.)	—	—	—	—	—	37.1
Employees	—	—	—	—	—	298

ING NORTH AMERICA INSURANCE CORPORATION

5780 Powers Ferry Rd. NW
Atlanta, GA 30327
Phone: 770-980-5100
Fax: 770-980-3301
Web: www.ing-usa.com

CEO: Thomas J. (Tom) McInerney
CFO: David A. Wheat
HR: Thomas P. (Tom) Waldron
FYE: December 31
Type: Subsidiary

From New York to Los Angeles, ING North America Insurance offers insurance and financial products including fixed and variable annuities, life insurance, individual life reinsurance, and 401(k), 403(b), and 457 retirement savings plans. One of the largest independent broker/dealers in the US, the company has 10,000 representatives serving more than 14 million customers. Operating units ING U.S. Financial Services (USFS) and ING Investment Management Americas (IIM) serve as principal operating units for ING North America, which includes subsidiaries and affiliates in Canada and Latin America. ING North America Insurance is a subsidiary of global financial giant ING Groep, which is based in the Netherlands.

INGLES MARKETS, INCORPORATED

NASDAQ (GM): IMKTA

2913 US Hwy. 70 West
Black Mountain, NC 28711
Phone: 828-669-2941
Fax: 828-669-3678
Web: www.ingles-markets.com

CEO: Robert P. Ingle
CFO: Ronald B. (Ron) Freeman
HR: Cynthia L. (Cindi) Brooks
FYE: Saturday nearest September 30
Type: Public

The Ingalls family could have used an Ingles market near its little house on the prairie. Ingles Markets operates nearly 200 supermarkets, primarily in suburbs, small towns, and rural areas of six southeastern states. The stores largely operate under the Ingles name; about five operate as Sav-Mor. In addition to brand-name products, Ingles has Laura Lynn and Ingles Best private labels. It owns a milk, fruit juice, and bottled water plant that supplies about 80% of its milk and sells the excess to other retailers and distributors. It also owns about 70 shopping centers, more than three-quarters of which contain an Ingles store. Founder and CEO Robert Ingle controls some 87% of the company's voting shares.

	Annual Growth	9/03	9/04	9/05	9/06	9/07
Sales ($ mil.)	9.4%	1,991.1	2,137.4	2,273.9	2,612.2	2,851.6
Net income ($ mil.)	36.3%	17.0	28.8	26.6	42.6	58.6
Market value ($ mil.)	35.6%	104.8	143.4	181.0	321.2	354.1
Employees	5.9%	—	—	15,200	16,100	—

INGRAM ENTERTAINMENT HOLDINGS INC.

2 Ingram Blvd.
La Vergne, TN 37089
Phone: 615-287-4000
Fax: 615-287-4982
Web: www.ingramentertainment.com

CEO: David B. Ingram
CFO: William D. (Donnie) Daniel
HR: Susan Gritton
FYE: December 31
Type: Private

Companies selling books and CDs might get the star treatment, but Ingram Entertainment doesn't mind a supporting role. The company is one of the largest independent video, DVD, and computer game distributors in the US. In addition, Ingram distributes software, audio books, electronics, and used videos and games. From some 15 sales and distribution centers, Ingram serves more than 10,000 video stores, mass retailers, drugstores, and supermarkets. The company also operates AccessIngram.com, a business-to-business e-commerce site, and creates and maintains personalized Web sites for its customers through its MyVideoStore.com offering. Ingram Entertainment was spun off from family-owned Ingram Industries in 1997.

	Annual Growth	12/02	12/03	12/04	12/05	12/06
Sales ($ mil.)	(8.9%)	—	—	—	839.0	764.0
Employees	(8.3%)	—	—	—	747	685

⊞ INGRAM INDUSTRIES INC.

1 Belle Meade Place, 4400 Harding Rd.
Nashville, TN 37205
Phone: 615-298-8200
Fax: 615-298-8242
Web: www.ingrambook.com

CEO: Orrin H. Ingram II
CFO: Mary K. Cavarra
HR: Dennis Delaney
FYE: December 31
Type: Private

Ingram Industries is heavy into books and boats. Ingram Book Group is one of the largest wholesale book distributors in the US; it ships books, as well as music, DVDs, and videos to retail outlets. It also ships internationally through its Ingram International arm. Ingram Marine Group operates Ingram Barge and ships grain, ore, and other products through about 4,000 barges and 100 boats. The Ingram family, led by chairman Martha (Rivers) Ingram (one of America's wealthiest active businesswomen), owns and runs Ingram Industries and controls about 20% of the shares of Ingram Micro (a top computer products wholesaler).

	Annual Growth	12/02	12/03	12/04	12/05	12/06
Est. sales ($ mil.)	(4.8%)	2,200.0	2,200.0	2,310.0	2,539.0	1,810.0
Employees	(6.8%)	6,900	6,730	5,767	5,200	5,200

INGRAM MICRO INC.

NYSE: IM

1600 E. St. Andrew Place
Santa Ana, CA 92799
Phone: 714-566-1000
Fax: 714-566-7900
Web: www.ingrammicro.com

CEO: Gregory M.E. (Greg) Spierkel
CFO: William D. Humes
HR: Lynn Jolliffe
FYE: Saturday nearest December 31
Type: Public

There's nothing micro about Ingram. Ingram Micro is the world's largest wholesale distributor of computer products. It provides thousands of products — desktop and notebook PCs, servers, storage devices, CD-ROM drives, monitors, printers, and software — to 170,000 reseller customers around the globe. The company also provides a wide range of services for its resellers and suppliers, including contract manufacturing and warehousing, customer care, financing, logistics, outsourcing management, and enterprise network support services. Customers include resellers such as CompUSA, Wal-Mart.com, Staples, and Office Depot.

	Annual Growth	12/03	12/04	12/05	12/06	12/07
Sales ($ mil.)	11.6%	22,613.0	25,462.1	28,808.3	31,357.5	35,047.1
Net income ($ mil.)	16.6%	149.2	219.9	216.9	265.8	275.9
Market value ($ mil.)	7.1%	2,413.2	3,301.7	3,236.0	3,457.6	3,175.2
Employees	7.4%	—	—	13,000	13,700	15,000

INHIBITEX, INC.

NASDAQ (GM): INHX

9005 Westside Pkwy.
Alpharetta, GA 30004
Phone: 678-746-1100
Fax: 678-746-1299
Web: www.inhibitex.com

CEO: Russell H. Plumb
CFO: –
HR: Maggie Feeney
FYE: December 31
Type: Public

Inhibitex aims to inhibit deadly viruses. The company is pursuing the development of small-molecule antiviral compounds targeting diseases including herpes zoster (shingles), HIV, hepatitis C, and cytomegalovirus (CMV). The company was previously focused on developing anti-infectives for deadly *Staphylococcus* and other hospital-associated infections. Inhibitex continues to work on its vaccine development program with Wyeth to target staph infections, and it is exploring diagnostics through a partnership with 3M.

	Annual Growth	12/03	12/04	12/05	12/06	12/07
Sales ($ mil.)	26.3%	1.1	0.6	0.9	0.9	2.8
Net income ($ mil.)	—	(22.3)	(25.9)	(38.6)	(31.1)	(41.5)
Market value ($ mil.)	(45.1%)	—	202.1	253.8	50.5	33.4
Employees	(53.8%)	—	—	80	37	—

INKSURE TECHNOLOGIES INC.

OTC: INKS

1770 NW 64th St., Ste. 350
Fort Lauderdale, FL 33309
Phone: 954-772-8507
Fax: 954-772-8509
Web: www.inksure.com

CEO: Elie Housman
CFO: Tzlil Peker
HR: –
FYE: December 31
Type: Public

InkSure Technologies markets custom security inks that are designed to prevent counterfeiting. The company also sells readers that use the company's proprietary software to identify and analyze marks printed with its inks, which can be used on a variety of paper and plastic materials and have a unique chemical code. Applications for InkSure Technologies systems include financial documents, product packaging, gift certificates, and tickets. Aviation security company ICTS International holds a 30% stake in InkSure Technologies.

	Annual Growth	12/03	12/04	12/05	12/06	12/07
Sales ($ mil.)	48.3%	0.6	1.0	1.6	2.0	2.9
Net income ($ mil.)	—	(3.0)	(2.1)	(2.2)	(3.1)	(3.1)
Market value ($ mil.)	(14.2%)	12.6	18.8	44.2	48.5	6.8
Employees	—	—	—	—	—	—

INLAND REAL ESTATE CORPORATION

NYSE: IRC

2901 Butterfield Rd.
Oak Brook, IL 60523
Phone: 630-218-8000
Fax: 630-218-7350
Web: www.inlandrealestate.com

CEO: Mark E. Zalatoris
CFO: Brett A. Brown
HR: –
FYE: December 31
Type: Public

Inland Real Estate, a member of the Inland Group, buys, develops, leases, and operates retail properties throughout the US. The self-administered real estate investment trust (REIT) owns about 150 properties, most of which are big box-anchored strip shopping centers. It also invests in single-tenant retail properties. The company primarily invests in shopping center properties in the Midwest (concentrating on the metropolitan markets of Chicago and Minneapolis/St. Paul); its portfolio totals about 15 million sq. ft. of leasable space. Supervalue, the REIT's largest tenant, accounts for about 6% of sales; other major tenants include Dominick's Finer Foods and TJX Companies.

	Annual Growth	12/03	12/04	12/05	12/06	12/07
Sales ($ mil.)	2.0%	175.3	187.1	182.7	178.4	189.4
Net income ($ mil.)	1.1%	41.9	49.4	47.3	45.2	43.8
Market value ($ mil.)	12.2%	585.8	1,069.0	998.4	1,217.9	929.9
Employees	—	—	—	78	—	—

THE INLAND REAL ESTATE GROUP OF COMPANIES, INC.

2901 Butterfield Rd.
Oak Brook, IL 60523
Phone: 630-218-8000
Fax: 630-218-4957
Web: www.inlandgroup.com

CEO: Daniel L. (Dan) Goodwin
CFO: Alan Kremin
HR: Barbara White
FYE: June 30
Type: Private

Feeling at sea in the real estate business? Go Inland. The Inland Real Estate Group invests in neighborhood, community, power, lifestyle, and single-tenant retail centers as well as office and industrial properties. The group includes public and private real estate investment trusts Inland Real Estate Corporation (focusing on properties in Chicago and Minneapolis), Inland Western Retail Real Estate Trust, Inc. (US and Canada), and Inland American Real Estate Trust (also US and Canada). Its Inland Real Estate Exchange Corporation lets investors exchange properties for capital gains benefits. The REITs own and manage more than 300 properties comprising 60 million sq. ft. of retail and other commercial space.

INNERWORKINGS, INC.

NASDAQ (GM): INWK

600 W. Chicago Ave., Ste. 850
Chicago, IL 60610
Phone: 312-642-3700
Fax: 312-642-3704
Web: www.iwprint.com

CEO: Steven E. (Steve) Zuccarini
CFO: Nicholas J. (Nick) Galassi
HR: –
FYE: December 31
Type: Public

Printing procurement company InnerWorkings has inserted itself into the process by which corporate customers get print jobs done. The company's proprietary software, PPM4, matches customers' jobs with printing companies' equipment and capacity. The InnerWorkings system submits a job to multiple printers, who then bid for the business. More than 6,000 suppliers participate in the company's network. InnerWorkings' customers include companies in the advertising, consumer products, publishing, and retail industries. Entities controlled by the families of two of InnerWorkings' founders own about 25% of the company, which was formed in 2001.

	Annual Growth	12/03	12/04	12/05	12/06	12/07
Sales ($ mil.)	105.4%	16.2	38.9	76.9	160.5	288.4
Net income ($ mil.)	138.1%	0.7	1.8	4.6	8.3	22.5
Market value ($ mil.)	18.5%	—	—	—	702.5	832.5
Employees	52.7%	43	85	154	153	—

An in-depth profile of this company is available to Hoover's Online members at hoovers.com.

INNODATA ISOGEN, INC.

NASDAQ (GM): INOD

3 University Plaza
Hackensack, NJ 07601
Phone: 201-488-1200
Fax: 201-488-9099
Web: www.innodata-isogen.com

CEO: Jack S. Abuhoff
CFO: Steven L. Ford
HR: –
FYE: December 31
Type: Public

Innodata Isogen handles information inundation. The company provides content management and process outsourcing services to businesses and government agencies. It oversees abstracting and indexing, data capture and entry, research and analysis, and technical writing. Customers turn to Innodata Isogen to manage such tasks as digitizing paper documents into a more manageable electronic form. Innodata also provides consulting, technology integration and implementation services, and software and systems engineering. The company has ten offshore facilites located in India, Israel, the Philippines, and Sri Lanka.

	Annual Growth	12/03	12/04	12/05	12/06	12/07
Sales ($ mil.)	16.5%	36.7	54.0	42.0	41.0	67.7
Net income ($ mil.)	74.2%	0.5	7.9	(1.6)	(7.3)	4.6
Market value ($ mil.)	10.8%	87.8	223.2	81.9	51.6	132.1
Employees	(10.0%)	—	—	6,087	5,476	—

INNOPHOS HOLDINGS, INC.

NASDAQ (GM): IPHS

259 Prospect Plains Rd.
Cranbury, NJ 08512
Phone: 609-495-2495
Fax: 609-860-0138
Web: www.innophos.com

CEO: Randolph (Randy) Gress
CFO: Richard Heyse
HR: Wilma Harris
FYE: December 31
Type: Public

Innophos Holdings adds a dash of its phosphate products to food, beverages, toothpaste, detergents, and ashphalt. Innophos manufactures specialty phosphates used in consumer products, pharmaceuticals, and industrial applications. The company was formed in 2004 when Bain Capital bought Rhodia's North American specialty phosphates business. Customers use the company's phosphates to improve the quality and performance of a broad range of products, from electronics and textiles to pharmaceuticals, water, and detergents. Innophos divides its business into three segments: specialty salts and specialty acids; purified phosphoric acid; and sodium tripolyphosphate.

	Annual Growth	12/03	12/04	12/05	12/06	12/07
Sales ($ mil.)	3.5%	503.9	538.3	535.5	541.8	579.0
Net income ($ mil.)	—	0.6	14.5	(11.7)	(32.8)	(5.5)
Market value ($ mil.)	4.4%	—	—	—	297.6	310.8
Employees	(1.3%)	1,100	—	1,148	1,101	1,045

INNOTRAC CORPORATION

NASDAQ (GM): INOC

6655 Sugarloaf Pkwy.
Duluth, GA 30097
Phone: 678-584-4000
Fax: 678-475-5840
Web: www.innotrac.com

CEO: Scott D. Dorfman
CFO: George M. Hare
HR: –
FYE: December 31
Type: Public

Behind your favorite catalog or online retailer might be a company like Innotrac, which handles customer support and fulfillment services. Innotrac takes orders through its call centers and via the Internet, and it processes them through its fulfillment centers, where customers' products are stored. The company's services include inventory tracking and management, packaging, and reverse logistics (handling of returned goods). Besides retailers such as Ann Taylor and Target, Innotrac's customers include telecom giants AT&T and Qwest, for which the company distributes DSL modems, Caller ID units, and phones. Chairman and CEO Scott Dorfman, who founded Innotrac in 1984, owns about 45% of the company.

	Annual Growth	12/03	12/04	12/05	12/06	12/07
Sales ($ mil.)	13.0%	74.7	78.3	73.9	82.3	121.8
Net income ($ mil.)	—	(12.0)	0.1	(4.7)	(5.3)	0.7
Market value ($ mil.)	(22.4%)	122.8	101.7	56.0	31.1	44.5
Employees	54.8%	—	—	840	1,300	—

IN-N-OUT BURGERS, INC.

3 University Plaza
Irvine, CA 92612
Phone: 949-509-6200
Fax: 949-509-6389
Web: www.in-n-out.com

CEO: Mark Taylor
CFO: Roger Kotch
HR: –
FYE: December 31
Type: Private

4199 Campus Dr., 9th Fl.

Made-to-order hamburgers are in and franchising is out at In-N-Out Burgers. The company owns and operates more than 210 popular burger joints located primarily in California. The chain's menu features just four basic items — hamburgers, cheeseburgers, the Double-Double (two patties and two slices of cheese), and French fries — but patrons are free to customize their hamburgers and add on shakes or sodas. The chain does not use microwaves, heat lamps, or freezers. Catering is offered via the In-N-Out Cookout Trailers. Harry and Esther Snyder started the family-owned company in 1948.

	Annual Growth	12/03	12/04	12/05	12/06	12/07
Est. sales ($ mil.)	—	—	—	—	—	216.8
Employees	—	—	—	—	—	10,000

INNOVA PURE WATER, INC.

Pink Sheets: IPUR

15851 N. Dallas Pkwy., Ste. 1200
Addison, TX 75001
Phone: 727-572-1000
Fax: 727-572-7391
Web: www.innovapurewater.com

CEO: Don Harris
CFO: Jim R. Davisson
HR: –
FYE: June 30
Type: Public

If cleanliness is next to godliness, Innova Pure Water is set. The company makes and sells portable water filtration and water treatment products under the WaterWay and Innova brand names. Its products are sold by mass merchandisers, outdoors and sporting goods retailers, and via the company's Web site. Innova manufactures a sports bottle with biological and heavy metal filters. The company expanded into software in mid-2005 through its purchase of Numera Software Corporation (a proprietary software firm) and into consultant services with its acquisition of DesertView Management Services (a management consulting company). Innova was founded in 1985.

	Annual Growth	6/02	6/03	6/04	6/05	*6/06
Sales ($ mil.)	—	—	—	—	—	0.5
Net income ($ mil.)	—	—	—	—	—	(0.5)
Employees	—	—	—	—	—	

*Most recent year available

INNOVATIVE CARD TECHNOLOGIES, INC.

NASDAQ (CM): INVC

10880 Wilshire Blvd., Ste. 950
Los Angeles, CA 90024
Phone: 310-312-0700
Fax: 310-312-5367
Web: www.incardtech.com

CEO: Steve Delcarson
CFO: Charles M. Caporale
HR: –
FYE: December 31
Type: Public

Innovative Card Technologies (ICT) is almost ready to make your plastic more powerful. The company has developed power inlay technology designed for information-bearing plastic cards. The company's primary product is the ICT DisplayCard which incorporates a battery, circuit, and display on a card the size of a credit card. The DisplayCard offers increased security by ensuring the card is physically present; at the push of a button, the card displays a one-time password that must be used in conjunction with the card for the transaction to be authorized. The DisplayCard can be configured for use as a payment card (debit or credit) or as an RFID access card serving electronic banking or data access needs.

	Annual Growth	12/03	12/04	12/05	12/06	12/07
Sales ($ mil.)	—	—	—	0.0	0.0	0.4
Net income ($ mil.)	—	—	—	(2.6)	(6.9)	(14.3)
Market value ($ mil.)	26.8%	—	—	44.9	125.1	72.2
Employees	46.4%	—	—	7	12	15

An in-depth profile of this company is available to Hoover's Online members at hoovers.com.

817

INNOVATIVE SOFTWARE TECHNOLOGIES, INC.

OTC: INIV

911 Ranch Rd. 620 North, Ste. 204
Austin, TX 78734
Phone: 512-266-2000
Fax: –
Web: www.istcompanies.com

CEO: Philip Ellett
CFO: Robert V. Rudman
HR: –
FYE: March 31
Type: Public

One can learn a lesson or two from Innovative Software Technologies (IST). The company provides business continuity services and products, primarily to small and midsized customers. Offerings include its AcXess Application Continuity Xchange, which provides Web-based access to enterprise applications and data during any IT downtime. Innovative Software entered the business continuity market through its 2006 purchase of AcXess, Inc.

	Annual Growth	12/03	12/04	12/05	*3/07	3/08
Sales ($ mil.)	(70.6%)	26.8	17.3	0.3	0.1	0.2
Net income ($ mil.)	—	(0.2)	(3.2)	(2.9)	(2.9)	(1.5)
Market value ($ mil.)	(27.7%)	—	—	—	3.6	2.6
Employees	66.7%	—	—	3	5	—

*Fiscal year change

INNOVATIVE SOLUTIONS AND SUPPORT, INC.

NASDAQ (GS): ISSC

720 Pennsylvania Dr.
Exton, PA 19341
Phone: 610-646-9800
Fax: 610-646-0149
Web: www.innovative-ss.com

CEO: Raymond J. (Ray) Wilson
CFO: John C. Long
HR: Thomas H. Watts
FYE: September 30
Type: Public

Pilots use products made by Innovative Solutions and Support (IS&S) to gauge their success. The company makes flight information computers, electronic displays, and monitoring systems that measure flight information such as airspeed, altitude, and engine and fuel data. IS&S's reduced vertical separation minimum (RVSM) products enable planes to fly closer together vertically; engine and fuel displays help the pilot track fuel and oil levels and other engine activities. IS&S uses flat-panel displays, which take up less cockpit space than conventional displays.

	Annual Growth	9/03	9/04	9/05	9/06	9/07
Sales ($ mil.)	(10.1%)	28.2	46.1	63.3	16.7	18.4
Net income ($ mil.)	—	5.5	11.9	18.6	(2.9)	(8.9)
Market value ($ mil.)	50.8%	62.0	193.4	280.3	244.4	320.4
Employees	5.7%	—	—	153	—	171

[logo] INNOVEX, INC.

NASDAQ (GM): INVX

3033 Campus Dr., Ste. E180
Plymouth, MN 55441
Phone: 763-383-4000
Fax: 763-383-4091
Web: www.innovexinc.com

CEO: Terry M. Dauenhauer
CFO: Randy Acres
HR: –
FYE: Saturday nearest September 30
Type: Public

Innovex is flexing its interconnect. The company manufactures high-density flexible circuits and interconnects used to control the flow of electrical signals within electronic devices, such as hard-disk drives, notebook computers, consumer entertainment products, LCDs, semiconductor packaging, and cellular phones. Innovex targets manufacturers in need of high-end and high-volume flexible circuits, and its leading customers are Seagate Technology (66% of sales), Hitachi Global Storage (17%), and Philips (11%). Other customers include Dell, Hewlett-Packard, and Samsung Electronics. More than 90% of the company's revenues come from outside the US, primarily from manufacturers in the Pacific Rim.

	Annual Growth	9/03	9/04	9/05	9/06	9/07
Sales ($ mil.)	(13.0%)	153.0	155.9	200.3	173.1	87.8
Net income ($ mil.)	—	(3.0)	(17.5)	(25.0)	(17.0)	(32.2)
Market value ($ mil.)	(40.2%)	188.1	77.8	81.7	40.1	24.1
Employees	(5.9%)	4,142	4,118	4,365	3,582	3,247

INNSUITES HOSPITALITY TRUST

AMEX: IHT

InnSuites Hotel Centre, 1625 E. Northern Ave., Ste. 102
Phoenix, AZ 85020
Phone: 602-944-1500
Fax: 602-678-0281
Web: www.innsuitestrust.com

CEO: James F. Wirth
CFO: Anthony B. Waters
HR: –
FYE: January 31
Type: Public

InnSuites Hospitality Trust is banking on its "suite-ness." The company has suite hotels in the southwestern US, four of which are branded as Best Westerns. The firm operates through its majority-owned RRF Limited Partnership, which in turn operates through subsidiary InnSuites Hotels. Family tree aside, InnSuite Hospitality Trust ultimately owns and operates five hotels in Arizona, New Mexico, and southern California. The company also provides management services for nearly ten (including its owned locations), and licenses the name InnSuite to 11 locations.

	Annual Growth	1/04	1/05	1/06	1/07	1/08
Sales ($ mil.)	(2.2%)	24.2	22.9	21.3	21.8	22.1
Net income ($ mil.)	—	(2.6)	0.2	0.5	(0.1)	1.1
Market value ($ mil.)	19.0%	4.6	13.0	12.3	12.8	9.3
Employees	(5.4%)	—	—	446	422	—

INNUITY, INC.

OTC: INNU

8644 154th Ave. NE
Redmond, WA 98052
Phone: 425-497-9909
Fax: 425-497-0409
Web: innuity.com

CEO: John R. Wall
CFO: Linden Barney
HR: –
FYE: December 31
Type: Public

Innuity has applied some ingenuity in transforming itself from an oil and gas exploration and production firm into an Internet technology services provider. The company offers integrated Internet technology services designed to help small businesses grow their revenues, improve services to customers, and maintain daily operations. Its operations are divided into three divisions: the Commerce Division provides commerce transaction services; the Productivity Division offers applications to help business operations; and the Promotion Division provides a Web presence and sales and marketing tools.

	Annual Growth	12/03	12/04	12/05	12/06	12/07
Sales ($ mil.)	183.9%	0.1	0.1	12.5	21.7	6.5
Net income ($ mil.)	—	0.0	0.0	(9.4)	(8.5)	(3.0)
Market value ($ mil.)	81.6%	—	1.9	76.9	11.1	11.5
Employees	—	—	—	—	—	—

INOVA HEALTH SYSTEM

2990 Telestar Ct.
Falls Church, VA 22042
Phone: 703-289-2000
Fax: 703-221-8381
Web: www.inova.org

CEO: J. Knox Singleton
CFO: Richard Magenheimer
HR: Kylanne Green
FYE: December 31
Type: Not-for-profit

Inova keeps NoVa (northern Virginia) healthy. Founded in 1956 in Fairfax, Virginia, Inova Health System is a not-for-profit health care provider, offering acute care, long-term care, home health care, mental health, and satellite emergency care services in the northern Virginia suburbs of Washington, DC. Inova's network consists of six hospitals (including a children's hospital) with about 1,700 beds, as well as family practice locations and assisted living centers for seniors. The health system has about 3,000 physicians on its medical staff. Its emergency departments receive around 400,000 visits each year. The company is supported by the Inova Health System Foundation.

	Annual Growth	12/02	12/03	12/04	12/05	12/06
Est. sales ($ mil.)	—	—	—	—	—	1,866.0
Employees	—	—	—	—	—	14,911

INOVA HEALTH SYSTEM FOUNDATION

8110 Gatehouse Rd., Ste. 200E
Falls Church, VA 22042
Phone: 703-289-2072
Fax: 703-289-2073
Web: www.inova.org/ways_to_give/foundation/about_us

CEO: Fred Sachs
CFO: –
HR: –
FYE: December 31
Type: Not-for-profit

While you might not want to go to the hospital in a Nova (Chevy, circa 1966), Inova Health System Foundation is not a bad idea. The organization provides financial support and assistance to Inova Health System, which operates about 10 not-for-profit community hospitals in northern Virginia. Inova Health System Foundation also supports home health, research, emergency and trauma care, and nurse training. The foundation hosts special events such as galas and golf tournaments to raise funds; it also provides a Web site for annual, memorial, one-time, corporate, and individual donations. It takes in about $17 million in contributions each year.

	Annual Growth	12/03	12/04	12/05	12/06	12/07
Est. sales ($ mil.)	—	—	—	—	—	1,706.4
Employees	—	—	—	—	—	14,911

INOVA TECHNOLOGY INC.

Pink Sheets: IVTH

501 Santa Monica Blvd., Ste. 601
Santa Monica, CA 90401
Phone: 310-857-6666
Fax: –
Web: www.inovatechnology.com

CEO: Adam Radly
CFO: Bob Bates
HR: –
FYE: April 30
Type: Public

Inova Technology, formerly Edgetech Services, offers IT consulting services and data storage solutions to government and corporate customers. It also provides radio frequency identification (RFID) equipment and consulting services. The constantly shifting company has most recently evolved from an Internet search firm — it previously operated Wiki-based search engine WebsBiggest.com and SponsorAnything.com, a Web-based product designed to bring together people seeking sponsorship funds with companies with money to spend. In 2007 the firm switched gears when it acquired radio RFID company RightTag. Chairman and CEO Adam Radly controls more than half of the company.

	Annual Growth	4/03	4/04	4/05	4/06	4/07
Sales ($ mil.)	3.4%	1.4	2.2	2.0	2.7	1.6
Net income ($ mil.)	—	(0.6)	(1.2)	(1.5)	0.7	(1.3)
Employees	—	—	—	—	2	—

INOVIO BIOMEDICAL CORPORATION

AMEX: INO

11494 Sorrento Valley Rd.
San Diego, CA 92121
Phone: 858-597-6006
Fax: 858-597-0451
Web: www.inovio.com

CEO: Avtar Dhillon
CFO: Peter D. Kies
HR: –
FYE: December 31
Type: Public

Inovio Biomedical is electrifying patients with its drug delivery technology. The firm focuses on electroporation, an infusion therapy that uses electrical pulses to open up cell membranes, thus optimizing the delivery of DNA vaccines and chemotherapies. The company is developing its MedPulser DNA Electroporation system (which consists of a generator and an applicator inserted into targeted tissue) to deliver chemotherapies directly into tumors. The firm is also exploring the use of the electroporation system for gene therapies and DNA vaccines, which contain large molecules that need assistance getting through cellular walls.

	Annual Growth	12/03	12/04	12/05	12/06	12/07
Sales ($ mil.)	163.2%	0.1	1.2	5.5	3.5	4.8
Net income ($ mil.)	—	(4.7)	(11.0)	(15.3)	(12.5)	(11.2)
Market value ($ mil.)	(40.4%)	318.4	72.6	66.9	125.6	40.3
Employees	17.1%	—	—	27	—	37

INOVIS, INC.

11720 Amber Park Dr., Ste. 100
Alpharetta, GA 30004
Phone: 404-467-3000
Fax: 404-467-3730
Web: www.inovis.com

CEO: Sean E. Feeney
CFO: Kenneth Williams
HR: Paul Trotti
FYE: December 31
Type: Private

Inovis understands that an efficient supply chain requires good communication. The company provides software that helps more than 20,000 retailers, suppliers, and other businesses standardize and manage communications. Inovis' electronic data interchange (EDI) and data translation software enables companies to use the Internet to securely exchange electronic documents, such as invoices and purchase orders. The company also offers its EDI system as a hosted service, and it provides industry-specific trading tools for the consumer packaged goods, electronics, petrochemicals, and automotive markets. Customers include Dell, Johnson & Johnson, Mervyn's, and Xerox.

	Annual Growth	12/03	12/04	12/05	12/06	12/07
Est. sales ($ mil.)	—	—	—	—	—	33.6
Employees	—	—	—	—	—	534

INPHONIC, INC.

NASDAQ (GM): INPC

1010 Wisconsin Ave., Ste. 600
Washington, DC 20007
Phone: 202-333-0001
Fax: 202-333-5007
Web: www.inphonic.com

CEO: Andrew B. (Andy) Zeinfeld
CFO: Kenneth D. (Ken) Schwarz
HR: –
FYE: December 31
Type: Public

InPhonic keeps the phone calls flowing. The company sells wireless services and devices through private-label Web sites that it creates and manages. The company's technology platform provides outsourced activation services for wireless telecommunications providers. Its portals allow wireless users to sign up for services, upgrade services, and configure their wireless devices. In addition, InPhonic offers wireless telecommunications providers a wide range of professional services, including application development, billing, and customer relationship management. Chairman David Steinberg owns a quarter of the company; Technology Crossover Ventures controls 30%.

	Annual Growth	12/02	12/03	12/04	12/05	*12/06
Sales ($ mil.)	55.6%	63.0	136.1	204.2	320.5	369.6
Net income ($ mil.)	—	(29.0)	(20.2)	(10.2)	(38.2)	(63.7)
Employees	16.0%	—	—	—	475	551

*Most recent year available

INPLAY TECHNOLOGIES, INC.

NASDAQ (CM): NPLA

234 S. Extension Rd., Ste. 103
Mesa, AZ 85210
Phone: 480-586-3300
Fax: 480-844-9625
Web: www.inplaytechnologies.com

CEO: Steven P. (Steve) Hanson
CFO: Mark R. Sokolowski
HR: –
FYE: December 31
Type: Public

InPlay Technologies has pulled the switch on manufacturing. Once a maker of electronic switches and integrated control panels, the company now licenses its magnetic-based DuraSwitch technology for switches to OEMs and component manufacturers. Its design combines the slim profile features of flat-panel membrane switches with the touch or "click" feedback of electromechanical switches. Companies that use InPlay's technology include appliance, automotive, aerospace, and industrial automation manufacturers. Quanta, a Taiwanese contractor that makes computers for Gateway and other clients, is a big customer; the Gateway business represents 21% of sales. InPlay gets three-quarters of its sales in the US.

	Annual Growth	12/03	12/04	12/05	12/06	12/07
Sales ($ mil.)	93.9%	0.8	1.8	6.5	9.5	11.3
Net income ($ mil.)	—	(2.5)	(1.3)	0.7	(3.2)	1.5
Market value ($ mil.)	(0.4%)	15.5	22.8	37.4	16.7	15.3
Employees	18.9%	14	14	24	21	28

An in-depth profile of this company is available to Hoover's Online members at hoovers.com.

INSERRA SUPERMARKETS, INC.

20 Ridge Rd.
Mahwah, NJ 07430
Phone: 201-529-5900
Fax: 201-529-1189

CEO: Lawrence R. Inserra Jr.
CFO: Theresa Inserra
HR: Marie Larson
FYE: December 31
Type: Private

The Big Apple need never be short of apples (or oranges, for that matter), thanks to Inserra Supermarkets. Inserra owns and operates about 20 ShopRite supermarkets and superstores in northern New Jersey and southeastern New York State (most are in Westchester and Rockland counties). Inserra's superstores feature bagel bakeries, cafes, and pharmacies. The regional grocery chain also offers banking services in selected stores through agreements with Poughkeepsie Savings Bank, Statewide Savings Bank, and others. Owned by the Inserra family, the retailer is one of about 40 members that make up cooperative Wakefern Food, the owner of the ShopRite name.

	Annual Growth	12/02	12/03	12/04	12/05	12/06
Sales ($ mil.)	0.0%	—	—	—	1,030.0	1,030.0
Employees	0.0%	—	—	—	4,000	4,000

INSIGHT COMMUNICATIONS COMPANY, INC.

810 7th Ave.
New York, NY 10019
Phone: 917-286-2300
Fax: 917-286-2301
Web: www.insight-com.com

CEO: Michael S. Willner
CFO: John Abbot
HR: Jim Morgan
FYE: December 31
Type: Private

Insight Communications had the foresight to jump on an industry trend and turn its cable TV systems into broadband networks. The firm's cable system (formerly a joint venture with Comcast known as Insight Midwest) serves about 650,000 subscribers in the Midwest, with the majority of customers in Kentucky. Insight upgraded its networks for two-way communications so it can offer interactive digital video and high-speed data services, including cable modem Internet access. Adding telephony to its list of services, the company has a deal with AT&T that provides co-branded broadband phone service.

	Annual Growth	12/02	12/03	12/04	12/05	12/06
Sales ($ mil.)	13.0%	—	—	—	1,117.7	1,262.6
Net income ($ mil.)	—	—	—	—	(84.9)	(36.6)
Employees	5.4%	—	—	—	3,829	4,035

⊞ INSIGHT ENTERPRISES, INC.

NASDAQ (GS): NSIT

1305 W. Auto Dr.
Tempe, AZ 85284
Phone: 480-902-1001
Fax: 480-902-1157
Web: www.insight.com

CEO: Richard A. Fennessy
CFO: Glynis A. Bryan
HR: Gary M. Glandon
FYE: December 31
Type: Public

With this company around the end of your technology woes could be in sight. Insight Enterprises is a top distributor of computer hardware and software in North America, carrying thousands of products from major manufacturers, such as Hewlett-Packard, IBM, and Microsoft. It uses direct telesales and field sales agents to reach customers in business, government, and education. Insight, which has boosted its services unit, also sells products through catalogs and its Web site. In addition to North America, it serves customers in Europe, the Middle East, Africa, and Asia/Pacific. It bought software and mobile solutions firm Software Spectrum, as well as Calence, a networking and communications company.

	Annual Growth	12/03	12/04	12/05	12/06	12/07
Sales ($ mil.)	13.3%	2,914.4	3,082.7	3,261.1	3,817.1	4,800.4
Net income ($ mil.)	19.8%	37.8	80.5	54.7	76.8	77.8
Market value ($ mil.)	(0.1%)	885.8	1,018.8	936.1	922.1	883.9
Employees	9.6%	—	—	3,967	4,568	4,763

INSIGHT HEALTH SERVICES HOLDINGS CORP.

26250 Enterprise Ct., Ste. 100
Lake Forest, CA 92630
Phone: 949-282-6000
Fax: 949-462-3292
Web: www.insighthealth.com

CEO: Louis E. (Kip) Hallman III
CFO: Mitch C. Hill
HR: –
FYE: June 30
Type: Public

InSight Health Services knows what evil lurks within the hearts, brains, and pancreases of men. The company, through its subsidiaries, offers diagnostic imaging services at about 100 hospital-based and freestanding centers (as well as more than 110 mobile units) in about 30 states. InSight provides MRI, CT, and PET scanning, as well as conventional X-ray, mammogram, and ultrasound services. In addition to diagnostic imaging, the company offers some therapeutic services, including radiation therapy and lithotripsy (kidney stone treatment). The company underwent a Chapter 11 reorganization in 2007 aimed at lightening its debt burden.

	Annual Growth	6/03	6/04	6/05	6/06	6/07
Sales ($ mil.)	4.8%	237.8	290.9	316.9	306.3	286.9
Net income ($ mil.)	—	4.9	2.9	(27.2)	(210.2)	(99.0)
Employees	4.8%	1,780	2,290	2,270	—	2,148

INSIGHTFUL CORPORATION

NASDAQ (CM): IFUL

1700 Westlake Ave. North, Ste. 500
Seattle, WA 98109
Phone: 206-283-8802
Fax: 206-283-8691
Web: www.insightful.com

CEO: Jeffrey (Jeff) Coombs
CFO: Richard P. (Rich) Barber
HR: –
FYE: December 31
Type: Public

Hindsight may be 20-20, but Insightful wants companies to have information before they make decisions. The company develops software tools for statistical analysis, data mining, business intelligence, and text analysis. Insightful's core products are its S-PLUS software suite, which enables technicians and professionals to perform advanced data mining and analysis, and its Insightful Miner application, which provides data analysis and visualization capabilities. Former chairman Samuel Meshberg owns 23% of Insightful.

	Annual Growth	12/03	12/04	12/05	12/06	12/07
Sales ($ mil.)	6.7%	17.2	18.9	22.3	24.0	22.3
Net income ($ mil.)	—	(1.6)	2.1	2.0	0.2	(1.7)
Market value ($ mil.)	(2.5%)	23.4	29.4	33.6	30.5	21.2
Employees	—	—	—	114	—	—

INSIGNIA SYSTEMS, INC.

NASDAQ (CM): ISIG

6470 Sycamore Ct. North
Maple Grove, MN 55369
Phone: 763-392-6200
Fax: 763-392-6222
Web: www.insigniasystems.com

CEO: Scott F. Drill
CFO: Justin W. Shireman
HR: –
FYE: December 31
Type: Public

Insignia Systems believes all signs point to greater sales. The company's point of purchase (POP) software and services help retailers and consumer goods manufacturers create in-store advertising and promotional displays. As part of its POPSign program, the company creates customized signs based on information from retailers and manufacturers. Its Stylus software suite is used to create signs, labels, and posters. Insignia also sells specialized cardstock and other supplies for its systems. The company's customers have included Kellogg and General Mills.

	Annual Growth	12/03	12/04	12/05	12/06	12/07
Sales ($ mil.)	(1.7%)	26.1	21.0	19.6	21.9	24.4
Net income ($ mil.)	—	(4.3)	(4.9)	(3.3)	2.4	2.3
Market value ($ mil.)	7.5%	32.7	32.6	10.8	46.2	43.7
Employees	18.4%	—	—	77	88	108

INSITE VISION INCORPORATED

AMEX: ISV

965 Atlantic Ave.
Alameda, CA 94501
Phone: 510-865-8800
Fax: 510-865-5700
Web: www.insitevision.com

CEO: S. Kumar Chandrasekaran
CFO: Louis C. (Lou) Drapeau
HR: Leslie Zuñiga-Arias
FYE: December 31
Type: Public

InSite Vision provides insight into the murky realm of eye disease. The company develops ophthalmic products using its DuraSite eyedrop-based drug delivery system. Its topical anti-infective product, AzaSite, is marketed in the US by licensing partner Inspire Pharmaceuticals as a treatment for conjunctivitis (pink eye). Various other AzaSite products are in development to treat eyelid inflammation and inner ear infections. InSite Vision has licensed rights to use azithromycin (the active ingredient in AzaSite) from Pfizer. Commercial supplies of AzaSite for the US and Canada are manufactured by Inspire, while international units are supplied by Catalent Pharma Solutions.

	Annual Growth	12/03	12/04	12/05	12/06	12/07
Sales ($ mil.)	292.8%	0.1	0.5	0.0	0.0	23.8
Net income ($ mil.)	—	(6.8)	(5.5)	(15.2)	(16.6)	5.5
Market value ($ mil.)	38.6%	19.2	54.9	66.1	144.9	70.9
Employees	—	—	—	30	—	—

INSITUFORM TECHNOLOGIES, INC.

NASDAQ (GS): INSU

17988 Edison Ave.
Chesterfield, MO 63005
Phone: 636-530-8000
Fax: 636-519-8010
Web: www.insituform.com

CEO: John J. (Joe) Burgess
CFO: David A. Martin
HR: Andrew (Andy) Straud
FYE: December 31
Type: Public

Under many a city lurks a decaying infrastructure, and that's what Insituform Technologies takes care of *in situ*. The company provides trenchless technologies for rehabilitating sewers, water mains, and industrial pipes, serving municipalities and industrial plants worldwide. Its Insituform CIPP Process involves installing a custom-manufactured tube or liner that forms a leakproof "pipe within a pipe." Its Tite Liner process is used to line steel pipe with corrosion-resistant polyethylene pipe. Other rehabilitation processes include the use of thermofusing resin and composite and polyethyline liners. The company exited the tunneling business in 2007, the better to focus on its core segments.

	Annual Growth	12/03	12/04	12/05	12/06	12/07
Sales ($ mil.)	0.4%	487.3	542.6	595.3	596.7	495.6
Net income ($ mil.)	(8.1%)	3.5	0.6	13.2	24.7	2.5
Market value ($ mil.)	(1.8%)	436.6	606.3	521.8	704.4	406.6
Employees	(16.2%)	—	—	2,281	2,000	1,600

INSMED INCORPORATED

NASDAQ (GM): INSM

8720 Stony Point Pkwy.
Richmond, VA 23235
Phone: 804-565-3000
Fax: 804-565-3500
Web: www.insmed.com

CEO: Geoffrey Allan
CFO: Kevin P. Tully
HR: –
FYE: December 31
Type: Public

Insmed is on a dual development path to discover drugs for everything from anemia to Lou Gehrig's disease. Its protein program is clinically focused on the FDA-approved IPLEX as a treatment for muscular dystrophy and possibly HARS (fat maldistribution associated with HIV) and retinopathy (abnormal growth of blood vessels in the retina). IPLEX is already available in Italy through an agreement with Cephalon. Insmed has also entered the field of biologics (versions of drugs produced through biological processes) to find treatments for anemia, neutropenia, and autoimmune diseases. Its early and preclinical oncology drug pipeline is targeting breast, prostate, and colon cancer, among others.

	Annual Growth	12/03	12/04	12/05	12/06	12/07
Sales ($ mil.)	147.5%	0.2	0.1	0.1	1.0	7.5
Net income ($ mil.)	—	(10.3)	(27.2)	(40.9)	(56.1)	(20.0)
Market value ($ mil.)	(2.9%)	114.0	99.0	152.0	89.2	101.2
Employees	—	—	—	85	—	—

INSPIRE PHARMACEUTICALS, INC.

NASDAQ (GM): ISPH

4222 Emperor Blvd., Ste. 200
Durham, NC 27703
Phone: 919-941-9777
Fax: 919-941-9797
Web: www.inspirepharm.com

CEO: Christy L. Shaffer
CFO: Thomas R. (Tom) Staab II
HR: –
FYE: December 31
Type: Public

Inspire Pharmaceuticals doesn't want to leave a dry eye in the house. The company targets treatments for various respiratory and ocular diseases caused by malfunctioning P2 receptors, which regulate the body's mucosal hydration. Inspire markets two eye products, Elestat for allergic conjunctivitis and Restasis for dry eye disease, that were developed in collaboration with Allergan. Another marketed product, AzaSite (licensed from InSite Vision), treats bacterial conjunctivitis. Other product candidates include treatments for cystic fibrosis, allergic rhinitis, and glaucoma.

	Annual Growth	12/03	12/04	12/05	12/06	12/07
Sales ($ mil.)	74.9%	5.2	11.1	23.3	37.1	48.7
Net income ($ mil.)	—	(31.4)	(44.1)	(31.9)	(42.1)	(63.7)
Market value ($ mil.)	10.7%	225.3	350.9	214.4	268.2	337.9
Employees	3.0%	—	—	165	170	—

INSTACARE CORP.

OTC: ISCR

2660 Townsgate Rd., Ste. 300
Westlake Village, CA 91361
Phone: 805-446-1973
Fax: 805-446-1983
Web: www.instacare.net

CEO: Keith Berman
CFO: Keith Berman
HR: –
FYE: December 31
Type: Public

instaCare (formerly CareDecision) hopes IT plus pharmaceuticals will equal success. Previously focused on wireless systems for the health care and lodging markets, in 2005 the company added a pharmaceuticals distribution unit through its purchases of CareGeneration and the Pharmaceutical Solutions unit of Kelly Company. instaCare drives customers to its pharmaceuticals business by providing wireless computing devices to doctors in clinics for the poor and uninsured; in return, doctors direct their patients to instaCare's discount mail-order prescription service. instaCare continues to sell its wireless PDA devices for the health care and lodging industries. Clearing company Cede & Co. owns 40% of instaCare.

	Annual Growth	12/03	12/04	12/05	12/06	12/07
Sales ($ mil.)	181.7%	0.1	0.2	5.6	19.2	6.3
Net income ($ mil.)	—	(2.4)	(4.6)	(4.8)	(2.8)	(1.4)
Market value ($ mil.)	—	—	—	—	2.8	—
Employees	—	—	—	—	—	—

INSTEEL INDUSTRIES, INC.

NASDAQ (GM): IIIN

1373 Boggs Dr.
Mount Airy, NC 27030
Phone: 336-786-2141
Fax: 336-786-2144
Web: www.insteel.com

CEO: Howard O. (H.O.) Woltz III
CFO: Michael C. Gazmarian
HR: Deborah Van Etten
FYE: Saturday nearest September 30
Type: Public

WIRE! What is it good for? Absolutely everything — if you're Insteel Industries. The company manufactures welded wire reinforcement (WWR), used primarily to reinforce concrete pipe (pipe mesh, building mesh, engineered structural mesh, and precast manholes), driveways, and slabs. Its PC strand products are used to reinforce concrete structures such as bridges and parking garages. Insteel's customers include members of the concrete product manufacturers, construction product distributors, and rebar fabricators. Insteel Industries operates six manufacturing facilities in the US. The majority of its sales (about 85%) come from nonresidential construction.

	Annual Growth	9/03	9/04	9/05	9/06	9/07
Sales ($ mil.)	8.9%	212.1	332.6	345.5	329.5	297.8
Net income ($ mil.)	37.9%	6.7	31.5	25.0	33.0	24.2
Market value ($ mil.)	206.8%	3.2	66.3	72.1	361.9	281.0
Employees	(10.0%)	—	—	—	621	559

An in-depth profile of this company is available to Hoover's Online members at hoovers.com.

821

INSTITUTIONAL SHAREHOLDER SERVICES, INC.

2099 Gaither Rd., Ste. 501
Rockville, MD 20850
Phone: 301-556-0500
Fax: 301-556-0491
Web: www.issproxy.com

CEO: Richard (Rich) Leggett
CFO: Robert J. (Bob) Baer
HR: Karen Meyer-Cain
FYE: December 31
Type: Private

So many proxies, so little time. Institutional Shareholder Services (ISS) provides proxy voting and corporate governance services to around 2,750 institutional investors and corporations around the world. For institutional investors, the firm researches proxies and offers vote recommendations for some 35,000 securities a year. ISS also offers Web-based tools and research to help companies develop and analyze their governance policies and practices. Units of ISS specialize in services to labor unions and to investment managers who are implementing social investment strategies. RiskMetrics Group acquired ISS in 2007.

	Annual Growth	12/03	12/04	12/05	12/06	12/07
Est. sales ($ mil.)	—	—	—	—	—	17.4
Employees	—	—	—	—	—	309

INSULET CORPORATION

NASDAQ (GM): PODD

9 Oak Park Dr.
Bedford, MA 01730
Phone: 781-457-5000
Fax: 781-457-5011
Web: www.myomnipod.com

CEO: Duane M. DeSisto
CFO: Carsten Boess
HR: —
FYE: December 31
Type: Public

Insulet wants to isolate an insolent disease. The medical device company manufactures an insulin pump for people with insulin-dependent diabetes. Its disposable, waterproof product, called the OmniPod Insulin Management System, weighs a mere 1.2 ounces and adheres directly to the patient's skin, making it more discrete than most insulin infusion systems that typically clip to a belt or fit in a pocket. The company markets its products to doctors, patients, and managed care companies. Insulet was founded in 2000 and received clearance in 2005 from the FDA to market its OmniPod system. The company conducted an IPO in 2007.

	Annual Growth	12/03	12/04	12/05	12/06	12/07
Sales ($ mil.)	—	0.0	0.0	0.1	3.7	13.4
Net income ($ mil.)	—	(11.9)	(13.8)	(21.6)	(36.0)	(53.5)
Market value ($ mil.)	—	—	—	—	—	639.2
Employees	—	—	—	—	—	—

🏠 INSURANCE AUTO AUCTIONS, INC.

2 Westbrook Corporate Center, Ste. 500
Westchester, IL 60154
Phone: 708-492-7000
Fax: 708-492-7078
Web: home.iaai.com

CEO: Thomas C. (Tom) O'Brien
CFO: John W. Kett
HR: —
FYE: December 31
Type: Subsidiary

Getting something out of nothing is what this junkyard doggedly pursues. Insurance Auto Auctions (IAA) is a leading US auto salvage company that auctions off cars declared a total loss for insurance purposes; it auctions either whole vehicles or, if they can't be fixed, just the parts. IAA has nearly 90 auction sites throughout the US. It primarily sells on consignment or buys the cars outright, negotiating salvage contracts with major insurers, but IAA is trying to transition more of its business to a percentage-of-sale basis, in which its salvage clients (including State Farm, Farmers Insurance, and Allstate) get a percentage of the auction sale price. IAA is owned by investment firm Kelso & Company.

	Annual Growth	12/03	12/04	12/05	12/06	12/07
Est. sales ($ mil.)	—	—	—	—	—	332.1
Employees	—	—	—	—	—	1,066

INSURANCE SERVICES OFFICE, INC.

Newport World Business Center, 545 Washington Blvd.
Jersey City, NJ 07310
Phone: 201-469-2000
Fax: 201-748-1472
Web: www.iso.com

CEO: Frank J. Coyne
CFO: Mark Anquillare
HR: —
FYE: December 31
Type: Private

In search of insurance info? Founded in 1971, Insurance Services Office (ISO) provides statistical, actuarial, and underwriting information for the property/casualty insurance and risk management industries. The company gathers premium, claim, and loss data that is filed with state regulators; the data is used to evaluate the price of insurance in each state. ISO's other services include developing standardized policy language, conducting site surveys of individual properties, and fraud identification. ISO has operations in the US, the UK, and in Israel.

	Annual Growth	12/03	12/04	12/05	12/06	12/07
Est. sales ($ mil.)	—	—	—	—	—	206.5
Employees	—	—	—	—	—	3,048

INSURE.COM, INC.

NASDAQ (CM): NSUR

8205 S. Cass Ave., Ste. 102
Darien, IL 60561
Phone: 630-515-0170
Fax: 630-515-0270
Web: www.insure.com

CEO: Robert S. Bland
CFO: Phillip A. Perillo
HR: William V. (Bill) Thoms
FYE: December 31
Type: Public

Got a computer? Get insurance. Insure.com gives Web surfers instant quotes for life insurance products from about 30 carriers through its online portal. Users can get comparative quotes and purchase policies online or from over-the-phone agents. The site provides information on other lines of personal insurance as well, including automobile, homeowners and rental, medical, long-term care, and travel insurance. Insure.com earns commissions on the policies it sells through its Web site and, for some lines of insurance, receives fees for passing on qualified leads to insurance companies.

	Annual Growth	12/03	12/04	12/05	12/06	12/07
Sales ($ mil.)	16.7%	9.7	15.9	17.1	17.2	18.0
Net income ($ mil.)	—	(1.3)	(1.8)	(4.9)	(3.6)	(0.2)
Market value ($ mil.)	2.3%	—	—	—	28.5	29.1
Employees	—	—	—	99	—	—

🏠 INSWEB CORPORATION

NASDAQ (GM): INSW

11290 Pyrites Way, Ste. 200
Gold River, CA 95670
Phone: 916-853-3300
Fax: 916-853-3325
Web: www.insweb.com

CEO: Hussein A. Enan
CFO: Kiran Rasaretnam
HR: —
FYE: December 31
Type: Public

It seems somehow appropriate to sell the least tangible of products — insurance coverage — via a virtual marketplace. InsWeb operates an Internet portal that allows consumers to shop for quotes on various insurance products, including automobile, term life, and homeowners insurance policies. InsWeb has alliances with more than two dozen insurance companies (including Allstate, AIG, and Liberty Mutual) which pay transaction fees to InsWeb for providing qualified customer leads. Quotes are available through the company's Web site at no charge to the consumer.

	Annual Growth	12/03	12/04	12/05	12/06	12/07
Sales ($ mil.)	8.3%	24.1	14.7	25.0	28.5	33.2
Net income ($ mil.)	24.5%	1.0	(8.9)	(5.9)	(3.4)	2.4
Market value ($ mil.)	17.8%	21.4	13.2	13.5	13.1	41.2
Employees	(28.7%)	—	—	122	—	62

INTEGRA BANK CORPORATION

NASDAQ (GM): IBNK

21 SE 3rd St.
Evansville, IN 47705
Phone: 812-464-9677
Fax: 812-464-9825
Web: www.integrabank.com

CEO: Michael T. (Mike) Vea
CFO: Martin M. Zorn
HR: Cheryl Steinbacher
FYE: December 31
Type: Public

Community banking is integral to Integra Bank Corporation. Its subsidiary, Integra Bank, operates more than 80 branches and loan production offices serving communities in southern Indiana and Illinois, Kentucky, and southwestern Ohio. The bank offers a variety of traditional deposit products for personal and business customers, including savings and money market accounts, CDs, and IRAs. Commercial, industrial, and agricultural loans account for nearly 30% of the bank's loan portfolio; construction and development loans account for another 25%. The portfolio also includes residential and commercial mortgages, economic development loans, lease financing, and home equity lines of credit.

	Annual Growth	12/03	12/04	12/05	12/06	12/07
Assets ($ mil.)	3.2%	2,958.3	2,757.2	2,708.1	2,684.5	3,350.1
Net income ($ mil.)	14.6%	17.8	(6.6)	27.3	19.5	30.7
Market value ($ mil.)	(6.5%)	380.8	401.5	372.7	489.7	291.4
Employees	0.3%	—	—	843	—	848

INTEGRA LIFESCIENCES HOLDINGS

NASDAQ (GS): IART

311 Enterprise Dr.
Plainsboro, NJ 08536
Phone: 609-275-0500
Fax: 609-275-5363
Web: www.integra-ls.com

CEO: Stuart M. Essig
CFO: John B. (Jack) Henneman III
HR: Richard D. Gorelick
FYE: December 31
Type: Public

Integra LifeSciences Holdings Corporation wants its products to be integral to the healing process. In fact, using its proprietary collagen matrix technology, the company makes biological implants for brain, spinal, and orthopedic surgeries that become part of a patient's body, helping it to generate new bone and tissue in place of what was damaged. In addition to its regenerative implants, grafts, and wound dressings, Integra LifeSciences makes surgical instruments, including ultrasonic surgical ablation systems and joint fixation devices, used primarily in neurosurgery and joint reconstruction. Integra LifeSciences sells products worldwide through several specialty sales forces and through distributors.

	Annual Growth	12/03	12/04	12/05	12/06	12/07
Sales ($ mil.)	31.2%	185.6	229.8	277.9	419.3	550.5
Net income ($ mil.)	5.6%	26.9	17.2	37.2	29.4	33.5
Market value ($ mil.)	7.5%	813.7	1,051.9	973.6	1,163.4	1,085.9
Employees	82.2%	—	—	1,180	2,150	—

INTEGRA TELECOM, INC.

1201 NE Lloyd Blvd., Ste. 500
Portland, OR 97232
Phone: 503-453-8000
Fax: 503-453-8221
Web: www.integratelecom.com

CEO: Dudley R. Slater
CFO: Matt Fahey
HR: Lisa Hillyer
FYE: December 31
Type: Private

Integra Telecom is an alternative integrated telecommunications carrier focused on small to midsized business customers primarily in Arizona, California, Idaho, Minnesota, North Dakota, Oregon, Utah, and Washington. The facilities-based provider maintains about 280,000 access lines and offers local access, domestic and international long-distance, Internet access, and data services, as well as voice messaging, and telecommunications system services and management. Investors in the company include Nautic Partners, Bank of America Capital Partners, and Boston Ventures. In mid-2006 Integra acquired service provider Electric Lightwave from Citizens Communications for $247 million.

	Annual Growth	12/03	12/04	12/05	12/06	12/07
Est. sales ($ mil.)	—	—	—	—	—	154.5
Employees	—	—	—	—	—	1,493

INTEGRAL SYSTEMS, INC.

NASDAQ (GS): ISYS

5000 Philadelphia Way
Lanham, MD 20706
Phone: 301-731-4233
Fax: 301-731-9606
Web: www.integ.com

CEO: Alan W. Baldwin
CFO: William M. Bambarger Jr.
HR: Jeffrey A. Rosolio
FYE: September 30
Type: Public

You might be wondering what the twinkling little star is, but Integral System knows that it might actually not even be a star. Integral provides satellite ground system components and systems as well as hardware and software for satellite communications signal monitoring, network and ground equipment monitoring, and satellite data processing. Its primary product is its EPOCH Integrated Product Suite software, which is used to manage satellite control and monitoring, off-line data trending, orbit analysis, and database configuration.

	Annual Growth	9/03	9/04	9/05	9/06	9/07
Sales ($ mil.)	11.7%	82.6	90.3	97.7	116.5	128.6
Net income ($ mil.)	26.5%	5.0	6.8	6.3	12.3	12.8
Market value ($ mil.)	3.5%	175.7	194.0	215.6	345.7	201.6
Employees	6.7%	—	—	400	—	455

INTEGRAL TECHNOLOGIES, INC.

OTC: ITKG

805 W. Orchard Dr., Ste. 7
Bellingham, WA 98225
Phone: 360-752-1982
Fax: 360-752-1983
Web: www.itkg.net

CEO: William S. Robinson
CFO: William A. Ince
HR: –
FYE: June 30
Type: Public

Integral Technologies hopes to discover that technology truly is integral to everyday life. The development state company is betting the bank on its registered "ElectriPlast" product, an electrically conductive resin-based polymer that can be molded into any shape. The company's "PlasTenna" technology uses ElectriPlast for antenna design and other manufacturing processes. It can become part of the cell phone casing itself. The company also has developed a GPS antenna used for fleet management and mobile data communications. Integral Technologies outsources its manufacturing and is marketing its products to cell phone and other wireless device manufacturers.

	Annual Growth	6/03	6/04	6/05	6/06	6/07
Sales ($ mil.)	—	0.0	0.0	0.1	0.0	0.1
Net income ($ mil.)	—	(1.4)	(2.5)	(1.8)	(2.1)	(6.0)
Market value ($ mil.)	21.7%	27.0	46.2	22.1	105.7	59.2
Employees	—	—	—	—	—	5

INTEGRAL VISION, INC.

OTC: INVI

49113 Wixom Tech Dr.
Wixom, MI 48393
Phone: 248-668-9230
Fax: 248-668-9384
Web: www.iv-usa.com

CEO: Charles J. Drake
CFO: Mark R. Doede
HR: –
FYE: December 31
Type: Public

Integral Vision wants manufacturers to take a closer look. The company makes machine vision systems that monitor and control manufacturing processes in the small flat-panel display industry. Its systems inspect for both cosmetic and functional defects in display components used in camcorders, cell phones, digital still cameras, computer monitors, and handheld video games. Integral Vision also offers software for developing machine vision inspection applications. Top customers include Liquavista, QUALCOMM (31% of sales), Samsung Electronics (24%), and Texas Instruments (10%).

	Annual Growth	12/03	12/04	12/05	12/06	12/07
Sales ($ mil.)	16.4%	0.6	1.5	0.7	0.8	1.1
Net income ($ mil.)	—	(1.9)	(2.5)	(2.7)	(3.0)	(3.0)
Market value ($ mil.)	(11.3%)	3.3	35.6	59.0	19.2	2.1
Employees	3.9%	12	16	21	18	14

An in-depth profile of this company is available to Hoover's Online members at hoovers.com.

823

INTEGRAMED AMERICA, INC.

NASDAQ (GM): INMD

2 Manhattanville Rd.	CEO: Jay Higham
Purchase, NY 10577	CFO: John W. Hlywak Jr.
Phone: 914-253-8000	HR: Angela Gizinski
Fax: 914-253-8008	FYE: December 31
Web: www.integramed.com	Type: Public

IntegraMed America provides fertile ground for the growth of reproductive services. The company provides a range of business, financial, and clinical services to a network of fertility clinics that span the US. Its network includes about 30 centers, located in major metropolitan areas, that provide in vitro fertilization (IVF), artificial insemination, and other reproductive assistance. IntegraMed offers those centers clinical support in the form of technical support through its ARTSworks practice management and electronic records information systems; accounting and human resource services; mail-order pharmacy services; and both traditional and online marketing and sales support.

	Annual Growth	12/03	12/04	12/05	12/06	12/07
Sales ($ mil.)	12.9%	93.7	107.7	128.8	126.4	152.0
Net income ($ mil.)	34.8%	1.0	1.2	1.7	3.2	3.3
Market value ($ mil.)	75.7%	10.3	20.5	43.2	78.2	98.6
Employees	—	—	—	881	—	—

INTEGRATED BIOPHARMA, INC.

NASDAQ (GM): INBP

225 Long Ave.	CEO: E. Gerald Kay
Hillside, NJ 07205	CFO: Dina L. Masi
Phone: 973-926-0816	HR: –
Fax: 973-926-1735	FYE: June 30
Web: www.ibiopharma.com	Type: Public

From aloe vera juice to chemotherapy drugs, Integrated BioPharma is making the most of plants. The company's Manhattan Drug subsidiary makes vitamins, nutritional supplements, and herbal products for sale to distributors, and retailers including Herbalife International. It also sells its products under the Vitamin Factory brand direct to consumers by mail and on the Internet and provides raw material sourcing through its IHT Health Products subsidiary. The company also owns AgroLabs, which produces health beverages extracted from pomegranates, aloe vera, and other fruits. Its pharmaceuticals unit makes paclitaxel, a chemotherapy agent extracted from yew trees used to treat breast cancer.

	Annual Growth	6/03	6/04	6/05	6/06	6/07
Sales ($ mil.)	28.3%	22.2	25.3	32.7	57.8	60.2
Net income ($ mil.)	—	0.9	(5.3)	(8.6)	8.4	(2.0)
Market value ($ mil.)	(1.4%)	76.6	102.1	47.9	116.8	72.3
Employees	3.1%	—	—	157	156	167

INTEGRATED DATA CORP.

Pink Sheets: ITDD

3422 Old Capitol Trail, Ste. 741	CEO: Abraham (Abe) Carmel
Wilmington, DE 19808	CFO: David C. Bryan
Phone: 484-212-4137	HR: –
Fax: 484-212-4141	FYE: June 30
Web: www.integrateddatacorp.com	Type: Public

Integrated Data (IDC) is leaving wireless in favor of land. The holding company previously operated through subsidiaries offering a variety of wireless communications services, including point-of-sale activation and financial transactions. In 2006 IDC began disposing of its wireless operations to begin a new focus on resort real estate development. It agreed to purcahse Montana Holdings, owner of the Rum Cay Resort Marina in the Bahamas. IDC sold off its Italian wireless subsidiary in 2006 and disposed of its stake in DataWave Systems to InComm Holdings in 2007.

	Annual Growth	6/02	6/03	6/04	6/05	*6/06
Sales ($ mil.)	—	—	—	—	—	0.1
Net income ($ mil.)	—	—	—	—	—	0.4
Employees	—	—	—	—	—	—

*Most recent year available

INTEGRATED DEVICE TECHNOLOGY, INC.

NASDAQ (GS): IDTI

6024 Silver Creek Valley Rd.	CEO: Theodore L. (Ted) Tewksbury III
San Jose, CA 95138	CFO: Brian White
Phone: 408-284-8200	HR: Roger Ervin
Fax: 408-284-2775	FYE: Sunday nearest March 31
Web: www.idt.com	Type: Public

Integrated Device Technology (IDT) knows about integrating devices. IDT offers some 1,300 high-performance semiconductors and modules, available in 15,000 configurations, primarily for the networking and communications markets, but also for other computer and computer peripheral applications. Much of IDT's sales come from its communications and high-performance logic products, which include processors, specialized memories, logic and clock management products, and chipsets and controllers for networking gear. The company gets about two-thirds of sales from the Asia/Pacific region.

	Annual Growth	3/04	3/05	3/06	3/07	3/08
Sales ($ mil.)	22.6%	345.4	390.6	527.8	803.6	781.5
Net income ($ mil.)	52.0%	6.4	13.3	(81.7)	(7.6)	34.2
Market value ($ mil.)	(0.6%)	1,504.6	1,245.0	2,948.1	3,026.4	1,466.2
Employees	(7.0%)	3,150	2,955	2,700	2,400	2,353

INTEGRATED ELECTRICAL SERVICES, INC.

NASDAQ (GM): IESC

1800 West Loop S., Ste. 500	CEO: Michael J. (Mike) Caliel
Houston, TX 77027	CFO: Raymond K. (Randy) Guba
Phone: 713-860-1500	HR: Robert B. (Bob) Callahan
Fax: 713-860-1599	FYE: September 30
Web: www.ies-co.com	Type: Public

Integrated Electrical Services (IES), a leading consolidator in the electrical contracting and maintenance industry, has a network of around 120 locations across the US, with its focus on the rapidly growing Sunbelt. Its services include design, installation, and maintenance of electrical wiring and data communication systems in offices, high-rise apartments, hospitals, factories, and airports. Its subsidiaries also work on above- and below-ground powerlines and high-voltage substations, and install wiring in new homes and apartments. In 2006 IES declared bankruptcy, emerging after three months.

	Annual Growth	9/03	9/04	9/05	9/06	9/07
Sales ($ mil.)	(11.4%)	1,448.6	1,424.1	1,102.8	950.2	892.8
Net income ($ mil.)	—	20.4	(124.9)	(129.6)	(0.4)	(4.4)
Market value ($ mil.)	61.4%	—	—	—	243.4	392.8
Employees	(19.6%)	—	—	8,900	7,183	5,746

INTEGRATED SECURITY SYSTEMS, INC.

OTC: IZZI

2009 Chenault Dr., Ste. 114	CEO: Vernon H. (Jay) Foersterling Jr.
Carrollton, TX 75006	CFO: –
Phone: 972-444-8280	HR: –
Fax: 972-869-3843	FYE: June 30
Web: www.integratedsecurity.com	Type: Public

Integrated Security Systems might not be able to stop a train, but the company will tell you when one is coming. Subsidiary B&B ARMR builds railroad crossing safety barriers and warning gates, along with traffic control products such as crash barriers and perimeter security gates used by businesses and government agencies. B&B Roadway, a joint venture with Causey Lyon Enterprises, makes traffic control products used on roads and bridges. Integrated Security Systems' Intelli-Site unit integrates security devices from different manufacturers onto a single PC-controlled platform, and the company's DoorTek unit makes access control systems. Director Russell Cleveland controls 92% of Integrated Security Systems.

	Annual Growth	6/03	6/04	6/05	6/06	6/07
Sales ($ mil.)	20.9%	5.0	9.8	13.5	12.3	10.7
Net income ($ mil.)	—	(2.0)	(3.7)	(4.9)	(4.2)	(4.8)
Employees	13.2%	—	—	—	38	43

⊞ INTEGRATED SILICON SOLUTION, INC.

NASDAQ (GM): ISSI

1940 Zanker Rd.
San Jose, CA 95112
Phone: 408-969-6600
Fax: 408-969-7800
Web: www.issi.com

CEO: Scott D. Howarth
CFO: John M. Cobb
HR: –
FYE: September 30
Type: Public

Memories light more than the corners of ISSI's mind. Integrated Silicon Solution, Inc. (ISSI) makes static random-access memory chips (SRAMs), DRAMs, specialized read-only memories, and other devices, including voice recording chips. SRAMs, which unlike DRAMs don't need periodic refreshing from the CPU to protect data from loss, are used in cars, computers, instrumentation, and telecommunications devices. ISSI's DRAMs are used in equipment such as set-top boxes, networking equipment, and disk drives. The company's customers — either directly or through distributors and contract manufacturers — include Cisco, Nokia, Sony, and VDO Automotive. Asian customers account for two-thirds of sales.

	Annual Growth	9/03	9/04	9/05	9/06	9/07
Sales ($ mil.)	25.9%	97.7	181.0	181.4	217.5	245.4
Net income ($ mil.)	—	(28.1)	3.5	(37.9)	(14.2)	15.4
Market value ($ mil.)	(4.8%)	281.6	263.0	312.5	209.5	230.9
Employees	11.1%	274	310	386	421	417

INTEGRATED SURGICAL SYSTEMS, INC.

Pink Sheets: ISSM

1433 N. Market Blvd., Ste. 1
Sacramento, CA 95834
Phone: 916-285-9943
Fax: 916-285-9104
Web: www.robodoc.com

CEO: Christopher A. Marlett
CFO: David H. Adams
HR: –
FYE: December 31
Type: Public

Integrated Surgical Systems (ISS) wanted to be the hippest company around with its ROBODOC Surgical Assistant System, a computer-controlled robot used in hip and knee replacements. However, ISS ceased operations in mid-2005 because of lawsuits and lack of funding, and it sold its ROBODOC assets to Novatrix Biomedical in 2007. Using those assets, Novatrix has set up a new company called Curexo Medical to continue development of ROBODOC, which is sold in Europe, Asia, and other regions but has not won FDA approval. Meanwhile, ISS used the money from the asset sale to pay its debtors and is looking for acquisition opportunities.

	Annual Growth	12/02	12/03	12/04	12/05	*12/06
Sales ($ mil.)	(15.9%)	5.2	5.8	2.4	3.4	2.6
Net income ($ mil.)	—	(2.8)	(3.3)	(0.6)	2.0	1.6
Employees	—	—	—	—	—	—

*Most recent year available

INTEGRYS ENERGY GROUP, INC.

NYSE: TEG

130 E. Randolph Dr.
Chicago, IL 60601
Phone: 312-228-5400
Fax: –
Web: www.integrysgroup.com

CEO: Larry L. Weyers
CFO: Joseph P. (Joe) O'Leary
HR: Bernard J. (Bud) Treml
FYE: December 31
Type: Public

Integrys Energy (formerly WPS Resources) provides power for the Windy City and Lake Wobegon. The energy holding company owns six regulated utilities: Michigan Gas Utilities Corporation (165,000 gas customers), Minnesota Energy Resources Corporation (206,000 gas customers), North Shore Gas Company (158,000 customers in the northern suburbs of Chicago), Peoples Gas Light and Coke Company (840,000 natural gas customers in Chicago), Wisconsin Public Service (450,000 electric customers and 314,000 natural gas customers in Wisconsin and Michigan), and Upper Peninsula Power (51,000 electricity customers). Integrys took its current name after the 2007 acquisition of Peoples Energy for $1.5 billion.

	Annual Growth	12/03	12/04	12/05	12/06	12/07
Sales ($ mil.)	24.2%	4,321.3	4,890.6	6,962.7	6,890.7	10,292.4
Net income ($ mil.)	27.0%	97.8	142.8	160.5	158.9	254.4
Market value ($ mil.)	68.3%	—	—	—	2,344.2	3,946.1
Employees	12.9%	—	—	2,945	3,326	—

⊞ INTEL CORPORATION

NASDAQ (GS): INTC

2200 Mission College Blvd.
Santa Clara, CA 95054
Phone: 408-765-8080
Fax: 408-765-3804
Web: www.intel.com

CEO: Craig R. Barrett
CFO: Stacy J. Smith
HR: Patricia Murray
FYE: Last Saturday in December
Type: Public

Intel — still #1 in semiconductors, and no longer complacent about holding the top spot. The company holds the lion's share of the market for microprocessors that go into desktop and notebook computers, and also into computer servers. Archrival AMD has eaten into Intel's market share in recent years, but the big guy has fought back with faster processors and advanced manufacturing technology. Intel also makes embedded semiconductors for the industrial equipment and networking gear markets. Most computer makers use Intel processors; PC giants Dell (18% of sales) and Hewlett-Packard (17%) are the company's largest customers. The Asia/Pacific region generates more than half of Intel's revenues.

	Annual Growth	12/03	12/04	12/05	12/06	12/07
Sales ($ mil.)	6.2%	30,141.0	34,209.0	38,826.0	35,382.0	38,334.0
Net income ($ mil.)	5.5%	5,641.0	7,516.0	8,664.0	5,044.0	6,976.0
Market value ($ mil.)	(6.5%)	203,432.3	147,195.6	147,738.2	116,761.5	155,689.7
Employees	2.0%	79,700	85,000	99,900	94,100	86,300

INTELLI-CHECK - MOBILISA, INC.

AMEX: IDN

191 Otto Street
Port Townsend, WA 98368
Phone: 360-344-3233
Fax: 360-344-3323
Web: www.icmobil.com

CEO: Nelson Ludlow
CFO: Peter J. Mundy
HR: –
FYE: December 31
Type: Public

Intelli-Check — Mobilisa will need to see some ID. The company provides handheld electronic card readers and related software for the commercial, government, and military markets. Used to secure military and federal government locations, its Defense ID System can read barcodes, magnetic stripes, optical character recognition (OCR), and radio frequency identification (RFID) codes. Its ID-Check systems are designed to verify the age and identity of customers who swipe a driver's license, military ID, or other magnetically encoded ID card. The company has installed systems in airports, bars, casinos, convenience stores, hotels, and stadiums.

	Annual Growth	12/03	12/04	12/05	12/06	12/07
Sales ($ mil.)	30.7%	1.2	1.1	2.4	3.2	3.5
Net income ($ mil.)	—	(6.4)	(6.9)	(3.2)	(2.9)	(2.7)
Market value ($ mil.)	(16.5%)	80.3	46.3	46.9	82.1	39.1
Employees	10.5%	—	—	19	21	—

INTELLIGENT SYSTEMS CORPORATION

AMEX: INS

4355 Shackleford Rd.
Norcross, GA 30093
Phone: 770-381-2900
Fax: 770-381-2808
Web: www.intelsys.com

CEO: J. Leland Strange
CFO: Bonnie L. Herron
HR: –
FYE: December 31
Type: Public

Intelligent Systems Corporation doesn't want to be accused of making dumb choices. The company invests in information technology and industrial products firms, primarily in the Southern US. Subsidiaries include ChemFree, which makes a non-solvent-based parts wash for automotive and industrial applications, and CoreCard, which develops software for banks and retailers to manage credit and debit card accounts. Other holdings include a stake in NKD Enterprises, dba CoreXpand, which provides software tools to manage e-commerce activities. The firm's Gwinnett Innovation Park is a small-business incubator providing office space and support systems to nascent businesses.

	Annual Growth	12/03	12/04	12/05	12/06	12/07
Sales ($ mil.)	9.3%	13.3	22.3	16.1	14.5	19.0
Net income ($ mil.)	—	(4.8)	2.6	(1.6)	4.5	(2.4)
Market value ($ mil.)	18.5%	7.6	9.0	9.6	14.3	15.0
Employees	—	—	—	205	—	—

⊞ An in-depth profile of this company is available to Hoover's Online members at hoovers.com.

825

⊞ INTELLIGROUP, INC.

Pink Sheets: ITIG

499 Thornall St.
Edison, NJ 08837
Phone: 732-590-1600
Fax: 732-362-2100
Web: www.intelligroup.com

CEO: Vikram Gulati
CFO: Alok Bajpai
HR: –
FYE: December 31
Type: Public

Intelligroup believes that two heads are better than one. The information technology (IT) company provides outsourced application management and hosting services, consulting, and offshore software development to large enterprises. Intelligroup also installs complex human resources, administration, database management, and other business process software applications from software makers such as SAP and Oracle. The company also offers proprietary software products Pharma Express and Contractor Express — industry-specific, SAP-based systems.

	Annual Growth	12/03	12/04	12/05	12/06	12/07
Sales ($ mil.)	5.2%	118.6	128.9	125.3	125.3	145.1
Net income ($ mil.)	—	(6.4)	(0.9)	(6.6)	(3.7)	3.0
Employees	—	—	—	—	—	—

INTELLON CORPORATION

NASDAQ (GM): ITLN

5100 W. Silver Springs Blvd.
Ocala, FL 34482
Phone: 352-237-7416
Fax: 352-237-7616
Web: www.intellon.com

CEO: Charles E. (Charlie) Harris
CFO: Brian T. McGee
HR: –
FYE: December 31
Type: Public

Intellon focuses its intelligence on powerline networking. The fabless semiconductor company designs analog, digital, and mixed-signal chips that enable high-speed network access over a home's existing power lines. The company also makes chips for low-bandwidth communications over power lines and wireless media. Its technology has been chosen as a standard for the HomePlug Powerline Alliance (an industry standards group for home networking) and has been tapped by manufacturers (and Intellon investors), including Motorola, Philips, and Samsung. Intellon gets most of its sales outside of the US.

	Annual Growth	12/03	12/04	12/05	12/06	12/07
Sales ($ mil.)	61.1%	—	12.5	16.6	33.7	52.3
Net income ($ mil.)	—	—	(12.1)	(12.5)	(7.8)	(7.3)
Market value ($ mil.)	—	—	—	—	—	228.7
Employees	20.4%	—	—	—	108	130

INTEPLAST GROUP, LTD.

9 Peach Tree Hill Rd.
Livingston, NJ 07039
Phone: 973-994-8000
Fax: 973-994-8005
Web: www.inteplast.com

CEO: John D. Young
CFO: Benjamin Tsao
HR: Brenda Wilson
FYE: December 31
Type: Private

The Inteplast Group hopes to turn plastic into gold. Composed of three divisions, Inteplast Group makes a wide range of plastic products. Its AmTopp division makes biaxially oriented polypropylene (BOPP) film, stretch wrap, and plastic concentrates; its World-Pak unit makes fluted boards, PVC sheets and foam, and cross-laminated film; and its Integrated Bagging Systems unit makes trash can liners, produce bags, and plastic packaging. Inteplast products are used in applications including food packaging, lamination, and shipping. Founded in 1991, Inteplast operates 11 plants at its 700-acre site in Texas, as well as in Massachusetts and British Columbia.

	Annual Growth	12/02	12/03	12/04	12/05	12/06
Sales ($ mil.)	—	—	—	—	—	850.0
Employees	—	—	—	—	—	1,550

⊞ INTER PARFUMS, INC.

NASDAQ (GS): IPAR

551 5th Ave., Ste. 1500
New York, NY 10176
Phone: 212-983-2640
Fax: 212-983-4197
Web: www.interparfumsinc.com

CEO: Jean Madar
CFO: Russell Greenberg
HR: Michelle Habert
FYE: December 31
Type: Public

Would a perfumer by any other name smell as sweet? Inter Parfums certainly hopes not. Most of the company's revenue is generated by sales of prestige fragrances, including Burberry, Christian Lacroix, Lanvin, Nickel, S.T. Dupont, Quiksilver/Roxy, Van Cleef & Arpels, Paul Smith, and S.T. Dupont. It also sells moderately priced perfumes and low-priced imitations of high-end perfumes. In addition Inter Parfums sells personal care products and cosmetics, including Aziza eye makeup, and owns men's skincare firm Nickel. Customers include department stores, mass merchandisers (Wal-Mart Stores), and drugstore chains. Founders Jean Madar (CEO) and Philippe Benacin (vice chairman) jointly own about 60% of the firm.

	Annual Growth	12/03	12/04	12/05	12/06	12/07
Sales ($ mil.)	20.4%	185.6	236.1	273.5	321.0	389.6
Net income ($ mil.)	14.6%	13.8	15.7	15.3	17.7	23.8
Market value ($ mil.)	(3.9%)	288.6	205.4	242.5	261.4	246.0
Employees	31.1%	117	144	201	—	—

INTERACT HOLDINGS GROUP, INC.

OTC: IHGR

550 Greens Pkwy., Ste. 230
Houston, TX 77067
Phone: 619-615-4242
Fax: 281-877-3561
Web: www.interactholdings.com

CEO: Jeffrey W. (Jeff) Flannery
CFO: Jeffrey W. (Jeff) Flannery
HR: –
FYE: December 31
Type: Public

Interact Holdings Group (formerly The Jackson Rivers Company) changed horses mid-stream and came out on the other bank as a technology company. It provides data collection and information management services for machine-to-machine (M2M) networks (primarily in the international oil and gas industries), energy and water utilities, and municipalities and telecom network operators. The company also designs and develops networks and offers engineering consulting services. In 2005 Jackson Rivers acquired Houston-based Diverse Networks, a provider of wired and wireless communications network engineering services. Prior to this acquisition, it was a development-stage company offering IT management services.

	Annual Growth	12/03	12/04	12/05	12/06	12/07
Sales ($ mil.)	—	—	0.0	2.2	3.2	4.5
Net income ($ mil.)	—	—	(4.8)	(1.8)	(2.8)	(3.3)
Employees	—	—	—	—	24	—

INTERACTIVE BRAND DEVELOPMENT, INC.

OTC: IBDI

3275 W. Hillsboro Blvd., Ste. 300
Deerfield Beach, FL 33442
Phone: 954-333-8747
Fax: 954-333-8679
Web: www.interactivebranddevelopment.com

CEO: Steven (Steve) Markley
CFO: Steven (Steve) Markley
HR: –
FYE: December 31
Type: Public

Interactive Brand Development (IBD) is more passive than interactive at the moment. The company has no operations, but holds stakes in Penthouse Media Group (more than 25%) and in Interactive Television Networks (more than 20%). In 2006 the company exited its most recent operating business — providing online payment processing to the adult entertainment world. IBD exited another line of business (online auction and marketing) in 2005. IBD also owns a collection of cels (original cartoon animation art). PHSL Worldwide (from which the company bought its now-defunct billing business) owns 28% of IBD.

	Annual Growth	12/02	12/03	12/04	12/05	*12/06
Sales ($ mil.)	(98.6%)	—	—	—	6.9	0.1
Net income ($ mil.)	—	—	—	—	(20.2)	(32.9)
Market value ($ mil.)	—	—	—	—	—	2.3
Employees	—	—	—	—	—	—

*Most recent year available

INTERACTIVE BROKERS GROUP, INC.

NASDAQ (GS): IBKR

1 Pickwick Plaza
Greenwich, CT 06830
Phone: 203-618-5800
Fax: 203-618-5770
Web: www.interactivebrokers.com

CEO: Thomas Peterffy
CFO: Paul J. Brody
HR: Tammy Silby
FYE: December 31
Type: Public

Interactive Brokers Group serves investors who interact with world markets, focusing on the use of technology in securities trading. It does business through electronic market-maker Timber Hill, as well as its Interactive Brokers brokerage subsidiaries; it executes some 700,000 trades daily in stocks, options, futures, foreign exchange, and corporate bonds. Customers may trade on about 70 exchanges and market centers in about 25 countries. The company caters to experienced individual and institutional investors. Large banks and brokerages can also provide the company's interface to their customers through a white-label arrangement. Founder and chairman Thomas Peterffy controls Interactive Brokers Group.

	Annual Growth	12/03	12/04	12/05	12/06	12/07
Sales ($ mil.)	29.5%	720.0	621.7	1,099.2	1,736.8	2,023.4
Net income ($ mil.)	3.6%	—	270.4	535.5	734.2	300.5
Market value ($ mil.)	—	—	—	—	—	1,297.4
Employees	10.7%	450	455	496	532	675

INTERACTIVE DATA CORPORATION

NYSE: IDC

32 Crosby Dr.
Bedford, MA 01730
Phone: 781-687-8500
Fax: 781-687-8005
Web: www.interactivedata.com

CEO: Stuart J. Clark
CFO: Andrew J. Hajducky III
HR: Peg Murphy
FYE: December 31
Type: Public

Interactive Data Corporation has something vital to the information superhighway — the information. The company offers subscription services that provide financial market data, analytics, and related services to financial institutions, active traders, and individual investors. Interactive Data Corporation conducts business through two segments: Institutional Services and Active Trader Services. Products include Interactive Data Fixed Income Analytics (fixed-income portfolio analytics for institutions), eSignal (real-time market data for individuals), and Interactive Data Pricing and Reference Data (securities information for institutions). Pearson plc owns about 60% of the company.

	Annual Growth	12/03	12/04	12/05	12/06	12/07
Sales ($ mil.)	11.7%	442.7	484.6	542.9	612.4	689.6
Net income ($ mil.)	14.9%	72.2	80.3	93.9	93.4	126.0
Market value ($ mil.)	19.3%	1,537.0	2,025.0	2,119.5	2,243.7	3,114.3
Employees	4.7%	—	—	2,100	2,200	2,304

INTERACTIVE INTELLIGENCE, INC.

NASDAQ (GM): ININ

7601 Interactive Way
Indianapolis, IN 46278
Phone: 317-872-3000
Fax: —
Web: www.inin.com

CEO: Donald E. Brown
CFO: Stephen R. (Steve) Head
HR: —
FYE: December 31
Type: Public

Interactive Intelligence knows that managing your communications is smart business. The company's software helps integrate a wide array of communication systems, from phone calls, voice mail, and e-mail to faxes and Web-based. Its applications integrate with enterprise messaging platforms such as Microsoft's Exchange and Lotus Notes and provides tools for connecting mobile workers to enterprise information systems. Interactive Intelligence also makes systems for call center operations. Founder and CEO Donald Brown owns about 54% of Interactive Intelligence.

	Annual Growth	12/03	12/04	12/05	12/06	12/07
Sales ($ mil.)	20.9%	51.5	55.1	62.9	83.2	109.9
Net income ($ mil.)	—	(5.9)	1.0	2.1	10.3	17.5
Market value ($ mil.)	54.9%	81.9	71.7	82.2	384.3	471.7
Employees	20.5%	—	340	390	—	595

INTERACTIVE SYSTEMS WORLDWIDE INC.

Pink Sheets: ISWI

2 Andrews Dr., 2nd Fl.
West Paterson, NJ 07424
Phone: 973-256-8181
Fax: 973-256-8211
Web: www.sportxction.com

CEO: Bernard Albanese
CFO: Bernard Albanese
HR: —
FYE: September 30
Type: Public

Interactive Systems Worldwide develops play-by-play sports wagering systems that couch potatoes can bet on. Its SportXction software system, designed for use with interactive television or the Internet, sets the odds and monitors and records bets for the final outcome or individual plays within a sporting event. (Anyone care to bet who fumbles next?) Co-founder and former chairman Barry Mindes owns about 25% of the company.

	Annual Growth	9/03	9/04	9/05	9/06	9/07
Sales ($ mil.)	—	0.0	0.0	0.2	0.1	0.5
Net income ($ mil.)	—	(5.6)	(6.0)	(5.8)	(4.4)	(2.2)
Market value ($ mil.)	(41.6%)	35.7	28.7	28.9	18.1	4.2
Employees	(37.6%)	—	—	18	—	7

INTER-AMERICAN DEVELOPMENT BANK

1300 New York Ave. NW
Washington, DC 20577
Phone: 202-623-1000
Fax: 202-623-3096
Web: www.iadb.org

CEO: Luis Alberto Moreno
CFO: Edward Bartholomew
HR: Manuel Labrado
FYE: December 31
Type: Member-owned banking authority

Inter-American Development Bank is like a mutual aid society that packs an economic punch. The institution was founded in 1959 to aid in the social and economic development of Latin America and the Caribbean. It uses grants, guarantees, investments, and loans to help fund public and private investment projects, policy reforms, financial crises or disasters, and national and regional technical cooperation. The bank is owned by its 47 member nations, which consist of 26 borrowing members in Central America, South America, and the Caribbean, plus nonborrowing members including the US, Canada, and 19 other countries.

	Annual Growth	12/03	12/04	12/05	12/06	12/07
Est. sales ($ mil.)	—	—	—	—	—	2,147.5
Employees	—	—	—	—	—	1,604

INTERBOND CORPORATION OF AMERICA

3200 SW 42nd St.
Hollywood, FL 33312
Phone: 954-797-4000
Fax: 954-797-4061
Web: www.brandsmartusa.com

CEO: Michael Perlman
CFO: Eric Beazley
HR: Janet Witczak
FYE: August 31
Type: Private

The only thing that isn't big about Interbond Corporation of America (which does business as BrandsMart USA) is its geographic scope. The company runs five BrandsMart USA stores in South Florida and three in the Atlanta area that each stock more than $8 million in merchandise. BrandsMart USA discount stores sell a wide selection of brand-name consumer electronics, including appliances, camcorders, cameras, car stereos, computers, DVD players, home theater components, phones, printers, and TVs. BrandsMart USA also offers delivery and installation services and store-branded credit cards. Chairman Robert Perlman founded the company in 1977.

	Annual Growth	8/02	8/03	8/04	8/05	8/06
Est. sales ($ mil.)	—	—	—	—	—	1,000.0
Employees	—	—	—	—	—	2,500

INTERCARE DX, INC.

OTC: ICCO

6080 Center Dr., Ste. 640
Los Angeles, CA 90045
Phone: 310-242-5634
Fax: 310-242-5676
Web: www.intercare.com

CEO: Anthony C. Dike
CFO: –
HR: –
FYE: December 31
Type: Public

Founded in 1991, Intercare DX provides health care management systems for clinical documentation, decision support, order entry, clinical data acquisition and storage, imaging and picture archiving, workflow and productivity management, and care communications management. The company's Mirage Systems Multimedia Biofeedback software is a program for neuromuscular re-education and biofeedback training. Its InterCare Clinical Explorer software integrates all aspects of health care organizations. Intercare DX has partnerships with Microsoft, Acer, and ViewSonic, among others. CEO Anthony Dike owns nearly 80% of Intercare DX.

	Annual Growth	12/02	12/03	12/04	12/05	*12/06
Sales ($ mil.)	—	—	—	—	0.0	1.6
Net income ($ mil.)	—	—	—	—	(1.7)	0.1
Employees	0.0%	—	—	—	12	12

*Most recent year available

INTER-CON SECURITY SYSTEMS, INC.

210 S. De Lacey Ave.
Pasadena, CA 91105
Phone: 626-535-2200
Fax: 626-685-9111
Web: www.icsecurity.com

CEO: Enrique (Rick) Hernandez Jr.
CFO: Neil Martau
HR: Pier Kuehn
FYE: December 31
Type: Private

There is no conning Inter-Con Security Systems. The company, one of the largest private security consulting firms in the US, provides custom-designed security programs for commercial, governmental, and industrial clients in North and South America, Europe, and Africa. Inter-Con's services include security consulting, investigations, and training. The company also provides security guard services. Inter-Con's clients have included General Motors, Kaiser Permanente, NASA, the US Marshals Service, and the US Department of State. The company was founded in 1973.

INTERCONTINENTALEXCHANGE, INC.

NYSE: ICE

2100 RiverEdge Pkwy., Ste. 500
Atlanta, GA 30328
Phone: 770-857-4700
Fax: 770-951-1307
Web: www.theice.com

CEO: Jeffrey C. Sprecher
CFO: Scott A. Hill
HR: Scott A. Hill
FYE: December 31
Type: Public

If there was money to be made in ice futures, IntercontinentalExchange (ICE) would probably trade that as well. The company is a leading online marketplace for global commodity trading, primarily of electricity, natural gas, crude oil, refined petroleum products, precious metals, and weather and emission credits. It also owns the ICE Futures Europe, a leading European energy futures and options platform. ICE's 10x Group unit provides real-time market data reports, and the company's eConfirm platform provides electronic trade confirmations. In a major expansion the company acquired the New York Board of Trade (renamed ICE Futures US) for $1 billion in 2007.

	Annual Growth	12/03	12/04	12/05	12/06	12/07
Sales ($ mil.)	57.3%	93.8	108.4	155.9	313.8	574.3
Net income ($ mil.)	105.8%	13.4	22.0	40.4	143.3	240.6
Market value ($ mil.)	347.9%	—	—	668.8	6,271.7	13,419.4
Employees	57.9%	—	—	203	226	506

INTERDIGITAL, INC.

NASDAQ (GS): IDCC

781 3rd Ave.
King of Prussia, PA 19406
Phone: 610-878-7800
Fax: 610-992-9432
Web: www.interdigital.com

CEO: William J. Merritt
CFO: Scott McQuilkin
HR: Gary D. Isaacs
FYE: December 31
Type: Public

InterDigital is more than just interested in digital telecommunications. The company develops and licenses circuitry designs, software, and other technology using CDMA and TDMA (code- and time-division multiple access) wireless telecommunications standards. InterDigital is also developing semiconductors and software to enable voice and data transmissions in mobile phones and portable computing devices. The company's top customers are LG Electronics (one-quarter of sales), NEC (14%), and Sharp (19%). InterDigital also licenses to Siemens and Sony Ericsson, and to many other makers of chips, software, and telecom equipment. The company gets about 80% of revenues from Asian customers.

	Annual Growth	12/03	12/04	12/05	12/06	12/07
Sales ($ mil.)	19.6%	114.6	103.7	163.1	480.5	234.2
Net income ($ mil.)	(12.7%)	34.5	0.2	54.7	225.2	20.0
Employees	4.4%	320	337	315	343	380

INTEREP NATIONAL RADIO SALES, INC.

Pink Sheets: IREP

100 Park Ave.
New York, NY 10017
Phone: 212-916-0700
Fax: 212-916-0790
Web: www.interep.com

CEO: David E. (Dave) Kennedy
CFO: William J. (Bill) McEntee Jr.
HR: Paul Parzuchowski
FYE: December 31
Type: Public

Interruptions to some, radio ads are music to this company's ears. A leading independent radio representation firm, advertising sales and marketing company Interep National Radio Sales sells advertising time for radio stations throughout the US. In addition, the company sells ads for Internet properties, television stations, and other media. Interep operates through a network of several representation firms, some of which are devoted to major radio station owners. The company is restructuring its finances under Chapter 11 bankruptcy protection.

	Annual Growth	12/02	12/03	12/04	12/05	*12/06
Sales ($ mil.)	(3.7%)	94.6	88.4	102.9	100.1	81.2
Net income ($ mil.)	—	(17.6)	(38.2)	(7.0)	(3.0)	(14.3)
Employees	(5.1%)	480	460	430	425	390

*Most recent year available

⊞ INTERFACE, INC.

NASDAQ (GM): IFSIA

2859 Paces Ferry Rd., Ste. 2000
Atlanta, GA 30339
Phone: 770-437-6800
Fax: 706-882-0500
Web: www.interfaceinc.com

CEO: Daniel T. Hendrix
CFO: Patrick C. Lynch
HR: –
FYE: Sunday nearest December 31
Type: Public

Interface goes underfoot and around the office with its line of modular carpet. The company, which puts an emphasis on environmentally friendly production, is the world's #1 producer of commercial carpets used in offices and other commercial facilities. Interface markets its modular (tiles and rolls) and broadloom carpets under such names as Heuga, Interface, Bentley, and FLOR. The company also offers an antimicrobial chemical, Intersept, which it provides in its modular carpet products and licenses for use in air filters. Interface manufactures carpet in North America, Europe, Asia, and Australia; it sells products in more than 110 countries. The company sold its panel and upholstery fabric business in 2007.

	Annual Growth	12/03	12/04	12/05	12/06	12/07
Sales ($ mil.)	4.0%	923.5	881.7	985.8	1,075.8	1,081.3
Net income ($ mil.)	—	(33.3)	(55.4)	1.2	10.0	(10.8)
Market value ($ mil.)	36.2%	264.5	453.7	386.0	766.9	910.6
Employees	(12.0%)	—	—	4,781	4,873	3,701

INTERGRAPH CORPORATION

170 Graphics Dr.
Madison, AL 35758
Phone: 256-730-2000
Fax: 256-730-2048
Web: www.intergraph.com

CEO: R. Halsey Wise
CFO: Anthony Colaluca Jr.
HR: –
FYE: December 31
Type: Private

They like wide open spaces at Intergraph — and city streets, too. The company provides spatial information management software, which enables mapping and design functions for local, state, and federal government agencies, and for businesses in the transportation, process plant design, power, marine, public safety, and utilities industries. Its systems (a combination of software, third-party hardware, and services) are used for a wide range of functions, including plant design, ship construction, public safety dispatch, aerial photography, and geospatial mapping and analysis. In 2006 the company was acquired by Texas Pacific Group and Hellman & Friedman LLC for about $1.3 billion.

	Annual Growth	12/03	12/04	12/05	12/06	12/07
Est. sales ($ mil.)	—	—	—	—	—	352.1
Employees	—	—	—	—	—	3,450

THE INTERGROUP CORPORATION

NASDAQ (CM): INTG

820 Moraga Dr.
Los Angeles, CA 90049
Phone: 310-889-2500
Fax: 310-889-2525

CEO: John V. Winfield
CFO: David T. Nguyen
HR: –
FYE: June 30
Type: Public

InterGroup buys, develops, and manages affordable housing and other projects with an eye toward social responsibility. The company, formerly a real estate investment trust (REIT), owns around 20 apartment complexes, two commercial real estate properties, two residential homes, and, through subsidiary Santa Fe Financial, majority interest in a San Francisco hotel. Its holdings are primarily concentrated in California and Texas. InterGroup also invests in securities and in real estate portfolios held by other corporations. Chairman and CEO John Winfield owns about 60% of the company. Winfield is also CEO of Santa Fe Financial and its subsidiary, Portsmouth Square.

	Annual Growth	6/03	6/04	6/05	6/06	6/07
Sales ($ mil.)	36.0%	14.1	13.8	13.0	17.6	48.3
Net income ($ mil.)	—	2.6	3.1	(3.1)	(1.9)	(3.6)
Market value ($ mil.)	15.5%	24.1	29.3	43.6	37.3	42.8
Employees	(58.3%)	—	—	46	—	8

INTERIM HEALTHCARE INC.

1601 Sawgrass Corporate Pkwy.
Sunrise, FL 33323
Phone: 954-858-6000
Fax: 954-858-2760
Web: www.interimhealthcare.com

CEO: Russ Cooper
CFO: Michael Slupecki
HR: Carolyn Garman
FYE: December 31
Type: Private

Interim HealthCare places health care staff where they are needed, whether in a hospital or in a patient's home. Its home health care business, marketed as Interim HomeStyle Services, provides nurses, therapists, and personal care aides to patients in their houses. The company also provides health care personnel to hospitals, long-term care facilities, and other home health care providers. Interim HealthCare has about 300 franchised locations in the US and Puerto Rico and serves some 50,000 patients daily. Investment firm Sentinel Capital Partners owns the company, which was founded in 1966 as Medical Personnel Pool.

	Annual Growth	12/03	12/04	12/05	12/06	12/07
Est. sales ($ mil.)	—	—	—	—	—	134.8
Employees	—	—	—	—	—	2,500

INTERLAKE MATERIAL HANDLING, INC.

1230 E. Diehl Rd., Ste. 400
Naperville, IL 60563
Phone: 630-245-8800
Fax: 630-245-8906
Web: www.interlake.com

CEO: Dan Wilson
CFO: Jackie Barry
HR: Lorene Flewellen
FYE: June 30
Type: Private

If you've got some material you need moved around, don't worry because Interlake's got a handle on it. Interlake Material Handling manufactures industrial storage racks and conveyor systems. It designs and builds material handling controls and machinery automation panels, consoles, and systems as well as providing related software and consulting. Interlake manufactures its racks for distribution centers, manufacturing facilities, warehouses, and retail outlets, among other industries. Brambles Industries sold Interlake to materials handling company United Fixtures in 2006.

	Annual Growth	6/03	6/04	6/05	6/06	6/07
Est. sales ($ mil.)	—	—	—	—	—	27.1
Employees	—	—	—	—	—	332

INTERLEUKIN GENETICS, INC.

AMEX: ILI

135 Beaver St.
Waltham, MA 02452
Phone: 781-398-0700
Fax: 781-398-0720
Web: www.ilgenetics.com

CEO: Lewis H. Bender
CFO: –
HR: –
FYE: December 31
Type: Public

Interleukin Genetics counts on the high failure rate of crystal balls. The company develops genetic tests to identify individuals' chances of developing certain diseases. Its first commercial product, the PST, is a test for gum disease and is available in the US and Europe. The company also offers predictive tests for heart disease and general nutrition under the Gensona brand through its partnership with Alticor. Interleukin Genetics has also teamed with Alticor to develop nutritional and skin care products. Through its Alan James Group unit, the company develops and markets nutritional supplements to consumers through retail channels. Alticor subsidiary Pyxis Innovations controls 58% of the company.

	Annual Growth	12/03	12/04	12/05	12/06	12/07
Sales ($ mil.)	46.6%	2.1	0.0	0.0	4.7	9.7
Net income ($ mil.)	—	(4.2)	(7.3)	(6.6)	(6.9)	(6.2)
Market value ($ mil.)	(25.3%)	108.2	83.8	128.0	160.3	33.6
Employees	22.7%	—	—	22	27	—

INTERLINE BRANDS, INC.

NYSE: IBI

801 W. Bay St.
Jacksonville, FL 32204
Phone: 904-421-1400
Fax: 904-358-2486
Web: www.interlinebrands.com

CEO: Michael J. Grebe
CFO: Thomas J. Tossavainen
HR: Annette A. Ricciuti
FYE: Last Friday in December
Type: Public

When something breaks, bursts, or drips, you can call Interline Brands, a national distributor and direct marketer of repair and maintenance products. The company sells more than 85,000 plumbing, hardware, electrical, janitorial, and related products under private labels (including AmSan, Hardware Express, Maintenance USA, Sexauer, U.S. Lock, Wilmar). It operates 75 regional distribution centers and some 40 showrooms serving professional contractors throughout North America. Its Florida Lighting business (acquired in 2003) distributes specialty lighting and electrical products. Interline Brands was formed in 2000 when the Wilmar, Barnett, and Sexauer companies merged. The company went public in late 2004.

	Annual Growth	12/03	12/04	12/05	12/06	12/07
Sales ($ mil.)	18.5%	—	743.9	851.9	1,067.6	1,239.0
Net income ($ mil.)	41.2%	—	18.1	28.8	31.2	51.0
Market value ($ mil.)	8.3%	—	561.4	733.0	725.4	713.7
Employees	37.8%	—	—	2,730	3,763	—

An in-depth profile of this company is available to Hoover's Online members at hoovers.com.

829

INTERLINK ELECTRONICS, INC.

Pink Sheets: LINK

546 Flynn Rd.
Camarillo, CA 93012
Phone: 805-484-8855
Fax: 805-484-8989
Web: www.interlinkec.com

CEO: John A. Buckett II
CFO: Charles C. Best
HR: Patrice R. Poleto
FYE: December 31
Type: Public

Interlink Electronics designs electronic signature capture devices and specialty interface products. The company's signature capture products include its ePad line of hardware devices and IntegriSign software. Its sensor interface components enable menu navigation, cursor control, and character input in devices such as computer mice and mobile phones. Interlink's patented force-sensing technology enables smaller, more touch-sensitive input devices. The company also provides design and integration services. Interlink sold its OEM remote control and branded presentation controls segments to electronics manufacturer SMK for $11.5 million in 2007. Special Situations Technology Fund owns about 40% of the company.

	Annual Growth	12/03	12/04	12/05	12/06	12/07
Sales ($ mil.)	(11.2%)	31.0	35.4	38.2	36.2	19.3
Net income ($ mil.)	—	1.1	(2.3)	(8.3)	(11.8)	(5.7)
Employees	—	—	—	—	226	—

INTERMATIC INCORPORATED

7777 Winn Rd.
Spring Grove, IL 60081
Phone: 815-675-2321
Fax: 815-675-7055
Web: www.intermatic.com

CEO: David W. (Dave) Schroeder
CFO: –
HR: Linnea Ten Bruin
FYE: December 31
Type: Private

From its start in 1891 as a maker of streetcar fare registers, Intermatic has evolved to become an integrated manufacturer of energy-control products for both industrial and residential use. The company makes home timers that include pool and spa controls, portable burglar alarms, and appliance timers. It makes night-lights and portable alarms, as well as outdoor lighting systems, such as its Malibu brand of low-voltage systems. Other products include industrial surge protectors, weatherproof covers for electrical outlets, and solar-powered lights. Intermatic sells its products through retailers and wholesalers. Chairman emeritus Douglas Kinney Sr. and his family own the company.

INTERMEC, INC.

NYSE: IN

6001 36th Ave. West
Everett, WA 98203
Phone: 425-265-2400
Fax: 425-355-9551
Web: www.intermec.com

CEO: Patrick J. (Pat) Byrne
CFO: Lanny H. Michael
HR: Sue Y. Taylor
FYE: December 31
Type: Public

Intermec keeps assets on track. The company manufactures and supports data collection and mobile computing products. Its offerings include bar code scanners, RFID readers, mobile and fixed vehicle computers, printers, and label media. The company also sells wireless LAN equipment from Cisco Systems. Intermec's products are used to manage distribution, warehouse, and manufacturing facilities. Formerly called UNOVA, the company discontinued its Industrial Automation Systems (IAS) segment in 2005 and changed its name to Intermec — the name already used by its automated data collection subsidiary — in 2006.

	Annual Growth	12/03	12/04	12/05	12/06	12/07
Sales ($ mil.)	(6.7%)	1,122.6	811.3	875.5	850.0	849.2
Net income ($ mil.)	—	(19.3)	(49.1)	61.8	32.0	23.0
Market value ($ mil.)	(23.6%)	—	—	2,128.9	1,463.9	1,242.8
Employees	(3.9%)	—	—	2,497	2,407	2,308

INTERMET CORPORATION

301 Commerce St., Ste. 2901
Fort Worth, TX 76102
Phone: 817-348-9190
Fax: 817-332-9606
Web: www.intermet.com

CEO: Jeffrey (Jeff) Mihalic
CFO: William H. (Bill) Whalen
HR: Donald H. Sabathier
FYE: December 31
Type: Private

INTERMET casts more than a giant shadow: It is one of the world's largest independent makers of castings for automakers. The company makes castings from ductile iron, gray iron, and aluminum. INTERMET's ferrous castings include wheel hubs, rear knuckles, tie rods, and driveline yokes. Its light casting parts include engine covers, instrument panel frames, and airbag controller enclosures. The company's products are used primarily in passenger cars, light trucks, and heavy-duty vehicles. Major customers include Chrysler, General Motors, and Ford Motor.

	Annual Growth	12/03	12/04	12/05	12/06	12/07
Est. sales ($ mil.)	—	—	—	—	—	340.6
Employees	—	—	—	—	—	3,650

INTERMETRO COMMUNICATIONS, INC.

2685 Park Center Dr., Bldg. A
Simi Valley, CA 93065
Phone: 805-433-8000
Fax: 805-582-1006
Web: www.intermetro.net

CEO: Charles Rice
CFO: Vincent Arena
HR: –
FYE: December 31
Type: Private

InterMetro Communications hopes to take over the VoIP market, city by city by city. The company has built a national, private Voice-over Internet Protocol (VoIP) network that enables it to deliver voice calling services to telecommunications providers and end users. InterMetro's customers include traditional long-distance carriers, broadband companies, VoIP service providers, and wireless providers. Its VoIP network utilizes proprietary software, switching equipment, and fiber-optic lines to deliver carrier-quality VoIP services, which are typically more cost efficient than circuit-based technologies used in traditional long-distance networks.

INTERMOUNTAIN HEALTH CARE, INC.

36 S. State St., Fl. 22
Salt Lake City, UT 84111
Phone: 801-442-2000
Fax: 801-442-3327
Web: www.ihc.com

CEO: William H. (Bill) Nelson
CFO: Burt Zimmerly
HR: –
FYE: December 31
Type: Not-for-profit

Intermountain Health Care (IHC) is a not-for-profit health system that operates some 20 hospitals. It also runs more than a dozen home health care agencies, an air ambulance service, and about 160 physician and urgent care clinics, counseling offices, rehabilitation centers, and other health care facilities in Utah and southern Idaho. Its emergency department treats more than 39,700 patients each year. IHC Health Plans also offers health insurance programs to large and small employers and to individuals. Affiliate IHC/AmeriNet is a group purchasing organization. The company was formed in 1975 when the Church of Jesus Christ of Latter Day Saints (the Mormons) donated 15 of its hospitals to their communities.

INTERMUNE, INC.

NASDAQ (GM): ITMN

3280 Bayshore Blvd.
Brisbane, CA 94005
Phone: 415-466-2200
Fax: 415-466-2300
Web: www.intermune.com

CEO: Daniel G. (Dan) Welch
CFO: John C. Hodgman
HR: Howard A. Simon
FYE: December 31
Type: Public

InterMune has found a good thing in interferon gamma. The company's sole marketed product is Actimmune (interferon gamma-1b), an FDA-approved treatment for two rare congenital disorders: chronic granulomatous disease, an immune condition; and osteopetrosis, a disease causing abnormal bone growth. Most of Actimmune's sales, however, are for off-label use of the drug to treat the deterioration of lung function from scarring caused by idiopathic pulmonary fibrosis (IPF). InterMune is developing another potential IPF treatment called pirfenidone, and it is also researching hepatitis C therapies with Roche.

	Annual Growth	12/03	12/04	12/05	12/06	12/07
Sales ($ mil.)	(18.9%)	154.1	151.0	110.5	90.8	66.7
Net income ($ mil.)	—	(97.0)	(59.5)	(5.2)	(107.2)	(89.6)
Market value ($ mil.)	(8.4%)	737.5	432.1	547.5	1,053.6	520.3
Employees	—	—	—	—	193	—

INTERNAP NETWORK SERVICES CORPORATION

NASDAQ (GM): INAP

250 Williams St.
Atlanta, GA 30303
Phone: 404-302-9700
Fax: 404-475-0520
Web: www.internap.com

CEO: James P. (Jim) DeBlasio
CFO: George E. Kilguss III
HR: Eric Suddith
FYE: December 31
Type: Public

Internap Network Services has a solution for CIOs losing sleep over slow network connections. The company helps businesses bypass congested public network access points (NAPs) — the crossroads where major backbone carriers connect and exchange Internet traffic — with its own private NAPs (P-NAPS). Internap has P-NAPs located in Asia, Australia, Europe, and North America. The company also provides application hosting and other data center services. Internap has a global platform of data centers, managed Internet services, a content delivery network, and content monetization services. Customers use its Flow Control Platform (FCP) routing hardware to manage the performance of multiple network architectures.

	Annual Growth	12/03	12/04	12/05	12/06	12/07
Sales ($ mil.)	14.0%	138.6	144.6	153.7	181.4	234.1
Net income ($ mil.)	—	(33.0)	(18.1)	(5.0)	3.7	(5.6)
Market value ($ mil.)	(7.2%)	560.4	314.5	146.9	712.8	414.8
Employees	12.8%	—	—	330	330	420

INTERNATIONAL ALUMINUM CORPORATION

767 Monterey Pass Rd.
Monterey Park, CA 91754
Phone: 323-264-1670
Fax: 323-264-4909
Web: www.intlalum.com

CEO: Cornelius C. Vanderstar
CFO: Mitchell K. Fogelman
HR: Susan L. Leone
FYE: June 30
Type: Private

Ooh, shiny! International Aluminum makes aluminum and vinyl building products for commercial and residential customers who want to build, remodel, or improve their homes or businesses. Commercial products include curtain and window walls, interior wall systems, office partitions, doors, and frames. Residential products include windows and doors, which International Aluminum sells to lumber yards and home improvement centers and to contractors, dealers, and distributors. It also produces custom aluminum extrusions for its own use and for other manufacturers. Private equity firm Genstar Capital acquired International Aluminum in 2007 for nearly $230 million.

	Annual Growth	6/02	6/03	6/04	6/05	6/06
Sales ($ mil.)	9.7%	193.7	192.6	213.0	251.6	280.8
Net income ($ mil.)	—	(8.0)	2.7	6.7	12.9	16.2
Employees	0.0%	1,500	1,400	1,500	1,500	—

INTERNATIONAL ASSETS HOLDING

NASDAQ (CM): IAAC

220 E. Central Pkwy., Ste. 2060
Altamonte Springs, FL 32701
Phone: 407-741-5300
Fax: 407-740-0808
Web: www.intlassets.com

CEO: Sean M. O'Connor
CFO: Brian T. Sephton
HR: —
FYE: September 30
Type: Public

Going global is the name of the game for securities broker International Assets Holding Corporation and its subsidiaries. The company specializes in niche international markets, offering expertise in securities, foreign exchange, and commodities trading. Its INTL Trading subsidiary is a market-maker for more than 400 foreign securities. INTL Consilium, a joint venture with Consilium Investment Capital, provides asset management services. International Assets Holding serves financial institutions, corporations, and other institutional investors in the US and abroad. It has four US offices and six more in Asia, South America, and Europe.

	Annual Growth	9/03	9/04	9/05	9/06	9/07
Sales ($ mil.)	349.8%	10.9	22.0	26.2	102.8	4,460.3
Net income ($ mil.)	—	1.3	(0.1)	2.6	3.5	(4.5)
Market value ($ mil.)	100.8%	13.1	56.6	60.9	183.1	212.5
Employees	59.3%	—	—	67	—	170

INTERNATIONAL BANCSHARES CORPORATION

NASDAQ (GS): IBOC

1200 San Bernardo Ave.
Laredo, TX 78042
Phone: 956-722-7611
Fax: 956-726-6637
Web: www.iboc.com

CEO: Dennis E. Nixon
CFO: Imelda Navarro
HR: —
FYE: December 31
Type: Public

International Bancshares is leading post-NAFTA banking in South Texas. The institution's International Bank of Commerce and Commerce Bank serve residents and businesses of Texas, Oklahoma, and northern Mexico through some 235 offices. The bulk of the company's portfolio is made up of business loans, including funding for northern Mexico's *maquiladoras*, US-owned plants in Mexico that temporarily import materials for assembly and then re-export to the US. About 30% of the company's deposits come from south of the border. With its large number of Hispanic shareholders, International Bancshares is one of the largest minority-owned banks in the nation.

	Annual Growth	12/03	12/04	12/05	12/06	12/07
Assets ($ mil.)	14.1%	6,578.3	9,918.0	10,391.8	10,911.5	11,167.2
Net income ($ mil.)	(0.2%)	122.1	119.0	140.8	117.0	121.3
Market value ($ mil.)	10.4%	965.3	1,323.2	1,546.3	1,607.1	1,436.3
Employees	(4.7%)	—	—	3,265	3,427	2,965

INTERNATIONAL BANK FOR RECONSTRUCTION & DEVELOPMENT

1818 H St. NW
Washington, DC 20433
Phone: 202-473-1000
Fax: 202-477-6391
Web: www.worldbank.org

CEO: Robert B. Zoellick
CFO: Vincenzo La Via
HR: Xavier Coll
FYE: June 30
Type: Private

Collectively known as the World Bank, the International Bank for Reconstruction & Development (IBRD) and its sister organization the International Development Association (IDA) are on a mission to improve the world. The IBRD strives to reduce poverty in creditworthy middle-income countries by promoting sustainable development through loans, guarantees, risk management products, and advisory services. The IBRD serves countries in Latin America, Asia, Africa, and Eastern Europe, funding activities by selling bonds in international capital markets. IDA assists the world's poorest countries, helping them develop effective health care, education, and government institutions. The World Bank has 185 member countries.

	Annual Growth	6/03	6/04	6/05	6/06	6/07
Est. sales ($ mil.)	—	—	—	—	—	618.8
Employees	—	—	—	—	—	10,000

An in-depth profile of this company is available to Hoover's Online members at hoovers.com.

831

INTERNATIONAL BROTHERHOOD OF TEAMSTERS

25 Louisiana Ave. NW	CEO: James P. (Jim) Hoffa
Washington, DC 20001	CFO: C. Thomas (Tom) Keegel
Phone: 202-624-6800	HR: Cheryl L. Johnson
Fax: 202-624-6918	FYE: December 31
Web: www.teamster.org	Type: Labor union

One of the largest and best-known labor unions in the US, the International Brotherhood of Teamsters has 1.4 million members. The Teamsters represents workers in some 20 industry sectors, including trucking, warehousing, parcel delivery, industrial trades, and government. More than 200,000 of the union's members are employees of package delivery giant United Parcel Service. Besides negotiating labor contracts with employers on behalf of its members, the union oversees pension funds and serves as an advocate in legislative and regulatory arenas. The union and its affiliates have about 1,900 local chapters in the US and Canada, including about 475 Teamsters locals. The Teamsters union was founded in 1903.

INTERNATIONAL BUILDING TECHNOLOGIES   OTC: INBGE

1151 Harbor Bay Pkwy., Ste. 202	CEO: Kenneth Yeung
Alameda, CA 94502	CFO: –
Phone: 510-814-3778	HR: –
Fax: 510-814-0366	FYE: December 31
Web: www.ibtgi.com	Type: Public

International Building Technologies Group, Inc. (formerly Motorsports Emporium) has raced into a new business. Formerly a seller of racing and motorsports accessories and apparel, the company has changed lanes. In 2007 it began a new life as a manufacturer of a specialty panel-based technology that helps buildings withstand earthquakes and hurricane-force winds. International Building Technologies also offers other services including site planning, engineering, contractor services, training, and supervision.

	Annual Growth	12/02	12/03	12/04	12/05	*12/06
Sales ($ mil.)	0.0%	0.1	0.1	0.0	0.2	0.1
Net income ($ mil.)	—	(0.2)	(0.6)	(1.7)	(1.0)	(1.2)
Market value ($ mil.)	—	—	—	—	—	—
Employees	—	—	—	—	—	—

*Most recent year available

INTERNATIONAL BUSINESS MACHINES   NYSE: IBM

New Orchard Rd.	CEO: Samuel J. Palmisano
Armonk, NY 10504	CFO: Mark Loughridge
Phone: 914-499-1900	HR: J. Randall (Randy) MacDonald
Fax: –	FYE: December 31
Web: www.ibm.com	Type: Public

Big Blue? Try Huge Blue. International Business Machines Corporation (IBM) is the world's top provider of computer products and services. Among the leaders in almost every market in which it competes, the company makes mainframes and servers, storage systems, and peripherals. Its service arm is the largest in the world and accounts for more than half of its revenue. IBM is also one of the largest providers of both software (ranking #2, behind Microsoft) and semiconductors. The company continues to use acquisitions to augment its software and service businesses, while streamlining its hardware operations with divestitures and organizational reengineering.

	Annual Growth	12/03	12/04	12/05	12/06	12/07
Sales ($ mil.)	2.6%	89,131.0	96,293.0	91,134.0	91,424.0	98,786.0
Net income ($ mil.)	8.3%	7,583.0	8,430.0	7,934.0	9,492.0	10,418.0
Market value ($ mil.)	(1.2%)	157,047.1	162,222.5	129,381.1	146,354.8	149,743.8
Employees	4.7%	355,157	369,277	366,345	355,766	426,969

INTERNATIONAL CARD ESTABLISHMENT, INC.   OTC: ICRD

555 Airport Way, Ste. A	CEO: William J. Lopshire
Camarillo, CA 93010	CFO: Candace Mills
Phone: 805-383-7047	HR: –
Fax: 866-423-2492	FYE: December 31
Web: www.cardnetone.com	Type: Public

International Card Establishment (ICE) believes that it's cool for every merchant, big or small, to have the ability to swipe your credit card. The company provides a variety of credit card servicing and leasing offerings. ICE targets small merchants and markets credit card processing systems, processing services, software, and related offerings for managing loyalty programs. The company also provides financing for purchasing point-of-sale equipment. ICE has used acquisitions to transition away from its previous business of providing Web-based event management software and services.

	Annual Growth	12/03	12/04	12/05	12/06	12/07
Sales ($ mil.)	66.4%	1.2	14.8	6.6	10.8	9.2
Net income ($ mil.)	—	(0.4)	(3.8)	(4.3)	(3.6)	(4.0)
Market value ($ mil.)	(23.7%)	12.0	14.5	5.9	7.8	4.1
Employees	—	—	—	—	—	—

INTERNATIONAL CENTER FOR ENTREPRENEURIAL DEVELOPMENT, INC.

12715 Telge Rd.	CEO: Stephen B. (Steve) Hammerstein
Cypress, TX 77429	CFO: –
Phone: 281-256-4100	HR: –
Fax: 281-373-4450	FYE: December 31
Web: www.iced.net	Type: Holding company

The International Center for Entrepreneurial Development (ICED) is a holding company offering franchise opportunities in the computer education, health care, and mail center and printing industries. ICED offers a number of franchise brands including Kwik Kopy, Parcel Plus, and Women's Health Boutique. Bud Hadfield founded the company in 1967 when he began franchising his Kwik Kopy centers.

	Annual Growth	12/03	12/04	12/05	12/06	12/07
Est. sales ($ mil.)	—	—	—	—	—	15.0
Employees	—	—	—	—	—	140

INTERNATIONAL COAL GROUP, INC.   NYSE: ICO

300 Corporate Centre Dr.	CEO: Bennett K. (Ben) Hatfield
Scott Depot, WV 25560	CFO: Bradley W. (Brad) Harris
Phone: 304-760-2400	HR: –
Fax: –	FYE: December 31
Web: www.intlcoal.com	Type: Public

International Coal Group focuses its energy on one nation, the US. The company produces coal from about 10 mining complexes in Northern and Central Appalachia (Kentucky, Maryland, and West Virginia) and from another in the Illinois Basin (in Illinois, strangely enough). International Coal Group produces low-sulfur steam coal, which is sold mainly to electric utilities, and metallurgical coal, which is sold to steelmakers. Steam coal accounts for two-thirds of the company's 950 million tons of coal reserves. International Coal Group was formed in 2004 when investor Wilbur Ross led a group that bought many of the assets of Horizon Natural Resources in a bankruptcy auction.

	Annual Growth	12/03	12/04	12/05	12/06	12/07
Sales ($ mil.)	14.5%	—	—	647.7	891.6	849.2
Net income ($ mil.)	—	—	—	31.8	(9.3)	(147.0)
Market value ($ mil.)	(24.7%)	—	—	1,447.1	833.3	820.0
Employees	43.6%	—	—	1,547	2,222	—

INTERNATIONAL COFFEE & TEA, LLC

1945 S. La Cienega Blvd.
Los Angeles, CA 90034
Phone: 310-237-2326
Fax: 310-815-3676
Web: www.coffeebean.com

CEO: Melvin (Mel) Elias
CFO: Angy Chin
HR: Faye Moseley
FYE: December 31
Type: Private

Don't be chai; stand your grounds and espresso yourself over a cup at The Coffee Bean. International Coffee & Tea operates and franchises more than 520 coffee shops operating under the name The Coffee Bean & Tea Leaf. The outlets, found mostly in California and in about a dozen foreign countries, feature a variety of fresh roasted coffees and specialty teas, along with baked goods and blended ice drinks. More than 270 locations are company owned, while the rest are franchised. The chain was started by Mona and Herbert Hyman in 1963. Chairman Sunny Sassoon, his brother Victor, and investor Severin Wunderman bought the company in 1998.

	Annual Growth	12/03	12/04	12/05	12/06	12/07
Est. sales ($ mil.)	—	—	—	—	—	292.4
Employees	—	—	—	—	—	4,400

INTERNATIONAL CREATIVE MANAGEMENT, INC.

10250 Constellation Blvd.
Los Angeles, CA 90067
Phone: 310-550-4000
Fax: 310-550-4100
Web: www.icmtalent.com

CEO: Jeffrey S. (Jeff) Berg
CFO: Joe Friedman
HR: Karen Abrams
FYE: July 30
Type: Private

If anyone can manage creativity internationally, it's International Creative Management (ICM). The agency represents actors and directors, as well as artists in theater, music, publishing, and new media. One of the major "10 percenteries" (along with CAA and William Morris), ICM represents high-profile clients including Richard Gere, Halle Berry, and Beyonce Knowles. ICM also arranged financing for Oscar-nominated films such as *Gosford Park, Moulin Rouge,* and *The Fellowship of the Ring.* The agency has lost several star agents in recent years, along with big-name clients (including Cameron Diaz and Julia Roberts) to its competitors. ICM was formed in 1975 by the merger of Creative Management Associates and The International Famous Agency.

INTERNATIONAL DAIRY QUEEN, INC.

7505 Metro Blvd.
Minneapolis, MN 55439
Phone: 952-830-0200
Fax: 952-830-0273
Web: www.dairyqueen.com

CEO: Charles W. (Chuck) Mooty
CFO: James S. Simpson
HR: Angela Rud
FYE: December 31
Type: Subsidiary

International Dairy Queen (IDQ) has been supplying brain-freezes for almost 70 years. The company is a leading franchiser of frozen treat stores, with more than 5,600 Dairy Queen quick-service restaurants popular for their ice cream treats, including Blizzards, sundaes, and cones. Many of the stores also serve burgers, fries, and other items. A small number of units are company-owned. In addition, IDQ franchises about 400 Orange Julius locations serving blended fruit drinks, and a small number of Karmelkorn stands offering a variety of popcorn treats. IDQ franchisees operate in the US, Canada, and 20 other countries. Tracing its roots back to 1938, the company is owned by Warren Buffett's Berkshire Hathaway.

	Annual Growth	12/03	12/04	12/05	12/06	12/07
Est. sales ($ mil.)	—	—	—	—	—	476.0
Employees	—	—	—	—	—	2,055

INTERNATIONAL DATA GROUP, INC.

1 Exeter Plaza, 15th Fl.
Boston, MA 02116
Phone: 617-534-1200
Fax: 617-423-0240
Web: www.idg.com

CEO: Patrick J. (Pat) McGovern
CFO: Ted Bloom
HR: Piper Sheer
FYE: September 30
Type: Private

International Data Group (IDG) is a publishing giant with digital appeal. The world's top technology publisher, IDG produces more than 300 magazines and newspapers (including *PC World* and *CIO*) in 85 countries and in dozens of languages. In addition to publishing, IDG provides technology market research through its IDC unit, and also produces technology-focused industry events. The company offers career services through sites such as ITcareers.com, and operates 450 Web sites featuring technology content. Chairman Patrick McGovern founded IDG in 1964.

	Annual Growth	9/02	9/03	9/04	9/05	9/06
Sales ($ mil.)	4.0%	2,580.0	2,410.0	2,500.0	2,680.0	3,020.0
Employees	1.1%	13,050	13,450	13,510	13,640	13,640

INTERNATIONAL FIGHT LEAGUE, INC.

OTC: IFLI

424 W. 33rd St., Ste. 650
New York, NY 10001
Phone: 212-356-4000
Fax: −
Web: www.ifl.tv

CEO: Jay Larkin
CFO: Michael C. Keefe
HR: −
FYE: December 31
Type: Public

You might say everybody is kung fu fighting at this company. International Fight League (IFL) operates a mixed martial arts (MMA) league in which fighters compete in a series of bouts, including title matches to determine belt holders in various weight classes. The events are televised through a broadcasting deal with FOX Sports Net; television fees and ticket sales account for the majority of IFL's revenue. League co-founder and commissioner Kurt Otto owns almost 30% of the company; co-founder and former CEO Gareb Shamus and Richard Kurtz each own about 20%.

	Annual Growth	12/03	12/04	12/05	12/06	12/07
Sales ($ mil.)	470.0%	—	—	—	1.0	5.7
Net income ($ mil.)	—	—	—	—	(9.6)	(21.3)
Market value ($ mil.)	(97.0%)	—	—	—	505.6	15.0
Employees	—	—	—	—	28	—

INTERNATIONAL FINANCE CORPORATION

2121 Pennsylvania Ave. NW
Washington, DC 20433
Phone: 202-473-3800
Fax: 202-974-4384
Web: www.ifc.org

CEO: Paul D. Wolfowitz
CFO: Nina Shapiro
HR: Dorothy H. Berry
FYE: June 30
Type: Member-owned banking authority

International Finance Corporation (IFC) is the lender known 'round the world. IFC promotes economic development worldwide by providing loans and equity financing for private-sector investment. The IFC typically focuses on small and midsized businesses, financing projects in all types of industries, including manufacturing, infrastructure, tourism, health, education, and financial services. Established in 1956, the IFC is part of the World Bank group. Although it often acts in concert with the World Bank, the IFC is legally and financially autonomous. It is owned by some 180 member countries.

	Annual Growth	6/03	6/04	6/05	6/06	6/07
Est. sales ($ mil.)	—	—	—	—	—	885.8
Employees	—	—	—	—	—	2,100

An in-depth profile of this company is available to Hoover's Online members at hoovers.com.

833

INTERNATIONAL FLAVORS & FRAGRANCES INC.
NYSE: IFF

521 W. 57th St.
New York, NY 10019
Phone: 212-765-5500
Fax: 212-708-7132
Web: www.iff.com

CEO: Robert M. (Rob) Amen
CFO: Douglas J. Wetmore
HR: Steven J. Heaslip
FYE: December 31
Type: Public

Iff you've got a taste for the sweet and the salty, then International Flavors & Fragrances (IFF) is your kind of company. It's one of the world's leading creators and manufacturers of artificial aromas and flavors, producing fragrances used in the manufacture of perfumes, cosmetics, soaps, and other personal care and household products. The company has nearly 20% of the world market, placing it right behind Givaudan as the #2 flavor and fragrance maker. IFF sells its flavors principally to producers of prepared foods, dairy foods, beverages, confections, and pharmaceuticals. The company sells its fragrances and flavors in solid and liquid forms in amounts that range from a few pounds to several tons.

	Annual Growth	12/03	12/04	12/05	12/06	12/07
Sales ($ mil.)	4.6%	1,901.5	2,033.7	1,993.4	2,095.4	2,276.6
Net income ($ mil.)	9.4%	172.6	196.1	193.1	226.5	247.1
Market value ($ mil.)	4.5%	3,273.0	4,055.8	3,105.9	4,395.7	3,898.3
Employees	(1.4%)	—	—	5,160	5,087	—

INTERNATIONAL FOOD PRODUCTS GROUP, INC.
OTC: IFDG

170 Newport Center Dr., Ste. 260
Newport Beach, CA 92660
Phone: 949-759-7775
Fax: 949-759-5490
Web: www.goldenchoice.com

CEO: Richard Damion
CFO: Joseph R. Rodriguez Jr.
HR: –
FYE: June 30
Type: Public

International Food Products Group is a marketer of salty snacks under the Golden Choice, G.O.T. Fries, and AH SHUCKS labels. It also imports and distributes breath strips, Colombian coffee, frozen vegetables and fruit, tea, and other items. However, the company ceased these operations in 2007 pending the acquisition of an unnamed cheese-making company, the completion of which will result in International's becoming a cheese manufacturer. International's chairman and CEO Richard Damion owns about 14% of the company; president Ketan Mehta owns about 19%.

	Annual Growth	6/03	6/04	6/05	6/06	6/07
Sales ($ mil.)	25.7%	0.2	0.1	0.2	0.8	0.5
Net income ($ mil.)	—	(0.7)	(1.8)	(1.4)	(1.6)	(1.2)
Market value ($ mil.)	23.1%	2.2	1.9	4.8	10.3	5.0
Employees	—	—	—	—	—	—

INTERNATIONAL GAME TECHNOLOGY
NYSE: IGT

9295 Prototype Dr.
Reno, NV 89521
Phone: 775-448-7777
Fax: 775-448-0719
Web: www.igt.com

CEO: Thomas J. Matthews
CFO: Daniel R. Siciliano
HR: Tami Corbin
FYE: September 30
Type: Public

International Game Technology (IGT) is looking to hit the jackpot in the casino gaining business. The company is one of the world's largest gaming machine manufacturers with a product portfolio that includes traditional reel slot machines, video slots and video poker, and progressive payout machines. IGT also makes casino management software systems for tracking activity on the casino floor, as well as multi-player game software and customer relationship management (CRM) systems. It sells products mostly in North America, but it also serves international customers in Europe and Japan.

	Annual Growth	9/03	9/04	9/05	9/06	9/07
Sales ($ mil.)	5.4%	2,128.1	2,484.8	2,379.4	2,511.7	2,621.4
Net income ($ mil.)	6.8%	390.7	488.7	436.5	473.6	508.2
Market value ($ mil.)	8.9%	9,727.0	12,442.0	9,131.4	13,869.3	13,658.4
Employees	4.0%	—	—	5,000	5,200	—

INTERNATIONAL ISOTOPES INC.
OTC: INIS

4137 Commerce Circle
Idaho Falls, ID 83401
Phone: 208-524-5300
Fax: 208-524-1411
Web: www.intisoid.com

CEO: Steve T. Laflin
CFO: Laurie A. McKenzie-Carter
HR: –
FYE: December 31
Type: Public

Despite its name, International Isotopes is confined to a single US state. The company operates primarily through subsidiary International Isotopes Idaho, where it makes nuclear medicine calibration and measurement equipment. The company also processes gemstones that have been treated to enhance their color. The company's high specific activity (HSA) cobalt is sold in bulk to medical device makers. The substance is a key component of non-surgical radiation treatment equipment. International Isotopes plans to add fluorine gases to its line of products.

	Annual Growth	12/03	12/04	12/05	12/06	12/07
Sales ($ mil.)	22.3%	2.1	2.8	3.0	4.5	4.7
Net income ($ mil.)	—	(0.6)	(0.8)	(1.0)	(1.0)	(1.7)
Market value ($ mil.)	137.3%	—	15.9	18.6	26.3	212.5
Employees	—	12	—	—	—	—

INTERNATIONAL LEASE FINANCE CORPORATION

10250 Constellation Blvd., Ste. 3400
Los Angeles, CA 90067
Phone: 310-788-1999
Fax: 310-788-1990
Web: www.ilfc.com

CEO: Steven F. Udvar-Hazy
CFO: Alan H. Lund
HR: –
FYE: December 31
Type: Subsidiary

John Travolta bought his own Boeing; if your cash flow is more limited, International Lease Finance Corporation (ILFC) would be glad to lease you one. The company, which leases the entire range of Boeing and Airbus commercial aircraft, lays claim to being the largest lessor of new aircraft and the largest lessor of widebody aircraft in the world. It also boasts of owning the world's most valuable fleet — reportedly more than 900 planes — of leasable aircraft. High-rollers and movie stars aside, commercial airlines outside the US account for most sales; ILFC counts about 145 airlines as customers. ILFC is a subsidiary of insurance firm American International Group.

	Annual Growth	12/02	12/03	12/04	12/05	12/06
Sales ($ mil.)	9.8%	2,848.9	3,053.9	3,293.4	3,628.6	4,142.7
Net income ($ mil.)	(1.4%)	528.5	506.3	501.9	423.0	499.3
Employees	8.5%	124	129	151	160	172

INTERNATIONAL LOTTERY & TOTALIZATOR SYSTEMS
OTC: ITSI

2131 Faraday Ave.
Carlsbad, CA 92008
Phone: 760-931-4000
Fax: 760-931-1789
Web: www.ilts.com

CEO: Jeffrey M. (Jeff) Johnson
CFO: T. Linh Nguyen
HR: Carla Montiel
FYE: April 30
Type: Public

This company lets you press your luck by computer. International Lottery & Totalizator Systems, Inc. (ILTS) is a leading manufacturer of computerized wagering systems used by pari-mutuel racing operators, off-track betting centers, and lottery operators. It also provides consulting and training services, along with its software and hardware. In addition to wagering, ILTS markets electronic voting systems through its Unisyn Voting Solutions subsidiary. Customers in Asia account for nearly 95% of the company's revenue. Berjaya Lottery Management, a subsidiary of Malaysia-based Berjaya Group, owns more than 70% of ILTS.

	Annual Growth	4/04	4/05	4/06	4/07	4/08
Sales ($ mil.)	4.7%	10.8	9.7	3.4	11.1	13.0
Net income ($ mil.)	—	(1.8)	(1.8)	(2.3)	0.5	3.9
Market value ($ mil.)	3.8%	5.7	4.5	6.2	8.0	6.6
Employees	—	—	—	—	—	—

An in-depth profile of this company is available to Hoover's Online members at hoovers.com.

INTERNATIONAL MONETARY SYSTEMS, LTD.

OTC: INLM

16901 W. Glendale Dr.
New Berlin, WI 53151
Phone: 800-559-8515
Fax: 262-780-3655
Web: www.internationalmonetary.com

CEO: Donald F. (Don) Mardak
CFO: Danny W. Weibling
HR: −
FYE: December 31
Type: Public

Who says the barter system is dead? Not International Monetary Systems (IMS). IMS runs one of the world's largest trade exchanges, or barter networks, that can help businesses convert excess inventory into goods and services — or even cold hard cash. Serving more than 16,000 business customers in some 40 US markets, the company operates the Continental Trade Exchange Barter Network. Through this wholly owned subsidiary, users can swap excess goods or services or purchase items with cash or special trade currency. Founder and CEO Donald Mardak and his family own 55% of the company, which has grown by acquiring other trade exchanges.

	Annual Growth	12/03	12/04	12/05	12/06	12/07
Sales ($ mil.)	38.7%	4.0	4.7	6.2	8.8	14.8
Net income ($ mil.)	—	(0.2)	0.0	(0.2)	(0.4)	(0.4)
Market value ($ mil.)	78.8%	3.1	11.9	12.2	53.2	32.1
Employees	—	—	—	—	—	—

INTERNATIONAL PAPER COMPANY

NYSE: IP

6400 Poplar Ave.
Memphis, TN 38197
Phone: 901-419-7000
Fax: 901-214-9682
Web: www.ipaper.com

CEO: John V. Faraci Jr.
CFO: Timothy (Tim) Nicholls
HR: Jerome N. (Jerry) Carter
FYE: December 31
Type: Public

International Paper is the world's largest forest products company. It produces uncoated paper, industrial and consumer packaging, and pulp. Together, paper and packaging account for nearly two-thirds of the company's sales. International Paper also distributes printing, packaging, and graphic-art supplies in North America through subsidiary xpedx and in Europe through multiple subsidiaries. Slimming down, the company has sold its specialty chemicals operations, the majority of its lumber and wood products business, and most of the 6.3 million acres of US forestland it once owned. It retains 300,000 acres of US land and owns or has harvesting rights to nearly 250,000 acres of forestland in Brazil.

	Annual Growth	12/03	12/04	12/05	12/06	12/07
Sales ($ mil.)	(3.4%)	25,179.0	25,548.0	24,097.0	21,995.0	21,890.0
Net income ($ mil.)	40.2%	302.0	(35.0)	1,100.0	1,050.0	1,168.0
Market value ($ mil.)	(9.8%)	20,757.2	20,474.1	16,482.0	15,464.3	13,765.4
Employees	(13.4%)	—	—	68,700	60,600	51,500

INTERNATIONAL PROFIT ASSOCIATES, INC.

1250 Barclay Blvd.
Buffalo Grove, IL 60089
Phone: 847-808-5590
Fax: 847-808-5599
Web: www.ipa-iba.com

CEO: John R. Burgess
CFO: Gregg M. Steinberg
HR: Shelley Bareck
FYE: December 31
Type: Private

International Profit Associates would like to help small companies get bigger. The firm, which works closely with affiliate Integrated Business Analysis and does business as IPA-IBA, provides business development and management consulting services for small and midsized companies in the US and Canada. Its offerings include helping clients establish strategies, set goals, and track progress. In addition, IPA-IBA maintains alliances with providers of tax and accounting services and even publishes a quarterly magazine, *IPA's BusinessToday*. The company was founded in 1991 by managing director John Burgess after he left rival George S. May.

INTERNATIONAL RECTIFIER CORPORATION

NYSE: IRF

233 Kansas St.
El Segundo, CA 90245
Phone: 310-726-8000
Fax: 310-252-7903
Web: www.irf.com

CEO: Oleg Khaykin
CFO: Peter B. Knepper
HR: −
FYE: June 30
Type: Public

In electronics as in politics, power tends to corrupt. International Rectifier (IR) doesn't apply itself to matters of statecraft, but it has plenty of ideas about the performance of power in electronic gear. IR is a top maker of power semiconductors, which refine the electricity flowing into a device from a battery or a power grid, thus enabling more efficient operation. Its products — including MOSFETs (metal oxide semiconductor field-effect transistors), diodes, and rectifiers — are used in consumer appliances, automobiles, computers, communication devices, lighting systems, and military equipment. Top customers include Robert Bosch, Cisco Systems, IBM, Lockheed Martin, Motorola, and Philips.

	Annual Growth	6/02	6/03	6/04	6/05	*6/06
Sales ($ mil.)	12.9%	720.2	864.4	1,060.5	1,174.4	1,171.1
Net income ($ mil.)	21.8%	48.7	(89.6)	89.8	137.5	107.2
Market value ($ mil.)	10.9%	1,856.8	1,721.4	2,748.6	3,189.0	2,813.3
Employees	1.7%	5,900	5,500	5,800	6,000	6,300

*Most recent year available

INTERNATIONAL SECURITIES EXCHANGE HOLDINGS, INC.

60 Broad St.
New York, NY 10004
Phone: 212-943-2400
Fax: 212-425-4926
Web: www.iseoptions.com

CEO: Gary Katz
CFO: Bruce Cooperman
HR: −
FYE: December 31
Type: Subsidiary

International Securities Exchange Holdings (ISE) wants you to consider all of your options. An electronic exchange for options trading, the ISE is the world's largest equity options exchange based on volume. In all, ISE trades some 6,000 products. Besides equity options, it offers forex, ETF, and index options. It also operates a stock exchange with both dark pool (secret pricing) and fully visible markets, alternative market investments such as real estate, and market tools and trading data. ISE is a subsidiary of Deutsche Börse's Eurex derivatives group. It reports to the US Securities and Exchange Commission (SEC) as a registered national securities exchange.

	Annual Growth	12/02	12/03	12/04	12/05	12/06
Sales ($ mil.)	28.8%	73.4	100.5	125.4	155.9	202.1
Net income ($ mil.)	188.2%	0.8	20.2	26.2	35.3	55.2
Employees	14.0%	125	—	—	185	—

INTERNATIONAL SHIPHOLDING CORPORATION

NYSE: ISH

11 N. Water St., Ste. 18290
Mobile, AL 36602
Phone: 251-243-9100
Fax: −
Web: www.intship.com

CEO: Niels M. Johnsen
CFO: Manuel G. (Manny) Estrada
HR: −
FYE: December 31
Type: Public

International Shipholding helps put the car in cargo. Most of the company's sales come from the chartering of vessels such as car and truck carriers, ships with strengthened hulls for use in polar regions, and coal and sulfur carriers. Overall, the International Shipholding fleet consists of more than 25 vessels. Charter customers have included Toyota, Hyundai Motor, Freeport-McMoRan's P.T. Freeport Indonesia unit, International Paper, and the US Navy's Military Sealift Command. International Shipholding has sold the assets of its lighter-aboard-ship (LASH) business, which provided scheduled ocean freight transportation services between the US and ports in Europe and the Middle East.

	Annual Growth	12/03	12/04	12/05	12/06	12/07
Sales ($ mil.)	(6.5%)	257.8	263.5	262.2	274.9	197.1
Net income ($ mil.)	33.4%	5.5	12.8	7.0	17.0	17.4
Market value ($ mil.)	16.8%	89.7	90.6	95.0	82.5	167.1
Employees	—	—	—	618	—	—

An in-depth profile of this company is available to Hoover's Online members at hoovers.com.

835

INTERNATIONAL SPECIALTY PRODUCTS, INC.

1361 Alps Rd.
Wayne, NJ 07470
Phone: 973-628-4000
Fax: 973-628-4423
Web: www.ispcorp.com

CEO: Sunil Kumar
CFO: –
HR: Marianne Spencer
FYE: December 31
Type: Private

If you've washed, shaved, and groomed, then you've probably shared a chemical experience with the folks at International Specialty Products (ISP). The company, also called ISP Chemco, makes about 300 types of specialty chemicals, including food and pharmaceutical ingredients, personal care, and fine chemicals, industrial chemicals (like butanediol for fibers and plastics), and minerals products. ISP also makes waterproofing agents, moisturizers, and preservatives for personal care products such as sunscreen and hair care products. Chairman Samuel Heyman owns ISP; after watching the company's stock dive in 2002, Heyman took ISP private.

	Annual Growth	12/02	12/03	12/04	12/05	12/06
Sales ($ mil.)	15.4%	845.3	892.9	1,023.0	1,360.0	1,500.0
Employees	5.5%	2,500	2,800	2,600	3,100	3,100

INTERNATIONAL SPEEDWAY CORPORATION

NASDAQ (GS): ISCA

1801 W. International Speedway Blvd.
Daytona Beach, FL 32114
Phone: 386-254-2700
Fax: 386-947-6816
Web: www.iscmotorsports.com

CEO: James C. (Jim) France
CFO: Daniel W. (Dan) Houser
HR: –
FYE: November 30
Type: Public

International Speedway Corporation (ISC) doesn't believe in slow and steady. The company is the top motorsports operator in the US, with about a dozen racetracks that host more than 100 auto racing events annually. Its portfolio of race facilities includes Daytona International Speedway (home of the Daytona 500), Talladega Superspeedway, and Michigan International Speedway. In addition, ISC operates MRN radio (motorsports radio programming) and the Daytona 500 Experience theme park and museum. CEO James France and his family own 35% of the company and control about 65% of the voting power. The France family also controls NASCAR. ISC earns more than 85% of its sales from NASCAR events.

	Annual Growth	11/03	11/04	11/05	11/06	11/07
Sales ($ mil.)	9.1%	575.7	647.8	740.1	798.4	816.6
Net income ($ mil.)	(4.9%)	105.4	156.3	159.4	116.8	86.2
Market value ($ mil.)	1.1%	1,224.0	1,410.9	1,604.0	1,610.8	1,278.7
Employees	10.0%	—	—	1,000	1,100	

INTERNATIONAL TEXTILE GROUP, INC.

OTC: ITXN

804 Green Valley Rd., Ste. 300
Greensboro, NC 29605
Phone: 336-379-2865
Fax: 336-379-6972
Web: www.burlington.com

CEO: Joseph L. Gorga
CFO: Willis C. (Billy) Moore III
HR: Robert (Bob) Garren
FYE: December 31
Type: Public

From airbags to denim, International Textile Group (ITG) is a safe bet. The company was created late in 2006 when investor Wilbur L. Ross, Jr. merged airbag fabric maker Safety Components International with International Textile Group. The new company now operates through five divisions: Automotive Safety (airbag fabrics and cushions, specialty fabrics), Cone Denim (denim for Levi Strauss 501 jeans, wool-worsted fabrics, and synthetic fabrics), Burlington WorldWide (apparel fabrics), Burlington House (interior fabrics), and Carlisle Finishing (jacquard fabrics and commission finishing).

	Annual Growth	12/03	12/04	12/05	12/06	12/07
Sales ($ mil.)	53.2%	183.7	247.9	220.1	720.9	1,010.8
Net income ($ mil.)	—	6.1	10.3	3.5	(50.1)	(80.2)
Employees	36.8%	—	—	—	8,700	11,900

INTERNATIONAL UNION, UAW

Solidarity House, 8000 E. Jefferson Ave.
Detroit, MI 48214
Phone: 313-926-5000
Fax: 313-926-5009
Web: www.uaw.org

CEO: Ron Gettelfinger
CFO: Elizabeth Bunn
HR: Robert Gavin
FYE: December 31
Type: Labor union

At contract time, the International Union, UAW stands up (or sits down across the table) on behalf of some 640,000 active members and 500,000 retirees. The UAW (officially, the United Automobile, Aerospace, and Agricultural Implement Workers of America), represents workers at large and small companies, universities, and government agencies. The union has about 3,100 contracts with some 2,000 employers in the US, Canada, and Puerto Rico. Along with negotiating over wages, benefits, and working conditions, the UAW provides education and training programs for its members, who belong to about 800 local unions. The organization was founded in Detroit in 1935.

	Annual Growth	12/03	12/04	12/05	12/06	12/07
Est. sales ($ mil.)	—	—	—	—	—	176.9
Employees	—	—	—	—	—	3,000

INTERNATIONAL WIRE GROUP, INC.

OTC: ITWG

12 Masonic Ave.
Camden, NY 13316
Phone: 315-245-3800
Fax: 315-245-0737
Web: www.iwg.com

CEO: Rodney D. Kent
CFO: Glenn J. Holler
HR: –
FYE: December 31
Type: Public

International Wire Group (IWG) bares it all in the wire business. The company makes bare tin-plated and copper wire in a variety of gauges. The wire is used in audio, communications, computer, digital, and video equipment. The company has also expanded its offerings of high-performance conductors used in medical devices and aerospace equipment. IWG has exited the insulated wire business to focus on its bare wire and conductors businesses. It maintains 15 facilities located in the US and Europe. Tennenbaum Capital Partners, with which IWG chairman Mark Holdsworth is affiliated, owns 28% of the company; investor James Bennett owns another 19%.

	Annual Growth	12/03	12/04	12/05	12/06	12/07
Est. sales ($ mil.)	—	—	—	—	—	730.8
Net income ($ mil.)	—	—	—	—	—	15.9
Employees	—	—	—	—	—	—

INTERNET AMERICA, INC.

OTC: GEEK

10930 W. Sam Houston Pkwy. North, Ste. 200
Houston, TX 77064
Phone: 214-861-2500
Fax: –
Web: www.internetamerica.com

CEO: William E. (Billy) Ladin Jr.
CFO: Jennifer S. LeBlanc
HR: –
FYE: June 30
Type: Public

Internet America is changing its "lines" of business. Traditionally a provider of dial-up Internet access and, to a lesser degree, of wire-line DSL broadband Internet access, the company is battling back against dwindling subscriber numbers by expanding its offering of wireless broadband Internet access. It offers installation and maintenance of the wireless networks from its three Texas operational centers in Corsicana, San Antonio, and Stafford (near Houston). The ISP, founded in 1995, is known regionally for its 1-800-BE-A-GEEK sign-up number.

	Annual Growth	6/03	6/04	6/05	6/06	6/07
Sales ($ mil.)	(17.8%)	17.5	12.0	10.6	9.9	8.0
Net income ($ mil.)	—	2.3	1.1	0.0	(0.6)	(0.3)
Market value ($ mil.)	(3.1%)	4.5	6.3	9.0	4.4	4.0
Employees	(1.5%)	—	—	—	67	66

INTERNET BRANDS, INC.
NASDAQ (GM): INET

909 N. Sepulveda Blvd., 11th Fl.
El Segundo, CA 90245
Phone: 310-280-4000
Fax: 310-280-4868
Web: www.internetbrandsinc.com

CEO: Robert N. (Bob) Brisco
CFO: Alexander Emil (Alex) Hansen
HR: –
FYE: December 31
Type: Public

Internet Brands takes shopping from research to retail with a few clicks of a mouse. The company helps customers research and purchase — online or at a physical location — big-ticket items, such as cars, real estate, mortgages, and travel. Its some 55 Web sites include those for automobiles (Autos.com, CarsDirect.com), homes and mortgages (Loan.com), and vacation rental properties (BBOnline.com, VacationHomes.com). The company offers financing and mortgages through various banks. More than 3,000 local car dealers have joined its nationwide network and it has alliances with Penske Automotive Group (formerly United Auto Group). Founded as CarsDirect.com in 1998, Internet Brands went public in late-2007.

	Annual Growth	12/03	12/04	12/05	12/06	12/07
Sales ($ mil.)	13.7%	—	61.1	78.1	84.8	89.9
Net income ($ mil.)	(68.2%)	—	9.3	13.4	93.1	0.3
Market value ($ mil.)	—	—	—	—	—	282.5
Employees	—	—	—	—	559	—

INTERNET CAPITAL GROUP, INC.
NASDAQ (GM): ICGE

690 Lee Rd., Ste. 310
Wayne, PA 19087
Phone: 610-727-6900
Fax: 610-727-6901
Web: www.internetcapital.com

CEO: Walter W. Buckley III
CFO: Raymond (Kirk) Morgan
HR: –
FYE: December 31
Type: Public

B2B or not B2B? That's a poignant question for Internet Capital Group (ICG). The company invests in companies involved in the business-to-business (B2B) Internet market, working with its holdings to develop strategy. It owns stakes in about 20 companies, including business process management software maker Metastorm; Marketron, which provides customer relationship management software for the media industry; scheduling software and services company StarCite; and international trade facilitator FreeBorders. ICG also has holdings in companies engaged in financial services (Creditex) and the food service industry (Tibersoft).

	Annual Growth	12/03	12/04	12/05	12/06	12/07
Sales ($ mil.)	(6.8%)	70.0	52.4	50.6	64.8	52.9
Net income ($ mil.)	—	(135.9)	(135.3)	72.5	15.6	(30.6)
Market value ($ mil.)	(45.8%)	5,251.8	345.5	323.2	396.0	453.8
Employees	4.4%	—	—	22	—	24

INTERNET SECURITY SYSTEMS, INC.

6303 Barfield Rd.
Atlanta, GA 30328
Phone: 404-236-2600
Fax: 404-236-2626
Web: www.iss.net

CEO: Val Rahmani
CFO: –
HR: –
FYE: December 31
Type: Business segment

Internet Security Systems (ISS) certainly isn't vague about what it does. The company provides network security monitoring, detection, and response software and services that are used to protect networks, servers, and desktops. ISS's products protect and respond to intrusions, assess vulnerabilities, collect and analyze data, and provide centralized security management. The company also offers a growing portfolio of managed security services, including security assessment, intrusion detection, firewalls, virtual private networks (VPNs), and virus filtering. A business unit of IBM Global Services, ISS was acquired by Big Blue for $1.3 billion in 2006.

	Annual Growth	12/03	12/04	12/05	12/06	12/07
Est. sales ($ mil.)	—	—	—	—	—	127.2
Employees	—	—	—	—	—	1,250

INTERPHARM HOLDINGS, INC.
AMEX: IPA

75 Adams Ave.
Hauppauge, NY 11788
Phone: 631-952-0214
Fax: 631-952-9587
Web: www.interpharminc.com

CEO: Maganlal K. Sutaria
CFO: Peter Giallorenzo
HR: –
FYE: June 30
Type: Public

Interpharm Holdings makes, and markets generic prescription and over-the-counter drugs. It makes about a dozen different generic drugs — including acetaminophen, hydrocodone, and ibuprofen — in various dosage strengths. Interpharm sells many of its products directly to major chains, wholesalers, and others, both under its own name and private labels. Through an agreement with Centrix Pharmaceutical, it makes a female hormone product that Centrix distributes in the US. Interpharm is trying to expand its product line in a number of areas, including hormones, scheduled narcotics, and specialized drug delivery products such as soft gels and liquids. Chairman Maganlal Sutaria and family control the company.

	Annual Growth	6/03	6/04	6/05	6/06	6/07
Sales ($ mil.)	50.1%	14.9	41.1	39.9	63.4	75.6
Net income ($ mil.)	—	0.7	3.1	(0.2)	(3.8)	(14.1)
Employees	17.5%	—	—	485	—	670

INTERPHASE CORPORATION
NASDAQ (GM): INPH

2901 N. Dallas Pkwy., Ste. 200
Plano, TX 75093
Phone: 214-654-5000
Fax: 214-654-5500
Web: www.iphase.com

CEO: Gregory B. (Greg) Kalush
CFO: Thomas N. Tipton
HR: Deborah A. Shute
FYE: December 31
Type: Public

Interphase keeps acronyms connected. The company makes adapters, controllers, and other connectivity devices for storage-area, local-area, and wide-area networks (SANs, LANs, and WANs). Its networking devices include adapters and controllers for connecting components in LANs and WANs. Interphase also offers adapters for telecom network embedded servers. Its Fibre Channel SAN systems feature utility software and adapters for connecting mass storage servers and other storage devices to networks. Interphase sells primarily through OEMs, distributors, and systems integrators.

	Annual Growth	12/03	12/04	12/05	12/06	12/07
Sales ($ mil.)	(1.3%)	32.5	35.0	30.9	33.4	30.8
Net income ($ mil.)	—	(0.8)	1.7	(2.3)	2.1	(1.2)
Market value ($ mil.)	(2.3%)	73.6	48.2	26.0	51.0	67.1
Employees	—	—	—	126	—	—

INTERPOOL, INC.

211 College Rd. East
Princeton, NJ 08540
Phone: 609-452-8900
Fax: 609-452-8211
Web: www.interpool.com

CEO: Martin Tuchman
CFO: Richard W. Gross
HR: Barbara Pantel
FYE: December 31
Type: Private

Interpool is into intermodal interaction: The company leases container chassis, which enable cargo containers to be moved between (and by) ships, trucks, and trains, as well as the containers themselves. Subsidiary Trac Lease manages Interpool's fleet of 238,000 container chassis and operates pools in the US that allow users to share and trade available chassis. Interpool also offers leases of standard dry freight containers. Under the trade name PoolStat, Interpool aggregates container chassis activity data from more than 400 locations in the US and reports patterns of usage and efficiency back to its customers.

	Annual Growth	12/02	12/03	12/04	12/05	12/06
Sales ($ mil.)	(3.8%)	—	—	404.4	416.5	374.2
Net income ($ mil.)	267.3%	—	—	7.9	60.5	106.6
Employees	—	—	—	—	254	—

An in-depth profile of this company is available to Hoover's Online members at hoovers.com.

THE INTERPUBLIC GROUP OF COMPANIES, INC.

NYSE: IPG

1114 Avenue of the Americas
New York, NY 10036
Phone: 212-704-1200
Fax: 212-704-1201
Web: www.interpublic.com

CEO: Michael I. Roth
CFO: Frank Mergenthaler
HR: Timothy A. Sompolski
FYE: December 31
Type: Public

Subsidiaries of this company come between brands and the general public. The Interpublic Group of Companies is the world's third-largest advertising and marketing services conglomerate (behind Omnicom Group and WPP Group), operating through offices in more than 100 countries. Its flagship creative agencies include McCann Worldgroup, DraftFCB, and Lowe & Partners, while such firms as Campbell-Ewald; Deutsch; and Hill, Holliday are leaders in the US advertising business. Interpublic also offers direct marketing, media services, and public relations through such agencies as Initiative and Weber Shandwick. Its largest clients include General Motors, Johnson & Johnson, Microsoft, and Unilever.

	Annual Growth	12/03	12/04	12/05	12/06	12/07
Sales ($ mil.)	2.8%	5,863.4	6,387.0	6,274.3	6,190.8	6,554.2
Net income ($ mil.)	—	(451.7)	(538.4)	(262.9)	(31.7)	167.6
Market value ($ mil.)	(12.5%)	6,522.4	5,691.0	4,148.5	5,735.7	3,821.4
Employees	(2.0%)	—	43,700	43,000	42,000	—

INTERSCOPE GEFFEN A&M RECORDS

2220 Colorado Ave.
Santa Monica, CA 90404
Phone: 310-865-1000
Fax: 310-865-7096
Web: www.interscope.com

CEO: Jimmy Iovine
CFO: –
HR: –
FYE: December 31
Type: Business segment

Interscope Geffen A&M Records shines like a supernova in the musical universe. A division of recording industry titan Universal Music Group (UMG), Interscope Geffen oversees a diverse collection of record labels, including three of UMG's flagship imprints: Interscope, Geffen Records, and A&M Records. Interscope, best known for its rap and R&B artists, is responsible for some of UMG's best-selling albums, including works from top-sellers 50 cent and Eminem. Venerable A&M Records promotes a variety of artists such as Bryan Adams and Sheryl Crow. Geffen Records' focus is shifting from a mix of genres to commercial pop.

	Annual Growth	12/03	12/04	12/05	12/06	12/07
Est. sales ($ mil.)	—	—	—	—	—	11.0
Employees	—	—	—	—	—	200

INTERSECTIONS INC.

NASDAQ (GM): INTX

14901 Bogle Dr., Ste. 300
Chantilly, VA 20151
Phone: 703-488-6100
Fax: 703-488-6223
Web: www.intersections.com

CEO: Michael R. Stanfield
CFO: Madalyn C. Behneman
HR: Daniela Gleason
FYE: December 31
Type: Public

Robert Johnson went to the crossroads to get the blues; consumers can go to Intersections to make sure they don't. Intersections, through financial services industry clients, provides credit management and identity-theft protection to nearly 3 million consumer subscribers in the US and the UK. Services include monitoring credit records at major reporting agencies Equifax, Experian, and Trans Union. Intersection's majority-owned Screening International provides risk management services including pre-employment background checks and driving records. Major clients, which together account for about two-thirds of total revenues, include Bank of America (about a third of sales), Discover, Citibank, and Capital One.

	Annual Growth	12/03	12/04	12/05	12/06	12/07
Sales ($ mil.)	16.5%	147.3	152.9	165.2	201.1	271.7
Net income ($ mil.)	(22.8%)	19.4	10.9	12.5	9.4	6.9
Market value ($ mil.)	(21.9%)	—	298.8	155.5	178.2	142.5
Employees	27.4%	—	—	630	—	1,022

INTERSIL CORPORATION

NASDAQ (GS): ISIL

1001 Murphy Ranch Rd.
Milpitas, CA 95035
Phone: 408-432-8888
Fax: 408-434-5351
Web: www.intersil.com

CEO: David B. Bell
CFO: David A. (Dave) Zinsner
HR: Vern Kelley
FYE: Friday nearest December 31
Type: Public

Intersil makes silicon chips that help interconnect the high-tech world. The company makes high-speed integrated circuits (ICs), primarily for high-end consumer electronics (such as cell phones, DVD recorders, LCD TVs, and MP3 players) and industrial equipment. Other leading applications are found in the communications and computing markets. The company's power management chips are used by manufacturers such as Dell and IBM in PCs, servers, and storage networking gear. Intersil, spun out of Harris in 1999, has gone through a series of acquisitions and divestitures in shaping its product portfolio. The Asia/Pacific region produces about 70% of the company's sales.

	Annual Growth	12/03	12/04	12/05	12/06	12/07
Sales ($ mil.)	10.5%	507.7	535.8	600.3	740.6	757.0
Net income ($ mil.)	32.3%	45.8	40.7	85.9	151.9	140.5
Market value ($ mil.)	(2.6%)	3,434.5	2,537.4	3,538.0	3,251.2	3,097.3
Employees	(1.7%)	1,598	1,481	1,336	1,423	1,494

INTERSTATE BAKERIES CORPORATION

Pink Sheets: IBCI

12 E. Armour Blvd.
Kansas City, MO 64111
Phone: 816-502-4000
Fax: 816-502-4138
Web: www.interstatebakeriescorp.com

CEO: Craig D. Jung
CFO: J. Randall Vance
HR: Warren N. Richards
FYE: Saturday nearest May 31
Type: Public

It's no Wonder that a Hostess would show her Home Pride by serving breads and sweet treats made by Interstate Bakeries (IBC). As one of the nation's largest wholesale bakers, it operates bakeries throughout the US and delivers baked goods to supermarkets and convenience stores. Its national and regional bread brands include Wonder, Merita, and Beefsteak. Its snack cake, doughnut, and sweet-good brands include Hostess, Dolly Madison, and Drake's. Interstate Bakeries also produces croutons and stuffing under the Mrs. Cubbison's and Marie Callender's brands. The company filed for bankruptcy protection in 2004 and is still in the process of reorganization.

	Annual Growth	5/03	5/04	5/05	5/06	5/07
Sales ($ mil.)	(5.6%)	—	3,467.6	3,403.5	3,060.5	2,917.3
Net income ($ mil.)	—	—	(33.4)	(379.3)	(128.3)	(112.8)
Employees	—	—	—	—	25,000	—

INTERSTATE BATTERY SYSTEM OF AMERICA, INC.

12770 Merit Dr., Ste. 400
Dallas, TX 75251
Phone: 972-991-1444
Fax: 972-458-8288
Web: www.ibsa.com

CEO: Carlos Sepulveda
CFO: Lisa Huntsberry
HR: Walter (Walt) Holmes
FYE: April 30
Type: Private

Interstate Battery System of America offers a battery of batteries. The company can provide the electrical juice for everything from cellular phones and laptops to automobiles, boats, and lawn equipment. Interstate Battery has 300-plus distributors throughout North America; consumers can purchase Interstate Battery's products at more than 200,000 retail locations, including a growing number of Interstate All Battery Centers. The company makes the official replacement battery for the vehicles of companies such as Land Rover, Subaru, and Toyota. Interstate Battery sponsors the Joe Gibbs Racing team on the NASCAR circuit. Chairman Norm Miller owns the company.

	Annual Growth	4/02	4/03	4/04	4/05	4/06
Sales ($ mil.)	11.4%	650.0	680.0	700.0	754.9	1,000.0
Employees	15.0%	800	900	900	1,251	1,400

INTERSTATE DISTRIBUTOR CO.

11707 21st Ave. South
Tacoma, WA 98444
Phone: 253-537-9455
Fax: 800-845-7074
Web: www.intd.com

CEO: George Payne
CFO: Jim Tener
HR: –
FYE: December 31
Type: Private

Driving on interstate highways and less-traveled roads, too, Interstate Distributor provides truckload freight transportation and a full set of complementary offerings. The company's services include standard dry van, temperature-controlled, and heavy cargo hauling, dedicated contract carriage, warehousing and distribution, and intermodal marketing (arrangement of freight transportation by multiple methods, such as truck and train). Interstate Distributor's fleet consists of some 2,500 tractors and 6,900 trailers. The company operates primarily in the western US, but it provides service throughout the 48 contiguous states and in Alaska, Canada, and parts of Mexico. Interstate Distributor was founded in 1933.

INTERSYSTEMS CORPORATION

1 Memorial Dr.
Cambridge, MA 02142
Phone: 617-621-0600
Fax: 617-494-1631
Web: www.intersystems.com

CEO: Phillip T. (Terry) Ragon
CFO: Susan M. Ragon
HR: Susan M. Ragon
FYE: December 31
Type: Private

Speeding is encouraged at InterSystems. The company's database systems and management software process heavy workloads at high speeds for corporate and government computer networks. The majority of InterSystems' customers are software developers who use its technology as a basis for custom programs for their own clients in markets such as financial services, manufacturing, health care, and government. The company's roster of clients has included American Airlines, QuadraMed, and SAIC.

	Annual Growth	12/03	12/04	12/05	12/06	12/07
Est. sales ($ mil.)	—	—	—	—	—	37.8
Employees	—	—	—	—	—	485

INTERSTATE HOTELS & RESORTS, INC.

NYSE: IHR

4501 N. Fairfax Dr.
Arlington, VA 22203
Phone: 703-387-3100
Fax: 703-387-3101
Web: www.ihrco.com

CEO: Thomas F. (Tom) Hewitt
CFO: Bruce A. Riggins
HR: Christopher L. (Chris) Bennett
FYE: December 31
Type: Public

If you're driving on the interstate and are looking for a hotel or a resort, Interstate Hotels & Resorts is your company. Interstate is the nation's largest independent hotel operator, managing some 200 hotels in about 35 US states and Washington, DC, and internationally in Canada, Belgium, Ireland, Mexico, and Russia. Its property portfolio boasts more than 40,000 rooms and includes locations affiliated with about 30 different hotel chains. Among its brands are Marriott, Hilton, Sheraton, Westin, Radisson, Doubletree, and Wyndham. Interstate also manages properties for some 15 independent hotels. In addition, the company wholly owns about 10 properties.

	Annual Growth	12/03	12/04	12/05	12/06	12/07
Sales ($ mil.)	(6.1%)	1,027.1	944.0	1,116.2	975.2	800.1
Net income ($ mil.)	—	(4.4)	(5.7)	12.9	29.8	22.8
Market value ($ mil.)	(6.0%)	161.0	164.7	133.8	235.3	125.6
Employees	(22.7%)	—	—	33,000	25,500	—

INTERVEST BANCSHARES CORPORATION

NASDAQ (GS): IBCA

1 Rockefeller Plaza, Ste. 400
New York, NY 10020
Phone: 212-218-2800
Fax: 212-218-8390
Web: www.intervestnatbank.com

CEO: Lowell S. Dansker
CFO: John J. Arvonio
HR: –
FYE: December 31
Type: Public

Intervest Bancshares is the holding company for Intervest National Bank, which operates one branch in New York City and six other branches in Pinellas County, Florida. Most of the company's lending activities are real estate-related: Commercial mortgages make up more than half of its loan portfolio, while multifamily residential mortgages account for another 40%. Some of its lending is carried out by subsidiary Intervest Mortgage Corporation, which primarily originates mortgages for apartment buildings and commercial properties in New York City. The family of chairman and CEO Lowell Dansker controls Intervest Bancshares.

	Annual Growth	12/03	12/04	12/05	12/06	12/07
Assets ($ mil.)	22.1%	910.6	1,316.8	1,706.4	1,971.8	2,021.4
Net income ($ mil.)	20.8%	9.1	11.4	18.2	23.5	19.4
Market value ($ mil.)	12.7%	82.1	116.2	184.1	274.8	132.4
Employees	2.2%	—	—	69	72	72

INTERSTATE POWER AND LIGHT COMPANY

Alliant Energy Tower, 200 1st St. SE
Cedar Rapids, IA 52401
Phone: 319-786-4411
Fax: 319-786-7633
Web: www.alliantenergy.com

CEO: William D. (Bill) Harvey
CFO: Eliot G. Protsch
HR: –
FYE: December 31
Type: Subsidiary

Interstate Power and Light (IP&L) got the bright idea of providing electricity and has hit the road to make it happen. The company, incorporated in 1925, provides energy in a tri-state portion of the Midwest. The Alliant Energy utility subsidiary serves more than 526,400 electricity customers and more than 233,900 natural gas customers. IP&L also has nearly 3,000 MW of generating capacity from fossil-fueled and nuclear power plants, and it provides steam and other energy-related services in selected areas. In 2007 Alliant Energy sold IP&L's transmission assets in Illinois, Iowa, and Minnesota, to ITC Holdings for $783 million.

	Annual Growth	12/02	12/03	12/04	12/05	12/06
Sales ($ mil.)	9.0%	1,242.4	1,371.2	1,459.6	1,681.7	1,754.8
Net income ($ mil.)	17.4%	90.9	100.7	125.7	165.1	172.4
Employees	(1.8%)	1,692	1,686	1,676	1,578	1,571

INTERVOICE, INC.

NASDAQ (GS): INTV

17811 Waterview Pkwy.
Dallas, TX 75252
Phone: 972-454-8000
Fax: 972-454-8707
Web: www.intervoice.com

CEO: Robert E. (Rob) Ritchey
CFO: Craig E. Holmes
HR: H. Don Brown
FYE: Last day of February
Type: Public

Intervoice tries to cool the fires of automated phone menu Hell. Formerly InterVoice-Brite, the company makes call automation hardware and software systems that allow telecom network operators to provide interactive services. Its products enable unified messaging (access to voice, e-mail, fax, and Web contact through a single software interface) to simplify the customer service process; it also assists with electronic payments. Intervoice's interactive voice response system allows users to access accounts and other information by phone. Intervoice also provides a range of support and hosting services.

	Annual Growth	2/04	2/05	2/06	2/07	2/08
Sales ($ mil.)	5.2%	165.3	183.3	168.1	196.3	202.4
Net income ($ mil.)	(16.5%)	11.3	22.5	16.5	(1.7)	5.5
Market value ($ mil.)	(10.8%)	433.3	403.6	329.7	248.6	274.6
Employees	0.1%	734	746	814	768	736

An in-depth profile of this company is available to Hoover's Online members at hoovers.com.

839

INTERWOVEN, INC.

NASDAQ (GM): IWOV

160 E. Tasman Dr.
San Jose, CA 95134
Phone: 408-774-2000
Fax: 408-774-2002
Web: www.interwoven.com

CEO: Joseph L. (Joe) Cowan
CFO: John E. Calonico Jr.
HR: –
FYE: December 31
Type: Public

Interwoven weaves content across organizations. The company's enterprise content management software suite helps companies create, manage, and store corporate content — such as documents, spreadsheets, e-mails, and presentations — then distribute it across intranets, portals, and the Internet. Interwoven's software products include tools for collaborative document management, e-mail management, image processing, Web content management, digital asset and records management, and content distribution. The company also offers installation, project management, and workflow strategy services.

	Annual Growth	12/03	12/04	12/05	12/06	12/07
Sales ($ mil.)	19.3%	111.5	160.4	175.0	200.3	225.7
Net income ($ mil.)	—	(47.5)	(23.7)	0.6	6.4	23.7
Market value ($ mil.)	5.7%	516.9	447.0	359.6	651.6	644.2
Employees	—	—	—	744	—	—

INTEST CORPORATION

NASDAQ (GM): INTT

7 Esterbrook Ln.
Cherry Hill, NJ 08003
Phone: 856-424-6886
Fax: 856-751-1222
Web: www.intest.com

CEO: Robert E. Matthiessen
CFO: Hugh T. Regan Jr.
HR: –
FYE: December 31
Type: Public

When semiconductor makers are testing their chips, inTEST handles the trickiest chores. The semiconductor test equipment supplier offers test head manipulators, docking hardware, and systems for managing temperatures during integrated circuit (IC) production and testing. inTEST's products facilitate testing procedures by quickly moving and connecting IC components to handling and testing equipment. The company's clients include Analog Devices, Freescale Semiconductor, Intel, Sony, STMicroelectronics, and Texas Instruments (20% of sales). inTEST has built up its product line through a series of acquisitions. The company gets three-quarters of its sales in the US.

	Annual Growth	12/03	12/04	12/05	12/06	12/07
Sales ($ mil.)	0.4%	48.0	71.2	53.4	62.3	48.7
Net income ($ mil.)	—	(5.4)	1.3	(3.6)	2.9	(6.7)
Market value ($ mil.)	(19.1%)	52.1	39.7	30.4	41.1	22.4
Employees	(5.3%)	260	255	231	224	209

INTEVAC, INC.

NASDAQ (GM): IVAC

3560 Bassett St.
Santa Clara, CA 95054
Phone: 408-986-9888
Fax: 408-727-5739
Web: www.intevac.com

CEO: Kevin Fairbairn
CFO: Jeff Andreson
HR: Kimberly Burk
FYE: December 31
Type: Public

Intevac's sputtering doesn't stem from a speech impediment. The company's Equipment division manufactures sputtering systems that deposit alloy films onto hard-disk drives; the films magnetize the drives and thus enable them to record information. The Equipment division also makes sputterers used to make flat-panel displays. Intevac's Imaging division develops sensitive electro-optical devices used in high-performance digital cameras and military targeting equipment. Leading customers include Fuji Electric, Hitachi Global Storage Technologies, and Seagate. Intevac gets more than three-quarters of its sales from the Asia/Pacific region.

	Annual Growth	12/03	12/04	12/05	12/06	12/07
Sales ($ mil.)	56.1%	36.3	69.6	137.2	259.9	215.8
Net income ($ mil.)	—	(12.3)	(4.3)	16.1	46.7	27.3
Market value ($ mil.)	7.1%	239.0	152.6	272.8	549.8	313.9
Employees	27.8%	180	191	362	540	480

INTIMATE BRANDS, INC.

3 Limited Pkwy.
Columbus, OH 43230
Phone: 614-415-8000
Fax: 614-415-7278
Web: www.intimatebrands.com

CEO: Leslie H. (Les) Wexner
CFO: –
HR: –
FYE: Saturday nearest January 31
Type: Subsidiary

Intimate Brands likes to get close to its customers — in more ways than one. Owned by Limited Brands, the Intimate Brands group is an umbrella organization for the Victoria's Secret (lingerie, underwear, clothing, cosmetics, and fragrances) and Bath & Body Works (personal care, beauty, and home fragrance products) retail companies. Victoria's Secret, which operates some 1,000 US stores and about 325 La Senza stores in Canada, also sells apparel online and mails out about 400 million copies a year of its famous namesake catalog, which serves as something of a poor man's *Playboy*. Candles, oils, and other home fragrance products are sold through White Barn Candle Co.

	Annual Growth	1/02	1/03	1/04	1/05	1/06
Sales ($ mil.)	7.6%	5,021.0	5,367.0	5,751.0	6,401.0	6,733.0
Employees	—					

INTOWN SUITES MANAGEMENT, INC.

2727 Paces Ferry Rd., Ste. 2-1200
Atlanta, GA 30339
Phone: 770-799-5000
Fax: 770-437-8190
Web: www.intownsuites.com

CEO: Mark Ticotin
CFO: Dennis Cassel
HR: –
FYE: December 31
Type: Private

"In town? Sweet!" That's what InTown Suites likes to hear traveling businesspeople say. The company operates more than 120 InTown Suites budget extended-stay properties in some 20 states. The accommodations, aimed at customers staying a week or longer, include kitchens, Internet access, laundry facilities, and weekly housekeeping. There are no swimming pools, onsite restaurants, or guest services. The company was founded in 1988 by former CEO David Vickers. Investors include the New York branch of investment firm Lazard.

	Annual Growth	12/03	12/04	12/05	12/06	12/07
Est. sales ($ mil.)	—	—	—	—	—	11.7
Employees	—	—	—	—	—	1,100

INTRADO INC.

1601 Dry Creek Dr.
Longmont, CO 80503
Phone: 720-494-5800
Fax: 720-494-6600
Web: www.intrado.com

CEO: George K. Heinrichs
CFO: Nancy Casey
HR: –
FYE: December 31
Type: Subsidiary

Dial 911 and Intrado sends for help. Intrado provides 911 operations support systems services to incumbent and competitive local-exchange carriers and wireless phone companies in North America. It also offers its services directly to state and local government agencies. Intrado's National Data Services Center ensures that 911 calls are routed to the appropriate public safety agency with the caller's call-back number and location. The company also licenses its software to carriers for in-house management of 911 services. It expanded into international markets in 2004 with the acquisition of Swiss network messaging firm bmd wireless. Intrado was acquired in 2006 by teleservices provider West Corporation.

	Annual Growth	12/03	12/04	12/05	12/06	12/07
Est. sales ($ mil.)	—	—	—	—	—	66.7
Employees	—	—	—	—	—	776

INTRAWARE, INC.

NASDAQ (CM): ITRA

25 Orinda Way, Ste. 101
Orinda, CA 94563
Phone: 925-253-4500
Fax: 925-253-4599
Web: www.intraware.com

CEO: Peter H. (Pete) Jackson
CFO: Wendy A. Nieto
HR: Melinda Ericks
FYE: February 28
Type: Public

Intraware hopes the decision to focus on software delivery and support serves it well. The company's SubscribeNet service enables software companies (including Vignette, Sybase, and Hyperion Solutions) to electronically manage the distribution, updating, and support of their software. Intraware's SubscribeNet service can be used to support software sold online, as well as through channel partners and direct sales. Strategic partners of the company include Akamai, Digital River, and Aspera.

	Annual Growth	2/04	2/05	2/06	2/07	2/08
Sales ($ mil.)	2.9%	10.9	10.8	11.1	10.9	12.2
Net income ($ mil.)	—	(2.4)	(1.9)	(1.7)	(3.2)	(0.5)
Market value ($ mil.)	(58.6%)	1,002.8	519.8	38.5	32.4	29.4
Employees	(4.0%)	—	—	50	48	—

INTREPID POTASH, INC.

NYSE: IPI

700 17th St., Ste. 1700
Denver, CO 80202
Phone: 303-296-3006
Fax: 303-298-7502
Web: www.intrepidpotash.com

CEO: Robert P. Jornayvaz III
CFO: Patrick A. Quinn
HR: James N. Whyte
FYE: December 31
Type: Public

Hungry plants turn to Intrepid Potash for their food supply. The mining company produces two potassium-containing minerals, potash and langbeinite, that are essential nutrients in plant and crop fertilizer. Intrepid culls these minerals from five mines in New Mexico and Utah, where it also operates production facilities. Potash accounts for 90% of its sales. The company sells primarily within the US to the agricultural, industrial, and feed markets; PotashCorp sells Intrepid's potash internationally. It supplies nearly 10% of US potash consumption annually and is the country's largest producer of the stuff. (The US imports the great majority of the potash it uses.)

	Annual Growth	12/03	12/04	12/05	12/06	12/07
Sales ($ mil.)	23.2%	—	114.3	153.0	154.3	213.5
Net income ($ mil.)	6.8%	—	24.4	34.5	36.0	29.7
Employees	3.4%	—	—	—	710	734

INTREPID TECHNOLOGY & RESOURCES, INC.

OTC: IESV

501 W. Broadway, Ste. 200
Idaho Falls, ID 83402
Phone: 208-529-5337
Fax: 208-529-1014
Web: www.intrepid21.com

CEO: John D. (Jack) Haffey
CFO: –
HR: Vicky Kenoyer
FYE: June 30
Type: Public

Intrepid Technology & Resources provides engineering, construction, and operation services for alternative energy facilities, including methane gas production plants and hydroelectric, geothermal, and wind generation facilities. It has three divisions: biofuels, science and technology, and engineering services. Its main division is the biofuels unit, which focuses on methane gas production from dairy cows. Engineering services contracts with the Idaho National Laboratory, the Oak Ridge Associated Universities in Tennessee, and 4D2 International generate most of the company's revenues.

	Annual Growth	6/03	6/04	6/05	6/06	6/07
Sales ($ mil.)	(41.1%)	2.5	2.1	0.4	0.4	0.3
Net income ($ mil.)	—	(0.1)	(0.6)	(1.5)	(2.0)	(1.6)
Market value ($ mil.)	117.7%	54.7	785.5	798.6	1,035.5	1,227.3
Employees	—	—	—	—	—	—

INTRICON CORPORATION

NASDAQ (GM): IIN

1260 Red Fox Rd.
Arden Hills, MN 55112
Phone: 651-636-9770
Fax: 651-636-9503
Web: www.intricon.com

CEO: Mark S. Gorder
CFO: Scott Longval
HR: –
FYE: December 31
Type: Public

IntriCon hears its future calling, and that future is in precision microminiature components and molded plastic parts, such as volume controls and switches, primarily for use in hearing aids. The company's Resistance Technology subsidiary develops digital signal processor chips for medical applications. The company's components are also used in professional audio equipment, such as headsets and microphones. In 2007 IntriCon acquired Tibbetts Industries, a manufacturer of components used in hearing aids, medical devices, and industrial equipment, for $4.5 million in cash and the assumption of liabilities. Intricon gets about 70% of its sales from customers in the US.

	Annual Growth	12/03	12/04	12/05	12/06	12/07
Sales ($ mil.)	17.5%	36.2	35.2	44.5	51.7	69.0
Net income ($ mil.)	—	(5.0)	0.2	1.5	1.2	1.9
Market value ($ mil.)	36.3%	19.1	10.6	21.8	25.8	66.1
Employees	7.1%	466	369	426	561	612

INTROGEN THERAPEUTICS, INC.

NASDAQ (GM): INGN

301 Congress Ave., Ste. 1850
Austin, TX 78701
Phone: 512-708-9310
Fax: 512-708-9311
Web: www.introgen.com

CEO: David G. Nance
CFO: James W. (Jim) Albrecht Jr.
HR: –
FYE: December 31
Type: Public

Introgen Therapeutics is looking inward for the cancer cure. The biotech drug developer is working on gene therapies that fight cancer by stimulating a patient's cells to produce cancer-attacking proteins. Its lead drug candidate, Advexin, is in late-stage clinical trials as a potential treatment for recurring head and neck cancer. Advexin has received orphan drug status from the FDA for this indication; it is also undergoing clinical testing for numerous other cancer types. In addition to Advexin, Introgen has several other anti-cancer products in various stages of clinical and preclinical development, including topical formulations for skin and oral cancers and a therapeutic cancer vaccine.

	Annual Growth	12/03	12/04	12/05	12/06	12/07
Sales ($ mil.)	35.1%	0.3	1.8	1.9	1.1	1.0
Net income ($ mil.)	—	(19.3)	(24.4)	(26.1)	(28.8)	(30.5)
Market value ($ mil.)	(13.0%)	225.4	258.4	195.9	191.8	128.9
Employees	—	—	—	80	—	—

INTRUSION INC.

OTC: INTZ

1101 E. Arapaho Rd., Ste. 200
Richardson, TX 75081
Phone: 972-234-6400
Fax: 972-301-3685
Web: www.intrusion.com

CEO: G. Ward Paxton
CFO: Michael L. Paxton
HR: –
FYE: December 31
Type: Public

Think of Intrusion as a virtual police force protecting and serving your network. The security specialist sells network intrusion detection and security monitoring systems. Its products include software and stand-alone security appliances that guard against misuse of classified or private information. Intrusion also provides consulting, design, installation, and technical support services. The company sells its products directly and through distributors and resellers. Intrusion markets its products to government agencies, as well as businesses ranging from health care providers to telecommunications service operators.

	Annual Growth	12/03	12/04	12/05	12/06	12/07
Sales ($ mil.)	(14.3%)	6.5	6.0	6.0	5.2	3.5
Net income ($ mil.)	—	(9.6)	(4.5)	(3.3)	(3.0)	(2.4)
Market value ($ mil.)	(55.1%)	48.7	15.8	14.5	3.8	2.0
Employees	(13.0%)	—	41	43	32	27

An in-depth profile of this company is available to Hoover's Online members at hoovers.com.

841

INTUIT INC.

NASDAQ (GS): INTU

2632 Marine Way
Mountain View, CA 94043
Phone: 650-944-6000
Fax: 650-944-3699
Web: www.intuit.com

CEO: Brad D. Smith
CFO: R. Neil Williams
HR: Sherry Whiteley
FYE: July 31
Type: Public

Intuit knows that good accounting takes more than a pocket calculator. The company is a leading provider of personal finance (Quicken), small business accounting (QuickBooks), and consumer tax preparation (TurboTax) software for consumers, accountants, and small businesses. Other software offerings include industry-specific accounting and management applications for construction, real estate, retail, and wholesale distribution organizations. Intuit also provides payroll services, financial supplies, and software for professional tax preparation.

	Annual Growth	7/03	7/04	7/05	7/06	7/07
Sales ($ mil.)	12.8%	1,650.7	1,867.7	2,037.7	2,342.3	2,672.9
Net income ($ mil.)	6.4%	343.0	317.0	381.6	417.0	440.0
Market value ($ mil.)	22.6%	4,301.6	3,558.5	4,302.5	10,624.6	9,713.5
Employees	8.2%	—	—	7,000	7,500	8,200

INTUITIVE SURGICAL, INC.

NASDAQ (GS): ISRG

1266 Kifer Rd.
Sunnyvale, CA 94086
Phone: 408-523-2100
Fax: 408-523-1390
Web: www.intuitivesurgical.com

CEO: Lonnie M. Smith
CFO: Marshall L. Mohr
HR: Heather Rider
FYE: December 31
Type: Public

Intuitive Surgical is haptic to meet you. Employing haptics (the science of computer-aided touch sensitivity), the firm has developed the da Vinci Surgical System, a combination of software, hardware, and optics that allows doctors to perform robotically aided surgery from a remote console. The da Vinci system faithfully reproduces the doctor's hand movements in real time, with surgery performed by tiny electromechanical arms and instruments inserted in the patient's body through small openings. The company also makes EndoWrist surgical instruments for use with its system. Intuitive sells its products in Asia, Australia, Europe, and North America through both a direct sales force and independent distributors.

	Annual Growth	12/03	12/04	12/05	12/06	12/07
Sales ($ mil.)	60.0%	91.7	138.8	227.3	372.7	600.8
Net income ($ mil.)	—	(9.6)	23.5	94.1	72.0	144.5
Market value ($ mil.)	116.6%	564.9	1,370.1	4,243.8	3,557.2	12,425.8
Employees	35.0%	—	—	419	563	764

INVACARE CORPORATION

NYSE: IVC

1 Invacare Way
Elyria, OH 44036
Phone: 440-329-6000
Fax: 440-366-9008
Web: www.invacare.com

CEO: A. Malachi Mixon III
CFO: Robert K. (Rob) Gudbranson
HR: Joseph S. (Joe) Usaj
FYE: December 31
Type: Public

Invacare's modern wheelchair design is the Ferrari to its predecessors' old Model T. Invacare is a leading maker of wheelchairs worldwide. It makes medical equipment for the home health and extended care markets. Products include crutches, bed systems, respiratory devices, and motorized scooters. It manufactures and sells its own products to more than 25,000 home health care and medical equipment dealers in North America, Europe, and the Asia/Pacific region, as well as to government agencies and distributors. Invacare also distributes other companies' equipment and disposable products such as home diabetic and wound care items.

	Annual Growth	12/03	12/04	12/05	12/06	12/07
Sales ($ mil.)	6.5%	1,247.2	1,403.3	1,529.7	1,498.0	1,602.2
Net income ($ mil.)	(64.0%)	71.4	75.2	48.8	(317.8)	1.2
Market value ($ mil.)	(10.4%)	1,209.8	1,400.5	964.8	757.7	779.3
Employees	(3.3%)	—	—	6,100	6,000	5,700

INVENTIV HEALTH, INC.

NASDAQ (GS): VTIV

200 Cottontail Ln., Vantage Court North
Somerset, NJ 08873
Phone: 732-537-4800
Fax: 732-537-4912
Web: www.ventiv.com

CEO: R. Blane Walter
CFO: David Bassin
HR: Jennifer Fosburgh
FYE: December 31
Type: Public

To sell a new drug, it may be time to get inVentiv. inVentiv Health provides commercial, clinical, communications, and patient assistance services for customers in the life sciences and pharmaceutical industries. The company's commercial services unit provides outsourced sales and marketing services, market research, data collection and management, recruitment, and training. The clinical services unit provides clinical staffing, clinical research and statistical analysis, and executive placement. Serving more than 300 clients such as Bayer Corporation, Bristol-Myers Squibb, and Noven Pharmaceuticals, inVentiv Health has been growing via a constant barrage of acquisitions.

	Annual Growth	12/03	12/04	12/05	12/06	12/07
Sales ($ mil.)	44.5%	224.4	352.2	556.3	766.2	977.3
Net income ($ mil.)	69.2%	5.8	31.1	43.9	51.2	47.5
Market value ($ mil.)	47.5%	211.3	522.3	658.1	1,059.6	1,000.8
Employees	16.5%	—	—	4,200	5,200	5,700

THE INVENTURE GROUP, INC.

NASDAQ (CM): SNAK

5050 N. 40th St., Ste. 300
Phoenix, AZ 85018
Phone: 623-932-6200
Fax: 602-522-2690
Web: www.inventuregroup.net

CEO: Terry McDaniel
CFO: Steve Weinberger
HR: –
FYE: December 31
Type: Public

It's always an adventure at The Inventure Group. The company — founded by Don and Jay Poore in 1986 and formerly known as Poore Brothers — makes snack chips and dips under Bob's Texas Style, Poore Brothers, Boulder Canyon Natural Foods, and Tato Skins brands. The company also makes savory snacks branded with the T.G.I. Friday's and BURGER KING names, and also manufactures store brands for several food chains in the southwestern US. The firm distributes its own and other companies' snack food products. Costco accounts for about 15% of the company's sales.

	Annual Growth	12/03	12/04	12/05	12/06	12/07
Sales ($ mil.)	8.2%	66.4	68.7	75.3	69.8	90.9
Net income ($ mil.)	—	1.0	2.1	0.3	1.1	(1.5)
Market value ($ mil.)	(10.3%)	63.9	62.5	56.6	49.4	41.4
Employees	—	—	—	270	—	—

INVERNESS MEDICAL INNOVATIONS, INC.

AMEX: IMA

51 Sawyer Rd., Ste. 200
Waltham, MA 02453
Phone: 781-647-3900
Fax: 781-647-3939
Web: www.invernessmedical.com

CEO: Ron Zwanziger
CFO: David Teitel
HR: –
FYE: December 31
Type: Public

When you really need an answer — fast — toss out the crystal ball and bring in Inverness Medical Innovations. The diagnostics maker's products include consumer and professional products including pregnancy tests and fertility monitors. Its professional diagnostic products include tests for infectious diseases, cancers, drugs of abuse, and serum cholesterol levels. Inverness' consumer diagnostics include the First Check brand of drug testing products. The firm's consumer vitamins and nutritional products include StressTabs vitamins and Posture-D calcium supplements while its Inverness Medical Nutritionals Group makes private-label vitamins and supplements.

	Annual Growth	12/03	12/04	12/05	12/06	12/07
Sales ($ mil.)	29.7%	296.7	374.0	421.9	569.5	839.5
Net income ($ mil.)	—	9.6	(16.6)	(19.2)	(16.8)	(244.8)
Market value ($ mil.)	77.2%	437.7	519.8	741.8	1,517.6	4,313.7
Employees	47.8%	—	—	2,360	2,561	5,153

INVESCO AIM MANAGEMENT GROUP INC.

11 Greenway Plaza, Ste. 100
Houston, TX 77046
Phone: 713-626-1919
Fax: 713-993-9890
Web: www.invescoaim.com

CEO: Mark H. Williamson
CFO: Dawn M. Hawley
HR: –
FYE: December 31
Type: Subsidiary

Ready, aim, invest! A I M Management Group (dba AIM Investments) administers and distributes mutual funds and provides investment management services to individual and institutional investors. The firm manages nearly 200 retail, variable annuity, institutional, and subadvised funds in a range of asset classes and investment disciplines for US investors; broker-dealer A I M Distributors underwrites and markets the funds, which are sold under the AIM and Invesco brands in the US and as AIM and Trimark in Canada. A I M Management is a unit of Invesco (formerly AMVESCAP).

	Annual Growth	12/03	12/04	12/05	12/06	12/07
Est. sales ($ mil.)	—	—	—	—	—	227.4
Employees	—	—	—	—	—	2,000

INVESCO INSTITUTIONAL (N.A.), INC.

1 Midtown Plaza, 1360 Peachtree St. NE
Atlanta, GA 30309
Phone: 404-892-0896
Fax: 404-892-4817
Web: www.institutional.invesco.com

CEO: G. Mark (Mark) Armour
CFO: Loren M. Starr
HR: –
FYE: December 31
Type: Subsidiary

Invesco Institutional puts the fun in fund. With more than $225 billion of assets under management, the firm is the institutional investment management division of Invesco. Clients include corporate pension plans, public pension funds, financial institutions, insurance companies, endowments, and foundations. The company's Invesco Perpetual unit offers mutual funds to retail customers in Asia and Europe. Other offerings include fixed income and US and global equity investment products. Invesco Institutional also provides real estate investment advisory services and dabbles in private equity.

INVESCO LTD.

NYSE: IVZ

1360 Peachtree St. NE
Atlanta, GA 30309
Phone: 404-479-1095
Fax: 404-439-4911
Web: www.invesco.com

CEO: Martin L. (Marty) Flanagan
CFO: Loren M. Starr
HR: –
FYE: December 31
Type: Public

Invesco (formerly AMVESCAP) is AIMing for the topmost position on the investment heap. One of the world's largest asset managment companies, the firm manages investments for individuals, corporations, foundations, endowments, and government institutions under the Invesco, Invesco AIM (in the US), Invesco (Europe and Asia), Invesco Perpetual (UK), and Trimark (Canada) brands. Subsidiary Atlantic Trust serves high-net-worth individuals and families. Invesco also offers managed accounts, separate accounts, and college investment plans. The company spreads its operations wide, with nearly 40 offices in some 20 countries. It has approximately $500 billion of assets under management.

	Annual Growth	12/03	12/04	12/05	12/06	12/07
Assets ($ mil.)	8.9%	9,184.4	9,874.6	9,460.2	11,190.8	12,925.2
Net income ($ mil.)	28.4%	247.5	(101.8)	223.6	474.5	673.6
Market value ($ mil.)	—	—	—	—	—	2,343.7
Employees	—	—	—	5,586		

INVESTMENT TECHNOLOGY GROUP, INC.

NYSE: ITG

380 Madison Ave.
New York, NY 10017
Phone: 212-588-4000
Fax: 212-444-6295
Web: www.itginc.com

CEO: Robert C. (Bob) Gasser
CFO: Howard C. Naphtali
HR: Peter Goldstein
FYE: December 31
Type: Public

As its name implies, Investment Technology Group (ITG) combines technology with investing. The company provides automated equity trading products and services related to order management and execution management; it serves institutional investors and brokers throughout the trading process, from analysis before the trade to post-trading evaluation. Core products include its Portfolio System for Institutional Trading (POSIT) crossing system, which lets institutional clients confidentially trade shares and stock portfolios among themselves; ITG Algorithms; and ITG Logic, for risk management. The company is active in the US, Australia, Canada, Asia, and Europe.

	Annual Growth	12/03	12/04	12/05	12/06	12/07
Sales ($ mil.)	21.6%	334.0	334.5	408.2	599.5	731.0
Net income ($ mil.)	27.5%	42.0	41.0	67.7	97.9	111.1
Market value ($ mil.)	30.1%	722.6	840.5	1,515.9	1,878.6	2,068.4
Employees	21.8%	—	—	714	1,060	1,060

INVESTORS BANCORP, INC.

NASDAQ (GS): ISBC

101 JFK Pkwy.
Short Hills, NJ 07078
Phone: 973-924-5100
Fax: 973-924-5192
Web: www.isbnj.com

CEO: Kevin Cummings
CFO: Thomas F. Splaine Jr.
HR: –
FYE: June 30
Type: Public

Apostrophe? Investors Bancorp don't need no stinking apostrophe. The firm is the holding company for Investors Savings Bank, which serves northern and eastern New Jersey from more than 50 branch locations. The bank offers such standard deposit products as savings and checking accounts, CDs, money market accounts, and IRAs. Investors Savings Bank's loan portfolio is composed almost entirely of single-family residential mortgages and home equity loans. It also offers commercial mortgages, construction loans, and consumer loans. Mutual holding company Investors Bancorp, MHC owns a majority of the bank, which was founded in 1926.

	Annual Growth	6/03	6/04	6/05	6/06	6/07
Assets ($ mil.)	1.1%	5,352.4	5,318.1	4,992.8	5,497.3	5,601.1
Net income ($ mil.)	(5.8%)	28.3	19.8	(3.1)	15.0	22.3
Market value ($ mil.)	(5.0%)	—	—	—	1,575.5	1,497.0
Employees	—	—	—	—	—	

INVESTORS CAPITAL HOLDINGS, LTD.

AMEX: ICH

230 Broadway E.
Lynnfield, MA 01940
Phone: 781-593-8565
Fax: 781-593-9464
Web: www.investorscapital.com

CEO: Theodore E. (Ted) Charles
CFO: Timothy B. (Tim) Murphy
HR: –
FYE: March 31
Type: Public

The name pretty much says it all. Investors Capital Holdings offers investment services to clients across the US through approximately 675 registered independent advisors. The company also sells through retail investment centers in Florida, Massachusetts, New Hampshire, and New Jersey. Its Investors Capital Corporation (ICC) broker-dealer subsidiary provides securities trading, research, online brokerage, and other services and generates nearly all of the company's sales. Subsidiary ICC Insurance Agency sells variable life insurance and annuities.

	Annual Growth	3/04	3/05	3/06	3/07	3/08
Sales ($ mil.)	16.7%	49.0	55.2	68.0	80.1	91.0
Net income ($ mil.)	—	0.8	0.6	0.4	(1.1)	(0.7)
Market value ($ mil.)	(0.9%)	32.1	28.7	18.5	34.0	30.9
Employees	15.3%	—	72	83		

An in-depth profile of this company is available to Hoover's Online members at hoovers.com.

843

INVESTORS REAL ESTATE TRUST

NASDAQ (GS): IRETS

12 S. Main St.
Minot, ND 58701
Phone: 701-837-4738
Fax: 701-838-7785
Web: www.upreits.com

CEO: Thomas A. Wentz Sr.
CFO: Diane K. Bryantt
HR: –
FYE: April 30
Type: Public

Investors Real Estate Trust (IRET) is a self-advised umbrella partnership real estate investment trust (UPREIT) that invests in, develops, and maintains a portfolio of office, retail, and multifamily residential properties. IRET owns more than 200 properties in the Upper Midwest and Texas, including around 70 apartment communities comprising more than 9,000 individual units; more than 60 office properties; nearly 40 retail properties; more than 30 medical properties (including senior housing and assisted living facilities); and about a dozen industrial properties.

	Annual Growth	4/04	4/05	4/06	4/07	4/08
Sales ($ mil.)	12.0%	140.5	156.4	172.8	197.8	221.2
Net income ($ mil.)	6.5%	9.4	15.1	11.6	14.1	12.1
Market value ($ mil.)	10.1%	400.3	408.9	444.3	512.4	588.9
Employees	0.0%	—	42	42	—	—

INVESTORS TITLE COMPANY

NASDAQ (GM): ITIC

121 N. Columbia St.
Chapel Hill, NC 27514
Phone: 919-968-2200
Fax: 919-968-2235
Web: www.invtitle.com

CEO: J. Allen Fine
CFO: James A. Fine Jr.
HR: –
FYE: December 31
Type: Public

Investors Title insures you in case your land is, well, not completely yours. It's the holding company for Investors Title Insurance and Northeast Investors Title Insurance, which underwrite land title insurance and sell reinsurance to other title companies. (Title insurance protects those who invest in real property against loss resulting from defective titles.) Investors Title Insurance serves customers from about 30 offices in North Carolina, South Carolina, Michigan, and Nebraska, and through branches or agents in about 20 additional states. Northeast Investors Title operates through an agency office in New York. Founder and CEO J. Allen Fine and his family own nearly 20% of Investors Title.

	Annual Growth	12/03	12/04	12/05	12/06	12/07
Assets ($ mil.)	10.5%	100.5	113.2	128.5	143.5	149.6
Net income ($ mil.)	(6.5%)	11.0	10.7	13.3	13.2	8.4
Market value ($ mil.)	4.5%	77.6	91.8	107.5	133.9	92.6
Employees	—	—	—	233	—	—

INVISA, INC.

OTC: INSA

290 Cocoanut St., Ste. 1A
Sarasota, FL 34243
Phone: 941-355-9361
Fax: 941-355-9373
Web: www.invisa.com

CEO: Edmund C. King
CFO: Edmund C. King
HR: –
FYE: December 31
Type: Public

Invisa develops and manufactures sensors used to ensure safety and security. The company's SmartGate safety sensors are used in traffic and parking control, fence and gate access, and industrial automation safety applications. The sensors are meant to keep doors and gates from closing on people or objects. Invisa's InvisaShield technology is designed to detect the presence of intruders in a monitored zone, such as the area around a museum exhibit. Customer Magnetic Automation Corp., a manufacturer of barrier gates, accounts for nearly 30% of product sales.

	Annual Growth	12/03	12/04	12/05	12/06	12/07
Sales ($ mil.)	(15.9%)	0.2	0.2	0.5	0.1	0.1
Net income ($ mil.)	—	(11.7)	(3.1)	(1.8)	(2.3)	(5.0)
Market value ($ mil.)	(74.2%)	66.6	6.3	3.3	1.1	—
Employees						

INVISTA B.V.

NASDAQ (GS): IVGN

4123 E. 37th St. North
Wichita, KS 67220
Phone: 316-828-1000
Fax: 316-828-1801
Web: invista.com

CEO: Jeff Gentry
CFO: Kelly Bulloch
HR: –
FYE: December 31
Type: Subsidiary

INVISTA has a fibrous outlook on life. Created in 2003, the company is a global leader in textile and polymer manufacturing. INVISTA is composed of five business units — Apparel, Interiors, Intermediates, Performance Materials, and Polymers and Resins — and its portfolio includes brand names Stainmaster, Lycra, and Thermolite. Its products are used in clothing, plastic packaging, automobile airbags, and pharmaceutical ingredients. DuPont sold INVISTA to Koch Industries in 2004. Koch then merged the company with its own fibers unit, KoSa, leaving only INVISTA remaining. INVISTA has operations in 86 countries worldwide.

INVITROGEN CORPORATION

NASDAQ (GS): IVGN

1600 Faraday Ave.
Carlsbad, CA 92008
Phone: 760-603-7200
Fax: 760-602-6500
Web: www.invitrogen.com

CEO: Gregory T. (Greg) Lucier
CFO: David F. Hoffmeister
HR: Peter M. Leddy
FYE: December 31
Type: Public

Need to make a quick clone? Invitrogen makes kits that not only simplify but also speed up gene cloning, expression, and analysis. Its TOPO TA Cloning Kit reduces one step in the cloning process that once took 12 hours to just five minutes. This and other products make up its BioDiscovery segment, which serves the functional genomics, cell biology, and drug discovery markets. Its Cell Culture Systems segment sells blood, cell, and tissue culture media used in life sciences research and to produce and test the purity of pharmaceuticals. Customers include life sciences researchers and drugmakers. In 2008 the company agreed to acquire Applera's Applied Biosystems unit in a deal worth $6.7 billion.

	Annual Growth	12/03	12/04	12/05	12/06	12/07
Sales ($ mil.)	13.3%	777.7	1,023.8	1,198.4	1,263.5	1,281.8
Net income ($ mil.)	24.2%	60.1	88.8	132.1	(191.1)	143.2
Market value ($ mil.)	5.0%	1,796.5	1,888.9	1,764.6	1,354.1	2,180.3
Employees	(5.4%)	—	—	4,800	4,835	4,300

INX INC.

NASDAQ (GM): INXI

6401 Southwest Fwy.
Houston, TX 77074
Phone: 713-795-2000
Fax: 713-795-2001
Web: www.inxi.com

CEO: James H. Long
CFO: Brian L. Fontana
HR: –
FYE: December 31
Type: Public

INX (formerly known as I-Sector) knows the IT sector. The company primarily offers Cisco-based IT infrastructure services and related hardware and software to customers in the educational, governmental, and private sectors. Its InterNetwork Experts division provides infrastructure services including network design and integration, as well as management and security audits. INX sold its Valerent unit — an outsourcer of IT staff for infrastructure management functions such as help desk support and network management — in 2006. Founder, chairman, and CEO James Long owns about 25% of INX.

	Annual Growth	12/03	12/04	12/05	12/06	12/07
Sales ($ mil.)	35.2%	62.2	93.1	107.3	156.0	208.0
Net income ($ mil.)	—	(1.8)	1.5	(7.9)	1.2	3.7
Market value ($ mil.)	6.3%	62.0	39.8	33.2	51.9	79.0
Employees	27.6%	—	—	225	287	—

I/OMAGIC CORPORATION

OTC: IOMG

4 Marconi
Irvine, CA 92618
Phone: 949-707-4800
Fax: 949-855-3550
Web: www.iomagic.com

CEO: Tony Shahbaz
CFO: Thomas L (Tom) Gruber
HR: –
FYE: December 31
Type: Public

I/OMagic has some input regarding computer peripheral output. It designs and markets optical storage products such as CD-ROM and DVD-ROM playback and read-write devices. Other products include audio cards, digital photo frames, external hard drives, headphones, and Web cameras. The company also markets LCD-based, high-definition televisions (HDTVs) and home theater speakers through its Digital Research Technologies (DRT) division. I/OMagic sells to retailers such as Staples (21% of sales in 2007), CompUSA, OfficeMax (20%), and Costco (17%) in the US and Canada. The company subcontracts the manufacturing of most of its products. Founder and CEO Tony Shahbaz owns about 53% of the company.

	Annual Growth	12/02	12/03	12/04	12/05	*12/06
Sales ($ mil.)	(13.9%)	83.5	62.2	44.4	37.8	45.9
Net income ($ mil.)	—	(8.4)	(0.3)	(8.1)	(1.8)	(0.3)
Market value ($ mil.)	(61.9%)	—	—	—	23.3	8.9
Employees	—	—	—	—	—	—

*Most recent year available

IOMAI CORPORATION

NASDAQ (GM): IOMI

20 Firstfield Rd., Ste. 250
Gaithersburg, MD 20878
Phone: 301-556-4500
Fax: 301-556-4501
Web: www.iomai.com

CEO: Stanley C. Erck
CFO: Russell P. Wilson
HR: Jin-Sook Chung
FYE: December 31
Type: Public

What to do when you don't want the flu but also don't want the flu shot? Iomai is developing needle-free alternatives to boost your immune system using a transcutaneous method, which delivers vaccines to cells found on the outer layers of the skin. It has a handful of product candidates in development, all in patch form, aimed at preventing seasonal flu and travelers' diarrhea (caused by E. coli, for instance). One of its patches is being funded under a contract from the US Department of Health and Human Services to aid in the treatment of pandemic flu. Iomai hopes to sell this product to the US government once it is approved. In 2008 the company agreed to be acquired by vaccine maker Intercell.

	Annual Growth	12/03	12/04	12/05	12/06	12/07
Sales ($ mil.)	60.8%	1.6	2.3	2.4	1.5	10.7
Net income ($ mil.)	—	(14.7)	(15.1)	(18.0)	(31.8)	(28.3)
Market value ($ mil.)	(72.4%)	—	—	—	95.6	26.4
Employees	24.5%	—	53	66		

IOMEGA CORPORATION

10955 Vista Sorrento Pkwy.
San Diego, CA 92130
Phone: 858-314-7000
Fax: 858-314-7001
Web: www.iomega.com

CEO: Jonathan S. Huberman
CFO: Preston S. Romm
HR: –
FYE: December 31
Type: Subsidiary

Iomega has cleared a new space for itself in the data storage market with a slash-and-burn strategy. The company provides rewritable CD and DVD drives, desktop and portable hard drives, and floppy disk drives for the consumer market. Iomega's business products include network attached storage (NAS) equipment, and its REV line of removable hard disk drives. It also provides managed services related to firewalls and remote access through its CSCI subsidiary. Iomega was acquired by data storage systems and software leader EMC for $213 million in 2008.

	Annual Growth	12/03	12/04	12/05	12/06	12/07
Sales ($ mil.)	(3.7%)	391.3	328.7	264.5	229.6	336.6
Net income ($ mil.)	—	(18.9)	(36.7)	(22.8)	(8.8)	10.1
Employees	(8.6%)	—	—	291	253	243

ION MEDIA NETWORKS, INC.

Pink Sheets: IION

601 Clearwater Park Rd.
West Palm Beach, FL 33401
Phone: 561-659-4122
Fax: 561-659-4252
Web: www.ionmedia.tv

CEO: R. Brandon Burgess
CFO: Richard Garcia
HR: Emma Cordoba
FYE: December 31
Type: Public

Airing programs made of sugar and spice and everything nice makes for some tough going in the cutthroat television broadcasting business. ION Media Networks is a leading TV company with about 60 stations that reach about 60% of the homes in the US. Its broadcasting outlets, most of which are low-powered UHF stations, offer programming from the company's ION Television network, which consists mostly of syndicated shows, movies and specials. It also broadcasts several hours of paid programming each day. In addition, ION's network is broadcast on cable and satellite services. The company is controlled by hedge fund operator Citadel Investment Group.

	Annual Growth	12/02	12/03	12/04	12/05	*12/06
Sales ($ mil.)	(4.6%)	276.9	270.9	276.6	254.2	228.9
Net income ($ mil.)	—	(303.9)	(76.2)	(188.0)	(235.7)	(173.7)
Employees	(0.4%)	530	—	—	483	521

*Most recent year available

ION GEOPHYSICAL CORPORATION

NYSE: IO

2105 CityWest Blvd., 4th Fl.
Houston, TX 77042
Phone: 281-933-3339
Fax: 281-879-3626
Web: www.i-o.com

CEO: Robert P. (Bob) Peebler
CFO: R. Brian Hanson
HR: Laura D. Guthrie
FYE: December 31
Type: Public

There's a whole lotta shakin' goin' on at ION Geophysical (formerly Input/Output). The seismic data-acquisition imaging and software systems company helps worldwide petroleum exploration contractors identify and measure subsurface geological structures that could contain oil and gas. ION Geophysical's data acquisition products are capable of processing 3-D, 4-D, and multi-component 3-C seismic data. Its systems include modules for land, marine, and transition areas (such as swamps, shoreline, marsh, and jungle). In 2007 the company changed its name to reflect its expanding range of technological services and programs.

	Annual Growth	12/03	12/04	12/05	12/06	12/07
Sales ($ mil.)	47.7%	150.0	247.3	362.7	503.6	713.1
Net income ($ mil.)	—	(23.1)	(3.0)	18.8	29.3	42.6
Market value ($ mil.)	59.0%	231.8	694.5	560.7	1,092.1	1,480.9
Employees	26.2%	—	—	804	1,015	—

IOWA TELECOMMUNICATIONS SERVICES, INC.

NYSE: IWA

115 S. 2nd Ave. West
Newton, IA 50208
Phone: 641-787-2000
Fax: 641-787-2001
Web: www.iowatelecom.com

CEO: Alan L. Wells
CFO: Craig A. Knock
HR: Timothy D. Lockhart
FYE: December 31
Type: Public

With more than 240,000 access lines, Iowa Telecommunications Services provides a variety of communications services to the residents of the Hawkeye State. Local, long-distance, and DSL Internet access are among some of the services the company provides to both residential and business customers. Iowa Telecom also offers wholesale and carrier services to other communications providers. It operates two competitive local exchange carrier (CLEC) subsidiaries: Iowa Telecom Communications and IT Communications. Iowa Telecom was founded in 1999 from assets acquired from several Regional Bell Operating Companies (RBOCs) and other telecom firms, including the Midwest division of GTE (now Verizon Communications).

	Annual Growth	12/03	12/04	12/05	12/06	12/07
Sales ($ mil.)	5.2%	205.5	228.1	231.6	234.1	251.4
Net income ($ mil.)	1.1%	28.1	14.2	46.4	34.0	29.3
Market value ($ mil.)	(8.4%)	—	665.7	481.2	618.5	511.2
Employees	—	—	—	625	—	—

IPALCO ENTERPRISES, INC.

1 Monument Cir.
Indianapolis, IN 46204
Phone: 317-261-8261
Fax: 317-630-5726
Web: www.ipalco.com

CEO: Ann D. Murtlow
CFO: Frank Marino
HR: —
FYE: December 31
Type: Subsidiary

IPALCO Enterprises ensures that the Indianapolis 500 tracks are lit up and the sound systems are crackling. Through its regulated utility unit, Indianapolis Power & Light (IPL), IPALCO generates, transmits, and distributes electricity to more than 470,000 customers in central Indiana. IPL has about 3,400 MW of generating capacity; most of its power is generated from coal-burning plants. IPALCO's nonregulated subsidiary, Mid-America Capital Resources, has an interest in a venture capital fund. The company has sold its steam distribution and metropolitan cooling system assets. IPALCO is a subsidiary of AES, a top independent power producer.

	Annual Growth	12/03	12/04	12/05	12/06	12/07
Est. sales ($ mil.)	—	—	—	—	—	1,032.1
Employees	—	—	—	—	—	1,471

IPARTY CORP.

AMEX: IPT

270 Bridge St., Ste. 301
Dedham, MA 02026
Phone: 781-329-3952
Fax: 781-326-7143
Web: www.iparty.com

CEO: Sal Perisano
CFO: David E. Robertson
HR: Rick Schnurbusch
FYE: Saturday nearest December 31
Type: Public

What do you get when you cross a couple of investment bankers with TV's most ubiquitous florist? One rollicking party — perhaps. iParty is a little firm founded by bigwigs: former Salomon Smith Barney executive Bob Lessin, Jim McCann of 1-800-Flowers, and LBO specialist Byron Hero. It sells more than 20,000 party-related items, including balloons, invitations and greeting cards, gag gifts, and Hawaiian luau items from about 50 iParty retail stores in Florida and New England. The company also operates an Internet site (strategic partner Taymark fulfills online orders) and offers party planning advice and information. Co-founder Lessin controls about 27% of iParty's shares.

	Annual Growth	12/03	12/04	12/05	12/06	12/07
Sales ($ mil.)	9.6%	56.7	64.3	72.5	78.5	81.8
Net income ($ mil.)	(6.9%)	0.8	1.0	(0.3)	0.4	0.6
Market value ($ mil.)	(26.1%)	16.7	15.2	8.8	9.0	5.0
Employees	—	—	—	—	887	

IPASS INC.

NASDAQ (GS): IPAS

3800 Bridge Pkwy.
Redwood Shores, CA 94065
Phone: 650-232-4100
Fax: 650-232-4111
Web: www.ipass.com

CEO: Kenneth D. (Ken) Denman
CFO: Frank E. Verdecanna
HR: —
FYE: December 31
Type: Public

On the information highway, iPass is in the passing lane. The company provides telecommuters and mobile employees with remote access to their businesses' internal networks. Through agreements with more than 550 carriers and ISPs, iPass operates a virtual network of more than 104,000 points of presence (POPs) in 160 countries. The network includes dial-up, Ethernet, and Wi-Fi access points. iPass was formed in 1996 when a group in Hong Kong and Canada's Sea Change developed a global Internet infrastructure. Customers of iPass include General Motors, The Hershey Company, and The Bank of New York Mellon.

	Annual Growth	12/03	12/04	12/05	12/06	12/07
Sales ($ mil.)	8.9%	136.1	166.3	169.4	182.7	191.7
Net income ($ mil.)	—	13.9	19.1	12.9	(8.1)	(34.2)
Market value ($ mil.)	(28.7%)	968.3	464.4	421.2	373.2	251.0
Employees	11.4%	—	—	406	575	504

IPAYMENT, INC.

40 Burton Hills Blvd., Ste. 415
Nashville, TN 37215
Phone: 615-665-1858
Fax: —
Web: www.ipaymentinc.com

CEO: Gregory S. (Greg) Daily
CFO: Clay M. Whitson
HR: —
FYE: December 31
Type: Private

iPayment doesn't want small businesses to pay an arm and a leg for credit and debit card processing. The company's more than 145,000 clients are mostly small US merchants, firms taking money over the phone or Internet, and those that previously may have accepted only cash or checks as payment. iPayment markets through independent sales organizations and has grown by consolidating its niche, buying a dozen competitors or merchant portfolios since 2003. A typical iPayment merchant generates less than $200,000 of charge volume per year, with an average transaction value of about $70. CEO Gregory Daily and his family own two-thirds of the company, while president Carl Grimstad and his family own the remainder.

	Annual Growth	12/03	12/04	12/05	12/06	12/07
Est. sales ($ mil.)	—	—	—	—	—	13.7
Employees	—	—	—	—	—	426

IPC THE HOSPITALIST COMPANY, INC.

NASDAQ (GM): IPCM

4605 Lankershim Blvd., Ste. 617
North Hollywood, CA 91602
Phone: 818-766-3502
Fax: —
Web: www.thehospitalistcompany.com

CEO: Adam D. Singer
CFO: Devra G. Shapiro
HR: —
FYE: December 31
Type: Public

IPC The Hospitalist Company is on the leading edge of the growing US trend toward hospitalist specialization. The staffing firm provides more than 500 hospitalists to more than 300 hospitals and other inpatient facilities. Hospitalists are health care providers (physicians, nurses, and physicians assistants) who oversee all of a patient's treatment from the beginning to the end of their stay. They answer questions and coordinate treatment programs to improve the quality of care and reduce the length of a patient's hospital stay. In addition to providing staff, the company also offers training, information management services, and risk management services for its medical professionals and clients.

	Annual Growth	12/03	12/04	12/05	12/06	12/07
Sales ($ mil.)	27.5%	—	91.7	110.9	148.1	190.0
Net income ($ mil.)	—	—	3.6	3.6	1.8	(0.9)
Employees	—	—	—	—	757	—

IPCS, INC.

NASDAQ (GS): IPCS

1901 N. Roselle Rd., Ste. 500
Schaumburg, IL 60195
Phone: 847-885-2833
Fax: 847-885-7125
Web: www.ipcswirelessinc.com

CEO: Timothy M. Yager
CFO: Stebbins B. (Steb) Chandor Jr.
HR: —
FYE: December 31
Type: Public

iPCS provides digital wireless phone service under the Sprint PCS brand to more than 560,000 customers in over a half dozen eastern and Midwestern states. The company's service area covers 80 markets between Chicago, New York, and Knoxville, Tennessee. iPCS sells its products and services through its own retail stores, as well as national retail outlets like Best Buy and RadioShack. Formerly known as Horizon PCS, the company was formed in 2000 but had operated since 1996 as part of Horizon Telcom; losses had forced it to file for Chapter 11 bankruptcy, from which it emerged in 2004. It then merged with iPCS and took that company's name the following year.

	Annual Growth	9/03	9/04	9/05	*12/06	12/07
Sales ($ mil.)	27.9%	—	201.2	280.0	492.4	538.1
Net income ($ mil.)	—	—	173.6	(50.9)	(46.0)	(69.3)
Market value ($ mil.)	39.0%	—	164.8	692.0	928.6	615.9
Employees	—	—	—	462	500	—

*Fiscal year change

An in-depth profile of this company is available to Hoover's Online members at hoovers.com.

IPG PHOTONICS CORPORATION

NASDAQ (GM): IPGP

50 Old Webster Rd.
Oxford, MA 01540
Phone: 508-373-1100
Fax: 508-373-1103
Web: www.ipgphotonics.com

CEO: Valentin P. Gapontsev
CFO: Timothy P. V. Mammen
HR: Coral Barry
FYE: December 31
Type: Public

IPG Photonics has its name in lights. The company makes fiber-optic signal amplifiers, fiber lasers, laser diodes, and pump lasers, which are primarily used in materials processing. Its fiber lasers also have applications in medicine and in telecommunications networks to enable voice and data transmission over optical lines, among other uses. IPG has shipped more than 21,000 units to hundreds of customers around the world. The company's customers include BAE SYSTEMS, Mitsubishi Heavy Industries, and Nippon Steel. IPG Photonics gets nearly three-quarters of its sales outside of North America.

	Annual Growth	12/03	12/04	12/05	12/06	12/07
Sales ($ mil.)	53.8%	33.7	60.7	96.4	143.2	188.7
Net income ($ mil.)	—	(28.2)	2.0	7.4	29.2	29.9
Market value ($ mil.)	(14.6%)	—	—	—	1,029.6	879.8
Employees	20.2%	—	—	900	1,040	1,300

IREX CONTRACTING GROUP

Pink Sheets: IREX

120 N. Lime St.
Lancaster, PA 17608
Phone: 717-397-3633
Fax: 717-399-5193
Web: www.irexcontracting.com

CEO: W. Kirk Liddell II
CFO: Lori A. Pickell
HR: Lori A. Pickell
FYE: December 31
Type: Public

Irex Contracting Group has its eye on the specialty contracting business. The group, formed in 1969, holds a parent service corporation, insulation and specialty contracting companies, an insurance company, and a finance company. The group's contracting companies provide new construction and maintenance services for offices, residential and institutional buildings, manufacturing facilities, power plants, process plants, and other heavy industrial facilities throughout North America. Services include mechanical insulation, fire protection, drywall installation, refractories, and removal of hazardous materials (including asbestos and mold).

	Annual Growth	12/03	12/04	12/05	12/06	12/07
Sales ($ mil.)	—	—	—	—	—	250.0
Employees	—	—	—	—	—	2,500

IRIDEX CORPORATION

NASDAQ (GM): IRIX

1212 Terra Bella Ave.
Mountain View, CA 94043
Phone: 650-940-4700
Fax: 650-940-4710
Web: www.iridex.com

CEO: Theodore A. Boutacoff
CFO: James H. Mackaness
HR: Antoinette Ryglisyn
FYE: Saturday nearest December 31
Type: Public

A meeting with IRIDEX can be an eye-opening experience. The company makes laser systems and peripheral devices used to treat three major causes of blindness: macular degeneration, glaucoma, and diabetic retinopathy. These ophthalmology products, which are sold primarily under the OcuLight name, account for about 60% of sales. IRIDEX also broadened its aesthetics business in 2007 when it acquired Laserscope from American Medical Systems, giving it a new suite of laser systems used in dermatology procedures and plastic surgery. The company markets its products through a direct sales staff and through distributors in more than 100 countries worldwide.

	Annual Growth	12/03	12/04	12/05	12/06	12/07
Sales ($ mil.)	15.0%	31.7	32.8	37.0	35.9	55.5
Net income ($ mil.)	—	0.4	(0.4)	1.7	(5.8)	(22.3)
Market value ($ mil.)	(13.8%)	37.7	31.0	59.1	69.6	20.8
Employees	—	—	—	114	—	—

IRIDIUM SATELLITE LLC

6707 Democracy Blvd., Ste. 300
Bethesda, MD 20817
Phone: 301-571-6200
Fax: 301-571-6250
Web: www.iridium.com

CEO: Matthew J. (Matt) Desch
CFO: Eric Morrison
HR: –
FYE: December 31
Type: Private

If you want to make a phone call from the North Pole, you want Iridium Satellite. The company offers mobile voice, data, and Internet services worldwide, targeting companies that operate in remote areas. It claims to be the only provider of truly global voice and data coverage. Iridium focuses on the defense, maritime, and mining industries; its main customer is the US Department of Defense. Boeing operates the Iridium system, which consists of 66 low-earth-orbit satellites linked to ground stations (the world's largest commercial satellite operation). An investor group led by former chairman and former Pan Am president Daniel Colussy formed Iridium Satellite in 2000.

	Annual Growth	12/03	12/04	12/05	12/06	12/07
Est. sales ($ mil.)	—	—	—	—	—	10.7
Employees	—	—	—	—	—	109

IRIS INTERNATIONAL, INC.

NASDAQ (GM): IRIS

9172 Eton Ave.
Chatsworth, CA 91311
Phone: 818-709-1244
Fax: 818-700-9661
Web: www.proiris.com

CEO: Cesar M. García
CFO: Peter L. Donato
HR: –
FYE: December 31
Type: Public

IRIS International provides urinalysis technology to medical institutions around the globe. IRIS International's three divisions include Iris Diagnostics, which develops imaging systems used in urinalysis and microscopic analysis, as well as related consumables (reagents and test strips) and services. Its primary product is the iQ family of microscopy analyzers, which automate the steps of routine urinalysis. Iris Sample Processing makes a variety of other small instruments and laboratory supplies, including centrifuges. IRIS International sells its products through a direct sales force in the US; international sales are generally conducted through independent distributors.

	Annual Growth	12/03	12/04	12/05	12/06	12/07
Sales ($ mil.)	28.1%	31.3	43.7	62.8	70.5	84.3
Net income ($ mil.)	—	(0.5)	2.3	6.1	(0.2)	7.6
Market value ($ mil.)	50.0%	72.0	155.6	381.6	230.1	365.0
Employees	—	—	—	236	—	—

IROBOT CORPORATION

NASDAQ (GM): IRBT

8 Crosby Dr.
Bedford, MA 01730
Phone: 781-430-3000
Fax: 781-430-3001
Web: www.irobot.com

CEO: Colin Angle
CFO: John J. Leahy
HR: –
FYE: December 31
Type: Public

If you're a fan of the old Jetsons episodes, you'll likely appreciate iRobot. The company makes robots for all sorts of applications, from government and military to toys and appliances. Its Roomba FloorVac and Scooba are the first of their kind to automatically clean floors. iRobot also makes the PackBot, which performs battlefield reconnaissance and bomb disposal for the US Army, as well as a limited version of the R-Gator, another unmanned ground vehicle model, alongside Deere & Company. iRobot has offices in California, Massachusetts, Virginia, and Hong Kong and sells through thousands of retailers globally. iRobot was founded in 1990 by robot engineers from the Massachusetts Institute of Technology.

	Annual Growth	12/03	12/04	12/05	12/06	12/07
Sales ($ mil.)	46.4%	54.3	95.0	142.0	189.0	249.1
Net income ($ mil.)	—	(7.4)	0.2	2.6	3.6	9.1
Market value ($ mil.)	(24.7%)	—	—	780.1	429.7	441.9
Employees	25.5%	—	—	214	276	371	423

IRON MOUNTAIN INCORPORATED

NYSE: IRM

745 Atlantic Ave.
Boston, MA 02111
Phone: 617-535-4766
Fax: 617-350-7881
Web: www.ironmountain.com

CEO: Robert T. (Bob) Brennan
CFO: Brian P. McKeon
HR: Linda Rossetti
FYE: December 31
Type: Public

You think you have a mountain of paperwork to deal with? Iron Mountain is one of the largest records storage and information management companies in the world. The company stores paper documents, computer disks and tapes, microfilm and microfiche, audio and videotapes, film, X-rays, and blueprints for more than 100,000 corporate customers. It provides such services as records filing, secure shredding, digital conversion, database management, packing, transportation, and disaster recovery. Its COMAC unit stores, builds, and mails information packets for companies. Iron Mountain traces its paper trail back to when it was established — in 1951.

	Annual Growth	12/03	12/04	12/05	12/06	12/07
Sales ($ mil.)	16.1%	1,501.3	1,817.6	2,078.2	2,350.3	2,730.0
Net income ($ mil.)	16.0%	84.6	94.2	111.1	128.9	153.1
Market value ($ mil.)	49.1%	1,503.8	2,638.8	3,705.9	5,487.5	7,429.7
Employees	86.2%	—	—	5,800	18,600	20,100

THE IRVINE COMPANY

550 Newport Center Dr.
Newport Beach, CA 92660
Phone: 949-720-2000
Fax: 949-720-2218
Web: www.irvinecompany.com

CEO: Donald L. Bren
CFO: Marc Ley
HR: –
FYE: June 30
Type: Private

At The Irvine Company, everything goes according to plan-- the *master* plan! The real estate investment company plans and designs office, retail, and residential villages in San Diego, Los Angeles, Silicon Valley, and Orange County. Its portfolio includes 400 office buildings, 40 retail centers, and 90 apartment communities, as well as several hotels, marinas, and golf clubs, not to mention The Irvine Ranch, one of the largest planned communities in the US. The ranch has some 260,000 residents and covers 93,000 acres, a drop from its original 120,000 acres back in the mid-1800s, when James Irvine bought out the debts of Mexican land-grant holders. Chairman Donald Bren, an American billionaire, owns the company.

	Annual Growth	6/03	6/04	6/05	6/06	6/07
Est. sales ($ mil.)	—	—	—	—	—	149.7
Employees	—	—	—	—	—	2,000

IRVINE SENSORS CORPORATION

NASDAQ (CM): IRSN

3001 Red Hill Ave., Bldg. 4, Ste. 108
Costa Mesa, CA 92626
Phone: 714-549-8211
Fax: 714-444-8773
Web: www.irvine-sensors.com

CEO: John C. Carson
CFO: John J. Stuart Jr.
HR: –
FYE: Sunday nearest September 30
Type: Public

Irvine Sensors puts its hopes in big returns from tiny products. Much of the company's sales comes from research and development contracts related to its minute solid-state microcircuitry technology, in which circuits are assembled in 3-D stacks (rather than flat layouts) to lower weight and boost performance. Irvine Sensors targets its lightweight components for space and aircraft applications. The US government and its military contractors account for more than 90% of sales. The company's Optex Systems subsidiary is a supplier of optical sighting systems and assemblies to the US Department of Defense.

	Annual Growth	9/03	9/04	9/05	9/06	9/07
Sales ($ mil.)	29.8%	12.6	13.9	23.0	30.8	35.8
Net income ($ mil.)	—	(6.3)	(4.2)	(1.8)	(8.5)	(22.1)
Market value ($ mil.)	16.2%	18.1	36.5	50.5	26.4	33.1
Employees	22.2%	87	93	114	165	194

IRVING OIL CORPORATION

190 Commerce Way
Portsmouth, NH 03801
Phone: 603-559-8736
Fax: 603-559-8793
Web: www.irvingoilco.com

CEO: Kenneth Irving
CFO: –
HR: Greg Bambury
FYE: –
Type: Private

Irving Oil Corporation, the US arm of Irving Oil Limited, is engaged in the refining and distribution of oil and natural gas. The Irving Oil Canaport refinery, located at the entrance to Saint John Harbour, New Brunswick, was the first deep-water terminal in the western hemisphere; it opened in 1970. Irving Oil Corporation has been serving customers in New England since opening its first site in Bangor, Maine in 1972. It serves retail customers via its 130 convenience stores and gas stations, and also has home heating and wholesale operations in Maine, Massachusetts, New Hampshire, and Vermont. In 2006 the company acquired Motiva's 55% stake in the Motiva/CITGO South Portland Marine Terminal in Maine.

IRWIN FINANCIAL CORPORATION

NYSE: IFC

500 Washington St.
Columbus, IN 47201
Phone: 812-376-1909
Fax: 812-376-1709
Web: www.irwinfinancial.com

CEO: William I. (Will) Miller
CFO: Gregory F. (Greg) Ehlinger
HR: Theresa L. (Terry) Hall
FYE: December 31
Type: Public

Irwin Financial banks on small business. Its commercial banking operations include Irwin Union Bank and Trust Company and Irwin Union Bank, which together operate about 35 offices in the Midwest and West. The banks target small businesses and their owners, offering a variety of banking products and services. Subsidiary Irwin Commercial Finance provides small-ticket equipment leases in the US and Canada, as well as financing for mostly fast food restaurant franchisees in the US. The company originates, purchases, securitizes, and services first mortgages and home equity loans through subsidiary Irwin Home Equity, which the company plans to merge into Irwin Union Bank and Trust.

	Annual Growth	12/03	12/04	12/05	12/06	12/07
Assets ($ mil.)	5.4%	4,988.4	5,235.8	6,646.5	6,238.0	6,166.1
Net income ($ mil.)	—	72.8	68.4	19.0	1.7	(54.7)
Market value ($ mil.)	(29.4%)	883.4	807.8	613.0	672.9	219.6
Employees	(28.3%)	—	—	2,445	1,542	1,256

ISCO INTERNATIONAL, INC.

AMEX: ISO

1001 Cambridge Dr.
Elk Grove Village, IL 60007
Phone: 847-391-9400
Fax: 847-299-9609
Web: www.iscointl.com

CEO: Gordon E. Reichard Jr.
CFO: Gary Berger
HR: –
FYE: December 31
Type: Public

ISCO International doesn't want anything interfering with your cellular experience. The company makes filters, duplexers, and combiners for cellular and PCS wireless telecommunications companies. Unlike conventional radio-frequency (RF) filters, the company's products use high-temperature superconductors to reject unwanted signals, improving call quality and decreasing the chance that calls will be blocked by interference. ISCO's products support domestic and international frequencies. Three customers — ALLTEL, Bluegrass Cellular, and Verizon Wireless — account for nearly all of sales.

	Annual Growth	12/03	12/04	12/05	12/06	12/07
Sales ($ mil.)	54.6%	—	2.6	10.3	15.0	9.6
Net income ($ mil.)	—	—	(7.0)	(3.0)	(4.4)	(6.4)
Market value ($ mil.)	(9.9%)	—	58.0	58.6	64.5	42.4
Employees	30.0%	—	—	30	39	—

ISECURETRAC CORP.

OTC: ISEC

5078 S. 111th St.
Omaha, NE 68137
Phone: 402-537-0022
Fax: 402-537-9847
Web: www.isecuretrac.com

CEO: Peter A. Michel
CFO: Lincoln Zehr
HR: –
FYE: December 31
Type: Public

Correctional authorities that need to account for the whereabouts of parolees and probationers can look to iSECUREtrac for answers. In the company's system, offenders wear devices that use GPS (global positioning system) technology to determine their locations; data is transmitted to a central monitoring station. iSECUREtrac also offers systems that enforce house-arrest orders by verifying an offender's presence within a building. The company leases its monitoring equipment to federal, state, and local criminal justice agencies.

	Annual Growth	12/03	12/04	12/05	12/06	12/07
Sales ($ mil.)	55.6%	1.5	4.7	5.6	8.1	8.8
Net income ($ mil.)	—	(7.0)	(9.7)	(3.9)	(5.4)	(7.2)
Market value ($ mil.)	(40.2%)	—	—	18.7	11.9	6.7
Employees	—	—	—	—	—	—

ISILON SYSTEMS, INC.

NASDAQ (GM): ISLN

3101 Western Ave.
Seattle, WA 98121
Phone: 206-315-7500
Fax: 206-315-7501
Web: www.isilon.com

CEO: Sujal M. Patel
CFO: William (Bill) Richter
HR: Gwen Weld
FYE: December 31
Type: Public

Isilon Systems isn't daunted by our ever-expanding digital world. The company develops clustered, disk-based storage systems. Its modular Isilon IQ nodes, which make use of the company's proprietary OneFS operating software, store and deliver large digital files, including photos, video, and audio content. The company markets its products to health care providers, media companies, oil and gas firms, and other enterprises with digital imaging and content delivery operations. The Atlas Venture investment firm owns about 24% of Isilon Systems, while Sequoia Capital holds 19% of the company.

	Annual Growth	12/03	12/04	12/05	12/06	12/07
Sales ($ mil.)	187.6%	1.3	7.7	21.1	62.3	89.0
Net income ($ mil.)	—	(8.3)	(12.5)	(19.2)	(25.4)	(26.9)
Market value ($ mil.)	(81.3%)	—	—	—	1,684.3	314.6
Employees	24.4%	—	—	—	258	321

ISIS PHARMACEUTICALS, INC.

NASDAQ (GM): ISIS

1896 Rutherford Rd.
Carlsbad, CA 92008
Phone: 760-931-9200
Fax: 760-603-2700
Web: www.isispharm.com

CEO: Stanley T. Crooke
CFO: B. Lynne Parshall
HR: –
FYE: December 31
Type: Public

Isis Pharmaceuticals is trying to make sense out of antisense. The biotechnology company is developing drug therapies based on antisense technology, in which drugs attach themselves to strands of RNA in order to prevent them from producing disease-causing proteins; the hoped-for end result is a therapy that fights disease without harming healthy cells. Isis Pharmaceuticals works by discovering potential compounds (primarily in the areas of cardiovascular and metabolic disease but also in a range of other categories) and finding larger pharmaceutical partners to license the drugs or collaborate in their development. Its lead candidate is high cholesterol drug mipomersen, which Isis has licensed to Genzyme.

	Annual Growth	12/03	12/04	12/05	12/06	12/07
Sales ($ mil.)	8.6%	50.0	42.6	40.1	24.5	69.6
Net income ($ mil.)	—	(95.0)	(142.5)	(72.4)	(45.9)	(11.0)
Market value ($ mil.)	39.7%	361.1	338.9	378.3	915.0	1,374.0
Employees	—	—	—	258	—	—

THE ISLAND DEF JAM GROUP

Worldwide Plaza, 825 8th Ave., 28th Fl.
New York, NY 10019
Phone: 212-333-8000
Fax: 212-603-7931
Web: www.islanddefjam.com

CEO: Antonio (L.A.) Reid
CFO: Joe Borrino
HR: –
FYE: December 31
Type: Business segment

A sea of music surrounds this island. The Island Def Jam Group operates several top notch recording labels offering a variety of musical styles, from rap to R&B to hard rock. Its flagship Island Records imprint trolls the waters of adult contemporary and alternative rock with such artists as Lionel Richie, Melissa Etheridge, The Killers, and PJ Harvey. Def Jam Recordings helms albums from top rap and R&B artists, including LL Cool J and Method Man. The business also oversees smaller imprints such as Def Soul, Lost Highway, and Roc-A-Fella Records. Island Def Jam is a division of recording industry giant Universal Music Group.

	Annual Growth	12/03	12/04	12/05	12/06	12/07
Est. sales ($ mil.)	—	—	—	—	—	5.0
Employees	—	—	—	—	—	34

ISLANDS RESTAURANTS, L.P.

5750 Fleet St., Ste. 120
Carlsbad, CA 92008
Phone: 760-268-1800
Fax: 760-918-1500
Web: www.islandsrestaurants.com

CEO: Anthony (Tony) DeGrazier
CFO: Rob Richards
HR: –
FYE: December 31
Type: Private

These eateries probably can't offer a Cheeseburger in Paradise (because that chain is owned by OSI Restaurant Partners) but it can serve up gourmet burgers in a tropical atmosphere. Islands Restaurants operates more than 55 Islands Fine Burgers & Drinks locations in California and three other southwestern states that specialize in beefy sandwiches with such names as Big Wave, Hula, and Pipeline. The chain's menu also includes chicken dishes, soft tacos, and salads. Restaurateur Tony DeGrazier started Islands in 1982 and continues to control the company.

	Annual Growth	12/03	12/04	12/05	12/06	12/07
Est. sales ($ mil.)	—	—	—	—	—	54.2
Employees	—	—	—	—	—	2,500

ISLE OF CAPRI CASINOS, INC.

NASDAQ (GS): ISLE

600 Emerson Rd., Ste. 300
St. Louis, MO 63141
Phone: 228-396-7000
Fax: –
Web: www.isleofcapricasino.com

CEO: James B. (Jim) Perry
CFO: Dale R. Black
HR: Robert F. Boone
FYE: Sunday nearest April 30
Type: Public

Rollin' on the river takes on new meaning when you're talking about Isle of Capri Casinos. The company owns and operates about 10 dockside, riverboat, and land-based casinos in Iowa, Louisiana, Mississippi, and Missouri. Its dockside and riverboat casinos all operate as tropically themed Isle casinos, except for the Rhythm City Casino in Iowa. The company also has 57% ownership of two casinos in Black Hawk, Colorado as well as a pari-mutuel harness racetrack and casino in Florida. International operations include two-thirds ownership of three casinos in the UK, and a casino in the Bahamas. The family of former CEO Bernard Goldstein owns about 38% of Isle of Capri.

	Annual Growth	4/03	4/04	4/05	4/06	4/07
Sales ($ mil.)	(5.7%)	1,265.5	1,113.1	1,111.6	988.0	1,001.4
Net income ($ mil.)	—	45.6	27.8	18.0	19.0	(4.6)
Market value ($ mil.)	16.4%	417.7	786.7	728.0	948.1	766.5
Employees	(18.9%)	—	—	10,500	8,516	—

An in-depth profile of this company is available to Hoover's Online members at hoovers.com.

849

ISOLAGEN, INC.

AMEX: ILE

405 Eagleview Blvd.
Exton, PA 19341
Phone: 484-713-6000
Fax: 484-713-6001
Web: www.isolagen.com

CEO: Declan Daly
CFO: Todd J. Greenspan
HR: –
FYE: December 31
Type: Public

No cow collagen here — Isolagen lets you be your vain self. The company's autologous cellular therapy process extracts fibroblasts (collagen-producing cells) from a small tissue sample taken from behind a patient's ear. The cells are allowed to reproduce over six to eight weeks and are then injected back into the patient, giving him or her a "natural" boost. Still in clinical trials, the company is hoping the technique will receive FDA approval for use on "wrinkle correction," burn and acne scars, and to help regenerate tissue lost from periodontal disease. Isolagen's Agera subsidiary markets and sells a line of skin care products sold through distributors and salons in the US and UK.

	Annual Growth	12/03	12/04	12/05	12/06	12/07
Sales ($ mil.)	36.8%	0.4	4.2	8.8	6.1	1.4
Net income ($ mil.)	—	(11.3)	(21.5)	(35.8)	(35.8)	(35.6)
Market value ($ mil.)	(10.8%)	149.4	237.8	56.0	89.0	94.5
Employees	—	—	—	141	—	—

ISOMET CORPORATION

Pink Sheets: IOMT

5263 Port Royal Rd.
Springfield, VA 22151
Phone: 703-321-8301
Fax: 703-321-8546
Web: www.isomet.com

CEO: Michael Hillier
CFO: Jerry W. Rayburn
HR: Vivian Hudson
FYE: December 31
Type: Public

Isomet never met a laser beam it couldn't control. The company makes acousto-optic systems that manipulate interactions between light and sound to control laser beams, especially in color image reproduction applications such as laser printing and phototypesetting. Isomet had long made graphic arts systems of its own — including digital scanners and graphics plotters — but has been winding down that business as it expands its production of birefringent materials (such as lead molybdate) used in fiber-optic applications. The company also offers components such as athermal filters, anti-reflection coatings, tunable filters, and optical switches.

	Annual Growth	12/03	12/04	12/05	12/06	12/07
Est. sales ($ mil.)	—	—	—	—	—	4.9
Employees	—	—	—	—	—	51

ISONICS CORPORATION

NASDAQ (CM): ISON

5906 McIntyre St.
Golden, CO 80403
Phone: 303-279-7900
Fax: 303-279-7300
Web: www.isonics.com

CEO: Christopher M. (Chris) Toffales
CFO: Gregory A. (Greg) Meadows
HR: –
FYE: April 30
Type: Public

Isonics knows its periodic table of elements. The company develops products based on stable and radioactive isotopes (chemical elements that differ from their parent elements only in the number of neutrons in the atom's nucleus). Among the company's products are carbon-13 (for diagnostic breath tests) and isotopically pure silicon-28 (for semiconductor devices). Isonics has developed uses for radioisotopes in biomedical research, medical imaging, and cancer therapy. It also provides security systems, personnel, and investigative and security services through subsidiary Protection Plus Security Consultants.

	Annual Growth	4/03	4/04	4/05	4/06	4/07
Sales ($ mil.)	32.1%	9.1	8.7	10.1	23.7	27.7
Net income ($ mil.)	—	(1.1)	(4.2)	(15.2)	(32.3)	(13.2)
Market value ($ mil.)	16.8%	10.1	23.6	50.7	54.3	18.7
Employees	22.8%	—	—	457	561	—

ISRAEL DISCOUNT BANK OF NEW YORK

511 5th Ave.
New York, NY 10017
Phone: 212-551-8500
Fax: 212-551-8540
Web: www.idbny.com

CEO: Reuven Spiegel
CFO: Michael A. Volpe
HR: –
FYE: December 31
Type: Subsidiary

Israel Discount Bank of New York (IDB Bank) is all over the map. The institution provides a comprehensive range of domestic and international private banking and commercial financial services to clients in the US and abroad. The bank offers a wide range of deposit and investment services, and originates a variety of commercial loans, including those for commercial real estate and construction. It also offers trade financing, equipment leasing, and factoring services. Subsidiaries include IDB Capital (a broker/dealer), IDB Leasing (equipment leasing and financing services), and Uruguay-based banking subsidiary Discount Bank Latin America. IDB Bank itself is a subsidiary of Israel Discount Bank Ltd.

	Annual Growth	12/03	12/04	12/05	12/06	12/07
Est. sales ($ mil.)	—	—	—	—	—	506.2
Employees	—	—	—	—	—	789

ISRAMCO, INC.

NASDAQ (CM): ISRL

11767 Katy Fwy., Ste. 711
Houston, TX 77079
Phone: 713-621-3882
Fax: 713-621-3988

CEO: Haim Tsuff
CFO: Haim Tsuff
HR: –
FYE: December 31
Type: Public

There may be milk and honey on the other side of the River Jordan, but to date, not much oil. In Israel, Isramco has stakes in two long-term offshore leases, and serves as the operator of one (the Med Ashdod Lease). In the US the company is engaged (through subsidiary Jay Petroleum) in oil and gas exploration in Louisiana, Oklahoma, Texas, and Wyoming. Isramco has proved reserves of almost 116,000 barrels of oil and 1.4 billion cu. ft. of gas. It also had a minority interest in a Congo offshore exploration venture, which it wrote off in 2003. In 2004, the company purchased a luxury cruise liner which it to leases to a European-based tour operator. Chairman and CEO Haim Tsuff owns 49.8% of Isramco.

	Annual Growth	12/03	12/04	12/05	12/06	12/07
Sales ($ mil.)	26.5%	8.9	8.9	7.7	12.4	22.8
Net income ($ mil.)	—	2.3	0.0	(1.1)	3.8	(6.4)
Market value ($ mil.)	67.8%	16.3	13.8	41.0	79.8	129.0
Employees	—	—	—	13	—	—

ISTA PHARMACEUTICALS, INC.

NASDAQ (GM): ISTA

15295 Alton Pkwy.
Irvine, CA 92618
Phone: 949-788-6000
Fax: 949-788-6010
Web: www.istavision.com

CEO: Vicente Anido Jr.
CFO: Lauren P. Silvernail
HR: Kathleen McGinley
FYE: December 31
Type: Public

ISTA Pharmaceuticals has set its sights on treating eye diseases. Through a collaboration with Japanese drug company Senju Pharmaceuticals, ISTA makes and sells Istalol (a glaucoma treatment) and Xibrom (used for pain and inflammation following cataract surgery) in the US. Its proprietary drug Vitrase is a spreading agent that promotes absorption of injected drugs. ISTA is developing Vitrase for other uses, such as the treatment of vitreous hemorrhaging. Other drug candidates in ISTA's pipeline include treatments for allergic conjunctivitis and dry eye syndrome, both licensed from Senju.

	Annual Growth	12/03	12/04	12/05	12/06	12/07
Sales ($ mil.)	274.3%	0.3	1.9	10.7	33.0	58.9
Net income ($ mil.)	—	(25.2)	(40.4)	(38.5)	(38.4)	(38.2)
Market value ($ mil.)	0.0%	161.2	195.8	164.7	187.0	161.3
Employees	—	—	—	161	—	—

ISTAR FINANCIAL INC.

NYSE: SFI

1114 Avenue of the Americas, 27th Fl.
New York, NY 10036
Phone: 212-930-9400
Fax: 212-930-9455
Web: www.istarfinancial.com

CEO: Jay Sugarman
CFO: Catherine D. (Katy) Rice
HR: –
FYE: December 31
Type: Public

iStar Financial (formerly Starwood Financial) buys loans from the hoi polloi, too. The real estate investment trust (REIT) originates, acquires, and services senior and subordinate loans that are unsecured or secured primarily by commercial real estate located throughout the US. iStar Financial makes a variety of loans, including first and second mortgages, mezzanine loans, and net-lease financings. Its corporate tenant leasing operations provide capital to owners of mission-critical facilities, such as company headquarters. Through subsidiaries AutoStar and TimberStar the company makes loans and investments in the automotive and timber industries, respectively. iStar Europe Limited is its London subsidiary.

	Annual Growth	12/03	12/04	12/05	12/06	12/07
Sales ($ mil.)	23.8%	606.5	694.4	798.5	980.2	1,425.6
Net income ($ mil.)	(4.9%)	292.2	260.5	287.9	374.8	239.0
Market value ($ mil.)	(4.4%)	4,170.7	5,043.4	4,035.9	6,052.3	3,488.9
Employees	18.2%	—	—	181	214	—

ISUZU MOTORS AMERICA INC.

13340 183rd St.
Cerritos, CA 90702
Phone: 562-229-5000
Fax: 562-229-5463
Web: www.isuzu.com

CEO: J. Terry Maloney
CFO: Matt Saito
HR: –
FYE: March 31
Type: Subsidiary

Isuzu Motors America was once a real Trooper, but most of its models have seen their last Rodeo. Once a distributor of Isuzu cars, pickups, and SUVs, the subsidiary of Isuzu Motors now offers only three vehicle models (the Ascender five-passenger SUV and the i290 and i370 pickups), and it is exiting the light vehicle market in the US altogether beginning in 2009. The company also makes 30 models of diesel engines that offer up to 300 horsepower; sister company Isuzu Commercial Truck of America distributes Isuzu H-series, N-series, and F-series commercial trucks. Production of the seven-passenger Ascender SUV ended in February 2006, and the once-popular Trooper, Rodeo, and Axiom also have been retired.

	Annual Growth	3/03	3/04	3/05	3/06	3/07
Est. sales ($ mil.)	—	—	—	—	—	198.9
Employees	—	—	—	—	—	600

ITC HOLDINGS CORP.

NYSE: ITC

39500 Orchard Hill Place, Ste. 200
Novi, MI 48375
Phone: 248-374-7100
Fax: 248-374-7140
Web: www.itc-holdings.com

CEO: Joseph L. Welch
CFO: Edward M. Rahill
HR: –
FYE: December 31
Type: Public

ITC Holdings owns and operates 2,700 miles of power transmission lines in southeastern Michigan (including Detroit and Ann Arbor). ITC was created to acquire International Transmission Company. Through its subsidiaries, ITCTransmission, Michigan Electric Transmission Company, LLC (METC) and ITC Midwest LLC, ITC operates regulated, high-voltage transmission systems in Michigan's Lower Peninsula and portions of Iowa, Minnesota, Illinois, and Missouri serving a combined peak load in excess of 25,000 MW. ITC is a member of the Midwest ISO, a regional transmission organization. Kohlberg Kravis Roberts (KKR) purchased the company from utility holding company DTE Energy.

	Annual Growth	12/03	12/04	12/05	12/06	12/07
Sales ($ mil.)	50.0%	—	126.4	205.3	223.6	426.3
Net income ($ mil.)	204.4%	—	2.6	34.7	33.2	73.3
Market value ($ mil.)	61.1%	—	—	933.4	1,691.6	2,421.4
Employees	62.8%	—	—	137	223	—

ITC^DELTACOM, INC.

OTC: ITCD

7037 Old Madison Pike
Huntsville, AL 35806
Phone: 256-382-5900
Fax: 256-264-9924
Web: www.deltacom.com

CEO: Randall E. (Randy) Curran
CFO: Richard E. (Rich) Fish Jr.
HR: –
FYE: December 31
Type: Public

Phone company ITC^DeltaCom *is* the competition. The competitive local-exchange carrier (CLEC) operates in eight southeastern states, offering integrated voice and data communications, including local and long-distance phone service and DSL Internet access, primarily to business customers. ITC^DeltaCom also wholesales transmission capacity on its fiber-optic network, which spans more than 10,000 miles from Florida to New York, to other carriers. The depressed telecom sector forced the company into bankruptcy in 2002, and it emerged with investment firm Welsh Carson owning a controlling equity stake (it now owns 72%).

	Annual Growth	12/03	12/04	12/05	12/06	12/07
Sales ($ mil.)	1.6%	461.6	583.6	520.4	487.6	492.1
Net income ($ mil.)	—	(24.3)	(247.2)	(50.8)	(53.5)	(177.0)
Market value ($ mil.)	(22.8%)	942.4	282.6	23.6	47.9	335.6
Employees	(3.9%)	—	—	1,950	1,975	1,800

ITERIS, INC.

AMEX: ITI

1700 Carnegie Ave., Ste. 100
Santa Ana, CA 92705
Phone: 714-774-5000
Fax: 714-780-7246
Web: www.iteris.com

CEO: Abbas Mohaddes
CFO: James S. Miele
HR: –
FYE: March 31
Type: Public

Iteris wants to make sure drivers get home quickly and safely. The company manufactures vision systems for use both inside and outside the vehicle. Its roadway sensors business segment includes video vehicle detection systems installed at intersections to help manage the flow of traffic and traffic data collection (Vantage). Through its automotive sensors business segment, Iteris makes a windshield-mounted video sensor that warns drivers if they drift out of their lanes (AutoVue). Iteris' transportation systems division offers engineering and consulting services and the development of transportation management and information systems. Company founder and director Joel Slutzky owns 6% of Iteris.

	Annual Growth	3/04	3/05	3/06	3/07	3/08
Sales ($ mil.)	9.5%	45.3	46.4	50.5	58.3	65.2
Net income ($ mil.)	—	0.0	(11.3)	0.1	2.9	12.2
Market value ($ mil.)	(1.5%)	81.9	66.1	72.4	74.9	77.2
Employees	5.1%	204	215	219	237	—

ITEX CORPORATION

OTC: ITEX

3326 160th Ave. SE, Ste. 100
Bellevue, WA 98008
Phone: 425-463-4000
Fax: 425-463-4040
Web: www.itex.com

CEO: Steven M. White
CFO: Steven M. White
HR: Rob Benson
FYE: July 31
Type: Public

ITEX provides a business-to-business payment system for corporate members through a licensed broker network across the US and Canada. In lieu of cash, some 24,000 member businesses of the company's ITEX Marketplace barter time-sensitive, slow-moving, or surplus goods and services valued in ITEX dollars. Members represent a variety of industries including advertising, construction, dining, health care, hospitality, media, printing, and professional services. ITEX administers the trade exchange; it (or any of its 95 franchisees or licensed brokers) also acts as a record keeper for member transactions. Looking to diversify its operations, restaurant chain operator Western Sizzlin is seeking to acquire ITEX.

	Annual Growth	7/03	7/04	7/05	7/06	7/07
Sales ($ mil.)	7.6%	10.6	10.3	10.4	14.7	14.2
Net income ($ mil.)	—	(0.6)	2.7	3.1	3.4	4.5
Market value ($ mil.)	54.1%	2.5	4.1	7.2	10.5	14.3
Employees						

An in-depth profile of this company is available to Hoover's Online members at hoovers.com.

851

ITOCHU INTERNATIONAL INC.

335 Madison Ave.
New York, NY 10017
Phone: 212-818-8000
Fax: 212-818-8543
Web: www.itochu.com

CEO: Yoshihisa Q. Suzuki
CFO: Shigeki Maeda
HR: Harry Glantz
FYE: March 31
Type: Subsidiary

Doing one thing and doing it well is fine for some, but ITOCHU International is looking for some variety in its life. The North American arm of Japanese trading giant ITOCHU Corporation runs the gamut of product offerings, from aerospace components and building products to textile manufacturing and solar power systems to produce distribution and the manufacture of high-performance adhesives. Among ITOCHU's subsidiary companies are Master-Halco (a maker of fencing material), PrimeSource Building Products (a distributor of nails and screws), and ITOCHU Prominent USA (a maker of men's and women's garment fabrics).

	Annual Growth	3/03	3/04	3/05	3/06	3/07
Sales ($ mil.)	(9.3%)	—	—	—	5,294.6	4,801.4
Employees	—	—	—	—	—	4,671

⊞ ITRON, INC.

NASDAQ (GS): ITRI

2111 N. Molter Rd.
Liberty Lake, WA 99019
Phone: 509-924-9900
Fax: 509-891-3355
Web: www.itron.com

CEO: LeRoy D. Nosbaum
CFO: Steven M. (Steve) Helmbrecht
HR: Jared P. Serff
FYE: December 31
Type: Public

Itron aims to make meter reading a desk job. The company is a global supplier of wireless data acquisition and communication products for electric, gas, and water utilities. Itron makes radio- and telephone-based automatic meter reading (AMR) systems, handheld meter reading computers, and meter data acquisition and analysis software. Its systems are installed at more than 2,000 utilities worldwide — many using more than one Itron product. The company also provides consulting, project management, and outsourcing services. Customers include BC Hydro, Ford, Electrabel, Old Dominion Electric Cooperative, and Progress Energy. Europe is Itron's biggest market, closely followed by North America.

	Annual Growth	12/03	12/04	12/05	12/06	12/07
Sales ($ mil.)	46.6%	317.0	399.2	552.7	644.0	1,464.1
Net income ($ mil.)	—	10.5	(5.3)	33.1	33.8	(16.1)
Market value ($ mil.)	67.0%	377.7	510.0	995.8	1,331.0	2,940.1
Employees	53.8%	1,500	2,100	2,000	2,400	8,400

ITRONICS, INC.

OTC: ITRO

6490 S. McCarran Blvd., Bldg. C, Ste. 23
Reno, NV 89509
Phone: 775-689-7696
Fax: 775-689-7691
Web: www.itronics.com

CEO: John W. Whitney
CFO: John W. Whitney
HR: –
FYE: December 31
Type: Public

Mary, Mary, quite contrary, how does your garden grow? Silver (recycled) from X-rays and photowaste turns plants green all in a row. Itronics operates its two business segments through subsidiaries. Itronics Metallurgical recycles photochemicals and turns the results into its GOLD'n GRO animal repellent and liquid fertilizer. GOLD'n GRO products are sold primarily in the western US. Another subsidiary, Whitney & Whitney, provides mineral planning and technical services (mineral economics, geologic studies, and project management services) to the mining industry.

	Annual Growth	12/03	12/04	12/05	12/06	12/07
Sales ($ mil.)	15.3%	1.3	1.7	1.4	1.9	2.3
Net income ($ mil.)	—	(2.8)	(2.8)	(4.9)	(3.8)	(10.5)
Market value ($ mil.)	(36.4%)	18.4	9.1	9.9	4.4	3.0
Employees	—	—	—	—	—	—

ITRONIX CORPORATION

12825 E. Mirabeau Pkwy.
Spokane Valley, WA 99216
Phone: 509-624-6600
Fax: 509-626-4203
Web: www.gd-itronix.com

CEO: Jim O'Book
CFO: –
HR: –
FYE: March 31
Type: Subsidiary

Itronix computers aren't known for their rugged good looks. Itronix makes rugged, portable computers that can withstand dust, water, vibrations, temperature extremes, and drop impacts. Field service workers, government and military personnel, and public safety staff are among the customers that use the company's GoBook notebook and handheld computers. Itronix also offers wireless networking software developed by NetMotion Wireless. The company's customers include BellSouth and the US Department of Defense. Previously a subsidiary of Acterna, Itronix was bought out by Golden Gate Capital in 2003. The company was acquired by General Dynamics in 2005.

	Annual Growth	3/03	3/04	3/05	3/06	3/07
Est. sales ($ mil.)	—	—	—	—	—	100.1
Employees	—	—	—	—	—	475

IT'S JUST LUNCH INTERNATIONAL LLC

75430 Gerald Ford Dr., Ste. 207
Palm Desert, CA 92211
Phone: 760-779-0101
Fax: 760-779-9191
Web: www.itsjustlunch.com

CEO: Kevin Bazner
CFO: –
HR: –
FYE: December 31
Type: Private

It's Just Lunch (IJL) doesn't offer high-tech hook-ups. The matchmaking service sets up busy, professional singles for lunch dates based on personal interviews instead of the much maligned introduction videos or online dating pools. The company, which franchises nearly 100 offices in the US, Singapore, Canada, Australia, Europe, and the Caribbean, charges singles around $1,000 for a series of dates (prices vary by location). It boasts having arranged more than 2 million dates since its inception. Founder Andrea McGinty established the company in 1992 after her fiancé jilted her weeks before their wedding. She sold IJL to The Riverside Company in 2006.

⊞ ITT CORPORATION

NYSE: ITT

4 W. Red Oak Ln.
White Plains, NY 10604
Phone: 914-641-2000
Fax: 914-696-2950
Web: www.itt.com

CEO: Steven R. Loranger
CFO: Denise L. Ramos
HR: Usha Wright
FYE: December 31
Type: Public

ITT Corporation (formerly ITT Industries) doesn't get defensive when you associate its name with fluid motion. The company has three primary segments: defense electronics (combat radios, night-vision devices, airborne electronic-warfare systems), fluid technology (pumps, mixers, heat exchangers, and valves for water and wastewater systems), and motion and flow control (connectors, boat pumps, shock absorbers, friction pads for communication and transportation applications). ITT, which traces its corporate roots more than 80 years to the old ITT phone empire, also provides repair and maintenance services for the products it manufactures.

	Annual Growth	12/03	12/04	12/05	12/06	12/07
Sales ($ mil.)	12.5%	5,626.6	6,764.1	7,427.3	7,807.9	9,003.3
Net income ($ mil.)	16.4%	403.9	432.3	359.5	581.1	742.1
Market value ($ mil.)	36.8%	3,423.7	3,896.9	9,492.2	10,399.0	11,985.6
Employees	(1.5%)	—	—	40,900	37,500	39,700

ITT EDUCATIONAL SERVICES, INC.

NYSE: ESI

13000 N. Meridian St.
Carmel, IN 46032
Phone: 317-706-9200
Fax: 317-706-3040
Web: www.ittesi.com

CEO: Kevin M. Modany
CFO: Daniel M. Fitzpatrick
HR: Nina F. Esbin
FYE: December 31
Type: Public

To get a mortarboard from ITT, you may need to know a little something about motherboards. One of the largest US providers of technical education, ITT Educational Services offers mainly associate and bachelor degree programs to some 53,000 students at about 100 ITT Technical Institutes in some 35 states. The company has traditionally offered a range of technology-focused degrees in areas such as computer-aided design, engineering technology, and information technology. However, ITT Educational Services also offers degrees in business, criminal justice, design, and health sciences. Some programs are offered exclusively online, while others are offered through a combination of classroom and online instruction.

	Annual Growth	12/03	12/04	12/05	12/06	12/07
Sales ($ mil.)	13.6%	522.9	617.8	688.0	757.8	869.5
Net income ($ mil.)	26.7%	58.9	75.3	109.7	118.5	151.6
Market value ($ mil.)	12.2%	2,133.9	2,187.0	3,196.0	2,723.8	3,384.6
Employees	9.5%	—	—	6,000	6,200	7,200

IVAX DIAGNOSTICS, INC.

AMEX: IVD

2140 N. Miami Ave.
Miami, FL 33127
Phone: 305-324-2338
Fax: 305-324-2395
Web: www.ivaxdiagnostics.com

CEO: Kevin D. Clark
CFO: Mark S. Deutsch
HR: —
FYE: December 31
Type: Public

Its products are used for screenings, but don't confuse it with IMAX. IVAX Diagnostics operates in the US and Italy through three subsidiaries. Delta Biologicals develops scientific instrumentation, makes the Mago and Aptus lines of instruments, and distributes *in vitro* diagnostic products to hospitals and medical laboratories in Italy. Diamedix makes *in vitro* diagnostic kits and markets them to clinical and hospital labs in the US. ImmunoVision develops, makes, and markets autoimmune reagents and research products for use by clinical and research labs and other diagnostic manufacturers. Top generic drug maker Teva Pharmaceutical Industries owns some 72% of IVAX Diagnostics.

	Annual Growth	12/03	12/04	12/05	12/06	12/07
Sales ($ mil.)	3.1%	17.7	18.9	19.8	19.5	20.0
Net income ($ mil.)	—	(0.7)	0.2	(0.5)	(2.8)	(10.4)
Market value ($ mil.)	(43.6%)	133.6	117.5	99.4	40.4	13.5
Employees	—	—	—	120	—	—

IVILLAGE INC.

500 7th Ave., 14th Fl.
New York, NY 10018
Phone: 212-600-6000
Fax: 212-600-6001
Web: www.ivillage.com

CEO: Deborah I. (Debi) Fine
CFO: Todd Saypoff
HR: —
FYE: December 31
Type: Subsidiary

iVillage offers a cyber retreat for the female Web surfer. The company operates a leading online destination targeting women with topic areas such as health, food, money, and pregnancy and parenting. In addition to its flagship Web portal, iVillage operates iVillage UK, iVillage Total Health, GardenWeb, Astrology.com, and gURL.com (content for teen readers). It also offers video clips via its iVillage Video feature. All total, iVillage attracts an audience of about 30 million unique visitors. The company also operates The Newborn Channel cable network. In 2006 NBC Universal (NBCU) acquired iVillage for $600 million.

	Annual Growth	12/03	12/04	12/05	12/06	12/07
Est. sales ($ mil.)	—	—	—	—	—	34.0
Employees	—	—	—	—	—	278

IVIVI TECHNOLOGIES, INC.

AMEX: II

224-S Pegasus Ave.
Northvale, NJ 07647
Phone: 201-784-8168
Fax: 201-784-0620
Web: www.ivivitechnologies.com

CEO: Andre' A. DiMino
CFO: Alan V. Gallantar
HR: —
FYE: March 31
Type: Public

Ivivi Technologies provides treatments for soft tissue disorders using electrotherapy. The development-stage company's FDA-approved SofPulse device products help treat conditions including acute and chronic wounds, as well as arterial, venous stasis, pressure, and diabetic ulcers. The SofPulse device transmits an electromagnetic signal that can penetrate non-metal materials to reach the skin. Ivivi Technologies continues to conduct research for other product applications for cardiac and circulatory impairment conditions, pain and swelling of the skin, and growth of implanted stem cells. In 2006 the company was spun off from ADM Tronics Unlimited.

	Annual Growth	3/04	3/05	3/06	3/07	3/08
Sales ($ mil.)	100.0%	0.1	0.3	0.8	1.2	1.6
Net income ($ mil.)	—	(0.1)	(2.6)	(10.8)	(7.8)	(7.5)
Market value ($ mil.)	(8.1%)	—	—	—	39.7	36.4
Employees	—	—	—	—	—	—

IVOICE, INC.

OTC: IVOI

750 Hwy. 34
Matawan, NJ 07747
Phone: 732-441-7700
Fax: 732-441-9895
Web: www.ivoice.com

CEO: Jerome R. (Jerry) Mahoney
CFO: —
HR: —
FYE: December 31
Type: Public

iVoice speaks the language of spinoffs and special dividends, as well as speech technology. The company has formed or acquired a variety of subsidiaries which have then been spun off to shareholders via special dividends; spin offs have included Trey Resources, iVoice Technology, Deep Field Technology, and SpeechSwitch. iVoice's long term plan, however, revolves around development and licensing of proprietary speech enabled technologies and applications for which it holds patents.

	Annual Growth	12/02	12/03	12/04	12/05	*12/06
Sales ($ mil.)	(15.9%)	0.6	0.4	0.4	0.0	0.3
Net income ($ mil.)	—	(2.1)	(2.0)	(3.0)	(1.3)	(3.2)
Market value ($ mil.)	(69.3%)	193.8	2,746.6	914.5	599.6	1.7
Employees	—	—	—	—	—	4

*Most recent year available

IWI HOLDING LIMITED

OTC: IWIHF

1010 Executive Ct., Ste. 300
Westmont, IL 60559
Phone: 630-887-8288
Fax: 630-887-8282

CEO: Joseph K. Lau
CFO: Joseph K. Lau
HR: —
FYE: December 31
Type: Public

IWI Holding keeps the world sparkling. The company, through its Imperial World subsidiary, designs and distributes affordable fine jewelry, primarily rings, earrings, pendants, bracelets, and necklaces made of diamonds, precious and semi-precious stones, pearls, silver, and gold. Most of the jewelry is imported from China and Hong Kong. IWI Holding hawks its wares in more than 7,000 retail outlets, mostly mass media marketers (including Wal-Mart) and department stores (such as J.C. Penney). Bamberg Company Ltd. controls some 60% of voting shares of the company.

	Annual Growth	12/02	12/03	12/04	12/05	*12/06
Sales ($ mil.)	1.8%	25.8	22.2	28.5	25.5	27.7
Net income ($ mil.)	—	0.3	(1.9)	0.2	(0.2)	(0.1)
Employees	—	—	—	—	—	—

*Most recent year available

An in-depth profile of this company is available to Hoover's Online members at hoovers.com.

853

IWT TESORO CORPORATION

OTC: IWTT

191 Post Rd. West, Ste. 10
Westport, CT 06880
Phone: 203-221-2770
Fax: 203-221-2797
Web: www.iwttesoro.com

CEO: Henry J. Boucher Jr.
CFO: David W. Whitwell
HR: –
FYE: December 31
Type: Public

IWT Tesoro has found its treasure in tiles from around the world. The company operates International Wholesale Tile, which distributes imported ceramic, porcelain, and stone tiles. IWT Tesoro obtains the majority of its product from Italy (47%), Brazil (21%), and the remainder from China, Spain, Turkey, and Venezuela. The company's proprietary Tesoro brand consists of porcelain tiles and decorative inserts and borders. Flooring retailers account for more than 50% of sales, but IWT Tesoro also distributes to home-improvement stores and national buying groups. SVPs Paul Boucher, Forrest Jordan, and Grey Perna each own more than 26% of the company, which was founded in 2000.

	Annual Growth	12/02	12/03	12/04	12/05	*12/06
Sales ($ mil.)	24.8%	25.4	32.6	44.9	55.6	61.6
Net income ($ mil.)	—	1.9	(1.9)	(1.2)	(4.3)	(3.4)
Employees	—	—	—	—	—	135

*Most recent year available

IXIA

NASDAQ (GS): XXIA

26601 W. Agoura Rd.
Calabasas, CA 91302
Phone: 818-871-1800
Fax: 818-871-1805
Web: www.ixiacom.com

CEO: Atul Bhatnagar
CFO: Thomas B. (Tom) Miller
HR: Thomas A. (Tim) Jones
FYE: December 31
Type: Public

Ixia nixes network glitches. The company designs interface cards that transmit and analyze signals over fiber-optic and copper-line networks. Its equipment evaluates the quantity and speed of transmission of data packets, how many packets are lost during transmission, and whether the packets are received intact and in order. Ixia also designs chassis to hold the interface cards, and software to operate them. The company primarily serves network equipment manufacturers, service providers, and communications chip makers. Customers include Alcatel-Lucent, AT&T, Broadcom, Cisco (about 24% of sales), Ericsson, Intel, NTT, Nokia, and Texas Instruments. Ixia gets around two-thirds of its sales in the US.

	Annual Growth	12/03	12/04	12/05	12/06	12/07
Sales ($ mil.)	20.2%	83.5	117.0	150.9	180.1	174.1
Net income ($ mil.)	(5.3%)	8.7	18.9	28.5	13.5	7.0
Market value ($ mil.)	(1.9%)	697.8	1,049.9	985.4	646.6	646.3
Employees	27.4%	287	403	640	750	756

IXYS CORPORATION

NASDAQ (GM): IXYS

1590 Buckeye Dr.
Milpitas, CA 95035
Phone: 408-457-9000
Fax: –
Web: www.ixys.com

CEO: Nathan Zommer
CFO: Uzi Sasson
HR: John Harris
FYE: March 31
Type: Public

If you like power semiconductors — and who doesn't? — you'll like IXYS. IXYS (pronounced ike-sys) makes a variety of power semiconductors (including transistors and rectifiers) and power modules, which convert and control electric power in electronic gear. The company sells these components for use in such equipment as power supplies, motor drives, and medical electronics. IXYS also sells digital power management integrated circuits, gallium arsenide field-effect transistors, and proprietary direct copper bond substrate technology. The company's 2,000-plus customers include ABB, Emerson Electric, GE, Philips, Samsung SDI, and Siemens. About three-quarters of its sales come from customers outside the US.

	Annual Growth	3/04	3/05	3/06	3/07	3/08
Sales ($ mil.)	12.9%	187.4	256.6	251.5	285.9	304.5
Net income ($ mil.)	—	(4.4)	16.2	(6.1)	30.2	23.3
Market value ($ mil.)	(9.0%)	309.5	381.6	314.9	332.9	212.3
Employees	5.1%	860	858	965	1,018	1,049

J. ALEXANDER'S CORPORATION

AMEX: JAX

3401 West End Ave.
Nashville, TN 37203
Phone: 615-269-1900
Fax: 615-269-1999
Web: www.jalexanders.com

CEO: Lonnie J. Stout II
CFO: R. Gregory Lewis
HR: J. Michael Moore
FYE: December 31
Type: Public

This restaurant chain is made up of distinctive links. J. Alexander's operates about 30 upscale casual-dining restaurants, each of which sports a different architectural design and interior. The establishments serve beef, chicken, and pasta dishes for lunch and dinner, as well as soups, sandwiches, and appetizers. Desserts and croissants are baked fresh at each location. The company's freestanding restaurants operate in a dozen states, primarily in Ohio, Florida, and Tennessee. Board member E. Townes Duncan owns nearly 30% of the company through his investment firm Solidus.

	Annual Growth	12/03	12/04	12/05	12/06	12/07
Sales ($ mil.)	7.2%	107.1	122.9	126.6	137.7	141.3
Net income ($ mil.)	8.7%	3.3	4.8	3.6	4.7	4.6
Market value ($ mil.)	10.1%	45.0	47.8	52.4	58.5	66.2
Employees	—	—	—	2,700	—	—

J.B. HUNT TRANSPORT SERVICES, INC.

NASDAQ (GS): JBHT

615 J.B. Hunt Corporate Dr.
Lowell, AR 72745
Phone: 479-820-0000
Fax: 479-820-3418
Web: www.jbhunt.com

CEO: Kirk Thompson
CFO: Jerry W. Walton
HR: –
FYE: December 31
Type: Public

When it comes to hauling freight, J.B. Hunt Transport Services is a leader of the pack. Its intermodal unit, the company's largest, maintains some 1,800 tractors and 34,000 containers and moves customers' cargo by combinations of truck and train. J.B. Hunt's dedicated contract services unit supplies customers with drivers and equipment; it operates about 5,000 company-controlled tractors. The company's truckload transportation unit, which has a fleet of about 3,600 tractors, provides dry van freight transportation service in the US, Canada, and Mexico. A fourth business segment, integrated capacity solutions (ICS), manages freight transportation via third-party carriers as well as J.B. Hunt equipment.

	Annual Growth	12/03	12/04	12/05	12/06	12/07
Sales ($ mil.)	9.4%	2,433.5	2,786.1	3,127.9	3,328.0	3,489.9
Net income ($ mil.)	22.2%	95.5	146.3	207.3	219.9	213.1
Market value ($ mil.)	33.5%	1,081.9	1,825.2	3,482.3	3,002.4	3,432.0
Employees	(63.9%)	—	—	16,367	5,916	—

J. CREW GROUP, INC.

NYSE: JCG

770 Broadway
New York, NY 10003
Phone: 212-209-2500
Fax: 212-209-2666
Web: www.jcrew.com

CEO: Millard S. (Mickey) Drexler
CFO: James S. Scully
HR: Linda Markoe
FYE: Saturday nearest January 31
Type: Public

The crews depicted in the flashy catalogs of the J. Crew Group are far from motley. The retailer is known for its preppy fashions, including jeans, khakis, and other basic (but pricey) items sold to young professionals through its catalogs, Web sites, and some 260 retail and outlet stores in the US under the J. Crew, crewcuts (for kids), and Madewell banners. Madewell, launched in 2006, is a women's-only collection of hip, casual clothes. Asian contractors produce about 80% of the company's merchandise. Chief executive Millard "Mickey" Drexler, recruited in 2003 from The Gap to revive J. Crew's ailing fortunes, has led a retail renaissance at the firm, marked by taking the company public in mid-2006.

	Annual Growth	1/04	1/05	1/06	1/07	1/08
Sales ($ mil.)	17.9%	690.0	804.2	953.2	1,152.1	1,334.7
Net income ($ mil.)	—	(50.2)	(100.3)	3.8	77.8	97.1
Market value ($ mil.)	28.6%	—	—	—	2,243.7	2,885.4
Employees	11.4%	5,500	—	6,800	7,600	—

THE J. JILL GROUP, INC.

4 Batterymarch Park
Quincy, MA 02169
Phone: 617-376-4300
Fax: 617-769-0177
Web: www.jjill.com

CEO: Paula Bennett
CFO: Edward L. Larsen
HR: –
FYE: January 31
Type: Subsidiary

The J. Jill Group's fortune has been catalog fashion, and catalogs aren't so fashionable anymore. To mend its bottom line, the direct marketer narrowed its focus to one brand and turned to retail outlets and online sales, with aggressive plans to open new stores across the US; it currently operates about 270 stores in 35 US states. The firm targets active, affluent women ages 35 and up, and banks on its J. Jill brand. The catalog and the Web site offer private-label casual wear made in the US and abroad. J. Jill Group's retail operations are its fastest-growing division. Nearly 90% of J. Jill's outside merchandise comes from vendors, primarily in China. J. Jill was acquired by Talbots in mid-2006.

	Annual Growth	1/03	1/04	1/05	1/06	1/07
Est. sales ($ mil.)	—	—	—	—	—	532.1
Employees	—	—	—	—	—	3,041

J2 GLOBAL COMMUNICATIONS, INC.

NASDAQ (GS): JCOM

6922 Hollywood Blvd., Ste. 500
Hollywood, CA 90028
Phone: 323-860-9200
Fax: –
Web: www.j2global.com

CEO: Nehemia (Hemi) Zucker
CFO: Kathleen M. (Kathy) Griggs
HR: Patty Brunton
FYE: December 31
Type: Public

Checked your messages? Customers of j2 Global Communications can retrieve e-mail, faxes, and voicemail from a single phone line. Customers receive a private phone number that can handle unlimited incoming messages. The company, formerly known as JFAX.COM, operates primarily under the eFax, JFAX, and jConnect brands and claims more than 11 million phone numbers for customers located in 37 countries worldwide, including major US cities and international business centers such as Frankfurt, London, and Tokyo. The company counts more than 900,000 paid subscribers with the balance of phone lines going to advertising-supported free subscribers.

	Annual Growth	12/03	12/04	12/05	12/06	12/07
Sales ($ mil.)	32.5%	71.6	106.3	143.9	181.1	220.7
Net income ($ mil.)	17.6%	35.8	31.6	51.3	53.1	68.5
Market value ($ mil.)	37.7%	286.2	407.2	529.2	1,343.9	1,030.3
Employees	19.3%	—	—	288	341	410

JABIL CIRCUIT, INC.

NYSE: JBL

10560 Dr. Martin Luther King Jr. St. North
St. Petersburg, FL 33716
Phone: 727-577-9749
Fax: 727-579-8529
Web: www.jabil.com

CEO: Timothy L. Main
CFO: Forbes I. J. Alexander
HR: William E. (Bill) Peters
FYE: August 31
Type: Public

Jabil Circuit takes more than a jab at contract electronics manufacturing. The company is one of the leading providers of electronics manufacturing services (EMS) in the world. Parts made by Jabil on a contract basis are used in communications products, computers and computer peripherals, and automobiles. Services range from product design and component procurement to order fulfillment and supply chain management. The company has been rapidly expanding into Asian and Eastern European markets in recent years, through acquisitions and new plants. Top customers include Cisco Systems (15% of sales), Hewlett-Packard, Nokia (13%), and Philips. The Americas provide about 40% of sales.

	Annual Growth	8/03	8/04	8/05	8/06	8/07
Sales ($ mil.)	27.0%	4,729.5	6,252.9	7,524.4	10,265.5	12,290.6
Net income ($ mil.)	14.2%	43.0	166.9	231.9	164.5	73.2
Market value ($ mil.)	(5.2%)	5,611.6	4,152.8	6,020.2	5,444.6	4,541.6
Employees	23.5%	—	—	40,000	—	61,000

JACK COOPER TRANSPORT CO., INC.

2345 Grand Blvd., Ste. 400
Kansas City, MO 64108
Phone: 816-983-4000
Fax: 816-983-5000
Web: www.jackcooper.com

CEO: Greg May
CFO: –
HR: –
FYE: December 31
Type: Private

Your new car's journey from the factory to your garage might include a trip on a Jack Cooper Transport trailer. The company hauls motor vehicles from assembly plants, ports, and railway terminals to dealers and other locations across the US. Through its Jack Cooper Transport and Pacific Motor Trucking units, the company moves more than 1 million new and used vehicles each year, including cars, light trucks, and sport utility vehicles. It maintains a fleet of about 730 tractor-trailer pairs. The company operates primarily in the western, midwestern, and southern US. Jack Cooper Transport is owned by Thom Cooper Jr., whose grandfather Jack Cooper founded the company in 1928.

	Annual Growth	12/03	12/04	12/05	12/06	12/07
Est. sales ($ mil.)	—	—	—	—	—	256.0
Employees	—	—	—	—	—	1,436

JACK HENRY & ASSOCIATES, INC.

NASDAQ (GS): JKHY

663 W. Hwy. 60
Monett, MO 65708
Phone: 417-235-6652
Fax: 417-235-4281
Web: www.jackhenry.com

CEO: John F. (Jack) Prim
CFO: Kevin D. Williams
HR: Ann Puddister
FYE: June 30
Type: Public

Although Jack Henry is no Jimmy Stewart, the man's software may have saved many a small bank from the clutches of an evil Mr. Potter. Jack Henry & Associates (JHA) provides integrated in-house and outsourced computer systems to banks and credit unions. Products include core processing systems, electronic funds transfer (EFT) systems, automated teller machine networking products, digital check and document imaging and storage systems, Internet banking tools, and customer relationship management (CRM) software. The company's Symitar division offers service bureau, data processing, and other software for credit unions, while its ProfitStar brand offers revenue management products.

	Annual Growth	6/03	6/04	6/05	6/06	6/07
Sales ($ mil.)	13.4%	404.6	467.4	535.9	592.2	668.1
Net income ($ mil.)	20.7%	49.4	62.3	75.5	89.9	104.7
Market value ($ mil.)	10.0%	1,568.3	1,813.1	1,675.3	1,792.8	2,294.4
Employees		—	—	2,989	—	—

JACK IN THE BOX INC.

NYSE: JBX

9330 Balboa Ave.
San Diego, CA 92123
Phone: 858-571-2121
Fax: 858-571-2101
Web: www.jackinthebox.com

CEO: Linda A. Lang
CFO: Jerry P. Rebel
HR: Carlo E. Cetti
FYE: Sunday nearest September 30
Type: Public

Led by an affable "CEO" with a Ping-Pong ball for a head, Jack in the Box is among the leading quick-service restaurant businesses in the US. The company operates and franchises more than 2,100 of its flagship hamburger outlets in California, Texas, and about 15 other states. Jack in the Box offers such standard fast-food fare as burgers, fries, and soft drinks, as well as salads, tacos, and breakfast items. More than 1,500 locations are company-owned, while the rest are franchised. In addition to its mainstay burger business, the company runs a chain of nearly 400 Qdoba Mexican Grill fast-casual eateries through its Qdoba Restaurant Corporation subsidiary.

	Annual Growth	9/03	9/04	9/05	9/06	9/07
Sales ($ mil.)	8.7%	2,058.3	2,322.4	2,507.2	2,765.6	2,876.0
Net income ($ mil.)	14.5%	73.6	74.7	91.5	108.0	126.3
Market value ($ mil.)	58.1%	309.7	592.5	532.9	933.1	1,936.6
Employees	(2.4%)	—	—	44,600	44,300	42,500

JACKSON HEWITT TAX SERVICE INC.

NYSE: JTX

3 Sylvan Way
Parsippany, NJ 07054
Phone: 973-630-1040
Fax: 973-496-2785
Web: www.jacksonhewitt.com

CEO: Michael C. (Mike) Yerington
CFO: Daniel P. (Dan) O'Brien
HR: Peter N. Karpiak
FYE: April 30
Type: Public

Jackson Hewitt can help you conquer your fear of the tax collector. The company — the #2 tax preparer in the US, behind H&R Block — prepares tax returns for low- and middle-income customers through more than 6,500 offices (primarily franchised), including locations within Wal-Mart Stores and mall kiosks. Tax preparers use the company's ProFiler decision-tree software. Other Jackson Hewitt products and services include electronic filing, refund-anticipation loans, tax school, and a MasterCard stored-value card. Founded in 1982, Jackson Hewitt became a subsidiary of Avis Budget Group (formerly Cendant) in 1998 and went public in 2004.

	Annual Growth	4/04	4/05	4/06	4/07	4/08
Sales ($ mil.)	7.9%	205.6	232.5	275.4	293.2	278.5
Net income ($ mil.)	(6.8%)	43.0	50.0	58.0	65.4	32.4
Market value ($ mil.)	(15.1%)	—	693.2	1,054.9	858.2	423.8
Employees	—	—	377	—	—	—

JACKSON NATIONAL LIFE INSURANCE COMPANY

IMG Service Center, 1 Corporate Way
Lansing, MI 48951
Phone: 517-381-5500
Fax: 517-706-5521
Web: www.jnl.com

CEO: Clark P. Manning Jr.
CFO: Andrew B. (Andy) Hopping
HR: Stephen A. (Steve) Hrapkiewicz
FYE: December 31
Type: Subsidiary

Folks who've been talking about insurance might want to go to Jackson. Jackson National Life Insurance Company, a subsidiary of UK insurer Prudential plc, offers financial services (fixed, indexed, and variable annuities) and life insurance products through banks, regional broker/dealers, and independent agents. Jackson National Life Insurance subsidiaries include Jackson National Life Distributors (the company's wholesale distribution arm), Curian Capital (managed accounts), and broker/dealers SII Investments and INVEST Financial. The company in 2004 sold its Jackson Federal Bank subsidiary to UnionBanCal and acquired the Life Insurance Company of Georgia (Life of Georgia) from the ING Groep.

JACKSON SAFETY, INC.

1859 Bowles Ave., Ste. 200
Fenton, MO 63026
Phone: 636-717-6600
Fax: 636-717-6800
Web: www.jacksonsafety.com

CEO: Thomas D. (Tom) Burns
CFO: Mike Pruss
HR: Cindy Humphries
FYE: December 31
Type: Private

Sparks might fly around Jackson Safety, but the company's customers won't see them. Jackson Safety makes and sells head, eye, face, and hearing protection equipment, such as safety goggles, hard hats, helmets, and ear phones to industries in North America and Europe. The company's personal safety equipment units include Silencio, Allsafe, SMC, Smith and Wesson Safety Products, Huntsman, and Contour. Jackson Safety also sells traffic safety equipment, such as barricades, cones, and signs. In 2007, the company acquired Wilson Industries, a manufacturer of welding curtains and blankets, and Safemaster OY, a manufacturer of welding blankets in the Nordic region.

	Annual Growth	12/03	12/04	12/05	12/06	12/07
Est. sales ($ mil.)	—	—	—	—	—	132.7
Employees	—	—	—	—	—	945

JACKSONVILLE BANCORP, INC.

NASDAQ (GM): JAXB

100 N. Laura St., Ste. 1000
Jacksonville, FL 32202
Phone: 904-421-3040
Fax: 904-421-3050
Web: www.jaxbank.com

CEO: Gilbert J. Pomar III
CFO: Valerie A. Kendall
HR: –
FYE: December 31
Type: Public

Need to stow some greenbacks in Jax? You might check out Jacksonville Bancorp, the holding company for The Jacksonville Bank, which has about five branches in Jacksonville, Florida. The community bank offers consumers and commercial customers standard deposit products, including checking and savings accounts, money market accounts, CDs, and IRAs. The bank's lending is focused on commercial real estate loans, which make up some 60% of its loan portfolio; residential real estate loans add another 20%. The bank also offers business, construction, and consumer loans. Bank subsidiary Fountain Financial is an insurance agency. Jacksonville Bancorp is unrelated to the Illinois corporation of the same name.

	Annual Growth	12/03	12/04	12/05	12/06	12/07
Assets ($ mil.)	22.0%	176.9	223.7	273.0	325.6	392.0
Net income ($ mil.)	31.6%	1.0	1.3	2.2	2.5	3.0
Market value ($ mil.)	9.6%	24.1	46.0	56.8	57.6	34.8
Employees	(52.5%)	—	—	120	57	—

JACKSONVILLE BANCORP, INC.

NASDAQ (CM): JXSB

1211 W. Morton Ave.
Jacksonville, IL 62650
Phone: 217-245-4111
Fax: 217-245-2010
Web: www.jacksonvillesavings.com

CEO: Richard A. (Rich) Foss
CFO: Diana S. Tone
HR: John D. Eilering
FYE: December 31
Type: Public

Jacksonville wants to hold onto your jack. Jacksonville Bancorp (unaffiliated with the Florida corporation of the same name) was formed in 2002 to be the holding company for Jacksonville Savings Bank. Founded in 1916, the bank serves consumers and businesses in western Illinois through a handful of offices. The bank's lending activities are focused on real estate, with residential mortgages and commercial real estate loans accounting for more than half of the bank's loan portfolio. Consumer and business loans round out the bank's portfolio. Subsidiary Financial Resources Group offers investment services.

	Annual Growth	12/03	12/04	12/05	12/06	12/07
Assets ($ mil.)	2.5%	261.8	253.3	253.9	267.4	288.5
Net income ($ mil.)	(6.9%)	0.8	0.9	0.9	0.9	0.6
Market value ($ mil.)	(7.1%)	32.7	33.3	30.0	25.7	24.3
Employees	9.7%	—	—	98	—	118

JACKSONVILLE GREYHOUND RACING, INC.

4555 Park Ave.
Orange Park, FL 32073
Phone: 904-646-0001
Fax: 904-646-0420
Web: www.jaxkennel.com

CEO: Howard Korman
CFO: Bob Kuhn
HR: Delynn Zebouni
FYE: December 31
Type: Private

Four-legged runners send this company off to the races. Jacksonville Greyhound Racing owns and operates three dog tracks in Florida, including the Orange Park Kennel Club which offers live racing year-round. Its other tracks, the Jacksonville Kennel Club and The "Best Bet" at St. Johns, show simulcast racing. All three of its facilities offer fine dining and other amenities; its St. Johns facility also features a poker room with about 40 tables. In addition to operating its race tracks, Jacksonville Greyhound Racing broadcasts races over the Internet.

	Annual Growth	12/03	12/04	12/05	12/06	12/07
Est. sales ($ mil.)	—	—	—	—	—	35.7
Employees	—	—	—	—	—	400

JACLYN, INC.

AMEX: JLN

197 W. Spring Valley Ave.
Maywood, NJ 07607
Phone: 201-909-6000
Fax: –
Web: www.jaclyninc.com

CEO: Robert Chestnov
CFO: Anthony C. Christon
HR: Margarita Del Moral
FYE: June 30
Type: Public

Jaclyn wants to give a hand — or, at the very least, a handbag — to women on the go. It designs and makes branded and private-label women's sportswear, sleepwear, and dresses (some 65% of sales) under the Topsville, I. Appel, Smart Time, and Emerson Road names. It also makes infant's and children's clothing. Jaclyn produces casual handbags in fabric, vinyl, and leather. Its product lines, manufactured by outside contractors, are sold through general merchandise, department, and specialty stores nationwide. Wal-Mart accounts for more than 40% of Jaclyn's sales; Estée Lauder contributed another 20%. Jaclyn is owned by the Ginsburg (24% stake) and Chestnov (about 7%) families.

	Annual Growth	6/03	6/04	6/05	6/06	6/07
Sales ($ mil.)	9.1%	109.0	123.8	126.5	126.6	154.5
Net income ($ mil.)	0.0%	0.7	1.5	1.0	1.5	0.7
Employees	(2.4%)	—	—	172	—	164

THE JACMAR COMPANIES

2200 W. Valley Blvd.
Alhambra, CA 91803
Phone: 626-576-0737
Fax: 626-458-9224
Web: thejacmarcompanies.com

CEO: William H. (Bill) Tilley
CFO: David Reid
HR: –
FYE: December 31
Type: Private

Food is the primary focus of this holding company. Along with interests in restaurants and real estate, the Jacmar Companies is a leading distributor of food and non-food products to restaurants in California. Its Jacmar Foodservice Distribution unit supplies fresh produce, dairy products, meat, and a variety of frozen items, along with paper products and janitorial supplies. Jacmar also operates the Shakey's Pizza chain through subsidiary Shakey's USA, and it owns a 20% stake in BJ's Restaurants. The company's Jacmar Builders division deals in real estate development and management. Chairman and CEO William Tilley started Jacmar with a single Shakey's franchise in 1964.

	Annual Growth	12/03	12/04	12/05	12/06	12/07
Est. sales ($ mil.)	—	—	—	—	—	324.6
Employees	—	—	—	—	—	900

JACO ELECTRONICS, INC.

NASDAQ (GM): JACO

145 Oser Ave.
Hauppauge, NY 11788
Phone: 631-467-1100
Fax: 631-467-9262
Web: www.jacoelectronics.com

CEO: Joel H. Girsky
CFO: Jeffrey D. Gash
HR: –
FYE: June 30
Type: Public

In the world of electronics distributors, this company is a Jaco of all trades. Jaco Electronics distributes electronic components to small and midsize electronics manufacturers throughout North America. The company stocks more than 45,000 items produced by manufacturers such as Samsung, KEMET, and Vishay. Products include active components (such as semiconductors, transistors, and diodes) and passive components (capacitors and resistors). Jaco also offers a number of services, including inventory management and flat-panel display system configuration, but has discontinued offering contract manufacturing services. The company still provides engineering support services for its customers.

	Annual Growth	6/03	6/04	6/05	6/06	6/07
Sales ($ mil.)	2.5%	218.0	249.1	231.8	228.5	240.2
Net income ($ mil.)	—	(3.0)	(0.6)	(4.9)	(7.0)	(3.1)
Market value ($ mil.)	(15.4%)	28.5	38.1	18.6	23.5	14.6
Employees	—	—	—	—	—	—

JACO OIL COMPANY

3101 State Rd.
Bakersfield, CA 93308
Phone: 661-393-7000
Fax: 661-393-8738
Web: www.fastrip.com

CEO: Thomas J. Jamieson
CFO: Brian Busacca
HR: –
FYE: December 31
Type: Private

Jaco Oil Company is jockeying for its piece of the convenience store pie. The company operates about 50 Fastrip Food Stores primarily in and around Bakersfield, California, but also in Arizona. The Fastrip chain is testing in-store financial service centers, which provide check cashing, payday loans, wire transfer services via The Western Union Company, and other services, at some locations.

	Annual Growth	12/03	12/04	12/05	12/06	12/07
Est. sales ($ mil.)	—	—	—	—	—	459.5
Employees	—	—	—	—	—	350

JACOBS ENGINEERING GROUP INC.

NYSE: JEC

1111 S. Arroyo Pkwy.
Pasadena, CA 91105
Phone: 626-578-3500
Fax: 626-578-6916
Web: www.jacobs.com

CEO: Craig L. Martin
CFO: John W. Prosser Jr.
HR: Patricia H. Summers
FYE: September 30
Type: Public

Jacobs Engineering Group climbs its own ladder of success by expanding services and markets. The company has evolved from a one-person engineering firm into a global provider of diverse professional technical services. Engineering and construction projects for the chemical, petroleum, and pharmaceutical and biotech industries generate much of its revenues. US government contracts, chiefly for aerospace and defense, also add significantly to Jacobs' bottom line. Projects include buildings, process plants, manufacturing facilities, and paper and pulp plants. Jacobs also works on roads, highways, railways, ports, and other infrastructure projects, and it provides operations and maintenance services.

	Annual Growth	9/03	9/04	9/05	9/06	9/07
Sales ($ mil.)	16.4%	4,615.6	4,594.2	5,635.0	7,421.3	8,474.0
Net income ($ mil.)	22.4%	128.0	129.0	151.0	196.9	287.1
Market value ($ mil.)	63.9%	1,259.1	1,085.5	1,959.0	2,204.4	9,086.4
Employees	(2.9%)	—	—	38,600	31,700	36,400

JACOBS ENTERTAINMENT, INC.

17301 W. Colfax Ave., Ste. 250
Golden, CO 80401
Phone: 303-215-5200
Fax: 303-215-5219
Web: www.bhwk-hr.com

CEO: Jeffrey P. Jacobs
CFO: Brett A. Kramer
HR: –
FYE: December 31
Type: Private

Jacobs Entertainment wants you to come out and play. The company operates The Lodge Casino and Gilpin Casino in Black Hawk, Colorado; and the Gold Dust West Casinos in Reno, Carson City, and Elko, Nevada. The company also has about 20 truck stop video gaming facilities throughout Louisiana, and the Colonial Downs horseracing track in New Kent, Virginia; and eight satellite pari-mutuel wagering locations throughout Virginia. Chairman and CEO Jeffrey Jacobs owns 50% of the company. His father, Richard Jacobs, who co-founded Jacobs Entertainment, owns the other half.

	Annual Growth	12/02	12/03	12/04	12/05	12/06
Sales ($ mil.)	21.8%	153.7	171.8	189.7	234.1	338.6
Net income ($ mil.)	—	2.9	2.7	5.0	(4.7)	(10.8)
Employees	(5.0%)	1,350	1,365	1,365	1,585	1,100

An in-depth profile of this company is available to Hoover's Online members at hoovers.com.

857

JACOBS FINANCIAL GROUP, INC.

OTC: JFGIE

300 Summers St., Ste. 970
Charleston, WV 25301
Phone: 304-343-8171
Fax: 304-342-9726

CEO: John M. Jacobs
CFO: John M. Jacobs
HR: –
FYE: May 31
Type: Public

Jacobs Financial Group, through its subsidiaries, provides investment advising, investment management, surety business, security brokerage, and related services. Subsidiaries include Jacobs & Co., which provides investment advisory services, and FS Investments (FSI), a holding company organized to develop surety business through the formation and acquisition of companies engaged in the issuance of surety bonds (bonds collateralized by accounts managed by Jacobs & Co.). FSI's wholly owned subsidiary Triangle Surety Agency places surety bonds with insurance companies in regulated industries. Subsidiary Crystal Mountain Water holds mineral property in Arkansas.

	Annual Growth	5/03	5/04	5/05	5/06	5/07
Assets ($ mil.)	157.6%	0.1	0.1	0.1	4.3	4.4
Net income ($ mil.)	—	(0.7)	(1.0)	(1.1)	(1.5)	(1.3)
Market value ($ mil.)	(3.5%)	3.6	1.6	1.1	6.2	3.1
Employees	—	—	—	—	—	—

JACQUES MORET, INC.

1411 Broadway, 8th Fl.
New York, NY 10018
Phone: 212-354-2400
Fax: 212-354-1052
Web: www.moret.com

CEO: Joseph (Joey) Harary
CFO: Irwin Luxemburg
HR: –
FYE: December 31
Type: Private

Jacques Moret sounds like a French Impressionist but its business is in outfitting casual athletes rather than galleries. The company, which caters to the fitness apparel industry, makes women's, men's, and kid's activewear and undergarments under the Jacques Moret, MoretUltra, and Jacques Moret Kids names. It also makes men's and women's undergarments marketed under the 2(x)ist and SBH Intimates monikers. Jacques Moret is the master licensee for Everlast Worldwide. The company also partners with the likes of Jockey, Spalding, Freestyle by Danskin, and Etonic. Jacques Moret's products are sold through department stores, mass merchandisers, and sporting goods chains nationwide.

	Annual Growth	12/03	12/04	12/05	12/06	12/07
Est. sales ($ mil.)	—	—	—	—	—	100.0
Employees	—	—	—	—	—	150

[H] JACUZZI BRANDS CORPORATION

14525 Monte Vista Ave.
Chino, CA 91710
Phone: 909-606-1416
Fax: –
Web: www.jacuzzibrands.com

CEO: Thomas D. Koos
CFO: Glen Ferguson
HR: Kevin Clegg
FYE: Saturday nearest September 30
Type: Private

Aaah, that feels good. Jacuzzi Brands makes the eponymous whirlpool baths, spas, and showers (it also sells bath products under the Sundance and Astracast brands) that soothe the aches and pains of customers in the US, Europe, Middle East, and South America. Besides spas, products include toilets and sinks, accessories such as bath pillows and heating kits, steam showers, and other Romanesque bathroom necessities. Investment firm Apollo Management acquired Jacuzzi Brands for about $1.25 billion in early 2007. Apollo then transferred Jacuzzi's institutional plumbing business, Zurn Industries, to its RBS Global division.

	Annual Growth	9/02	9/03	9/04	9/05	9/06
Sales ($ mil.)	0.9%	1,159.5	1,192.6	1,347.2	1,210.0	1,202.4
Net income ($ mil.)	(0.3%)	40.9	(31.1)	28.5	(5.6)	40.4
Employees	(7.0%)	6,562	6,150	5,929	4,507	4,907

JAFRA WORLDWIDE HOLDINGS (LUX), S.ÀR.L.

2451 Townsgate Rd.
Westlake Village, CA 91361
Phone: 805-449-3000
Fax: 805-449-3254
Web: www.jafra.com

CEO: Frank P. Mineo
CFO: Enrique Marco Arenas
HR: –
FYE: December 31
Type: Private

Move over, Avon; step aside, Mary Kay. There's an international sales force of money-hungry women banding together. Jafra (a combination of the first names of the company's founders, Mailbu, California couple Jan and Frank Day, who created the company in 1956) sells and distributes high-end cosmetics and fragrances internationally through about 500,000 independent beauty consultants in more than 20 countries. Products include skin care cleansers and lotions, shampoos and conditioners, and nail polishes, as well as a variety of products for men.

	Annual Growth	12/03	12/04	12/05	12/06	12/07
Est. sales ($ mil.)	—	—	—	—	—	90.5
Employees	—	—	—	—	—	762

JAG MEDIA HOLDINGS, INC.

Pink Sheets: JAGH

6865 SW 18th St., Ste. B-13
Boca Raton, FL 33433
Phone: 561-892-0821
Fax: 561-892-0821
Web: www.jagnotes.com

CEO: Thomas J. Mazzarisi
CFO: Stephen J. Schoepfer
HR: –
FYE: July 31
Type: Public

Investors on a jag might be interested in JAG Media Holdings. The company provides financial and investment information. Its subscription-based JAGNotes (Upgrade/Downgrade) Report offers a daily investment report summarizing newly issued research, analyst opinions, upgrades, downgrades, and analyst coverage changes from various investment banks and brokerage houses. The company's Rumor Room is a space where JAG Media posts rumors that have been heard on the street about various stocks. JAG's UK-based Pixaya subsidiary is a software firm that delivers on-demand video and audio clips and text messages to mobile phones (Pixaya Mobile), and technology that enables real-time video streams (SurvayaCam).

	Annual Growth	7/03	7/04	7/05	7/06	7/07
Sales ($ mil.)	(15.9%)	0.4	0.3	0.2	0.2	0.2
Net income ($ mil.)	—	(2.6)	(2.0)	(1.9)	(3.6)	(11.8)
Employees	0.0%	5	5	—	—	—

JAGGED PEAK, INC.

OTC: JGPK

13577 Feather Sound Dr., Ste. 330
Clearwater, FL 33762
Phone: 800-430-1312
Fax: 800-749-4998
Web: www.jaggedpeak.com

CEO: Paul Demirdjian
CFO: Andrew J. Norstrud
HR: –
FYE: December 31
Type: Public

Jagged Peak rises up to help customers reach the peak of supply chain management. The company's E-Business Dynamic Global Engine (EDGE) is a ready-to-use Web-based application that captures, processes, and distributes orders from multiple sources, sending them in real-time to warehouses. With automated purchases and orders, companies can streamline their supply chain processes to improve delivery, reduce costs, and integrate inventory information. Jagged Peak took its present form in 2005, when publicly traded Absolute Glass Protection acquired the private company and adopted its name, officers, and operations.

	Annual Growth	12/03	12/04	12/05	12/06	12/07
Est. sales ($ mil.)	—	—	—	—	—	14.4
Net income ($ mil.)	—	—	—	—	—	(0.4)
Market value ($ mil.)	(64.1%)	—	—	34.0	7.6	4.4
Employees	—	—	—	—	—	—

JAKKS PACIFIC, INC.

NASDAQ (GS): JAKK

22619 Pacific Coast Hwy.
Malibu, CA 90265
Phone: 310-456-7799
Fax: 310-317-8527
Web: www.jakkspacific.com

CEO: Jack Friedman
CFO: Joel M. Bennett
HR: Tom Gerner
FYE: December 31
Type: Public

JAKKS Pacific is ready to rumble. JAKKS, one of the US's top toy companies, makes and sells action figures (including an exclusive license for World Wrestling Entertainment figures), activity sets (Flying Colors), die-cast and plastic cars (Road Champs, Remco), preschool toys (Child Guidance), pens and markers (Pentech), and fashion dolls. Its inexpensive toys are sold to US retailers such as Target, Toys "R" Us, and Wal-Mart (which together account for more than 50% of company sales); hobby stores; and other retailers. JAKKS was founded in 1995 by chairman and CEO Jack Friedman and president Stephen Berman.

	Annual Growth	12/03	12/04	12/05	12/06	12/07
Sales ($ mil.)	28.4%	315.8	574.3	661.5	765.4	857.1
Net income ($ mil.)	53.8%	15.9	43.6	63.5	72.4	89.0
Market value ($ mil.)	19.5%	327.0	580.0	564.2	606.6	667.6
Employees	(2.1%)	—	—	624	702	598

JAMBA INC.

NASDAQ (GM): JMBA

6475 Christie Ave., Ste. 150
Emeryville, CA 94608
Phone: 510-596-0100
Fax: 510-653-0764
Web: www.jambajuice.com

CEO: Paul E. Clayton Jr.
CFO: Donald D. (Don) Breen
HR: Karen A. Kelley
FYE: January 1
Type: Public

This company is blending up business with its fruit-filled drinks. Jamba operates the Jamba Juice chain, the leading outlet for blended fruit drinks with more than 700 smoothie stands in about two dozen states and the Bahamas. Its menu includes more than 30 varieties of custom smoothies (including Mango Mantra, Orange Berry Blitz, and Strawberry Nirvana) and Jamba Boosts (smoothies made with vitamin and protein supplements), along with other fruit juices and baked goods. Jamba Juice locations include freestanding units as well as on-site kiosks in high traffic areas, such as college campuses, gyms, and airports. More than 500 Jamba Juice locations are company-owned, while the rest are franchised.

	Annual Growth	1/04	1/05	1/06	1/07	1/08
Sales ($ mil.)	1,273.2%	—	—	—	23.1	317.2
Net income ($ mil.)	—	—	—	—	(59.0)	(113.3)
Employees	33.3%	—	—	—	7,500	10,000

JAMES AVERY CRAFTSMAN, INC.

145 Avery Rd. North
Kerrville, TX 78028
Phone: 830-895-1122
Fax: 830-895-6601
Web: www.jamesavery.com

CEO: Homer J. (James) Avery
CFO: –
HR: –
FYE: February 28
Type: Private

James Avery crafted himself a quite successful enterprise. James Avery Craftsman is a leading jewelry designer, manufacturer, and retailer in the southern US. Its jewelry collection, numbering some 1,100 designs and 14,000 items made in sterling silver, 14-, and 18-karat yellow and white gold, and gemstones, is sold through about 200 independent retailers and nearly 40 of its own stores in Colorado, Georgia, Oklahoma, Louisiana, and Texas. James Avery also sells through a catalog and via the Internet. The company got its start in 1954 when James Avery himself set up shop in a two-car garage with about $250 in capital.

	Annual Growth	2/03	2/04	2/05	2/06	2/07
Est. sales ($ mil.)	—	—	—	—	—	80.0
Employees	—	—	—	—	—	1,000

JAMES RIVER COAL COMPANY

NASDAQ (GM): JRCC

901 E. Byrd St., Ste. 1600
Richmond, VA 23219
Phone: 804-780-3000
Fax: 804-780-0643
Web: www.jamesrivercoal.com

CEO: Peter T. Socha
CFO: Samuel M. (Sam) Hopkins II
HR: –
FYE: December 31
Type: Public

James River Coal hopes the coal keeps flowing. The company operates about 25 mines in eastern Kentucky (in the Central Appalachian Basin) and southern Indiana (in the Illinois Basin) that produce some 10 million tons of coal annually. James River Coal controls approximately 265 million tons of proved and probable reserves. The company expanded in 2005 with the acquisition of Triad Mining, which brought to James River Coal the Indiana mines. More than three-quarters of its coal is sold to utilities. Georgia Power and South Carolina Public Service are its biggest customers, collectively accounting for nearly half of its business.

	Annual Growth	12/03	12/04	12/05	12/06	12/07
Sales ($ mil.)	14.4%	304.1	345.6	454.0	564.8	520.6
Net income ($ mil.)	—	(59.8)	110.0	(12.3)	(26.2)	(54.0)
Market value ($ mil.)	(23.3%)	—	627.2	636.4	154.7	283.1
Employees	18.5%	1,018	—	1,429	—	—

JAMES RIVER GROUP, INC.

300 Meadowmont Village Cir., Ste. 333
Chapel Hill, NC 27517
Phone: 919-883-4171
Fax: 919-883-4177
Web: www.james-river-group.com

CEO: J. Adam Abram
CFO: Michael T. Oakes
HR: –
FYE: December 31
Type: Private

When other insurance carriers reject you, don't cry a river, *call* one! James River Group writes specialty property/casualty insurance through its two primary operating subsidiaries. James River Insurance offers excess & surplus lines (policies that have been rejected by standard carriers), including general casualty, professional liability, and environmental coverage in 48 states and Washington, DC. Stonewood Insurance provides workers' compensation in North Carolina and Virginia, primarily for homebuilders. The company distributes its products through a network of independent brokers and agents. In 2007 the firm was acquired by private investment firm D. E. Shaw.

	Annual Growth	12/02	12/03	12/04	12/05	12/06
Assets ($ mil.)	24.2%	—	—	—	597.0	741.7
Net income ($ mil.)	186.8%	—	—	—	12.1	34.7
Employees	—	—	—	—	160	—

JAMESON INNS, INC.

4770 S. Atlanta Rd.
Smyrna, GA 30080
Phone: 404-350-9990
Fax: 404-601-6106
Web: www.jamesoninns.com

CEO: Aaron Walker
CFO: Jeff Brashear
HR: –
FYE: December 31
Type: Private

Jameson Inns owns some 110 limited-service hotels in about 12 southeastern and midwestern states. The hotels are operated under the Jameson Inns and Signature Inns names. Many properties offer such amenities as swimming pools, fitness facilities, and meeting and conference rooms; some rooms feature perks such as whirlpool tubs and refrigerators. The first Jameson Inn opened in 1987 in Winder, Georgia. In 2004 Jameson Inns ditched its status as a real estate investment trust (REIT). Formerly a public company, Jameson became a private firm in 2006, and is now jointly owned by JER Partners and Longhouse Hospitality. The hotel company's properties are managed by Park Management Group.

An in-depth profile of this company is available to Hoover's Online members at hoovers.com.

859

J & J SNACK FOODS CORP.

NASDAQ (GS): JJSF

6000 Central Hwy.
Pennsauken, NJ 08109
Phone: 856-665-9533
Fax: 856-665-6718
Web: www.jjsnack.com

CEO: Gerald B. Shreiber
CFO: Dennis G. Moore
HR: Harry Fronjan
FYE: Saturday nearest September 30
Type: Public

Giving you a brain-freeze and maybe a little mustard on the corner of your mouth, J & J Snack Foods makes snack items, including soft pretzel products sold under the SuperPretzel name, and ICEE and Arctic Blast frozen beverages. It also makes frozen desserts and juice treats (Luigi's, Mama Tish's), churros, funnel cakes (Tio Pepe's), and other snacks. It also offers a line of ready-to-bake cookies under the brand name Mrs. GoodCookie and CinnaPretzel under the Cinnabon name. J & J is the licensed manufacturer of Coca-Cola's Minute Maid soft frozen lemonade and frozen squeeze tubes.

	Annual Growth	9/03	9/04	9/05	9/06	9/07
Sales ($ mil.)	11.8%	364.6	416.6	457.1	514.8	568.9
Net income ($ mil.)	12.7%	19.9	22.7	26.0	29.5	32.1
Market value ($ mil.)	44.9%	147.6	183.9	251.9	574.4	651.2
Employees	5.2%	—	—	2,350	—	2,600

J & R ELECTRONICS INC.

23 Park Row
New York, NY 10038
Phone: 212-238-9000
Fax: 212-238-9191
Web: www.jandr.com

CEO: Joseph (Joe) Friedman
CFO: Zvi Hirsch
HR: Dean Shilenok
FYE: June 30
Type: Private

J & R Electronics redefines block party. The company is a leading electronics retailer with 10 specialty electronics stores in the same New York City block. The stores make up one retail megastore, J & R Music and Computer World. The combined stores measure about 300,000 sq. ft. and are known for discount prices and customer service. The firm also sells its products online and through a catalog. J & R's merchandise includes audio and video products, computers, cameras, software, office products, music, movies, and games. The company also operates an in-store shop at Macy's in Herald Square. Co-owners Joe and Rachelle Friedman used their wedding money to finance the founding of J & R Electronics in 1971.

J. & W. SELIGMAN & CO. INCORPORATED

100 Park Ave.
New York, NY 10017
Phone: 212-850-1864
Fax: 212-922-5726
Web: www.jwseligman.com

CEO: Brian T. Zino
CFO: Lawrence P. (Larry) Vogel
HR: Nick Martino
FYE: December 31
Type: Private

One of the oldest asset managers in the US, J. & W. Seligman & Co. offers a variety of investment products to individual and institutional investors. Founded in 1864, the company manages more than 40 mutual funds with prominent holdings in communications, information, and technology firms, as well as municipal debt. It also oversees more than $6 billion in assets for public funds, corporations, and foundations. Services for individuals include 401(k) plans and IRAs. Seligman also manages the Tri-Continental Corporation, one of the oldest and largest closed-end investment funds traded on the NYSE.

	Annual Growth	12/03	12/04	12/05	12/06	12/07
Est. sales ($ mil.)	—	—	—	—	—	56.0
Employees	—	—	—	—	—	417

JANEL WORLD TRADE LTD.

OTC: JLWT

150-14 132nd Ave.
Jamaica, NY 11434
Phone: 718-527-3800
Fax: 718-527-1689
Web: www.janelgroup.net

CEO: James N. Jannello
CFO: Linda Bieler
HR: –
FYE: September 30
Type: Public

Janel World Trade puts it all together for customers that ship by air, land, or sea. The freight forwarding and logistics management company gets lower bulk shipping rates for its clients by consolidating cargo headed to the same destination. Janel also provides customs brokerage, warehousing and distribution, and other logistics services. The company primarily handles clothing and textiles, household appliances, machinery and machine parts, and sporting goods shipped to and from the US, Europe, and the Far East. In addition to offices in the US, Janel has franchise operations in China, Hong Kong, and Thailand; the company works with agents in other parts of the world.

	Annual Growth	9/03	9/04	9/05	9/06	9/07
Sales ($ mil.)	7.1%	56.9	70.0	73.5	77.2	74.9
Net income ($ mil.)	10.7%	0.2	0.3	0.4	0.1	0.3
Market value ($ mil.)	(7.8%)	11.8	7.6	11.1	7.8	8.5
Employees	—	—	—	—	—	69

JANI-KING INTERNATIONAL, INC.

16855 Dallas Pkwy.
Addison, TX 75001
Phone: 972-991-0900
Fax: 972-991-5723
Web: www.janiking.com

CEO: James A. (Jim) Cavanaugh Jr.
CFO: Steven B. Hawkins
HR: –
FYE: December 31
Type: Private

Jani-King fights its royal battle with mop and broom. The company, which has more than 12,000 franchised businesses around the world, offers commercial cleaning services to office buildings, hotels, manufacturing facilities, health care institutions, universities, and sport arenas. Services include general cleaning, floor care, carpet care, trash disposal, and window washing, as well as outsourced hotel guest room cleaning, laundry service, event venue cleaning, porter services, and post-construction clean-up. Operating through 115 offices, the company was founded in 1969 by CEO Jim Cavanaugh, who created the company while still in college.

	Annual Growth	12/03	12/04	12/05	12/06	12/07
Est. sales ($ mil.)	—	—	—	—	—	154.8
Employees	—	—	—	—	—	550

JANNEY MONTGOMERY SCOTT LLC

1801 Market St.
Philadelphia, PA 19103
Phone: 215-665-6000
Fax: 215-564-9597
Web: www.janneys.com

CEO: Timothy C. (Tim) Scheve
CFO: Mark Knowt
HR: –
FYE: March 31
Type: Subsidiary

Janney Montgomery Scott offers a bevy of financial products and services through about 100 offices up and down the East Coast. One of the nation's largest regional broker-dealers, the firm offers fixed-income underwriting and trading, equity research, wealth management, and retirement planning, and acts as a market maker for nearly 150 Nasdaq-listed stocks. It also provides investment banking services such as public offerings, private placements, and mergers and acquisitions support to emerging and middle-market companies. Janney Montgomery Scott has approximately $13 billion of assets under management.

JANUS CAPITAL GROUP INC.

NYSE: JNS

151 Detroit St.
Denver, CO 80206
Phone: 303-333-3863
Fax: 303-336-7497
Web: www.janus.com

CEO: Gary D. Black
CFO: Gregory A. (Greg) Frost
HR: –
FYE: December 31
Type: Public

If you've got two faces, you may have twice the capacity to see and monitor the business landscape. Named after the ancient Roman god with two faces, Janus Capital Group provides investment management and advisory services for institutional and individual customers. Janus Capital Management administers more than 30 funds in all. Its flagship Janus Fund, formed in 1969, established itself as an investor in growth industries. (The fund and its sister fund, Janus Twenty, have made comebacks after experiencing heavy losses related to the Internet bust.) The INTECH fund bases its investment strategies on mathematical analysis of the stock market. Janus Capital has more than $206 billion in assets under management.

	Annual Growth	12/03	12/04	12/05	12/06	12/07
Assets ($ mil.)	(4.8%)	4,332.2	3,767.6	3,628.5	3,537.9	3,564.1
Net income ($ mil.)	(40.8%)	949.9	169.5	87.8	133.6	116.3
Market value ($ mil.)	8.6%	3,925.3	3,940.9	4,024.7	4,177.2	5,462.6
Employees	(8.8%)	—	—	1,457	1,518	1,213

JARDEN CORPORATION

NYSE: JAH

555 Theodore Fremd Ave., Ste. B-302
Rye, NY 10580
Phone: 914-967-9400
Fax: 914-967-9405
Web: www.jarden.com

CEO: Martin E. Franklin
CFO: Ian G. H. Ashken
HR: J. David Tolbert
FYE: December 31
Type: Public

Jarden is beaming with consumer products for inside and outside the home. It manufactures a diverse set of branded consumer products, including Sunbeam appliances, Coleman outdoor gear, and First Alert home safety products. It also makes Ball home canning products, Diamond matches and plastic cutlery, Crawford home storage products, Loew-Cornell artist supplies, and Bicycle playing cards. Jarden sells its products primarily to retailers, such as Wal-Mart Stores, Dick's Sporting Goods, and Target. It also makes plastic and zinc products for other companies and supplies copper-plated zinc penny blanks to the US Mint and the Royal Canadian Mint. It bought outdoor products maker K2 for about $1.2 billion in 2007.

	Annual Growth	12/03	12/04	12/05	12/06	12/07
Sales ($ mil.)	67.8%	587.4	838.6	3,189.1	3,846.3	4,660.1
Net income ($ mil.)	(3.0%)	31.8	42.4	60.7	106.0	28.1
Market value ($ mil.)	38.5%	492.3	846.0	2,052.2	2,491.0	1,813.2
Employees	19.5%	—	—	17,500	20,000	25,000

▥ JASON INCORPORATED

411 E. Wisconsin Ave., Ste. 2120
Milwaukee, WI 53202
Phone: 414-277-9300
Fax: 414-277-9445
Web: www.jasoninc.com

CEO: David Westgate
CFO: John Hengel
HR: –
FYE: Last Friday in December
Type: Private

Whether you're making the Sturgis run or just mowing your lawn, Jason Incorporated keeps your behind nice and comfy. The company's motor vehicle products segment has supplied seats for Harley-Davidson motorcycles since the 1930s, and it also makes seats for lawn care, construction, and agricultural equipment makers. Jason's motor vehicle unit also makes fiber insulation for the automotive industry. The company's industrial products include power brushes, buffing wheels, and metal and wire components. Investors in Jason include the company's management team and private equity firm Saw Mill Capital.

	Annual Growth	12/03	12/04	12/05	12/06	12/07
Est. sales ($ mil.)	—	—	—	—	—	385.9
Employees	—	—	—	—	—	3,500

JASPER ENGINES AND TRANSMISSIONS

815 Wernsing Rd.
Jasper, IN 47547
Phone: 812-482-1041
Fax: 812-634-1820
Web: www.jasperengines.com

CEO: Douglas A. (Doug) Bawel
CFO: Ralph Schwenk
HR: –
FYE: December 31
Type: Private

The maxim "one man's junk is another man's treasure" is a saying Jasper Engines and Transmissions takes to the bank. The company is a leading remanufacturer of automotive drive train parts. Jasper Engines and Transmissions takes worn out auto parts or "cores" and remanufactures them for sale to the automotive aftermarket. Products remanufactured by Jasper Engines and Transmissions include gasoline and diesel engines, transmissions, and differentials. The company also remanufactures high-performance engines and transmissions, marine engines, alternative fuel engines, and electric motors. Jasper Engines and Transmissions was founded in 1942.

	Annual Growth	12/03	12/04	12/05	12/06	12/07
Est. sales ($ mil.)	—	—	—	—	—	139.6
Employees	—	—	—	—	—	1,500

JAVO BEVERAGE COMPANY, INC.

OTC: JAVO

1311 Specialty Dr.
Vista, CA 92081
Phone: 760-560-5286
Fax: 760-560-5287
Web: www.javobeverage.com

CEO: Cody C. Ashwell
CFO: Richard A. Gartrell
HR: –
FYE: December 31
Type: Public

Javo puts the S-Q-U-E-E-Z-E on coffee. Javo Beverage Company makes and markets coffee and tea concentrates, drink mixes, iced and hot ready-to-drink beverages, and flavor and dispenser systems. Its national and international customers do business in the retail, food and beverage manufacturing and foodservice industries. Of note is Javo's line of "bag-in-a-box" products that allows restaurants, hotels, and hospitals to offer fresh-tasting coffee without having to do any actual brewing. In business since 1987, the company has never been profitable, reporting a net loss every year, and has yet to pay dividends to its stockholders, most of whom are Javo officers.

	Annual Growth	12/03	12/04	12/05	12/06	12/07
Sales ($ mil.)	106.0%	0.7	2.1	6.2	10.3	12.6
Net income ($ mil.)	—	(6.3)	(4.8)	(4.8)	(9.9)	(7.4)
Market value ($ mil.)	50.4%	22.6	59.7	44.1	209.3	115.5
Employees	—	—	—	—	—	—

JAYCO, INC.

903 S. Main St.
Middlebury, IN 46540
Phone: 574-825-5861
Fax: 574-825-7354
Web: www.jayco.com

CEO: Wilbur Bontrager
CFO: –
HR: –
FYE: August 31
Type: Private

Jayco's motto could be "have trailer, will travel." The company sells its line of camping trailers, travel trailers, fifth-wheels, sport-utility trailers, and motor homes through a network of about 300 dealers in the US and Canada. Products are marketed under model names including Eagle, Greyhawk, Jay Feather, Jay Flight, and Octane. Chairman and CEO Wilbur Bontrager and his family own Jayco. His father, the late Lloyd Bontrager, founded the company in 1968.

	Annual Growth	8/03	8/04	8/05	8/06	8/07
Est. sales ($ mil.)	—	—	—	—	—	585.0
Employees	—	—	—	—	—	1,770

JAZZ PHARMACEUTICALS, INC.

NASDAQ (GM): JAZZ

3180 Porter Dr.	CEO: Samuel R. Saks
Palo Alto, CA 94304	CFO: Matthew K. (Matt) Fust
Phone: 650-496-3777	HR: Lynn M. Hughes
Fax: 650-496-3781	FYE: December 31
Web: www.jazzpharmaceuticals.com	Type: Public

Jazz Pharmaceuticals wants to paint the town with successful treatments for niche psychiatric and neurological conditions. The company has several products on the market, including narcolepsy treatment Xyrem (which is also in clinical trials for the treatment of fibromyalgia) and Antizol, an antidote for ethylene glycol and methanol poisoning. The company acquired both drugs through its 2005 purchase of Orphan Medical. Jazz Pharmaceuticals also has US marketing rights for Solvay Pharmaceuticals' Luvox CR, a treatment for obsessive compulsive disorder (OCD) and social anxiety disorder that the FDA approved in 2008.

	Annual Growth	12/03	12/04	12/05	12/06	12/07
Sales ($ mil.)	—	—	0.0	21.4	44.9	65.3
Net income ($ mil.)	—	—	(24.8)	(85.2)	(59.4)	(138.8)
Market value ($ mil.)	—	—	—	—	—	361.9
Employees	—	—	—	—	185	—

JAZZ SEMICONDUCTOR, INC.

4321 Jamboree Rd.	CEO: Gilbert F. (Gil) Amelio
Newport Beach, CA 92660	CFO: Brent Jensen
Phone: 949-435-8000	HR: Daniel T. (Dan) Lynch
Fax: 949-435-8200	FYE: December 31
Web: www.jazzsemi.com	Type: Private

Making semiconductors in exotic materials and processes is the specialty of Jazz Semiconductor, a contract manufacturer of chips, also known as a silicon foundry. Jazz also uses the ol' reliable material, plain old silicon, but many chips for networking and wireless applications call for fabrication in silicon germanium and other compound semiconductors. Customers in the US account for most of Jazz Semiconductor's sales. Rival foundry Tower Semiconductor agreed in 2008 to acquire Jazz Technologies, the parent company of Jazz Semiconductor, for about $169 million, including the assumption of debt.

JAZZERCISE, INC.

2460 Impala Dr.	CEO: Judi Sheppard Missett
Carlsbad, CA 92010	CFO: Sally Baldridge
Phone: 760-476-1750	HR: Rick Colson
Fax: 760-602-7180	FYE: June 30
Web: www.jazzercise.com	Type: Private

Jazzercise has shown people how to shake their booties toward fitness for more than 30 years. The company's franchised fitness classes, taught by more than 6,000 instructors, blend jazz dancing with an aerobic workout for nearly a half million students worldwide. Jazzercise makes money through franchise fees as well as the sale of clothing, books, and other merchandise online and through catalogs. The company's JM DigitalWorks unit produces Jazzercise workout tapes and provides video production services to other clients. Its Jazzertogs division offers fitness apparel and accessories. CEO Judi Sheppard Missett, a professional dancer, founded Jazzercise in 1969 and began franchising in 1980.

J.B. POINDEXTER & CO., INC.

1100 Louisiana, Ste. 5400	CEO: John B. Poindexter
Houston, TX 77002	CFO: Robert S. Whatley
Phone: 713-655-9800	HR: –
Fax: 713-951-9038	FYE: December 31
Web: www.jbpoindexter.com	Type: Private

No matter what you're hauling, J.B. Poindexter & Co. has got you covered. Through its Morgan Corporation subsidiary, the company makes medium-duty commercial van bodies that are mounted on truck chassis made by other manufacturers. A separate unit, Morgan Olson, makes bodies for step vans. J.B. Poindexter's truck accessories unit makes pickup bed enclosures such as tonneaus and campers under brands including Leer and LoRider. The company's specialty manufacturing group includes subsidiaries EFP (expandable foam plastics), Specialty Vehicle Group (funeral coaches and other funeral vehicles), and MIC Group (precision metal parts, casting, and machining). Chairman and CEO John B. Poindexter owns the company.

	Annual Growth	12/02	12/03	12/04	12/05	12/06
Est. sales ($ mil.)	—	—	—	—	—	795.4
Net income ($ mil.)	—	—	—	—	—	8.9
Employees	—	—	—	—	—	4,500

JBS SWIFT & COMPANY

1770 Promontory Cir.	CEO: Wesley Mendonça Batista
Greeley, CO 80634	CFO: Andre Nogueira
Phone: 970-506-8000	HR: John W. (Jack) Shandley
Fax: 970-506-8307	FYE: Last Sunday in May
Web: www.swiftbrands.com	Type: Subsidiary

JBS Swift & Company (formerly Swift & Company) has a hoof up on other companies in the meat industry. A subsidiary of Brazilian beef giant JBS since 2007, the company is one of the leading beef processors in the world, with operations in Australia as well as the US. Its products include fresh, further-processed, and value-added meats. Beef is its biggest seller, although it also offers pork and a small amount of lamb. In addition to the US market, JBS Swift's products are available in Australia, Mexico, China, Japan, and other Pacific Rim countries. Its brand names include G.F. Swift 1855, Swift Angus Select, Swift Premium Black Angus, and Miller Blue Ribbon Beef.

	Annual Growth	5/02	5/03	5/04	5/05	5/06
Sales ($ mil.)	2.5%	8,476.2	8,431.6	9,879.5	9,669.1	9,350.0
Net income ($ mil.)	—	75.5	57.7	44.5	40.8	(129.5)
Employees	(1.4%)	21,400	21,300	21,100	20,700	20,200

J. C. PENNEY COMPANY, INC.

NYSE: JCP

6501 Legacy Dr.	CEO: Myron E. (Mike) Ullman III
Plano, TX 75024	CFO: Robert B. Cavanaugh
Phone: 972-431-1000	HR: Michael T. Theilmann
Fax: 972-431-9140	FYE: Saturday nearest January 31
Web: www.jcpenney.com	Type: Public

J. C. Penney Company was created in 2002 as a holding company for department store operator J. C. Penney Corporation, its wholly owned subsidiary, which exchanged the "Company" in its 89-year-old moniker for "Corporation" after the holding company was formed. J. C. Penney Corporation is one of the largest department store, catalog, and e-commerce retailers in the US. In 2004 J. C. Penney Company sold its Eckerd drugstores chain to The Jean Coutu Group and CVS for $4.5 billion in cash. The retailer runs more than 1,000 JCPenney department stores throughout the US and Puerto Rico. In 2005 J. C. Penney sold its controlling stake in the 62-unit Lojas Renner chain in Brazil through a public stock offering.

	Annual Growth	1/04	1/05	1/06	1/07	1/08
Sales ($ mil.)	2.8%	17,786.0	18,424.0	18,781.0	19,903.0	19,860.0
Net income ($ mil.)	—	(928.0)	524.0	1,088.0	1,153.0	1,111.0
Market value ($ mil.)	10.7%	7,173.3	11,298.0	13,096.9	18,916.2	10,767.0
Employees	1.3%	—	—	151,000	155,000	155,000

An in-depth profile of this company is available to Hoover's Online members at hoovers.com.

J. C. PENNEY CORPORATION, INC.

6501 Legacy Dr.
Plano, TX 75024
Phone: 972-431-1000
Fax: 972-431-1362
Web: www.jcpenney.net

CEO: Myron E. (Mike) Ullman III
CFO: Robert B. Cavanaugh
HR: Michael T. Theilmann
FYE: Saturday nearest January 31
Type: Subsidiary

An old name in retailing, J. C. Penney has been busy reinventing itself to bring style to Middle America's department store shoppers. The company's chain of about 1,065 JCPenney department stores in the US and Puerto Rico has found itself squeezed between upscale competitors and major discounters (Target, Wal-Mart). Following the sale of its ailing Eckerd drugstore chain (formerly 45% of Penney's sales) to The Jean Coutu Group and CVS for $4.5 billion in 2004, the retailer has focused firmly on fashion. The firm runs one of the top catalog operations in the US. J. C. Penney Corporation is a wholly owned subsidiary of holding company J. C. Penney Company (created in 2002), which is the publicly traded entity.

	Annual Growth	1/03	1/04	1/05	1/06	1/07
Sales ($ mil.)	(11.4%)	32,347.0	17,786.0	18,424.0	18,781.0	19,903.0
Net income ($ mil.)	29.9%	405.0	(928.0)	524.0	1,088.0	1,153.0
Employees	(9.2%)	228,000	147,000	151,000	151,000	155,000

JCM PARTNERS, LLC

2151 Salvio St., Ste. 325
Concord, CA 94520
Phone: 925-676-1966
Fax: 925-676-1744

CEO: Gayle M. Ing
CFO: Douglas W. Toovey
HR: –
FYE: December 31
Type: Private

At the upper end of the Golden State is where you'll find JCM Partners, which invests in, renovates, manages, markets, and sells multifamily residential and commercial real estate in Northern California. It owns about 45 properties, including nearly 40 apartment communities (containing a total of about 5,000 units), one multi-tenant office/retail property, two office properties, and four industrial properties. Nearly half of JCM Partners' residential properties are located in Sacramento County; the remainder are in San Joaquin, Solano, Stanislaus, and Contra Costa counties (the Central Valley and the San Francisco metro area).

	Annual Growth	12/02	12/03	12/04	12/05	12/06
Sales ($ mil.)	1.8%	51.3	52.4	50.3	47.2	55.0
Net income ($ mil.)	91.7%	0.6	1.6	5.9	15.9	8.1
Employees	(4.9%)	—	222	205	191	191

J.D. ABRAMS, LP

111 Congress Ave., Ste. 2400
Austin, TX 78701
Phone: 512-322-4000
Fax: 512-322-4018
Web: www.jdabrams.com

CEO: Jon F. Abrams
CFO: Kelly Gallagher
HR: Dean Bernal
FYE: October 31
Type: Private

J.D. Abrams builds bridges and highways across Texas. The civil engineering and construction firm has also worked on flood control dams, reservoirs, waterways, railroad test track, airport taxiways, and other infrastructure projects in Texas and elsewhere in the Sun Belt. It has two subsidiaries, Transmountain Equipment and Austin Prestressed, which runs a concrete casting plant. The Texas Department of Transportation is J.D. Abrams' largest customer. Chairman James D. Abrams founded the company in El Paso in 1966. It is owned and managed by members of the Abrams family.

	Annual Growth	10/03	10/04	10/05	10/06	10/07
Est. sales ($ mil.)	—	—	—	—	—	182.2
Employees	—	—	—	—	—	750

J.D. POWER AND ASSOCIATES

2625 Townsgate Rd.
Westlake Village, CA 91361
Phone: 805-418-8000
Fax: 805-418-8900
Web: www.jdpower.com

CEO: Stephen C. (Steve) Goodall
CFO: Gary Tucker
HR: Kenneth (Ken) Caruso
FYE: December 31
Type: Subsidiary

They've got the power. Marketing information firm J.D. Power and Associates (best known for its car ratings) awards badges of excellence in dozens of categories based on yearly customer satisfaction surveys. Its studies are independently financed and then sold for use in marketing. Only top-rated performers are allowed to license the use of the awards. The company also provides its satisfaction ratings for businesses in the financial, home building, and travel industries. In addition to surveys, J.D. Power offers forecasting and other market research services. The company was founded in 1968 by its namesake, chairman James D. Power, III. In 2005 it was acquired by publisher McGraw-Hill.

JDA SOFTWARE GROUP, INC.

NASDAQ (GM): JDAS

14400 N. 87th St.
Scottsdale, AZ 85260
Phone: 480-308-3000
Fax: 480-308-3001
Web: www.jda.com

CEO: Hamish N. J. Brewer
CFO: Kristen L. Magnuson
HR: Kristen L. Magnuson
FYE: December 31
Type: Public

JDA Software Group supplies the links in the supply chain. The company's supply and demand optimization (SDO) software helps retailers and other businesses manage supply and demand chains, as well as business processes ranging from planning and forecasting to e-commerce and store operations. The company also offers point-of-sale applications to handle back-office functions, including inventory management, receipts, and returns. Other products include analytic applications for decision support and collaborative tools for maintaining product and catalog information with partners, distributors, and suppliers. JDA boasts more than 5,600 customers worldwide, including Kraft Foods, OfficeMax, and Mervyns.

	Annual Growth	12/03	12/04	12/05	12/06	12/07
Sales ($ mil.)	15.9%	207.4	216.9	215.8	277.5	373.6
Net income ($ mil.)	77.0%	2.7	2.0	7.0	(0.4)	26.5
Market value ($ mil.)	6.6%	479.0	397.5	494.3	404.7	617.7
Employees	23.0%	—	—	1,055	1,701	1,596

JDS UNIPHASE CORPORATION

NASDAQ (GS): JDSU

430 N. McCarthy Blvd.
Milpitas, CA 95035
Phone: 408-546-5000
Fax: 408-546-4300
Web: www.jdsu.com

CEO: Kevin J. Kennedy
CFO: David W. Vellequette
HR: Alan (Al) Etterman
FYE: June 30
Type: Public

JDS Uniphase (JDSU) is drawn to the warming glow of optical networks. Through a series of acquisitions, primarily suppliers of network monitoring and test instruments, the company has reorganized from two segments — the Communications Products Group and the Commercial and Consumer Products Group — into three businesses. Communications Test & Measurement consists of the T&M acquisitions. Optical Communications makes components, modules, and equipment used to build fiber-optic telecom, data, and cable television networks. Advanced Optical Technologies contains JDSU's Flex Products and Custom Optics businesses. JDSU sells to customers in the communications, commercial, consumer, and military markets.

	Annual Growth	6/03	6/04	6/05	6/06	6/07
Sales ($ mil.)	19.9%	675.9	635.9	712.2	1,204.3	1,396.8
Net income ($ mil.)	—	(933.8)	(115.5)	(261.3)	(151.2)	(26.3)
Market value ($ mil.)	(12.5%)	5,009.6	5,459.1	2,511.3	4,140.3	2,941.3
Employees	6.3%	5,489	6,041	5,022	7,099	7,000

An in-depth profile of this company is available to Hoover's Online members at hoovers.com.

863

JE DUNN CONSTRUCTION GROUP, INC.

929 Holmes
Kansas City, MO 64106
Phone: 816-474-8600
Fax: 816-391-2510
Web: www.jedunn.com

CEO: Terrence P. (Terry) Dunn
CFO: Gordon E. Lansford III
HR: Rick Beyer
FYE: December 31
Type: Private

JE Dunn Construction Group prides itself on getting the job done. Owned by descendants of founder John E. Dunn, the firm holds a group of construction companies, including flagship J. E. Dunn Construction and Atlanta-based R.J. Griffin & Company. The group builds institutional, commercial, and industrial structures. It also provides construction and program management and design/build services. J. E. Dunn Construction, which ranks among the top 10 US general builders, was one of the first contractors to offer the construction management delivery method. Major projects it has completed include the IRS complex and world headquarters for H&R Block in Kansas City.

	Annual Growth	12/02	12/03	12/04	12/05	12/06
Sales ($ mil.)	11.6%	1,655.0	1,497.0	1,633.0	2,305.0	2,563.0
Employees	0.0%	3,000	3,000	3,000	3,000	3,000

JEA

21 W. Church St.
Jacksonville, FL 32202
Phone: 904-665-6000
Fax: 904-665-7008
Web: www.jea.com

CEO: James A. (Jim) Dickenson
CFO: Paul McElroy
HR: Susan Hughes
FYE: September 30
Type: Government-owned

As long as sparks are flying in Jacksonville, everything is A-OK with JEA. The municipal utility provides electricity to more than 360,000 customers in Jacksonville and surrounding areas in northeastern Florida. Managing an electric system that dates back to 1895, JEA has a net generating capacity of 2,361 MW (primarily from fossil-fueled plants). The company also resells electricity to other utilities, including FPL. JEA also provides water and wastewater services; it serves more than 240,000 water customers and 186,000 wastewater customers. The utility's water supply comes from 150 artesian wells tapping the Floridian Aquifer.

	Annual Growth	9/03	9/04	9/05	9/06	9/07
Est. sales ($ mil.)	—	—	—	—	—	1,443.2
Employees	—	—	—	—	—	2,356

⊞ JEFFERIES GROUP, INC.

NYSE: JEF

520 Madison Ave., 12th Fl.
New York, NY 10022
Phone: 212-284-2300
Fax: 212-284-2111
Web: www.jefco.com

CEO: Richard B. Handler
CFO: Peregrine C. de M. (Peg) Broadbent
HR: Melvin W. (Mel) Locke Jr.
FYE: December 31
Type: Public

Because smaller companies need hostile takeover advice, too. Jefferies Group raises capital, performs securities trading and research, and provides advisory services for small and midsized companies in the US through its Jefferies & Company subsidiary. Its Jefferies Execution Services subsidiary trades more than 30 billion shares per year for institutional investors. The company also has been building its asset management business, and now oversees more than $5.5 billion on behalf of its clients. Jefferies Group has more than 25 offices in North America, Europe, and Asia.

	Annual Growth	12/03	12/04	12/05	12/06	12/07
Sales ($ mil.)	30.9%	926.7	1,198.6	1,497.9	1,963.2	2,718.9
Net income ($ mil.)	14.5%	84.1	131.4	157.4	205.8	144.7
Market value ($ mil.)	28.5%	1,052.3	1,153.8	1,306.9	3,206.2	2,868.6
Employees	10.2%	—	—	2,045	2,254	—

JEFFERSON BANCSHARES, INC.

NASDAQ (GM): JFBI

120 Evans Ave.
Morristown, TN 37814
Phone: 423-586-8421
Fax: 423-587-2605
Web: www.jeffersonfederal.com

CEO: Anderson L. (Andy) Smith
CFO: Jane P. Hutton
HR: –
FYE: June 30
Type: Public

Here's a bank that will definitely *volunteer* its financial services. Jefferson Bancshares is the holding company for Jefferson Federal Bank, which has locations in Knoxville and Morristown, Tennessee. Founded in 1963 as a building and loan association, the bank serves individuals and businesses in Hamblen County and neighboring Jefferson County with such standard services as checking, money market, and NOW accounts, as well as CDs and IRAs. The bank's lending activities consist primarily of one- to four-family real estate loans and commercial real estate loans, which combined, account for nearly 60% of the company's portfolio.

	Annual Growth	6/03	6/04	6/05	6/06	6/07
Assets ($ mil.)	(1.7%)	363.6	305.5	295.0	327.1	339.7
Net income ($ mil.)	(17.1%)	3.6	1.4	3.5	2.3	1.7
Market value ($ mil.)	(11.4%)	—	108.9	93.3	85.6	75.7
Employees	—	—	—	80	—	—

JEFFERSON HEALTH SYSTEM INC.

259 N. Radnor-Chester Rd., Ste. 290
Radnor, PA 19087
Phone: 610-225-6200
Fax: 610-225-6254
Web: www.jeffersonhealth.org

CEO: Joesph T. Sebastianelli
CFO: Kirk E. Gorman
HR: –
FYE: June 30
Type: Not-for-profit

This health care system's freedom-loving namesake might approve of its work to preserve the people's freedom of choice in health care. Jefferson Health System is a not-for-profit alliance of five health systems with more than ten hospitals serving the Delaware Valley. Members include the Thomas Jefferson University Hospital family (one of the system's founders), Albert Einstein Healthcare Network, Frankford Health Care System, Main Line Health (the other founding organization), and Magee Rehabilitation. The Jefferson network has some 3,700 beds. The health system is affiliated with Thomas Jefferson University.

	Annual Growth	6/03	6/04	6/05	6/06	6/07
Est. sales ($ mil.)	—	—	—	—	—	2,147.5
Employees	—	—	—	—	—	20,700

JEFFERSONVILLE BANCORP

NASDAQ (CM): JFBC

4864 State Rte. 52
Jeffersonville, NY 12748
Phone: 845-482-4000
Fax: 845-482-3544
Web: www.jeffbank.com

CEO: Raymond L. Walter
CFO: Charles E. Burnett
HR: Claire A. Pecsi
FYE: December 31
Type: Public

Jeffersonville Bancorp is the holding company for The First National Bank of Jeffersonville. The bank serves businesses and consumers through about 10 locations in southeastern New York's Sullivan County. First National Bank of Jeffersonville offers such standard retail services as demand deposit, savings, and money market accounts; NOW accounts; CDs; and IRAs to fund a variety of loans. Nearly 40% of the bank's loan portfolio consists of residential mortgages, while commercial mortgages account for another 35%. The bank also provides home equity, business, consumer, construction, and agricultural loans.

	Annual Growth	12/03	12/04	12/05	12/06	12/07
Assets ($ mil.)	2.4%	352.2	363.9	387.3	397.3	387.4
Net income ($ mil.)	(6.8%)	5.7	6.2	5.7	4.9	4.3
Market value ($ mil.)	(7.9%)	82.6	85.6	106.2	81.6	59.3
Employees	—	—	—	135	—	—

An in-depth profile of this company is available to Hoover's Online members at hoovers.com.

JEL SERT CO.

Rte. 59 and Conde St.
West Chicago, IL 60185
Phone: 630-231-7590
Fax: 630-231-3993
Web: www.jelsert.com

CEO: Kenneth (Ken) Wegner
CFO: Tony D'Anna
HR: Juan Chavez
FYE: October 31
Type: Private

Just call Jel Sert Company the king of freezer pops. The company made its name in the early 1960s with its popular Pop-Ice "stick 'em in the freezer and squeeze 'em out of the tube" treats. Since then it has expanded its product line to include Flavor-Aid and Wyler's powdered drink mixes; Fla-Vor-Ice, Otter Pops and Wyler's Italian Ice freezer pops; and MONDO Fruit Squeezers fruit drinks. As a result of a 2000 purchase from Nabisco, Jel Sert also makes My*T*Fine and Royal pudding mixes. In addition, it makes Pooch Pops, beef- and cheese-flavored icy treats for the family pet. Founded in 1926, Jel Sert is still owned by the Wegner family; Charles Wegner (grandson of the founder) is chairman.

JELD-WEN, INC.

401 Harbor Isles Blvd.
Klamath Falls, OR 97601
Phone: 541-882-3451
Fax: 541-885-7454
Web: www.jeld-wen.com

CEO: Roderick C. (Rod) Wendt
CFO: Douglas P. (Doug) Kintzinger
HR: –
FYE: December 31
Type: Private

JELD-WEN can improve your outlook by providing new windows and doors for your home or by offering accommodations at a scenic resort. A leading manufacturer of windows and doors (some designed to withstand hurricane winds), JELD-WEN offers aluminum, vinyl, and wood windows; interior and exterior doors; garage doors; swinging and sliding patio doors; and door frames and moldings. It sells its products mainly in North America, Europe, and Australia. If you get tired of looking out your own doors and windows, JELD-WEN owns several resorts and communities in Oregon and Idaho, including Oregon's Eagle Crest Resort and Idaho's Silver Mountain Resort.

	Annual Growth	12/02	12/03	12/04	12/05	12/06
Est. sales ($ mil.)	12.1%	2,000.0	2,200.0	2,300.0	2,600.0	3,160.0
Employees	4.4%	20,000	21,000	21,000	25,000	23,750

JELLY BELLY CANDY COMPANY

1 Jelly Belly Ln.
Fairfield, CA 94533
Phone: 707-428-2800
Fax: 707-423-4436
Web: www.jellybelly.com

CEO: Herman (Herm) Rowland Sr.
CFO: –
HR: Jeff Brown
FYE: March 31
Type: Private

It has Cheesecake, Orange Sherbet, and Jalapeño — who could ask for anything more? But ask for more anyway. The Jelly Belly Candy Company makes Jelly Belly jelly beans in 50 flavors. Other company products include JBz, a combination of Jelly Bellies and chocolate in 20 flavors, as well as gumballs in various Jelly Belly flavor. It also makes variously shaped gummie candies including Jelly Slugs. Introduced in 1976 and named by former president Ronald Reagan as his favorite candy, the company's jelly beans are exported worldwide. Other products include candy corn, chocolate candies, and licorice.

	Annual Growth	3/03	3/04	3/05	3/06	3/07
Est. sales ($ mil.)	—	—	—	—	—	58.9
Employees	—	—	—	—	—	650

JENNIFER CONVERTIBLES, INC.

AMEX: JEN

419 Crossways Park Dr.
Woodbury, NY 11797
Phone: 516-496-1900
Fax: 516-496-0008
Web: www.jenniferfurniture.com

CEO: Harley J. Greenfield
CFO: Rami Abada
HR: Judith Weissman
FYE: Last Saturday in August
Type: Public

Houseguests can get a good night's sleep with Jennifer Convertibles. The company owns or licenses some 180 Jennifer Convertibles stores throughout the US that sell sofa beds, loveseats, recliners, and chairs. The company runs another 16 stores that specialize in leather living room furniture under the banner Jennifer Leather. Stores offer name-brand products, as well as the company's private-label Bellissimo Collection. Jennifer Convertibles is the largest dealer of Sealy sofa beds in the US. The firm buys more than 14% of its products from Klaussner Furniture, which owns a 20% stake in Jennifer Convertibles. Chairman and CEO Harley Greenfield owns nearly 20% of the company; EVP Edward Seidner owns nearly 19%.

	Annual Growth	8/03	8/04	8/05	8/06	8/07
Sales ($ mil.)	1.9%	126.6	134.2	121.9	140.4	136.6
Net income ($ mil.)	—	(3.4)	(4.1)	(3.9)	5.2	4.0
Market value ($ mil.)	7.3%	23.3	16.6	13.1	39.3	30.8
Employees	5.5%	—	—	443	—	493

JENNY CRAIG, INC.

5770 Fleet St.
Carlsbad, CA 92008
Phone: 760-696-4000
Fax: 760-696-4009
Web: www.jennycraig.com

CEO: Patricia A. (Patti) Larchet
CFO: Jim Kelly
HR: Chris Hilker
FYE: December 31
Type: Subsidiary

Jenny Craig would like for everyone to lighten up, at least a little. The weight-control company is one of the world's two largest diet firms (along with Weight Watchers). It owns or franchises about 650 centers in the US, Canada, Australia, New Zealand, Puerto Rico, and Guam. Jenny's Cuisine prepared foods, along with DVDs, journals, CDs, workout accessories, and cookbooks, are sold to participants at its centers. The program is also available at home with telephone consultations and home delivery of food and support materials. Nestlé, the largest food and drink company in the world, acquired Jenny Craig for $600 million in June 2006. Jenny Craig's management team still runs the business.

JENZABAR, INC.

Prudential Tower, 800 Boylston St., 35th Fl.
Boston, MA 02199
Phone: 617-492-9099
Fax: 617-492-9081
Web: www.jenzabar.net

CEO: Robert A. (Bob) Maginn Jr.
CFO: Mimi Jespersen
HR: –
FYE: December 31
Type: Private

Raising the bar on higher learning, Jenzabar provides enterprise software and executive services developed to meet the unique requirements of colleges and universities. The company's products and services focus on simplifying the processes and tools that drive enrollment, retention, and advancement and integrating them into a single Web-based portal. Jenzabar's Total Campus Management framework combines student information and business office systems with an Internet portal, alumni and student services modules, and a learning management system. Jenzabar provides services to some 700 higher education institutions, including The Claremont Colleges, Harvard Medical School, and William Mitchell College of Law.

	Annual Growth	12/03	12/04	12/05	12/06	12/07
Est. sales ($ mil.)	—	—	—	—	—	65.0
Employees	—	—	—	—	—	283

An in-depth profile of this company is available to Hoover's Online members at hoovers.com.

865

JER INVESTORS TRUST INC.

NYSE: JRT

1650 Tysons Blvd., Ste. 1600
McLean, VA 22102
Phone: 703-714-8000
Fax: 703-714-8100
Web: www.jer.com

CEO: Joseph E. Robert Jr.
CFO: J. Michael McGillis
HR: –
FYE: December 31
Type: Public

A real estate investment trust (REIT), JER Investors Trust invests in and originates real estate structured finance products, primarily commercial mortgage-backed securities (CMBS) and nonconforming mezzanine and other mortgage loans. Its portfolio is secured by a variety of property types (mainly retail, residential, and office properties, but also hospitality and industrial properties) located throughout the US. Founded in 2004, the company is managed by an affiliate of real estate investment management firm J.E. Robert Company (JER). It went public the following year.

	Annual Growth	9/03	9/04	*12/05	12/06	12/07
Sales ($ mil.)	155.8%	—	8.0	36.4	74.0	133.9
Net income ($ mil.)	—	—	(6.1)	19.6	31.7	23.1
Market value ($ mil.)	(20.0%)	—	—	435.4	532.4	279.0
Employees	—	—	150	—	—	0

*Fiscal year change

JERRY'S ENTERPRISES, INC.

5101 Vernon Ave. South
Minneapolis, MN 55436
Phone: 952-922-8335
Fax: 952-929-9281

CEO: Gerald A. (Jerry) Paulsen
CFO: Kent Dixon
HR: David Gerdes
FYE: September 30
Type: Private

Jerry's Enterprises operates about 25 grocery stores under the Cub Foods, Save-a-Lot, and Jerry's Foods banners in Minnesota and Florida. In 2004 the company expanded its market to include Wisconsin when it purchased two County Market stores from Dick Schmitz, a Hudson-based businessman, for an undisclosed price. Jerry's Enterprises was founded in 1947.

	Annual Growth	9/03	9/04	9/05	9/06	9/07
Est. sales ($ mil.)	—	—	—	—	—	379.5
Employees	—	—	—	—	—	3,500

JERSEY CENTRAL POWER & LIGHT COMPANY

c/o FirstEnergy Corp., 76 S. Main St.
Akron, OH 44308
Phone: 800-736-3402
Fax: 330-384-3866
Web: www.firstenergycorp.com

CEO: Stephen E. (Steve) Morgan
CFO: Richard H. (Rich) Marsh
HR: Lynn M. Cavalier
FYE: December 31
Type: Subsidiary

New Jersey native son Bruce Springsteen may be the boss, but Jersey Central Power & Light (JCP&L) electrifies more fans every day. The company, a FirstEnergy subsidiary, transmits and distributes electricity to about 2.6 million homes and businesses in central and northern New Jersey. JCP&L operates more than 19,280 miles of distribution lines; its 2,135-mile transmission system is overseen by PJM Interconnection, a regional transmission organization (RTO). The utility, which was organized under the laws of the State of New Jersey in 1925, also has power plant interests.

	Annual Growth	12/02	12/03	12/04	12/05	12/06
Sales ($ mil.)	3.5%	2,328.4	2,364.2	2,207.0	2,602.2	2,667.6
Net income ($ mil.)	(6.7%)	251.9	68.0	111.6	182.9	190.6
Employees	(1.5%)	—	1,557	1,444	1,416	1,488

JERSEY CITY MEDICAL CENTER

355 Grand St.
Jersey City, NJ 07302
Phone: 201-915-2000
Fax: 201-915-2002
Web: www.libertyhealth.org/jcmc.html

CEO: E. Stephen Kirby
CFO: Don Parseghian
HR: Mary Cataudella
FYE: December 31
Type: Not-for-profit

Originally dedicated by Franklin Delano Roosevelt in the 1930s, Jersey City Medical Center is an acute-care hospital serving the residents of New Jersey's Hudson county area. Operated by Liberty HealthCare System, the hospital includes a trauma center, a children's hospital, a perinatal center, and a heart institute. Founded in 1808, the hospital is also a teaching affiliate for the Mount Sinai School of Medicine. Among its specialized services are neurology, oncology, hematology, and geriatrics. In addition, the medical center provides a variety of behavioral health services, including inpatient and outpatient care.

	Annual Growth	12/03	12/04	12/05	12/06	12/07
Est. sales ($ mil.)	—	—	—	—	—	90.7
Employees	—	—	—	—	—	1,942

JESUP & LAMONT, INC.

AMEX: JLI

2170 W. State Rd. 434, Ste. 100
Longwood, FL 32779
Phone: 407-774-1300
Fax: 407-682-5867
Web: www.jesuplamont.com

CEO: Donald A. Wojnowski Jr.
CFO: James M. Matthew
HR: –
FYE: December 31
Type: Public

Jesup & Lamont performs brokerage services for retail investors and small to midsized financial institutions (e.g., credit unions, hedge funds, and money managers) throughout the US and in Europe and Asia. Related services include investment advice, market data, and portfolio management. The company also provides administrative support for a network of independent and employee broker/advisors in some 30 independently owned offices. Then named Empire Financial, the company acquired Jesup & Lamont Securities in 2006 and changed its own name to Jesup & Lamont in 2008. Other subsidiaries include Empire Financial Group and Empire Investment Advisors.

	Annual Growth	12/03	12/04	12/05	12/06	12/07
Sales ($ mil.)	30.7%	17.4	21.6	22.5	35.6	50.7
Net income ($ mil.)	—	(3.1)	(1.6)	2.5	0.0	(10.7)
Employees	(9.7%)	—	—	222	—	181

JETBLUE AIRWAYS CORPORATION

NASDAQ (GS): JBLU

118-29 Queens Blvd.
Forest Hills, NY 11375
Phone: 718-286-7900
Fax: 718-709-3621
Web: www.jetblue.com

CEO: David (Dave) Barger
CFO: Edward (Ed) Barnes
HR: Vinny Stabile
FYE: December 31
Type: Public

JetBlue Airways is counting on more than low fares to make its ledgers jet-black. The carrier offers one-class service — with leather seats, satellite TV (with programming from DIRECTV), satellite radio (from XM), and movies (from FOX InFlight) — to about 55 cities in more than 20 states and in Mexico and the Caribbean (including Puerto Rico and the Dominican Republic). The majority of its flights arrive or depart from one of five key markets: Boston; Fort Lauderdale, Florida; Long Beach, California; New York; and Washington, DC. The company's fleet of about 135 aircraft consists mainly of Airbus A320s but also includes Embraer 190s.

	Annual Growth	12/03	12/04	12/05	12/06	12/07
Sales ($ mil.)	29.9%	998.3	1,266.0	1,701.0	2,363.0	2,842.0
Net income ($ mil.)	(35.5%)	103.9	47.5	(20.0)	(1.0)	18.0
Market value ($ mil.)	(7.5%)	1,804.6	1,613.6	2,661.1	2,522.1	1,323.0
Employees	12.2%	—	—	9,248	10,624	11,632

JETRO CASH & CARRY ENTERPRISES, LLC

1524 132 St.
College Point, NY 11356
Phone: 718-939-6400
Fax: 718-661-9627
Web: www.jetro.com

CEO: Stanley Fleishman
CFO: Bryan Emmert
HR: Stuart (Stu) Kipilman
FYE: December 31
Type: Private

Jetro Cash & Carry Enterprises is a leading wholesale grocery distributor that operates more than a dozen Cash & Carry outlets in the New York City area and a half dozen other states. The warehouse outlets offer a full line of food and non-food products, including national brands and private label goods, for grocery retailers and foodservice operators. Parent company Jetro Holdings also operates more than 50 wholesale outlets serving foodservice operators through its Restaurant Depot subsidiary. Founded in 1976, Jetro is a portfolio company of private equity firm CCMP Capital.

	Annual Growth	12/03	12/04	12/05	12/06	12/07
Est. sales ($ mil.)	—	—	—	—	—	361.1
Employees	—	—	—	—	—	1,000

JEWEL-OSCO

1955 W. North Ave.
Melrose Park, IL 60160
Phone: 708-531-6000
Fax: 708-531-6047
Web: www.jewelosco.com

CEO: Keith Nielsen
CFO: -
HR: Tim Corry
FYE: Last Saturday in February
Type: Business segment

Jewel-Osco operates about 190 combination food-and-drug stores in Illinois and Indiana. The regional supermarket chain is the #1 seller of groceries in Chicago with about 40% of the market, trailed by Safeway-owned Dominick's and deep-discounter ALDI. Jewel-Osco trails rival Walgreen in pharmacy sales there. The company abandoned the Wisconsin market in 2007. Started as the Jewel Tea Company in 1899 and formerly the Midwest division of Albertson's (now Albertsons LLC), Jewel-Osco was sold to grocery retailer and wholesaler SUPERVALU in mid-2006. The company's new owner is taking aim at Dominick's with plans for the biggest Chicago-area expansion of Jewel-Osco stores in decades.

	Annual Growth	2/03	2/04	2/05	2/06	2/07
Est. sales ($ mil.)	—	—	—	—	—	2,147.5
Employees	—	—	—	—	—	32,000

JEWETT-CAMERON TRADING COMPANY LTD.

NASDAQ (CM): JCTCF

32275 NW Hillcrest
North Plains, OR 97133
Phone: 503-647-0110
Fax: 503-647-2272
Web: www.jewettcameron.com

CEO: Donald M. Boone
CFO: Donald M. Boone
HR: Janet Strand
FYE: August 31
Type: Public

Jewett-Cameron Trading Company (JCTC) puts the lumber in lumberyards, the air in pneumatic tools, and seeds in the ground. Its Jewett-Cameron Lumber Company (JCLC) subsidiary supplies wood and other building materials to home improvement chains in the western US from distribution centers in Oregon and Utah. The MSI-PRO subsidiary imports pneumatic air tools and industrial clamps from Asia. The Jewett-Cameron Seed business distributes processed agricultural seeds and grain in the US. It also owns plywood panel maker Greenwood Products. President Donald Boone owns nearly 25% of the company, while employees own about 16% of the company.

	Annual Growth	8/03	8/04	8/05	8/06	8/07
Sales ($ mil.)	6.2%	55.4	71.3	74.6	76.1	70.5
Net income ($ mil.)	66.4%	0.3	0.6	0.9	2.3	2.3
Market value ($ mil.)	43.7%	5.1	5.9	8.9	11.5	21.8
Employees	17.2%	—	—	67	—	92

J.F. SHEA CO., INC.

655 Brea Canyon Rd.
Walnut, CA 91789
Phone: 909-594-9500
Fax: 909-594-0917
Web: www.jfshea.com

CEO: Peter O. Shea Jr.
CFO: James G. (Jim) Shontere
HR: -
FYE: December 31
Type: Private

J.F. Shea didn't build Shea Stadium but it could have. The family-owned construction and real estate company takes on commercial and civil engineering projects and offers design/build services through its flagship group, J.F. Shea Construction. The group's heavy civil engineering division builds tunnels and water treatment and water storage facilities. The company has seven other companies that offer residential construction and mortgage services, aggregate supply, concrete foundation construction and machinery, venture capital (investments include water management system developer HydroPoint, which dovetails with Shea's area of expertise), and golf courses.

	Annual Growth	12/02	12/03	12/04	12/05	12/06
Sales ($ mil.)	12.4%	1,994.0	2,597.0	3,080.0	3,429.0	3,180.0
Employees	3.9%	2,315	2,685	2,668	3,299	2,700

JFC INTERNATIONAL INC.

540 Forbes Blvd.
South San Francisco, CA 94080
Phone: 650-871-1660
Fax: 650-952-3272
Web: www.jfc.com

CEO: Hiroyuki Enomoto
CFO: Takashi Ozawa
HR: -
FYE: March 31
Type: Subsidiary

JFC International is spreading the joy of Asian flavors. A subsidiary of Kikkoman Corporation, JFC International makes and markets about 15,000 Asian cooking items, under brand names such as Dynasty, Hapi, Hime, JFC, Nishiki, and Wel-Pac. Products of the California company include canned and dried seaweeds; frozen fruits and vegetables; crackers and other salty snacks, oils and vinegars; teas and canned coffees; rice, flours, and beans; and soy and other sauces. JFC also distributes Tanzan, Daishichi, and Tomoju sakes, Nikka whisky, and Kikkoman shochu.

	Annual Growth	3/03	3/04	3/05	3/06	3/07
Est. sales ($ mil.)	—	—	—	—	—	111.8
Employees	—	—	—	—	—	573

J.G. BOSWELL COMPANY

101 W. Walnut St.
Pasadena, CA 91103
Phone: 626-583-3000
Fax: 626-583-3090

CEO: James W. Boswell
CFO: -
HR: -
FYE: December 31
Type: Private

J.G. Boswell grows and mills cotton on some 150,000 acres in the San Joaquin Valley of California which it sells to textile manufacturers worldwide. The secretive company is the country's largest cotton producer and is said to be the largest privately held farming venture in the US. It also grows tomatoes, wheat, sunflowers, and safflowers. The company was established in 1921.

	Annual Growth	12/03	12/04	12/05	12/06	12/07
Est. sales ($ mil.)	—	—	—	—	—	150.0
Employees	—	—	—	—	—	2,000

An in-depth profile of this company is available to Hoover's Online members at hoovers.com.

867

J.H. COHN LLP

4 Becker Farm Rd.
Roseland, NJ 07068
Phone: 973-228-3500
Fax: 973-228-0330
Web: www.jhcohn.com

CEO: Thomas J. (Tom) Marino
CFO: –
HR: –
FYE: January 31
Type: Partnership

Cup or Cohn? To help you decide, here's some scoop on the latter: J.H. Cohn is one of the largest independently owned accounting and consulting firms in the New York area, offering business and personal accounting, auditing, planning, and consulting services. Through Cohn Benefits Consultants it designs, implements, and administers pension, profit sharing, and 401(k) plans, employee health and welfare programs, executive and deferred compensation, and wealth transfer and business succession plans. Its Cohn Executive Search helps recruit senior level management; Cohn Capital provides funding resources to middle-market companies. The company is part of international accounting network Nexia International.

	Annual Growth	1/03	1/04	1/05	1/06	1/07
Est. sales ($ mil.)	—	—	—	—	—	36.5
Employees	—	—	—	—	—	600

JIFFY LUBE INTERNATIONAL, INC.

700 Milam St.
Houston, TX 77002
Phone: 713-546-4100
Fax: –
Web: www.jiffylube.com

CEO: Luis Scoffone
CFO: Simone Noordegraaf
HR: Carl Reed
FYE: December 31
Type: Subsidiary

A leading oil change provider, Jiffy Lube doesn't expect to see its customers every day — every three months or 3,000 miles will be often enough. The company has more than 2,200 outlets in North America, about 80% of which are franchised; the rest are company-owned and operated. Besides oil changes, Jiffy Lube facilities provide maintenance services for air conditioning, fuel systems, transmissions, and other automotive systems. The company serves vehicle fleet operators as well as individual consumers. Jiffy Lube, which is a subsidiary of Shell Oil, was founded in 1979.

	Annual Growth	12/03	12/04	12/05	12/06	12/07
Est. sales ($ mil.)	—	—	—	—	—	150.0
Employees	—	—	—	—	—	3,000

JIMMY JOHN'S FRANCHISE, LLC

2212 Fox Dr.
Champaign, IL 61820
Phone: 217-356-9900
Fax: 217-359-2956
Web: www.jimmyjohns.com

CEO: James John (Jimmy) Liautaud
CFO: Pam Hersch
HR: –
FYE: December 31
Type: Private

For some sandwich fans, the company with two first names is the first choice for subs. Jimmy John's Franchise operates and franchises more than 550 quick service restaurants popular for their submarine sandwiches in about 35 states. The chain's menu features sub sandwiches made with a variety of toppings (and carrying such names as Big John, J.J. Gargantuan, and Vito) along with club sandwiches made with whole wheat or French bread. Jimmy John's locations typically offer limited seating as well as delivery service. Chairman "Jimmy" John Liautaud, who founded the company in 1983, controls the company.

	Annual Growth	12/03	12/04	12/05	12/06	12/07
Est. sales ($ mil.)	—	—	—	—	—	7.6
Employees	—	—	—	—	—	350

JLG INDUSTRIES, INC.

1 JLG Dr.
McConnellsburg, PA 17233
Phone: 717-485-5161
Fax: 717-485-6417
Web: www.jlg.com

CEO: Craig E. Paylor
CFO: Russell (Rusty) Rye
HR: –
FYE: July 31
Type: Subsidiary

JLG Industries gets its customers all worked up. The company's products include aerial work platforms, which are sold under the JLG, Manlift, and Toucan brands; telescopic material handlers (telehandlers), sold under brands such as JLG, SkyTrak, Lull, and Gradall; and related accessories. JLG sells through a network of distributors, as well as via the Internet and through integrated supply programs. Customers include rental companies and others in the industrial, commercial, institutional, and construction markets. JLG offers after-sales service and support and provides factory remanufacturing and repair programs, equipment rentals, and used equipment. JLG was acquired by Oshkosh Truck in 2006.

	Annual Growth	7/03	7/04	7/05	7/06	7/07
Est. sales ($ mil.)	—	—	—	—	—	473.2
Employees	—	—	—	—	—	4,088

JLL PARTNERS INC.

450 Lexington Ave., Ste. 3350
New York, NY 10017
Phone: 212-286-8600
Fax: 212-286-8626
Web: www.jllpartners.com

CEO: Paul S. Levy
CFO: Michael Schwartz
HR: Anita Arguirro
FYE: December 31
Type: Private

Jack and JLL went up the hill, to fetch a pail of . . . portfolio companies? JLL Partners (formerly Joseph, Littlejohn & Levy) is anything but child's play. The private equity firm invests in companies in a range of industries, including broadcasting, chemicals, consumer products, financial services, health care, and manufacturing. An active investor, it specializes in leveraged buyouts, restructurings, and turnaround situations. Portfolio companies include Motor Coach Industries International, IASIS Healthcare Corporation, and Ace Cash Express. Since its founding in 1988, JLL Partners has managed private equity funds totaling some $4 billion.

	Annual Growth	12/03	12/04	12/05	12/06	12/07
Est. sales ($ mil.)	—	—	—	—	—	259.2
Employees	—	—	—	—	—	2,635

JM FAMILY ENTERPRISES, INC.

100 Jim Moran Blvd.
Deerfield Beach, FL 33442
Phone: 954-429-2000
Fax: 954-429-2300
Web: www.jmfamily.com

CEO: Colin Brown
CFO: Mark S. Walter
HR: Amy Kropp
FYE: December 31
Type: Private

JM Family Enterprises is a family affair. JM, owned by the family of founder James Moran, is a holding company (Florida's second-largest private company, in fact, after Publix Super Markets) with about a dozen automotive-related businesses, including the world's largest-volume Lexus retailer, JM Lexus, in Margate, Florida. JM's major subsidiary, Southeast Toyota Distributors, is the nation's largest independent Toyota and Scion distribution franchise, delivering Toyota cars, trucks, and SUVs to more than 165 dealers in Alabama, Florida, Georgia, Texas, and Ohio. Following the recent retirement of chairwoman Pat Moran, daughter of the firm's founder, the company is run by CEO Colin Brown.

	Annual Growth	12/03	12/04	12/05	12/06	12/07
Sales ($ mil.)	13.9%	—	—	9,400.0	11,100.0	12,200.0
Employees	4.5%	—	—	4,300	4,600	4,700

J.M. HUBER CORPORATION

333 Thornall St.
Edison, NJ 08837
Phone: 732-549-8600
Fax: 732-549-7256
Web: www.huber.com

CEO: Peter T. Francis
CFO: Jeffrey (Jeff) Prosinski
HR: Niall Mulkeen
FYE: December 31
Type: Private

As great as toothpaste, paint, and tires may be, J.M. Huber claims to make them even better. Hard to believe, we know. Founded in 1890 by Joseph M. Huber and still owned by his heirs, the company makes specialty additives and minerals used to thicken and improve the cleaning properties of toothpaste, the brightness and gloss of paper, the strength and durability of rubber, and the flame retardant properties of wire and cable. The diverse company also makes oriented strand board (a plywood substitute), explores for and produces oil and gas, and provides technical and financial services. Huber also makes hydrocolloids (thickeners for gums) through subsidiary CP Kelco.

	Annual Growth	12/02	12/03	12/04	12/05	12/06
Sales ($ mil.)	15.9%	1,231.0	1,805.0	2,400.0	2,300.0	2,220.0
Employees	11.1%	3,278	4,850	5,000	5,000	5,000

THE J. M. SMUCKER COMPANY

NYSE: SJM

1 Strawberry Ln.
Orrville, OH 44667
Phone: 330-682-3000
Fax: 330-684-3370
Web: www.smucker.com

CEO: Timothy P. Smucker
CFO: Mark R. Belgya
HR: –
FYE: April 30
Type: Public

The J. M. Smucker Company is known for the sweet, sticky stuff, but hopes shortening and biscuits will fatten its bottom line. The #1 US producer of jams, jellies, and preserves also makes dessert toppings, juices, and specialty fruit spreads under names such as Laura Scudder's and Dickinson's. In order to diversify, the company added what have become market leaders — Jif peanut butter and Crisco oils and shortening. Smucker owns other brands as well. As the parent of International Multifoods, Smucker's roster also includes baking-goods brands Hungry Jack, Martha White, and Pillsbury, along with Pet evaporated milk.

	Annual Growth	4/04	4/05	4/06	4/07	4/08
Sales ($ mil.)	15.5%	1,417.0	2,043.9	2,154.7	2,148.0	2,524.8
Net income ($ mil.)	11.2%	111.3	129.1	143.4	157.2	170.4
Market value ($ mil.)	0.9%	2,624.1	2,904.8	2,235.8	3,169.5	2,724.6
Employees	(9.6%)	—	3,700	3,500	3,025	

JMAR TECHNOLOGIES, INC.

OTC: JMAR

10905 Technology Place
San Diego, CA 92127
Phone: 858-946-6800
Fax: 858-946-6899
Web: www.jmar.com

CEO: C. Neil Beer
CFO: Edward C. (Ned) Hall
HR: –
FYE: December 31
Type: Public

Like Steve Martin in his stand-up comedy days, JMAR Technologies likes to get small. The company is developing highly specialized systems that employ cutting-edge X-ray lithography (which JMAR calls collimated plasma lithography) to make advanced integrated circuits; development of these systems was mostly funded by grants from the US Army. JMAR has developed the technology into the diode-pumped modular solid state (DPSS) BriteLight laser for a variety of applications. The company also is addressing the biotechnology, homeland security, nanotechnology, and water quality fields. JMAR's top customers are the US government, which accounts for 36% of sales, and Lawrence Livermore National Laboratory (about 26%).

	Annual Growth	12/03	12/04	12/05	12/06	12/07
Sales ($ mil.)	(52.2%)	17.3	10.1	9.2	4.9	0.9
Net income ($ mil.)	—	(3.3)	(5.6)	(8.0)	(13.1)	(1.6)
Market value ($ mil.)	(58.2%)	65.0	54.6	46.6	7.1	2.0
Employees	(30.9%)	70	50	65	40	16

JMB REALTY CORP.

900 N. Michigan Ave., Ste. 1400
Chicago, IL 60611
Phone: 312-440-4800
Fax: 312-915-2310

CEO: H. Rigel Barber
CFO: Gailen J. Hull
HR: Gail Silver
FYE: December 31
Type: Private

JMB Realty wants to make State Street a great street again and bring glitter back to the Steel City's Golden Triangle. A major US commercial real estate investment firm, JMB Realty is heavily involved in ambitious retail developments in Chicago's Loop and downtown Pittsburgh. It owns, develops, and manages projects throughout North America, including regional malls, hotels (the Chicago Ritz-Carlton), planned communities, and office complexes. JMB Realty was founded in 1968 by Robert Judelson, Judd Malkin, and Neil Bluhm; Judelson (the "J" of JMB) is no longer involved with JMB, but Malkin remains as chairman and Bluhm is president. Bluhm also owns casino company Midwest Gaming and Entertainment.

	Annual Growth	12/03	12/04	12/05	12/06	12/07
Est. sales ($ mil.)	—	—	—	—	—	47.0
Employees	—	—	—	—	—	650

JMP GROUP INC.

NYSE: JMP

600 Montgomery St., Ste. 1100
San Francisco, CA 94111
Phone: 415-835-8900
Fax: 415-835-8910
Web: www.jmpg.com

CEO: Joseph A. Jolson
CFO: Thomas B. Kilian
HR: –
FYE: December 31
Type: Public

JMP Group wants to get the jump on the competition. The company provides equity research, trading, and investment banking services to small and mid-sized companies. It provides brokerage services to institutional clients while its investment banking arm provides assistance with mergers and acquisitions, divestitures, restructurings, and valuations. Its research department covers some 270 public companies. The company possesses expertise in the technology, health care, consumer goods, financial services, real estate, and business services sectors, with a special focus on financial services and homebuilding. The company went public in 2007.

	Annual Growth	12/03	12/04	12/05	12/06	12/07
Sales ($ mil.)	13.6%	58.8	74.8	94.7	86.8	97.9
Net income ($ mil.)	—	3.2	3.5	3.9	3.4	(105.2)
Market value ($ mil.)	—	—	—	—	—	174.9
Employees	0.0%	—	—	187	187	—

JO-ANN STORES, INC.

NYSE: JAS

5555 Darrow Rd.
Hudson, OH 44236
Phone: 330-656-2600
Fax: 330-463-6675
Web: www.joann.com

CEO: Darrell D. Webb
CFO: James C. Kerr
HR: Rosalind Thompson
FYE: Saturday nearest January 31
Type: Public

Jo-Ann Stores has sewn up the leadership of the fabric store market. The company is the #1 fabric retailer in the US, well ahead of Hancock Fabrics. Jo-Ann Stores sells fabrics and sewing supplies, craft materials, decorating and floral items, and seasonal goods. Most of the company's roughly 600 stores, located mainly in strip shopping centers, operate under the Jo-Ann Fabrics and Crafts name. The company also operates some 200 Jo-Ann superstores. Jo-Ann Stores has been closing shops in response to weak sales. Recognizing that sewing these days is more often a hobby than a necessity, the company is luring creative customers with arts and crafts and home-decorating items.

	Annual Growth	1/04	1/05	1/06	1/07	1/08
Sales ($ mil.)	2.0%	1,734.1	1,812.4	1,882.8	1,850.6	1,878.8
Net income ($ mil.)	(21.7%)	41.0	46.2	(23.0)	(1.9)	15.4
Market value ($ mil.)	(11.6%)	513.8	601.9	323.1	611.5	313.9
Employees	(5.0%)	—	—	24,060	22,280	21,707

An in-depth profile of this company is available to Hoover's Online members at hoovers.com.

869

JOCKEY INTERNATIONAL, INC.

2300 60th St.
Kenosha, WI 53141
Phone: 262-658-8111
Fax: 262-658-1812
Web: www.jockey.com

CEO: Debra S. Waller
CFO: Frank Schneider
HR: –
FYE: December 31
Type: Private

Jockey International has nothing to do with horses and everything to do with the classic men's brief (its invention). The company makes men's, women's, and children's underwear and loungewear. Its products are sold through several thousand department and specialty stores, such as Bloomingdale's and JCPenney. Jockey International licenses and distributes its apparel in more than 120 countries and holds numerous licensing agreements. Chairman and CEO Debra Waller and her family own the company. Jockey International was founded by Samuel Cooper in 1876 as a hosiery company intended to relieve lumberjacks of blisters and infections resulting from shoddy wool socks.

	Annual Growth	12/03	12/04	12/05	12/06	12/07
Est. sales ($ mil.)	—	—	—	—	—	213.7
Employees	—	—	—	—	—	5,000

JOE G. MALOOF & CO.

701 Comanche Rd., NE
Albuquerque, NM 87107
Phone: 505-243-2293
Fax: 505-768-1552

CEO: Tammy Maloof
CFO: –
HR: –
FYE: December 31
Type: Private

Joe G. Maloof & Co. is a wholesale beer and liquor distributor in New Mexico. The company distributes major brands including Miller and Heineken, Boston Beer, and more, as well as nonalcoholic beverages such as AriZona iced tea. In 2003, the company purchased the New Mexico Beverage Company, which boosted the company's sales levels to nearly half of all the cases of beer distributed in New Mexico. Maloof & Co. is owned by the Maloof family, which also owns California's Sacramento Kings professional basketball team, the Palms Casino in Las Vegas, and is a major shareholder in Wells Fargo Bank. The Maloof family's presence in New Mexico dates back to the 1890s, when Joe Maloof opened a small general-goods store.

	Annual Growth	12/03	12/04	12/05	12/06	12/07
Est. sales ($ mil.)	—	—	—	—	—	308.7
Employees	—	—	—	—	—	2,000

JOE'S JEANS INC.

NASDAQ (CM): JOEZ

5901 S. Eastern Ave.
Commerce, CA 90040
Phone: 323-837-3700
Fax: 323-837-3790
Web: joesjeans.com

CEO: Marc B. Crossman
CFO: Hamish S. Sandhu
HR: –
FYE: November 30
Type: Public

Joe's Jeans has jettisoned just about everything but its jeans. Following its acquisition of the Joe's brand from JD Holdings in 2007, the private-label apparel maker changed its name from Innovo Group to Joe's Jeans and revised its business plan to focus on building the Joe's and Joe's Jeans brands of denim and denim-related products. Joe's Jeans sells its apparel online at the Joe's Jeans Web site, and in the US and Europe through high-end retailers, such as Barneys and Bergdorf Goodman, and in specialty stores including Atrium and Fred Segal. Founded in 1987, the firm changed its name in October 2007 and adopted a new ticker, JOEZ.

	Annual Growth	11/03	11/04	11/05	11/06	11/07
Sales ($ mil.)	(6.8%)	83.1	104.7	108.6	46.6	62.8
Net income ($ mil.)	—	(8.3)	(9.6)	(16.4)	(9.3)	2.3
Market value ($ mil.)	(10.2%)	105.8	69.4	45.3	27.6	68.7
Employees	—	—	—	124	—	—

JOE'S SPORTS AND OUTDOOR

9805 Boeckman Rd.
Wilsonville, OR 97070
Phone: 503-682-2242
Fax: 503-682-7200
Web: www.joessports.com

CEO: Norman P. Daniels
CFO: Philip M. (Phil) Pepin
HR: Jill R. Inskeep
FYE: January 31
Type: Private

Joe's Sports and Outdoor (formerly G.I. Joe's) knows it's a jungle out there, and it has the gear to tame it. The sporting goods and outdoor supplies retailer has some 30 locations in Idaho, Oregon, and Washington. Its stores carry items for outdoor activities (camping, fishing, hunting, snowboarding, and snow and water skiing), including apparel and footwear. It also sells trailer hardware, storage racks, radar detectors, and other automotive gear to make your ride roadtrip-ready. Joe's also sells through catalogs and online. The firm outsourced its Internet operations to GSI Commerce in 2001. Founded as a war surplus store in 1952, the privately held company was sold to Gryphon Investors in early 2007.

	Annual Growth	1/03	1/04	1/05	1/06	1/07
Est. sales ($ mil.)	—	—	—	—	—	98.5
Employees	—	—	—	—	—	1,350

JOHN B. SANFILIPPO & SON, INC.

NASDAQ (GM): JBSS

1703 N. Randall Rd.
Elgin, IL 60123
Phone: 847-289-1800
Fax: 847-289-1843
Web: www.jbssinc.com

CEO: Jeffrey T. Sanfilippo
CFO: Michael J. Valentine
HR: –
FYE: Last Thursday in June
Type: Public

A bunch of nuts make money for John B. Sanfilippo & Son (JBSS). The company gets approximately 90% of its sales from peanuts, almonds, pecans, walnuts, cashews, and mixed nuts. JBSS processes, packages, and sells nuts under private labels and its own brands, which include Evon's, Fisher, Flavor Tree, Sunshine Country, and Texas Pride. It also produces and distributes other foods and snacks such as peanut butter, ice cream toppings, trail mixes, corn snacks, and candy. JBSS's products are sold worldwide to retail, wholesale, vending, industrial, foodservice, and government customers.

	Annual Growth	6/03	6/04	6/05	6/06	6/07
Sales ($ mil.)	6.6%	419.7	520.8	581.7	579.6	541.4
Net income ($ mil.)	—	15.0	22.6	14.5	(16.7)	(13.7)
Market value ($ mil.)	(1.5%)	95.0	206.8	186.8	105.5	89.6
Employees	—	—	—	1,740	—	—

JOHN CRANE INC.

6400 W. Oakton St.
Morton Grove, IL 60053
Phone: 847-967-2400
Fax: 847-967-2857
Web: www.johncrane.com

CEO: Robert (Bob) Wasson
CFO: Tom Whipple
HR: Andrea Skobel
FYE: July 31
Type: Subsidiary

John Crane seals the fate — or at least the openings — of lots of industrial equipment. The company, which is a subsidiary of UK-based Smiths Group plc, manufactures seals, packings, lubrication systems, and power transmission couplings. John Crane serves customers in the oil and gas, pharmaceutical, chemical, automotive, pulp and paper, mining, food and beverage, and power generation industries, among others. It has more than 25 offices across the US and a presence in more than 20 other countries throughout the world.

JOHN D. OIL AND GAS COMPANY

OTC: JDOG

8500 Station St., Ste. 345
Mentor, OH 44060
Phone: 440-255-6325
Fax: 440-205-8680

CEO: Richard M. Osborne
CFO: C. Jean Mihitsch
HR: C. Jean Mihitsch
FYE: December 31
Type: Public

John D. Oil and Gas (formerly Liberty Self-Stor) has shed its sheds in favor of oil and natural gas extraction. In 2005 the company moved to concentrate on drilling oil and gas wells in northeastern Ohio. In 2006 John D. Oil and Gas reported proved reserves of 1.4 billion cu. ft. of natural gas and 14,800 barrels of oil. Previously, the firm operated as a real estate investment trust (REIT); it acquired and developed self-storage facilities in Ohio and New York. The company sold all but two of its portfolio of 20 self-storage properties to U-Store-It for $33.7 million. The two facilities are located in Ohio. Chairman and CEO Richard Osborne owns 49% of the company.

	Annual Growth	12/03	12/04	12/05	12/06	12/07
Sales ($ mil.)	(12.0%)	5.5	0.5	0.6	1.9	3.3
Net income ($ mil.)	—	(0.1)	0.0	1.8	(2.0)	(0.9)
Market value ($ mil.)	30.8%	2.0	1.5	1.8	4.7	5.9
Employees	—	—	—	—	—	—

JOHN HANCOCK FINANCIAL SERVICES, INC.

601 Congress St.
Boston, MA 02210
Phone: 617-663-3000
Fax: 617-572-6015
Web: www.johnhancock.com

CEO: John D. DesPrez III
CFO: Charles A. Rizzo
HR: Diane M. Bean
FYE: December 31
Type: Subsidiary

For insurance, all you have to do is sign on the dotted line. John Hancock Financial Services offers insurance, investment products, investment management, and other services. Its insurance products include variable, universal, and term life. John Hancock also provides retirement savings products — annuities, mutual funds, and long-term care insurance. One of the US's largest investors, John Hancock offers institutional asset management services, providing clients with specialty funds in such industries as timber and agriculture. It has more than $220 billion under management. John Hancock is owned by Canada's Manulife.

JOHN J. KIRLIN, LLC

515 Dover Rd., Ste. 2100
Rockville, MD 20850
Phone: 301-424-3410
Fax: 301-738-8888
Web: www.jjkllc.com

CEO: Robert W. (Rob) Bacon
CFO: –
HR: –
FYE: December 31
Type: Private

John J. Kirlin isn't just blowing hot air. The mechanical contractor specializes in large heating, air-conditioning, and plumbing construction jobs. John J. Kirlin's clients represent a wide range of sectors, from sports and entertainment complexes to correctional facilities. The company in 1994 established a special projects division to handle federal medical and laboratory facilities renovation contracts; since that time medical and laboratory facilities work has become one of the company's specialties. John J. Kirlin operates through divisions in Florida, Maryland, and North Carolina. The company was founded in 1960.

	Annual Growth	12/03	12/04	12/05	12/06	12/07
Est. sales ($ mil.)	—	—	—	—	—	113.2
Employees	—	—	—	—	—	1,200

JOHN PAUL MITCHELL SYSTEMS

9701 Wilshire Blvd., Ste. 1205
Beverly Hills, CA 90212
Phone: 310-248-3888
Fax: 310-248-2780
Web: www.paulmitchell.com

CEO: John Paul (J. P.) DeJoria
CFO: Rick Battaglini
HR: –
FYE: December 31
Type: Private

From pomades to pompadours, John Paul Mitchell Systems offers its best to those who do 'dos. The #1 privately owned haircare firm in the US makes more than 90 different haircare products that sell in about 90,000 hair salons worldwide. John Paul Mitchell was founded in Hawaii in 1980 by John Paul "J. P." DeJoria and the late Paul Mitchell. The firm's signature white bottles with distinctive black lettering (because the founders couldn't afford color ink) have attracted the attention of counterfeiters on more than one occasion. Chairman and CEO DeJoria, a former gang member who sports a ponytail, beard, and an easy smile, is a vocal supporter for consumer-product safety.

JOHN Q. HAMMONS HOTELS & RESORTS, LLC

300 John Q. Hammons Pkwy., Ste. 900
Springfield, MO 65806
Phone: 417-864-4300
Fax: 417-873-3540
Web: www.jqhhotels.com

CEO: John Q. Hammons
CFO: Christopher Smith
HR: Kent S. Foster
FYE: Friday nearest December 31
Type: Private

John Q. Hammons Hotels & Resorts has several rooms with a view. The company owns and operates some 70 hotels in about 20 states. Most of its properties operate under the Embassy Suites, Holiday Inn, Marriott, Radisson, and Renaissance banners, and many are located near convention centers, universities, and corporate headquarters. The company was established in 1958. In 2005, the company's founder John Q. Hammons sold the firm to JQH Acquisition, a group that includes investor Jonathan Eilian and iStar Financial.

	Annual Growth	12/03	12/04	12/05	12/06	12/07
Est. sales ($ mil.)	—	—	—	—	—	430.8
Employees	—	—	—	—	—	9,000

JOHN T. MATHER MEMORIAL HOSPITAL

75 N. Country Rd.
Port Jefferson, NY 11777
Phone: 631-473-1320
Fax: 631-476-2792
Web: www.matherhospital.org/pages

CEO: Kenneth D. (Ken) Roberts
CFO: –
HR: –
FYE: December 31
Type: Not-for-profit

Looking out over the southern coast of the Long Island Sound, shipbuilder John T. Mather envisioned a legacy that would keep his community of Port Jefferson in good health. One year after his death in 1929, John T. Mather Memorial Hospital came to fruition. The not-for-profit hospital has some 250 beds and provides a variety of health care services to the residents of Port Jefferson and Suffolk county. It is a member of Long Island Health Network, a network of about a dozen hospitals all serving Long Island. Services include emergency care, orthopedics, occupational therapy, psychiatry, and radiology.

	Annual Growth	12/03	12/04	12/05	12/06	12/07
Est. sales ($ mil.)	—	—	—	—	—	168.6
Employees	—	—	—	—	—	1,700

An in-depth profile of this company is available to Hoover's Online members at hoovers.com.

JOHN WIELAND HOMES AND NEIGHBORHOODS, INC.

1950 Sullivan Rd.
Atlanta, GA 30337
Phone: 770-996-1400
Fax: 770-907-3485
Web: www.jwhomes.com

CEO: Terry Russell
CFO: Doug Ray
HR: John Wood
FYE: September 30
Type: Private

John Wieland Homes and Neighborhoods develops land and builds cluster homes, townhomes, and upscale single-family homes in the Southeast US. The company sells homes at prices ranging from $200,000 to more than $1 million. John Wieland Homes also provides remodeling and landscaping services. In cities where it builds, the company operates New Home Center design centers that provide interior and exterior design services. Wieland Financial Services offers mortgage lending to John Wieland Homes' customers and others. Chairman John Wieland owns his namesake firm.

JOHN WILEY & SONS, INC.

NYSE: JWA

111 River St., Ste. 2000
Hoboken, NJ 07030
Phone: 201-748-6000
Fax: 201-748-6088
Web: www.wiley.com

CEO: William J. (Will) Pesce
CFO: Ellis E. Cousens
HR: William J. Arlington
FYE: April 30
Type: Public

John Wiley & Sons might not adorn its books with shirtless hunks, but with such titles as *Patty's Industrial Hygiene and Toxicology*, who needs Fabio? The company publishes scientific, technical, and medical works, including journals and reference works such as *Current Protocols* and *Kirk-Othmer Encyclopedia of Chemical Technology*. It also produces professional and non-fiction trade books and is a leading publisher of college textbooks. The firm publishes the *For Dummies* how-to series and *CliffsNotes* study guides, as well. In addition to printed materials, John Wiley produces titles on CD-ROM and provides online access to some of its content. The Wiley family controls the majority of voting stock through a trust.

	Annual Growth	4/04	4/05	4/06	4/07	4/08
Sales ($ mil.)	16.0%	923.0	974.0	1,044.2	1,234.9	1,673.7
Net income ($ mil.)	13.5%	88.8	83.8	110.3	99.6	147.5
Market value ($ mil.)	9.9%	1,543.9	1,757.7	1,718.1	1,784.6	2,255.5
Employees	—	—	—	3,600	—	—

THE JOHNNY ROCKETS GROUP, INC.

25550 Commercentre Dr., Ste. 200
Lake Forest, CA 92630
Phone: 949-643-6100
Fax: 949-643-6200
Web: www.johnnyrockets.com

CEO: Lee Sanders
CFO: Rick Rosen
HR: Renee Atwood
FYE: April 30
Type: Private

Hep cats still hang out at Johnny Rockets restaurants, where U-shaped counters, padded booths, table-top jukeboxes, and white uniforms salute the classic American diner. The Johnny Rockets Group operates and franchises more than 200 restaurants in 30 states and a dozen other countries that specialize in such classic diner fare as hamburgers, malts, fries, and apple pie. About two-thirds of the locations are operated by franchisees. The chain was founded by Ronn Teitelbaum, who opened the first Johnny Rockets on Los Angeles' fashionable Melrose Avenue in 1986. The company was acquired by RedZone Capital, an investment fund led by Washington Redskins owner Dan Snyder, in 2007.

	Annual Growth	4/02	4/03	4/04	4/05	4/06
Sales ($ mil.)	35.0%	60.0	55.0	147.0	177.1	199.2
Employees	(9.1%)	2,200	2,000	—	—	—

JOHNS HOPKINS MEDICINE

720 Rutland Ave.
Baltimore, MD 21205
Phone: 410-955-5000
Fax: 410-955-4452
Web: www.hopkinsmedicine.org

CEO: Edward D. Miller Jr.
CFO: Richard A. (Rich) Grossi
HR: –
FYE: June 30
Type: Not-for-profit

Hopping John is a recipe for black-eyed peas; Johns Hopkins Medicine is a recipe for more than Baltimore health care. Consisting of Johns Hopkins University School of Medicine and the Johns Hopkins Health System, Johns Hopkins Medicine fosters the education of physicians and medical scientists as well as facilitating biomedical research, and the application of medical knowledge. The system utilizes the numerous resources offered by the hospitals and clinics in the Health System in addition to the academic offerings of the school. In 2007 Johns Hopkins Medicine announced it entered a five-year partnership agreement with Greater Baltimore Medical Center.

	Annual Growth	6/03	6/04	6/05	6/06	6/07
Est. sales ($ mil.)	—	—	—	—	—	11.1
Employees	—	—	—	—	—	7,000

JOHNS MANVILLE CORPORATION

717 17th St.
Denver, CO 80202
Phone: 303-978-2000
Fax: 303-978-2318
Web: www.jm.com

CEO: Todd Raba
CFO: Mary K. Rhinehart
HR: D. Fred Lowe
FYE: December 31
Type: Subsidiary

When you want to be insulated from the vagaries of life, turn to Johns Manville (JM). JM produces commercial and industrial roofing systems and formaldehyde-free fiberglass building insulation for the commercial and residential building industries. One of the nation's top makers of residential building insulation, JM also produces specialty insulation for OEMs in the transportation, acoustics, appliance, and HVAC industries. Other offerings include fire-protection systems, thermal and acoustical insulation, glass textile wallcoverings, and fibers and nonwoven mats used in roofing and flooring. JM operates more than 40 plants in China, Europe, and North America. Warren Buffett's Berkshire Hathaway owns JM.

	Annual Growth	12/03	12/04	12/05	12/06	12/07
Est. sales ($ mil.)	—	—	—	—	—	697.2
Employees	—	—	—	—	—	8,500

JOHNSON & JOHNSON

NYSE: JNJ

1 Johnson & Johnson Plaza
New Brunswick, NJ 08933
Phone: 732-524-0400
Fax: 732-214-0332
Web: www.jnj.com

CEO: William C. (Bill) Weldon
CFO: Dominic J. Caruso
HR: Kaye I. Foster-Cheek
FYE: Sunday nearest December 31
Type: Public

It's nearly impossible to get well without Johnson & Johnson (J&J). The diversified health care giant operates in three segments through more than 250 operating companies located in some 60 countries. Its Pharmaceuticals division makes drugs (including schizophrenia medication Risperdal and psoriasis drug Remicade) for an array of ailments, such as neurological conditions, blood disorders, autoimmune diseases, and pain. J&J's Medical Devices and Diagnostics division offers surgical equipment, monitoring devices, orthopedic products, and contact lenses, among other things. Its Consumer segment makes over-the-counter drugs and products for skin and hair care, oral care, first aid, and women's health.

	Annual Growth	12/03	12/04	12/05	12/06	12/07
Sales ($ mil.)	9.9%	41,862.0	47,348.0	50,514.0	53,324.0	61,095.0
Net income ($ mil.)	10.1%	7,197.0	8,509.0	10,411.0	11,053.0	10,576.0
Market value ($ mil.)	6.2%	150,238.8	188,422.3	178,766.1	191,011.0	191,374.2
Employees	5.7%	—	—	115,600	122,200	—

An in-depth profile of this company is available to Hoover's Online members at hoovers.com.

JOHNSON BROTHERS LIQUOR COMPANY

1999 Shepard Rd.
St. Paul, MN 55116
Phone: 651-649-5800
Fax: 651-649-5894
Web: www.johnsonbrothers.com

CEO: Lynn W. Johnson
CFO: Scott Belsaas
HR: Susan Ewers
FYE: December 31
Type: Private

The Johnson brothers have become winners by quenching the thirsts of "winers." Johnson Brothers Liquor Company is one of the country's top wine and liquor distributors. The company distributes mainly domestic brands of wines and distilled spirits throughout 12 mainly midwestern and southern US states, as well as in Nevada in the West, Rhode Island in the East, and in Hawaii (in paradise). Johnson Brothers is owned by the Johnson brothers — CEO Lynn Johnson and president Mitchell Johnson. In 2005 Dallas-based Glazer's Wholesale Drug Company purchased Johnson Brothers operations in Illinois. The sale resulted in the closing of the Johnson Brothers distribution center in Lincoln, Illinois.

JOHNSON CONTROLS, INC.

NYSE: JCI

5757 N. Green Bay Ave.
Milwaukee, WI 53209
Phone: 414-524-1200
Fax: 414-524-2077
Web: www.johnsoncontrols.com

CEO: Stephen A. Roell
CFO: R. Bruce McDonald
HR: Susan F. Davis
FYE: September 30
Type: Public

Johnson Controls wants to put you in the driver's seat. The company makes car seats, interior systems, and batteries, as well as environmental control systems for commercial buildings and HVAC systems. Interior components include consoles and instrument panels. Major OEM customers include GM, Daimler, Chrysler, and Ford. The battery unit makes car batteries for retailers such as Wal-Mart, Advance Auto, AutoZone, Pep Boys, and Sears. The building efficiency division makes, installs, and services control systems that monitor temperatures and detect fires in non-residential buildings. The unit also offers on-site facility management for buildings.

	Annual Growth	9/03	9/04	9/05	9/06	9/07
Sales ($ mil.)	11.2%	22,646.0	26,553.4	27,479.4	32,235.0	34,624.0
Net income ($ mil.)	16.4%	682.9	817.5	909.4	1,028.0	1,252.0
Market value ($ mil.)	101.4%	1,421.5	3,620.3	3,989.1	4,681.5	23,376.6
Employees	10.8%	—	—	114,000	136,000	140,000

JOHNSON FINANCIAL GROUP, INC.

555 Main St., Ste. 400
Racine, WI 53403
Phone: 262-619-2700
Fax: –
Web: www.johnsonbank.com

CEO: Richard A. Hansen
CFO: –
HR: Joan Iorio
FYE: December 31
Type: Private

Johnson Financial Group is the holding company for Johnson Bank, which has more than 40 offices in Wisconsin and nearly 10 more in Arizona and Nevada. In addition to standard banking fare such as checking and savings accounts and mortgages and loans, the company also offers insurance, investment, trust, and retirement services. The group also provides international and private banking services through Switzerland-based Banque Franck, Galland & Cie and TransOcean Bank & Trust in the Cayman Islands. Chairman Helen Johnson-Leopold and her family, which control consumer goods giant S.C. Johnson & Son, also own Johnson Financial Group, which was founded in 1970.

	Annual Growth	12/03	12/04	12/05	12/06	12/07
Est. sales ($ mil.)	—	—	—	—	—	263.8
Employees	—	—	—	—	—	1,233

JOHNSON MATTHEY INC.

435 Devon Park Dr., Ste. 600
Wayne, PA 19087
Phone: 610-971-3000
Fax: 610-971-3191
Web: www.jmusa.com

CEO: Neil A. P. Carson
CFO: –
HR: Anthony (Tony) Trifiletti
FYE: March 31
Type: Subsidiary

Johnson Matthey serves the precious metals, catalysts, coatings, and pharmaceutical businesses in the US. The company provides contract research and development for the pharmaceutical industry. Its Fine Chemicals and Catalysts unit manufactures active pharmaceutical ingredients and products for chemicals makers. The Precious Metals division sells platinum sheet, tube, and wire to jewelers in addition to refining precious metals. Johnson Matthey Fuel Cells is also based in the US. The company is the North American operations for the UK chemicals and catalysts maker Johnson Matthey.

	Annual Growth	3/03	3/04	3/05	3/06	3/07
Est. sales ($ mil.)	—	—	—	—	—	470.7
Employees	—	—	—	—	—	1,650

JOHNSON OUTDOORS INC.

NASDAQ (GM): JOUT

555 Main St.
Racine, WI 53403
Phone: 262-631-6600
Fax: 262-631-6601
Web: www.johnsonoutdoors.com

CEO: Helen P. Johnson-Leipold
CFO: David W. Johnson
HR: Sara Vidian
FYE: Friday nearest September 30
Type: Public

Johnson Outdoors keeps sports buffs from staying indoors. The company makes and sells camping and outdoor equipment (Eureka! tents and backpacks), diving gear (Scubapro and Uwatec masks, fins, snorkels, and tanks), trolling motors (Minn Kota), fishfinders (Humminbird), and watercraft (Old Town canoes, Dimension kayaks). Johnson Outdoors' marine electronics division accounts for nearly half of sales. The S.C. Johnson & Son family, including CEO Helen Johnson-Leipold, owns a majority stake in the company.

	Annual Growth	9/03	9/04	9/05	9/06	9/07
Sales ($ mil.)	8.1%	315.9	355.3	380.7	395.8	432.1
Net income ($ mil.)	14.2%	5.4	8.7	7.1	8.7	9.2
Market value ($ mil.)	14.6%	99.7	146.7	129.9	135.9	172.2
Employees	3.8%	—	—	1,300	1,300	1,400

JOHNSON PUBLISHING COMPANY, INC.

820 S. Michigan Ave.
Chicago, IL 60605
Phone: 312-322-9200
Fax: 312-322-0918
Web: www.johnsonpublishing.com

CEO: Linda Johnson Rice
CFO: Treka Owens
HR: Sheila Jenkins
FYE: December 31
Type: Private

Snubbed by advertisers when he founded his company 60 years ago, the late John Johnson pushed his magazine company to the front of the pack. Led by its flagship publication, *Ebony*, family-owned Johnson Publishing Company is a black-owned global publishing firm. The company also publishes *Jet* and operates the JPC Book Division. In addition, Johnson Publishing produces a line of cosmetics (Fashion Fair Cosmetics) marketed for African-American women, and each year it hosts the Ebony Fashion Fair, a traveling fashion show that raises money for scholarships and charities in cities across the US and Canada.

	Annual Growth	12/02	12/03	12/04	12/05	12/06
Sales ($ mil.)	1.9%	424.7	488.5	498.2	495.7	458.0
Employees	(14.7%)	2,076	2,000	—	1,707	1,100

An in-depth profile of this company is available to Hoover's Online members at hoovers.com.

JOHNSONDIVERSEY, INC.

8310 16th St.
Sturtevant, WI 53177
Phone: 262-631-4001
Fax: 262-631-4282
Web: www.johnsondiversey.com

CEO: Edward F. (Ed) Lonergan
CFO: Joseph F. (Joe) Smorada
HR: James W. (Jim) Larson
FYE: December 31
Type: Private

JohnsonDiversey is the industrial-strength version of S.C. Johnson & Son. Split off from the well-known private company in 1999, JohnsonDiversey provides professional commercial cleaning, hygiene, pest control, and food sanitation products to retailers, building service contractors, hospitality firms, and food service operators. It is the #2 global industrial and institutional cleaning products firm (behind Ecolab), selling its products in more than 170 countries, with Europe representing more than half of its sales. It operates across 33 manufacturing facilities located in almost 25 countries. The Johnson family controls two-thirds of the company; Unilever controls the rest.

	Annual Growth	12/02	12/03	12/04	12/05	12/06
Sales ($ mil.)	7.5%	2,196.4	2,947.8	3,169.3	3,310.3	2,928.3
Net income ($ mil.)	41.4%	29.6	24.1	13.7	(166.6)	118.3
Employees	(5.0%)	13,530	13,000	12,000	12,000	11,000

JOHNSONVILLE SAUSAGE, LLC

950 Woodlake Rd.
Kohler, WI 53044
Phone: 920-453-6900
Fax: 920-459-7824
Web: www.johnsonville.com

CEO: Ralph C. Stayer
CFO: Kris Dirkse
HR: Leah Glaub
FYE: December 31
Type: Private

This is a company you ought to link up with. Johnsonville Sausage makes a wide array of top-selling fresh, precooked, and smoked sausage products, including bratwurst, breakfast sausage, and Italian sausage. Its link and bulk meats are sold primarily through retail grocery stores, but the company also operates an online store that offers gift packs, cheeses, breads and rolls, and the company's cookbook, ephemera in addition to sausage. Johnsonville sausage is available in about 40 countries worldwide. In the US, Johnsonville products can be found on the menu at more than 4,000 McDonald's restaurants.

	Annual Growth	12/03	12/04	12/05	12/06	12/07
Est. sales ($ mil.)	—	—	—	—	—	125.4
Employees	—	—	—	—	—	750

JOINT COMMISSION ON ACCREDITATION OF HEALTHCARE ORGANIZATIONS

1 Renaissance Blvd.
Oakbrook Terrace, IL 60181
Phone: 630-792-5000
Fax: 630-792-5005
Web: www.jcaho.org

CEO: Mark R. Chassin
CFO: Paige A. Rodgers
HR: Ruth Metsch
FYE: December 31
Type: Not-for-profit

Its not really about joints, per se, unless they are aching and in need of repair. The Joint Commission on Accreditation of Healthcare Organizations is a not-for-profit group that provides accreditation services to more than 15,000 health care organizations in the US. Its Board of Commissioners includes physicians, medical doctors, nurses, consumers, and administrators. They evaluate hospitals, health care networks, nursing homes and other long term care facilities, clinical laboratories, and other health-related groups. Founded in 1951, The Joint Commission also hands out the Disease-Specific Care Certification to disease management companies.

	Annual Growth	12/03	12/04	12/05	12/06	12/07
Est. sales ($ mil.)	—	—	—	—	—	137.5
Employees	—	—	—	—	—	1,100

JONES APPAREL GROUP, INC.

NYSE: JNY

1411 Broadway
New York, NY 10018
Phone: 212-642-3860
Fax: 215-785-1795
Web: www.jny.com

CEO: Wesley R. (Wes) Card
CFO: John T. McClain
HR: Aida Tejero-DeColli
FYE: December 31
Type: Public

While some are busy keeping up with the Joneses, Jones Apparel Group is too busy taking stock in its portfolio of brands to take notice. It provides a wide range of women's and men's clothing and shoes. Brands include Jones New York and Evan-Picone, among many others. Subsidiary Nine West Group designs shoes under names Easy Spirit, Enzo Angiolini, Bandolino, and Gloria Vanderbilt. Gloria Vanderbilt and l.e.i. design twill and denim casualwear, swimwear, and accessories, among other items. In 2007 the company sold luxury fashion retailer Barneys New York (acquired in 2004) to focus on its other brands. Jones currently owns and operates about 1,030 stores.

	Annual Growth	12/03	12/04	12/05	12/06	12/07
Sales ($ mil.)	(3.2%)	4,375.3	4,649.7	5,074.2	4,742.8	3,848.5
Net income ($ mil.)	(1.4%)	328.6	301.8	274.3	(144.1)	311.1
Market value ($ mil.)	(25.6%)	4,446.0	4,468.9	3,560.4	3,607.1	1,363.9
Employees	(32.3%)	—	—	18,430	16,485	8,450

THE JONES COMPANY, INC.

215 Pendleton St.
Waycross, GA 31501
Phone: 912-285-4011
Fax: 912-285-0811
Web: www.jonescoinc.com

CEO: James C. (Jimmy) Jones III
CFO: Greg Higginson
HR: –
FYE: December 31
Type: Private

After more than a quarter of a century, The Jones Company has proven it isn't just a flash in the pan. The company operates more than 165 Flash Foods convenience stores and 20 Branded Foods outlets in Georgia and north Florida. Its Fuel South subsidiary supplies those stores with fuel. Other subsidiaries of The Jones Company include Distribution South, a wholesale grocery supply business, and Walker-Jones auto dealership, which sells new and used cars (Buick, Chevrolet, Honda, and Toyota). Founded in 1979 by J. C. Jones Jr. and his father, the company is still owned and run by the Jones family.

	Annual Growth	12/03	12/04	12/05	12/06	12/07
Est. sales ($ mil.)	—	—	—	—	—	860.6
Employees	—	—	—	—	—	1,800

JONES DAY

North Point, 901 Lakeside Ave.
Cleveland, OH 44114
Phone: 216-586-3939
Fax: 216-579-0212
Web: www.jonesday.com

CEO: Stephen J. Brogan
CFO: –
HR: Kristin G. Edwards
FYE: December 31
Type: Partnership

Legal leviathan Jones Day ranks as one of the world's largest law firms, providing counsel to about half of the FORTUNE 500 companies. It has some 2,200 attorneys in about 30 offices worldwide. Outside the US, Jones Day has offices in the Asia/Pacific region and in Europe. The firm's practice areas include capital markets, government regulation, intellectual property, real estate, and tax. Jones Day has counted Bridgestone/Firestone, General Motors, IBM, RJR Nabisco, and Texas Instruments among its clients. The firm traces its roots to the Cleveland law partnership founded by Edwin Blandin and William Rice in 1893.

	Annual Growth	12/02	12/03	12/04	12/05	12/06
Est. sales ($ mil.)	1.9%	—	—	—	1,285.0	1,310.0
Employees	2.6%	—	—	—	4,850	4,977

THE JONES FINANCIAL COMPANIES, L.L.L.P.

12555 Manchester Rd.
Des Peres, MO 63131
Phone: 314-515-2000
Fax: 314-515-2622
Web: www.edwardjones.com

CEO: James D. (Jim) Weddle
CFO: Steven (Steve) Novik
HR: Ken Dude
FYE: December 31
Type: Partnership

This isn't your father's broker. Well, maybe it is. The Jones Financial Companies is the parent of Edward Jones, an investment brokerage network catering to individual investors. Most of its clients are retirees and small-business owners in rural communities and suburbs. The "Wal-Mart of Wall Street" has thousands of satellite-linked offices in all 50 states plus Canada and the UK. Brokers preach a conservative buy-and-hold approach, offering relatively low-risk investment vehicles such as government bonds, blue-chip stocks, and high-quality mutual funds. The company also sells insurance and engages in investment banking, underwriting and distributing securities for corporate and municipal clients.

	Annual Growth	12/02	12/03	12/04	12/05	12/06
Sales ($ mil.)	11.6%	2,270.0	2,538.9	2,891.4	3,190.4	3,517.8
Employees	4.8%	28,469	29,200	31,400	32,400	34,300

JONES LANG LASALLE INCORPORATED

NYSE: JLL

200 E. Randolph Dr.
Chicago, IL 60601
Phone: 312-782-5800
Fax: 312-782-4339
Web: www.joneslanglasalle.com

CEO: Colin Dyer
CFO: Lauralee E. Martin
HR: Nazneen Razi
FYE: December 31
Type: Public

Borders mean little to Jones Lang LaSalle. The giant real estate services company helps its customers buy, sell, and manage property in more than 60 countries on five continents. It offers property and project management, leasing, and tenant representation. Jones Lang LaSalle's financial services include investment banking and corporate and real estate financing. The firm also offers real estate investment management services to pension funds, insurance firms, and money managers. It has nearly $50 billion in assets under management and a total portfolio of about 1.2 billion sq. ft. worldwide.

	Annual Growth	12/03	12/04	12/05	12/06	12/07
Sales ($ mil.)	29.3%	949.8	1,167.0	1,390.6	2,013.6	2,652.1
Net income ($ mil.)	63.5%	36.1	64.2	103.7	176.4	257.8
Market value ($ mil.)	36.1%	658.4	1,243.6	1,772.3	3,372.8	2,257.4
Employees	21.9%	—	—	22,000	25,500	32,700

JONES SODA CO.

NASDAQ (CM): JSDA

234 9th Ave. North
Seattle, WA 98109
Phone: 206-624-3357
Fax: 206-624-6857
Web: www.jonessoda.com

CEO: Stephen C. (Steve) Jones
CFO: Hassan N. Natha
HR: Nancy Bucher
FYE: December 31
Type: Public

There's nothing average about Jones Soda. The company manufactures brightly colored beverages with wacky flavors like Fufu Berry and Blue Bubble Gum. Seasonal offerings include Turkey and Gravy for Thanksgiving and Chocolate Fudge for Valentine's Day. It regularly discontinues flavors and adds new ones. Jones, which distributes its drinks through retailers such as Barnes & Noble cafés and Starbucks, also customizes its beverage labels with photos submitted by customers. The company sells a line of noncarbonated beverages (Jones Naturals), with added ginseng, zinc, and other ingredients, and citrus-flavored energy drinks under the Jones Energy and WhoopAss labels, and bottled tea (Jones Organics).

	Annual Growth	12/03	12/04	12/05	12/06	12/07
Sales ($ mil.)	18.9%	20.1	27.5	34.2	39.7	40.2
Net income ($ mil.)	—	0.3	1.3	1.3	4.6	(11.6)
Market value ($ mil.)	46.9%	42.0	72.3	116.7	315.7	195.3
Employees	21.2%	38	51	52	67	82

JORDACHE ENTERPRISES, INC.

1400 Broadway, 15th Fl.
New York, NY 10018
Phone: 212-944-1330
Fax: 212-239-0063
Web: www.jordachecorporate.com

CEO: Joseph (Joe) Nakash
CFO: Joe Taylor
HR: –
FYE: December 31
Type: Private

It was the 1980s: Robin Williams wore rainbow suspenders, Tom Hanks wore a dress, and if you were hot, you had the Jordache look. Fast-forward more than two decades: Jordache Enterprises offers jeans, apparel, and accessories (shoes, purses) primarily for teens, mostly through decidedly non-designer retailers, such as Wal-Mart. It also licenses the Jordache name for eyewear and luggage. Jordache makes jeans under license for Gasoline, Sasson, KIKIT, FUBU, and U.S. Polo Association. Its premium Jordache Vintage line is sold at specialty stores. In 1977 a New York City store, owned by brothers and Israeli immigrants Joe, Ralph, and Avi Nakash, was burned and looted; insurance enabled them to launch Jordache.

	Annual Growth	12/03	12/04	12/05	12/06	12/07
Est. sales ($ mil.)	—	—	—	—	—	193.4
Employees	—	—	—	—	—	8,000

THE JORDAN COMPANY, L.P.

767 5th Ave., 48th Fl.
New York, NY 10153
Phone: 212-572-0800
Fax: 212-755-5263
Web: www.thejordancompany.com

CEO: John W. (Jay) Jordan II
CFO: Paul R. Rodzevik
HR: –
FYE: December 31
Type: Private

The Jordan Company takes the long view. The investment company and its affiliate The Jordan/Zalaznick Capital Company are long-term investors that seek out profitable established firms and work with management to use infused capital to strengthen the acquisition. The Jordan Company holds stakes in some 15 firms; it has invested in more than 300 firms since its founding in 1974 and has approximately $5 billion worth of committed capital. Target industries include manufacturing, health care supplies, consumer products, and insurance. The Jordan Company invests between $50 million and $400 million in each transaction.

	Annual Growth	12/03	12/04	12/05	12/06	12/07
Est. sales ($ mil.)	—	—	—	—	—	30.0
Employees	—	—	—	—	—	410

JORDAN INDUSTRIES, INC.

Arbor Lake Centre, Ste. 550, 1751 Lake Cook Rd.
Deerfield, IL 60015
Phone: 847-945-5591
Fax: 847-945-0198
Web: www.jordanindustries.com

CEO: John W. (Jay) Jordan II
CFO: Lisa M. Ondrula
HR: –
FYE: December 31
Type: Private

Jordan Industries operates four business units: Beemak (point-of-purchase plastic displays), Sate-Lite (safety reflectors for bicycles and commercial vehicles), Deflecto (assorted plastics products), and GramTel USA (IT disaster recovery infrastructure). Late in 2006 Jordan sold its Kinetek division (electric motors and gears) to The Resolute Fund for about $442 million. The company has also exited three other businesses — Valmark (promotional products), Welcome Home (gift items), and a catalytic converter remanufacturing business. Director David Zalaznick owns 20% of the company; chairman and CEO John W. Jordan II owns 18%.

	Annual Growth	12/02	12/03	12/04	12/05	12/06
Sales ($ mil.)	(22.7%)	720.0	720.0	723.3	729.5	256.7
Net income ($ mil.)	—	(64.4)	(33.1)	(20.1)	(6.0)	163.4
Employees	(33.7%)	7,200	6,605	6,500	6,363	1,393

An in-depth profile of this company is available to Hoover's Online members at hoovers.com.

JORDAN'S FURNITURE, INC.

450 Revolutionary Dr.
Taunton, MA 02718
Phone: 508-828-4000
Fax: 508-580-8953
Web: www.jordans.com

CEO: Eliot Tatelman
CFO: David Stavros
HR: Jill Franklin
FYE: December 31
Type: Subsidiary

Barry and Eliot Tatelman, furniture icons renowned for their quirky television ad campaigns and unorthodox business tactics, have built a furniture fortress around what they term "shoppertainment." Jordan's Furniture operates four stores in Massachusetts and New Hampshire that sell furniture for the bedroom, dining room, living room, and home office, as well as rugs, mattresses, and more. Taking furniture sales to the next level, stores feature a 48-seat flight-simulator, a replica of New Orleans' Bourbon Street (complete with Mardi Gras beads), and two Imax theaters. Founded in 1918 by the Tatelman brothers' grandfather, Samuel, Jordan's Furniture is owned by billionaire Warren Buffett's Berkshire Hathaway.

	Annual Growth	12/03	12/04	12/05	12/06	12/07
Est. sales ($ mil.)	—	—	—	—	—	174.7
Employees	—	—	—	—	—	1,600

JOS. A. BANK CLOTHIERS, INC.

NASDAQ (GS): JOSB

500 Hanover Pike
Hampstead, MD 21074
Phone: 410-239-2700
Fax: 410-239-5700
Web: www.josbank.com

CEO: Robert N. Wildrick
CFO: David E. Ullman
HR: Robert B. Hensley
FYE: Saturday nearest January 31
Type: Public

When casual Fridays put a wrinkle in the starched selling philosophy of Jos. A. Bank Clothiers, the company dressed down. Although it is still best known for making tailored clothing for the professional man, including suits, sport coats, dress shirts, and pants, it has added casual wear suitable for those dress-down Fridays and weekends. It also debuted the David Leadbetter line of golf wear. The company sells its Jos. A. Bank clothes and a few shoe brands through its catalogs, Web site, and some 420 company-owned or franchised stores in about 42 states and the District of Columbia. For corporate customers, it offers a credit card that provides users with discounts.

	Annual Growth	1/04	1/05	1/06	1/07	1/08
Sales ($ mil.)	19.1%	299.7	372.5	464.6	546.4	604.0
Net income ($ mil.)	31.9%	16.6	24.5	35.3	43.2	50.2
Market value ($ mil.)	39.3%	131.7	307.1	693.8	564.6	495.4
Employees	16.6%	—	—	2,995	3,375	4,069

JOSTENS, INC.

3601 Minnesota Dr.
Minneapolis, MN 55435
Phone: 952-830-3300
Fax: 952-830-3293
Web: www.jostens.com

CEO: Timothy M. Larson
CFO: Marjorie J. (Marge) Brown
HR: –
FYE: Saturday nearest December 31
Type: Subsidiary

Are you *sure* you want to remember high school? If so, look to Jostens, the leading US producer of yearbooks and class rings. Class rings are sold on school campuses and through bookstores, retail jewelers, and the Web, while Jostens' sports rings commemorate professional sports champions (it has made 27 Super Bowl rings). Other graduation products include diplomas, announcements, caps, and gowns. The company sold its school photography business in mid-2006. Founded in 1897, Jostens was sold to a unit of CSFB in 2003. The next year Jostens was recapitalized and became part of a newly created publishing and marketing services company, Visant, co-owned by an affiliate of CSFB and Kohlberg Kravis Roberts.

	Annual Growth	12/03	12/04	12/05	12/06	12/07
Est. sales ($ mil.)	—	—	—	—	—	850.0
Employees	—	—	—	—	—	6,700

JOURNAL COMMUNICATIONS, INC.

NYSE: JRN

333 W. State St.
Milwaukee, WI 53203
Phone: 414-224-2000
Fax: 414-224-2469
Web: www.jc.com

CEO: Steven J. Smith
CFO: Paul M. Bonaiuto
HR: –
FYE: December 31
Type: Public

You might say this company chronicles the news in Milwaukee. Journal Communications is a leading diversified media company with operations including newspapers, radio, and television. The company's publishing business is anchored by its flagship paper the *Milwaukee Journal Sentinel*, a leading daily newspaper with a circulation of 220,000. Its Journal Community Publishing Group also runs about 50 community newspapers and shoppers serving markets in Wisconsin and Florida. In addition, Journal Communications owns 35 radio stations and about a dozen TV stations in more than 10 states through its Journal Broadcast unit. It also operates several Web sites in conjunction with its media properties.

	Annual Growth	12/03	12/04	12/05	12/06	12/07
Sales ($ mil.)	(7.6%)	798.3	820.8	764.5	671.8	582.7
Net income ($ mil.)	13.3%	66.8	78.5	66.2	64.4	110.1
Market value ($ mil.)	2.6%	374.1	494.6	586.0	607.1	414.5
Employees	(9.5%)	—	—	5,500	350	4,500

JOURNAL REGISTER COMPANY

Pink Sheets: JRCO

790 Township Line Rd., Ste. 300
Yardley, PA 19067
Phone: 215-504-4200
Fax: –
Web: www.journalregister.com

CEO: James W. Hall
CFO: Julie A. Beck
HR: –
FYE: December 31
Type: Public

You might say this company publishes all the local news that fits. Journal Register Company is a leading newspaper publisher with about 20 daily papers covering small towns and suburban areas in a half dozen states, including Pennsylvania, Michigan, and New York. Its dailies, including the flagship *New Haven Register* (Connecticut), boast a combined circulation of more than 500,000. In addition, the company publishes about 320 non-daily papers and operates more than 220 Web sites offering news, employment listings, and other regional information. Journal Register also operates four commercial printing plants in three states.

	Annual Growth	12/03	12/04	12/05	12/06	12/07
Sales ($ mil.)	3.4%	406.0	475.7	556.6	506.1	463.2
Net income ($ mil.)	—	72.0	116.5	46.9	(6.2)	(102.5)
Employees	—	—	—	6,000	—	—

JOY GLOBAL INC.

NASDAQ (GS): JOYG

100 E. Wisconsin Ave., Ste. 2780
Milwaukee, WI 53202
Phone: 414-319-8500
Fax: 414-319-8520
Web: www.joyglobal.com

CEO: Michael W. Sutherlin
CFO: James H. (Jim) Tate
HR: Dennis R. Winkleman
FYE: Saturday nearest October 31
Type: Public

Joy Global is pretty peppy for a company that builds equipment destined to spend the majority of its life down in a hole. The company makes heavy equipment for the mining industry through two subsidiaries. Its Joy Mining Machinery subsidiary makes underground coal-mining equipment that includes armored face conveyors, roof supports, long-wall shearers, and shuttle cars. Subsidiary P&H Mining Equipment makes draglines, blasthole drills, and other equipment used by surface miners; it also provides parts and services to mines through its P&H MinePro Services distribution group. Joy Global operates manufacturing and service facilities worldwide.

	Annual Growth	10/03	10/04	10/05	10/06	10/07
Sales ($ mil.)	20.3%	1,216.0	1,432.2	1,927.5	2,401.7	2,547.3
Net income ($ mil.)	97.2%	18.5	55.3	148.1	416.4	279.8
Market value ($ mil.)	94.7%	420.6	799.6	3,671.7	4,805.1	6,045.3
Employees	12.7%	—	—	7,900	8,900	—

An in-depth profile of this company is available to Hoover's Online members at hoovers.com.

JOYCE LESLIE, INC.

135 W. Commercial Ave.
Moonachie, NJ 07074
Phone: 201-804-7800
Fax: 877-253-5060
Web: www.joyceleslie.com

CEO: Joyce Segal
CFO: –
HR: –
FYE: January 31
Type: Private

Club-hoppers (and high schoolers) hoping to look like Paris Hilton without spending like her do their shopping at Joyce Leslie. The northeastern retail chain specializes in trendy and inexpensive women's and junior's clothing aimed primarily at teens and tweens. It operates nearly 50 shops filled with high-fashion knockoffs in Connecticut, New Jersey, New York, and Pennsylvania. Joyce Leslie is named for the daughter of the company's founder and former chairman, Julius Gewirtz, who died in 2006. Gewirtz founded the chain, which originally sold women's dresses, in Brooklyn in 1945.

	Annual Growth	1/03	1/04	1/05	1/06	1/07
Est. sales ($ mil.)	—	—	—	—	—	89.0
Employees	—	—	—	—	—	900

JPI

600 E. Las Colinas Blvd., Ste. 1800
Irving, TX 75039
Phone: 972-556-1700
Fax: 972-556-3889
Web: www.jpi.com

CEO: J. Frank Miller III
CFO: Frank B. Schubert Jr.
HR: –
FYE: December 31
Type: Private

JPI is looking for a new way to spell apartments. One of the largest luxury apartment developers in the US, JPI also manages multifamily residential communities in the US and Canada. The company typically buys underperforming properties in desirable areas and upgrades them with such features as parking garages, fitness centers, and 24-hour concierge services. JPI's 24 student complexes (many of which have "Jefferson" in their name) include game rooms and fitness centers. Founded in 1976 as Jefferson Properties, Inc., JPI was a subsidiary of Southland Financial until the early 1990s when Hunt Realty invested in it.

JPMORGAN CHASE & CO.

NYSE: JPM

270 Park Ave.
New York, NY 10017
Phone: 212-270-6000
Fax: 212-270-1648
Web: www.jpmorganchase.com

CEO: James (Jamie) Dimon
CFO: Michael J. Cavanagh
HR: John F. Bradley
FYE: December 31
Type: Public

JPMorgan Chase was born with a silver spoon in its mouth, but it hasn't let that stop it. The #3 financial services firm in the US, behind Citigroup and Bank of America, is keen on its retail operations (more than 3,000 bank branches and growing) and is also among the nation's top mortgage lenders, automobile loan writers, and credit card issuers. It also boasts formidable investment banking and asset management operations. The company's subsidiaries include the prestigious JPMorgan Private Bank and institutional investment manager JPMorgan Asset Management (with $1.6 trillion in assets under management). In 2008 JPMorgan Chase bought Bear Stearns.

	Annual Growth	12/03	12/04	12/05	12/06	12/07
Assets ($ mil.)	19.3%	770,912.0	1,157,248.0	1,198,942.0	1,351,520.0	1,562,147.0
Net income ($ mil.)	23.0%	6,719.0	4,466.0	8,483.0	14,444.0	15,365.0
Market value ($ mil.)	18.3%	75,025.4	138,727.0	138,386.7	167,199.3	146,986.3
Employees	3.4%	—	—	168,847	174,360	180,667

JPS INDUSTRIES, INC.

Pink Sheets: JPST

55 Beattie Place, Ste. 1510
Greenville, SC 29601
Phone: 864-239-3900
Fax: 864-271-9939
Web: www.jpselastomerics.com

CEO: Michael L. Fulbright
CFO: Charles R. (Chuck) Tutterow
HR: –
FYE: Saturday nearest October 31
Type: Public

JPS Industries' products can be found surfing the waves and saving lives. The company's subsidiary, JPS Composite Materials, makes high-strength fiberglass and synthetic fabrics for the aeronautics, military, and other industries. Products include body armor, insulation, and even surfboards. JPS Industries is the holding company for JPS Elastomerics, which operates Stevens Geomembranes, Stevens Urethane, and Stevens Roofing Systems. In an apparent effort to focus on its composite materials and urethane products, the company announced in 2008 that it would sell Steven Geomembranes and Steven Urethane to Dow Building Solutions, a part of The Dow Chemical Company.

	Annual Growth	10/03	10/04	10/05	10/06	10/07
Sales ($ mil.)	28.1%	—	—	—	171.5	219.7
Net income ($ mil.)	200.0%	—	—	—	6.0	18.0
Employees	—	—	—	—	—	—

J.R. SIMPLOT COMPANY

999 Main St., Ste. 1300
Boise, ID 83702
Phone: 208-336-2110
Fax: 208-389-7515
Web: www.simplot.com

CEO: Lawrence S. (Larry) Hlobik
CFO: Annette Elg
HR: Erin Nuxoll
FYE: August 31
Type: Private

J.R. Simplot hopes you'll have fries with that. Potato potentate J. R. "Jack" Simplot simply shook hands with McDonald's pioneer Ray Kroc in the mid-1960s, and his company's french fry sales have sizzled ever since. The company still remains the major french fry supplier for McDonald's and supplies Burger King, KFC, and Wendy's, as well. It produces more than 3 billion pounds of french fries and hash browns annually, making it one of the world's largest processors of frozen potatoes. The company sells its potato products mainly to food service customers under Simplot and private-label brands.

	Annual Growth	8/02	8/03	8/04	8/05	8/06
Sales ($ mil.)	2.4%	3,000.0	3,100.0	3,100.0	3,100.0	3,300.0
Employees	(6.3%)	13,000	12,000	11,500	10,200	10,000

JTH TAX, INC.

1716 Corporate Landing Pkwy.
Virginia Beach, VA 23454
Phone: 757-493-8855
Fax: 800-880-6432
Web: www.libertytax.com

CEO: John T. Hewitt
CFO: Mark Baumgartner
HR: –
FYE: April 30
Type: Private

JTH Tax wants to free you from those tax preparation shackles. Doing business as Liberty Tax Service, it is now the third-largest tax chain (behind H&R Block and Jackson Hewitt). Liberty Tax Service provides computerized tax preparation services to clients through its approximately 2,500 offices throughout the US and in Canada. The company's acquisition of E Tax Services in 2007 expanded its online self-filing services, a fast-growing part of the tax preparation sector. Liberty Tax Service also offers tax-preparation courses, IRS forms, tax calculators, and related programs and services.

	Annual Growth	4/03	4/04	4/05	4/06	4/07
Est. sales ($ mil.)	—	—	—	—	—	66.2
Employees	—	—	—	—	—	125

An in-depth profile of this company is available to Hoover's Online members at hoovers.com.

877

THE JUDGE GROUP, INC.

300 Conshohocken State Rd., Ste. 300
West Conshohocken, PA 19428
Phone: 610-667-7700
Fax: 610-667-1058
Web: www.judge.com

CEO: Martin E. Judge Jr.
CFO: Rob G. Alessandrini
HR: –
FYE: December 31
Type: Private

If your business requires staffing, technology consulting, or training services, The Judge Group will be predisposed to render a verdict in your favor. The company offers temporary and permanent employee placement services in a wide variety of service and manufacturing sectors. It specializes in technology staffing. The company's technology consulting services address such areas as enterprise content management and strategy. Through its Berkeley unit, the company offers training for IT-related and other professional functions. The Judge Group operates from a network of about 30 offices throughout the US. CEO Martin Judge founded the company in 1970.

	Annual Growth	12/03	12/04	12/05	12/06	12/07
Est. sales ($ mil.)	—	—	—	—	—	129.8
Employees	—	—	—	—	—	570

JUJAMCYN THEATERS

246 W. 44th St.
New York, NY 10036
Phone: 212-840-8181
Fax: –

CEO: Rocco Landesman
CFO: –
HR: –
FYE: June 30
Type: Private

Jujamcyn Theaters screws in a lot of the light bulbs on the Great White Way. The company owns and operates five theaters in New York City that house plays and musicals such as the Tony award-winning show *The Producers* and Pulitzer Prize winner *Angels in America*. Its theaters include the St. James and the August Wilson Theatre (formerly the Virginia). Jujamcyn — along with The Shubert Organization and the Nederlander Producing Company — controls most Broadway productions. The company is owned by president Rocco Landesman, also a creative producer, who bought it in 2005 for about $30 million. Jujamcyn was founded in the 1970s by James Binger. It's named after his children, Ju[dith], Jam[es], and Cyn[thia].

	Annual Growth	6/03	6/04	6/05	6/06	6/07
Est. sales ($ mil.)	—	—	—	—	—	24.1
Employees	—	—	—	—	—	473

JUNIATA VALLEY FINANCIAL CORP.

OTC: JUVF

Bridge and Main Streets
Mifflintown, PA 17059
Phone: 717-436-8211
Fax: 717-436-7551
Web: www.jvbonline.com

CEO: Francis J. Evanitsky
CFO: JoAnn N. McMinn
HR: Pamela S. Eberman
FYE: December 31
Type: Public

Need a bank in Pennsylvania? Juniata Valley Financial may be the place for you. The institution is the holding company for Juniata Valley Bank, which serves central Pennsylvania from more than a dozen banking locations. The bank, which has been doing business since 1867, offers standard deposit products and services, including checking and savings accounts, money market accounts, IRAs, and CDs. It also provides credit card services and originates a variety of consumer and business loans. Consumer loans make up more than 70% of its loan portfolio. Additionally, Juniata Valley Bank sells insurance and investment products.

	Annual Growth	12/03	12/04	12/05	12/06	12/07
Assets ($ mil.)	2.0%	387.8	396.8	410.8	415.9	420.1
Net income ($ mil.)	(1.3%)	5.7	5.8	4.6	5.0	5.4
Market value ($ mil.)	23.1%	39.4	47.9	108.1	93.8	90.4
Employees	—	—	—	—	—	150

JUNIPER GROUP, INC.

OTC: JUNIE

20283 State Rd. 400, Ste. 400
Boca Raton, FL 33498
Phone: 561-482-9327
Fax: –

CEO: Vlado P. Hreljanovic
CFO: Vlado P. Hreljanovic
HR: –
FYE: December 31
Type: Public

The Juniper Group corporate tree has two main branches. The company provides technology services through Juniper Services and film distribution through Juniper Entertainment. The technology services branch concentrates on the installation of wireless and cable broadband network infrastructure for residential and business customers under contract from mobile communications and cable services providers, as well as from equipment vendors. The company's other business has withered on the vine and has ceased operations; Juniper Communications had provided installation support to Cablevision but had difficulties collecting monies owed it by the cable system operator.

	Annual Growth	12/03	12/04	12/05	12/06	12/07
Sales ($ mil.)	12.2%	1.2	1.3	0.6	4.7	1.9
Net income ($ mil.)	—	(3.0)	(2.2)	(4.9)	(1.7)	(9.8)
Employees	—	—	—	—	—	—

JUNIPER NETWORKS, INC.

NASDAQ (GS): JNPR

1194 N. Mathilda Ave.
Sunnyvale, CA 94089
Phone: 408-745-2000
Fax: 408-745-2100
Web: www.juniper.net

CEO: Scott G. Kriens
CFO: Robyn M. Denholm
HR: Steven Rice
FYE: December 31
Type: Public

Juniper Networks has managed to grow in a landscape dominated by Cisco. The company designs and sells network infrastructure for private and public access networks. Customers use its products to securely deploy and manage services and applications across IP networks. The company's product portfolio includes routers, network traffic management software, virtual private network (VPN) and firewall devices, data center and WAN acceleration tools, intrusion detection and prevention (IDP) systems, and support services. Juniper sells directly and through resellers to network service providers, enterprises, government agencies, and schools.

	Annual Growth	12/03	12/04	12/05	12/06	12/07
Sales ($ mil.)	41.8%	701.4	1,336.0	2,064.0	2,303.6	2,836.1
Net income ($ mil.)	74.2%	39.2	135.8	354.0	(1,001.4)	360.8
Market value ($ mil.)	24.2%	7,290.3	14,696.9	12,671.8	10,781.3	17,357.5
Employees	19.1%	—	—	4,145	4,833	5,879

JUNO LIGHTING, INC.

1300 S. Wolf Rd.
Des Plaines, IL 60017
Phone: 847-827-9880
Fax: 847-296-4056
Web: www.junolighting.com

CEO: Amelia (Amy) Huntington
CFO: John Vitacco
HR: Edward Laginess
FYE: November 30
Type: Subsidiary

Sharing its name with Jupiter's wife, Juno Lighting can bask in the light of its own glow. Juno Lighting makes light fixtures for commercial, institutional, and residential buildings under nine brand names. It also makes showcase lighting fixtures, fiber-optic lighting products, and emergency and exit lighting signs based on LED technology. Juno's other products include recessed lighting and track-lighting systems. The company also sells under-cabinet and casework lighting products under the Juno and Danalite brands. Juno counts contractors and remodelers as its chief customers. Founded in 1976, the company is a subsidiary of Schneider Electric SA.

	Annual Growth	11/03	11/04	11/05	11/06	11/07
Est. sales ($ mil.)	—	—	—	—	—	103.3
Employees	—	—	—	—	—	1,000

JUPITER MARINE INTERNATIONAL HOLDINGS

Pink Sheets: JMIH

1103 12th Avenue East
Palmetto, FL 34221
Phone: 941-729-5000
Fax: 941-729-5005
Web: www.jupitermarine.com

CEO: Carl Herndon Sr.
CFO: Lawrence S. Tierney
HR: Carisa Albrecht
FYE: Saturday nearest July 31
Type: Public

Women are from Venus, men are from Mars, and fishing boats are from Jupiter, as in Jupiter Marine International Holdings, Inc. The company designs and manufactures offshore sport fishing boats that range in length from 29 feet to 38 feet and in price from about $140,000 to $270,000. Jupiter Marine offers open center console and forward-seating center console models, as well as a model with a cabin. It manufacutures all of its boats at its plant in Palmetto, Florida, after closing a second facility in Ft. Lauderdale. President and CEO Carl Herndon owns about 53% of the company.

	Annual Growth	7/03	7/04	7/05	7/06	7/07
Sales ($ mil.)	13.1%	9.3	10.3	11.5	15.1	15.2
Net income ($ mil.)	—	0.3	0.4	0.4	0.2	(1.4)
Employees	—	—	—	—	120	—

JUPITERMEDIA CORPORATION

NASDAQ (GS): JUPM

23 Old Kings Hwy. South
Darien, CT 06820
Phone: 203-662-2800
Fax: 203-655-4686
Web: www.jupitermedia.com

CEO: Alan M. Meckler
CFO: Donald J. O'Neill
HR: Michelle Burnham
FYE: December 31
Type: Public

Owner of Internet.com, Jupitermedia isn't the homepage for the entire Web, but it does put lots of information within reach of your mouse. Targeting IT, business, and creative professionals, the company's JupiterOnlineMedia unit publishes industry news, information, and resources through five online networks, including Internet.com and EarthWeb.com (for IT professionals), DevX.com (for developers), and Mediabistro.com and Graphics.com (for media professionals). Jupitermedia provides online images through Jupiterimages, which sells subscriptions to its libraries. The firm has been expanding its rapidly growing digital asset collection through acquisitions.

	Annual Growth	12/03	12/04	12/05	12/06	12/07
Sales ($ mil.)	31.4%	47.0	71.9	124.6	137.5	140.3
Net income ($ mil.)	—	1.4	15.7	78.4	13.1	(82.3)
Market value ($ mil.)	3.8%	118.2	768.4	515.4	282.3	137.4
Employees	6.1%	—	—	639	678	—

JUST BORN, INC.

1300 Stefko Blvd.
Bethlehem, PA 18017
Phone: 610-867-7568
Fax: 610-867-9931
Web: www.justborn.com

CEO: Ross Born
CFO: Ronald J. (Ron) Izewski
HR: Mark McLaughlin
FYE: December 31
Type: Private

Just Born gave birth to tiny marshmallow treats for all occasions. The family-owned and -operated company makes the popular Easter candy Marshmallow Peeps — those little chicklettes that appear in Easter baskets everywhere. Peeps come in five standard colors (blue, lavender, pink, white, and yellow). The company makes snowmen and tree Peeps for Christmas; cats, ghosts, and pumpkins for Halloween; and hearts for Valentine's Day. And not forgetting dieting Peep lovers, Just Born makes sugar-free versions of its little critters. Moviegoers will recognize the company's Hot Tamales and Mike & Ike brands. Other candy treats include Just Born Jelly Beans, Teenee Beanee Gourmet jelly beans, Peanut Chews, and Zours.

	Annual Growth	12/03	12/04	12/05	12/06	12/07
Est. sales ($ mil.)	—	—	—	—	—	49.6
Employees	—	—	—	—	—	550

JUSTIN BRANDS, INC.

610 W. Daggett Ave.
Fort Worth, TX 76104
Phone: 817-332-4385
Fax: 817-348-2037
Web: www.justinboots.com

CEO: Randy Watson
CFO: Herbert (Herb) Beckwith
HR: Donna Lasater
FYE: December 31
Type: Subsidiary

Once a subsidiary of Justin Industries, Justin Brands sauntered away and returned to its cowboy roots. The footwear firm's four brand names include Justin, Nocona, Chippewa, and Tony Lama. Justin Brands is better known as a manufacturer of western boots, but it also makes and markets work, safety, and sports footwear. Western boots come in a variety of exotic leathers, including lizard and ostrich. The company also caters to cowboys and fillies who want to learn more about the West and its culture. It publishes books on Western history and art and Native American culture through its Northland Publishing unit. Warren Buffett's Berkshire Hathaway owns the company.

	Annual Growth	12/03	12/04	12/05	12/06	12/07
Est. sales ($ mil.)	—	—	—	—	—	54.0
Employees	—	—	—	—	—	1,000

J.W. CHILDS ASSOCIATES, L.P.

111 Huntington Ave., Ste. 2900
Boston, MA 02199
Phone: 617-753-1100
Fax: 617-753-1101
Web: www.jwchilds.com

CEO: John W. Childs
CFO: Allan A. Dowds
HR: –
FYE: December 31
Type: Partnership

J.W. Childs Associates (JWC) makes private equity investment look like mere child's play. The firm, created by four former Thomas H. Lee partners, conducts friendly leveraged buyouts (LBOs) and recapitalizations of middle-market growth companies. Upon takeover of a firm, JWC typically installs management teams that include individuals with a stake in the buyout. The firm, which has been active since 1995, pursues deals mostly in North America and Asia. It focuses on the consumer products, specialty retail, asset management, and health care sectors. JWC's portfolio includes menswear line Joseph Abboud, NutraSweet, Mattress Firm, and Sunny Delight Beverages.

	Annual Growth	12/03	12/04	12/05	12/06	12/07
Est. sales ($ mil.)	—	—	—	—	—	897.6
Employees	—	—	—	—	—	9,100

J. W. MAYS, INC.

NASDAQ (CM): MAYS

9 Bond St.
Brooklyn, NY 11201
Phone: 718-624-7400
Fax: 718-935-0378

CEO: Lloyd J. Shulman
CFO: Mark S. Greenblatt
HR: –
FYE: July 31
Type: Public

J. W. Mays could sell you some property in Brooklyn, but it's office buildings, not a bridge. The company owns and leases about 10 properties in and around New York City — mostly former MAYS department stores — and a warehouse in central Ohio. J. W. Mays leases its properties to retail stores, restaurants, offices, and other enterprises. The department store chain, founded in 1924 by Russian immigrant Joe Weinstein, closed in 1989 when management realized the New York real estate it occupied was worth more than its struggling discount retail business. Weinstein's descendants, including CEO Lloyd Shulman, control more than half of the company, although relations among the heirs have not always been harmonious.

	Annual Growth	7/03	7/04	7/05	7/06	7/07
Sales ($ mil.)	8.4%	13.2	14.0	12.9	13.7	18.2
Net income ($ mil.)	17.5%	1.1	1.1	0.3	1.4	2.1
Market value ($ mil.)	14.8%	26.3	26.3	32.3	36.3	45.7
Employees				31		

An in-depth profile of this company is available to Hoover's Online members at hoovers.com.

879

JWM PARTNERS, LLC

1 E. Weaver St.
Greenwich, CT 06831
Phone: 203-552-5400
Fax: 203-552-5422

CEO: John W. Meriwether
CFO: –
HR: –
FYE: December 31
Type: Private

John W. Meriwether (the JWM in JWM Partners) hopes his latest venture is more long-term than his last. A pioneer in quantitative and model-based investing, the former Salomon Brothers vice chairman founded hedge fund JWM Partners barely a year after his previous co-managed fund, the heavily leveraged Long-Term Capital Management, crashed spectacularly in 1998. It received a $3.6 billion bailout organized by the Federal Reserve Bank of New York. JWM Partners has about $3 billion under management.

	Annual Growth	12/03	12/04	12/05	12/06	12/07
Est. sales ($ mil.)	—	—	—	—	—	44.0
Employees	—	—	—	—	—	51

JWT

466 Lexington Ave.
New York, NY 10017
Phone: 212-210-7000
Fax: 212-210-7770
Web: www.jwt.com

CEO: Bob Jeffrey
CFO: Lewis J. (Lew) Trencher
HR: –
FYE: December 31
Type: Subsidiary

If you call on this advertising firm, don't bother asking for J. Walter. JWT, formerly J. Walter Thompson, is the leading advertising agency in the US and one of the largest in the world (along with McCann Worldgroup and BBDO Worldwide). It provides creative ad development, campaign management, and strategic planning services to such clients as Ford, Kimberly-Clark, and Shell. JWT also offers brand development and specialized marketing services, including customer relationship marketing, event marketing, and sponsorships. The firm operates in almost 90 countries through more than 300 offices. Founded in 1877, it is one of the flagship agency networks of UK-based media conglomerate WPP Group.

K12 INC.

NYSE Arca: LRN

2300 Corporate Park Dr.
Herndon, VA 20171
Phone: 703-483-7000
Fax: 703-483-7330
Web: www.k12.com

CEO: Ronald J. (Ron) Packard
CFO: John F. Baule
HR: Nancy Hauge
FYE: June 30
Type: Public

K12 isn't a missing element from the periodic table, but it could help struggling kids learn the periodic table. The "virtual public school" company offers online educational programs for children in kindergarten through 12th grade (K-12). Products include full-time online public schools (in about a dozen states), course material and product sales directly to parents, and individualized supplemental programs offered through traditional public schools. K12's programs are targeted at kids who underperform in public school, aren't safe in public school, or can't attend public school because of travel issues, disabilities, or because they are athletes or performers. CEO Ron Packard founded the company in 2000.

	Annual Growth	6/03	6/04	6/05	6/06	6/07
Sales ($ mil.)	25.3%	—	71.4	85.3	116.9	140.6
Net income ($ mil.)	—	—	(7.4)	(3.5)	1.4	3.9
Employees	14.0%	—	—	—	558	636

KADANT INC.

NYSE: KAI

1 Technology Park Dr.
Westford, MA 01886
Phone: 978-776-2000
Fax: 978-635-1593
Web: www.kadant.com

CEO: William A. Rainville
CFO: Thomas M. O'Brien
HR: –
FYE: Saturday after December 31
Type: Public

Seeking to hear the "Ka-ching" of increased profits, Kadant makes recycling equipment that turns wastepaper into white and brown grades of recycled paper. The company's main products are stock-preparation equipment, including pulping and trash removal systems; cleaning, screening, and de-inking systems; accessories to clean the rolls of paper-making equipment and to cut and remove sheets of paper; and equipment that recycles water from pulp slurry and processes reusable fiber. Formerly a subsidiary, Kadant was spun off from Thermo Electron (now Thermo Fisher Scientific) in 2001. The company gets more than half of its sales in the US.

	Annual Growth	12/03	12/04	12/05	12/06	12/07
Sales ($ mil.)	15.8%	203.5	195.0	243.7	341.6	366.5
Net income ($ mil.)	17.8%	11.8	0.6	6.9	17.1	22.7
Market value ($ mil.)	11.3%	294.0	285.3	250.7	341.0	450.5
Employees	18.9%	1,000	1,000	1,400	2,000	2,000

▥ KAHALA CORP.

9311 E. Via de Ventura, Ste. 104
Scottsdale, AZ 85258
Phone: 480-362-4800
Fax: –
Web: www.kahalacorp.com

CEO: Kevin Blackwell
CFO: Walt Schultz
HR: –
FYE: December 31
Type: Private

Life is a quick-service beach at Kahala Corp. The company is a leading multi-franchise operator with more than a dozen restaurant brands encompassing more than 4,600 locations across the US and in a small number of other countries. Its flagship brands include ice cream purveyor Cold Stone Creamery, the Taco Time Mexican fast-food chain, and Blimpie (the #3 sub sandwich chain behind Subway and Quiznos). Most of Kahala's locations are typically found in malls, airports, and other high-traffic areas. The company is controlled by chairman Kevin Blackwell and former CFO David Guarino.

	Annual Growth	12/02	12/03	12/04	12/05	12/06
Sales ($ mil.)	—	—	—	—	—	1,100.0
Employees	—	—	—	—	—	260

KAIRE HOLDINGS INCORPORATED

OTC: KAIH

7700 Irvine Center Dr., Ste. 870
Irvine, CA 92618
Phone: 949-861-3560
Fax: –

CEO: Steven R. Westlund
CFO: Steven R. Westlund
HR: –
FYE: December 31
Type: Public

Moving items from point A to point B is the only thing Kaire Holdings seems consistent on. In early 2007 the company ditched its prescription medicine delivery business and acquired H&H Glass, a glass packaging distribution business. Previous endeavors have included selling herbal supplements online and marketing diagnostic imaging products. Its last business consisted of delivering prescription medications and other medical products to residents of assisted-living facilities in California through its Effective Health subsidiary. Kaire Holdings used a small retail pharmacy as its base of operations and served about 15 small to midsized facilities.

	Annual Growth	12/03	12/04	12/05	12/06	12/07
Sales ($ mil.)	—	—	—	—	—	18.9
Net income ($ mil.)	—	—	—	—	—	(0.3)
Employees	—	—	—	—	—	—

KAISER ALUMINUM CORPORATION

NASDAQ (GM): KALU

27422 Portola Pkwy., Ste. 350
Foothill Ranch, CA 92610
Phone: 949-614-1740
Fax: 949-614-1930
Web: www.kaiseral.com

CEO: Jack A. Hockema
CFO: Daniel J. Rinkenberger
HR: James E. McAuliffe
FYE: December 31
Type: Public

Kaiser Aluminum went on a diet, slimmed down considerably, and now operates just 11 fabricated products manufacturing plants in the US and Canada and has minority ownership of one aluminum smelting facility in the UK (Anglesey Aluminum). Kaiser's main customers are in the aerospace, engineering, and transportation markets. Following a 2002 filing for Chapter 11 bankruptcy protection, the company sold its bauxite and alumina mining businesses and closed up shop in its commodities marketing unit. Kaiser emerged from Chapter 11 in mid-2006. Since then, the company has initiated several expansion projects at its aluminum fabrication facilities, increasing production capacity.

	Annual Growth	12/03	12/04	12/05	12/06	12/07
Sales ($ mil.)	2.5%	1,365.3	942.4	1,089.7	1,357.3	1,504.5
Net income ($ mil.)	—	(788.3)	(746.8)	(753.7)	3,167.4	101.0
Market value ($ mil.)	42.4%	—	—	—	1,149.0	1,635.8
Employees	—	—	—	—	—	2,600

KAISER GROUP HOLDINGS, INC.

OTC: KGHI

9300 Lee Hwy.
Fairfax, VA 22031
Phone: 703-934-3665
Fax: 703-934-3199
Web: www.kaisergroup.com

CEO: Douglas W. McMinn
CFO: Nicholas Burakow
HR: –
FYE: December 31
Type: Public

The primary asset of Kaiser Group Holdings is its 50% stake in Kaiser-Hill Company, a joint venture with CH2M HILL that was formed to clean up the US Department of Energy's Rocky Flats site, a former nuclear weapons production facility in Colorado (completed ahead of schedule in 2005). Subsidiary Kaiser Analytical Management Services provides analytical management services in areas such as health and safety and environmental and waste management and accounted for all of the company's revenue in 2006, but the company expects no future revenues from this unit. Kaiser Group also has an insurance unit (MS Builders Insurance Company), but it has not written any policies. Kaiser Group deregistered its stock in 2008.

	Annual Growth	12/03	12/04	12/05	12/06	12/07
Sales ($ mil.)	—	—	1.0	1.8	0.2	0.0
Net income ($ mil.)	—	—	7.4	45.3	(2.4)	(0.7)
Employees	—	—	—	—	4	—

KAISER PERMANENTE

1 Kaiser Plaza
Oakland, CA 94612
Phone: 510-271-5800
Fax: 510-267-7524
Web: www.kaiserpermanente.org

CEO: George C. Halvorson
CFO: Kathy Lancaster
HR: –
FYE: December 31
Type: Not-for-profit

Kaiser Permanente hopes to be a permanent leader in US health care. The not-for-profit entity is among the largest integrated health care systems in the US. The company offers health care services through a network of nearly 14,000 physicians belonging to Permanente Medical Groups; 32 medical centers and more than 415 medical offices that form the Kaiser Foundation Hospitals; and the Kaiser Foundation Health Plan, which covers some 8.7 million lives (most of which are in California). Kaiser Permanente is primarily bicoastal, active in California, Colorado, Georgia, Hawaii, Maryland, Ohio, Oregon, Virginia, Washington, and Washington, DC.

	Annual Growth	12/03	12/04	12/05	12/06	12/07
Sales ($ mil.)	10.6%	25,300.0	28,000.0	31,100.0	34,400.0	37,800.0
Employees	2.1%	147,000	140,356	148,884	156,853	159,700

KAISER-FRANCIS OIL COMPANY

6733 S. Yale Ave.
Tulsa, OK 74136
Phone: 918-494-0000
Fax: 918-491-4694
Web: www.kfoc.net

CEO: George B. Kaiser
CFO: Don Millican
HR: Gwen Johnson
FYE: June 30
Type: Private

King of the Tulsa oil patch, oil and gas exploration and production independent Kaiser-Francis Oil Company buys, sells, and develops oil and gas properties, primarily in Arkansas, Colorado, Kansas, Nebraska, New Mexico, North Dakota, Oklahoma, Texas, and Wyoming. In 2005 and 2006 the company teamed up with fellow Tulsa-based energy firm SemGas LP to build the Wyckoff Gas Storage facility in Steuben County, New York. The underground natural gas storage project provides 6 billion cu. ft. of working gas storage and is capable of delivering up to 250 million cu. ft. of natural gas a day to local distribution companies and other gas users. Local billionaire George Kaiser owns and manages Kaiser-Francis Oil.

	Annual Growth	6/03	6/04	6/05	6/06	6/07
Est. sales ($ mil.)	—	—	—	—	—	247.1
Employees	—	—	—	—	—	2,067

KAJIMA U.S.A. INC.

395 W. Passaic St.
Rochelle Park, NJ 07662
Phone: 201-518-2100
Fax: 201-518-1539
Web: www.kajimausa.com

CEO: Keisuke (KC) Koshijima
CFO: Kiyoshi Sugasawa
HR: –
FYE: March 31
Type: Subsidiary

US businesses are saying *konichiwa* to Kajima U.S.A. The planning, design, construction, and real estate development company serves such clients as Costco, Federal Express, Hitachi, Mazda, and Mitsubishi Motors. Kajima U.S.A. is the North American arm of Kajima, one of the world's largest global contractors. Kajima U.S.A., established in 1961, has about 20 subsidiaries including The Austin Company, KBD Group, Hawaiian Dredging Construction, Anglebrook Golf Club, and KUD International. In 2008 Kajima U.S.A. increased its presence in the Southeast by acquiring construction services firm Batson-Cook.

	Annual Growth	3/03	3/04	3/05	3/06	3/07
Est. sales ($ mil.)	—	—	—	—	—	1,065.1
Employees	—	—	—	—	—	488

KALEIDA HEALTH

100 High St.
Buffalo, NY 14203
Phone: 716-859-5600
Fax: 716-859-3323
Web: www.kaleidahealth.org

CEO: James R. (Jim) Kaskie
CFO: Joseph (Joe) Kessler
HR: David R. Whipple
FYE: December 31
Type: Not-for-profit

Kaleida Health tries to catch you if you fall somewhere in the Snow Belt. Operating five acute-care facilities with some 1,200 beds total, Kaleida Health serves the residents of western New York. The health system's hospitals are Buffalo General Hospital, The Women & Children's Hospital of Buffalo, DeGraff Memorial Hospital, Millard Fillmore Gates Circle Hospital, and Millard Fillmore Suburban Hospital. Primary care needs are met through a network of community and school-based clinics. Kaleida Health also operates four skilled nursing care facilities and provides home health care. To help train future medical professionals, Buffalo General Hospital is a teaching affiliate of the State University of New York.

	Annual Growth	12/02	12/03	12/04	12/05	12/06
Sales ($ mil.)	6.7%	—	824.0	871.6	935.2	1,000.0
Net income ($ mil.)	192.0%	—	2.0	7.5	26.1	49.8
Employees	(0.8%)	—	9,724	10,000	9,500	9,500

An in-depth profile of this company is available to Hoover's Online members at hoovers.com.

881

KALIL BOTTLING CO.

931 S. Highland Ave.
Tucson, AZ 85719
Phone: 520-624-1788
Fax: 520-623-6662
Web: www.kalilbottling.com

CEO: George Kalil
CFO: William (Bill) Ourand
HR: –
FYE: December 31
Type: Private

Kalil Bottling has been all in the family since 1948. President George Kalil grew up learning the business from his father and grandfather. Today, he oversees a company that serves Arizona and parts of Colorado, New Mexico, and Texas, supplying them with a variety of beverages. Among the beverages are AriZona, Arrowhead, and Vernors, along with more widely known brands, such as Gatorade, Big Red, 7UP, and Snapple (from Dr Pepper Snapple Group), and SoBe. The company operates from its production facility in Tucson, Arizona; and four distribution warehouses — Tucson, Phoenix, and Flagstaff, Arizona; and one in El Paso, Texas.

	Annual Growth	12/03	12/04	12/05	12/06	12/07
Est. sales ($ mil.)	—	—	—	—	—	32.0
Employees	—	—	—	—	—	800

KALITTA AIR, LLC

818 Willow Run Airport
Ypsilanti, MI 48198
Phone: 734-484-0088
Fax: 734-484-3640
Web: www.kalittaair.com

CEO: Conrad (Connie) Kalitta
CFO: Greg Strzynski
HR: –
FYE: December 31
Type: Private

Although its freighters might not be as fast off the line as the drag-racers once driven by its namesake, cargo carrier Kalitta Air is quick enough for its customers. The company offers both scheduled and chartered transportation services with a fleet of more than 15 Boeing 747 freighters, which have been used to transport cargo ranging from delicate medical equipment to heavy machinery to livestock to US mail. Drag-racing legend Conrad Kalitta owns the company, which began operations in 2000. Kalitta, who also owns an aircraft leasing company, entered the aviation business in 1967 to transport parts for auto manufacturers and suppliers.

	Annual Growth	12/03	12/04	12/05	12/06	12/07
Est. sales ($ mil.)	—	—	—	—	—	495.0
Employees	—	—	—	—	—	1,000

KAMAN CORPORATION

NASDAQ (GM): KAMN

1332 Blue Hills Ave.
Bloomfield, CT 06002
Phone: 860-243-7100
Fax: 860-243-6365
Web: www.kaman.com

CEO: Neal J. Keating
CFO: Robert M. Garneau
HR: Lowell J. Hill
FYE: December 31
Type: Public

Kaman makes military helicopters, but it's the distribution of industrial products that makes the company fly. The company distributes industrial products such as bearings, power transmission, and motion control products through more than 200 locations in North America. Subsidiary Kaman Aerospace makes aerospace components and produces the SH-2G maritime helicopter and the K-MAX aerial truck (designed for repetitive lifting) helicopter. Kaman also distributes Ovation, Hamer, and Takamine guitars, as well as percussion instruments and accessories, through its music division, which it has sold to Fender.

	Annual Growth	12/03	12/04	12/05	12/06	12/07
Sales ($ mil.)	5.0%	894.5	995.2	1,101.2	1,206.2	1,086.0
Net income ($ mil.)	30.3%	19.4	(11.8)	13.0	31.8	55.9
Market value ($ mil.)	34.9%	279.6	279.5	470.7	540.6	926.9
Employees	(1.3%)	—	—	3,712	3,906	3,618

KANA SOFTWARE, INC.

OTC: KANA

181 Constitution Dr.
Menlo Park, CA 94025
Phone: 650-614-8300
Fax: 650-614-8301
Web: www.kana.com

CEO: Michael S. (Mike) Fields
CFO: Michael J. (Mike) Shannahan
HR: –
FYE: December 31
Type: Public

Kana Software provides customer service management software used to manage a variety of client interactions. The company's software includes applications that manage call centers, automate marketing campaigns, and analyze customer data. The Web-based software ties together multiple channels of customer interaction, including online contact and collaboration, e-mail, and telephone. The company also provides consulting, technical support, and training services.

	Annual Growth	12/03	12/04	12/05	12/06	12/07
Sales ($ mil.)	(0.1%)	61.0	48.9	43.1	54.0	60.8
Net income ($ mil.)	—	(21.2)	(21.8)	(18.0)	(2.4)	(8.0)
Market value ($ mil.)	0.8%	95.8	55.3	45.5	114.0	98.9
Employees	24.3%	—	—	—	181	225

K&F INDUSTRIES HOLDINGS, INC.

50 Main Street
White Plains, NY 10606
Phone: 914-448-2700
Fax: 914-448-2719
Web: www.kandfindustries.com

CEO: Kenneth M. Schwartz
CFO: Dirkson R. Charles
HR: –
FYE: December 31
Type: Subsidiary

K&F Industries Holdings wants to bring aviation to a screeching halt. Through its subsidiaries, the company makes brake products and fuel tanks for commercial, military, and general aviation aircraft. Its Aircraft Braking Systems unit, which accounts for more than 80% of K&F's sales, makes wheels, carbon- and steel-based brakes, and brake control systems. Aircraft Braking Systems' products are sold mainly as replacement parts. K&F's other main subsidiary, Engineered Fabrics, makes bladder fuel tanks and crash-resistant polyurethane fuel tanks for aircraft, along with ice guards and specialty coated fabrics. UK-based aerospace firm Meggitt owns K&F.

	Annual Growth	12/02	12/03	12/04	12/05	12/06
Sales ($ mil.)	5.0%	348.6	342.8	353.3	384.6	424.1
Net income ($ mil.)	6.6%	42.1	40.6	(29.3)	23.6	54.3
Employees	0.7%	1,261	1,281	1,294	1,288	—

KANSAS CITY LIFE INSURANCE COMPANY

NASDAQ (CM): KCLI

3520 Broadway
Kansas City, MO 64111
Phone: 816-753-7000
Fax: 816-753-0138
Web: www.kclife.com

CEO: R. Philip Bixby
CFO: Tracy W. Knapp
HR: Charles R. Duffy Jr.
FYE: December 31
Type: Public

They're not just standing on the corner of 12th Street and Vine! Kansas City Life Insurance and subsidiary Sunset Life sell their products throughout the US to individuals (life insurance and annuities) and to groups (life, dental, vision, and disability insurance). The companies sell through independent agents, brokers, and third-party marketers. Subsidiary Old American Insurance focuses on burial and related insurance. Kansas City Life Insurance also offers brokerage services through its Sunset Financial Services unit. The company's insurance products are also marketed by American Republic Insurance. CEO Philip Bixby and his family control more than half of the company.

	Annual Growth	12/03	12/04	12/05	12/06	12/07
Assets ($ mil.)	(1.1%)	4,551.9	4,666.1	4,559.0	4,460.4	4,352.1
Net income ($ mil.)	24.6%	14.8	57.7	36.2	36.9	35.7
Market value ($ mil.)	(1.8%)	550.9	569.1	596.9	593.7	512.8
Employees	—	—	—	541	—	—

KANSAS CITY SOUTHERN

NYSE: KSU

427 W. 12th St.
Kansas City, MO 64105
Phone: 816-983-1303
Fax: 816-983-1108
Web: www.kcsi.com

CEO: Michael R. (Mike) Haverty
CFO: Patrick J. (Pat) Ottensmeyer
HR: John E. Derry
FYE: December 31
Type: Public

Kansas City Southern (KCS) rides the rails of a 6,000-mile network that stretches from Missouri to Mexico. The company's Kansas City Southern Railway (KCSR) owns and operates more than 3,200 miles of track in the midwestern and southern US. KCS offers rail freight service in Mexico through Kansas City Southern de México (KCSM, formerly TFM), which maintains more than 2,600 miles of track and serves three major ports. Another KCS unit, Texas Mexican Railway, connects the KCSR and KCSM systems. The KCS railroads transport such freight as forest products and metals, agricultural and mineral products, and chemical and petroleum products.

	Annual Growth	12/03	12/04	12/05	12/06	12/07
Sales ($ mil.)	31.6%	581.3	639.5	1,352.0	1,659.7	1,742.8
Net income ($ mil.)	88.4%	12.2	24.4	100.9	108.9	153.8
Market value ($ mil.)	31.3%	890.4	1,121.8	1,793.5	2,200.2	2,642.6
Employees	34.3%	—	2,680	3,060	6,470	6,485

KAO BRANDS COMPANY

2535 Spring Grove Ave.
Cincinnati, OH 45214
Phone: 513-421-1400
Fax: 513-263-7328
Web: www.kaobrands.com

CEO: William J. (Bill) Gentner
CFO: Joe Workman
HR: –
FYE: March 31
Type: Subsidiary

Kao wants to keep its customers clean and feeling fresh. Kao Brands Company, a subsidiary of Kao Corporation, was established in 1882 as a maker of coconut oil soap. The company (its name is pronounced "cow") now formulates and manufactures a wide range of personal care products for men and women. Its brand names include Jergens, Curél, Soft Sense, Bioré, John Frieda, Guhl, and Ban. Kao Brands' Jergens body wash became popular when liquid soap hit the market. Kao Brands, which sells its products in more than 50 countries, was bought by the American Brands Company in 1970 and the Kao Corporation in 1988.

	Annual Growth	3/03	3/04	3/05	3/06	3/07
Est. sales ($ mil.)	—	—	—	—	—	66.2
Employees	—	—	—	—	—	560

KAPLAN, INC.

888 7th Ave.
New York, NY 10106
Phone: 212-492-5800
Fax: 212-492-5933
Web: www.kaplan.com

CEO: Jonathan Grayer
CFO: Robert L. (Bob) Lane
HR: –
FYE: December 31
Type: Subsidiary

Kaplan likes being put to the test. A subsidiary of The Washington Post Company, Kaplan is one of the nation's leading providers of educational and career services. Its Test Preparation and Admissions division publishes course materials, books, software, and Web content to help prime students for standardized tests and licensing examinations (SAT, GRE, medical board exam). Kaplan also provides training, software, and continuing education services for a variety of industries, operates about 160 SCORE! after-school learning centers, and offers certificate and degree programs online and through some 70 campuses in the US and abroad. The company also publishes books on business, finance, and real estate.

KAPSTONE PAPER AND PACKAGING

NASDAQ (GM): KPPC

1101 Skokie Blvd., Ste. 300
Northbrook, IL 60062
Phone: 847-239-8800
Fax: 847-205-7551
Web: www.kapstonepaper.com

CEO: Roger W. Stone
CFO: Andrea K. Tarbox
HR: –
FYE: December 31
Type: Public

For customers of KapStone Paper and Packaging Corporation, it's a wrap! Focused on producing unbleached kraft paper (strong wrapping paper) and linerboard (a type of paperboard), the company serves customers who convert its paper products into grocery bags and packaging for pet food, agricultural products, cement, and chemicals, among other materials. Established in 2005, KapStone Paper and Packaging also makes inflatable paper dunnage bags (sold under the Ride Rite Converting trademark) that use layers of kraft paper or linerboard to reduce movement and damage to products in shipping. Its pulp and paper mill in North Carolina operates with an annual capacity of about 440,000 tons.

KARSTEN MANUFACTURING CORPORATION

2201 W. Desert Cove
Phoenix, AZ 85029
Phone: 602-870-5000
Fax: 602-687-4482
Web: www.pinggolf.com

CEO: John A Solheim
CFO: Mike Trueblood
HR: Dorothy Glueck
FYE: December 31
Type: Private

If there's a PING in your swing, it's got to be Karsten. Founded in 1959 after Karsten Solheim designed a revolutionary putter in his garage, Karsten Manufacturing designs and manufactures customized PING golf clubs; the clubs are named for the sound they make when striking the ball. Karsten's offerings also include the PING titanium driver (which the company claims can improve the distance of a player's drive), G5 and i5 clubs, youth clubs, golf bags and other accessories, and apparel. John A. Solheim, the founder's youngest son, leads the family-owned company.

KATE SPADE LLC

48 W. 25th St.
New York, NY 10010
Phone: 212-739-6550
Fax: 212-739-6544
Web: www.katespade.com

CEO: Deborah J. Lloyd
CFO: –
HR: Elyce Arons
FYE: July 31
Type: Subsidiary

kate spade's story is one of simplicity, like the bags it peddles. Begun by designer Kate Spade and her husband, Andy, in 1993, signature kate spade bags were an instant success because of their uncomplicated design. Since then, the company has expanded into stationery, various functional bags (think diaper bags), and now, licensing that brings to the world a line of homewares, including sheets, tablewares, and wallpaper, as well as beauty products, eyewear, and shoes. kate spade's products are distributed through more than 20 of its own stores and in upscale department stores, including those of its previous owner, Neiman Marcus. Neiman's sold the company to Liz Claiborne for about $124 million.

	Annual Growth	7/02	7/03	7/04	7/05	7/06
Est. sales ($ mil.)	—	—	—	—	—	84.0
Employees	—	—	—	—	—	—

An in-depth profile of this company is available to Hoover's Online members at hoovers.com.

KATUN CORPORATION

10951 Bush Lake Rd.
Minneapolis, MN 55438
Phone: 952-941-9505
Fax: 952-941-4307
Web: www.katun.com

CEO: Carlyle S. Singer
CFO: Kathleen P. Pepski
HR: Chris Coleman
FYE: December 31
Type: Private

Katun wants you to exercise your options — to not buy OEM parts. The company designs and makes alternative parts and supplies for copiers, printers, and fax machines. Other sales come from toner cartridges, drums, and rollers. Also included among Katun's more than 6,000 products are ink jet cartridges, thermal ribbons, ball bearings, and tools — many for products made by companies such as Hewlett-Packard and Canon. Katun (Mayan for "a period of twenty years") sells its wares to more than 19,000 office equipment dealers and distributors in more than 170 countries. Founded in 1979, the company was acquired in 2002 by investors led by Banc of America Capital Investors, Svoboda, Collins, and management.

	Annual Growth	12/03	12/04	12/05	12/06	12/07
Est. sales ($ mil.)	—	—	—	—	—	138.7
Employees	—	—	—	—	—	1,060

KATY INDUSTRIES, INC.

OTC: KATY

2461 S. Clark St., Ste. 630
Arlington, VA 22202
Phone: 703-236-4300
Fax: 703-236-3170
Web: www.katyindustries.com

CEO: David J. Feldman
CFO: Amir Rosenthal
HR: Joseph E. Mata
FYE: December 31
Type: Public

Katy Industries gives janitors the tools to clean up the acts of others. The firm makes and markets maintenance products, including cleaning supplies, abrasives, and stains. Its Continental Commercial Products (CCP) subsidiary operates six divisions: Contico, Disco, Glit, Wilen, CCP Canada, and Gemtex. The Contico business includes the Continental, Contico, and Container names. CCP operates in the US in Missouri, California, and Georgia, as well as in Canada. Its products are sold under the Continental, Kleen Aire, Huskee, KingKan, Unibody, Tilt-N-Wheel, and Trim-Kut brand names. Since its 1967 founding, Katy Industries has sold everything from shrimp to shoes. The Carroll family owns about 40% of the firm.

	Annual Growth	12/03	12/04	12/05	12/06	12/07
Sales ($ mil.)	(19.0%)	436.4	457.6	455.2	396.2	187.8
Net income ($ mil.)	—	(9.4)	(36.1)	(13.2)	(12.4)	(1.5)
Market value ($ mil.)	(25.4%)	—	—	—	21.3	15.9
Employees	(24.1%)	—	—	1,544	1,172	—

KAYDON CORPORATION

NYSE: KDN

315 E. Eisenhower Pkwy., Ste. 300
Ann Arbor, MI 48108
Phone: 734-747-7025
Fax: 734-747-6565
Web: www.kaydon.com

CEO: James O'Leary
CFO: Kenneth W. Crawford
HR: Anthony T. Behrman
FYE: December 31
Type: Public

Just about everything has a bearing on the business of Kaydon Corporation. The company custom designs, engineers, and manufactures bearings and bearing systems, slip rings, filtration products, and seals. Kaydon Corporation operates in four segments: friction and motion control products (antifriction bearings, split roller bearings, and specialty balls), velocity control products (industrial shock absorbers and velocity controls), and sealing products (engine rings and shaft seals); other products include metal alloys, machine tool components, presses, dies, and benders. Customers include the aerospace, defense, and construction industries.

	Annual Growth	12/03	12/04	12/05	12/06	12/07
Sales ($ mil.)	11.3%	294.1	333.8	354.6	404.0	451.4
Net income ($ mil.)	23.1%	33.8	38.4	73.9	69.5	77.7
Market value ($ mil.)	19.8%	727.3	931.3	904.9	1,116.4	1,500.5
Employees	5.6%	—	—	1,800	1,900	—

KAZ, INC.

1775 Broadway, Ste. 2405
New York, NY 10019
Phone: 212-586-1630
Fax: 212-265-9248
Web: www.kaz.com

CEO: Richard Katzman
CFO: Jon Kosheff
HR: George Bowen
FYE: December 31
Type: Private

For Kaz, its business is blowing off a little steam. Kaz makes humidifiers, vaporizers, air purifiers, thermometers, heating pads, steam facials, and lawn and garden items. Its products, made under the Kaz, Honeywell, Stinger, Softheat, and Vicks brands, are sold worldwide through its Web site and through drug retailers and mass merchants such as CVS, Kmart, Target, and Wal-Mart. Vicks is licensed from Procter & Gamble, which in 2006 sold its Braun thermometers and blood pressure monitoring business to Kaz. Max Katzman invented the first electric vaporizer and founded Kaz in 1926; his grandson Richard is CEO.

	Annual Growth	12/03	12/04	12/05	12/06	12/07
Est. sales ($ mil.)	—	—	—	—	—	352.3
Employees	—	—	—	—	—	1,457

KB HOME

NYSE: KBH

10990 Wilshire Blvd., 7th Fl.
Los Angeles, CA 90024
Phone: 310-231-4000
Fax: 310-231-4222
Web: www.kbhome.com

CEO: Jeffrey T. (Jeff) Mezger
CFO: William R. (Bill) Hollinger
HR: John Staines
FYE: November 30
Type: Public

If Mr. Blandings still wants to build his dream house, he might turn to KB Home. KB Home builds mainly for first-time, trade-up, and active adult buyers primarily in the southern, western, and southwestern US. KB Home markets homes under its Built to Order brand, allowing buyers to customize their homes through KB Home Studio. The program lets customers choose from thousands of options to be included in the construction of their new homes. The company also has branding deals with Martha Stewart and the Walt Disney Company. KB Home offers financing, mortgage assistance, and home insurance through Countrywide KB Home Loans, a joint venture with Countrywide Financial.

	Annual Growth	11/03	11/04	11/05	11/06	11/07
Sales ($ mil.)	2.3%	5,850.5	7,052.7	9,441.7	11,003.8	6,416.5
Net income ($ mil.)	—	370.8	480.9	842.4	482.4	(929.4)
Market value ($ mil.)	0.1%	1,862.4	2,423.0	6,620.1	4,619.7	1,870.2
Employees	(32.0%)	—	—	6,700	5,100	3,100

KB TOYS, INC.

100 West St.
Pittsfield, MA 01201
Phone: 413-496-3000
Fax: 413-496-3616
Web: www.kbtoys.com

CEO: Andrew (Andy) Bailen
CFO: Joel R. Wiest
HR: Gerald P. (Gerry) Murray
FYE: January 31
Type: Private

The retail toy business is not all fun and games, as the nation's largest mall-based toy chain KB Toys can surely attest. The struggling toy seller operates about 380 stores in malls nationwide, following the closure of about 120 stores in early 2008. (Previously, KB Toys shuttered more than 600 locations and laid off thousands of employees following a stint in Chapter 11 bankruptcy protection.) To survive, the company hopes to sell inexpensive toys and games to impulse buyers in malls, while leaving the fiercely competitive market for more popular products to market leader Toys "R" Us and discounters Wal-Mart and Target. KB Toys is owned by investment firm Prentice Capital Management (PCM).

	Annual Growth	1/03	1/04	1/05	1/06	1/07
Est. sales ($ mil.)	—	—	—	—	—	53.5
Employees	—	—	—	—	—	650

KBR, INC.

NYSE: KBR

601 Jefferson St., Ste. 3400
Houston, TX 77002
Phone: 713-753-3011
Fax: 713-753-5353
Web: www.kbr.com

CEO: William P. (Bill) Utt
CFO: Charles (Chip) Schneider
HR: –
FYE: December 31
Type: Public

If you thought KBR was only about Iraqi contracts, think again. The construction and engineering company operates in four segments: civil infrastructure, government contracts, energy and chemical services, and joint ventures. Although its contracts in Iraq account for about 50% of its sales, the company focuses on its engineering and construction operations. KBR builds, designs, and manages airports and energy and chemical plants; provides engineering, environmental, and transportation services; performs security and threat analyses; and designs and manages urban rail projects. Oil field services giant Halliburton spun off about 20% of KBR through an IPO in 2006 and divested the rest in 2007.

	Annual Growth	12/03	12/04	12/05	12/06	12/07
Sales ($ mil.)	(0.3%)	8,867.0	11,903.0	10,138.0	9,633.0	8,745.0
Net income ($ mil.)	—	(133.0)	(303.0)	240.0	168.0	302.0
Market value ($ mil.)	—	—	—	—	—	6,584.7
Employees	(5.1%)	64,000	60,000	57,000	56,000	52,000

KBW, INC.

NYSE: KBW

The Equitable Bldg., 787 7th Ave., 4th Fl.
New York, NY 10019
Phone: 212-887-7777
Fax: 212-541-6668
Web: www.kbw.com

CEO: John G. Duffy
CFO: Robert (Bob) Giambrone
HR: Josephine Fink
FYE: December 31
Type: Public

KBW is an investment bank for bankers. Clients of the firm include banks, insurance companies, broker/dealers, asset managers, and others in the financial services sector. The company specializes in investment banking; securities sales and trading; and research. Operating through subsidiary Keefe, Bruyette & Woods, KBW provides mergers and acquisitions advice, securities underwriting, and structured finance. KBW Asset Management offers investment advisory services to financial institutions and other institutional clients, as well as to wealthy individuals. In what has become an industry trend, KBW went public via an IPO in 2006.

	Annual Growth	12/03	12/04	12/05	12/06	12/07
Sales ($ mil.)	12.0%	271.6	300.3	307.9	406.6	427.5
Net income ($ mil.)	(8.1%)	38.2	31.3	17.4	53.3	27.3
Market value ($ mil.)	(12.7%)	—	—	—	858.3	749.5
Employees	16.3%	—	—	—	455	529

KEANE INTERNATIONAL, INC.

210 Porter Dr., Ste. 315
San Ramon, CA 94583
Phone: 925-838-8600
Fax: 925-838-7138
Web: www.keane.com

CEO: Mani Subramanian
CFO: Chris Setterington
HR: Kalyan Sundaram Mahalingam
FYE: December 31
Type: Private

This company's customers are keen on letting someone else take care of their technology systems. Keane is a leading provider of outsourcing and information technology consulting services. It manages enterprise information systems and provides system integration services for both private and public sector customers. The company offers a range of business process outsourcing services through its Keane Worldzen subsidiary. Other services include application development, consulting, project management, and strategic staffing. The company, which does much of its business in the US, counts agencies of the federal government among its top customers.

	Annual Growth	12/02	12/03	12/04	12/05	12/06
Sales ($ mil.)	5.9%	873.2	805.0	911.5	955.9	1,100.0
Employees	17.6%	7,331	7,847	8,548	9,586	14,000

KEARNY FINANCIAL CORP.

NASDAQ (GS): KRNY

120 Passaic Ave.
Fairfield, NJ 07004
Phone: 973-244-4500
Fax: –
Web: www.kearnyfederalsavings.com

CEO: John N. Hopkins
CFO: William C. (Bill) Ledgerwood
HR: –
FYE: June 30
Type: Public

Kearny Financial Corp. wants northern New Jersey to trade up from the old piggy bank. It is the holding company for savings and loan Kearny Federal Savings Bank, which has more than two dozen branches in New Jersey's Bergen, Essex, Hudson, Passaic, Morris, Middlesex, Ocean, and Union counties. Kearny Federal Savings Bank offers such standard services as checking and savings accounts, CDs, ATM and debit cards, IRAs, and loans. Residential mortgages make up about two-thirds of a loan portfolio that also includes consumer loans, commercial mortgages, and other products. Mutual holding company Kearny MHC owns 70% of Kearny Financial.

	Annual Growth	6/03	6/04	6/05	6/06	6/07
Assets ($ mil.)	(1.0%)	1,996.5	1,936.5	2,107.0	2,007.5	1,917.3
Net income ($ mil.)	(17.5%)	4.1	12.9	18.9	9.6	1.9
Market value ($ mil.)	5.7%	—	—	858.3	1,076.5	959.0
Employees	—	—	—	284	—	—

KEHE FOOD DISTRIBUTORS, INC.

900 N. Schmidt Rd.
Romeoville, IL 60446
Phone: 815-886-0700
Fax: 815-886-7530
Web: www.kehefood.com

CEO: Brandon Barnholt
CFO: Chris Meyers
HR: Annette Roder
FYE: April 30
Type: Private

Want to know the key to success in the wholesale specialty foods business? You might want to ask this company. Kehe Food Distributors is a leading wholesale supplier of ethnic and gourmet foods, serving about 9,000 retail grocery stores across the country. Its ethnic offerings include African American, Asian, Hispanic, and Kosher food products. Kehe Food also distributes a wide variety of organic and natural food products. Its customers include such supermarket chains as Albertson's, Kroger, and H.E.B. Arthur Kehe started the employee-owned company in 1952.

	Annual Growth	4/04	4/05	4/06	4/07	4/08
Est. sales ($ mil.)	—	—	—	—	—	750.0
Employees	—	—	—	—	—	2,500

KEITHLEY INSTRUMENTS, INC.

NYSE: KEI

28775 Aurora Rd.
Solon, OH 44139
Phone: 440-248-0400
Fax: 440-248-6168
Web: www.keithley.com

CEO: Joseph P. Keithley
CFO: Mark J. Plush
HR: Philip R. Etsler
FYE: September 30
Type: Public

A wailing guitar? For the Rolling Stones, that's Keith's lead instrument. The company, Keithley Instruments, is more familiar to engineers, scientists, and technicians than to geezer rockers or their fans. Keithley makes some 500 different products, tools used to control, measure, and trace signals, whether they take the form of electrical current, light, or radio waves. Its portfolio includes digital multimeters, semiconductor parametric test and device characterization systems, signal analyzers and generators, and plug-in boards that enable PCs to be used for data acquisition. About three-quarters of Keithley's sales are to customers located outside the US.

	Annual Growth	9/03	9/04	9/05	9/06	9/07
Sales ($ mil.)	7.7%	106.7	140.3	141.6	155.2	143.7
Net income ($ mil.)	—	(4.2)	11.4	10.1	8.4	(0.3)
Market value ($ mil.)	(5.6%)	194.7	245.5	208.8	183.7	154.6
Employees	3.5%	608	632	651	673	698

An in-depth profile of this company is available to Hoover's Online members at hoovers.com.

885

KELLEY BLUE BOOK CO., INC.

195 Technology
Irvine, CA 92618
Phone: 949-770-7704
Fax: 949-837-1904
Web: www.kbb.com

CEO: Paul Johnson
CFO: John Morrison
HR: –
FYE: December 31
Type: Private

Kelley Blue Book helps steer people to avoid something yellow — a lemon. The company publishes information on vehicle pricing, including automobile trade-in values, as well as car ratings and reviews. While the company still publishes the traditional print *Blue Book Official Guide*, it has shifted its focus to the Web, offering all of its information online. The company was established in 1926 by car buff Les Kelley, who owned one of the nation's largest car dealerships, the Kelley Kar Company. He chose to name the company "Blue Book" after the Blue Book social register, which listed prestigious people in the community.

	Annual Growth	12/03	12/04	12/05	12/06	12/07
Est. sales ($ mil.)	—	—	—	—	—	11.7
Employees	—	—	—	—	—	100

KELLOGG COMPANY

NYSE: K

1 Kellogg Sq.
Battle Creek, MI 49016
Phone: 269-961-2000
Fax: 269-961-2871
Web: www.kelloggcompany.com

CEO: A. D. David Mackay
CFO: John A. Bryant
HR: Kathleen Wilson-Thompson
FYE: December 31
Type: Public

Kellogg does more business before 8 a.m. than most companies do all day. It is the #1 US breakfast cereal maker (a mere corn flake ahead of General Mills). Among its well-known brands are Frosted Flakes and Rice Krispies. As on-the-go consumers grow impatient with the traditional cereal-milk combo, Kellogg increasingly relies on snacks and convenience foods such as Eggo waffles, Nutri-Grain cereal bars, and Pop-Tarts to buff up its bottom line. Furthering its non-cereal offerings, the company bought cookie and cracker giant Keebler Foods (Fudge Shoppe, Cheez-It), which became its Kellogg Snacks Division. The W. K. Kellogg Foundation, one of the world's largest private charities, owns about 25% of the company.

	Annual Growth	12/03	12/04	12/05	12/06	12/07
Sales ($ mil.)	7.5%	8,811.5	9,613.9	10,177.2	10,906.7	11,776.0
Net income ($ mil.)	8.8%	787.1	890.6	980.4	1,004.1	1,103.0
Market value ($ mil.)	7.4%	15,486.6	18,445.6	17,518.4	19,908.7	20,641.5
Employees	0.8%	—	—	25,600	26,000	26,000

KELLWOOD COMPANY

600 Kellwood Pkwy.
Chesterfield, MO 63017
Phone: 314-576-3100
Fax: 314-576-3460
Web: www.kellwood.com

CEO: Robert C. (Bob) Skinner Jr.
CFO: Gregory W. (Greg) Kleffner
HR: J. David (Dave) LaRocca
FYE: January 31
Type: Private

Who would be one of the most dominant apparel makers in the US? Kellwood would. It generates nearly 60% of its sales from women's wear, including its Koret and Sag Harbor lines. It also produces men's and children's clothes and hats. Other Kellwood brands include Kelty, Baby Phat, Phat Farm, and Sierra Designs. The apparel manufacturer sells its products through department stores, mass retailers, specialty boutiques, and catalogs. Kellwood has gained a foothold in new niches and grown through acquisitions, including Vince, Briggs New York, Group B Clothing, Romance du Jour, Phat Fashions, Gerber Childrenswear, Royal Robbins, and Hanna Andersson. The company was taken private by Sun Capital Partners in 2008.

	Annual Growth	1/03	1/04	1/05	1/06	1/07
Sales ($ mil.)	(2.9%)	2,204.7	2,346.5	2,555.7	2,062.1	1,961.8
Net income ($ mil.)	(7.0%)	42.0	71.1	66.3	(38.4)	31.4
Employees	1.7%	28,000	—	—	30,000	30,000

KELLY SERVICES, INC.

NASDAQ (GS): KELYA

999 W. Big Beaver Rd.
Troy, MI 48084
Phone: 248-362-4444
Fax: 248-244-4360
Web: www.kellyservices.com

CEO: Carl T. Camden
CFO: Michael E. Debs
HR: Nina M. Ramsey
FYE: Sunday nearest December 31
Type: Public

These days a lot of "Kelly Girls" are men. Once a business that supplied only female clerical help, Kelly Services has expanded to include light industrial, technical, and professional employees of both genders, including information technology specialists, engineers, and accountants. It also places lawyers (Kelly Law Registry), scientists (Kelly Scientific Resources), substitute teachers (Kelly Educational Staffing), nurses and other medical staff (Kelly Healthcare Resources), and teleservices personnel (KellyConnect). Overall, Kelly Services provides some 750,000 employees through about 2,500 offices in more than 35 countries. Chairman Terence Adderley owns a controlling stake in the company.

	Annual Growth	12/03	12/04	12/05	12/06	12/07
Sales ($ mil.)	7.0%	4,325.2	4,984.0	5,289.8	5,605.8	5,667.6
Net income ($ mil.)	86.0%	5.1	21.2	39.3	63.5	61.0
Market value ($ mil.)	(8.3%)	861.4	966.7	848.2	953.1	609.5
Employees	3.6%	—	—	708,600	750,000	760,000

KELLY-MOORE PAINT COMPANY, INC.

987 Commercial St.
San Carlos, CA 94070
Phone: 650-592-8337
Fax: 650-508-8563
Web: www.kellymoore.com

CEO: Steven (Steve) DeVoe
CFO: Dan Stritmatter
HR: Debbie Culmer
FYE: December 31
Type: Private

You'd call them red, yellow, and green. Kelly-Moore Paint Company calls them High Society, Feisty, and Center Field. But never mind silly names for paint colors, Kelly-Moore aims to show that the paint business isn't entirely run by multinational big brushes like Sherwin-Williams and DuPont. The regional firm produces approximately 20 million gallons of paint per year at its three manufacturing facilities and has more than 170 stores in eight states west of the Mississippi River. Kelly-Moore sells about 400 types of paints, finishes, and sundries to professional contractors and painters and to the do-it-yourself market. The employee-owned company was formed by William Moore and William Kelly in 1946.

	Annual Growth	12/03	12/04	12/05	12/06	12/07
Est. sales ($ mil.)	—	—	—	—	—	333.0
Employees	—	—	—	—	—	2,000

KELSO & COMPANY

320 Park Ave.
New York, NY 10022
Phone: 212-751-3939
Fax: 212-223-2379
Web: www.kelso.com

CEO: Frank T. Nickell
CFO: Howard A. Matlin
HR: –
FYE: December 31
Type: Private

They're the softer side of private equity. Kelso & Company is a private equity firm that specializes in supporting management buyouts. It eschews hostile takeovers and liquidations and is often a "white knight" investor that helps companies dodge unsolicited bids. The firm's investments generally center around industrial and consumer products concerns. Kelso & Company's most recent investment fund, its seventh, garnered about $2.1 billion of investment capital. The firm was founded in 1971 by the late renowned economist Louis O. Kelso and has invested in more than 90 companies since establishing its first investment partnership in 1980.

KEMET CORPORATION

NYSE: KEM

2835 KEMET Way
Simpsonville, SC 29681
Phone: 864-963-6300
Fax: –
Web: www.kemet.com

CEO: Per-Olof Lööf
CFO: David E. Gable
HR: Larry C. McAdams
FYE: March 31
Type: Public

KEMET cannot resist the tantalizing call of capacitors. The company is one of the world's largest makers of tantalum and multilayer ceramic capacitors, devices that store, filter, and regulate electrical energy and that are used in virtually all electronic devices. The acquisitive KEMET focuses on making surface-mount capacitors, including specialized units for communications systems, computers, and military equipment. The company also makes solid aluminum capacitors for high-frequency applications. KEMET sells its vast array of products primarily to manufacturers, such as Alcatel-Lucent, Cisco Systems, Dell, Hewlett-Packard, Hon Hai, IBM, Intel, Motorola, Northrop Grumman, Raytheon, and Siemens.

	Annual Growth	3/04	3/05	3/06	3/07	3/08
Sales ($ mil.)	18.3%	433.9	425.3	490.1	658.7	850.1
Net income ($ mil.)	—	(112.0)	(174.1)	0.4	6.9	(17.6)
Market value ($ mil.)	(28.5%)	1,240.4	670.9	822.7	640.7	324.4
Employees	7.2%	8,800	8,100	9,000	9,100	11,600

KEMPER INSURANCE COMPANIES

1 Kemper Dr.
Long Grove, IL 60049
Phone: 847-320-2000
Fax: 847-320-3818
Web: www.kemperinsurance.com

CEO: David B. Mathis
CFO: Fredrick Thomas Griffith
HR: –
FYE: December 31
Type: Mutual company

The Kemper Companies could be called The Scamper Companies since hard times have the company reeling. No longer writing new policies, the once-proud Kemper Insurance Companies traditionally offered a wide array of personal, risk management, and commercial property/casualty products, mostly through what was its flagship Lumbermens Mutual Casualty Company. But the axe has come down and the company is voluntarily liquidating by running off all of its remaining property/casualty business. Its claims handling has been outsourced to third-party administrators including BroadSpire.

	Annual Growth	12/03	12/04	12/05	12/06	12/07
Est. sales ($ mil.)	—	—	—	—	—	61.4
Employees	—	—	—	—	—	9,000

THE KENAN ADVANTAGE GROUP, INC.

4895 Dressler Rd., Ste. 100
Canton, OH 44718
Phone: 330-491-0474
Fax: 330-491-1471
Web: www.kenanadvantagegroup.com

CEO: Dennis A. Nash
CFO: Carl H. Young
HR: Ryan Walls
FYE: December 31
Type: Private

Not only do the trucking subsidiaries of The Kenan Advantage Group burn diesel fuel, but they also haul it. The Kenan Advantage Group transports gasoline, diesel fuel, other petroleum and petrochemical products, and food throughout the US. The company operates a fleet of some 3,100 tractors and 4,100 tank trailers from a network of about 100 terminals in more than 30 states. Customers include major oil companies and other petroleum marketers, along with food manufacturers. In addition to trucking, Kenan Advantage Group provides fuel-related logistics services. Investment firm Littlejohn & Co. owns the company.

	Annual Growth	12/03	12/04	12/05	12/06	12/07
Est. sales ($ mil.)	—	—	—	—	—	253.2
Employees	—	—	—	—	—	3,545

KENCO GROUP, INC.

2001 Riverside Dr.
Chattanooga, TN 37406
Phone: 423-622-1113
Fax: –
Web: www.kencogroup.com

CEO: Gary Mayfield
CFO: Kevin Dew
HR: Eddy Register
FYE: December 31
Type: Private

Kenco Group, which does business as Kenco Logistic Services, specializes in providing warehousing and distribution services. The company operates more than 90 facilities in the US and Canada with about 22 million sq. ft. of warehouse space. Kenco also provides truckload freight transportation, mainly within a 600-mile radius of its Chattanooga, Tennessee, headquarters, and offers transportation management services. Customers have included Bristol-Myers Squibb, DuPont, General Mills, GlaxoSmithKline, and Whirlpool. Together with their families, chairman Jim Kennedy III and vice chairman Sam Smartt Jr. own Kenco, which was founded by their fathers in 1950 with a single warehouse.

	Annual Growth	12/03	12/04	12/05	12/06	12/07
Est. sales ($ mil.)	—	—	—	—	—	126.9
Employees	—	—	—	—	—	2,500

KENDALL-JACKSON WINE ESTATES, LTD.

421 Aviation Blvd.
Santa Rosa, CA 95403
Phone: 707-544-4000
Fax: 707-569-0105
Web: www.kj.com

CEO: Jess S. Jackson Jr.
CFO: –
HR: Fred Philpott
FYE: June 30
Type: Private

Kendall-Jackson Wine Estates plucks its success from vines. One of California's largest winemakers, Kendall-Jackson produces the top-selling chardonnay in the US, Vintner's Reserve. Its other leading (and most expensive) wine is Grand Reserve. Sold in restaurants, stores, and via the company's Web site (where legal), Kendall-Jackson's wines — in addition to its well-known chardonnay — include merlot, sauvignon blanc, pinot noir, cabernet sauvignon, and zinfandel. Kendall-Jackson owns and farms some 12 thousand acres of vineyards, running along the California coast. Founder Jess Jackson and his family own Kendall-Jackson.

KENDLE INTERNATIONAL INC.

NASDAQ (GS): KNDL

1200 Carew Tower, 441 Vine St.
Cincinnati, OH 45202
Phone: 513-381-5550
Fax: 513-381-5870
Web: www.kendle.com

CEO: Candace Kendle
CFO: Karl (Buzz) Brenkert III
HR: Karen Crone
FYE: December 31
Type: Public

When it comes to research and development, few can hold a candle to Kendle International. A leading contract research organization (CRO) for the biotechnology and pharmaceutical industries, the company provides services that facilitate Phase I through Phase IV clinical trials; those services include patient recruitment, clinical monitoring, statistical analysis, and consulting on regulatory issues. Additionally, Kendle's TrialWare software helps customers manage research and clinical trial data. The company has expertise in a range of therapeutic areas, including oncology, the central nervous system, cardiovascular disease, and inflammation. Kendle has operations around the globe.

	Annual Growth	12/03	12/04	12/05	12/06	12/07
Sales ($ mil.)	28.3%	209.7	215.9	250.6	373.9	568.8
Net income ($ mil.)	—	(1.7)	3.6	10.7	8.5	18.7
Market value ($ mil.)	71.5%	82.9	116.5	362.6	454.3	717.1
Employees	32.3%	—	—	1,900	3,050	3,325

An in-depth profile of this company is available to Hoover's Online members at hoovers.com.

KENEXA CORPORATION

NASDAQ (GM): KNXA

650 E. Swedesford Rd., 2nd Fl.
Wayne, PA 19087
Phone: 610-971-9171
Fax: 610-971-9181
Web: www.kenexa.com

CEO: Nooruddin S. (Rudy) Karsan Sr.
CFO: Donald F. (Don) Volk
HR: Tim Geisert
FYE: December 31
Type: Public

Kenexa wants to streamline your HR processes. The company markets Web-based applications that automate human resources activities, such as recruitment, skills testing, and tracking of employee development. Kenexa also offers outsourcing options to clients, taking over part or all of the recruitment and hiring process. In addition, the company conducts employee surveys for its customers. Kenexa sells its services and software products mostly on a subscription basis to about 4,000 large and medium-sized corporations. The company, which has been growing through acquisitions, was founded in 1987.

	Annual Growth	12/03	12/04	12/05	12/06	12/07
Sales ($ mil.)	52.1%	34.0	46.3	65.6	112.1	181.9
Net income ($ mil.)	—	(12.2)	(4.1)	6.1	15.9	23.5
Market value ($ mil.)	12.6%	—	—	368.4	695.1	466.7
Employees	40.8%	—	—	693	1,220	1,373

KENNAMETAL INC.

NYSE: KMT

1600 Technology Way
Latrobe, PA 15650
Phone: 724-539-5000
Fax: 724-539-6657
Web: www.kennametal.com

CEO: Carlos M. Cardoso
CFO: Frank P. Simpkins
HR: Kevin R. Walling
FYE: June 30
Type: Public

Kennametal welcomes cutting-edge remarks. The company offers a host of metal-cutting tools, mining and highway construction equipment, and engineering services across its two divisions: the Metalworking Solutions and Services Group and the Advanced Materials Solutions Group. Kennametal's products include cutting, milling, and drilling tools used in metalworking; drums, bits, and accessories used in mining; and bits, grader blades, and snowplow blades used in construction. Kennametal and its subsidiaries sell products worldwide under the Cleveland, Conforma Clad, Drill-Fix, Fix-Perfect, Greenfield, Kendex, Kenloc, Kennametal, and Kyon brand names.

	Annual Growth	6/03	6/04	6/05	6/06	6/07
Sales ($ mil.)	7.9%	1,759.0	1,971.4	2,304.2	2,329.6	2,385.5
Net income ($ mil.)	76.1%	18.1	73.6	119.3	256.3	174.2
Market value ($ mil.)	27.8%	600.2	838.9	874.1	1,201.6	1,599.0
Employees	(0.2%)	—	—	14,000	13,300	13,947

KENNECOTT UTAH COPPER CORPORATION

8362 W. 10200 South
Bingham Canyon, UT 84006
Phone: 801-569-6000
Fax: 801-569-6045
Web: www.kennecott.com

CEO: Andrew Harding
CFO: Robert L (Rob) Light
HR: Chris Crowl
FYE: December 31
Type: Subsidiary

Kennecott Utah Copper, a subsidiary of mining giant Rio Tinto, operates Bingham Canyon, one of the world's biggest open pit mines. Annual production at Bingham Canyon is nearly 300,000 tons of copper, nearly 400,000 ounces of gold, 4 million ounces of silver, and 24 million pounds of molybdenum. In operation since 1906, Bingham Canyon has produced about 17 million tons of copper — more than any other mine in history. It has plenty of ore left, and Kennecott expects to continue open pit mining until 2013, followed by years of underground mining. The company has its own smelter and refinery; Kennecott also produces sulfuric acid as a by-product of the smelting process.

KENNETH COLE PRODUCTIONS, INC.

NYSE: KCP

603 W. 50th St.
New York, NY 10019
Phone: 212-265-1500
Fax: 866-741-5753
Web: www.kennethcole.com

CEO: Jill Granoff
CFO: David P. Edelman
HR: Linda Nash Merker
FYE: December 31
Type: Public

Kenneth Cole is a trendy old sole. Most known for its shoes, Kenneth Cole Productions also makes stylish apparel and accessories under the Kenneth Cole New York, Kenneth Cole Reaction, Unlisted, Tribeca, and Gentle Souls names. It licenses the Bongo and Le Tigre brands. Kenneth Cole licenses its name for hosiery, luggage, watches, and eyewear. It continues to expand, adding new lines for women and children, as well as men's and women's fragrances. About 6,000 department and specialty stores carry its products. Kenneth Cole operates more than 90 retail and outlet stores and sells through catalogs and Web sites. Chairman Kenneth Cole owns about 50% of the firm and controls almost all of the voting rights.

	Annual Growth	12/03	12/04	12/05	12/06	12/07
Sales ($ mil.)	2.2%	468.4	516.2	518.0	536.5	510.7
Net income ($ mil.)	(31.7%)	32.6	35.8	33.5	26.8	7.1
Market value ($ mil.)	(12.7%)	342.4	464.6	310.7	287.7	198.8
Employees	0.0%	—	—	1,800	1,900	1,800

KEN'S FOODS, INC.

1 D'angelo Dr.
Marlborough, MA 01752
Phone: 508-485-7540
Fax: 508-485-6882
Web: www.kensfoods.com

CEO: Frank A. (Andy) Crowley III
CFO: James (Jim) Sutherby
HR: –
FYE: April 30
Type: Private

Having a green salad with that steak? Then ask Ken for some dressing. It's a pretty sure bet he'll have one you like. Ken's Foods manufactures more than 400 different varieties and flavors of bottled salad dressings, marinades, and sauces under the Ken's Steak House brand name. The company's products are distributed to retail food companies and food service operators throughout the US. Ken's also offers custom production, labeling, and packaging services for other manufacturers. Ken's Foods owns and operates production facilities in Massachusetts, Georgia, and Nevada.

	Annual Growth	4/03	4/04	4/05	4/06	4/07
Est. sales ($ mil.)	—	—	—	—	—	158.5
Employees	—	—	—	—	—	760

KENSEY NASH CORPORATION

NASDAQ (GS): KNSY

735 Pennsylvania Dr.
Exton, PA 19341
Phone: 484-713-2100
Fax: 484-713-2900
Web: www.kenseynash.com

CEO: Joseph W. Kaufmann
CFO: Wendy F. DiCicco
HR: June E. Sheets
FYE: June 30
Type: Public

Kensey Nash works not in vain — rather, in arteries. The firm developed the Angio-Seal, a bio-absorbable material to seal arterial punctures, which can occur during cardiovascular procedures. St. Jude Medical has licensed the rights to manufacture and market Angio-Seal worldwide. Other biomaterial products include bone grafting material and fixation devices for orthopedic sports medicine, collagen-based burn treatments and wound dressings, and dental surgery aids. Kensey Nash also made a range of endovascular devices, including the QuickCat and ThromCat catheters for removing blood clots, but it sold the product line to Spectranetics in 2008.

	Annual Growth	6/03	6/04	6/05	6/06	6/07
Sales ($ mil.)	11.9%	44.3	58.2	61.4	60.4	69.5
Net income ($ mil.)	(20.0%)	8.8	12.9	12.9	3.7	3.6
Market value ($ mil.)	2.4%	291.2	397.2	345.2	342.7	319.9
Employees	—	—	—	333	—	—

KENT FINANCIAL SERVICES, INC.

NASDAQ (CM): KENT

211 Pennbrook Rd.
Far Hills, NJ 07931
Phone: 908-766-7221
Fax: 908-766-4160
Web: www.kentfinancialservices.com

CEO: Paul O. Koether
CFO: Bryan P. Healey
HR: –
FYE: December 31
Type: Public

Kent Financial Services (once known as Texas American Energy) has moved from the oil patch to the financial services field. The investment firm holds a majority stake in publicly traded Kent International Holdings (formerly Cortech), which scrapped its pharmaceutical research and is seeking new business opportunities in the US, eastern Europe, and China. Subsidiary Kent Educational Services owns 60% of The Academy for Teaching and Leadership, which provides educational programs to teachers and schools. Chairman Paul Koether owns approximately 55% of Kent Financial Services.

	Annual Growth	12/03	12/04	12/05	12/06	12/07
Sales ($ mil.)	(21.7%)	3.2	1.9	0.9	1.1	1.2
Net income ($ mil.)	—	0.4	0.9	(0.2)	(0.6)	(0.6)
Market value ($ mil.)	17.2%	3.1	7.8	6.9	6.6	5.9
Employees	(29.3%)	—	—	6	—	3

KENT INTERNATIONAL HOLDINGS, INC.

Pink Sheets: KNTH

376 Main St.
Bedminster, NJ 07921
Phone: 908-234-1881
Fax: 908-234-9355

CEO: Paul O. Koether
CFO: Bryan P. Healey
HR: –
FYE: December 31
Type: Public

Kent International Holdings (formerly Cortech) is a company without a core. The firm, which previously developed drugs for inflammatory disorders, lost its research partners because of disappointing test results and has since discontinued its drug development operations. In 2006 Cortech merged with wholly owned subsidiary Kent International and took on the moniker of the latter to get a fresh start. It is looking into opportunities in China and has set up an advertiser-supported social networking site aimed at promoting interaction among Chinese and US users. Through his Kent Financial Services investment firm, chairman Paul Koether owns more than half of the company. Biotechnology Value Fund owns another 20%.

	Annual Growth	12/03	12/04	12/05	12/06	12/07
Sales ($ mil.)	49.5%	0.1	0.1	0.3	0.6	0.5
Net income ($ mil.)	—	(0.3)	(0.3)	(0.1)	(0.2)	(0.3)
Employees	—	—	—	—	—	—

KENTUCKY FIRST FEDERAL BANCORP

NASDAQ (GM): KFFB

479 Main St.
Hazard, KY 41702
Phone: 502-223-1638
Fax: –

CEO: Tony D. Whitaker
CFO: R. Clay Hulette
HR: –
FYE: June 30
Type: Public

Kentucky First Federal wants to be second to none for banking in the Bluegrass State. Through subsidiaries First Federal Savings and Loan of Hazard and First Federal Savings Bank of Frankfort, the company operates three branches in the state's capital and one in the town of Hazard. The banks offer traditional deposit products, such as checking, savings, NOW, and retirement accounts, as well as CDs. Lending is focused on residential mortgages, but the banks also offer other property loans, as well as consumer and construction loans. Kentucky First Federal acquired Frankfort First Bancorp in 2005. First Federal MHC, a mutual holding company, owns 55% of Kentucky First Federal.

	Annual Growth	6/03	6/04	6/05	6/06	6/07
Assets ($ mil.)	18.1%	138.3	138.1	273.9	261.9	268.9
Net income ($ mil.)	(8.8%)	1.3	0.9	1.6	1.6	0.9
Market value ($ mil.)	(5.6%)	—	—	94.6	90.0	84.2
Employees	38.3%	—	14	40	40	37

KENTUCKY INVESTORS, INC.

OTC: KINV

200 Capital Ave.
Frankfort, KY 40601
Phone: 502-223-2361
Fax: 502-875-7084
Web: www.investorsheritage.com

CEO: Harry Lee Waterfield II
CFO: Raymond L. Carr
HR: Bobby Russell
FYE: December 31
Type: Public

Forget coonskin caps and racehorses — these Kentucky investors put their money into insurance. Kentucky Investors' primary subsidiary, Investors Heritage Life Insurance, provides group and individual life insurance, burial insurance, credit insurance, and similar products, which are sold through independent agents and through funeral homes in about 30 states. Investor Heritage Life Insurance does most of its business in the East and Southeast. The company also owns noninsurance subsidiaries, which offer commercial printing, investment holding services, and funeral lending services. Chairman and president Harry Lee Waterfield controls 46% of the company's stock.

	Annual Growth	12/03	12/04	12/05	12/06	12/07
Assets ($ mil.)	(0.6%)	429.5	422.7	433.5	415.2	419.8
Net income ($ mil.)	29.7%	0.6	2.2	2.2	1.2	1.7
Market value ($ mil.)	0.7%	30.2	25.6	26.5	32.8	31.0
Employees	—	—	—	—	—	—

KERR DRUG, INC.

3220 Spring Forest Rd.
Raleigh, NC 27616
Phone: 919-544-3896
Fax: 919-544-3796
Web: www.kerrdrug.com

CEO: Anthony N. (Tony) Civello
CFO: Ken Jones
HR: Briony Voorhees
FYE: December 31
Type: Private

Oh, you can buy knick-knacks and doo-dads at a Kerr Drug store, but the company that bills itself as "Carolina's Drugstore" puts its primary focus on pharmacy operations, which account for the majority of sales. Kerr Drug operates about 100 stores in the Carolinas in several formats, ranging from upscale stores featuring cosmetologists, expanded gift sections, and even Starbucks coffee to the basic pharmacy format offering more cleaning supplies, health and beauty aids, and soft goods. Founded by Banks Kerr in 1951, the chain was sold in 1995 to retailer J. C. Penney. A management group led by Kerr CEO Anthony Civello and former CFO Richard Johnson took Kerr Drug private in 1996.

	Annual Growth	12/03	12/04	12/05	12/06	12/07
Est. sales ($ mil.)	—	—	—	—	—	212.7
Employees	—	—	—	—	—	2,400

KERYX BIOPHARMACEUTICALS, INC.

NASDAQ (GM): KERX

750 Lexington Ave., 20th Fl.
New York, NY 10022
Phone: 212-531-5965
Fax: 212-531-5961
Web: www.keryx.com

CEO: Michael S. Weiss
CFO: James F. Oliviero
HR: –
FYE: December 31
Type: Public

Drugs are a life-or-death business for Keryx Biopharmaceuticals. The company specializes in developing treatments for life-threatening ailments, such as cancer and kidney disease. Its lead candidate is Zerenex, a compound that may reduce high phosphate levels in patients with end-stage renal disease. The company is also developing KRX-0401 (also known as perifosine) to fight renal cell carcinoma and other cancers. Keryx suffered a major blow in 2008 when its previous lead candidate Sulonex failed in a pivotal clinical trial; the drug had been intended to treat diabetic nephropathy, a diabetes-related kidney disease.

	Annual Growth	12/03	12/04	12/05	12/06	12/07
Sales ($ mil.)	7.7%	—	0.8	0.6	0.5	1.0
Net income ($ mil.)	—	—	(32.9)	(26.9)	(73.8)	(90.1)
Market value ($ mil.)	0.4%	—	362.3	555.8	578.0	366.8
Employees	—	—	—	29	—	—

An in-depth profile of this company is available to Hoover's Online members at hoovers.com.

889

KETTLE FOODS, INC.

3125 Kettle Ct. SE
Salem, OR 97301
Phone: 503-364-0399
Fax: 503-371-1447
Web: www.kettlefoods.com

CEO: Timothy G. (Tim) Fallon
CFO: Marc Cramer
HR: –
FYE: December 31
Type: Private

A good-tasting, low-fat potato chip is not an oxymoron at Kettle Foods. The company produces all-natural, hand-cooked chips. It also manufactures and sells tortilla chips, roasted nuts, trail mixes, and nut butter spreads. In the past, Kettle Foods' products were only available in natural food stores, but now the company is trying to expand its market reach by moving into mainstream supermarkets. It currently lays claim to about a 50% share in the natural potato chip market, but only about 1% in the mainstream potato chip market. Founded in 1978, the company is owned by private investment firm Lion Capital.

	Annual Growth	12/03	12/04	12/05	12/06	12/07
Est. sales ($ mil.)	—	—	—	—	—	184.7
Employees	—	—	—	—	—	550

KEWAUNEE SCIENTIFIC CORPORATION

NASDAQ (GM): KEQU

2700 W. Front St.
Statesville, NC 28677
Phone: 704-873-7202
Fax: 704-873-1275
Web: www.kewaunee.com

CEO: William A. Shumaker
CFO: D. Michael Parker
HR: –
FYE: April 30
Type: Public

The nutty professor once wreaked havoc on furniture like that made by Kewaunee Scientific. The company makes furniture for laboratories, including wood and steel cabinets, fume hoods, and work surfaces. Its primary customers are labs (pharmaceutical, biotech, industrial, chemical, and commercial research), schools, and health care institutions. Kewaunee also makes technical workstations, workbenches, and computer enclosures for local area networking applications. The company's products are sold through VWR International, a school and lab products supplier (about 13% of sales), and through Kewaunee dealers. Director James Rhind and his wife own about 16% of capital stock in the company.

	Annual Growth	4/03	4/04	4/05	4/06	4/07
Sales ($ mil.)	3.4%	71.2	94.7	73.5	84.1	81.4
Net income ($ mil.)	—	(0.3)	1.5	(0.2)	0.2	1.5
Market value ($ mil.)	7.1%	20.8	26.5	18.7	22.1	27.4
Employees	16.9%	—	—	484	566	—

⊞ KEY ENERGY SERVICES, INC.

NYSE: KEG

1301 McKinney St., Ste. 1800
Houston, TX 77010
Phone: 713-651-4300
Fax: 713-652-4005
Web: www.keyenergy.com

CEO: Richard J. (Dick) Alario
CFO: William M. (Bill) Austin
HR: Kim B. Clarke
FYE: December 31
Type: Public

Energy is the key to growth for Key Energy Services, one of the US's largest well-servicing and workover companies. The company provides maintenance, workover, and recompletion of wells, primarily for onshore drilling. It also provides services such as contract drilling, well completion and abandonment, oil field fluid transportation, production testing, and storage and disposal services to major and independent oil companies. It has a fleet of 975 well service rigs, which operate primarily in the Permian Basin, the Mid-Continent region, and California.

	Annual Growth	12/03	12/04	12/05	12/06	12/07
Sales ($ mil.)	7.5%	—	—	—	1,546.2	1,662.0
Net income ($ mil.)	(1.0%)	—	—	—	171.0	169.3
Market value ($ mil.)	—	—	—	—	—	1,887.1
Employees	—	—	—	—	9,400	—

KEY FOOD STORES CO-OPERATIVE, INC.

1200 South Ave.
Staten Island, NY 10314
Phone: 718-370-4200
Fax: 718-370-4225
Web: www.keyfoodstores.com

CEO: Richard Pallitto
CFO: Ronald (Ron) Phillips
HR: –
FYE: April 30
Type: Cooperative

Key Food Stores Co-Operative is a friend to independent New York grocers. Founded in 1937, the co-op provides retail support and other services to more than 100 independently owned food retailers in the New York City area. Key Food's member-owners run stores mainly in Brooklyn and Queens, but also in the other boroughs and surrounding counties. The co-op operates stores primarily under the Key Food banner. It has also begun opening Key Food Marketplace locations, which include expanded meat, deli, and produce departments. Among the co-op's members are Pick Quick Foods, Dan's Supreme Super Markets, Man-dell Food Stores, Gemstone Supermarkets, Queens Supermarkets, and Penguin Key Food Supermarkets.

KEY PLASTICS L.L.C.

21700 Haggerty Rd., Ste. 100 North
Northville, MI 48167
Phone: 248-449-6100
Fax: 248-449-4105
Web: www.keyplastics.com

CEO: B. Edward Ewing
CFO: Thomas Gougherty
HR: –
FYE: December 31
Type: Private

Key Plastics has a lock on plastic parts for cars, trucks, and SUVs. The company makes exterior, interior, trim, and underhood products, including air louvers, door handles, mirror shells, pressurized bottles, radio bezels, and speaker grilles. The company's major customers have included Ford, General Motors, and Chrysler. Other customers include suppliers to the world's major carmakers. Key Plastics operates more than 25 manufacturing facilities in Asia, Europe, and North America. Key Plastics is a unit of Ewing Management's Key Automotive Group.

	Annual Growth	12/03	12/04	12/05	12/06	12/07
Est. sales ($ mil.)	—	—	—	—	—	673.0
Employees	—	—	—	—	—	6,000

⊞ KEY SAFETY SYSTEMS, INC.

7000 Nineteen Mile Rd.
Sterling Heights, MI 48314
Phone: 586-726-3800
Fax: 586-726-4150
Web: www.keysafetyinc.com

CEO: Jason Luo
CFO: Dave Smith
HR: Anthony Penner
FYE: December 31
Type: Private

This Key won't start your car, but it will protect the occupants. Key Safety Systems is a leading maker of air bags and air bag components. The company also makes steering wheels and seat belts. Key Safety Systems' line of air bag products includes sensors, inflators, driver-side and steering-wheel air bag combinations, and side-impact air bag systems. The company supplies air bag systems to most of the world's carmakers. Key Safety Systems also makes a line of interior trim products, including automatic and manual shift knobs, parking brake handles, shift and brake boots, armrest covers, and pull handles. The company is controlled by investment firm Crestview Partners.

	Annual Growth	12/02	12/03	12/04	12/05	12/06
Sales ($ mil.)	(1.6%)	1,100.0	1,100.0	1,100.0	1,100.0	1,030.0
Employees	(14.1%)	16,000	10,000	8,000	9,000	8,700

KEY TECHNOLOGY, INC.

NASDAQ (GM): KTEC

150 Avery St.
Walla Walla, WA 99362
Phone: 509-529-2161
Fax: 509-527-1331
Web: www.keyww.com

CEO: David M. Camp
CFO: John J. (Jack) Ehren
HR: Dennis T. Hopwood
FYE: September 30
Type: Public

When good french fries go bad, Key Technology comes to the rescue. The company makes food- and material-processing automation equipment. Its electro-optical automated inspection and sorting systems and product preparation systems can be used to evaluate fresh fruits and vegetables, beans, potato chips, and other snacks. Items can be sorted by color, size, and shape to identify defective or inconsistent products for removal. The company also makes conveyor and sorting systems for the pharmaceutical, tobacco, and coffee industries. McCain Foods accounted for 9% of Key Technology's sales in 2007.

	Annual Growth	9/03	9/04	9/05	9/06	9/07
Sales ($ mil.)	6.8%	82.6	80.6	80.3	84.8	107.5
Net income ($ mil.)	6.3%	5.8	3.7	2.7	(0.8)	7.4
Market value ($ mil.)	30.7%	56.8	56.1	75.9	68.8	165.8
Employees	5.5%	—	—	478	—	532

KEY TRONIC CORPORATION

NASDAQ (GM): KTCC

N. 4424 Sullivan Rd., Lower Level
Spokane, WA 99216
Phone: 509-928-8000
Fax: 509-927-5383
Web: www.keytronic.com

CEO: Jack W. Oehlke
CFO: Ronald F. (Ron) Klawitter
HR: –
FYE: Saturday nearest June 30
Type: Public

Contract electronics manufacturing holds the key for Key Tronic. The company, which does business as KeyTronicEMS to highlight its focus on electronic manufacturing services, provides printed circuit board assembly, tooling and prototyping, box build (completely built) systems, and plastic injection molding. In addition, Key Tronic offers services such as engineering, logistics, and testing. The company also makes customized and standard keyboards and mice for PCs, terminals, and workstations. Major customers include Zebra Technologies (22% of sales), Lexmark (18%), International Game Technology (17%), and Transaction Printer Group.

	Annual Growth	6/03	6/04	6/05	6/06	6/07
Sales ($ mil.)	11.4%	130.9	148.9	202.9	187.7	201.7
Net income ($ mil.)	(21.1%)	13.4	0.1	4.4	9.8	5.2
Market value ($ mil.)	19.2%	25.1	34.4	33.3	38.1	50.5
Employees	—	—	—	—	—	—

KEYCORP

NYSE: KEY

127 Public Sq.
Cleveland, OH 44114
Phone: 216-689-6300
Fax: 216-689-0519
Web: www.key.com

CEO: Henry L. Meyer III
CFO: Jeffrey B. Weeden
HR: Thomas E. (Tom) Helfrich
FYE: December 31
Type: Public

Financial services giant KeyCorp has the clout of mean Henry Potter of Bedford Falls, but wants to be the sweet George Bailey of bankers. With a focus on relationship banking and retail operations, flagship subsidiary KeyBank operates more than 950 branches (KeyCenters) in more than a dozen states. Its operations are divided into two groups. Community banking offers local banking services including deposits, loans, and financial planning, while national banking provides real estate capital, equipment financing, and capital markets services to large corporate clients. Non-bank subsidiaries offer insurance, brokerage, investment banking, and credit card processing for small businesses.

	Annual Growth	12/03	12/04	12/05	12/06	12/07
Assets ($ mil.)	4.3%	84,487.0	90,739.0	93,126.0	92,337.0	99,983.0
Net income ($ mil.)	0.4%	903.0	954.0	1,129.0	1,055.0	919.0
Employees	(1.4%)	—	—	19,485	20,006	18,934

KEYNOTE SYSTEMS, INC.

NASDAQ (GM): KEYN

777 Mariners Island Blvd.
San Mateo, CA 94404
Phone: 650-403-2400
Fax: 650-403-5500
Web: www.keynote.com

CEO: Umang Gupta
CFO: Andrew (Drew) Hamer
HR: –
FYE: September 30
Type: Public

Measuring Web site performance is the keystone of this company's operations. Keynote Systems provides Internet performance management services to all manner of companies with a Web presence. Using a network of computers connected to Internet backbones in more than 60 cities worldwide, Keynote monitors the speed of such activities as conducting e-commerce transactions, downloading Web pages, or using wireless applications to help clients identify information bottlenecks. The company also offers qualitative research and consulting services covering online behavior, industry trends, and customer satisfaction to help clients improve the customer experience.

	Annual Growth	9/03	9/04	9/05	9/06	9/07
Sales ($ mil.)	15.3%	38.3	42.4	53.7	55.5	67.8
Net income ($ mil.)	—	(4.7)	4.7	7.4	(7.5)	(4.7)
Market value ($ mil.)	4.7%	210.6	280.4	244.9	180.6	253.1
Employees	—	—	—	191	—	—

KEYS FITNESS PRODUCTS, LP

4009 Distribution Dr., Ste. 250
Garland, TX 75041
Phone: 214-340-8888
Fax: 214-340-1768
Web: www.keysfitness.com

CEO: Tim Chen
CFO: Neil Bishkin
HR: –
FYE: June 30
Type: Private

Known primarily for its treadmills, Keys Fitness Products also makes exercise bikes, ellipticals, steppers, home gyms, and other exercise equipment. The company sells its products through more than 3,000 retailers in the US, as well as stores in more than 30 other countries. Brand names include CardioMax, Power System HealthTrainer, Ironman, Keys, and Karen Voight. In 2005 Keys Fitness acquired ICON Health & Fitness' Image Spa unit as part of its growth strategy. The company has rebranded its complete line of personal health and fitness accessories under the Ironman Fitness brand.

	Annual Growth	6/03	6/04	6/05	6/06	6/07
Est. sales ($ mil.)	—	—	—	—	—	19.0
Employees	—	—	—	—	—	84

KEYSTONE AUTOMOTIVE INDUSTRIES, INC.

700 E. Bonita Ave.
Pomona, CA 91767
Phone: 909-624-8041
Fax: 909-624-9136
Web: www.keystone-auto.com

CEO: Richard L. (Rick) Keister
CFO: Jeffrey T. (Jeff) Gray
HR: Robert E. (Bob) Hedrick
FYE: Last Friday in March
Type: Subsidiary

Wonder why the gang at Keystone Automotive Industries salivates during the car chases from the old *Smokey and the Bandit* movies? The company is a leading distributor of unbranded new and recycled automotive parts used to repair damaged vehicles as well as materials used in painting. It also recycles bumpers and refurbishes alloy wheels. Keystone serves auto body shops through about 135 service centers under the names Fenders, North Star, AM, Midwest Bumper, Stockton, Nordan, and others in the US and Canada. The company has about a dozen wheel remanufacturing plants and about 55 bumper recycling facilities. LKQ Corporation acquired Keystone Automotive for some $811 million in October 2007.

	Annual Growth	3/03	3/04	3/05	3/06	3/07
Sales ($ mil.)	12.9%	439.1	501.1	557.7	628.3	714.0
Net income ($ mil.)	19.6%	14.8	17.7	14.3	22.3	30.3
Employees	0.5%	—	—	—	3,761	3,778

An in-depth profile of this company is available to Hoover's Online members at hoovers.com.

KEYSTONE CONSOLIDATED INDUSTRIES, INC.

OTC: KYCN

5430 LBJ Fwy., Ste. 1740, 3 Lincoln Centre
Dallas, TX 75240
Phone: 972-458-0028
Fax: 972-448-1408

CEO: David L. Cheek
CFO: Bert E. Downing Jr.
HR: –
FYE: Last Sunday In December
Type: Public

If you're born to be wired, Keystone Consolidated Industries can rock your world. The company, mainly through its Keystone Steel & Wire division, makes fabricated wire products, including fencing, barbed wire, welded wire, and woven wire mesh for the agricultural, construction, and do-it-yourself markets. Many of its products are sold under the Red Brand label. A vertically integrated company with its own steel mininmill, Keystone also makes industrial wire and carbon steel rod. Through holding company Contran, Dallas billionaire Harold Simmons (brother of Keystone chairman Glenn Simmons) is the largest investor in Keystone.

	Annual Growth	12/03	12/04	12/05	12/06	12/07
Sales ($ mil.)	10.1%	306.7	364.3	367.5	440.5	451.2
Net income ($ mil.)	—	(37.5)	16.1	39.2	57.7	64.8
Market value ($ mil.)	(7.2%)	—	—	—	150.0	139.2
Employees	(4.1%)	1,300	1,200	—	1,100	1,100

KEYSTONE FOODS LLC

300 Barr Harbor Dr., Ste. 600
West Conshohocken, PA 19428
Phone: 610-667-6700
Fax: 610-667-1460
Web: www.keystonefoods.com

CEO: Jerry Dean
CFO: John Coggins
HR: Jerry Gotro
FYE: December 31
Type: Private

Beef is just one of the cornerstones of this food company. Keystone Foods is one of the largest makers of hamburger patties and processed poultry, with more that 25 distribution and processing centers located throughout the world. A major supplier to McDonald's restaurants, it serves more than 24,000 restaurants worldwide with hamburgers, chicken wings, breast fillets, and chicken patties, as well as fish and pork products. Keystone also provides logistics services to thousands of customers throughout the world. Chairman Herb Lotman owns the company, which began as a beef-boning business in the 1960s.

	Annual Growth	12/02	12/03	12/04	12/05	12/06
Est. sales ($ mil.)	6.2%	2,600.0	2,800.0	3,000.0	3,119.0	3,310.0
Employees	4.5%	6,700	6,500	7,800	7,800	8,000

KEYSTONE GROUP, L.P.

201 Main St., Ste. 3100
Fort Worth, TX 76102
Phone: 817-390-8400
Fax: 817-338-2064

CEO: Robert M. Bass
CFO: –
HR: –
FYE: December 31
Type: Private

Keystone Group is owned and led by Texas financier Robert Bass, renowned for buying troubled businesses and making them profitable. (He is also among the richest men in America and is a prominent philanthropist and contributor to the Democratic Party.) His investment firm has holdings in real estate and the financial services, manufacturing, information services, and oil and gas industries. It is a principal investor in Oak Hill Capital Partners, which manages approximately $4.6 billion in private equity capital and owns stakes in more than 20 companies.

	Annual Growth	12/03	12/04	12/05	12/06	12/07
Est. sales ($ mil.)	—	—	—	—	—	92.5
Employees	—	—	—	—	—	1,513

KEYSTONE HEALTH PLAN CENTRAL

2500 Elmerton Ave.
Harrisburg, PA 17110
Phone: 717-541-7000
Fax: 717-541-6915
Web: www.khpc.com

CEO: Anita M. Smith
CFO: Michael R. Cleary
HR: –
FYE: December 31
Type: Not-for-profit

This keystone bridges the gap between Medicare coverage and a more robust health insurance plan for many senior citizens in the Keystone State. Keystone Health Plan Central provides health insurance products and related administrative services in central Pennsylvania and the Lehigh Valley. Keystone Health Plan Central's key products also include SeniorBlue, a Medicare Advantage HMO insurance plan that provides supplemental coverage to Medicare, and CHIP, which provides low-cost insurance to uninsured children. The company is a subsidiary of Capital BlueCross.

	Annual Growth	12/03	12/04	12/05	12/06	12/07
Est. sales ($ mil.)	—	—	—	—	—	494.5
Employees	—	—	—	—	—	450

KEYSTONE MERCY HEALTH PLAN

200 Stevens Dr.
Philadelphia, PA 19113
Phone: 215-937-8000
Fax: 215-863-5673
Web: www.keystonemercy.com

CEO: Daniel J. Hilferty
CFO: Alan Krigstein
HR: Regina Heffernan
FYE: December 31
Type: Private

Keystone Mercy Health Plan provides health care benefits to about a quarter of a million Medicaid recipients in five southeastern Pennsylvania counties: Bucks, Chester, Delaware, Montgomery, and Philadelphia. Operating as a health maintenance organization (HMO), the company manages care for its members through a network of primary care physicians, specialists, pharmacies, and hospitals; it provides benefits including dental and prescription coverage, pregnancy programs, and assistance with transportation needs. Keystone Mercy Health Plan is a 50/50 joint venture belonging to Mercy Health System and Keystone First, a unit of Independence Blue Cross.

	Annual Growth	12/03	12/04	12/05	12/06	12/07
Est. sales ($ mil.)	—	—	—	—	—	1,335.8
Employees	—	—	—	—	—	1,200

KFC CORPORATION

1441 Gardiner Ln.
Louisville, KY 40213
Phone: 502-874-8300
Fax: –
Web: www.kfc.com

CEO: Roger Eaton
CFO: –
HR: –
FYE: Last Saturday in December
Type: Subsidiary

KFC rules the roost when it comes to chicken. One of the world's largest fast-food chains, the company owns and franchises more than 14,800 outlets in more than 100 countries. (More than 5,300 locations are in the US.) The restaurants offer the Colonel's trademark fried chicken (in both Original Recipe and Extra Tasty Crispy varieties) along with chicken sandwiches, chicken pot pies, crispy chicken strips, mashed potatoes and gravy, and potato wedges. Its locations can be found operating as free-standing units and kiosks in high traffic areas. More than 20% of the restaurants are company-operated; the rest are franchised or licensed. KFC is a division of global fast-food franchiser YUM! Brands.

	Annual Growth	12/03	12/04	12/05	12/06	12/07
Est. sales ($ mil.)	—	—	—	—	—	520.3
Employees	—	—	—	—	—	24,000

K-FED BANCORP

NASDAQ (GM): KFED

1359 N. Grand Ave.
Covina, CA 91724
Phone: 626-339-9663
Fax: –
Web: www.k-fed.com

CEO: Kay M. Hoveland
CFO: Dustin Luton
HR: –
FYE: June 30
Type: Public

K-Fed Bancorp had the name *before* a certain notorious baby daddy did. K-Fed Bancorp is the holding company of Kaiser Federal Bank, a community thrift operating in Southern California and the San Francisco Bay area. With about 10 full-service branches and financial services offices, Kaiser Federal Bank offers such traditional retail deposit products as checking accounts, savings accounts, and CDs. The company uses deposit funds to originate or purchase a variety of loans; residential mortgages make up two-thirds of a lending portfolio that also includes multifamily and commercial real estate loans and auto and other consumer loans. K-Fed Mutual Holding Company owns more than 60% of K-Fed Bancorp.

	Annual Growth	6/03	6/04	6/05	6/06	6/07
Assets ($ mil.)	16.5%	433.8	584.4	639.9	738.9	799.6
Net income ($ mil.)	18.3%	2.4	3.2	5.0	4.9	4.7
Market value ($ mil.)	5.7%	—	185.5	175.9	205.8	218.9
Employees	—	—	—	95	—	—

KFORCE INC.

NASDAQ (GS): KFRC

1001 E. Palm Ave.
Tampa, FL 33605
Phone: 813-552-5000
Fax: 813-254-9640
Web: www.kforce.com

CEO: David L. Dunkel
CFO: Joseph J. (Joe) Liberatore
HR: –
FYE: December 31
Type: Public

Kforce is a corporate matchmaker, placing highly skilled workers with the companies that need them. The specialty staffing firm provides primarily temporary staffing services (and to a lesser extent permanent placement) in such areas as information technology, accounting, health care, clinical research, and government. Kforce operates about 70 field offices across the US and serves *FORTUNE* 1000 corporations, as well as small and midsized firms, in all 50 states. Formed in 1994, the company also offers Web-based services such as online resumes, job postings, career management information, and interactive interviews.

	Annual Growth	12/03	12/04	12/05	12/06	12/07
Sales ($ mil.)	20.3%	495.6	661.5	802.3	938.5	1,036.9
Net income ($ mil.)	67.8%	5.1	25.0	22.3	32.5	40.4
Market value ($ mil.)	9.1%	285.7	413.8	431.4	498.1	405.2
Employees	(5.5%)	—	—	11,193	12,460	10,000

KGB

655 Madison Ave., 21st Fl.
New York, NY 10021
Phone: 212-909-8282
Fax: 610-997-1050
Web: www.kgb.com

CEO: Robert Pines
CFO: David Freedman
HR: Kevin Gaugush
FYE: December 31
Type: Private

You don't need cold war spies to find that phone number thanks to this company. Formerly INFONXX, kgb is a leading provider of outsourced directory assistance services in Europe and the US. Through subsidiary The Number UK, it offers phone number lookup and other information services primarily through its 118 118 number (akin to 411 in the US), as well as through its Web site and text messaging services. The company works directly with telecom carriers in the US to offer outsourced assistance services; it boasts customers such as Sprint Nextel and Verizon Wireless. Boasting such investors as the Tisch family (who control diversified holding company Loews), kgb plans to go public through an IPO.

	Annual Growth	12/02	12/03	12/04	12/05	12/06
Sales ($ mil.)	32.6%	—	—	283.8	308.0	499.1
Net income ($ mil.)	—	—	—	40.1	1.8	(20.8)
Employees	64.2%	—	—	—	5,482	9,000

KI

1330 Bellevue St.
Green Bay, WI 54302
Phone: 920-468-8100
Fax: 920-468-2270
Web: www.ki.com

CEO: Richard J. Resch
CFO: Mark Olsen
HR: –
FYE: December 31
Type: Private

KI can be found in cubicles, classrooms, cafeterias, and college dorms. Formerly known as Krueger International, KI makes ergonomic seating, cabinets, and other furniture used by businesses, health care organizations, schools, and other institutions. The company offers everything from desks to daybeds, not to mention tables, filing systems, and even trash cans. KI operates manufacturing facilities in Canada and the US, and markets its products through sales representatives, furniture dealers, architects, and interior designers. Founded in 1941, KI was bought in the 1980s by its managers, who later allowed the company's employees to buy its stock. KI is now 100% owned by its employees.

	Annual Growth	12/03	12/04	12/05	12/06	12/07
Est. sales ($ mil.)	—	—	—	—	—	610.2
Employees	—	—	—	—	—	2,800

KIA MOTORS AMERICA, INC.

111 Peters Canyon Rd.
Irvine, CA 92606
Phone: 949-468-4800
Fax: 949-468-4905
Web: www.kia.com

CEO: Byung Mo Ahn
CFO: N.K. (David) Kim
HR: John Yoon
FYE: December 31
Type: Subsidiary

With a growing stable of models and a generous 10-year/100,000 mile warranty, Kia is turning more and more heads in the US. Kia Motors America is the US marketing, sales, and service subsidiary of South Korea-based Kia Motors. Models sold in the US include the Optima (sedan), Sorento (compact SUV), Sedona (minivan), Sportage (SUV), Spectra (four-door and five-door), Rio (compact sedan), Amanti (premium sedan), and Rondo crossover. Kia Motors America has dealerships all over the country (every US state except North Dakota). Fellow Korean automaker Hyundai Motor controls about 36% of Kia Motors.

	Annual Growth	12/03	12/04	12/05	12/06	12/07
Est. sales ($ mil.)	—	—	—	—	—	165.6
Employees	—	—	—	—	—	500

KIK TECHNOLOGY INTERNATIONAL, INC.

OTC: KKTI

590 Airport Rd.
Oceanside, CA 92054
Phone: 760-967-2777
Fax: 760-967-4071
Web: www.kiktire.com

CEO: Donald P. (Don) Dean
CFO: –
HR: –
FYE: January 31
Type: Public

Bringing a whole new meaning to the phrase "tire kicking," KIK Technology International makes flat-free tires for use in the health care, industrial, recreational, and lawn and garden industries. The company makes tires and related products using micro-cellular polyurethane technology. KIK Technology produces up to 5 million tires a year. Its tires are used in such end products as baby carriages, bicycles, factory carts, farm carts, garden mowers, golf carts, Go-Karts, hand dollies, luggage handling equipment, mopeds, power scooters, snow blowers, wheel barrows, and wheel chairs.

	Annual Growth	1/03	1/04	1/05	1/06	*1/07
Sales ($ mil.)	(12.2%)	3.2	3.6	2.5	2.0	1.9
Net income ($ mil.)	—	0.0	(0.2)	(0.4)	(0.4)	(0.4)
Employees	0.0%	—	—	—	15	15

*Most recent year available

An in-depth profile of this company is available to Hoover's Online members at hoovers.com.

893

KILLBUCK BANCSHARES, INC.

OTC: KLIB

165 N. Main St.
Killbuck, OH 44637
Phone: 330-276-2771
Fax: 330-276-0216
Web: www.killbuckbank.com

CEO: Luther E. Proper
CFO: Diane S. Knowles
HR: –
FYE: December 31
Type: Public

Interestingly enough, if you want to *save* a buck, you can take your *doe* to Killbuck. Killbuck Bancshares is the holding company for The Killbuck Savings Bank, which operates branches in northeast Ohio. It offers traditional retail products to individuals and small to midsized businesses, including checking and savings accounts, credit cards, and IRAs. Residential mortgages make up the largest portion of its loan portfolio, which also includes commercial mortgages and business loans. Killbuck Bancshares is the #1 financial institution in Holmes County, where most of its offices are located. It also has branches in Knox and Tuscarawas counties.

	Annual Growth	12/03	12/04	12/05	12/06	12/07
Assets ($ mil.)	4.3%	284.1	293.9	298.0	313.2	336.3
Net income ($ mil.)	11.2%	3.2	3.4	4.2	5.2	4.9
Market value ($ mil.)	4.9%	59.8	61.8	65.7	70.7	72.4
Employees	—	—	—	—	—	127

KILROY REALTY CORPORATION

NYSE: KRC

12200 W. Olympic Blvd., Ste. 200
Los Angeles, CA 90064
Phone: 310-481-8400
Fax: 310-481-6580
Web: www.kilroyrealty.com

CEO: John B. Kilroy Jr.
CFO: Richard E. Moran Jr.
HR: –
FYE: December 31
Type: Public

Kilroy is *still* here, especially if you're referring to Southern California. A real estate investment trust (REIT), Kilroy Realty owns, manages, and develops office and industrial properties, mostly in suburban Orange County, San Diego, and Los Angeles. Its portfolio includes about 85 office and 45 industrial properties, including the Kilroy Airport Center in Long Beach and the Westside Media Center in Los Angeles. Of its more than 350 tenants, the REIT counts among its largest Intuit (about 7% of total rent) and Cardinal Health (some 4% of rent), as well as AMN Healthcare and DIRECTV. The company also develops properties for itself and for other parties. It owns about 12 million sq. ft. of rentable space.

	Annual Growth	12/03	12/04	12/05	12/06	12/07
Sales ($ mil.)	3.2%	227.8	218.6	241.7	251.2	258.5
Net income ($ mil.)	23.1%	49.6	33.5	33.8	81.9	113.8
Market value ($ mil.)	18.2%	923.9	1,228.8	1,793.3	2,527.1	1,800.8
Employees	—	—	—	139	—	—

KIMBALL HILL, INC.

5999 New Wilke Rd., Ste. 504
Rolling Meadows, IL 60008
Phone: 847-364-7300
Fax: 847-439-0875
Web: www.kimballhill.com

CEO: C. Kenneth Love
CFO: Edward J. Madell
HR: –
FYE: September 30
Type: Private

Chicagoland's GI generation and their offspring, who have long thrived in the 'burbs, can thank lawyer-turned-builder D. Kimball Hill, a pioneer of the city's suburbs and founder of Kimball Hill, Inc. The company, still owned and operated by the Hill family, builds mid-priced, single-family detached homes, town homes, and condominiums under the name Kimball Hill Homes in the Chicago area, as well as in California, Florida, Nevada, Texas, and Wisconsin. Subsidiary KH Financial offers mortgage financing and refinancing of investment properties in about half a dozen states. Kimball Hill and several of its subsidiaries (excluding its financial service businesses) filed for Chapter 11 bankruptcy in April 2008.

	Annual Growth	6/02	*9/03	9/04	9/05	9/06
Sales ($ mil.)	13.6%	700.0	792.9	927.3	1,100.0	1,163.8
Employees	9.1%	654	700	700	958	926

*Fiscal year change

KIMBALL INTERNATIONAL, INC.

NASDAQ (GS): KBALB

1600 Royal St.
Jasper, IN 47549
Phone: 812-482-1600
Fax: 812-482-8300
Web: www.kimball.com

CEO: James C. (Jim) Thyen
CFO: Robert F. Schneider
HR: Randall L. Catt
FYE: June 30
Type: Public

These days, keyboards on Kimball products are used for entering data, not making music. Once a leader in the domestic piano business, Kimball International now has two business segments. Its Furniture and Cabinets unit — which generates about half of its revenue — makes furniture and cabinets for the office, hospitality, and retail industries. Kimball's Electronics Contract Assemblies segment sells contract electronics and electromechanical assemblies primarily to the transportation and industrial markets. Combined, the founding Habig and Thyen families control Kimball and fill its executive and board suites.

	Annual Growth	6/03	6/04	6/05	6/06	6/07
Sales ($ mil.)	2.7%	1,154.7	1,148.6	1,124.2	1,142.6	1,286.9
Net income ($ mil.)	35.9%	5.6	21.7	16.6	15.4	19.1
Market value ($ mil.)	0.3%	372.0	362.5	327.0	503.4	376.8
Employees	—	—	—	—	7,512	—

KIMBERLY-CLARK HEALTH CARE

1400 Holcomb Bridge Rd.
Roswell, GA 30076
Phone: 770-587-8000
Fax: 770-587-7676
Web: www.kchealthcare.com

CEO: Joanne B. Bauer
CFO: –
HR: Joe Recker
FYE: December 31
Type: Subsidiary

Kimberly-Clark cares about more than runny noses; it has solutions to more serious health problems, too. A division of the consumer products giant (and maker of Kleenex), Kimberly-Clark Health Care is a leading supplier of surgical drapes, gowns, gloves, and other staples of the operating room. It offers a wide array of infection control products, from hand sanitizers and soaps to ventilator tubes that prevent contaminants from invading the lungs and causing pneumonia. The unit also makes feeding tubes, oral suction systems, electrodes used to regulate heart beats, and epidural needles for administering pain meds. It sells its products under the Kimberly-Clark, Ballard Medical, and Safeskin brand names.

	Annual Growth	12/02	12/03	12/04	12/05	12/06
Est. sales ($ mil.)	—	—	—	—	—	1,000.0
Employees	—	—	—	—	—	—

KIMBERLY-CLARK CORPORATION

NYSE: KMB

351 Phelps Dr.
Irving, TX 75038
Phone: 972-281-1200
Fax: 972-281-1490
Web: www.kimberly-clark.com

CEO: Thomas J. (Tom) Falk
CFO: Mark A. Buthman
HR: Lizanne C. (Liz) Gottung
FYE: December 31
Type: Public

Nobody knows noses and diapering babies better than Kimberly-Clark, the world's top maker of personal paper products. It operates under four business segments: personal care, consumer tissue, K-C Professional, and health care. Under brand names such as Cottonelle, Kleenex, and Scott, Kimberly-Clark makes facial and bathroom tissues, paper towels, and other household items. Its personal care products include Huggies, Kotex, and Depend. The firm also makes WypAll and Kimwipes commercial wipes. It spun off its paper (Neenah Paper, Technical Paper), pulp, and timber operations to create Neenah Paper. The firm kicked off a multiyear reorganization in 2005 and bought Germany's Microcuff GmbH.

	Annual Growth	12/03	12/04	12/05	12/06	12/07
Sales ($ mil.)	6.2%	14,348.0	15,083.2	15,902.6	16,746.9	18,266.0
Net income ($ mil.)	1.8%	1,694.2	1,800.2	1,568.3	1,499.5	1,822.9
Market value ($ mil.)	(0.1%)	29,259.3	31,779.6	27,528.5	30,958.0	29,186.7
Employees	(3.6%)	—	—	57,000	55,000	53,000

An in-depth profile of this company is available to Hoover's Online members at hoovers.com.

KIMCO REALTY CORPORATION

NYSE: KIM

3333 New Hyde Park Rd.
New Hyde Park, NY 11042
Phone: 516-869-9000
Fax: 516-869-9001
Web: www.kimcorealty.com

CEO: Milton Cooper
CFO: Michael V. Pappagallo
HR: –
FYE: December 31
Type: Public

Kimco Realty is the real deal. The self-managed and self-administered real estate investment trust (REIT) owns or has interests in more than 1,900 community shopping centers — totaling around 180 million sq. ft. of space — in 45 states, Canada, and Central and South America. Kimco is involved in land acquisition, development of new properties, and redevelopment of existing ones with a goal of long-term investment. It also offers related real estate services, including preferred equity and mezzanine debt financing, leasing and property services, and real estate investing. Kimco properties are usually anchored by discount department stores or large supermarkets, such as Home Depot or Kohl's.

	Annual Growth	12/03	12/04	12/05	12/06	12/07
Sales ($ mil.)	13.6%	450.2	587.6	522.5	653.4	750.6
Net income ($ mil.)	9.5%	307.9	297.1	363.6	428.3	442.8
Market value ($ mil.)	—	—	—	—	—	9,202.1
Employees	—	—	—	503	—	—

KIMLEY-HORN AND ASSOCIATES, INC.

3001 Weston Pkwy.
Cary, NC 27513
Phone: 919-677-2000
Fax: 919-677-2050
Web: www.kimley-horn.com

CEO: Mark S. Wilson
CFO: Nicholas L. (Nick) Ellis
HR: Barry Barber
FYE: December 31
Type: Private

Once "east bound and down," Kimley-Horn and Associates has been making tracks across the Mississippi for several years. Founded by a pair of transportation engineers, Kimley-Horn and Associates provides design and consulting services for landscape architecture, structural engineering, environmental, water resource, and aviation projects. A leading urban planning consultant and top intelligent transportation systems specialist, Kimley-Horn has worked on airports, bridges, highways, water supply, and telecommunications projects. It also specializes in multifamily residential and retail property projects. Incorporated in 1967 by Bob Kimley, Bill Horn, and Ed Vick, the firm is now employee-owned.

KIMPTON HOTEL & RESTAURANT GROUP, INC.

222 Kearney St., Ste. 200
San Francisco, CA 94108
Phone: 415-397-5572
Fax: 415-296-8031
Web: www.kimptongroup.com

CEO: Michael Depatie
CFO: Gregory J. (Greg) Wolkom
HR: Greg Smith
FYE: December 31
Type: Private

Kimpton Hotel & Restaurant Group hopes a little style can help it stand out in the crowded leisure industry. The company targets business and leisure travelers at more than 40 boutique hotels in about 20 markets in the US and Canada, about 10 of which are in California. Unlike most chains, Kimpton hotels are modeled in different styles, creating a unique environment for travelers in mostly smaller, European-style accommodations, some in renovated historic buildings. Upscale Kimpton Restaurants are located next to most hotels.

	Annual Growth	12/02	12/03	12/04	12/05	12/06
Sales ($ mil.)	—	—	—	—	—	486.0
Employees	—	—	—	—	—	1,440

KINDER MORGAN ENERGY PARTNERS, L.P.

NYSE: KMP

500 Dallas St., Ste. 1000
Houston, TX 77002
Phone: 713-369-9000
Fax: 713-369-9410
Web: www.kindermorgan.com

CEO: Richard D. (Rich) Kinder
CFO: C. Park Shaper
HR: James E. Street
FYE: December 31
Type: Public

Kinder Morgan Energy Partners (KMP) keeps energy on the move throughout the US. The company operates 14,700 miles of natural gas pipelines and owns 153 bulk terminals and rail transloading facilities that handle more than 87 million tons of coal, petroleum coke, and bulk products annually. KMP transports refined petroleum products (gasoline, diesel, and jet fuel) through 8,300 miles of pipelines and stores the products in 60 terminals in the US. Through its CO2 subsidiary, KMP transports carbon dioxide. Knight owns 13.9% of KMP, and through its Kinder Morgan Management unit, acts as general partner.

	Annual Growth	12/03	12/04	12/05	12/06	12/07
Sales ($ mil.)	8.6%	6,624.3	7,932.9	9,787.1	8,954.6	9,217.7
Net income ($ mil.)	(4.1%)	697.3	831.6	812.2	972.1	590.3
Market value ($ mil.)	8.5%	6,638.1	6,540.4	7,508.0	7,798.9	9,190.2
Employees	—	—	—	0	0	—

KINDER MORGAN MANAGEMENT, LLC

NYSE: KMR

500 Dallas St., Ste. 1000
Houston, TX 77002
Phone: 713-369-9000
Fax: 713-495-2817
Web: www.kindermorgan.com

CEO: Richard D. (Rich) Kinder
CFO: Kimberly A. (Kim) Dang
HR: James E. Street
FYE: December 31
Type: Public

This can get Kinder complicated: Kinder Morgan Management (KMM) was created in 2001 by pipeline operator Knight (formerly Kinder Morgan, Inc., or KMI), to become general partner of Kinder Morgan Energy Partners (KMP). KMM oversees KMP's business segments: pipelines that transport refined petroleum products (including gasoline, diesel, jet fuel, and natural gas liquids); natural gas pipelines; pipelines that transport carbon dioxide for oil field use; bulk terminals that handle coal, petroleum coke, and other products; and liquids terminals that handle refined petroleum products and chemicals. Knight controls KMM and, indirectly, KMP.

KINDRED HEALTHCARE, INC.

NYSE: KND

680 S. 4th St.
Louisville, KY 40202
Phone: 502-596-7300
Fax: 502-596-4170
Web: www.kindredhealthcare.com

CEO: Paul J. Diaz
CFO: Richard A. (Rich) Lechleiter
HR: –
FYE: December 31
Type: Public

Kindred Healthcare is one of the largest long-term health care providers in the US. Kindred operates some 225 nursing homes and more than 80 long-term acute care hospitals located in about 35 states. It owns some of its facilities, but operates most of them under lease agreements with Ventas and other third parties. Kindred also operates a contract rehabilitation therapy business, which serves its own and other long-term care facilities, through its People-first Rehabilitation division. In 2007 Kindred spun off its Kindred Pharmacy Services unit, which distributed drugs to long-term care facilities.

	Annual Growth	12/03	12/04	12/05	12/06	12/07
Sales ($ mil.)	6.5%	3,284.0	3,531.2	3,924.0	4,266.7	4,220.3
Net income ($ mil.)	—	(75.3)	70.6	144.9	78.7	(46.9)
Market value ($ mil.)	26.5%	373.7	881.3	760.9	798.7	957.7
Employees	(14.0%)	—	—	51,600	55,000	38,200

An in-depth profile of this company is available to Hoover's Online members at hoovers.com.

895

KINECTA FEDERAL CREDIT UNION

1440 Rosecrans Ave.
Manhattan Beach, CA 90266
Phone: 310-643-5458
Fax: 310-643-8350
Web: www.kinecta.org

CEO: Simone F. Lagomarsino
CFO: Edward (Ed) Resendez
HR: Toni D. Daniels
FYE: December 31
Type: Mutual company

You don't have to be an eccentric gazillionaire to join Kinecta Federal Credit Union. Formerly Hughes Aircraft Employees Federal Credit Union, Kinecta provides financial services to more than 220,000 members from 100-plus employers in Southern California. The member-owned credit union offers savings, checking, money market, and IRA accounts, and savings bonds. Lending activities include the origination of auto, home equity, and residential mortgage loans, as well as credit card services. In addition to the more than two dozen branches Kinecta operates, members can also access their accounts through a worldwide network of some 1,800 affiliated credit unions.

	Annual Growth	12/03	12/04	12/05	12/06	12/07
Est. sales ($ mil.)	—	—	—	—	—	172.1
Employees	—	—	—	—	—	450

KINETEK, INC.

ArborLake Center, 1751 Lake Cook Rd., Ste. 550
Deerfield, IL 60015
Phone: 847-267-4473
Fax: 847-945-9645
Web: www.kinetekinc.com

CEO: Thomas H. Quinn
CFO: Daniel D. Drury
HR: –
FYE: December 31
Type: Subsidiary

Kinetek keeps its power under control. The company makes a range of electrical products, such as subfractional motors used in vending machines and controllers found in elevators. Other products include electric motors (AC and DC), gearboxes, gearmotors, gears, and transaxles. In addition to elevators and vending machines, Kinetek's products are used in appliances, floor-care equipment, conveyor systems, golf carts, ventilation equipment, lift trucks, and sewing machines. In late 2006 Jordan Industries sold Kinetek to The Resolute Fund (managed and operated by The Jordan Company) for nearly $442 million.

KINETIC CONCEPTS, INC.

NYSE: KCI

8023 Vantage Dr.
San Antonio, TX 78230
Phone: 210-524-9000
Fax: 210-255-6998
Web: www.kci1.com

CEO: Catherine M. (Cathy) Burzik
CFO: Martin J. (Marty) Landon
HR: R. James Cravens
FYE: December 31
Type: Public

Kinetic Concepts makes its bed and has no problems lying in it. The company's products include hospital beds, specialized mattresses, and pressure relief and pulmonary care systems. Such "therapeutic surfaces" treat and prevent complications associated with patient immobility, such as pressure sores and buildup of fluid in the lungs. Kinetic Concepts also makes vacuum-based wound care systems and critical-care therapy systems that rotate immobilized patients to reduce the incidence of pulmonary complications. Customers include acute and long-term care facilities, home health agencies, wound care clinics, and individuals in the US and abroad.

	Annual Growth	12/03	12/04	12/05	12/06	12/07
Sales ($ mil.)	20.5%	763.8	992.6	1,208.6	1,371.6	1,609.9
Net income ($ mil.)	35.8%	69.7	96.5	122.2	195.5	237.1
Market value ($ mil.)	(9.7%)	—	5,241.4	2,795.4	2,786.7	3,864.5
Employees	5.6%	—	—	5,735	6,300	6,400

KINETICS GROUP, INC.

4226 Surles Ct., Ste. 500
Durham, NC 27703
Phone: 919-474-4600
Fax: 919-474-4219
Web: www.kineticsgroup.com

CEO: Michael R. D'Appolonia
CFO: Harry J. Soose Jr.
HR: –
FYE: December 31
Type: Private

Kinetics Group stays in motion. Through its Kinetic Systems division, the company provides high-purity process and mechanical systems primarily to the semiconductor and biopharmaceutical industries in the Americas, Asia, and Europe. It also serves retail facilities, schools and municipalities, sports and entertainment venues, and water treatment plants. The company provides installation of gas, chemical, water, and utility systems, as well as fabricated steel pipe, HVAC (heating, ventilation, and air-conditioning), and plumbing systems. Founded in 1973, Kinetics Group counts Advanced Micro Devices, Merck, and Pepsi among its clients.

	Annual Growth	12/03	12/04	12/05	12/06	12/07
Est. sales ($ mil.)	—	—	—	—	—	108.5
Employees	—	—	—	—	—	1,150

KING & SPALDING LLP

1180 Peachtree St. NE
Atlanta, GA 30309
Phone: 404-572-4600
Fax: 404-572-5100
Web: www.kslaw.com

CEO: Robert D. Hays Jr.
CFO: Steve Jacobs
HR: Christopher Jackson
FYE: December 31
Type: Partnership

With a client list that has included Brown & Williamson Tobacco, Coca-Cola, and Scientific-Atlanta, law firm King & Spalding is well-established as one of the South's leading legal lights. The firm has more than 800 attorneys; counted among them have been such Georgia luminaries as former US Attorney General Griffin Bell and former US Sen. Sam Nunn. Its leading practice area is litigation; others include corporate, energy, intellectual property, public finance, and tax law. Outside Atlanta, King & Spalding has offices in Charlotte, North Carolina; Dubai; Houston; London; New York; Riyadh; and Washington, DC. Alex King and Jack Spalding founded the firm in 1885.

	Annual Growth	12/03	12/04	12/05	12/06	12/07
Est. sales ($ mil.)	—	—	—	—	—	500.0
Employees	—	—	—	—	—	1,893

KING KULLEN GROCERY CO., INC.

185 Central Ave.
Bethpage, NY 11714
Phone: 516-733-7100
Fax: 516-827-6325
Web: www.kingkullen.com

CEO: Bernard D. Kennedy
CFO: James Flynn
HR: –
FYE: September 30
Type: Private

How's this for a crowning achievement? King Kullen Grocery claims to have been the originator of the supermarket format. Heralding itself as "America's first supermarket," the firm operates some 50 supermarkets, mainly on Long Island, New York, but also on Staten Island. King Kullen also owns three Wild By Nature natural foods stores and offers a line of vitamins and supplements under the same name in some King Kullen stores. Most outlets average about 35,000 sq. ft., but the company has a 62,000-sq.-ft. upscale market with features such as ethnic fare, catering, and a Wild By Nature section. Started in a Queens, New York, warehouse in 1930 by Michael Cullen, the firm is owned and operated by Cullen's descendants.

KING PHARMACEUTICALS, INC.

NYSE: KG

501 5th St.
Bristol, TN 37620
Phone: 423-989-8000
Fax: 423-274-8677
Web: www.kingpharm.com

CEO: Brian A. Markison
CFO: Joseph Squicciarino
HR: C. Diane Holbrook
FYE: December 31
Type: Public

King Pharmaceuticals may not be the monarch of the US drug market, but there are a few therapeutic kingdoms it would like to rule. The firm makes branded drugs in several niche markets, including neuroscience and critical care. Its best seller has been cardiovascular drug Altace, but when the drug unexpectedly lost patent protection in 2007, King shifted its focus to other products, including insomnia drug Sonata and muscle relaxant Skelaxin, as well as a portfolio of primary care antibiotics and hospital-administered drugs. The company also contracts its excess manufacturing capacity to outside drug companies. Its Meridian Medical Technologies subsidiary makes the EpiPen, a prefilled auto-injection device.

	Annual Growth	12/03	12/04	12/05	12/06	12/07
Sales ($ mil.)	8.9%	1,521.4	1,304.4	1,772.9	1,988.5	2,136.9
Net income ($ mil.)	14.7%	105.9	(160.3)	117.8	289.0	183.0
Market value ($ mil.)	(9.1%)	3,680.6	2,997.2	4,096.0	3,871.0	2,518.4
Employees	(14.3%)	—	—	2,795	2,800	2,052

KING RANCH, INC.

3 River Way, Ste. 1600
Houston, TX 77056
Phone: 832-681-5700
Fax: 832-681-5759
Web: www.king-ranch.com

CEO: Jack Hunt
CFO: Bill Gardiner
HR: Martha McGee
FYE: December 31
Type: Private

Meanwhile, back at the ranch . . . the sprawling King Ranch, to be exact. Founded in 1853, King Ranch's operations extend beyond its original 825,000 cattle-raising acres. The ranch is still home to cattle and horses, of course. However, King Ranch oversees considerable farming interests in Texas and elsewhere (cotton, sorghum, sod, citrus, pecans, vegetables, and cane sugar). It also has varied retail operations (hardware, designer saddles and other leather goods, publishing and printing). In addition, King Ranch also beefs up revenues with tourist dollars from birdwatchers, hunters, and sightseers who visit its Texas ranch lands. The descendants of founder Richard King own King Ranch.

	Annual Growth	12/03	12/04	12/05	12/06	12/07
Est. sales ($ mil.)	—	—	—	—	—	34.2
Employees	—	—	—	—	—	683

KING WORLD PRODUCTIONS, INC.

2401 Colorado Ave., Ste. 110
Santa Monica, CA 90404
Phone: 310-264-3300
Fax: 310-264-3301
Web: www.kingworld.com

CEO: John Nogawski
CFO: Steven A. LoCascio
HR: –
FYE: December 31
Type: Subsidiary

King World Productions reigns supreme in the syndicated television business. The US's leading syndicator of TV programming, the company distributes the top two game shows on TV: *Wheel of Fortune* (one of the most-watched TV shows in the world) and *Jeopardy!* (the #2 nationally syndicated TV program). King World also distributes *The Oprah Winfrey Show,* the most successful talk show in TV history, and its sister program, *Dr. Phil.* Other programming includes CBS hits *Everybody Loves Raymond* and *CSI: Crime Scene Investigation,* and celebrity news magazine *Inside Edition.* King World is a part of CBS Television Distribution Group, the global production and distribution arm of media firm CBS Corporation.

	Annual Growth	12/03	12/04	12/05	12/06	12/07
Est. sales ($ mil.)	—	—	—	—	—	24.8
Employees	—	—	—	—	—	440

KINGS SUPER MARKETS, INC.

700 Lanidex Plaza
Parsippany, NJ 07054
Phone: 973-463-6300
Fax: 973-463-6512
Web: www.kingswebsite.com

CEO: Bruce Weitz
CFO: Patrick Dentato
HR: Cherie Bliwise
FYE: March 31
Type: Private

Kings Super Markets has severed all ties to the British monarchy. The regional supermarket chain operates about 25 upscale grocery stores in northern New Jersey and a single store in Garden City, New York. Formerly owned by UK clothing retailer Marks and Spencer, which first put Kings up for sale in 1999, the chain was finally sold — after several unsuccessful attempts — in 2006 to a pair of New York-based private equity firms (Angelo, Gordon & Co. and MTN Capital Partners) and Bruce Weitz, a former CEO of Duane Reade, for about $61 million. Kings Super Markets was founded in 1936.

	Annual Growth	3/02	3/03	3/04	3/05	3/06
Sales ($ mil.)	—	—	—	—	—	706.1
Employees	—	—	—	—	—	—

KINGSTON TECHNOLOGY COMPANY, INC.

17600 Newhope St.
Fountain Valley, CA 92708
Phone: 714-435-2600
Fax: 714-435-2699
Web: www.kingston.com

CEO: John Tu
CFO: Koichi Hosokawa
HR: Daniel Hsu
FYE: December 31
Type: Private

Kingston Technology cuts a regal figure in the realm of memory. The company is a top maker of memory modules — circuit boards loaded with DRAM or other memory chips that increase the capacity and speed of printers and computers. Kingston also makes flash memory cards used in portable electronic devices, such as digital still cameras, MP3 players, and wireless phones. Kingston has taken on some manufacturing chores for customers through its sister company Payton Technology, which runs a specialized factory that tests and packages memory chips before assembling them into customized memory modules. Founders John Tu (president and CEO) and David Sun (COO) own the company.

	Annual Growth	12/02	12/03	12/04	12/05	12/06
Sales ($ mil.)	26.4%	1,450.0	1,800.0	2,400.0	3,000.0	3,700.0
Employees	20.7%	1,884	2,200	2,000	2,900	4,000

THE KINGTHOMASON GROUP, INC.

OTC: KGTHE

21702 Evalyn Ave.
Torrance, CA 90277
Phone: 310-540-1960
Fax: –

CEO: Thomas E. (Tim) King III
CFO: Thomas E. (Tim) King III
HR: –
FYE: December 31
Type: Public

Physician, heal thy accounts receivable! The KingThomason Group (through its Credit Card division) converts doctors' and hospitals' delinquent accounts into credit card balances. The idea is to make payment easier for the uninsured (as opposed to demand of total payment in one sum), or to consolidate the debt for sale on the asset-backed securities market. The division offers its outsourced accounts receivable services to doctors and hospitals nationwide. The company's health care and insurance division markets health and dental insurance plans and other such products to insurance brokers.

	Annual Growth	12/02	12/03	12/04	12/05	*12/06
Sales ($ mil.)	—	0.0	0.0	0.1	0.1	0.0
Net income ($ mil.)	—	(0.6)	(0.5)	(0.2)	(0.8)	(0.2)
Employees	—	—	—	—	—	—

*Most recent year available

An in-depth profile of this company is available to Hoover's Online members at hoovers.com.

KINNEY DRUGS, INC.

520 E. Main St.
Gouverneur, NY 13642
Phone: 315-287-3600
Fax: 315-287-9781
Web: kinneydrugs.com

CEO: Craig C. Painter
CFO: Stephen McCoy
HR: —
FYE: December 31
Type: Private

Founded by Burt Orrin Kinney, who opened the company's first drugstore in 1903, Kinney Drugs has grown to number about 90 stores in central and northern New York and Vermont. Most of Kinney's stores are freestanding units, some of which offer drive-through pharmacy and one-hour photo developing services, as well as expanded selections of convenience foods. The employee-owned company operates its own distribution warehouse to service its retail locations, and it offers about 800 different household items, food and beverage products, vitamins and nutritional supplements, personal care items, and over-the-counter medicines under its own Kinney brand. Prescription drugs account for the majority of Kinney's sales.

	Annual Growth	12/03	12/04	12/05	12/06	12/07
Est. sales ($ mil.)	—	—	—	—	—	606.5
Employees	—	—	—	—	—	2,000

KINRAY INC.

152-35 10th Ave.
Whitestone, NY 11357
Phone: 718-767-1234
Fax: 718-767-4388
Web: www.kinray.com

CEO: Stewart Rahr
CFO: Howard Hirsch
HR: —
FYE: December 31
Type: Private

Kinray, the US's top private wholesale drug distributor, is nothing if not independent. It provides generic, branded, and repackaged drugs, health and beauty products, medical equipment, vitamins and herbals, and diabetes-care products. The distributor also offers some 800 private-label products under the Preferred Plus Pharmacy brand. It serves more than 3,000 independent pharmacies in eight northeastern US states; its customers also include long-term care facilities and specialty pharmacies. The firm was founded in 1944 by Joseph Rahr. His son, CEO and president Stewart Rahr, has owned Kinray since 1975.

	Annual Growth	12/02	12/03	12/04	12/05	12/06
Sales ($ mil.)	15.2%	2,500.0	2,910.0	3,510.0	4,000.0	4,400.0
Employees	5.7%	800	700	1,000	800	1,000

KINTERA, INC.

NASDAQ (GM): KNTA

9605 Scranton Rd., Ste. 240
San Diego, CA 92121
Phone: 858-795-3000
Fax: 858-795-3010
Web: www.kintera.com

CEO: Richard N. (Rich) LaBarbera
CFO: Richard Davidson
HR: —
FYE: December 31
Type: Public

Kintera helps organizations tap into the billions of charitable dollars donated online each year. The company markets software and services to help not-for-profit organizations use the Internet to raise money. Charities, affinity groups, universities, and other institutions utilize its hosted Kintera Sphere suite to put together Web sites and manage membership, communications, reporting, collections, and wealth prospecting. The company also provides account and project management, creative services, database integration, and consulting. Kintera's customers have included the American Cancer Society and The Salvation Army. Kintera agreed to be acquired by rival Blackbaud for $46 million in cash in 2008.

	Annual Growth	12/03	12/04	12/05	12/06	12/07
Sales ($ mil.)	53.9%	8.0	23.7	40.9	41.1	44.9
Net income ($ mil.)	—	(9.9)	(19.2)	(41.9)	(33.1)	(15.8)
Market value ($ mil.)	(32.8%)	294.5	280.6	107.7	50.2	60.2
Employees	(22.8%)	—	—	471	366	281

KIRBY CORPORATION

NYSE: KEX

55 Waugh Dr., Ste. 1000
Houston, TX 77007
Phone: 713-435-1000
Fax: 713-435-1464
Web: www.kirbycorp.com

CEO: Joseph H. (Joe) Pyne
CFO: Norman W. Nolen
HR: Jack M. Sims
FYE: December 31
Type: Public

Where Kirby hauls cargo, the only curbs are riverbanks. Kirby Corporation is the largest inland tank barge operator in the US. Its fleet, operated by subsidiary Kirby Inland Marine, consists of about 915 barges and 260 towboats. The vessels are used to transport liquid bulk cargo such as petrochemicals, crude and refined petroleum products, and agricultural chemicals. Major customers include Exxon Mobil affiliate SeaRiver Maritime and Dow Chemical, each of which accounts for about 10% of Kirby's sales. In addition to its marine transportation operations, the company is a leading provider of diesel engine services for marine, rail, and industrial customers.

	Annual Growth	12/03	12/04	12/05	12/06	12/07
Sales ($ mil.)	17.6%	613.5	675.3	795.7	984.2	1,172.6
Net income ($ mil.)	31.8%	40.9	49.5	68.8	95.4	123.3
Market value ($ mil.)	55.6%	424.1	551.6	677.5	1,808.3	2,488.1
Employees	(1.0%)	—	—	2,450	3,000	2,400

KIRKLAND & ELLIS LLP

Aon Center, 200 E. Randolph Dr.
Chicago, IL 60601
Phone: 312-861-2000
Fax: 312-861-2200
Web: www.kirkland.com

CEO: Douglas (Doug) McLemore
CFO: Nicholas J. (Nick) Willmott
HR: Gary Beu
FYE: January 31
Type: Partnership

The lawyers of Kirkland & Ellis practice in areas that include antitrust, employee benefits, intellectual property, litigation, mergers and acquisitions, and venture capital. Over the years the firm's clients have included companies such as 3M, General Motors, and Motorola. Kirkland & Ellis has more than 1,300 lawyers in eight offices: five in the US (Chicago, Los Angeles, New York, San Francisco, and Washington, DC); two in Europe (London and Munich, Germany); and one in the Asia/Pacific region (Hong Kong). The firm was founded in 1908.

	Annual Growth	1/02	1/03	1/04	1/05	1/06
Sales ($ mil.)	21.2%	530.0	611.0	725.0	970.0	1,145.0
Employees	—	—	—	—	—	3,200

KIRKLAND'S, INC.

NASDAQ (GM): KIRK

431 Smith Lane
Jackson, TN 38301
Phone: 615-872-4995
Fax: —
Web: www.kirklands.com

CEO: Robert E. Alderson
CFO: W. Michael (Mike) Madden
HR: Michelle R. Graul
FYE: Saturday nearest January 31
Type: Public

When you just deplore your bare wood floor and feel the need to improve your home's décor, Kirkland's hopes you'll explore its stores for affordable rugs, art, lamps, and more. The company operates about 325 stores in some 35 states, which stock decorative home accessories and gifts, including framed art, mirrors, candles, lamps, picture frames, artificial flowers, rugs, garden accessories, and coffee-table books. Kirkland's also offers holiday items during Christmas and Easter. Stores operate under the names Kirkland's, Kirkland's Home, and several Briar Patch by Kirkland's locations, which the company is phasing out. Kirkland's was founded in 1966 by Carl Kirkland.

	Annual Growth	1/04	1/05	1/06	1/07	1/08
Sales ($ mil.)	1.8%	369.2	394.4	415.1	446.8	396.7
Net income ($ mil.)	—	18.1	6.6	0.2	(0.1)	(25.9)
Market value ($ mil.)	(50.1%)	284.2	198.0	112.2	102.1	17.6
Employees	(11.2%)	—	—	4,878	4,312	3,843

KIRKPATRICK & LOCKHART PRESTON GATES ELLIS LLP

599 Lexington Ave.
New York, NY 10022
Phone: 212-536-3900
Fax: 212-536-3901
Web: www.klgates.com

CEO: Peter J. Kalis
CFO: Glenn H. Graner
HR: Susan V. Fried
FYE: December 31
Type: Partnership

Comprising about 1,500 lawyers and more than 20 offices located in North America, Europe, and Asia, Kirkpatrick & Lockhart Preston Gates Ellis (K&L Gates) represents a number of major multinational companies, large banks and mutual funds, and public sector entities. The firm divides its wide array of practices into five main areas: corporate and transactional; intellectual property; financial services; litigation and dispute resolution; and regulatory and policy. K&L Gates took its current shape in 2007 when New York-based Kirkpatrick & Lockhart Nicholson Graham merged with Seattle-based firm Preston Gates & Ellis.

KIT DIGITAL, INC.

OTC: KITD

228 E. 45th St., 8th Fl.
New York, NY 10017
Phone: 212-661-4111
Fax: 646-619-4074
Web: www.kit-digital.com

CEO: Kaleil Isaza Tuzman
CFO: Robin Smyth
HR: –
FYE: December 31
Type: Public

A talking car won't help your company achieve its online goals, but maybe KIT digital can help. Formerly ROO Group, KIT digital operates an online video platform designed to enable clients to publish, manage, and distribute content for marketing purposes. In its previous incarnation as ROO Group, the company was a syndicator of video-on-demand content for broadcast through the Internet, set top boxes, and wireless devices. In 2008 the firm refocused its operations on interactive marketing and changed its name to KIT ("Knowledge, Imagination and Technology") digital. Subsidiaries include online marketing services company Sputnik Agency and integrated marketing communication services provider Reality Group.

	Annual Growth	12/03	12/04	12/05	12/06	12/07
Sales ($ mil.)	188.7%	0.2	3.9	6.6	9.8	13.9
Net income ($ mil.)	—	(0.6)	(4.2)	(9.0)	(14.6)	(34.6)
Market value ($ mil.)	(61.0%)	—	—	43.5	79.5	6.6
Employees	—	—	—	—	—	—

KITCHELL CORPORATION

1707 E. Highland Ave., Ste. 100
Phoenix, AZ 85016
Phone: 602-264-4411
Fax: 602-631-9112
Web: www.kitchell.com

CEO: William C. Schubert
CFO: –
HR: Marie Theel
FYE: December 31
Type: Private

Not everything blooms in the Arizona desert, but Kitchell's buildings do. The employee-owned company, which operates in the western US, has two segments in construction management and general contracting: Kitchell Contractors works with private customers in the health care, custom home, master-planned community, and Native American markets; Kitchell CEM works with public-sector clients, building schools, jails, municipal buildings, and performing arts centers. Kitchell also has a real estate development arm that develops community, retail, office, and industrial projects. Lastly, American Refrigeration Supplies is a refrigeration and air conditioning equipment wholesaler.

KITE REALTY GROUP TRUST

NYSE: KRG

30 S. Meridian St., Ste. 1100
Indianapolis, IN 46204
Phone: 317-577-5600
Fax: 317-577-5605
Web: www.kiterealty.com

CEO: John A. Kite
CFO: Daniel R. Sink
HR: Charlie Ehrlich
FYE: December 31
Type: Public

A real estate investment trust (REIT), Kite Realty Group Trust acquires, develops, builds, and operates retail properties. It owns about 50 strip malls and anchored shopping centers with 7.4 million sq. ft. of leasable space in 10 states, with a good chunk in Indiana. The REIT also has interests in a dozen retail sites under development, four commercial properties, and more than 100 acres of land held for possible future development. Kite Realty also provides third-party management, development, and construction services. Its largest tenants include Lowe's, Circuit City, Publix, Marsh Supermarkets, and the State of Indiana, though no single tenant accounts for more than 4% of the company's rental income.

	Annual Growth	12/03	12/04	12/05	12/06	12/07
Sales ($ mil.)	41.4%	—	49.1	99.4	131.9	138.8
Net income ($ mil.)	—	—	(0.5)	13.4	10.2	13.5
Market value ($ mil.)	14.8%	—	292.6	441.7	537.1	442.5
Employees	—	—	—	95	—	—

⊞ KKR & CO. L.P.

9 W. 57th St., Ste. 4200
New York, NY 10019
Phone: 212-750-8300
Fax: 212-750-0003
Web: www.kkr.com

CEO: Henry R. Kravis
CFO: William J. Janetschek
HR: Robert D. (Bob) Gottlieb
FYE: December 31
Type: Private

Have the barbarians at the gate become civilized? KKR (formerly Kohlberg Kravis Roberts), the master of the leveraged buyout, has shed its old name and is going public in a $1.25 billion IPO. The company long ago updated its hostile takeover image for a kinder, gentler, buy-and-build strategy. The firm assembles funds from institutional and wealthy investors and profits from management fees and its direct interests. An active investor, it often supervises or installs new management and revamps strategy and corporate structure, selling underperforming units or adding new ones. KKR has some $53 billion in assets under management.

	Annual Growth	12/02	12/03	12/04	12/05	12/06
Sales ($ mil.)	16.0%	—	—	3,278.0	3,973.8	4,411.3
Net income ($ mil.)	19.9%	—	—	773.4	941.5	1,112.7
Employees	—	—	—	—	—	399

KKR FINANCIAL HOLDINGS LLC

NYSE: KFN

555 California St., 50th Fl.
San Francisco, CA 94104
Phone: 415-315-3620
Fax: 415-391-3077
Web: www.kkrkfn.com

CEO: Saturnino S. Fanlo
CFO: Jeffrey B. Van Horn
HR: –
FYE: December 31
Type: Public

KKR Financial Holdings is a specialty finance company that invests in secured and unsecured corporate loans, including mezzanine loans, high-yield corporate bonds, asset-backed securities, and debt and equity securities. It has more than $18 billion of assets under management. The company is managed by KKR Financial Advisors; both companies are affiliates of private equity and leveraged buyout firm Kohlberg Kravis Roberts. Formerly a real estate investment trust (REIT), KKR Financial had significant investments in residential mortgages and related securities, but with the mortgage market melting down, the company restructured, dropped its REIT status, and stopped investing in residential mortgages in 2007.

	Annual Growth	12/03	12/04	12/05	12/06	12/07
Sales ($ mil.)	368.1%	—	7.1	407.5	970.8	728.4
Net income ($ mil.)	—	—	(6.7)	55.1	135.3	(100.2)
Market value ($ mil.)	(8.4%)	—	—	1,928.2	2,155.6	1,619.2
Employees	13.7%	—	41	44	53	—

KLA-TENCOR CORPORATION

NASDAQ (GS): KLAC

160 Rio Robles
San Jose, CA 95134
Phone: 408-875-3000
Fax: 408-875-4144
Web: www.kla-tencor.com

CEO: Richard P. (Rick) Wallace
CFO: John H. Kispert
HR: –
FYE: June 30
Type: Public

KLA-Tencor is hard-core when it comes to hunting down flaws in chips. The company — one of the world's largest makers of semiconductor equipment — offers yield management systems that monitor and analyze wafers at various stages of chip production, inspecting reticles (which make circuit patterns) and measuring crucial microscopic layers. The systems' feedback allows flaws to be corrected before they can ruin the costly wafers. KLA-Tencor has long dominated the market for equipment that inspects semiconductor photomasks and reticles. The company gets more than three-quarters of its sales from outside the US, and uses selective acquisitions as well as intensive R&D to keep up with advances in chip fabrication.

	Annual Growth	6/03	6/04	6/05	6/06	6/07
Sales ($ mil.)	19.9%	1,323.1	1,496.7	2,085.1	2,070.6	2,731.2
Net income ($ mil.)	40.1%	137.2	243.7	466.7	380.5	528.1
Market value ($ mil.)	4.2%	8,907.9	9,719.8	8,588.5	8,278.4	10,515.5
Employees	4.4%	—	—	5,500	5,900	6,000

KLAUSSNER FURNITURE INDUSTRIES, INC.

405 Lewallen Rd.
Asheboro, NC 27205
Phone: 336-625-6174
Fax: 336-626-0905
Web: www.klaussner.com

CEO: J. B. Davis
CFO: David O. (Dave) Bryant
HR: Randy Timmerman
FYE: December 31
Type: Private

Klaussner Furniture Industries makes accoutrements for the couch potato in all of us. A leading US maker of upholstered furniture, Klaussner sells fabric- and leather-upholstered sofas and recliners, chairs, ottomans, occasional tables, home entertainment, and dining furniture under the Distinctions, Realistic, and Klaussner names. Licensed brands include Sealy and Dick Idol "rustic" furnishings, including Dick Idol's World Vineyard collection. Its 15 some plants produce items exported to more than 60 countries. Klaussner also owns about 20% of furniture retailer Jennifer Convertibles. Chairman Hans Klaussner has owned the company since 1979; it was founded in 1964 as Stuart Furniture Industries.

KLEIN TOOLS, INC.

450 Bond St.
Lincolnshire, IL 60069
Phone: 847-821-5500
Fax: –
Web: www.klein-tools.com

CEO: Mathias A. (Mat) Klein III
CFO: Verne Tuite
HR: Bruce Beebe
FYE: December 31
Type: Private

Five generations of Kleins have had a grip on Klein Tools, a maker of non-powered hand tools. The company, founded by Mathias Klein in 1857 to make pliers, sells its products through distributors worldwide. Klein tools can be found in the tool pouches of professionals in the construction, electronics, mining, telecommunications, and general industries. (Klein makes the pouches, too.) Products include bolt cutters, cable cutters, chisels, drill bits, hammers, screwdrivers, sheet metal cutters, wire strippers, and wrenches. Klein also sells occupational protective gear. The Klein family owns the company. Longtime executive Richard Klein was ousted in 2006 and his cousin, Mathias, took over as chairman.

KLEINER PERKINS CAUFIELD & BYERS

2750 Sand Hill Rd.
Menlo Park, CA 94025
Phone: 650-233-2750
Fax: 650-233-0300
Web: www.kpcb.com

CEO: John Denniston
CFO: –
HR: Juliet Flint
FYE: December 31
Type: Private

Let Kleiner Perkins Caufield & Byers (KPCB) beware — or, at the very least, be on the lookout. The venture capital firm invests money, time, and talent in innovative companies that sometimes become the foundations for new industries. KPCB has invested in such notable outfits as Amazon.com, Google, and Intuit. The firm focuses its investments in four main areas: information technology, life sciences, pandemic and bio-defense, and green technology. Its portfolio includes stakes in nearly 100 companies. KPCB often forms networks among its investments so they can use one another to develop and expand.

	Annual Growth	12/03	12/04	12/05	12/06	12/07
Est. sales ($ mil.)	—	—	—	—	—	3.2
Employees	—	—	—	—	—	29

THE KLEINFELDER GROUP, INC.

5015 Shoreham Place
San Diego, CA 92122
Phone: 858-320-2000
Fax: 858-320-2001
Web: www.kleinfelder.com

CEO: Gerald J. (Gerry) Salontai
CFO: Jon S. Holmgren
HR: Denise Howe
FYE: March 31
Type: Private

The Kleinfelder Group isn't afraid to get its hands dirty. Since its start as a materials testing lab in 1961, the company has expanded rapidly to become one of the largest engineering consulting and design groups in the US. In addition to its traditional soil and materials testing, engineering, and inspection operations, Kleinfelder, through subsidiary companies, offers geotechnical engineering, engineering geology, construction management, and environmental services. To expand its presence in Oregon, it has acquired Squier Associates (now Squier/Kleinfelder). Jim Kleinfelder, who retired in 1993, founded the employee-owned company.

	Annual Growth	3/03	3/04	3/05	3/06	3/07
Est. sales ($ mil.)	—	—	—	—	—	130.3
Employees	—	—	—	—	—	1,100

KLIPSCH, LLC

3502 Woodview Trace, Ste. 200
Indianapolis, IN 46268
Phone: 317-860-8100
Fax: 317-860-9170
Web: www.klipsch.com

CEO: Fred S. Klipsch
CFO: Nancy Mills
HR: Steve Klipsch
FYE: December 31
Type: Private

Klipsch delivers the primo sound. The company, a division of Klipsch Group, makes high-end audio products and sound systems for personal, professional, and commercial use. Klipsch's loudspeakers are used in a variety of businesses such as Regal Cinemas and in more than 100 Hard Rock Cafes globally. Through its acquisition of Mondial Designs in 2001, the company also makes Aragon high-end amplifiers, processors, and other related items. In 2006 Klipsch acquired Canadian speaker maker Audio Products International, better known as API. Founded in 1946 by audio engineer Paul W. Klipsch (designer of the Klipschorn loudspeaker), the company is run by Paul's cousin Fred and his wife Judy, who purchased it in 1989.

	Annual Growth	12/03	12/04	12/05	12/06	12/07
Est. sales ($ mil.)	—	—	—	—	—	21.2
Employees	—	—	—	—	—	180

KMART CORPORATION

3333 Beverly Rd.
Hoffman Estates, IL 60179
Phone: 847-286-2500
Fax: 847-286-5500
Web: www.kmartcorp.com

CEO: W. Bruce Johnson
CFO: J. Miles Reidy
HR: William R. Harker
FYE: Last Wednesday in January
Type: Subsidiary

Attention Kmart shoppers: Kmart is the #3 discount retailer in the US, behind Wal-Mart and Target. It sells name-brand and private-label goods (including its Martha Stewart label), mostly to low- and mid-income families. It runs about 1,380 off-mall stores (including 55 Supercenters) in 49 US states, Puerto Rico, Guam, and the US Virgin Islands. About 1,060 Kmart stores contain in-store pharmacies. The company also operates the kmart.com Web site. Dismal sales and the erosion of supplier confidence led Kmart to file for Chapter 11 bankruptcy in 2002. (It emerged from Chapter 11 in 2003.) Kmart then bought and merged with Sears, Roebuck in 2005 to form both chains' parent company, Sears Holdings.

	Annual Growth	1/03	1/04	1/05	1/06	1/07
Sales ($ mil.)	(11.8%)	30,762.0	23,253.0	19,701.0	19,094.0	18,647.0
Employees	(20.8%)	212,000	158,000	133,000	—	—

KMG CHEMICALS, INC.

NASDAQ (GM): KMGB

10611 Harwin Dr., Ste. 402
Houston, TX 77036
Phone: 713-600-3800
Fax: 713-600-3850
Web: www.kmgb.com

CEO: J. Neal Butler
CFO: John V. Sobchak
HR: –
FYE: July 31
Type: Public

KMG Chemicals saves dead trees and kills weeds. The company makes and distributes wood preservatives and agricultural chemicals. Its wood preservatives are pentachlorophenol (penta), sodium penta, and creosote. KMG sells penta and creosote in the US, primarily to the railroad, construction, and utility industries. Sodium penta is sold in Latin America. The company makes herbicides used to protect cotton from weeds (Bueno) and to kill weeds along highways (Ansar), and its Rabon and Ravap pesticide lines keep pests from livestock and poultry. KMG also sells hydrochloric acid, a by-product of penta manufacturing, to the oil and steel industries. Chairman David Hatcher owns more than 60% of KMG.

	Annual Growth	7/03	7/04	7/05	7/06	7/07
Sales ($ mil.)	26.1%	35.5	43.6	59.2	71.0	89.8
Net income ($ mil.)	47.1%	1.9	1.8	3.0	3.8	8.9
Market value ($ mil.)	76.0%	23.3	23.8	75.8	84.3	223.6
Employees	12.6%	—	—	93	—	118

KNAPE & VOGT MANUFACTURING COMPANY

2700 Oak Industrial Dr. NE
Grand Rapids, MI 49505
Phone: 616-459-3311
Fax: 616-459-3467
Web: www.knapeandvogt.com

CEO: Peter J. Martin
CFO: Leslie J. Cummings
HR: –
FYE: Saturday nearest June 30
Type: Private

Knape & Vogt Manufacturing (KV) believes in easy access to your drawers — and all your stuff, whether it's at home or the office. The company makes drawer slides, shelving systems, closet rods, and other storage-related hardware items, plus ideaWORK office lighting and computer-related ergonomic products. KV sells its products mostly to original equipment manufacturers and specialty distributors in the US and Canada, but it also sells directly to consumers. The Knape family, including former chairman and CEO Bill Dutmers (a descendant of one of the founders), sold its controlling interest in the company to private equity firm Wind Point Partners for about $106 million in mid-2006.

	Annual Growth	6/03	6/04	6/05	6/06	6/07
Est. sales ($ mil.)	—	—	—	—	—	52.8
Employees	—	—	—	—	—	640

KNIGHT CAPITAL GROUP, INC.

NASDAQ (GS): NITE

545 Washington Blvd.
Jersey City, NJ 07310
Phone: 201-222-9400
Fax: 201-557-6853
Web: www.knighttradinggroup.com

CEO: Thomas M. (Tom) Joyce
CFO: Steven Bisgay
HR: Bronwen Bastone
FYE: December 31
Type: Public

A day trader is one thing, but a Knight trader is something altogether different. Knight Capital Group is one of the top market makers for US and foreign stocks, as well as futures, options, foreign exchange and fixed income, through subsidiaries Knight Equity Markets, Knight Capital Markets, Direct Trading, Hotspot, and Knight BondPoint. It makes approximately four billion trades per day. Customers include brokerages, institutional investors, and issuers of securities. Majority-owned subsidiary Deephaven Capital Management manages some $4 billion in assets for institutional clients and wealthy individuals.

	Annual Growth	12/03	12/04	12/05	12/06	12/07
Sales ($ mil.)	7.8%	670.0	625.8	634.6	951.2	905.3
Net income ($ mil.)	33.5%	38.5	91.1	66.4	158.4	122.2
Market value ($ mil.)	(6.0%)	1,687.5	1,240.6	1,018.3	1,987.2	1,318.1
Employees	9.8%	—	—	720	844	868

KNIGHT INC.

500 Dallas St., Ste. 1000
Houston, TX 77002
Phone: 713-369-9000
Fax: 713-369-9100
Web: www.kindermorgan.com

CEO: Richard D. (Rich) Kinder
CFO: Kimberly A. (Kim) Dang
HR: James E. Street
FYE: December 31
Type: Private

Knight (formerly Kinder Morgan) pipes in profits by operating 37,000 miles of natural gas pipelines in the US and Canada. The company also distributes natural gas to more than 1.1 million customers, primarily in the Midwest, and operates gas-fired power plants along its pipelines. Through Kinder Morgan Management, it controls Kinder Morgan Energy Partners, which transports refined products and operates 165 terminals that handle coal, petroleum coke, and other materials. In 2007 chairman and CEO Richard Kinder, who owns 31% of the company, led a group of investors in taking Kinder Morgan private and changed its name to Knight.

	Annual Growth	12/03	12/04	12/05	12/06	12/07
Sales ($ mil.)	79.9%	1,097.9	1,164.9	1,585.8	11,846.4	11,500.0
Employees	8.3%	5,530	6,072	8,481	8,602	7,600

KNIGHT TRANSPORTATION, INC.

NYSE: KNX

5601 W. Buckeye Rd.
Phoenix, AZ 85043
Phone: 602-269-2000
Fax: 602-269-8409
Web: www.knighttrans.com

CEO: Kevin P. Knight
CFO: David A. Jackson
HR: –
FYE: December 31
Type: Public

Knight Transportation drivers don't drive long hours into the night. The truckload carrier instead focuses on short- to medium-haul trips, averaging about 540 miles. From more than 30 regional operations centers, mainly in the southern, midwestern, and western US, Knight carries such cargo as consumer goods, food and beverages, and paper products. It has a fleet of about 3,750 tractors and 8,800 trailers, including about 550 refrigerated trailers. Besides for-hire hauling, Knight provides dedicated contract carriage, in which drivers and equipment are assigned to a customer long-term. The company also offers freight brokerage services. Four members of the Knight family collectively own 33% of the company.

	Annual Growth	12/03	12/04	12/05	12/06	12/07
Sales ($ mil.)	20.4%	340.1	442.3	566.8	664.4	713.6
Net income ($ mil.)	15.5%	35.5	47.9	61.7	73.0	63.1
Market value ($ mil.)	31.7%	427.4	936.8	1,775.9	1,468.2	1,284.0
Employees	8.3%	—	3,465	3,531	4,176	4,404

An in-depth profile of this company is available to Hoover's Online members at hoovers.com.

901

KNIGHTS OF COLUMBUS

1 Columbus Plaza
New Haven, CT 06510
Phone: 203-752-4000
Fax: 203-752-4100
Web: www.kofc.org

CEO: Carl A. Anderson
CFO: Robert J. Lane
HR: –
FYE: December 31
Type: Not-for-profit

Good Knight! The Knights of Columbus is not only a formidable volunteer group, boasting about 1.7 million Roman Catholic men as members in the US, Canada, Mexico, Poland, Puerto Rico, and several other countries; it's also a force to be reckoned with in the insurance world, providing life insurance, annuities, and long-term care insurance to its members and their families. The organization also manages the Knights of Columbus Museum in New Haven, Connecticut, featuring exhibits of religious art and history. The Knights of Columbus was founded by Father Michael J. McGivney in 1882 and has been selling insurance since its founding.

KNOBIAS, INC.

OTC: KBAS

875 Northpark Dr., Bldg. 2, Ste. 500
Ridgeland, MS 39157
Phone: 601-978-3399
Fax: 601-978-3675
Web: www.knobias.com

CEO: Steven B. Lord
CFO: Donald A. (Don) Bernard
HR: –
FYE: December 31
Type: Public

Knobias knows there's more to the world of securities than the NYSE. The company provides research data on small-cap public companies traded through exchanges such as Nasdaq, Pink Sheets, and the Over-the-Counter (OTC) Bulletin Board. Knobias (pronounced "no-be-us") provides its users with real-time stock quotes and charts, financial data, alerts for news and SEC filings, reports, and company profiles. The firm provides this information for more than 16,000 US securities. It markets its products to investors, brokers, and financial institutions. Knobias was founded in 1999.

	Annual Growth	12/03	12/04	12/05	12/06	12/07
Sales ($ mil.)	0.0%	—	2.0	2.1	2.3	2.0
Net income ($ mil.)	—	—	(2.8)	(2.6)	(2.3)	(9.9)
Employees	—	—	—	—	—	—

KNOLL, INC.

NYSE: KNL

1235 Water St.
East Greenville, PA 18041
Phone: 215-679-7991
Fax: 215-679-1755
Web: www.knoll.com

CEO: Andrew B. Cogan
CFO: Barry L. McCabe
HR: Marcia A. Thompson
FYE: December 31
Type: Public

From Bauhaus to business chic, Knoll has designs on the furniture market. The company makes a variety of distinctively designed, curvilinear office furniture and related accessories, including office systems (a.k.a. cubicles). Its products are sold under such names as Equity, Dividends, and Currents. Other products include ergonomic seating, tables and desks, and filing systems. The firm offers an upscale line of designed furniture (KnollStudio), computer and desk accessories (KnollExtra), and fabric and leather upholstery (KnollTextiles). Columbia Wanger Asset Management owns more than 11% of Knoll.

	Annual Growth	12/03	12/04	12/05	12/06	12/07
Sales ($ mil.)	10.9%	697.3	706.4	808.0	982.2	1,055.8
Net income ($ mil.)	18.4%	36.3	26.7	35.9	58.6	71.4
Market value ($ mil.)	(2.2%)	—	865.8	895.5	1,078.8	809.8
Employees	11.9%	—	—	3,775	4,224	—

KNOLOGY, INC.

NASDAQ (GM): KNOL

1241 O. G. Skinner Dr.
West Point, GA 31833
Phone: 706-645-8553
Fax: 706-645-0148
Web: www.knology.com

CEO: Rodger L. Johnson
CFO: M. Todd Holt
HR: Brad M. Vanacore
FYE: December 31
Type: Public

Knology knows the way to a couch potato's heart is through its hybrid fiber-coaxial cable connection. The facilities-based telecommunications company provides integrated voice, video, and data services through its interactive broadband network. Knology offers bundled cable TV, local and long-distance phone, and high-speed Internet access to residential and business customers primarily in midsized markets in the southeastern US. The company provides video, voice, and data services in Alabama, Florida, Georgia, Iowa, Minnesota, South Carolina, South Dakota, and Tennessee.

	Annual Growth	12/03	12/04	12/05	12/06	12/07
Sales ($ mil.)	19.1%	172.9	211.5	230.9	259.0	347.6
Net income ($ mil.)	—	(87.8)	(75.6)	(54.8)	(38.8)	(43.9)
Market value ($ mil.)	24.8%	186.1	92.4	92.7	370.1	451.3
Employees	10.3%	—	—	1,386	—	1,686

THE KNOT, INC.

NASDAQ (GM): KNOT

462 Broadway, 6th Fl.
New York, NY 10013
Phone: 212-219-8555
Fax: 212-219-1929
Web: www.theknot.com

CEO: David Liu
CFO: Richard Szefc
HR: –
FYE: December 31
Type: Public

Here comes the bride, surfing online. Where is the groom? He's in a chat room. The Knot is a leading online publisher serving the wedding market sector with content and services through TheKnot.com. The site offers advice and information on topics from engagement to honeymoon, as well as wedding planning tools (budget planner, gown finder), chat rooms, a directory of local resources, and an online gift store. The company's WeddingChannel.com offers online registry services. The firm also licenses its content to Web portal MSN and cable operator Comcast. In addition to online content, The Knot publishes *The Knot Weddings Magazine*, more than a dozen regional magazines, and books on lifestyle topics.

	Annual Growth	12/03	12/04	12/05	12/06	12/07
Sales ($ mil.)	28.1%	36.7	41.4	51.4	72.7	98.7
Net income ($ mil.)	81.4%	1.1	1.3	4.0	23.4	11.9
Market value ($ mil.)	55.1%	86.9	112.4	263.7	816.8	503.4
Employees	31.7%	—	—	260	367	451

KNOUSE FOODS, INC.

800 Peach Glen Rd.
Peach Glen, PA 17375
Phone: 717-677-8181
Fax: 717-677-7069
Web: www.knouse.com

CEO: Kenneth (Ken) Guise Jr.
CFO: Thomas DeNisco
HR: Scott Briggs
FYE: June 30
Type: Cooperative

Is there a Knouse in the house? Might be. With retail brand names that include Apple Time, Lucky Leaf, Musselman's, Lincoln, and Speas Farm, Knouse Foods' apple products are in many a pantry. The company is a growers' cooperative made up of some 1,500 Appalachian Mountain and Midwestern farmers that processes its members' apples for sale as canned and bottled applesauce, juice, vinegar, butter, pie fillings, and snack packs. Its products are available nationwide. The co-op, founded in 1949, also supplies the food service and industrial-ingredients markets with apple products. It also offers private-label and co-packing services.

	Annual Growth	6/03	6/04	6/05	6/06	6/07
Est. sales ($ mil.)	—	—	—	—	—	248.1
Employees	—	—	—	—	—	1,200

⊞ KNOWLEDGE LEARNING CORPORATION

650 NE Holladay St., Ste. 1400
Portland, OR 97232
Phone: 503-872-1300
Fax: 503-872-1349
Web: www.knowledgelearning.com

CEO: Elanna S. Yalow
CFO: Mark D. Moreland
HR: Donna J. Lesch
FYE: December 31
Type: Private

Curious kids are welcome at Knowledge Learning Corporation. Its KinderCare Learning Centers provide day care and educational programs for more than 300,000 children throughout the US. The company provides care for children from their infancy to primary school years, including back-up child care, before- and after-school care, and summer camps. It operates about 2,000 community centers, 600 school-partnership sites, and 130 corporate child care centers. Clients include *FORTUNE* 500, mid-sized, and small companies; local and state governments; hospitals; and universities. The company became the nation's largest private child care provider following its 2005 acquisition of KinderCare Learning Centers.

	Annual Growth	12/02	12/03	12/04	12/05	12/06
Est. sales ($ mil.)	(6.3%)	—	—	—	1,654.0	1,550.0
Employees	0.0%	—	—	—	41,000	41,000

KOCH ENTERPRISES, INC.

14 S. 11th Ave.
Evansville, IN 47744
Phone: 812-465-9800
Fax: 812-465-9613
Web: www.kochenterprises.com

CEO: Robert L. (Bob) Koch II
CFO: Susan E. Parsons
HR: –
FYE: December 31
Type: Private

Koch gets straight A's. Koch Enterprises is a diversified firm with interests in aluminum, automotive finishing systems, air-conditioning equipment, and adhesives. Subsidiaries include George Koch Sons (engineers, installs, and services a range of finishing systems for the auto industry), Koch Air (distributes heating and air-conditioning equipment), Gibbs Die Casting (supplies automotive aluminum die castings), Brake Supply Company (repairs and replaces brakes and hydraulic systems for the auto and mining industries), and Uniseal (makes adhesives and sealants for carmakers, and connectors for drain and waste pipes). George Koch, president Bob Koch's great grandfather, founded the family-owned firm in 1873.

	Annual Growth	12/03	12/04	12/05	12/06	12/07
Est. sales ($ mil.)	—	—	—	—	—	819.1
Employees	—	—	—	—	—	2,900

KOCH ENTERTAINMENT LIMITED PARTNERSHIP

22 Harbor Park Dr.
Port Washington, NY 11050
Phone: 516-484-1000
Fax: 516-484-4746
Web: www.kochent.com

CEO: Michael Koch
CFO: Lawrence Sapadin
HR: Nancy Young
FYE: December 31
Type: Subsidiary

Independents rock! A leading independent music and DVD distributor, KOCH Entertainment (formerly KOCH Entertainment Distribution) distributes music to retailers in the US and Canada through its KOCH Entertainment Distribution arm. The company also operates a record label, KOCH Records, established when KOCH acquired Velvel Records from Velvel founder Walter Yetnikoff, the former head of CBS Records. KOCH also operates video and publishing divisions that distribute DVDs (films, TV shows, and concerts) and publish music for KOCH artists, respectively. CEO Michael Koch founded the company in 1987. He sold it to Canada-based Entertainment One (formerly ROW Entertainment) in 2005.

	Annual Growth	12/03	12/04	12/05	12/06	12/07
Est. sales ($ mil.)	—	—	—	—	—	51.1
Employees	—	—	—	—	—	280

KOCH FOODS INCORPORATED

1300 W. Higgins Rd.
Park Ridge, IL 60068
Phone: 847-384-5940
Fax: 847-384-5961
Web: www.kochfoods.com

CEO: Joseph C. (Joe) Grendys
CFO: Mark Kaminsky
HR: –
FYE: December 31
Type: Private

Kids, always ready with a joke, ask why the chicken crossed the road. But it's you who should cross the road — to get to Koch Foods — because the company is ready with a whole henhouse full of chicken products. Koch is one of the top chicken producers in the US, and its products include value-added fresh and frozen chicken products, including chicken tenderloins, tenders, strips, boneless breasts, and wings, along with diced and pulled white and dark meat, and whole and whole cut-up chickens. Its customers include companies in the retail food and food service sectors throughout the country and overseas.

	Annual Growth	12/02	12/03	12/04	12/05	12/06
Est. sales ($ mil.)	28.6%	—	—	—	1,400.0	1,800.0
Employees	6.7%	—	—	—	7,500	8,000

⊞ KOCH INDUSTRIES, INC.

4111 E. 37th St. North
Wichita, KS 67220
Phone: 316-828-5500
Fax: 316-828-5739
Web: www.kochind.com

CEO: Charles G. Koch
CFO: Steve Feilmeier
HR: –
FYE: December 31
Type: Private

Following the assimilation of forest products giant Georgia-Pacific (for a reported $21 billion), Koch Industries has become a real paper tiger. Koch (pronounced "coke") is one of the largest private companies in the US. Its operations include refining and chemicals, process equipment, and technologies; fibers and polymers; commodity and financial trading; and forest and consumer products. Koch's Flint Hills Resources subsidiary owns three refineries that process 800,000 barrels of crude oil daily. Koch operates crude gathering systems and pipelines across North America as well as cattle ranches in Kansas, Montana, and Texas. Brothers Charles and David Koch control the company.

	Annual Growth	12/03	12/04	12/05	12/06	12/07
Sales ($ mil.)	25.1%	40,000.0	40,000.0	80,000.0	90,000.0	98,000.0
Employees	27.8%	30,000	30,000	80,000	80,000	80,000

KODIAK OIL & GAS CORP.   AMEX: KOG

1625 Broadway, Ste. 330
Denver, CO 80202
Phone: 303-592-8075
Fax: 303-592-8071
Web: www.kodiakog.com

CEO: Lynn A. Peterson
CFO: Keith Doss
HR: –
FYE: December 31
Type: Public

Kodiak Oil & Gas bears the responsibility for exploration, development, and production of oil and natural gas in the Rockies. The company, which focuses on assets in the Vermillion Basin of the Green River Basin and the Williston Basin (located in Montana and North Dakota), had proved reserves of 5.6 billion cu. ft. of natural gas equivalent in 2006. Kodiak Oil & Gas has 80,130 net acres of land holdings. In the Green River Basin it is exploring for unconventional gas through the exploitation of coalbed methane, over-pressured shales, and tight-gas-sands.

	Annual Growth	12/03	12/04	12/05	12/06	12/07
Sales ($ mil.)	—	0.0	0.0	0.4	5.0	9.3
Net income ($ mil.)	—	(0.3)	(1.1)	(2.0)	(2.8)	(38.2)
Market value ($ mil.)	21.6%	—	—	130.9	343.2	193.6
Employees		—	—	—	—	—

⊞ An in-depth profile of this company is available to Hoover's Online members at hoovers.com.

903

KOHLBERG & COMPANY, L.L.C.

111 Radio Cir.
Mt. Kisco, NY 10549
Phone: 914-241-7430
Fax: 914-241-7476
Web: www.kohlberg.com

CEO: James A. Kohlberg
CFO: Shant Mardirossian
HR: –
FYE: December 31
Type: Private

Call it the Kohlberg Variations: Kohlberg & Company specializes in buyouts, recapitalizations, and equity investments of middle-market companies (valued between $100 million and $500 million) in industries ranging from machinery and equipment, to food and consumer, to health care. The firm typically invests $30 million to $125 million, and works with the management of its portfolio companies to guide their growth. Kohlberg was founded in 1987 by Jerome Kohlberg Jr., the senior founding partner of KKR (formerly Kohlberg Kravis Roberts), and James A. Kohlberg, but is not affiliated with that company.

	Annual Growth	12/03	12/04	12/05	12/06	12/07
Est. sales ($ mil.)	—	—	—	—	—	1,114.0
Employees	—	—	—	—	—	4,500

KOHLER CO.

444 Highland Dr.
Kohler, WI 53044
Phone: 920-457-4441
Fax: 920-457-1271
Web: kohlerco.com

CEO: Herbert V. Kohler Jr.
CFO: Jeffrey P. Cheney
HR: Laura Kohler
FYE: December 31
Type: Private

Kohler's profits are in the toilet, literally. The company makes bathroom and kitchen products — from toilets and baths to showers and sinks — under the names Kohler, Hytec, and Sterling. It also makes furniture under the names Baker and McGuire, as well as ceramic, stone, and mosaic tile under the brand Ann Sacks. Lesser-known operations include Kohler's manufacturing of small engines, generators, and power supplies for both consumer and industrial applications. Kohler's real estate operations include Destination Kohler, a resort in Wisconsin, and Old Course Hotel Golf Resort and Spa in Scotland. Chairman Herbert Kohler Jr. and his sister Ruth Kohler, grandchildren of the founder, control Kohler.

	Annual Growth	12/02	12/03	12/04	12/05	12/06
Est. sales ($ mil.)	13.6%	3,000.0	3,005.0	3,000.0	3,000.0	5,000.0
Employees	7.2%	25,000	25,000	28,000	31,000	33,000

KOHL'S CORPORATION

NYSE: KSS

N56 W17000 Ridgewood Dr.
Menomonee Falls, WI 53051
Phone: 262-703-7000
Fax: 262-703-6143
Web: www.kohls.com

CEO: R. Lawrence (Larry) Montgomery
CFO: Wesley S. (Wes) McDonald
HR: Telvin Jeffries
FYE: Saturday nearest January 31
Type: Public

Kohl's wants to be easy on shoppers and tough on competition. The company operates about 950 discount department stores in 47 states. Nearly a third of its stores are in the Midwest, where Kohl's continues to grow while rapidly expanding into other markets. Moderately priced name-brand and private-label apparel, shoes, accessories, and housewares are sold through centrally located cash registers, designed to expedite checkout and keep staff costs down. Kohl's competes with discount and mid-level department stores. Merchandising relationships allow Kohl's to carry top brands (NIKE, Levi's, OshKosh B'Gosh) not typically available to discounters; it sells them cheaper than department stores by controlling costs.

	Annual Growth	1/04	1/05	1/06	1/07	1/08
Sales ($ mil.)	12.5%	10,282.1	11,700.6	13,402.2	15,544.2	16,473.7
Net income ($ mil.)	16.4%	591.2	730.4	842.0	1,108.7	1,083.8
Market value ($ mil.)	(1.4%)	15,068.2	15,663.4	15,252.9	23,480.1	14,259.8
Employees	16.8%	—	—	107,000	125,000	—

KOKOSING CONSTRUCTION CO., INC.

17531 Waterford Rd.
Fredericktown, OH 43019
Phone: 740-694-6315
Fax: 740-694-1481
Web: www.kokosing-inc.com/new_page_1.htm

CEO: Brian Burgett
CFO: –
HR: –
FYE: March 31
Type: Private

Regional general contractor Kokosing Construction is one of the largest non-residential builders in Ohio. The company operates through three divisions: its highway and heavy industrial divisions in Ohio and its Durocher Marine division (piers, docks, and breakwaters and environmental remediation) in Michigan. The company's projects include commercial and institutional buildings, heavy industrial process plants, waste and water-treatment plants, underground sewer and utility lines, heavy/highway construction, and industrial waste management projects. It also provides renovation work. The company, which was founded in 1951 by Bill Burgett and Les Rinehart, is owned and run by the Burgett family.

	Annual Growth	3/03	3/04	3/05	3/06	3/07
Est. sales ($ mil.)	—	—	—	—	—	534.1
Employees	—	—	—	—	—	1,061

KOLLSMAN, INC.

220 Daniel Webster Hwy.
Merrimack, NH 03054
Phone: 603-889-2500
Fax: 603-889-7966
Web: www.kollsman.com

CEO: Randy Moore
CFO: Bob Goodnow
HR: Jack McStravock
FYE: December 31
Type: Subsidiary

Kollsman helps you gauge your progress. The company develops advanced avionics and electro-optic instruments and systems for aerospace, defense, and medical applications. Two units deal with aerospace and defense: Its Commercial Aviation Systems unit makes air data instruments and test equipment, cabin pressurization systems, and vision landing systems for commercial aircraft; its Defense EO Systems unit makes infrared and laser-based optic systems for military and homeland security use. Kollsman's subsidiary, KMC Systems, provides contract services for the development and manufacture of electromechanical instruments for the medical industry. Kollsman is a unit of Israel-based defense concern Elbit Systems.

	Annual Growth	12/03	12/04	12/05	12/06	12/07
Est. sales ($ mil.)	—	—	—	—	—	44.7
Employees	—	—	—	—	—	550

KOLORFUSION INTERNATIONAL, INC.

OTC: KOLR

1605 E. 32nd Ave., Ste. A
Aurora, CO 80011
Phone: 303-340-9994
Fax: 303-340-9982
Web: www.kolorfusion.com

CEO: Stephen Nagel
CFO: Stephen Nagel
HR: –
FYE: June 30
Type: Public

Beauty might be more than skin-deep, but surface appearances are what matter most to Kolorfusion International. Via the Kolorfusion process, the company's customers can print colors and patterns onto coatings on metal, wood, and glass products, and directly onto plastic products. The company maintains production capabilities for clients in the US and Canada and licenses the process internationally to other clients. Customers have included Daisy Manufacturing, Moen, and Polaris. Investor Philippe Nordman owns 42% of Kolorfusion International, and company president Stephen Nagel holds a 26% stake.

	Annual Growth	6/03	6/04	6/05	6/06	6/07
Sales ($ mil.)	(2.9%)	1.8	2.5	2.3	2.1	1.6
Net income ($ mil.)	5.7%	0.4	(0.6)	(0.6)	(0.3)	0.5
Market value ($ mil.)	(31.0%)	10.5	12.1	2.9	2.1	2.4
Employees	—	—	—	—	—	9

KOMATSU AMERICA CORP.

1701 W. Golf Rd.
Rolling Meadows, IL 60008
Phone: 847-437-5800
Fax: 847-437-5814
Web: www.komatsuamerica.com

CEO: David W. (Dave) Grzelak
CFO: Yoshio (Phil) Yanai
HR: John Angster
FYE: March 31
Type: Subsidiary

You would need a very big sandbox to play with Komatsu America's dump trucks and dozers. The company, a subsidiary of Japanese construction equipment giant Komatsu (#2 worldwide after Caterpillar), manufactures, sells, and maintains earth-moving machinery for the North American construction and mining markets. Komatsu America divides its operations into utility equipment (compact construction equipment) and mining systems. Its products include dump trucks, backhoes, crushers, graders, hydraulic excavators, crawler carriers, wheel loaders, bulldozers, and a computer-based mine management system. Komatsu America also provides financing and rents and sells used equipment.

KONICA MINOLTA BUSINESS SOLUTIONS U.S.A., INC.

101 Williams Dr.
Ramsey, NJ 07446
Phone: 201-825-4000
Fax: 201-825-7605
Web: www.kmbs.konicaminolta.us

CEO: Jun Haraguchi
CFO: Michael Leonczyk
HR: Donald Warwick
FYE: December 31
Type: Subsidiary

Konica Minolta Business Solutions (KMBS U.S.A.) is part of Konica Minolta Holdings, which was created from the 2003 merger of Konica and Minolta. KMBS U.S.A. offers copiers, fax machines, printers, and other office machines. In addition to standard customer support, it provides services such as document process streamlining and infrastructure management through its professional services group. KMBS U.S.A. serves organizations ranging from small offices to large production operations. The company operates branch offices and distribution centers throughout the US.

KONA GRILL, INC.

NASDAQ (GM): KONA

7150 E. Camelback Rd., Ste. 220
Scottsdale, AZ 85251
Phone: 480-922-8100
Fax: 480-991-6811
Web: www.konagrill.com

CEO: Marcus E. Jundt
CFO: Mark S. Robinow
HR: Debbie Shelton
FYE: December 31
Type: Public

This company is pinning its hopes on the flavor of the Big Island to draw a few mainlanders into its restaurants. Kona Grill operates more than 15 upscale casual-dining restaurants offering both seafood and American dishes with an island twist. The restaurants serve both lunch and diner menus, and they offer a wide selection of sushi. In addition to dining, each location typically has a bar area for happy hour with margaritas and martinis. The restaurants are found in Arizona, Texas, and about 10 other states. Chairman and CEO Marcus Jundt and his family own about 20% of Kona Grill.

	Annual Growth	12/03	12/04	12/05	12/06	12/07
Sales ($ mil.)	44.5%	16.6	25.0	36.8	50.7	72.3
Net income ($ mil.)	—	(0.7)	0.3	(0.4)	(2.7)	(0.7)
Market value ($ mil.)	41.0%	—	—	48.5	120.2	96.5
Employees	—	—	—	1,108	—	—

KOPIN CORPORATION

NASDAQ (GM): KOPN

200 John Hancock Rd.
Taunton, MA 02780
Phone: 508-824-6696
Fax: 508-824-6958
Web: www.kopin.com

CEO: John C. C. Fan
CFO: Richard A. Sneider
HR: Joan Evans
FYE: Last Saturday in December
Type: Public

Kopin's semiconductor wafers are good at copin' with high speeds. The company makes specialized gallium arsenide (GaAs) wafers with heterojunction bipolar transistors engineered onto the surface vertically (horizontal is the industry norm). Companies such as Skyworks Solutions (26% of sales) use the specialized GaAs wafers — costlier than silicon but with higher performance — to make integrated circuits for wireless and fiber-optic gear that demands high speed or low power consumption. Kopin also makes tiny display devices used by Matsushita, Samsung Electronics, SANYO Electric (16% of sales), and Victor Company of Japan in digital camcorders. The company gets more than half of its sales in the Americas.

	Annual Growth	12/03	12/04	12/05	12/06	12/07
Sales ($ mil.)	6.4%	76.6	87.3	90.3	71.1	98.2
Net income ($ mil.)	—	(6.9)	(13.8)	11.7	(2.2)	(6.6)
Market value ($ mil.)	(18.7%)	470.0	269.3	371.0	240.7	205.3
Employees	(3.5%)	418	379	317	299	363

KONE INC.

1 Kone Ct.
Moline, IL 61265
Phone: 309-764-6771
Fax: 309-743-5469
Web: www.kone.com/en_US/main

CEO: Vance Tang
CFO: W.A. Bowers
HR: Charles Moore
FYE: December 31
Type: Subsidiary

KONE began its elevator business on the ground floor and is working its way up. The US subsidiary of Finland's KONE sells, manufactures, upgrades, and maintains elevators, escalators, and automatic building doors. The KONE EcoSpace line of elevators is an environmentally friendly (using no oil) traction elevator that offers more space while conserving energy for residential, office, and public access use. Other brand names include the KONE HH Series and MX Series line of hydraulic elevators, as well as the KONE EcoSystem MR elevator. KONE USA accounts for about one-fifth of its parent company's elevator and escalator sales.

	Annual Growth	12/03	12/04	12/05	12/06	12/07
Est. sales ($ mil.)	—	—	—	—	—	288.7
Employees	—	—	—	—	—	4,100

KOPPERS HOLDINGS INC.

NYSE: KOP

436 7th Ave.
Pittsburgh, PA 15219
Phone: 412-227-2001
Fax: 412-227-2333
Web: www.koppers.com

CEO: Walter W. Turner
CFO: Brian H. McCurrie
HR: Steven R. (Steve) Lacy
FYE: December 31
Type: Public

Koppers Holdings treats wood right. The company makes carbon compounds and treated-wood products for the chemical, railroad, aluminum, utility, construction, and steel industries around the world. Its carbon materials and chemicals unit makes materials for producing aluminum, polyester resins, plasticizers, and wood preservatives. The railroad and utility products unit supplies treated cross ties and utility poles and treats wood for vineyard, construction, and other uses. Koppers Holdings owns 50% of KSA Limited — Lehigh Cement owns the other half — which produces concrete cross ties. Investment firm Saratoga Partners had owned Koppers before taking it public in 2006.

	Annual Growth	12/03	12/04	12/05	12/06	12/07
Sales ($ mil.)	12.0%	842.9	952.5	1,030.2	1,159.5	1,327.9
Net income ($ mil.)	—	(37.1)	9.6	9.9	15.2	63.3
Market value ($ mil.)	66.6%	—	—	—	540.4	900.5
Employees	(2.5%)	—	—	2,026	1,983	1,927

An in-depth profile of this company is available to Hoover's Online members at hoovers.com.

KORN/FERRY INTERNATIONAL

NYSE: KFY

1900 Avenue of the Stars, Ste. 2600	CEO: Gary D. Burnison
Los Angeles, CA 90067	CFO: Stephen J. Giusto
Phone: 310-552-1834	HR: Janet Clardy
Fax: 310-553-6452	FYE: April 30
Web: www.kornferry.com	Type: Public

High-level executives can jump ship via Korn/Ferry International. The world's largest executive recruitment firm, Korn/Ferry has 70 offices in more than 35 countries. The company's some 400 consultants help prominent public and private companies, as well as government and not-for-profit organizations, find qualified job applicants for openings in a variety of executive level positions (including CEOs, CFOs, and other senior-level jobs). Through Futurestep, job seekers use the Internet and videotaped job interviews to find mid-level management positions. In addition, the company provides management assessment as well as coaching and executive development services. Korn/Ferry was founded in 1969.

	Annual Growth	4/03	4/04	4/05	4/06	4/07
Sales ($ mil.)	19.5%	338.5	350.7	476.4	551.8	689.2
Net income ($ mil.)	—	(22.9)	5.4	38.6	59.4	55.5
Market value ($ mil.)	44.0%	258.6	571.8	574.4	865.2	1,111.9
Employees	—	—	—	—	1,841	—

KOSAN BIOSCIENCES INCORPORATED

NASDAQ (GM): KOSN

3832 Bay Center Place	CEO: Helen S. Kim
Hayward, CA 94545	CFO: Gary S. Titus
Phone: 510-732-8400	HR: –
Fax: 510-732-8401	FYE: December 31
Web: www.kosan.com	Type: Public

Kosan Biosciences has a way with polyketides. The development-stage firm alters the naturally occurring compounds (which are produced by microorganisms) to help cure cancer. Kosan Biosciences' drug candidate tanespimycin is in clinical trials for the treatment of multiple myeloma (a kind of blood cancer) and breast and skin cancer. Another drug candidate, dubbed KOS-1584, may treat patients with solid tumors, including lung, ovarian, and pancreatic cancers. In addition, Pfizer has licensed some drug candidates from Kosan for the treatment of gastrointestinal conditions. Kosan agreed to be acquired by Bristol-Myers Squibb in 2008.

	Annual Growth	12/03	12/04	12/05	12/06	12/07
Sales ($ mil.)	(7.8%)	31.4	22.9	13.4	13.5	22.7
Net income ($ mil.)	—	(9.7)	(22.1)	(29.6)	(29.5)	(28.7)
Market value ($ mil.)	(14.2%)	283.5	201.6	130.4	196.4	153.3
Employees	6.7%	—	—	80	—	91

KOSS CORPORATION

NASDAQ (GM): KOSS

4129 N. Port Washington Ave.	CEO: Michael J. Koss
Milwaukee, WI 53212	CFO: Michael J. Koss
Phone: 414-964-5000	HR: Cheryl Mike
Fax: 414-964-8615	FYE: June 30
Web: www.koss.com	Type: Public

Koss makes sure you can turn up the volume without disturbing the neighbors. It makes stereo headphones, or "stereophones," and related accessories. Koss products include headphones for home and on-the-go. It also sells headphones for communications purposes (DJ, home recording, telephone). It has two subsidiaries: Koss Classics and Bi-Audio. Koss products are sold through more than 15,000 US retail outlets, including audio specialty stores, catalogs, discount stores, and national retailers, as well as to fire and police units. It has an international office in Switzerland. The Koss family — including founder John Koss (inventor of stereo headphones) and his son, CEO Michael — owns more than 75% of the firm.

	Annual Growth	6/03	6/04	6/05	6/06	6/07
Sales ($ mil.)	8.1%	33.8	40.5	40.3	50.9	46.2
Net income ($ mil.)	5.5%	4.2	5.4	4.5	6.2	5.2
Market value ($ mil.)	(0.2%)	69.3	79.6	64.3	92.3	68.8
Employees	—	—	—	95	—	—

KPMG L.L.P.

757 Third Ave.	CEO: Timothy P. (Tim) Flynn
New York, NY 10017	CFO: Thomas Löhmer
Phone: 212-909-5600	HR: Douglas K. (Doug) Jukes
Fax: 212-909-5699	FYE: September 30
Web: www.us.kpmg.com	Type: Partnership

KPMG L.L.P. is the US member firm of KPMG International, one of accounting's Big Four (which also includes Deloitte Touche Tohmatsu, Ernst & Young, and PricewaterhouseCoopers). KPMG has about 95 offices across the US, offering a wide range of accounting, audit, and tax-related services to customers in such target industries as banking, media and entertainment, consumer products, health care providers, insurance, and pharmaceuticals. KPMG has admitted to "unlawful conduct" in an ongoing investigation by the Department of Justice for its work on questionable tax shelters that the firm developed and marketed in between 1996 and 2002; KPMG has agreed to pay a $456 million penalty and accept an outside monitor.

	Annual Growth	9/02	9/03	9/04	9/05	9/06
Sales ($ mil.)	—	—	—	—	—	4,800.0
Employees	—	—	—	—	—	23,600

KRAFT FOODS INC.

NYSE: KFT

3 Lakes Dr.	CEO: Irene B. Rosenfeld
Northfield, IL 60093	CFO: Timothy R. (Tim) McLevish
Phone: 847-646-2000	HR: Karen J. May
Fax: 847-646-6005	FYE: December 31
Web: www.kraft.com	Type: Public

Mac & cheese if you please. Kraft Foods is the US's #1 food company and #2 in the world (behind Nestlé). Its North America unit makes the world's largest cheese brand (Kraft), owns the cookie and cracker business (Nabisco) and makes that slam-dunk favorite, Oreos. Its international business unit offers most of its US brands, plus national favorites. The Oscar Mayer, Kraft, Philadelphia, Maxwell House, Nabisco, Oreo, Jacobs, Milka, and LU brands have revenues of at least $1 billion; more than 50 hit the $100 million mark. Kraft extricated itself from the haze of second-hand tobacco smoke when it was spun off from Altria in 2007; later the same year, it announced the sale of its Post Cereals business to Ralcorp.

	Annual Growth	12/03	12/04	12/05	12/06	12/07
Sales ($ mil.)	4.7%	31,010.0	32,168.0	34,113.0	34,356.0	37,241.0
Net income ($ mil.)	(7.1%)	3,476.0	2,665.0	2,632.0	3,060.0	2,590.0
Market value ($ mil.)	30.1%	17,461.2	18,707.9	13,799.9	16,278.2	50,047.2
Employees	4.7%	—	—	94,000	90,000	103,000

KRAFT INTERNATIONAL

3 Lakes Dr.	CEO: Sanjay Khosla
Northfield, IL 60093	CFO: –
Phone: 847-646-2000	HR: –
Fax: 847-646-2922	FYE: December 31
Web: www.kraft.com	Type: Business segment

"Velveeta" may not translate beyond North America, but Kraft International has plenty of brands that do. As a business segment of the world's #2 food company, Kraft Foods Inc., Kraft International sells food products in some 150 countries worldwide. In addition to many of the same products sold by its sister segment, Kraft North America (Kraft cheeses, Miracle Whip salad dressing, and Tang powdered drink), Kraft International's products include Jacobs and Carte Noire coffees, and Milka and Toblerone candy. Kraft Foods bought Nabisco in 2000 and integrated its international food brands (Oreo, Ritz, and Club Social biscuits) into the Kraft International fold.

KRAFT NORTH AMERICA

3 Lakes Dr.
Northfield, IL 60093
Phone: 847-646-2000
Fax: 847-646-6005

CEO: Richard G. (Rick) Searer
CFO: –
HR: –
FYE: December 31
Type: Business segment

What do you get when you mix Jell-O, Miracle Whip, Oreos, and Velveeta? You get a big slice of the Kraft Foods pie called Kraft North America. A business segment of the world's #2 food company, it "houses" the company's North American consumer sectors, including beverages, cheese and dairy, convenient meals, grocery, snacks and cereals, and food service operations. Other segments' brands include Kraft, Maxwell House, Oscar Mayer, Kool-Aid, Post, South Beach Living, and Tombstone. Former parent Philip Morris (now Altria Group) acquired Nabisco in 2000 and folded its operations (including Ritz crackers and Chips Ahoy!) into its North American unit. Altria spun Kraft off in 2007.

	Annual Growth	12/02	12/03	12/04	12/05	12/06
Sales ($ mil.)	12.5%	21,485.0	21,907.0	22,060.0	23,293.0	34,356.0
Employees	—	—	—	—	—	—

KRAFTMAID CABINETRY

15535 S. State Ave.
Middlefield, OH 44062
Phone: 440-632-5333
Fax: 440-632-0726
Web: www.kraftmaid.com

CEO: Mike Newton
CFO: John Pederson
HR: –
FYE: December 31
Type: Subsidiary

KraftMaid Cabinetry can dish it with the best of them. The company, a subsidiary of Masco Corporation, is one of the largest cabinetmakers in the world and a leading manufacturer of built-to-order cabinetry. Set in the heart of Amish country, the company operates plants in Middlefield, Ohio (cabinetry parts milling, cabinet assembly, frame construction and finishing, and specialty part finishing) and Orwell, Ohio (cabinetry doors and drawer fronts). It sells products through distributors and home centers throughout the US as well as international markets. The company was founded in 1969 and was purchased by Masco in 1990.

	Annual Growth	12/03	12/04	12/05	12/06	12/07
Est. sales ($ mil.)	—	—	—	—	—	200.8
Employees	—	—	—	—	—	3,022

KRANSON INDUSTRIES, INC.

10330 Old Olive Street Rd.
St. Louis, MO 63141
Phone: 314-569-3633
Fax: 314-569-5087
Web: www.tricorbraun.com

CEO: Keith Strope
CFO: Neil Tzinberg
HR: –
FYE: December 31
Type: Private

Kranson Industries (primarily doing business as TricorBraun) doesn't have a genie in a bottle, but it has a bottle for just about everything else. The company's three subsidiaries, TricorBraun, Caliber Wine, and Clinton Packaging, distribute glass and plastic bottles and jars for the personal care, food and beverage, health care, and chemical industries. Kranson Industries also supplies sprayers, boxes, corks, tanks and drums, and linerboard. The company has about 30 distribution centers across the US, and represents every major closure and container maker in Canada and the US. AEA Investors took control of Kranson Industries in 2004, then sold it to Code Hennessy & Simmons in 2006.

	Annual Growth	12/03	12/04	12/05	12/06	12/07
Est. sales ($ mil.)	—	—	—	—	—	540.0
Employees	—	—	—	—	—	370

KRASDALE FOODS INC.

65 W. Red Oak Ln.
White Plains, NY 10604
Phone: 914-694-6400
Fax: 914-697-5225
Web: www.krasdalefoods.com

CEO: Charles A. Krasne
CFO: Steve Silver
HR: Bernie Patton
FYE: December 31
Type: Private

Krasdale Foods is a leading independent grocery wholesaler that supplies more than 7,000 products to food retailers, mostly in the New York metropolitan area. From its distribution center in the Bronx, the company offers both private-label and regional brands, as well as ethnic and specialty food items. Krasdale also provides merchandising and marketing services to its customers. Abraham Krasne founded the company as A. Krasne Inc. in 1908. (The name was changed in 1972.) Krasdale is led by Krasne's son, CEO Charles Krasne; the family continues to own and operate the business.

	Annual Growth	12/03	12/04	12/05	12/06	12/07
Est. sales ($ mil.)	—	—	—	—	—	189.4
Employees	—	—	—	—	—	530

KRATON POLYMERS LLC

15710 John F. Kennedy Blvd., Ste. 300
Houston, TX 77032
Phone: 281-504-4700
Fax: 281-504-4817
Web: www.kraton.com

CEO: Kevin M. Fogarty
CFO: Stephen E. (Steve) Tremblay
HR: Richard A. (Rick) Ott
FYE: December 31
Type: Private

When the rubber meets the road, KRATON Polymers is responsible for both ends of the equation. Its styrenic block copolymers (SBCs) are important ingredients in both footwear and road building materials. SBCs are a kind of polymer used in a variety of plastic, rubber, and chemicals, as well as for improving the stability of asphalt. More specifically, the KRATON family of polymers is used in adhesives, toys, and packaging, and to make shoe soles. The company has six manufacturing facilities in Asia, Europe, and North and South America. Private investment firm Texas Pacific Group (TPG) has owned KRATON since late 2003.

	Annual Growth	12/03	12/04	12/05	12/06	12/07
Sales ($ mil.)	11.6%	702.6	807.4	975.6	1,048.1	1,089.6
Net income ($ mil.)	—	7.8	(32.7)	22.7	(3.6)	(43.7)
Employees	0.0%	—	850	940	800	850

KRATOS DEFENSE & SECURITY SOLUTIONS, INC.

NASDAQ (GS): KTOS

4810 Eastgate Mall
San Diego, CA 92121
Phone: 858-228-2000
Fax: 858-228-2001
Web: www.kratosdefense.com

CEO: Eric M. DeMarco
CFO: Deanna H. Lund
HR: –
FYE: December 31
Type: Public

Kratos Defense & Security Solutions (formerly Wireless Facilities) designs technology systems and provides engineering, IT, and other technical services primarily to defense and security agencies of the federal government as well as state and local agencies. The company also creates and maintains in-building IT networks that integrate voice, data, security, and building automation. Additionally, it provides program requirement development, operational testing, and software customization services. Customers have included the US Department of Defense.

	Annual Growth	12/03	12/04	12/05	12/06	12/07
Sales ($ mil.)	(7.2%)	261.0	397.0	375.3	327.8	193.6
Net income ($ mil.)	—	9.5	5.0	3.7	(57.9)	(40.8)
Market value ($ mil.)	(33.1%)	929.5	672.2	368.2	210.6	185.6
Employees	—	—	—	2,300	—	—

An in-depth profile of this company is available to Hoover's Online members at hoovers.com.

907

KRAUSE GENTLE CORP.

6400 Westown Pkwy.
West Des Moines, IA 50266
Phone: 515-226-0694
Fax: 515-226-0995
Web: www.kumandgo.com

CEO: Kyle Krause
CFO: Craig Bergstrom
HR: Greg Grove
FYE: December 31
Type: Private

If you're in a hurry in Iowa, Krause Gentle provides an assist. The company runs about 450 Kum & Go convenience stores, mostly in Iowa, but also in a dozen other states. The stores provide basic gas station amenities, as well as the company's private-label line (Hiland) of coffee, potato chips, sandwiches, and other foods. Some stores have fast food outlets, such as Blimpie. The company has more than doubled its Kum & Go store count since 1997, mostly through acquisitions. Solar Transport, a petroleum products and fertilizer hauler, Liberty Bank, and the Des Moines Menace soccer team are affiliated with Krause Gentle, which was founded in 1959. The founding Krause and Gentle families still own Krause Gentle.

KREISLER MANUFACTURING CORPORATION

NASDAQ (CM): KRSL

180 Van Riper Ave.
Elmwood Park, NJ 07407
Phone: 201-791-0700
Fax: 201-791-8015
Web: www.kreisler-ind.com

CEO: Michael D. Stern
CFO: Edward A. Stern
HR: Lisa Sibrel
FYE: June 30
Type: Public

Your Chrysler might have a hemi under the hood, but this Kreisler focuses on bigger engines. Kreisler Manufacturing, through subsidiary Kreisler Industrial, makes precision metal components for commercial and military aircraft engines and industrial gas turbines. Tube assemblies — used to transfer fuel for combustion, hydraulic fluid for thrust reversers, and oil for lubrication — account for most of the company's sales. A second subsidiary, Kreisler Polska, supplies machined components to Kreisler Industrial from a manufacturing plant in Krakow, Poland. Chairman Wallace Kelly controls a 38% stake in Kreisler Manufacturing.

	Annual Growth	6/03	6/04	6/05	6/06	6/07
Sales ($ mil.)	17.6%	12.5	12.3	14.4	19.7	23.9
Net income ($ mil.)	—	(0.7)	(0.7)	0.2	1.2	2.0
Market value ($ mil.)	36.1%	8.5	12.7	9.7	24.5	29.0
Employees	27.3%	—	—	124	155	201

KRISPY KREME DOUGHNUTS, INC.

NYSE: KKD

370 Knollwood St., Ste. 500
Winston-Salem, NC 27103
Phone: 336-725-2981
Fax: 336-733-3791
Web: www.krispykreme.com

CEO: James H. (Jim) Morgan
CFO: Douglas R. (Doug) Muir
HR: Kenneth J. Hudson
FYE: Sunday nearest January 31
Type: Public

This sweet treats outlet doesn't use any digging equipment, but it does make a lot of holes. Krispy Kreme Doughnuts operates a chain of almost 300 doughnut shops and more than 180 smaller-format satellite locations throughout the US and in more than a dozen other countries. The shops are popular for glazed doughnuts that are served fresh and hot out of the fryer. In addition to its original glazed variety, Krispy Kreme serves cake and filled doughnuts, crullers, and fritters, as well as hot coffee and other beverages. About 100 locations are company-owned, while the rest are franchised. Krispy Kreme also markets its doughnuts through grocery stores and supermarkets.

	Annual Growth	1/04	1/05	1/06	1/07	1/08
Sales ($ mil.)	(10.4%)	665.6	707.8	543.4	461.2	429.3
Net income ($ mil.)	—	57.1	(198.3)	(135.8)	(42.2)	(67.1)
Market value ($ mil.)	(45.8%)	2,184.2	534.8	329.6	807.2	188.9
Employees	(11.1%)	—	5,733	4,759	4,759	4,033

⊞ THE KROGER CO.

NYSE: KR

1014 Vine St.
Cincinnati, OH 45202
Phone: 513-762-4000
Fax: 513-762-1160
Web: www.kroger.com

CEO: David B. Dillon
CFO: J. Michael Schlotman
HR: Della Wall
FYE: Saturday nearest January 31
Type: Public

Kroger is the nation's #1 pure grocery chain, but it still must watch out for falling prices; Wal-Mart has overtaken Kroger as the largest seller of groceries in the US. While Kroger has diversified through acquisitions, adding jewelry and general merchandise to its mix, food stores still account for about 85% of sales. The company operates about 3,660 stores, including some 2,485 supermarkets and multi-department stores, under two dozen banners, in about 30 states. It also runs some 780 convenience stores under names such as Quik Stop and Kwik Shop. Kroger's Fred Meyer Stores subsidiary operates more than 120 supercenters, which offer groceries, general merchandise, and jewelry, in the western US.

	Annual Growth	1/04	1/05	1/06	1/07	1/08
Sales ($ mil.)	6.9%	53,791.0	56,434.0	60,553.0	66,111.0	70,235.0
Net income ($ mil.)	39.5%	312.0	(100.0)	958.0	1,115.0	1,181.0
Market value ($ mil.)	5.8%	13,767.8	12,550.7	13,426.1	18,224.3	17,224.7
Employees	5.5%	—	—	290,000	310,000	323,000

⊞ KROLL INC.

1166 Avenue of the Americas
New York, NY 10036
Phone: 212-593-1000
Fax: 212-593-2631
Web: www.krollworldwide.com

CEO: Ben F. Allen
CFO: Michael C. (Mike) Hellriegel
HR: Jim Kelly
FYE: December 31
Type: Subsidiary

Kroll could tell you what it does, but then, of course, it would have to charge you. The risk consulting company is made up of business units such as Background Screening (pre-employment background checking, drug testing, and surveillance services), Security Services (travel risk management, crisis emergency management, security consulting), Corporate Advisory & Restructuring Services (financial services, operational turnaround), Technology Services (computer forensics and data recovery), and Identity Fraud Solutions.

KRONOS ADVANCED TECHNOLOGIES, INC.

OTC: KNOS

464 Common St., Ste. 301
Belmont, MA 02478
Phone: 617-993-9965
Fax: –
Web: www.kronosati.com

CEO: Daniel R. Dwight
CFO: Daniel R. Dwight
HR: –
FYE: June 30
Type: Public

Kronos Advanced Technologies wants to be crowned king of the air purification industry. The company develops proprietary products using its air-movement and air-purification technology for residential and commercial applications, as well as for filtration system applications in operating rooms, manufacturing clean rooms, and other clinical and health care, military, transportation, and industrial markets. The Kronos system moves and purifies air by using high voltage to create an ion exchange. Kronos is working to commercialize its products and fully capitalize its businesses.

	Annual Growth	6/03	6/04	6/05	6/06	6/07
Sales ($ mil.)	(24.0%)	0.6	0.5	0.4	0.2	0.2
Net income ($ mil.)	—	(2.8)	(2.5)	(7.1)	(4.0)	(2.3)
Market value ($ mil.)	(25.6%)	11.8	10.1	6.6	6.9	3.6
Employees		—	—	—	—	—

KRONOS INCORPORATED

297 Billerica Rd.
Chelmsford, MA 01824
Phone: 978-250-9800
Fax: 978-367-5900
Web: www.kronos.com

CEO: Aron J. Ain
CFO: Mark V. Julien
HR: Patrick J. (Pat) Moquin
FYE: September 30
Type: Private

You won't ever catch Kronos taking a nap in the company supply closet. The company's Workforce Central systems collect attendance data and automatically post it to payroll. Kronos data collection systems keep track of factory production and labor hours. It also makes labor management analysis software and payroll processing applications. Kronos sells its products through its own sales force and through an alliance with payroll service company ADP. The company focuses on the health care, manufacturing, government, retail, and hospitality markets. Kronos was acquired by an investment group led by private equity firm Hellman & Friedman in 2007.

	Annual Growth	9/02	9/03	9/04	9/05	9/06
Sales ($ mil.)	14.0%	342.4	397.4	450.7	518.7	578.2
Net income ($ mil.)	9.5%	28.8	34.7	46.3	53.9	41.4
Employees	11.5%	2,200	2,400	2,500	2,900	3,400

KRONOS WORLDWIDE, INC.

NYSE: KRO

5430 LBJ Fwy., Ste. 1700
Dallas, TX 75240
Phone: 972-233-1700
Fax: 972-448-1445
Web: www.kronostio2.com

CEO: Harold C. Simmons
CFO: Gregory M. (Greg) Swalwell
HR: −
FYE: December 31
Type: Public

Kronos can't take credit for Moby Dick being called the White Whale, but as for the brightly white paper the whale's tale is told on . . . that's a different story. Kronos, formerly a wholly owned subsidiary of NL Industries, is among the top manufacturers of titanium dioxide (TiO2 or Tioxide), the most-used whitening pigment for paper, paints, and plastic. With its six manufacturing plants in North America and Europe, Kronos has been able to carve out a place among the top companies in its industry. Kronos has 20% of the European market and about 15% in North America. In 2003 NL spun off Kronos to its own shareholders; NL and its parent company, Valhi, retain majority control of the company.

	Annual Growth	12/03	12/04	12/05	12/06	12/07
Sales ($ mil.)	6.8%	1,008.2	1,128.6	1,196.7	1,279.4	1,310.3
Net income ($ mil.)	—	87.6	314.9	71.0	82.0	(66.7)
Market value ($ mil.)	(5.9%)	1,086.5	1,994.5	1,420.0	1,593.9	853.3
Employees	(0.3%)	—	—	2,415	2,450	2,400

THE KRYSTAL COMPANY

1 Union Sq.
Chattanooga, TN 37402
Phone: 423-757-1550
Fax: 423-757-5610
Web: www.krystal.com

CEO: James F. (Fred) Exum Jr.
CFO: James W. (Jim) Bear
HR: Michael C. Bass
FYE: Sunday nearest December 31
Type: Private

The Krystal Company is a fast-food gem of the South. The company's chain of more than 400 restaurants in almost a dozen southern states are known for their petite, square hamburgers (what Northerners might call a Slyder). In addition, Krystal's menu includes chicken sandwiches (Krystal Chik), chili, corn dogs, breakfast sandwiches, and dessert items. Krystal also sells its burgers through several grocery chains. The company owns and operates about 230 of its locations, while the rest are franchised. Krystal is owned by Port Royal Holdings, which is controlled by former CEO Philip Sanford. The chain got its start in 1932 when R.B. Davenport Jr. and J. Glenn Sherrill opened up shop in Chattanooga, Tennessee.

K-SEA TRANSPORTATION PARTNERS L.P.

NYSE: KSP

1 Tower Center Blvd., 17th Fl.
East Brunswick, NJ 10303
Phone: 732-339-6100
Fax: 732-339-6140
Web: www.k-sea.com

CEO: Timothy J. Casey
CFO: John J. Nicola
HR: Dennis Luba
FYE: June 30
Type: Public

If you're transporting refined petroleum products, it's OK to go by K-Sea. K-Sea Tranportation operates a fleet of more than 70 tank barges and about 60 tugboats to propel them. Overall, the company's fleet has a carrying capacity of more than 4.2 million barrels. K-Sea serves major oil companies, refiners, and oil traders, primarily along the east and west coasts of the US. About 80% of its business comes from one-year or longer contracts; major customers include BP, Chevron, ConocoPhillips, Exxon Mobil, and Rio Energy. Investment funds managed by Jefferies Capital Partners, an affiliate of Jefferies Group, own a controlling stake in K-Sea.

	Annual Growth	6/03	6/04	6/05	6/06	6/07
Sales ($ mil.)	33.2%	—	95.8	121.4	182.8	226.6
Net income ($ mil.)	(9.3%)	—	21.2	8.1	5.9	15.8
Market value ($ mil.)	44.0%	—	107.7	159.9	185.0	321.5
Employees	37.4%	—	—	490	690	925

KSW, INC.

AMEX: KSW

37-16 23rd St.
Long Island City, NY 11101
Phone: 718-361-6500
Fax: 718-784-1943

CEO: Floyd Warkol
CFO: Richard W. Lucas
HR: Rudy Bisnauth
FYE: December 31
Type: Public

KSW may have a need to vent on occasion, but the company still knows how to keep its cool. KSW installs heating, ventilating, and air conditioning (HVAC) and pipe systems through its operating subsidiary, KSW Mechanical Services. The company installs these systems for industrial, commercial, residential, and public works projects mainly in the New York metropolitan area. It generally does not bid on projects less than $3 million. Its top customer is Bovis Lend Lease, which accounts for about 45% of the company's revenues. Rounding out the company's top customers are Newmark Construction Services (20%) and Plaza Construction (13%). Chairman, president, CEO, and secretary Floyd Warkol owns about 12% of KSW.

	Annual Growth	12/03	12/04	12/05	12/06	12/07
Sales ($ mil.)	21.9%	35.0	26.3	53.4	77.1	77.3
Net income ($ mil.)	46.6%	0.8	(1.3)	2.7	2.8	3.7
Market value ($ mil.)	91.6%	3.2	2.1	14.6	40.6	43.5
Employees	0.0%	45	31	43	45	45

K-SWISS INC.

NASDAQ (GS): KSWS

31248 Oak Crest Dr.
Westlake Village, CA 91361
Phone: 818-706-5100
Fax: 818-706-5390
Web: www.kswiss.com

CEO: Steven Nichols
CFO: George Powlick
HR: Yvette Conen
FYE: December 31
Type: Public

K-Swiss refuses to remain neutral in the sports shoe wars. K-Swiss sells athletic, training, and children's shoes; apparel; and accessories. Shoppers keep coming back to the K-Swiss Classic, the white, all-weather, leather tennis shoe that was introduced in 1966 by its founders. Apparel from K-Swiss is aimed at upscale buyers of athletic gear and suburban casualwear. K-Swiss products, marketed under its namesake and Royal Elastics brands, are made by independent suppliers — almost entirely in China — and are sold in department and specialty retail stores, chiefly in the US. Chairman, president, and CEO Steven Nichols owns about 93% of the company's voting shares. It's buying footwear maker Palladium in 2008.

	Annual Growth	12/03	12/04	12/05	12/06	12/07
Sales ($ mil.)	(1.1%)	429.2	484.1	508.6	501.1	410.4
Net income ($ mil.)	(6.0%)	50.1	71.3	75.3	76.9	39.1
Market value ($ mil.)	(7.0%)	644.8	762.8	839.7	814.8	483.2
Employees	5.9%	—	—	510	236	572

An in-depth profile of this company is available to Hoover's Online members at hoovers.com.

909

K-TRON INTERNATIONAL, INC.

NASDAQ (GM): KTII

Rtes. 55 and 553
Pitman, NJ 08071
Phone: 856-589-0500
Fax: 856-589-8113
Web: www.ktron.com

CEO: Edward B. (Ed) Cloues II
CFO: Ronald R. Remick
HR: —
FYE: Saturday nearest December 31
Type: Public

K-Tron International helps keep manufacturers well fed. The company makes feeders that let manufacturers control the flow of solid bulk and liquid materials during manufacturing processes by weight (gravimetric) and volume (volumetric). It also makes pneumatic conveying systems, including vacuum and pressure systems that precisely control the flow of ingredients used by the pharmaceutical, food, chemical, and plastics industries. K-Tron also makes size reduction equipment used to crush coal and wood products. Subsidiary K-Tron Electronics produces electronic assemblies and controller hardware.

	Annual Growth	12/03	12/04	12/05	12/06	12/07
Sales ($ mil.)	20.8%	94.7	112.5	118.9	148.1	201.7
Net income ($ mil.)	54.9%	3.7	6.6	7.3	12.9	21.3
Market value ($ mil.)	62.3%	47.0	67.1	95.6	195.1	325.7
Employees	—	—	—	460	—	—

KUBOTA TRACTOR CORPORATION

3401 Del Amo Blvd.
Torrance, CA 90503
Phone: 310-370-3370
Fax: 310-370-2370
Web: www.kubota.com

CEO: Tetsuji (Mike) Tomita
CFO: Toby Anderson
HR: —
FYE: March 31
Type: Subsidiary

If you need a tractor but are worried about fitting it into tight parking spaces, the products sold by Kubota Tractor Corporation (KTC) fit the bill just right. The company acts as the American distribution arm of Japanese heavy-equipment industry heavy hitter Kubota Corporation and specializes in compact tractors, construction equipment, and lawn and garden machinery. It's the leading marketer and distributor of under-40 horsepower tractors in the US, offering four lines of tractors. Kubota Credit Corporation U.S.A. provides financing options for the company's products, for both purchase and lease.

	Annual Growth	3/03	3/04	3/05	3/06	3/07
Est. sales ($ mil.)	—	—	—	—	—	72.6
Employees	—	—	—	—	—	360

KUEHNE + NAGEL, INC.

10 Exchange Place, 19th Fl.
Jersey City, NJ 07302
Phone: 201-413-5500
Fax: 201-413-5777
Web: http://www.kn-portal.com/location.cfm?page=na/US

CEO: Rolf Altorfer
CFO: Michael Schimpf
HR: —
FYE: December 31
Type: Subsidiary

Kuehne + Nagel, Inc. (pronounced KOO-nuh and NAH-gel) is the primary US-based unit of freight forwarding and logistics giant Kuehne + Nagel International AG. It operates from a network of some 30 distribution centers and 45 import/export offices throughout the US. Kuehne + Nagel, Inc., specializes in contract logistics services, including warehousing and distribution. In addition, it participates in the parent company's international freight forwarding operations by coordinating air, sea, and ground transportation. Like other freight forwarders, Kuehne + Nagel, Inc., doesn't own transportation assets; instead, it buys capacity from carriers and resells it to customers.

	Annual Growth	12/03	12/04	12/05	12/06	12/07
Est. sales ($ mil.)	—	—	—	—	—	1,949.7
Employees	—	—	—	—	—	2,900

KULICKE AND SOFFA INDUSTRIES, INC.

NASDAQ (GM): KLIC

1005 Virginia Dr.
Fort Washington, PA 19034
Phone: 215-784-6000
Fax: 215-784-6001
Web: www.kns.com

CEO: C. Scott Kulicke
CFO: Maurice E. Carson
HR: —
FYE: September 30
Type: Public

"Some assembly required" is music to Kulicke and Soffa Industries' ears. Kulicke and Soffa (K&S) is the world's top supplier of assembly equipment for the semiconductor industry. Its die bonders and wire bonders use fine wires to connect an integrated circuit to its package leads, thereby completing the chip's electrical circuit. K&S also makes bonding wire, packaging materials, and other assembly equipment. The company sells its products to such contractors and chip makers as Advanced Semiconductor Engineering, Amkor, STMicroelectronics, and Texas Instruments. Customers in Asia account for more than three-quarters of sales.

	Annual Growth	9/03	9/04	9/05	9/06	9/07
Sales ($ mil.)	9.1%	494.3	717.8	561.3	696.3	700.4
Net income ($ mil.)	—	(76.7)	55.9	(104.1)	52.2	37.7
Market value ($ mil.)	(4.5%)	543.5	289.1	377.5	505.7	451.3
Employees	(2.2%)	3,169	3,294	3,610	2,454	2,903

KURT SALMON ASSOCIATES, INC.

1355 Peachtree St. NE, Ste. 900
Atlanta, GA 30309
Phone: 404-892-0321
Fax: 404-898-9590
Web: www.kurtsalmon.com

CEO: Jerry T. Black
CFO: William Beckemeyer
HR: Pam Beckerman
FYE: December 31
Type: Subsidiary

Retailers can call on Kurt Salmon Associates (KSA) when their cash registers stop ringing. The firm, a unit of UK-based Management Consulting Group, offers a range of consulting services aimed at streamlining supply chain and business operations for retailers and consumer products makers. Operating from about 15 offices in Asia, Europe, and North America, its consultants offer expertise in logistics, marketing and merchandising, and information technology. The firm also provides reports on industry and consumer trends. In addition, KSA has a health care unit that offers consulting services for hospitals and physician groups in the US. Textile engineer Kurt Salmon started the firm in 1935.

K-V PHARMACEUTICAL COMPANY

NYSE: KVA

2503 S. Hanley Rd.
St. Louis, MO 63144
Phone: 314-645-6600
Fax: 314-644-2419
Web: www.kvpharma.com

CEO: Marc S. Hermelin
CFO: Ronald J. Kanterman
HR: —
FYE: March 31
Type: Public

Just a spoonful of K-V Pharmaceutical helps the medicine go down. The firm owns a portfolio of drug delivery technologies — including the know-how to create controlled-release pills, bioadhesive creams, and quick dissolving tablets — that its subsidiaries use to develop new drugs and generic versions of existing ones. Its generics unit, ETHEX, makes hard-to-copy generic drugs in a number of therapeutic categories, including cardiovascular disease, women's health, pain management, and respiratory disease. Ther-Rx handles K-V's branded drugs, with a focus on women's health, cardiovascular, and anemia therapies. Its products include prenatal vitamins, as well as prescription yeast infection treatment Gynazole.

	Annual Growth	3/04	3/05	3/06	3/07	3/08
Sales ($ mil.)	20.7%	283.9	303.5	367.6	443.6	601.9
Net income ($ mil.)	17.8%	45.8	33.3	15.8	58.1	88.3
Market value ($ mil.)	3.6%	811.6	834.0	889.1	917.0	935.4
Employees	6.8%	—	1,072	1,145		

An in-depth profile of this company is available to Hoover's Online members at hoovers.com.

K-VA-T FOOD STORES, INC.

201 Trigg St.
Abingdon, VA 24211
Phone: 276-628-5503
Fax: 276-623-5440
Web: www.foodcity.com

CEO: Steven C. (Steve) Smith
CFO: Robert L. Neeley
HR: Donnie Meadows
FYE: December 31
Type: Private

What do you call a chain of supermarkets in Kentucky, Virginia, and Tennessee? How about K-VA-T Food Stores? K-VA-T is one of the largest grocery chains in the region, with about 95 supermarkets primarily under the Food City banner (and a handful of Super Dollar Supermarkets). Originally a Piggly Wiggly franchise with three stores, K-VA-T was founded in 1955. It has expanded by acquiring stores from other regional food retailers, opening new stores, and adding services such as about 45 pharmacies, nearly 30 Gas'N Go gasoline outlets, and banking. Its Mid-Mountain Foods provides warehousing and distribution services. The founding Smith family owns a majority of K-VA-T; employees own the rest of the company.

	Annual Growth	12/02	12/03	12/04	12/05	12/06
Sales ($ mil.)	10.2%	1,063.0	1,200.0	1,310.0	1,400.0	1,570.0
Employees	5.5%	9,300	10,000	10,400	—	11,500

KVH INDUSTRIES, INC.

NASDAQ (GM): KVHI

50 Enterprise Center
Middletown, RI 02842
Phone: 401-847-3327
Fax: 401-849-0045
Web: www.kvh.com

CEO: Martin A. Kits van Heyningen
CFO: Patrick J. Spratt
HR: –
FYE: December 31
Type: Public

KVH Industries makes products for people (or boats or armies) on the go. The company's mobile satellite communications products include antennas for yachts and commercial ships, mobile DIRECTV antennas for automobiles, and mobile satellite telephones. KVH sells its satellite products to retailers and distributors, as well as boat and other vehicle manufacturers. The company's guidance and stabilization products include digital compasses, fiber-optic gyros for tactical navigation, and guidance systems for torpedoes and unmanned aerial vehicles. It sells its guidance and stabilization products to US and allied governments and defense contractors.

	Annual Growth	12/03	12/04	12/05	12/06	12/07
Sales ($ mil.)	9.3%	56.7	62.3	71.3	79.0	80.9
Net income ($ mil.)	—	(1.5)	(6.2)	2.9	3.7	2.5
Market value ($ mil.)	(21.8%)	319.5	142.2	143.3	157.7	119.5
Employees	—	—	—	300	—	—

KWIK TRIP, INC.

1626 Oak St.
La Crosse, WI 54602
Phone: 608-781-8988
Fax: 608-781-8950
Web: www.kwiktrip.com

CEO: Donald P. (Don) Zietlow
CFO: Scott Teigen
HR: –
FYE: September 30
Type: Private

Midwesterners who need to make a quick trip to get gas or groceries, cigarettes or donuts, race on over to Kwik Trip stores. Kwik Trip operates more than 380 Kwik Trip and Kwik Star convenience stores throughout Iowa, Minnesota, and Wisconsin. The company also runs several Hearty Platter restaurants and nearly 40 Tobacco Outlet Plus (TOP) cigar stores. All Kwik Trip stores built since 1990 are owned by Convenience Store Investments, a separate company, which leases the land and stores to Kwik Trip. Kwik Trip, which opened its first store in 1965 in Eau Claire, Wisconsin, is owned by the family of CEO Don Zietlow.

	Annual Growth	9/03	9/04	9/05	9/06	9/07
Est. sales ($ mil.)	—	—	—	—	—	932.6
Employees	—	—	—	—	—	7,000

KYOCERA INTERNATIONAL, INC.

8611 Balboa Ave.
San Diego, CA 92123
Phone: 858-576-2600
Fax: 858-492-1456
Web: www.kyocera.com

CEO: Rodney N. Lanthorne
CFO: –
HR: –
FYE: March 31
Type: Subsidiary

Kyocera International, the holding company for the North American operations of Japan's Kyocera Corporation, makes a variety of products ranging from semiconductor casings to knives and utensils. Having expanded through acquisitions beyond its origins in specialty ceramics, Kyocera International also makes cameras, LCD panels, thin-film devices, printers, cutting tools, and solar energy systems. Its Kyocera Wireless unit, formed after Kyocera acquired QUALCOMM's consumer wireless phone business in 2000, is a major producer of wireless phones in the US. Kyocera International's Kyocera Solar subsidiary is one of the world's largest producers of photovoltaic solar cells.

	Annual Growth	3/03	3/04	3/05	3/06	3/07
Est. sales ($ mil.)	—	—	—	—	—	644.9
Employees	—	—	—	—	—	4,299

KYOCERA MITA AMERICA, INC.

225 Sand Rd.
Fairfield, NJ 07004
Phone: 973-808-8444
Fax: 973-882-6000
Web: usa.kyoceramita.com

CEO: Michael (Mike) Pietrunti
CFO: Nicholas (Nick) Maimone
HR: –
FYE: March 31
Type: Subsidiary

Representing Kyocera Mita in the US, Kyocera Mita America provides copiers, fax machines, printers, and multifunction devices. Its printer line includes monochrome, wide-format, and color devices, ranging from small desktop models to departmental models designed for large corporations. The company also provides document management software, as well as service and support services. It sells directly and through independent dealers and resellers to customers in the enterprise and government sectors. Kyocera Mita is the document imaging division of manufacturing giant Kyocera.

	Annual Growth	3/03	3/04	3/05	3/06	3/07
Est. sales ($ mil.)	—	—	—	—	—	6.5
Employees	—	—	—	—	—	700

L-1 IDENTITY SOLUTIONS, INC.

NYSE: ID

177 Broad St.
Stamford, CT 06901
Phone: 203-504-1100
Fax: 203-504-1150
Web: www.l1id.com

CEO: Robert V. LaPenta
CFO: James (Jim) DePalma
HR: –
FYE: December 31
Type: Public

L-1 Identity Solutions, formerly Viisage, handles security problems face-to-face. The company develops face, finger, and iris recognition technologies used for protecting and securing personal identities and assets, with a focus on the federal, civil, criminal, commercial, border, and management markets. The federal government accounts for nearly 70% of revenues. L-1 Identity Solutions was formed in 2006 as a result of the merger between rival security firms Viisage Technology and Identix Incorporated. Viisage and Identix both specialized in biometric facial recognition technologies. A group of executives own a majority stake in L-1 through investment vehicles L-1 Investment Partners and Aston Capital Partners.

	Annual Growth	12/03	12/04	12/05	12/06	12/07
Sales ($ mil.)	79.6%	37.4	67.5	66.2	164.4	389.5
Net income ($ mil.)	—	(17.7)	(7.0)	(7.3)	(31.0)	17.7
Market value ($ mil.)	58.3%	215.0	1,083.2	509.8	1,095.7	1,348.9
Employees	102.5%	126	211	223	1,047	—

An in-depth profile of this company is available to Hoover's Online members at hoovers.com.

911

L-3 COMMUNICATIONS HOLDINGS, INC.

NYSE: LLL

600 3rd Ave.
New York, NY 10016
Phone: 212-697-1111
Fax: 212-805-5477
Web: www.l-3com.com

CEO: Michael T. Strianese
CFO: Ralph G. D'Ambrosio
HR: Kenneth W. Manne
FYE: December 31
Type: Public

L-3's good defense is its best commercial offense. L-3 Communications Holdings makes secure and specialized systems for satellite, avionics, and marine communications. The US government (primarily the Department of Defense) accounts for about 80% of the company's business, but L-3 is using acquisitions to expand its commercial offerings. Commercial products include flight recorders (black boxes), display systems, and wireless telecom gear. L-3 has added to its aircraft repair, overhaul, and technical services with the purchase of Spar Aerospace and what are now L-3 Communications Integrated Systems, L-3 Communications Vertex Aerospace, and L-3 Communications Cincinnati Electronics.

	Annual Growth	12/03	12/04	12/05	12/06	12/07
Sales ($ mil.)	28.9%	5,061.6	6,897.0	9,444.7	12,476.9	13,960.5
Net income ($ mil.)	28.5%	277.6	381.9	508.5	526.1	756.1
Market value ($ mil.)	27.4%	4,985.9	8,472.5	8,949.7	10,242.0	13,155.1
Employees	4.2%	—	—	59,500	63,700	64,600

L-3 COMMUNICATIONS VERTEX AEROSPACE LLC

555 Industrial Dr. South
Madison, MS 39110
Phone: 601-856-2274
Fax: 801-594-3284
Web: www.l-3vertex.com

CEO: John E. (Ed) Boyington Jr.
CFO: Shannon D. Nichol
HR: Robert C. James
FYE: December 31
Type: Subsidiary

L-3 Communications Vertex Aerospace services the government. No tabloid fodder here, however: The company, previously known as Vertex Aerospace (and before that, Raytheon Aerospace), provides aerospace and technical services — logistics support, maintenance, repair and overhaul, supply chain management, and pilot training — for the US government. Its monied client list includes the armed forces, the Customs Service, the DEA, and NASA. Among the products supported are training aircraft (T-6A Texan II), attack helicopters (AH-64 Apache), stealth bombers (B-2), missile systems (Patriot), and tanks (M1 Abrams). L-3 Communications Vertex Aerospace is a subsidiary of L-3 Communications.

LA BREA HOLDINGS, INC.

15963 Strathern St.
Van Nuys, CA 91406
Phone: 818-742-4242
Fax: 818-742-4276
Web: www.labreabakery.com

CEO: John Yamin
CFO: –
HR: –
FYE: July 31
Type: Subsidiary

La Brea Bakery Holdings knows it takes some crust to win the hearts of foodies. The company is a leading US producer of partially baked artisan breads, which it supplies to restaurants and food stores throughout the US under the La Brea brand name. It also operates two casual dining restaurants, the La Brea Bakery Cafes, in California. As demand for upscale bread has continued to steadily grow, the company has expanded to two production facilities in California and New Jersey. Parent company IAWS Group purchased 80% of La Brea in 2001 for $79 million and now controls 100% of its voting stock.

	Annual Growth	7/03	7/04	7/05	7/06	7/07
Est. sales ($ mil.)	—	—	—	—	—	150.0
Employees	—	—	—	—	—	699

L.A. GEAR, INC.

844 Moraga Dr.
Los Angeles, CA 90049
Phone: 310-889-3499
Fax: 310-889-3500
Web: www.lagear.com

CEO: Steven Jackson
CFO: David Mankowitz
HR: –
FYE: November 30
Type: Private

Named for the City of Angels, L.A. Gear has been reincarnated. Best known in the 1990s for its L.A. Lights shoes (with blinking LED lights) for kids, the firm is now a licensor for a variety of products, including footwear, apparel, and watches. It now targets teens and adults, as well. Kidfusion makes a collection of L.A. Gear swimwear and related apparel for kids. L.A. Gear also has a licensing deal with Nouveau Eyewear for optical frames and eyewear. Los Angeles-based footwear company ACI International, which L.A. Gear had licensed to sell men's, women's, and children's footwear under the L.A. Gear name in the US and Canada, acquired L.A. Gear in 2001.

	Annual Growth	11/03	11/04	11/05	11/06	11/07
Est. sales ($ mil.)	—	—	—	—	—	10.4
Employees	—	—	—	—	—	30

LA MADELEINE, INC.

6688 North Central Expwy., Ste. 700
Dallas, TX 75206
Phone: 214-696-6962
Fax: 214-692-8496
Web: www.lamadeleine.com

CEO: Jean-Roch Vachon
CFO: William (Bill) Schaffler
HR: Tina Hebert
FYE: June 30
Type: Private

This company hopes its crème brulee, croissants, and quiche prove as memorable as Proust's famous tea cake. La Madeleine operates a chain of more than 60 la Madeleine Bakery, Café & Bistro casual dining locations in six states, offering French country cuisine for breakfast, lunch, and dinner. The restaurants, which welcome patrons with such interior appointments as a stone hearth and handcrafted wood tables, use a cafeteria-style serving line and limited table service. Each location also sells a variety of fresh baked goods. French native Patrick Leon Esquerré started the business in 1983. La Madeleine is owned by a group of investors including Paris-based restaurant operator Groupe Le Duff.

LA MESA RV CENTER, INC.

7430 Copley Park Place
San Diego, CA 92111
Phone: 858-874-8000
Fax: 858-874-8021
Web: www.lamesarv.com

CEO: James R. (Jim) Kimbrell
CFO: –
HR: Yvette Broderick
FYE: December 31
Type: Private

The folks at La Mesa RV Center want to make everyone a happy camper. One of the world's largest Winnebago dealers, La Mesa RV also sells new and used campers and RVs from Tiffin, Western RV, Georgie Boy, Coachmen, and others at about 10 locations in California, Arizona, Georgia, and Florida. It also has several seasonal locations to service motorhomes in spring and winter as they come out of or go into off-season storage. The company offers RV repair and service as well as parts for new and used vehicles. Its special RV financing includes terms up to 20 years. La Mesa RV was founded in 1972.

	Annual Growth	12/03	12/04	12/05	12/06	12/07
Est. sales ($ mil.)	—	—	—	—	—	127.3
Employees	—	—	—	—	—	700

L.A. MODELS, INC.

7700 W. Sunset Blvd.
Los Angeles, CA 90046
Phone: 323-436-7700
Fax: 323-436-7755
Web: www.lamodels.com

CEO: Heinz Holba
CFO: Irma Bermudez
HR: –
FYE: –
Type: Private

California girls, bi-coastal business model, global reach. L.A. Models is a full-service modeling agency focusing on clients on the West Coast. Its sister company, New York Model Management, does business in the traditional fashion hub of Manhattan. Founded by Heinz Holba in the mid-1980s, L.A. Models is the largest international modeling agency on the West Coast. The company is a leading sponsor of the annual L.A. Looks Model Search Contest, a professional talent contest that provides the winner and runner-up with modeling contracts. Holba also runs sister agency L.A. Talent, which seeks commercial and theatrical opportunities for its modeling clients.

LAB SAFETY SUPPLY, INC.

401 S. Wright Rd.
Janesville, WI 53547
Phone: 608-754-7160
Fax: 608-754-1806
Web: www.labsafety.com

CEO: Larry J. Loizzo
CFO: Randy Scheuneman
HR: Tim Markus
FYE: December 31
Type: Subsidiary

Lab Safety Supply knows that there is safety in numbers — especially a huge number of products in stock. The company, a subsidiary of W.W. Grainger, distributes safety and industrial supplies, such as air monitors, chemical storage and spill clean-up products, eyewash stations, fire extinguishers, and cleaning solutions. Other products distributed include office furniture, material handling equipment, tools, electrical and HVAC equipment, and forestry and agricultural gear. Lab Safety's products number around 120,000 and are sold through its Web site and catalogs. Founded in 1973, the company became a Grainger subsidiary in 1992.

LABARGE, INC.

AMEX: LB

9900 Clayton Rd.
St. Louis, MO 63124
Phone: 314-997-0800
Fax: 314-812-9438
Web: www.labarge.com

CEO: Craig E. LaBarge
CFO: Donald H. Nonnenkamp
HR: Robert Mihalco
FYE: Sunday nearest June 30
Type: Public

Despite its name, LaBarge is more spacecraft than boat. As a contract manufacturer, LaBarge makes complex electronics and interconnect systems that are able to withstand the physical extremes of combat, space, sea, and inner earth. The company's printed circuit boards, cables, electronic assemblies, and other products are used in demanding applications such as military communication systems, commercial aircraft, satellites, and oil drilling equipment. LaBarge's customers include Northrop Grumman (about 13% of sales), Owens-Illinois (10%), Schlumberger (also 10%), and Lockheed Martin.

	Annual Growth	6/03	6/04	6/05	6/06	6/07
Sales ($ mil.)	23.0%	102.9	131.5	182.3	190.1	235.2
Net income ($ mil.)	48.9%	2.3	6.9	10.9	9.7	11.3
Market value ($ mil.)	36.7%	53.7	108.9	270.9	201.3	187.6
Employees	—	—	—	—	1,200	—

LABORATORY CORPORATION OF AMERICA HOLDINGS

NYSE: LH

358 S. Main St.
Burlington, NC 27215
Phone: 336-229-1127
Fax: 336-436-1205
Web: www.labcorp.com

CEO: David P. (Dave) King
CFO: William B. (Brad) Hayes
HR: –
FYE: December 31
Type: Public

This company pricks and prods for profit. Laboratory Corporation of America Holdings (LabCorp) is one of the top providers of clinical laboratory services in the world. LabCorp performs tests on more than 420,000 patient specimens each day on behalf of managed care organizations, hospitals, doctors, government agencies, drug companies, and employers. Most of its tests are routine tests such as urinalyses, HIV tests, and Pap smears. LabCorp also offers specialty testing services, including diagnostic genetics, oncology diagnosis and monitoring, infectious disease testing, clinical drug trials testing, and allergy testing.

	Annual Growth	12/03	12/04	12/05	12/06	12/07
Sales ($ mil.)	8.5%	2,939.4	3,084.8	3,327.6	3,590.8	4,068.2
Net income ($ mil.)	10.4%	321.0	363.0	386.2	431.6	476.8
Market value ($ mil.)	11.1%	5,500.2	7,507.9	6,812.0	8,978.0	8,383.8
Employees	4.1%	—	—	24,000	25,000	26,000

LABRANCHE & CO INC.

NYSE: LAB

33 Whitehall St.
New York, NY 10004
Phone: 212-425-1144
Fax: 212-344-1469
Web: www.labranche.com

CEO: George M. L. (Michael) LaBranche IV
CFO: Jeffrey A. McCutcheon
HR: –
FYE: December 31
Type: Public

LaBranche & Co specializes in being a specialist. The company makes markets for the common stock of more than 600 NYSE-listed firms, including Dow Jones components American Express, AT&T, DuPont, Exxon Mobil, Merck, and 3M. One of the oldest and largest specialists, LaBranche & Co matches buyers and sellers and compensates for demand imbalances by buying or selling stocks for its own account. The company also has a unit that focuses on options, futures, and exchange-traded funds, as well as others that focus on foreign markets. Subsidiary LaBranche Financial Services performs brokerage and clearing services for institutional clients.

	Annual Growth	12/03	12/04	12/05	12/06	12/07
Sales ($ mil.)	10.0%	306.0	319.0	340.2	674.0	448.7
Net income ($ mil.)	—	(179.4)	(43.8)	37.5	136.8	(350.5)
Market value ($ mil.)	(18.4%)	697.8	542.4	612.9	597.0	309.9
Employees	(30.0%)	—	—	525	429	257

LACKS ENTERPRISES, INC.

5460 Cascade Rd. SE
Grand Rapids, MI 49546
Phone: 616-949-6570
Fax: 616-285-2367
Web: www.lacksenterprises.com

CEO: Richard Lacks Jr.
CFO: Brad Kirk
HR: Jim Green
FYE: July 31
Type: Private

It's not hipp if your car lacks a wheel cover or has a rusty grille. Lacks Enterprises makes high-impact plated plastic (HIPP) alternatives to die-cast and stainless steel automotive products such as wheel covers and grilles. The company's HIPP parts, plated with coppernickel chrome, are lighter and cheaper than all-metal alternatives, as well as more resistant to dents and rust. Other products include molding, rocker panels, and trim. Automotive OEM customers have included Chrysler and General Motors. The Lacks family owns Lacks Enterprises, which was founded in 1961.

	Annual Growth	7/03	7/04	7/05	7/06	7/07
Est. sales ($ mil.)	—	—	—	—	—	172.4
Employees	—	—	—	—	—	2,286

An in-depth profile of this company is available to Hoover's Online members at hoovers.com.

THE LACLEDE GROUP, INC.

NYSE: LG

720 Olive St.
St. Louis, MO 63101
Phone: 314-342-0500
Fax: 314-421-1979
Web: www.thelacledegroup.com

CEO: Douglas H. Yaeger
CFO: Mark D. Waltermire
HR: Richard A. Skau
FYE: September 30
Type: Public

In the "Show Me" state, The Laclede Group is saying, "Show me the money." To create a more balanced earnings mix, the company is emphasizing its nonutility operations. The group's main revenue source is still utility Laclede Gas, which distributes natural gas to about 631,600 customers in eastern Missouri, including St. Louis. Laclede Group provides gas transportation services and operates underground gas storage fields; it also transports and stores propane. Other operations include wholesale gas marketing (Laclede Energy Resources), underground infrastructure locating (SM&P Utility Resources), insurance (Laclede Gas Family Services), and real estate development.

	Annual Growth	9/03	9/04	9/05	9/06	9/07
Sales ($ mil.)	17.8%	1,050.3	1,250.3	1,597.0	1,997.6	2,021.6
Net income ($ mil.)	9.5%	34.7	36.1	40.1	49.0	49.8
Market value ($ mil.)	7.9%	515.4	613.3	687.9	685.3	698.7
Employees	(2.6%)	—	—	1,933	1,874	1,835

LACROSSE FOOTWEAR, INC.

NASDAQ (GM): BOOT

17634 NE Airport Way
Portland, OR 97230
Phone: 503-262-0110
Fax: 503-262-0115
Web: www.lacrossefootwear.com

CEO: Joseph P. Schneider
CFO: David P. Carlson
HR: J. Gary Rebello
FYE: December 31
Type: Public

If customers are wearing its protective boots, LaCrosse Footwear doesn't care who steps on their toes. The company offers sturdy footwear for sporting, outdoors, and occupations such as farming, general utility, and construction. LaCrosse makes rubber, vinyl, and leather footwear, as well as rainwear and protective clothing, for adults and children. Its brands include LaCrosse, Red Ball, Danner, Camohide, and Rainfair, among other names. LaCrosse's products are sold nationwide to catalog merchants, retailers, wholesalers, and the US government, as well as through company Web sites and outlet stores. The Schneider family owns about 45% of LaCrosse.

	Annual Growth	12/03	12/04	12/05	12/06	12/07
Sales ($ mil.)	5.4%	95.7	105.5	99.4	107.8	118.2
Net income ($ mil.)	29.4%	2.6	7.0	5.2	6.3	7.3
Market value ($ mil.)	23.9%	46.3	63.7	64.9	80.2	108.9
Employees	—	—	—	276	—	—

LACTALIS USA, INC.

950 Third Ave., 22nd Fl.
New York, NY 10022
Phone: 212-758-6666
Fax: 212-758-7383
Web: www.lactalis-usa.com

CEO: Fréderick Bouisset
CFO: –
HR: –
FYE: December 31
Type: Business segment

Lactalis USA is not a party animal; the company is a party to cheese. The company is a leading maker of specialty cheeses in the US and a division of the French cheese and dairy products maker Groupe Lactalis. Featuring both domestic and imported cheeses, Lactalis USA markets products under the Président, Sorrento, Galbani, Valbreso, and Rondelé brands. Varieties include feta, brie, camembert, baby Swiss, emmental, roquefort, goat's milk, and sheep's milk. In addition to whole and sliced cheeses, the company also makes cheese spreads, fondue mixes, and butter. In 2007 the company acquired California-based soft cheese maker, Mozzarella Fresca.

	Annual Growth	12/03	12/04	12/05	12/06	12/07
Est. sales ($ mil.)	—	—	—	—	—	232.3
Employees	—	—	—	—	—	765

THELADDERS.COM, INC.

137 Varick St., 8th Fl.
New York, NY 10013
Phone: 646-453-1800
Fax: 646-453-1932
Web: www.theladders.com

CEO: Marc Cenedella
CFO: Rick Eaton
HR: David F. (Dave) Carvajal
FYE: December 31
Type: Private

You'll have to climb a few ladders to get to the top, and TheLadders.com can help ensure that the ladders you climb lead to the best view. Targeting high-level executive positions, the company lists job postings on its Web site (more than 35,000 jobs are typically featured). TheLadders.com only lists jobs that come with salaries of at least $100,000; industries covered include sales and marketing, finance, technology, and law. Rather than charging companies to post available positions, the firm chooses and publishes the pick of the job crop; job hunters subscribe to receive full access to the postings. TheLadders.com has signed more than 1.5 million members since it was founded in 2003.

	Annual Growth	12/03	12/04	12/05	12/06	12/07
Est. sales ($ mil.)	—	—	—	—	—	7.4
Employees	—	—	—	—	—	120

LADENBURG THALMANN FINANCIAL SERVICES INC.

AMEX: LTS

4400 Biscayne Blvd., 12th Fl.
Miami, FL 33137
Phone: 212-409-2000
Fax: 305-572-4199
Web: www.ladenburg.com

CEO: Richard J. (Dick) Lampen
CFO: Brett H. Kaufman
HR: Kelly Cronin
FYE: December 31
Type: Public

Ladenburg Thalmann's offerings menu is laden with retail and institutional brokerage, investment banking, and asset management services for corporate, institutional, and retail clients. The company focuses its investment banking — which includes equity underwriting, specified purpose acquisition (or blank-check) company underwriting, mergers and acquisitions advice, and corporate finance — on middle-market, emerging growth companies. Asset management offerings include wealth management, financial planning, and alternative investments. Ladenburg Thalmann manages approximately 200,000 private client and institutional accounts nationwide.

	Annual Growth	12/03	12/04	12/05	12/06	12/07
Sales ($ mil.)	11.8%	61.4	38.4	30.7	46.9	95.8
Net income ($ mil.)	—	(5.5)	(9.9)	(26.0)	4.7	9.4
Market value ($ mil.)	93.5%	24.4	27.1	65.1	191.5	342.8
Employees	3.3%	—	—	162	—	173

LADISH CO., INC.

NASDAQ (GM): LDSH

5481 S. Packard Ave.
Cudahy, WI 53110
Phone: 414-747-2611
Fax: 414-747-2963
Web: www.ladishco.com

CEO: Kerry L. Woody
CFO: Wayne E. Larsen
HR: Lawrence C. Hammond
FYE: December 31
Type: Public

Ladish got its start in 1905 when Herman Ladish bought a 1,500-pound steam hammer, and the company's been swinging ever since. Today the company designs and manufactures high-strength forged and cast metal components for aerospace and industrial markets. Jet engine parts, missile components, landing gear, helicopter rotors, and other aerospace products generate some 80% of the company's sales; general industrial components account for the remaining 20%. Aerospace industry giants Rolls-Royce, United Technologies, and General Electric together account for 50% of Ladish's sales.

	Annual Growth	12/03	12/04	12/05	12/06	12/07
Sales ($ mil.)	23.9%	179.9	208.7	266.8	369.3	424.6
Net income ($ mil.)	—	0.0	3.8	13.7	28.5	32.3
Market value ($ mil.)	56.1%	105.7	158.5	313.2	537.8	627.7
Employees	(19.3%)	—	—	1,950	1,200	1,270

LAFARGE NORTH AMERICA INC.

12950 Worldgate Dr., Ste. 500
Herndon, VA 20170
Phone: 703-480-3600
Fax: 703-796-2215
Web: www.lafargenorthamerica.com

CEO: Bruno Lafont
CFO: Eric C. Olsen
HR: −
FYE: December 31
Type: Subsidiary

Lafarge North America is knitting together a skein of concrete and related building products businesses across the US and Canada. One of North America's largest building materials manufacturers, the company operates around 300 concrete plants, another 300 aggregates plants, and some 20 cement plants in the US and Canada (through Lafarge Canada). Lafarge North America's construction materials products include asphalt, gypsum wallboard, ready-mixed concrete, and concrete pipes and blocks. French building materials conglomerate Lafarge S.A. owns the company. Lafarge North America accounts for more than 25% of its parent's sales.

	Annual Growth	12/03	12/04	12/05	12/06	12/07
Est. sales ($ mil.)	—	—	—	—	—	2,147.5
Employees	—	—	—	—	—	16,400

LAFAYETTE COMMUNITY BANCORP

Pink Sheets: LFYC

2 N. 4th St.
Lafayette, IN 47901
Phone: 765-429-7200
Fax: 765-429-7100
Web: www.lafayettecommunitybank.com

CEO: Richard D. Murray
CFO: Dennis R. Hardwick
HR: −
FYE: December 31
Type: Public

Tippecanoe and community banking, too. Lafayette Community Bancorp is the holding company for Lafayette Community Bank, which serves individuals and small to midsized businesses in Tippecanoe County, Indiana, and surrounding areas northwest of Indianapolis. Through three branches, Lafayette Community Bank offers such traditional retail products as checking accounts, savings and money market accounts, and CDs. The bank uses deposits mainly to originate one- to-four-family residential mortgages, and also business loans, commercial mortgages, and construction and land development loans.

	Annual Growth	12/03	12/04	12/05	12/06	12/07
Est. sales ($ mil.)	—	—	—	—	—	11.7
Employees	—	—	—	—	—	33

LAHEY CLINIC, INC.

41 Mall Rd.
Burlington, MA 01805
Phone: 781-273-5100
Fax: 781-744-8928
Web: www.lahey.org

CEO: David M. Barrett
CFO: Timothy P. O'Connor
HR: Joan Robbio
FYE: September 30
Type: Not-for-profit

In need of special care? Lahey Clinic is here for you. The organization provides primary and tertiary care to residents of northeastern Massachusetts along with patients from other states and other countries. Lahey Clinic has two hospitals: Lahey Clinic Medical Center has about 315 beds and is a teaching facility for Tufts University School of Medicine, and Lahey Clinic North Shore has 10 beds. Founded in 1923, the not-for-profit company also operates several community-based primary care physician practices. Lahey Clinic has some 450 doctors and offers a range of health care services, including cancer treatment, surgery, family medicine, and organ transplantation.

	Annual Growth	9/03	9/04	9/05	9/06	9/07
Est. sales ($ mil.)	—	—	—	—	—	679.5
Employees	—	—	—	—	—	4,000

LAKE SHORE BANCORP, INC.

NASDAQ (GM): LSBK

125 E. 4th St.
Dunkirk, NY 14048
Phone: 716-366-4070
Fax: 716-366-3010
Web: www.lakeshoresavings.com

CEO: David C. Mancuso
CFO: Rachel A. Foley
HR: Janinne F. Dugan
FYE: December 31
Type: Public

Lake Shore Bancorp was formed to be the holding company for Lake Shore Savings Bank (formerly Lake Shore Savings and Loan Association). The savings bank serves local consumers and businesses through branches in Chautauqua and Erie counties in Western New York State, near Lake Erie. It focuses on residential real estate lending, with one- to four-family mortgages accounting for more than 70% of its loan portfolio, while home equity loans and lines of credit come in at nearly 15%. The bank also offers commercial and consumer loans, as well as checking and savings accounts, CDs, and IRAs. Mutual holding company Lake Shore, MHC owns about 55% of Lake Shore Bancorp, which went public in 2006.

	Annual Growth	12/03	12/04	12/05	12/06	12/07
Assets ($ mil.)	2.8%	—	329.8	333.7	354.2	357.8
Net income ($ mil.)	4.7%	1.5	2.2	2.0	1.8	1.8
Market value ($ mil.)	(33.4%)	—	—	—	83.1	55.3
Employees	—	—	—	—	—	—

LAKELAND BANCORP, INC.

NASDAQ (GS): LBAI

250 Oak Ridge Rd.
Oak Ridge, NJ 07438
Phone: 973-697-2000
Fax: 973-697-8385
Web: www.lakelandbank.com

CEO: Thomas J. Shara Jr.
CFO: Joseph F. Hurley
HR: Connie Ann Meehan
FYE: December 31
Type: Public

Lakeland Bancorp is shoring up in the Garden State. It's the holding company for Lakeland Bank, which serves northern New Jersey from about 50 branch offices. Targeting individuals and small to midsized businesses, the bank offers standard retail products such as checking and savings accounts, money market and NOW accounts, and CDs. It also offers financial planning and advisory services for consumers. The bank's lending activities primarily consist of commercial loans (about half of the company's loan portfolio) and residential mortgages (about a third of all loans). Its Lakeland Bank Equipment Leasing Division offers commercial equipment lease financing.

	Annual Growth	12/03	12/04	12/05	12/06	12/07
Assets ($ mil.)	12.2%	1,585.3	2,141.0	2,206.0	2,263.6	2,513.8
Net income ($ mil.)	4.5%	15.1	16.5	20.2	17.0	18.0
Market value ($ mil.)	5.2%	220.7	313.5	281.6	313.0	269.8
Employees	(0.7%)	—	—	548	—	540

LAKELAND FINANCIAL CORPORATION

NASDAQ (GS): LKFN

202 E. Center St.
Warsaw, IN 46581
Phone: 574-267-6144
Fax: 574-267-6063
Web: www.lakecitybank.com

CEO: Michael L. Kubacki
CFO: David M. Findlay
HR: Jill A. DeBatty
FYE: December 31
Type: Public

American dollars are preferred over Polish zloty in this Warsaw bank. Lakeland Financial is the holding company for Lake City Bank, which serves area business customers and individuals through more than 40 branches scattered across about a dozen northern Indiana counties. Founded in 1872 in Warsaw, Indiana, the bank offers such standard retail services as checking and savings accounts, money market accounts, and CDs. Commercial loans, including agricultural loans, make up about 80% of the bank's loan portfolio. Lake City Bank also offers investment products and services such as corporate and personal trust, brokerage, employee benefit plans, and estate planning.

	Annual Growth	12/03	12/04	12/05	12/06	12/07
Assets ($ mil.)	11.8%	1,271.4	1,453.1	1,634.6	1,836.7	1,989.1
Net income ($ mil.)	8.4%	13.9	14.5	18.0	18.7	19.2
Market value ($ mil.)	25.4%	102.2	117.3	120.1	307.2	253.1
Employees	1.5%	—	—	434	—	447

An in-depth profile of this company is available to Hoover's Online members at hoovers.com.

LAKELAND INDUSTRIES, INC.

NASDAQ (GM): LAKE

701 Koehler Ave., Ste. 7
Ronkonkoma, NY 11779
Phone: 631-981-9700
Fax: 631-981-9751
Web: www.lakeland.com

CEO: Christopher J. Ryan
CFO: Gary Pokrassa
HR: –
FYE: January 31
Type: Public

Lakeland Industries isn't your average haberdasher — it's like a love child of the EPA and OSHA. The company manufactures protective clothing for on-the-job hazards. Lakeland uses DuPont specialty fabrics such as Kevlar, Tychem, and Tyvek, as well as its own fabrics, to make industrial disposable garments, toxic-waste cleanup suits, fire- and heat-resistant apparel (including Fyrepel turnout gear for firefighters), industrial work gloves, and industrial and medical garments. Lakeland manufactures its products in China, India, Mexico, and the US; customers outside the US account for more than 10% of the company's sales.

	Annual Growth	1/04	1/05	1/06	1/07	1/08
Sales ($ mil.)	1.6%	89.7	95.3	98.7	100.2	95.7
Net income ($ mil.)	(2.2%)	3.6	5.0	6.3	5.1	3.3
Market value ($ mil.)	7.8%	39.7	81.9	84.5	81.0	53.7
Employees	2.0%	—	—	1,634	1,667	—

LAKES ENTERTAINMENT, INC.

NASDAQ (GM): LACO

130 Cheshire Ln., Ste. 101
Minnetonka, MN 55305
Phone: 952-449-9092
Fax: 952-449-9353
Web: www.lakesgaming.com

CEO: Lyle Berman
CFO: Timothy J. (Tim) Cope
HR: Christine (Chris) Moon
FYE: Sunday nearest December 31
Type: Public

Even though Lakes Entertainment doesn't own a casino, it still keeps its eye on the slots. The company develops and manages Indian-owned casino properties. Lakes Entertainment has agreements with four tribes for new casino development projects in Michigan, California, and Oklahoma. It is also developing a non-Indian casino in Mississippi, and new casino table games to market, distribute, and license to casinos. In addition, Lakes Entertainment owns some 60% of WPT Enterprises, creator of the *World Poker Tour*, a TV show based on a series of poker tournaments that airs on the Travel Channel. Chairman and CEO Lyle Berman owns about 20% of Lakes Entertainment.

	Annual Growth	12/03	12/04	12/05	12/06	12/07
Sales ($ mil.)	60.5%	4.3	17.6	23.4	81.6	28.5
Net income ($ mil.)	—	(4.0)	(4.0)	(11.9)	19.8	(13.6)
Market value ($ mil.)	20.0%	85.4	362.5	148.3	247.6	177.3
Employees	(2.0%)	—	—	—	50	49

LAKESHORE LEARNING MATERIALS

2695 E. Dominguez St.
Carson, CA 90895
Phone: 310-537-8600
Fax: 310-537-5403
Web: www.lakeshorelearning.com

CEO: Michael Kaplan
CFO: –
HR: –
FYE: December 31
Type: Private

Lakeshore Learning Materials aims to make learning fun. The company provides educational toys and classroom tools through about 40 retail stores in nearly 20 states, and through its catalogs and Web site. Products include furniture, games, art supplies, learning kits, text books, and teacher resource packets. Most of its educational materials are broken down by age group and subject. The company also offers items that address multicultural learning environments and special needs children as well as in-store workshops for teachers. Ethelyn Kaplan founded the company in 1954; her sons Michael (president and CEO) and Charles (VP, merchandising) run Lakeshore Learning Materials.

	Annual Growth	12/03	12/04	12/05	12/06	12/07
Est. sales ($ mil.)	—	—	—	—	—	78.6
Employees	—	—	—	—	—	1,200

LAKEVILLE MOTOR EXPRESS, INC.

2833 Fairview Ave. North
Roseville, MN 55113
Phone: 651-636-8900
Fax: 651-638-9694
Web: www.lakevillemotor.com

CEO: John Wren
CFO: Karen Vanney
HR: Roger Wilsey
FYE: December 31
Type: Private

From its beginnings hauling milk from Lakeville, Minnesota, to Minneapolis, Lakeville Motor Express has expanded to provide less-than-truckload (LTL) services throughout 10 states in the Midwest. (LTL carriers combine freight from multiple shippers into a single truckload.) The company operates a fleet of about 1,400 tractors and trailers from a network of some 35 terminals. It offers service elsewhere in North America through its partners in The Reliance Network, a group of regional LTL carriers. Lakeville Motor Express also offers freight brokerage and logistics services. The company, founded by Vincent Wren in 1921, is owned by the Wren family.

	Annual Growth	12/03	12/04	12/05	12/06	12/07
Est. sales ($ mil.)	—	—	—	—	—	111.8
Employees		—	—	—	—	300

LAM RESEARCH CORPORATION

NASDAQ (GS): LRCX

4650 Cushing Pkwy.
Fremont, CA 94538
Phone: 510-572-0200
Fax: 510-572-2935
Web: www.lamrc.com

CEO: Stephen G. (Steve) Newberry
CFO: Martin B. Anstice
HR: –
FYE: Last Sunday in June
Type: Public

It's not uncommon for chip makers in need of critical manufacturing equipment to go on the Lam. Lam Research is a top maker of semiconductor processing equipment. The company's products address two key steps in the chip-making process. Its plasma etch machines are used to create tiny circuitry patterns on silicon wafers. Lam also makes cleaning equipment that keeps unwanted particles from contaminating processed wafers. The company's customers include many large chip makers, such as Hynix Semiconductor (about 14% of sales), Samsung Electronics (also 14%), STMicroelectronics, and Toshiba. About three-quarters of the company's sales are to customers in the Asia/Pacific region, primarily in Taiwan and South Korea.

	Annual Growth	6/03	6/04	6/05	6/06	6/07
Sales ($ mil.)	35.8%	755.2	936.0	1,502.4	1,642.2	2,566.6
Net income ($ mil.)	—	(7.7)	83.0	299.3	335.8	685.8
Market value ($ mil.)	29.2%	2,355.0	3,504.3	3,965.6	6,095.3	6,560.9
Employees	9.3%	2,100	2,200	2,200	2,430	3,000

LAMAR ADVERTISING COMPANY

NASDAQ (GS): LAMR

5551 Corporate Blvd., Ste. 2-A
Baton Rouge, LA 70808
Phone: 225-926-1000
Fax: 225-926-1005
Web: www.lamar.com

CEO: Kevin P. Reilly Jr.
CFO: Keith A. Istre
HR: Tammy Duncan
FYE: December 31
Type: Public

Here's a company that shows all the signs of being a successful outdoor advertising business. Lamar Advertising is one of the top billboard operators in the US, along with CBS Outdoor and Clear Channel Outdoor. The company maintains more than 160,000 billboards in about 45 states, plus Canada and Puerto Rico. It also sells advertising space on more than 28,000 signs placed on buses and at bus stops in more than 15 states, and it maintains some 100,000 logo signs (highway exit signs with logos of nearby hotels and restaurants) along interstates in about 20 states and Canada. Chairman, president, and CEO Kevin Reilly Jr., together with members of his family, controls a two-thirds voting stake in the company.

	Annual Growth	12/03	12/04	12/05	12/06	12/07
Sales ($ mil.)	10.5%	810.1	883.5	1,021.7	1,120.1	1,209.6
Net income ($ mil.)	—	(80.0)	13.2	41.8	43.9	46.2
Market value ($ mil.)	3.7%	3,256.8	3,796.4	4,145.4	5,514.7	3,759.8
Employees	0.0%	—	—	3,200	3,300	3,200

LAMPS PLUS, INC.

20250 Plummer St.
Chatsworth, CA 91311
Phone: 818-886-5267
Fax: 818-886-1011
Web: www.lampsplus.com

CEO: Dennis Swanson
CFO: Clark Linstone
HR: –
FYE: December 31
Type: Private

Hey buddy, gotta light? Sure, but not that kind of light and for a price. LAMPS PLUS sells lights for ceilings, walls, and the outdoors to about 5 million customers a year. Plus it offers ceiling and desk fans as well as home decoration items such as rugs, mirrors, pillows, and vases. The company sells its products from more than 40 stores in five western states (Arizona, California, Colorado, Nevada, and Texas). For those who don't live near a store, it offers online shopping, too. LAMPS PLUS also provides in-home lighting consulting, in-store lighting seminars, and installation. The company was founded in 1976.

	Annual Growth	12/03	12/04	12/05	12/06	12/07
Est. sales ($ mil.)	—	—	—	—	—	80.2
Employees	—	—	—	—	—	1,200

THE LAMSON & SESSIONS CO.

25701 Science Park Dr.
Cleveland, OH 44122
Phone: 216-464-3400
Fax: 216-464-1455
Web: www.lamson-sessions.com

CEO: Michael J. (Mike) Merriman Jr.
CFO: –
HR: Eileen E. Clancy
FYE: Saturday nearest December 31
Type: Subsidiary

The Lamson & Sessions Co. channels its energies into a diversified mix of thermoplastic and electrical products. Founded in 1866, the company makes plastic pipe, conduit, and consumer electrical devices. Its Carlon unit produces watertight conduit, outlet boxes, fittings, and similar products for the electrical contracting, utility, and telecommunications industries. The Lamson Home Products subsidiary targets do-it-yourselfers with its light dimmers, door chimes, electrical fittings, and outlet boxes. The company's PVC pipe division makes electrical, power, and communications conduit, as well as sewer pipe. Thomas & Betts acquired Lamson & Sessions in 2007 for about $450 million in cash.

	Annual Growth	12/02	12/03	12/04	12/05	12/06
Sales ($ mil.)	15.6%	314.5	343.8	387.1	494.2	561.3
Net income ($ mil.)	—	(41.2)	1.0	6.6	27.4	39.1
Employees	3.5%	1,116	—	—	1,263	1,281

LANCASTER COLONY CORPORATION — NASDAQ (GS): LANC

37 W. Broad St.
Columbus, OH 43215
Phone: 614-224-7141
Fax: 614-469-8219
Web: www.lancastercolony.com

CEO: John B. (Jay) Gerlach Jr.
CFO: John L. Boylan
HR: Gary E. Thompson
FYE: June 30
Type: Public

Lancaster Colony provides the ingredients for romantic meals: caviar and candles. The company makes specialty foods, including Marzetti salad dressings, Chatham Village croutons, Romanoff caviar, Texas Toast, and other bread, pasta, and sauce products. Lancaster's food products are available in food retailers throughout the US, as well as to food service operations, including restaurants. It also offers private-label services. In addition to food, the company supplies other amenities for that special dinner mentioned above: Lancaster produces Candle-lite candles and potpourri.

	Annual Growth	6/03	6/04	6/05	6/06	6/07
Sales ($ mil.)	(0.4%)	1,106.8	1,096.9	1,131.5	1,175.3	1,091.2
Net income ($ mil.)	(20.2%)	112.6	80.0	93.1	82.9	45.7
Market value ($ mil.)	(1.8%)	1,384.0	1,477.1	1,470.1	1,272.7	1,288.1
Employees	(6.6%)	—	—	5,500	5,600	4,800

LANCE, INC. — NASDAQ (GS): LNCE

8600 South Blvd.
Charlotte, NC 28273
Phone: 704-554-1421
Fax: 704-554-5562
Web: www.lance.com

CEO: David V. Singer
CFO: Richard D. (Rick) Puckett
HR: Earl D. Leake
FYE: Saturday nearest December 31
Type: Public

If you're familiar with the munchies named Toastchee, Cheese on Nipchee, and Captain's Wafers, Lance has undoubtedly helped you fend off a snack attack. The company produces single-serve, multi-pack, and family-sized packages of bakery products and sweet and savory snack foods, including cookies, crackers, nuts, and potato chips. Its products are sold primarily under the Lance, Cape Cod, and Tom's brand names at food retailers; mass merchandisers; and convenience, club, and discount stores. It also supplies products to food service operators and it produces private-label and branded-label snacks for other manufacturers.

	Annual Growth	12/03	12/04	12/05	12/06	12/07
Sales ($ mil.)	7.9%	562.5	600.5	679.3	730.1	762.7
Net income ($ mil.)	6.8%	18.3	24.9	18.5	18.5	23.8
Market value ($ mil.)	10.7%	433.3	567.0	555.3	619.6	650.5
Employees	(7.6%)	—	—	5,500	4,800	4,700

LANCER CORPORATION

6655 Lancer Blvd.
San Antonio, TX 78219
Phone: 210-310-7000
Fax: 210-310-7183
Web: www.lancercorp.com

CEO: Christopher D. Hughes
CFO: Mark L. Freitas
HR: –
FYE: December 31
Type: Private

"Make it a Coke," is music to Lancer Corporation's ears. The company, a manufacturer of fountain drink-dispensing equipment for the food service and beverage industries, makes products including systems for dispensing soft drinks and juice, post-mix dispensing valves (which mix syrup and carbonated water), ice dispensers, beer dispensing systems, and various syrup pumps, carbonators, and valves. Coca-Cola traditionally has been one of Lancer's biggest customers; the two companies have been linked throughout Lancer's history. In 2006 Lancer was acquired by Hoshizaki America, the US arm of Hoshizaki Electric, a Japanese manufacturer of commercial kitchen equipment.

	Annual Growth	12/03	12/04	12/05	12/06	12/07
Est. sales ($ mil.)	—	—	—	—	—	45.8
Employees	—	—	—	—	—	515

LAND O'LAKES PURINA FEED LLC

1080 County Rd. F
Shoreview, MN 55126
Phone: 651-481-2222
Fax: –
Web: www.lolfeed.com

CEO: Fernando J. Palacios
CFO: Daniel E. Knutson
HR: Nancy Giacchetti
FYE: December 31
Type: Subsidiary

Whether rodent, fowl, bovine, or swine, Land O'Lakes Purina Feed will have something for it to eat. As the largest US producer of animal feeds, the company addresses the dietary needs of livestock (poultry, swine, and dairy and beef cattle); specialty animals (such as llamas and emus); zoo and lab animals; wild birds; and companion animals (pets). In addition to feed, the company makes milk-replacer products for young animals, as well as premixes, supplements, and custom-mixed feeds, and it offers farm management advice and services. It is a subsidiary of dairy giant Land O'Lakes, Inc.

An in-depth profile of this company is available to Hoover's Online members at hoovers.com.

917

LAND O'LAKES, INC.

4001 Lexington Ave. North
Arden Hills, MN 55112
Phone: 651-481-2222
Fax: 651-481-2000
Web: www.landolakesinc.com

CEO: Chris Policinski
CFO: Daniel E. Knutson
HR: Karen Grabow
FYE: December 31
Type: Cooperative

Land O'Lakes butters up its customers, and shows you what life is like if everyone cooperates. Owned by and serving more than 7,000 dairy farmer members and 1,300 community cooperatives, Land O'Lakes is the one of the largest dairy co-ops in the US (along with Dairy Farmers of America and California Dairies). It provides its members with wholesale fertilizer and crop protection products, seed, and animal feed. Its oldest and best known product, LAND O' LAKES butter, is the top butter brand in the US. Land O'Lakes also produces packaged milk, margarine, sour cream, and cheese. The co-op's animal-feed division, Land O'Lakes Purina Feed, is a leading animal and pet food maker.

	Annual Growth	12/02	12/03	12/04	12/05	12/06
Sales ($ mil.)	5.6%	5,846.9	6,320.5	7,676.5	7,556.7	7,274.9
Net income ($ mil.)	(2.7%)	98.9	83.5	21.4	128.9	88.7
Employees	1.5%	8,000	8,000	8,000	7,500	8,500

LANDAMERICA FINANCIAL GROUP, INC.

NYSE: LFG

5600 Cox Rd.
Glen Allen, VA 23060
Phone: 804-267-8000
Fax: 804-267-8836
Web: www.landam.com

CEO: Theodore L. (Ted) Chandler Jr.
CFO: G. William (Bill) Evans
HR: Ross W. Dorneman
FYE: December 31
Type: Public

This land is *my* land, and that land is *your* land, and LandAmerica will insure the titles that prove it. As one of the US's top title insurance companies, the company issues title policies to protect the insured from outstanding liens and title encumbrances in real estate transactions. Operating through its subsidiaries, including Lawyers Title Insurance, Commonwealth Land Title Insurance, and Transnation Title Insurance, LandAmerica provide services and products to real estate agents, lenders, and property buyers through some 8,500 agents in 700 offices. Its also provides credit reporting, property inspection, appraisal and valuation, closing and escrow services, buyers' warranties, and real estate tax services.

	Annual Growth	12/03	12/04	12/05	12/06	12/07
Assets ($ mil.)	9.1%	2,717.5	3,290.0	3,695.0	4,174.8	3,853.7
Net income ($ mil.)	—	192.1	146.3	165.6	98.8	(54.1)
Market value ($ mil.)	(15.0%)	983.2	968.7	1,079.0	1,111.0	513.5
Employees	(8.7%)	—	—	13,250	14,250	11,050

LANDAUER, INC.

NYSE: LDR

2 Science Rd.
Glenwood, IL 60425
Phone: 708-755-7000
Fax: 708-755-7016
Web: www.landauerinc.com

CEO: William E. Saxelby
CFO: Jonathon M. Singer
HR: –
FYE: September 30
Type: Public

If your employees are glowing — and not with joy — Landauer can tell you why. Landauer manufactures and markets dosimeters (radiation detection monitors) for use in nuclear plants, hospitals, and university and government laboratories. Landauer's services include radiation detection badge distribution, radiation monitoring, and reporting on exposures. Its HomeBuyer's Preferred subsidiary provides residential radon monitoring services primarily used for corporate employee relocation programs. The company operates worldwide from offices in France, the US, and the UK. It also operates through joint ventures in Australia, Brazil, China, and Japan.

	Annual Growth	9/03	9/04	9/05	9/06	9/07
Sales ($ mil.)	6.6%	64.8	69.8	75.2	79.0	83.7
Net income ($ mil.)	6.5%	15.0	17.8	17.2	19.0	19.3
Market value ($ mil.)	10.5%	315.0	420.0	445.2	461.5	469.4
Employees	(5.7%)	—	—	450	420	400

LANDEC CORPORATION

NASDAQ (GS): LNDC

3603 Haven Ave.
Menlo Park, CA 94025
Phone: 650-306-1650
Fax: 650-368-9818
Web: www.landec.com

CEO: Gary T. Steele
CFO: Gregory S. (Greg) Skinner
HR: Shirley Hilton
FYE: Last Sunday in May
Type: Public

Landec's products don't turn into pumpkins at midnight, but the changes are nearly as sudden and much more practical. The company has developed a technology that allows polymers to change physical characteristics when exposed to temperature changes. Its Intellipac permeable membrane packaging is designed to allow oxygen and CO2 to enter and escape from sealed fresh-cut produce packages to keep produce fresh. It's used primarily by subsidiary Apio, which grows and packages fresh vegetables. The company also produces Intellicoat seed coatings, which allow early planting of crops by preventing germination until warm weather arrives. Landec has licensing deals with Air Products and Chemicals and Monsanto.

	Annual Growth	5/03	5/04	5/05	5/06	5/07
Sales ($ mil.)	17.0%	112.3	192.1	205.2	231.9	210.5
Net income ($ mil.)	100.7%	1.8	2.9	5.4	8.6	29.2
Market value ($ mil.)	53.6%	63.1	163.7	147.4	209.1	351.1
Employees	11.4%	—	—	167	186	—

LANDMARK BANCORP, INC.

NASDAQ (GM): LARK

701 Poyntz Ave.
Manhattan, KS 66505
Phone: 785-565-2000
Fax: 785-537-0619
Web: www.banklandmark.com

CEO: Patrick L. Alexander
CFO: Mark A. Herpich
HR: Marsha Kemper
FYE: December 31
Type: Public

Landmark Bancorp is a tourist attraction for Kansas money. The holding company for Landmark National Bank has about 20 offices throughout central, eastern, and southwestern Kansas, targeting consumer and business customers. The bank offers traditional products such as checking, savings, and money market accounts, as well as certificates of deposit, individual retirement accounts, credit and debit cards, and trust services. Residential one- to four-family loans account for one-third of a loan portfolio that also includes commercial mortgages (about 30%) and business, construction, and consumer loans. Unlike many other thrifts, Landmark does not have insurance or asset management operations.

	Annual Growth	12/03	12/04	12/05	12/06	12/07
Assets ($ mil.)	16.1%	334.0	442.1	465.1	590.6	606.5
Net income ($ mil.)	3.0%	4.8	4.3	3.9	6.0	5.4
Market value ($ mil.)	5.7%	49.1	52.4	50.4	60.6	61.4
Employees	19.6%	—	—	142	—	203

LANDMARK COMMUNICATIONS, INC.

150 W. Brambleton Ave.
Norfolk, VA 23510
Phone: 757-446-2010
Fax: 757-446-2489
Web: www.landmarkcom.com

CEO: Frank Batten Jr.
CFO: Teresa F. Blevins
HR: Charlie W. Hill
FYE: December 31
Type: Private

You might say this company's media properties are all over the map. Landmark Communications is a diversified holding company with operations in newspaper publishing and television. Its flagship subsidiary, The Weather Channel Companies, operates the popular 24-hour cable weather channel and syndicates weather information to other media outlets. Landmark also publishes three major daily newspapers (*The Virginian-Pilot, News & Record*, and *The Roanoke Times*) in North Carolina and Virginia, as well as more than 50 community papers in about 15 states. In addition, the company has subsidiaries offering marketing and data services. Chairman Frank Batten Jr. and his family own the company.

	Annual Growth	12/02	12/03	12/04	12/05	12/06
Est. sales ($ mil.)	1.8%	—	—	—	1,719.0	1,750.0
Employees	2.1%	—	—	—	11,750	12,000

LANDRY'S RESTAURANTS, INC.

NYSE: LNY

1510 W. Loop South	CEO: Tilman J. Fertitta
Houston, TX 77027	CFO: Richard H. (Rick) Liem
Phone: 713-850-1010	HR: –
Fax: 713-850-7205	FYE: December 31
Web: www.landrysseafood.com	Type: Public

This company's empire stretches from surf to turf to Fremont Street. Landry's Restaurants is a leading operator of casual-dining places with about 180 locations in Texas and about 30 other states. The company's portfolio of eateries is anchored by its flagship Landry's Seafood House chain; other concepts include Rainforest Cafe, Saltgrass Steak House, and the upscale Chart House. In addition to casual dining, Landry's owns and operates the iconic Golden Nugget Hotel & Casino in Las Vegas, along with a number of other entertainment properties, including aquariums, hotels, and other tourist attractions. The company has agreed to be taken private by chairman and CEO Tilman Fertitta, who already has a 40% stake.

	Annual Growth	12/03	12/04	12/05	12/06	12/07
Sales ($ mil.)	1.5%	1,105.8	1,167.5	1,254.8	1,134.3	1,171.9
Net income ($ mil.)	(20.8%)	45.9	66.5	44.8	(21.8)	18.1
Market value ($ mil.)	(18.2%)	711.3	744.2	576.8	666.0	318.0
Employees	(7.1%)	25,000	26,000	28,000	20,055	—

LANDS' END, INC.

1 Lands' End Ln.	CEO: David McCreight
Dodgeville, WI 53595	CFO: Susan Healy
Phone: 608-935-9341	HR: Kelly A. Ritchie
Fax: 608-935-4831	FYE: Saturday nearest December 31
Web: www.landsend.com	Type: Subsidiary

Lands' End has surrounded a number of sales channels. The firm markets its products through its folksy flagship and specialty catalogs and Web site. It also runs about 15 retail stores in the US, UK, and Germany, and operates 200 in-store Lands' End Shops at Sears locations. Its traditional, casual apparel for men, women, and children is generally immune to the changing tides of fashion. Lands' End also sells accessories, home goods, luggage, and corporate gifts to its primarily middle-aged customers. Lands' End is expanding its Web presence worldwide, but catalogs continue to be its primary means of marketing. Sears, Roebuck, which acquired Lands' End in 2002, was bought by Kmart Holding (now Sears Holdings).

LANDSTAR SYSTEM, INC.

NASDAQ (GS): LSTR

13410 Sutton Park Dr. South	CEO: Henry H. Gerkens
Jacksonville, FL 32224	CFO: James B. (Jim) Gattoni
Phone: 904-398-9400	HR: –
Fax: 904-390-1437	FYE: Last Saturday in December
Web: www.landstar.com	Type: Public

Truckload freight carrier Landstar System has hitched its star to an asset-light business model. The company's fleet of about 8,600 tractors and 14,300 trailers (including flatbed, refrigerated, and heavy-duty units as well as standard dry vans) is operated primarily by independent contractors, and the company's services are marketed by sales agents. Landstar's freight carrier units transport general commodities and goods such as automotive products, building materials, and machinery, as well as ammunition. Major customers include third-party logistics providers and government agencies such as the US Department of Defense. In addition to truckload transportation, Landstar offers logistics services.

	Annual Growth	12/03	12/04	12/05	12/06	12/07
Sales ($ mil.)	11.8%	1,597.8	2,021.3	2,520.5	2,518.0	2,492.6
Net income ($ mil.)	21.3%	50.7	71.9	120.0	113.1	109.7
Market value ($ mil.)	40.6%	576.0	2,264.9	2,454.6	2,136.7	2,250.5
Employees	1.0%	—	—	1,285	1,298	

L&W SUPPLY CORPORATION

550 W. Adams St.	CEO: Brendan J. Deely
Chicago, IL 60606	CFO: Mark Hickman
Phone: 847-622-9400	HR: Kevin Corrigan
Fax: 847-622-9600	FYE: December 31
Web: www.lwsupply.com	Type: Subsidiary

At the construction job site A&W can supply the root beer, while L&W can deliver the wallboard and other building materials. L&W Supply distributes more than 40,000 building products made by its parent company, USG, and other manufacturers through nearly 200 locations in about 36 states. Besides wallboard, L&W Supply's products include ceilings, insulation, joint treatment and texture products, metal framing, and roofing supplies. It also offers such services as delivery of less-than-truckload quantities, stocking, and lending. The company's customers are primarily builders and contractors. USG organized L&W Supply in 1971.

THE LANE CONSTRUCTION CORPORATION

90 Fieldstone Ct.	CEO: Robert E. (Bob) Alger
Cheshire, CT 06410	CFO: James M. (Jim) Ferrell
Phone: 203-235-3351	HR: –
Fax: 203-237-4260	FYE: December 31
Web: www.laneconstruct.com	Type: Private

For more than a century Lane Construction has been a transportation specialist — building everything from horseless carriage lanes to airport runways. The heavy civil contractor evolved from a stone-crushing plant opened in 1890 by railroad engineer John Lane. The group is known for building highways, roads, bridges, railroads, and mass transit systems, primarily in the eastern and southern US. Projects include the construction of a pedestrian tunnel at Dulles International Airport and the reconstruction of a Texas interstate. The firm also produces bituminous concrete and aggregates from plants in the northeastern, mid-Atlantic, and southern US. Additionally, it sells and leases construction equipment.

	Annual Growth	12/03	12/04	12/05	12/06	12/07
Est. sales ($ mil.)	—	—	—	—	—	554.8
Employees	—	—	—	—	—	3,500

LANE INDUSTRIES, INC.

1200 Shermer Rd., 4th Fl.	CEO: Forrest M. Schneider
Northbrook, IL 60062	CFO: Richard R. (Rich) Fabbrini
Phone: 847-498-6789	HR: Debra W. Stinson
Fax: 847-498-2104	FYE: December 31
Web: www.lanehospitality.com	Type: Private

From the seeds of a humble office machine and supplies manufacturer grew the mighty oak of Lane Industries. The diversified holding company is active in the lodging industry through Lane Hospitality, which owns or operates about 20 hotels and time-share properties under brands such as Hilton, Intercontinental Hotels Group, Marriott, and Radisson. The company also breeds cattle and horses on its Bell Ranch in New Mexico. Its RedBell cattle are raised for beef, and guests are invited to stay at its 1930s Hacienda and experience old-fashioned cowboy life, including trail rides and antelope hunts. Lane Industries is owned by the Lane family.

An in-depth profile of this company is available to Hoover's Online members at hoovers.com.

LANGER, INC.

NASDAQ (GM): GAIT

450 Commack Rd.
Deer Park, NY 11729
Phone: 631-667-1200
Fax: 631-667-1203
Web: www.langerbiomechanics.com

CEO: W. Gray Hudkins
CFO: Kathleen P. Bloch
HR: –
FYE: December 31
Type: Public

Langer has a foot fetish. The firm makes some 500 orthopedic products to help people support, correct, or comfort foot and ankle discomfort caused by joint misalignment or injury. It Regal Medical subsidiary serves patients in long-term care facilities. Products include Sporthotics sneaker inserts, orthotic shells for Birkenstocks, and gel-based sheaths and liners to protect amputees' skin and sockets from undue wear from their prosthetics. Langer also makes around 50 skin-care products. The NouveauDerm-branded products include creams to promote scar healing and gloves and socks to lubricate and nourish skin.

	Annual Growth	12/03	12/04	12/05	12/06	12/07
Sales ($ mil.)	26.3%	24.7	30.1	40.1	35.2	62.9
Net income ($ mil.)	—	0.0	0.4	(4.6)	(4.8)	(4.5)
Market value ($ mil.)	18.8%	15.2	30.7	51.5	52.6	30.3
Employees	71.3%	—	—	335	574	—

LANNETT COMPANY, INC.

AMEX: LCI

9000 State Rd.
Philadelphia, PA 19136
Phone: 215-333-9000
Fax: 215-333-9004
Web: www.lannett.com

CEO: Arthur P. Bedrosian
CFO: Brian J. Kearns
HR: –
FYE: June 30
Type: Public

Lannett is banking on the designation of "bioequivant" for its products. The firm manufactures and markets generic prescription drugs including painkillers (including two versions of Novartis' migraine treatment Fiorinal), anticonvulsants for epileptics, and a drug for congestive heart failure (a version of Lanoxin). The company has also developed a generic version of Abbott Laboratories' Synthroid. While it manufactures some of its products, Jerome Stevens Pharmaceuticals manufactures a significant portion of Lannett's inventories. Lannett prefers to focus on products with few generic competitors. Chairman William Farber owns more than half of the company.

	Annual Growth	6/03	6/04	6/05	6/06	6/07
Sales ($ mil.)	18.1%	42.5	63.8	44.9	64.1	82.6
Net income ($ mil.)	—	11.7	13.2	(32.8)	5.0	(6.9)
Market value ($ mil.)	(25.2%)	469.9	361.7	125.9	137.4	147.2
Employees	7.3%	—	—	172	—	198

LANTRONIX, INC.

NASDAQ (CM): LTRX

15353 Barranca Pkwy.
Irvine, CA 92618
Phone: 949-453-3990
Fax: 949-450-7249
Web: www.lantronix.com

CEO: Jerry D. Chase
CFO: Reagan Y. Sakai
HR: –
FYE: June 30
Type: Public

Lantronix gets electronics online. The company designs servers that allow electronic devices such as bar code scanners, vending machines, thermostats, point-of-sale terminals, and security cameras to be accessed and controlled over the Internet and across LANs. It also develops print servers that let users across a network share printers. Lantronix, which outsources its manufacturing, sells primarily through OEMs, resellers, systems integrators, and distributors. Ingram Micro and Tech Data together account for about 20% of sales. Former chairman Bernhard Bruscha, who is a primary shareholder of computer systems maker transtec AG (a key Lantronix customer), owns about 34% of Lantronix.

	Annual Growth	6/03	6/04	6/05	6/06	6/07
Sales ($ mil.)	2.8%	49.5	48.9	48.5	51.9	55.3
Net income ($ mil.)	—	(47.5)	(15.6)	(7.0)	(3.0)	(1.7)
Market value ($ mil.)	19.4%	41.0	72.7	77.0	129.1	83.2
Employees	—	—	—	—	—	—

LANXESS CORPORATION

111 RIDC Park West Dr.
Pittsburgh, PA 15275
Phone: 412-809-1000
Fax: 412-809-3599
Web: www.us.lanxess.com

CEO: Randall S. (Randy) Dearth
CFO: –
HR: –
FYE: December 31
Type: Subsidiary

LANXESS Corporation is trying to move forward successfully. Its synthetic rubber products are used by the tire, auto, and industrial goods industries, while its plastics are marketed toward makers of medical and electronic communications products. LANXESS Corp.'s largest unit is its chemicals division, which supplies the textiles, pharmaceutical, and automobile industries, among others. Its parent company, Germany's LANXESS AG, was spun off from Bayer in 2004 and began to trade publicly the following year. It comprises the former chemicals, plastics, and rubber businesses of Bayer Corporation. The LANXESS name derives from a mash-up of the French word *lancer* (to thrust forward) and the English *success*.

LAPOLLA INDUSTRIES, INC.

AMEX: LPA

15402 Vantage Pkwy. East, Ste. 322
Houston, TX 77032
Phone: 281-219-4100
Fax: 281-219-4102
Web: www.lapollaindustries.com

CEO: Douglas J. Kramer
CFO: Paul Smiertka
HR: –
FYE: December 31
Type: Public

LaPolla Industries would hate for its customers to have leaky roofs over their heads or insufficiently protected exterior walls. The company makes foam products used to protect roofs and the "building envelope," which is the separation of the exterior and interior parts of a building. It also makers coatings for weatherproofing concrete and metal roofing and other materials. The company changed its name in 2005 when it absorbed subsidiary LaPolla Industries, a provider of roof coatings and polyurethane foam construction systems. The former IFT Corp., which had previously been called Urecoats, acquired LaPolla in 2005. Chairman Richard Kurtz owns 62% of LaPolla.

	Annual Growth	12/03	12/04	12/05	12/06	12/07
Sales ($ mil.)	67.9%	4.0	2.6	20.2	30.3	31.8
Net income ($ mil.)	—	(11.3)	(5.8)	(1.5)	(2.8)	(5.1)
Market value ($ mil.)	7.5%	—	—	26.1	30.5	30.2
Employees	—	—	—	39	—	—

LARGO VISTA GROUP, LTD.

OTC: LGOV

4570 Campus Dr.
Newport Beach, CA 92660
Phone: 949-252-2180
Fax: 949-252-2181
Web: www.largovista.com

CEO: Deng Shan
CFO: Denise Deng
HR: –
FYE: December 31
Type: Public

In the big picture Largo Vista buys and resells liquid petroleum gas (LPG) in China. The company conducts its operations through strategic partnerships with Chinese companies Zunyi Shilin Xinmao Petrochemical Industries and Jiahong Gas. It purchases and resells LPG in the retail and wholesale markets to both residential and commercial customers in the city of Zunyi, in Guizhou Province. Largo Vista has closed its unprofitable storage depot operations in that city and is focusing on supplying LPG in bottles and via pipelines. The company is eyeing further expansion in both China and Vietnam.

	Annual Growth	12/03	12/04	12/05	12/06	12/07
Sales ($ mil.)	(9.6%)	0.6	0.4	0.4	0.7	0.4
Net income ($ mil.)	—	(0.5)	(0.3)	(0.3)	(0.2)	(0.6)
Market value ($ mil.)	(44.2%)	—	—	8.1	7.8	2.5
Employees	—	—	—	—	—	—

LARRY H. MILLER GROUP

9350 S. 150 E., Rte. 1000
Sandy, UT 84070
Phone: 801-563-4100
Fax: 801-563-4191
Web: www.lhm.com

CEO: Clark Whitworth
CFO: Clark Whitworth
HR: –
FYE: December 31
Type: Private

You wouldn't hire the Larry H. Miller Group for your late night bebop, but the firm does know a little something about all that jazz. The company operates about 45 auto dealerships in Arizona, Colorado, Idaho, New Mexico, Oregon, and Utah. The company also owns the NBA's Utah Jazz, its home (EnergySolutions Arena), Fanzz retail stores, and Salt Lake City TV station KJZZ. In addition the Larry H. Miller Group operates three movie theatres with about 40 screens in Salt Lake City, Lehi, and Sandy, Utah. The company also owns Jordan Commons, an office and entertainment center in Sandy. Owned by Larry H. Miller, the company was founded in 1979.

LARSEN & TOUBRO INFOTECH LTD.

2035 Lincoln Hwy., Ste. 3000-3005, Edison Square West
Edison, NJ 08817
Phone: 732-248-6111
Fax: 732-248-6122
Web: www.lntinfotech.com

CEO: Vijay K. Magapu
CFO: Sunil Sapre
HR: –
FYE: March 31
Type: Private

On the far side of the world, folks are providing outsourced IT services for US companies. Larsen & Toubro Infotech (L&T Infotech) implements third-party mobile and enterprise software in such areas as enterprise resource planning, customer relationship management, and e-procurement and supply chain management. The company also provides application development and infra-structure management services. Subsidiary GDA Technologies designs semi-conductors and circuit boards for technology manufacturers. Customers include companies in the financial services, insurance, and manufacturing industries. L&T Infotech, which operates from offices worldwide, is owned by India's Larson & Toubro Limited.

	Annual Growth	3/03	3/04	3/05	3/06	3/07
Est. sales ($ mil.)	—	—	—	—	—	170.7
Employees	—	—	—	—	—	7,500

LAS VEGAS SANDS CORP.

NYSE: LVS

3355 Las Vegas Blvd. South
Las Vegas, NV 89109
Phone: 702-414-1000
Fax: 702-414-4884
Web: www.lasvegassands.com

CEO: Sheldon G. Adelson
CFO: Scott A. Henry
HR: Mike Gentry
FYE: December 31
Type: Public

Rising from the ashes of the bulldozed Sands Hotel, the Venetian Casino Resort (owned by Las Vegas Sands) brings a touch of Venice to the Las Vegas Strip. Replete with gondoliers and a replica of the Rialto Bridge, the Venetian offers a 120,000-sq.-ft. casino and a 4,000-suite hotel, as well as a shopping, dining, and entertainment complex. Las Vegas Sands also operates the Congress Center conference facility that links the casino to the nearby Sands Expo Center trade show and convention center. In addition, the firm operates The Sands Macao casino in China, and The Palazzo Casino next door to the Venetian in Las Vegas. Chairman and CEO Sheldon Adelson and trusts for his family own nearly 70% of the firm.

	Annual Growth	12/03	12/04	12/05	12/06	12/07
Sales ($ mil.)	43.7%	691.8	1,197.1	1,740.9	2,236.9	2,950.6
Net income ($ mil.)	15.1%	66.6	495.2	283.7	442.0	116.7
Market value ($ mil.)	29.1%	—	16,999.7	13,979.5	31,720.0	36,610.7
Employees	51.3%	—	—	12,230	15,280	28,000

LASALLE BRANDS CORPORATION

Pink Sheets: LSAL

7702 E. Doubletree Ranch Rd., Ste. 300
Scottsdale, AZ 85258
Phone: 480-905-5550
Fax: 480-945-3472
Web: www.lasalleicecream.com

CEO: Medhat (Tony) Mohamed
CFO: Scott Campbell
HR: –
FYE: December 31
Type: Public

LaSalle Brands (formerly Diners Acquisition Corp.) owns LaSalle Ice Cream, a premium frozen dairy brand that is distributed primarily in the New York City area. LaSalle is popular for its variety of ice cream flavors, as well as gelato and fruit sorbet. The company also sells branded coffee and imported cookies. LaSalle Brands is focused on developing a national retail chain to sell LaSalle branded treats.

	Annual Growth	12/02	12/03	12/04	12/05	*12/06
Sales ($ mil.)	—	0.0	0.0	0.0	0.0	0.1
Net income ($ mil.)	—	(0.7)	(0.7)	(0.8)	(5.6)	(2.9)
Employees	—	—	—	—	—	—

*Most recent year available

LASALLE HOTEL PROPERTIES

NYSE: LHO

3 Bethesda Metro Center, Ste. 1200
Bethesda, MD 20814
Phone: 301-941-1500
Fax: 301-941-1553
Web: www.lasallehotels.com

CEO: Jon E. Bortz
CFO: Hans S. Weger
HR: Hans S. Weger
FYE: December 31
Type: Public

LaSalle Hotel Properties is a self-administered and self-managed real estate investment trust (REIT) that invests in, renovates, and leases luxury full-service hotel properties. It owns more than 30 hotels in about a dozen states. Its hotels, which together have about 8,500 rooms, are typically located in major urban markets near convention centers, business districts, and resorts. The properties are managed by outside hotel operators under such brand names as Marriott, Sheraton, Holiday Inn, and Hilton. LaSalle Hotel Properties became self-managing in 2001 after three years under the wing of global real estate investment firm Jones Lang LaSalle.

	Annual Growth	12/03	12/04	12/05	12/06	12/07
Sales ($ mil.)	34.6%	202.0	280.6	394.6	626.8	662.4
Net income ($ mil.)	23.3%	38.8	23.2	35.4	99.1	89.8
Market value ($ mil.)	30.0%	447.8	951.1	1,447.1	1,839.0	1,280.5
Employees	7.2%	—	—	27	31	31

LASERCARD CORPORATION

NASDAQ (GM): LCRD

1875 N. Shoreline Blvd.
Mountain View, CA 94043
Phone: 650-969-4428
Fax: 650-969-3140
Web: www.lasercard.com

CEO: Robert T. (Bob) DeVincenzi
CFO: Steven G. Larson
HR: –
FYE: March 31
Type: Public

Green cards are no longer green — but they are high-tech, thanks to LaserCard. The company makes wallet-sized, recordable optical data cards that permanently store electronic text, graphics, photos, and security marks such as fingerprints and holograms. The tamper-resistant cards store data and can be read to display information on a computer screen. It also offers optical card drives and card system software. LaserCard's products are used by the US Immigration and Naturalization Service for immigrant identification; other applications include health record storage, security access, and e-commerce transactions.

	Annual Growth	3/04	3/05	3/06	3/07	3/08
Sales ($ mil.)	21.5%	17.0	28.5	39.9	32.3	37.0
Net income ($ mil.)	—	(12.4)	(8.9)	0.8	(12.4)	(7.2)
Market value ($ mil.)	(9.5%)	151.8	57.0	264.0	139.8	101.7
Employees	(16.1%)	—	—	261	219	—

An in-depth profile of this company is available to Hoover's Online members at hoovers.com.

LASERLOCK TECHNOLOGIES, INC.

OTC: LLTI

837 Lindy Ln.
Bala Cynwyd, PA 19004
Phone: 610-668-1952
Fax: 610-668-2771
Web: www.laserlocktech.com

CEO: Norman A. Gardner
CFO: –
HR: –
FYE: December 31
Type: Public

Willy Wonka could have used LaserLock Technologies to help ensure that each Golden Ticket was the genuine article. A development-stage company, LaserLock plans to license an invisible ink to third parties that can be used to authenticate documents. The company's system is targeted to the gambling industry, where uses could include verification of cashless tickets from slot machines and detection of counterfeit cards, chips, or dice. LaserLock has plans to raise additional capital and/or enter into strategic alliances or partnerships with other companies in order to do business.

	Annual Growth	12/03	12/04	12/05	12/06	12/07
Sales ($ mil.)	31.6%	0.1	0.1	0.2	0.1	0.3
Net income ($ mil.)	—	(1.1)	(1.4)	(1.3)	(1.6)	(1.0)
Market value ($ mil.)	(40.7%)	8.8	5.8	2.5	1.8	—
Employees	—	—	—	—	—	—

LASON, INC.

1305 Stephenson Hwy.
Troy, MI 48083
Phone: 248-837-7100
Fax: 248-837-7150
Web: www.lason.com

CEO: Ronald C. Cogburn
CFO: James G. Reynolds
HR: Kenneth L. Shaw
FYE: December 31
Type: Private

Companies drowning in paperwork can call on Lason for help. The firm helps document- and data-intensive companies streamline such business processes as accounts receivable, claims processing, electronic medical records management, and loan processing. Services offered include document scanning and indexing, mail services, data entry, data conversion, and printing. Additionally, Lason's proprietary document management program — called document DNA — lets companies store and retrieve documents online. The company's operations span the globe, with more than 35 offices in the US and Canada, as well as facilities in China, India, and Mexico.

LATHAM & WATKINS LLP

885 3rd Ave.
New York, NY 10022
Phone: 212-906-1200
Fax: 212-751-4864
Web: www.lw.com

CEO: Robert M. (Bob) Dell
CFO: Grant Johnson
HR: Mimi A. Krumholz
FYE: December 31
Type: Partnership

Latham & Watkins' founders Dana Latham and Paul Watkins flipped a coin in 1934 to determine which of their names would go first on the law firm's shingle. From that coin toss, the firm has grown into one of the largest in the US, and today it has about 2,100 lawyers in some two dozen offices around the world. Latham & Watkins organizes its practices into five main areas: corporate; environment, land, and resources; finance; litigation; and tax. The firm has counted companies such as Amgen, Time Warner Inc., and Morgan Stanley among its clients.

	Annual Growth	12/02	12/03	12/04	12/05	12/06
Sales ($ mil.)	14.9%	—	—	—	1,413.0	1,624.0
Employees	6.3%	—	—	—	4,234	4,500

LATTICE INCORPORATED

OTC: LTTC

7150 N. Park Dr., Ste. 500
Pennsauken, NJ 08109
Phone: 856-910-1166
Fax: 856-910-1811
Web: www.latticeincorporated.com

CEO: Paul Burgess
CFO: Joseph (Joe) Noto
HR: –
FYE: December 31
Type: Public

Lattice has constructed a diverse product framework. The company provides communications products and services to corporate and government clients. Deriving the majority of its revenue through contracts with the federal government, it develops applications related to business management, geographic information systems (GIS), Web services, and geospatial systems. The company also provides technology that allows prison officials to monitor and control inmate collect-only phone calls. Formerly called Science Dynamics, the company changed its name to Lattice in 2007.

	Annual Growth	12/03	12/04	12/05	12/06	12/07
Sales ($ mil.)	38.8%	4.1	1.6	4.2	7.5	15.2
Net income ($ mil.)	—	(0.3)	(0.5)	(0.9)	(15.6)	3.7
Market value ($ mil.)	—	—	—	—	—	5.9
Employees	—	—	—	—	59	

LATTICE SEMICONDUCTOR CORPORATION

NASDAQ (GM): LSCC

5555 NE Moore Ct.
Hillsboro, OR 97124
Phone: 503-268-8000
Fax: 503-268-8347
Web: www.latticesemi.com

CEO: Jan Johannessen
CFO: Jan Johannessen
HR: Todd Llewelyn
FYE: December 31
Type: Public

Lattice Semiconductor provides a latticework of programmable-chip products. The company is a top supplier of programmable logic devices (PLDs), including in-system programmable (ISP) devices that electronics manufacturers can configure and reconfigure after the chips have been attached to a circuit board. Lattice also makes low-density logic devices, and sells the software needed to customize its chips, which are used in communications, computing, industrial, and military applications. The fabless semiconductor company has also expanded into the market for field-programmable gate arrays, another type of programmable chip. More than three-quarters of its sales comes from customers outside the US.

	Annual Growth	12/03	12/04	12/05	12/06	12/07
Sales ($ mil.)	2.2%	209.7	225.8	211.1	245.5	228.7
Net income ($ mil.)	—	(91.8)	(52.0)	(49.1)	3.1	(239.8)
Market value ($ mil.)	(24.0%)	1,094.2	647.6	491.0	743.5	365.0
Employees	(4.2%)	1,048	1,008	909	960	883

LAUREATE EDUCATION, INC.

650 S. Exeter St.
Baltimore, MD 21202
Phone: 410-843-6100
Fax: –
Web: www.laureate-inc.com

CEO: Douglas L. (Doug) Becker
CFO: Rosemarie Mecca
HR: –
FYE: December 31
Type: Private

If higher education is a matter of degrees, Laureate must be hot. Laureate Education, formerly Sylvan Learning Systems, provides full-time and working adult career education through online and campus-based programs in Asia, the Americas, and Europe. Laureate's educational institutions offer more than 100 bachelor's, master's, and doctoral degrees and specializations to a combined enrollment of more than 240,000. Students can earn degrees in areas such as business, education, hospitality management, law, and medicine. Laureate's Canter unit provides professional development and training programs for teachers. An investment group headed by chairman and CEO Douglas Becker owns the company.

	Annual Growth	12/02	12/03	12/04	12/05	12/06
Sales ($ mil.)	17.4%	604.0	472.8	648.0	875.4	1,145.8
Net income ($ mil.)	—	(95.9)	46.1	63.0	75.2	105.6
Employees	9.2%	16,200	13,374	17,534	22,800	23,000

LAW ENFORCEMENT ASSOCIATES CORPORATION

AMEX: AID

100 Hunter Place
Youngsville, NC 27596
Phone: 919-554-4700
Fax: 919-556-6240
Web: www.leacorp.com

CEO: Paul Feldman
CFO: Paul Feldman
HR: –
FYE: December 31
Type: Public

Criminals can run, but they can't hide. At least not if Law Enforcement Associates (LEA) has anything to say about it. The company makes surveillance equipment for law enforcement agencies worldwide. Its products include transmitters, receivers, video recording systems, and global positioning tracking systems. Law Enforcement Associates also makes audio surveillance equipment that lets law enforcement agencies monitor conversations. The company's under-vehicle inspection system (UVIS) is used to view the underside of vehicles entering and exiting secure areas in order to detect explosives or contraband. Sirchie Finger Print Laboratories owns a 51% stake in Law Enforcement Associates.

	Annual Growth	12/03	12/04	12/05	12/06	12/07
Sales ($ mil.)	2.4%	6.1	6.2	8.2	7.6	6.7
Net income ($ mil.)	—	0.2	(0.2)	(0.3)	0.0	(1.0)
Market value ($ mil.)	26.3%	5.6	128.9	57.1	21.2	14.2
Employees	—	—	—	25	—	—

LAWSON PRODUCTS, INC.

NASDAQ (GS): LAWS

1666 E. Touhy Ave.
Des Plaines, IL 60018
Phone: 847-827-9666
Fax: –
Web: www.lawsonproducts.com

CEO: Thomas J. Neri
CFO: Scott F. Stephens
HR: James J. Smith
FYE: December 31
Type: Public

Lawson Products' stock in trade may sound boring to some, but to manufacturing companies it's positively riveting. The company supplies screws, rivets, and related fasteners to industrial and commercial maintenance, repair, and operations (MRO) customers, as well as original equipment manufacturers (OEMs). Founded in 1952, Lawson distributes products — including industrial supplies (hoses, lubricants, cleansers), fasteners (screws, nuts, rivets), and car parts (electrical supplies) — throughout North America. Other services include inventory and information systems and supply chain management.

	Annual Growth	12/03	12/04	12/05	12/06	12/07
Sales ($ mil.)	7.0%	389.1	419.6	450.2	518.2	509.7
Net income ($ mil.)	(10.1%)	16.2	21.4	26.7	12.6	10.6
Market value ($ mil.)	0.7%	314.0	465.8	338.6	391.0	323.2
Employees	(7.3%)	—	—	1,630	1,540	1,400

LAWSON SOFTWARE, INC.

NASDAQ (GS): LWSN

380 St. Peter St.
St. Paul, MN 55102
Phone: 651-767-7000
Fax: –
Web: www.lawson.com

CEO: Harry Debes
CFO: Robert A. Schriesheim
HR: Kristin Trecker
FYE: May 31
Type: Public

Lawson Software just wants to bring a little law and order to managing enterprises. The company makes enterprise resource planning software for the health care, professional services, retail, public sector, and telecommunications industries. Its applications handle such tasks as distribution, procurement, human resources, customer service, professional services automation, and accounting. The company also offers consulting, implementation, and maintenance services. Co-founders Richard Lawson and John Cerullo collectively own about a third of the company. Lawson acquired Intentia International in early 2006.

	Annual Growth	5/04	5/05	5/06	5/07	5/08
Sales ($ mil.)	23.7%	363.6	335.2	390.8	750.4	851.9
Net income ($ mil.)	14.4%	8.0	5.3	16.0	(20.9)	13.7
Market value ($ mil.)	22.4%	675.6	746.7	1,253.1	1,679.7	1,515.8
Employees	(11.3%)	1,579	1,400	—	—	—

LAYNE CHRISTENSEN COMPANY

NASDAQ (GS): LAYN

1900 Shawnee Mission Pkwy.
Mission Woods, KS 66205
Phone: 913-362-0510
Fax: 913-362-0133
Web: www.laynechristensen.com

CEO: Andrew B. Schmitt
CFO: Jerry W. Fanska
HR: John Wright
FYE: January 31
Type: Public

Layne Christensen cuts its way through the upper crust. The company provides drilling and construction services primarily related to water, wastewater treatment, and mineral exploration. Layne Christensen serves such clients as public and private water utilities, industrial companies, mining firms, and heavy civil construction contractors. It has operations throughout the Americas, as well as in Africa, Australia, and Europe. Layne Christensen's Water and Wastewater Infrastructure segment accounts for about two-thirds of the company's sales; mineral exploration work accounts for most of the remainder. The group has also entered the energy field, producing coalbed methane.

	Annual Growth	1/04	1/05	1/06	1/07	1/08
Sales ($ mil.)	33.7%	272.0	343.5	463.0	722.8	868.3
Net income ($ mil.)	92.8%	2.7	9.8	14.7	26.3	37.3
Market value ($ mil.)	45.7%	156.8	233.4	459.3	543.6	707.0
Employees	10.0%	—	—	3,551	3,919	4,300

LAZARE KAPLAN INTERNATIONAL INC.

AMEX: LKI

19 W. 44th St.
New York, NY 10036
Phone: 212-972-9700
Fax: 212-972-8561
Web: lazarediamonds.com

CEO: Leon Tempelsman
CFO: William H. Moryto
HR: –
FYE: May 31
Type: Public

Sometimes plain old diamonds just aren't good enough. Lazare Kaplan International specializes in premium-priced diamonds and diamond jewelry. The firm buys rough diamonds (primarily from Diamond Trading Company, the sales arm of De Beers), cuts and polishes the gems for maximum sparkle, and laser-inscribes the branded Lazare Diamonds with the firm's logo and an ID number. Plants in Namibia, South Africa, and Russia handle the processing. Lazare sells to wholesalers, manufacturers, and jewelry retailers worldwide. Chairman Maurice Tempelsman (longtime companion of Jackie Onassis), his son Leon (vice chairman and president), and their family own almost 90% of Lazare.

	Annual Growth	5/03	5/04	5/05	5/06	5/07
Sales ($ mil.)	20.9%	203.2	235.8	421.4	528.0	434.4
Net income ($ mil.)	—	1.1	2.4	5.2	1.5	(3.0)
Market value ($ mil.)	10.5%	48.2	74.8	72.4	69.5	71.9
Employees	—	—	—	—	223	—

LA-Z-BOY INCORPORATED

NYSE: LZB

1284 N. Telegraph Rd.
Monroe, MI 48162
Phone: 734-242-1444
Fax: 734-457-2005
Web: www.lazboy.com

CEO: Kurt L. Darrow
CFO: Louis M. (Mike) Riccio Jr.
HR: Steven P. (Steve) Rindskopf
FYE: Last Saturday in April
Type: Public

The kickback that La-Z-Boy gives its customers is perfectly legal. The top US maker of upholstered furniture, La-Z-Boy sells its ubiquitous recliners (#1 in the world), plus chairs, sofas, tables, and modular seating units. One recliner sports a drink cooler, phone, and massage and heat system. La-Z-Boy sells through about 70 company-owned stores, some 330 independent La-Z-Boy Furniture Galleries, and about 280 in-store galleries at furniture dealers, department stores, and other outlets. La-Z-Boy also makes wood furniture (desks, cabinets, and bedroom items) and licenses its name for use on furniture for the health care industry. Its brands include La-Z-Boy, Bauhaus USA, Hammary, Lea, and Kincaid.

	Annual Growth	4/04	4/05	4/06	4/07	4/08
Sales ($ mil.)	(7.7%)	1,998.9	2,048.4	1,916.8	1,617.3	1,450.9
Net income ($ mil.)	—	(5.8)	37.2	(3.0)	4.1	(13.5)
Market value ($ mil.)	(25.2%)	1,136.9	618.3	793.3	617.0	355.4
Employees	(12.1%)	—	14,822	13,404	11,729	10,057

An in-depth profile of this company is available to Hoover's Online members at hoovers.com.

923

LAZY DAYS RV CENTER, INC.

6130 Lazy Days Blvd.
Seffner, FL 33584
Phone: 813-246-4999
Fax: 813-246-4408
Web: www.lazydays.com

CEO: John Horton
CFO: Randall R. (Randy) Lay
HR: Debbie Dube
FYE: December 31
Type: Private

Plenty of hard work has turned Lazy Days RV Center into one of the largest dealers of recreational vehicles in the US. At its 126-acre site, Lazy Days sells about 20 brands of new and used RVs. The dealership also has some 230 service bays for repair and maintenance. Besides the RV dealership, the Lazy Days location includes RallyPark, a 300-lot RV campground. Lazy Days' grounds also include a Cracker Barrel restaurant, Camping World retail store, and RV gas station. The company was founded in 1976 by chairman Don Wallace (who owns more than 10%), his late father, H. K. Wallace, and brother, Ron Wallace. In 2004 a New York investment company paid $206 million for a controlling stake in the company.

	Annual Growth	12/03	12/04	12/05	12/06	12/07
Est. sales ($ mil.)	—	—	—	—	—	757.3
Employees	—	—	—	—	—	669

L. B. FOSTER COMPANY

NASDAQ (GS): FSTR

415 Holiday Dr.
Pittsburgh, PA 15220
Phone: 412-928-3417
Fax: 412-928-7891
Web: www.lbfoster.com

CEO: Stan L. Hasselbusch
CFO: David J. Russo
HR: Brian Kelly
FYE: December 31
Type: Public

L. B. Foster can help keep you on track whether you're riding the rails or cruising the open road. The company manufactures rail and trackwork for railroads and mass transit systems, and for industrial applications such as mining. It also sells and rents steel sheet piling and earth wall systems used in highway construction and repair, and H-bearing piling that supports bridges and high-rise buildings. L. B. Foster also supplies pipe coatings to the oil and natural gas industries and pipe products for industrial, municipal, and agricultural water wells.

	Annual Growth	12/03	12/04	12/05	12/06	12/07
Sales ($ mil.)	17.8%	264.3	297.9	353.5	389.8	509.0
Net income ($ mil.)	138.9%	3.4	1.5	5.4	13.5	110.7
Market value ($ mil.)	72.8%	63.3	95.6	151.5	273.1	564.6
Employees	—	—	—	—	641	—

LCA-VISION INC.

NASDAQ (GS): LCAV

7840 Montgomery Rd.
Cincinnati, OH 45236
Phone: 513-792-9292
Fax: 513-792-5620
Web: www.lca-vision.com

CEO: Steven C. Straus
CFO: Alan H. Buckey
HR: Stephen M. Jones
FYE: December 31
Type: Public

LCA-Vision thinks its services are a sight better than glasses. The company provides laser vision correction procedures at some 75 LasikPlus free-standing facilities. LCA-Vision's facilities treat nearsightedness, farsightedness, and astigmatism primarily using laser-assisted in situ keratomileusis (LASIK), which reshapes the cornea with a computer-guided excimer laser. Additionally, the company's centers offer photorefractive keratectomy (PRK) and other corrective procedures. LCA-Vision operates through centers located in major cities across more than 30 states.

	Annual Growth	12/03	12/04	12/05	12/06	12/07
Sales ($ mil.)	37.7%	81.4	127.1	192.4	238.9	292.6
Net income ($ mil.)	45.3%	7.3	32.0	31.6	28.4	32.5
Market value ($ mil.)	18.5%	187.4	472.9	986.7	681.1	369.1
Employees	22.0%	—	—	574	700	—

LCC INTERNATIONAL, INC.

NASDAQ (GM): LCCI

7900 Westpark Dr., Ste. A-315
McLean, VA 22102
Phone: 703-873-2000
Fax: 703-873-2100
Web: www.lcc.com

CEO: Dean J. Douglas
CFO: Louis (Lou) Salamone
HR: –
FYE: December 31
Type: Public

In the war of wireless standards, LCC International plays all sides — from CDMA to GSM. The radio-frequency engineering and consulting firm serves wireless carriers in every stage of operations. It helps aspiring carriers apply for licenses, buy cell sites, and design and deploy networks; it aids established carriers in expanding and upgrading technology; and it helps mature wireless firms streamline their operations. It also provides outsourced daily operations and maintenance of networks. In addition to wireless service providers, the company serves telecommunications equipment vendors, systems integrators, and tower operators.

	Annual Growth	12/03	12/04	12/05	12/06	12/07
Sales ($ mil.)	7.7%	108.4	193.2	194.0	129.9	145.7
Net income ($ mil.)		(6.5)	(6.3)	(12.5)	(8.0)	(30.8)
Market value ($ mil.)	(17.9%)	104.8	117.8	66.3	103.9	47.6
Employees	(19.9%)	—	—	977	783	—

LCNB CORP.

OTC: LCNB

2 N. Broadway
Lebanon, OH 45036
Phone: 513-932-1414
Fax: 513-933-5262
Web: www.lcnb.com

CEO: Stephen P. Wilson
CFO: Robert C. Haines II
HR: –
FYE: December 31
Type: Public

It just makes *cents* that LCNB counts bucks in the Buckeye State. The firm is the holding company for LCNB National Bank (formerly Lebanon Citizens National Bank), which operates some two dozen branches in southwestern Ohio. The bank offers personal and commercial banking services such as checking and savings accounts, money markets, IRAs, and CDs. Its primary lending activity is originating residential mortgages, which account for about half of the company's loan book. Other offerings include commercial mortgages, consumer loans, including credit cards, and business loans. Trust services are also provided; subsidiary Dakin Insurance Agency sells commercial and personal property/casualty insurance.

	Annual Growth	12/03	12/04	12/05	12/06	12/07
Assets ($ mil.)	3.6%	523.6	522.3	539.5	548.2	604.1
Net income ($ mil.)	(3.1%)	6.7	6.6	6.7	6.5	5.9
Market value ($ mil.)	26.7%	29.8	64.6	66.0	57.4	76.9
Employees	—	—	—	—	—	241

LEADIS TECHNOLOGY, INC.

NASDAQ (GM): LDIS

800 W. California Ave., Ste. 200
Sunnyvale, CA 94086
Phone: 408-331-8600
Fax: 408-331-8601
Web: www.leadis.com

CEO: Antonio R. (Tony) Alvarez
CFO: John Allen
HR: –
FYE: December 31
Type: Public

Leadis Technology aspires to market leadership in display driver chips. The fabless company designs semiconductors used in the LCD and organic light-emitting diode (OLED) flat-panel displays of wireless phones. More than half of all wireless handsets shipped now have color displays in them, leading to demand for sophisticated display drivers. The company is diversifying into audio chips for portable electronics. Taiwan's TPO Displays (53% of sales) is Leadis Technology's leading customer, followed by Japanese distributor Rikei Corp. (29%). Those customers in turn supply display modules to wireless handset manufacturers, such as LG Electronics, Nokia, and Samsung Electronics.

	Annual Growth	12/03	12/04	12/05	12/06	12/07
Sales ($ mil.)	(17.3%)	84.5	150.3	64.2	101.2	39.6
Net income ($ mil.)	—	12.8	17.6	(11.4)	(11.9)	(30.9)
Market value ($ mil.)	(34.8%)	—	298.5	146.7	137.4	82.7
Employees	32.3%	60	89	139	141	184

An in-depth profile of this company is available to Hoover's Online members at hoovers.com.

LEAP WIRELESS INTERNATIONAL, INC.

NASDAQ (GS): LEAP

10307 Pacific Center Ct.	CEO: Stewart D. (Doug) Hutcheson
San Diego, CA 92121	CFO: Stewart D. (Doug) Hutcheson
Phone: 858-882-6000	HR: Leonard C. (Len) Stephens
Fax: 858-882-6010	FYE: December 31
Web: www.leapwireless.com	Type: Public

Leap Wireless International wants to hurdle the competition. The company's Cricket Communications mobile wireless operating unit serves nearly 3 million customers in more than 50 markets in 23 US states. The Cricket service features unlimited flat-rate local calling and a prepaid roaming option, as well as wireless data and multimedia services. Leap Wireless also offers Cricket service in some markets (El Paso, Texas; Colorado Springs, Colorado) through a joint venture with Alaska Native Broadband (managed by Arctic Slope Regional Corporation). The company touts itself as a minority-focused carrier with more than half of its customers coming from the African-American or Latino communities.

	Annual Growth	12/03	12/04	12/05	12/06	12/07
Sales ($ mil.)	21.4%	751.3	344.4	914.7	1,167.2	1,630.8
Net income ($ mil.)	—	(597.4)	(8.6)	30.0	(24.4)	(75.9)
Market value ($ mil.)	25.5%	—	1,620.0	2,318.4	4,037.6	3,203.0
Employees	26.9%	—	—	1,507	2,034	2,425

LEAPFROG ENTERPRISES, INC.

NYSE: LF

6401 Hollis St.	CEO: Jeffrey G. (Jeff) Katz
Emeryville, CA 94608	CFO: William B. (Bill) Chiasson
Phone: 510-420-5000	HR: Hilda S. West
Fax: 510-420-5001	FYE: December 31
Web: www.leapfrog.com	Type: Public

If putting pen to interactive paper helps your little Einstein learn, LeapFrog Enterprises wants to spend some time with your pint-size genius. The toy maker's line includes more than 100 interactive learning toys and books covering subjects ranging from math to music. LeapFrog's best-selling LeapPad learning system looks like a laptop and helps to teach spelling, reading, and phonics. The company's School division sells directly to schools. Former vice chairman and CEO Michael Wood founded LeapFrog in 1995 because the toy market offered nothing to help his three-year-old learn phonics. The company is controlled by Oracle CEO Larry Ellison and one-time junk bond trader Michael Milken.

	Annual Growth	12/03	12/04	12/05	12/06	12/07
Sales ($ mil.)	(10.2%)	680.0	640.3	649.8	502.3	442.3
Net income ($ mil.)	—	72.7	(6.5)	17.5	(145.1)	(101.3)
Market value ($ mil.)	(26.6%)	829.7	454.4	406.0	336.1	241.3
Employees	0.4%	—	—	837	916	844

LEAR CORPORATION

NYSE: LEA

21557 Telegraph Rd.	CEO: Robert E. Rossiter
Southfield, MI 48033	CFO: Matthew J. (Matt) Simoncini
Phone: 248-447-1500	HR: Roger A. Jackson
Fax: 248-447-1772	FYE: December 31
Web: www.lear.com	Type: Public

Lear Corporation doesn't take a back seat to anyone when it comes to manufacturing automotive seats. A major supplier of automotive electronics, the company is also a leader in the global market for car seat systems. In addition to seating systems and their components, Lear manufactures wire harnesses, junction boxes, terminals and connectors, sound systems, and video entertainment systems. Lear, which has more than 200 facilities in 34 countries, sells to automakers such as Ford and General Motors, BMW, Fiat, Toyota, and Volkswagen. Lear has divested its interest in automotive interiors.

	Annual Growth	12/03	12/04	12/05	12/06	12/07
Sales ($ mil.)	0.4%	15,746.7	16,960.0	17,089.2	17,838.9	15,995.0
Net income ($ mil.)	(10.7%)	380.5	422.2	(1,381.5)	(707.5)	241.5
Market value ($ mil.)	(15.5%)	4,180.4	4,113.1	1,912.1	2,251.7	2,135.1
Employees	(11.0%)	—	—	115,000	104,000	91,000

LEARJET INC.

1 Learjet Way	CEO: Michael (Mike) Kanaley
Wichita, KS 67209	CFO: –
Phone: 316-946-2000	HR: Justin Welner
Fax: 316-946-2200	FYE: January 31
Web: www.learjet.com	Type: Subsidiary

Learjet Inc., a subsidiary of Bombardier, builds high-performance business jets — the limos of the skies. A pioneer in the business jet industry, the company has built more than 2,000 aircraft at its Wichita, Kansas, plant since its first jet rolled off the assembly line in 1964. Current Learjet models include the Learjet 40 XR (light jet), Learjet 45 XR (midsize jet), and Learjet 60 (super midsize jet). And what better way to round out your busy jet-setting executive image than Learjet's line of branded gear? The line includes apparel, luggage, martini glasses and shakers, cufflinks, and watches.

	Annual Growth	1/03	1/04	1/05	1/06	1/07
Est. sales ($ mil.)	—	—	—	—	—	62.3
Employees	—	—	—	—	—	850

LEARNING CARE GROUP, INC.

21333 Haggerty Rd., Ste. 300	CEO: William D. (Bill) Davis
Novi, MI 48375	CFO: Frank M. Jerneycic
Phone: 248-697-9000	HR: Scott W. Smith
Fax: 248-697-9002	FYE: June 30
Web: learningcaregroup.com	Type: Subsidiary

Take your seats and pay attention, class: Learning Care Group (formerly Childtime Learning Centers) takes care of children who are between the ages of six weeks and 12 years. The company provides both full-time and part-time child care, educational and developmental programs, and workplace child care. Most of its more than 1,100 sites in the US (operated under brand names: The Children's Courtyard, Childtime Learning Centers, La Petite Academy, Montessori Unlimited, and Tutor Time Child Care) are in suburban areas, but some centers are on or near company work sites. In 2006 Learning Care Group was bought by Australia-based child care services provider A.B.C. Learning Centres for some $160 million.

	Annual Growth	6/03	6/04	6/05	6/06	6/07
Sales ($ mil.)	—	—	—	—	—	522.0
Employees	—	—	—	—	—	23,000

LEARNING TREE INTERNATIONAL, INC.

NASDAQ (GM): LTRE

1805 Library St.	CEO: Nicholas R. (Nick) Schacht
Reston, VA 20190	CFO: Charles R. (Bob) Waldron
Phone: 703-709-9119	HR: Nancy J. McKinley
Fax: 703-709-6405	FYE: Friday nearest September 30
Web: www.learningtree.com	Type: Public

Learning Tree International says, "Leave no IT professional behind." The company offers more than 160 courses, including about 40 professional certification programs, to IT managers in corporations and government agencies. The bulk of the company's course library focuses on information technology topics such as Web development, programming languages, network security, and operating systems. Learning Tree has a growing list of management training offerings, however, with courses in business skills, leadership development, and project management. Learning Tree offers its classes in Japan, Europe, and North America.

	Annual Growth	9/03	9/04	9/05	9/06	9/07
Sales ($ mil.)	2.4%	151.9	152.1	151.6	154.1	167.2
Net income ($ mil.)	34.5%	5.2	0.6	(0.7)	(3.1)	17.0
Market value ($ mil.)	0.6%	286.9	244.3	219.9	134.1	293.8
Employees	4.1%	—	—	457	—	495

An in-depth profile of this company is available to Hoover's Online members at hoovers.com.

925

LECG CORPORATION

NASDAQ (GS): XPRT

2000 Powell St., Ste. 600
Emeryville, CA 94608
Phone: 510-985-6700
Fax: 510-653-9898
Web: www.lecg.com

CEO: Michael J. Jeffery
CFO: Steven R. Fife
HR: Tina M. Bussone
FYE: December 31
Type: Public

You ask, "Can I get a witness?" and LECG answers, "Yes!" The firm provides expert testimony to a wide range of corporate clients and government agencies on issues such as competition and antitrust, intellectual property, labor and employment, and mergers and acquisitions. In addition, LECG offers in-depth studies and consulting services. Clients typically come from industries such as energy, financial services, health care and pharmaceuticals, and telecommunications. LECG operates primarily in the US; the firm also has offices elsewhere in the Americas and in Europe and the Asia/Pacific region.

	Annual Growth	12/03	12/04	12/05	12/06	12/07
Sales ($ mil.)	22.3%	165.6	216.6	286.7	353.9	370.4
Net income ($ mil.)	(19.2%)	26.7	17.1	22.4	21.5	11.4
Market value ($ mil.)	(6.3%)	496.6	425.5	421.4	460.3	383.2
Employees	(0.7%)	—	—	1,151	1,196	1,134

LECROY CORPORATION

NASDAQ (GM): LCRY

700 Chestnut Ridge Rd.
Chestnut Ridge, NY 10977
Phone: 845-425-2000
Fax: 845-425-8967
Web: www.lecroy.com

CEO: Thomas H. (Tom) Reslewic
CFO: Sean B. O'Connor
HR: –
FYE: June 30
Type: Public

If only LeCroy made an instrument to analyze signals exchanged between the sexes. The company makes high-performance, real-time oscilloscopes under the WaveExpert, WaveJet, WaveMaster, WavePro, WaveRunner, and WaveSurfer brand names that capture electronic signals, convert them to digital form, and perform measurements and analysis. LeCroy makes other products such as differential amplifiers, electrical probes, production test digitizers and analyzers, serial data analyzers, and waveform generators. The company also provides technical support, maintenance, and recalibration services. Customers include BAE, IBM, and Siemens. About two-thirds of the company's sales come from outside North America.

	Annual Growth	6/03	6/04	6/05	6/06	6/07
Sales ($ mil.)	8.8%	107.9	124.9	165.0	160.5	151.3
Net income ($ mil.)	—	(1.7)	8.0	2.1	6.6	(13.2)
Market value ($ mil.)	4.7%	99.8	215.6	173.7	182.8	120.0
Employees	—	—	—	402		

LECTEC CORPORATION

OTC: LECT

5610 Lincoln Dr.
Edina, MN 55346
Phone: 952-933-2291
Fax: 952-942-5369
Web: www.lectec.com

CEO: Judd A. Berlin
CFO: Judd A. Berlin
HR: –
FYE: December 31
Type: Public

It's all a skin game at LecTec. The company formerly made (and now licenses) topical patches that deliver over-the-counter drugs through the skin. Its products include cooling, anti-itch, and pain relief patches, as well as acne treatments and wart removers. LecTec ceased manufacturing a few years ago, and is now licensing its intellectual property. The company currently licenses its technology to Novartis for that company's Triaminic Vapor Patch, a children's cough suppressant; the patch was recalled in 2006 after children who ate it got sick. LecTec is pursuing additional licensing agreements with Novartis, as well as seeking other licensing partners.

	Annual Growth	12/03	12/04	12/05	12/06	12/07
Sales ($ mil.)	(65.7%)	7.2	1.1	0.4	0.1	0.1
Net income ($ mil.)	—	(1.3)	2.3	(0.5)	(0.4)	(0.8)
Market value ($ mil.)	13.9%	3.2	6.0	2.1	2.7	5.4
Employees	—	—	—	—	—	—

LEE ENTERPRISES, INCORPORATED

NYSE: LEE

201 N. Harrison St., Ste. 600
Davenport, IA 52801
Phone: 563-383-2100
Fax: 563-323-9609
Web: www.lee.net

CEO: Mary E. Junck
CFO: Carl G. Schmidt
HR: Vytenis P. (Vito) Kuraitis
FYE: September 30
Type: Public

This Lee commands an army of newspapers. Lee Enterprises owns or has stakes in about 50 daily newspapers and more than 300 weekly papers and niche publications serving primarily small and midsized markets in more than 20 states. Its portfolio is anchored by the *St. Louis Post Dispatch*, which boasts a daily circulation of more than 265,000. Lee also owns 50% of Madison Newspapers, publisher of the *Wisconsin State Journal*. In addition to traditional publishing, Lee operates a number of Web sites in conjunction with its newspapers, and it has about 10 commercial printing units in a half dozen states. Former chairman Lloyd Schermer and his family have nearly 30% voting control of the company.

	Annual Growth	9/03	9/04	9/05	9/06	9/07
Sales ($ mil.)	14.5%	656.7	683.3	860.9	1,128.7	1,127.7
Net income ($ mil.)	0.9%	78.0	86.1	76.9	70.8	81.0
Market value ($ mil.)	(17.9%)	1,372.7	1,715.9	1,631.6	996.7	622.5
Employees	(6.0%)	—	—	10,000	9,400	—

LEE HECHT HARRISON LLC

50 Tice Blvd.
Woodcliff Lake, NJ 07677
Phone: 201-930-9333
Fax: 201-307-0878
Web: www.lhh.com

CEO: Ekkehard (Ekkie) Kuppel
CFO: Daniel C. Schlotterbeck
HR: –
FYE: December 31
Type: Subsidiary

Lee Hecht Harrison, a unit of the world's #1 employment services firm, Adecco, provides career and leadership consulting through its more than 240 offices around the globe. The company offers services in areas such as career and leadership development, outplacement, and executive coaching. Clients include organizations, individuals, and recruiters. It additionally offers clients the opportunity to access career information from home. Lee Hecht Harrison sponsors events featuring experts on human resources topics. The company was founded in 1974 and resides within its parent company's Human Capital Solutions division.

	Annual Growth	12/03	12/04	12/05	12/06	12/07
Est. sales ($ mil.)	—	—	—	—	—	46.8
Employees	—	—	—	—	—	850

LEE LEWIS CONSTRUCTION, INC.

7810 Orlando Ave.
Lubbock, TX 79423
Phone: 806-797-8400
Fax: 806-797-8492
Web: www.leelewis.com

CEO: Lee Lewis
CFO: –
HR: –
FYE: June 30
Type: Private

General builder Lee Lewis Construction has waltzed across Texas and beyond to keep in step with the top US contractors. The company provides construction-related services and construction management for commercial, institutional, and industrial projects. Among its projects is the Garland ISD Special Events Center in Garland, Texas; it also worked on the Grand Floridian Resort at Walt Disney World. The company earns much of its revenue from projects for Texas school systems. Projects for hometown neighbor Texas Tech University have generated a significant portion of the company's business. CEO Lee Lewis founded the company in 1976.

	Annual Growth	6/03	6/04	6/05	6/06	6/07
Est. sales ($ mil.)	—	—	—	—	—	245.1
Employees	—	—	—	—	—	250

LEFRAK ORGANIZATION INC.

40 W. 57th St.
New York, NY 10019
Phone: 212-708-6600
Fax: 212-708-6641
Web: www.lefrak.com

CEO: Richard S. LeFrak
CFO: Richard N. Papert
HR: John Farrelly
FYE: Last Sunday in November
Type: Private

Horace Greeley said, "Go west, young man!" and the Lefrak Organization listened — at least, if you take the famous *New Yorker* comic strip's view that you're in the Midwest once you cross the Hudson. The Lefrak Organization is a real estate development company and one of the US's largest private landlords, managing hundreds of apartment buildings (affordable and upscale) in New York, New Jersey, and more recently California, as well as millions of square feet of commercial space. Lefrak's office and retail holdings include its flagship office tower at 40 West 57th Street in midtown Manhattan, home to such tenants as Bank of America, Nautica, and Wells Fargo. Still family-owned and run, Lefrak was founded in 1901.

LEGACY BANCORP, INC.

NASDAQ (GM): LEGC

99 North St.
Pittsfield, MA 01202
Phone: 413-443-4421
Fax: 413-442-8155
Web: www.legacy-banks.com

CEO: J. Williar Dunlaevy
CFO: Paul H. Bruce
HR: Amy Sullivan Thompson
FYE: December 31
Type: Public

A name change, demutualization, and a listing on Nasdaq will be this bancorp's Legacy. In 2005 Legacy Bancorp (formerly Mutual Bancorp of the Berkshires) shed its mutual status, through which depositors owned stakes in the bank, and offered its shares to the public. It is the holding company for Legacy Banks, which has about 15 branches in western Massachusetts' Berkshire County and eastern New York. In addition to traditional deposit accounts, the bank and other subsidiaries offer trust services, insurance, investment products, and portfolio management. Legacy Bancorp traces its history to 1890.

	Annual Growth	12/03	12/04	12/05	12/06	12/07
Assets ($ mil.)	9.0%	—	—	778.3	808.3	924.5
Net income ($ mil.)	—	—	—	(2.2)	2.8	1.2
Market value ($ mil.)	(5.6%)	—	—	137.6	163.4	122.5
Employees	—	—	—	151	—	—

LEGACY HEALTH SYSTEM

1919 NW Lovejoy St.
Portland, OR 97209
Phone: 503-415-5600
Fax: 503-415-5777
Web: www.legacyhealth.org

CEO: Pamela S. (Pam) Vukovich
CFO: Pamela S. (Pam) Vukovich
HR: Sonja Steves
FYE: March 31
Type: Not-for-profit

Legacy Health System strives to create a legacy of positive impact for the Oregon communities it serves. It is the largest nonprofit group of hospitals and home health agencies — and the second-largest overall health care system — in the state. Hospitals include Legacy Emanuel Hospital & Health Center and five others, all founded by a variety of secular organizations. Legacy Health has nearly 900 total beds and its facilities provide such services as acute and critical care, inpatient and outpatient treatment, and health education programs. It also operates hospice and research facilities, as well as a number of regional clinics.

	Annual Growth	3/03	3/04	3/05	3/06	3/07
Est. sales ($ mil.)	—	—	—	—	—	90.0
Employees	—	—	—	—	—	8,000

LEGACY RESERVES LP

NASDAQ (GS): LGCY

303 W. Wall St., Ste. 1600
Midland, TX 79701
Phone: 432-689-5200
Fax: 432-684-3774
Web: www.legacylp.com

CEO: Cary D. Brown
CFO: Steven H. (Steve) Pruett
HR: –
FYE: December 31
Type: Public

Legacy Reserves has its sights set on creating its very own prosperous legacy. The independent oil and gas company explores for oil and gas deposits in the Permian Basin of West Texas and southeast New Mexico and exploits those resources. In 2006 Legacy Reserves reported proved reserves of 20 million barrels of oil equivalent (70% oil; 82% proved developed). The company was formed in 2005 to own and operate the oil and natural gas properties that it acquired from the Moriah Group, the Brothers Group, and MBN Properties. These investors, along with the firm's directors and executive officers, own about 34% of Legacy Reserves.

	Annual Growth	12/03	12/04	12/05	12/06	12/07
Sales ($ mil.)	98.7%	—	14.3	19.4	69.1	112.2
Net income ($ mil.)	—	—	9.2	5.9	4.4	(55.7)
Market value ($ mil.)	—	—	—	—	—	615.1
Employees	—	—	—	—	—	—

LEGAL SEA FOODS, INC.

1 Seafood Way
Boston, MA 02210
Phone: 617-530-9000
Fax: 617-530-9649
Web: www.legalseafoods.com

CEO: Roger S. Berkowitz
CFO: Mark Synnott
HR: Susan J. (Sue) Lorenz
FYE: December 31
Type: Private

Everything at this seafood chain is above board. Legal Sea Foods operates a popular chain of more than 30 upscale casual-dining spots known for their fresh seafood. The restaurants offer a variety of fish, lobster, and shrimp dishes, along with chowder, soup, and sandwiches. Legal also offers carry-out, catering, and private dining services. The chain operates in seven Eastern states, though most are in the Boston area. George Berkowitz got started in the seafood business in 1950 when he opened a fish market next to his father's grocery store, the Legal Cash Market, in Cambridge, Massachusetts. He and his wife opened their first restaurant in 1968 and their son, Roger, took control of the business in the 1990s.

	Annual Growth	12/03	12/04	12/05	12/06	12/07
Est. sales ($ mil.)	—	—	—	—	—	65.1
Employees	—	—	—	—	—	3,000

LEGEND MOBILE, INC.

OTC: LGMB

244 Fifth Avenue, Ste. P203
New York, NY 10001
Phone: 212-252-2459
Fax: –
Web: www.legendm.com

CEO: Peter Klamka
CFO: Peter Klamka
HR: –
FYE: December 31
Type: Public

Legend Mobile would like you to see its face when you pick up the phone. The company develops and markets faceplates and other mobile phone accessories, along with text-messaging services and mobile data applications. Several of Legend Mobile's products feature NASCAR themes. The company's 50%-owned Legend Credit unit develops and markets stored-value cards, such as gift cards; its offerings include a debit card sold under the Hello Kitty brand. Neither of Legend Mobile's main business lines has generated significant revenue, however, and the company's auditor has questioned whether Legend Mobile will be able to continue as a going concern. CEO Peter Klamka controls a majority of the company's voting stock.

	Annual Growth	12/02	12/03	12/04	12/05	*12/06
Sales ($ mil.)	—	0.1	0.0	0.0	0.0	0.0
Net income ($ mil.)	—	(1.9)	(1.5)	(1.4)	(0.7)	(0.6)
Market value ($ mil.)	(40.6%)	8.2	3.0	1.8	—	1.0
Employees	—	—	—	—	—	—

*Most recent year available

An in-depth profile of this company is available to Hoover's Online members at hoovers.com.

927

LEGG MASON, INC.

NYSE: LM

100 Light St.
Baltimore, MD 21202
Phone: 410-539-0000
Fax: 410-454-4923
Web: www.leggmason.com

CEO: Mark R. Fetting
CFO: Charles J. Daley Jr.
HR: –
FYE: March 31
Type: Public

Legg Mason's feats include wealth management and mutual fund management. The financial services firm has several subsidiaries that offer asset management, trust services, and annuities to retail and institutional investors. The company manages more than 150 mutual funds under the Legg Mason, Legg Mason Partners, Western Asset, and The Royce Funds banners. Other offerings include closed-end funds and separate accounts. Legg Mason distributes its products through its own offices, retirement plans, insurance companies, and other channels. The company operates primarily in the US and the UK, but has locations in about 15 other countries.

	Annual Growth	3/04	3/05	3/06	3/07	3/08
Assets ($ mil.)	13.0%	7,263.0	8,219.5	9,302.5	9,604.5	11,830.3
Net income ($ mil.)	(2.6%)	297.8	408.4	1,144.2	646.8	267.6
Market value ($ mil.)	17.2%	4,116.2	8,336.3	16,256.5	12,220.1	7,756.4
Employees	(15.0%)	—	5,580	3,800	4,030	—

LEGGETT & PLATT, INCORPORATED

NYSE: LEG

No. 1 Leggett Rd.
Carthage, MO 64836
Phone: 417-358-8131
Fax: 417-358-5840
Web: www.leggett.com

CEO: David S. (Dave) Haffner
CFO: Matthew C. (Matt) Flanigan
HR: John G. Moore
FYE: December 31
Type: Public

That spring in your step after a good night's sleep may be there courtesy of Leggett & Platt — the pioneer of coiled bedsprings. Primarily using aluminum and steel, it makes finished furniture (headboards), commercial furnishings (store displays, shelving), and die-cast products (components for gas barbecue grills and outdoor lighting fixtures). (It is divesting its die-cast products unit.) Leggett & Platt also produces industrial materials (wire, steel tubing) and specialized items (quilting machinery, commercial truck equipment). Customers include furniture retailers and manufacturers of automobiles, construction-related products, furniture and bedding, and garden and yard equipment.

	Annual Growth	12/03	12/04	12/05	12/06	12/07
Sales ($ mil.)	(0.5%)	4,388.2	5,085.5	5,299.3	5,505.4	4,306.4
Net income ($ mil.)	—	205.9	285.4	251.3	300.3	(11.2)
Market value ($ mil.)	(8.3%)	4,155.1	5,427.3	4,192.5	4,254.2	2,942.1
Employees	(14.7%)	—	—	33,000	32,828	24,000

LEHIGH CEMENT COMPANY

7660 Imperial Way
Allentown, PA 18195
Phone: 610-366-4600
Fax: 610-366-4851
Web: www.lehighcement.com

CEO: Albert Scheuer
CFO: Michael J. Lewis
HR: –
FYE: December 31
Type: Subsidiary

Lehigh Cement Company has built a solid foundation in the cement business. One of the largest cement producers in the US, the company produces ready-mix concrete, concrete pipe, concrete block, precast concrete, portland, blended and specialty cements, and aggregates in the US and Canada. Other products include pre-stressed cement products, custom color portland and masonry cement, fly ash, and other pozzolanic materials. The company serves customers in the cement and construction industries who use its products in highway, architectural, industrial, and marine applications. Founded in 1897, the company is a subsidiary of Germany-based HeidelbergCement.

LEHIGH VALLEY HOSPITAL AND HEALTH NETWORK

1200 S. Cedar Crest Blvd.
Allentown, PA 18103
Phone: 610-402-8000
Fax: 610-402-7523
Web: www.lvhhn.org

CEO: Elliot J. Sussman
CFO: Vaughn C. Gower
HR: Mary Kay Grim
FYE: June 30
Type: Not-for-profit

Billy Joel painted a bleak portrait of Allentown and Bethlehem in the 1970s, but Lehigh Valley Hospital and Health Network (LVHHN) has a slightly more optimistic view of eastern Pennsylvania. At the center of the health system are Lehigh Valley Hospital and Lehigh Valley Hospital-Muhlenberg, both acute care community hospitals with a combined total of 700 beds. The hospitals offer a comprehensive array of inpatient and outpatient services, and are home to centers of excellence in various areas of general and internal medicine. Other services include health centers and hospice services. In 2007 LVHHN added to its services a Pneumatic Mobile Surge Hospital that can serve up to 20 critical care patients at a time.

	Annual Growth	6/03	6/04	6/05	6/06	6/07
Est. sales ($ mil.)	—	—	—	—	—	708.7
Employees	—	—	—	—	—	4,000

LEHMAN BROTHERS HOLDINGS INC.

NYSE: LEH

745 7th Ave.
New York, NY 10019
Phone: 212-526-7000
Fax: 212-526-8766
Web: www.lehman.com

CEO: Richard S. (Dick) Fuld Jr.
CFO: Ian T. Lowitt
HR: –
FYE: November 30
Type: Public

Lehman Brothers is a lean, mean, investment banking machine. One of the top bulge-bracket firms, the company is perennially among the industry leaders in mergers and acquisitions advice, debt and equity underwriting, and global finance. Capital markets activities (by far its largest segment) entail institutional brokerage, market making, equity and debt research, securities lending, and mortgage banking. Investment banking provides advisory services and underwriting of debt and equity instruments. The investment management segment includes private banking, trust services, private equity, and money manager Neuberger Berman; it oversees some $282 billion for clients.

	Annual Growth	11/03	11/04	11/05	11/06	11/07
Sales ($ mil.)	35.9%	17,287.0	21,250.0	32,420.0	46,709.0	59,003.0
Net income ($ mil.)	25.3%	1,699.0	2,369.0	3,260.0	4,007.0	4,192.0
Market value ($ mil.)	36.4%	9,628.4	11,570.1	17,100.5	39,293.2	33,312.1
Employees	11.8%	—	—	22,900	25,900	28,600

LEMAITRE VASCULAR, INC.

NASDAQ (GM): LMAT

63 2nd Ave.
Burlington, MA 01803
Phone: 781-221-2266
Fax: 781-425-5049
Web: www.lemaitre.com

CEO: George W. LeMaitre
CFO: Joseph P. Pellegrino
HR: Cornelia W. (Connie) LeMaitre
FYE: December 31
Type: Public

LeMaitre Vascular makes the veins run on time. The company makes both disposable and implanted surgical vascular devices, including catheters and stents, under such brands as AnastoClip, EndoFit, and Pruitt-Inahara. LeMaitre was founded in 1983 by vascular surgeon George D. LeMaitre, who developed a valvulotome used to prepare veins for arterial bypass. The company has since expanded its offerings to include a device to create dialysis access sites and another to treat aortic aneurysms. Its products are sold to hospitals in North America, Europe, and Japan through a direct sales force. Dr. LeMaitre's son George W. LeMaitre (the company's chairman, president, and CEO) holds a controlling stake in the company.

	Annual Growth	12/03	12/04	12/05	12/06	12/07
Sales ($ mil.)	19.0%	20.7	26.2	30.7	34.6	41.5
Net income ($ mil.)	—	(0.2)	0.9	0.1	(1.2)	(2.9)
Market value ($ mil.)	4.5%	—	—	—	91.9	96.0
Employees	—	—	—	—	218	—

LEMANS CORPORATION

3501 Kennedy Rd.
Janesville, WI 53545
Phone: 608-758-1111
Fax: 608-758-4677
Web: www.parts-unlimited.com

CEO: Jeffrey (Jeff) Fox
CFO: Mark Scharenbroch
HR: –
FYE: September 30
Type: Private

Lemans has a role to play with plenty of parts for those who live to ride (and ride to live). Through its Parts Unlimited division, Lemans distributes parts and accessories for street and off-road motorcycles, snowmobiles, personal watercraft, and all-terrain vehicles (ATVs). Lemans also makes and distributes boots, gloves, goggles, helmets, jackets, jerseys, safety gear, and other riding apparel and accessories for motorcyclists through its Thor and Drag Specialties subsidiaries. Its Moose Utility Division specializes in parts for ATVs and apparel for their riders.

	Annual Growth	9/03	9/04	9/05	9/06	9/07
Est. sales ($ mil.)	—	—	—	—	—	127.5
Employees	—	—	—	—	—	1,000

LENDINGTREE, LLC

11115 Rushmore Dr.
Charlotte, NC 28277
Phone: 704-541-5351
Fax: 704-541-1824
Web: www.lendingtree.com

CEO: Douglas R. (Doug) Lebda
CFO: Matthew Packey
HR: Claudette Hampton
FYE: December 31
Type: Subsidiary

LendingTree helps borrowers cut through a forest of loan options. The loan exchange's customers complete one mortgage, credit card, auto loan, or other loan application which is shopped around to some 200 lenders, including industry leaders such as Bank of America, Citibank, and Wachovia Mortgage. The service is free for borrowers, who choose the lender with the most favorable terms. LendingTree charges corporate participants transaction fees upon submission of the loan application and again at closing. LendingTree is being spun off from IAC/InterActiveCorp, which bought the company in 2003.

LENNAR CORPORATION

NYSE: LEN

700 NW 107th Ave., Ste. 400
Miami, FL 33172
Phone: 305-559-4000
Fax: 305-229-6453
Web: www.lennar.com

CEO: Stuart A. Miller
CFO: Bruce E. Gross
HR: –
FYE: November 30
Type: Public

Lennar is one of the largest homebuilding, land-owning, loan-making leviathans in the US. Delivering some 33,000 homes in 2007, the company is second only to D.R. Horton and leads other top builders Pulte Homes and Centex. Lennar builds primarily detached homes for first-time buyers, move-up buyers, and active adults in nearly 20 states. Home prices average some $297,000. Lennar also provides financial services including mortgage financing, title insurance, and closing services. Lennar markets its homes through its Everything's Included program, in which houses come complete with most top-of-the-line features. CEO Stuart Miller controls 47% of the company.

	Annual Growth	11/03	11/04	11/05	11/06	11/07
Sales ($ mil.)	3.4%	8,907.6	10,504.9	13,867.0	16,266.7	10,186.8
Net income ($ mil.)	—	751.4	945.6	1,355.2	593.9	(1,941.1)
Market value ($ mil.)	(24.1%)	6,134.8	5,554.8	7,197.3	6,664.1	2,037.1
Employees	(28.8%)	—	—	13,687	12,605	6,934

LENNOX INTERNATIONAL INC.

NYSE: LII

2140 Lake Park Blvd.
Richardson, TX 75080
Phone: 972-497-5000
Fax: 972-497-5299
Web: www.lennoxinternational.com

CEO: Todd M. Bluedorn
CFO: Susan K. Carter
HR: Daniel M. Sessa
FYE: December 31
Type: Public

Lennox International makes products so cool they're hot, and vice versa. The company makes heating, ventilation, air conditioning, and refrigeration products for residential and commercial uses. It sells furnaces, heat pumps, fireplaces, and air conditioners under such brands as Lennox, Armstrong Air, and Aire-Flo; chillers and condensing units are sold under the Bohn and Larkin brands. Its products are sold to about 7,000 independent dealers in the US and Canada. The company also owns and operates 120 service and installation centers. Lennox has interests and facilities in Asia, Australia, Europe, and South America. Named after inventor Dave Lennox, the company in 1904 was sold to newspaper publisher D.W. Norris.

	Annual Growth	12/03	12/04	12/05	12/06	12/07
Sales ($ mil.)	5.0%	3,085.1	2,982.7	3,366.2	3,671.1	3,749.7
Net income ($ mil.)	19.0%	84.4	(134.4)	150.7	166.0	169.0
Market value ($ mil.)	25.9%	1,022.1	1,288.6	2,003.2	2,055.6	2,570.2
Employees	(3.2%)	—	—	16,000	16,000	15,000

LENOVO GROUP LIMITED

Pink Sheets: LNVGY

1009 Think Place
Morrisville, NC 27560
Phone: 866-458-4465
Fax: 877-411-1329
Web: www.lenovo.com

CEO: William J. (Bill) Amelio
CFO: Wong Wai Ming
HR: Kenneth A. (Ken) DiPietro
FYE: March 31
Type: Public

Lenovo may not be considered technology royalty, but it's definitely blue-blooded. The company was already the largest PC maker in the world's most populous country when it acquired IBM's PC operations for approximately $1.75 billion in 2005. It remains a leader in China, but the company now has a global presence. Lenovo's products include desktop and notebook PCs, displays, storage drives, and IT services. In China it also sells mobile phone handsets and servers. Legend Holdings, which is controlled by the Chinese government, owns 49% of Lenovo. IBM holds about 6%.

	Annual Growth	3/04	3/05	3/06	3/07	3/08
Sales ($ mil.)	53.2%	2,971.2	2,891.5	13,347.7	14,590.2	16,352.0
Net income ($ mil.)	37.6%	135.0	143.6	22.3	161.1	484.0
Employees	30.1%	11,408	20,600	19,500	25,100	—

LENOX GROUP INC.

NYSE: LNX

1 Village Place, 6436 City West Pkwy.
Eden Prairie, MN 55344
Phone: 952-944-5600
Fax: 952-943-4500
Web: www.department56.com

CEO: Marc L. Pfefferle
CFO: Fred Spivak
HR: Branka Hannon
FYE: Saturday nearest December 31
Type: Public

Department 56 may have taken over Lenox, but the bigger name prevailed. Called Lenox Group, the company sells collectibles and giftware, primarily in the US. It is best known for its Village Series — winter scenes complete with tiny, lit ceramic or porcelain houses and accessories. Other items include Snowbabies figurines, holiday and home decorative products, and tableware. The company exited its Time to Celebrate division, which sold products through home-based parties, at the end of 2005. Customers include independent gift retailers, department stores, and catalog firms. Lenox Group also sells products through corporate showrooms, company stores, and trade shows. It bought Willitts in 2006.

	Annual Growth	12/03	12/04	12/05	12/06	12/07
Sales ($ mil.)	23.9%	191.7	164.7	330.9	502.5	452.1
Net income ($ mil.)	—	16.4	23.8	15.2	(49.3)	(15.8)
Employees	0.6%	—	—	2,310	2,324	—

An in-depth profile of this company is available to Hoover's Online members at hoovers.com.

929

LENOX HILL HOSPITAL

100 E. 77th St.
New York, NY 10021
Phone: 212-434-2000
Fax: 212-434-2003
Web: www.lenoxhillhospital.org

CEO: Gladys George
CFO: Michael Breslin
HR: –
FYE: December 31
Type: Not-for-profit

Lenox Hill Hospital provides acute care to patients from facilities located on Manhattan's Upper East Side. The hospital has more than 650 beds and provides such services as cardiac care, high-risk obstetrics, pediatrics, ophthalmology, and orthopedics and sports medicine. In addition, the facility serves as a teaching affiliate for NYU Medical Center. Lenox Hill Hospital also owns Manhattan Eye, Ear & Throat Hospital, a leading provider of specialty care for vision, hearing, speech, and even swallowing disorders. The hospital was established in 1857.

	Annual Growth	12/03	12/04	12/05	12/06	12/07
Est. sales ($ mil.)	—	—	—	—	—	626.3
Employees	—	—	—	—	—	2,955

LENSCRAFTERS, INC.

4000 Luxottica Place
Mason, OH 45040
Phone: 513-765-6000
Fax: 513-765-6249
Web: www.lenscrafters.com

CEO: Kerry Bradley
CFO: Jack Dennis
HR: Mildred Curtis
FYE: December 31
Type: Subsidiary

LensCrafters brings eyewear and malls together. Part of the growing retail arm (Luxottica Retail) of Italy's Luxottica Group, LensCrafters is North America's largest retailer of eyewear and related services, with about 900 stores in the US, Canada, and Puerto Rico. The company-owned stores, mainly located in shopping malls, offer prescription glasses, contact lenses, and sunglasses, as well as vision exams by an on-site optometrist. Outside North America, Luxottica is introducing the LensCrafters brand in China. LensCrafters was founded in 1983 and acquired by Luxottica in 1995.

	Annual Growth	12/03	12/04	12/05	12/06	12/07
Est. sales ($ mil.)	—	—	—	—	—	881.1
Employees	—	—	—	—	—	14,000

LEO BURNETT WORLDWIDE, INC.

35 W. Wacker Dr.
Chicago, IL 60601
Phone: 312-220-5959
Fax: 312-220-3299
Web: www.leoburnett.com

CEO: Thomas (Tom) Bernardin
CFO: Paul Eichelman
HR: Patrick Venetucci
FYE: December 31
Type: Subsidiary

This company has come up with some gr-r-reat ideas to promote brands. The #2 ad agency in the US (behind WPP Group's JWT), Leo Burnett Worldwide has helped create some of the top consumer brands, including Kellogg's Frosted Flakes cereal and its Tony the Tiger icon. It offers creative development and campaign planning services through about 95 offices in almost 85 countries. Its Arc Worldwide subsidiary provides promotional and direct marketing services, as well as multimedia and interactive marketing development. Vigilante acts as an urban marketing firm, while Lápiz Integrated Hispanic Marketing creates campaigns for Spanish-speaking audiences. Leo Burnett is owned by French ad conglomerate Publicis.

LEONARD GREEN & PARTNERS, L.P.

11111 Santa Monica Blvd., Ste. 2000
Los Angeles, CA 90025
Phone: 310-954-0444
Fax: 310-954-0404
Web: www.leonardgreen.com

CEO: John G. Danhakl
CFO: Cody L. Franklin
HR: –
FYE: December 31
Type: Private

This Green's thumb is you-know-what when it comes to management buyouts. Leonard Green & Partners (LGP) specializes in friendly buyouts, focusing on retailers and consumer products companies such as FTD Group, Neiman Marcus, Rand McNally, Varsity Brands, The Sports Authority, and Rite Aid. The investment firm generally doesn't participate in the day-to-day operations of its holdings; it does, however, take seats on the board to help direct strategic and financial development. Currently investing its fifth private equity fund, LGP owns stakes in about 20 firms and manages some $9 billion in equity capital.

	Annual Growth	12/03	12/04	12/05	12/06	12/07
Est. sales ($ mil.)	—	—	—	—	—	1,348.4
Employees	—	—	—	—	—	13,666

LEPRINO FOODS COMPANY

1830 W. 38th Ave.
Denver, CO 80211
Phone: 303-480-2600
Fax: 303-480-2605
Web: www.leprinofoods.com

CEO: Larry Jensen
CFO: Ron Klump
HR: Bradley (Brad) Olsen
FYE: October 31
Type: Private

Don't try to butter up Leprino Foods — it's into mozzarella with a capital "M." The company is the worldwide leader in mozzarella making. It sells its mozzarella to pizza purveyors large and small, including Domino's, Papa John's, and Pizza Hut, as well as to food manufacturers. Leprino's other products include whey protein concentrate and lactose for use in animal feeds, yogurt, baby formula, and baked goods. Supplied by the nation's large dairy co-ops, Leprino hitches its sales to the continuing rise in the global popularity of pizza. The company has a joint venture located in the UK called Glanbia Cheese with Glanbia. It is a top maker of pizza cheese in Europe.

	Annual Growth	10/02	10/03	10/04	10/05	10/06
Est. sales ($ mil.)	8.2%	1,750.0	1,900.0	2,600.0	2,285.0	2,400.0
Employees	0.0%	3,000	3,350	3,350	3,000	3,000

LES SCHWAB TIRE CENTERS

646 NW Madras Hwy.
Prineville, OR 97754
Phone: 541-447-4136
Fax: 541-416-5488
Web: www.lesschwab.com

CEO: Dick Borgman
CFO: Tom Freedman
HR: Jodie Hueske
FYE: December 31
Type: Private

If you need new tires after heeding Greeley's advice, go to Les Schwab Tire Centers. And it doesn't hurt that the owner wrote the bible of tire retailing: Pride in Performance — Keep It Going. Les Schwab Tire Centers prides itself on continued customer service; it sells tires and batteries and does alignment, brake, and shock work at 400-plus stores in California, Idaho, Montana, Nevada, Oregon, Utah, Alaska, and Washington. With a story that rivals Moses', late founder Les Schwab was reared in a logging camp and went to school in a converted boxcar. In 1952 he bought a tire shop that grew into Les Schwab Tire Centers. The firm, owned by Schwab's family, plans to open about 20 stores a year.

	Annual Growth	12/02	12/03	12/04	12/05	12/06
Est. sales ($ mil.)	8.0%	1,000.0	1,000.0	1,150.0	1,200.0	1,360.0
Employees	6.4%	6,000	6,000	5,800	6,000	7,700

LESCARDEN INC.

OTC: LCAR

420 Lexington Ave., Ste. 212
New York, NY 10170
Phone: 212-687-1050
Fax: 212-687-1051
Web: www.catrix.com

CEO: William E. (Bill) Luther
CFO: William E. (Bill) Luther
HR: –
FYE: May 31
Type: Public

Lescarden lessens scarring when it can. Lescarden develops cancer therapies, clinical dermatological care, osteoarthritis, and wound care. The company focuses on developing natural therapies. Many of its products utilize bovine cartilage which has been shown to possess beneficial healing qualities. Its lead product, Catrix, is sold as a wound dressing and topical skin care line. Poly-Nag is an anti-arthritic compound made from chitin, a material found in the shells of invertebrates like lobsters, crabs, and various insects. Its Biocar Laboratories offers variations on a nutritional supplement made from bovine cartilage, under the brand name Bio-Cartilage. Director Charles Maxwell owns 41% of the company.

	Annual Growth	5/03	5/04	5/05	5/06	5/07
Sales ($ mil.)	38.4%	0.3	0.3	2.4	1.6	1.1
Net income ($ mil.)	—	(0.3)	(0.3)	0.4	0.1	0.1
Market value ($ mil.)	7.8%	4.1	6.3	11.7	7.8	5.6
Employees	—	—	—	—	—	—

LESCO, INC.

1301 E. 9th St., Ste. 1300
Cleveland, OH 44114
Phone: 216-706-9250
Fax: 800-673-3030
Web: www.lesco.com

CEO: David P. Werning
CFO: Michael A. Weisbarth
HR: Kathleen M. Minahan
FYE: December 31
Type: Subsidiary

When LESCO sees a golf course or a lawn, it sees green. The company sells fertilizer, grass seed, and turf-protection products used on golf courses and lawns, primarily under the LESCO name, but also under brands such as NOVEX (a longer-acting turf fertilizer). Customers include landscapers, municipalities, and country clubs. Consumable goods (fertilizer, grass seed, herbicides, insecticides, and fungicides) account for most of LESCO's sales, but it also sells hard goods like rotary mowers, spreaders, and sprayers. Lesco sells its products through about 350 service centers and a fleet of 100 tractor-trailer-based stores. It is a subsidiary of the John Deere Landscapes unit of Deere & Company.

	Annual Growth	12/02	12/03	12/04	12/05	12/06
Sales ($ mil.)	1.8%	511.7	523.5	561.0	575.7	550.6
Net income ($ mil.)	—	(17.5)	(5.3)	(5.6)	(26.7)	(19.7)
Employees	(10.3%)	1,399	1,303	1,341	1,009	—

LESLIE'S POOLMART, INC.

3925 E. Broadway Rd., Ste. 100
Phoenix, AZ 85040
Phone: 602-366-3999
Fax: 602-366-3934
Web: www.lesliespool.com

CEO: Lawrence H. Hayward
CFO: Steven L. Ortega
HR: –
FYE: Saturday nearest September 30
Type: Private

Leslie's Poolmart is the big fish of pool product retailers. The company sells pool chemicals, cleaning and testing equipment, covers, and recreational items through about 575 stores in some 35 states, mostly in Arizona, California, Florida, and Texas. It also sells through catalogs and its Web site. Leslie's makes chlorine tablets and repackages other chemicals to be sold under the Leslie name. (Leslie's brand products account for nearly 40% of sales.) Pool chemicals, major equipment, and parts account for a majority of sales. Founded in 1963, Leslie's went private in a 1997 management LBO backed by Leonard Green & Partners, which owns more than 80% of the company.

	Annual Growth	9/02	9/03	9/04	9/05	9/06
Sales ($ mil.)	8.9%	313.3	327.2	356.0	388.5	440.6
Net income ($ mil.)	44.5%	4.7	10.3	16.2	(4.4)	20.5
Employees	4.5%	1,843	2,006	1,892	2,026	2,201

LETTUCE ENTERTAIN YOU ENTERPRISES, INC.

5419 N. Sheridan Rd.
Chicago, IL 60640
Phone: 773-878-7340
Fax: 773-878-1205
Web: www.leye.com

CEO: Kevin Brown
CFO: –
HR: Susan (Susie) Southgate-Fox
FYE: December 31
Type: Private

With such names as R.J. Grunts, Cafe Ba-Ba-Reeba, and Mity Nice Grill, it's clear that these restaurants serve up a helping of humor along with the food. Lettuce Entertain You Enterprises (LEYE) operates more than 40 upscale and casual-dining restaurants primarily in the Chicago area, encompassing more than 25 concepts. At the high end, LEYE operates the sophisticated Everest (located in the Chicago Stock Exchange building), one of the top-rated dining rooms in Chicago. At the lower end, the company offers quick bites from Chicago Flat Sammies and foodlife. In addition to the Windy City, LEYE has operations in Atlanta, Las Vegas, Minneapolis, and Washington, DC. Richard Melman started the company in 1971.

LEUCADIA NATIONAL CORPORATION

NYSE: LUK

315 Park Ave. South
New York, NY 10010
Phone: 212-460-1900
Fax: 212-598-4869
Web: www.leucadia.com

CEO: Joseph S. Steinberg
CFO: Joseph A. Orlando
HR: Laura E. Ulbrandt
FYE: December 31
Type: Public

Holding company Leucadia National owns stakes in firms involved in manufacturing, medical products, gaming, oil and gas drilling, and real estate. The investment firm typically seeks out troubled companies that it believes are undervalued; its holdings include Idaho Timber, Conwed Plastics, Goober Drilling, and medical products firm Sangart, which is developing a therapy it hopes will be an alternative to red blood cell transfusions. Leucadia also holds stakes in two US wineries (Pine Ridge and Archery Summit) and a 30% stake in a copper mine in Spain.

	Annual Growth	12/03	12/04	12/05	12/06	12/07
Sales ($ mil.)	20.0%	556.4	2,262.1	1,041.2	862.7	1,154.9
Net income ($ mil.)	49.4%	97.1	145.5	1,636.0	189.4	484.3
Market value ($ mil.)	76.1%	1,089.0	2,492.3	2,564.6	6,101.1	10,483.3
Employees	1.1%	—	—	3,969	1,323	4,057

LEVCOR INTERNATIONAL, INC.

OTC: LEVC

1065 Avenue of the Americas, 28th Fl.
New York, NY 10018
Phone: 212-354-8500
Fax: 212-354-4938

CEO: Robert A. Levinson
CFO: Pramila Devi (Devi) Shaheed
HR: –
FYE: December 31
Type: Public

Button. Button. Who's got the button? Levcor does. Buttons and other accoutrements are the core of Levcor International's business. The company makes and sells buttons, decorations, craft products, and complementary product lines, including iron-ons, kits, and fashion and jewelry accessories. Levcor's products are sold to the home sewing and craft markets through mass merchandisers and retailers, such as Wal-Mart and Jo-Ann Stores. Levcor operated a textile division that made women's coordinated apparel but it exited the unprofitable business in mid-2006 after several years of tweaking it. Chairman, president, and CEO Robert Levinson controls about 30% of Levcor.

	Annual Growth	12/03	12/04	12/05	12/06	12/07
Sales ($ mil.)	(10.9%)	30.8	33.7	29.4	21.9	19.4
Net income ($ mil.)	—	(6.0)	0.7	(8.3)	1.6	0.1
Market value ($ mil.)	(47.2%)	20.6	10.9	4.0	2.1	1.6
Employees	—	—	—	—	—	—

An in-depth profile of this company is available to Hoover's Online members at hoovers.com.

931

⊞ LEVEL 3 COMMUNICATIONS, INC.　　NASDAQ (GS): LVLT

1025 Eldorado Blvd.
Broomfield, CO 80021
Phone: 720-888-1000
Fax: 720-888-5085
Web: www.level3.com

CEO: James Q. (Jim) Crowe
CFO: Sunit S. Patel
HR: Margaret E. (Meg) Porfido
FYE: December 31
Type: Public

Level 3 Communications owns the communications networking market, or at least a piece of it. The company operates one of the world's largest Internet protocol (IP)-based fiber-optic networks. Its services include broadband and dial-up Internet access, wholesale voice origination and termination, enterprise voice, content distribution, broadband transport, and colocation. Its wholesale customers include ISPs, telecom carriers, cable TV operators, wireless service providers, and the federal government. It markets directly to businesses, state agencies, and schools. Its content delivery unit targets video distribution companies, Web portals, online gaming and software companies, and social networking sites.

	Annual Growth	12/03	12/04	12/05	12/06	12/07
Sales ($ mil.)	1.5%	4,026.0	3,712.0	3,613.0	3,378.0	4,269.0
Net income ($ mil.)	—	(711.0)	(458.0)	(638.0)	(790.0)	(1,114.0)
Market value ($ mil.)	4.9%	3,863.6	2,327.2	2,347.0	6,599.2	4,675.1
Employees	18.0%	—	—	4,800	7,400	6,680

LEVENGER

420 S. Congress Ave.
Delray Beach, FL 33445
Phone: 561-274-0904
Fax: 561-266-2181
Web: www.levenger.com

CEO: Steven Leveen
CFO: Larry Jenkins
HR: Vincent G. Dunn
FYE: December 31
Type: Private

Levenger began when Lori Granger Leveen and her husband, Steve, said, "Let there be lighting." Since starting off in 1987 by selling halogen lights for reading, Levenger has fashioned itself as the provider of "Tools for Serious Readers." The direct marketer offers an assortment of branded and private-label home and office furniture and accessories. Its products include bookcases, briefcases, chairs, clocks, desks, inkwells, Palm cases, pens, pillows, stationery, wallets, and of course, lighting products. Levenger, which derives its name from combining Leveen and Granger, sells its merchandise through its catalog, Web site, and at about a half dozen retail stores.

	Annual Growth	12/03	12/04	12/05	12/06	12/07
Est. sales ($ mil.)	—	—	—	—	—	59.2
Employees	—	—	—	—	—	350

⊞ LEVI STRAUSS & CO.

1155 Battery St.
San Francisco, CA 94111
Phone: 415-501-6000
Fax: 415-501-7112
Web: www.levistrauss.com

CEO: R. John Anderson
CFO: Hans Ploos van Amstel
HR: Julie Davidson
FYE: Last Sunday in November
Type: Private

Levi Strauss & Co. (LS&CO.) strives to provide the world's casual workday wardrobe, inside and out. LS&CO., a top maker of brand-name clothing globally, sells jeans and sportswear under the Levi's, Dockers, and Levi Strauss Signature names in more than 110 countries. It also markets men's and women's underwear and loungewear. Levi's jeans — department store staples — were once the uniform of American youth, but LS&CO. has been working to reconnect with the niche and expand outside the US. It transformed its product offerings to include wrinkle-free and stain-resistant fabrics used in the making of some of its Levi's and Dockers slacks. The Haas family (relatives of founder Levi Strauss) owns LS&CO.

	Annual Growth	11/02	11/03	11/04	11/05	11/06
Sales ($ mil.)	(0.2%)	4,136.6	4,090.7	4,072.5	4,125.2	4,106.6
Net income ($ mil.)	75.8%	25.0	(349.3)	30.4	155.9	239.0
Employees	(3.7%)	12,400	12,300	8,850	9,635	10,680

LEVITON MANUFACTURING CO., INC.

59-25 Little Neck Pkwy.
Little Neck, NY 11362
Phone: 718-229-4040
Fax: 800-832-9538
Web: www.leviton.com

CEO: Donald J. Hendler
CFO: Ralph DeBiasi
HR: Mark Fogel
FYE: December 31
Type: Private

Its more than 22,000 products make Leviton Manufacturing a leviathan of electrical and electronic components. The company makes switches, plugs, connectors, and integrated networks designed for home, commercial, and industrial uses. The company's divisions also produce lighting controls and voice and data equipment. Its American Insulated Wire subsidiary makes both thermoset and thermoplastic electrical wire, cable, cord, and cord sets for utility customers. Its products are sold in North America to distributors, manufacturers, and retail outlets such as Home Depot, Sears, and Wal-Mart. The Leviton family holds the majority ownership in the company, which started out making tip mantles for gaslights in 1906.

	Annual Growth	12/03	12/04	12/05	12/06	12/07
Est. sales ($ mil.)	—	—	—	—	—	799.6
Employees	—	—	—	—	—	6,100

LEVITZ FURNITURE

233 Broadway, 23rd Fl.
New York, NY 10279
Phone: 212-634-2200
Fax: 212-634-2168
Web: www.levitz.com

CEO: Larry J. Zigerelli
CFO: Kathleen M. (Kathy) Guinnessey
HR: –
FYE: April 30
Type: Private

Levitz Furniture (formerly Levitz Home Furnishings) believes that the third time's a charm. Once one of the largest US furniture retailers, Levitz filed for Chapter 11 bankruptcy protection for the third time in 10 years in November 2007. The retailer plans to reorganize and consider its options, which include a possible sale. The firm operates about 80 stores in the Northeast and on the West Coast. Levitz had filed for Chapter 11 bankruptcy protection about two years earlier, in 2005, and sold its assets later that year to investment firm Prentice Capital Management and Pride Capital, the parent of liquidator Great American Group. Its new owners shuttered some 30 Levitz stores.

LEVY RESTAURANTS, INC.

980 N. Michigan Ave., Ste. 400
Chicago, IL 60611
Phone: 312-664-8200
Fax: 312-280-2739
Web: www.levyrestaurants.com

CEO: Andrew J. (Andy) Lansing
CFO: Bob Seiffert
HR: Cindy Noble
FYE: December 31
Type: Subsidiary

This company's menu of operations feeds people out on the town and at the game. Levy Restaurants is a leading restaurant operator and contract food services provider. Its fine dining spots, found mostly in Chicago, include Bistro 110, Fulton's on the River, and Spiaggia. Most of the company's business, though, comes from running food service operations at more than 75 sports stadiums, convention centers, and race tracks, including Churchill Downs (Louisville, Kentucky), Lambeau Field (Green Bay, Wisconsin), and Wrigley Field (Chicago). Levy Restaurants also runs dining locations at Walt Disney's Disney World resort and theme park in Orlando. The company is a subsidiary of UK-based Compass Group.

LEWIS BAKERIES, INC.

500 N. Fulton Ave.
Evansville, IN 47710
Phone: 812-425-4642
Fax: 812-425-7609
Web: www.lewisbakeries.com

CEO: R.J. (Jack) Lewis Jr.
CFO: Rodger Lesh
HR: Bob Renock
FYE: December 31
Type: Private

Lewis Bakeries manufactures low-fat, low-carbohydrate breads under the Healthy Life label. The company's products include whole grain and white breads, buns, muffins, and bagels, including sugar-free varieties. Its fresh products are available in retail food outlets in the Midwestern and northeastern US. Lewis Bakeries also provides frozen bakery products nationwide. Its Bunny Bread division supplies loaves and buns in the Midwest. In 2004 the company shut down the operations of its Chicago Baking business, maker of the well-known regional brand Butternut Bread. Lewis Bakeries was established in 1925 by three brothers, Amos, Armold, and Jack Lewis using $300 they obtained by mortgaging their mother's house.

	Annual Growth	12/03	12/04	12/05	12/06	12/07
Est. sales ($ mil.)	—	—	—	—	—	240.0
Employees	—	—	—	—	—	2,500

LEXAR MEDIA, INC.

47300 Bayside Pkwy.
Fremont, CA 94538
Phone: 510-413-1200
Fax: 510-440-3499
Web: www.lexar.com

CEO: Mark W. Adams
CFO: Ronald C. (Ron) Foster
HR: Esther Clayson
FYE: December 31
Type: Subsidiary

Lexar Media is banking on a digital picture being worth more than a thousand words. The company designs and markets memory cards and connectivity products (USB flash drives) for the digital photography, consumer electronic, and communications markets. Lexar's products (which are made by third parties) are sold mostly in the US (which accounts for more than half of sales), as well as in Japan, Korea, the UK, Europe, and Canada. Customers include retailers, OEMs, and licensees. Lexar has a licensing agreement with Kodak to make and distribute Kodak-branded memory cards. Micron Technology bought Lexar in mid-2006 for about $850 million.

LEXICON MARKETING CORPORATION

640 S. San Vicente Blvd.
Los Angeles, CA 90048
Phone: 323-782-7400
Fax: 323-782-7481
Web: www.lexiconmarketing.com

CEO: Valeria Rico
CFO: Robert Ro
HR: Rosa N. Hernandez
FYE: January 31
Type: Private

Inglés sin Barreras (or English without barriers) is Lexicon Marketing's motto and its flagship educational product. This English-as-a-Second-Language (ESL) learning program incorporates audio/visual and print materials to aid Spanish speakers in America. The company also provides marketing, call center, and collection services to businesses trying to reach Hispanic markets. Through its subsidiary Lexicon Training Services, the firm develops live-instruction and self-study training programs for the Spanish-speaking workforce in a variety of industries, from education and government to food service and manufacturing. José Luis Nazar, who emigrated to the US from Chile, founded Lexicon in Miami in 1974.

	Annual Growth	1/03	1/04	1/05	1/06	1/07
Est. sales ($ mil.)	—	—	—	—	—	115.0
Employees	—	—	—	—	—	800

LEXICON PHARMACEUTICALS, INC

NASDAQ (GM): LEXG

8800 Technology Forest Place
The Woodlands, TX 77381
Phone: 281-863-3000
Fax: 281-863-8088
Web: www.lexpharma.com

CEO: Arthur T. Sands
CFO: Julia P. Gregory
HR: Walter F. (Skip) Colbert
FYE: December 31
Type: Public

Lexicon Pharmaceuticals (formerly Lexicon Genetics) works with some of the biggest words in the dictionary — words like deoxyribonucleic acid. The company uses knockout mice — mice whose DNA has been modified to disrupt, or "knock out" certain gene functions — to study the potential effects of drugs on various genetic targets. Lexicon distributes its knockout mice to life sciences researchers, partly through an agreement with Taconic Farms. It also is working on its own pipeline of drug candidates, both independently and with such partners as Bristol-Myers Squibb, Genentech, Organon, and Takeda. Its lead candidate is LX-6171, a potential treatment for cognitive disorders such as Alzheimer's disease.

	Annual Growth	12/03	12/04	12/05	12/06	12/07
Sales ($ mil.)	4.0%	42.8	61.7	75.7	72.8	50.1
Net income ($ mil.)	—	(64.2)	(47.2)	(36.3)	(54.3)	(58.8)
Market value ($ mil.)	—	—	—	—	—	414.5
Employees	—	—	—	755	—	—

LEXINGTON B & L FINANCIAL CORP.

Pink Sheets: LXMO

205 S. 13th St.
Lexington, MO 64067
Phone: 660-259-2247
Fax: 660-259-2384
Web: www.bl-bank.com

CEO: E. Steva Vialle
CFO: William J. Huhmann
HR: –
FYE: September 30
Type: Public

Lexington B & L Financial is the holding company for B & L Bank, which serves individuals and businesses through four branches in western central Missouri. Founded in 1887 as The Building and Loan Association, the bank offers standard retail products, including checking, savings, money market, individual retirement, and NOW accounts, as well as certificates of deposit. One- to four-family residential mortgages represent a majority of the bank's loan portfolio; it also originates business and personal installment loans and auto loans. Lexington B & L Financial expanded in 2001 when it acquired competitor Lafayette County Bank.

	Annual Growth	9/03	9/04	9/05	9/06	9/07
Est. sales ($ mil.)	—	—	—	—	—	6.3
Employees	—	—	—	—	—	26

LEXINGTON PRECISION CORPORATION

Pink Sheets: LEXP

800 3rd. Ave
New York, NY 10022
Phone: 212-319-4657
Fax: 212-319-4659
Web: www.lexingtonprecision.com

CEO: Warren Delano
CFO: Dennis J. Welhouse
HR: –
FYE: December 31
Type: Public

Lexington Precision may be wired to the auto industry, but it has injected itself into the medical industry as well. The company makes rubber and metal component parts used mostly in automotive and medical applications. Lexington Precision's Rubber Group manufactures rubber components such as rubber wire seals and insulators for ignition wiring, as well as rubber parts for medical products such as syringes and catheters. The company's Metals Group produces machined aluminum, brass, and steel components. Lexington Precision filed for Chapter 11 protection from creditors in April 2008.

	Annual Growth	12/03	12/04	12/05	12/06	12/07
Sales ($ mil.)	(7.7%)	121.6	110.3	96.8	87.9	88.4
Net income ($ mil.)	—	(6.4)	1.6	(3.8)	(7.3)	(7.0)
Employees	(9.9%)	1,010	978	797	706	666

An in-depth profile of this company is available to Hoover's Online members at hoovers.com.

933

LEXINGTON REALTY TRUST

NYSE: LXP

1 Penn Plaza, Ste. 4015
New York, NY 10119
Phone: 212-692-7200
Fax: 212-594-6600
Web: www.lxp.com

CEO: T. Wilson Eglin
CFO: Patrick Carroll
HR: –
FYE: December 31
Type: Public

Lexington Realty Trust (formerly Lexington Corporate Properties Trust) lays down the law when it comes to commercial real estate. The umbrella partnership real estate investment trust (UPREIT) owns and manages about 280 properties throughout the US and Netherlands. Its properties include warehouses, manufacturing facilities, offices, and retail sites totaling some 45 million sq. ft. of rentable space. Most properties are rented under triple net leases. Tenants include Baker Hughes, Bank of America, and The Shaw Group. Lexington Realty Trust became a REIT when it acquired Newkirk Realty Trust in 2007.

	Annual Growth	12/03	12/04	12/05	12/06	12/07
Sales ($ mil.)	37.6%	120.5	151.2	197.1	207.4	431.8
Net income ($ mil.)	22.9%	33.7	44.8	32.7	7.8	76.8
Market value ($ mil.)	2.1%	815.6	1,097.9	1,110.9	1,548.1	887.9
Employees	—	—	—	52	—	—

LEXMARK INTERNATIONAL, INC.

NYSE: LXK

1 Lexmark Centre Dr., 740 W. New Circle Rd.
Lexington, KY 40550
Phone: 859-232-2000
Fax: 859-232-2403
Web: www.lexmark.com

CEO: Paul J. Curlander
CFO: John W. Gamble Jr.
HR: Jeri L. Isbell
FYE: December 31
Type: Public

Lexmark attacks printing with a host of jets and lasers. Lexmark International is a leading maker of computer printers and related products. Its printer line includes laser printers (designed primarily for corporate networks and desktops) and ink jet printers (for home and business use). Unlike many of its competitors, Lexmark develops and manufactures its own devices, thereby speeding product cycles. The company sells its products in more than 150 countries through distributors including Ingram Micro and Tech Data, and through retailers in the US (CompUSA and Best Buy), France (Carrefour), and the UK (DSG International); it also supplies products to other equipment manufacturers.

	Annual Growth	12/03	12/04	12/05	12/06	12/07
Sales ($ mil.)	1.1%	4,754.7	5,313.8	5,221.5	5,108.1	4,973.9
Net income ($ mil.)	(9.0%)	439.2	568.7	356.3	338.4	300.8
Market value ($ mil.)	(24.4%)	10,113.1	10,846.0	5,016.5	7,100.4	3,301.2
Employees	0.7%	—	—	13,600	14,900	13,800

LFP, INC.

8484 Wilshire Blvd., Ste. 900
Beverly Hills, CA 90211
Phone: 323-651-5400
Fax: 323-651-3525
Web: hustler.com

CEO: Larry Flynt
CFO: James Chamberlain
HR: –
FYE: December 31
Type: Private

The founding fathers probably never imagined anything like this company when they wrote the First Amendment. LFP (which also does business as Larry Flynt Publications) runs the adult entertainment empire owned by infamous porn purveyor Larry Flynt, including his flagship magazine *Hustler*. The company's publishing portfolio includes about 10 titles, including *Barely Legal* and *Busty Beauties*. In addition, LFP produces and distributes adult videos, has a number of adult Web sites, and runs a dozen Hustler Hollywood retail stores. Flynt started publishing *Hustler* magazine in 1974 and founded Larry Flynt Publications two years later.

	Annual Growth	12/03	12/04	12/05	12/06	12/07
Est. sales ($ mil.)	—	—	—	—	—	13.8
Employees	—	—	—	—	—	117

LG ELECTRONICS MOBILECOMM U.S.A., INC.

10101 Old Grove Rd.
San Diego, CA 92131
Phone: 858-635-5300
Fax: 858-635-5225
Web: us.lge.com/about/company/us_mobile.jsp

CEO: Myeong-Kyu (Michael) Ahn
CFO: –
HR: –
FYE: December 31
Type: Subsidiary

LG Electronics Mobilecomm USA sums it up pretty well: the company, which also operates as LG Mobile Phones, manufactures and markets mobile phones and related accessories. The company also provides sales and marketing support in North America for its parent company, LG Electronics, a Korea-based manufacturer of consumers electronics, information technology, and communications products. LG Mobile Phones also has marketing partnerships with wireless carriers including AT&T Mobility, Verizon, and US Cellular, as well as retail outlets such as Best Buy.

	Annual Growth	12/03	12/04	12/05	12/06	12/07
Est. sales ($ mil.)	—	—	—	—	—	2,147.5
Employees	—	—	—	—	—	150

THE LGL GROUP, INC.

AMEX: LGL

2525 Shader Rd.
Orlando, FL 32804
Phone: 407-298-2000
Fax: 407-293-2979
Web: www.lynchcorp.com

CEO: Robert R. Zylstra
CFO: Howard D. Castle
HR: –
FYE: December 31
Type: Public

The LGL Group is hoping that one isn't the loneliest number. Previously made up of two separate businesses, the company has a sole remaining line of business: its MtronPTI subsidiary, which produces frequency control devices, such as crystals and oscillators, used primarily in communications equipment. MtronPTI was formed in the 2004 merger of M-tron Industries and Piezo Technology, Inc. In 2007 The LGL Group sold certain assets of its unprofitable Lynch Systems subsidiary for about $3 million. The company gets the majority of its sales from outside the US.

	Annual Growth	12/03	12/04	12/05	12/06	12/07
Sales ($ mil.)	9.0%	28.0	33.8	46.2	49.3	39.5
Net income ($ mil.)	—	0.1	(3.3)	1.2	0.9	(2.5)
Market value ($ mil.)	(1.5%)	15.7	23.7	17.8	15.1	14.7
Employees	10.4%	204	355	355	386	303

LHC GROUP, INC.

NASDAQ (GM): LHCG

420 W. Pinhook Rd., Ste. A
Lafayette, LA 70503
Phone: 337-233-1307
Fax: 337-235-8037
Web: www.lhcgroup.com

CEO: Keith G. Myers
CFO: Peter J. (Pete) Roman
HR: Lolanda Butler Brown
FYE: December 31
Type: Public

LHC Group operates care facilities and provides home health care services to rural markets in the southern US. The company's some 150 home health nursing agencies provide care to Medicare beneficiaries, offering such services as private duty nursing, physical therapy, and medically oriented social services. LHC also operates around 10 hospices that provide palliative care for terminal patients, as well as several long-term, acute-care hospital facilities (mostly within host hospitals) that serve patients who no longer need intensive care but still require complex care in a hospital setting. The company also provides rehabilitation services.

	Annual Growth	12/03	12/04	12/05	12/06	12/07
Sales ($ mil.)	42.4%	72.4	123.0	162.6	215.3	298.0
Net income ($ mil.)	62.7%	2.8	9.3	10.1	20.6	19.6
Market value ($ mil.)	24.0%	—	—	288.6	505.5	444.0
Employees	15.9%	—	—	3,415	3,959	—

LIBBEY INC.

NYSE: LBY

300 Madison Ave.
Toledo, OH 43604
Phone: 419-325-2100
Fax: 419-325-2117
Web: www.libbey.com

CEO: John F. Meier
CFO: Gregory T. Geswein
HR: Timothy T. Paige
FYE: December 31
Type: Public

The sound of breaking glass is music to Libbey's ears. It signals potential sales for the firm, which primarily sells glassware and flatware to the foodservice industry and to retailers in the US and Canada. Libbey's products are exported to more than 100 countries. Its brands include Libbey, Crisa, Royal Leerdam, and Traex, among others. Subsidiary Syracuse China makes ceramic dinnerware, and World Tableware peddles metal flatware and hollowware. Libbey owns Vitrocrisa, the largest Mexican glassware maker. Zesiger Capital Group owns about 14% of the company's stock. After multiple challenges from the FTC, Libbey abandoned its proposed purchase of Anchor Hocking (formerly owned by Newell Rubbermaid).

	Annual Growth	12/03	12/04	12/05	12/06	12/07
Sales ($ mil.)	12.0%	518.6	546.8	570.1	692.4	816.4
Net income ($ mil.)	—	29.1	8.3	(19.4)	(20.9)	(2.3)
Market value ($ mil.)	(12.2%)	387.7	306.6	143.2	176.9	230.7
Employees	104.3%	—	—	3,500	7,150	—

LIBERMAN BROADCASTING, INC.

1845 W. Empire Ave.
Burbank, CA 91504
Phone: 818-563-5722
Fax: 818-567-1062
Web: www.lbimedia.com

CEO: Jose Liberman
CFO: Wisdom W. Lu
HR: –
FYE: December 31
Type: Private

If you prefer el radio to emit español, then turn to the Libermans. Liberman Broadcasting (LBI) owns and operates more than 15 Spanish-language radio stations and four Spanish-language television stations in California and Texas. The company also owns television production facilities in Dallas, Houston, and Burbank, California. LBI is expanding through acquisitions, such as its 2006 purchase of five Dallas radio stations from Entravision. Father-and-son team Jose and Lenard Liberman founded Liberman Broadcasting in 1987 and own more than 95% of the company.

	Annual Growth	12/03	12/04	12/05	12/06	12/07
Est. sales ($ mil.)	—	—	—	—	—	32.1
Employees	—	—	—	—	—	400

LIBERTY BANCORP, INC.

NASDAQ (CM): LBCP

16 W. Franklin St.
Liberty, MO 64068
Phone: 816-781-4822
Fax: 816-781-6851
Web: www.libertysb.com

CEO: Brent M. Giles
CFO: Marc J. Weishaar
HR: –
FYE: September 30
Type: Public

Liberty Bancorp was formed in 2006 to be the holding company for BankLiberty (formerly Liberty Savings Bank), which operates seven branches in the Kansas City area. It offers traditional deposit services such as checking and savings accounts, CDs, and IRAs, in addition to newfangled offerings like Internet banking, bill payment, and cash management services. Construction loans, mainly to custom homebuilders, make up the largest portion of the company's loan portfolio (more than 45%). It also offers business, residential and commercial real estate, and consumer loans.

	Annual Growth	9/03	9/04	9/05	9/06	9/07
Assets ($ mil.)	15.9%	—	—	—	287.6	333.2
Net income ($ mil.)	26.7%	—	—	—	1.5	1.9
Market value ($ mil.)	4.7%	—	—	—	48.7	51.0
Employees	10.4%	—	—	—	67	74

LIBERTY BELL BANK

NASDAQ (CM): LBBB

2099 Rte. 70 East
Cherry Hill, NJ 08003
Phone: 856-489-8401
Fax: 856-489-8405
Web: www.libertybellbank.com

CEO: Kevin L. Kutcher
CFO: Dennis Costa
HR: –
FYE: December 31
Type: Public

You won't find Liberty Bell Bank in Philadelphia but rather across the Delaware River in South Jersey. It serves businesses and individuals from three branches in Cherry Hill, Evesham, and Moorestown, New Jersey. The bank offers traditional retail deposit products including checking, savings, and money market accounts, and certificates of deposit. The company's lending activities mainly consist of commercial mortgages (more than 40% of its loan portfolio), followed by one- to four-family residential mortgages and business loans (about 25% each).

	Annual Growth	12/02	12/03	12/04	12/05	*12/06
Assets ($ mil.)	100.4%	—	13.5	76.0	94.7	108.7
Net income ($ mil.)	—	—	(1.7)	(2.4)	(1.6)	(1.4)
Employees	38.7%	—	12	25	32	32

*Most recent year available

LIBERTY CAPITAL GROUP

NASDAQ (GS): LCAPA

12300 Liberty Blvd.
Englewood, CO 80112
Phone: 720-875-5400
Fax: 720-875-7469
Web: www.libertymedia.com

CEO: Gregory B. (Greg) Maffei
CFO: Christopher W. (Chris) Shean
HR: –
FYE: December 31
Type: Public

Liberty Capital Group is a tracking stock of Liberty Media, a holding company controlled by John Malone with interests in media, retail, and telecommunications. Liberty Capital includes holdings related to cable television programming and telecommunications services, including Starz Media (media production and distribution) and TruePosition (wireless positioning applications). Liberty Capital also owns Leisure Arts (a publisher of lifestyle and instructional books, DVDs, newsletters, and Web content) and two television stations (WFRV-TV in Green Bay, Wisconsin, and WJMN-TV in Escanaba, Michigan). The Liberty Capital tracking stock was formed in 2006 along with Liberty Interactive Group.

	Annual Growth	12/03	12/04	12/05	12/06	12/07
Sales ($ mil.)	15.4%	—	1,056.0	1,145.0	1,287.0	1,621.0
Employees	—	—	—	—	—	—

LIBERTY DIVERSIFIED HOLDINGS, INC.

OTC: LDHIE

2100 W. Orangewood, Ste. 220
Orange, CA 92868
Phone: 949-376-4846
Fax: 949-640-0430
Web: www.libertydiversifiedholdings.com

CEO: Ronald C. (Ron) Touchard
CFO: Wayne K. Bailey
HR: –
FYE: December 31
Type: Public

Now that it is focused on packaging, Liberty Diversified Holdings has set its former subsidiaries free. Liberty's primary subsidiary is MCR Printing and Packing Corp, which it acquired in the tail end of 2005. MCR makes packaging products that include folding cartons, insert cards, and small trays from its manufacturing facilities in Mexico. Electronics manufacturer Leviton is the company's largest customer, representing about 30% of total sales. In 2006, Liberty sold off its eWorldMedia subsidiary, an e-mail marketing services company, as well as its Peaceful Feet Shoeshine subsidiary, which provided shoe shines and shoe services. Co-chairmen Ronald Touchard and Mario Ramirez collectively own 28% of Liberty.

	Annual Growth	12/02	12/03	12/04	12/05	*12/06
Sales ($ mil.)	—	0.8	0.8	1.3	0.5	0.0
Net income ($ mil.)	—	(1.5)	(3.2)	(3.0)	(3.9)	(14.4)
Employees	—	—	—	—	—	—

*Most recent year available

An in-depth profile of this company is available to Hoover's Online members at hoovers.com.

935

LIBERTY DIVERSIFIED INDUSTRIES INC.

5600 N. Hwy. 169
New Hope, MN 55428
Phone: 763-536-6600
Fax: 763-536-6685
Web: www.libertydiversified.com

CEO: Michael (Mike) Fiterman
CFO: Steve Richardson
HR: –
FYE: May 31
Type: Private

Freedom means — among other things — the right to diversify; Liberty Diversified Industries has done just that. It designs, manufactures, markets, and distributes corrugated paper, plastic, and metal packaging products. The company has nine operating units, including Diversi-Plast (corrugated plastic products), LDI Fibres (recycling programs and services), Liberty Carton (specialty corrugated paper packaging), and Protecta-Pack Systems (plastic shipping pallets). Other operating units such as Valley Craft and SAFCO design and manufacture fabricated metal shipping containers and office storage supplies.

	Annual Growth	5/03	5/04	5/05	5/06	5/07
Est. sales ($ mil.)	—	—	—	—	—	219.0
Employees	—	—	—	—	—	1,820

LIBERTY ENTERTAINMENT GROUP

NASDAQ (GS): LMDIA

12300 Liberty Blvd.
Englewood, CO 80112
Phone: 720-875-5400
Fax: 720-875-7469
Web: www.libertymedia.com

CEO: Gregory B. (Greg) Maffei
CFO: Christopher W. (Chris) Shean
HR: –
FYE: December 31
Type: Public

Liberty Entertainment Group is a tracking stock of Liberty Media, a holding company controlled by John Malone with interests in telecommunications, cable television, and online media. The tracking stock includes Starz Entertainment, which operates the Encore and Starz pay-TV services, and Liberty's 48% holding in direct broadcast satellite (DBS) provider DIRECTV. Liberty Entertainment also includes interactive game producer FUN Technologies, a 32% interest in satellite broadband Internet access company WildBlue Communications, and a 50% stake in the Game Show Network cable channel.

LIBERTY GLOBAL, INC.

NASDAQ (GS): LBTYA

12300 Liberty Blvd.
Englewood, CO 80112
Phone: 303-220-6600
Fax: 303-220-6601
Web: www.lgi.com

CEO: Michael T. Fries
CFO: Bernard G. Dvorak
HR: Amy M. Blair
FYE: December 31
Type: Public

Liberty Global's consolidated operations provide cable TV programming and content distribution, telephone service, and Internet access to nearly 15 million subscribers in 15 European, Asian, and Latin American countries. The company's core market is Western Europe where it does more than half of its business through subsidiary UPC Holding and in Belgium through a controlling stake in Telenet Holding. The company's European programming business is overseen by Chellomedia. Other key subsidiaries include Jupiter Telecommunications (J:COM), which serves customers in Japan, and VTR, which leads Liberty Global's presence in Chile. The company also offers satellite television in some markets.

	Annual Growth	12/03	12/04	12/05	12/06	12/07
Sales ($ mil.)	32.2%	—	—	5,151.3	6,487.5	9,003.3
Net income ($ mil.)	—	—	—	(80.1)	706.2	(422.6)
Market value ($ mil.)	14.4%	—	—	5,227.5	5,739.5	6,846.0
Employees	0.9%	—	—	21,600	20,500	22,000

LIBERTY HOMES, INC.

Pink Sheets: LIBHA

1101 Eisenhower Dr. North
Goshen, IN 46526
Phone: 574-533-0431
Fax: 574-533-0438
Web: www.libertyhomesinc.com

CEO: Edward J. Hussey
CFO: Marc A. Dosmann
HR: Brian L. Christner
FYE: December 31
Type: Public

Liberty Homes gives houses the freedom to move about the land. The company builds builds multi-section homes (most of its shipments) and single-section homes on wheel-mounted undercarriages for relocation to customer sites. The company's two- to five-bedroom manufactured homes range in length from 36 ft. to 76 ft. and in width from 12 ft. to 16 ft. Multi-section homes cost from $35,000 to $125,000; single-section homes cost from $25,000 to $50,000. The company also builds modular homes. Liberty Homes sells through independent US dealers and company-owned retail centers. Chairman Edward Hussey and his family own a controlling stake in the company.

	Annual Growth	12/99	12/00	12/01	12/02	*12/03
Sales ($ mil.)	(16.8%)	176.3	128.2	112.3	91.9	84.4
Net income ($ mil.)	—	2.2	(5.9)	(1.6)	(4.6)	(4.6)
Employees	(16.0%)	1,350	1,100	930	800	—

*Most recent year available

LIBERTY INTERACTIVE GROUP

NASDAQ (GM): LINTA

12300 Liberty Blvd.
Englewood, CO 80112
Phone: 720-875-5400
Fax: 720-875-7469
Web: www.libertymedia.com

CEO: Gregory B. (Greg) Maffei
CFO: Christopher W. (Chris) Shean
HR: –
FYE: December 31
Type: Public

Liberty Interactive Group stands by your right to shop from home and online. One of three tracking stocks of Liberty Media, it includes home shopping network QVC, perishable goods e-tailer Provide Commerce (Proflowers.com), and online costume shop Buyseasons. Liberty Interactive also owns about a quarter of Barry Diller's Internet conglomerate IAC/InteractiveCorp, which operates such diverse businesses as Ticketmaster, search engine Ask.com, and QVC rival HSN. Liberty Media spun off Liberty Interactive in 2006 along with Liberty Capital, a similar tracking stock that includes Starz Media, True Position, and the Atlanta Braves baseball team. (A third tracking stock, Liberty Entertainment, was created in 2008.)

	Annual Growth	12/03	12/04	12/05	12/06	12/07
Sales ($ mil.)	11.1%	—	5,687.0	6,501.0	7,326.0	7,802.0
Employees	—	—	—	—	—	—

⊞ LIBERTY MEDIA CORPORATION

12300 Liberty Blvd.
Englewood, CO 80112
Phone: 720-875-5400
Fax: 720-875-5401
Web: www.libertymedia.com

CEO: Gregory B. (Greg) Maffei
CFO: David J. A. Flowers
HR: –
FYE: December 31
Type: Holding company

Liberty Media takes the freedom to arrange its varied businesses as it pleases. The holding company comprises publicly traded Liberty Capital Group, Liberty Entertainment Group, and Liberty Interactive Group. The arrangement effectively splits the fast-growing video and online commerce operations and the company's less robust cable TV and entertainment businesses. Liberty Media's biggest holding, the QVC home shopping network, falls under the Liberty Interactive umbrella, as does e-tailer Provide Commerce. Movie channel Starz Media and the Atlanta Braves baseball team both belong to Liberty Capital, while Liberty Entertainment is the receptacle for a stake in DIRECTV. Liberty Media is chaired by John Malone.

	Annual Growth	12/03	12/04	12/05	12/06	12/07
Sales ($ mil.)	30.7%	3,230.0	7,051.0	7,960.0	8,613.0	9,423.0
Net income ($ mil.)	151.7%	—	—	—	840.0	2,114.0
Employees	17.9%	—	—	13,660	14,765	19,000

LIBERTY MUTUAL HOLDING COMPANY INC.

175 Berkeley St.
Boston, MA 02116
Phone: 617-357-9500
Fax: 617-350-7648
Web: www.libertymutual.com

CEO: Edmund F. (Ted) Kelly
CFO: Dennis J. Langwell
HR: Helen E. R. Sayles
FYE: December 31
Type: Mutual company

Boston boasts of baked beans, the Red Sox, and the Liberty Mutual Group. Liberty Mutual Holding is the parent of Liberty Mutual Group and its three principal mutual insurance companies, Liberty Mutual Insurance, Liberty Mutual Fire Insurance, and Employers Insurance Company of Wausau. Liberty Mutual is one of the top property/casualty insurers in the US and among the top 10 providers of automobile insurance. The company also offers homeowners' insurance and commercial lines for small to large companies. Liberty Mutual Group is a diversified global insurer with operations in nearly 900 offices throughout the world.

	Annual Growth	12/02	12/03	12/04	12/05	12/06
Assets ($ mil.)	11.2%	55,877.0	64,422.0	72,359.0	78,824.0	85,498.0
Net income ($ mil.)	33.8%	508.0	851.0	1,245.0	1,027.0	1,626.0
Employees	2.7%	35,000	38,000	38,000	39,000	39,000

LIBERTY PROPERTY TRUST

NYSE: LRY

500 Chesterfield Pkwy.
Malvern, PA 19355
Phone: 610-648-1700
Fax: 610-644-4129
Web: www.libertyproperty.com

CEO: William P. Hankowsky
CFO: George J. Alburger Jr.
HR: Craig Waring
FYE: December 31
Type: Public

There's "Land of the Free" but no such thing as "free land" to Liberty Property Trust. The self-managed real estate investment trust (REIT) owns and leases industrial and office properties in suburban areas in the Southeast, Mid-Atlantic, and Midwest regions of the US, as well as in the UK. It provides leasing, development, and property management services to its portfolio of about 350 industrial properties (including distribution, service, assembly, light manufacturing, and research and development facilities) and nearly 300 office properties. The company's properties encompass some 60 million sq. ft. Top tenants include The Vanguard Group and GlaxoSmithKline.

	Annual Growth	12/03	12/04	12/05	12/06	12/07
Sales ($ mil.)	2.8%	625.0	655.4	680.7	666.7	698.8
Net income ($ mil.)	0.2%	163.6	161.4	249.4	266.6	164.8
Market value ($ mil.)	(4.9%)	3,229.2	3,701.2	3,786.1	4,470.4	2,638.1
Employees	1.9%	—	—	470	474	488

LIBERTY TRAVEL, INC.

69 Spring St.
Ramsey, NJ 07446
Phone: 201-934-3500
Fax: 201-934-3651
Web: www.libertytravel.com

CEO: Gilbert Haroche
CFO: –
HR: –
FYE: December 31
Type: Private

Give me liberty, or give me . . . travel? Liberty Travel gives you both. The company offers leisure travel services to consumers in the Northeast and Florida. Liberty's sister company GOGO Worldwide Vacations serves the travel agent community with customized land-only and air-inclusive travel packages from almost 90 offices in more than 30 states. Overall, Liberty Travel offers trips to more than 200 destinations, including Colorado Rockies ski excursions, Alaskan cruises, and family vacations to Walt Disney World. The company was founded in 1951 and was acquired by Australian-based travel agency Flight Centre in early 2008 for about $135 million.

	Annual Growth	12/03	12/04	12/05	12/06	12/07
Est. sales ($ mil.)	—	—	—	—	—	668.5
Employees	—	—	—	—	—	2,200

LICT CORPORATION

Pink Sheets: LICT

401 Theodore Fremd Ave.
Rye, NY 10580
Phone: 914-921-8821
Fax: 914-921-6410
Web: www.lictcorp.com

CEO: Robert E. Dolan
CFO: Robert E. Dolan
HR: –
FYE: December 31
Type: Public

Spun off from Lynch Corporation (now The LGL Group) in 1999, LICT (formerly Lynch Interactive) has holdings in small local-exchange phone companies and wireless operations, including PCS providers. It also owns stakes in cable TV operations and in two TV stations: ABC affiliate WOI (Iowa) and CBS affiliate WHBF (Iowa/Illinois). The company bought local-exchange carrier California-Oregon Telecommunications Company (Cal-Ore) in 2005. Chairman Mario Gabelli, who also heads GAMCO Investors (formerly Gabelli Asset Management), owns 24% of Lynch Interactive.

	Annual Growth	12/02	12/03	12/04	12/05	*12/06
Sales ($ mil.)	3.4%	86.3	87.4	87.8	93.7	98.8
Net income ($ mil.)	(10.9%)	1.9	7.4	4.5	4.3	1.2
Employees	(0.3%)	369	—	356	370	365

*Most recent year available

LIFE CARE CENTERS OF AMERICA

3570 Keith St. NW
Cleveland, TN 37312
Phone: 423-476-3254
Fax: 423-476-5974
Web: www.lcca.com

CEO: Beecher Hunter
CFO: Steve Ziegler
HR: Michelle Meadows
FYE: December 31
Type: Private

Life Care Centers of America is a privately owned operator of retirement and health care centers. The company manages more than 260 facilities throughout 28 states — including retirement communities, assisted-living facilities, and nursing homes — and provides specialized services such as home health care, as well as occupational, speech, and physical therapies. Additional services include adult day care, hospice, short-term care, and wound care. In addition, Life Care operates centers specifically for people with Alzheimer's disease or related dementia.

	Annual Growth	12/02	12/03	12/04	12/05	12/06
Sales ($ mil.)	8.9%	1,460.0	1,600.0	1,800.0	1,957.0	2,050.0
Employees	0.0%	30,000	30,000	40,000	30,000	30,000

LIFE FITNESS

5100 N. River Rd.
Schiller Park, IL 60176
Phone: 847-288-3300
Fax: 847-288-3703
Web: www.lifefitness.com

CEO: John E. Stransky
CFO: Dan Tanner
HR: Judy L. Gustafson
FYE: December 31
Type: Business segment

Life Fitness wants to pump you up. It manufactures fitness equipment for the consumer and commercial markets under the Life Fitness, Life Fitness Sport, ParaBody, Essential, and Hammer Strength names. Products include strength systems, exercise bikes, treadmills, cross-trainers, and stair-climbers. Founded in 1977 as Lifecycle, the company distributes its products through about 190 dealers in more than 120 countries. Recreational products maker Brunswick Corporation purchased Life Fitness in 1997 from Mancuso & Co. Life Fitness purchased Hammer Strength (maker of plate-loaded equipment) later that year and ParaBody (home strength training equipment maker) in 1998.

	Annual Growth	12/03	12/04	12/05	12/06	12/07
Est. sales ($ mil.)	—	—	—	—	—	145.7
Employees	—	—	—	—	—	1,400

An in-depth profile of this company is available to Hoover's Online members at hoovers.com.

937

LIFE PARTNERS HOLDINGS, INC.

NASDAQ (GM): LPHI

204 Woodhew
Waco, TX 76712
Phone: 254-751-7797
Fax: 254-751-1025
Web: www.lphi.net

CEO: Brian D. Pardo
CFO: Nina Piper
HR: –
FYE: February 28
Type: Public

Life Partners Holdings, parent company of Life Partners, Inc., makes its bucks by helping its customers make a buck. The company facilitates viatical and life settlement transactions, in which an institution or wealthy investor purchases individual life insurance policies (at a discount) and becomes the beneficiary of those policies when they mature. Viatical settlements involve terminally ill policyholders with only a couple of years to live; life settlement transactions involve sellers with longer life expectancies. Life Partners makes its money from fees earned by facilitating viatical and life settlements.

	Annual Growth	2/04	2/05	2/06	2/07	2/08
Assets ($ mil.)	37.2%	9.0	10.3	12.0	16.6	31.9
Net income ($ mil.)	65.6%	2.5	2.7	1.1	3.6	18.8
Market value ($ mil.)	40.6%	46.3	45.2	44.2	77.5	180.9
Employees	0.0%	—	—	37	37	—

LIFE SCIENCES RESEARCH INC.

Pink Sheets: LSRI

Mettlers Road
East Millstone, NJ 08875
Phone: 201-525-1819
Fax: –
Web: www.lsrinc.net

CEO: Andrew H. Baker
CFO: Richard A. Michaelson
HR: –
FYE: December 31
Type: Public

Life Sciences Research stands ready to test everything that humans, animals, and the environment eat, use, and are exposed to. As the world's third-largest contract research organization (CRO) — behind Charles River and Covance — the company performs safety and efficacy tests on pharmaceutical and chemical compounds used in products being developed by drug, agricultural, industrial, and veterinary companies. Life Sciences Research and its subsidiaries provide both large and start-up drugmaker clients worldwide with toxicology, metabolism, and stability studies for preclinical candidates that are applying for product approval. Pharmaceutical trials account for more than 85% of the company's revenue.

	Annual Growth	12/03	12/04	12/05	12/06	12/07
Sales ($ mil.)	15.6%	132.4	157.6	172.0	192.2	236.8
Net income ($ mil.)	—	3.7	17.6	1.5	(14.9)	(14.0)
Market value ($ mil.)	37.0%	—	—	—	185.2	253.8
Employees	0.2%	1,467	1,387	1,407	1,477	—

LIFE TIME FITNESS, INC.

NYSE: LTM

2902 Corporate Place
Chanhassen, MN 55317
Phone: 952-947-0000
Fax: 952-947-9137
Web: www.lifetimefitness.com

CEO: Bahram Akradi
CFO: Michael R. (Mike) Robinson
HR: –
FYE: December 31
Type: Public

Life Time Fitness wants to help you keep your New Year's resolutions. The company operates some 70 exercise and recreation centers in about 15 states, including Illinois, Indiana, Michigan, Texas, and Virginia. Life Time Fitness facilities offer swimming pools, basketball and racquet courts, child care centers, spas, dining services, and climbing walls, in addition to some 400 pieces of exercise equipment. The company's members can access the facilities 24 hours a day, seven days a week. About 40 of the company's locations are larger than 100,000 square feet and are designed to serve as an all-in-one sports and athletic club, professional fitness facility, family recreation center, and spa and resort.

	Annual Growth	12/03	12/04	12/05	12/06	12/07
Sales ($ mil.)	26.4%	256.9	312.0	390.1	511.9	655.8
Net income ($ mil.)	34.8%	20.6	28.9	41.2	50.6	68.0
Market value ($ mil.)	30.5%	—	874.5	1,354.9	1,786.0	1,944.4
Employees	21.3%	—	8,400	9,500	12,350	15,000

LIFECELL CORPORATION

NASDAQ (GS): LIFC

1 Millennium Way
Branchburg, NJ 08876
Phone: 908-947-1100
Fax: 908-947-1200
Web: www.lifecell.com

CEO: Paul G. Thomas
CFO: Steven T. Sobieski
HR: –
FYE: December 31
Type: Public

LifeCell puts new life into the tissue graft market. The firm manufactures skin graft materials processed from cadaver skin, a category of products known as allografts. Its products include AlloDerm, used in reconstructive plastic, dental, and burn surgeries; Repliform, used in urologic and gynecological surgeries; and GraftJacket, used in some orthopedic procedures. Orthopedic surgeons also use the company's AlloCraft DBM as a bone void filler. The company markets its products in the US and abroad through a direct sales force and distributors, including Boston Scientific, Wright Medical, and Stryker. LifeCell was acquired by wound care company Kinetic Concepts in 2008.

	Annual Growth	12/03	12/04	12/05	12/06	12/07
Sales ($ mil.)	47.6%	40.3	61.1	94.4	141.7	191.1
Net income ($ mil.)	9.5%	18.7	7.2	12.0	20.5	26.9
Market value ($ mil.)	74.6%	158.7	297.7	625.3	815.5	1,473.6
Employees	24.5%	—	—	269	335	—

LIFECORE BIOMEDICAL, INC.

3515 Lyman Blvd.
Chaska, MN 55318
Phone: 952-368-4300
Fax: 952-368-3411
Web: www.lifecore.com

CEO: Dennis J. Allingham
CFO: David M. Noel
HR: Kristen Weiss-Todd
FYE: June 30
Type: Private

Lifecore Biomedical hopes you like most of your medical products *al dente*. Its dental division produces dental implants to replace lost or extracted teeth; it also makes tissue regeneration products for treatment of periodontal disease and tooth loss. Lifecore's hyaluronan division makes products using hyaluronan, a natural lubricating compound found in animal and human connective tissues. The products are used in cataract surgeries, bone grafting, pain treatments for osteoarthritis, and veterinary orthopedics. Lifecore has supply agreements with Alcon and Advanced Medical Optics, who use its hyaluronan solution in cataract surgery products. In 2008 the firm was taken private by Warburg Pincus.

	Annual Growth	6/03	6/04	6/05	6/06	6/07
Sales ($ mil.)	13.2%	42.4	47.0	55.2	63.1	69.6
Net income ($ mil.)	—	(0.4)	0.7	17.5	7.0	7.7
Employees	—	—	—	—	233	—

LIFEPOINT HOSPITALS, INC.

NASDAQ (GS): LPNT

103 Powell Ct., Ste. 200
Brentwood, TN 37027
Phone: 615-372-8500
Fax: 615-372-8575
Web: www.lifepointhospitals.com

CEO: William F. (Bill) Carpenter III
CFO: David M. Dill
HR: Melissa Clontz
FYE: December 31
Type: Public

Folks who get sick in the country but are sick of the city can go to one of LifePoint's hospitals. The company, a spin-off of hospital giant HCA, operates some 50 hospitals (with about 6,000 total beds) that are located in non-urban areas where they are in most cases the only available acute care facilities. LifePoint's hospitals are located in 18 states, with the heaviest concentrations in Alabama, Kentucky, Louisiana, New Mexico, and Virginia. The company participates in the HealthTrust Purchasing Group, a group purchasing organization that negotiates competitive contracts on medical supplies and equipment.

	Annual Growth	12/03	12/04	12/05	12/06	12/07
Sales ($ mil.)	30.5%	907.1	996.9	1,855.1	2,439.7	2,630.1
Net income ($ mil.)	10.5%	68.5	85.7	72.9	146.2	102.0
Market value ($ mil.)	10.9%	1,115.7	1,908.7	2,141.4	1,933.2	1,687.6
Employees	5.1%	—	—	19,000	20,000	21,000

LIFEQUEST WORLD CORPORATION

OTC: LQWC

1181 Grier Dr., Ste. C
Las Vegas, NV 89119
Phone: 702-914-9688
Fax: 702-914-9625
Web: www.jurak.com

CEO: Anthony C. Jurak
CFO: –
HR: Maria J. Guedes
FYE: May 31
Type: Public

Are you tired, run-down, listless? Do you poop out at parties? Are you unpopular? Time to call on Tonicman! LifeQuest World (formerly PhytoLabs and before that Jurak) uses its Tonicman radio shows to help get the word out about its Jurak Classic Whole Body Tonic, but its primary distribution is through multi-level marketing. The company's primary product is a liquid herbal formula created in 1943 by Carl Jurak, father of founder and CEO Anthony Jurak. Some of the tonic's ingredients include peppermint, licorice, chamomile, and hops. LifeQuest World has more than 9,000 active distributors. The company was founded in 1997. Mr. Jurak owns 68% of the company.

	Annual Growth	5/03	5/04	5/05	5/06	5/07
Sales ($ mil.)	(21.2%)	2.6	2.7	2.4	1.5	1.0
Net income ($ mil.)	—	(0.6)	(0.4)	(0.5)	(1.1)	(1.4)
Market value ($ mil.)	—	—	—	—	—	157.2
Employees	—	—	—	7	—	—

LIFESCAN, INC.

1000 Gibraltar Dr.
Milpitas, CA 95035
Phone: 408-263-9789
Fax: 408-942-6070
Web: www.lifescan.com

CEO: Tom West
CFO: –
HR: –
FYE: December 31
Type: Subsidiary

LifeScan is sugar sweet for diabetes patients. A subsidiary of health care giant Johnson & Johnson, the company is a leading supplier of blood glucose monitoring systems, sold under the OneTouch brand name, that help diabetes patients monitor and manage their disease. Many of the company's products — including meters, test strips, lancing devices, and software — allow users to test with tiny amounts of blood taken from the forearm or palm rather than using painful finger pricks. In addition to products for home use, LifeScan sells glucose monitoring systems (branded SureStep and OneTouch Flexx) that are used in hospitals and other institutional settings.

LIFESPAN CORPORATION

167 Point St.
Providence, RI 02903
Phone: 401-444-3500
Fax: 401-444-5433
Web: www.lifespan.org

CEO: George A. Vecchione
CFO: –
HR: V. Brandon Melton
FYE: September 30
Type: Private

Lifespan Corporation helps to increase the longevity of the residents of Rhode Island. Founded in 1994, the health system includes Rhode Island Hospital (about 720 beds) and Miriam Hospital (nearly 250 beds), as well as Hasbro Children's Hospital (the pediatric division of Rhode Island Hospital), Bradley Hospital (a children's psychiatric hospital), and Newport Hospital (about 150 beds).

	Annual Growth	9/03	9/04	9/05	9/06	9/07
Est. sales ($ mil.)	—	—	—	—	—	1,348.3
Employees	—	—	—	—	—	8,000

LIFESPAN, INC.

Pink Sheets: LSPN

27 Oakmont Dr.
Rancho Mirage, CA 92270
Phone: 866-883-9971
Fax: –

CEO: Stuart V. Brame
CFO: Karl Harz
HR: –
FYE: December 31
Type: Public

Lifespan, Inc., formerly NationsRx, wants to make it cheaper and easier for people to get their drugs. The company markets a self-activating pharmacy benefit card that holders can use at more than 55,000 member pharmacies. Both insured and noninsured consumers receive savings on all prescriptions. The company has acquired Nanotech's (formerly Lifespan) Health Science Program, which it previously had rights to through a licensing agreement. The program offers customized health and dietary programs for individuals based on lifestyle, food allergy tests, and other factors.

	Annual Growth	12/02	12/03	12/04	12/05	*12/06
Sales ($ mil.)	—	—	—	—	—	0.0
Net income ($ mil.)	—	—	—	—	—	(0.6)
Employees	—	—	—	—	—	—

*Most recent year available

LIFESTEM INTERNATIONAL, INC.

OTC: LSTM

23341 Del Lago
Laguna Hills, CA 92853
Phone: 949-450-9910
Fax: 949-597-1408
Web: www.lifesteminternational.com

CEO: James DeOlden
CFO: –
HR: –
FYE: December 31
Type: Public

LifeStem International (formerly CalbaTech) sees a world of opportunity in a vial of blood. Through acquisitions, the biotech company has built a portfolio of research supply companies that develop new technologies to sell or license. The company's subsidiaries include K-D Medical (microbiological culture media supplier), LifeStem (adult stem cell supplier and banker), Molecula (reagent supplier), and MolecularWare (biological data management software development and supplier). Its customers include federally funded, academic, and private pharmaceutical research centers, medical distributors, and other research suppliers.

	Annual Growth	12/03	12/04	12/05	12/06	12/07
Sales ($ mil.)	—	0.0	0.3	1.3	1.3	1.1
Net income ($ mil.)	—	(3.7)	(2.7)	(5.0)	0.0	0.0
Employees	—	—	—	—	—	—

LIFETIME BRANDS, INC.

NASDAQ (GS): LCUT

1000 Stewart Ave.
Garden City, NY 11530
Phone: 516-683-6000
Fax: 516-683-6116
Web: www.lifetimebrands.com

CEO: Jeffrey (Jeff) Siegel
CFO: Laurence Winoker
HR: Mindy Ross
FYE: December 31
Type: Public

Take-out meals and frozen dinners? Not in this lifetime. Lifetime Brands designs and distributes cutlery, cutting boards, bakeware, home decor, and kitchen widgets under the Cuisinart, Farberware, KitchenAid, Elements, Melannco, Kamenstein, Wallace Silversmiths, and Pomerantz names, among others. The company also offers items under licensed brands and sells its varied lines in the US, Canada, and Europe through high-end retailers, supermarkets, and discount stores. The firm operates about 80 Farberware and Pfaltzgraff outlet stores in 32 states. Founder Milton Cohen and his family own 26% of the firm; his late partners' descendants, CEO Jeffrey Siegel and SVP Craig Phillips, own 22%.

	Annual Growth	12/03	12/04	12/05	12/06	12/07
Sales ($ mil.)	32.5%	160.4	189.5	307.9	457.4	493.7
Net income ($ mil.)	1.5%	8.4	8.5	14.1	15.5	8.9
Market value ($ mil.)	(4.1%)	183.2	175.7	267.1	218.2	155.3
Employees	(6.7%)	—	—	1,686	1,199	1,469

An in-depth profile of this company is available to Hoover's Online members at hoovers.com.

LIFETIME ENTERTAINMENT SERVICES

309 W. 49th St.
New York, NY 10019
Phone: 212-424-7000
Fax: 212-957-4449
Web: www.lifetimetv.com

CEO: Andrea Wong
CFO: James Wesley
HR: Patricia (Pat) Langer
FYE: December 31
Type: Joint venture

Lifetime Entertainment Services hopes viewers make a long-term commitment to its television programs. The company operates three cable-TV networks (Lifetime, Lifetime Movie Network, Lifetime Real Women) focused on serving female viewers with original movies, talk shows, and syndicated shows. Its Lifetime channel reaches more than 95 million US households. Lifetime Entertainment also offers lifestyle and entertainment content online. The company was formed by the merger of channels Daytime and Cable Health Network in 1984. It's jointly owned by Walt Disney (through Disney ABC Cable) and publishing giant Hearst.

LIFETOUCH INC.

11000 Viking Dr., Ste. 400
Eden Prairie, MN 55344
Phone: 952-826-4000
Fax: 952-826-4557
Web: www.lifetouch.com

CEO: Paul Harmel
CFO: Randolph (Randy) Pladson
HR: Ted Koenecke
FYE: June 30
Type: Private

When it's picture day at school and the kids are all lined up with new haircuts and scrubbed faces, odds are good that their toothy grins are directed at someone from Lifetouch. One of the largest US portrait photographers, employee-owned Lifetouch also runs about 600 photography studios inside J. C. Penney and Target stores across the nation. In addition, Lifetouch takes baby, family, business, and sports portraits; publishes church directories and yearbooks; and offers event digital imaging (which combines photography, graphics, and text), CD business imaging, and video production services. The firm operates in the US and Canada. Lifetouch was founded in 1936 as National School Studios.

	Annual Growth	6/02	6/03	6/04	6/05	6/06
Est. sales ($ mil.)	0.9%	—	—	—	1,070.0	1,080.0
Employees	0.0%	—	—	—	22,000	22,000

LIFEWAY CHRISTIAN RESOURCES OF THE SOUTHERN BAPTIST CONVENTION

1 LifeWay Plaza, MSN 146
Nashville, TN 37234
Phone: 615-251-2000
Fax: 615-251-3899
Web: www.lifeway.com

CEO: Thom S. Rainer
CFO: Jerry Rhyne
HR: –
FYE: September 30
Type: Not-for-profit

LifeWay Christian Resources of the Southern Baptist Convention helps to spread the teachings of Jesus. The company is a non-profit Christian publisher; it also sells books, CDs, and church furniture, signs, and supplies through more than 140 LifeWay Christian Stores throughout the US and its catalog. In addition, LifeWay operates two of the country's largest Christian conference facilities — LifeWay Ridgecrest Conference Center in North Carolina and LifeWay Glorieta Conference Centers in New Mexico. Together they welcome about 2,000 conference and overnight guests per year. The company was founded in 1891 by Dr. J.M. Frost.

	Annual Growth	9/03	9/04	9/05	9/06	9/07
Est. sales ($ mil.)	—	—	—	—	—	449.3
Employees	—	—	—	—	—	4,000

LIFEWAY FOODS, INC.

NASDAQ (GM): LWAY

6431 W. Oakton St.
Morton Grove, IL 60053
Phone: 847-967-1010
Fax: 847-967-6558
Web: lifeway.net

CEO: Julie Smolyansky
CFO: Edward P. (Ed) Smolyansky
HR: –
FYE: December 31
Type: Public

Kefir is not milk with a pedigree but it *is* cultured, and it's the lifeblood of Lifeway Foods. In addition to the yogurt-like dairy beverage called kefir, the company's products include Farmer's Cheese, Sweet Kiss (a sweetened cheese spread), and Soy-Treat, a soy-based kefir. A drinkable yogurt product is aimed at the Hispanic market under the brand name, La Fruta. Its Probugs offering, a flavored drink with live kefir cultures packaged in pouches, is aimed at children. A longtime staple in the dairy cases of health-food stores, Lifeway's products are available throughout the US, as well as internationally.

	Annual Growth	12/03	12/04	12/05	12/06	12/07
Sales ($ mil.)	26.9%	14.9	16.3	20.1	27.7	38.7
Net income ($ mil.)	9.8%	2.2	2.0	2.5	2.9	3.2
Market value ($ mil.)	62.6%	28.5	38.6	52.2	157.9	199.1
Employees	39.5%	—	—	86	120	—

LIGAND PHARMACEUTICALS

NASDAQ (GM): LGND

10275 Science Center Dr.
San Diego, CA 92121
Phone: 858-550-7500
Fax: 858-550-7506
Web: www.ligand.com

CEO: John L. Higgins
CFO: John P. Sharp
HR: Audrey Warfield
FYE: December 31
Type: Public

Ligand Pharmaceuticals Incorporated is receptive to new ideas. The company, which develops small-molecule drugs that interact with hormone-activated cellular receptors, has sold off its commercial operations, including its FDA-approved cancer and pain drugs, and has refocused on developing a pipeline of new compounds. It sold pain medication Avinza to King Pharmaceuticals in 2007; Eisai bought its oncology product lines the previous year. Its current R&D efforts include treatments for thrombocytopenia (low platelet count) and osteoporosis, developed internally and in collaboration with the likes of GlaxoSmithKline, Wyeth, and Pfizer.

	Annual Growth	12/03	12/04	12/05	12/06	12/07
Sales ($ mil.)	(45.0%)	141.1	163.5	176.6	141.0	12.9
Net income ($ mil.)	—	(37.5)	(45.1)	(36.4)	(31.7)	281.7
Market value ($ mil.)	(19.3%)	1,075.2	849.4	814.6	1,089.3	455.4
Employees	(75.3%)	—	—	493	122	—

LIGHTING SCIENCE GROUP CORPORATION

OTC: LSCG

2100 McKinney Ave., Ste. 1555
Dallas, TX 75201
Phone: 214-382-3630
Fax: 214-382-3631
Web: www.lsgc.com

CEO: Govi Rao
CFO: Stephen A. (Steve) Hamilton
HR: Lynn Vera
FYE: December 31
Type: Public

Lighting Science Group has seen the light. The company offers a line of energy-efficient, low-cost LED (light-emitting diode) light bulbs and other lighting products for commercial and residential uses. Applications for Lighting Science's products include outdoor and parking garage lighting, floodlights, retail displays, and cabinet lighting. Lighting Science Group products can also be seen illuminating bridges and roadways, as well as gaming devices in casinos. The company also manufactures power and data supplies, dimmers, and converters. Lighting Science distributes its products through traditional commercial and retail distribution channels.

	Annual Growth	12/02	12/03	12/04	12/05	*12/06
Sales ($ mil.)	—	—	0.0	0.0	0.1	0.4
Net income ($ mil.)	—	—	(0.4)	(3.8)	(3.1)	(9.8)
Employees	—	—	4	—	—	—

*Most recent year available

LIGHTPATH TECHNOLOGIES, INC.

NASDAQ (CM): LPTH

2603 Challenger Tech Ct., Ste. 100
Orlando, FL 32826
Phone: 407-382-4003
Fax: 407-382-4007
Web: www.lightpath.com

CEO: Joseph (Jim) Gaynor
CFO: Dorothy M. Cipolla
HR: –
FYE: June 30
Type: Public

LightPath Technologies is lighting the optical networking way. The company, which has traditionally used its patented GRADIUM glass to make distortion-reducing lenses for inspection equipment, is developing new applications for its technologies in the optoelectronics and fiber-optic communications fields. Its optoelectronics products include collimators (optical network components) and optical isolators (filters that prevent light waves from reflecting backwards). LightPath serves such customers as Intel, Santur (14% of sales), and CyOptics (12%). The company targets aerospace, telecommunications, health care, instrumentation, and the military. LightPath gets about three-quarters of its sales in the US.

	Annual Growth	6/03	6/04	6/05	6/06	6/07
Sales ($ mil.)	18.5%	6.8	8.3	11.8	12.2	13.4
Net income ($ mil.)	—	(21.2)	(5.6)	(3.5)	(3.4)	(2.6)
Market value ($ mil.)	31.6%	7.3	19.8	11.1	18.1	22.0
Employees	27.5%	81	125	115	207	214

LILLIAN VERNON CORPORATION

2600 International Pkwy.
Virginia Beach, VA 23452
Phone: 757-427-7700
Fax: 757-427-7819
Web: www.lillianvernon.com

CEO: Tim Arland
CFO: Robert J. Eveleigh
HR: Mark McGowan
FYE: December 31
Type: Subsidiary

Whether you're decorating a Christmas tree or a dining table, Lillian's your lady. Mail-order and online retailer Lillian Vernon offers thousands of items, including gift, gardening, holiday, household, and kids' products. The company is known for its "personalization" department that offers customers the option to monogram items, such as bags and bath towels, at a reasonable charge. Lillian Vernon filed for Chapter 11 Bankruptcy protection in February 2008 after laying off about half its year-round work force; it was acquired by Current USA in April 2008.

	Annual Growth	12/03	12/04	12/05	12/06	12/07
Est. sales ($ mil.)	—	—	—	—	—	175.0
Employees	—	—	—	—	—	5,300

LIMCO-PIEDMONT INC.

NASDAQ (GM): LIMC

5304 S. Lawton Ave.
Tulsa, OK 74107
Phone: 918-445-4300
Fax: –
Web: www.limcopiedmont.com

CEO: Shaul Menachem
CFO: Carla S. Covey
HR: –
FYE: December 31
Type: Public

Limco-Piedmont wants to keep planes out of limbo while waiting for repairs. The company (formerly Limco-Airepair) performs aircraft component maintenance, repairs, and overhaul services for commercial and military planes, as well as air cargo carriers. Most of its work is on heat transfer parts. Limco-Piedmont also makes heat transfer equipment used in airplanes and offers inventory management and parts procurement for airlines. Parts services account for about a quarter of the company's business. Major customers include the US government, KLM Royal Dutch Airlines, Lufthansa, and Bell Helicopter. The company, which had been a subsidiary of Israeli aircraft parts maker TAT Technologies, went public in 2007.

	Annual Growth	12/03	12/04	12/05	12/06	12/07
Sales ($ mil.)	70.4%	—	14.1	31.7	59.0	69.8
Net income ($ mil.)	73.2%	—	1.0	1.9	4.3	5.2
Market value ($ mil.)	—	—	—	—	—	163.9
Employees	—	—	—	—	283	—

LIME ENERGY CO.

NASDAQ (CM): LIME

1280 Landmeier Rd.
Elk Grove Village, IL 60007
Phone: 847-437-1666
Fax: 847-437-4969
Web: www.lime-energy.com

CEO: David R. Asplund
CFO: Jeffrey R. Mistarz
HR: Jeffrey R. Mistarz
FYE: December 31
Type: Public

Lime Energy wants to shine a little less light for a lot less money. The company's Energy Services segment installs energy efficient lighting upgrades for commercial and industrial customers. It works with each customer to determine the best lighting set-up given several factors, such as hours of operation, energy costs, and building environment. It also provides energy engineering services, including energy management planning and assistance with applying for energy rebates. Additionally, the company sells a line of controllers under the eMAC and uMAC brands that offer wireless monitoring of HVAC and lighting equipment designed to help reduce energy usage. Top customers include Washington Mutual and Kohl's.

	Annual Growth	12/03	12/04	12/05	12/06	12/07
Sales ($ mil.)	43.5%	4.6	2.4	4.8	8.1	19.5
Net income ($ mil.)	—	(5.5)	(5.2)	(6.9)	(16.5)	(15.6)
Market value ($ mil.)	(76.7%)	—	—	—	313.7	73.0
Employees	(10.3%)	—	—	41	77	33

LIMELIGHT NETWORKS, INC.

NASDAQ (GM): LLNW

2220 W. 14th St.
Tempe, AZ 85281
Phone: 602-850-5000
Fax: 602-850-5001
Web: www.limelightnetworks.com

CEO: Jeffrey W. (Jeff) Lunsford
CFO: Matthew (Matt) Hale
HR: –
FYE: December 31
Type: Public

Limelight Networks wants to be the center of attention for digital content providers. The company offers services for delivering media files such as video, music, games, software, and social media, via the Internet. Limelight Networks also provides on-demand and live streaming services for all major formats, including Adobe Flash, MP3 audio, QuickTime, RealNetworks RealPlayer, and Windows Media. Its more than 700 customers include movie studio DreamWorks, video game company Electronic Arts, and software giant Microsoft, which accounds for more than 10% of sales. Limelight Networks' clients provide content through a variety of devices, including PCs, mobile phones, and digital video recorders.

	Annual Growth	12/03	12/04	12/05	12/06	12/07
Sales ($ mil.)	109.6%	—	11.2	21.3	64.3	103.1
Net income ($ mil.)	—	—	0.5	0.4	(3.7)	(73.0)
Market value ($ mil.)	—	—	—	—	—	568.7
Employees	—	—	—	—	—	—

LIMITED BRANDS, INC.

NYSE: LTD

3 Limited Pkwy.
Columbus, OH 43216
Phone: 614-415-7000
Fax: 614-415-7440
Web: www.limitedbrands.com

CEO: Leslie H. Wexner
CFO: Stuart Burgdoerfer
HR: Jane L. Ramsey
FYE: Saturday nearest January 31
Type: Public

Limited Brands is as much of a shopping-mall mainstay as food courts and teenagers. The company operates about 2,925 stores throughout North America under the Victoria's Secret, Bath & Body Works (BBW), and La Senza (in Canada) banners, as well as corresponding Web sites. Originally focused on apparel, Limited Brands sold its ailing Limited Stores and Express chains, leaving the company free to focus on its core brands: Victoria's Secret and BBW. Limited Brands also owns apparel importer MAST Industries, luxe department store operator Henri Bendel, and The White Barn Candle Co. The company is controlled by founder and chairman Leslie Wexner, whose family owns about 16% of the firm.

	Annual Growth	1/04	1/05	1/06	1/07	1/08
Sales ($ mil.)	3.2%	8,934.0	9,408.0	9,699.0	10,671.0	10,134.0
Net income ($ mil.)	0.0%	717.0	705.0	683.0	676.0	718.0
Employees	(3.2%)	111,100	115,300	110,000	125,500	97,500

An in-depth profile of this company is available to Hoover's Online members at hoovers.com.

941

LIN TV CORP.

NYSE: TVL

4 Richmond Sq., Ste. 200
Providence, RI 02906
Phone: 401-454-2880
Fax: 401-454-0089
Web: www.lintv.com

CEO: Vincent L. Sadusky
CFO: Bart W. Catalane
HR: Dan Donohue
FYE: December 31
Type: Public

This company spells success with TV call letters. LIN TV owns and operates about 30 stations serving nearly 20 markets in about a dozen states. Its portfolio of stations includes affiliates with all the major networks — mostly CBS and FOX — as well as those affiliated with smaller networks The CW Network and MyNetworkTV. It also has a handful of Spanish-language stations affiliated with TeleFutura and Univision (both owned by Univision Communications). In addition, the company owns 20% of a joint venture with NBC Universal parent General Electric that operates NBC stations in Dallas and San Diego. Board member Royal W. Carson owns about 35% voting control of LIN TV.

	Annual Growth	12/03	12/04	12/05	12/06	12/07
Sales ($ mil.)	(7.1%)	—	—	—	426.1	395.9
Net income ($ mil.)	—	—	—	—	(234.5)	53.7
Market value ($ mil.)	15.0%	—	—	—	289.1	332.5
Employees	—	—	—	—	—	—

LINCARE HOLDINGS INC.

NASDAQ (GS): LNCR

19387 US 19 North
Clearwater, FL 33764
Phone: 727-530-7700
Fax: 727-532-9692
Web: www.lincare.com

CEO: John P. Byrnes
CFO: Paul G. Gabos
HR: Shelia Dilley
FYE: December 31
Type: Public

Lincare Holdings doesn't take breathing for granted. With more than 1,000 offices across the US, the company helps some 700,000 patients with chronic obstructive pulmonary diseases (sicknesses like emphysema and severe asthma) by providing oxygen therapy services. Through its local service centers, Lincare delivers oxygen equipment to patients in their homes, and it trains them and monitors their use of the equipment. It also supplies other home medical equipment such as hospital beds and wheelchairs. And in some markets, it provides home infusion services, such as chemotherapy, parenteral nutrition, and other procedures.

	Annual Growth	12/03	12/04	12/05	12/06	12/07
Sales ($ mil.)	8.6%	1,147.4	1,268.5	1,266.6	1,409.8	1,596.0
Net income ($ mil.)	(0.7%)	232.1	273.4	213.7	213.0	226.1
Market value ($ mil.)	(3.3%)	2,978.3	4,318.0	4,028.3	3,597.5	2,608.7
Employees	7.0%	—	—	8,258	9,070	9,450

LINCOLN BANCORP

NASDAQ (GM): LNCB

905 Southfield Dr.
Plainfield, IN 46168
Phone: 317-839-6539
Fax: 317-837-3928
Web: www.lincolnbankonline.com

CEO: Jerry R. Engle
CFO: John M. Baer
HR: Jennifer Dawson
FYE: December 31
Type: Public

Oh, what Lincoln could do with your pennies! Lincoln Bancorp is the parent company for Lincoln Bank, which serves the areas west and south of Indianapolis through about 20 branches and loan offices. The bank offers traditional retail products such as checking, savings, money market, and NOW accounts, as well as CDs and IRAs. About one-third of the loans it writes are for commercial real estate. One- to four-family residential mortgages make up another quarter of the portfolio, which also includes construction and consumer loans. The bank traces its roots to 1884, although it did not adopt the Lincoln name until 100 years later.

	Annual Growth	12/03	12/04	12/05	12/06	12/07
Assets ($ mil.)	10.7%	591.7	809.0	844.5	883.5	889.3
Net income ($ mil.)	(15.9%)	3.6	3.7	1.2	2.9	1.8
Market value ($ mil.)	(4.1%)	88.0	103.5	88.6	106.5	74.5
Employees	0.6%	—	—	243	—	246

LINCOLN EDUCATIONAL SERVICES

NASDAQ (GM): LINC

200 Executive Dr., Ste. 340
West Orange, NJ 07052
Phone: 973-736-9340
Fax: 973-736-1750
Web: www.lincolneducationalservices.com

CEO: David F. Carney
CFO: Cesar Ribeiro
HR: Sally Williams
FYE: December 31
Type: Public

You won't find courses on the Civil War and the Gettysburg Address taught here — Lincoln Educational Services Corporation focuses more on career-oriented training. The for-profit company offers degrees and diplomas in automotive technology, health sciences, skilled trades (including HVAC and electronics), cosmetology, culinary arts, and business and information technology. More than 17,000 students are enrolled at some 40 campuses, most of which operate under the Lincoln brand name (Lincoln College of Technology and Lincoln Technical Institute). Private investment fund Stonington Partners (through subsidiary Back to School Acquisition) owns 76% of Lincoln Educational Services.

	Annual Growth	12/03	12/04	12/05	12/06	12/07
Sales ($ mil.)	13.3%	198.9	261.3	299.2	321.5	327.8
Net income ($ mil.)	0.3%	8.2	13.0	18.7	15.6	8.3
Market value ($ mil.)	3.0%	—	—	358.9	343.3	381.1
Employees	8.5%	—	—	2,270	—	2,671

LINCOLN ELECTRIC HOLDINGS, INC.

NASDAQ (GS): LECO

22801 St. Clair Ave.
Cleveland, OH 44117
Phone: 216-481-8100
Fax: 216-486-1751
Web: www.lincolnelectric.com

CEO: John M. Stropki Jr.
CFO: Vincent K. Petrella
HR: Gretchen Farrell
FYE: December 31
Type: Public

With this thing, I thee weld. Lincoln Electric is a leading manufacturer of arc-welding and cutting products, as well as supplies such as arc-welding power sources, automated wire-feeding systems, and consumable electrodes for arc welding. Lincoln Electric also makes coated manual electrodes, solid electrodes produced in coil form, and cored electrodes produced in solid form. Lincoln Electric's welding products unit accounts for the majority of its revenues. The company operates 35 manufacturing facilities in the US and 18 other countries. More than half of its sales are in North America.

	Annual Growth	12/03	12/04	12/05	12/06	12/07
Sales ($ mil.)	21.7%	1,040.6	1,333.7	1,601.2	1,971.9	2,280.8
Net income ($ mil.)	38.9%	54.5	80.6	122.3	175.0	202.7
Market value ($ mil.)	32.1%	1,004.6	1,438.5	1,672.9	2,586.4	3,058.0
Employees	10.7%	5,992	6,835	7,485	8,430	8,992

LINCOLN NATIONAL CORPORATION

NYSE: LNC

150 N. Radnor Chester Rd.
Radnor, PA 19807
Phone: 215-448-1400
Fax: 215-448-3962
Web: www.lfg.com

CEO: Dennis R. Glass
CFO: Frederick J. (Fred) Crawford
HR: Elizabeth L. (Beth) Reeves
FYE: December 31
Type: Public

Who better to trust with your nest egg than the company that took its name from Honest Abe? Lincoln National, which operates as Lincoln Financial Group, provides retirement planning and life insurance to individuals and employers in the form of annuities and a variety of life insurance products. It sells through such subsidiaries as Lincoln National Life Insurance and Lincoln Life & Annuity Company of New York. The company is also active in the investment management business, offering individual and institutional clients such financial services as pension plans, trusts, and mutual funds through Delaware Investments and other subsidiaries.

	Annual Growth	12/03	12/04	12/05	12/06	12/07
Assets ($ mil.)	15.7%	106,744.9	116,219.3	124,787.6	178,494.0	191,435.0
Net income ($ mil.)	24.1%	511.9	707.0	831.1	1,316.0	1,215.0
Market value ($ mil.)	20.8%	7,213.3	8,101.7	9,214.9	18,310.0	15,383.7
Employees	17.8%	5,644	5,441	5,259	10,744	10,870

LINCOLN PROPERTY COMPANY

3300 Lincoln Plaza, 500 N. Akard
Dallas, TX 75201
Phone: 214-740-3300
Fax: 214-740-3441
Web: www.lincolnproperty.com

CEO: A. Mack Pogue
CFO: Nancy Davis
HR: Luanne Hudson
FYE: June 30
Type: Private

Lincoln Property is one of the largest diversified real estate companies in the US — honest! Lincoln Property began by building apartments in the Dallas area, then expanded into commercial and retail projects. It owns, leases, and manages around 290 residential communities throughout the US. Its commercial division provides management, development, and brokerage services for industrial, office, retail, and mixed-use real estate. Lincoln Property is also one of the largest developers and managers of military housing. CEO Mack Pogue co-founded Lincoln Property in 1965 with Trammell Crow, whose stake Pogue bought out in 1977.

	Annual Growth	6/03	6/04	6/05	6/06	6/07
Est. sales ($ mil.)	—	—	—	—	—	80.7
Employees	—	—	—	—	—	3,985

LINDSAY CORPORATION

NYSE: LNN

2707 N. 108th St., Ste. 102
Omaha, NE 68164
Phone: 402-428-2131
Fax: 402-428-7232
Web: www.lindsaymanufacturing.com

CEO: Richard W. (Rick) Parod
CFO: Timothy J. (Tim) Paymal
HR: Randy S. Hester
FYE: August 31
Type: Public

Drought conditions can sometimes be a blessing for Lindsay Corporation. The company is a leading maker of center-pivot and lateral-move irrigation systems for agriculture. Lindsay sells its Zimmatic irrigation systems through a worldwide network of dealers to farmers in more than 90 countries. Its electrically powered irrigation systems are designed to use both water and labor more efficiently than do traditional "flood" or "surface" irrigation systems. Lindsay also offers replacement parts for its irrigation products. The company's infrastructure division makes movable barriers for traffic management and crash cushions for improved roadway safety.

	Annual Growth	8/03	8/04	8/05	8/06	8/07
Sales ($ mil.)	14.6%	163.4	196.7	177.3	226.0	281.9
Net income ($ mil.)	4.9%	12.9	9.3	4.8	11.7	15.6
Market value ($ mil.)	29.0%	259.4	293.8	291.4	502.0	719.2
Employees	18.1%	—	—	645	763	899

LINEAR TECHNOLOGY CORPORATION

NASDAQ (GS): LLTC

1630 McCarthy Blvd.
Milpitas, CA 95035
Phone: 408-432-1900
Fax: 408-434-0507
Web: www.linear.com

CEO: Lothar Maier
CFO: Paul Coghlan
HR: –
FYE: Sunday nearest June 30
Type: Public

Linear Technology's chips keep real-world information right in line. The company's linear integrated circuits (ICs) transform analog signals — which convey information about real-world phenomena such as temperature, pressure, sound, or speed — into digital form so they can be used by electronic devices. The company also makes linear devices that control power and regulate voltage in electronic systems. Its products are found in a wide variety of equipment, including cable modems, cellular phones, disk drives, radar systems, satellites, and scientific and industrial instruments. Customers in the US provide around one-third of sales.

	Annual Growth	6/03	6/04	6/05	6/06	6/07
Sales ($ mil.)	15.6%	606.6	807.3	1,049.7	1,093.0	1,083.1
Net income ($ mil.)	14.9%	236.6	328.2	434.0	428.7	411.7
Market value ($ mil.)	(4.7%)	10,059.8	12,193.8	11,208.8	10,150.6	8,308.9
Employees	16.7%	—	—	3,217	3,755	—

LINENS 'N THINGS, INC.

6 Brighton Rd.
Clifton, NJ 07015
Phone: 973-778-1300
Fax: 973-815-2990
Web: www.lnt.com

CEO: Michael F. Gries
CFO: Francis M. (Frank) Rowan
HR: –
FYE: December 31
Type: Private

From pillow talk to coffee talk, Linens 'n Things has it covered. The #2 US home goods chain (after Bed Bath & Beyond) sells bedding, towels, housewares, and other home accessories, such as bath items and window treatments. Linens 'n Things has some 585 superstores (33,000 sq. ft. and larger), emphasizing low-priced, brand-name merchandise, in more than 45 states and about seven Canadian provinces. Brands include Braun, Krups, Calphalon, Laura Ashley, Croscill, Waverly, and the company's own label. Linens 'n Things was acquired by the private equity firm Apollo Management in 2006. The ailing company filed for Chapter 11 Bankruptcy protection in May 2008 and began shuttering about 120 stores.

	Annual Growth	12/02	12/03	12/04	12/05	12/06
Sales ($ mil.)	(6.0%)	—	—	—	2,695.0	2,534.4
Employees	(2.6%)	—	—	—	19,000	18,500

LINN ENERGY, LLC

NASDAQ (GS): LINE

J P Morgan Chase Tower, 600 Travis, Ste. 7000
Houston, TX 77002
Phone: 281-810-4000
Fax: –
Web: www.linnenergy.com

CEO: Michael C. (Mike) Linn
CFO: Kolja Rockov
HR: –
FYE: December 31
Type: Public

It's a Linn-Linn situation. CEO Michael Linn's namesake company Linn Energy has successfully drilled for natural gas across the US. The natural gas exploration and production company has made 24 property acquisitions between 2003 and early 2008 in California, New York, Oklahoma, Pennsylvania, Texas, Virginia, and West Virginia. The company has proved reserves of 1,616.1 billion cu. ft. of natural gas equivalent. Linn Energy has focused on shallow drilling (2,500 to 5,500 ft.). In 2007 the company acquired Dominion Resource's exploration and production Mid-Continent assets for $2.05 billion. Lehman Brothers Holdings owns about 13% of Linn Energy; CEO Linn, 4%.

	Annual Growth	12/02	12/03	12/04	12/05	*12/06
Sales ($ mil.)	286.9%	—	3.3	21.9	49.7	191.1
Net income ($ mil.)	—	—	(1.3)	(4.0)	(56.3)	79.2
Market value ($ mil.)	—	—	—	—	—	1,074.1
Employees	69.2%	—	—	—	130	220

*Most recent year available

LINSCO/PRIVATE LEDGER CORP.

9785 Towne Centre Dr.
San Diego, CA 92121
Phone: 858-450-9606
Fax: 858-546-8324
Web: www.lpl.com

CEO: Mark S. Casady
CFO: Charles W. (Bill) Maher
HR: –
FYE: December 31
Type: Private

Linsco/Private Ledger (LPL) is one of the largest independent brokerage firms in the US. The company's more than 10,000 advisors offer stocks and bonds, mutual funds, annuities, insurance, and other investments, as well as trust, research, and financial planning services. As an independent, LPL doesn't sell its own investment products, but provides access to those of other firms. It operates more than 6,500 offices in all 50 states and the District of Columbia. LPL expanded its client base with its purchase of UVEST Financial Services, which provides independent brokerage services to more than 300 regional and community banks and credit unions throughout the US.

	Annual Growth	12/02	12/03	12/04	12/05	12/06
Est. sales ($ mil.)	30.8%	—	—	—	1,300.0	1,700.0
Employees	83.3%	—	—	—	1,200	2,200

An in-depth profile of this company is available to Hoover's Online members at hoovers.com.

943

LION, INC.

OTC: LINN

2801 Hollycroft St.
Gig Harbor, WA 98116
Phone: 206-577-1440
Fax: 206-577-1441
Web: www.lionmts.com

CEO: David (Dave) Stedman
CFO: Steve Thomson
HR: –
FYE: December 31
Type: Public

LION (Lenders Interactive Online Network) wants its share of the online mortgage market, but a downturn in the industry has been a thorn in its paw. The firm provides software and online services connecting mortgage brokers with consumers and lenders. Its flagship Precision LPX product is a lending transaction and pricing engine which also allows customers access to the LION Broker (formerly LION Pro) wholesale mortgage database. In 2007, LION began restructuring in light of the troubled housing and credit markets. It sold its Mortgage 101 and TRMS businesses and reduced its workforce by 60%. The company has agreed to sell its assets to Beanstalk Networks Acquisition.

	Annual Growth	12/03	12/04	12/05	12/06	12/07
Assets ($ mil.)	(0.7%)	7.4	10.6	9.7	8.5	7.2
Net income ($ mil.)	(56.5%)	2.8	0.6	(0.1)	(1.3)	0.1
Market value ($ mil.)	(18.7%)	8.0	17.6	12.7	12.7	3.5
Employees	—	—	—	—	—	45

LIONBRIDGE TECHNOLOGIES, INC.

NASDAQ (GM): LIOX

1050 Winter St.
Waltham, MA 02451
Phone: 781-434-6000
Fax: 781-434-6034
Web: www.lionbridge.com

CEO: Rory J. Cowan
CFO: Donald M. (Don) Muir
HR: Eileen Sweeney
FYE: December 31
Type: Public

Lionbridge Technologies wants to bridge the language gap. The company offers translation, or globalization, of material such as software, user manuals, and Web content, preparing materials for international use by tailoring them to individual languages and cultures. It also supplies human interpreters to government agencies and businesses. In addition to its language-related businesses, Lionbridge provides testing services: Under the VeriTest brand, the company checks Web sites, software, and hardware to ensure their quality. Lionbridge customers come from industries such as consumer products, financial services, life sciences, manufacturing, and technology; Microsoft accounts for about 20% of sales.

	Annual Growth	12/03	12/04	12/05	12/06	12/07
Sales ($ mil.)	33.6%	141.7	154.1	236.3	418.9	452.0
Net income ($ mil.)	—	2.5	7.1	(3.9)	(4.9)	(4.2)
Market value ($ mil.)	(17.7%)	444.9	315.3	416.1	387.0	204.5
Employees	8.3%	—	—	3,921	4,295	4,600

LIONS GATE ENTERTAINMENT CORP.

NYSE: LGF

2700 Colorado Ave.
Santa Monica, CA 90404
Phone: 310-449-9200
Fax: 310-255-3870
Web: www.lionsgatefilms.com

CEO: Jon Feltheimer
CFO: James (Jim) Keegan
HR: –
FYE: March 31
Type: Public

Independent films are the cat's meow at Lions Gate Entertainment. The firm, which operates as Lionsgate, is the leading producer and distributor of independent films such as Academy Award winner *Crash* and top documentary *Fahrenheit 9/11* through its Lionsgate Films division. It produces TV programming (*The Dead Zone*) through Lionsgate Television. Lionsgate also releases films under the Trimark brand, and owns a library of more than 8,000 movie titles. In addition, it owns a minority stake in CinemaNow, an online video-on-demand service, and production studio Roadside Attractions. Lionsgate's 2003 purchase of rival Artisan Entertainment for $160 million created the industry's largest indie studio.

	Annual Growth	3/04	3/05	3/06	3/07	3/08
Sales ($ mil.)	37.1%	384.9	842.6	951.2	976.7	1,361.0
Net income ($ mil.)	—	(93.5)	20.3	6.1	27.5	(74.0)
Market value ($ mil.)	17.8%	600.2	1,125.4	1,059.9	1,335.8	1,157.0
Employees	13.0%	—	—	354	400	—

LIONS GATE TELEVISION CORP.

2700 Colorado Blvd.
Santa Monica, CA 90404
Phone: 310-449-9200
Fax: 310-255-3870
Web: http://lionsgate.com/?section=television

CEO: Kevin Beggs
CFO: –
HR: –
FYE: March 31
Type: Subsidiary

You might say this production company aims to be the king of the television jungle. Lions Gate Television is the TV production arm of independent film maker Lions Gate Entertainment. Operating as Lionsgate Television, the studio produces shows primarily for distribution through cable channels; its portfolio of productions includes *The Dead Zone* (shown on USA Network), *Mad Men* (AMC), and *Weeds* (Showtime). Lionsgate has also created such reality series as *Dirty Dancing* (WE Network) and *I Pity the Fool* (MTV Networks' TV Land). The studio's vault boasts more than 3,800 television episodes.

LIPID SCIENCES, INC.

NASDAQ (CM): LIPD

7068 Koll Center Pkwy., Ste. 401
Pleasanton, CA 94566
Phone: 925-249-4000
Fax: 925-249-4040
Web: www.lipidsciences.com

CEO: S. Lewis Meyer
CFO: Sandra A. Gardiner
HR: –
FYE: December 31
Type: Public

Lipid Sciences wants to knock out fat — the kind that coats arteries with plaque, not the kind that plagues dieters. The company is using its HDL Therapy platform to find treatments for patients with atherosclerosis (hardening of the arteries) that reverse the buildup of cholesterol and other artery-clogging fats in blood vessels. The HDL Therapy technology removes blood from the patient, cleanses the blood plasma of harmful lipids, and returns blood and plasma to the patient. The procedure is intended to jump-start the patient's own lipid management capabilities.

	Annual Growth	12/03	12/04	12/05	12/06	12/07
Sales ($ mil.)	—	—	0.0	0.0	0.1	0.3
Net income ($ mil.)	—	—	(11.6)	(10.2)	(11.2)	(12.8)
Market value ($ mil.)	(28.4%)	—	91.2	66.2	50.5	33.4
Employees	—	—	—	16	—	—

LIQUIDITY SERVICES, INC.

NASDAQ (GM): LQDT

1920 L St. NW, 6th Fl.
Washington, DC 20036
Phone: 202-467-6868
Fax: 202-467-5475
Web: www.liquidityservicesinc.com

CEO: William P. (Bill) Angrick III
CFO: James M. Rallo
HR: –
FYE: September 30
Type: Public

Hey, bidder, bidder. Take a swing at Liquidity Services (LSI). The online auction firm provides manufacturers, retailers, and corporations with an electronic business-to-business marketplace to dispose of, liquidate, and track goods in the reverse supply chain. Some 685,000 registered buyers can bid for wholesale, surplus, and salvage assets like retail customer returns, overstock products, and end-of-life goods. LSI also offers valuation, appraisal, inventory, marketing, sale, and logistical management of assets; warehousing and inspection of inventory; and transaction support such as payment collection and dispute mediation.

	Annual Growth	9/03	9/04	9/05	9/06	9/07
Sales ($ mil.)	34.5%	60.7	75.9	89.4	147.8	198.6
Net income ($ mil.)	40.8%	2.8	5.3	4.1	8.0	11.0
Market value ($ mil.)	(28.6%)	—	—	—	430.0	307.1
Employees	32.4%	—	—	304	—	533

LIQUIDMETAL TECHNOLOGIES, INC.

OTC: LQMT

25800 Commercentre Dr., Ste. 100	CEO: Larry E. Buffington
Lake Forest, CA 92630	CFO: Gerald E. Morrow
Phone: 949-206-8000	HR: –
Fax: 949-206-8008	FYE: December 31
Web: www.liquidmetal.com	Type: Public

It's not liquid, it's not metal — well, OK, it is metal. Still, Liquidmetal Technologies has built on research done at the California Institute of Technology by company officers William Johnson and Atakan Peker to sell amorphous metal alloys. Those products include an alloy that's lighter than titanium but twice as strong as conventional titanium alloys. The company's products are sold as bulk alloys, coatings, composites, and powders. Applications include casings for cell phones, defense products (armor-piercing ammunition), industrial coatings, and sporting goods (baseball bats, tennis rackets). Electronics giant Samsung is among the company's largest customers.

	Annual Growth	12/03	12/04	12/05	12/06	12/07
Sales ($ mil.)	14.5%	16.9	17.4	16.4	27.7	29.0
Net income ($ mil.)	—	(33.6)	(14.9)	(7.1)	(14.5)	(5.6)
Market value ($ mil.)	(31.1%)	—	95.7	37.1	67.4	31.3
Employees	—	120	—	—	—	—

LIQUIDNET, INC.

498 7th Ave., 12th Fl.	CEO: Seth Merrin
New York, NY 10018	CFO: William (Bill) Maw
Phone: 646-674-2000	HR: –
Fax: 646-674-2003	FYE: December 31
Web: www.liquidnet.com	Type: Private

Liquidity has a place at the table at Liquidnet, an institution where loose lips are not tolerated. The company has pioneered an electronic marketplace for institutional trading that brings buyers and sellers together and enables them to anonymously negotiate trades among each other without intermediaries or information leaks. Liquidnet's global membership community of institutional firms today represents more than $10 trillion in equity assets under management. The company operates in the fragmented Asian region, as well as in Australia, Canada, and Europe. Liquidnet was founded in 1999. Two years later, the company launched its US electronic exchange with some 40 members.

	Annual Growth	12/03	12/04	12/05	12/06	12/07
Est. sales ($ mil.)	—	—	—	—	—	346.5
Net income ($ mil.)	—	—	—	—	—	115.0
Employees	—	—	—	—	—	379

LITHIA MOTORS, INC.

NYSE: LAD

360 E. Jackson St.	CEO: Sidney B. (Sid) DeBoer
Medford, OR 97501	CFO: Jeffrey B. (Jeff) DeBoer
Phone: 541-776-6899	HR: Barbara Perkins
Fax: 541-774-7617	FYE: December 31
Web: www.lithia.com	Type: Public

Lithia Motors is driving the acquisition autobahn. The company operates about 110 stores in about 45 markets in 15 states, including California and Texas. The firm sells about 30 makes of domestic and imported new and used vehicles through its stores and the Internet. Daimler AG (Chrysler, Dodge, Jeep) and GM (Buick, Chevrolet, Saturn, Cadillac, Hummer) are the top sellers. Lithia Motors also offers financing and parts, and operates about 15 collision-repair service centers. Unlike most consolidators, it prefers to pay cash (rather than stock) for dealerships in smaller markets. Chairman and CEO Sidney DeBoer, through Lithia Holding Co., controls Lithia Motors, which was founded in 1946 by his father Walt.

	Annual Growth	12/03	12/04	12/05	12/06	12/07
Sales ($ mil.)	6.4%	2,513.5	2,745.8	2,935.4	3,172.9	3,219.0
Net income ($ mil.)	(11.8%)	35.5	42.7	53.6	37.3	21.5
Market value ($ mil.)	(12.3%)	370.4	406.1	491.4	454.1	219.1
Employees	10.0%	—	—	5,692	6,261	—

LITHIUM TECHNOLOGY CORPORATION

Pink Sheets: LTHU

5115 Campus Dr.	CEO: Klaus Brandt
Plymouth Meeting, PA 19462	CFO: Amir Elbaz
Phone: 610-940-6090	HR: –
Fax: 610-940-6091	FYE: December 31
Web: www.lithiumtech.com	Type: Public

Lithium Technology is engaged in the development of large-format rechargeable lithium-ion batteries for aerospace, automotive, stationary power, and national security applications. Customers include Lockheed Martin Space Systems and the UK Ministry of Defense. Lithium Technology acquired lithium polymer battery maker GAIA Holding from Arch Hill Capital in a 2002 share exchange transaction that gave Arch Hill Capital 64% control of Lithium Technology. Lithium's auditor has expressed doubt about the company's ability to continue as a going concern, due to its accumulated deficit of $131 million and its need for additional financing.

	Annual Growth	12/03	12/04	12/05	12/06	12/07
Sales ($ mil.)	89.9%	0.2	0.8	1.8	2.8	2.6
Net income ($ mil.)	—	(10.2)	(14.8)	(10.6)	(20.3)	(24.4)
Employees	15.1%	45	49	71	66	79

LITLE & CO.

900 Chelmsford St., Tower Three	CEO: Tom Litle
Lowell, MA 01851	CFO: Andrew Sutherland
Phone: 978-275-6500	HR: Andrew Sutherland
Fax: 978-937-7250	FYE: December 31
Web: www.litle.com	Type: Private

Litle & Co. sees eye-to-eye with non-face-to-face merchants. The company provides credit card payment processing services to direct marketers and e-commerce merchants. Its products include e-check and international payment processing and fraud protection. It also offers customers — more than half of whom are Internet marketers — a chargeback management system and a proprietary online reporting platform. The company operates an office in the US and one in Canada. Founder and chairman Tim Litle started the first Litle & Co. in 1986, but sold it in 1995 to then First USA for about $80 million. In 2001 he started the latest Litle & Co.

	Annual Growth	12/02	12/03	12/04	12/05	12/06
Sales ($ mil.)	—	—	—	—	—	34.8
Employees	—	—	—	—	—	38

LITTELFUSE, INC.

NASDAQ (GS): LFUS

800 E. Northwest Hwy.	CEO: Gordon B. Hunter
Des Plaines, IL 60016	CFO: Philip G. (Phil) Franklin
Phone: 847-824-1188	HR: Ryan K. Stafford
Fax: 847-391-0894	FYE: December 31
Web: www.littelfuse.com	Type: Public

Littelfuse is big on circuit protection. The company is the world's #1 fuse maker. In addition to its vast assortment of fuses, Littelfuse's other circuit-protection devices include positive temperature coefficient devices that limit current when too much is being supplied, and electrostatic discharge suppressors that redirect transient high voltage. The company's thyristors protect telecom circuits from transient voltage caused by lightning strikes. Littelfuse's 10,000-plus customers include electronics manufacturers (Hewlett-Packard and Samsung), automakers (Ford, GM, Honda, and Toyota), and the automotive aftermarket (AutoZone and Pep Boys). Customers outside of the US account for more than 60% of sales.

	Annual Growth	12/03	12/04	12/05	12/06	12/07
Sales ($ mil.)	12.1%	339.4	500.2	467.1	534.9	536.1
Net income ($ mil.)	24.5%	15.3	36.0	17.7	23.8	36.8
Market value ($ mil.)	3.6%	631.2	770.3	605.7	704.9	725.9
Employees	6.1%	4,896	5,822	5,646	6,550	6,200

An in-depth profile of this company is available to Hoover's Online members at hoovers.com.

945

LITTLE CAESAR ENTERPRISES, INC.

2211 Woodward Ave.
Detroit, MI 48201
Phone: 313-983-6000
Fax: 313-983-6390
Web: www.littlecaesars.com

CEO: Michael (Mike) Ilitch
CFO: Darrel Snygg
HR: Joni C. Nelson
FYE: December 31
Type: Subsidiary

I came, I saw, I bought a pizza. Little Caesar Enterprises operates and franchises more than 2,300 Little Caesars carryout pizza restaurants throughout the US and in about ten other countries. The chain offers a variety of original and deep-dish pizzas along with cheese bread, salads, and sandwiches. While some stores are stand-alone units, many Little Caesars locations can be found in strip malls and other high-traffic areas; the units typically do not offer dine-in seating. About 80% of the chain's outlets are run by franchisees. Little Caesars was founded in 1959 by Mike and Marian Ilitch, who also control a sports and entertainment empire through Ilitch Holdings.

	Annual Growth	12/03	12/04	12/05	12/06	12/07
Est. sales ($ mil.)	—	—	—	—	—	130.1
Employees	—	—	—	—	—	6,000

LITTLE LEAGUE BASEBALL, INCORPORATED

539 Rt. 15 Hwy.
Williamsport, PA 17702
Phone: 570-326-1921
Fax: 570-326-1074
Web: www.littleleague.org

CEO: Stephen D. Keener
CFO: David Houseknecht
HR: Carol Kester
FYE: September 30
Type: Not-for-profit

Little League Baseball's players might be small, but the organization's reach is anything but. Little League Baseball oversees more than 7,500 baseball and softball programs for some 2.7 million children in more than 100 countries worldwide, including China, Israel, Russia, and Venezuela. On the local level, Little League Baseball programs are organized and operated by volunteers. The season ends with the annual Little League World Series played in Williamsport, Pennsylvania. The organization also runs the Peter J. McGovern Little League Museum in Pennsylvania, baseball summer camps, and a Little League shop online. Little League Baseball was founded by Carl Stotz with only three teams in 1939.

	Annual Growth	9/03	9/04	9/05	9/06	9/07
Est. sales ($ mil.)	—	—	—	—	—	22.0
Employees	—	—	—	—	—	105

LITTLE SWITZERLAND, INC.

6800 Broken Sound Pkwy. NW
Boca Raton, FL 33487
Phone: 561-241-1115
Fax: 561-912-9138
Web: www.littleswitzerland.com

CEO: R. Christopher Cooper
CFO: —
HR: —
FYE: December 31
Type: Private

There's nothing neutral about Little Switzerland's definitively upscale stores. The company operates about 25 mostly duty-free stores that sell jewelry, watches, crystal, china, and other gift items priced from $20 to more than $10,000. Its stores, located on 11 Caribbean islands and in Florida, appeal to tourists (mostly from the US) looking to avoid the import taxes they would pay at home — especially passengers on the cruise ship lines that ply the waters in those areas. The chain was acquired by Tiffany & Co. in 2002, but Tiffany sold Little Switzerland to NXP Corp. in 2007.

	Annual Growth	12/03	12/04	12/05	12/06	12/07
Est. sales ($ mil.)	—	—	—	—	—	38.3
Employees	—	—	—	—	—	447

LITTLEFIELD CORPORATION

OTC: LTFD

2501 N. Lamar Blvd.
Austin, TX 78705
Phone: 512-476-5141
Fax: 512-476-5680
Web: www.littlefield.com

CEO: Jeffrey L. (Jeff) Minch
CFO: Richard S. (Rich) Chilinski
HR: —
FYE: December 31
Type: Public

A game of bingo is serious business for this company. Littlefield Corporation owns and operates more than 30 bingo halls in Texas, South Carolina, and Alabama. Its gaming locations generate revenue from renting out space to charitable organizations that use the halls for bingo and other fund-raising activities. In addition to bingo parlors, the company owns party rental company Premiere Tents & Events, which rents tables, tents, and foodservice equipment to customers in Austin, Texas and surrounding areas. President and CEO Jeffrey Minch owns more than 25% of the company.

	Annual Growth	12/02	12/03	12/04	12/05	*12/06
Sales ($ mil.)	4.1%	11.4	10.0	9.9	11.3	13.4
Net income ($ mil.)	—	(2.7)	0.2	(1.1)	1.0	0.8
Market value ($ mil.)	23.6%	3.7	5.2	5.2	4.2	8.8
Employees	—	125	—	—	—	—

*Most recent year available

LIVE NATION, INC.

NYSE: LYV

9348 Civic Center Dr.
Beverly Hills, CA 90210
Phone: 310-867-7000
Fax: 310-867-7001
Web: www.livenation.com

CEO: Michael (Mike) Rapino
CFO: Kathy Willard
HR: —
FYE: December 31
Type: Public

Live Nation holds center stage as the world's largest producer and promoter of live entertainment. The company owns or operates some 150 venues in North America and Europe. Annually, more than 60 million people attend some 28,000 Live Nation events. Live Nation also owns House of Blues venues through HOB Entertainment. The firm is focused on its music operations, and sold its North American theatrical business, which produced touring Broadway shows. Through a deal with pop star Madonna, Live Nation owns a stake in the Material Girl's music, including albums, tours, and merchandise. It has a similar deal with Jay-Z. Once a part of radio giant Clear Channel Communications, Live Nation was spun off in 2005.

	Annual Growth	12/03	12/04	12/05	12/06	12/07
Sales ($ mil.)	11.5%	2,704.4	2,802.0	2,936.8	3,691.6	4,185.0
Net income ($ mil.)	—	57.0	16.3	(130.6)	(31.4)	(11.9)
Market value ($ mil.)	12.5%	—	—	860.3	1,504.7	1,088.1
Employees	6.9%	3,600	3,200	3,000	4,400	4,700

LIVEDEAL, INC.

NASDAQ (CM): LIVE

4840 E. Jasmine St., Ste. 105
Mesa, AZ 85205
Phone: 480-654-9646
Fax: 480-654-9727
Web: www.livedeal.com

CEO: Michael (Mike) Edelhart
CFO: Gary L. Perschbacher
HR: —
FYE: September 30
Type: Public

LiveDeal (formerly YP Corp.) is an Internet yellow pages and online classifieds provider. The company publishes listings for some 16 million US businesses through its Yellow-Page.Net, YP.Net, and YP.Com Web sites. Its Internet Advertising Package (IAP) product lets advertisers buy exposure by purchasing a Mini-WebPage. The IAP includes enhanced presentation features such as larger font, bolded business name, a map and directions, and a link to the advertiser's Web site. Other offerings include Web site development and a low-cost Internet dial-up package. The company changed its name from YP Corp. after its 2007 purchase of online local classifieds marketplace LiveDeal.

	Annual Growth	9/03	9/04	9/05	9/06	9/07
Sales ($ mil.)	(3.9%)	30.8	57.2	25.2	36.9	26.3
Net income ($ mil.)	(30.2%)	7.6	9.0	(0.6)	(1.0)	1.8
Market value ($ mil.)	(51.1%)	819.2	550.8	423.3	455.2	46.8
Employees	—	—	—	—	79	—

LIVEPERSON, INC.

NASDAQ (CM): LPSN

462 7th Ave., 3rd Fl.
New York, NY 10018
Phone: 212-609-4200
Fax: 212-609-4201
Web: www.liveperson.com

CEO: Robert P. LoCascio
CFO: Timothy E. (Tim) Bixby
HR: –
FYE: December 31
Type: Public

LivePerson wants to inject some life into your customer service operations. The company provides online, hosted software applications that enable retailers and other companies selling goods online to communicate with customers. LivePerson's Timpani software enables communications through multiple channels, including text-based chat, e-mail, and customer self-service tools. Clients install an icon on their Web sites that, when clicked, opens a dialogue window with customer service representatives. As part of its services, LivePerson also maintains transcripts of customer interactions and offers the option of conducting user exit surveys.

	Annual Growth	12/03	12/04	12/05	12/06	12/07
Sales ($ mil.)	44.4%	12.0	17.4	22.3	33.5	52.2
Net income ($ mil.)	—	(0.8)	2.1	2.5	2.2	5.8
Market value ($ mil.)	8.6%	184.1	117.9	213.1	214.8	255.7
Employees	60.4%	—	—	111	178	—

LIVEWORLD, INC.

OTC: LVWD

170 Knowles Dr., Ste. 211
Los Gatos, CA 95030
Phone: 408-871-5200
Fax: 408-871-5300
Web: www.liveworld.com

CEO: Peter H. Friedman
CFO: David S. Houston
HR: –
FYE: December 31
Type: Public

LiveWorld hopes that online collaboration is the key to its livelihood. Promoting itself as an "online community agency", LiveWorld creates custom communities that are targeted at three distinct areas: loyalty marketing (community of enthusiasts loyal to the clients' business), customer support (used for directly supporting and answering customer questions), and business intelligence (analysis on participating customers' behavior). LiveWorld has created online communities for such prominent companies as AOL, eBay, The Campbell Soup Company, and Warner Brothers. Chairman and CEO Peter Friedman and EVP Jenna Woodul founded LiveWorld in 1996 from remnants of Apple's now-defunct eWorld online service.

	Annual Growth	12/03	12/04	12/05	12/06	12/07
Est. sales ($ mil.)	—	—	—	—	—	10.9
Net income ($ mil.)	—	—	—	—	—	(2.4)
Market value ($ mil.)	—	—	—	—	—	10.2
Employees						

LIZ CLAIBORNE, INC.

NYSE: LIZ

1441 Broadway
New York, NY 10018
Phone: 212-354-4900
Fax: 212-626-3416
Web: www.lizclaiborne.com

CEO: William L. McComb
CFO: Andrew C. Warren
HR: Lawrence D. (Larry) McClure
FYE: Saturday nearest December 31
Type: Public

Liz Claiborne is dressed for success as a leading US seller of clothes and accessories for women. It markets its products as designer items but prices them for a broader market. Its brands — including Enyce, Liz & Co., Concepts by Claiborne, kate spade, and Dana Buchman — are sold worldwide in department stores, in some 430 specialty stores, in about 350 outlets, and among numerous brand Web sites. Liz Claiborne also makes men's clothing and licenses its name for shoes, sunglasses, swimwear, formalwear, home furnishings, and stationery. Liz Claiborne acquired trendy kate spade. The company is cutting jobs and completed a strategic review of its operations in early 2008.

	Annual Growth	12/03	12/04	12/05	12/06	12/07
Sales ($ mil.)	1.9%	4,241.1	4,632.8	4,847.8	4,994.3	4,577.3
Net income ($ mil.)	—	279.7	313.6	317.4	254.7	(372.8)
Market value ($ mil.)	(16.0%)	3,831.7	4,589.7	3,760.6	4,483.2	1,909.1
Employees	3.5%	—	—	15,400	17,000	16,500

LKQ CORPORATION

NASDAQ (GS): LKQX

120 N. LaSalle St., Ste. 3300
Chicago, IL 60602
Phone: 312-621-1950
Fax: 312-621-1969
Web: www.lkqcorp.com

CEO: Joseph M. Holsten
CFO: Mark T. Spears
HR: –
FYE: December 31
Type: Public

Ever wonder what happens to a car once the insurance company declares it "totaled"? Enter LKQ. An acquisitive nationwide recycler of damaged cars, LKQ buys wrecked cars (popular models such as the Honda Accord, Toyota Camry, and Ford Explorer) at auction and salvages reusable parts, including engines, front-end assemblies, doors, and fenders. It then distributes those parts to collision repair and mechanical repair shops; mechanical parts that can't be reused are sold as-is to parts reconditioners and items such as fluids, batteries, and tires are marketed to other recyclers. LKQ, which also distributes supplies to paint and body shops, operates from about 300 locations across North America.

	Annual Growth	12/03	12/04	12/05	12/06	12/07
Sales ($ mil.)	36.1%	328.0	424.8	547.4	789.4	1,126.8
Net income ($ mil.)	45.8%	14.6	20.6	30.9	44.4	65.9
Market value ($ mil.)	138.3%	87.4	103.5	445.0	612.7	2,819.8
Employees	64.3%	—	—	3,370	4,270	9,100

L.L. BEAN, INC.

3 Campus Dr.
Freeport, ME 04033
Phone: 207-552-3028
Fax: 207-552-3080
Web: www.llbean.com

CEO: Chris McCormick
CFO: Mark Fasold
HR: Martha Cyr
FYE: February 28
Type: Private

With L.L. Bean, you can tame the great outdoors — or just look as if you could. The outdoor apparel and gear maker mails more than 200 million catalogs per year. L.L. Bean's library includes about 10 specialty catalogs offering products in categories such as children's clothing, fly-fishing, outerwear, sportswear, housewares, footwear, camping and hiking gear, and the Maine hunting shoe upon which the company was built. L.L. Bean also operates about a dozen retail stores and some 15 factory outlets throughout the Northeast. In addition, it sells online through English- and Japanese-language Web sites. L.L. Bean was founded in 1912 by Leon Leonwood Bean and is controlled by his descendants.

	Annual Growth	2/02	2/03	2/04	2/05	2/06
Sales ($ mil.)	7.8%	1,140.0	1,070.0	1,150.0	1,400.0	1,540.0
Employees	4.2%	4,500	3,800	3,800	3,900	5,300

LL&E ROYALTY TRUST

NYSE: LRT

919 Congress Ave.
Austin, TX 78701
Phone: 512-236-6599
Fax: 512-479-2553

CEO: Michael J. (Mike) Ulrich
CFO: –
HR: –
FYE: December 31
Type: Public

LL&E Royalty Trust owns royalty interests in oil and gas properties located in Alabama, Florida, Texas, and offshore Louisiana. Formed in 1983, the trust receives and distributes royalties to shareholders based on the amount of oil and gas sold either to affiliates or on the spot market. Royalty trusts distribute essentially all royalties received to their shareholders, but their profitability is dependent upon the price of oil and gas and the productivity of the properties. LL&E Royalty Trust has proved reserves of 294,000 barrels of oil and 319 million cu. ft. of natural gas.

	Annual Growth	12/03	12/04	12/05	12/06	12/07
Sales ($ mil.)	(30.4%)	8.5	10.9	7.3	3.1	2.0
Net income ($ mil.)	(47.5%)	7.9	10.2	6.6	2.1	0.6
Market value ($ mil.)	(17.8%)	88.3	119.5	52.0	52.0	40.3
Employees	—	—	—	—	—	0

An in-depth profile of this company is available to Hoover's Online members at hoovers.com.

947

LMI AEROSPACE, INC.

NASDAQ (GM): LMIA

411 Fountain Lakes Blvd.
St. Charles, MO 63301
Phone: 636-946-6525
Fax: 636-949-1576
Web: www.lmiaerospace.com

CEO: Ronald S. (Ron) Saks
CFO: Lawrence E. (Ed) Dickinson
HR: Cindy Maness
FYE: December 31
Type: Public

It don't mean a thing if it ain't got a wing. LMI Aerospace makes key airplane structures, including door frames, cockpit window-frame assemblies, wing leading-edge skins, flap slats, fuselage skins, and interior components. The company fabricates, machines, finishes, and integrates more than 30,000 aluminum and specialty alloy components for commercial, corporate, and military aircraft. LMI's Tempco unit offers machining services to companies in the medical and semiconductor technology industries, as well as for aircraft manufacturers. Major customers include Boeing, Gulfstream, Bombardier, Sikorsky, and Spirit AeroSystems. CEO Ronald Saks owns about 17% of the company.

	Annual Growth	12/03	12/04	12/05	12/06	12/07
Sales ($ mil.)	22.1%	75.9	85.9	101.1	123.0	168.5
Net income ($ mil.)	—	(4.0)	0.4	5.2	10.7	13.2
Market value ($ mil.)	107.7%	16.3	44.6	118.4	173.2	303.1
Employees	36.1%	—	—	673	916	—

LNB BANCORP, INC.

NASDAQ (GM): LNBB

457 Broadway
Lorain, OH 44052
Phone: 440-244-6000
Fax: 440-244-4815
Web: www.4lnb.com

CEO: Daniel E. (Dan) Klimas
CFO: Sharon L. Churchill
HR: Mary E. Miles
FYE: December 31
Type: Public

LNB Bancorp is the holding company for The Lorain National Bank, which operates more than 20 branches in Ohio's Cuyahoga, Erie, Lorain, and Summit counties. The bank serves local businesses and individuals, offering such deposit products as checking and savings accounts, money market accounts, CDs, and IRAs. It also offers trust services and credit cards. The bank's lending activities primarily consist of commercial loans (approximately 60% of its portfolio) and real estate mortgages, as well as installment and home equity loans. The Lorain National Bank offers brokerage and investment services to customers through an agreement with Investment Centers of America.

	Annual Growth	12/03	12/04	12/05	12/06	12/07
Assets ($ mil.)	9.3%	741.2	781.7	801.1	851.1	1,056.6
Net income ($ mil.)	(8.1%)	7.7	7.5	6.4	5.4	5.5
Market value ($ mil.)	(5.6%)	134.3	133.6	117.1	103.4	106.9
Employees	—	—	—	257	—	—

LNR PROPERTY CORPORATION

1601 Washington Ave., Ste. 800
Miami Beach, FL 33139
Phone: 305-695-5500
Fax: 305-695-5589
Web: www.lnrproperty.com

CEO: Ronald E. Schrager
CFO: Steven N. Bjerke
HR: –
FYE: November 30
Type: Private

LNR is a real estate investment and management company spun off from homebuilding giant Lennar in 1997. LNR owns and manages a portfolio of real estate properties and real estate finance investments (unrated and junk-grade commercial mortgage-backed securities and collateralized debt obligations, high-yield mortgage loans, and mezzanine financing). LNR was acquired by LNR Property Holdings for $3.8 billion in 2005. LNR Property Holdings is 75%-owned by investment firm Cerberus Capital Management, 20% owned by the family of former chairman Stuart Miller, and 5% owned by management.

	Annual Growth	11/03	11/04	11/05	11/06	11/07
Est. sales ($ mil.)	—	—	—	—	—	11.9
Employees	—	—	—	—	—	480

LOCAL.COM CORPORATION

NASDAQ (CM): LOCM

1 Technology Dr., Bldg. G
Irvine, CA 92618
Phone: 949-784-0800
Fax: 949-784-0880
Web: corporate.local.com

CEO: Heath B. Clarke
CFO: Douglas S. Norman
HR: Heather A. Dilley
FYE: December 31
Type: Public

Local.com, formerly Interchange, traffics in keywords. Specializing in paid-search advertising, the company connects businesses hawking their wares to consumers surfing the Web via its distribution network of more than 200 Web sites and search engines. It makes money from direct advertisers who bid for placement (based on keywords) and pay for click-throughs, and from indirect advertisers that gain inclusion on the network through paid-search firms that have partnered with Local.com (such as LookSmart and Yahoo!). In an effort to capitalize on the awareness of its primary search engine, which it bought in 2005, the company changed its name to Local.com from Interchange in late 2006.

	Annual Growth	12/03	12/04	12/05	12/06	12/07
Sales ($ mil.)	25.0%	8.8	19.1	18.1	14.2	21.5
Net income ($ mil.)	—	0.1	1.5	(6.5)	(13.3)	(18.2)
Market value ($ mil.)	(22.1%)	—	144.3	50.7	37.7	68.3
Employees	—	—	—	67	—	—

LOCATEPLUS HOLDINGS CORPORATION

Pink Sheets: LPHC

100 Cummings Center, Ste. 235M
Beverly, MA 01915
Phone: 978-921-2727
Fax: 978-524-8767
Web: www.locateplus.com

CEO: James C. Fields
CFO: James C. Fields
HR: –
FYE: December 31
Type: Public

LocatePLUS Holdings provides databases of public and non-public background information for law enforcement agencies, government agencies, law firms, private investigators, and insurance companies. Its Internet-based LocatePLUS database provides searchable and cross-referenced data about individuals, including names, addresses, birth dates, social security numbers, court records, and motor vehicle records. Its Worldwide Information CD-ROM databases provide motor vehicle and driver's license information. Its Certifion Corporation unit, operating under the Entersect name, provides screening for resumé and online dating services. LocatePLUS also offers information on phone numbers through its Dataphant unit.

	Annual Growth	12/03	12/04	12/05	12/06	12/07
Sales ($ mil.)	25.4%	3.4	6.3	11.6	12.3	8.4
Net income ($ mil.)	—	(4.4)	(7.6)	(5.6)	(6.0)	(7.3)
Employees	—	—	—	—	88	—

LOCKHEED MARTIN CORPORATION

NYSE: LMT

6801 Rockledge Dr.
Bethesda, MD 20817
Phone: 301-897-6000
Fax: 301-897-6704
Web: www.lockheedmartin.com

CEO: Robert J. Stevens
CFO: Bruce L. Tanner
HR: Kenneth J. Disken
FYE: December 31
Type: Public

Lockheed Martin moves product in times of crisis — the company is the world's #1 defense contractor (ahead of Boeing and Northrop Grumman). Its business segments include: Aeronautics, which includes the F-16 and F-22 fighters, and the upcoming F-35 Joint Strike Fighter (Lightning II); Electronic Systems, encompassing everything from missiles and submarine warfare systems to homeland security systems, radar, and postal automation systems; Space Systems, which includes satellites, strategic missiles, and airborne defense systems; and Information Systems & Global Services, which provides IT solutions, mission solutions, and command, control, and communication systems and reconnaissance/surveillance systems.

	Annual Growth	12/03	12/04	12/05	12/06	12/07
Sales ($ mil.)	7.1%	31,824.0	35,526.0	37,213.0	39,620.0	41,862.0
Net income ($ mil.)	30.3%	1,053.0	1,266.0	1,825.0	2,529.0	3,033.0
Market value ($ mil.)	16.9%	22,988.8	24,442.0	27,800.7	38,761.5	42,959.0
Employees	3.7%	—	—	135,000	140,000	—

THE LOCKTON COMPANIES, LLC

444 W 47th St., Ste. 900
Kansas City, MO 64112
Phone: 816-960-9000
Fax: 816-960-9099
Web: www.lockton.com

CEO: John L. Lumelleau
CFO: Alan L. Salts
HR: Jo-Ann Gastin
FYE: April 30
Type: Private

The largest privately held insurance brokerage, Lockton offers risk management services, commercial property/casualty insurance, surety bonds, mergers and acquisition support services, and employee benefit planning services. Initially targeting construction businesses, Lockton has expanded its expertise to other industries, including energy, health care, hospitality, manufacturing, retail, and transportation. The company operates from about 20 domestic offices and more than 30 international offices and serves globally based companies operating in more than 125 countries. Lockton was founded in 1966 by Jack Lockton, brother of chairman David Lockton; it is owned by company executives.

	Annual Growth	4/03	4/04	4/05	4/06	4/07
Est. sales ($ mil.)	—	—	—	—	—	91.8
Employees	—	—	—	—	—	1,350

LODGENET INTERACTIVE CORPORATION

NASDAQ (GM): LNET

3900 W. Innovation St.
Sioux Falls, SD 57107
Phone: 605-988-1000
Fax: 605-988-1511
Web: www.lodgenet.com

CEO: Scott C. Petersen
CFO: Gary H. Ritondaro
HR: Shannon E. Grogan
FYE: December 31
Type: Public

Enjoy your stay: Watch a movie, play Nintendo, surf the Internet, use the shampoo, but please don't steal the towels. LodgeNet Interactive (formerly LodgeNet Entertainment) provides free and fee-based guest services, including cable TV, on-demand movies, Nintendo video games, DIRECTV broadcast satellite (DBS) TV programming, and Internet access to more than 9,000 hotels serving about 2 million rooms. To provide its Internet and interactive services, the company installs broadband LANs (local-area networks); its interactive services include video checkout and room service menus. LodgeNet is spreading its system architecture and technology through licensing partners outside North America.

	Annual Growth	12/03	12/04	12/05	12/06	12/07
Sales ($ mil.)	18.0%	250.1	266.4	275.8	288.2	485.6
Net income ($ mil.)	—	(35.0)	(20.8)	(7.0)	1.8	(65.2)
Market value ($ mil.)	14.6%	232.6	311.8	253.2	477.7	400.6
Employees	(0.7%)	—	—	809	803	—

LODGIAN, INC.

AMEX: LGN

3445 Peachtree Rd. NE, Ste. 700
Atlanta, GA 30326
Phone: 404-364-9400
Fax: 404-364-0088
Web: www.lodgian.com

CEO: Peter T. Cyrus
CFO: James A. MacLennan
HR: —
FYE: December 31
Type: Public

If you're living in hotel lodgings, does that make you a Lodgian? Lodgian is a multi-brand hospitality franchisee that operates some 45 hotels in nearly 25 states and one hotel in Windsor, Canada. The company's portfolio is focused mostly on the mid-market segment serving both leisure and business travels with full-service brands franchised from InterContinental Hotels (including Crowne Plaza and Holiday Inn) and Marriott (Marriott, Courtyard by Marriott). It also runs a handful of Hilton hotels and a couple of properties unaffiliated with a national brand. The company sold 23 hotels in 2007.

	Annual Growth	12/03	12/04	12/05	12/06	12/07
Sales ($ mil.)	(2.8%)	311.4	322.1	319.3	261.8	278.1
Net income ($ mil.)	—	(31.7)	(31.8)	12.3	(15.2)	(8.4)
Market value ($ mil.)	(0.4%)	—	—	264.2	334.7	262.3
Employees	(33.0%)	—	—	5,277	3,534	—

LOEHMANN'S HOLDINGS INC.

2500 Halsey St.
Bronx, NY 10461
Phone: 718-409-2000
Fax: 718-518-2766
Web: www.loehmanns.com

CEO: Jerald (Jerry) Politzer
CFO: –
HR: Nancy Straface
FYE: Saturday nearest January 31
Type: Private

Humorist Erma Bombeck claimed that *All I Know About Animal Behavior I Learned in Loehmann's Dressing Room* — and if you've ever tussled over the last discounted Donna Karan blouse at one of this retailer's stores, you know what she was talking about. With 60-plus Loehmann's stores in more than 15 states (nearly a third are in California), Loehmann's Holdings sells designer and brand-name women's and men's apparel, accessories, intimate apparel, fragrances, shoes, and gifts at deep discounts. But caution to the shy: Loehmann's is famous for its communal dressing rooms. Founded in Brooklyn in 1921 by Frieda Loehmann, the company was acquired by Dubai-based Istithmar PJSC in mid-2006 for about $300 million.

	Annual Growth	1/03	1/04	1/05	1/06	1/07
Est. sales ($ mil.)	—	—	—	—	—	122.1
Employees	—	—	—	—	—	1,784

LOEWS CORPORATION

NYSE: LTR

667 Madison Ave.
New York, NY 10065
Phone: 212-521-2000
Fax: 212-521-2525
Web: www.loews.com

CEO: James S. Tisch
CFO: Peter W. Keegan
HR: Alan Momeyer
FYE: December 31
Type: Public

This diversified holding company not only drills deep and makes the bed — it'll insure others that do, too. Loews' main interest is insurance through publicly traded subsidiary CNA Financial, which offers commercial property/casualty coverage. Other wholly owned and partially owned holdings include hotels in the US and Canada through its Loews Hotels subsidiary. Its energy holdings include contract oil-drilling operator Diamond Offshore Drilling (which operates more than 40 offshore oil rigs), natural gas transmission pipeline systems operator Boardwalk Pipelines, and HighMount Exploration & Production.

	Annual Growth	12/03	12/04	12/05	12/06	12/07
Assets ($ mil.)	(0.6%)	77,880.9	73,634.9	70,675.6	76,880.9	76,079.0
Net income ($ mil.)	—	(610.7)	1,235.3	1,211.6	2,491.3	2,489.0
Market value ($ mil.)	71.9%	3,056.7	4,348.8	5,875.9	22,568.1	26,664.3
Employees	0.2%	—	—	21,600	21,600	21,700

LOGAN'S ROADHOUSE, INC.

3011 Armory Dr., Ste. 300
Nashville, TN 37204
Phone: 615-885-9056
Fax: 615-885-9057
Web: www.logansroadhouse.com

CEO: G. Thomas (Tom) Vogel
CFO: Amy L. Bertauski
HR: –
FYE: Friday nearest July 31
Type: Private

A trip to this roadhouse is rewarded with steak. Logan's Roadhouse operates and franchises about 170 casual-dining steakhouses in some 20 states, offering a menu of steaks, ribs, seafood, and chicken entrees. The eateries also serve such items as grilled wings, Southern-fried catfish, and baked sweet potatoes. Designed to resemble roadhouses dating from the 1930s and 1940s, the restaurants feature rough-hewn cedar, corrugated metal, and neon, along with Wurlitzer jukeboxes playing a mix of jazz, blues, and country music. Patrons snacking on peanuts are encouraged to toss the shells on the floor. Logan's was acquired in 2006 by a private investment group that included Bruckmann, Rosser, Sherrill & Co.

LOGANSPORT FINANCIAL CORP.

OTC: LOGN

723 E. Broadway
Logansport, IN 46947
Phone: 574-722-3855
Fax: 574-722-3857
Web: www.logansportsavings.com

CEO: David G. Wihebrink
CFO: Dottye Robeson
HR: –
FYE: December 31
Type: Public

Community banking is the main sport at Logansport. Logansport Financial is the holding company for Logansport Savings Bank, which serves customers in Cass County, Indiana. From a single office in Logansport, the bank offers individuals and businesses a variety of financial services, including such deposit products as checking, savings, and NOW accounts, as well as IRAs and certificates of deposit. Logansport Savings Bank uses funds from deposits to originate residential mortgages, which account for almost half of its loan portfolio. The bank, originally chartered in 1925, also offers home equity, home improvement, commercial real estate, business, and consumer loans.

	Annual Growth	12/03	12/04	12/05	12/06	12/07
Est. sales ($ mil.)	—	—	—	—	—	9.8
Employees	—	—	—	—	—	26

LOGIC DEVICES INCORPORATED

NASDAQ (GM): LOGC

395 W. Java Dr.
Sunnyvale, CA 94089
Phone: 408-542-5400
Fax: 408-542-0080
Web: www.logicdevices.com

CEO: William J. (Bill) Volz
CFO: Kimiko Milheim
HR: –
FYE: September 30
Type: Public

LOGIC Devices doesn't produce philosophical machines. Rather, LOGIC specializes in high-end digital signal processor (DSP) chips used in applications including medical imaging, instrumentation, telecommunications, and military weapons systems. The company outsources production of its chips to Asian foundries, primarily Taiwan Semiconductor Manufacturing. LOGIC works with sales representatives and international distributors, and also sells directly to OEMs, including Lockheed Martin, QUALCOMM, Raytheon, Sony, Teradyne, and Texas Instruments. The company gets one-third of its sales from outside the US.

	Annual Growth	9/03	9/04	9/05	9/06	9/07
Sales ($ mil.)	(1.5%)	5.0	4.4	3.5	4.6	4.7
Net income ($ mil.)	—	(2.5)	(1.5)	(1.4)	0.1	(1.5)
Market value ($ mil.)	8.8%	10.0	7.6	7.4	18.1	14.0
Employees	(9.3%)	31	16	16	20	21

LOGICVISION, INC.

NASDAQ (GM): LGVN

25 Metro Dr., 3rd Fl.
San Jose, CA 95110
Phone: 408-453-0146
Fax: 408-573-7640
Web: www.logicvision.com

CEO: James T. (Jim) Healy
CFO: Bruce M. Jaffe
HR: Jean Knudtson
FYE: December 31
Type: Public

LogicVision helps semiconductors evaluate themselves from a logical viewpoint. The company offers specialized diagnostic circuit design and manufacturing software that allow semiconductor makers to embed testing functions into their chips. LogicVision's proprietary designs — which it licenses to clients such as Agere Systems, Sun Microsystems, and Intel — test logic and memory chips, as well as chip interconnections. The technology allows such tests to be run even after the chips are incorporated into larger electronics systems. LogicVision also provides design and manufacturing support.

	Annual Growth	12/03	12/04	12/05	12/06	12/07
Sales ($ mil.)	6.6%	9.0	10.1	10.9	10.5	11.6
Net income ($ mil.)	—	(12.0)	(8.4)	(10.0)	(7.1)	(3.7)
Market value ($ mil.)	(39.3%)	177.5	133.1	59.0	73.4	24.2
Employees	—	—	—	78	—	—

LOGILITY, INC.

NASDAQ (GM): LGTY

470 E. Paces Ferry Rd. NE
Atlanta, GA 30305
Phone: 404-261-9777
Fax: 404-264-5206
Web: www.logility.com

CEO: J. Michael (Mike) Edenfield
CFO: Vincent C. (Vince) Klinges
HR: –
FYE: April 30
Type: Public

Logility brings logic and agility to the task of managing global supply chains. The company's Voyager software helps large corporations manage relationships with raw materials suppliers, distributors, partners, and customers. Compatible with a variety of enterprise resource planning software, including offerings from IBM and SSA Global Technologies, Logility's products address specific supply chain needs, such as boosting inventory in response to promotions, or collaborating online with partners and suppliers. Customers have included Haverty's Furniture, Mercury Marine, and Pfizer. The company sells its products both directly and through American Software, which owns an 88% stake in Logility.

	Annual Growth	4/04	4/05	4/06	4/07	4/08
Sales ($ mil.)	18.5%	22.8	24.9	37.3	43.8	44.9
Net income ($ mil.)	37.1%	1.7	(0.6)	8.0	6.0	6.0
Market value ($ mil.)	9.9%	64.8	55.8	125.0	127.2	94.5
Employees	(1.4%)	—	141	139	137	—

LOGISTICARE, INC.

1800 Phoenix Blvd., Ste. 120
Atlanta, GA 30349
Phone: 770-907-7596
Fax: 770-907-7598
Web: www.logisticare.com

CEO: John L. Shermyen
CFO: Thomas E. Oram
HR: Jenny Southern
FYE: December 31
Type: Subsidiary

LogistiCare is a go-between for getting between your house and the doctor's office. The company brokers non-emergency transportation services for commercial health plans, government entities (such as state Medicaid agencies), and hospitals throughout the US. Using its call centers and a network of some 900 independent, contracted transportation providers, the company coordinates the medical-related travel arrangements of its clients' members. In addition, it contracts with local school boards to coordinate transportation for special needs students. The company provides more than 14 million trips each year for clients in more than a dozen states. Logisticare was acquired by Providence Service in late 2007.

	Annual Growth	12/03	12/04	12/05	12/06	12/07
Est. sales ($ mil.)	—	—	—	—	—	20.7
Employees	—	—	—	—	—	650

LOJACK CORPORATION

NASDAQ (GS): LOJN

200 Lowder Brook Dr., Ste. 1000
Westwood, MA 02090
Phone: 781-251-4700
Fax: 781-251-4649
Web: www.lojack.com

CEO: Richard T. Riley
CFO: Michael (Mike) Umana
HR: Mark Bornemann
FYE: December 31
Type: Public

LoJack's signature product helps police recover stolen vehicles — a chilling thought for those driving hot cars. When a car equipped with a LoJack transmitter is stolen, its radio signal is activated and tracked by police. LoJack rents tracking computers to law enforcement agencies, then markets transponders to dealers and operators in about 25 states and the District of Columbia, and some 30 countries internationally. The company also markets products for cargo and equipment tracking and recovery. LoJack provides installation and maintenance of its units, which are manufactured by third parties. Canada-based subsidiary Boomerang Tracking uses cellular technology to track stolen vehicles.

	Annual Growth	12/03	12/04	12/05	12/06	12/07
Sales ($ mil.)	15.4%	125.8	145.7	190.7	213.3	222.8
Net income ($ mil.)	29.5%	7.6	10.4	18.4	16.5	21.4
Market value ($ mil.)	26.4%	120.7	208.2	456.8	317.3	307.9
Employees	2.6%	—	—	890	913	—

LOMA LINDA UNIVERSITY MEDICAL CENTER

11234 Anderson St.
Loma Linda, CA 92354
Phone: 909-558-4000
Fax: 909-558-2446
Web: www.llu.edu/llumc

CEO: Ruthita J. Fike
CFO: Steven Mohr
HR: Mark L. Hubbard
FYE: December 31
Type: Not-for-profit

Loma Linda University Medical Center (LLUMC), affiliated with Loma Linda University, has some 900 beds. The center includes an acute care hospital, a children's hospital, a community health center, and a behavioral care facility. LLUMC primarily serves the Inyo, Mono, Riverside, and San Bernardino counties in California. Founded in 1967, the medical center offers specialized services such as behavioral medicine, neurology, pediatrics, and rehabilitation. Among its staff are some 400 physicians. The medical center provides health care for 33,000 inpatients and about 500,000 outpatients every year.

	Annual Growth	12/03	12/04	12/05	12/06	12/07
Est. sales ($ mil.)	—	—	—	—	—	879.6
Employees	—	—	—	—	—	4,676

LOMBARDI SOFTWARE, INC.

4516 Seton Center Pkwy., Ste. 250
Austin, TX 78759
Phone: 512-382-8200
Fax: 512-382-8201
Web: www.lombardisoftware.com

CEO: Rod Favaron
CFO: Jim Luttenbacher
HR: —
FYE: December 31
Type: Private

Lombardi Software can coach you through the process of business management. The company develops and implements business process management (BPM) software that helps companies monitor business activities, automate responses, and measure performance. Lombardi's software also includes applications for modifying business rules and routing notifications and workflows. The company's products integrate with a variety of enterprise systems and can be used for tasks such as monitoring and managing shipping, payment, supply chains, and settlement processes. Founded in 2000, Lombardi has received funding from firms including Austin Ventures, Goldman Sachs, and Sanders Morris Harris.

	Annual Growth	12/03	12/04	12/05	12/06	12/07
Est. sales ($ mil.)	—	—	—	—	—	15.7
Employees	—	—	—	—	—	75

LONE STAR STEAKHOUSE & SALOON, INC.

224 E. Douglas, Ste. 700
Wichita, KS 67202
Phone: 316-264-8899
Fax: 316-264-5988
Web: www.lonestarsteakhouse.com

CEO: Marc A. Buehler
CFO: John D. White
HR: Reeve Zimmerman
FYE: Last Tuesday in December
Type: Private

There are actually two stars in this steakhouse constellation. Lone Star Steakhouse & Saloon owns and operates more than 150 steakhouse restaurants offering mesquite-grilled steaks, ribs, chicken, and fish dishes. The casual dining spots, found in 30 states, are punctuated by Texas paraphernalia, neon beer signs, and country music. The company also runs the Texas Land & Cattle Steak House chain, which has more than 30 locations in Texas and six other states. Founded by Jamie Coulter in 1992, Lone Star Steakhouse is owned by Dallas-based private equity firm Lone Star Funds.

LONESTAR TRANSPORTATION, INC.

1100 Northway Dr.
Fort Worth, TX 76131
Phone: 817-306-1000
Fax: 817-306-1999
Web: www.lstinc.com

CEO: Tex Robbins
CFO: Don Murray
HR: —
FYE: December 31
Type: Private

By no means bound by the borders of Texas, LoneStar Transportation hauls freight throughout North America on flatbed trailers. The company specializes in transporting equipment for wind power generation facilities, along with other heavy and complex loads for customers in industries such as aerospace, construction, and oil and gas. It operates a fleet of about 800 tractors and 1,700 trailers from more than 20 facilities throughout the US and in Canada. In addition to freight transportation, LoneStar provides a variety of logistics services, which include arranging the transportation of customers' freight by air, ocean, and rail carriers. Company CEO Tex Robbins owns LoneStar, which began operations in 1988.

	Annual Growth	12/03	12/04	12/05	12/06	12/07
Est. sales ($ mil.)	—	—	—	—	—	212.8
Employees	—	—	—	—	—	436

THE LONG & FOSTER COMPANIES, INC.

11351 Random Hills Rd.
Fairfax, VA 22030
Phone: 703-359-1500
Fax: 703-591-6978
Web: www.longandfoster.com

CEO: P. Wesley Foster Jr.
CFO: Bruce Enger
HR: Jackie Thiel
FYE: December 31
Type: Private

Long & Foster wants to be your one-stop shopping center, at least when it comes to buying a home. Flagship subsidiary Long & Foster Real Estate is one of the largest residential real estate brokerage firms in the mid-Atlantic. Some 16,000 agents represent Long & Foster Real Estate in nearly 240 sales offices, primarily in the Washington, DC/Baltimore, Maryland metropolitan area. The company also operates in Delaware, New Jersey, North Carolina, Pennsylvania, Virginia, and West Virginia. Other subsidiaries provide such products and services as commercial brokerage, homeowners insurance, title insurance, and mortgage financing. Long & Foster Real Estate was founded in 1968.

LONG JOHN SILVER'S, INC.

1441 Gardiner Ln.
Louisville, KY 40213
Phone: 502-874-3000
Fax: 502-874-3050
Web: www.ljsilvers.com

CEO: Ben Butler
CFO: —
HR: —
FYE: Last Saturday in December
Type: Subsidiary

Avast ye and prepare to board the largest quick-service seafood restaurant chain. Taking its name from a character in Robert Louis Stevenson's *Treasure Island*, Long John Silver's (LJS) operates and franchises more than 1,100 nautically themed eateries offering such menu items as batter-dipped fish, chicken, shrimp, and hushpuppies. Patrons can also select from sandwiches and salads, as well as chicken items. About 30% of the restaurants are corporate-owned, while the rest are franchised; the chain also has a small number of international locations. Tracing its roots back to 1929, LJS is part of the YUM! Brands fast food empire.

	Annual Growth	12/03	12/04	12/05	12/06	12/07
Est. sales ($ mil.)	—	—	—	—	—	216.8
Employees	—	—	—	—	—	10,000

An in-depth profile of this company is available to Hoover's Online members at hoovers.com.

THE LONGABERGER COMPANY

1 Market Sq., 1500 E. Main St.
Newark, OH 43055
Phone: 740-322-5588
Fax: 740-322-5240
Web: www.longaberger.com

CEO: Tami Longaberger
CFO: Stephanie Imhoff
HR: –
FYE: December 31
Type: Private

A tisket, a tasket, a Longaberger basket. The Longaberger Company is the #1 maker of handmade baskets in the US, selling nearly 10 million a year. The baskets are sold through in-home shows conducted by Longaberger's nearly 60,000 independent sales associates. Baskets account for about half of sales, but the company also sells fabrics, pottery, and wrought-iron home accessories. Longaberger's home office is a seven-story rendition of a basket with two 75-ton handles on top. The company also owns a golf course, a hotel, and Longaberger Homestead (an events area with shops and restaurants). The family-owned firm is run by the daughters of the late Dave Longaberger, who founded the company in 1973.

LONGS DRUG STORES CORPORATION

NYSE: LDG

141 N. Civic Dr.
Walnut Creek, CA 94596
Phone: 925-937-1170
Fax: 925-210-6886
Web: www.longs.com

CEO: Warren F. Bryant
CFO: Steven F. (Steve) McCann
HR: Linda M. Watt
FYE: Last Thursday in January
Type: Public

Longs Drug Stores wants to be known for being short on hassle and long on service. A leading drugstore chain with about 510 stores in the western US and Hawaii, Longs prides itself on customer service. Known for giving store managers autonomy to select merchandise, its stores add local flavor by carrying specialty items popular in the neighborhoods they serve. With larger stores (23,000 square feet on average) than its rivals — such as CVS and Walgreen — the company surpasses the industry average when it comes to selling higher-margin, front-store items such as cosmetics, food, greeting cards, and over-the-counter medications. Longs Drug's RxAmerica subsidiary provides pharmacy benefit management services.

	Annual Growth	1/04	1/05	1/06	1/07	1/08
Sales ($ mil.)	3.8%	4,526.5	4,607.9	4,670.3	5,097.0	5,262.6
Net income ($ mil.)	34.0%	29.8	36.6	73.9	74.5	96.2
Market value ($ mil.)	19.1%	829.0	982.6	1,293.6	1,603.6	1,666.8
Employees	(0.2%)	—	—	22,000	21,900	21,900

LONGVIEW FIBRE COMPANY

300 Fibre Way
Longview, WA 98632
Phone: 360-425-1550
Fax: 360-575-5934
Web: www.longviewfibre.com

CEO: Frank V. McShane
CFO: Heidi Pozzo
HR: Sally Nelson
FYE: December 31
Type: Subsidiary

Taking the long view, "paper or plastic?" is not an option at Longview Fibre. The company owns and operates tree farms, a pulp and paper mill, and 15 converting plants in a dozen states. Its paper mill and converting plants produce a broad range of paper products, including kraft paper, containerboard, and converted products such as shipping containers. Longview Fibre owns tree farms on nearly 590,000 acres in Oregon and Washington and produces logs for sale to nearby independent sawmills and plywood plants, as well as to customers in Japan. In 2006 the company converted itself into a real estate investment trust (REIT). The following year Longview Fibre was acquired by Brookfield Asset Management.

	Annual Growth	10/02	10/03	10/04	10/05	*12/06
Sales ($ mil.)	5.4%	769.3	773.3	831.2	898.1	950.7
Net income ($ mil.)	38.9%	5.1	5.3	13.9	10.4	19.0
Employees	(3.8%)	3,500	3,250	3,200	3,200	3,000

*Fiscal year change

LONZA INC

90 Boroline Rd.
Allendale, NJ 07401
Phone: 201-316-9200
Fax: 201-785-9973
Web: www.lonza.com

CEO: Stephan Kutzer
CFO: Vincent L. DiVito
HR: Joan Desiderio
FYE: December 31
Type: Subsidiary

From poisoning garden pests to exfoliating dry skin, Lonza puts itself in the middle of things. As the US operations of its parent company, Lonza accounts for about a third of the Lonza Group's $2 billion in annual sales. While Lonza doesn't actually make consumer products, the company provides chemical ingredients and intermediates for the personal care, water treatment, pharmaceutical, and plastics industries, from its nine manufacturing and R&D locations throughout the US.

	Annual Growth	12/03	12/04	12/05	12/06	12/07
Est. sales ($ mil.)	—	—	—	—	—	75.9
Employees	—	—	—	—	—	536

LOOKSMART, LTD.

NASDAQ (GM): LOOK

625 2nd St.
San Francisco, CA 94107
Phone: 415-348-7000
Fax: 415-348-7050
Web: www.looksmart.com

CEO: Edward F. (Ted) West
CFO: R. Brian Gibson
HR: Stacey A. Giamalis
FYE: December 31
Type: Public

It's hard to find anything online without looking unless you're talking about ads. LookSmart helps publishers, advertisers, and consumers see what they want when it comes to online advertising. The company earns most of its revenue through its Advertiser Networks offering, which provide advertisers with targeted, pay-per-click (PPC) search advertising, contextual advertising, and banner products. It also offers Publisher Solutions that help content publishers maintain advertiser relationships online. LookSmart sold most of its consumer Web site operations in 2007. It retained Furl.net, an online social bookmarking service that lets users publicly share links to bookmarked Web pages.

	Annual Growth	12/03	12/04	12/05	12/06	12/07
Sales ($ mil.)	(22.6%)	156.2	77.0	41.4	48.7	56.2
Net income ($ mil.)	(12.5%)	5.8	(9.6)	(17.8)	(13.7)	3.4
Market value ($ mil.)	(49.0%)	835.5	1,245.5	86.1	102.5	56.7
Employees	(5.5%)	—	—	127	120	—

LOOMIS, FARGO & CO.

2500 CityWest Blvd., Ste. 900
Houston, TX 77042
Phone: 713-435-6700
Fax: 713-435-6905
Web: www.loomisfargo.com

CEO: Alf Göransson
CFO: –
HR: –
FYE: December 31
Type: Subsidiary

This company gets paid to take the money and run. Loomis, Fargo & Co., the cash handling services division of Swedish security giant Securitas, provides customers with armored transport, ATM, cash handling, check processing, and coin processing services. It operates a fleet of armored vehicles and provides emergency transport and worldwide logistics services. Doing business as Loomis, the company operates through locations across the US and Western Europe. Loomis was founded in 1852 by Lee Loomis and William Fargo as Loomis, Fargo & Co. Parent company Securitas is transitioning Loomis, Fargo & Co. to the new Loomis identity and plans to spin off the company in 2008.

	Annual Growth	12/03	12/04	12/05	12/06	12/07
Est. sales ($ mil.)	—	—	—	—	—	500.0
Employees	—	—	—	—	—	9,000

LOOPNET, INC.

NASDAQ (GM): LOOP

185 Berry St., Ste. 4000
San Francisco, CA 94107
Phone: 415-243-4200
Fax: 415-764-1622
Web: www.loopnet.com

CEO: Richard J. (Rich) Boyle Jr.
CFO: Brent Stumme
HR: –
FYE: December 31
Type: Public

Feeling out of the loop when it comes to commercial real estate? LoopNet provides information services to the commercial real estate market through its namesake Web site, LoopNet.com, an online marketplace that includes approximately 560,000 property listings. The company offers a free basic membership, as well as a subscription-based premium membership. LoopNet has about 2.5 million registered members and more than 88,000 premium members. The company also offers LoopLink, which helps real estate brokers integrate LoopNet listings into their own Web sites; BizBuySell, an online marketplace for operating businesses that are for sale; and commercial real estate network CityFeet.com.

	Annual Growth	12/03	12/04	12/05	12/06	12/07
Sales ($ mil.)	61.1%	10.5	17.0	31.0	48.4	70.7
Net income ($ mil.)	87.7%	1.7	3.7	18.9	15.5	21.1
Market value ($ mil.)	(3.7%)	—	—	—	567.7	546.7
Employees	43.5%	—	—	138	198	—

LORAL SPACE & COMMUNICATIONS INC.

NASDAQ (GM): LORL

600 3rd Ave.
New York, NY 10016
Phone: 212-697-1105
Fax: 212-338-5662
Web: www.loral.com

CEO: Michael B. (Mickey) Targoff
CFO: Harvey B. Rein
HR: Stephen L. Jackson
FYE: December 31
Type: Public

Loral Space & Communications has a higher purpose. The company's main business unit, Space Systems/Loral (SS/L), makes satellites and related systems and components for digital broadcasters, data distribution, commercial weather forecasting, and digital audio service providers. The company also holds a majority stake in fixed satellite services provider Telesat Canada. The unit leases satellite transponder capacity to cable and satellite broadcasters, voice and data networks, and other users. Loral's customers include DIRECTV, DISH Network, and Sirius Satellite Radio.

	Annual Growth	12/03	12/04	12/05	12/06	12/07
Sales ($ mil.)	13.4%	533.4	522.1	626.3	797.3	882.5
Net income ($ mil.)	—	(382.7)	(176.7)	1,029.6	(22.7)	29.7
Market value ($ mil.)	10.9%	—	—	565.6	814.4	695.0
Employees	12.2%	—	—	1,700	2,100	2,140

LORD & TAYLOR LLC

424 5th Ave.
New York, NY 10018
Phone: 212-391-3344
Fax: 212-768-0743
Web: www.lordandtaylor.com

CEO: Jane T. Elfers
CFO: Michael Cuhlane
HR: Bruce Kelso
FYE: December 31
Type: Private

Venerable Lord & Taylor is a Fifth Avenue institution trying not to become a retail industry dinosaur. The department store chain operates nearly 50 stores in nine states and the District of Columbia, as well as a Web site. Its stores sell better women's, men's, and children's apparel and accessories, and cosmetics. Services include personal shopping and in-store restaurants at some locations. Its Fifth Avenue flagship store's Christmas windows are a New York holiday tradition. Founded in 1826, the firm has changed hands as its industry has consolidated. In 2006 Macy's sold Lord & Taylor for nearly $1.1 billion to NRDC Equity Partners, owner of the Fortunoff jewelry and housewares chain.

	Annual Growth	12/03	12/04	12/05	12/06	12/07
Est. sales ($ mil.)	—	—	—	—	—	1,300.0
Employees	—	—	—	—	—	9,000

LORD CORPORATION

111 Lord Dr.
Cary, NC 27511
Phone: 919-468-5979
Fax: 919-469-5777
Web: www.lordcorp.com

CEO: Richard L. McNeel
CFO: Arthur B. (Art) Belden
HR: Mark Boris
FYE: December 31
Type: Private

When it comes to adhesives and vibration control products, LORD knows. LORD is a leading maker of adhesives and coatings, as well as vibration, noise, and motion control products. Its adhesive products are used by the automotive industry for rubber-to-metal bonding for engine mounts, bushings, and hoses, as well as for body panel assembly. LORD's adhesives also are used in circuit assembly. Motion and vibration products are used in aerospace (avionic mounts), automotive (engine mounts), and industrial applications. Noise control products are used mainly in aircraft. Outside the US, LORD has operations in the Asia/Pacific region and in Europe. The company was founded in 1919.

L'ORÉAL USA, INC.

575 5th Ave.
New York, NY 10017
Phone: 212-818-1500
Fax: 212-984-4999
Web: www.lorealusa.com

CEO: Laurent Attal
CFO: Howard Geiger
HR: David Greenberg
FYE: December 31
Type: Subsidiary

The changes made by L'Oréal USA since its 1953 founding have been anything but cosmetic. The US arm of L'Oréal (the world's #1 cosmetics firm), L'Oréal USA has acquired a host of big-name brands, including Maybelline and Redken. It also owns salon product makers Matrix and Kérastase, as well as consumer-focused SoftSheen/Carson and perfume brands Ralph Lauren and Gloria Vanderbilt. The unit's upscale Lancôme (makeup, skin care) and Biotherm (skin care) lines are sold nationwide in department stores. Its parent bought Dallas-based SkinCeuticals in 2005. Laurent Attal took over as president and CEO in April 2006, when former president and CEO Jean-Paul Agon became CEO of L'Oréal SA.

LORILLARD, INC.

NYSE: LO

714 Green Valley Rd.
Greensboro, NC 27408
Phone: 336-335-7000
Fax: 336-335-7550
Web: http://www.lorillard.com/index.php?id=1

CEO: Martin L. (Marty) Orlowsky
CFO: Thomas R. Staab
HR: William G. Crump
FYE: December 31
Type: Public

Newport news provides the best read on Lorillard, the #3 cigarette maker in the US and the nation's oldest continuously operating tobacco firm. Newport, Lorillard's flagship brand, is the #1 menthol cigarette and the second-largest cigarette brand in the US. Newport generates about 91% of Lorillard's sales by volume. Other brands include Kent, Max, Old Gold, Satin, True, and Maverick, its discount brand. Lorillard, which was named Carolina Group until June 2008, accounted for about 22% of sales for former parent company Loews. Loews established Carolina Group in 2002 as a tracking stock for its tobacco holdings and owned 62% of its shares until it spun off Lorillard to Carolina Group and Lowes shareholders.

	Annual Growth	12/03	12/04	12/05	12/06	12/07
Est. sales ($ mil.)	—	—	—	—	—	864.2
Employees	—	—	—	—	—	3,100

An in-depth profile of this company is available to Hoover's Online members at hoovers.com.

953

LOS ANGELES DODGERS INC.

1000 Elysian Park Ave.
Los Angeles, CA 90012
Phone: 323-224-1500
Fax: 323-224-1269
Web: losangeles.dodgers.mlb.com

CEO: Jamie McCourt
CFO: Peter Wilhelm
HR: Leonor Romero
FYE: October 31
Type: Private

Taking Horace Greeley's advice to go west literally, the Los Angeles Dodgers rocked Major League Baseball in 1957 when the team moved from its proud Brooklyn home (where it was founded in 1884) and made baseball a coast-to-coast sport. One of the game's most successful franchises (and the first to break MLB's color barrier with the signing of Jackie Robinson), the Dodgers have won six World Series championships (its last in 1988) and 21 National League titles. Real estate developer Frank McCourt has owned the Dodgers since 2004 when he bought the team from Rupert Murdoch's Fox Entertainment Group.

	Annual Growth	10/02	10/03	10/04	10/05	10/06
Est. sales ($ mil.)	—	—	—	—	—	211.0
Employees	—	—	—	—	—	—

⊞ LOUD TECHNOLOGIES INC.

NASDAQ (CM): LTEC

16220 Wood-Red Rd. NE
Woodinville, WA 98072
Phone: 425-892-6500
Fax: 425-487-4337
Web: www.loud-technologies.com

CEO: James T. (Jamie) Engen
CFO: Gerald Ng
HR: –
FYE: December 31
Type: Public

LOUD Technologies helps musicians bring their music to the masses. Best known for its multi-channel mixing consoles, which allow engineers to combine some 100 sound channels, the company also manufactures amplifiers, monitor speakers, and digital mixing consoles. In addition to studio recording, LOUD Technologies' equipment is used in CD and CD-ROM authoring, live sound reinforcement, and video postproduction. It also owns loudspeaker manufacturer Eastern Acoustic Works (EAW). LOUD Technologies' products are sold through thousands of retail outlets and a network of installed sound contractors in the US, as well as through distributors worldwide. It acquired Martin Audio in April 2007.

	Annual Growth	12/03	12/04	12/05	12/06	12/07
Sales ($ mil.)	12.3%	130.8	123.3	204.3	215.0	208.3
Net income ($ mil.)	—	(21.8)	(2.3)	3.8	0.6	(12.6)
Market value ($ mil.)	(36.9%)	198.0	221.4	73.1	68.9	31.4
Employees	12.0%	468	408	704	658	—

THE LOUIS BERGER GROUP, INC.

412 Mount Kemble Ave.
Morristown, NJ 07960
Phone: 973-407-1000
Fax: 973-267-6468
Web: www.louisberger.com

CEO: Nicholas J. (Nick) Masucci
CFO: Salvatore (Sal) Pepe
HR: Terry Williams
FYE: June 30
Type: Private

An archeologist, an engineer, and an environmentalist walked into a bar. Turns out it wasn't a joke — it was The Louis Berger Group, a New Jersey-based engineering firm. The company, which provides civil, structural, mechanical, electrical, and environmental engineering services, has worked on high-profile projects such as the Pennsylvania Turnpike, the first toll expressway in the US. Louis Berger also has a significant overseas presence, and has built highways, airports, seaports, and dams and contributed to cultural and environmental preservation on projects in 140 countries. The company has also worked on Iraq reconstruction projects.

LOUIS DREYFUS CORPORATION

20 Westport Rd.
Wilton, CT 06897
Phone: 203-761-2000
Fax: 203-761-2375

CEO: Peter B. Griffin
CFO: Jeffrey R. Gilman
HR: Veronica Pitaro
FYE: December 31
Type: Subsidiary

A subsidiary of global conglomerate Louis Dreyfus Group, Louis Dreyfus Corporation handles the Group's grains and oilseeds exports in the US and Canada. One of the world's largest merchants of grains and oilseeds, the company's annual volume has represented some 15% of total world trade. The unit also oversees grain activities in Australia and Mexico, handles sales for the US and Canadian coffee (Arabica) markets, and offers various risk management products and services for agribusiness customers through its Agricultural Financial Risk Management Group. The company has several facilities throughout the US.

	Annual Growth	12/03	12/04	12/05	12/06	12/07
Est. sales ($ mil.)	—	—	—	—	—	149.8
Employees	—	—	—	—	—	900

LOUIS VUITTON NORTH AMERICA, INC.

19 E. 57th St.
New York, NY 10022
Phone: 212-931-2700
Fax: 212-931-2739
Web: www.lvmh.com

CEO: Mark Weber
CFO: Patrice Pfistner
HR: –
FYE: December 31
Type: Subsidiary

Louis Vuitton North America is the North American operations subsidiary of French luxury goods giant LVMH Moët Hennessy Louis Vuitton, which boasts brands such as Clicquot, Dom Pérignon, Moët & Chandon, Christian Dior, Givenchy, Donna Karan (DKI), and TAG Heuer. The firm specializes in wines and spirits, fashion and leather goods, perfumes and cosmetics, watches and jewelry, and duty free shopping, as well as French media (La Tribune, Investir Hebdo, Investir Magazine, le Monde de la Musique, Défis, SID Presse). LVMH opened its biggest store — a four-story emporium on New York's Fifth Avenue — in 2004.

⊞ LOUISIANA-PACIFIC CORPORATION

NYSE: LPX

414 Union St., Ste. 2000
Nashville, TN 37219
Phone: 615-986-5600
Fax: 615-986-5666
Web: www.lpcorp.com

CEO: Richard W. (Rick) Frost
CFO: Curtis M. Stevens
HR: Ann P. Harris
FYE: December 31
Type: Public

Orient yourself to the fact that Louisiana-Pacific (LP) is one of the world's largest producers of oriented strand board (OSB) siding and other OSB-based products. LP also produces hardboard siding products, engineered/composite wood products (I-joists, laminated veneer lumber), plastic building products (vinyl siding, composite decking products, and mouldings), trim products, radiant barrier sheathing, and concrete form products. LP sells to wholesale distributors, building material dealers, retail "do-it-yourself" home centers, manufactured housing producers, and industrial manufacturers.

	Annual Growth	12/03	12/04	12/05	12/06	12/07
Sales ($ mil.)	(7.2%)	2,300.2	2,849.4	2,598.9	2,235.1	1,704.9
Net income ($ mil.)	—	272.5	420.7	455.5	123.7	(179.9)
Market value ($ mil.)	(7.2%)	1,903.5	2,945.2	2,905.8	2,244.1	1,410.2
Employees	(4.6%)	—	—	5,600	5,600	5,100

LOVE'S TRAVEL STOPS & COUNTRY STORES, INC.

10601 N. Pennsylvania Ave.
Oklahoma City, OK 73120
Phone: 405-751-9000
Fax: 405-749-9110
Web: www.loves.com

CEO: Tom Love
CFO: Doug Stussi
HR: Carl Martincich
FYE: December 31
Type: Private

If you're a trucker or RVer on the road, all you need is Love's. Love's Travel Stops & Country Stores operates more than 200 travel stop locations throughout a swath of about 35 states from California to Virginia, including convenience stores in Colorado, Kansas, New Mexico, Oklahoma, and Texas. Each travel stop includes a convenience store, a fast-food restaurant, such as Taco Bell or Subway, and gas outlets for cars, trucks, and RVs. The travel stops also provide shower rooms, laundry facilities, game rooms, and mail drops. Love's Travel Stops & Country Stores is owned by the family of CEO Tom Love, who founded the company in 1964.

	Annual Growth	12/02	12/03	12/04	12/05	12/06
Sales ($ mil.)	48.5%	1,300.0	1,900.0	2,210.0	3,807.0	6,330.0
Employees	10.2%	3,800	3,500	3,800	4,400	5,600

LOWE ENTERPRISES, INC.

11777 San Vicente Blvd., Ste. 900
Los Angeles, CA 90049
Phone: 310-820-6661
Fax: 310-207-1132
Web: www.loweenterprises.com

CEO: Robert J. (Bob) Lowe
CFO: William T. Wethe
HR: Avedick B. (Dick) Poladian
FYE: December 31
Type: Private

Lowe knows how to be hospitable. Through subsidiaries, Lowe Enterprises invests in and manages commercial real estate, primarily in the western US. Units include Lowe Hospitality Group, a hotel development and management firm and parent of Destination Hotels & Resorts; Lowe Enterprises Investment Management, which invests on the behalf of pension plans; and Lowe Enterprises Real Estate, which develops and manages commercial and residential real estate. Notable properties include Inverness Hotel in Denver and Teton Mountain Lodge in Jackson Hole, Wyoming. Founded in 1972 by CEO Robert Lowe, the firm is owned by about 50 shareholders and has offices in California, Arizona, Colorado, Florida, and Washington, DC.

	Annual Growth	12/03	12/04	12/05	12/06	12/07
Est. sales ($ mil.)	—	—	—	—	—	142.4
Employees	—	—	—	—	—	7,050

LOWER COLORADO RIVER AUTHORITY

3700 Lake Austin Blvd.
Austin, TX 78703
Phone: 512-473-3200
Fax: 512-473-3298
Web: www.lcra.org

CEO: Thomas G. Mason
CFO: Brady Edwards
HR: –
FYE: June 30
Type: Government-owned

The stars at night may be big and bright, but more than one million people deep in the heart of Texas still need electricity from the Lower Colorado River Authority (LCRA). Serving more than 50 counties along the lower Colorado River from Central Texas' Hill Country to the Gulf of Mexico, the not-for-profit, state-run entity supplies wholesale electricity to more than 40 retail utilities (primarily municipalities and cooperatives). It operates three fossil-fuel powered plants and six hydroelectric dams that give it a capacity of about 2,300 MW; it also purchases electricity from Texas wind farms. The LCRA provides water and wastewater utility services to more than 30 communities as well.

	Annual Growth	6/02	6/03	6/04	6/05	6/06
Sales ($ mil.)	16.3%	556.1	643.1	694.4	802.6	1,018.7
Employees	1.0%	2,112	2,211	2,224	2,200	2,200

LOWE'S COMPANIES, INC.

NYSE: LOW

1000 Lowe's Blvd.
Mooresville, NC 28117
Phone: 704-758-1000
Fax: 336-658-4766
Web: www.lowes.com

CEO: Robert A. Niblock
CFO: Robert F. (Bob) Hull Jr.
HR: Maureen K. Ausura
FYE: Friday nearest January 31
Type: Public

No longer a low-profile company, Lowe's Companies has evolved from a regional hardware store operator into a nationwide chain of home improvement superstores. The #2 US home improvement chain (after The Home Depot), Lowe's has more than 1,500 superstores in 50 states and expanded into Canada in late 2007. The company's stores sell about 40,000 products for do-it-yourselfers and professionals for home improvement and repair projects, such as gardening products, home fashion items, lumber, millwork, plumbing and electrical supplies, and tools, as well as appliances and furniture. Lowe's is the second-largest US home appliance retailer after Sears.

	Annual Growth	1/04	1/05	1/06	1/07	1/08
Sales ($ mil.)	11.9%	30,838.0	36,464.0	43,243.0	46,927.0	48,283.0
Net income ($ mil.)	10.6%	1,877.0	2,176.0	2,765.0	3,105.0	2,809.0
Market value ($ mil.)	15.3%	21,071.9	21,736.0	49,799.7	52,078.5	37,251.9
Employees	8.1%	—	—	185,000	210,000	216,000

LOZIER CORPORATION

6336 Pershing Dr.
Omaha, NE 68110
Phone: 402-457-8000
Fax: 402-457-8297
Web: www.lozier.com

CEO: Sheri Andrews
CFO: Steve Franz
HR: Vickey Thayer
FYE: December 31
Type: Private

In the market for a pallet rack or an end cap? Lozier can satisfy your wildest shelving desires. The company makes retail store fixtures including front room display fixtures and back room storage systems for supermarkets, discount stores, mass merchandisers, and a variety of other retail formats. It has manufacturing operations in Alabama, Missouri, Nebraska, Utah, and Pennsylvania. Lozier distributes fixtures across the US, as well as internationally; the firm maintains a sales and service network for its international retailers. In addition to selling fixtures, Lozier also offers installation services.

	Annual Growth	12/03	12/04	12/05	12/06	12/07
Est. sales ($ mil.)	—	—	—	—	—	411.1
Employees	—	—	—	—	—	2,050

LQ CORPORATION, INC.

OTC: LQCI

888 Seventh Ave., 17th Fl.
New York, NY 10019
Phone: 212-974-5730
Fax: –

CEO: Sebastian E. (Sam) Cassetta
CFO: Melvyn (Mel) Brunt
HR: –
FYE: December 31
Type: Public

LQ Corporation, formerly Liquid Audio, liquidated its audio. The company sold its patent rights to Microsoft as part of a plan to be acquired by media distribution company Alliance Entertainment Corp., but the deal was called off when shareholders voiced opposition. Liquid Audio subsequently sold its digital music fulfillment business to Geneva Media in 2003. Prior to selling the bulk of its assets, Liquid Audio offered software that allowed users to download, listen to, and buy digital songs off the Web. The company now operates through two subsidiaries: Sielox (access control products) and SES Resources International (business and security consulting).

	Annual Growth	12/02	12/03	12/04	12/05	*12/06
Sales ($ mil.)	—	—	—	—	—	6.4
Net income ($ mil.)	—	—	—	—	—	(1.9)
Employees	—	—	—	—	—	

*Most recent year available

An in-depth profile of this company is available to Hoover's Online members at hoovers.com.

955

LQ MANAGEMENT LLC

909 Hidden Ridge, Ste. 600
Irving, TX 75038
Phone: 214-492-6600
Fax: 214-492-6616
Web: www.lq.com

CEO: Wayne B. Goldberg
CFO: Robert M. Harshbarger
HR: Jeffrey M. (Jeff) Schagren
FYE: December 31
Type: Subsidiary

LQ Management, owner of the La Quinta (which is Spanish for the villa) brand, wants you to stay at its place. The company owns, operates, or franchises some 600 hotels under the La Quinta Inns and La Quinta Inn & Suites brands. The company's properties, which operate in the limited service segment, are located in about 45 US states and Canada. LQ Management is expanding by adding franchises and through corporate development and acquisitions. In addition, the company is spending $275 million on property upgrades. LQ Managament is owned by investment firm The Blackstone Group.

LRN CORPORATION

1100 Glendon Ave.
Los Angeles, CA 90024
Phone: 310-209-5400
Fax: 310-209-5401
Web: www.lrn.com

CEO: Dov L. Seidman
CFO: Gary P. Rolfes
HR: Diane Nott-Kilfoil
FYE: December 31
Type: Private

Helping employees do what's right isn't as simple as it sounds, and LRN wants to make it easier. The company's applications and services enable its corporate customers to implement ethics and compliance management programs. LRN's offerings include Web-based and in-person training, certifications, help lines, and consulting services to help clients disseminate corporate values, policies, and regulations to employees at all levels. LRN also provides legal research and analysis via a network of attorneys and law professors. The company's clients, drawn from a variety of industries, have included Dow Chemical, Procter & Gamble, and Raytheon. Chairman and CEO Dov Seidman founded LRN in 1994.

	Annual Growth	12/03	12/04	12/05	12/06	12/07
Est. sales ($ mil.)	—	—	—	—	—	55.1
Employees	—	—	—	—	—	220

THE L.S. STARRETT COMPANY

NYSE: SCX

121 Crescent St.
Athol, MA 01331
Phone: 978-249-3551
Fax: 978-249-8495
Web: www.starrett.com

CEO: Douglas A. Starrett
CFO: Randall J. (Randy) Hylek
HR: Joel Shaughnessy
FYE: Last Saturday in June
Type: Public

L.S. Starrett has forged its business inch by inch. The company makes more than 5,000 products, including hand measuring tools (steel rules, combination squares, micrometers) and precision instruments (vernier calipers and height and depth gauges). Other products include levels, vises, lubricants, saw blades, and vocational and educational materials. Machinists in the metalworking industry are Starrett's primary market; it also serves the automotive, aviation, construction, marine, and farm equipment industries, as well as tradesmen and do-it-yourselfers. In 2006 the company acquired Tru-Stone Technologies, adding high-precision, custom-engineered machine bases and accessories to its product lines.

	Annual Growth	6/03	6/04	6/05	6/06	6/07
Sales ($ mil.)	6.1%	175.7	180.0	195.9	200.9	222.4
Net income ($ mil.)	—	(10.6)	(2.3)	4.0	(3.8)	6.7
Market value ($ mil.)	10.5%	69.3	85.3	98.2	73.6	103.2
Employees	—	—	—	2,219	—	—

LSB CORPORATION

NASDAQ (GM): LSBX

30 Massachusetts Ave.
North Andover, MA 01845
Phone: 978-725-7500
Fax: 978-725-7593
Web: www.riverbk.com

CEO: Gerald T. Mulligan
CFO: Diane L. Walker
HR: Teresa K. Flynn
FYE: December 31
Type: Public

LSB Corporation helps those with common (and uncommon) wealth in Massachusetts. It owns RiverBank (formerly Lawrence Savings Bank), which has about a half dozen offices in northeastern Massachusetts and nearby southern New Hampshire. Founded in 1868, RiverBank offers checking and savings accounts, NOW and money market accounts, CDs, and IRAs. Commercial mortgages dominate the company's lending activities — they account for some 50% of all loans. Residential mortgages account for more than 20%; home equity, construction, business, and consumer loans round out its loan book.

	Annual Growth	12/03	12/04	12/05	12/06	12/07
Assets ($ mil.)	7.5%	466.1	518.5	521.8	543.0	621.7
Net income ($ mil.)	(2.5%)	4.1	4.7	4.2	0.1	3.7
Market value ($ mil.)	(0.4%)	73.3	80.3	77.5	76.1	72.3
Employees	—	—	—	101	—	—

LSB FINANCIAL CORP.

NASDAQ (GM): LSBI

101 Main St.
Lafayette, IN 47901
Phone: 765-742-1064
Fax: 765-742-1507
Web: www.lsbank.com

CEO: Randolph F. (Randy) Williams
CFO: Mary Jo David
HR: –
FYE: December 31
Type: Public

There's nothing psychedelic about LSB. Straight-laced LSB Financial is the holding company for Lafayette Savings Bank, which has been serving northern Indiana since 1869. Today the bank has a handful of branches in the communities of Lafayette and West Lafayette, offering checking, savings, and money market accounts, NOW accounts, and CDs. It primarily writes real estate loans, with residential mortgages making up more than half of the company's loan portfolio. Other types of loans offered include commercial and multifamily residential mortgages, real estate construction loans, and land development loans.

	Annual Growth	12/03	12/04	12/05	12/06	12/07
Assets ($ mil.)	1.7%	319.3	355.0	372.7	368.4	342.0
Net income ($ mil.)	(14.5%)	3.0	3.3	3.3	3.3	1.6
Market value ($ mil.)	(1.8%)	32.2	33.9	40.7	39.3	29.9
Employees	3.2%	—	—	91	—	97

LSB INDUSTRIES, INC.

AMEX: LXU

16 S. Pennsylvania Ave.
Oklahoma City, OK 73107
Phone: 405-235-4546
Fax: 405-235-5067
Web: www.lsbindustries.com

CEO: Jack E. Golsen
CFO: Tony M. Shelby
HR: –
FYE: December 31
Type: Public

LSB Industries makes a wide variety of chemicals (including nitric acid) and climate-control products. Its chemicals segment manufactures nitrate fertilizers and acids for agricultural, mining, and industrial markets. The climate-control division makes hydronic fan coils and a variety of heat pumps. Additionally, its industrial products segment distributes industrial milling, drilling, turning, and fabricating machines. The company's chemical unit accounts for more than half of sales; geographically, the US accounts for pretty much all of its sales. CEO Jack Golsen and family members own about 40% of the company, which conducts most of its business through subsidiary ThermaClime.

	Annual Growth	12/03	12/04	12/05	12/06	12/07
Sales ($ mil.)	16.6%	317.3	363.6	396.7	492.0	586.4
Net income ($ mil.)	97.2%	3.1	1.4	5.1	15.5	46.9
Market value ($ mil.)	78.9%	—	104.0	84.6	194.2	595.6
Employees	23.5%	—	—	1,267	1,565	—

⊞ LSI CORPORATION

NYSE: LSI

1621 Barber Ln.
Milpitas, CA 95035
Phone: 408-433-8000
Fax: 408-954-3220
Web: www.lsi.com

CEO: Abhijit Y. (Abhi) Talwalkar
CFO: Bryon Look
HR: Jon R. Gibson
FYE: December 31
Type: Public

LSI Corp. (formerly LSI Logic) offers lots more than logic chips. The fabless semiconductor developer provides standard integrated circuits (ICs) and custom-designed application-specific ICs, focusing on broadband and wireless communications, data storage, and networking markets. LSI was a pioneer of system-on-a-chip (SoC) devices, which combine elements of an electronic system — especially a microprocessor, memory, and logic — onto a single chip. LSI's top customers include Hewlett-Packard, IBM (15% of sales), and Seagate (19%). LSI also provides hardware and software for storage area networks. The Asia/Pacific region accounts for more than half of the company's sales.

	Annual Growth	12/03	12/04	12/05	12/06	12/07
Sales ($ mil.)	11.4%	1,693.1	1,700.2	1,919.3	1,982.2	2,603.6
Net income ($ mil.)	—	(308.5)	(463.5)	(5.6)	169.6	(2,486.8)
Market value ($ mil.)	1.7%	3,383.8	2,124.9	3,152.1	3,633.1	3,614.0
Employees	7.0%	4,722	4,414	4,322	4,010	6,193

⊞ LSI INDUSTRIES INC.

NASDAQ (GS): LYTS

10000 Alliance Rd.
Cincinnati, OH 45242
Phone: 513-793-3200
Fax: 513-984-1335
Web: www.lsi-industries.com

CEO: Robert J. (Bob) Ready
CFO: Ronald S. Stowell
HR: Stan Adams
FYE: June 30
Type: Public

LSI Industries likes to spread a little artificial sunshine. The company and its subsidiaries make lighting, graphics, and menu board systems for gas stations, convenience stores, fast-food restaurants, car dealerships, retail chain stores, and other businesses. Its lighting group concentrates on convenience stores, gas stations, multi-site retailers, and commercial and industrial markets, providing indoor, outdoor, and landscape lighting. LSI's graphics group concerns itself with printed, as well as indoor and outdoor graphic services such as menu board systems and digital billboards. Customers include Best Buy, Wal-Mart, Ford, Target, and Burger King.

	Annual Growth	6/03	6/04	6/05	6/06	6/07
Sales ($ mil.)	12.2%	213.1	241.4	282.4	280.5	337.5
Net income ($ mil.)	—	(10.8)	8.7	14.6	14.4	20.8
Market value ($ mil.)	21.8%	175.0	226.9	277.0	364.4	384.7
Employees	—	—	—	—	1,640	—

LTC PROPERTIES INC.

NYSE: LTC

31365 Oak Crest Dr., Ste. 200
Westlake Village, CA 91361
Phone: 805-981-8655
Fax: 805-981-8663
Web: www.ltcproperties.com

CEO: Wendy L. Simpson
CFO: –
HR: –
FYE: December 31
Type: Public

Specializing in TLC, LTC Properties sees real estate as a healthy investment. The self-administered real estate investment trust (REIT) primarily invests in health care and long-term care facilities. The company owns properties in 23 states. Its portfolio includes more than 80 assisted living centers (homes for elderly residents not requiring constant supervision), some 60 skilled nursing facilities (which provide rehabilitative and restorative nursing care), and a New Jersey charter school. Major tenants include Extendicare, Alterra Healthcare, and Preferred Care, Inc. The REIT also invests in mortgage loans and provides financing on its properties.

	Annual Growth	12/03	12/04	12/05	12/06	12/07
Sales ($ mil.)	4.2%	63.5	66.9	73.0	73.2	74.8
Net income ($ mil.)	18.4%	24.3	36.4	52.7	78.8	47.8
Market value ($ mil.)	21.6%	262.5	425.6	489.5	643.7	572.9
Employees	4.1%	—	—	12	—	13

LTD COMMODITIES, LLC

2800 Lakeside Dr.
Bannockburn, IL 60015
Phone: 847-295-5532
Fax: 847-604-7600
Web: www.ltdcommodities.com

CEO: Juliana Furlong
CFO: –
HR: Brian Will
FYE: December 31
Type: Private

You won't find soybeans or pork bellies, but you can buy a little silver (as in a pair of sterling silver earrings) from LTD Commodities. The company is a business-to-business supplier of apparel for women, men, and children, as well as home and garden accessories, jewelry, electronics, luggage, toys, furniture, gift items, and other general merchandise. LTD Commodities sells its products through numerous catalogs as well as the Internet and ships only to US business addresses. LTD Commodities was founded in 1963 as a small mail-order business.

	Annual Growth	12/03	12/04	12/05	12/06	12/07
Est. sales ($ mil.)	—	—	—	—	—	261.3
Employees	—	—	—	—	—	1,500

⊞ LTX CORPORATION

NASDAQ (GM): LTXX

825 University Ave.
Norwood, MA 02062
Phone: 781-461-1000
Fax: 781-329-8836
Web: www.ltx.com

CEO: David G. (Dave) Tacelli
CFO: Mark J. Gallenberger
HR: Richard L. Bove
FYE: July 31
Type: Public

LTX isn't a fancy sports car, but it does help chip makers rev up their production. The company makes equipment used to test semiconductors as they're being manufactured. Its Fusion X-Series product line (which evolved from LTX's earlier mixed-signal, discrete-device, and digital-device test systems) offers a single-platform system for testing digital, mixed-signal, and system-on-a-chip integrated circuits. The company's customers include Texas Instruments (38% of sales), Freescale Semiconductor, Infineon Technologies, National Semiconductor, NXP, Samsung Electronics, and STMicroelectronics. Customers outside the US account for two-thirds of LTX's sales.

	Annual Growth	7/03	7/04	7/05	7/06	7/07
Sales ($ mil.)	5.4%	119.4	255.8	134.5	216.5	147.6
Net income ($ mil.)	—	(145.1)	2.0	(132.7)	12.2	(10.7)
Market value ($ mil.)	(13.5%)	511.7	490.3	406.7	334.2	286.6
Employees	(7.2%)	611	690	499	438	454

⊞ THE LUBRIZOL CORPORATION

NYSE: LZ

29400 Lakeland Blvd.
Wickliffe, OH 44092
Phone: 440-943-4200
Fax: 440-943-5337
Web: www.lubrizol.com

CEO: James L. Hambrick
CFO: Charles P. Cooley
HR: Mark W. Meister
FYE: December 31
Type: Public

Lubrizol is a smooth operator — the company is the world's #1 maker of additives for lubricants and fuels. Its Lubrizol Additives segment includes engine oil additives that fight sludge buildup, viscosity breakdown, and component wear; fuel additives designed to control deposits and improve combustion; and additives for paints, inks, greases, metalworking, and other industrial markets. Lubrizol's Advanced Materials segment sends its products to the personal care and rubber and plastics markets. The company bought Noveon in 2004; Noveon's former businesses make up the bulk of the Advanced Materials segment. (That segment bore the Noveon name until 2006 when Lubrizol quit using that trademark.)

	Annual Growth	12/03	12/04	12/05	12/06	12/07
Sales ($ mil.)	21.7%	2,052.1	3,159.5	4,042.7	4,040.8	4,499.0
Net income ($ mil.)	32.9%	90.8	93.5	189.3	103.6	283.4
Market value ($ mil.)	21.9%	1,677.6	2,461.5	2,962.4	3,460.0	3,703.7
Employees	(4.1%)	—	—	7,500	6,700	6,900

⊞ An in-depth profile of this company is available to Hoover's Online members at hoovers.com.

LUBY'S, INC.

NYSE: LUB

13111 NW Fwy., Ste. 600
Houston, TX 77040
Phone: 713-329-6800
Fax: 713-329-6809
Web: www.lubys.com

CEO: Christopher J. (Chris) Pappas
CFO: K. Scott Gray
HR: Paulette Gerukos
FYE: Last Wednesday in August
Type: Public

When Mom wants a salad, Dad craves fried chicken, and little Johnny is screaming for enchiladas, what's an all-American family to do? A simple trip to the cafeteria line at Luby's may do the trick. Luby's owns and operates about 130 cafeteria-style restaurants in Texas and four other states that offer dozens of different entrees, salads, vegetable dishes, and desserts. The chain's menu is heavy on such comfort foods as mashed potatoes, macaroni and cheese, and fried chicken. Some of its eateries also offer a breakfast buffet on the weekends; select locations offer an all-you-can-eat menu.

	Annual Growth	8/03	8/04	8/05	8/06	8/07
Sales ($ mil.)	0.1%	318.5	308.8	322.1	324.6	320.4
Net income ($ mil.)	—	(33.1)	(6.0)	3.5	19.6	10.9
Market value ($ mil.)	53.0%	53.2	147.2	340.8	270.8	291.7
Employees	(1.2%)	—	—	7,680	—	7,500

LUCASFILM LTD.

1110 Gorgas Ave.
San Francisco, CA 94129
Phone: 415-662-1800
Fax: –
Web: www.lucasfilm.com

CEO: Micheline (Mich) Chau
CFO: –
HR: –
FYE: March 31
Type: Private

The Force is definitely with Emperor George Lucas. With three of the 20 highest-grossing movies of all time, Lucasfilm is one of the most successful independent movie studios in the history of film. Owned by filmmaker George Lucas (the brains behind the *Star Wars* and *Indiana Jones* films), Lucasfilm's productions have won 19 Academy Awards. Its most recent movie is 2008's *Indiana Jones and the Kingdom of the Crystal Skull* (in partnership with Paramount); 1999's *Episode I — The Phantom Menace* is Lucasfilm's biggest money-maker, with a gross of more than $920 million worldwide. Other subsidiaries in the Lucas empire are responsible for licensing, special effects, and software. Lucasfilm was created in 1971.

LUCOR, INC.

790 Pershing Rd.
Raleigh, NC 27608
Phone: 919-828-9511
Fax: 919-828-4847

CEO: Stephen P. Conway
CFO: Kendall A. Carr
HR: –
FYE: December 31
Type: Private

Lucor deals with dipsticks all day. One of the largest US franchisees of Jiffy Lube International, the company runs more than 210 automotive service centers in Georgia, Kentucky, Michigan, North Carolina, Ohio, Pennsylvania, Tennessee, and Virginia. Basic services include changing a vehicle's oil and oil filter, lubricating the chassis, checking the battery, replacing air filters, inflating tires, vacuuming the interior, and washing exterior windows. Lucor also offers emissions inspections and other preventive maintenance services. The company is owned primarily by CEO Stephen Conway and president Jerry Conway, brothers who founded Lucor in 1986.

	Annual Growth	12/03	12/04	12/05	12/06	12/07
Est. sales ($ mil.)	—	—	—	—	—	100.5
Employees	—	—	—	—	—	2,011

LUFKIN INDUSTRIES, INC.

NASDAQ (GS): LUFK

601 S. Raguet
Lufkin, TX 75904
Phone: 936-634-2211
Fax: 936-637-5272
Web: www.lufkin.com

CEO: John F. (Jay) Glick
CFO: Christopher L. (Chris) Boone
HR: Paul G. Perez
FYE: December 31
Type: Public

Lufkin Industries is all geared up to help pump oil. Through its Oil Field division, the company manufactures and services pumping units, automation equipment, and foundry castings. It also provides computer control equipment and analytical services used to maximize well efficiency. Through its Power Transmission unit, Lufkin manufactures and services gearboxes used in large-scale industrial applications. It has expanded its product offerings through the acquisition of Basin Technical Services. Lufkin has strengthened its presence in Canada through the acquisition of D&R Oilfield Services.

	Annual Growth	12/03	12/04	12/05	12/06	12/07
Sales ($ mil.)	22.8%	262.3	356.3	492.2	605.5	597.2
Net income ($ mil.)	66.3%	9.7	14.4	44.5	73.0	74.2
Market value ($ mil.)	75.1%	94.8	138.5	754.3	890.0	890.0
Employees	11.1%	—	—	2,700	3,000	—

LUMBER LIQUIDATORS, INC.

NYSE: LL

3000 John Deere Rd.
Toano, VA 23168
Phone: 757-259-4280
Fax: –
Web: www.lumberliquidators.com

CEO: Jeffrey W. (Jeff) Griffiths
CFO: Daniel E. Terrell
HR: E. Jean Matherne
FYE: December 31
Type: Public

Thanks to the resurgence of hardwoods, Lumber Liquidators is in the money. The nation's largest specialty retailer of hardwood flooring, Lumber Liquidators sells more than 25 domestic and exotic wood species of both pre-finished and unfinished hardwood flooring from about 125 stores in more than 40 states. The company also sells flooring online, by catalog, and from its Virginia call center. Brands include Bellawood, Builder's Pride, Schön, and more. Founded in 1994 by its chairman Tom Sullivan, Boston-based private equity firm TA Associates acquired a one-third stake in the company in 2004 (with Sullivan holding on to the rest). Three years later, Sullivan and TA Associates took Lumber Liquidators public.

	Annual Growth	12/03	12/04	12/05	12/06	12/07
Sales ($ mil.)	33.1%	—	171.8	244.9	332.1	405.3
Net income ($ mil.)	12.2%	—	8.0	10.7	12.9	11.3
Market value ($ mil.)	—	—	—	—	—	240.5
Employees	—	—	—	—	490	—

LUMERA CORPORATION

NASDAQ (CM): LMRA

19910 N. Creek Pkwy.
Bothell, WA 98011
Phone: 425-415-6900
Fax: 425-398-6599
Web: www.lumera.com

CEO: Joseph J. (Joe) Vallner
CFO: Peter J. Biere
HR: –
FYE: December 31
Type: Public

Lumera hopes its light shines bright in an optical universe. The company develops polymer materials and products based on those materials for use in wireless and optical communications networks and in biochemical analysis. Products in development include compact panel wireless antennas, disposable biochips used to isolate DNA and protein samples for testing (NanoCapture), a surface plasmon resonance instrument for molecular research (ProteomicProcessor), and electro-optic modulators and optical interconnects for use in telecommunications applications. Lumera plans to merge with GigOptix LLC, a California-based supplier of optical modulator drivers and receivers, in a stock-swap transaction.

	Annual Growth	12/03	12/04	12/05	12/06	12/07
Sales ($ mil.)	13.3%	1.7	1.0	1.5	3.4	2.8
Net income ($ mil.)	—	(8.1)	(8.9)	(10.4)	(12.1)	(16.0)
Market value ($ mil.)	(25.6%)	—	127.4	62.6	122.5	52.4
Employees	17.6%	34	38	46	56	65

An in-depth profile of this company is available to Hoover's Online members at hoovers.com.

LUMINENT MORTGAGE CAPITAL, INC.

OTC: LUMC

1 Commerce Sq., 21st Fl., 2005 Market St.
Philadelphia, PA 19103
Phone: 215-564-5900
Fax: 215-564-5990
Web: www.luminentcapital.com

CEO: Zachary H. Pashel
CFO: Karen Chang
HR: –
FYE: December 31
Type: Public

Luminent Mortgage Capital has seen the lights dim in the mortgage market. The company, like industry peers in 2007, has been experiencing cash problems as its lenders call in their notes. It was formed in 2003 to invest in highly rated mortgage-backed securities (MBS) acquired in the secondary market. A real estate investment trust (REIT), Luminent Mortgage Capital also invests in MBS with credit ratings below AAA (although it does not invest in subprime loans); it is also involved in mortgage loan acquisition and securitization. It profits primarily from the spread between funds borrowed and the yield on purchased securities. Most of the REIT's investments are backed by Fannie Mae, Freddie Mac, or Ginnie Mae.

	Annual Growth	12/03	12/04	12/05	12/06	12/07
Sales ($ mil.)	119.1%	22.6	124.8	181.4	365.9	520.9
Net income ($ mil.)	—	2.8	57.1	(83.0)	46.8	(721.0)
Market value ($ mil.)	(57.6%)	—	441.6	304.8	—	33.7
Employees	27.5%	—	—	16	—	26

LUMINEX CORPORATION

NASDAQ (GM): LMNX

12212 Technology Blvd.
Austin, TX 78727
Phone: 512-219-8020
Fax: 512-219-5195
Web: www.luminexcorp.com

CEO: Patrick J. Balthrop
CFO: Harriss T. Currie
HR: Eddie Chien
FYE: December 31
Type: Public

Luminex Corporation sheds new light on genetic mysteries. The company's xMAP technology — which consists of instruments, software, and disposable microspheres, or tiny beads on which tests are performed — allows users to run up to 100 bioassays on one drop of fluid. Luminex licenses the technology to other life sciences companies which develop reagent-based tests to go with the instrumentation systems and then distribute them to end users, or else use them to perform testing services for their customers. Its strategic partners include companies focused on drug discovery and biomedical research (Millipore, Invitrogen) and clinical diagnostics (Bio-Rad, Inverness Medical).

	Annual Growth	12/03	12/04	12/05	12/06	12/07
Sales ($ mil.)	30.0%	26.3	35.9	42.3	53.0	75.0
Net income ($ mil.)	—	(4.2)	(3.6)	(2.7)	1.5	(2.7)
Market value ($ mil.)	19.2%	284.2	276.8	367.8	412.4	574.8
Employees	—	—	—	185	—	—

LUMMUS TECHNOLOGY

1515 Broad St.
Bloomfield, NJ 07003
Phone: 973-893-1515
Fax: 973-893-2000
Web: www.cbi.com/lummus

CEO: Daniel M. McCarthy
CFO: –
HR: Kaye Bell-Reiter
FYE: December 31
Type: Subsidiary

Lummus Technology (formerly ABB Lummus Global) looms large across the globe in engineering projects. The company provides engineering, procurement, and construction-related services for the oil and gas and petrochemical and refining industries. It oversees the construction of process plants and offshore facilities, performing a range of services, including process design, project management, project financing, engineer training, and technical support. Chicago Bridge & Iron Company (CBI) acquired the company from Swiss company ABB for some $950 million in 2007.

	Annual Growth	12/03	12/04	12/05	12/06	12/07
Sales ($ mil.)	(69.0%)	—	—	1,087.8	988.4	104.6
Net income ($ mil.)	44.2%	—	—	5.0	(80.0)	10.4
Employees	(4.0%)	—	—	2,500	2,400	—

LUNA INNOVATIONS INCORPORATED

NASDAQ (GM): LUNA

1703 S. Jefferson St. SW, Ste. 400
Roanoke, VA 24016
Phone: 540-769-8400
Fax: 540-769-8401
Web: www.lunainnovations.com

CEO: Kent A. Murphy
CFO: Dale E. Messick
HR: Lori Engebritson
FYE: December 31
Type: Public

R&D firm Luna Innovations endeavors to make practical use of cutting-edge technologies in the areas of molecular technology and sensing. Its molecular technology efforts focus on materials (including polymers, reagents, and nanomaterials) with enhanced performance characteristics; Luna has developed contrast agents for MRI testing, nanomaterials used in solar cells, and protective coatings. It has also created sensing technologies used in medical monitoring equipment, as well as wireless and fiber-optic monitoring systems for defense and industrial instrumentation. Luna makes its money from contract research services provided to corporate and government entities, as well as product sales and licensing fees.

	Annual Growth	12/03	12/04	12/05	12/06	12/07
Sales ($ mil.)	14.2%	—	22.6	16.5	23.5	33.7
Net income ($ mil.)	—	—	4.1	(2.0)	(9.4)	(7.8)
Market value ($ mil.)	137.5%	—	—	—	35.8	85.0
Employees	—	—	—	—	—	—

LUND FOOD HOLDINGS, INC.

4100 W. 50th St., Ste. 2100
Minneapolis, MN 55424
Phone: 952-927-3663
Fax: 952-915-2600
Web: www.lundsmarket.com

CEO: Russell T. (Tres) Lund III
CFO: Von Martin
HR: Tamra Laska
FYE: September 30
Type: Private

Lund Food Holdings operates about 20 Lunds and Byerly's upscale grocery markets in the Twin Cities area of Minnesota. The company took its present form in 1997 with the merger of Lunds and Byerly's. Both chains specialize in gourmet, high-quality foods, with locations offering artisan breads, bakeries, a line of organic foods and natural products, wine stores, florists, catering services, housewares, cooking demos, and community meeting rooms. Byerly's also runs a culinary school out of one of its stores. Through a partnership with Minnetonka-based PrairieStone Pharmacy, Lund Food Holdings has been adding pharmacies to its stores. The grocer launched an online shopping and home delivery service in 2006.

	Annual Growth	9/03	9/04	9/05	9/06	9/07
Est. sales ($ mil.)	—	—	—	—	—	488.0
Employees	—	—	—	—	—	4,500

🔲 LUND INTERNATIONAL HOLDINGS, INC.

300 Horizon Dr.
Suwanee, GA 30024
Phone: 678-804-3767
Fax: –
Web: www.lundinternational.com

CEO: Dennis W. Vollmershausen
CFO: Edmund (Ed) Schwartz
HR: J. Timothy Yungers
FYE: December 31
Type: Private

Whether you favor form or function, Lund International Holdings manufactures accessories to make your car or truck stand out while it holds up. The company sells more than 150 vehicle-accessory product lines to both OEMs and the automotive aftermarket. Lund's aftermarket products are sold through a network of dealers, warehouse distributors, specialty chain stores, and catalog companies. The company's products include bug deflectors, external windshield visors, grill and brush guards, hood shields, rear-window air deflectors, rock guards, running boards, taillight and headlight covers, and tonneau covers for pickup beds. Investment firm Harvest Partners controls the company.

	Annual Growth	12/03	12/04	12/05	12/06	12/07
Est. sales ($ mil.)	—	—	—	—	—	116.1
Employees	—	—	—	—	—	1,249

🔲 An in-depth profile of this company is available to Hoover's Online members at hoovers.com.

959

LUXOTTICA RETAIL

4000 Luxottica Place
Mason, OH 45040
Phone: 513-765-6000
Fax: 513-765-6249
Web: www.luxottica.com

CEO: Valerio Giacobbi
CFO: Jack Dennis
HR: –
FYE: December 31
Type: Business segment

If you need glasses, Luxottica Retail has you in its sights. A business segment of Italian eyewear giant Luxottica Group, Luxottica Retail is one of the world's leading operators of optical stores. The company has more than 5,700 locations in North America, the Asia/Pacific region, Europe, and the Middle East. Its chains include LensCrafters, Pearle Vision, and Sunglass Hut, as well as in-store businesses Sears Optical, Target Optical, and BJ's Optical. About 5,300 of Luxottica Retail's stores are company-owned; the rest are franchised. In addition, Luxottica Retail oversees a leading US managed vision care plan, EyeMed Vision Care.

LYDALL, INC.

NYSE: LDL

1 Colonial Rd.
Manchester, CT 06040
Phone: 860-646-1233
Fax: 860-646-4917
Web: www.lydall.com

CEO: Dale G. Barnhart
CFO: Thomas P. Smith
HR: Mona G. Estey
FYE: December 31
Type: Public

Lydall's products help to beat the heat and nix the noise. The company makes thermal and acoustical barriers, automotive heat shields, and insulation products that offer protection in temperatures ranging from near absolute zero to 3,000 degrees Fahrenheit. Lydall's thermal and acoustical products are used by the automotive industry and in industrial kilns and furnaces. The company rounds out its offerings with industrial and commercial air and liquid filtration products and — through its subsidiary Charter Medical — fluid management systems for the medical and biopharmaceutical markets. Its Lydall Transport unit provides trucking and logistics services.

	Annual Growth	12/03	12/04	12/05	12/06	12/07
Sales ($ mil.)	5.7%	271.4	292.4	306.5	326.4	338.9
Net income ($ mil.)	4.6%	7.6	(0.5)	5.1	10.2	9.1
Market value ($ mil.)	1.3%	165.9	191.5	132.1	175.7	174.4
Employees	—	—	—	1,500		

LYDIAN

180 Royal Palm Blvd.
Palm Beach, FL 33480
Phone: 561-514-4900
Fax: 561-541-4908
Web: www.lydian.com

CEO: Rory A. Brown
CFO: Stephen C. (Steve) Wilhoit
HR: –
FYE: December 31
Type: Private

Lydian is the parent of Lydian Bank & Trust and its Lydian Private Bank division. The company offers deposit, lending, and investment services through three offices in Florida, as well as through its VirtualBank.com Web site. Deposits gathered from these sources are mainly used to originate single-family residential mortgages. Among other subsidiaries, Lydian Data Services performs mortgage banking services for investment banks and other institutional lenders, while Fortigent provides outsourced wealth management services to other banks, trust companies, and financial advisors.

	Annual Growth	12/03	12/04	12/05	12/06	12/07
Est. sales ($ mil.)	—	—	—	—	—	182.7
Employees	—	—	—	—	—	850

LYNDEN INCORPORATED

18000 International Blvd., Ste. 800
Seattle, WA 98188
Phone: 206-241-8778
Fax: 206-243-8415
Web: www.lynden.com

CEO: James H. (Jim) Jansen
CFO: Richard A. Korpela
HR: –
FYE: December 31
Type: Private

Lynden will haul your freight by truck, barge, or airplane. Through its network of more than 15 subsidiaries, the company also provides airfreight and ocean freight forwarding and logistics services. Lynden provides surface transportation of freight primarily in Alaska, Canada, and the northwestern US; it offers service elsewhere in the Lower 48 and internationally mainly through arrangements with other carriers. Besides standard dry freight, Lynden's trucking units haul bulk chemicals, heavy equipment, and refrigerated cargo. Overall, the company's fleet includes about 600 tractors and 2,500 trailers. Lynden offers barge service between Seattle and southeastern Alaska and airfreight service within Alaska.

LYONDELLBASELL NORTH AMERICA INC.

1 Houston Center, 1221 McKinney St., Ste. 700
Houston, TX 77010
Phone: 713-652-7200
Fax: –
Web: www.lyondellbasell.com

CEO: Michael P. Mulrooney
CFO: –
HR: –
FYE: December 31
Type: Subsidiary

LyondellBasell North America is North America's leading producer of polypropylene. The company also makes polyethylene and other advanced polyolefin materials. It is the American division of global petrochemical giant LyondellBasell, formerly a joint venture of Shell and BASF but now a privately owned company. It operates manufacturing plants, technical and R&D centers, as well as sales offices located throughout North America. The company also operates a petroleum refinery in Houston and acts as the exclusive marketer of polypropylene resins manufactured at a plant owned by ConocoPhillips. Private investment group Access Industries, controlled by industrialist Len Blavatnik, has owned the company since 2005.

	Annual Growth	12/03	12/04	12/05	12/06	12/07
Est. sales ($ mil.)	—	—	—	—	—	81.4
Employees	—	—	—	—	—	1,500

LYRIS, INC.

OTC: LYRI

5858 Horton St., Ste. 270
Emeryville, CA 94608
Phone: 800-768-2929
Fax: –
Web: www.lyrisinc.com

CEO: Luis A. Rivera
CFO: Heidi Mackintosh
HR: –
FYE: June 30
Type: Public

Lyris is a firm believer in the far-reaching power of e-mail. The company provides a variety of e-mail marketing software and services. Clients use the company's products to manage e-mail lists and to create and monitor e-mail marketing campaigns. Its customers come from a wide range of industries including financial services, consumer goods, health care, retail, media, and transportation. The company also provides professional services such as consulting, support, and training. Formerly called J. L. Halsey, the company changed its name in 2007.

	Annual Growth	6/03	6/04	6/05	6/06	6/07
Sales ($ mil.)	321.0%	—	—	2.2	24.4	39.0
Net income ($ mil.)	—	—	—	(0.2)	2.6	0.3
Market value ($ mil.)	37.5%	—	—	42.3	76.6	80.0
Employees	—	—	—	—	—	162